GEORGIA continued

GAU	Atlanta University, Atlanta.
GAuA	Augusta College, Augusta.
GColuC	Columbus College, Columbus.
GCuA	Andrews College, Cuthbert.
GDC	Columbia Theological Seminary, Decatur.
GDS	Agnes Scott College, Decatur.
GDecA*	Agnes Scott College, Decatur.
GDecCT*	Columbia Theological Seminary, Decatur.
GDoS	South Georgia College, Douglas.
GEU	Emory University, Atlanta.
GHi	Georgia Historical Society, Savannah.
GMM	Mercer University, Macon.
GMW	Wesleyan College, Macon.
GMiW	Woman's College of Georgia, Milledgeville.
GMilvC*	Woman's College of Georgia, Milledgeville.
GOgU	Oglethorpe University, Oglethorpe University.
GSDe*	University of Georgia, DeRenne Library.
GU	University of Georgia, Athens.
GU-De	— DeRenne Georgia Library.
GU-Ex	— Georgia State College of Business Administration Library, Atlanta.

HAWAII

HU	University of Hawaii, Honolulu.
HU-EWC	Center for Cultural and Technical Interchange between East and West, Honolulu.

ILLINOIS

I	Illinois State Library, Springfield.
IC	Chicago Public Library.
ICA	Art Institute of Chicago, Chicago.
ICF	Chicago Natural History Museum, Chicago.
ICF-A	— Edward E. Ayer Ornithological Library.
ICHi	Chicago Historical Society, Chicago.
ICIP	Institute for Psychoanalysis, Chicago.
ICJ	John Crerar Library, Chicago.
ICMILC*	Center for Research Libraries, Chicago.
ICMcC	McCormick Theological Seminary, Chicago.
ICN	Newberry Library, Chicago.
ICRL	Center for Research Libraries, Chicago.
ICU	University of Chicago, Chicago.
ICarbS	Southern Illinois University, Carbondale.
IEG	Garrett Theological Seminary, Evanston.
IEN	Northwestern University, Evanston.
IEdS	Southern Illinois University, Edwardsville.
IGK	Knox College, Galesburg.
IHi	Illinois State Historical Library, Springfield.
ILS	St. Procopius College, Lisle.
IMunS	Saint Mary of the Lake Seminary, Mundelein.
INS	Illinois State University, Normal.
IRA	Augustana College Library, Rock Island.
IRivfR	Rosary College, River Forest.
IU	University of Illinois, Urbana.
IU-M	— Medical Sciences Library, Chicago.
IU-U	— Chicago Undergraduate Division, Chicago.

IOWA

IaAS	Iowa State University of Science and Technology, Ames.
IaDL	Luther College, Decorah.
IaDuC	Loras College, Dubuque.
IaDuU	University of Dubuque, Dubuque.
IaDuU-S	— Theological Seminary Library.
IaDuW	Wartburg Theological Seminary, Dubuque.
IaU	University of Iowa, Iowa City.

IDAHO

IdB	Boise Public Library.
IdPI	Idaho State University, Pocatello.
IdPS*	Idaho State University, Pocatello.
IdU	University of Idaho, Moscow.

INDIANA

In	Indiana State Library, Indianapolis.
InAndC	Anderson College, Anderson.
InCollS*	St. Joseph's College, Rensselaer.
InGo	Goshen College Biblical Seminary Library, Goshen.
InHi	Indiana Historical Society, Indianapolis.
InIB	Butler University, Indianapolis.

INDIANA continued

InLP	Purdue University, Lafayette.
InNd	University of Notre Dame, Notre Dame.
InOlH*	St. Leonard College Library, Dayton, Ohio.
InRE	Earlham College, Richmond.
InRenS	St. Joseph's College, Rensselaer.
InStme	St. Meinrad's College & Seminary, St. Meinrad.
InU	Indiana University, Bloomington.

KANSAS

K	Kansas State Library, Topeka.
KAS	St. Benedict's College, Atchison.
KAStB*	St. Benedict's College, Atchison.
KHi	Kansas State Historical Society, Topeka.
KKcB	Central Baptist Theological Seminary, Kansas City.
KMK	Kansas State University, Manhattan.
KStMC*	St. Louis University, School of Divinity Library, St. Louis, Mo.
KU	University of Kansas, Lawrence.
KU-M	— Medical Center Library, Kansas City.
KWiU	Wichita State University, Wichita.

KENTUCKY

Ky-LE	Library Extension Division, Frankfort.
KyBgW	Western Kentucky State College, Bowling Green
KyHi	Kentucky Historical Society, Frankfort.
KyLo	Louisville Free Public Library.
KyLoS	Southern Baptist Theological Seminary, Louisville.
KyLoU	University of Louisville, Louisville.
KyLx	Lexington Public Library.
KyLxCB	Lexington Theological Seminary, Lexington. (Formerly College of the Bible)
KyLxT	Transylvania College, Lexington.
KyMoreT	Morehead State College, Morehead.
KyU	University of Kentucky, Lexington.
KyWA	Asbury College Library, Wilmore.
KyWAT	Asbury Theological Seminary, Wilmore.

LOUISIANA

L	Louisiana State Library, Baton Rouge.
L-M	Louisiana State Museum Library, New Orleans.
LCA	Not a library symbol.
LCS	Not a library symbol.
LHi	Louisiana History Society, New Orleans.
LNHT	Tulane University Library, New Orleans.
LNT-MA	Tulane University, Latin American Library, New Orleans.
LU	Louisiana State University, Baton Rouge.
LU-M	— Medical Center Library, New Orleans.
LU-NO	— Louisiana State University in New Orleans.

MASSACHUSETTS

M	Massachusetts State Library, Boston.
MA	Amherst College, Amherst.
MB	Boston Public Library.
MBAt	Boston Athenaeum, Boston.
MBBC*	Boston College, Chestnut Hill.
MBCo	Countway Library of Medicine. (Harvard-Boston Medical Libraries)
MBH	Massachusetts Horticultural Society, Boston.
MBHo*	Massachusetts Horticultural Society, Boston.
MBM*	Countway Library of Medicine (Harvard-Boston Medical Libraries).
MBMu	Museum of Fine Arts, Boston.
MBU	Boston University.
MBdAF	U.S. Air Force Cambridge Research Center, Bedford.
MBrZ	Zion Research Library, Brookline.
MBrigStJ*	St. John's Seminary, Brighton.
MBtS	St. John's Seminary Library, Brighton.
MCM	Massachusetts Institute of Technology, Cambridge.
MCR	Radcliffe College, Cambridge.
MCSA	Smithsonian Institution, Astrophysical Observatory, Cambridge.
MChB	Boston College, Chestnut Hill.
MH	Harvard University, Cambridge.
MH-A	— Arnold Arboretum.
MH-AH	— Andover-Harvard Theological Library.
MH-BA	— Graduate School of Business Administration Library.
MH-FA	— Fine Arts Library. (Formerly Fogg Art Museum)
MH-G	— Gray Herbarium Library.
MH-HY	— Harvard-Yenching Institute. (Chinese-Japanese Library)

MASSACHUSETTS continued

MH-L	— Law School Library.
MH-P	— Peabody Museum Library.
MH-PR	— Physics Research Library.
MHi	Massachusetts Historical Society, Boston.
MMeT	Tufts University, Medford.
MNF	Forbes Library, Northampton.
MNS	Smith College, Northampton.
MNoeS	Stonehill College Library, North Easton.
MNtcA	Andover Newton Theological School, Newton Center.
MSaE	Essex Institute, Salem.
MShM	Mount Holyoke College, South Hadley.
MU	University of Massachusetts, Amherst.
MWA	American Antiquarian Society, Worcester.
MWAC	Assumption College, Worcester.
MWC	Clark University, Worcester.
MWH	College of the Holy Cross, Worcester.
MWalB	Brandeis University, Waltham.
MWelC	Wellesley College, Wellesley.
MWhB	Marine Biological Laboratory, Woods Hole.
MWiW	Williams College, Williamstown.
MWiW-C	— Chapin Library.

MARYLAND

MdAN	U.S. Naval Academy, Annapolis.
MdBE	Enoch Pratt Free Library, Baltimore.
MdBG	Goucher College, Baltimore.
MdBJ	Johns Hopkins University, Baltimore.
MdBJ-G	— John Work Garrett Library.
MdBP	Peabody Institute, Baltimore.
MdBWA	Walters Art Gallery, Baltimore.
MdU	University of Maryland, College Park.
MdW	Woodstock College, Woodstock.

MAINE

MeB	Bowdoin College, Brunswick.
MeBa	Bangor Public Library.
MeU	University of Maine, Orono.
MeWC	Colby College, Waterville.
MeWaC*	Colby College, Waterville.

MICHIGAN

Mi	Michigan State Library, Lansing.
MiAC	Alma College, Alma.
MiD	Detroit Public Library.
MiD-B	— Burton Historical Collection.
MiDA	Detroit Institute of Arts, Detroit.
MiDU	University of Detroit, Detroit.
MiDW	Wayne State University, Detroit.
MiEM	Michigan State University, East Lansing.
MiEalC*	Michigan State University, East Lansing.
MiGr	Grand Rapids Public Library.
MiH*	Michigan College of Mining and Technology, Houghton.
MiHM	Michigan College of Mining and Technology, Houghton.
MiU	University of Michigan, Ann Arbor.
MiU-C	— William L. Clements Library.

MINNESOTA

MnCS	St. John's University, Collegeville.
MnH*	Minnesota Historical Society, St. Paul.
MnHi	Minnesota Historical Society, St. Paul.
MnRM	Mayo Clinic and Foundation Library, Rochester.
MnSJ	James Jerome Hill Reference Library, St. Paul.
MnSSC	College of St. Catherine, St. Paul.
MnU	University of Minnesota, Minneapolis.

MISSOURI

MoHi	Missouri State Historical Society, Columbia
MoK	Kansas City Public Library.
MoKL	Linda Hall Library, Kansas City
MoKU	University of Missouri at Kansas City, Kansas City.
MoS	St. Louis Public Library.
MoSB	Missouri Botanical Garden, St. Louis.
MoSC*	Concordia Seminary Library, St. Louis.
MoSCS	Concordia Seminary Library, St. Louis.
MoSM	Mercantile Library Association, St. Louis.
MoSU	St. Louis University, St. Louis.
MoSU-D	— School of Divinity Library, St. Louis.
MoSW	Washington University, St. Louis.
MoU	University of Missouri, Columbia.

The National Union Catalog

Pre-1956 Imprints

The National Union Catalog

Pre-1956 Imprints

A cumulative author list representing Library of Congress printed cards and titles reported by other American libraries. Compiled and edited with the cooperation of the Library of Congress and the National Union Catalog Subcommittee of the Resources Committee of the Resources and Technical Services Division, American Library Association

Volume 407

NATIONAL EXTEMPORE - NATIONAL SONGS OF THE ALLIES

Mansell 1975

© 1975 Mansell Information/Publishing Limited

© 1975 The American Library Association

Mansell Information/Publishing Limited
3 Bloomsbury Place, London WC1

The American Library Association
50 East Huron Street, Chicago, Illinois 60611

The paper on which this catalog has been printed is supplied by
P. F. Bingham Limited and has been specially manufactured by the
Guard Bridge Paper Company Limited of Fife, Scotland.
Based on requirements established by the late William J. Barrow
for a permanent/durable book paper it is laboratory certified
to meet or exceed the following values:

Substance 89 gsm
pH cold extract 9·4
Fold endurance (MIT $\frac{1}{2}$kg. tension) 1200
Tear resistance (Elmendorf) 73 (or 67 × 3)
Opacity 90·3%

Library of Congress Card Number: 67–30001
ISBN: 0 7201 0500 5

Printed by Balding & Mansell Limited, London and Wisbech, England
Bound by Bemrose & Sons Limited, Derby, England

American Library Association

Resources and Technical Services Division

RESOURCES COMMITTEE

SUBCOMMITTEE ON THE NATIONAL UNION CATALOG

Chairman GORDON R. WILLIAMS
Director CENTER FOR RESEARCH LIBRARIES
5721 Cottage Grove Avenue, Chicago, Illinois 60637

Members

DOUGLAS W. BRYANT *University Librarian*
Widener Library, Harvard University
Cambridge, Massachusetts 02138

VERNER W. CLAPP 1901-1972 *formerly*
Consultant Council on Library Resources, Inc.

JOHN W. CRONIN *formerly*
Director Processing Department
Library of Congress
2129 32nd Place, S.E.
Washington, D.C. 20020

CHARLES W. DAVID *formerly*
Director of Library Development
Marine Historical Association
854 Radnor Road
St. Davids, Pennsylvania 19087

WILLIAM S. DIX *University Librarian*
Princeton University
Princeton, New Jersey 08540

RALPH E. ELLSWORTH *formerly*
Director University of Colorado Libraries
Boulder, Colorado 80302

HERMAN H. FUSSLER *Professor*
Graduate Library School
University of Chicago
Chicago, Illinois 60637

WARREN J. HAAS *Vice President*
for Libraries and Information Services
Columbia University
New York City, New York 10027

RUTHERFORD D. ROGERS *University Librarian*
Yale University
New Haven, Connecticut 06520

GEORGE A. SCHWEGMANN, JR. *formerly*
Chief Union Catalog Division
3534 Porter Street, N.W.
Washington, D.C. 20016

FREDERICK H. WAGMAN *Director*
University of Michigan Libraries
Ann Arbor, Michigan 48104

WILLIAM J. WELSH *Director*
Processing Department
Library of Congress
Washington, D.C. 20540

Publisher's Note

Because of the large number of sources from which the information in the National Union Catalog has been collected over a long period of time an understanding of its scope and an acquaintance with its methods is necessary for the best use to be made of it. Users are therefore earnestly advised to make themselves familiar with the introductory matter in Volume 1. This fully defines the scope of the Catalog and sets out the basis on which the material reported to the National Union Catalog has been edited for publication in book form.

National Union Catalog Designation

Each main entry in the Catalog has been ascribed a unique identifying designation. This alphanumeric combination appears uniformly after the last line of the entry itself and consists of:

1   The letter N, signifying National Union Catalog.
2   The initial letter under which the entry is filed.
3   A number representing the position of the entry within the sequence under its initial letter.

This National Union Catalog designator is sufficient both to identify any main entry in the Catalog and to establish its position within the sequence of volumes. It is, however, recommended that when referring to titles by the National Union Catalog designation a checking element, such as the key word or initials of the title, be added.

Reported Locations

Alphabetic symbols which represent libraries in the United States and Canada follow the National Union Catalog designation. These groups of letters signify which libraries have reported holding copies of the work. The first library so represented usually is the one that provided the catalog information.

Printed on the end sheets of each volume is a list of most frequently used symbols, each followed by the full name of the library. *List of Symbols*, containing a comprehensive list of symbols used, is published as a separate volume with the Catalog. The Library of Congress has also issued *Symbols Used in the National Union Catalog of the Library of Congress*. In cases where a symbol is not identified in these lists the National Union Catalog Division of the Library of Congress will, on enquiry, attempt to identify the library concerned.

Other Developments

Under the terms of their agreement with the American Library Association, the publishers have undertaken to apply, as far as is practicable, new developments in library science and techniques which may have the effect of further enhancing the value of the Catalog. To this end, the publishers will be pleased to receive suggestions and enquiries relating to technical and production aspects of the Catalog and will be glad to consider proposals calculated to improve its utility and amenity. Mansell Information/Publishing Limited will be pleased also to advise libraries on possible applications of the methods and techniques developed for this and similar projects to their own requirements.

J.C.
London, *August 1968*

VOLUME 407

The **National** extempore-discussion contest on inter-American affairs for colleges and universities. Sponsored by Office of coordinator of inter-American affairs. 1942. New York city, National public discussions committee, inc. [1942]

2 p. l., [7]-22 p., 1 l. illus. (port.) 21½ᶜᵐ.

Bibliography: p. 14-21.

1. American republics.   I. National public discussions committee.

41-46465

Library of Congress   F1418.N3

[6]   341.1

NN   0050637   DLC OrCS OrU Or

1.913
C3N216   National Extension Young Adult Planning
         Conference, Jackson's Mill, W. Va., 1949.
         Preliminary program.   Washington, 1949.
         3 p.

Issued Jan. 1949.

1. Youth.   2. Agricultural extension.
Congresses.   I. U.S. Extension Service.

NN   0050638   DNAL

630.717 National Extension Young Adult Planning Con-
N21r   ference, Weston, W. Va., 1949.
1949   Report of National Extension Young Adult
         Planning Conference.   Weston, W. Va.,
         State 4-H Camp, 1949.
         cover-title, 74p.   28cm.

1. Agricultural extension work.   I. Association of Land-Grant Colleges. Committee on Extension Organ-   ization and Policy.

NN   0050639   LU IU OrCS IdU DNAL

National FAO Committee of Finland
    see   Food and Agriculture Organization of
the United Nations. National FAO Committee of
Finland.

National Fabric and Finishing Company, inc.
[Pamphlets. Financial history]
31 cm.

NN   0050641   CtY

GV403 National Facilities Conference 1st,
.C6   Jackson's Mill, W. Va., 1946.
       College Physical Education Association.
       College facilities for physical education, health education,
       and recreation. [Standards for design and construction]
       Pub. by the College Physical Education Assn. with the as-
       sistance of the National Collegiate Athletic Assn. and the
       National Conference on Facilities for Athletics, Recreation,
       Health and Physical Education, as sponsored by the Ath-
       letic Institute, Jackson's Mill, W. Va., Dec. 1-15, 1946.
       Karl W. Bookwalter, editor. [n. p.] 1947 [i. e. 1948]

National Facilities Conference, *1st, Jackson's Mill, W. Va.,
1946.*
    A guide for planning facilities for athletics, recreation,
physical & health education.   Chicago, Athletic Institute
[1947]
    xi, 127 p.   illus.   28 cm.
    Bibliography: p. 121-123.

1. Recreation—Congresses.   2. Physical education facilities.
I. Title.

GV401.N33 1946c   796.06373   49-2407

MiD IaU N OO ViU MdBJ FMU TxU NIC TU DI NN NcU MiU
CaBVaU IdU OrCS OrP OrPS OrU WaT WaWW PPT PSt MH
NN   0050643   DLC InU MiU OkU CU WU WaU CLU TxU OCl

National Facilities Conference, 1st, Jackson's
Mill, W. Va., 1946.
    NEMA standard floodlight layouts for
floodlighting sports areas
    see under   National Electric Manu-
facturers Association.

National Facilities Conference. 1st, Jackson's
Mill, W. Va., 1946.
    The physical education instructor and
safety.   Washington, D.C., National Education
Association, 1948.
    48 p.   23 cm.   (Its High-school series,
bulletin no. 2)

NN   0050646   PSt

National fact book; a current statistical service
    see under   National Association of Manu-
facturers of the United States of America.
Research Dept.

National fact book: Mutual savings banking
    see under   National Association of Mutual
Savings Banks.

National fair for the exhibition of American manu-
factures. *1st, Washington, D. C., 1846.*
    see
Washington, D. C.   National fair for the exhibition of
American manufactures. *1st, 1846.*

National Fair-trade League, London.
The fair-trade position explained ...
    see under   Lloyd, Sampson S

SPECIAL COLLECTIONS
Seligman
Per.
N218   National Fair-Trade League, London.
         Fair-trade tracts.
         No.
         London, Issued by the National Fair-Trade League
         [188
         v.   22cm.

NN   0050651   NNC

941.58 National fair-trade league, London
C692   Import and export statistics: their
v.56   bearing on the fair-trade controversy.
no.11   A full report of the discussion at the
        Statistical society, 4th April, 1882, to-
        gether with further notes, forming a re-
        ply to Mr. Robert Giffen's paper read be-
        fore the Statistical society, 21st March,
        1882, on "The use of import and export
        statistics"   London, 1882.
        48p.

[Collins pamphlets. v.56, no.11]
"Reprint from the "Morning Post" of
Thursday, April 6th, 1882, with corrections made by the several speakers, excepting in the case of Mr. Giffen ..."

NN   0050652   IU

A national faith
    see under   Conservative Central Education
Committee, London.

Ayb31   The National family almanac for the year
N213   of our Lord 1847 ... calculated for
        New York and New Jersey ...   New
        York: Published by William H. Graham[etc.]
        48p.   illus.   21cm.

By Aaron Maynard.
Numbered at head of title: vol.2, no.2.
No more published?

1. Almanacs - U.S.   I. Maynard, Aaron

NN   0050654   CtY

WA
100   **National Family Health Week.**
N28
        [Collection of publications]
        The Library has a collection of miscellaneous
        publications of this organization kept as recieved. These
        publications are not listed or bound separately.
        1. General Practice   2. Health

NN   0050655   DNLM

National family opinion, Inc.
    A family survey of current living costs.
Toledo, Ohio, 1948.
    15p.

NN   0050656   PPCuP

National Family Opinion, Inc.
    A national survey of major purchases; period
covered, recall of purchases October 15, 1951 to
March 19, 1952.   [Chicago? 1952?]
    32 p.
    1. Shopping - U.S.   2. Consumers - U.S.
I. Title.

NN   0050657   ICarbS

Pamphlet
HF
81+   National Family Opinion, Inc.
        A study of coffee purchasing and con-
        sumption. Survey period: March 3 through
        March 29, 1954.   [Toledo, Ohio] 1954.
        21 l.   29cm.

1. Coffee—Tables, etc.

NN   0050658   NIC

R
917.631 National farm and live stock show.
N27   Premium list.   November 11th-19th, 1916.
1916   New Orleans, n.p., 1916?
         38 p.

1. Live stock exhibitions.   I. Title.

NN   0050659   LN

National Farm and Power Equipment Dealers
Association.
    Farm equipment retailer's handbook
    see under   Merrifield, Arch S

5677   National Farm and Power Equipment Dealers
O35   Association.

Official tractor and farm equipment guide.

St. Louis, Farm Equipment Retailing.

National farm and tractor implement blue book
    see   National farm tractor and implement
blue book

VOLUME 407

National Farm and Power Equipment Dealers Association.
Cost of doing business in the farm equipment retailing industry. St. Louis, Mo., Farm Equipment Retailing, inc.
Cover title.

NN 0050663   OC1

R658.34
F4N2
National Farm and Power Equipment Dealers Association.
Cost of doing business in the farm equipment retailing industry. St. Louis, Farm Equipment Retailing, Inc., 1955.
16 ₍2₎ p. charts.

Cover title.

1. Farm equipment   2. Agricultural machinery   I. T.

NN 0050664   MiD

Pamphlet
HD
257+
National Farm and Power Equipment De lers Association.
The retail farm equipment cost of doing business in 1954. ₍n.p., 1955?₎
16p. illus. 28cm.

Cover title.

1.Agricultural machinery--Trade and manufacture--U.S. I.Title.

NN 0050665   NIC

National Farm and Power Equipment Dealers Association.
Standard accounting procedure for the farm equipment retailers' accounting system.....
Oklahoma City, 1940.

2 p. l., ix 45 p. ₍16₎ l. of fold.

NN 0050666   OC1

National Farm Building Improvements Conference, Des Moines, 1918.
...Report of the National Farm Building Improvements Conference, Sept. 26-27-28, 1918, Des Moines, Iowa, called by Successful farming... ₍Des Moines: E. T. Meredith, 1918.₎
96 p. illus. 4°.

1. Agriculture.--Congresses, Des   Moines, Iowa. 2. Farmhouses and
buildings.
N. Y. P. L.   October 21. 1919.

NN 0050667   NN

National Farm Bureau Institute
see   American Farm Bureau Institute.

---

q660.282
M213
1939
National Farm Chemurgic Conference. 5th, Jackson, Miss., etc., 1939.
₍Papers₎ Columbus, Ohio, National Farm Chemurgic Council ₍1939₎
38 pieces in 1v. 29cm.

1. Chemurgy. I. National Farm Chemurgic Council.

NN 0050669   TxU

---

q660
N21p
National Farm Chemurgic Conference, 6th, Chicago, Ill., 1940.
₍Papers presented at₎ sixth annual National farm chemurgic conference, Chicago, Illinois, March 27-29, 1940 ... Columbus, O., National farm chemurgic council, inc.₍1940₎
37 no. in portfolio.

Mimeographed; no.20 and 27 printed; no.15 lacks t.-p.

NN 0050670   IU MiD WaS

National Farm Chemurgic Council.
Addresses presented at the annual Chemurgic Conference ... ₍Columbus, Ohio₎National Farm Chemurgic Council, Inc.; etc., etc., 1935-   ₎
Library has no. 1, 1935, to date. illus., plates, ports., maps, diagrs. 26-30ᶜᵐ.
The Farm Chemurgic Council was organized in May 1935 at the first Dearborn Conference; incorporated in June 1937 as National Farm Chemurgic Council.
Title varies: no. 1-2, Proceedings of the ... Dearborn Conference of Agriculture, Industry and Science.
No. 3, ₍ Proceedings of the ... Dearborn Conference.
No. 3, and selected papers from no. 4, issued in the Farm chemurgic journal,   have call number L660.51

No. 5-   issued only in the form of mimeographed papers read at the conferences.
No. 1 printed and distributed by Chemical Foundation, Inc., New York; no. 2, by Chemical Foundation, Inc., New York, and National Farm Chemurgic Council, Dearborn, Mich.
Wanting: no. 5-6, 1939-1940.

NN 0050672   ICJ

₍National farm chemurgic council₎
... ₍Addresses given₎ at the ... annual southern chemurgic conference ... 1st-1941-   ₍n.p., 1941?₎-
v.

Manifold copy.

NN 0050673   MH-BA

National Farm Chemurgic Council.
... Bulletin ... Columbus, Ohio, National Farm Chemurgic Council ₍1940-   ₎
Library has no. 1 to date. illus. 26ᶜᵐ.
At head of title: National Farm Chemurgic Council.
Issued without series numbering (listed in no. 4)

NN 0050674   ICJ NN

TP149
.C52
National farm chemurgic council.
The Chemurgic digest. v. 1-
Jan. 15, 1942-
Columbus, O., National farm chemurgic council, 1942-

National farm chemurgic council.
Chemurgy, progress and promise, by twenty-seven distinguished Americans. Columbus, O., New York, N. Y., The National farm chemurgic council incorporated, 1946.

1 p. l., 62 p. illus. (ports.) 23½ᶜᵐ.

1. Chemurgy.

TP149.N3   660   47-23814

NN 0050676   DLC MiU OrCS OC1 NN Mi IU ICJ PSt TU

630.1606 **National farm chemurgic council.**
NA2c   ... Constitution and by-laws ... 1937-1938.
Dearborn, Mich.₍1938?₎
cover-title, 16p.

At head of title: National farm chemurgic council ... coördinating agriculture, industry and science.

1. Agricultural chemistry--Societies.

NN 0050677   IU DNAL

National farm chemurgic council.
... The domestic production of essential oils from aromatic plants; a compilation of research papers relating to problems in the agricultural production of essential oils from the cultivation of aromatic plants. Columbus, O., National farm chemurgic council ₍1940₎
77 p. incl. illus., map, tables, diagrs. 25½ᶜᵐ. (Its Bulletin. ₍No. 1₎)
Bibliography: p. 62-63; p. 75-77.
CONTENTS.--Raw materials for essential oils, by H. F. Willkie and P. J. Kolachov.--The role of agricultural engineer in the production of essential oils, by P. J. Kolachov.--The preferential odour rating of essential oils from coriander seeds, by E. H. Scofield.--Laboratory assayment of raw materials for essential oils.
1. Herbs. 2. Essences   and essential oils.   I. Willkie,
Herman Frederick, 1890-   II. Kolachov, Paul John, 1899-
III. Scofield, E. H.   IV. Title.
Library of Congress   SB305.N35   41-9942
            ₍a45g1₎   633.85

OrCS DNAL
NN 0050678   DLC MB OC1FRB MH ICJ MH-BA OC1 OrP

TP149
.F3
National farm chemurgic council.
Farm chemurgic journal. v. 1, no. 1-3; Sept. 1937-Dec. 1938.
Dearborn, Mich., National farm chemurgic council, inc., 1937-38.

National Farm Chemurgic Council.
Kok-Sagyz
see under Kolachov, Paul John, 1899-

National farm chemurgic council.
Modern plastics
see under Demuth, H. M.

National Farm Chemurgic Council.
New fields for American agriculture.
see under Kolachov, Paul John, 1899-

National farm chemurgic council.
News bulletin ... v. 1-
Columbus, O. ₍19
v. diagr. 28ᵐᵐ. semimonthly.
Caption title.
Reproduced from type-written copy.

1. Chemurgy--Societies.
                        42-44973 Revised
Library of Congress   TP1.N3
            ₍r46c2₎   660.6273

NN 0050683   DLC ICJ PPAmP NN

NATIONAL FARM CHEMURGIC COUNCIL.
₍Publications₎ no. ₍1-10, 12₎-152, 154-230, 232-249, 251-264, 266-309, 311-320.
Columbus, O., 1940-44. no.   21-28cm.

Irregular.
Many issues lack numbering.
No. 11 withdrawn from circulation.

No. 1-320, various no. are reports made at the annual National farm chemurgic conference, no. 6-10, 1940-43. (Name of conference, 1941-43: Chemurgic conference.) For reports of the 1st-2d conference, see: Chemurgic conference. Proceedings of the Dearborn conference of agriculture, industry and science, Dearborn, Michigan; for the 3d, see Farm chemurgic journal.
Other numbers are reports made at various local chemurgic conferences.
For later file, see   Chemurgic papers.
1. Chemurgy.--Per. and soc.   publ. 2. Chemistry--Per. and
soc. publ.

NN 0050684   NN

SB
109
.N3
National Farm Chemurgic Council.
United States imports as possible new crops for experimentation and large scale domestic cultivation. Columbus, O., National Farm Chemurgic Council ₍1941₎
32p. 27cm. (Its Bulletin)

1. Plant introduction. 2. Domestication.
I. Title.

OrCS
NN 0050685   OrU OC1FRB DNAL OC1 OU MB MiD Or

VOLUME 407

HC
107
V5N52+
National Farm Chemurgic Council.
Vermont survey 1954. Prepared for
the Vermont Development Commission.
New York [1954]
[63] p. 28 cm.

NN 0050686 NIC

660
N213
National Farm Chemurgic Council. Oregon State
Committee.
Preliminary report of chemurgic achievements
for Oregon, 1946, by H.W. Derry, secretary.
[n.p.], 1946.
35 l. 29cm.

Processed.

1. Chemurgy. I. Derry, H.W.

NN 0050687 OrU

S583
qN3
National Farm Chemurgic Council. Oregon
State Committee.
Report of chemurgic achievements for
Oregon, 1944-45.
[n.p.] 1944-45.
v. 28cm.

Processed.

1. Agricultural chemistry. 2. Chemurgy.
x: Oregon State Committee National Farm
Chemurgic Council. x: Oregon.
State Committee National Farm

NN 0050688 OrCS

281.12
N217
National farm chemurgic council. Re-
search committee.
Chemurgic potentialities, for the con-
sideration of the Research committee of the
National farm chemurgic council, Columbus,
Ohio. [Columbus? Ohio, 1939]
unp. 28cm.
Processed.

NN 0050689 DNAL

National Farm Chemurgic Council. *Research Committee.*
Minutes of New York meeting, November 8, 1935. Dearborn, Mich. [1935]
37 l. (incl. cover) 28 cm.

At head of title: Not for publication.
Pub. by the committee under an earlier name of the council:
Farm Chemurgic Council.

1. Chemurgy—Societies.

TP149.N32 660.72 48-39803*

NN 0050690 DLC

National Farm Chemurgic Council. Research
Division.
Chemurgic papers
see under title

The **National** farm holiday news.
v. 1–2, no. 9 (Aug. 28, 1936 – Dec. 31, 1937)
Minneapolis, Minn.: National farm holiday news, inc., 1936–37.
2 v. illus. (incl. ports.) 33½cm.

Weekly, Aug. 28, 1936 – July 2, 1937; biweekly, July 16 – Dec. 31, 1937.
Formed by the union of Farm holiday news and Farmers national weekly.
Published by the National farmers' holiday association.
Vol. 1 complete in 50 numbers (no. 47 omitted in numbering); v. 2 complete in 9
numbers.
No more published.

1. Farmers—U. S. 2. Credit. Agricultural—U. S. 3. Agriculture
—Per. and soc. publ. I. National farmers' holiday association.
N. Y. P. L. January 26, 1939

NN 0050692 NN

National farm institute, *Des Moines.*
Proceedings... v. 1–
1937–
[Des Moines, Ia., Agricultural department, Des Moines
chamber of commerce, 1937–
v. 22 cm. annual.

"Sponsored by Agricultural department, Des Moines chamber of
commerce."

1. Agriculture—Congresses. 2. Agriculture—Economic aspects.
3. Agriculture—U. S.

S1.N17 630.6373 A 41–881
Oregon. State College. Library
for Library of Congress [a51d1]†

NN 0050693 OrU OrCS CU IU CtY KEmT NN DLC

The **National** farm journal
see
Farm journal and country gentleman.

National farm labor union
For publications before 1946

see

Southern tenant farmers' union

National Farm Labor Union
see also
National Agricultural Workers Union.
Southern Tenant Farmers' Union.

HFBA29
+N213
MIS
National Farm Labor Union.
Constitution. Washington, D.C., 1949–
v. 28 cm.

Library has: 1949

NN 0050697 WHi

283
N2122
National Farm Labor Union.
Statement of H.L. Mitchell, president [on]
amending Fair Labor Standards Act to include
agricultural workers. [n.p.] 1949.
2 l.

1. Wages, Agricultural. U.S. 2. Wages.
Minimum wage. U.S. I. Mitchell, Harold
Loren, 1906–

NN 0050698 DNAL

HFBA29
+N213
MIS
National Farm Labor Union. Executive
board.
Agricultural labor in 1948. Report...
to the 15th annual convention...Cincin-
nati...[1948] [Washington, D.C.? 1948]
14 l. 28 cm.

Reproduced from typewritten copy.

NN 0050699 WHi

283.9
N215
National Farm Labor Union. Executive Board.
Report ... to the ... annual convention.

[n. p.]

NN 0050700 DNAL

The **National** farm news...
v.

Washington, D. C.: The Independent Pub. Co., 1927– f°.
v. illus.

Weekly.

1. Agriculture—Per. and soc. publ.
N. Y. P. L. August 27, 1929

NN 0050701 NN

National farm poultry journal.
v.

Minneapolis, 19 4°.
v. illus.

Monthly.
Formed by the union of The Northwestern poultry journal and Farm poultry
(Kearney, Neb.).
Editor : 19 W. M. Phelps.

1. Poultry—Per. and soc. publ.
N. Y. P. L. May 7, 1928

NN 0050702 NN

NATIONAL FARM POWER.
Chart showing principal agricultural
publications of the United States, with
circulation by states. New York, etc., 1918.

1 sheet 25 1/2 x 16 in.

NN 0050703 MH-BA

NATIONAL FARM POWER.
A complete report of the automobile
survey of the National farm power. [1915]

NN 0050704 MH-BA

National farm radio forum (Radio program)
Farm forum handbook. [Toronto, Nat. farm radio forum,
1944] 39 p. illus. 15cm.

1. Forums, Radio—Canada. I. Title.
N. Y. P. L. April 24, 1947

NN 0050705 NN

281.9
N216F
1949
National Farm Radio Forum (Radio program)
Farm forum handbook. [Toronto, 1949]
40 p.
1. Forums (Discussion and debate)
2. Radio broadcasting. Agricultural applications.
3. National Farm Radio Forum, Toronto.
I. Title.

NN 0050706 DNAL

281.9
N216Ff
National Farm Radio Forum (Radio program)
Farm forum program guide.
Toronto.

NN 0050707 DNAL

281.9
N216Fa
[National farm radio forum (Radio program)
Farm forum questionnaire ... Summary of
replies.
[Toronto?

NN 0050708 DNAL

VOLUME 407

281.9
N216H   National Farm Radio Forum (Radio program)
      Handbook. Farm radio forums explained.
      [Toronto? 194-]
      26 p.

NN   0050709   DNAL

National farm radio forum (*Radio program*)
      Health can be planned. Four broadcasts on health planning, from National farm radio forum broadcasts, over CBC national network, December 6-27, 1943. Toronto, Health study bureau [1944]
      31 p. 25½ᶜᵐ.
      "These four broadcasts were part of the Planning for plenty series from November 8th, 1943 to March 20th, 1944."—Foreword.
      CONTENTS.—How stands health?—The draft bill for health insurance—The C. F. A. health plan.—What the forums say about 'Health can be planned.'—Suggested reading (p. 31)
      1. Insurance, Health—Canada. 2. Canada—Statistics, Medical. I. Health study bureau, Toronto. II. Title.
                             45-14283
      Library of Congress   HG9309.C22N35
                    [2]   331.25442

NN   0050710   DLC

281.9
N216N   National Farm Radio Forum (Radio program)
      National Farm Radio Forum.

      [Toronto]

NN   0050711   DNAL

National farm radio forum (Radio program)
      Planning for plenty series. no. 1-5. Toronto, 1943-44.
      5 nos. 18cm.
      No more published.
                       CONTENTS.
      no. 1. Planning, prices and controls. [1943]
      no. 2. Planning for health. [1943]
      no. 3. Planning farm credit. [1943]
      no. 4. Planning for rural living. [1944]
      no. 5. Planning reaches the family farm. [1944]

      1. Country life—Canada. I. Title.
      N. Y. P. L.   June 28, 1944

NN   0050712   NN DNAL

281.9
N216R   National farm radio forum (Radio program)
      Report for year ending

      [Toronto?

NN   0050713   DNAL

National Farm School, Farm School, Pa.
      see Farm School, Pa. National Agricultural College [Supplement]

National farm school conference, *New York, 1926.*
      An American contribution; a resumé of the National farm school conference ... June 2-7, 1926, New York city. [New York city, Pace press, inc., 1926]
      148 p. plates, ports. 27½ᶜᵐ.

      1. Agricultural education—Congresses. 2. Doylestown, Pa. National farm school. I. Title.
                              29-859
      Library of Congress   S533.N32 1926

NN   0050715   DLC IU NN OU MtHi MtBC ICU DNAL OCH

National farm survey studies
      see under Bristol, Eng. University. Dept. of Economics (Agricultural economics)

National farm tractor and implement **blue book.**
      Chicago, National Market Reports.
          v. 18 cm. annual.
          Began publication in 1939.

      1. Tractor industry—U. S. 2. Agricultural machinery—Trade and manufacture—U. S.
      HD9486.U3N3   62-32340

NN   0050717   DLC DNAL LU MiD NIC IU

National farm tractor directory; a complete list of **farm** tractors, their manufacturers, horse power, type, traction and other particulars ... [1st-1916-
      New York, The Agricultural press, inc. [1916-]
         v. 31½ᶜᵐ.
      Compiler: 1916-   C. E. Stone.

      1. Traction-engines.   I. Stone, Charles E., comp.
                              16-18581
      Library of Congress   S711.N3

NN   0050718   DLC DNAL

SD
118
N27+   National Farm Woodlot Conference, Chicago, 1953.
1953   Proceedings National Farm Woodlot Conference, Chicago, Illinois, June 25 and 26, 1953. Washington, D. C., American Forest Products Industries, Inc. [1955?]
      101 p. 28cm.

      Reproduced from typewritten copy.

         AAP IU MiU
NN   0050719   NIC DNAL CaBVaU ICarbS NcU PPF TxU

National farm youth foundation.

La Salle extension university, *Chicago.*
      Farm engineering and management ... **especially prepared** for National farm youth foundation by La Salle extension university ... Chicago [°1940-]

NATIONAL FARM YOUTH FOUNDATION.
      Making it possible for young men to stay on the land. [Dearborn, Michigan, Ferguson-Sherman Mfg. Corp., cop.1941.]

      28 cm.

NN   0050721   MH

NATIONAL FARM YOUTH FOUNDATION
      National farm youth foundation. Dearborn, Mich., Author, 1941.
      [12] p. illus.

NN   0050722   Or

National farm youth foundation.
      Progress bulletin... Students of 1940-41 classes graduate. [Dearborn, Mich., 1941]
      11 p. illus. 28 cm.

NN   0050723   DNAL

275.1
N214T   National farm youth foundation.
      Trained army of young farm women ready for victory drive in battle of food production. [Dearborn, Mich., c1942]
      11 p. illus. 28cm.

      Caption title.
      At head of title: Progress bulletin ...
      Lithographed.

NN   0050724   DNAL

630.5
qN277   The National farmer and home magazine. v. 1-18 -   Augusta, Me., E. Allen & Co.
      v. illus. 37-46 cm. monthly.

      1. Agriculture. Period.

NN   0050725   N DLC

S1
.N3   The National farmer and stock grower. v. 4, Jul.-Dec. 1900; v. 6, Jul.-Dec. 1901. St. Louis, 1900-01.
      2 v. 23.5 cm.

NN   0050726   DLC

National farmer and stock grower.

Hale, Philip Henry.
      The book of live stock champions, being an artistic souvenir supplement of the monthly National farmer and stock grower. Comp. and published by Philip H. Hale ... 1st complete ed., 1905. St. Louis, Mo., P. H. Hale, 1905.

National farmer and stock grower.

Hale, Philip Henry, *ed.*
      Hale's history of agriculture by dates. A simple record of historical events and victories of peaceful industries. Pub. in connection with the National farmer and stock grower ... 5th ed. ... St. Louis, Mo., The Hale publishing co., 1915.

National Farmers' Alliance.   630.6128 3
      Constitution of the National Farmers' Alliance as adopted at the eleventh annual meeting held at Omaha, Nebraska, Jan. 27, 28 & 29, 1891. .... Moulton, Iowa, [1891].
      7 p. 12½ᶜᵐ, bound 24ᶜᵐ.
      —— [Constitution of the] National Farmers' Alliance [and of subordinate Alliances. Moulton, Iowa.]
      15 p. 24ᶜᵐ.
      Advertisements, p. 11-15.
      Barrett, T. H. Address to the American people, p. 7-9.
      Bound together.

NN   0050729   ICJ

630.973 National farmers' alliance.
N214h   History of the Alliance movement. [Chicago, The Western rural, 1883?]
      [16]p.

      Caption title.

      1. Agricultural societies--U.S. I. The Western rural.

NN   0050730   IU ICJ

National Farmers' Alliance.   332.42 01
      Memorial from the National Farmers' Alliance to the Honorable the Congress of the United States. [188-]
      [2], 5 p. 24ᶜᵐ.

NN   0050731   ICJ IEN

National Farmers' Alliance.   630.6128 4
      Proceedings of the National Farmers' Alliance at its ... annual meeting. .... Des Moines, Iowa, 1890-1891.
      No. [9], 11, 1889, 1891. 17-24ᶜᵐ.
      1889 title reads: Proceedings of the annual session of the Farmers and Laborers Union of America; published in Washington, D. C.

NN   0050732   ICJ WHi

VOLUME 407

National farmers' alliance and co-operative
        union of America
  see

National farmers' alliance and industrial union.

Pam. National farmers' alliance and industrial
Coll. union.

15628 The consolidation of the Alliance and
    Wheel [n.p., 1888?]
     12 p. 22cm.

     Caption title.
    "Constitution and by-laws of the Farmers'
    and laborers' union of America": p. [3]-12.
     1. National Farmers Alliance and Coopera-
    tive Union. 2. National Agricultural
    Wheel.

  NN 0050734 NcD

FILM National Farmers' Alliance and Industrial Union.
HGFF Constitution. [n.p.,
N277
   Microfilm copy, made in 1957 by the State
  Historical Society of Wisconsin. Original dis-
  carded because of excessive deterioration.
  Negative.
   Collation of the original:
  On film with other related material.
  Library has:

  NN 0050735 WHi

  National Farmers Alliance and Industrial Union.
   Constitution and by-laws. [n.p., 189-?]
    66 p. folder 8°.
    n.t.-p.

  NN 0050736 NN

**National farmers' alliance and industrial
  union.**
Loucks, Henry Langford, 1846–
  ... Government ownership of railroads and telegraph,
as advocated by the National farmers' alliance and industrial union. By President H. L. Loucks ... Huron, S. D.,
1893.

  National farmers alliance and industrial
   union.
   Hand-book of facts and Alliance information. Specially prepared for members of the order ... Washington, D. C., The National economist publishing co., 1890.

T630.6273
N214m
  National Farmers' Alliance and Cooperative
   Union of America.
   Message of President C.W. Macune, to the
  National Farmers Alliance and Co-operative
  Union of America, at Meridian, Mississippi,
  December 5th, 1888. Dallas, Circular
  Letter Office, 1888.
   16p. 21cm.

   Cover title.

   I. Macune, Charles William, 1851-1940.

  NN 0050739 TxU

  National farmers' alliance and industrial union.
   N. F. A. and I. U. ritual. Washington.
  National economist pub. co., 1891.
   16 p. D.

  NN 0050740 NcD

National farmers alliance and industrial union.

The *National* economist. Official organ of the National farmers alliance and industrial union. Devoted to social, financial, and political economy. v. 1– Mar. 14, 1889–

  Washington [The National economist publishing co., 1889–

National Farmers' Alliance and Industrial Union.
 Proceedings,...and the Colored farmers' national
 alliance and co-operative union,... YA16913
 Ocala, Florida, 1890?

  NN 0050742 DLC

630.6273
N21 National Farmers' Alliance and Industrial
  Union.
   Ritual. [Washington, National Economist
  Publishing Co.] 1890.
   21p. 18cm.

   1. National Farmers' Alliance and
  Industrial Union. Rituals.

  NN 0050743 KU NN NcU

FILM National Farmers' Alliance and Industrial
HGFF Union.
N277   Ritual. [Washington, D.C.] 1890.
   Microfilm copy, made in 1957 by the State
  Historical Society of Wisconsin from the origi-
  nal held by the Colorado State Agricultural
  College, Fort Collins. Negative.
   Collation of the original: 21 p.
  On film with other related material.

  NN 0050744 WHi

  National Farmers Alliance and Industrial Union.
   What it is – where it was started – what its
  objects are ... [n.p., 189-?]
    1 leaf 4°.

  NN 0050745 NN

HGF National Farmers' Alliance and Industrial
.FA Union. Iowa Executive committee.
   Summary of the doings of the Executive committee. Des Moines, 1890.
   [6] p. 26 cm.

   Caption title.

  NN 0050746 WHi

  National farmers' alliance and industrial union. *Supreme council.*
   Proceedings of the annual session of the Supreme
  council of the National farmers alliance and industrial
  union ...   Washington, D. C., 18

   v. 20½ᶜᵐ.

   1. Agriculture—U. S.—Societies. 2. U. S.—Econ. condit.

            CA 11–2805 Unrev'd
   Library of Congress   HD1485.F2A2

  NN 0050747 DLC NcD

S414 National farmer's almanac; a year-book for stock-
.N27 breeders, stud-owners, dairymen, poultry-
   keepers &c. New York, H. Peacock [1904]
    1 v. 20 cm.

  NN 0050748 DLC

The national farmer's and housekeeper's
  cyclopaedia
   see under [Lupton, Frank M]
 1854-1910, comp.

National farmers' and laborers' union of America.
  Constitution of the National farmers' and
  laborers' union of America. The constitution
  of the Farmers' and laborers' union of Mo., and
  the Rochdale plan of co-operation. St. Louis,
  Journal of agriculture, 1889.

   cover-title, 64 (i.e. 45) p. 14 cm.

  NN 0050750 MoKU

B979.1
N213
  National farmers' association.
   Office of the National farmers' association,
  no. 7, Exchange place ... Boston, April 8,
  1879. 1879.
   20 p. 19cm. (Principia club papers. 10)

   Object of pamphlet is to encourage emigration
  to Texas.

   1. Texas.

  NN 0050751 NNC MdBJ

Mann
S
22 National Farmers' Association.
N24 Proceedings of first annual convention,
  Kansas City, Missouri, Feb. 21-23, 1916.
  [Kansas City, Mo., 1916]
   16 p. 23 cm.

   1. Agriculture - Congresses. . 2. Agriculture - U. S.

  NN 0050752 NIC

National farmers' congress of the U.S.
   see
Farmers' national congress.

National farmers magazine
  see Farmers magazine. Washington,
D.C.

HGF National Farmers' Organization.
N269
MIS [Miscellaneous ephemeral materials not
  fully catalogued]

   NB. - Such materials are shelved in
  pamphlet-boxes marked with a period (.),
  a plus (+) or a quotation-mark (") ahead
  of the second line of the call-number.
  Search should be made in all three locations, although material may not be found
  in any one or two of them.

  NN 0050755 WHi

National Farmers Organization.
  The NFO reporter
   see under title

National Farmers' Union
  see
Farmer's Educational and Co-operative Union of America.

VOLUME 407

National farmers' union (*Gt. Brit.*)
Agriculture; the home market and national security. Views of the National farmers' union on current agricultural problems ... London, National farmers' union, 1935.
cover-title, ii, 40 p. incl. tables, diagrs. 25 cm.
"N. F. U. no. 49."
Most of the alternate pages blank for "Notes."

1. Agriculture—Gt. Brit. 2. Agriculture—Economic aspects—Gt. Brit.   I. Title.
A 36–618 rev
Stanford University.   Libraries
for Library of Congress   [r62d4]

NN   0050758   CSt

National farmers' union (*Gt. Brit.*)
... Agriculture and the nation; interim report on post-war food production policy. London, National farmers' union, 1943.
24 p. 24ᶜᵐ.

1. Agriculture—Economic aspects—Gt. Brit. 2. Food supply—Gt. Brit.   I. Title.
Library of Congress   HD1927.1943.N3   43–11422
[3]   338.1

NN   0050759   DLC DNAL CtY

NATIONAL FARMERS' UNION (Gt. Br.)
Annual report.
London.   v.   16cm.

No. 12, 1920/21, issued as a supplement to the union's Year book for 1921.
For later years see its Year book.

NN   0050760   NN DNAL ICJ

National farmers' union (*Gt. Brit.*)
... The basis of economic security. London, The National farmers' union [1945]
cover-title, 71, [1] p. illus. 21¼ᶜᵐ.
At head of title: A policy for the nation's greatest industry.

1. Agriculture—Economic aspects—Gt. Brit.   I. Title.
46–17008
Library of Congress   HD1927 1945.N26
[3]   338.1

NN   0050761   DLC NIC DNAL

280.347
N213
National farmers' union (Gt. Brit.)
... Egg marketing organisation; report of Joint committee of the National farmers' union and the National poultry council on marketing. [n.p., 1937?]
8 p.   25cm.

At head of title: National farmers' union.

NN   0050762   DNAL

National farmers' union (*Gt. Brit.*)
The food of the people. The nation and its greatest industry. Being a summary of the proposals advanced by the National farmers' union for the effective reconstruction of British agriculture and the increase of home-grown food supplies ... London, National farmers' union, 1920.
cover-title, 36 p. 21½ cm.

1. Reconstruction (1914–1939)—Gt. Brit. 2. Agriculture—Gt. Brit. [2. Gt. Brit.—Agriculture]   I. Title.
Agr 20–1659 rev
U. S. Nat'l Agr. Libr.   281N21
for Library of Congress   [r62c¾]

NN   0050763   DNAL ICU ICJ

National farmers' union (*Gt. Brit.*)
Methods of milk production & distribution in the United States and Canada, the report of an inquiry made on behalf of the National farmers' union, by E. W. Langford ... London, National farmers' union, 1922.
24 p.   21½ cm.

1. Milk supply—Canada. [1. Canada—Milk supply] 2. Milk supply—U. S. [2. U. S.—Milk supply]   I. Langford, E. W.
Agr 23–873 rev
U. S. Nat'l Agr. Libr.   44N213
for Library of Congress   [r62c¾]

NN   0050764   DNAL

National Farmers' Union (Gt. Brit.)
N.F.U. annual
see   N.F.U. year book.

281.171
N213G
1945
National farmers' union (Gt. Brit.)
N.F.U. guide to wartime control.
[London] 1945–
1 v.

"Revised."
Kept up to date by supplements which are inserted.

NN   0050766   DNAL

281.171
N213G
1950
National Farmers' Union (Gt. Brit.)
N.F.U. guide to wartime control. [London, 1950–
1 v.

Kept up to date by supplements which are inserted.

NN   0050767   DNAL

National Farmers' Union (*Gt. Brit*)
The N. F. U. information service.

London.
v. in   22 cm.   monthly.
Began publication in 1936.

1. Agriculture—Economic aspects—Period. 2. Agriculture—Economic aspects—Gt. Brit.   I. Title.
HD101.N3   338.1   50–16618

NN   0050768   DLC DNAL NIC

National farmers' union (Gt. Brit.)
The N.F.U. record; official organ
see under title

National Farmers' Union (Gt. Brit.)
The N.F.U. year book
see under title

National farmers' union (Gt. Br.)
National farmers' union news sheet
see under title

National Farmers' Union (Gt. Brit.)
Register of records in laying trials, recognised by the National Farmers' Union. London, 19
v. tables. 23 cm.

1. Eggs – Production.

NN   0050772   OrCS

280.370
N21
National farmers' union (Gt. Brit.)
Scheme under the Agricultural marketing act, 1931, regulating the marketing of English hops. London, National farmers' union [1933?]
23 p.   19cm.

NN   0050773   DNAL

National Farmers' Union (Gt. Brit.)
Scheme under the Agricultural marketing acts, 1931 to 1949 regulating the marketing of wool. [London] 1949.
25 p.
1. Wool. Marketing. 2. Wool trade and industry. Gt. Brit.

NN   0050774   DNAL

National farmers' union (*Gt. Brit.*)
What the N. F. U. is doing for the farmer. A brief record of the work of some of the committees at headquarters during the year 1919–20. London, The National farmers' union, 1920.
47 p. 22 cm.

1. [Farmers' unions]
Agr 20–1660 rev
U. S. Nat'l Agr. Libr.   280.81N21W
for Library of Congress   [r62c¾]

NN   0050775   DNAL

National Farmers' Union (Gt. Brit.)
see also   Joint Committee of the National Poultry Council and the National Farmers' Union on Marketing.

National Farmers' Union (Gt. Brit.)
see also   Joint Working Party of National Farmers' Union of England and Wales, National Farmers' Union of Scotland, Ulster Farmers' Union.

National farmers' union (Gt. Brit.) Kent branch.
The Kent farmers' journal
see under title

National Farmers Union. Mutual insurance society. (Gt. Brit.)
A short history of the first thirty-five years [the story of our own insurance society] [Stratford-on-Avon, 1945?]

NN   0050779   MH

National Farmers' Union, Somerset County Branch. (Gt. Brit.)
Meat from marginal land, a draft policy suggested by "The Exmoor Survey" and other recent investigations. [Taunton, Eng., 1949]
10 p.

NN   0050780   DNAL

91.45
N21
National Farmers' Union, Watercress Branch. (Gt. Brit.)
News sheet.

[London?]

1. Water-cress. Periodicals.

NN   0050781   DNAL

VOLUME 407

NATIONAL farmers' union news sheet. 1945-   June, 1952
   (incomplete)
   London.   v.   35cm.
   Weekly (slightly irregular).
   Includes occasional "Press statements."
   Ceased publication with June 10, 1952.
   1. Agriculture -- Per. and soc. publ.   2. Agriculture -- Economics --
Gt. Br.   I. National farmers' union (Gt. Br.)

NN   0050782   NN DNAL

National farmers union ...program.

   See under

«Farmers' educational and co-operative union
   of America.»

23
N21   **National Farmers' Union of Australia.**
        Annual conference; collected addresses.

      ¡Stonehaven, Victoria¡

      1. Australia. Agriculture. Congresses.

NN   0050784   DNAL

National Farmers' Union of Scotland.
   Annual report. 1925/26-1959-60.
   [Glasgow] 19   -1960.
      Later included in The Farming leader
   (280.28 F224) cf. letter from issuing office,
   dated June 5, 1962.
      At head of title, 1938/39 —
National Farmers Union and Chamber
of agriculture of Scotland.

NN   0050785   DNAL

National Farmers' Union of Scotland.
   Farming leader
      see under title

National Farmers' Union of Scotland
      see also   Joint Working Party of National
Farmers' Union of England and Wales, National
Farmers' Union of Scotland, Ulster Farmers'
Union.

National Farmers Union Washington newsletter. 1.-
   Denver, 1954-

NN   0050788   KMK

National Fascist Institute of Social Insurance
      see   Istituto nazionale della previdenza
sociale.

The NATIONAL fast; March 24, 1847. Sermons preached
   by eminent divines, on the day of solemnities of a
   great national calamity.   London: J. Gilbert [1847]
   24 p.   18½cm.

   On cover: No. I.
   No more published.

   1. Fast days—Gt.Br., 1847.

NN   0050790   NN

National Federal Council of Scotland for Women's Trades.
   Women's employment in shops.   Report of an inquiry conducted for the National Federal Council of Scotland for Women's
Trades, by Margaret Irwin.   ¡Glasgow, 1894.¡   24 p. incl. tables.
f°.

   Cover-title.

1. Woman—Employment—Gt. Br.—   Scotland. 2. Irwin, Margaret H.
N. Y. P. L.   July 17, 1925

NN   0050791   NN

National Federated Craft news.

   ¡Buffalo, etc.¡
         v. in   illus. 24 cm. bimonthly.

      1. Freemasons. U. S.—Period. 2. Civil service—U. S.—Societies,
etc.
   HS2721.N3   59-31427 ‡

NN   0050792   DLC

National federation conference of the provincial educational associations of China.   *Curriculum committee.*
   The outline standards of the new system curriculum,
prepared by the Curriculum committee of the Conference
of federated provincial associations of China.   Shanghai,
China, The Commercial press limited, 1925.
   vi, 143 p. 19ᶜᵐ.

      1. Education—China—Curricula.   2. ¡Course of study—China¡
                                                      E 26-347
   Library, U. S. Bur. of   Education LA1131.N2

NN   0050793   DHEW OrU

National Federation for Constitutional Liberties
   see also   **Civil Rights Congress.**

National federation for constitutional liberties.
   Action letter.

   Washington, D. C. ¡etc.¡ 19   v.   28 – 35cm.
      Irregular.

1. Liberty—Per. and soc. publ.—   U. S. I. Title.
N. Y. P. L.   April 9, 1948

NN   0050795   NN

CPA
VF
1078   National Federation for Constitutional
         Liberties.
         Alarm! Anti-labor bills threaten defense.
      Washington, D.C. ¡1941?¡
      8 p.

         1. Labor laws and legislation - U.S.
      I. Title.   II. Title: Anti-labor bills
      threaten   defense.

NN   0050796   MiEM

National Federation for Constitutional Liberties.
   Conscription and civil liberties...
      see under title

CPA
VF
1080.5   National Federation for Constitutional
           Liberties.
           Conscription and civil liberties.
        ¡Washington, D.C., 1940?¡
        30 p.

        "Reprinted from International Juridical
        Association monthly bulletin, August, 1940."
        On cover: An analysis of the Burke-Wadsworth
        Bill.
        "Notes:" p.28-30.

        1. Military Service,   Compulsory - U. S. I. Association
     Juridique Internationale,   II. Title.

NN   0050798   MiEM

F130
.A1I8   National federation for constitutional
          liberties.
        ¡Isserman, A   J   ¡
        Everybody's business, a summary of New York state anti-
      discrimination laws and how to use them.   ¡New York, Na-
      tional federation for constitutional liberties, 1946¡

NN   0050800   NcD

Pam.   National Federation for Constitutional Liberties.
Coll.
        For victory over Fascism in our schools. A
23763   call to a conference to protect our free public
        schools from Coudertism and defeatism.   New York
        1942.
           folder (6 p.)   22 cm.

           1. Education. U. S.   2. Fascism. U. S.
        I. Title.

NN   0050800   NcD

National federation for constitutional liberties.
   ...Full employment as a safeguard to civil liberties.   ¡New
York¡ Nat. federation for constitutional liberties ¡1945¡   15 p.
23cm.

   At head of title: " — to secure the blessings of liberty —."

1. Unemployed—U. S., 1929-   2. Liberty—U. S.
N. Y. P. L.   January 19, 1948

NN   0050801   NN NcD

National federation for constitutional liberties.
   "In the matter of Harry R. Bridges"
      see under   Citizens committee for
Harry Bridges.

National federation for constitutional liberties.
   Investigate Martin Dies!   The case for a grand jury investigation of Martin Dies, submitted to the Department of justice
on August 6, 1942 by the National federation for constitutional
liberties ...   ¡New York, Washington, 1942¡
   47, ¡5¡ p. 23ᶜᵐ.
   "First printing, August 1942."

   1. Dies, Martin, 1901-   2. U. S. Congress. House. Special committee on un-American activities, 1938-   I. Title.

   Library of Congress   E743.5.N3   42-21707
                                        ¡4¡   335.0973

NN   0050803   DLC WHi

HWT   National Federation for Constitutional
.N277   Liberties.
MIS   Investigating committees and civil rights.
         [Washington, 1941]
         23 p.   19 cm.

         Cover title.

            1. Civil rights - U. S.

NN   0050804   WHi

VOLUME 407

National federation for constitutional liberties.
Legislation for victory; a summary of federal legislation affecting civil rights, 78th Congress — 1943...   Washington, Nat. federation for constitutional liberties [1943] 22 p. illus. 27cm.

1. World war, 1939-1945—Law and   legislation—U. S. 2. Liberty—U. S.
N. Y. P. L.   July 8, 1946

NN 0050805   NN

NATIONAL FEDERATION FOR CONSTITUTIONAL LIBERTIES.
Memorandum. no. [1]- ; Feb. 9, 1942-
New York [etc.]   no.   28cm.

Irregular.
Ceased publication with no. 13, Mar. 1946?

1. Liberty--Per. and soc. publ.--   U. S

NN 0050806   NN

National federation for constitutional liberties.
A message to the House of Representatives.   [New York, 1943]
[8] p.   28cm.
Caption title.

1. United States. Un-American   activities, Special committee on.

NN 0050807   NN

National federation for constitutional liberties.
National action conference for civil rights, Washington, D. C., April 19-20 ...
see under   National action conference for civil rights, Washington, D. C., 1941.

National federation for constitutional liberties.
"The only sound policy for a democracy." A statement by leading Americans on the criteria for Army commissions and other appointments. [New York, 1944?]
16 p. 21 x 9cm.

NN 0050809   MH-L

[National federation for constitutional liberties]
The people's rights and the 1944 elections. A comparative record, Franklin D. Roosevelt vs. Thomas E. Dewey. [New York, 1944]
47 p. 18½ᵐ.
"Prepared and published by the National federation for constitutional liberties."
"First printing October 1944."

1. Civil rights—U.S. 2. Suffrage—U. S. 3. Campaign literature, 1944.
I. Title.
Library of Congress   JC599.U5N33   45-3897
[4]   329.01

NN 0050810   DLC NN IEN WHi

National federation for constitutional liberties.
600 prominent Americans ask President to rescind Biddle decision; an open letter sponsored by the National federation for constitutional liberties. [New York, Washington, 1942]
32 p. 18ᵐ.
"First printing, September 11, 1942."

1. Bridges, Harry Renton, 1900–   2. Communism—U. S.
I. Title.
Library of Congress   HD8073.B7N3   42-50085
[2]   325.78

NN 0050811   DLC NcD

National Federation for Constitutional Liberties.
Speed the way !
see under   Watson, Morris.

[National federation for constitutional liberties]
Witch hunt, 1941, hits government workers. [Washington, 1941?]
1 p. l., 24 p., 1 l. 18½ᵐ.

1. Civil service—U. S.   I. Title.
Library of Congress   JK765.N34   46-42786
[2]   351.1

NN 0050813   DLC NN MH

Pam.   National Federation for Constitutional Liberties.
Coll.   Committee on Free Elections.
23676   Keeping elections free; a model election law. New York [1942?]
30 p. 21 cm.
Cover title.

1. Election law. I. Title.

NN 0050814   NcD NN

National Federation for Majority Rule.
... History of the Winnetka System, January–June, 1902. Program to secure majority rule in state and nation in this year's campaign. Washington, D. C., Published by the National Federation for Majority Rule, [1902].
vi, 66 p. 25½ᶜᵐ.
At head of title: Advance sheets released for publication Sunday, June 29, 1902.
Addendum slip inserted.

NN 0050815   ICJ

HE206   National federation of American shipping.
.V3   Washington, D. C.
Van Metre, Thurman William, 1884–
American transportation policy, by T. W. Van Metre ...
Washington, D. C., National federation of American shipping, 1944.

qR533.67 NATIONAL federation of American shipping, inc.
N2134A   The American merchant marine in the air.
Wash., D.C., Author. [1945?] [11] p.

NN 0050817   WaS

National federation of American shipping, inc., Washington, D. C.
... Brief in support of request for the removal of administrative restraints on the integration of sea and air service ... [Washington? 1946]
cover-title, 2 p.l., 31 p. 23cm.
At head of title: Before the Committee on interstate and foreign commerce, U.S. House of Representatives.
"Submitted to the subcommittee on

transportation in response to questionaire released July 24, 1945, in connection with a national transportation inquiry."

NN 0050819   MH-L

National federation of American shipping, *Washington, D. C.*
Brief on the right of steamship carriers to participate in transoceanic air service. [Washington] National federation of American shipping, inc. [194-]
cover-title, 1 p. l., 44 p. 26½ x 20½ᵐ.

1. Aeronautics, Commercial—U. S. 2. Steamboat lines—U. S. I. Title: Right of steamship carriers to participate in transoceanic air service.
46-28968
Library of Congress   TL521.N28
[3]   387.5127

NN 0050820   DLC OrU

387   National Federation of American Shipping, Washington, D.C.
N2132e   The emergency in domestic shipping. A statement by the National Federation of American Shipping, Washington, D.C., submitted to Committee on Interstate and Foreign Commerce, Subcommittee on Transportation, House of Representatives. [n.p.] 1946.
20 p. 28cm.

1. Merchant marine.
U.S. I. Title.

NN 0050821   OrU NNC

National Federation of American Shipping, Washington, D.C.
Industry faces new crisis; "the overtime-on-overtime problem" affects all industry; collective bargaining threatened; another round of strikes? Washington [194-]
7 p.
1. Wages, overtime.

NN 0050822   MH-IR

387   National Federation of American Shipping,
N2132   Washington, D.C.
Our fourth arm. [Washington, 1951]
[24] p. illus. 28cm.

1. Shipping. U.S. I. Title.

NN 0050823   OrU

National Federation of American Shipping, *Washington, D. C.*
Report.
[Washington]
v. 28 cm. annual.

1. Merchant marine—U. S.
HE730.N324   52-33694

NN 0050824   DLC

National Federation of American Shipping, Washington, D. C.
Shipping subsidies
see under   Bailey, Frazer A.

National federation of American shipping, *Washington, D.C.*
Statement of policy on overseas aviation by the National federation of American shipping.   Washington [1944] 6 p. 23cm.

1. Aeronautics, Commercial—U. S.
N. Y. P. L.   June 29, 1945

NN 0050826   NN NNC

VOLUME 407

U.S.
HE
Pam
National Federation of American Shipping, Washington, D.C.
    U.S. Flag Cargo Services; for trade, travel, defense-The American Merchant Marine. Member lines of National Federation of American Shipping, Inc. Washington, D.C., 1949.
        8 p. 28 cm.

    Cover-title.
    "No.2, September 1, 1949."

NN   0050827   DPU

National Federation of Anglers.
    Angling. [1st ed.] London, Educational Productions [1953]
        36 p. illus. 14 x 21 cm. ("Know the game" series)

    1. Fishing.
        SH439.N3 1953   799.12   54-16086 ‡

NN   0050828   DLC

National Federation of Associated Paint, Colour and Varnish Manufacturers of the United Kingdom. *Joint Technical Panel J/P1*
    see
Joint Technical Panel J/P1.

National Federation of Austrian Social Insurance Institutions
    see
Hauptverband der Österreichischen Socialversicherungsträger.

National Federation of British Launderers
    see   Institution of British Launderers.

HD9715
.G7B8
National federation of builders' merchants' associations of Great Britain and Ireland.
    The Builders' merchants' journal and builders' ironmonger.
        London [19

National federation of building industries
    see
National federation of construction industries.

The National federation of building trades employers
    see under   National Builder, Chicago.

National Federation of Building Trade Employers in South Africa.
    Building and allied trades official handbook.
        Johannesburg, South African Builder (Pty) Ltd.

National Federation of Building Trade Employers in South Africa.
    Membership rolls of affiliated associations.
        Johannesburg, South African builder.
            v. 21 cm.

        HD6869.B9N27   59-25533

NN   0050835   DLC

HD6869
.B9N3
National federation of building trade employers in South Africa.
    The South African builder.
        [Johannesburg, 19

NATIONAL FEDERATION OF BUILDING TRADE OPERATIVES.
    ...Air-raid precautions; civil defence measures. London: Federal house [1939] 7 p. 20½cm.

    At head of title: National federation of building trades operatives.

    1. Air defenses—Gt.Br. I. Title.

NN   0050837   NN

National Federation of Building Trade operatives.
    Barlow's building bluff
        see under   Hicks, George, 1879-

National federation of building trade operatives.
    Gt. Brit. *Ministry of labour.*
        ... Correspondence between the Ministry of labour and the National federation of building trade operatives respecting the admission of ex-service men into the building trades ... London, H. M. Stationery off [1921?]

HD7334
.L6L6
National federation of building trade operatives (London area)
    London trades council.
        London's housing ... reports, conference convened by London trades council and National federation of building trade operatives (London area) ... [Watford, Herts, Farleigh press ltd, 1946]

NATIONAL FEDERATION OF BUILDING TRADES EMPLOYERS. (South Western region)
    Year book.
    Bristol.   v.   ports.   23cm.

    1. Building trades--Gt. Br.

NN   0050841   NN

National Federation of Building Trades Employers, London.
    Annual report.
        London.
            v. 25 cm.

    1. Building trades—Gt. Brit.
        HD6668.B8N3   690.6242   49-37830*‡

NN   0050842   DLC

National federation of building trades employers, London.

Walker-Smith, Derek, 1910–
    "The standard form of building contract" (1939) being a critical annotation of the new form of building contract (issued under the sanction of the Royal institute of British architects and the National federation of building trades employers) and a guide to its use, by Derek Walker-Smith ... and Howard A. Close ... With a foreword by Mr. Justice Hallett and preface by Sydney Tatchell, F. R. I. B. A. London, Pub. by the Federated employers' press ltd. [1939]

National Federation of Building Trades Employers, *London.*
    A survey of technical education in the building industry. With messages from the Minister of Education and from the president (The National Federation of Building Trades Employers) and a foreword by F. M. Sleeman. London [1951]
        81 p. 22 cm.

    1. Building—Study and teaching. I. Title.
        TH165.N38   690.7   53-23212 ‡

NN   0050844   DLC

National federation of business and professional women's clubs, inc.

Byrne, Harriet Anne.
    ... The age factor as it relates to women in business and the professions, by Harriet A. Byrne ... Washington, U. S. Govt. print. off., 1934.

607
.N2132a
National federation of business and professional women's clubs, inc.
    Are there opportunities for women? Vocational radio series. [New York, The National federation of business and professional women's clubs, 1935]
            v.

    Mimeographed.

NN   0050846   IU DL

National federation of business and professional women's clubs.
    Are you giving a vocational talk? Suggestions for a vocational talk. N.Y.,National federation of business and professional women's clubs,n.d.
        7 p. 18X24cm.

    Processed.

NN   0050847   OrU

374.2
B9646a
National federation of business and professional women's clubs, inc.
    Articles of incorporation and by-laws ...
        New York, 1926-

NN   0050848   WaPS

National Federation of Business and Professional Women's Clubs.
    Bulletin
        see
National business woman.

D396
N21
National federation of business and professional women's clubs, inc.
    ... Business women in a democracy. New York, The National federation of business & professional women's clubs, 1940.
        100 p.

    At head of title: The program book, 1939-1940.

NN   0050850   NNC

VOLUME 407

National Federation of Business and Professional Women's Clubs.
Constitution. ₍n. p., 1919?₎ 3 f., 3 l. 4°.
Reproduced from typewritten sheets, written on one side of leaf only.
By-laws, 3 l.

1. Woman.—Assoc. and organiza-   tions.
N. Y. P. L.

October 25, 1922.

NN   0050851   NN

Natiohal Federation of Business and
Professional Women's Clubs, inc.
Convention program. 1919?–
Kansas City, Mo., etc.
v. 28ᶜᵐ

Title varies.

1. Woman. Societies and clubs.
2. Woman. History and condition of women.

NN   0050852   KU-RH

National federation of business and professional women's clubs, inc.
The current outlook, in ... series of thirty pamphlets giving findings of Institute of occupations, July 10–11, 1933. New York, N. Y., National federation of business and professional women's clubs, inc. ₍1933–34₎
30 pt. 28ᶜᵐ
Mimeographed.
CONTENTS.—Accounting and bookkeeping.—Advertising and promotion.—Art as a profession.—Aviation.—Cosmetology.—Credit management.—Finance.—General office positions.—Home economics.—Hotel and restaurant positions.—Insurance.—Journalism.—Legal profession.—Library work.—Medicine and dentistry.—Motion picture positions.—Music.—Nursing.—Office management.—Osteopathy.—Ownership and management.—Personnel and employment management.—Public office.—Radio.—Railroad positions.—Real estate.—Retail store service.—Secretarial work.—Social work.—Teaching.

1. Profession, Choice of. 2. Occupations. I. Title.
E 34–582
Library, U. S. Office of   Education HF5381.N25

NN   0050854   DHEW CU Or OrU WaS OrCS IU NNC MH

National federation of business and professional women's clubs, inc.

Council for democracy.
... Defense on Main street; a guide-book for local activities for defense and democracy. ₍New York, Council for democracy, 1941₎

National Federation of Business and Professional Women's Clubs.
₍Directory.₎
1920/21
₍New York, 1921
v. illus.
4°.

NN   0050856   NN MB DNAL ICJ

National federation of business and professional women's clubs, inc.

Elliott, Margaret.
... Earnings of women in business and the professions, by Margaret Elliott ... and Grace E. Manson ... Ann Arbor, University of Michigan, School of business administration, Bureau of business research, 1930.

National federation of business and professional women's clubs, inc.

Schneider, Mrs. Florence Hemley.
An economic challenge to American women, by Florence Hemley Schneider. New York, N. Y., The National federation of business and professional women's clubs, inc., 1941.

D6095   **National Federation of Business and Professional**
.34   **Women's Clubs.**

Kass, Babette.
The economic strength of business and professional women, by Babette Kass and Rose C. Feld. Research conducted at the Bureau of Applied Social Research, Columbia University. New York, National Federation of Business and Professional Women's Clubs, 1954.

---

607   National federation of business and professional
N2132f   women's clubs,
Five vocational issues ... ₍New York, The National federation of business and professional women's clubs, inc., 1938₎
62p.

Bibliography: p.27.

NN   0050860   IU OrU

National federation of business and professional women's clubs.

Clark, Rita Elizabeth, 1915–
A guide to world affairs; a guide for club members, creating interest-finding material-suggesting programs for world affairs. Compiled by Rita E. Clark. August, 1939. New York, N. Y., The National federation of business and professional women's clubs, inc. ₍1939₎

National federation of business and professional women's clubs.
Handbook of federation procedures. New York city, The National federation of business and professional women's clubs, inc. ₍1936₎
192, xiv, ₍2₎ p. 17ᶜᵐ.
Blank pages for notes (₍2₎ at end)

                                                    36–17499
Library of Congress   HD6050.N33
——— Copy 2.
Copyright AA 209588   ₍3₎   367

NN   0050862   DLC

National Federation of Business and Professional Women's Clubs.
Handbook of federation procedures. New York ₍1950₎
211 p. map, diagr. 18 cm.

HD6050.N33 1950   396.06273   50–4349

NN   0050863   DLC

National Federation of Business and Professional Women's Clubs.
Handbook of federation procedures. New York ₍1952₎
212 p. illus. 18 cm.

HD6050.N33 1952   396.06273   53–17866 ‡

NN   0050864   DLC OCl

National Federation of Business and Professional Women's Clubs.
A history of the National Federation of business and professional women's clubs
see under Bowman, Geline Macdonald.

National federation of business and professional women's clubs,
Independent woman; a magazine for business and professional women. v. 1–   Dec. 1, 1919–
₍New York, 1919–

National federation of business and
professional women's clubs,
Institute of occupations, Chicago ...
July 10–11, 1933. Biennial convention of the National federation of business and professional women's clubs ... New York₍1933₎

NN   0050867   CtY

National federation of business and professional women's clubs.
... Making democracy work; business women in a democracy. New York, The National federation of business and professional women's clubs, inc. ₍c1940₎
80 p.

NN   0050868   DLC OLak

HD6050   National Federation of Business and Professional
.N3   Women's Clubs.

National business woman. v. 1–
1919–
₍Washington, etc., National Federation of Business and Professional Women's Clubs₎

National federation of business and professional women's clubs,
Manson, Grace Evelyn, 1893–
... Occupational interests and personality requirements of women in business and the professions, by Grace E. Manson ... Ann Arbor. University of Michigan, School of business administration, Bureau of business research, 1931.

National Federation of Business and Professional Women's Clubs.
Opportunities for careers for women
see under Bacon, Elizabeth Mickle.

331.4   National federation of business and professional
N21p   women's clubs.
Position of married women in the economic world July, 1940. Report of special research project. New York, N. Y., The National federation of business and professional women's clubs, inc.₍1940₎
cover-title, viii, 69, 10 numb.l. incl.tables. Mimeographed.
"Brief bibliography": leaves 7–10(last group of leaves)

1. Woman--Employment. I. Title.

NN   0050872   IU

National Federation of Business and Professional Women's Clubs.
Proceedings ₍of the₎ annual convention. 10th–
1928–
New York.
v. 23 cm.
Proceedings of the first nine conventions were not published.

1. Woman—Employment—Societies, etc.
HD6050.N32   396.06273   54–45420

NN   0050873   DLC

National Federation of Business and Professional Women's Clubs, Inc.
Proceedings of the biennial convention. 1. July, 1931.
— New York. 1931. v. Portrait. Autograph facsimile. 23 cm.

D5714 — Women's clubs. Period. — Societies. Proc., trans., etc.

NN   0050874   MB NN Vi

VOLUME 407

National Federation of Business and Professional Women's Clubs.
Proceedings of the Board of Directors' meeting.
19

New York₍, 19
v.   ports.   8°.

1. Woman—Clubs—U. S.
N. Y. P. L.   April 6, 1932

NN   0050875   NN

National federation of business and professional women's clubs.
Program book.
19

New York ₍c19
nos.   illus.   19 – 28cm.

Title varies slightly.
Each number has also special title: 1937/38, Our town's business; 1939/40, Business women in a democracy; etc., etc.

1. Woman in business—U. S.
N. Y. P. L.   2. Woman—Occupations—U. S.
                                                  July 22, 1942

NN   0050876   NN MiD

NATIONAL FEDERATION OF BUSINESS AND PROFESSIONAL
WOMEN'S CLUBS,
Recent legislative and executive action restricting the right of married women to work. Rev. ed.   1819 Broadway, New York, Author, 1940.
₍15₎ ℓ.

NN   0050877   Or WaU

National federation of business and professional women's clubs,
Shallcross, Ruth Enalda, 1906–
Should married women work? By Ruth Shallcross for the National federation of business and professional women's clubs. ₍New York, Public affairs committee, inc.₎ °1940.

National federation of business and professional women's clubs,
... Strengthen democracy for defense. New York, The National federation of business and professional women's clubs, inc. ₍1941₎
96 p.   19ᶜᵐ.   (Its Program book, 1941–1942)
Text on p. ₍3₎ of cover.
"References" for each month. "General references for the year": p. 67–68.

1. Woman—Societies and clubs. 2. Democracy. 3. World war, 1939– —U. S.   I. Title.

Library of Congress   HQ1904.N3   42–19617
                             ₍2₎   321.80714

NN   0050879   DLC

National Federation of Business and Professional Women's Clubs.
Studies on the employability of women
see under title

National federation of business and professional women's clubs.
331.42   ... A study of the employability of women in
N277   Alabama, 1929-1935. A study conducted by the National federation of business and professional women's clubs, inc., and the Alabama federation of business and professional women's clubs, in collaboration with Alabama college, Montevallo, Alabama. ₍Montevallo, Ala.₎ 1936₎
   88 p. incl.tables,diagrs.,forms.   23ᵐ.(Alabama college₎ Special bulletin. vol.xxix, no.1. Total no.119. July, 1936)

NN   0050881   CSt DL MH NN DHEW

National Federation of Business and Professional Women's Clubs.
Survey of the position of married woman in the economis world. n.p.,n.d.

NN   0050882   OrU

A607   National federation of business and professional
N21v   women's clubs.
   A vocational bibliography; a brief list of book, magazine and pamphlet sources on vocations; indexes, directories of training schools; books on self-analysis and for the job seeker.   New York, N.Y., The National federation of business and professional women's clubs, inc., 1939.
   cover-title, 7 numb.l.
   Mimeographed.

   1. Profession, Choice of--Bibl. 2. Vocational education--Bibl.   I. Title.

NN   0050883   IU

---

607   National federation of business and professional
N2132v women's clubs,
   Vocations for women ...   New York city, The National federation of business and professional women's clubs ₍1939-40₎
   7v.

   Reprinted from the Independent woman.
   Contents.- ₍v.1₎ Airways to earning.- ₍v.2₎ Chemistry.- ₍v.3₎ Occupational therapy.- ₍v.4₎ Office management.- ₍v.5₎ Penology.- ₍v.6₎ Social work.- ₍v.7₎ Statistical work.

NN   0050884   IU

National federation of business and professional women's clubs.
   We sing ... New York, N. Y., The National federation of business & professional women's clubs, inc. ₍1938₎
128 p.   22ᵐ.
Songs with piano accompaniment.

1. Songs, English.   I. Title.

Library of Congress   M1629.N27W3   43–11251
                             ₍2₎   784.88

NN   0050885   DLC IdPI

National Federation of Business and Professional Women's Clubs.
   Why women work, based on a study made by the National federation of business and professional women's clubs, inc. New York, Public affairs committee, incorporated, 1938.
32 p. illus. 21¼ cm. (On cover: Public affairs pamphlets, no. 17)
   "The work was carried forward under the general direction of the Department of education, the National federation of business and professional women's clubs, inc. The report here presented was written by Beulah Amidon."--p. 2.

   1. Woman—Employment—U. S. 2. Wages—U. S.   I. Amidon, Beulah, 1894–   II. Title.

HD6095.N23   331.40973   38–13775 rev

NN   0050886   DLC OrU OrPR ViU OOxM OO OCU NBuC

HD6095   National federation of business and pro-
.N23   fessional women's clubs,
1939   Why women work, based on a study made by the National federation of business and professional women's clubs, inc. New York, Public affairs committee, incorporated, 1938 ₍i.e. 1939₎
   31, ₍1₎ p. illus. 21½cm. (On cover: Public affairs pamphlets. no.17)

   "The work was carried forward under the general direction of the Department of education, the National federation of business and professional women's clubs, inc. The report here presented was written by Beulah Amidon."-- p.2.
   "First printing, March, 1938 ... third printing, November, 1939."

NN   0050888   DLC

National federation of business and professional women's clubs.
   Why women work, based on a study made by the National federation of business and professional women's clubs, inc. New York, Public affairs committee, incorporated, 1941.
   31, ₍1₎ p. diagrs. 21¼ᵐ. (On cover: Public affairs pamphlets. no. 17 (revised))
   "The work was carried forward under the general direction of the Department of education, the National federation of business and professional women's clubs, inc. The report here presented was written by Beulah Amidon."--p. 2.
   "First edition, March, 1938 ... Revised edition, February, 1941."

   1. Woman—Employment—U. S. 2. Wages—U. S.   I. Amidon, Beulah, 1894–   II. Title.

Library of Congress   HD6095.N23 1941   41–10103
                             ₍3₎   331.40973

NN   0050889   DLC NcGU

National federation of business and professional women's clubs.
   You have an educational fund.   New York, Nat. federation of business and professional women's clubs, 1940.   29 p.   illus. 24cm.

1. Schools—Endowment—U. S.
N. Y. P. L.   April 25, 1947

NN   0050890   NN DLC

National Federation of Canadian University Students.
Rapport
see its Report.

National Federation of Canadian University Students.
Report.
   ₍London? Ont.₎
   v. 28 cm.
   English and French.

LA417.7.N325   378.71   53–24232 ‡

NN   0050892   DLC CaBVaU

National Federation of Canadian University Students.
Yearbook. Annuaire. v. 1–
1951–
₍Lennoxville? Que.₎
   v. illus., ports. 28 cm.

LA417.7.N32   378.71   52–64978 ‡

NN   0050893   DLC

National federation of Catholic college students.
   ...Handbook for student leaders, compiled by the national office of the NFCCS... Youth series, no. 2... ₍Washington, D.C.₎ N.C.W.C. The Youth department ₍1941₎
   61, ₍3₎p. diagram. 19½cm.
   (National Catholic welfare conference. Youth department. Youth series, no. 2)
   1. Leadership

NN   0050894   KAS OC1

National Federation of Catholic College Students.
₍Program of annual congress₎
₍n.p., 1937?₎
   v. illus. 23-28cm. annual.

   Title varies.

NN   0050895   KAS

R15   National Federation of Catholic Physicians'
.L58   Guilds.
The Linacre quarterly.

₍St. Louis₎

VOLUME 407

National Federation of Churches and Christian
Workers.
Church federation
see under   Inter-church Conference on
Federation, New York, 1905.

National Federation of Clay Industries.

TH1301
.B7

Brick bulletin. v. 1–
Sept. 1947–
₁London, National Federation of Clay Industries₎

NATIONAL FEDERATION OF CLOTH WEAVERS.
... PROCEEDINGS OF THE 1ST–   ...CONVEN-
TION ... 1908– ·
[N.P.,1908?–

     V.   22CM.

NAME OF UNION VARIES.

NN   0050899   MdBJ

National Federation of Coffee Growers of Colombia
see
Federación Nacional de Cafeteros de Colombia.

295.9
N217   National Federation of Cold Storage &
Ice Trades.
Year book. 1951/52–

London [1952–

1. Ice industry. Societies. 2. Refrigeration and refrigerating machinery. Societies.

NN   0050901   DNAL

National Federation of College and University
Business Officers Association.

For works by this body issued under its
later name see

National Association of College and University Business Officers.

**National Federation of College and University Business
Officers Associations.**
A study of income and expenditures in sixty colleges, year
1953–1954. Consultation by Cresap, McCormick and Paget,
management consultants. ₁n. p., 1955?₎
183 p. diagrs. tables. 31 cm.

1. Universities and colleges—Finance.

LB2342.N35   379.11   56–3697

    FU OC1W PPCCH FMU OrCS IdPI WaWW WaSpG Wa PPLT
    CU IU PSt PPT ICU TxU TU PPD PPCuP MtBuM OrU MiU
NN   0050903   DLC WU OYesA NcD PSt TNJ-P N IdU NcD

National Federation of Commercial Teachers' Associations. Mana-
gers' section.
Private business schools. Report of Asbury Park meeting
July 5-6, 1905. ₁Brooklyn, N. Y.: Pulis Prtg. Co., 1905.₎ 29 p.
8°.
Includes report of the mid-summer meeting of the Private Commercial Schools
Managers' Association; and of the American Commercial Schools Institution.

1. Commerce.—Education, U. S.   NAT. SHORTHAND REP. ASSOC.
Managers' Association. 3. American   2. Private Commercial Schools
N. Y. P. L.   Commercial Schools Institution.
                           August 6, 1914.

NN   0050904   NN

National Federation of Community Associations.
Community centres and community associations
in new town developments. n.p. [1946?]

4 p.
Signed: F.S.Milligan.

NN   0050905   MH

National federation of community associations.
Conference report. ₁no.₎ 1

₁London, 1946₎   no.   illus.   21cm.

1. Community centers—Per. and   soc. publ.—Gt. Br.
N. Y. P. L.   June 30, 1950

NN   0050906   NN

National Federation of Community Associa-
tions.
Constitution for a community associa-
tion, issued as a guide. ₁London, Pub-
lished for the₎ National Federation of
Community Associations ₁by the National
Council of Social Service, 1954₎
18 p. 19cm.
Cover title.
"Reference no. 2/242"
I. T1.

NN   0050907   MnU

National Federation of Community Associations.
Our neighborhood; a handbook of information
for community centres and associations
see under   National Council of Social Service.

National federation of construction industries.

Provisionally organized July 16, 1918 as National federation of
building industries; permanently organized December 6-7, 1918 as
National federation of construction industries. Headquarters, Philadelphia.

National Federation of Construction Industries.
The National federation of building industries;
an association of organizations in the building
industry, formed voluntarily by its members
at the suggestion of the Chamber of commerce of
the United States of America; a report of the
proceedings of the National conference at
Atlantic City, July 15th and 16th, 1918, where
national organization was effected
see under   National conference of the organizations in the building industry, Atlantic City,
1918.

HD6515   National Federation of Construction Industries.
. B89N5   Building industries and the government basis
for cooperation suggested to the Chairman Baruch
of the War industries board by the War Service
committee of the National Federation of Building
Industries. [Washington, 1918]
8 p. 23 cm.

NN   0050911   DLC

HD6515   National Federation of Construction Industries.
. B89N4   [Bulletin] Philadelphia, [1918]
6 v. 23 cm.

NN   0050912   DLC

National federation of construction industries.
Constitution and by-laws of the National federation
of construction industries. Philadelphia ₁1918?₎
8 p. 22½ᶜᵐ.

                       CA 22–349 Unrev'd

Library of Congress   TA1.N15

NN   0050913   DLC

HD9715   National Federation of Construction Industries.
.U54N3   Members' service letter. Philadelphia,
1919–22.
27 nos. in 2 v. illus. 27.5 x 21.5 cm.
(In binders, 34.5 cm.)

NN   0050914   DLC

National federation of construction industries.

Philadelphia conference on the construction industries,
1921.
Proceedings of the Philadelphia and National conferences on the construction industries: Philadelphia conference held in Philadelphia on February 15, 16, 17 and
18, 1921; National conference held in Chicago on March
2 and 3, 1921. Under the auspices of the Industrial relations committee of the Philadelphia chamber of commerce, Philadelphia, Pa.; the National federation of construction industries, general offices ... Philadelphia, Pa.
Chairman both conferences, Ernest T. Trigg ... Philadelphia, 1921.

HD6515   National Federation of Construction Industries.
. B89N5   A statement by the Executive board of the
National federation of building industries to
representatives of U. S. government administrative
boards. Washington, D. C., 1918.
15 p. 23 cm.

NN   0050916   DLC

National federation of constructional glass associations.
Glass age
see under title

National federation of consumers' cooperative
societies ₁of France₎
see
Fédération nationale des cooperatives de consomma-
tion.

National federation of credit traders.
Retail credit trading in the U.S.A., with
some notes on Canadian conditions; report by
Messrs.A.W.Dupont ... A.W.McGiff ... W.A.Phil-
lips ... and G.H.Denney ... September,1927.
London, National federation of credit traders
₁1927?₎
24 p.incl.forms. 18ᶜᵐ.

1.Retail trade--U.S. 2.Credit--U.S. I.Dupont,A.W.

NN   0050919   MiU

National Federation of Day Nurseries.
... Bulletin. ₁New York, N. Y., 1924–   ₎
Library has vol. 1, no. 2, Dec. 1924, *to date.* illus. 19½ᶜᵐ.
Caption title.
At head of title: National Federation of Day Nurseries, Inc.
Title varies: vol. 1–6, no. 2, Day nursery bulletin.
Monthly (vol. 6– , except Aug.–Sept.)
Wanting: vol. 3, no. 8–10, June–Aug. 1927.

NN   0050920   ICJ NN DL

VOLUME 407

National Federation of Day Nurseries.

HV701
.C52   **Child** welfare.

          ₁New York₎

National Federation of Day Nurseries.
Day nurseries in a changing world
see under   Hart, Helen.

National Federation of Day Nurseries.
Every child's dietary for mothers and
children
see under   Shackelford, Pearl S

National federation of day nurseries.
Leaflet, no 2-8
New York city
7 v. 14½ x 20½ cm.

NN 0050923   DL

National Federation of Day Nurseries.
Report of the conference.
19
New York ₁19
v.   8°.

1. Crèches, U. S.
N. Y. P. L.   July 14, 1924

NN 0050924   NN DHEW ICJ OC1

National federation of day nurseries.
A symposium : Case work programs in day nurseries. **Five**
papers presented at the twentieth biennial conference of the
National federation of day nurseries, New York city, April
1937. New York, Child welfare league of America, inc., and
the National federation of day nurseries, inc. ₁1937?₎

1 p. l., 17, ₁1₎ p. 22ᵐ.
Reproduced from type-written copy.
"Edited by Miss Luna E. Kenney."

1. Day nurseries.   i. Kenney, Luna Elizabeth, ed. ii. Child welfare
league of America, inc. iii. Title. iv. Title: Case work programs in day
nurseries.

Northwestern univ. Libr.   A 40-2085
  for Library of Congress   ₁2₎

NN 0050925   IEN ICJ NN

National federation of day nurseries. *Standards committee.*
Day nursery manual for the use of the boards of managers,
superintendents and staff members of day nurseries, **prepared**
by the Standards committee of the National federation of day
nurseries, inc. Mary F. Bogue, editor ... New York **city,**
National federation of day nurseries, inc., 1931.

5 p. l., 136 p. 22½ᵐ.
"List of references" : p. 132-136.

1. Day nurseries.   i. Bogue, Mary Florensia, 1886–   ed. ii. Title.
                                                         A 35—1899
Teachers college library,   Columbia univ.
  for Library of Congress   HV854.N3

NN 0050926   NNC-T NcD OC1W ICU OC1W NN

UA647   National Federation of Discharged and Demobilised
.A1N35   Sailors and Soldiers.
             The bulletin, the official organ of the
          National Federation of Discharged Sailors and
          Soldiers. [London] 1919-
             1 v.   illus.   29 cm.

NN 0050927   DLC

LA1131   National federation of educational asso-
.N27   ciations of China. Curriculum committee.
          The outline standards of the new system
          curriculum prepared by the Curriculum
          committee of the Conference of federated
          provincial associations of China.
          Shanghai, China, The Commercial press, 1925
          vi, 143p. 19cm.

          1. Education-China.   I. Title.

NN 0050928   NNU

A371.335 National Federation of Educational Film Groups.
N217s   Survey of pictorial materials.   Birmingham
          ₁Eng., 1948₎
             2v. 21cm.

          Cover title.
          Contents._ list 1. Nature study. Biology.
          Botany. Zoology._ list 2. Geographical sub-
          jects.

          1. Moving pictures in education--Bibl.

NN 0050929   IU

National federation of employees' approved societies.
    The Beveridge report on the social insurance and allied
services; memorandum issued by the National federation of
employees' approved societies. ₁London₎ 1943.

    cover-title, 22, ₁1₎ p. 20ᵐ.

    1. Gt. Brit. Inter-departmental committee on social insurance and
allied services. Social insurance and allied services.
                                                    45-18540
      Library of Congress   HD7165.A72N35
                               ₁2₎   331.2544

NN 0050930   DLC MH-BA NN

National Federation of Employees' Approved Societies.
    Unemployment insurance, with special reference to individual
firms and industries, by Henry Lesser...with contributions by
Lord Askwith, Lord Robert Cecil, Sir W. H. Beveridge...issued
by the National Federation of Employees' Approved Societies.
₁London, 1922?₎   30 p. incl. forms.   8°. .

    508995A. 1. Labor, Unemployed—   Insurance. I. Lesser, Henry.
    N. Y. P. L.   January 13, 1931

NN 0050931   NN

National Federation of Engineers and Tool
  Manufacturers.
    The German engineers' tool industry
      see under   Booth, C   H

National Federation of Federal Employees.
    Constitution...as revised by convention.
19
Washington, D. C.: Gibson Bros., Inc., etc.₁, 19   24°.
  nos.
    Cover-title.
    Title varies slightly.

    1. Civil service—Assoc. and org.—   U. S.
    N. Y. P. L.   February 5, 1929

NN 0050933   NN DL MH

National federation of federal employees.
    The **Federal** employee; devoted to the interests of the em-
ployees and of the civil service of the United States. Official magazine of National federation of federal employees.
    v. 1–   July 1916–
    Washington, D. C., 1916–

National federation of federal employees.
    The **Federal** news; a weekly newspaper published in the in-
terests of all employees of the U. S. government by the National federation of federal employees in cooperation with
the District of Columbia federation of federal employees
unions. v. 1–3; June 20, 1931–Dec. 30, 1933. Washington,
D. C. ₁1931–33₎

National federation of federal employees.
    ...History of the break in the affiliation with the American
federation of labor. ₁Washington? D. C.₎ 1933.   21 p.   23cm.

    1. Civil service—Assoc. and org.—   U. S.
    N. Y. P. L.   January 4, 1938

NN 0050936   NN InU

National federation of federal employees.
    ... Methods of computing annuities and other essential in-
formation in regard to retirement, Act of May 29, 1930. Washington, 1933.
    52 p. 23ᵐ.

    1. Civil service pensions—U. S.   i. Title.
    Library of Congress   JK791.N35   33-22463
    ——— Copy 2.
    Copyright AA 127043   ₁3₎   351.50073

NN 0050937   DLC OCU OC1

HFBF4   National Federation of Federal Employees.
N213
MIS   [Miscellaneous ephemeral materials not
           fully catalogued]

NN 0050938   WHi

National federation of federal employees.
    The National federation of federal employees; tenth anni-
versary. ₁Washington, D. C., 1928?₎
    1 p. l., ₁5₎–95 p. incl. ports. 30½ᵐ.
    This tenth anniversary book represents the personnel of every civilian
activity of the Federal government. cf. Foreword.
    Advertising matter : p. 73–94.

    1. U. S.—Officials and employees.
    Library of Congress   HD8008.N3   CA 29–21 Unrev'd

NN 0050939   DLC DL

HFBF4   National Federation of Federal Employees.
.N213   Proceedings. 6-25, 1922-1960.
P   Washington, D. C.
            13 v. in 3 . 23cm.
            20, 22-25 uns.

            1. U.S. – Officials + employees -
            Societies.

NN 0050940   WHi

HD8008   National Federation of Federal Employees.
.A1N3   ... Prospectus, September 1917...
         Washington, Press of Gibson Bros., inc. [1917]
            cover title, 36 p.   23 x 9.5 cm.

NN 0050941   DLC DPU

National Federation of Federal Employees.
    Resolutions submitted to the Convention.

    ₁Washington?₎
       v. 23 cm.

    1. Civil service—U. S.

    HD8008.N33   351.1   47-26252 rev*

NN 0050942   DLC MiD OC1 WHi NN MdBJ

VOLUME 407

National Federation of Federal Employees.
Summary of proceedings of the convention.
₍n. p.₎
v. 23 cm.

1. Civil service—Congresses. 2. Civil service—U. S.

HD8008.A1N152   331.88113511   49–15060*‡

NN   0050943   DLC OCU NN NNU

National federation of federal employees.
Local union no. 2.
Constitution of federal employees union
no. 2, Washington,...Washington, D. C., 1919
cover-title, 11 p. 15 cm.

NN   0050944   DL

National federation of federal employees.
Local union no. 73.
Cleveland federal employees, local no. 73
of the National federation of federal employees. Federal directory and program, nineteen
hundred and twenty-seven. (Cleveland, 1927)
cover-title, 52 p. incl. illus, ports,
25 cm.
Advertising matter interspereed.

NN   0050945   DL

National federation of federal employees, *Philadelphia.*
Union no. 23.
... Year book and federal directory, Federal employees
union no. 23 of Philadelphia, National federation of federal employees ... Phila₍delphia₎ Bradley bros. print.,
19
v. 27¼ᶜᵐ.
Cover-title: Pennsylvania federal employee year book.

1. Civil service—Philadelphia—Year-books.   I. Title.

Library of Congress   HD8008.A1N25   CA 24–743 Unrev'd

NN   0050946   DLC

National Federation of Financial Analysts Societies.
Directory of memberships, with officers, committees, directors, and federation constitution and by-laws.
Boston.
v. 21 cm.

Continued by the Membership directory issued
by the federation under its later name: Financial
Analysts Federation.
1. Brokers—Direct.

HG4907.N3   64–5309–‡

NN   0050947   DLC TU NN MH-BA NNC OCl

HG4501
.A7
   National Federation of Financial Analysts
      Societies.
   The **Financial** analysts journal. v. 1–
    Jan. 1945–
    ₍New York₎ National Federation of Financial **Analysts**
    Societies.

National federation of financial analysts societies
General management of profits

see under

Sears, Roebuck & Company.

HB3730
.N3
   National Federation of Financial Analysts
      Societies.
     Proceedings... 1st–
   annual convention. 1948–
   ₍New York₎
     v. 28cm.

NN   0050950   NNU-W WaS ICU NNC MH-BA

NATIONAL FEDERATION OF FINANCIAL ANALYSTS
     SOCIETIES.
    Report to the membership.
[New York?]   v.   24cm.

Annual.
Report year ends June 30.

NN   0050951   NN IU NIC

National Federation of Financial Analysts,
   Societies. Corporate Information Committee.
   Report (including subcommittee reports)

   ₍Chicago₎

NN   0050952   OCl

636.9
N213
   National federation of Flemish giant breeders.
     Guide book and standard. ₍Kalamazoo,
   Chambers pub.co.₎ illus.

NN   0050953   WaSp

HD9251
.1
.F7
     National Federation of Fruit and Potato Trades.

   Fruitation.

    ₍London₎

    National Federation of Fruit and Potato Trades.
     Handbook, including list of members, officers and com-
    mittees, annual report and accounts.
    ₍London₎
       v. 19 cm.

HD9251.1.N328   55–36526 ‡

NN   0050955   DLC NN

FR
   National Federation of Fruit and Potato Trades.
   Monthly bulletin. v.1–2, no.3; Sept.1921–
   Jan.1923.
   London.
    2v. 20cm.

    Issued by the National Federation of Fruit and
   Potato Trades' Association.
   No more published?

NN   0050956   IU

338.106 National federation of fruit and potato trades.
NAF
     ... Monthly news summary. v.1(no.1-6); Feb.-
   July/Aug.1935. ₍London, 1935₎
   1v. ports., facsim.

    Supersedes the National federation of fruit and
   potato trades' association (incorporated) limited.
   Monthly report.
   Superseded by Fruitation.

NN   0050957   IU

National Federation of Fruit and Potato Trades'
   Association
     see   National Federation of Fruit and Potato
   Trades.

58
N217
Ed.2
   National federation of gas coke associations.
     London.
     Combine harvesting and grain drying. 2d ed.
   London, 1944.
    72 p. (Modern agricultural equipment ser-
   ies. no. 1, 2d ed.)

    "First edition (1942) issued by the London
   and counties coke association." q.v. (58 L842)

NN   0050959   DNAL MiD

National federation of gas coke associations, *London.*
   Producer gas plant for industrial purposes; its operation and
   maintenance, issued by the National federation of gas coke
   associations ... the British hard coke association ... ₍and₎ the
   South Wales anthracite and dry coal committee ... ₍London₎
   1942.
   viii, 86, ₍2₎ p. illus., diagrs. (part fold.) 21½ᵐ.
   Bibliography: p. 5.

   1. Gas-producers.   I. British hard coke association.   II. South Wales
   anthracite and dry coal committee.   III. Title.

                    43–16755
   Library of Congress   TP762.N3
                 ₍3₎   665.7

NN   0050960   DLC NN CU

National federation of general workers.
   ... Report of the executive council together with state-
   ment of accounts ...
   and minutes of the proceedings at the
   annual general council meeting ...
   London, Co-operative printing society limited, 19
     v. 21½ᵐ.
   At head of title: National federation of general workers.
   Report year ends June 30.

               CA 21–481 Unrev'd
   Library of Congress   HD6661.N2

NN   0050961   DLC DL

National Federation of German American Catholics
     see
Catholic Central Union of America.

National federation of gospel missions.
   A directory of gospel missions in the United States of
   America and report of the addresses and sermons delivered at the district convention of the National federation of gospel missions held at Philadelphia, Pa., October 28 to November 1, 1908. By A. S. Longacre, Philadelphia, Pa., of the Palmer school of business. ₍Philadel-
   phia, 1908₎
   91 p. 23ᵐ.
   1. Missions, Home—Direct. 2. Missions, Home—Societies.   I. Longacre, Aaron S., 1876–   comp.   II. Title.

              CA 19–50 Unrev'd
   Library of Congress   BV2763.N4

NN   0050963   DLC

HD9031
.C6
   National federation of grain cooperatives.
     Co-op grain quarterly. v.1–
   Nov. 1943–
   ₍St. Paul, 1943–

914.238
N2770
   National Federation of Grocers Associations.
     Official programme and souvenir. 1913
   Conference at Bath. Bath, 1913.
    47 p. illus. 18 cm.

    With this is bound: Hatton, John. Bath,
   Britain's historic spa. ... ₍Bath, 1913?₎

    1. Grocery trade. Gt. Brit. Congresses.

NN   0050965   NcD

VOLUME 407

National Federation of Hotel and Accommodation
Establishments.

TX910
.A37G63
Guide to the hotels and other accommodation establish-
ments of South Africa and adjacent territories.

₍Johannesburg, South African Tourist Corporation₎

National federation of housing societies.
... Official bulletin ...
no. 1-
April 1936-
₍London, 1936-
v. illus., ports., diagrs. 26½cm.
quarterly.

Cover-title.
1. Housing - Gt. Brit. 2. Housing - Gt. Brit. -
Societies.

NN 0050967 NNC

National federation of implement dealers'
associations.
Standard accounting procedure for the farm
equipment retailers' accounting system; instruction manual ... Oklahoma City, National
federation of implement dealers' associations,
c1939.
2 p. l., ix, 45, ₍1₎ p. forms. 28½cm.

Cover-title: Farm equipment retailers' uniform accounting system; instruction manual.
Designed and prepared for the National

federation of implement dealers' associations
by a committee consisting of F. C. Scott,
C. H. Chase, S. E. Larsen, and W. L. Oliver.

1. Agricultural machinery - Accounting.
2. Accounting - Agricultural machinery.
I. Title: Farm equipment retailers' accounting
system.

NN 0050969 NNC

58.9
N21   National federation of implement dealers'
associations.
...United tractor and combine trade-in
manual,
16° ₍Abilene₎ Kan.,

NN 0050970 DNAL

National federation of implement dealers
associations. Committee on standard accounting.
The implement dealers simplified system of
bookkeeping. ₍30₎ p. incl. forms. ₍Chicago.
New York? n.d.₎

NN 0050971 OC1

National Federation of Independent Business.

HC101
N312
The Mandate.
Chicago ₍etc.₎

National Federation of Indian Women.

HQ1742
.N33
1954
National Congress of Women, *Calcutta, 1954.*
Indian women meet in conference; report of the National
Congress of Women, Calcutta, June, 1954. ₍New Delhi, Mrs.
Anasuya Gyanchand for the National Federation of Indian
Women₎ 1954.

National Federation of Indian Women. *National Congress
of Women*
see
National Congress of Women.

National Federation of Iron and Steel Manufacturers, *London*
see
British Iron and Steel Federation.

National Federation of Ironmongers.
Year book and directory.
Birmingham ₍Eng.₎
v. 24 cm.

1. Iron industry and trade—Gt. Brit.—Societies, etc.

HD9521.1.N323   55-16706 ‡

NN 0050976 DLC

National federation of jazz organizations of Great
Britain.
N. F. J. O. blue book, jazz club guide
see under Asman, James, comp.

National federation of labor youth.
British Columbia youth must have jobs;
brief submitted to the members of the
British Columbia legislature, Victoria,
B.C., March 15th, 1954. N.p. The Federation,1954.
3p. sq. Q.

NN 0050978 CaBViP

National Federation of Launderers
see
Institution of British Launderers.

National Federation of Liberal Associations.
Proceedings attending the formation of the
Federation with Report of conference, held in
Birmingham, on May 31, 1877. B., 1877.
48 p. 8°. [In College Pamphlets, v. 1608]

NN 0050980 CtY

National Federation of Liberal Women of Canada.
Report ₍of the₎ Assembly...
no. 1

Ottawa, 1928   8°.
no.

1. Woman in politics—Canada.
N. Y. P. L.   April 8, 1929

NN 0050981 NN

National Federation of Men's Bible Classes.
Men's Bible class songs
see under Montgomery, Joseph B

National Federation of Merchant Tailors.

HD9940
.G78M4
The Merchant tailor.

₍London, National Federation of Merchant Tailors₎

National Federation of Merchant Tailors. Log
Committee.
The national time log. Bolton ₍England₎
Printed by W. & T.R. Morris, Ltd., 1898.
179p. 22cm.

NN 0050984 NcU

National Federation of Miners and Mine Laborers.
The National Federation of Miners and Mine Laborers (organized
in 1885) and the National Progressive Union (organized in 1889)
merged in 1890 to form the United Mine Workers of America.
Works by these bodies are found under the name used at the time
of publication.

National Federation of Miners and Mine Laborers.
Constitution of the National Federation of Miners and Mine
Laborers of the United States and territories. Adopted at
Indianapolis, Indiana, September 12th, 1885. Columbus, O.,
Myers Brothers, printers, 1886.
8 p. 17cm.

NN 0050986 ICJ

NATIONAL FEDERATION OF MINERS AND MINE LABORERS.
₍MISCELLANEA: CONSTITUTIONS, PROCEEDINGS, ETC.,
1.-
COLUMBUS, O., ETC. 1885 -

v. 24 CM.

VOL. I CONTAINS ALSO PROCEEDINGS OF THE 9TH
ANN. CONV. OF THE ILLINOIS MINERS' PROTECTIVE ASSO-
CIATION ... JAN. 1889.

NN 0050987 MdBJ

National Federation of Miners and Mine Laborers.
Official proceedings of the ... annual convention of the National
Federation of Miners and Mine Laborers of the United States
and Territories, ... Columbus, Myers Brothers, printers,
1887-1888.
No. 3-4, 1887-1888. 24cm.
No. 3 title reads: Proceedings.

NN 0050988 ICJ IHi MiD

National federation of modern language teachers.

U. S. *Bureau of education.*
... Americans should study foreign languages. Resolutions
adopted by the Modern language association of America at
the Columbus meeting, March 29-31, 1920 ... ₍Washington,
Govt. print. off., 1921₎

National federation of modern language teachers.

Tharp, James Burton, *1892-*
A basic French vocabulary ... by James B. Tharp ... Arthur
G. Bovée ... Algernon Coleman ... Helen M. Eddy ... ₍and₎
Russell P. Jameson ... Washington, D. C., The Modern lan-
guage journal (National federation of modern language teach-
ers) 1934.

National federation of modern language teachers.

"Language leaflets." no. 1-
Washington, D. C., 1939-

National federation of modern language teachers.

The Modern language journal ... v. 1-
Oct. 1916-
₍Menasha, Wis., etc., 1916-

National Federation of Modern Language Teachers.
The Modern language journal supplementary
series
see under title

VOLUME 407

National federation of modern language teachers.
FOR OTHER EDITIONS
SEE MAIN ENTRY
Schwartz, William Leonard, 1888–
Vocational opportunities for foreign language students ...
by William Leonard Schwartz, Lawrence A. Wilkins ₍and₎
Arthur Gibbon Bovée. Buffalo, N. Y., The Modern language
journal (National federation of modern language teachers)
1941.

National federation of modern language teachers. *Committee on the place of the modern foreign languages in American education.*
Suggestions for state and local committees. National federation of modern language teachers, Committee on the place of the modern foreign languages in American education. Wilfred Attwood Beardsley—Henry Grattan Doyle, co-chairmen. Washington, D. C., 1941.
₍14₎ p. 21½ᶜᵐ.
Bibliography: p. ₍7₎–14₎
1. Languages, Modern—Study and teaching.
                    42–19051
    Library of Congress   PB38.U6N3
             ₍2₎   407

    NN   0050995   DLC OU NNC NN

National federation of music clubs.

Buchanan, *Mrs.* **Annabel (Morris)** 1889–   *comp.*
American folk music, compiled by Annabel Morris Buchanan ... Native folk music found in America, including Anglo-American (English, Scotch, Irish) Indian, Negro, Creole, Canadian, Mexican and Spanish-American, and a small amount from German, Norwegian, Hungarian and Portuguese sources. Sacred and secular forms presented in songs, tunes, bibliography, collections, choral and instrumental settings, American compositions based on native traditional material with old-world forms for comparison. For National federation of music

clubs. Ithaca, N. Y., National federation publications and business office (Music clubs magazine) ᵉ1939.

National federation of music clubs.
Book of proceedings of the National federation of music clubs. vol. I–   19th–   biennial meeting ...
1935–
Ithaca, N. Y., National federation of music clubs, 1935–
    v. 23½ᶜᵐ.
Editor: vol. I–   Hazel G. Weaver.

1. Music—Societies. 2. Music—U. S.   I. Weaver. Mrs. Hazel
(Gantt) ed.
                        35–31007
    Library of Congress   ML27.U5N36
    ———— 2d set.
    Copyright   A 80307   ₍2₎   780.6273

    NN   0050998   DLC OC1 OO T WaS NBuG MB

National federation of music clubs.

   ₍Contest bulletins₎

   Library has:
   Junior division.

   Student musicians.

   Young artists.

    NN   0050999   OrP

National federation of music clubs.
MT125
.S89
Surette, Thomas Whitney, 1861–1941.
... Course of study on the development of symphonic music, by Thomas Whitney Surette. ₍Chicago₎ N. F. M. C. press, 1915.

National Federation of Music. Clubs.
   Directory.
19
₍Chicago, 19   8°.
   v.

1. Music—Assoc. and org.—U. S.
N. Y. P. L.   June 20, 1929

    NN   0051001   NN ICJ MB

National Federation of Music Clubs.
Directory of officers and clubs / The National Federation of Musical Clubs. — Chicago : The Federation, 1916.
36 p. ; 23 cm.

1. National Federation of Music Clubs. 2. Musical societies—United States—Directories.
ML27.U5N333   1916   74–194150
                                MAP

    NN   0051002   DLC

National Federation of Music Clubs.
Directory of the National Federation of Music Clubs. —
₍s. l.₎ : The Federation, 1930.
149 p. ; 25 cm.

1. National Federation of Music Clubs. 2. Musical societies—United States—Directories.
ML27.U5N333   1930   74–194149
                              MARC

    NN   0051003   DLC

National federation of music-clubs.
MT6
.H215
Hamilton, Clarence Grant, 1865–
Epochs in musical progress, by Clarence G. Hamilton ... fourth year of a study course in music understanding, adopted by the National federation of music clubs. Boston, Oliver Ditson company; New York, C. H. Ditson & co.; ₍etc., etc.,₎ ᵉ1926₎

National federation of music clubs.
MT6
.M343
Mason, Daniel Gregory, 1873–
From song to symphony; a manual of music appreciation, by Daniel Gregory Mason ... Second year of a study course in music understanding, adopted by the National federation of music clubs. Boston, Oliver Ditson company; New York, C. H. Ditson & co.; ₍etc., etc.,₎ ᵉ1924₎

National federation of music clubs.
FOR OTHER EDITIONS
SEE MAIN ENTRY
Gehrkens, Karl Wilson, 1882–
The fundamentals of music, by Karl W. Gehrkens ... first year of a study course in music understanding, adopted by the National federation of music clubs. Boston, Oliver Ditson company; New York, C. H. Ditson & co.; ₍etc., etc.,₎ ᵉ1924₎

782
N213g
National Federation of Music Clubs.
Grass roots opera; a handbook for those interested in developing grass roots interest in opera as a form of musical expression. ₍Prepared by A. J. Fletcher and others₎ Rev. and reprinted. New York, 1954.
11 numb. ℓ.

Cover title.
"List of operas": ℓ. 7–9.

    NN   0051007   MiD OrP OU

National federation of music clubs,
Handbook, compiled and edited by Mrs. Charles H. Pascoe. New York ₍1951?₎ 85 p. 21cm.

I. Pascoe, Eleanor F   ,ed,

    NN   0051008   NN OrP

National federation of music clubs.
Junior bulletin, National federation of music clubs ...
v. 1–   ; Feb. 1927–
₍Merchantville, N. J., 1927–
   v. in   illus. (incl. ports.) 27½ᶜᵐ. monthly (except June-August)
Editor: Feb. 1927–   Julia E. Williams.

1. Music—Societies.   I. Williams, Julia E., ed. II. Title.
    Library of Congress   ML1.N135   30–25673

    NN   0051009   DLC TxU NN

016.78
N2767L
National Federation of Music Clubs.
List of American music for program planning...
New York, NFMC Information Service ₍195 ₎
Music   60p. 22cm.
lib.   Cover title.
"Supplementary list, to be used with The parade of American music."

1. Music, American – Bibliography. I. Title:
American music for program planning. II. Title:
Program planning,   List of American music for.

    NN   0051010   NcD NcU

R
780.6
N26m
National Federation of Music Clubs.

The master yearbook.

   1.Musical   societies.

    NN   0051011   OrP

MT6
.G62
National federation of music clubs.
Goetschius, Percy, 1853–1943.
Masters of the symphony, by Percy Goetschius ... Fifth year of a study course in music understanding, adopted by the National federation of music clubs ... Boston, Oliver Ditson company; New York, C. H. Ditson & co.; ₍etc., etc.,₎ 1929₎

National federation of music clubs.

A music club in every city, in every county, in every state in the union and Junior boys' and girls' clubs auxiliary. Birmingham ₍1923₎

    NN   0051013   NcU

MT6
.K35
National federation of music clubs.
Kelley, Edgar Stillman, 1857–
Musical instruments, by Edgar Stillman Kelley ... third year of a study course in music understanding, adopted by the National federation of music clubs. Boston, Oliver Ditson company; New York, C. H. Ditson & co.; ₍etc., etc.,₎ ᵉ1925₎

VOLUME 407

National federation of musical clubs.

The **Musical** monitor; the official magazine of the National federation of musical clubs.

₁Chicago, Ill., Mrs. D. A. Campbell,

National federation of music clubs.
... Official bulletin. v. 1–
Jan. 1922–
Peoria, Ill., National federation of music clubs ₁1922–
v. illus. (incl. ports.) 27ᶜᵐ (v. 1, no. 1: 23ᶜᵐ) monthly (except July and August)
Nos. 2–3 of v. 2 are misnumbered "no. 3–4".
Caption title.
Editor: Jan. 1922–   Mrs. Helen H. Mills.
Prior to 1922 the Musical monitor was the organ of the federation.
The issue for June, 1923, is "Special festival issue, thirteenth biennial convention, Asheville, N. C."
1. Music—Societies.   ɪ. Mills, Mrs. Helen Harrison, ed.

Library of Congress   ML1.N14   26–22282

NN   0051016   DLC NN MB AzTeS DCU MiU IU

National Federation of Music Clubs.
Official bulletin
see also its later title   Showcase; music clubs magazine.

National federation of music clubs.

Wardwell, Linda Bell (Free) *"Mrs. F. S. Wardwell,"* 1865–
Plan of study, recommended by the National federation of musical clubs ...   Prepared by Mrs. F. S. Wardwell ...
Stamford, Conn., Mrs. F. S. Wardwell, ₑ1905–

National federation of music clubs.
Study outline for use with Aaron Copland's What to listen for in music; ninth book in the course of study prepared by the National federation of music clubs. New York, London, Whittlesey house, McGraw-Hill book company, inc. ₑ1939₁
32 p. 23ᵐ.
1. Copland, Aaron, 1900–   What to listen for in music. 2. Music—Analysis, interpretation, appreciation. 3. Music—Examinations, questions, etc.   ɪ. Title.
                                          40–7692
Library of Congress   MT6.C78W42
——————— Copy 2.
Copyright AA 312146   ₍2₎   780.1

NN   0051019   DLC OO OU KMK NIC

National federation of music clubs.
A study outline in music appreciation, for use with McKinney and Anderson's Discovering music; eighth course of study book, National federation of music clubs. New York, Boston ₑetc.₁ American book company ₑ1937₁
35 p. 23ᵐ.
On cover: A study outline for Discovering music ₑby₁ McKinney and Anderson.
Bibliography: p. 34–35.
1. McKinney, Howard Decker, 1889–   Discovering music. 2. Music—Analysis, appreciation. 3. Music—Manuals, textbooks, etc.   ɪ. Title.
ML6.M152   780.1   37–16789

NN   0051020   DLC OU WaS

National federation of music clubs.
A study outline in music history, for use with McKinney and Anderson's Music in history; tenth course of study book, National federation of music clubs. New York, Boston ₑetc.₁ American book company ₑ1942₁
28 p. 23ᵐ.
Includes lists of "Suggested topics for papers or reports" and "Books (in addition to those listed in the Selective bibliography)."
1. McKinney, Howard Decker, 1889–   Music in history.
2. Music—Hist. & crit.—Outlines, syllabi, etc.   ɪ. Title.
                                          42–22666
Library of Congress   ML161.N2S7
                        ₍2₎   780.9

NN   0051021   DLC

National federation of music clubs
see also
California federation of music clubs.
District of Columbia federation of music clubs.
See also similar headings beginning with names of states.

National federation of music clubs
see also
Story of music (*Radio program*)

National **federation of music clubs.** Extention Dept.
Organization handbook. Port Huron, 1926.

NN   0051024   NcU

National Federation of Music Clubs. Junior Division.
History and outlook
see under   Hall, Addye (Yeargain)

National federation of music clubs. *Junior division.*
Competitive festivals.
₁Ithaca, N. Y., 19
nos. 23½ᵐ. annual.
1. Music—Competitions. 2. Musical festivals.
                                          45–48920
Library of Congress   ML37.U5N27
                        ₍2₎   780.7973

NN   0051026   DLC

National Federation of Music Clubs. *Junior Division.*
Junior bulletin
see
Junior keynotes.

National Federation of Music Clubs. Junior
ML1   Division.
.N135   **Junior** keynotes. v. 1–
        Feb. 1927–
        ₁Mount Morris, Ill., etc.₁

National Federation of Music Clubs. Past
Presidents Assembly.
Blue book. 1st ed. ₑn.p.₁ 1927.
126 p. ports.
1. Music – Societies

NN   0051029   MiD

National Federation of Music Clubs. Past Presidents Assembly.
Past presidents assembly of The National Federation of Music Clubs, its aims, activities and history.
= [Boston. 1923.] 8 pp. Autograph facsimile. 27 cm.

NN   0051030   MB

National federation of music societies.
...Catalogue of choral works; performed by societies affiliated to the National federation of music societies during the period between its inauguration in 1936 and the year 1949.   London [1950]
63 p.   21cm.

1. Choral music—Bibl.

NN   0051031   NN

National Federation of Music Societies.
Catalogue of choral works performed by societies affiliated to the National Federation of Music Societies during the period between its inauguration in 1936 and the year 1953. 2d ed. London, 1953.
72 p. 23 cm.
1. Choral music—Bibl.
ML128.V7N34 1953   781.9734   56–21471 ‡

NN   0051032   DLC IU

MT883   National Federation of Music Societies.
N2C4   Choral Latin; some notes for the guidance of choirs in the pronunciation of Latin.   London ₑ195–?₁
25p. 25cm.
Cover title.
Bibliography: p.3.
1. Latin language – Pronunciation. 2. Choral singing – Diction. I. Title.

NN   0051033   IaU WaS CoU

MUSIC LIB.
ML27   National Federation of Music Societies.
G7N5   Register of members and handbook.
London.
v. 22 cm.
1. Music – Societies, etc. – Direct.

NN   0051034   OU CaBVa

National federation of paper box manufacturers.
Joint cost committee.
Denham, Robert S.
Manual of cost engineering and estimating for paper box manufacturers, by Robert S. Denham; with Addenda by Joint cost committee. Cleveland, R. S. Denham, 1917.

NATIONAL FEDERATION OF PLASTERING CONTRACTORS.
Year book.
London, Coram publishers.   v.   ports.
20cm.
1. Plaster and plastering--Gt. Br. --Yearbooks. 2. Plaster and plastering--Direct. --Gt. Br.

NN   0051036   NN

National federation of Post office clerks.
Brief for the reduction of hours of night work in the postal service. Submitted by National federation of post office clerks, the Railway mail association.
(n.p., 1926)
cover-title, 52 p.   23 cm

NN   0051037   DL Or

VOLUME 407

HFBP75
.N219
MIS
National Federation of Post Office Clerks.
Brief history of militant organization
that has 'fought the fight and kept the
faith.' Washington, D.C.? [1931?]
8 p. 23cm.

Cover title.

--- ---- Another edition. [1936?] (8 p.)
--- ---- Another edition. [1941?] (8 p.)

NN   0051038   WHi MH

National federation of post office clerks.
Constitution and by-laws of the National federation of
post office clerks : affiliated with the A. F. of L. As adopted at Chicago, Illinois, August 27, 1906, and amended ...
1907-   Milwaukee, Allied printing trades council
[1908?-
   v. 14-15½ᶜᵐ.

                                        12-25516

Library of Congress   HE6001.N4

NN   0051039   DLC NN ICJ MH

National Federation of Post Office Clerks.
Convention [of the] National Federation of Post Office
Clerks.
   St. Paul.
     v. ports. 30 cm.
       Issues for 19   in 2 pts., each with special t. p.: [1] Reports
of officers. [2] Proceedings of the convention.

    HE6001.N42   331.8811383   54-15059 ‡

NN   0051040   DLC

HFBP75
N219
MIS
National Federation of Post Office Clerks.

[Miscellaneous ephemeral materials not
fully catalogued]

NB. - Such materials are shelved in
pamphlet-boxes marked with a period (.),
a plus (+) or a quotation-mark (") ahead
of the second line of the call-number.
Search should be made in all three locations, although material may not be found
in any one or two of them.

NN   0051041   WHi

HFBP75
"N219
.P
National Federation of Post Office Clerks.
Proceedings. v.   -   , 19 -19
[Washington, D.C.]
   v. illus., ports. 31cm. biennial.
   Resolutions, v.   bound with
the Proceedings.

   1. Postal service - U.S. - Employees.

NN   0051042   WHi NNC MB MiD

NATIONAL FEDERATION OF POST OFFICE CLERKS.
A record of progress. Washington,1940.

   pp.7.

NN   0051043   MH

National Federation of Post Office Clerks.
Reports of officers.
   [n. p.]
     v. 29-31 cm.

    HE6001.N43   331.8811383   49-37166*‡

NN   0051044   DLC MH-BA WHi NN MH-L

National federation of post office clerks.
The Union postal clerk ... Devoted to the interest of the
postal service and post office clerks.
Chicago, The Union postal clerk publishing co., 19

National Federation of Pos Office Clerks. Local
10, New York City.
New York fed; monthly publication of Local
Number 10, National Federation of Post Office
Clerks
    see under title

HFBP75
.N219
MIS
National Federation of Post Office Clerks.
Local no. 10, New York.
Official hand-book of New York branch,
National Association of Post Office Clerks.
[New York, 1896]
[98] p. illus., ports. 26cm.

A digest of postal laws and regulations.
Contains: "New York Post Office" by
Charles W. Dayton, postmaster.

NN   0051047   WHi

National federation of post office clerks.
Local 28, Seattle.
   Local 28 news.   Seattle.
   Monthly.

NN   0051048   WaS

F869
S33N33
National Federation of Post Office Clerks.
Local no. 73, San Jose, Calif. Woman's
Auxiliary.
Constitution and by-laws. [n. p., 19--?]
[8] p. 14cm.

Cover title.

1. San Jose, Calif. - Clubs.

NN   0051049   CU-B

National federation of post office clerks. *Local no. 251 Brooklyn*
Local bulletin...
   v.
Brooklyn, N. Y., 193   32cm.
   v.
   Monthly (except July - Aug.).
   Vol. 6, no. 4 - v. 7, no. 3 omitted in numbering; other irregularities in numbering.
   Vol. 5 (1939) includes an extra unnumbered issue, called Special convention issue,
dated Aug., 1939.

   1. Trade unions, Postal service   employees'--U.S.--N.Y.--
New York.
N. Y. P. L.   January 30, 1942

NN   0051050   NN

R331.881 National Federation of Post Office Clerks.
P72N22m Local No.295, Detroit
         Minutes. [Detroit] 1929 -

     Library has

NN   0051051   MiD

NATIONAL FEDERATION OF POST OFFICE MOTOR
    VEHICLE EMPLOYEES.
     Official proceedings of the biennial national
convention.
   [v. p.]   v.   ports.   23cm.

   Title varies slightly.
   1. Trade unions, Postal   employees'--U.S. 2. Trade
unions, Automobile drivers'--   U.S.

NN   0051052   NN

PN4841
N28
National Federation of Press Women, Inc.
Directory for the years

   Hibbing, Minn., 19_

     _vols. 21cm.

NN   0051053   NBuG NN

BX1912
.P775
National Federation of Priests' Councils.
   Priests' forum.
   [South Hackensack, N. J., Color Reproductions, inc.]

National Federation of Professional Workers.
   Annual report.
   London.
     v. 21 cm.

    HD6668.P75N3   331.880942   49-37708*‡

NN   0051055   DLC NN

National federation of property owners.
   The Civil defence act, 1939, together with an
introduction and explanatory notes by H. Heathcote-
Williams ...
     see under   Gt. Brit. Laws, statutes,
etc., 1936-1952 (George VI)

National Federation of Property Owners.
Law
   Property owners' gazette.
   [London]

National Federation of Property Owners.
   Question & answer on the Town and country planning act,
1947. Property problems simply and briefly explained.
Interim ed. Westminster [London, 1947]
   11 p. 21 cm.

   1. Cities and towns—Planning—Gt. Brit. 2. Real property—Gt.
Brit.   I. Title: Town and country planning act, 1947.

                                     48-23946*

NN   0051058   DLC

National federation of Protestant patriotic
   societies of the United States.
   The Protestant standard; the new voice of the old menace.
   v. 1-   May 24, 1920-
   East Orange, N. J., 1920-

VOLUME 407

National federation of religious liberals.
Theodore Parker anniversaries...
see under title

CT
211
A52
v.21
no.14
National Federation of Religious Liberals.
Theodore Parker commemoration
programme, Tuesday evening, May 10 ...
[Philadelphia? 1910]
[7] p. 25cm.
Caption title.
Cover title: You are invited to
attend ...

1. Parker, Theodore, 1810-1860.
I. Title

NN 0051061   NIC

National federation of religious liberals. *1st congress,
Philadelphia, 1909.*
The unity of the spirit; proceedings and papers of the
first congress of the National federation of religious liberals, held at Philadelphia, Penn., in the meeting house
of the Religious society of Friends, April 27, 28, 29 and
30, 1909; ed. by Charles W. Wendte, D. D. Boston, Mass.
[1909]
3 p. l., 287 p. 23½ᶜᵐ.

I. Wendte, Charles William, 1844-   ed.

9-31873

NN 0051062   DLC OC1W OO CU MB NNUT IEG OCH MB

National federation of religious liberals. *3d congress,
New York, 1911.*
The unity of life. Proceedings and papers of the third
congress of the National federation of religious liberals,
held in New York, April 26, 27, 28, 1911. Ed. by Henry
W. Wilbur. Philadelphia, The Federation, 1911.
216 p. 22½ᶜᵐ.

I. Wilbur, Henry Watson, 1851-   II. Title.

15-3370

NN 0051063   DLC OO

National federation of religious liberals.
4th congress, Rochester, N.Y., 1913.
The promotion of sympathy and goodwill
between orthodox and liberal in religion.
[n. p., 1913]
cover-title, 33 p.   18.5 cm.
Contents:— I. A juster appreciation of
religious radicals by orthodox believers, by
Ambrose White Vernon. II. A juster appreciation of orthodox believers by religious radicals,
by William Channing Gannett.

NN 0051064   NNUT N

National federation of religious liberals. *5th congress,
Philadelphia, 1915.*
... Program, proceedings, and papers. Boston, The
National federation of religious liberals [1915]
62 p. 19ᶜᵐ.
Foreword signed: Charles W. Wendte.

I. Wendte, Charles William, 1844-

16-7473

NN 0051065   DLC OO

280
N21
1917
National federation of religious liberals--7th
congress, Pittsburgh, 1917.
... Seventh congress at Pittsburgh, Pa., March
6, 7, and 8, 1917. Program, proceedings, and papers. [Boston] National federation of religious liberals [1917?]
75p.

1. Christian union. 2. Liberalism (Religion)
3. Religion--Congresses.

NN 0051066   IU DLC MH MiU

National federation of religious liberals. *8th congress,
Boston, 1917.*
Religious liberals in council. Eighth congress of the
National federation of religious liberals at Boston, Mass.
November 25 and 26, 1917. Proceedings and papers ...
[Boston, 1917?]
96 p. 19ᶜᵐ.

I. Title.

Library of Congress   BX6.N4A5 1917 a

19-15719

NN 0051067   DLC OCH MiU

National federation of religious liberals. *9th congress,
Longwood, Pa., 1919.*
A world league of nations and religions. Ninth congress of
the National federation of religious liberals at Longwood, Pa.,
May 31 and June 1, 1919. Proceedings and papers ... [n. p.,
1919]
77 p. 19ᶜᵐ.

1. Liberalism (Religion)—Congresses.   I. Title.

20-2572 Revised

Library of Congress   BX6.N4A5 1919

NN 0051068   DLC MiU OO

National federation of religious liberals. *10th congress,
Boston, 1920.*
Tenth meeting of the National federation of religious
liberals, held in connection with the seventh session of
the International congress of religious liberals, at Unity
house, Boston, Massachusetts, October 6, 1920. [Newton,
Mass., The Graphic press, 1921]
48 p. 19ᶜᵐ.

I. International congress of free Christians and other religious liberals.
7th, Boston, 1920.

21-9102

Library of Congress   BX6.N4A5 1920

NN 0051069   DLC MBU-T MiU OCH

National federation of remedial loan associations.
Bulletin of the National federation of remedial loan
associations.
[n. p.] The ... Federation [1912]–
v. 23ᶜᵐ.
Supersedes the Proceedings of the federation, 1909-11.

1. Interest and usury—U. S.

13-17354

Library of Congress   HG2083.N32

NN 0051070   DLC NjP ICJ OU CU

National Federation of Remedial Loan Associations.
Proceedings of annual convention... Published by
the National Federation of Remedial Loan Association [New York?] 1912-

NN 0051071   ICJ CaBViP OrPR

National federation of remedial loan associations.
Proceedings of the National federation of remedial loan
associations. 1909-11. [Buffalo? etc.] The Federation [1909-
11]
3 v. in 1. fold. tables. 23ᶜᵐ.
Meetings held in conjunction with the National conference of charities and correction.
Superseded in 1912 by the Bulletin of the federation.

1. Interest and usury—U. S.

Library of Congress   HG2083.N3

11—18624

NN 0051072   DLC CU OrPR NjP

[National Federation of remedial loan associations]
... Work of the remedial loan societies, 1912- [13-15.
[New York, The Clover press] 19[12 – 1915.
3 sheet. 43½ x 70ᶜᵐ. fold. to 21½ x 14ᶜᵐ.
Title on recto of first fold.

1. Credit—U. S.   I. Title.

15—3780

Library of Congress   HG2066.N3

NN 0051073   DLC ICJ OU CU

JK
2283
.A4
no.2
National Federation of Republican Women.
Campaign manual. Washington, D. C.
[n.d.]
26 p. 22cm. (NFRW leadership manual
series, 2)

Cover title.

1. Campaign management--Handbooks, manuals,
etc. I. Title. II. Series: National Federation of Republican Women./Leadership manual
series, no. 2.

NN 0051074   KyLoU

JK
2283
.A4
no.3
National Federation of Republican Women.
Fund raising manual. Washington, D. C.
[n.d.]
12 p. illus. 22cm. (NFRW leadership
manual series, 3)

Cover title.

1. Campaign funds--Handbooks, manuals, etc.
I. Title. II. Series: National Federation of
Republican Women./Leadership manual series,
no. 3.

NN 0051075   KyLoU

National Federation of Republican Women.
Handbook for women who win. [Washington,
1953]
cover-title, 44 p.   20 cm.

NN 0051076   NcD

JK
2283
.A4
no.1
National Federation of Republican Women.
Leadership manual. Washington, D. C.
[n.d.]
47 p. 22cm. (NFRW leadership manual
series, 1)

Cover title.

1. Politics, Practical. 2. Leadership--
Handbooks, manuals, etc. I. Title. II.
Series: National Federation of Republican
Women./Leader-   ship manual series, no.1.

NN 0051077   KyLoU

VOLUME 407

JK
2283
.A4
no.4

National Federation of Republican Women.
Membership manual. Washington, D. C.
₍n.d.₎
8 p. illus. 22cm. (NFRW leadership
manual series, 4)

Cover title.

1. Party affiliation--Handbooks, manuals, etc.
2. Membership campaigns--Handbooks, manuals,
etc. I. Title. II. Series: National Federation of Republican Women./Leadership manual
series, no. 4.

NN   0051078   KyLoU

Pam.
Coll.
10642

National Federation of Republican Women.
Plan of action for "more in 54". Washington ₍1953₎
cover-title, ₍24₎ p. illus. 23cm.

NN   0051079   NcD

JK
2283
.A4
no.5

National Federation of Republican Women.
Program manual. Washington, D. C. ₍n.d.₎
32 p. illus. 22cm. (NFRW leadership
manual series, 5)

Cover title.

1. Politics, Practical--Handbooks, manuals,
etc. I. Title. II. Series: National Federation of Republican Women./Leadership manual
series, no. 5.

NN   0051080   KyLoU

JK
2283
.A4
no.6

National Federation of Republican Women.
Public relations manual. Washington, D.C.
₍n.d.₎
28 p. 22cm. (NFRW leadership manual
series, 6)

Cover title.

1. Public relations and politics--Handbooks,
manuals, etc. I. Title. II. Series: National
Federation of Republican Women./Leadership
manual series, no. 6.

NN   0051081   KyLoU

National federation of sales executives.
...Annual conference...
₍no.₎
New York, 19   28cm.
nos.   illus.

No. 6 has title: A condensed report of the proceedings of the annual convention.
No.   "made available by the International business machines corporation."

1. Salesmanship and salesmen—   Per. and soc. publ.—U.S.
N. Y. P. L.   February 16, 1944

NN   0051082   NN OU

T7
.U62
no. 65

National Federation of Sales Executives.
Metz, Herbert, 1892–   ed.
Opportunities in selling. Prepared in cooperation with the
National Federation of Sales Executives. Washington, U. S.
Govt. Print. Off., 1947.

658.85
N2151

NATIONAL FEDERATION OF SALES EXECUTIVES.
Report of the first-
annual meeting ... 1936-   [New York,
National federation of sales executives, 1936-
v. diagrs. 27-28cm.

1. Salesmen and salesmanship.

NN   0051084   TxU

National Federation of Settlements
see
National Federation of Settlements and Neighborhood
Centers.

National Federation of Settlements and Neighborhood Centers.
Agency prospectus.
₍New York₎
v. 28 cm.

1. Social settlements—United States.

HV4195.N3   361.8   72-627539

NN   0051086   DLC

National Federation of Settlements and Neighborhood Centers.
Bulletin.

Library has
no.1-2; Jan.-Apr. 1922.

NN   0051087   MiD OCl

National Federation of Settlements and Neighborhood Centers.
City or community; patterns of community
organisation in urban areas
see under   Handasyde, Elizabeth.

National Federation of Settlements and
Neighborhood Centers.
... Conference of the National Federation of Settlements ...
₍Boston, 1913-1919₎
Library has no. 3-9, 1913-1919. 24ᶜᵐ.
No. 1, 2, 4, never published?
Wanting: no. 7, 1917.

NN   0051089   ICJ CU DNAL DL

National Federation of Settlements and Neighborhood
Centers.
Digest of action, Board of directors meeting.

New York ₍1948–   nos.   28cm.

Continues its Conference. ₍Report of proceedings₎
1949–   issued under the later name of the federation: National federation of
settlements and neighborhood centers.
Various issues include, or are accompanied, by Business meeting of the delegate
body.

1. Social settlements—Assoc.   and org.—U.S.   *Card revised*

NN   0051090   NN

National Federation of Settlements and Neighborhood
Centers.
Directory of summer resident camping programs.
New York.   no.   28cm.

Title also as: Directory of camps.

1. Camping--Direct.--U.S. I. Title. II. Title: Directory of camps.
III. National federation of settlements. Directory of camps.

NN   0051091   NN

National Federation of Settlements and Neighborhood Centers.
Bruère, *Mrs.* Martha S   (Bensley)
Does prohibition work? A study of the operation of the
Eighteenth amendment made by the National federation of
settlements, assisted by social workers in different parts of the
United States. Martha Bensley Bruère, director of the study,
with a foreword by Lillian D. Wald ... New York and London, Harper & brothers, 1927.

National federation of settlements and neighborhood centers.
Health costs and how met.   1954.

NN   0051093   PU-PSW

National Federation of Settlements and Neighborhood Centers.
Kingman, John Macoun, 1894–   ed.
A manual of settlement boys' work, edited by John M. Kingman ... and Edward Sidman ... ₍New York₎ National federation of settlements, 1935.

National Federation of Settlements and Neighborhood Centers. Music Division.
Music activities in the National federation
of settlements. ∕ v.1- New York, 1941-

Reproduced from type-written copy.

NN   0051095   OCl

HV
4195
.N28

National Federation of Settlements and Neighborhood Centers.
Neighborhood improvement projects. New York
₍1953₎
47 p.   23 cm.
Cover title.
"Seven papers presented at settlement con-
ference₍s₎ in 1952 and 1953."

1.Neighborhood. 2.Social settlements.

NN   0051096   MiU OrU IaU NN OEac PU-PSW

National federation of settlements and neighborhood
centers.
Papers presented at annual conference...
June 9-12, 1949, Cleveland, Ohio.   Cleveland,
Ohio, Author, 1949.

NN   0051097   OCl

National Federation of Settlements and Neighborhood Centers.
₍Publications₎

Library has
Oct. Dec. 1920; Feb. June 1921.

NN   0051098   MiD

National Federation of Settlements and Neighborhood
Centers.
Report and forecast. Boston 1920.
7 p. 23½ cm.

NN   0051099   DL ICJ

VOLUME 407

National federation of settlements. and neighborhood centers.
Resolutions adopted at the Delegate meeting, May 8th, 1954, New York, N. Y.   New York ₍1954₎   9 l.   28cm.

At head of title: National federation of settlements and neighborhood centers... New York...

1. Children—Congresses—U.S.   —N. Y.—New York, 1954.   2. Children—Charities—U.S.

NN   0051100   NN

331.853   National Federation of Settlements and Neigh-
N213s   borhood Centers.
Selected conference papers, 1952-1953.
New York, 1953.
83 l.   28cm.

1. Social settlements.

NN   0051101   OrU

HV   National Federation of Settlements and
4178   Neighborhood Centers.
N3   Settlement goals for the next third of
HULL   a century; a symposium. Boston, 1926.
HOUSE   70 p. (Settlement monographs, 7)

Statement by Jane Addams: p. 12.

1. Social settlements--Congresses.
I. Title.

NN   0051102   ICIU NN OC1 OO MnU ICU MiD

National Federation of Settlements and Neighborhood Centers.
· Summer in the city. ₍New York, 1942₎
38 p. illus. 22 cm.

Cover title.
Issued by the federation under its earlier name: National Federation of Settlements.
Foreword signed: Margaret Day, editor.
"Permission to adapt the Handbook of play schools was ... granted by the Play Schools Association of New York."
"Resources": p. 36-38.

1. Play schools.   I. Day, Margaret, ed.   II. Play Schools Association. Handbook on play schools for group leaders and teachers.   III. Title.

GV424.N3   796   44-880 rev*

NN   0051103   DLC NN

National Federation of Settlements and
331.852   Neighborhood Centers.
N21w   We believe; ₍a₎ tentative statement of
desirable standards for settlements and
neighborhood centers, by Jean M. Maxwell
₍and₎ John McDowell.   New York ₍1950₎
17 l.   28cm.

1. Social settlements.   I. Maxwell,
Jean M   II. McDowell, John.
III. Title.

NN   0051104   LU

National Federation of Settlements and Neighborhood Centers.
Young working girls; a summary of evidence from two thousand social workers. Edited for the National Federation of Settlements, by Robert A. Woods and Albert J. Kennedy, its secretaries; with an introd. by Jane Addams. Boston, Houghton Mifflin, 1913.
xiii, 185 p. 20 cm.

1. Girls.   2. Young women.   3. Woman—Employment.   I. Woods, Robert Archey, 1865-1925, ed.   II. Kennedy, Albert Joseph, 1879- ed.   III. Title.

HQ798.N3   13-21035 rev*

MB NN OU MiU MH ICJ
NN   0051105   DLC OrCS WaS OKentU RPB NcC CU NIC

National Federation of Settlements and Neighborhood Centers. Boys' and Girls' Work Division.
Round table, Boys' and Girls' Work Division...
v. ₍1₎

New York, 193
v.   28cm.

Monthly (except Aug.–Oct.; irregular).
Reproduced from typewritten copy, v. 1

Full title: v. 1   –v. 2   – May, 1938) Round table of the Boys' work, Girls' work divisions, National federation of settlements; v. 3–   (Nov., 1938 – Round table, Boys' and girls' work division, National federation of settlements.
Includes proceedings of various regional conferences.
Occasional issues include book reviews, reading lists, separately paged suppl.

NN   0051107   NN CaBVaU DPU OC1

National Federation of Settlements and Neighborhood Centers. *Camp Committee.*
Adventures in camping. ₍New York, National Federation of Settlements, 1940₎
48 p. 27 cm.
Cover title.

1. Camping.   I. Title.

SK601.N42   796.54   42-51662 rev*

NN   0051108   DLC OrU NN IU OrCS

National Federation of Settlements and Neighborhood Centers. Dramatists Division.
... List of plays. 36, ₍1₎p. New York,
1936.

Planographed.
Cover-title.

NN   0051109   OC1

National Federation of Settlements and Neighborhood Centers. Music Division.
Welfare council of New York city.
Music in thirty-eight settlements in New York city; a study made by the Welfare council of New York city, in cooperation with the Music division of the National federation of set-
tlements; by Frances McElwee McFarland ... ₍New York, 1930₎

National Federation of Settlements and Neighborhood   4048.402
Centers. Music Division.
Suggestions on curriculum.
(*In* Schenck, Janet D. Music schools and settlement music depart-
ments. Pp. 63-76. Boston. 1923.)

M6182 — Musical education. — Courses of study.

NN   0051111   MB

National Federation of Settlements and Neighborhood Centers. Music Division.
Year book.
19

New York, 19   8°.
no.

1. Music settlements.
N. Y. P. L.   October 28, 1929

NN   0051112   NN

National Federation of Settlements and Neighborhood
Centers. *Unemployment Committee.*
Case studies of unemployment, compiled by the Unemployment Committee of the National Federation of Settle-
ments, with an introd. by Helen Hall and a foreword by Paul U. Kellogg. Edited by Marion Elderton. Philadelphia, University of Pennsylvania Press, 1931.
x, 418 p. 24 cm. (Industrial Research Department, Wharton School of Finance and Commerce, University of Pennsylvania. Research studies, 12)
1. Unemployed—U. S.—Case studies.   I. Elderton, Marion, 1806-
ed.   II. Title.   (Series: Pennsylvania. University. Wharton School of Finance and Commerce. Industrial Research Dept. Research studies, 12)

HD5724.N25   331.137973   31-8098 rev

OU MiU OO OrU DL MB CU WHi NcD OrPR NN
NN   0051113   DLC MtU WaSp WaTC WaS RPB ViU OrP TxU

HFBT4   National Federation of Silk Workers.
.NA   Constitution.   New York, East-Side Union
print., 1888.
28 p. 13cm.

Cover title.
"In English, German and French" each section having caption-title.

1. Textile workers – U.S.

NN   0051114   WHi

BX809   National Federation of Sodalities of the United
.W6A3   States.
World Federation of the Sodalities of Our Lady.
Proceedings of the world congress of Sodalities of Our Lady. 1st–   1954–
₍v. p.₎

National federation of spiritual science churches.
Textbook of spiritual science, National federation of spiritual science churches. Los Angeles, Calif. ₍1932₎
2 p. l., 7–110 p. 23½ᶜᵐ.

1. Spiritualism.   I. Title.   II. Title: Spiritual science, Textbook of.

Library of Congress   BX9798.S7N3
——— Copy 2.   33-6356
Copyright A 48689   ₍2₎   289.9

NN   0051116   DLC

GV876   National Federation of State High School Ath-
.N38   Associations.
Baseball umpires manual.
Chicago.
v. illus. 18 cm.

At head of title, 5th-   eds.:
National Alliance edition.
Prepared under direction of National
Alliance Baseball Rules Committee.

NN   0051117   TU

796.357   National Federation of State High School
N265   Athletic Associations.
Baseball rules.

1.Baseball.   I.Title.

NN   0051118   OrP Or WaT

796.357   National Federation of State High School
N265b   Athletic Associations.
Baseball case book; official rule interpre-
tations.

Library has

1.Baseball.   I.Title.

NN   0051119   OrP Or

VOLUME 407

National Federation of State High School
Athlethic Associations.
Basketball case book
see under title

National Federation of State High School Athletic
Associations.
Basketball official's manual. 1st-   ed.
19 -
Chicago, 19 -
v. illus. 18 cm.

NN   0051121   OU

National federation of state high school athletic associations.
Basketball play situations. [1932]-   ed.
Chicago, Ill., °1931-
v. diagrs. 17ᶜᵐ.

1982-   consist of interpretations of the rules of the
National basketball committee of the United States and Canada.

1. Basket-ball.   I. National basketball committee of the United
States and Canada.   II. Title.
32-34480 Revised
Library of Congress   GV885.A1N3
[r43c2]   796.32

NN   0051122   DLC N OLak NN CoGrS Wa

NATIONAL FEDERATION OF STATE HIGH SCHOOL ATHLETIC
ASSOCIATIONS
Basketball player handbook, |1952/53 -
Author, 1953.
v. illus.

Editor: H.V. Porter.

NN   0051123   Or

National federation of state high school athletic associations.
...Basketball rules. National federation edition.
19

Chicago, c194   nos. 17cm.
"Rules of the National basketball committee of the United States and Canada."

1. Basket-ball.
N.Y.P.L.   March 16, 1944

NN   0051124   NN

GV 955   National Federation of State High School
A1 N28   Athletic Associations.
Football case book. 19 -
Chicago.
v. illus. 18 cm.

1. Football - Rules. I. Title.

NN   0051125   OU OrP

National Federation of State High School Athletic
Associations.
Football officiating manual, compiled by
Carl Kopelk and E.A. Thomas.   Chicago, Author
[1950?]
32 p.   ilus., diagrs.
1. Football. 2. Sports officiating.
I. Kopelk, Carl, comp. II. Title.

NN   0051126   OrP

GV 955   National Federation of State High School
A1 N32   Athletic Associations.
Football official's manual. 1st-   edition.
19 -
Chicago.
v. illus. 17-18 cm.

Title varies: 19 -   , Football officiating
manual.

1. Football - Umpiring. I. Title.

NN   0051127   OU

National federation of state high school athletic associa-
tions.
Football play situations ... for the benefit of officials, coaches
and players, edited by Hugh L. Ray. [Chicago] National
federation of state high school athletic associations, °1931.
82, [1] p. illus., diagr. 17ᶜᵐ.
"1931 edition."

1. Foot-ball.   I. Ray, Hugh L., ed.
Library of Congress   GV951.N3   32-34790
————— Copy 2.
Copyright A 46653   [3]   796.33

NN   0051128   DLC MoU

National federation of state high school
athletic associations.
Football play situations based on N.C.
A.A. official football rules. Published...
for the benefit of officials, coaches and
players. Edited by Hugh L. Ray. [Chicago,
Ill.] National federation of state high
school athletic associations, c1932.
78 p., 1 l. illus., diagrs. S

NN   0051129   OO

National federation of state high school athletic associa-
tions.
Football play situations, based on N. C. A. A. official football
rules ... for the benefit of officials, coaches and players, edited
by Hugh L. Ray. [Chicago] National federation of state high
school athletic associations, °1933.
86, [1] p. illus., diagrs. 17ᶜᵐ.

1. Foot-ball.   I. Ray, Hugh L., ed.   II. National collegiate athletic
association.
Library of Congress   GV951.N3 1933   34-6311
————— Copy 2.
Copyright AA 134499   [3]   796.33

NN   0051130   DLC

National Federation of State High School Athletic
Association.
Football player handbook.   19 -
Chicago, 19 -
v. illus. 18 cm.

NN   0051131   OU

National federation of state high school athletic associa-
tions.
Football rules ... including 6-man and touch rules. 1932-
[Chicago, 1932-
v. illus., diagr. 17ᶜᵐ.
Cover-title.
Title varies: 1932-41, Official interscholastic football rules.
1942-   Interscholastic football rules.
19   Football rules.
Editors: 19   E. A. Thomas, H. L. Ray, H. V. Porter.

1. Foot-ball.   I. Thomas, Ernest A., ed.   II. Ray, Hugh L., ed.
III. Porter, Henry Van Arsdale, ed.   IV. Title.

GV955.N325   796.33   41-25913 rev

OCl
NN   0051132   DLC IU OLak WaSp WaPS OrP Or WaT NN

National federation of state high school athletic associations.
Game administration handbook in basketball ... edited by
H. V. Porter ... Chicago, Ill., National federation of state
high school athletic associations, °19
v. illus. 17½ᶜᵐ.

1. Basket-ball.   I. Porter, Henry Van Arsdale, ed.   II. Title.
44-45883
Library of Congress   GV885.A1N33
[2]   796.32

NN   0051133   DLC NN

GV 565   National Federation of State High School
N27   Athletic Associations.
Handbook. 19 -
[Chicago]
v. illus. 18 cm.

Includes constitution, by-laws and directory.
Title varies: 19 -   Constitution and by-laws.

NN   0051134   OU

National Federation of State High School Athletic
Associations.
Interscholastic football rules
see its   Football rules.

National Federation of State High School Athletic
Associations.
Official basketball rules
see under title

National Federation of State High School Athletic
Associations.
Official interscholastic football rules
see its   Football rules.

National Federation of State High School Athletic Associa-
tions.
The official National Federation of State High School
Athletic Associations all-sports rule book, edited by H. V.
Porter. New York, A. S. Barnes [1952]
185 p. illus. 28 cm.

1. School sports.   I. Porter, Henry Van Arsdale, ed.   II. Title.
III. Title : All-sports rule book.
GV731.N314   796   52-8287 ‡

CaQMM
NN   0051138   DLC NN WaT WaS CaBVa WaE OrP Wa Or PP

National Federation of State High School Athletic
Associations.
Official six-man football guide and rule book
see its   Official six-man football rules and
handbook.

National Federation of State High School Athletic Asso-
ciations.
Official six-man football rules and handbook (including
touch football rules) for schools, military camps and playground groups. 1935-
[Chicago]
v. illus., ports. 18 cm.
Issues for 1940-   pub. as Spalding's athletic library, no. 433.

"Official publication of the National Six-Man Football Rules Committee," 1940-   : issued by the federation, 19
Title varies: 1935-   Six-man football; a handbook for players,
coaches, and schoolmen (subtitle varies)—19   Official six-man

Continued in next column

VOLUME 407

Continued from preceding column

football guide and rule book.— -1942, Six-man football rules.—
1943– Official six-man football rules and handbook ... (cover title:
6-man football rules and hand book (varies slightly))
  Editors: 1935– Stephen Epler.—19 H. V. Porter, Stephen
Epler.
  Imprint varies: 1935-39, Lincoln, Univ. Pub. Co.—1940– New
York, American Sports Pub. Co.
  1. Foot-ball. I. Epler, Stephen Edward, 1909– ed. II. Porter,
Henry Van Arsdale, ed. III. National Six-Man Football Rules Com-
mittee. IV. Title. V. Title: Six-man football rules.   (Series:
Spalding's athletic library, no. 433.

GV953.N3   796.33   35–16457 rev 2*

NN   0051141   DLC MB WaSp MB NN ViU Or OrMonO

**National Federation of State High School Athletic
Associations.**
        Six-man football; a handbook
        see its Official six-man football rules
and handbook.

**National Federation of State High School Athletic Associa-
tions.** *Six-man football rules*
see its Official six-man football rules and handbook.

**National Federation of State High School Athletic Associa-
tions.**
        Track and field rules and records.
(Chicago)
        v. illus. 17 cm.

    1. Track-athletics—Yearbooks. I. Title.
GV563.N276   371.74   51–17243 ‡

NN   0051144   DLC NN

GV 881   **National Federation of State High School**
A1 N26   **Athletic Associations.**
           12-inch baseball rules.   1st   edition.
         19 -
         Chicago.
           v. illus. 18 cm.

           1. Softball. I. Title.

NN   0051145   OU

National federation of telephone workers.
        ... Analysis of existing-proposed pension plans for telephone
workers, June 1943. (Baltimore) National federation of telephone workers, [1944.
        cover-title, 3 p. l., 40 numb. l., 77 l. 27½ x 21½ᶜᵐ.
        Reproduced from type-written copy.

        1. Old age pensions—U. S. 2. Telephone—U. S.   I. Title.
                                                            44–35527
        Library of Congress   HD7116.T36U65
                                      [2]   331.252

NN   0051146   DLC

National Federation of Telephone Workers.
HD6350
.T23C2
        The CWA news. v. 1–
        May 1941–
        (Washington)

National Federation of Telephone Workers.
        A general study on leaves of absence for full-time union
officers, by Mildred Galloway, statistical assistant, under general supervision of Ann J. Herlihy, research director.
(Washington) 1945.
        94 l. 29 cm.
        Cover title: Leaves of absence for union officers.
        Bibliography: leaves 89–92.

        1. Leave of absence. 2. Trade-unions—U. S.—Officers.   I. Gallo-
way, Mildred.
HD6490.O4N3   331.816   51–28910

NN   0051148   DLC OCl NNC MH-BA

National Federation of Telephone Workers.
        Summarized report of the national assembly.
        [n. p.]
        v. 23 cm.

        1. Telephone—U. S.—Employees.
HD6515.T33N3   331.88121385   49–15059*‡

NN   0051149   DLC

National Federation of Telephone Workers
see also **Communications Workers of America.**

331.91   National federation of telephone workers.
N21   National assembly.
           Official proceedings.

           (Chicago, etc., 19
             v.   24ᶜᵐ.

           1. Telephone - U. S. - Societies.

NN   0051151   NNC WHi

BM700   National federation of temple brotherhoods.
.I3
           Idelsohn, Abraham Zebi, 1882–1938.
               The ceremonies of Judaism, by A. Z. Idelsohn ... Cin-
           cinnati, The National federation of temple brotherhoods,
           1929.

BM   **National Federation of Temple**
197   **Brotherhoods.**
N3   The findings of an inquiry on the
           layman's attitude toward the reform
           synagogue service. Compiled by Arthur
           L. Reinhart. With a foreword by Hon.
           Samuel B. Finkel. Cincinnati [193-
             30 l.   28 cm.

             1. Reform Judaism—United States.
           I. Reinhart, Arthur L II. Title
           III. Title: The layman's attitude
           toward the reform synagogue service.

NN   0051153   OCH

BM1   **National Federation of Temple Brotherhoods.**
.J4
           The Jewish layman. v. 1–22, no. 5; Nov. 1926–May/June
           1948. (Cincinnati)

National federation of temple brotherhoods.
        The voice of the Jewish laity; a survey of the Jewish lay-
man's religious attitudes and practices, by Arthur L. Rein-
hart; conducted by the National committee on religious propaganda, the National federation of temple brotherhoods. Cincinnati, O., 1928.
        x p., 1 l., 91 p. incl. 1 illus., tables, diagrs. 23ᶜᵐ.
        A. Cahn, chairman; A. L. Reinhart, secretary.

        1. Jews—Religion. 2. Jews in the U. S.   I. Reinhart, Arthur L.
II. Cahn, Alexander, 1875– III. Title.
        Library of Congress   BM650.N7
                                                            29–946

NN   0051155   DLC OCH NN

National federation of temple sisterhoods.
        Child study outlines
        see under title

DS141   **National federation of temple sisterhoods.**
.G466
           Gittelsohn, Roland Bertram, 1910–
               The Jew faces his problems, by Rabbi Roland B. Gittelsohn.
           (Cincinnati, National federation of temple sisterhoods, ᶜ1938)

JX1953   **National federation of temple sisterhoods.**
.G63
           Gittelsohn, Roland Bertram, 1910–
               The Jew looks at war and peace, by Roland B. Gittelsohn ...
           Cincinnati, O., The National federation of temple sisterhoods
           [1935]

National Federation of Temple Sisterhoods.
        Money-money; suggestions for fund raising.
[New York, 1953.]
        22 l. 29 cm.
        Alternate pages blank.

NN   0051159   OCH

           National Federation of Temple
             Sisterhoods.
             National museum for Jewish ceremonial
           objects. [n. p., 19—]
             [6 p.   [7 cm.
             Caption title.
             Cover title: National museum of
           Jewish ceremonial objects.

             1. Jewish art and symbolism—
           Exhibitions. I. Title II. Title:
           Jewish ceremonial objects.

NN   0051160   OCH

National Federation of Temple Sisterhoods.
        The Oppenheim pictures, depicting Jewish ceremonial life.
Cincinnati: The National Federation of Temple Sisterhoods, 1930.
45 p.   illus.   20½ cm.

        1. Oppenheim, Moritz, 1800–1882.   2. Rites and ceremonies—Jews.
N. Y. P. L.   March 6, 1934

NN   0051161   NN OCH

National federation of temple sisterhoods.

        Langsdorf, Mrs. Elsie (Hirsch) 1880–
           ... The pre-school child, prepared by (Mrs. A. S.) Elsie H.
Langsdorf ... (Cincinnati) The National federation of temple
sisterhoods [ᶜ1930]

VOLUME 407

National federation of temple sisterhoods.
Proceedings of the National federation of temple sisterhoods; first general convention, Cincinnati, January 21–23, 1913, first biennial meeting, Chicago, January 19–21, 1915. ₍Cincinnati? 1915₎
6 p. l., 15–92 p. 25¼ᵐ.
"Membership list": p. 81–85.

15–14852

NN 0051163   DLC NN MB

NATIONAL FEDERATION OF TEMPLE SISTERHOODS.
Proceedings. 1913/15–
New York [etc.]   v.   25cm.

Proceedings for 1913/15–1934 called v. 1–14.
Vol. for 1913/15 contains Proceedings of the 1st general convention, 1913, and of the 1st biennial meeting, 1915 1917 contains Proceedings of the 2d biennial meeting, 1919 contains Proceedings of the 3d biennial assembly (no. 3 called biennial meeting) and the Annual reports,

no. 5/6– , 1916/18– . (Some vols. contain only the Annual reports.
Report year ends Oct. 31.

1. Woman, Jewish--Assoc. and org.--U.S. 2. Woman--Assoc. and org. --U.S. I. National federation of temple sisterhoods. Reports.

NN 0051165   NN

The National Federation of Temple Sisterhoods.
The Seder service
see under Barnet, Mrs. Henry.

LD
2219   National Federation of Temple Sisterhoods.
N3   National Committee on Hebrew Union College
        Scholarships.
        Report.

        [Cincinnati?]
        v. 26 cm.

        1.Hebrew Union College–Jewish Institute of
        Religion--Funds and scholarships.

NN 0051167   OCH

National federation of temple youth.
Jewish youth; official organ
see under title

HFBT4   National Federation of Textile Operatives
+N213   of America.
MIS   Annual official souvenir. [Fall River,
        Mass.? 1899 –1900.
        2 v. illus., ports. 25–27cm.

        Library has: 1899/1900
                      1900/1901

        1899/1900 contains Proceedings of its
        2d Convention, 1899. 1900/1901 contains
        Proceedings of ɣ 3d Convention, 1900.

NN 0051169   WHi

HFBT4   National Federation of Textile Operatives
.N213   of America.
MIS   Constitution and by-laws. Fall River,
        Mass., Press of A.L. Hathaway, 1900.
        8 p. 14½cm.

NN 0051170   WHi

HFBT4   National Federation of Textile Operatives
N213   of America.
MIS
        [Miscellaneous ephemeral materials not
        fully catalogued]

        NB. – Such materials are shelved in
        pamphlet-boxes marked with a period (.),
        a plus (+) or a quotation-mark (") ahead
        of the second line of the call-number.
        Search should be made in all three loca-
        tions, although material may not be found
        in any one or two of them.

NN 0051171   WHi

National Federation of Textile Works Managers·
Association.
HD9861
.1   The Textile weekly.
.T47
        Manchester, Eng.

National Federation of Textiles.
Activities, officers, members.
New York.
        v. 23 cm.

1. Textile industry and fabrics--U. S.—Societies, etc.

HD9851.N33   677.06273   55–34440 ‡

NN 0051173   DLC

National federation of textiles.
Brief to support the recommendation of Industry committee no. 1 for the textile industry to the administrator of the wage and hour division, submitted by the National federation of textiles, inc. ... ₍New York, 1939₎ 7 f. 28cm.

Reproduced from typewritten copy.

1. Textile trade and statistics—   U. S. 2. Wages, Textile workers'—
U.S.
N.Y.P.L.   June 4, 1940

NN 0051174   NN

National Federation of Textiles.
Annual report
see its Report.

National Federation of Textiles.
Bulletin.
New York.
        ₍no. 1₎ v. 28 cm. weekly.
Began publication with Oct. 1936 issue. Cf. Union list of serials.
Title varies: Federation news bulletin.
Supplements accompany some numbers.

1. Textile industry and fabrics—U. S.—Period.

HD9851.N34   338.47677   57–43595

NN 0051176   DLC DNAL

National Federation of Textiles.
Imports of raw ₍and manufactured₎ silk.
New York, Silk Association of America, 1874.
        4 f.

        "No.6–1874"
        Later statistics included in its Mid year
report.

NN 0051177   MH-BA

National federation of textiles.
The only hope for our industry is in united self-government through code administration; a resume of the first five months in 1934 by the National federation of textiles, inc., code authority for the silk textile industry... ₍New York: The Marchbanks press₎ 1934. 21 p. illus. (chart, ports.) 25½cm.

1. Industrial codes of fair com-   petition. 2. Textile trade and statistics—U. S.
N. Y. P. L.   November 10, 1939

NN 0051178   NN NNC

National Federation of Textiles.
Production and distribution of silk and rayon broad goods, prepared by Melvin T. Copeland ₍and₎ W. Homer Turner for the Textile Foundation, inc. ₍and₎ the National Federation of Textiles, inc. ₍New York, 1935₎

xiv, 100 p. map, diagrs. 28 cm.
Work on this study was done by a committee of the National Federation of Textiles, M. T. Copeland, consultant, and W. H. Turner and F. J. G. Duck, editors. cf. Foreword.
Bibliography: p. ₍95₎–99.

1. Silk manufacture and trade—U. S. 2. Rayon.   I. Copeland,
Melvin Thomas, 1884–   II. Title: Silk and rayon broad goods.

HD9915.N3   338.4   35–3843 rev*

MtBC
NcRS NcD WaS DeU WaWW OrCS OrU MtU TU CoU IdU
NN 0051179   DLC MH OCl OO OU ViU MB WU FMU ICJ

338.47677   National Federation of Textiles.
N277R   Report. 1st–   1873–
            New York.
                  v. in   20–26 cm. annual.
            Report year varies.
            13th–14th reports issued in one.
            9th report, 2d ed.
            Title varies: 1873, Meeting.
            Issued by the body under its earlier names:
            1873–1933, Silk Association of America; 1934,
            Federated Textile Industries, inc.
                  1. Silk manu- facture and trade.
            Societies, etc.

NN 0051180   NcD ICJ MH-A DL ICRL

National federation of textiles.
Statement presented for the National federation of textiles, inc. to the Committee on ways and means, House of representatives, Washington, D. C. on May 11, 1945, by Irene Blunt, secretary and treasurer of the federation. Re: Opposition to H. R. 2652 on renewal of the reciprocal trade agreement section 350 of the Tariff act of 1930. ₍New York, 1945₎ 9 f. 28cm.

Caption-title.

1. Textile fabrics—Tariff—U. S.   2. Textile trade and statistics—U. S.
I. Blunt, Irene.
N. Y. P. L.   July 12, 1948

NN 0051181   NN

National Federation of Textiles
see also American Cotton Manufacturers
Institute, inc. ; Silk Association of America.

280.2   National Federation of the Agricultural
N218   Guidance Co-operative Associations.
        Outline of the agricultural co-operative
        movement in Japan. Tokyo, 1954.
        81.

        1. Agriculture, Cooperative. Japan.

NN 0051183   DNAL

---

292   National Federation of the Agricultural
N217   Guidance Co-operative Associations.
        Water resources utilization system in
        Japan.   Tokyo ₍1952?₎
        24 p.

        1. Water. Utilization. 2. Japan. Water-
        supply. 3. Irrigation. Japan.

NN 0051184   DNAL

VOLUME 407

HV1783
.B7

National Federation of the Blind.

The Braille monitor. Ink print ed.
Berkeley, Calif., National Federation of the Blind.

R362.4
N27w National Federation of the Blind
Who are the blind who lead the blind?
Berkeley, Calif. [1954]
20p. 24cm.

1. Blind - U.S. - Direct. I. Title.

NN 0051186 TNJ

National Federation of the Import and Export Trades of
France
see Fédération nationale des commerces d'importation
et d'exportation de France.

NATIONAL FEDERATION OF THE PROFESSIONAL ASSO-
CIATIONS OF PUBLIC SCHOOLMISTRESSES
AND SCHOOLMASTERS OF FRANCE AND THE
COLONIES.
To the schoolmistresses and schoolmasters
of all countries/ [n.p., 1915]
pp.4.
Signed: Montjotin, Mme Mauger, Cadelen.

NN 0051188 MH

National Federation of Theatre Clubs.
Souvenir program... ["The road to Arcady"; aims and
objects of the federation; members.   New York, 1912.]   6 l.
illus.   4°.

1. Stage.—Periodicals, etc.
N. Y. P. L.   May 13, 1914.

NN 0051189 NN

TL1
.I56

National Federation of Vehicle Trades.

Institute of British Carriage and Automobile Manufacturers.
The institute bulletin.

[London]

National federation of women workers.
... Report and balance sheets. 1907–1918/1919. London
[etc.] 1907–1920.
10 v. 18½–27ᶜᵐ.
Report year irregular.
Combined reports were issued for the years 1915–1917 and 1918–1919
respectively.
Title varies slightly.
A report for 1920 is contained in the First report of the National
union of general workers, Women workers' section, for year ended Dec.
31st, 1921.
1. Trade-unions—Gt. Brit. 2. Woman—Societies.
                                                L 13–74 Revised
Library, U. S. Bur. of   Labor Statistics HD6661.N5

NN 0051191 DL ICJ

AP7
.W6

National federation of women's clubs of the
Philippines.

Woman's home journal-world.

[Manila, Woman's home journal, inc., 19

National federation of women's institutes.
County fare. Ideal home exhibition. [London] 1954.   47 p.
22cm.

1. Cookery, English, 1926–

NN 0051193 NN KMK

281.29
N214H National federation of women's institutes.

Handbook.
London

1. Women's institutes.

NN 0051194 DNAL

National Federation of Women's Institutes.
Home made wines, syrups, and cordials; recipes of
Women's Institute members, edited by F. W. Beech. With
a foreword by Sir Stephen Tallents, illustrated by Roger
Nicholson. [London, 1954]
117 p. illus. 22 cm.

1. Wine and wine making. 2. Syrups. 3. Liqueurs.   I. Beech,
Frederick Walter, ed. II. Title.

TP548.N3   55–26347 ‡

NN 0051195 DLC NN CaBVa

National Federation of Women's Institutes.
Music handbook. [New ed.] London [195–]
47 p. 22 cm.

1. Music—Manuals, text-books, etc.

ML27.G7N39   55–17297 ‡

NN 0051196 DLC

National federation of women's institutes.
...Public questions; the annual meeting record.   Oxford,
University press, 1951.   115 p.   21cm.
8. ed.

1. Country life—Gt. Br.

NN 0051197 NN MiD

National Federation of Women's Institutes.
Report.
[London]
v. 21 cm.
Report year ends Feb. 28.

HQ1945.N3A4   396.06242   49–37557*‡

NN 0051198 DLC NN

National federation of women's institutes.
Town children through country eyes; a survey
on evacuation 1940. Dorking, Surrey, National
federation of women's institutes [1940]
cover-title, p. 3–23.   22 cm.
Consists of "comments of Women's institute
members on the condition and habits of the evac-
uees whom they received into their homes in
September 1940." cf. p. 3.
Inside of back cover included in paging.
1. Children - Care and hygiene. 2. Children in
Gt. Britain. 3. World war, 1939–   Children.
I. Title.

NN 0051199 CU

TX
717
N386

National Federation of Women's Institutes.
Traditional fare of England and Wales.
With illus. by Patricia Winnington.
Foreword by the Countess of Albemarle.
[London, 1948]
92 p. illus.

COOKERY, ENGLISH

NN 0051200 KMK

National federation of women's institutes.
Yeast cookery.   London, 1954.   20 p.   22cm.

1. Yeast. 2. Baking.

NN 0051201 NN

NATIONAL FEDERATION OF WOMEN'S REPUBLICAN CLUBS
OF AMERICA.
Foreign relations.   [Washington, D.C., 1939?].

22 cm. pp.11, (1).

NN 0051202 MH

Z5071
.A1N3

National Federation of Young Farmers' Clubs.

National Book League, *London.*
Country books; a list of bibliographies and the organisations that publish them, produced jointly by the National
Book League and the National Federation of Young Farmers' Clubs. London [1953]

203
N21

National Federation of Young Farmers'
Clubs.
Dictionary of agricultural terms,
English-French, French-English.   [London,
1950]
45 p.

1. Agriculture. Dictionaries. 2. French
language. Dictionaries.

NN 0051204 DNAL

National Federation of Young Farmers' Clubs.
Dictionary of agricultural terms, English-
German: German-English, for the use of Young
Farmers and others on their travels. [Bristol,
Printed by J. W. Arrowsmith for the National
Federation of Young Farmers' Clubs, 1952]
cover-title, 51 p. 19cm.

Title in German also.

1. Agriculture - Dictionaries, German.
2. German language - Dictionaries - English.

NN 0051205 OCU IU

National Federation of Young Farmers' Clubs.
A farm dictionary

see under

Chapman, Derek H

VOLUME 407

10
N21H
National Federation of Young Farmers Clubs.
 [Handbook on young farmers' clubs]
 London [1951-53]
  8 pts.

  1. Young farmers' clubs.

NN 0051207 DNAL

National Federation of Young Farmers Clubs.
 Just your meat

 see under

 Jones, Elwyn.

275.1
N215
National federation of Young farmers' clubs
 School and countryside; suggestions for
 teachers on the use of the Young farmers'
 club Booklets in schemes of study. [Lon-
 don] Pilot press [1946]
  23 p. illus. 21 1/2cm.

NN 0051209 DNAL

10
N21Y
National federation of young farmers' clubs.
 Young farmers. [London, National federation
 of young farmers' clubs, 1936?]
 [32] p. illus. 25cm.

 On cover: Young farmers' club.

NN 0051210 DNAL

HD 651 5
.R 267 J
... THE NATIONAL FEDERATIONIST. [A MONTHLY PAPER
DEVOTED TO THE INTERESTS OF ORGANIZED LABOR
IN GENERAL] VOL.1, NO.
[INDIANAPOLIS, IND.,

  v. 37½CN.

AT HEAD OF TITLE, VOL.1- : IN IN THE INTERESTS
OF THE SUPREME COUNCIL OF THE FEDERATED ORDERS OF
RAILWAY EMPLOYEES.

NN 0051211 MdBJ

SF
95
N37
National Feed Ingredients Association.
 Complete texts of the speeches given
 at the annual convention. 1st-
 [19-]-
 Des Moines, Iowa.
  v. illus. ports. 28 cm.

 Cover title.
 1. Feeds - Congresses. I. Title.

NN 0051212 CaBVaU

---

*EC8
A100
821n
 National feeling; or, The history of
Fitzsimon; a novel. With historical and
political remarks. In two volumes. By an
Irishman ...
 Dublin:Printed,for the author,by A.O'Neil,
at the Minerva printing-office,17,Chancery-lane.
1821.
 2v. 20cm.,in case 21cm.
 Errata slip pasted inside back cover to each
vol. (spelled "Erratta" in v.1).
 Original half blue paper & pink boards; paper
label on spines; in cloth case.

NN 0051213 MH

National feldspar association.

Sharp, Donald Ellsworth, 1896-   *ed.*
 Feldspar as a constituent of glass, prepared by members of
the staff of the Bailey & Sharp co.. inc.; edited by Donald E.
Sharp. New York, N. Y., National feldspar association [*1937]

National Fellowship of Brethren Churches
see also
The Brethren Church (Progressive Dunkers)

F805
"ZN24
N5
National Fellowship of Indian Workers.
 Newsletter. No.2-81, 1936-1964. New
 York, Division of Home Missions, National
 Council of Churches.
  1 box. 23-31 cm.

  1. Indians of North America - Periodicals.

NN 0051216 WHi

National Fellowship of Indian Workers. *Eastern Regional
Conference, Thomas Indian School, Iroquois, N. Y., 1944.*
 Eastern Regional Conference of the Fellowship of Indian
Workers, Thomas Indian School, Iroquois, N. Y., October
20-22, 1944. [Principal addresses. Iroquois? 1944?]
  34 p. 23 cm.

 1. Indians of North America.

 E77.N35 1944   49-44421*

NN 0051217 DLC

National fertilizer association.
  Three associations have borne the name of National fertilizer association.
  1st, founded 1883 as National fertilizer association, existed
until 1887.
  From 1887 to 1893, no organization existed.
  2d, founded 1893 as Fertilizer manufacturers' association in
the West; known (after 1902) as Fertilizer manufacturers'
association; name changed 1907 to National fertilizer association.
  3d, founded 1925 by the union of the former National fertilizer association (*cf.* no. 2, above) and the Southern fertilizer association. The new organization took the name of National fertilizer association.
  The three associations are distinguished by dates, in their
respective entries.

Agriculture
TP
963
N27
National Fertilizer Association (1883-1887)
 Abstract of the minutes of the 1st-
 annual meeting. Baltimore, Guggenheimer
 & Weil, Printer, 18 -
  v. 23 cm.

  1. Fertilizers & manures - Societies.

NN 0051219 NIC

HD9483
.G5
1886
National fertilizer association (1883-1887)
     FOR OTHER EDITIONS
     SEE MAIN ENTRY
[Ghequier, A de] *comp.*
 The fertilizer movement during the season 1885-86, with
an appendix containing the laws of the several states on the
subject of fertilizers. [Baltimore] National fertilizer association, 1886.

NN 0051221 DLC

National fertilizer association (1883-1887)
 On the outlook for uniform legislation on the inspection and sale of fertilizers. Pub. by the National fertilizer association, March, 1885. In Baltimore. Baltimore, Guggenheimer & Weil, printers, 1885.
  13 p. 23ᶜᵐ.

 1. Fertilizers and manures. I. Title.

         CA 17-3846 Unrev'd

Library of Congress   S641.N3

NN 0051221 DLC

National fertilizer association (1883-1887)
 ...Special meeting...June 15th, 1886, in New
York City. 1886.

NN 0051222 DNAL

National fertilizer association (1893-1925)
 How transportation companies can help
reduce the cost of growing food and clothes
and thereby increase their earnings. [New
York city] National fertilizer association
[n.d.]
 [8] p.

NN 0051223 OU

National fertilizer association (1893-1925)
 The National fertilizer association.
[Nashville? 1915]

HD9483
.N3

NN 0051224 DLC

National Fertilizer Association (1893-1925)
 Proceedings of the annual convention...
[no.]
[Hot Springs, Va.?,   8°.

  v.

 1. Fertilizers (Commercial).—Peri- odicals and soc. publ.
N. Y. P. L.   January 25, 1916.

NN 0051225 NN WvU MnU DNLM TU DLC NMScS

National Fertilizer Association (1893-1925).
 Twenty-fifth anniversary. The National Fertilizer Association; a history of its organization and growth. 1894-1918. Atlantic City, 1918. 42 p. illus. 8°.

526578A. 1. No subject.
N. Y. P. L.   May 26, 1931

NN 0051226 NN TU

657
N2152c
1924
National fertilizer association (1893-1925) Cost
 accounting committee.
  Cost accounting and cost estimating
 for dry mixers of fertilizers. [2d ed.]
 Norfolk, Va., 1924.
  71p. forms(part fold.)

NN 0051227 IU

National fertilizer association Middle West
 improvement committee. (1893-1925)
Bowker, William Henry, 1850-1916.
 Sources of fertility and their conservation. An address delivered at a conference of the Soil improvement
committee of the National fertilizer association and the
farm press of the Middle west at Chicago, December 1,
1915, by William H. Bowker. Chicago, Soil improvement
committee of the National fertilizer association [1916]

N214
National Fertilizer Association (1893-) *Soil Improvement Committee.*
 ... Bulletin ... [Chicago, Soil Improvement Committee of the
National Fertilizer Association, 1911-1919?]

 Library has no. 1-24. illus. 20-23½ᶜᵐ.

 Previous to 1916: Middle West Soil Improvement Committee of the National
Fertilizer Association.
 No. 25 last published?
 No. 2, 14, 16, 17 also in revised editions.
 Wanting: no. 10.

NN 0051229 ICJ NN ViU

VOLUME 407

National Fertilizer Association (1893-) Soil Improvement Committee.
News bulletin.
v. 1–

Chicago, 1917–   4°.
v.

Bi-weekly, April 19, 1917–Oct. 14, 1920; monthly, Nov. 1920–

1. Fertilizers and manures.—Per.   and soc. publ.
N. Y. P. L.   October 13, 1923.

NN   0051230   NN OU

National fertilizer association (1893-) Soil improvement committee.
A statement of a project to secure information as soon as possible on the maximum amount of fertilizer which may be used with greatest profit on the soils and crops of this country. [1924?]
27 numb. l.
wanting: leaves 1-5.

NN   0051231   DNAL

National Fertilizer Association (1893-) Soil Improvement Committee.
What fertilizer shall I use on wheat?   Chicago, Ill.: Soil Improvement Committee of the National Fertilizer Assoc. [1919?]
15(1) p.   illus.   12°.   (Its: Bull. 23.)

1. Fertilizers and manures. 2. Series.
N. Y. P. L.   December 8, 1919.

NN   0051232   NN

National fertilizer association (1893-1925) Statistics committee.
Report.
[n. p.,
v. 27cm.

1. Fertilizers and manures—Stat.
                                                    17–29395
Library of Congress   TP963.N33

NN   0051233   DLC

281.12   National fertilizer association (1925-1955)
N216   The Agricultural adjustment act of 1938; its general background and a summary of some of its provisions, prepared by the National fertilizer association. Washington, D.C., 1938.
34p.   28cm.
Processed.

NN   0051234   DNAL

National fertilizer association (1925-)
American fertilizer practices; a series of reports relating to the use of commercial plant food, presenting information obtained by a survey among 48,000 farmers in 35 states ... Washington, D. C., Prepared and published by the National fertilizer association, 1929.
2 p. l., 147, 10 p. incl. charts, tables, diagrs. 27½cm.
Errata slip mounted on p. 45.

1. Fertilizers and manures. 2. Agriculture—U. S.   I. Title.
Library of Congress   S633.N3   30–32237
[2]   631.8

NN   0051235   DLC OC1 ICJ ICU NN Ok Or Wa NcRS NIC

National fertilizer association (1925-)
American fertilizer practices (second survey), a report relating to the use of commercial plant food, presenting information obtained by a survey among 32,000 farmers in 35 states, by H. R. Smalley ... Robert H. Engle ... Herbert Willett ... [of] the National fertilizer association, Washington, D. C. [Washington, D. C., The Association, 1939.
128, 12 p. incl. illus., tables, diagrs.   27 x 21½cm.
"American fertilizer practices (second survey) Supplementary tables" (with special t.-p.) : 12 p. at end.
1. Fertilizers and manures. 2. Agriculture—U. S.   I. Smalley, Harold Ryland, 1887-   II. Engle, Robert H., 1895-   III. Willett, Herbert, 1902-   IV. Title.
Library of Congress   S633.N32   41–4508
[2]   631.8

OC1 OU MB ICJ Ok NIC NcRS
NN   0051236   DLC DNAL TU WaSp MtBC Or Wa WaS OrCS

National fertilizer association (1925-).
Are fertilizer prices rigid? By Herbert Willett ... Prices farmers pay for all commodities, for fertilizer. Prepared and published by the National fertilizer association ...   Washington [1938]   15 p.   illus.   23cm.

1. Prices, Fertilizers and manures   —U. S., 1938. I. Willett, Herbert, 1902-
N. Y. P. L.   January 8, 1945

NN   0051237   NN NIC

National Fertilizer Association, (1925-)
Board of directors.   -1954.
[Washington?]
Ceased. cf letter from National Plant Food Institute, 4/3/56.

NN   0051238   DNAL

MANN
SB   National Fertilizer Association (1925-1955)
742   A catalogue of kodachrome slides showing
N27   nutrient deficiency symptoms, assembled by H. R. Smalley and Robert H. Engle [and] the National Fertilizer Association in cooperation with agronomists, horticulturists and plant physiologists. Washington, 1944.
21 p.   28 cm.

1. Deficiency diseases in plants - Audio-visual aids - Bibl. I. Smalley, Harold Ryland, 1887-   II. Engle, Robert H
III. Title.

NN   0051239   NIC

S   [National Fertilizer Association] (1925-
633   A century of progress with fertilizers.
N270   [Washington, 1950]
40 p.   illus.   20x27 cm.

Cover title.

1. Fertilizers and manures.
I. Title.

NN   0051240   NIC Or

National Fertilizer Association (1925-)
HD3616   U. S. National Recovery Administration.
.U452   Code of fair competition for the fertilizer industry; hearing before the National Recovery Administration, September 6, 1933. Washington, National Fertilizer Association [1933?]
F45
I(mim)h

National Fertilizer Association (1925-)
Code of fair competition for the fertilizer industry under the National industrial recovery act. [Miscellaneous documents. Washington, 193-
v. illus. 24 cm.
Vol. 4 contains the Prelim. ed., Nov. 1933, the 2d ed., May 1934, and the 3d ed., Mar. 1935 of the Fertilizer industry zone list.
Contents.—[1] Interpretations and explanations in question and answer form.—[2] Application for presentation of a code of fair competition to the National Recovery Administration, etc.—[3] Zone recommendations as presented to the Administrative Committee.—[4] Fertilizer industry zone lists.
1. Fertilizers and manures.
HD3616.U452F45   III (rev.) doc.   49–55908*

NN   0051242   DLC

National Fertilizer Association (1925-)
HD3616   U. S. National Recovery Administration.
.U452   Code of fair competition for the fertilizer industry under the National industrial recovery act; administrative orders pertaining to the fertilizer industry. [Washington, National Fertilizer Association, 1935?]
F45
I(mim)o

National Fertilizer Association (1925-)
HD3616   U. S. National Recovery Administration.
.U452   Drafts of Code of fair competition for the fertilizer industry under the National industrial recovery act, compiled by the National Fertilizer Association. Washington [1933?]
F45
I(mim)d

National fertilizer association (1925-)
Economic service letters covering fertilizer tag sales, production, shipments and stocks of superphosphate, imports and exports of fertilizers and fertilizer materials, general business conditions including review of weekly wholesale commodity price index. Washington, D. C., Published by the National fertilizer association [19
v. illus., tables, diagrs. 28 x 21½cm.
On cover. 19   : Service letters including superphosphate reports. The individual letters have title: N. F. A. service letter. Mimeographed.
1. Fertilizers and manures—Societies. 2. Phosphates—U. S.
I. Title. II. Title: N. F. A. service letter.
                                                    CA 32–647 Unrev'd
Library of Congress   TP963.N33   338.4

NN   0051245   DLC

HD   National Fertilizer Association (1925-1955)
1769   Farm income and fertilizer consumption, [
N27   compiled by Herbert Willett. Washington, 1939.
16 p.   maps, tables. 28 cm.

Cover title.

1. Fertilizers and manures - U. S. - Stat.
2. Farm income - U. S. I. Willett, Herbert, 1902-
II. Title.

NN   0051246   NIC OC1FRB DFT

National Fertilizer Association (1925-)
Fertilizer consumption by counties [1939] based on the Sixteenth Census of the United States: 1940. Washington, 1942.
87 p.   maps, diagrs. 28 cm.

1. Fertilizers and manures.
HD9483.N34   339.486318   48–39685*

NN   0051247   DLC

NATIONAL FERTILIZER ASSOCIATION (1925-)
Fertilizer consumption in 1940. 616 Investment bldg., Washington, D.C., Author [1941?]
[4] p. illus.

Processed.

NN   0051248   Or

VOLUME 407

NATIONAL FERTILIZER ASSOCIATION (1925-)
Fertilizer consumption in 1941.   Author
[1942]
[4] p. illus.

NN   0051249   Or

National fertilizer association (1925-).
...Fertilizer consumption in the United States, / by Herbert
Willett... Prepared and published by the National fertilizer
association...   Washington, D. C., 1937.   8 p. illus.
(charts), table.   23cm.

Cover-title.

1. Fertilizers and manures—   Trade and stat.—U. S. I. Willett,
Herbert, 1902-
N. Y. P. L.   May 12, 1938

NN   0051250   NN ICJ MoU NIC DNAL

National fertilizer association (1925-)
Fertilizer industry forges ahead, a story of fertilizer industry
progress. Washington, D. C., The National fertilizer association [1944]
cover-title, 1 p. l., 30 p. illus. (incl. maps) diagrs. 23ᶜᵐ.

1. Fertilizers and manures.   I. Title.
                                                    44-8858
Library of Congress   HD9483.N27
[3]   338.476686

NN   0051251   DLC

NATIONAL FERTILIZER ASSOCIATION (1925-).
Fertilizer industry zone list (second edition), prepared
for use in administering the code of fair competition of
the fertilizer industry. Washington, D.C.: Printed and
distributed in furtherance of the national recovery program
by the National Fertilizer Assoc., 1934. vii, 134 p.
chart. 23cm.

797551A. 1. Industrial codes of fair competition.
2. Fertilizers and manures—Trade and stat.—U.S., 1934.

NN   0051252   NN

225
F412
Ed.3
National Fertilizer Association (1925-   )
Fertilizer industry zone list; prepared for
use in administering the Code of fair
competition of the fertilizer industry.
3d ed.   Washington, National Fertilizer
Association, 1935.
140 p.

Additions and corrections issued in National
Fertilizer Association. NFA news (57.9 N21Nf)

NN   0051253   DNAL

284.357
N21
National fertilizer association (1925-   ).
...Fertilizer prices and price indexes,
by Herbert Willett, economist of the
Association. Washington, D.C., The National
fertilizer association, 1937.
40 numb.l.   27 1/2cm.

At head of title: The National fertilizer
association.
Processed.

NN   0051254   DNAL

National fertilizer association (1925-)
... Fertilizer prices and price indexes, by Herbert Willett,
economist of the association. Prepared and published by the
National fertilizer association ... Washington, D. C., 1938.

cover-title, 32 p. diagrs. 28ᶜᵐ.

At head of title: The National fertilizer association.

1. Fertilizers and manures.   2. Index numbers (Economics)
I. Willett, Herbert, 1902-
                                                    39-16739
Library of Congress   HD9483.N28
———— Copy 2.   [2]   338.4

NN   0051255   DLC DFT OU NN OrCS Or NIC

National fertilizer association (1925-)
... Fertilizer prices and price indexes; a summary of available information on fertilizer price levels, trends, and relationships. (3d ed.) Compiled by Herbert Willett, economist of
the association, foreword by Charles J. Brand ... Washington,
D. C., The National fertilizer association, 1941.

27 p. diagrs. 28ᶜᵐ.

At head of title: The National fertilizer association.

1. Fertilizers and manures.   2. Index numbers (Economics)
I. Willett, Herbert, 1902-
                                                    41-17145
Library of Congress   HD9483.N28 1941
                          [5]   338.4

NN   0051256   DLC OCl MH-BA Or OrCS TU

National fertilizer association (1925-1955)
The Fertilizer review; published ... by the National fertilizer
association. v. 1-
Jan. 1926-
Washington, D. C., 1926-

HD
9483
N271
National Fertilizer Association (1925-1955)
Fertilizer use at the half-century mark; a
regional survey dealing with the distribution and
application of mixed fertilizers and fertilizer
materials in regard to individual crops.
Washington [1951?]
20 p. tables. 28 cm. (Its Publication no. 155)

Cover title.

NN   0051258   NIC OrCS DNAL

National fertilizer association (1925-1955)
A guide to pasture management and fertiliz-
ation...   [1930]
19 p.

NN   0051259   DNAL

QK867
.H24
National fertilizer association (1925-   )

Hambidge, Gove, ed.
Hunger signs in crops, a symposium, prepared by George M.
Bahrt [and others] ... edited by Gove Hambidge. Washington,
D. C., The American society of agronomy and the National fer-
tilizer association [1941]

QK867
.A5
1949
National Fertilizer Association (1925-   )

American Society of Agronomy.
Hunger signs in crops; a symposium, prepared by Firman
E. Bear [and others. Rev., i. e. 2d, ed.] Washington, American Society of Agronomy and National Fertilizer Association [1949]

National fertilizer association (1925-   )
Interpretations of the code of trade practices
of the fertilizer industry. [1927] 16 numb. l.

NN   0051262   DNAL

57.9
N21M
National Fertilizer Association (1925-   )
Making the anvil ring; the National
Fertilizer Association forges a public
service program. [Washington, 1951]
[13] p.

1. National Fertilizer Association.

NN   0051263   DNAL

National Fertilizer Association, (1925-   )
Minutes of a conference of agronomists, state
control officials and fertilizer manufacturers,
called by the National fertilizer association and
held at the hotel McAlpin, New York, August 19,
1931.   [n. p., 1931?]
10 numb. l.   28.5 cm.
Caption title.
Mimeographed.

NN   0051264   OrCS

National Fertilizer Association (1925-   ) 668.06161 S700
160294 Minutes of the special convention of the fertilizer industry held
at Washington, D. C., January 10, 1927, under the auspices of
the National Fertilizer Association. [Washington?], Published
by the Association, 1927.
69 p. 23½ᵐ.

NN   0051265   ICJ MiD DNAL NIC OrCS DLC

National fertilizer association (1925-   )
Muscle shoals and fertilizer.....a
plea on behalf of the fertilizer industry
...... (1928)
48, (2)p.

NN   0051266   DNAL

National Fertilizer Association (1925-   )
NFA news
see under title

National fertilizer association (1925-   )
The N.F.A. Service letter
see under title

S631
.N33
National Fertilizer Association (1925-   )

National fertilizer review. v. 1-
Jan. 1926-
[Washington, National Fertilizer Association]

NATIONAL FERTILIZER ASSOCIATION (1925-1955).
Pamphlet.
Washington.   no.   illus.   11-28cm.

Various numbers lack series title.

No. 55-95 prepared by the association's Soil improvement committee
(no. 55-78, 80-95 by its Northern division, no. 79? by its Southern division).

No. 154 has title: Publication.
Ceased publication.

1. Fertilizer and manures—Per. and soc. publ. I. National fertilizer
association (1925-1955). Soil improvement committee. Pamphlet.

NN   0051271   NN DNAL OrCS

VOLUME 407

National Fertilizer Association. (1925–   )
Price indexes of complete fertilizer.
Washington, 1927.
16 p.   tables, diagr.

NN   0051272   MH-BA

National fertilizer association (1925–   )
Proceedings of the ... annual convention of the National fertilizer association.
2d–   1926–
₍Washington, D. C.₎ The Association, 1926–
v. illus. (incl. ports.) 23ᶜᵐ.
"No formal proceedings were published covering the first annual convention which was held at White Sulphur Springs, West Virginia, June, 1925. The present association is a consolidation of the former National fertilizer association and the former Southern fertilizer association, which was effected on June 11, 1925. Relatively complete accounts of the first convention will be found in the June and July numbers of the American fertilizer, published at Philadelphia, Pa., and the Commercial fertilizer, published at Atlanta, Ga."—Memorandum (type-written) mounted on half-title of   Proceedings of 2d convention, 1926.
1. Fertilizers and   manures—Societies.
Library of Congress   TP963.N32   27—16642

NN   0051273   DLC NcRS OrP TU ViU ICJ MB NN Ok IdU

National fertilizer association (1925–   )

National joint committee on fertilizer application.
Proceedings of the ... annual meeting of the National joint committee on fertilizer application ...
₍Washington, D. C.₎ The National fertilizer association ₍193

National fertilizer association (1925–

Pasture and hayland conference, *New York,* **1936.**
Proceedings of the Pasture and hayland conference, held at New York, N. Y., September 24, 1936, American agricultural editors' association and the National fertilizer association co-operating. ₍Washington?₎ D. C., Pub. by the National fertilizer association, 1936.

National Fertilizer Association. (1925–   )
Recent developments in the fertilizer industry...
see under   Brand, Charles John, 1879–

National fertilizer association (1925–
FOR OTHER EDITIONS
SEE MAIN ENTRY
National joint committee on fertilizer application.
Reports and proceedings of the Joint committee on fertilizer application, 1925–1928. Compiled by E. Truog and Ove F. Jensen ... Washington, D. C., The National fertilizer association ₍1928₎

National Fertilizer Association (1925–   )   T100
... The significance of the word "guano" in fertilizer terminology, prepared by Charles J. Brand ... Washington, D. C., 1931.
5 leaves, 78 numb. l. incl. illus., 1 form, facsims, tables. 23ᶜᵐ.
Title on slip mounted on t.-p.
At head of title: United States of America, before the Federal Trade Commission in the matter of Patuxent Guano Co., a corporation. Docket 1939. Brief of the National Fertilizer Association as amicus curiae.
Mimeographed.
"Code of trade practices of the fertilizer industry, amended and revised ... First edition ... 1930. Published by the National fertilizer association, Washington, D. C." ₍4₎ 23 p. 18ᶜᵐ.—Mounted on leaf 3 as Exhibit 1.
"List of references": leaf ₍4–5₎

NN   0051278   ICJ DNAL

National fertilizer association (1925–   ).
Summary of state fertilizer control laws, regulations, and rulings (as of September 1, 1939), prepared by the National fertilizer association. Washington, D. C. ₍1939?₎ table. 33 x 61cm.

1. Fertilizers and manures—   Jurisp.—U. S.
N. Y. P. L.   May 8, 1942

NN   0051279   NN

National fertilizer association (1925–   )
Superphosphate reports ...   calendar years 19
₍Washington, D. C.₎ The national fertilizer association, 19
v. 28ᶜᵐ.
Mimeographed.

1. Phosphates—U. S.   I. Title.
                         CA 30–1204 Unrev'd
Library of Congress   TP963.N34   338.4

NN   0051280   DLC

National Fertilizer Association. (1925–   )
A survey of fertilizer application practices in connection with field crops
see under   National Joint Committee on Fertilizer Application.

National Fertilizer Association. (1925–   )
A survey of fertilizer distributing machines on the market
see under   National Joint Committee on Fertilizer Application.

633.6 National fertilizer association (1925–   )
N21s   A survey of pasture experiments now being conducted in the humid regions of the United States, by H. R. Smalley ... and A. L. Grizzard ... ₍Washington D.C.₎ The National fertilizer association, 1938.
145p.

Mimeographed.

1. Pastures. 2. Fertilizers and manures. I. Smalley, Harold Ryland, 1887–   II. Grizzard, A. L. III. Title.

NN   0051281   IU DNAL

National fertilizer association (1925–   )
A survey of plant food consumption in the United States for the year ended June 30, 1934
see under   Mehring, Arnon Lewis, 1892–

National fertilizer association (1925–   )
A survey of plant-food consumption in the United States in the year ended June 30, 1939, by A. L. Mehring and Lola S. Deming ... and Herbert Willett ... With a foreword by Charles J. Brand ... Washington, D. C., The National fertilizer association, 1940.
86 p. incl. illus. (map) tables, diagr. 23ᶜᵐ.
The National fertilizer association and the U. S. Bureau of plant industry cooperated in making this survey. cf. Introd.
1. Fertilizers and manures. I. U. S. Bureau of plant industry. II. Mehring, Arnon Lewis, 1892– III. Deming, Mrs. Lola Elizabeth (Shupe) 1906– IV. Willett, Herbert, 1902– V. Title: Plant-food consumption in the United States.
                                  41–18658
Library of Congress   HD9483.N33
                         ₍3₎   338.4

NN   0051283   DLC DNAL ICJ OrCS MtBC TU

National Fertilizer Association (1925–1955)
United States of America before the Federal trade commission in the matter of Patuxent Guano Co., a corporation. Brief ...
see its   The significance of the word "guano"...

HD9483
N3   National fertilizer association (1925–   )
         The weekly wholesale price index of the National fertilizer association ...

         Washington, D. C., Prepared and published by the National fertilizer association, 1924

         __vols.   tables, charts.   23cm.

         1924–
              by W. Arthur Shelton.

         1. Fertilizers   and manures.   Prices.
         I. Shelton, William Arthur, 1878–

NN   0051285   NBuG

National fertilizer association (1925–   )
The weekly wholesale price index of the National fertilizer association, by W. Arthur Shelton ... Washington, D. C., The National fertilizer association, 1929.
47 p. diagrs. 23ᶜᵐ.
Covers the period July 7, 1927–July 27, 1929. Later information is issued in the N. F. A. service letter.

1. Index numbers (Economics) I. Shelton, William Arthur, 1878– II. Title.

U. S. Dept. of agr. Library   284.3N212
for Library of Congress   HB235.W6N3
                                   Agr 30—233

NN   0051286   DNAL WaTC Or ICJ NN

284.3   National fertilizer association (1925–   )
N212   ...The weekly wholesale price index, by
1936   Herbert Willett, economist of the Association.
        Washington, D. C., The National fertilizer association, 1936.
        23 p.   23cm.

        At head of title: The National fertilizer association.

NN   0051287   DNAL OC1FRB OC1 IU NNC ICJ NN

National fertilizer association (1925–   )
The weekly wholesale price index (3d ed.) by Herbert Willett, economist of the association, with a foreword by Charles J. Brand ... Washington, D. C., The National fertilizer association, 1941.
42 p. diagrs. 23ᶜᵐ.
Describes the wholesale price index issued weekly by the association. cf. p. 5.

1. Index numbers (Economics) I. Willett, Herbert, 1902– II. Title.
                                          41–13902
Library of Congress   HB235.U6N3 1941
                         ₍3₎   338.50973

NN   0051288   DLC OC1 OU ICJ NNC NN MB OrCS DNAL

National fertilizer association (1925–   )
Working for the common good; an illustrated summary of the work of the National fertilizer association, Washington, D. C. Submitted for consideration in the American trade association executives award, by Charles J. Brand, executive secretary and treasurer, February 15, 1930. ₍Washington, D. C., National fertilizer association, 1930₎
1 p. l., 40 numb. l. illus., plates. 28ᶜᵐ.
Autographed from type-written copy.

I. Brand, Charles John, 1879–   II. Title.

Library of Congress   S631.N3
                         ₍2₎   30–32238
                                   668.606273

NN   0051289   DLC DNAL

S633   National fertilizer association (1925–   )
.I5
1926   **Institute of politics,** *Williams college,* **1926.**
        World conditions as to mineral raw materials for the fertilizer industry; addresses delivered at the meeting of the Institute of politics at Williamstown, Mass., August 12–14, 1926. ₍Washington, D. C.₎ The National fertilizer association, 1926.

VOLUME 407

National fertilizer association (1925-1955)
  Year book. 1925/26-
  ₍Washington, 1925?-
    nos. 15½ᶜᵐ.

  1. Fertilizers and manures—Societies.
                                        43-40492
  Library of Congress   TP963.N36

NN 0051291   DLC

National Fertilizer Association (1925-1955)
  see also
National Plant Food Institute.

National fertilizer association (1925-   ) *Cost account-
    ing committee.*
  Cost accounting and cost estimating for plants producing
sulphuric acid and acid phosphate, prepared by the Cost accounting committee of the National fertilizer association; text
and forms by B. A. McKinney ... ₍Washington? D. C.₎ 1926.
    63 p. diagr., fold. forms. 23½ᶜᵐ.

  1. Chemicals—Manufacture and industry—Costs. 2. Cost—Accounting. I. McKinney, Byron Avery, 1882- II. Title.
                                        33-33180
  Library of Congress   HF5686.C35N3   661.2

NN 0051293   DLC NN ICJ IU

---

657   National fertilizer association ∧ Cost accounting
N2152d   committee.
            Digest of cost accounting manual for producers
          of sulphuric acid, superphosphate, and mixed
          fertilizers and for producers of superphosphate
          and mixed fertilizers, containing exhibits and
          schedules ... Prepared for use in administering
          the code of fair competition of the fertilizer
          industry ... and approved by the code authority
          and the National recovery administration.
          ₍Washington, D.C., The National fertilizer asso-

          ciation₎ 1934.
            48p. fold.forms.

            1. Fertilizers and manures. 2. Cost--Account-
          ing.

NN 0051295   IU DNAL OC1

National fertilizer association (1925-1955) *Cost account-
    ing committee.*
  A manual of accounting for dry mixers of fertilizers,
prepared by B. A. McKinney ... chairman, Cost accounting
committee, the National fertilizer association and William
B. McCloskey ... cost accountant of the Association, under
the direction of the Cost accounting committee. ₍Washing-
ton, D. C.₎ Published by the Association, 1927.
    48 p. fold. diagr., fold. forms. 23¼ cm.
    Seal of the National fertilizer association on t.-p.
  1. Cost accounting. 2. Fertilizer industry—Accounting. I. Mc-
Kinney, Byron Avery, 1882- II. McCloskey, William B., joint
author. III. Title: Dry mixers of fertilizers, A manual of accounting
for.
    HF5686.F4N3   668.6
                                        33-33181
NN 0051296   DLC ICJ IU

57.05   National Fertilizer Association (1925-   )
N212   Middle West
          Soil Improvement Committee.
          History of fertilizer ratios and grade
          recommendations in the Middle West, 1938-
          1954. Chicago ₍1954₎
            16 p.

            1. Fertilizers. Grading and standardization.

NN 0051297   DNAL

56.9   National Fertilizer Association (1925-   )
N214   Middle West
          Soil Improvement Committee.
          Minutes of joint agronomist-industry meeting.

          Chicago.

            1. Central states. Soils. 2. Soil. Con-
          gresses. 3. Fertilizers. Congresses.

NN 0051298   DNAL

463.34   National Fertilizer Association (1925-   )
N21   Middle
          West Soil Improvement Committee.
          Signs that show on hungry legumes.
          ₍Chicago, 1951₎
          folder.

            1. Deficiency diseases in plants.
          2. Legumes. Growth. I. Title.

NN 0051299   DNAL

National Fertilizer Association (1925-1955)
  Pasture Committee.
    Pasture top-dressing with fertilizer and
  lime ...
          see under   National Fertilizer Associa-
  tion (1925-1955) Soil Improvement Committee.

National Fertilizer Association (1925-   )
  Plant Food Research Committee.
SB351   The Peanut, the unpredictable legume; a symposium, pre-
.P3P4   pared by Frank Selman Arant ₍and others₎ Sponsored by
         the Plant Food Research Committee of the National Ferti-
         lizer Association. Washington, National Fertilizer Asso-
         ciation ₍1951₎

National Fertilizer Association (1925-   ) *Plant Food
Research Committee.*
  Report.
  Washington.
    v. illus. 23 cm. annual.

  1. Fertilizers and manures—Societies. 2. Field crops—U. S.
3. Agricultural research.
    S631.N3674   631.8072   51-37555 ‡

NN 0051302   DLC TU CU DNAL

National Fertilizer Association (1925-   ) Plant Food
  Research Committee.
  Report of the Sub-committee on Fertilizing
Fruit Trees. French Lick, Ind., 1946.
    38 p. 28cm.

  Processed.

  1. Fertilizers and manures. 2. Fruit culture.
I. Title: Fertilizing fruit trees.

NN 0051303   OrCS

National fertilizer association (1925-   ) Soil improvement committee.
    Pasture top-dressing with fertilizer and
  lime in the hay and pasture belt. A progress
  report. ₍Prepared by J. B. Abbott and others₎
  Washington, D. C., 1929?₎
    31 p. illus. 23cm.

NN 0051304   DNAL

S667   National Fertilizer Association (1925-   )
.H3N3   Soil Improvement Committee.
          Pasture top-dressing with fertilizer and
        lime in the hay and pasture belt.
        ₍Washington, D.C., 1929-1930₎
          2 nos. in 1. illus. 25 cm. (Its Progress
        report. ₍no.1-2₎)

            1. Pastures. 2. Fertilizers and manures.
          I. Title.

NN 0051305   TU

National fertilizer association (1925-   ) Soil
  improvement committee. Northern division.
    Sales opportunity reports... Washington
  1928?
    16 pts. in iv. 28cm.

NN 0051306   DNAL

National fertilizer association ∧ Soil improvement committee.
  Northern division.
    Soil-fertility conferences in the northern states, 1926.
  ₍Washington, D. C., National fertilizer association, Soil im-
  provement committee, Northern division, 1926₎
    78 p. illus. 23ᶜᵐ.

  1. Fertilizers ₍and manures₎
                                        Agr 28-680
  Library, U. S. Dept. of   Agriculture 57N214

NN 0051307   DNAL IU

National fertilizer association ∧ Soil
  improvement committee. Northern division.
    Soil improvement program for Lawrence
  County Missouri 1927. 24 p.

NN 0051308   DNAL

National fertilizer association ∧ Soil improvement
  committee - Northern division.
    Survey of the present status of soil fertility
  research in the Northern states...1926.
    15 numb. 1.

NN 0051309   dnal

National Fertilizer Association (1925-   ) Soil Improvement
Committee. Southern Division.
  Fertilizer data—Southern States. Compiled by staff, Southern
  Division, Soil Improvement Committee, National Fertilizer
  Association. [Washington, D. C., 1927?.]
    [8], 351 leaves incl. tables. 28ᶜᵐ.
    Mimeographed.
    The tests were made on four specific crops: cotton, corn, tobacco, and wheat.

NN 0051310   ICJ WaPS DNAL DLC

S631   National Fertilizer Development Center.
.N3   Fertilizer summary data, by States and
          geographic areas.
          Muscle Shoals, Ala.

            (13) 1. Fertilizers. Statistics.
          I. Title.

NN 0051311   DNAL

VOLUME 407

National fertilizer review. v. 1–
Jan. 1926–
[Washington, National Fertilizer Association]
v. in   illus., ports. 28 cm.   quarterly.
Title varies: Jan. 1926–Apr./June 1952, Fertilizer review.

1. Fertilizers and manures—Period.   ɪ. National Fertilizer Association (1925–   )
S631.N33   631.805   27–18151 rev*

DFT IaAS NcRS MiU DNLM ScCleU ICJ ICU NN
NN   0051312   DLC CaBVaU WaS OrCS OrP WaS TxDaM

National fibre can and tube association.
...Studies of the industry with respect to uniform accounting, cost finding and cost estimating.   [New York, 1936]   2 l.
62 p.   diagrs., tables.   28cm.

Caption-title.
Reproduced from typewritten copy.

901198A. 1. Accounting and book-   keeping for container industry.
2. Containers—Cost of production.
N. Y. P. L.   July 13, 1938

NN   0051313   NN

The **National field.**
v.

Salina, Kan., 19   v.   illus.   41 – 43cm.

Weekly (slightly irregular).
Various mistakes in numbering.

Official organ of the National farmers' union.   have title: The National field and Texas
farm co-operator.   – Sept. 30, 1915.
Published at Atlanta, Ga.,
Absorbed the Texas farm co-operator, Jan. 8, 1914.

Ceased publication with v. 8, no. 6 (Feb. 8, 1918)?

NN   0051315   NN

National Field Archery Association.
The basic technique of instinctive field shooting. Redlands, California, n.d.

NN   0051316   OrLgE

National field archery association.
Official handbook... 19

[Redlands, Calif., 19   v.   illus.   14 – 17cm.

19   ha   cover-title: Archery handbook.

1. Archery.   ɪ. Archery hand-   book.
N. Y. P. L.   December 8, 1950

NN   0051317   NN IU CSt N CLSU

HC101
.F53   **National fifty years in business club.**

The Fifty years in business magazine. v. 1, no. 1–4; Nov. 1939–Oct. 1940. [Nashville, The National fifty years in business club, 1939–40]

National Film Archive, *London*
see
London. National Film Archive.

National film association (Gt. Brit.)
The NFA journal
see under title

National film awards.
London, D. Yates.
v.   illus. 19 cm. annual.
"The leading films, actors and actresses in the ballot organised by the 'Daily mail.'"

1. Moving-pictures—Gt. Brit.   ɪ. Daily mail, London.
PN1993.5.G7N3   791.4   50–15411

NN   0051321   DLC CLSU

National film board of Canada
see
Canada. *National film board.*

National Film Finance Corporation.
Report and statement of accounts.
London, H. M. Stationery Off.
v. 25 cm. annual.
Issued in the series of parliamentary papers as Papers by command.
Report year ends Mar. 31.

PN1999.N3A3   791.4   51–34174 ‡

NN   0051323   DLC DS

National Film Library, London
see   **London. National Film Archive.**

ML1
.F315   **National Film Music Council.**

Film and TV music. v. 1–   Oct. 1941–
[New York, etc.]

YA   **National Film productions, S. A.**
23112   Prospecto de... [Mexico, n.d.]
unp.

NN   0051326   DLC

National Film Society of Canada
see
Canadian Film Institute.

National finance. A journal of American financial progress.
Chicago [W. Goodhue]
v.   illus. 31ᶜᵐ. monthly.
Preceded by Educational news.

1. Finance—Period.
CA 10–2691 Unrev'd
Library of Congress   HG1.N3

NN   0051328   DLC

National Finance Corporation of South Africa.
Report of the ordinary general meeting of stockholders.
[Pretoria]
v. 25 cm. annual.

HG3729.A38N33   55–33585 ‡

NN   0051329   DLC

National finances. [1864?]
see under   **Walley, Samuel Hurd.**

The **national finances,** 1973
see under   [**Grubb, Joseph C**   ]

The **National finances.** no. 1–   1954–55
see under   **Canadian Tax Foundation.**

336.73
N2125
The national finances: a letter addressed to the Hon. Secretary of the Treasury, and to the Hon. members of the Senate and House of Representatives of the United States, on the subject of the New York financiers, their modesty, wisdom, patriotism, and intentions, and upon the subject of demand treasury notes, taxation, &c. By a patriot.
New York, January 12th, 1862.   New York, Baker & Godwin, Printers, 1862.
8p. 23cm.
1. Finance -   U.S. ɪ A Patriot.

NN   0051333   TxU MWA OClWHi

National finances. A vindication of Republican statesmanship, fidelity, and economy. [n. p., 1872?]
8 p. 24½ᶜᵐ.
Caption title.

1. Finance—U. S.
Library of Congress   HJ256.N26   7–42128

NN   0051334   DLC OClWHi MB ViU

HG2557
1861   ... The national finances and a national bank.
.N3   New-York, Pub. at the office of the Bankers' magazine, 1861.
cover-title, 20 p.
Dedication signed: R. S.

NN   0051335   ICU

The national finances and the public faith.
see under
Adirondack, pseud.

National, The, finances. Letter to Congress. [Signed, a citizen]
n. t.-p.   [Washington City, 1862]   6 p., 1 l.   8°.

1. Finance, U. S., 1862.
N. Y. P. L.   July 22, 1911.

NN   0051337   NN

VOLUME 407

The **National** financial news; a weekly newspaper of American finance. v. 1–   May 7, 1923–
New York, N. Y., Plummer publications, inc., 1923–

v. illus. 25ᶜᵐ.

Caption title.
Editor: May 1923–   A. N. Plummer.

1. Finance—Period. 2. Investments—Period. 3. Securities—Period.
I. Plummer, A. Newton, ed.

Library of Congress   HG4501.N3   26–18224

NN   0051338   DLC

The national financial statement interpreter
     see under   Hemingway, Wilfrid Hubert,
     1879–

National Financing Corporation of Cuba
     see
Financiera Nacional de Cuba.

National fingerprint and identification bureau, inc., *New York.*
   A complete course in fingerprinting, by National fingerprint and identification bureau, inc., New York city. ₍New York₎ National fingerprint and identification bureau, inc., ᶜ1940.

cover-title, 68 p. illus. (incl. forms) 28ᶜᵐ.

1. Finger-prints.   I. Title: Fingerprinting, A complete course in.

Library of Congress   HV6074.N3   40–35842
——— Copy 2.
Copyright AA 341210   ₍2₎   573.6

NN   0051341   DLC ICJ

National fingerprint and identification bureau, inc., *New York.*
   The fingerprint quizzer; over 650 questions and answers, 10 actual sets of fingerprints included, previous city, state & federal fingerprint examinations.   Compiled & edited by Sgt. A. J. Berman, F. P. E., identification consultant & Joseph D. Schneeweiss, director, National fingerprint & identification school. New York city, National fingerprint & identification bureau, inc., National fingerprint & identification school, ᶜ1942.

51 l.   diagrs.   27¼ x 21¼ᶜᵐ.
Ten plates laid in.
Reproduced from type-written copy.
1. Finger-prints. 2. Civil   service—U. S.—Examinations.   I. Berman, Abraham Jacob,   1907–   II. Schneeweiss, Joseph Daniel, 1910–   III. Title.
Library of Congress   HV6074.N32   42–17483
                      ₍4₎   351.30973

NN   0051342   DLC OCl

Pam.   National Finnish Socialist Organization of
Coll.   United States. Middle District Committee.

23944   The controversy within the Finnish Socialist Organization of United States, its issues and reasons. ₍Superior, Wis., 1914₎
      16 p.   20 cm.

     Caption title.
     1. National Finnish Socialist Organization of United States. 2. Socialism in the U. S. I. Title.

NN   0051343   NcD

National Fire and Life Insurance Company of Scotland.
   The National Fire and Life Insurance Company of Scotland... Established in 1841.   Edinburgh ₍1843?₎   30 p., 1 l.
Tables.   8°.

Cover-title.

1. Insurance companies, Gt. Br.:   Scotland.
N. Y. P. L.   January 21, 1916.

NN   0051344   NN

National Fire and Life Insurance Company of Scotland.
   Report of the proceedings at the...annual general meeting.
no.
Edinburgh,   8°.

1. Insurance companies, Gt. Br.: Scot-   land.
N. Y. P. L.   July 7, 1916.

NN   0051345   NN

National Fire Brigades' Association, London.
   Annual report.
    ₍London₎
     v. illus.
   Began 1913.

NN   0051346   ICRL ICJ

National fire brigades' association, London.

   Bevir, Harold.
     The Auxiliary fire service and its organisation, by Harold Bevir ... London, The National fire brigades association ₍1940₎

National Fire Brigades' Association, London
   Manual for the use of fire brigades.   Issued by the National Fire Brigades' Union...   London: National Fire Brigades' Union ₍1912?₎   4 p.l., (1)12–362 p., 3 l., 8 fold. diagr. (7 in pocket.) illus. (incl. diagr.), tables.   12°.

1. Fires.—Prevention and extinc-   tion. 2. Fire departments, Gt. Br.
N. Y. P. L.   May 9, 1916.

NN   0051348   NN

National Fire Brigades' Association, London.
   The National Fire Brigades' Association.   Its activities, organization, and development.   ₍London, 1919.₎   14 p.   illus.
8°.

Cover-title.

1. Firemen—Assoc. and org.—   Gt. Br.
N. Y. P. L.   September 24, 1926

NN   0051349   NN OCl

National Fire Brigades' Association, London.
   Proceedings of the annual conference.
London.
     v. illus.

   Began 1913.

NN   0051350   ICRL

National fire brigades' association. Fire prevention department committee
   ...Fire test with a metal fire-resisting cabinet, submitted by Messrs. Chubb & son's lock & safe co., ltd., London.
    20 p. illus., diagrs., tables.
   London, National fire brigades' association, 1931. (Red books no. 259)

NN   0051351   OCl

National fire brigades' association Fire prevention department committee
   ...Fire test with a partition constructed with fire-resisting slabs known as "Heraklith" slabs, submitted by Messrs. Newman & Holt, ltd., London,
    16 p. illus., diagrs' association, 1931.
   (Red books no. 255)

NN   0051352   OCl

National fire brigades' association, London.
   Fire prevention dept. committee
   ... Fire tests with a fire-resisting paint known as Colorado "Fireproof" paint, submitted by Messrs. Colorado products, ltd., Reading. The committee's report.
    16 p. illus., diagrs.
   ₍London₎ National fire brigades' association, 1930.

NN   0051353   OCl

National fire brigades' association. Fire prevention department committee
   ... Fire tests with an automatic fire alarm, submitted by Messrs. John Kerr & Co., Manchester. The committee's report.
    15, ₍1₎ p. diagrs., table.
   ₍London₎ National fire brigades' association, 1929.
    At head of title "Red books" of the National fire brigades' association , no. 253.

NN   0051354   OCl

National fire brigades' association- Fire prevention dept. committee
   ...Fire tests with flame-proofing salts; a test with textiles, packing material and other articles before and after treatment with "cellon" flame-proofing salts, submitted by the Sprenger corporation, ltd. The Committee's report.
    16 p. illus. table.
   ₍London₎ National fire brigades' association ₍1929₎ (Its red books, no. 248)

NN   0051355   OCl

National fire brigades' association- Fire prevention department committee
   ...Fire tests with flame proofing solution; a test with textiles, packing material and other articles before and after treatment with "Neocellon" flame-proofing solution, submitted by Messrs. Neocellon, limited.
    16 p. illus.
   London, National fire brigades' association, 1925. (Red books" no. 255)

NN   0051356   OCl

National Fire Brigades' Association, London.
   Fire Prevention Department Committee
   "Red books" of the National Fire Brigades Association. Edited by the Committee of the Fire Prevention Department. ... London ₍1898–   ₎

   Library has no. 1 *to date.* illus., plates, tables, diagrs. 22ᶜᵐ.

   At head of title, no. 231–232, 234?, 237–239, 242–244, 246, 249–252, 256–257: Department of Scientific and Industrial Research.   These numbers were reports on tests undertaken for the Government and were published by H. M. Stationery Office.
   No. 1–244 issued by the British Fire Prevention Committee which was absorbed by the National Fire Brigades Association.
   Title varies: no. 1–89, Publications ...
   No. 1, 2d edition; have also reissues, 1911, of no. 8, 42.
   Wanting: no. 168, 234.

NN   0051357   ICJ DLC ICRL

National Fire Brigades Association, London. Fire Prevention Dept. Committee.
   "Red books"
     see also   British Fire Prevention Committee.
Publications.

National Fire Brigades' Union
     see   National Fire Brigades' Association.

VOLUME 407

National fire insurance co., Hartford, Conn.
Facts and figures relating to the presidential
campaign of Nineteen hundred. [Chicago, G.E.
Marshall & co. [19-]

[21] p. ports. 15.5 cm.

NN 0051360 MH

National fire insurance company, *Hartford, Conn.*
A quarter-century's fire underwriting, 1871–1896. An
historical and biographical milestone in the life of the
National fire insurance co. of Hartford, Conn. New-York,
The De Vinne press [1897]

1 p. l., v–vii, 164 p. incl. tables. front., plates, ports., 2 facsim. 26 x 21 cm.

1. Insurance, Fire—U. S.—Hist. I. Title.

Library of Congress HG9780.N2

7—19959

NN 0051361 DLC OkU CU ICU PP NcU NN Nh

National Fire Insurance Co., Hartford, Conn.
Pacific Dept.
Choice recipes, compiled by practical
housekeepers of Sonoma County, California,
1900. Prepared for... the Pacific Dept. of
the National Fire Insurance Company... and
Springfield Fire and Marine Insurance Co.
San Francisco, Whitaker & Ray [c1900]
57p. 22cm.

1. Cookery, American. The West.
I. Springfield Fire and Marine Insurance
Company, jt. auth.

NN 0051362 OrU

National Fire Insurance Company, New York

CT275
D75
N3

Drowne
Collection

An act to incorporate the National Fire Insurance Co., in the City of New York, passed
April 9, 1838, and the several amendments thereto March 11, 1857. New York, G. F. Nesbitt &
co., 1857.
20 p. 17 cm.

Henry T. Drowne, secretary of the co.

1. Drowne, Henry Thayer, 1822–1897.

NN 0051363 RPB

National Fire Insurance Company, New York.
Semi-annual statement. New York.
obl. 48°.

NN 0051364 NN

National Fire Insurance Company of Scotland.
Contract of copartnery. [Edinburgh,] 1841. 32 p. 8°.

1. Insurance (Fire).—Companies,
N. Y. P. L.

Gt. Br.: Scotland. December 18, 1916.

NN 0051365 NN

NATIONAL FIRE PREVENTION CONVENTION

See AMERICAN NATIONAL FIRE PREVENTION
CONVENTION.

National fire proofing company.
Catalogue of the National fire proofing company of
Pittsburgh, U. S. A. Abridged ed. ... Author and compiler: Henry L. Hinton, engineer, National fire proofing
company. New York, National fire proofing company,
1903.

[496] p. illus., diagrs. 18½ cm.

Part of the pages blank.

1. Building, Fire-proof. I. Hinton, Henry L.

Library of Congress TH1083.N26

3—13602

NN 0051367 DLC OCl MB ICJ

National Fire Proofing Company.
The city unburnable and the building on which it
can be modeled. [Chicago, Rogers and Co.,
1908 ?]
8 l. illus. 8°.

NN 0051368 NN

National Fire Proofing Company.
Fireproof construction for houses and other buildings of
moderate cost... New York, N. Y.: National Fire Proofing
Company, 1909. 93 p. incl. tables. diagrs., illus. (incl. facsims., plans). sq. 8°.

On cover: Fireproof houses of terra cotta hollow title, and how to build them.

401558A. 1. Fireproof construction.
N. Y. P. L.

May 31, 1929

NN 0051369 NN

National fire proofing company.
Fireproof construction, for houses and other buildings
of moderate cost. 2d ed. ... Pittsburgh, Pa., New York
[etc.] National fire proofing company, 1909.
93 p. illus. 23 cm.

1. Building, Terra-cotta.

Library of Congress TH1375.N3

10-7653

NN 0051370 DLC

TH 1083
.N3

National fire proofing company.
Fireproof construction for houses and other
buildings of moderate cost. 4th ed.
Pittsburgh, 1910.

NN 0051371 DLC

National fire proofing company.
Fireproof construction, for houses and other buildings
of moderate cost. 5th ed. ... Pittsburgh, Pa., New York
[etc.] National fire proofing company, 1911.
93 p. illus. 23 cm.

NN 0051372 ICJ

National fire proofing company.
Fireproof construction for houses and other buildings
of moderate cost ... [6th ed.] Pittsburgh, Pa., New York
[etc.] National fire proofing company, c1912.
[3]–64 p. illus. (part col.) 30½ cm.
Illustrated lining-papers.

1. Building, Terra-cotta.

Library of Congress TH1375.N3 1912

13–365

NN 0051373 DLC MiU NN MB

528.93
N27f
.4

National fire proofing company.
Fireproof houses of moderate cost. Natco
hollow tile. Pittsburg, Pennsylvania,
National fire proofing company, [1914]
30 p. illus. 26 cm.
Illus.t.-p.
7th ed.
Loose blue fold.pl.

NN 0051374 MiU

National Fire Proofing Company. 693.8 Q500
Fire proofing catalogue of the National Fire Proofing Company,
manufacturers and contractors dense and porous terra cotta fire
proofing. ... . [New York, Bartlett & Company, The Orr
Press], c1905.
39, [1] p. incl. front., illus. 24 cm.

NN 0051375 ICJ

National Fire Proofing Company.
First mortgage. National Fire Proofing Company to the
New York Trust Company, as trustee. National Fire Proofing
Company to O. T. Bannard, as trustee. To secure first mortgage
five per cent. gold notes. Total authorized issue, $2,500,000.
Dated April 1, 1906. New York: C. G. Burgoyne [1906]. 1 p.l.,
111 p., 1 l., 17(1) p. 4°.

Title from cover.

1. Mortgages. 2. New York Trust Co. 3. Bannard, Otto Tremont.
N. Y. P. L.

August 31, 1912.

NN 0051376 NN NjP

728
N213h
1910-17

National Fire Proofing Company.
[House designing] Boston, Rogers &
Manson [1910-1917]
5v. in 1. illus. 27cm.

1. Architecture , Domestic. Designs
and plans. I. Title.

NN 0051377 KU

[National Fire Proofing Company]
Industrial housing. [Pittsburgh, cop. 1918.] 12 p.
diagrs., illus. 4°. (Bull. [no.] 172.)

Cover-title.

1. Building (Tile). 2. Habitations for the working classes.—Architecture.
N. Y. P. L.

January 12, 1922.

NN 0051378 NN

National Fire Proofing Company.
Long span fireproof construction in reinforced terra cotta
hollow tile. Pittsburgh, 1910. 60 p. 2. ed. 4°.

1. Fireproof construction.
N. Y. P. L.

March 22, 1912.

NN 0051379 NN

National Fire Proofing Company.
McRoy camp vitrified, salt glazed conduit for electrical sub-
ways. Pittsburgh: National Fire Proofing Company, 1916.
46 p., incl. illus., tables 8°.

Cover-title: McRoy camp conduits.

1. Electricity.—Conduits.
N. Y. P. L.

December 7, 1921.

NN 0051380 NN

VOLUME 407

National fire proofing company.
    The Natco bungalow for four thousand dollars; attractive, economical, durable, fireproof ... Pub. for the National fire proofing company, Pittsburgh. Boston, Rogers and Manson company [1913]

    80 p. illus. (incl. plans) 26½ᶜᵐ.

    "The material recommended is Natco hollow tile."

    1. Bungalows.   I. Title.

    Library of Congress   NA7571.N3   13–10858

NN 0051381   DLC MiU NN ICJ ICRL

National fire proofing company.
    The Natco double house, semi-detached; attractive, economical, durable, fireproof ... Pub. for the National fire proofing company, Pittsburgh. Boston, Rogers and Manson company [1914]

    80 p. illus. (incl. plans) 26½ᶜᵐ.

    1. Architecture, Domestic—Designs and plans.   I. Title.

    Library of Congress   NA7127.N4   14–15762

NN 0051382   DLC MiU OC1

[National Fire Proofing Company.]
    Natco grain bins, corn cribs and storage bins. / [Pittsburgh, cop. 1920.] 9 p. incl. diagrs., illus., table. 4°. (Bull. [no.] 175.)

    Cover-title.

    1. Building (Tile). 2. Bins.
N. Y. P. L.   January 12, 1922.

NN 0051383   NN

National Fire Proofing Company.
    Natco homes. Pittsburgh [192–?]. 16 p. illus., plans. 4°.

    1. Building (Tile). 2. Architecture   (Domestic).—Designs and plans.
N. Y. P. L.   January 6, 1922.

NN 0051384   NN

National Fire Proofing Company.
    Natco homes for workingmen. [Pittsburgh,] cop. 1918. 10 p. illus., plans. 4°. (Bull. [no.] 173.)

    Cover-title.

    1. Building (Tile). 2. Habitations   for the working classes.—Architecture.
N. Y. P. L.   January 11, 1922.

NN 0051385   NN

National fire proofing company.
    The Natco house for six thousand dollars, attractive, economical, durable, fireproof ... Pub. for the National fire proofing company, Pittsburgh. Boston, Rogers & Manson [1912]

    72 p. illus. (incl. plans) 26½ x 20ᶜᵐ. $0.50

    1. Architecture, Domestic—Designs and plans.   I. Title.

    Library of Congress   NA7125.N3   12–13454

NN 0051386   DLC ICJ MiU OC1 ICRL

National Fire Proofing Company.
    Natco imperishable silo built of vitrified hollow clay tile... Pittsburgh: the company, 1915.   47(1) p. illus. 8°.

    1. Silos.—Dealers' catalogues. 2.   Title.
N. Y. P. L.   November 18, 1915.

NN 0051387   NN

[National Fire Proofing Company.]
    Natco on the farm. [Pittsburgh, cop. 1919.] 36 p. incl. diagrs., illus., tables. 4°.

    Cover-title.

    1. Farmhouses and buildings (Tile).
N. Y. P. L.   January 9, 1922.

NN 0051388   NN

National Fire Proofing Company.
    Natco standard fire proofing.   [Pittsburgh, cop. 1917.] 31 p. incl. diagrs., illus., tables. 4°. (Bull. no. 171.)

    Cover-title.

    1. Building (Tile). 2. Fireproof   construction.
N. Y. P. L.   January 12, 1922.

NN 0051389   NN

National fire proofing company.
    The Natco suburban house and garage, attractive, economical, durable, fireproof ... Pub. for the National fire proofing company, Pittsburgh. Boston, Rogers and Manson company [1915]

    80 p. illus. (incl. plans) 26½ᶜᵐ.

    1. Architecture, Domestic—Designs and plans. 2. Hollow brick, tile, etc.
I. Title.

    Library of Congress   NA7155.N35   15–25962

NN 0051390   DLC ICRL ICJ

National fire proofing company.
    The Natco tex-tile one-family house; a selection of designs submitted in competition by architects, with illustrations of houses built of Natco tex-tile; together with articles treating of design, plan, and construction of dependable houses of moderate cost ... Pub. for the National fire proofing company, Pittsburgh. Boston, Rogers and Manson company, [1917]

    72 p. illus. (incl. plans) 27 cm.

    1. Architecture, Domestic—Designs and plans. 2. Tile construction. I. Title.

    NA7155.N355   17—27910

NN 0051391   DLC NcRS

National fire proofing company.
    The Natco two-apartment house; a selection of designs submitted in competition by architects; with illustrations of houses built of Natco hollow tile; together with articles treating of design, plan, and construction of dependable houses of moderate cost ... Pub. for the National fire proofing company, Pittsburgh. Boston, Rogers and Manson company [1916]

    72 p. illus. (incl. plans) 27ᶜᵐ.

    1. Apartment houses. 2. Architecture, Domestic—Designs and plans.
I. Title.

    Library of Congress   NA7155.N36   16–23028

NN 0051392   DLC ICJ ICRL

[National Fire Proofing Company.]
    Natco wall construction. / [Pittsburgh, cop. 1919.] 32 p. 4°. (Bull. [no.] 174.)

    Cover-title.

    1. Building (Tile).
N. Y. P. L.   January 9, 1922.

NN 0051393   NN

---

*K
.B68885 The National Fire Proofing Company, plaintiff in error.
v.20
no. 11
    The National Fire Proofing Company, a corporation, plaintiff in error. v. J. V. Bickford, defendant in error. Record 1147. From the Circuit Court of Elizabeth City County, Va. [Richmond? 1924?]
    37 p. 23cm. [Braxton legal pamphlets]
    Cover title.
    "In the Supreme Court of Appeals of Virginia at Richmond."
    I. Bickford, James Van Allen, 1876– , defendant in error. II. Virginia. Supreme Court of Appeals.

NN 0051394   ViU

National fire proofing company.
TH1083
.N28   Terra cotta hollow tile fireproofing as used in the construction of standard steel frame fireproof buildings.
    [Pittsburgh?] c1910.

NN 0051395   DLC

National fire proofing company.
    Trial by fire at San Francisco; the evidence of the camera. Pub. by National fire proofing company ... [New York? 1906]
    [61] p. illus. 26½ x 33½ᶜᵐ.

    1. San Francisco—Earthquake and fire, 1906. 2. Building, Fire-proof.
I. Title.
    Library of Congress   TH1093.N27   7—4534

NN
0051396   DLC WaS NjP IEN PSt OU OO ViU ICJ MB

614.8405 **National Fire Protection Association.**
N2772a   Advance reports to the ... annual meeting.
    Boston.
        v. illus. 23cm.

    1. Fire prevention - Period. 2. Fire extinction - Period.

NN 0051397   CLSU WaS

NATIONAL FIRE PROTECTION ASSOCIATION.
    Advisory outline of the scope and contents of a fire prevention code for cities with suggestions on sources of material.
    [Boston, Mass., 192-].

    pp.11/.

NN 0051398   MH

National Fire Protection Association.
    ... Aims, activities and current publications. Boston, Mass. [19
        v. 23 cm.
    At head of title: The National fire protection association.

NN 0051399   DLC MH DL

VOLUME 407

National Fire Protection Association.
Airplane crash fire fighting manual
see under   National Fire Protection Association. Committee on Aircraft Fire Fighting.

National Fire Protection Association.
... American recommended practice for the installation, maintenance and use of piping and fittings for city gas
see under   American standards association.

National fire protection association.
... American standard safety code for the installation of pulverized fuel systems. Approved, American standards association, September 4, 1930, Sponsors, National fire protection association, United States Department of agriculture. American engineering and industrial standards. New York (1930)
1 p.l., 30 p. 20 cm.
At head of title: ASA Z12a-1930-

NN 0051402   DL

National fire protection association.
... American standard safety code for the installation of pulverizing systems for sugar and cocoa. Approved, American standards association, January 10, 1930. Sponsors, National fire protection association, United States Department of agriculture. American engineering and industrial standards. (New York, 1930)
1 p.l., 14 p. 20 cm.
At head of title: ASA 212b 1930-

NN 0051403   DL

NATIONAL FIRE PROTECTION ASSOCIATION.
Annual fire survey of Moline, Illinois; sponsored by the Moline Association of Commerce Fire Prevention Committee, with the cooperation of city officials. Boston, [1931].

Manifold copy. ff.39. Maps and tables.
"Made September 7-12, 1931, by the Field Engineering Department."

NN 0051404   MH

NATIONAL FIRE PROTECTION ASSOCIATION.
Annual fire survey of Wilmington, Delaware; sponsored by the Wilmington Chamber of Commerce, Fire Prevention Committee, with the cooperation of the Department of Public Safety. Boston, [1932].

Manifold copy. ff.40. Map and tables.
"Made July 25-30, 1932, by the Field Engineering Department."

NN 0051405   MH

TH9111
.N2

National Fire Protection Association.   Articles of association.

National Fire Protection Association.
Year book, officers and committees.   -1932/33.
Boston.

National Fire Protection Association.
Augusta, Georgia, conflagration, March 22-23, 1916.   Boston, 1916.   14 p.   illus.   4°.

1. Fires, U. S.: Ga.: Augusta.
N. Y. P. L.   January 17, 1917.

NN 0051407   NN OU MB

National fire protection association.
The Baltimore conflagration. Report of the Committee on fire-restrictive construction of the National fire protection association. 1904. 2d ed. Chicago, Office of the secretary of the association [1904?]
130 p. illus. 23ᶜᵐ.

1. Baltimore—Fire, 1904. 2. Building, Fire-proof.

Library of Congress   TH1093.N29   6—46771

NN 0051408   DLC MB ICJ NN CU

NATIONAL FIRE PROTECTION ASSOCIATION.
The Baltimore conflagration. Report of the committee on fire-resistive construction of the National Fire Protection Association, 1904. [2. ed.] Chicago, Office of the Secretary of the Association [1904?] 130 p. illus. 23cm.

Film reproduction. Negative.
1. Fires—U.S.—Md.—Balti-   more, 1904. 2. Fireproof
construction—U. S.—Md.—   Baltimore. 3. Baltimore—Fires,
1904. i. 1904.   1904.

NN 0051409   NN

National Fire Protection Association.
Binghampton clothing company fire...1913; special report by H. W. Forster. Boston: the assoc. [1913]. 6 l. illus. 4°.

1. Fires in factories, U. S.: N. Y.:   Binghamton.
N. Y. P. L.   February 6, 1914.

NN 0051410   NN

614.85
N213n
1951
Arch
Lib'y

National fire protection association.
Building construction and equipment, compiled by Robert S. Moulton ... and James K. McElroy ... Boston, 1951.
717p. illus., diagrs. 24cm. (Its The National fire codes, vol. III)

Includes advertising matter.

1. Fire prevention. I. Moulton, Robert Selden, 1894- comp. II. Series.

NN 0051411   TxU DI

National Fire Protection Association.
Building exits code.

Boston.
v. 19-23 cm.
Issued   as the association's NFPA no. 101 (TH9115.N28)
Began publication in 1917.

1. Public buildings—Fires and fire prevention. 2. Building laws—
U. S. 3. Fire-escapes.   i. Title.   (Series: National Fire Protection Association. NFPA no. 101)

TH2274.N27   614.847   51-3095 rev

N DNAL
OU CLL TU MH MB TxU NcD PPL PWpM MiD MiU NIC IU
NN 0051412   DLC OrCS OrU WaS Wa Or NN OCI DL CU

296.6
N21B

National fire protection association.
Building exits for fire safety.   Boston [1938?]
[8] p.

1. Fire prevention. I. Moulton, Robert Selden, 1894-   II. Title.

NN 0051413   DNAL

E 286
A 14

National fire protection association.
[Bulletin. Boston, 1911]

NN 0051414   DLC

National Fire Protection Association.
[Bulletin on a rational celebration of Independence Day.] Boston, 1916.   2 l.   illus.   4°.

1. Independence day.—Celebrations,   1916. 2. Fires.—Prevention.
N. Y. P. L.   August 29, 1917.

NN 0051415   NN

National Fire Protection Association.   4011.85
[Bulletins.]
= Boston. 1915-   v. Illus. 28 cm.

K7039 — Societies. Proc., trans., etc. — Fire. Prevention. Periodicals.

NN 0051416   MB

614.846 National fire protection association.
N213c   Care of fire hose; suggestions for the selection, maintenance and use of fire hose …   Boston, Mass., National fire protection association, international, 1936.
11p. diagr.

1. Hose. 2. Fire extinction. I. Title.

NN 0051417   IU

National Fire Protection Association.
Chimneys and flues.   n. t.-p.   Boston [1912?].   2 l.   4°.

1. Chimneys.—Construction.
N. Y. P. L.   August 18, 1913.

NN 0051418   NN OU

National Fire Protection Association.
Church fires, a record of one hundred and fifty-four fires...
see under title

National Fire Protection Association.
Churches are burning ...   Boston, National fire protection association, c1948.
40 p. illus. 23 cm. (National fire protection association. Quarterly, v. 42, no. 3, pt. 2)

NN 0051420   OU

National Fire Protection Association.   L368.06161 31
[Circulars and other minor publications.]

NN 0051421   ICJ

National Fire Protection Association.
The Cleveland clinic fire, May 15, 1929.
Boston, National fire protection association, 1929.
[4] p. illus. 28 cm.
Caption title.
"Reference material": last page.
1. Fires – Cleveland, Ohio. I. Title.

NN 0051422   CU

VOLUME 407

National fire protection association.
The Cocoanut Grove night club fire, Boston, November 28, 1942 ... Boston, Mass., National fire protection association ₁1943₎

19, ₁1₎ p. illus. (incl. plans) 28 x 21½ᵐ.

A preliminary report prepared by Robert S. Moulton, technical secretary, National fire protection association.

1. Cocoanut Grove, Boston—Fire, 1942.   I. Moulton, Robert Selden, 1804–   44–18663
  Library of Congress   TH9449.B7N3
                                   ₁2₎   614.84

NN 0051423   DLC DNAL IU CtY OCl OU NNC

M94.2212 National Fire Protection Association.
N277c   Code for protection against lightning.
            1925–
            Boston.
            v. illus. 23cm. (Its NFPA no.78)

            1. Lightning. Protection. 2. Fire prevention. I. t. ser.

NN 0051424   DAS

TH   National Fire Protection Association.
2274   Code for safety to life from fire in
.N28   buildings and structures.
            Boston.

            Issued   as the association's NFPA
            no.101.
            Began publication in 1917.
            Title varies: Building exits
            code.
            Cover title   : Life safety code.

NN 0051425   MiU NdU

National fire protection association.
Code for the construction and installation of liquefied petroleum gas systems recommended for enforcement by fire marshals or other regulatory authorities, 1937 ... Adopted by National fire protection association ₁and₎ National board of fire underwriters. Boston, Mass., U.S.A.: National fire protection assoc. ₁1937₎ 16 p. 23cm.

1. Oil fuel—Jurisp.—U. S.   I. National board of fire underwriters.
N. Y. P. L.   March 12, 1940

NN 0051426   NN

National fire protection association.
Code for the prevention of dust explosions in
the plastics industry (ASA Z12.16–1945) Boston,
National fire protection association, 1945.

22 p.

NN 0051427   MH-C

National Fire Protection Association.
Code for the use of flammable anesthetics
(recommended safe practice for hospital operating rooms). 1941?–
Boston.

Title varies: Recommended safe
practice for hospital operating rooms.
Latest edition only

NN 0051428   MiU

TH9145 **National Fire Protection Association.**
N38   **[Codes approved by the American Standards**
          Association]   No.12A   no.60–60A
          651–655   663
          Boston, 1941–
            v. diagrs.; tables.   18 cm.
            No. 60, 653–655, reprinted, 1953.

            1. Fire prevention. I. American Standards
Association.

NN 0051429   DI

TK260   **National fire protection association.**
.N387
1940   **National board of fire underwriters.**
          Código eléctrico nacional, 1940. La norma de la Junta nacio-
nal de compañías de seguros contra incendio (National board of
fire underwriters) para las instalaciones de canalizaciones y
aparatos eléctricos en los Estados Unidos de América, en la
forma recomendada por la Asociación nacional de protección
contra incendio (National fire protection association) y apro-
bada, como norma americana, por la Asociación de normas
americanas (American standards association) ... Traducido

e impreso por la Business publishers international corporation,
Nueva York, N. Y., y publicado bajo los auspicios de la National electrical manufacturers association. ₁Nueva York₎
1943.

368.1   National fire protection association.
N21c   Comparative statistics of fire loss,
          American and foreign.   (In its Quar-
          terly, vol.6, no.1, July, 1912. p.16–22)

NN 0051432   IU

S   National Fire Protection Association.
614.84   Conflagrations in America since 1900, a record of the
N2725c   principal conflagrations in the United States and Canada during
            the first half of the twentieth century. Boston, ᶜ1954.
            64 p. illus. 24 cm.

            Caption title.

            1. Fires, U.S.   I. Title.

NN 0051433   N WaU DI ICJ TxU NN WHi

National fire protection association.
Conflagrations in America since 1914; a record of the principal
conflagrations in the United States and Canada since the burning
of Salem ...   Boston, Mass.: National fire protection assoc.
₁1942₎ 39 p. illus. 23cm.

"This record supersedes '100 conflagrations since 1900' (Quarterly, October, 1935);
it is a reprint from the Quarterly, April, 1942."

1. Fires—U. S. 2. Fires—Canada.
N. Y. P. L.   November 19, 1942

NN 0051434   NN OCl

National Fire Protection Association.   4019.263
Constructional particulars. . . . Plan.
(In British Fire Protection Committee. The fire at the Iroquois
Theatre, Chicago, ... Pp. 41–47. London. 1904.)

G4854 — Iroquois Theatre, Chicago, Ill. — Fire-proof buildings.

NN 0051435   MB

National Fire Protection Association.
Crosby-Fiske Forster handbook of fire
protection
     see Fire protection handbook.

National Fire Protection Association.
Don't give fires a place to start

see under

U.S. Dept. of Agriculture.

TH   National Fire Protection Association.
9117   Dust explosion prevention; an American
N27   standard.   Boston, 1954–
            nos. 20cm.

            Cover title.
            Contents.--no.60. Pulverized fuel systems,
            1961.
            no.65. Aluminum processing, 1963.--no.651.
            Aluminum powder, 1963.

NN 0051438   NIC

National Fire Protection Association.
Dwelling house hazards. How to prevent fires in the home.
Boston: the assoc. ₁1913.₎ 2 l. illus. 4°.

1. Fires in dwellings.
N. Y. P. L.   January 22, 1914.

NN 0051439   NN

TK225   **National fire protection association.**
.A7A5
1933   Atlanta. *Ordinances, etc.*
            ... Electrical ordinances and rules. National electrical code.
₁Atlanta?₎ 1933.

₁National fire protection association₎
  Employee organization for fire safety. ₁Boston, National
fire protection association, 1942₎

47, ₁1₎ p. illus. 23ᵐ.

"This text, drafted by the executive office staff, presents no new or
untried suggestions. They are based principally on three N. F. P. A.
standards: exit drills and alarm systems (a part of the Building exits
code) ... suggestions for the organization, drilling and equipment of private fire brigades ... and The watchman ... each ... printed in recent
editions."—Foreword.
  "Some other N. F. P. A. publications": p. ₁48₎

1. Mill and factory buildings—Fires and fire prevention. 2. Civilian
defense.   I. Title.
  Library of Congress   TH9445.M4N335   42–22082
                                   ₁3₎   614.84

NN 0051441   DLC OrP OCl OC1FRB IU NN

National fire protection association.
Employee organization for fire safety ... Boston, Mass., National fire protection association, international, ᶜ1945.

40 p. illus. (part col.) 23ᵐ.

"The ... text, drafted by the N. F. P. A. Executive office staff, is a revision of the first edition ... but the emphasis on air raid precautions has
been eliminated."—Foreword.

1. Mill and factory buildings—Fires and fire prevention.   I. Title.
                                                  45–8318
  Library of Congress   TH9445.M4N335 1945
                                   ₁2₎   614.84

NN 0051442   DLC

National Fire Protection Association.
Employee organization for fire safety. ₁3d ed.₎ Boston,
ᶜ1951.

42 p. illus. 23 cm.

1. Factories—Fires and fire prevention.   I. Title.
TH9445.M4N335 1951   614.84   52–3713 ‡

NN 0051443   DLC DI TxU

VOLUME 407

National Fire Protection Association.
The evil shingle roof.   Boston: the assoc. [1913.]   2 l.   illus.   4°.

1. Roofs (Shingle). 2. Fires.—   Causes.
N. Y. P. L.   January 23, 1914.

NN   0051444   NN OU

National Fire Protection Association.
Explosion venting 1954.   1954.

NN   0051445   CaBVaU

TH9148   National fire protection association.
N29   Facts about fire.   Fire prevention week
             supplement for fire prevention week

             Boston, Mass., National fire protection
             association, 19-

             _vols.   illus.   23cm.

             Title varies slightly.

             Published as supplements to the National
             fire protection association Fire prevention
             week handbooks.

             1. Fire prevention.
             I. National fire protection association.
             Fire prevention week handbook;
             supplement.

NN   0051447   NBuG NNC CtY OC1 DL

National Fire Protection Association.
Facts, texts and slogans for Fire Prevention week, October 4-10, 1925...   Boston[, 1925].   16 p.   illus.   12°.

1. Fires—Prevention and extinction.
N. Y. P. L.   September 28, 1926

NN   0051448   NN

National fire protection association.
The Fall River conflagration, February 2-3, 1928 ...   Boston, Mass., National fire protection association [1928]
cover-title, 39 p.   illus.   23ᶜᵐ.

1. Fall River, Mass.—Fires and fire prevention.
                                                29-6054
Library of Congress   F74.F2N3

NN   0051449   DLC WaS OU OC1 MB IU NN

296.8   National fire protection association.
N21fa   Farm publicity packet for fire prevention
             week ... October 3-9, 1943.   Boston [1943]
             17 pieces in folder.

NN   0051450   DNAL

National fire protection association.
Field practice; an inspection manual for property owners, fire departments and inspection offices, covering fire hazards and their safeguarding and fire protection and upkeep.   1914 ed. ...   Boston, Mass., National fire protection association [1914]
199 p.   17½ᶜᵐ. $1.50

1. Fire prevention. 2. Insurance, Fire—Inspectors.   I. Title.
Library of Congress   HG9715.N3
                                                15—1835

NN   0051451   DLC NIC CU OC1 NN MB ICJ NcU

National fire protection association.
Field practice; an inspection manual for property owners, fire departments and inspection offices, covering common fire hazards and their safeguarding and fire protection and upkeep. 2d ed., 1922 ...   Boston, Mass., National fire protection association [*1922]
206 p.   illus.   17½ᶜᵐ.

1. Fire prevention. 2. Insurance, Fire—Inspectors.   I. Title.
Library of Congress   HG9715.N3   1922
                                                22—11005

NN   0051452   DLC Or ICJ CU NcU

National fire protection association.
Field practice; an inspection manual for property owners, fire departments and inspection offices, covering common fire hazards and their safeguarding and fire protection and upkeep. 2d ed., 1922 (reprint, 1929) ...   Boston, Mass., National fire protection association [1929]
206 p.   illus.   17½ᶜᵐ. $1.50

1. Fire prevention. 2. Insurance, Fire—Inspectors.   I. Title.
Library of Congress   HG9715.N3   1929
                                                29—7381

NN   0051453   DLC OC1U

National Fire Protection Association.
The field work of the National Fire Protection Association; is it worth sustaining?...   Boston, 1924.   8 p.   8°.

1. Fires—Prevention and extinction—   U.S.
N. Y. P. L.   September 28, 1926

NN   0051454   NN

              National Fire Protection Association.
Uit12   Financial report.
N23q   Boston.
                                                23cm.

NN   0051455   CtY

NATIONAL FIRE PROTECTION ASSOCIATION.
    Fire alarm central stations,[by W.J.Carroll].
Boston,Mass.,1929.

    pp.19. Illustr.
    "From Quarterly of the National Fire Protection Association. April 1924. Revised and reprinted."

NN   0051456   MH

National fire protection association.
Fire and the air war; a compilation of expert observations on fires of the war set by incendiaries and the atomic bombs, wartime fire fighting, and the work of the fire protection engineers who helped plan the destruction of enemy cities and industrial plants. Edited by Horatio Bond, chief engineer, N. F. P. A. Boston, Mass., National fire protection association, international [1946]
xii, 262 p.   illus. (incl. maps) diagrs.   23½ᶜᵐ.
"First printing, August, 1946."
"A partial bibliography": p. 253-255.
1. Fire prevention. 2. Fires. 3. Atomic bomb. 4. Projectiles, Incendiary.   I. Bond, Horatio, ed.   II. Title.

UG447.N3   623.45   47—448

            ICJ
NN   0051457   DLC CaBViP WaS MH NNC NcRS NcD NIC

UG447   National Fire Protection Association.
.N3   Fire and the air war; a compilation
1951   of expert observations on fires of the
          war set by incendiaries and the atomic
          bombs, wartime fire fighting, and the
          work of the fire protection engineers
          who helped plan the destruction of
          enemy cities and industrial plants.
          Edited by Horatio Bond. Boston [1951,
          c1946]
              xii, 262 p. illus., maps, diagrs.
          24 cm.
              "A partial bibliography": p. 253-255.
              1. Fire prevention. 2. Fires.
          3. Atomic bomb. 4. Projectiles,
          Incendiary.   I. Bond, Horatio, ed.
          II. Title.

NN   0051458   [1] MB

National Fire Protection Association.
The fire at the Edison Phonograph Works, New Jersey, U. S. A. of December, 1914, being a report by F. J. T. Stewart...   London: British Fire Prevention Committee, 1916.   61 p. (incl. plans, pl., 3 fold. plans, 2 fold. tables.   8°.   (British Fire Prevention Committee.   Red books, no. 204.)

1. Fires, U. S.: N. J.: West Orange,   1914. 2. Fireproof construction.—
Factories. 3. Stewart, F. J. T. 4.   Series.
N. Y. P. L.   January 2, 1917.

NN   0051459   NN

National fire protection association.
Fire defense; a compilation of available material on air-set fires, bombs and sabotage, civilian defense, fire fighting and the safeguarding of industrial production for defense. Edited by Horatio Bond, chief engineer N. F. P. A. Boston, Mass., National fire protection association, international [1941]
x, 221 p. illus. (incl. plans) 23ᵐ.
Pages 220-221, advertising matter.
"A selected bibliography": p. 214-215.
1. Fire prevention. 2. Air defenses. 3. Projectiles, Incendiary.
I. Bond, Horatio, ed. II. Title.
Library of Congress   TH9145.N35   41-51785
                                        [30]

            KEmT CU MU Wa MH OOxM OC1 OLak TU ICJ DAL
NN   0051460   DLC OrU IdU CaBVa Or NcD NcRS NcC MiD

National fire protection association.
Fire defense in munitions production; principles for the guidance of manufacturers engaged in the production of munitions ...   Boston, Mass., National fire protection association [*1941]
cover-title, 52 p. illus. (incl. map, plans) 23ᵐ.
"A reprint of part vi, Defense production, from the N. F. P. A. book Fire defense, published ... 1941."
1. Mill and factory buildings—Fires and fire prevention. 2. Munitions.
I. Title.
Library of Congress   TH9445.M4N34   42-16283
                                        [2]   614.84

NN   0051461   DLC

NATIONAL FIRE PROTECTION ASSOCIATION.
Fire defense programs; suggestions for defense councils and committees. A staff report... Boston, Mass.: National fire protection assoc. [1941]   11 p.   22½cm.

1. Fires in war time. I. Title.

NN   0051462   DLC IU MH

National fire protection association.
A fire department manual; hose and hose couplings. Informative material on the selection, care and testing of hose and hose couplings, compiled from recommendations of N. F. P. A. committees and other authoritative sources ... Boston, Mass., National fire protection association, international [1937]
cover-title, 40 p. incl. illus., form. 22½ᵐ.
1. Hose. 2. Hose-couplings.   I. Title. II. Title: Hose and hose couplings.
Library of Congress   TH9380.N35   42-3678

NN   0051463   DLC WaS OC1 NN

National fire protection association.

Bond, Horatio.
A fire department manual; hose and ladder work, by Horatio Bond ... and Warren Y. Kimball ... Boston, Mass., National fire protection association, international [1939]

VOLUME 407

National fire protection association.
... Fire department members news-letter. no. 1–9 (Dec., 1936 – May, 1939). Boston, 1936–39. 9 nos. 28cm.

Irregular.
Reproduced from typewritten copy.
No more published.

1. Firemen—Assoc. and org.—   U. S.
N. Y. P. L.   May 13, 1941

NN   0051465   NN

National Fire Protection Association
.·. Fire fighting equipment in metal mines.
see under American Standards Association.

[National fire protection association]
Fire losses in the U.S. $30,000 an hour and what individuals and communities can do to reduce them.
[n.p., 1912?]

HG9748
.N3

NN   0051467   DLC

National Fire Protection Association.
Fire news
see under title

National Fire Protection Association.
Fire prevention clean-up campaign. A clean house seldom burns... Boston: National Fire Protection Assoc., 1927.
7 p.   8°.

405651A. 1. Fires—Prevention and   extinction.
N. Y. P. L.   March 14, 1929

NN   0051469   NN CtY DNAL

National Fire Protection Association.   614.84 S100
.... Fire Prevention Day handbook. Suggestions for guidance in planning the observance of Fire Prevention Day. .... [Boston, Mass., 1921.]
cover-title, 47, [1] p. illus. 23¼cm.
At head of title: National Fire Protection Association.
——— Suggestions for ... Fire and Accident Prevention Day (fire section) ... for public parade, school exercises, ... [Boston, 1921.]
cover-title, 28 p. 23¼cm.
At head of title: National Fire Protection Association and National Safety Council cooperating.
——— Suggested programs for ... Fire Prevention Day. .... [Boston, 1921.]
cover-title, 15 p. 23¼cm.
Bound together.

NN   0051470   ICJ NN DL MB

TH9445
D9N3   **National Fire Protection Association.**
1953   Fire prevention standards for homes and camps in forested areas, September 1953.
Boston, 1953.
21 p. 19 cm. (Its NFPA no. 224)
Bibliography: p. 18.

1. Fire prevention. 2. Dwellings - Fires and fire prevention. 3. Camps - Fires and fire prevention.

NN   0051471   DI

National fire protection association.
... Fire prevention week handbook; suggestions for guidance in planning the observance of fire prevention week ... [Boston, 1924]

cover-title, 48 p. illus. 23cm.
At head of title: National fire protection association, international.

1. Fire prevention. i. Title.

                                              24–25613

Library of Congress   TH9148.N29

NN   0051472   DLC NN

National fire protection association.
... Fire prevention week handbook; suggestions for guidance in planning the observance of fire prevention week. 5th ed. ... [Boston, 1926]
cover-title, 48 p. illus. 23cm.
At head of title: National fire protection association, international.
TH9148.N29 1926
——— Fire prevention week supplement 1926; fire facts, texts, slogans ... contributed by T. Alfred Fleming ... Montague Glass [and others] ... for fire prevention week, October 3–9, 1926 ... Boston, Mass., National fire protection association [1926]
15, [1] p. 23cm.
1. Fire prevention.   i. Title.
                                              26–16679
Library of Congress   TH9148.N29 1926 Suppl.

NN   0051473   DLC MH OU MB

National Fire Protection Association.
... Fire prevention week handbook; suggestions for [guidance in planning the observance of] fire prevention week. 6th ed. ... (Boston, 1931)
cover-title, 48 p. illus. 23 cm.
At head of title: Fire prevention week.
———Fire prevention week supplement 1926; fire facts, texts, slogans ... contributed by T. Alfred Fleming ... (and others) ... for fire prevention week, October 4–10, 1931 ... Boston, Mass., National fire protection association (1931)

? p.   23 cm.
I. Fire prevention.

NN   0051475   DHEW OU

NATIONAL FIRE PROTECTION ASSOCIATION.
Fire prevention week handbook; suggestions for the organization and conduct of fire prevention week. [Boston, 1935].

pp.48. Illustr.
"6th ed., (2d printing)."

NN   0051476   MH

TH9111   **National Fire Service Officers' Association.**
.F754
Fire protection and accident prevention review.

[London, Benn Bros., etc.]

National Fire Protection Association.
Fire protection and prevention for summer homes in forested areas ...
see under National Fire Protection Association. Forest Committee.

National fire protection association.

Conference on fire protection engineering. *Massachusetts institute of technology, 1942.*
Fire protection engineering; a symposium of papers presented at a summer conference at the Massachusetts institute of technology, Cambridge, Massachusetts, June, 1942. Boston, Mass., National fire protection association [1943]

National fire protection association.
Fire protection for hospitals, asylums, and similar institutions
see under Forster, Hans Walter, 1883–

National fire protection association.
Fire protection for schools
see under Forster, Hans Walter, 1883–

TH9150   **National Fire Protection Association.**
.F47
Fire protection handbook.
Boston [etc.]

National fire protection association.
... Fire protection in schools ... [Boston, 1916?]
16 p. illus. (incl. maps, plans, charts) 26¼cm.
Illus. t.-p.
At head of title: National fire protection association ... Boston, Mass.

1. School-houses—Fires and fire prevention. [1. Fire prevention—School-houses] i. Title.
                                              E 16–409
Library, U. S. Bur. of   Education LB3248.N22

NN   0051483   DHEW OO MiU OU NN

National fire protection association.
Fire protection regulations for motor craft, pleasure and commercial (part D: Regulations governing marine fire hazards) ... Prepared and revised by Marine section, National fire protection association. [Boston, Mass.] 1937. 30 p. 16½cm.

"This [pam]phlet is a complete revision of Appendix D: Regulations governing marine fire hazards, edition of 1930."

1. Motor boats. 2. Fires—Pre-   vention and extinction.
N. Y. P. L.   March 10, 1938

NN   0051484   NN

National fire protection association.
Fire protection regulations for motor craft, pleasure and commercial. (Part D, regulations governing marine fire hazards) Prepared and revised by Marine section, National fire protection association. Boston, Mass., National fire protection, 1939.
v.

NN   0051485   OU

National fire protection association.
FOR OTHER EDITIONS
SEE MAIN ENTRY
U. S. *Bureau of chemistry and soils.*
... Fire-protective construction on the farm. [Prepared by the bureaus of chemistry and soils, public roads, and agricultural economics, in cooperation with the National fire protection association. Washington, U. S. Govt. print. off., 1929]

National fire protection association.
Fire record of cities, 1943. Bost. [The Author] 1944.
14 p. illus.

Reprint from Quarterly, April, 1944 (Revised edition)

NN   0051487   MiD

VOLUME 407

[National fire protection association]
⊙Fire waste overtaking insurance capitol.
[n.p., 1912?]

HG9748
.N4

NN   0051488   DLC 00

TH9111 National Fire Protection Association.
.V6
Firemen. v. 1–   Oct. 1933–
[Boston] National Fire Protection Association.

TH1093 National Fire Protection Association.
N3   Fires in "fireproof" buildings. Boston,
c1950.
31 p. illus.

"Reprinted from Quarterly of the National
Fire Protection Association"

1. Fires. 2. Building, Fire-proof.
I. Title.

NN   0051490   CU

National fire protection association.
Fires in hospitals and institutions ... Boston, Mass., National fire protection association, °1945.
48 p. illus., diagrs. 23ᵐ.

1. Hospitals—Fires and fire prevention. 2. Asylums—Fires and fire prevention. 3. Fires—U. S. I. Title.
                                                    46–5678
Library of Congress   TH9445.H7N3

NN   0051491   DLC MnU-B OrU-M

National fire protection association.
Fires in one year of war, Dec. 7, 1941 – Dec. 7, 1942... Boston: National fire protection assoc. [1942] 15 p. 27cm.

1. Fires—U. S., 1942.
N. Y. P. L.   February 9, 1944

'NN   0051492   NN OCl OrP

National fire protection association.
Fires in the second year of war, Dec. 7, 1942–Dec. 7, 1943 ... Boston, Mass., National fire protection association, international [1943]
23 p. 27 x 21½ᵐ.

1. Fires—U. S. I. Title.
                                                    44–34104
Library of Congress   TH9503.N19
                                [2]   614.84

NN   0051493   DLC NNC

National Fire Protection Association.
Flammable liquid trade name index,
July 1954. Boston, c1954.
80 p. 19cm.
Cover title.
At head of title: NFPA no. 325A.

1. Inflammable liquids.   I. Title.

NN   0051494   MB WaS PP

National Fire Protection Association.
Flammable liquids, gases, chemicals and explosives. Comp. by Robert S. Moulton. Boston, 1948.
608 p. diagrs., tables. (Its National fire codes, v.1)
"Revised to December 31, 1947."

I. Series. II. Moulton, Robert Selden, 1894–

NN   0051495   ICJ

R614.83 NATIONAL fire protection association.
N213FLa   Flash point index of trade name liquids.
Boston.

Preceded by its Flammable liquid trade name index.

NN   0051496   WaS

National fire protection association.
Food dehydration, by Gerald W. Hallowell ... Boston, Mass., National fire protection association, international [1944]
cover-title, 19, [1] p. incl. illus., diagr. 23cm.

1. Drying apparatus--Food. I. Title.
2. Food, Dried.

NN   0051497   MB

National fire protection association.
[Fourth of July circular] [Boston, 1914]
[4] p.

NN   0051498   OU

296.6
N21G   National Fire Protection Association.
Gasoline on the farm. [Boston, 1948]
folder ([4] p.)

NN   0051499   DNAL

National Fire Protection Association.
Guide for hotel fire safety law, 1948 ...
see under   National Fire Protection
Association. Fire marshals' section.
Committee on model hotel fire safety law.

National Fire Protection Association.
... A guide for training auxiliary fireman ...
see under   National Fire Protection Association. Committee on Firemen's Training.

National Fire Protection Association.
Handbook of fire protection
see   Fire protection handbook.

National Fire Protection Association.
Handling hose and ladders

see under

National Fire Protection Association.
Committee on Firemen's Training.

National Fire Protection Association.
Holiday fire bulletin. A mercantile sacrifice to Christmas decorations. Boston: the assoc. [1912] 2 l. 4°.

1. Fires.—Prevention : Associations.   U. S.
N. Y. P. L.   April 14, 1914.

NN   0051504   NN

National Fire Protection Association.
Holiday fire bulletin. A mercantile sacrifice to Christmas decorations. Boston, [1914]. 2 l. illus. 4°.

1. Fires.—Prevention, etc.
N. Y. P. L.   August 27, 1914.

NN   0051505   NN OU

National Fire Protection Association.   4011.93
Holiday fire bulletin.
= Boston. [1916.] (4) pp. Illus. 28 cm.

L1320 — Fire. Prevention.

NN   0051506   MB

National Fire Protection Association.
Hospital fire safety, 1949. Boston [1949]
136 p. illus. 23 cm. (Its NFPA no. 104)
Cover title.

1. Hospitals—Fires and fire prevention.   I. Title.   (Series)
TH9115.N28 no. 104   614.84   50–1252 rev

NN   0051507   DLC WaS ICRL CU MnU-B DNLM OrU OrU-M

National Fire Protection Association.
Hospital fire safety, 1951. 2. ed. Boston
[c1951]
144 p. illus., plans. 23cm.
At head of title: NFPA no. 104.
Cover title.

1. Hospitals—Fires and fire prevention.

NN   0051508   MB DNLM DI

TH9445 National Fire Protection Association.
H7N35   Hospital fire safety. 3d ed.   Boston
1954   [c1954]
176p. illus. 23cm. (Its [publication, no.104]

Cover title.

1. Hospitals - Fires and fire prevention.
I. Title.

NN   0051509   IaU NIC

National Fire Protection Association.   4011.90
Independence Day: 1916.
= Boston. [1916.] (4) pp. Illus. 28 cm.
A plea for a sane Fourth of July.

K9204 — Fourth of July.

NN   0051510   MB

VOLUME 407

A614.841 National fire protection association.
N2131   Index. I. Publications on fire
prevention and fire protection avail -
able in the files of the National fire
protection association. II. Index to
subjects covered in the printed records
from September 30, 1928, to September
30, 1929 ... Boston, 1929.
28p.

NN 0051511   IU DL

National fire protection association
... Index. 1. Publications on fire prevention and fire protection available in the
files of the National fire protection association. II. Index to subjects covered in the
printed records from September 30, 1926, to
December 31, 1941.... Boston, National fire
protection association, international ₁1942₎
72 p.

Part 2, Quarterly of the National fire
protection association.
Cover title.

NN 0051513   OCl

National fire protection association.
... Index to publications ...
1911, 1913, 1916, 1918, 1920, 1926.
1934-
Boston, Mass., National fire protection
association, 1911-26.
v. in   23 cm.
1926 index covers all material from
1896 to September 30, 1926.
Title varies: 1911, Index to subjects
covered in the printed records; 1913-1926,
Publications on the subjects of fire preven-

tion and fire protection available in the files,
and Index to subjects covered in the printed
records; 1934-1941, Index. I. Publications
on fire prevention and fire protection available in the files of the National fire protection association. II. Index to subjects covered
in the printed records from September 30, 1926,
to [December 31, 1941] ... 1945
Index to publications ... [Part I. The various
books and separate pamphlets currently available for distribution. Part II. The general index of all material published by the Association

during the period covered.
1. Fire prevention - Bibl. 2. Fire extinction - Bibl.
The following indexes were issued as part 2
of various numbres of the Quarterly of the National fire protection association: Sept. 30, 1926-
Jan. 2, 1934, issued at v. 27, no. 3, part.
Sept. 30, 1926 - Jan. 2, 1937, issued as v. 30,
no. 3, part 2. Sept. 30, 1926 - Dec. 31, 1941,
issued as v. 35, no. 3, part 2. Jan. 1, 1942—
Jan. 1, 1945, issued as v. 38, no. 3, part 2.

NN 0051516   CU

National Fire Protection Association.   4014.91
Index to subjects covered in the printed records.
=Chicago. 1909. 47, (1) pp. 23 cm.

H6432 — Fire. Prevention. Bibl.

NN 0051517   MB

National fire protection association.
... Index to subjects covered in the printed records,
January, 1911. ₁Boston, F. Wood, printer, 1911₎
51, ₁1₎ p. 23ᶜᵐ.
At head of title: National fire protection association.

1. Fire prevention—Bibl. 2. Fire extinction—Bibl.

12–37056

Library of Congress   HG9753.A1N6

NN 0051518   DLC

National Fire Protection Association.
Individual liability for fires due to carelessness or neglect.
Suggested state law and arguments therefor. Boston: the assoc.,
1915. 23 p. 8°.

1. Fires.—Jurisprudence. 2. Title.
N. Y. P. L.   September 28, 1915.

NN 0051519   NN OU MB MH

NATIONAL FIRE PROTECTION ASSOCIATION.
Individual liability for fires due to carelessness or neglect; state laws and city ordinances and arguments therefor. Boston, 1935.

pp.15.

NN 0051520   MH

National fire protection association.
Industrial fire brigades training manual, edited by Emmett T. Cox ... W. Fred Heisler ... and Horatio Bond ... as
a subcommittee of the Firemen's training committee, National fire protection association. Boston, Mass., National
fire protection association international, ᶜ1943.

viii, 176 p. illus. 28 x 21½ cm.

On cover : 1st ed.
Bibliography at end of some of the chapters.

1. Factories—Fires and fire prevention. I. Cox, Emmett T., ed.
II. Title.

TH9445.M4N35   658.284   43–8831 rev

NN 0051521   DLC DNAL MiD OrP WaS ViU TU IU OU OCl

National fire protection association.
Industrial fire brigades training manual. 2d ed. Sponsored by Committee on firemen's training. Boston, National
fire protection association, international, ᶜ1946.

4 p. l., 188 p. illus., diagrs. 23 cm.

"A revision and rearrangement of the first edition issued in 1943."—
Pref.
Bibliography at end of some of the chapters.

1. Factories—Fires and fire prevention. I. Title.

TH9445.M4N35 1946   658.284   47–2285 rev

NN 0051522   DLC MB OrP WaS PPUSDA

NATIONAL FIRE PROTECTION ASSOCIATION.
Industrial fire brigades training manual. 2. ed. ...   Boston.
c1946 [i. e. 1951] 188 p. illus. 23cm.

Issued 1951.

1. Fires— Prevention and extinction. 2. Firemen— Training— U. S.

NN 0051523   NN

National Fire Protection Association.
Industrial fire brigades training manual, by Horatio Bond,
chief engineer, and Warren Y. Kimball, manager, Fire Services Dept. ₁3d ed.₎ Boston, ᶜ1954.

158 p. illus. 28 cm.

1. Factories—Fires and fire prevention. I. Bond, Horatio.
II. Title.

TH9445.M4N35 1954   *614.84 658.284   54–12296 ‡

NN 0051524   DLC OrP WaS CaBVa IU AAP CLSU NN MB

National Fire Protection Association.
... International publications on the subjects of
fire prevention and fire protection available in the
files and index to subjects covered in the printed
records. Correct to May 1, 1923. Boston
National fire protection association, [1923?]
79 p.

NN 0051525   WaU

National Fire Protection Association.
Large loss fires ₁of₎ 1944. Boston ₁1945₎
47 p. illus., map.

"Reprinted from January, 1945, Quarterly."

NN 0051526   NNC

National Fire Protection Association.   *4014.94
[Leaflets, programs, etc.]
= [New York? 1911.] Various sizes.

H6430 — Fire. Prevention.

NN 0051527   MB

National Fire Protection Association.
Lessons from dust explosions
see under   National Fire Protection
Association.   Committee on Dust Explosion
Hazards.

National fire protection association.

National board of fire underwriters.
... List of electrical fittings, pub. by the National board
of fire underwriters at the recommendation of Underwriters' laboratories, inc., following examinations and
tests conducted under the standards of the National electrical code as recommended by the National fire protection association ...
₁Chicago₎ 19

National fire protection association.

National board of fire underwriters.
List of manufacturers of fire appliances, pub. by the
National board of fire underwriters at the recommendation of underwriters' laboratories, inc., following examinations and tests conducted under standards recommended by the National fire protection association.

Chicago

National fire protection association.
Magnesium and its alloys...
see under   Hirst, Heston S.

National fire protection association.
Melvin apartment house fire, Boston, Mass.,
April 14, 1914... ₁Chicato, 1914.₎
4 p.

NN 0051532   OU

TH9111   National Fire Protection Association. Member-
.N2   ship directory.

National Fire Protection Association.
Year book, officers and committees.   –1932/33.
Boston.

NATIONAL FIRE PROTECTION ASSOCIATION.
The menace of the wooden shingle. n.p.,
[192-].

pp.16,₂2₎. Illustr.
Cover serves as title-page.
2nd edition.

NN 0051534   MH

VOLUME 407

National Fire Protection Association.   L368.06161 31
[Minor publications.]
5269
b   Includes educational publications, special bulletins, fire reports and news
letters.

NN   0051535   ICJ

National fire protection association
⌐Miscellaneous publications⌐

Open entry.

NN   0051536   MiD

S
791.6   National Fire Protection Association.
N27   Model state fireworks law. Boston, 1941.
7 p. 24 cm.

1. Fireworks. Laws and regulations. U.S.
I. Title.

NN   0051537   N

National fire protection association.
Must stores burn? ... Boston, ⌐1946.
48 p. illus. 23⌐.

1. Mercantile buildings—Fires and fire prevention.
TH9445.S8N3   614.84   47–21638
     Brief cataloging

NN   0051538   DLC

National Fire Protection Association.
NFPA.
Boston.
no. in   v. illus., diagrs. 22 cm.
Many no. in rev. editions.

1. Fire prevention—Collected works.
TH9115.N28   614.841082   56–36486 ‡

NN   0051539   DLC FU

National Fire Protection Association.
NFPA handbook of fire protection
    see   Fire protection handbook.

TK260
.N2   National Fire Protection Association.

NFPA handbook of the National electrical code. 1932–
New York, McGraw-Hill.

National Fire Protection Association.
NFPA inspection manual. 1st-
ed.; 1950–
⌐Boston⌐
v. illus. 17 cm.

1. Fire prevention—Inspection. 2. Insurance, Fire—Inspectors.
I. Title.
TH9176.N48   614.84   63–40314
     rev

NN   0051542   DLC NN NcU MB DNAL ICJ OrP WaS CaBVa

National Fire Protection Association.
NFPA technical committee reports.

Boston.
v. illus. 20 cm.
Vols. for   issued in parts.

1. Fire prevention—United States—Laws and regulations—Con-
gresses. I. Title.
TH9503.N19a   628.9'22   73–647042
ISSN 0077-4553   MARC-S

NN   0051543   DLC

National fire protection association.
The Nashua conflagration, May 4, 1930 ... Boston, National fire protection association ⌐1930⌐
cover-title, 19, ⌐1⌐ p. illus. (incl. map) 23⌐.

1. Nashua, N. H.—Fire, 1930. I. Title.
                           CA 30–1375 Unrev'd
Library of Congress   F44.N2N32   974.28

NN   0051544   DLC WaS MB NN

National Fire Protection Association.
Nashville conflagration; sweeping fire in residential section
of Nashville, Tennessee, March 22nd, 1916... Special report by
Tennessee Inspection Bureau... Boston, 1916. 3 l., 1 fold.
map, 1 fold. pl. 4°.

At head of title: National Fire Protection Association.

1. Fires, U. S.: Tenn.: Nashville.
N. Y. P. L.   July 7, 1916.

NN   0051545   NN OU CtY

National Fire Protection Association.
National defense fires. [Boston, 1941]
[20] p. illus. 28 cm.
1. Fire prevention. 2. Fires. 3. U.S.
Defenses. I. Title.

NN   0051546   DNAL OCl

National fire protection association.
National defense fires. 2d ed. ⌐Boston⌐ National fire protection association ⌐1942⌐
⌐23⌐ p. illus. 27½ x 21⌐.
Mainly illustrations.

1. Fires—U. S. I. Title.
                           42–51019
Library of Congress   TH9448.N3 1942
       ⌐2⌐   614.84

NN   0051547   DLC NN NBuG

National fire protection association.
National defence fires. 3d ed. ⌐Boston⌐ National fire protection association ⌐1942⌐
⌐24⌐ p. illus. 27½ x 21⌐.
Mainly illustrations.

1. Fires—U. S. I. Title.
                           45–3844
Library of Congress   TH9448.N3 1942 a
       ⌐2⌐   614.84

NN   0051548   DLC NBuG

National Fire Protection Association.
National fire codes. 1938–

Boston.
v. in   illus. 20-30 cm. annual.
Titles varies slightly.
Issued in parts.

1. Fire prevention — United States — Periodicals. 2. Fire extinction—Periodicals. I. Title.
TH9111.N375a   614.8'41'0973   38–27236
            rev 3   MARC-S

OClW PSt MiU MB
NcRS MnU NIC ICJ IU OrU OLak NBuU CtY NcD MiHM
WaT ViU UCl OrCS NcC CLL GU PPT NjN ViU-L NcD Mi
LU NNC Or IdU PPAtR PPPEC MH PP CU OClW OrP CU
OrCS NcU DNAL NbU AzU Wa MsSM WaS InU DI UU NSyU
NN   0051549   DLC DSI OU OkU CaBVaU CaBVa NN TxU TU

TK260   National Fire Protection Association.
.N38

National Board of Fire Underwriters.
National electrical code. Standard ... for electric wiring
and apparatus as recommended by the National Fire Protection Association. American standard approved ... by American Standards Association.

⌐New York⌐

National fire protection association.
The National fire protection association,
1896-1946. ⌐1946⌐
cover-title, 32 p. illus., ports.

"By Percy Bugbee."
I. Bugbee, Percy   jt. au.

NN   0051552   NNC OrP

NATIONAL FIRE PROTECTION ASSOCIATION.
National standard fire hose couplings and fire department hose connections for sprinkler and standpipe systems.
Boston, Mass.: National Fire Protection Assoc. [1934]
11 p. illus. 16cm.

868235A. 1. Hose, Fire—Couplings.

NN   0051553   NN OU

National fire protection association.
News letter.
Boston,
27⌐.
Later title: Fire news.

1. Insurance engineering—Societies. 2. Fire prevention—Societies.
                         CA 20–121 Unrev'd
Library of Congress   TH9201.N3

NN   0051554   DLC DNAL OU OCl MB NN

National Fire Protection Association.
News letter
    see also   Fire news.

614.84   National Fire Protection Association.
N213oc   Occupancy fire record. Fire record bulletin.
FR 54-1-
1954-
Boston.
v. illus., diagrs. 28cm. irregular.

Some nos. issued in rev. editions.
Numbering consists of year and no., i.e.,
54-1 is first issue for 1954.
None issued in 1959.

NN   0051556   IU

VOLUME 407

TH9111   **National Fire Protection Association. Officers**
.N2   **and committees.**

     National Fire Protection Association.
     Year book, officers and committees.   -1932/33.
     Boston.

614.84   National fire protection association.
N213s   1000 school fires ...   Boston, Mass., National
1939   fire protection association [1939]
      72p. illus., diagrs.

     "Reprinted from Quarterly, October, 1939."
     "Designed to supersede the pamphlet, School
     fires."

     1. Fire prevention. 2. Schools--Fires and fire
     prevention. I. Title. II. Title: School fires.

    NN   0051558   IU OCl

     National Fire Protection Association.
     Operating fire department pumpers

     see under

     Kimball, Warren Young.

     National fire protection association.
TH9503
.N17
     National board of fire underwriters.
     An ordinance providing for fire limits and the construction
     and equipment of buildings in small towns and villages, recom-
     mended by the National board of fire underwriters, New York,
     N. Y., and the National fire protection association, Boston, Mass.
     1st ed. [New York?] 1914.

NATIONAL FIRE PROTECTION ASSOCIATION.
     Organization plan for fire prevention commit-
tee work. Boston, 1935.

     pp.(2).
     "4th ed."
     Issued by Field Service Department.

    NN   0051561   MH

     National Fire Protection Association.
     Outside stairs for fire exits; recommendations
     for their construction and installation ...
     see under   National Fire Protection
     Association. Committee on Safety to Life.

     National fire protection association.
     Pamphlets. [Chicago, Boston, etc.,
     1905-   ]
     6 v. illus., plates (part col., fold.)
     maps (part fold. tables, diagrs.   17-28 cm.
     Binder's title.
     Includes folded broadsides and posters;
     some pamphlets are folded.
     Includes pamphlets jointly sponsored by
     the National fire protection association and
     the National board of fire underwriters.

    NN   0051563   CU

National Fire Protection Association.   **614.84 5**
     [Papers and addresses.]
157790   Mostly extracts or reprints from various serials.

    NN   0051564   ICJ

National Fire Protection Association.
     Paris, Texas, conflagration, March 21st, 1916...   Boston,
1916.   4 l.   illus. (incl. diagr.)   4°.

     At head of title: National Fire Protection Association.

     1. Fires, U. S.: Texas: Paris.
   N. Y. P. L.   July 7, 1916.

    NN   0051565   NN OU MB

     National Fire Protection Association. A partial
TH9111   **record of the transactions at annual meeting.**
.N18

     National Fire Protection Association.
     Proceedings of annual meeting.   1st-35th; 1897-1931.
     Boston.

     National Fire Protection Association.
     Photo contest fire photographs. 1951-
     [Boston]
     v. illus. 24 cm.

     1. Photography—Yearbooks.   2. Photography—Competitions.
     3. Fires.   i. Title.
     TR1.N275   779.961484   52-43421

    NN   0051567   DLC

D669.11   National fire protection association.
N21   Preventing cutting and welding fires. [Bos-
     ton] National fire protection association
     [1942]
     [16] p. illus. 21½cm.

     1. Fire prevention. 2. Welding.

    NN   0051568   NNC OU

     National Fire Protection Association.
     Proceedings of annual meeting. 1st-
     1897-
     Boston.
       v. in   illus. 24 cm.
     Title varies: 1897   A partial record of the transactions at
     annual meeting.
     Issues for 19   -08 published in Chicago.
     Issued 1932-   as pt. 2 of each July number of the association's
     Quarterly.

     1. Fire prevention—Societies, etc.

     TH9111.N18   614.8406273   2-21120 rev 2*

    NN   0051569   DLC WaS ICRL ICJ NcD OrP CU DL

National Fire Protection Association.   **368.06161 36**
     Program ... annual meeting of the National Fire Protection
187797   Association ... [Boston, 1912-.]
     Library has no. 16, 1912, to date. 13½ᶜᵐ.
     Cover-title.
     Wanting: no, 24, 28-30, 1920, 1924-1926.

    NN   0051570   ICJ CU

     National fire protection association.
     Proposed code for explosion and fire protection in plants pro-
     ducing or handling magnesium powder or dust...   Boston:
     National fire protection assoc., 1943.   12 p.   23cm.

     1. Magnesium.   2. Fires—Pre-   vention and extinction.
   N. Y. P. L.   September 27, 1943

    NN   0051571   NN

     National fire protection association
     Proposed code for the prevention of dust ex-
     plosions in the plastics industry... Boston,
     National fire protection association, 1945.
     22 p. tables, diagrs.

     Cover-title

    NN   0051572   OCl

     National fire protection association.
     Protection of records; consolidated reports
     of the Committee on protection of records ...
     see under   National Fire Protection
     Association. Committee on Protection of
     Records.

     National Fire Protection Association
     A public relations manual for fire departments.
     [Boston, ᶜ1947]
     30 p. illus.

    NN   0051574   MiD

TH9111   National fire protection association.
N3P2   ... Publications on the subjects of fire
     prevention and fire protection available in
     the files and Index to subjects covered in
     the printed records

     Boston, Mass., National fire protection
     association, 19-
       vols.   23cm.

     Title varies; 1929, Index ...

     1. Fire prevention.--Bibliography.
     2. Fire extinction.--Bibliography.
     I. National fire protection association.
     Index to subjects covered in the
     printed records.

    NN   0051576   NBuG

National Fire Protection Association.   ***4014.91**
     Publications on the subjects of fire prevention and fire protection
     available in the files and index to subjects, covered in the printed
     records.   January, 1909; June, 1913; January, 1916.
     Boston [etc. 1909-15].   3 v.   23 cm.
     The 1909 edition contains only index to subjects covered in the printed
     records.

     K7500 — Fire. Prevention. Bibl.

    NN   0051577   MB OCl ICJ NN IU

     National fire protection association.
     ... Publications on the subjects of fire prevention and
     fire protection available in the files; and Index to subjects
     covered in the printed records, September 1, 1918.   Bos-
     ton, National fire protection association [1918]
     83 p. 23ᶜᵐ.

     1. Fire prevention—Bibl.   2. Fire extinction—Bibl.

                                   18-21675

     Library of Congress   Z5853.F6N2   1918

    NN   0051578   DLC

     National fire protection association.
     ... Publications on the subjects of fire prevention and
     fire protection available in the files, and Index to subjects
     covered in the printed records, September, 1920.   Bos-
     ton, National fire protection association [1920]
     88 p. 22½ᶜᵐ.
     At head of title: National fire protection association (International)

     1. Fire prevention—Bibl.   2. Fire extinction—Bibl.

                                     21-3583

     Library of Congress   Z5853.F6N2   1920

    NN   0051579   DLC DL

VOLUME 407

Z5853 National Fire Protection Association.
.F6 ... Publications on the subjects of fire pre-
N2 vention and fire protection available in the files
1923 and Index to subjects covered in the printed records. Correct to May 1, 1923. Boston, **Mass.**,
National Fire Protection Association ₁1923₎
79p. 23cm.

At head of title: National fire protection
association international.

1. Fire prevention - Bibl. 2. Fire extinction
- Bibl.

NN 0051580 PSt MH DL

National fire protection association.
... Publications on the subjects of fire prevention and fire
protection available in the files, and Index to subjects covered
in the printed records corrected to September 30, 1926. Boston, Mass., National fire protection association ₁1926₎
87 p. 22½ᶜᵐ.
At head of title: National fire protection association, international.

1. Fire prevention—Bibl. 2. Fire extinction— Bibl.

Library of Congress Z5853.F6N2 1926 27–426

NN 0051581 DLC WaS ICJ

National Fire Protection Association.
Quarterly. v. 1–
July 1907–
Boston.
v. illus., plans (part fold.) 24 cm.
Issues for July 1907– published in Hartford.
Beginning in 1932, pt. 2 of each July issue is the association's
Proceedings.
Beginning in 1933, pt. 2 of each October issue is the association's
year book and directory.
Pt. 2 of January issues, 1934, 1937, 1942, 1945 are lists of and sub-
ject indexes to, the association's publications, Sept. 30, 1926–Jan. 1,
1945.
1. Fire prevention—Societies, etc.

TH9111.N3 614.8406273 12–20232 rev*

WvU AzU NcU MB CU ICRL NNC NN DL WaS
NN 0051582 DLC OC1 NNC ICJ IU LU PPF OU MiU TxU

TP757 National fire protection association.
.N3
1932 **National board of fire underwriters.**
Recommended good practice requirements of the National
board of fire underwriters for the installation, maintenance and
use of piping and fittings for city gas as recommended by the
National fire protection association. Effective December 1,
1932. New York, N. Y., Chicago, Ill. ₁etc.₎ National board of
fire underwriters ₁1932₎

National fire protection association.
Recommended requirements for flameproofing
of textiles ...
see under National Fire Protection
Association. Committee on Fireproofing and
Preservative Treatments.

National Fire Protection Association.
Recommended safe practice for hospital
operating rooms

see under

National Fire Protection Association. **Committee**
on Hospital Operating Rooms.

NATIONAL FIRE PROTECTION ASSOCIATION.
Regulations for air conditioning and blower systems,
1938 revision. Adopted by National fire protection
association 1937, 1938... Boston, Mass.: National fire
protection assoc., international, 1938. 27 p. incl.
diagrs. 23cm.

1. Ventilation—Jurisp.—U.S. 2. Blowers and exhausters.

NN 0051586 NN

TH9445 National fire protection association.
.M4N25
1937 **National board of fire underwriters.**
Regulations of the National board of fire underwriters for
paint spraying and spray booths as recommended by the National fire protection association. New York, N. Y., Chicago,
Ill. ₁etc.₎ National board of fire underwriters. 1937.

TH9445 National fire protection association.
.C6N3
1936 **National board of fire underwriters.**
... Regulations of the National board of fire underwriters
for safeguarding dry cleaning and dry dyeing plants as recommended by the National fire protection association. New York,
N. Y., Chicago, Ill. ₁etc.₎ National board of fire underwriters,
1936.

TH9363 National fire protection association.
.N27
1939 **National board of fire underwriters.**
... Regulations of the National board of fire underwriters for
the installation and operation of centrifugal fire pumps as
recommended by the National fire protection association. New
York, N. Y., Chicago, Ill. ₁etc.₎ National board of fire underwriters, 1939.

TH9176 National fire protection association.
.N27
1936 **National board of fire underwriters.**
Regulations of the National board of fire underwriters for
the installation and operation of gas systems for welding and
cutting as recommended by the National fire protection association. New York, N. Y., Chicago, Ill. ₁etc.₎ National board of
fire underwriters, 1936.

TK7271 National fire protection association.
.N3
1934 **National board of fire underwriters.**
... Regulations of the National board of fire underwriters
for the installation, maintenance and use of municipal fire
alarm systems as recommended by the National fire protection
association. Effective September 1, 1934. New York, N. Y.,
Chicago, Ill. ₁etc.₎ National board of fire underwriters ₁1934₎

TK7271 National fire protection association.
.N32
1936 **National board of fire underwriters.**
... Regulations of the National board of fire underwriters
for the installation, maintenance and use of proprietary, auxiliary and local systems for watchman, fire alarm and supervisory service, as recommended by the National fire protection
association. 1931 (With amendments made 1936) New York,
N. Y., Chicago, Ill. ₁etc.₎ National board of fire underwriters
₁1936₎

TH7697 National fire protection association.
.F2N35
1937 **National board of fire underwriters.**
Regulations of the National board of fire underwriters for
the installation of blower and exhaust systems for dust, stock
and vapor removal as recommended by the National fire protection association. New York, N. Y., Chicago, Ill. ₁etc.₎ National board of fire underwriters, 1937.

HD9156 National fire protection association.
.A2N3
1937 **National board of fire underwriters.**
... Regulations of the National board of fire underwriters
for the storage and handling of combustible fibres as recommended by the National fire protection association. New York,
N. Y., Chicago, Ill. ₁etc.₎ National board of fire underwriters,
1937.

National fire protection association.
Report of committee of the National fire protection
association on the relative fire hazard of cotton as baled
by various methods. 1902. ₁New York₎ 1902₎
83 p. illus. 23ᶜᵐ.

1. Cotton baling. I. Title: Fire hazard of cotton.

CA 17–1051 Unrev'd

Library of Congress TH9446.C7N3

NN 0051595 DLC ICJ MH-BA MB

National Fire Protection Association.
Report of secretary F. H. Wentworth at annual meeting, May
23, 1911. / n. t.-p. New York ₁1911₎. 21. 8°.

1. Fires.—Prevention of.
N. Y. P. L. October 17, 1911.

NN 0051596 NN

NATIONAL FIRE PROTECTION ASSOCIATION.
Report of the⁵Committee on field practice./
Pt.I. n.p.,[191-].

Contents:I.Manual of fire protection inspec-
tions and tests for use of inspectors,laymen,
factory superintendents,fire department inspection corps.

NN 0051597 MH

National Fire Protection Association.
Report of the committee on high pressure systems for fire
service; presented at annual meeting, May 24, 1905. / Chicago
₁1905₎. 91. 8°.

1. Fires.—Prevention, etc.: Apparatus.
N. Y. P. L. September 15, 1911.

NN 0051598 NN

National fire protection association.
Report on fire. The Edison phonograph works, Thomas
A. Edison, inc., West Orange, N. J., December 9, 1914.
Prepared jointly by the National fire protection associa-
tion and the National board of fire underwriters ... ₁New
York?₎ 1915.
61 p. illus., 3 fold. plans, 2 fold. tab. 23ᶜᵐ.

I. National board of fire underwriters. II. Title: Edison phonograph
works.

17–3240

Library of Congress TH1093.N32

NN 0051599 DLC OC1 MB IU NN

National Fire Protection Association.
Report on trailer pumpers and specifications
for auxiliary pumpers
see under National Fire Protection
Association. Committee on Municipal Fire
Apparatus.

National Fire Protection Association. 614.84 6
₁Reports, specifications, etc.₎
187731

NN 0051601 ICJ

VOLUME 407

National Fire Protection Association.
Safeguarding factory workers from fire
    see under   National Fire Protection
Association. Committee on Safety to Life.

National Fire Protection Association.
Safeguarding school children from fire. A. Planning school
buildings for safety. B. Exit drills. C. The care of school buildings... Boston: the assoc., 1916. 54 p. illus., plans. 8°.

Repr.: National Fire Protection Assoc. Proc. 1916.

1. Fires in schools.
N. Y. P. L.   October 2, 1916.

NN 0051603   NN OU IU

National fire protection association.
... Safety codes for the prevention of dust explosions. National fire protection association and United States Department
of agriculture, sponsors. Tentative American standard, approved July 2, 1925, by American engineering standards committee. January, 1927. Washington, Govt. print. off., 1927.
    iv, 40 p. 23ᶜᵐ. (Bulletin of the United States Bureau of labor statis-
tics, no. 433. Safety code series)
    At head of title: U. S. Department of labor. James J. Davis, secre-
tary. Bureau of labor statistics. Ethelbert Stewart, commissioner.
    Issued also as House doc. 526, 69th Cong., 2d sess.
    1. Accidents, ¡Industrial¡—Prevention. 2. Dust explosion. ¡2. Dust—
Explosions¡ 3. Explosions. I. U. S. Dept. of agriculture. II. Title.
                                                            L 27—56
U. S. Dept. of labor. Libr.   HD8051.A5 no. 433
    for Library of Congress   HD8051.A62 no. 433

NN 0051604   DL OrP OC1 OCU OU ICJ MB DLC

National fire protection association.
... Safety codes for the prevention of dust explosions. National fire protection association and United States Department of agriculture, sponsors. American standard, approved by the American standards association. December,
1931. Washington, U. S. Govt. print. off., 1932.
    vii, 87 p. incl. illus., tables. plates. 23 cm. (U. S. Bureau of
labor statistics. Bulletin no. 562. Safety code series)
    At head of title: United States Department of labor. W. N. Doak,
secretary. Bureau of labor statistics. Ethelbert Stewart, commissioner.
    David J. Price, chairman, of Committee on dust explosion hazards,
U. S. Bureau of chemistry and soils, Department of agriculture.

    A "Tentative American standard" was issued in 1924 as Bulletin
no. 433 of the United States Bureau of labor statistics.
    Issued also as House doc. 118, 73d Cong., 1st sess.
    ————...Supplement to Bulletin no. 562 ... Wash-
ington, U. S. Govt. print. off., 1936.
    iii, 29 p. 4 pl. on 2 l. 23 cm. (U. S. Bureau of labor statistics.
Bulletin no. 617)
    At head of title: United States Department of labor. Frances Per-
kins, secretary. Bureau of labor statistics. Isador Lubin, commissioner ...
                              HD8051.A62 no. 617
    1. Dust explosion. I. U. S. Dept. of agriculture. II. American
standards association. III. Title.
HD8051.A62   no. 562   L 32—28 rev 2
    ————Copy 3.   HD7262.N25 1932
U. S. Dept. of Labor.   Library
    for Library of Congress   ¡r57o2¡†

NN 0051606   DL CU DLC OU OCU OC1 KMK WaWW PPPEC

National Fire Protection Association.
Salem conflagration, Salem, Massachusetts,
June 25, 26, 1914 ...
    see under   Wentworth, Franklin Harcourt,
1866-

National Fire Protection Association.
Sanity versus gunpowder. ¡July 4, 1912. Statistics of Independence day in America, 1903-1911.¡ Boston: the association
¡1912¡. 21. 4°.

1. Independence day.—Celebrations.
N. Y. P. L.   August 12, 1912.

NN 0051608   NN DLC

National fire protection association.
School fires ... Boston, °1946.
    48 p. illus. 23ᵐ.

1. Schools—Fires and fire prevention.
TH9445.S3N32   614.84   47–21432
                                              Brief cataloging

NN 0051609   DLC OrU IaU

National Fire Protection Association.
School fires; a record of eight hundred and seventy-five school
fires reported to the National Fire Protection Association...
Boston, Mass. ¡1931?¡ 63 p. incl. tables. illus. (incl. plan.)
23cm.
    Cover-title.
    "The original text...appeared in the Quarterly magazine of the National Fire
Protection Association, October, 1927. The present text, prepared in June, 1931, is
completely revised, with all statistical matter brought up to date."

869643A. 1. Fires in schools—U. S.
N. Y. P. L.   February 25, 1937

NN 0051610   NN CLSU

National Fire Protection Association.
A selection of fire department terminology. –2d. ed.,
19 55. Boston.
    v. illus. 22 cm.
    Continued by: National Fire Protection Association. A selection
of fire terminology.

    1. Fire extinction—Dictionaries. I. Title. II. Title: Fire
department terminology.
TH9116.N37   56–23965

NN 0051611   DLC CaBVa NjN CLSU NN MiD MB

National Fire Protection Association.
The shame of Pittsburg, as revealed by the conflagration of
January 27th, 1917. Boston, 1917. 4 l. illus. 4°.

1. Fires. U. S.: Pa.: Pittsburg. 1917.
N. Y. P. L.   May 25, 1917.

NN 0051612   NN OU MB MiD

National fire protection association.
Soybean plant explosions ... Boston, Mass.,
National fire protection association (1936)
    12 p. illus., diagrs. 23 cm.
    Reprint from Quarterly, January, 1936,
National fire protection association.

NN 0051613   DL

National Fire Protection Association.
Specifications for construction of a standard
building ...
    see under   National Fire Protection
Association. Committee on Fire-Resistive
Construction.

National Fire Protection Association
Specifications for motor fire apparatus, 1951.
¡Boston, Mass.¡ °1951.
    42 p. (NFPA, no. 19)

    Cover title.

NN 0051615   MiD

National Fire Protection Association.
Spring 1953, clean-up and be free from fires
in fifty-three

    see under

    U.S. Dept. of Agriculture. Safety Council.

National fire protection association.
Sprinkler protection in war industries... Boston, National
fire protection assoc. ¡1943¡ 11 p. illus. 23cm.

    1. Fires—Prevention and extinc-   tion—Apparatus—Sprinkler system.
N. Y. P. L.   March 10, 1944

NN 0051617   NN

TH9338 **National Fire Protection Association.**
.N3
1946   **National Board of Fire Underwriters.**
    Standards of the National Board of Fire Underwriters
for carbon dioxide fire extinguishing systems and inert gas
for fire and explosion prevention, as recommended by the
National Fire Protection Association. Prepared by the committees on special extinguishing systems and dust explosion
hazards, National Fire Protection Association. New York,
1946.

        National fire protection association.

    National board of fire underwriters.
    ... Standards of the National board of fire underwriters for
dip tanks containing flammable liquids ... as recommended by
the National fire protection association. New York, N. Y., Chicago, Ill. ¡etc.¡ National board of fire underwriters, 1941.

TH9339 **National Fire Protection Association.**
.N3
1950   **National Board of Fire Underwriters.**
    Standards of the National Board of Fire Underwriters
for foam extinguishing systems as recommended by the National Fire Protection Association. New York, 1950.

TS1061 **National Fire Protection Association.**
.N3   FOR OTHER EDITIONS
1951   SEE MAIN ENTRY
        National Board of Fire Underwriters.
    Standards of the National Board of Fire Underwriters
for fur storage, as recommended by the National Fire Protection Association. New York, 1951.

TH9445 **National fire protection association.**
.M4N25
1941   **National board of fire underwriters.**
    ... Standards of the National board of fire underwriters for
paint spraying and spray booths using flammable materials as
recommended by the National fire protection association. New
York, N. Y., Chicago, Ill. ¡etc.¡ National board of fire underwriters, 1941.

TH9445 **National fire protection association.**
.C6N3
1944   **National board of fire underwriters.**
    ... Standards of the National board of fire underwriters for
safeguarding dry cleaning and dry dyeing plants, as recommended by the National fire protection association. New York,
N. Y., Chicago, Ill. ¡etc.¡ National board of fire underwriters,
1944.

TH9445 **National Fire Protection Association.**
.M4N25
1950   **National Board of Fire Underwriters.**
    Standards of the National Board of Fire Underwriters for
spray finishing, using flammable materials, as recommended
by the National Fire Protection Association. New York,
1950.

        National fire protection association.

    National board of fire underwriters.
    ... Standards of the National board of fire underwriters for
the construction and installation of gravity and pressure tanks,
as recommended by the National fire protection association.
New York, N. Y., Chicago, Ill. ¡etc.¡ National board of fire
underwriters, 1941.

VOLUME 407

National Fire Protection Association.

TH9332
.N3
1950
National Board of Fire Underwriters.
Standards for the construction and installation of water tanks for private fire protection service as recommended by the National Fire Protection Association. New York, 1950.

National Fire Protection Association.
FOR OTHER EDITIONS
SEE MAIN ENTRY

TH9176
.N37
1950
National Board of Fire Underwriters.
Standards of the National Board of Fire Underwriters for the design, installation and construction of containers and pertinent equipment for the storage and handling of liquefied petroleum gases as recommended by the National Fire Protection Association. New York, 1950.

National fire protection association.

TH9363
.N27
1944
National board of fire underwriters.
... Standards of the National board of fire underwriters for the installation and operation of centrifugal fire pumps as recommended by the National fire protection association. New York, N. Y., Chicago, Ill. ₍etc.₎ National board of fire underwriters, 1944.

National Fire Protection Association.

TH9176
.N27
1950
National Board of Fire Underwriters.
Standards of the National Board of Fire Underwriters for the installation and operation of gas systems for welding and cutting as recommended by the National Fire Protection Association. New York, 1950.

National Fire Protection Association.
FOR OTHER EDITIONS
SEE MAIN ENTRY

TH9275
.N26
1949
National Board of Fire Underwriters.
Standards of the National Board of Fire Underwriters for the installation, maintenance and use of central station protective signaling systems for watchman, fire alarm and supervisory service, as recommended by the National Fire Protection Association. New York, 1949.

National Fire Protection Association.
FOR OTHER EDITIONS
SEE MAIN ENTRY

TH9338
.N27
1950
National Board of Fire Underwriters.
Standards of the National Board of Fire Underwriters for the installation, maintenance and use of first aid fire appliances as recommended by the National Fire Protection Association. New York, 1950.

National fire protection association.

TK7271
.N3
1941
National board of fire underwriters.
... Standards of the National board of fire underwriters for the installation, maintenance and use of municipal fire alarm systems as recommended by the National fire protection association. New York, N. Y., Chicago, Ill. ₍etc.₎ National board of fire underwriters, 1941.

National fire protection association.

TP757
.N3
1943
National board of fire underwriters.
... Standards of the National board of fire underwriters for the installation, maintenance and use of piping, appliances and fittings for city gas as recommended by the National fire protection association. New York, N. Y., Chicago, Ill. ₍etc.₎ National board of fire underwriters, 1943.

National Fire Protection Association.
FOR OTHER EDITIONS
SEE MAIN ENTRY

TK7271
.N32
1949
National Board of Fire Underwriters.
Standards of the National Board of Fire Underwriters for the installation, maintenance and use of proprietary, auxiliary and local systems for watchman, fire alarm and supervisory service as recommended by the National Fire Protection Association. New York, 1949.

National Fire Protection Association.

TH9176
.N38
1950
National Board of Fire Underwriters.
Standards of the National Board of Fire Underwriters for the installation of air conditioning, warm air heating, air cooling and ventilating systems as recommended by the National Fire Protection Association. New York, 1950.

National Fire Protection Association.
FOR OTHER EDITIONS
SEE MAIN ENTRY

TH7697
.F2N35
1949
National Board of Fire Underwriters.
Standards of the National Board of Fire Underwriters for the installation of blower and exhaust systems for dust, stock and vapor removal or conveying, as recommended by the National Fire Protection Association. New York, 1949.

National Fire Protection Association.

TP757
.N3
1950
National Board of Fire Underwriters.
Standard of the National Board of Fire Underwriters for the installation of gas piping and gas appliances in buildings (does not apply to undiluted liquefied petroleum gas) as recommended by the National Fire Protection Association. New York, 1950.

National Fire Protection Association.

TH7466
.O 6N312
National Board of Fire Underwriters.
Standards ... for the installation of oil burning equipments as recommended by the National Fire Protection Association.
New York.

National fire protection association.
FOR OTHER EDITIONS
SEE MAIN ENTRY

TH9336
.N25
1947
National board of fire underwriters.
... Standards of the National board of fire underwriters for the installation of sprinkler equipments as recommended by the National fire protection association. New York, N. Y., Chicago, Ill. ₍etc.₎ National board of fire underwriters, 1947.

National Fire Protection Association.
FOR OTHER EDITIONS
SEE MAIN ENTRY

National Board of Fire Underwriters.
Standards of the National Board of Fire Underwriters for the storage and handling of combustible fibres as recommended by the National Fire Protection Association. New York. 1947.

National Fire Protection Association.
Standards for the storage and handling of liquefied petroleum gases, May 1954. Boston, 1954.
72 p. tables. (NFPA no. 58, file 50, series: Gases)

Includes editorial revision Appendix A.
Bound with North American Utility and Construction Corporation. Propane manual. 1954.

NN   0051641   NNC NIC

National Fire Protection Association.

TH9323
.N33
1950
National Board of Fire Underwriters.
Standards of the National Board of Fire Underwriters for water spray systems for fire protection as recommended by the National Fire Protection Association. New York, 1950.

National Fire Protection Association.

HD7262
.N2
National Board of Fire Underwriters.
Standards of the National Board of Fire Underwriters on the fundamental principles for the prevention of dust explosions in industrial plants, as recommended by the National Fire Protection Association. New York, 1949.

National Fire Protection Association.
Static electricity; report ...
see under   National Fire Protection Association. Committee on Static Electricity.

TH9111
.N33
[National fire protection association]
The story of the National fire protection association ...   [Boston, 1912?]
8 p.   23 cm.

NN   0051645   DLC

National fire protection association.
The story of the National fire protection association and list of its publications ...   ₍Boston, 1914₎
12 p. 23ᶜᵐ.

1. Fire prevention—Bibl. 2. Fire extinction—Bibl.

Library of Congress   Z5853.F6N2   15–20786

NN   0051646   DLC OU OO MiU MB NN MH IU

National fire protection association.
The story of the National fire protection association, and list of its publications ...   ₍Boston₎ 1922.
12 p. 21½ᶜᵐ.

1. Fire prevention—Bibl. 2. Fire extinction—Bibl.

23–15665

Library of Congress   Z5853.F6N2 1922

NN   0051647   DLC

National fire protection association.
The story of the National fire protection association, and list of its publications. ₍Boston, 1929₎
12 p. 23ᶜᵐ.
Correct to January 15, 1929.

1. Fire prevention—Bibl. 2. Fire extinction—Bibl.

CA 31–109 Unrev'd

Library of Congress   Z5853.F6N2 1929

NN   0051648   DLC DHEW NNC MH

National fire protection association.
The story of the National fire protection association.   Boston, 1940.
12 p.
Contains bibliography.

NN   0051649   DAL

VOLUME 407

National Fire Protection Association.
The story of the National fire protection
association. [Boston, 1948]
12 p. 21 cm.
"Publications of the association (corrected
to January 1, 1948)" p. 6-12.

NN 0051650 NN

National Fire Protection Association.
Studies of fire department fog or water spray
nozzles

see under

Committee on Fire Department Equipment.

National fire protection association.
Suggested explosives ordinance for cities, 1941, adopted by
National fire protection association, National board of fire underwriters ... Boston, Mass.: National fire protection assoc.,
1941. 15 p. 23cm.

1. Explosives—Jurisp.—U. S.   I. National board of fire underwriters.
N. Y. P. L.   December 8, 1942

NN 0051652 NN

662   National fire protection association.
N21s   Suggested explosives ordinance for cities, 1941
1942   (Reprint, 1942) Adopted by National fire protection association [and] National board of fire underwriters ... Boston, Mass., National fire protection association, international [1942]
15p.

1. Explosives. 2. Accidents—Prevention.

NN 0051653 IU MH

National Fire Protection Association.
Suggested fire prevention speech texts and
slogans for luncheon addresses, radio broadcasts,
etc., during fire prevention week. Boston,
Mass., 1924.
15 (1) p. 22 cm.

NN 0051654 DL

National Fire Protection Association.
Suggested fire prevention speech texts for
luncheon addresses, radio broadcasts, etc.,
during fire prevention week. Boston, Mass.,
National fire protection association, 1923.
11 p. 21.5 cm.

NN 0051655 DL IU

National fire protection association.
Suggested ordinance regulating construction and protection
of piers and wharves, adopted by American association of port
authorities, National fire protection association [and] National
board of fire underwriters ... Boston, Mass., National fire protection association international, 1941.

24 p. illus. 23ᶜᵐ.

Includes (p. 4-11) material from reports, etc. of the Committee on
piers and wharves.

1. Piers—Fires and fire prevention. 2. Wharves—Fires and fire prevention.   I. National fire protection association. Committee on piers
and wharves.
                                   42-51058
Library of Congress   TH9445.P5N3
                   [3]   614.85

NN 0051656 DLC MB OC1 NN

NATIONAL FIRE PROTECTION ASSOCIATION.
Suggested ordinance regulating oil burning
equipments, and oil storage in connection there-
with, adopted by the National Fire Protection
Association. Boston, 1933.

pp.(2).
"Edition of 1927, reprint 1933."

NN 0051657 MH

NATIONAL FIRE PROTECTION ASSOCIATION.
Suggested ordinance regulating the use,
handling, storage and sale of flammable liquids
and the products thereof. 1929. [Boston, Mass
1929].

pp.30,[2]. Plans

NN 0051658 MH

[National Fire Protection Association.]
Suggested programs for guidance in the observation of fire
prevention day, comprising public parade, school exercises, evening assembly... [Boston, 1913.] 15(1) p. 8°.

Title from cover.

1. Fires.—Prevention.   February 16, 1914.
N. Y. P. L.

NN 0051659 NN OU MB

National fire protection association.
Suggestions for fire prevention day.
Saturday, October 9th 1920.

NN 0051660 MiU

National Fire Protection Association.
Suggestions for the organization and execution of exit drills
in factories, schools, department stores and theatres, 1912.
Boston: the assoc. 15(1) p. 8°.

1. Fire drill.   October 21, 1913.
N. Y. P. L.

NN 0051661 NN MB OO OU

              National Fire Protection Association.
TH9176   FOR OTHER EDITIONS
.N3P67   SEE MAIN ENTRY
1949   **National Board of Fire Underwriters.**
Suggestions of the National Board of Fire Underwriters
for the organization, drilling and equipment of private fire
brigades as recommended by the National Fire Protection
Association. New York, 1949.

National fire protection association.
Syllabus for public instruction in fire prevention. 1916.
Boston, Mass., National fire protection association [1916]
8 p. 23ᶜᵐ.

1. Fire prevention.   I. Title.
                          CA 18-55 Unrev'd
Library of Congress   TH9148.N3

NN 0051663 DLC

National fire protection association.
Syllabus for public instruction in fire
prevention...1919.

NN 0051664 MiU

National Fire Protection Association.
TH9123   **National Commission on Safety Education.**
.N28   The teacher fireman team. [Washington, National Commission on Safety Education of the National Education Association and the National Fire Protection Association, Bos-
ton] ⁺1953.

National fire protection association.
Tentative code for explosion and fire protection
in plants producing or handling magnesium powder
or dust
      see under   National Fire Protection
Association. Committee on Dust Explosion
Hazards.

WO
241   National Fire Protection Association.
N277t   Tentative recommended safe practice for the use
of combustible anesthetics in hospital operating
rooms. Boston, 1941.
24 p., 23 cm.

2 p.   1. Operating rooms. Hazards. 2. Anesthetics,
combustible. 3. Gases.

NN 0051667 IParkA

National Fire Protection Association.
Topics for fire prevention meetings and suggestions for their
arrangement, designed to assist local organizations in considering
the subject of fire prevention. Boston: the assoc. 1916. 6 p.,
1 l. 8°.

1. Fires.—Prevention and extinction: Outlines, syllabi, etc.
N. Y. P. L.   January 18, 1917.

NN 0051668 NN MiU OU MB

          National Fire Protection Association.
VK1258   **Marine Chemists' Association.**
.M28   Transcript of the annual conference.
[Boston, National Fire Protection Association]

National fire protection association.
Uniform requirements recommended by the National
board of fire underwriters for use of boards, bureaus
and inspectors relating to standard mill construction,
"inferior" construction, general hazards, oil rooms, general protection, stairway and elevator closures, watch-
men, thermostats and miscellaneous matters. Prepared
by the National fire protection association. [Boston]
1911.

cover-title, 33, [3] p. incl. diagrs. 14ᶜᵐ.

1. Fire prevention. 2. Building, Fireproof.   I. National board of fire
underwriters.   13-8208

Library of Congress   TH1065.N3

NN 0051670 DLC NN MB

National fire protection association.
Brinckloe, William Draper, 1872-1933.
The volunteer fire company, by William Draper Brinckloe.
Boston, The National fire protection association [*1934]

National fire protection association.
Wartime fires. 4. ed. [Boston] Nat. fire protection assoc.
[c1943] 12 l. illus. 28cm.

1. Fires in war time—U. S.   February 7, 1946
N. Y. P. L.

NN 0051672 NN DNAL NNC

VOLUME 407

National fire protection association.
Wartime fires. 5th ed. ₍Boston, National
fire protection association ₍1944₎
₍20₎ p. illus. 28ᶜᵐ.

Mainly illustrations.

1. Fires - U. S. I. Title.

NN 0051673 NNC

[National fire protective association]
Will you be a fire warden and life-saver in the
store and factory? /
TH9146   [n.p., 1912?]
.N3

NN 0051674 DLC OO

National Fire Protection Association.
Will you be a fire warden and saver of
life? ₍In the home?₎ n.p. n.d.
₍4.p.₎ T

NN 0051675 OO

National Fire Protection Association.
Will you help to keep her out? ₍July 4, 1913. Statistics of
Independence day in America, 1903-1912.₎ Boston: the assoc.
₍1913.₎ 2 l. 4°.

1. Fires.—Prevention : Associations,   U. S.
N. Y. P. L.   April 14, 1914.

NN 0051676 NN

National Fire Protection Association.
Year book, officers and committees.   –1932/33.
Boston.
v. in   21–23 cm.
Title varies :   Articles of association ;
officers and committees ; membership, active, honorary, associate and
subscribing ; directory.—   –1931/32, Year book, articles of
association, officers and committees, membership directory.
Vols. for   published in Chicago.
Beginning with 1933/34, issued as pt. 2 of each October number of
the association's Quarterly.
1. Insurance, Fire—Direct.   I. National Fire Protection Association: Articles of association. II. National Fire Protection Association.
Officers and committees. III. National Fire Protection Association.
Membership directory.

TH9111.N2   614.8406273   54–55269

ICJ CU OCl IParkA
NN 0051677 DLC OrP OU MB DL KU NNC NN NcU TxU

National Fire Protection Association. Aviation
Committee
see National Fire Protection Association.
Committee on Aviation.

National fire protection association. Chamber of commerce and
safety council section.
...Bulletins for fire prevention committees of chambers of
commerce and safety councils.
no. 1–

Boston ₍1928–
nos.   23cm.

Irregular.
Nos. 1–13 (Nov., 1928–July, 1932) have title: Bulletins outlining tested activities
for fire prevention committees of chambers of commerce and safety councils.
Each number has also a special title.

NN 0051680 NN DLC IU

₍National fire protection association. *Committee on aircraft
fire fighting₎*
Airplane crash fire fighting manual. / Boston, Mass., National fire protection association, international, °1945.

96 p. illus. (part col. incl. maps) diagrs. 23ᶜᵐ.

Text on p. ₍2₎ of cover.
Prepared by a sub-committee of the Committee on aircraft fire fighting
of the National fire protection association. *cf.* Foreword.

1. Aeronautics—Accidents. 2. Fire extinction. I. Title.
                                                            45–8059
Library of Congress *   TL553.5.N3
                                ₍8₎   614.843

NN 0051681 DLC OrP ICJ WaS OCl MH MB

National fire protection association. *Committee on automatic sprinklers.*
Care and maintenance of sprinkler systems. Adopted by
N. F. P. A., 1940. Prepared by the Committee on automatic
sprinklers of the National fire protection association ... ₍Bos-
ton, 1940₎
28 p. 16ᶜᵐ.

1. Fire sprinklers.   I. Title.   II. Title: Sprinkler systems.
Library of Congress   TH9336.N3   41–22235

NN 0051682 DLC OCl NcRS

National Fire Protection Association. *Committee on Automatic Sprinklers.*
Care and maintenance of sprinkler systems. New York,
1951.
18 p. illus. 23 cm.

1. Fire sprinklers.   I. Title.
TH9336.N3 1951   614.844   53–23672 ‡

NN 0051683 DLC CLSU OU

NATIONAL fire protection association. Committee
on aviation.
Advance publication of the Report of the
Aviation committee. Recommended good practice
requirements for fire and life safety in avi-
ation.
Bost. Author. 1930. 32p.
S.D. McComb, chairman.

NN 0051684 WaS

National fire protection association. Committee
on blower systems for heating, ventilating,
stock and refuse conveying.
Regulations for the installation of blower,
and exhaust systems for heating and ventilating,
removal of flammable vapors, and conveying of
dust, stock and refuse. Prepared by N.F.P.A.
Committee on blower systems for heating, ventilating, stock and refuse conveying; adopted by
National fire protection association, 1933.
American standard approved January 31, 1935
by American standards association ... Boston,
Mass., National fire protection association, international [1935?]

19, [1] p. diagrs. 26 cm.
1. Blowing-engines. I. American standards
association.

NN 0051686 CU NN

NA9105   NATIONAL FIRE PROTECTION ASSOCIATION. Commit-
.N27   tee on city planning and zoning.
City planning and zoning in relation to fire prevention and fire protection; prepared by N.F.P.A.
Committee on city planning and zoning; adopted by
National fire protection association 1934. Boston
₍1934₎
cover-title, 39 p. incl. illus., tables, plans. 23cm.
Bibliography : p. 36–39.
1. Cities and towns--Planning--Zone system. 2. Fire
prevention.

NN 0051687 ICU Or MH IU

National Fire Protection Association. Committee
on Dust Explosion Hazards.
Dust explosion prevention
see under National Fire Protection
Association.

National fire protection association.
Committee on dust explosion hazards
Fundamental principles for the prevention
of dust explosions in industrial plants. n.d.
6 p.

Reproduced from typewritten copy.
Caption-title.

NN 0051689 OCl

                                              Dust Explosion Hazards.
National fire protection association. *Committee on* ^
Lessons from dust explosions. A record of
the past four years of dust explosions as
assembled in reports, prepared under the
direction of the officers of the committee on
dust explosion hazards of the National fire
protection association... N. Y., America fore
group of insurance companies. Research dept.
₍1936?₎
78 ₍15₎ p. illus.

NN 0051690 MiD OCl

TH9115   National Fire Protection Association. Committee
.N3   on Dust Explosion Hazards. The prevention of
             dust explosions.
National Fire Protection Association.
National fire codes. Boston, 1938–

National fire protection association. Committee
on dust explosion hazards.
Regulations for coal pneumatic cleaning
plants, prepared by N.F.P.A. Committee on
dust explosion hazards; adopted by National
fire protection association, 1930. American
standard approved December 31, 1930, by
American standards association. Boston,
Mass. (1930)
9 p. 23 cm.
At head of title: ASA Z12f-1930.

NN 0051692 DL Or

National fire protection association. *Committee on dust
explosion hazards.*
... Standards of the National board of fire underwriters for
the prevention of dust explosions in starch factories, terminal
grain elevators, flour and feed mills as recommended by the
National fire protection association. American standard approved January 9, 1940 by American standards association.
New York, N. Y., Chicago, Ill. ₍etc.₎ National board of fire
underwriters, 1940.
cover-title, 40 p. 15ᶜᵐ. (NBFU pamphlet no. 61)

"Prepared by the Committee on dust explosion hazards of the National
fire protection association."—p. ₍2₎.
"This pamphlet supersedes the previous issue of 1926."

1. Dust explosion. 2. Fire prevention. 3. Accidents--Prevention.
I. National board of fire   underwriters. II. American stand-
ards association.
Library of Congress   HD7262.N27   42–5251

NN 0051694 DLC OU

National Fire Protection Association. *Committee on Dust
Explosion Hazards.*
Standards of the National Board of Fire Underwriters for
the prevention of dust explosions in starch factories, terminal grain elevators, flour and feed mills as recommended by
the National Fire Protection Association. New York, National Board of Fire Underwriters, 1948.
40 p. 16 cm. (NBFU pamphlet no. 61)
Cover title.
"Supersedes the edition of March, 1940."
1. Dust explosion. 2. Fire prevention. 3. Accidents—Prevention.
I. National Board of Fire Underwriters. (Series: National Board
of Fire Underwriters. NBFU pamphlet no. 61)
HD7262.N27 1948   614.83   48–21344*

NN 0051695 DLC

VOLUME 407

Committee on
National fire protection association. Dust explosion hazards.

Tentative code for explosion and fire protection in plants producing or handling magnesium powder or dust... Boston, Mass.: National fire protection assoc. international, 1942. 11 p. 23cm.

1. Magnesium. 2. Fires—Preven-   tion and extinction.
N. Y. P. L.   November 20, 1942

NN   0051696   NN OC1

National fire protection association. *Committee on Farm Fire Protection.*
[Secor, Alson] ed.
Prevention and control of farm fires; a handbook on the causes of fires and best methods of safeguarding against loss of life and property. Chicago, 1932.

National fire protection association-Committee on farm fire protection
Rural fire departments. I. Equipment, apparatus. II. Organization. III. Volunteer fire department ordinance and rules. IV. State legislation for fire department organization... Boston, National fire protection association, 1940.
32 p. diagrs.
Cover-title.

NN   0051698   OC1 MH NN

National fire protection association. Committee on farm fire protection.
Volunteer fire departments for rural and small community service ... Prepared by N.F.P.A. Committee on farm fire protection; adopted by National fire protection association, 1943 ... Boston, National fire protection association [1943] cover-title, 32p. illus. 23cm.

Contents.— I. Equipment, apparatus.— II. Organization.— III. Volunteer fire department ordinance and rules.— IV. State legislation for fire department organization.

NN   0051699   PSt Or

National Fire Protection Association. Committee on Farm Fire Protection.
Water systems for fire protection on farms. Boston, 1935.
11 p.
1. Water-supply, Rural. 2. Fire prevention.
I. Title. II. Title: Fire protection on farms.

NN   0051700   DNAL

National Fire Protection Association. Committee on Field Practice.
Report of the Committee on field practice
see under   National Fire Protection Association.

National Fire Protection Association. *Committee on Fire Department Equipment*
see   Committee on Fire Department Equipment.

National Fire Protection Association. *Committee on Fire Hose.*
Advance publication of the report of the committee on fire hose. [New York? 1911] 31 p. 8°.

I. Hose (Fire).
     October 17, 1911.

NN   0051703   NN DLC

National Fire Protection Association. Committee on Fire Hose.
Report.   4019a.59
= Boston, Massachusetts. 1912. 19 pp. Plates. 23 cm.
Reprinted from published Proceedings of annual meeting [4014.163.15].

H8823 — Hose.

NN   0051704   MB IU OO NN

614.85 National fire protection association—
N215s Committee on fire-resistive construction.
Specifications for construction of a standard building. Report. Boston, 1913.
[9]p.

Reprinted with amendments from Proceedings of annual meeting, 1913.

NN   0051705   IU NN

National fire protection association. *Committee on firemen's training.*
... A guide for training auxiliary firemen ... Boston, Mass., National fire protection association, international, 1942.
14 p. 23°.
At head of title: Preliminary advance publication of the report of the N. F. P. A. Committee on firemen's training.
"Sources of information": p. 12-14.

1. Fire prevention—U. S. 2. Firemen. 3. Fire extinction. I. Title. II. Title: Training auxiliary firemen.
     42-25055

Library of Congress   TH9123.N3
     [3]   614.84

NN   0051706   DLC OC1 NN NcRS

National Fire Protection Association. Committee on Firemen's Training
Handling hose and ladders. Civil defense edition, based on pictures and text prepared cooperatively by the Committee on Firemen's Training of the National Fire Protection Association, International Association of Fire Chiefs, [and] Fire Department Instructors Conference. Boston [°1951]
175 p. illus.   (NFPA no.608-M)

NN   0051707   MiD DI

352.3 National Fire Protection Association. Com-
N223ha mittee on Firemen's Training
Handling hose and ladders. Based on pictures and text prepared cooperatively by the Committee on Firemen's Training of the National Fire Protection Association, International Association of Fire Chiefs [and] Fire Department Instructors Conference. Boston, °1953.
190 p. illus.

1. Fire extinc-   tion   I. Title

NN   0051708   MiD NN CLSU OrP

614.84 National Fire Protection Association—Com-
N213ii mittee on Firemen's Training.
The individual fireman's responsibility in public relations. 1st ed. Boston [1950]
20p. illus. 23cm. (NFPA no.613-M)

1. Firemen.

NN   0051709   IU

National Fire Protection Association. Committee on Firemen's Training.
Industrial fire brigades training manual see under   National Fire Protection Association.

National fire protection association. *Committee on firemen's training.*
Training manual for auxiliary firemen, edited by Horatio Bond ... W. Fred Heisler ... and R. J. Douglas ... Based on a Guide for training auxiliary firemen, prepared by the Committee on firemen's training, National fire protection association. Boston, Mass., National fire protection association, international [1942]
x, 406 p. incl. illus., tables, diagrs. 19½°.
"First edition."
Bibliography at end of most of the chapters.
1. Fire extinction. 2. U. S.—Civilian defense. I. Bond, Horatio, ed. II. Heisler, William Frederick, joint ed. III. Douglas, Raymond J., joint ed. IV. Title.   42-36261

Library of Congress   TH9811.N3   1942
     [10]   614.843

TU
NN   0051711   DLC NcRS CU OrP Or NcC OC1 OLak ViU

National Fire Protection Association. *Committee on Firemen's Training*
see also   Joint Committee on Evolutions.

National fire protection association. *Committee on fireproofing and preservative treatments.*
Recommended requirements for flame-proofing of textiles, 1941 ... Boston, Mass., National fire protection association, international [1941]
cover-title, 3-18 p. incl. tables, diagrs. 23°.
"This pamphlet presents a series of related standards, prepared by the N. F. P. A. Committee on fireproofing and preservative treatments and adopted by the association in 1940 and 1941."—p. [2] of cover.

1. Textile industry and fabrics—Testing. 2. Fireproofing. I. Title: Flameproofing of textiles.

Library of Congress   TP287.N3   42-15221
     [2]   677.0287

NN   0051713   DLC NN OC1

Committee on
National Fire Protection Association. Flammable Liquids.
Fire-hazard properties of certain flammable liquids, gases and volatile solids; compiled by Committee on Flammable Liquids of the National Fire Protection Association, as part 1 of the report of the committee to the 1935 annual meeting of the association. Boston, Mass., U. S. A.: National Fire Protection Assoc., 1934. 43 p. incl. tables. 23cm.

Pages 6-43 are tables.

869643A. 1. Liquids, Inflammable.   I. Title.
N.Y.P.L.   February 25, 1937

NN   0051714   NN

National fire protection association. *Committee on flammable liquids.*
Fire-hazard properties of certain flammable liquids, gases and volatile solids, compiled by Committee on flammable liquids of the National fire protection association. Rev. ed., 1941 ... Boston, Mass., National fire protection association, international [1941]
cover-title, 48 p. 23°.
"This table ... was originally presented at the 1935 annual meeting of the Association."—p. [2] of cover.
"References": p. [3] of cover.
1. Inflammable liquids. 2. Gases. 3. Solids. 4. Explosions. I. Title.
     42-1055

Library of Congress   QD516.N3   1941
     [5]   614.83

NN   0051715   DLC DAU OU CoBBS NN NcRS PBL

National Fire Protection Association. Committee on Flammable Liquids.
Fire-hazard properties of certain flammable liquids, gases and volatile solids, comp. by Committee on flammable liquids. Rev. ed. Boston, Author, 1946.
56 p. tab.

NN   0051716   WaS

VOLUME 407

National Fire Protection Association. Committee
on Hazardous Chemicals and Explosives.
Hazardous chemicals data. 1928-
Boston, National Fire Protection Association.
(NFPA no. 49)
Title varies: 1928-   , A Table of common
hazardous chemicals.
Prepared by the association's Committee on
Hazardous Chemicals and Explosives in coopera-
tion with the American Chemical Society; 1961
by the association's Sectional Committee on
Properties of Hazardous Chemicals.

NN 0051717   MiU

National Fire Protection Association. Committee
on Hazardous Chemicals and Explosions.
A table of common hazardous chemicals.
Prepared by Committee on hazardous chemicals
and explosives of the National fire protection
association and American chemical society.
Fourth edition 1939.   Boston, Mass., National
fire protection association [1939]
23 p.   tables.

NN 0051718   OCl

National fire protection association. *Committee on hazardous chemicals and explosives.*
A table of common hazardous chemicals, prepared by Committee on hazardous chemicals and explosives of the National
fire protection association and American chemical society ...
4th ed. 1939 (reprint 1940) Boston, Mass., National fire protection association [1940]
23, [1] p. 23ᶜᵐ.
"Tentatively adopted 1928, adopted 1929, amended 1931, 1935, 1938,
1939."—p. 4.
"References": p. 3.
1. Chemicals. 2. Fire prevention.   I. American chemical society.
II. Title: Hazardous chemicals.

A 41-449

Michigan. Univ. Library   TP200.N28 1940
for Library of Congress   [2]

NN 0051719   MiU OU ODW ICJ

National fire protection association. *Committee on hazardous chemicals and explosives.*
A table of common hazardous chemicals, prepared by Committee on hazardous chemicals and explosives of the National
fire protection association and American chemical society ...
5th ed. 1941. Boston, Mass., National fire protection association [1941]
23 p. 23ᶜᵐ.
"Tentatively adopted 1928, adopted 1929, amended 1931, 1935, 1938,
1939, 1941."—p. 5.
"References": p. 5.
1. Chemicals. 2. Explosives. 3. Fire prevention. 4. Fire extinction.
I. American chemical society.

42-25056

Library of Congress   TH9446.C5N3 1941
                                [3]   614.831

NN 0051720   DLC NN

National fire protection association. *Committee on hazardous chemicals and explosives.*
A table of common hazardous chemicals prepared by Committee on hazardous chemicals and explosives of the National
fire protection association and American chemical society ...
6th ed. 1942 (2d printing) Boston, Mass., National fire protection association [1942]
23 p. 23ᶜᵐ.
"Tentatively adopted 1928, adopted 1929, amended 1931, 1935, 1938,
1939, 1941."—p. 6.
1. Chemicals. 2. Explosives. 3. Fire prevention. 4. Fire extinction.
I. American chemical society.

45-16432

Library of Congress   TH9446.C5N3 1942
                                [3]   614.831

NN 0051721   DLC PBL

296.6   National fire protection association. Commit-
N2114   tee on hazardous chemicals and explosives.
Ed.7   A table of common hazardous chemicals, pre-
1945   pared by Committee on hazardous chemicals and
         explosives ... and American chemical society.
         7th ed. 1944 (reprint 1945) Boston, Mass.,
         1945.
         31 p.   23cm.

NN 0051722   DNAL MH OU

National Fire Protection Association. Committee
on High Pressure Systems for Fire Service.
Report of the committee on high pressure
systems for fire service; presented at annual
meeting, May 24, 1905
    see under   National Fire Protection
Association.

WX   NATIONAL Fire Protection Association.
140   Committee on Hospital Operating Rooms
N277r   Recommended safe practice for
1949   hospital operating rooms, adopted by
         National Fire Protection Association [and]
         National Board of Fire Underwriters.
         Boston, National Fire Protection Assn.,
         1949.
             31 p. (N. F. P. A. [Publication] no.
         56)
             Earlier ed. has title: Combustible

anesthetics in hospital operating rooms.
         1. Hospitals - Designs and plans
Title

NN 0051725   DNLM

National Fire Protection Association. Committee
on Hospital Operating Rooms.
Recommended safe practice for hospital
operating rooms ...   Boston, Mass., 1950.
    32 p.   19 cm.   (Its: standards no. 56)
    Cover title.
    1. Operating Rooms. Hazards.
    2. Anesthetics, combustible.

NN 0051726   IParkA

WX   NATIONAL Fire Protection Association.
140   Committee on Hospital Operating Rooms
N277r   Recommended safe practice for
1952   hospital operating rooms, June, 1952.
         Boston [1952]
             39 p. (NFPA [Publication] no. 56)
             Cover title.
             Prepared by the Committee on Hospital
         Operating Rooms, and acted upon by the
         Committee on Gases.
             1. Hospitals - Designs & plans
Title

NN 0051727   DNLM

WX   NATIONAL Fire Protection Association.
140   Committee on Hospital Operating Rooms
N277r   Recommended safe practice for hospi-
1954   tal operating rooms, endorsed by Ameri-
         can College of Surgeons, American Hospi-
         tal Association [and] U. S. Veterans
         Administration.   Boston, 1955, c1954.
             40 p. (NFPA [Publication] no. 56)
             Cover title
             Incorporates changes recommended by
         the Committee on Hospital Operating

Rooms, concurrently acted upon by the
Committee on Gases.
    1. Hospitals - Plans

NN 0051729   DNLM PPSKF NIC IParkA

RA   National Fire Protection Association. Committee on
968   Hospital Operating Rooms.
.N28   Standard for nonflammable medical gas systems,
1951   adopted by National Fire Protection Association
        [and] National Board of Fire Underwriters. Boston,
        National Fire Protection Association, 1951.
            14 p. (incl.cover) illus. 19 cm. (NFPA
        no. 565)
            "Supersedes the 'Recommended good practice re-
        quirements for the construction and installation
        of piping systems for the distribution of anesthe-
        tic gases and oxygen in hospitals and similar oc-
        cupancies' adopted   by the National Fire Pro-
        tection Association   in 1934 (reprint 1946)"
            1.Gases. 2.Hospitals--Safety measures. I.Title.

NN 0051730   MiU DNLM

National Fire Protection Association. *Committee on Libraries, Museums, and Historic Buildings.*
Protecting our heritage; historic buildings, museums, &
libraries. Boston, ᶜ1948.
28 p. col. illus. 23 cm.

1. Historic houses, etc.—Fires and fire prevention. 2. Museums—
Fires and fire prevention. 3. Library architecture—Fires and fire prevention.   I. Title.

TH9445.M8N3   614.84   51-3823

NN 0051731   DLC NBuC NIC DSI DI CU

National fire protection association. *Committee on manufacturing risks and special hazards.*
Structural defects influencing the spread of fire; suggestions for their elimination and protection. Prepared
by the Committee on manufacturing risks and special
hazards ... Boston, Mass., National fire protection association [1921]
cover-title, 3-18 p. illus. 22ᶜᵐ.
"Presented at annual meeting, 1916; revised and reprinted, 1916, 1921."—
p. 3.
1. Building, Fireproof.   I. Title.

CA 21-300 Unrev'd

Library of Congress   TH1065.N25 1921

NN 0051732   DLC

National fire protection association. *Committee on
manufacturing risks and special hazards.*
Structural defects: suggestions for their elimination
and protection, prepared by the Committee on manufacturing risks and special hazards. 1916. Boston, Mass.,
National fire protection association [1916]
17 p. illus. 23ᶜᵐ.

1. Building, Fireproof.   I. Title.

CA 18-52 Unrev'd

Library of Congress   TH1065.N35

NN 0051733   DLC OU NN

National Fire Protection Association. Committee
on Manufacturing Risks and Special Hazards.
Tanneries: suggestions for their improvement as fire risks. Prepared by the committee
on manufacturing risks and special hazards ...
Boston, Mass., National Fire Protection Association, 1912.
    1 p.l., 10 p. 8°.
    1. Tanneries. 2. Fireproof construction.-
Tanneries.

NN 0051734   NN DLC OO

National fire protection association. Committee on ᴧMunicipal fire apparatus.
    ...Advance publication of the report of the Committee on
municipal fire apparatus. Specifications for automobile fire apparatus, 1939. [Boston? 1938] 32 p. 23cm.
    "This report is a revision of that submitted at the 1938 annual meeting of the
N.F.P.A."

1. Fires—Prevention and extinc-   tion—Apparatus—U. S.
N. Y. P. L.   April 6, 1939

NN 0051735   NN

National fire protection association. Committee on Municipal Fire Apparatus
    Report on trailer pumpers and specifications for auxiliary
pumpers (Tentative). Report of the Committee on municipal fire
apparatus, presented at the 1941 annual meeting of the National
fire protection association...   Boston, Mass., U. S. A.: National fire protection assoc. (Internat.) [1941] 7 p. 22½cm.

1. Pumping machinery.
N. Y. P. L.   January 11, 1943

NN 0051736   NN MH

VOLUME 407

621.67   National fire protection association--Committee
N22r   on municipal fire apparatus.
     Report on trailer pumpers and specifications for
auxiliary pumpers; report of the Committee on municipal fire apparatus, adopted at the 1942 annual
meeting of the National fire protection association   Boston, Mass., National fire protection
association, international [1942]
     7p.

     1. Pumping machinery. I. Title: Trailer pump-
ers and specifications for auxiliary pumpers.

NN   0051737   IU OCl

     National fire protection association. Com-
mittee on piers and wharves.

     National fire protection association.
     Suggested ordinance regulating construction and protection
of piers and wharves, adopted by American association of port
authorities, National fire protection [and] National
board of fire underwriters ... Boston, Mass., National fire protection association international, 1941.

     **National fire protection association. Committee on
protection against lightning.**
     Safety code for the protection of life and property
against lightning. Edition of 1925. Boston. n. d.
     30 p.   23 cm.

NN   0051739   DAS

              Committee on
National fire protection association. ∧ Protection of records.

     Protection of records; consolidated reports of the Committee
on protection of records.... Boston, Mass., U.S.A.: National fire protection assoc., 1939.   88 p. incl. forms. illus.
23cm.

     Cover-title.
     On cover: A114–2M–8–39.
     "Reprinted from Proceedings of annual meetings, 1923–1939 inclusive."

     1. Fires—Prevention and extinc-   tion. 2. Archives—Preservation.
N. Y. P. L.   June 11, 1942

NN   0051740   NN OCl NNC IU MH

     NATIONAL FIRE PROTECTION ASSOCIATION - COMMITTEE
         ON PROTECTION OF RECORDS
     Protection of records; consolidated reports
of the Committee on protection of records.
Author, 1947.
     63 p.

NN   0051741   Or NIC MH-BA

TH   National Fire Protection Association. Commit-
9446   tee on Protection of Records.
R4   Protection of records, 1947; reprint 1955.
N3   Boston, 1955.
1955   63 p. illus. 19 cm. (NFPA no. 38B)

     Cover title.
     "Supersedes a publication originally printed in 1938."

     1. Business records. 2. Public records. 3. Fire pre-
vention. 4. Files and filing (Documents) 5. Building,
Fireproof. I. Title.

NN   0051742   Vi FU

     National Fire Protection Association. Committee
on Publicity and Education.
     [Publication]
     no.
     Chicago [1
         sq. 16°.
         1. Fires. Prevention, etc.

NN   0051743   NN

National fire protection association. *Committee on safety
to life.*
     Outside stairs for fire exits; recommendations for their
construction and installation, prepared by Committee on
safety to life. 1916 ... Boston, Mass., National fire protection association [1916]
     13, [1] p. 23ᶜᵐ.

     1. Fire-escapes.   I. Title.

                                          CA 18–53 Unrev'd
     Library of Congress   TH2274.N3

NN   0051744   DLC NN OU MB

     National Fire Protection Association. Committee
on Safety to Life.
     Safeguarding factory workers from fire.
Rules for measuring exit capacities and for determining permissible numbers of occupants of
factory buildings. Prepared by Committee on
safety to life, 1918. Boston, National fire
protection association (1918)
     16 p. fold. table. 22.5 cm.

NN   0051745   DL

National fire protection association. *Committee on signaling systems and thermostats.*
     Advance publication of the report of the N. F. P. A. Com-
mittee on signaling systems and thermostats. Subject: Municipal fire alarm systems, central station systems, proprietary
systems ... Boston, Mass., National fire protection association, international [1940]
     32 p. 23ᶜᵐ.
     "This report will be considered at the annual meeting in Atlantic
City, May 8–11, 1940."
     Stamped on cover: On the program of the N. F. P. A. annual meeting
this report is item no. 16.
     1. Fire-alarms—U. S.   I. Title: Municipal fire alarm systems.

                                          41–12041
     Library of Congress   TH9275.N3
            [2]   654.7

NN   0051746   DLC

National fire protection association. *Committee on special hazards and fire record.*
     Quarterly bulletin.
     [Hartford? Conn., 19
         v. illus., diagrs. 27–28ᶜᵐ.

     1. Fire prevention—Societies. 2 Fire prevention—U. S.

                                   CA 13–196 Unrev'd
     Library of Congress   TH9111.N32

NN   0051747   DLC ICJ

National fire protection association. *Committee on
spontaneous heating and ignition.*
     Spontaneous heating and ignition of coal and other mining
products ... 1936 (Reprint 1942) Boston, Mass., 1942.
     7 p. 23ᶜᵐ.
     "The result of the Committee's investigation on this subject, adopted as
an informative report at the 1935 annual meeting ... Proceedings, 1935,
page 311."

     1. National fire protection association. Proceedings. 1935.

NN   0051748   ICJ

National fire protection association. *Committee on static electricity*
     Static electricity; report of the Committee on static electricity,
presented at the 1937 annual meeting of the National fire protection association, and accepted as a preliminary report, subject to
change at a subsequent meeting... Boston, Mass., U. S. A.:
National fire protection assoc., 1937.   44 p. incl. diagrs., tables.
illus.   23cm.

     1. Electricity, Frictional.   2. Electric currents—Grounding.
     3. Electric wiring—Fire risks.   I. Title.
N. Y. P. L.   April 6, 1939

NN   0051749   NN

                  Committee on
National fire protection association. ∧ Static electricity.

     Static electricity; report of the Committee on static electricity,
tentatively adopted at the 1941 annual meeting of the National
fire protection association... Boston, Mass.: National fire
protection assoc., 1941.   50 p. incl. diagrs. illus. 23cm.

     1. Electric engineering—Safety   measures.
N. Y. P. L.   January 11, 1943

NN   0051750   NN NNC

---

                          static electricity.
National fire protection association. *Committee on* ∧
     Static electricity ... Boston, Mass.,
National fire protection association, inter-
national, 1947.
     cover-title, 51 p. illus., diagrs. 23 cm.

NN   0051751   OU

     National fire protection association.
     Committee on trailer and trailer
     camps.
     Standards for trailer coaches and
trailer coach camps. 1.Trailer vehicle
construction; 2.Safety features pertaining to trailers in transit; 3.Regu-
lation of trailers while not in transit. 14p. Author, 1940.

     Cover title.

NN   0051752   OrP

NATIONAL FIRE PROTECTION ASSOCIATION ⌐ Committee
     on Trailers and Trailer Camps.
     Trailer camps; regulation of trailers while
not in transit. Prepared by N.F.P.A. Committee
on Trailers and Trailer Camps, adopted by
National Fire Protection Association. 1939.
Boston, [1939].

     pp. 4.

NN   0051753   MH

TH   National Fire Protection Association. Committee
9339   on Wetting Agents.
.N29   Standards for wetting agents. July 1955. [Rev.]
     Boston, ᶜ1955.
     22 p. illus. 19 cm.
     At head of title: NFPA no. 18.
     Cover title.

     1. Wetting agents. 2. Fire extinction.

NN   0051754   MiU

     National fire protection association.   Electrical committee.
     ...Reports of the article committees of the Electrical commit-
tee, N F P A for the revision of the 1940 edition of the national
electrical code... [Boston, 1942]   114 p. 22½cm.

     1. Electric engineering—Regula-   tions—U. S. 2. Electric engineering
     —Safety measures.
N. Y. P. L.   January 14, 1943

NN   0051755   NN

     National Fire Protection Association. Farm Fire
     Protection Committee
         see   National Fire Protection Association.
     Committee on Farm Fire Protection.

VOLUME 407

614.8406 National fire protection association--Fire
NAF   marshals section.
      ... Proceedings of annual meeting, Chicago, May
10, 1937.   Boston, Mass. ₍1937₎
      61p. illus., ports.

      Proceedings for other years contained in the
Proceedings of the annual meeting of the National fire protection association.

      1. Fire prevention--Societies.

NN   0051757   IU

NATIONAL FIRE PROTECTION ASSOCIATION. Fire marshals' section.
     Committee on model hotel fire safety law.
     Guide for hotel fire safety law, 1948... Boston [1948]   17 p.
23cm.

     1. Fires in hotels.   2. Fires— Prevention and extinction— U. S.

NN   0051758   NN MH

NATIONAL FIRE PROTECTION ASSOCIATION. Forest Committee.
    Fire protection and prevention for summer homes in
forested areas, prepared by the Forest Committee of the
National Fire Protection Association. Adopted 1935...
Boston, Mass., U.S.A.: National Fire Protection Assoc.
[1935]   16 p.   23cm.

    869643A. 1. Fires—Prevention and extinction—U.S.

NN   0051759   NN OrCS

NATIONAL FIRE PROTECTION ASSOCIATION. Marine section.
    ...Advance publication of the report of the Committee
on motor craft (pleasure and commercial)...   [Boston?
Mass.] 1936.   18 p.   23cm.

    1. Ships—Fires and fire prevention. 2. Motor boats.

NN   0051760   NN

     National Fire Protection Association.   Marine
     Section.
        ... Fire protection regulations for motor
    craft, pleasure and commercial ...
        see under   National Fire Protection
    Association.

National Fire Protection Association.—New York Chapter.
    Membership; articles of association, January, 1915.   New
York, 1915.   26 p.   nar. 16°.

    Cover-title.
    At head of title: New York chapter.

    1. Fires.—Prevention, etc.: Associa-   tions.
N. Y. P. L.   October 5, 1915.

NN   0051762   NN

National Fire Protection Association.   Technical Committee.
192   Technical committee program.

₍Boston, 192   8°.
    no.
       192   caption-title.

    1. Fires—Prevention and extinction—   Assoc. and org.—U. S
N. Y. P. L.   August 13, 1926

NN   0051763   NN

TH9111   National Fire Protection Association.   Volunteer
.V6   Firemen's Section.

     Firemen.   v. 1–   Oct. 1933–
     ₍Boston₎ National Fire Protection Association.

     National fire service (*Gt. Brit.*)
       see
     Gt. Brit.   *National fire service.*

TH9111   National Fire Service Officers' Association.
.F754

     Fire protection review.

      ₍London, Benn Bros., etc.₎

     National Fire Waste Council.
       Promoting community fire prevention through
    chambers of commerce.
        see under   Chamber of commerce of the
    United States of America.

     National fire waste council.   Agricultural
       committee.
     ₍Secor, Alson₎ ed.
       Prevention and control of farm fires; a handbook on the
causes of fires and best methods of safeguarding against loss
of life and property.   Chicago, 1932.

296.6   National Fire Waste Council.   Agricultural
N2142   Committee.
     Rural fire prevention and protection through
Chambers of Commerce.   ₍Chicago, 1948?₎
    ₍12₎ p.

     1. Farm fires. Prevention. ₍I.₎ Chamber of
Commerce of the United States of America.
II. Title.

NN   0051769   DNAL

National firemen's association of the United States.
    Convention review and a synoptical history of
the New York and Chicago fire department: 20th
annual convention, Hotel La Salle, Chicago,
May 21, 22, 23, 1918.   [Chicago, 1918]
    167 p., ports.

NN   0051770   ICHi

National firemen's association of the United States.
    Report of the proceedings of the ... annual convention
of the National firemen's association of the United States
...
₍Bushnell, Ill.,
      v.   illus. ports.   23ᶜᵐ.
     10th, 22½ x 31ᶜᵐ.
     Title varies: 19   Proceedings of the ... annual convention of the Na-
    tional firemen's association.
     1907, National firemen's association of the United States.
     1906, Report of the proceedings ...

     1. Firemen—Societies.

                                  CA 12-645 Unrev'd

    Library of Congress   TH9503.N2

NN   0051771   DLC NN

     National first aid association of America.

     Wells, Roscoe G₍reen₎ 1878–
       Boys' drill regulations of the National first aid associa-
tion of America, arranged by Roscoe G. Wells ... The
setting up exercises and the section on rescuing the
drowning have been taken from "First aid in illness and
injury," through the courtesy of the author, Major James
Evelyn Pilcher, u. s. v.   Boston, Mass. ₍*1906₎

     National first aid association of America.

     First aid; official organ of the National first aid associa-
tion of America ...   v. 1, no. 1–
     Feb. 1, 1912–
     ₍Arlington? Mass., 1912–

W 1   NATIONAL First Aid Association of America.
NA433   Report of the annual meeting.
    1st-4th; 1906-09.   Boston.
     4 v.   illus., ports.

      Cover title of 1906 issue: Annual
report.

NN   0051774   DNLM ICRL ICJ NN MB

    National fish culture association of Great Britain
and Ireland.
       ... The journal of the national fish culture
association, including a summary of current information on fish, fish culture, and fisheries ...
    v. 1, no. 1-4.   Jan.-Oct. 1887.   London, 1887.
    496 p.   22.cm.   quarterly.
     Editor: J. W. Willis Bund.
     No more published.
     1. Fish-culture - Period.   I. Willis Bund,
John William Bund, 1843–

NN   0051775   CU DLC MH NN

NATIONAL FISH CULTURE ASSOCIATION OF GREAT
       BRITAIN AND IRELAND.
    [Objects of the association and rules]
[London, Partridge & Cooper, printers, 1883]

    12 p. 21 1/2 cm.

NN   0051776   MH

     National Fisheries Company
       see
     Atco Chemical-Industrial Products, inc.

     National Fisheries Institute.
       Fisheries blue book.
     Washington.
       v.   illus., ports.   20-31 cm.   annual.
      Began publication with 1946 issue.
      Title varies: Yearbook.

     1. Fisheries—U. S.—Direct. 2. Fish-trade—U. S.—Direct.
I. Title.
    SH1.N343   51-32630 rev ‡

NN   0051778   DLC DI DNAL CaBViP OrCS WaS CaBVaU CU

     National Fisheries Institute.
       Membership roster.
     Washington.
       v.   19 cm.

     1. Fisheries—U. S.—Direct. 2. Fish trade—U. S.—Direct.

    SH1.N347   64-5113 ⧧

NN   0051779   DLC

VOLUME 407

National Fisheries Institute.
N.F.I. flashes
   see under title

National Fisheries Institute.
Proceedings of annual convention.

Washington.

v. 28 cm.

1. Fisheries—Societies, etc.

SH1.N34   55–25914 ‡

NN   0051781   DLC OrCS

National Fisheries Institute.
Yearbook
   see its   Fisheries blue book.

National fisherman.

₍Goffstown, etc., N. H., G. Lamson, etc.₎
   v. illus. 20–31 cm. monthly.
"Established 1919."
Title varies: –May 1954, Atlantic fisherman.

1. Fisheries—Period. 2. Fisheries—U. S.—Period. **3. Fisheries—**
Atlantic Ocean—Period.

SH1.A8   338.3727   44–10721 rev*

NN   0051783   DLC FTaSU PPESB ICRL CU-S CSt TxU

NATIONAL fisherman combined with Main coast fisherman. v.41, no. 8-date; Nov. 1960-date
Belfast, Me.   v.   illus.
44cm.
Film reproduction. Positive.

Monthly.
Continues the numbering of the National fisherman, which in Nov.
1960 absorbed the Maine coast   fisherman.
1. Fish trade --Per. and soc.   publ. --U.S.   2. Fishing boats--
U.S.

NN   0051784   NN

NATIONAL FISHERY ASSOCIATION.
   Organization, platform and by-laws of the
National fishery association. Gloucester,
Mass., February 1887. Gloucester, Cape Ann,
Advertiser office, 1887.

15 p. 22 1/2 cm.

NN   0051785   MH

National fishery congress, *Tampa, Fla., 1898.*
   ... Proceedings and papers of the National fishery con-
gress, held at Tampa, Florida, January 19–24, 1898 ...
Washington, Govt. print. off., 1898.

1 p. l., 145–371 p., ₍v p. illus., pl. 10–31. 28 cm. ₍U. S. Commission of fish and fisheries. Doc. 363–396₎

"Extracted from U. S. fish commission bulletin for 1897."
A. N. Cheney, president. Hugh M. Smith, secretary.

CONTENTS.—Proceedings of the congress.—Methods of plankton investigation in their relation to practical problems, by Reighard.—The
importance of extended scientific investigation, by H. C. Bumpus.—
The utility of a biological station on the Florida coast in its relation
to the commercial fisheries, by S. E. Meek.—Establishment of a biological station on the gulf of Mexico, by W. E. Taylor.—Some notes on
American shipworms, by C. P. Sigerfoos.—An economical consideration of fish parasites, by Edwin Linton.—The fish fauna of Florida,
by B. W. Everman.—The lampreys of central New York, by H. A.
Surface.—The protection of the lobster fishery, by F. H. Herrick.—
The Florida commercial sponges, by H. M. Smith.—On the feasibility
of raising sponges from the egg, by H. V. Wilson.—The Hudson river
as a salmon stream, by A. N. Cheney.—A plea for the development
and protection of Florida fish and fisheries, by J. A. Henshall.—International protection for the denizens of the sea and waterways, by
B. W. James.—The restricted inland range of shad due to artificial
obstructions and its effect on natural reproduction, by C. H. Steven-

Continued in next column

Continued from preceding column

son.—The green turtle, and the possibilities of its protection and
consequent increase on the Florida coast, by R. M. Munroe.—Some
factors in the oyster problem, by H. F. Moore.—The oyster grounds of
the west Florida coast: their extent, condition and peculiarities, by
F. Swift.—The oysters and oyster-beds of Florida, by J. G. Ruge.—
The Louisiana oyster industry, by F. C. Zacharie.—The oyster-bars of
the west coast of Florida: their depletion and restoration, by H. A.
Smeltz.—Notes on the fishing industry of eastern Florida, by J. Y.
Detwiler.—Oysters and oyster-culture in Texas, by I. P. Kibbe.—The
methods, limitations, and results of white-fish culture in lake Erie, by
J. J. Stranahan.—A brief history of the gathering of fresh-water
pearls in the United States, by G. F. Kunz.—The red snapper fisheries:

---

their past, present, and future, by A. F. Warren.—Some brief reminiscences of the early days of fish-culture in the United States, by L.
Stone.—The relations between state fish commissions and commercial
fishermen, by W. E. Meehan.—Possibilities for an increased development of Florida's fishery resources, by J. N. Cobb.—The utility and
methods of mackerel propagation, by J. P. Moore.—The large-
mouthed black bass in Utah, by John Sharp.—Florida fur-farming, by
J. M. Wilson, jr.—Index.

1. Fisheries. 2. ₍Oyster fisheries₎ 3. ₍Sponge fisheries₎ 4. Biological laboratories. 5. Fisheries—Congresses.

F 12—110

U. S. Bureau of Fish.   Library
for Library of Congress   ₍a58e‡₎

NN   0051789   DI WaSp OC1W FU OU OC1WHi Nh CaBVaU

National fishing company, Dublin.

₍Yates, Michael₎
   Report of a deputation ₍Michael Yates and John
Hughes₎ from the directors of the National fishing company, on the subject of the fisheries on the south and
western coasts of Ireland. Dublin, M. Goodwin, 1825.

National fishing guide. 1946–
New York, A. S. Barnes & company, °1946–
   v. illus. (incl. maps) 27½ᵐ. annual.

Compiler: 1946–   William Voigt, jr.

1. Fishing—U. S.   ɪ. Voigt, William, comp. ɪɪ. Title: Fishing guide.

                  Agr 46–202

U. S. Dept. of agr. Library   414.8N21
for Library of Congress   SH463.N3
                ₍4₎†   799.1

NN   0051791   DNAL WaSp PSt MiD OEac OC1 DLC

National fitness council.
   In work or play fitness wins; twenty-four ways of keeping
fit. ₍London₎ National fitness council ₍1938₎
   cover-title, 64 p. illus. 21½ᵐ.
   Includes advertisements.

1. Exercise. ɪ. Title.
                    E 39–78

U. S. Off. of educ. Library   RA781.N19
for Library of Congress   ₍2₎

NN   0051792   DHEW

National fitness council (*New South Wales*)
   see
New South Wales. *National fitness council.*

Pam.   National Flag Conference.
Coll.
     The code of the flag, as adopted by the
48521   National Flag Conference, Washington, D. C.,
    June 14–15, 1923. Little Rock, Ark., Women
    of the Ku Klux Klan, Inc., Supreme Headquart-
    ers [1923?]
       16 p. 18 cm.

     1. United States. Flags. I. Women of the
Ku Klux Klan. II.   Title.

NN   0051794   NcD

CR113   (The) National flag conference.
N2
     The flag code.. Adopted at the National flag
conference ... 1923 as revised and endorsed at
the Second national flag conference ... 1924.
Washington, Author, 1924.

   unp. illus. 25½cm.

   ɪ. Title.
   1. Flags.

NN   0051795   NBuG OC1 DS

National flag conference.
   Report of the Sub-committee on the flag code appointed by
the National flag conference at its second session, held in
Washington, D. C., May 15, 1924. Indianapolis, Allied printing trades council 43 ₍1924?₎
   11, ₍1₎ p. illus. 23ᵐ.

1. Flags—U. S.
                    E 32–377

Library, U. S. Office of   Education CR113.N18

NN   0051796   DHEW

National flax fiber company, *Boston.*
   Linen, how it grows and how it is made. Boston, The
National flax fiber co., 1900.
   21 p. illus. sq. 8°.

                    May 31, 1900–66

NN   0051797   DLC

307.9   **National Flaxseed Processors Association.**
N213   Year book and trading rules.

   Washington.

     1. Flaxseed. Societies. 2. Linseed-
oil. Societies.

NN   0051798   DNAL

National Flight Test Instrumentation Symposium
   see
ISA Aerospace Instrumentation Symposium.

FOR OTHER EDITIONS
SEE MAIN ENTRY
National flood prevention and river regulation
commission
Kemper, James Parkerson, 1868–
   Plan for flood control in the Mississippi Valley by means
of lower flood levels through outlets and spillways below the
Arkansas River, prepared under the auspices of the National
flood prevention and river regulation commission and the
Atchafalaya Basin protection association, by J. P. Kemper,
c. ᴇ. New Orleans, La., 1927.

TC5   National flood prevention and river regulation con-
•N3   ference, New Orleans, 1913.
    Resolutions...

NN   0051801   DLC

National flood relief commission
   see   China, Chiu chi shu tsai wei yüan
hui.

VOLUME 407

The **National** floorcoverings review.
v. 1–

London: Metropolitan Press Agency, Ltd., 1931–   28½cm.
  v. illus. (incl. ports.)
  Monthly.
  Title varies: April, 1931–March, 1932, Carpets, rugs, linoleums and floorcoverings; April, 1932–   The National floorcoverings review.
  Absorbed Floorcoverings, March, 1932.

1. Carpets and rugs—Per. and soc.   publ. I. Carpets, rugs, linoleums
and floorcoverings.
N. Y. P. L.   October 30, 1934

NN 0051803   NN

National Florence Crittenton Mission.
  ...Annual report.
19

₍New York, 19   8°.
  nos. illus.
  1922–24 in 1 v., pub. ₍1925.₎
1   are   reports.

1. Woman—Rescue work—U. S.
N. Y. P. L.   December 28, 1929

NN 0051804   NN DL DLC

National Florence Crittenton Mission.
  Constitution and by-laws, with charters. The
association, 218 3d St., Washington, D. C., n. d.
  28 p.

NN 0051805   Or

National Florence Crittenton mission.

Wilson, Otto, 1885–
  Fifty years' work with girls, 1883–1933; a story of the
Florence Crittenton homes, by Otto Wilson, in collaboration
with Robert South Barrett ... Alexandria, Va., The National
Florence Crittenton mission, 1933.

National Florence Crittenton mission.
  Fourteen years' work among "erring girls" as conducted
by the National Florence Crittenton mission, with practical
suggestions for the same. Washington, D. C., The National
Florence Crittenton mission ₍1897₎
  vi, 209 p. front., plates, ports. 24ᶜᵐ.

  Published also under title: Fourteen years' work among street girls.
  "Report of the 1st general convention of the National Florence Crittenton mission and school of methods, held at Mountain Lake Park, Md., July 13 to 19, 1897": p. ₍95₎–202.

  1. Florence Crittenton missions.   I. Title.

Library of Congress   HQ316.W3N3   1–14512

NN 0051807   DLC DNLM MiU DN MB ICJ OC1

National Florence Crittenton mission.
  Life sketch and work of evangelist Charles N. Crittenton.
Washington, D. C., The National Florence Crittenton mission
₍1897?₎
  cover-title, 19 p. plates, ports. 28ᶜᵐ.

  1. Crittenton, Charles Nelson, 1833–1910.

                                  40–36613

Library of Congress   BV2657.C7N3

NN 0051808   DLC WaS

QK85
N2

(The) national flower for America.   Buffalo,
  N. Y., c1897.

  ₍4₎p. 23cm.

  1. National flowers.– United States.

NN 0051809   NBuG

National flower show, Detroit.
  ...Official program... ₍Detroit₎

  Library has
  8th, 1927.

NN 0051810   MiD-B

National flower show, conducted by the
  Society of American florists and ornamental
  horticulturalists.

  Library has 6th, 1924

  p 14, 863

NN 0051811   OClWHi

National Fluid Power Association.
  Design, operation & maintenance of hydraulic
equipment for use with fire resistant fluids.
Evanston, Ill. [1955]
  20 p.
  "Bibliography of hydraulic fluids and their
application": p. 16–19.
  1. Hydraulic machinery. 2. Fluids. I. Title.
II. Title: Fire resistant fluids.

NN 0051812   MsSM

QA
901
N27+

National Fluid Power Association.
  A glossary of terms for fluid power.
  1st ed.   Evanston, Ill., 1955.
  11 p. 28cm.

  1. Fluid dynamics--Terminology.

NN 0051813   NIC

---

f
RA591.5
A1N37

National fluoridation news.   v.1–
  Jan. 1955–
  Hempstead, N. Y. ₍etc.₎
    v. illus.   6 no. a year.

  Sponsored by the Association for the Pro-
tection of Our Water Supply, inc. and the
Pure Water Association of America, inc.,
California Committee.

  1. Water - Fluoridation - Period.
I Association for the Protection of Our Water
   Supply, inc.
II. Pure Water Association of America, inc.
   California Committee.

NN 0051815   HU KU

32

National flute folio. A choice collection of pieces
  for the flute.   Chicago, national music co.,
  [1890]
      38 p. 4°.

NN 0051816   DLC

The **National** flying farmer, v. 1–
  Oct. 1947–
  ₍Nowata, Okla.₎
    v. illus. 28 cm. monthly.
    "Magazine of the National Flying Farmers Association."

  1. Aeronautics—Period.   I. National Flying Farmers Association.

TL501.N343   629.13863   51–24560

NN 0051817   DLC IU NN DNAL NIC

National Flying Farmers Association.
  The National flying farmer
    see under title

National Flying Farmers' Association
    see also   National Agricultural Aviation
Conference. 1st, Fort Worth, Tex., 1949.

GT3930
.E9

National Folk Festival Association.

Evening Bulletin Folk Festival Association, *Philadelphia.*
  The folk festival handbook, a practical guide for local
communities. Philadelphia, ᶜ1944.

National fonds voor wetenschappelijk onderzoek,
  Brussels
    see   Fonds national de la recherche
scientifique, Brussels.

National food and fur association.
  Fortune in hares.   1919.
  32 p.

NN 0051822   DNAL

HF5417
.N36

National food and grocery conference committee.
  State unfair sales act recommended by the
National food and grocery conference committee as
a model for enactment in all states. ₍n.p.₎
  11 p. 22 cm.
  Contains comments by Associated grocery manufacturers of America, inc.; National association of
retail grocers; National voluntary groups institute;
National American wholesale grocers; Cooperative
food distributors of America; National association
of food chains.

  1. Grocery trade. 2. Unfair practices acts. 3. Prices– Laws and regulations– U.S. 4. Competition,
Unfair– U.S. I. Tit₎   II. Unfair sales act.

NN 0051823   DFT

National food and grocery distributors' code
  authority.
Ndx57 Bulletin to code authorities. v.[1]–2, Jan.29,
U2   1934–April 30,1935. Washington,D.C.[1934–35]
+N188e   2v. in 1. 28cm. weekly (irreg.)

  Title varies: [v.1],no.1/46, Jan.29–[July]
1934, Release; v.2, July 26,1934–April 30,1935,
Bulletin to code authorities.
  No more published?

NN 0051824   CtY

National Food and Nutrition Institute, *Washington, D. C.*
  see
  Nutrition Education Conference, *Washington, D. C.*

VOLUME 407

TX600
.N3   National food brokers association.

National canners association.
    Canners directory ... 1909–
Washington, D. C. [etc.] *1909–

National Food Brokers Association.
    Directory of members.
Washington.
        v. 20 cm. biennial.

    1. Food industry and trade—U. S.—Direct.

    HD9003.N3   52–34263 ‡

NN   0051827   NNC NBuG OU
                  DLC ICJ OrP WaS NN MB WM PPT MiD OC1

National food brokers association.
    The food broker ... Indianapolis, Ind., National food
brokers association, 1941.
    1 p. l., 86 p. 22½ᵐ.

    1. Grocery trade—U. S. 2. Wholesale trade—U. S.   I. Title.

    Library of Congress   HD9821.5.N28   42–20700
                           [2]   658.896414

NN   0051828   DLC TxU DFT OU WU DNAL

Pamphlet
HD   **National Food Brokers Association.**
104+   Food brokers' operations and services;
        a survey sponsored by the National Food
        Brokers Association and the Saturday
        evening post. [Philadelphia, Curtis, 1954]
        64 p. 28cm.

        Cover title.

        1. Food industry and trade--U. S.
    I. The Saturday evening post. II. Title.

NN   0051829   NIC

658.9414   **NATIONAL FOOD BROKERS ASSOCIATION.**
N213f   Food brokers, who they are - what they do -
1945   how they do it - where they fit properly in
        the economical distribution of food and grocery
        products as sales agents. Washington, D.C.,
        National food brokers association, 1945.
        2p.l.,83p. 24cm.

        "1945 edition."

        1. Grocery trade - U.S. 2. Wholesale trade
        - U.S. I. Title.

NN   0051830   TxU

National food brokers association.
    Food brokers; who they are, what they do, how
they do it, where they fit properly in the economical distribution of food and grocery products as sales agents. Washington, D. C., National food brokers association [1944]
    2 p. l., 83 p. 22½cm.

    On cover: How food brokers operate and how
to use them.

    1. Food industry and trade - U. S. I. Title.

NN   0051831   NNC

---

658   National Food Brokers Association.
N2143f   Food brokers ... Washington, D.C., 1945.
1945   83p.

        Cover title: How food brokers operate and how
    to use them.
        "1945 edition."

        1. Grocery trade--U.S. 2. Wholesale trade--U.S.
    I. Title. II. Title: How food brokers operate.

NN   0051832   IU OrP

---

286   **National Food Brokers Association.**
N217H   History defines the food broker. Wash-
        ington, D.C. [1947]
        10 p.

NN   0051833   DNAL

280.32   National Food Brokers Association.
N21   Joint marketing study. [Philadelphia,
        Curtis, 1949]
        25 p.

        1. Food industry and trade. U.S. 2. Chain
    stores. 3. Food. Advertising. 4. Grocery
    trade. U.S. 5. Market surveys. U.S.
    I. Saturday evening post.

NN   0051834   DNAL

National Food Brokers Association.
    Students view the food broker, the prize
winning manuscripts of three college students.
Wash. [n.d.]
    23p. illus. 24cm.

NN   0051835   PPD

National food brokers association.
    Unfairness in the food industry; a critical analysis from the
key view point of the food broker; discrimination in price, dis-
counts, allowances and other unfair trade practices which stifle
competition and lead to monopoly ... 1st ed. Indianapolis,
National food brokers association, 1935.
    120 p. 22½ᵐ.

    Text on pages [2] and [3] of cover.

    1. Grocery trade—U. S. 2. Wholesale trade—U. S.   I. Title. II.
Title: The food industry, Unfairness in. III. Title: The food broker.

    Library of Congress   HD9821.5.N3   35–35344
    ———— Copy 2.
    Copyright AA 190177   [5]   658.9414

NN   0051836   DLC

National food conference of consumers and producers.
    The complete proceedings of the ... conference ... [1st]–
        1943–
[Rochester, N. Y., 1943?]–
        v. 23ᵐ.

    1. Food supply—U. S. 2. World war, 1939–   —Food question—U. S.
3. Agriculture—Economic aspects—U. S.

    Library of Congress   HD9001.N263   44–29638
                               [3]   338.106873

NN   0051837   DLC DNAL

National food conference of consumers and producers. *1st,
    Chicago, 1943.*
    Highlights; significant passages from addresses delivered
at the National food conference, Chicago, Illinois, Sept. 16th–
17th, 1943. [Rochester, N. Y., Henderson-Mosher inc., printers,
1943?]
    2 p. l., 18 p., 1 l. 21½ᵐ.

    Library of Congress   HD9001.N264 1943 b   44–29433
                               [2]   338.1

NN   0051838   DLC DNAL

National Food Distributors Association.
    National food distributors' journal
        see under title

National food distributors' journal.
    [Chicago]
        v. illus., ports. 30 cm. monthly.
    Began publication in 1927. Cf. N. W. Ayer & Sons directory, 1958.
    Official organ of the National Food Distributors Association.

    1. Grocery trade—U. S.—Period.   I. National Food Distributors
Association.

    HD9321.1.N343   58–45889

NN   0051840   DLC DNAL NN

TX357   **National food economy league, London.**
.N3   [Publications] no. 1–2,
        London, 1917

NN   0051841   DLC NN

National Food Fund.
    Handbook for housewives. How to save money in war time;
one shillingsworth of food for tenpence. London [National Food
Fund, 1915?] 31(1) p. 8°. (National Food Fund Handbook. no. 1.)

    1. Food. 2. Domestic economy.   3. Title: How to save money in
war time.   war time.
    N. Y. P. L.   September 14, 1915.

NN   0051842   NN

National food journal. / Issued by the Ministry of Food. [Lon-
        don, 1917–1920.]
        *   Library has vol. 1, no. 2–vol. 3, no. [5], (*i.e.* no. 2–53), Sept. 26, 1917–June
    9, 1920. 27½ᵐ.

    Caption title.
    Sept. 1917–April 1919 semimonthly; May 1919–June 1920 monthly.
    Ceased publication June 9, 1920.

NN   0051843   ICJ CU

National food magazine. v. 1–40; Aug. 1896–Mar. 1916.
    Minneapolis [etc.] Pierce & Pierce, 1896–1900; Chicago [etc.]
    Pierce publishing co., 1900–16.
        40 v. in 26. illus. (part col.) 25–31ᵐ. monthly.
    Title varies: Aug. 1896–Dec. 1908, What to eat; the national food maga-
    zine (subtitle varies)
        Jan. 1909–Mar. 1916, National food magazine.
        P. A. Pierce, editor.
    Absorbed the International culinary magazine in Nov. 1915.
    Merged into Table talk, which continued as Table talk; the national
    food magazine, assuming the volume numbering of the National food
    magazine.
        1. Food — Period. 2. Food adulteration and inspection — Period. 3.
    Cookery—Period.   I. Pierce, Paul Ashville, 1866–   ed.   II. What to
    eat ; the national food   magazine.
    Library of Congress   TX341.N4   20–8145

NN   0051844   DLC NcGU KMK ICRL OrCS ICJ MU

1.9422   National food preservation workshop training
N2N21   conference, Peoria-Pekin, Ill., 1944.
            Report. Washington [1944]
            22 p.
            1. Community food preservation centers.
        2. Canning and preserving. Congresses.
        I. U. W. War food administration. Office of
        distribution.

NN   0051845   DNAL

National food reform association
        see
Food education society, *London.*

VOLUME 407

The **National** food situation.
₍Washington₎
v. in   27 cm. quarterly.
Issued 19 –53 by the U. S. Bureau of Agricultural Economics;
1954–   by the U. S. Agricultural Marketing Service.

1. Produce trade—U. S.—Period. I. U. S. Bureau of Agricultural
Economics. II. U. S. Agricultural Marketing Service.

HD9001.N28   338.1973   59–33311

NN   0051847   DLC FU MiU NIC

National football league.
... Constitution and by-laws, approved 1941, amended 1942,
amended 1943, amended 1944. Chicago, Ill., °1944.
31, ₍1₎ p. 18ᶜᵐ.

45–1030

Library of Congress °   GV955.N326 1944
₍2₎   796.33

NN   0051848   DLC

National Football League. Football record and rule book
see its Record and rules manual.

National Football League. Life story of ...
see its Record and rules manual.

National football league.
GV939
.S7S6
Spink, John George Taylor, 1888–   *comp.*
Life story of Amos Alonzo Stagg, grand old man of football,
by Francis J. Powers. Favorite plays of famous coaches.
Greatest grid thrills and Official 1946 rules, National pro foot-
ball league. Compiled by J. G. Taylor Spink, Hugo G. Autz
₍and₎ Paul A. Rickart. St. Louis, Mo., C. C. Spink & son,
°1946.

National football league.
Official football rules. 1939–
New York, A. S. Barnes & company; ₍etc., etc., 1939–
v. diagrs. 17ᶜᵐ.
1935–38 published in the league's Official guide.
On cover, 1939–40: Spalding's athletic library; 1941–   American
sports library.

1. Foot-ball. I. Title.
43–49000
Library of Congress   GV955.N327
₍2₎   796.33

NN   0051852   DLC NN

National Football League. Official guide
see its Record and rules manual.

National Football League.
Official record manual.
New York.
v. illus. 19 cm. annual.
Continues, in part, its Record and rules manual.
Title varies slightly.
Cover title: : Official National Football League record
book.

1. Football—Yearbooks. I. Title: Official National Football
League record book.

GV955.N328   796.33′264′0973   72–626572

NN   0051854   DLC FTaSU

National Football League. Official rules and statistics
see its Record and rules manual.

GV951
.A1P7
National football league.
Pro football illustrated; the picture magazine of pro football.
₍Chicago, F. T. Kable, 19

GV937
.N3
National Football League.
Professional football; yearbook of the National Football
League.
₍New York, Don Spencer Co.₎

National Football League. Professional football rules
see its Record and rules manual.

National Football League.
Record and rules manual. 1935–
₍Philadelphia? etc.₎
v. illus., ports. 18 cm. annual.
Issues for 1935–   pub. as Spalding's athletic library.
Title varies: 1935–   Official guide (cover title, 1935–38, Professional football rules; official guide (varies slightly))—1945, Football record and rule book.—1946, Favorite plays of famous coaches,
greatest grid thrills and official rules (cover title: Official pro play-)—
–1948, Official rules and statistics (cover title,   –1948,
Official National League football; pro record and rule book)
Each issue, 1946–48, has special title: Life story of ₍name of a
coach₎ ... and official rules ...

Issues for 1935–38, 19   include section entitled : The official
playing rules as devised, amended and authenticated for professional
football by the ... league (1935–38, 19   Official football rules;
issued also separately)

GV955.N33   796.33   36–29869 rev 3*‡

NN   0051860   DLC NN OkU OCl OCU MiD MB OCl FU

796.33
N2775ro
National Football League.
Roster manual.
Chicago [etc.]
v. 17cm. annual.
Title varies slightly.

1. Football - Yearbooks

NN   0051861   FU MiD

National forecast council.
Proceedings ₍of the meeting₎ ₍1st–
1944–
₍Columbus, O., 1944–
v. 23ᶜᵐ.
Meeting sponsored by the Ohio Development and publicity commission.

1. U. S.—Indus.—Congresses. I. Ohio. Development and publicity
commission.
44–42535
Library of Congress   HC101.N314
₍2₎   330.6373

NN   0051862   DLC DNAL

The National forecast magazine.   –8 (no.   –92) ;
–Feb. 1948.
₍Washington, National Forecast Publications₎
v. in   20 cm. monthly.
Editor: –Feb. 1948, C. O. Benham.

1. Anglo-Israelism. I. Benham, Charles Orville, 1911–   ed.

DS131.A1N3   52–35190 ‡

NN   0051863   DLC

National foreign trade association.
Foreign trade and the domestic welfare; a graphic outline of
the basic elements underlying a choice between a liberal
interchange of goods or economic isolation. New York,
N. Y., Publication division of the National foreign trade
council, inc. and the National foreign trade association
₍1936?₎

National Foreign Trade Convention.
Final declaration.
New York, National Foreign Trade Council.
v. 21–23 cm.

1. U. S.—Commercial policy. I. National Foreign Trade Council.

HF3008.N6   382.06373   17–23715 rev*‡

WaWW DPU KMK NNC TxU DS MB PSt NNC CU
NN   0051865   DLC NIC KU IU LU NN FU KEmT OrCS OrU

National Foreign Trade Convention.
Official Report
see its Proceedings.

National Foreign Trade Convention.
Proceedings. ₍1st₎–
1914–
New York, National Foreign Trade Council ₍etc.₎
v. 24 cm. annual.
Title varies: 1914–37, Official report.—1938–63, Report.
Vols. for 1927–33 have also a distinctive title: Foreign trade.

1. U. S.—Comm.—Congresses. I. National Foreign Trade Council. II. National Foreign Trade Convention. Official report. III. National Foreign Trade Convention. Report. IV. National Foreign
Trade Convention. Foreign trade.

HF3008.N5   22–14508 rev 3

NhD MoU TxLT WHi FTaSU WaS KMK WaE
Or IU CaBViP CaBVa ICJ CaBVaU UU MiGr MsU AAP
OClFRB MH–BA PPD DL WaSp WaSpG ICJ OrCS WaU–L
NjP NN PSt IU OrPR OrU WaPS MNS PBL NcU ICJ
NN   0051867   DLC DS TxU MiU GEU IdU DPU MtU KU

National Foreign Trade Convention. 5th, Cincinnati, 1918.
Foreign markets work and plans of the Bureau of Markets,
United States Department of Agriculture.   Cincinnati: National
Foreign Trade Convention, 1918. 7 p. 8°.

1. Commerce, U. S., 1918– . 2. Eu-   ropean war, 1914– .—Reconstruction (Economic), U. S.
N. Y. P. L.   May 15, 1919.

NN   0051868   NN

National foreign trade convention. 7th, San
Francisco, 1920.
Pacific shipping illustrated, *Seattle.*
Trading overseas. ₍Seattle, °1920₎

VOLUME 407

332   National Foreign Trade Convention. 39th,
N217d   New York. 1952.
Discussion period of the International
Finance Session, November 17, 1952.   New
York, National Foreign Trade Council ₍1952?₎
17p.   28cm.

Cover title.
"Ref. No. M-4921"

1. Finance.   I. Title.

NN   0051870   IU

National Foreign Trade Convention. 39th,
New York, 1952.
Panel discussion of the Merchandising,
Transportation and Insurance Session,
November 18, 1952.   New York, National
Foreign Trade Council [1952?]
19 p.   28 cm.
Cover title.
"Ref. No. M-4820."
1. Commerce.   I. Title.

NN   0051871   IU

Pamphlet
HF   National Foreign Trade Convention. 41st,
115   New York, 1954.
Educational session. Report of proceedings ... New York, N.Y., November 6, 1954
New York, National Foreign Trade Council,
1954.
30 p.   21cm.

Cover title.

1. U.S.--   Commercial policy.

NN   0051872   NIC

National foreign trade council.
American export manufacturers.   New York city, Members
of National foreign trade council, inc. ₍1938?₎
128 p.   28½ᶜᵐ.
English, Spanish, Portuguese, French and German.
Includes advertising matter.

1. U. S.—Comm.—Direct.   ɪ. Title.   42–7087

Library of Congress   HF3011.N28
₍2₎   382.058

NN   0051873   DLC NN

National foreign trade council, inc.
American foreign trade definitions, adopted at a conference
participated in by committees representing the National foreign
trade council, inc., Chamber of commerce of U. S. A., National
association of manufacturers ₍and others₎...   New York, Nat.
foreign trade council, 1936.   15 p.   23cm.

1. Commerce—Dictionaries,   English. 2. Shipping—Dictionaries.
N. Y. P. L.   June 11, 1946

NN   0051874   NN

National foreign trade council.
Smith, Joseph Russell, 1874–
... The American trade balance and probable tendencies; an analysis of the foreign trade of the United States
during recent years, with some consideration of its future
course, prepared by J. Russell Smith ...   New York city,
National foreign trade council, 1919.

HF3003   National Foreign Trade Council.
.N3   Annual report.
New York.

(12) 1. U.S. Commerce.

NN   0051876   DNAL

National foreign trade council.
Argentine-American trade relations; submitted by National
foreign trade council, inc.   William S. Culbertson, counsel...
February 1, 1937. ₍New York, 1937?₎   31 p.   23cm.

1. Commerce—U.S. and Argentine   Republic. 2. Commerce—Argentine
Republic and U. S. I. Culbertson,   William Smith, 1884–
N. Y. P. L.   April 25, 1945

NN   0051877   NN DPU

National Foreign Trade Council.
A bargaining tariff; memorandum submitted
... to the House ways and means committee
see under   National foreign trade council.
Committee on foreign trade aspect of the tariff.

National Foreign Trade Council.
Comments on the revised charter for an international
trade organization in terms of foreign economic policy, presented at public hearings before an interdepartmental committee, New York, February 27th, 1947.   New York ₍1947₎
vii, 152 p.   23 cm.
Cover title.
Bibliography: p. 118–119.

1. International Trade Organization (Proposed)   2. Commercial
policy.
HF55.N3   380.611   49–714*

NN   0051879   DLC NNC

NATIONAL FOREIGN TRADE COUNCIL.
Commercial possibilities of the Dutch
East Indies; a description of trade conditions
in an undeveloped market of great size, large
population, and immense resources.   New York,
1919.

Map.

NN   0051880   MH-BA

National foreign trade council.
... Commercial possibilities of the Union of South
Africa.   A survey of the recent industrial expansion and
the mineral and agricultural resources of a market presenting great possibilities for American enterprise.   New
York city, National foreign trade council, 1921.
31 p. incl. double map.   23ᶜᵐ.
"Eighth National foreign trade convention, Cleveland, Ohio, May 4, 5, 6,
7, 1921."
1. Africa, South—Comm. 2. Africa, South—Econ. condit.—1918–
ɪ. Title.
Library of Congress   HC517.S7N3
22—6879

NN   0051881   DLC NN

National foreign trade council.
Nicaragua. *Ministerio de hacienda y crédito público.*
... Contrato, decretos, acuerdos y disposiciones referentes a
la "deuda comercial congelada de Nicaragua" ...   Managua,
D. N., Talleres nacionales, 1938.

National foreign trade council.
₍Copy for release   Oct. 1934₎-1950 (incomplete).
New York.   v.   28cm.

CURRENT IN ECONOMICS DIVISION (Current issues
received after 1950 will be discarded at the end
of each year).
Irregular

1. Commerce—Per. and soc. publ.—U.S.

NN   0051883   NN

National Foreign Trade Council.
Current developments in the British trade and
financial situation; a review prepared by the
European Division, NFTC.   New York, 1949.
16 p.   (Its Ref. no. M-1838)

NN   0051884   MH-BA

National foreign trade council.
Directory of foreign buyers ...   New York city, National
foreign trade council, inc. ₍1938?₎
75 p.   28½ᶜᵐ.
"A companion volume to 'American export manufacturers, members
of the National foreign trade council, inc.' "—p. 3.

1. Commerce—Direct. 2. U. S.—Comm.—Direct.   ɪ. Title.
44–45896
Library of Congress   HF5030.N3
₍2₎   382.058

NN   0051885   DLC NN

National foreign trade council.
Economic proposals for consideration of ninth
International conference of American states scheduled
to meet in Bogota, Colombia, March 30, 1948.   New
York, National foreign trade council, Council for
inter-American cooperation, 1947.   22 p.   21cm.

2. ed.

1. Co-operation, Commercial—America. I. Council for
inter-American cooperation, inc.

NN   0051886   NN

National Foreign Trade Council.
Education session

see under

National Foreign Trade Convention. 39th,
New York.

National foreign trade council.
Stuart, Charles Edward, 1881–
European conditions in their relationship to international
trade and export credits; a report by Charles E. Stuart.   England, Germany, France, Turkey, Russia, Italy.   New York
city, National foreign trade council, 1955.

National foreign trade council.
... European economic alliances; a compilation of information on international commercial policies after the
European war and their effect upon the foreign trade of
the United States, also an analysis of European and
united commercial inter-dependence and treaty relations,
comp. under the direction of the secretary of the National
foreign trade council.   New York city, 1916.
118 p. fold. tables.   23ᶜᵐ.
Robert H. Patchin, secretary.

1. European war, 1914–   —Economic aspects. 2. Commercial policy.
3. U. S.—Comm.   ɪ. Patchin, Robert Halsey, 1881–   ɪɪ. Title.
16—20583
Library of Congress   D635.N3

OCU ODW MH   NBuU NN MB NjP
NN   0051889   DLC DNW WaSp WaS OrCS OKentU ICRL OO

VOLUME 407

National foreign trade council.
... European economic alliances; a compilation of information on international commercial policies after the European war and their effect upon the foreign trade of the United States, also an analysis of European and United States commercial inter-dependence and treaty relations, comp. under the direction of the secretary of the National foreign trade council. New York city, 1916.
128 p. fold. tables. 23ᶜᵐ.
"Second edition."
1. European war, 1914-1918—Economic aspects. 2. Commercial policy. 3. U. S.—Comm. I. Title.

Library of Congress   D635.N3 1916 a   24—11756

NN   0051890   DLC NIC ICRL OCU Or WaS WaTC

National Foreign Trade Council.
Examples of American export enterprise; a report of the National Foreign Trade Council, submitted to the fourth National Foreign Trade Convention, Pittsburgh, Pa., January 25-27, 1917 ... New York, 1917.   11 p.   8°.

1. Commerce, U. S.
N. Y. P. L.   March 19, 1917.

NN   0051891   NN

National foreign trade council.
Exchange restrictions pamphlets of the National foreign trade council. no. 1–
New York, National foreign trade council, 1933–
v. 23ᶜᵐ.
"Prepared for the National foreign trade council in collaboration with the Council on inter-American relations, Committee on inter-American commerce, Committee on exchange restrictions ₍etc.₎"
1. Commercial policy. 2. U. S.—Comm. 3. Foreign exchange. I. Title.

                                           35–14496
Library of Congress   HF1401.N3
                              ₍2₎   382.0973

NN   0051892   DLC OrU OCU NN

National foreign trade council.
Expansion plans and program for 1946.   New York, Nat. foreign trade council ₍1946₎   5 l.   illus.   28cm.

NN   0051893   NN

National Foreign Trade Council.
Exports control; a statement of the development of the War Trade Board and its relation to American foreign trade, submitted at the Fifth National Foreign Trade Convention, Cincinnati, Ohio, April 18, 1918.   New York City: National Foreign Trade Council ₍1918₎.   29 p.   8°.

1. United States.   War Trade Board.   2. Commerce, U. S. 1917. 3. Euro-
N. Y. P. L.   —Economic aspects,   U. S. 4. Title.
                                           September 4, 1918.

NN   0051894   NN NNC

HF   **National Foreign Trade Council.**
81   Fact finding brief in foreign trade.
N3   no.1-14; 1926-1933.   New York.
        no.   23cm.

Set consists of various editions.
Title varies: no.1-10, Fact finding pamphlets in foreign trade.

1.Commerce - Collections. 2.U.S. - Comm.
I.Title.

NN   0051895   CLSU OrU ICJ ICU NN TU CU

HF3008   **National Foreign Trade Council.**
.N6
       National Foreign Trade Convention.
          Final declaration.
       New York, National Foreign Trade Council.

National Foreign Trade Council.
The foreign economic policy of the United States. Three declarations formulated by the National Foreign Trade Council, inc. and approved by the National Foreign Trade Conventions of 1945, 1946 and 1947.   New York ₍1948₎
29 p.   23 cm.

1. U. S.—Commercial policy.   I. Title.

                                           A 49–8175*
North Carolina.   Univ.   Library
for Library of Congress   ₍2₎

NN   0051897   NcU NNC DNAL CaBViP NN

National foreign trade council.

Foreign trade and the domestic welfare; a graphic outline of the basic elements underlying a choice between a liberal interchange of goods or economic isolation.   New York, N. Y., Publication division of the National foreign trade council, inc. and the National foreign trade association ₍1936?₎

NATIONAL FOREIGN TRADE COUNCIL.
"Foreign trade week." Addresses at Latin American and world trade meetings in New York, May 20 and 22, 1935. New York: National Foreign Trade Council [1935]   43 p. 23cm.

824621A. 1. Commerce—U.S., 1935.

NN   0051899   NN

National foreign trade council, inc.
"Foreign trade week." Addresses at world trade meetings. New York: National foreign trade council, inc. ₍etc.₎ 1936.   56 p. 23cm.
Addresses by J. A. Farrell, H. F. Grady, F. H. LaGuardia, Cordell Hull, and others.

1. Commerce—Congresses—   U. S.—N. Y.—New York, 1936.
I. Title.
N. Y. P. L.   May 31, 1938

NN   0051900   NN DNAL

National Foreign Trade Council.
"Greater prosperity through greater foreign trade"
     see under   Fess, Simeon Davidson, 1861–

National foreign trade council, inc.
...Hearing before the Committee on foreign affairs, House of representatives, 81st Congress, 2nd session on H. J. Res 236—International trade organization act.   Statement of National foreign trade council, inc.   Presented...by Mr. Robert F. Loree, chairman.   New York, National foreign trade council ₍1950₎   10 f. 28cm.
At head of title: Ref. no. M–2545.

1. International trade organization   (Proposed).

NN   0051902   NN

Mex   **National Foreign Trade Council.**
HC   Mexican industrial development; statement
135   by the NFTC Committee for Mexico.   New York,
.N9   1949.
          18 l.   28 cm.

Mimeographed.
"Ref.no. M–1299."

NN   0051903   DPU NN

National Foreign Trade Council.   380.973 85
121536   [Minor publications.]

NN   0051904   ICJ

National foreign trade council.
... The National foreign trade council, its purpose, personnel, accomplishments.   New York city, The National foreign trade council, 1918.
15, ₍1₎ p.   23ᶜᵐ.
Issued January 1918.

1. U. S.—Comm.   CA 19–392 Unrev'd
Library of Congress   HF3029.N34 1918

NN   0051905   DLC NN MH

NATIONAL FOREIGN TRADE COUNCIL.
...The National Foreign Trade Council; purposes and personnel, activities and achievements... Twelfth edition. [New York? 1932.]   24 p.   23x10½cm.

NN   0051906   NN

National foreign trade council.
... The new American merchant marine; report and recommendations of the National foreign trade council to the United States Shipping board upon the policy necessary to secure to the American people the permanent retention of the new American merchant fleet, rehabilitated by the emergency of war.   New York city, Issued by the National foreign trade council, 1917.
11 p.   23ᶜᵐ.
1. Merchant marine—U. S.   I. U. S.   Shipping board.   II. Title.

Library of Congress   HE746.N3   20–14887

NN   0051907   DLC NN

National foreign trade council.
Ocean shipping; the basic principles of marine transportation, with particular reference to the foreign trade of the United States; copyright, 1915, the National foreign trade council ...   ₍New York, The National foreign trade council, 1915₎
1 p. l., 152 p.   diagr.   23ᶜᵐ. $0.25

1. Shipping—U. S.   I. Title.
Library of Congress   HE745.N25   15–26914

NN   0051908   DLC OrU OCl DN NN MB NjP

National foreign trade council.
... Ocean shipping: the basic principles of marine transportation, with particular reference to the foreign trade of the United States.   Prepared by the National foreign trade council ...   2d ed., rev. March 1917.   Washington ₍Govt. print. off.₎ 1917.
v, 3–110 p.   23ᶜᵐ.   (₍U. S.₎ 64th Cong. 2d sess.   House.   Doc. 2112)
Bibliography: p. 102.
"Supplement.   First report of the National foreign trade council on the merchant marine": p. 103–110.
1. Shipping.   2. Merchant marine—U. S.   I. Title.

                                           17—26334
Library of Congress   HE745.N25 1917

NN   0051909   DLC NjP OO MiU OU OrU WaS

National foreign trade council.
... Our imports and who use them ...   Classroom ed. ... 4th printing.   New York city, Issued by the National foreign trade council, 1923.
cover-title, 3–30 p.   illus.   27ᶜᵐ.
Index on p. 3 of cover.

1. U. S.—Comm.   I. Title.
                                           24–9462
Library of Congress   HF3031.N3 1923

NN   0051910   DLC DI MiU IU OO WaU Or OrU

VOLUME 407

National foreign trade council.
...Our trade with Latin America...
New York, c 1927.
10 p. (Fact finding pamphlets in foreign
trade: no. 4)

NN   0051911   OClFRB

HF3001
.N3   National Foreign Trade Council.
no.4
1929   Our trade with Latin America; facts from
the record show its vast development and
steady gain. New York [1929]
11 p.   23cm. (Its Fact finding pamphlets in
Foreign trade: no. 4)

1. U. S.—Comm.—Spanish America. 2. Spanish
America—Comm.—U. S. I. Ser.

NN   0051912   ViU

National Foreign Trade Council.
Position of the National Foreign Trade Council
with respect to the Havana charter for an international trade organization
see under   Loree, Robert F

HF1431
.E3   National foreign trade council.

The Economist, *London*.
The principles of trade. New York city, National foreign
trade council, inc. [1944]

National foreign trade council, inc.
...Private enterprise and the point IV program. Recommendations of the National foreign trade council, inc. New York,
1949.   29 p.   23cm.

At head of title: Advance copy.

1. Investments, American, in   foreign countries. 2. Investments,
Foreign. 3. Point four (Economic   policy).
N. Y. P. L.   March 26, 1951

NN   0051915   NN PPFRB

HF3008
.N5   National Foreign Trade Council.

National Foreign Trade Convention.
Proceedings. [1st]–
1914–
New York, National Foreign Trade Council [etc.]

National Foreign Trade Council.
Purposes and personnel, activities and
achievements. Author, 1927.
18 p.

NN   0051917   Or

National Foreign Trade Council.
Record.
New York.
v. 28 cm.

HF296.A162   53–16684 ‡

NN   0051918   DLC MH-BA NN ICRL ViU-L FU

National foreign trade council.

American economic mission to the Far East.
Report of the American economic mission to the Far East;
American trade prospects in the Orient. New York, National
foreign trade council, 1935.

National Foreign Trade Council.
Report of the National Foreign Trade Council on the merchant marine; submitted at the second annual meeting of the
council, New York City, September 23, 1915.   New York, 1915.
15 p.   8°.

1. Shipping—U. S., 1915.
N. Y. P. L.   August 27, 1926

NN   0051920   NN ViU

National foreign trade council.
... Report on European conditions, prepared for the
tenth national foreign trade convention, New Orleans,
La., May 2, 3, 4, 1923. New York city, National foreign
trade council, 1923.
20 p.   22cm.

1. Europe—Econ. condit.—1918– 2. European war, 1914–1918—Reparations.

Library of Congress   HC240.N3   23–18895

NN   0051921   DLC

National foreign trade council, inc.
Resolution on international business agreements adapted by the
board of directors of the National foreign trade council, inc., January 26, 1945.   New York, National foreign trade council [1945]
2 l.   22cm.

1. Cartels, International.
N. Y. P. L.   January 20, 1949

NN   0051922   NN

National Foreign Trade Council.
Revised American foreign trade definitions,
1941. New York [1941?]
16 p.   22 x 10cm.

"Adopted July 30, 1941 by a Joint Committee
representing the Chamber of Commerce of the
United States of America, National Council of
American Importers, Inc. [and] National Foreign
Trade Council, Inc."

NN   0051923   NNC-L WaU-L

National foreign trade council.
Save our mail trade with Cuba...
New York n. d.
21 p.

NN   0051924   OClFRB

National foreign trade council.
... Selected bibliography of foreign trade ...
a carefully digested list of titles representing the con-
census [!] of opinion among leading foreign trade economists, editors, educators and exporters, issued by the National foreign trade council ... New York city, 1922–
v. 23cm.

1. Commerce—Bibl. 2. U. S.—Comm.—Bibl.

Library of Congress   Z7164.C8N2   22–23912

NN   0051925   DLC ICJ MiU OO OCl CU

National Foreign Trade Council.
Sinews of war; a statement of principles by the National Foreign Trade Council recommending to the President and the Congress the co-ordination of price fixing and taxation, with the
maintenance of foreign trade, so as to stimulate production, insure
uninterrupted supplies, maintain national credit and provide a
steady source of war funds.   New York City: National Foreign
Trade Council, 1917.   15(1) p.   8°.

1. Commerce, U. S., 1917. 2. Prices,   —Regulations, U. S. 3. Taxation,
U. S., 1917. 4. European war,   1914– .—Economic aspects, U. S.
5. Title.
N. Y. P. L.   September 4, 1918.

NN   0051926   NN MH

National foreign trade council.
... Sources of our exports; a graphic presentation of
the national service of foreign trade, showing how and
why every man, woman, and child in the United States is
concerned in the steadfast maintenance of our international commerce. New York city, Issued by the National
foreign trade council [1920]
[38] p. illus. (maps) 37½ᶜᵐ.
Thirteen short articles by American business men.

1. U. S.—Comm. I. Title.

Library of Congress   HF3011.N3   21–487

NN   0051927   DLC MiU MB NN ICJ

National foreign trade council.
South American handbook; a compilation of information and statistics regarding the public indebtedness,
foreign commerce and railway development of the South
American republics. New York city, The National trade
council [1915]
xxi, 55 p. incl. tables. 23ᶜᵐ.
"This pamphlet ... is a compilation of the information contained in the
reports of the Department of commerce, the publications of the Pan
American union, the South American, Brazilian and Argentine year books
and the reports of the Council of foreign bondholders (British)"—Foreword.
"Report of the Latin-American trade committee, October 2, 1914":
p. ix–xxi.
1. South America—Econ.   condit. 2. South America—Comm.
3. Debts, Public—South   America. I. U. S. Dept. of commerce. Latin-American   trade committee. II. Title.
15–21661

Library of Congress   HC165.N3

NN   0051928   DLC OO OU MiU OrU WaS OrPR CU

National foreign trade council.

Martínez Fraga, Pedro, 1898–
... Speech delivered at the opening of the Cuban pavilion,
New York World's fair, on May 20, 1939; with appendices on
the outstanding Cuban foreign debt, the civic-military-rural
schools, distribution of national lands, Cuban-American trade
1928–1938, Cuban trade with the United States and the American merchant marine, Cuban sugar and the United States
(world war, 1917), Cuban sugar and the United States (present
conditions), Cuba among the first ten nations trading with the
United States. Washington. D. C., 1939.

National Foreign Trade Council.
... Starting to export; an analysis of the
elementary problems confronting the smaller
manufacturer who is considering becoming an
exporter.   New York, 1919.
21 p.

NN   0051930   MH-BA

National Foreign Trade Council.
...Statement by the National Foreign Trade Council to the
Merchant Marine Committee of the House of Representatives on
the Administration Shipping Bill, H. R. 10,500, in the form intro-
duced January 31, 1916...   New York: National Foreign Trade
Council, 1916.   20 p.   8°.

1. Shipping, U. S. 2. United States.   Shipping Board. 3. United States.
Merchant Marine Committee on   (House, 64:1.).
N. Y. P. L.   October 27, 1917.

NN   0051931   NN

VOLUME 407

137   National foreign trade council.
269.   ... Statement in support of renewal
2.8   of trade agreements act. New York,
          1948.
             5 numb. l. 28cm.
             "Thirty-fifth National foreign trade
          convention, New York City, November
          8,9,10, 1948."

NN   0051932   MH-L

National foreign trade council.
   A statement on foreign economic policy...
New York, 1951. 15 p. 21cm. .

1. United States—Economic relations with foreign
countries.

NN   0051933   NN

National foreign trade council, inc.
   Stenotype report of the proceedings of the Latin
American group session
      see under   Council on inter-American
relations.

National foreign trade council.
   Sterling since the convertibility crisis ...
      see under   National Foreign Trade Council.
International Finance Committee.

National Foreign Trade Council.
   Suggested methods of co-operation in foreign trade; for dis-
cussion at the fourth National Foreign Trade Convention, William
Penn Hotel, Pittsburgh, Pa., January 25–27, 1917... New York,
1917. 30 p.   8°.
   At head of title: Advance sheets.

1. Commerce, U. S. 2. Co-operation   (Commercial), U. S.
N. Y. P. L.   March 24, 1917.

NN   0051936   NN

National Foreign Trade Council.
   Summary of current activities.
New York.
      v.

   Frequency varies.
   Includes supplements: its Bulletin.

NN   0051937   ICRL NN

National Foreign Trade Council.
   Survey of the Netherlands income taxes and
   property taxes

      see under

   Netherlands (Kingdom, 1815-   ) Departement
   van financiën.

HJ4653
.A83C3
Carroll, Mitchell Benedict, 1898–
   Taxation of foreign individuals and companies in the
United States; a survey of legislative and treaty provisions.
New York, National Foreign Trade Council [1946]

National foreign trade council.
   Tributes to Eugene Peeples Thomas; World trade luncheon,
National foreign trade week, May 19, 1941; October 7, 1941,
World trade dinner, twenty-eighth National foreign trade con-
vention. [New York, National foreign trade council, inc. 1942]
      4 p. l., 51 p. front., ports. 23½ᵐ.
   Cover-title: Presentation to Eugene Peeples Thomas of the Captain
Robert Dollar memorial award, 1941.

1. Thomas. Eugene Peeples.   I. Title.
                                                    42–12986
Library of Congress   HF3023.T45N3
                                      [2]   923.373

NN   0051940   DLC

National foreign trade council.
   Tributes to Mr. James A. Farrell. Twenty-fifth anniversary
of the National foreign trade council, inc., and the National
foreign trade convention. New York, National foreign trade
council, inc. [°1939]
      ix p., 1 l., 38 p., 1 l. front. 24½ᵐ.

1. Farrell, James Augustine, 1863–   I. Title.
Library of Congress   CT275.F4255N3   39–18145
——— Copy 2.
Copyright A 131265   [2]   923.373

NN   0051941   DLC MH

National Foreign Trade Council.
   United Kingdom income tax - individuals and
corporations
      · see under   Gt. Brit. British information
services.

National Foreign Trade Council.
   United States foreign trade statistics. New York [1949?]
      iii, 31 p.   28 cm.
   Cover title.
   At head of title: Ref. no. M-1557.

1. U. S.—Comm.   I. Title.

HF3001.N3   382   49–48447*

NN   0051943   DLC

National foreign trade council.
   The war and South American trade, issued September
8, 1914, by the National foreign trade council ... [New
York city, 1914]
      8 p. 23ᵐ. (Information bulletin, no. 1)
   Signed: James A. Farrell, chairman; Robert H. Patchin, secretary.

1. South America—Comm.—U. S. 2. U. S.—Comm.—South America.
3. European war, 1914—   —Economic aspects—South America.   I. Far-
rell, James A., 1863–   II. Title.
Library of Congress   HF3080.N4   16–3324
——— Copy 2.
——— Copy 3.

NN   0051944   DLC

National Foreign Trade Council.
   "The Webb Bill"; report of the National Foreign Trade Coun-
cil on co-operation in foreign trade... Submitted to the fourth
National Foreign Trade Convention, William Penn Hotel, Pitts-
burgh, Pa., at the afternoon session, January 25, 1917.   New
York, 1917.   43 p.   8°.
   Cover-title.

1. Commerce.—Jurisprudence, U. S.,   1917. 2. Co-operation (Commercial),
U. S. 3. European war, 1914— —   Economic aspects, U. S. 4. Title.
N. Y. P. L.   March 22, 1917.

NN   0051945   NN

National Foreign Trade Council.
   World shipping conditions and the American merchant marine; a report by the Committee on the Merchant Marine of
the National Foreign Trade Council, for discussion at the fourth
National Foreign Trade Convention, William Penn Hotel, Pittsburgh, Pa., January 25–27, 1917... New York, 1917. 12 p.
8°.
   At head of title: Advance sheets.

1. Shipping, 1914–   . 2. Shipping,   U. S., 1914–   . 3. European war,
1914–   —Economic aspects.   1914–   .
N. Y. P. L.   March 24, 1917.

NN   0051946   NN

National Foreign Trade Council.
   World trade conditions after the European war; a presenta-
tion of the results of research by the National Foreign Trade
Council to the fourth National Foreign Trade Convention, Wil-
liam Penn Hotel, Pittsburgh, Pa., January 25–27, 1917...   New
York, 1917.   44 p.   8°.

1. European war, 1914–   .—Economic   aspects. 2. Commerce, 1914–   .
N. Y. P. L.   March 24, 1917.

NN   0051947   NN

National foreign trade council.
   ... World trade conditions after the war; an analysis of the
preparations England, France and Germany are now making
to extend their foreign trade. New York city, The National
foreign trade council, 1918.
      72 p. 23ᵐ.

1. European war, 1914–1918—Economic aspects. 2. Commercial policy.
3. Competition, International.   I. Title.
                                                    18—23904
Library of Congress   HC56.N2

NN   0051948   DLC MiU NN

HF3001
.N3   National Foreign Trade Council.
no.1
1928   The world's export trade recovery from the
          war, with comparative statistics for eighty-
          two countries. New York [1928]
             14 p. 24cm. (Its Fact finding pamphlets in
          foreign trade, no. 1)

             1. Commerce—Stat. I. Title. II. Ser.

NN   0051949   ViU

National foreign trade council
      see also
International business conference, Rye, N. Y., 1944.

National Foreign Trade Council
      see also   Joint Committee Representing
   the Chamber of Commerce of the United States
   of America, National Council of American
   Imposters, inc. [and] National Foreign Trade
   Council, inc.

National Foreign Trade Council. *Committee for France.*
   Franco-American economic relations; report. New York,
National Foreign Trade Council, 1947.
      60 p. 23 cm.
   Cover title.

1. U. S.—Comm.—France. 2. France—Comm.—U. S. 3. Reconstruction (1939-   )—France.   I. Title.

HF3098.N3   382   50–17525

NN   0051952   DLC NN

National Foreign Trade Council. *Committee for India and
Pakistan.*
   American economic relations with India and Pakistan;
report. New York, National Foreign Trade Council, 1948.
      50 l. 28 cm.
   Cover title.
   At head of title: Ref. No. M-865.

1. U. S.—Comm.—India. 2. India—Comm.—U. S.   I. Title.

HF3121.N3   330.954   51–38409

NN   0051953   DLC NNC TxU

VOLUME 407

National Foreign Trade Council. Committee for
Mexico.
  Mexican industrial development ...
      see under National Foreign Trade
Council.

National Foreign Trade Council. *Committee for the Low
Countries.*
  Netherlands-American economic relations; report. New
York, National Foreign Trade Council, 1948.
  87 l. 28 cm.

    1. U. S.—Comm.—Netherlands. 2. Netherlands—Comm.—U. S.
  I. Title.
      HF3104.N38   382   52-29087 ‡

NN   0051955   DLC

National Foreign Trade Council. Committee on Co-operation in
Foreign Trade.
  Report of the Committee on Co-operation in Foreign Trade
of the National Foreign Trade Council, on the Webb Bill (H. R.
17350) 1st Session, 64th Congress. ₍New York: the council,
1916.₎ 5 p. 8°.

  Caption-title.

1. Commerce, U. S., 1916.
N. Y. P. L.   August 20, 1917.

NN   0051956   NN

National foreign trade council. *Committee on co-operation in foreign trade.*
  ... Report of the Committee on co-operation in foreign
trade of the National foreign trade council, submitted to
the Judiciary committee of the House of representatives,
July 20, 1916, relative to H. R. 16707 (Webb bill), "An
act to promote export trade, and for other purposes."
July 21, 1916 ... issued by the National foreign trade
council. New York city ₍1916₎
  27 p. 22¼ᶜᵐ.

  1. U. S.—Comm.

                                        17-7851

  Library of Congress   HF3029.N35

NN   0051957   DLC NN

National foreign trade council.
  Committee on foreign trade aspect of the
tariff.
  A bargaining tariff; memorandum submitted
... to the House ways and means committee.
N.Y. 1917.
  15 p.

NN   0051958   ODW MH

National foreign trade council. *Committee on international
business agreements.*
  Memorandum on regulatory measures affecting American
foreign trade. New York, National foreign trade council,
inc., 1944.
  cover-title, vi, 130 p. 21¼ cm.

  "This memorandum has been prepared at the instance of the Committee on international business agreements of the National foreign
trade council, inc., and is submitted, together with covering letter by
counsel, dated August 28, 1944, for information and study."

    1. U. S.—Commercial policy. 2. Trusts, Industrial—U. S.
  I. Title.
      HF1456 1944.N28   337   A 45-3361
  Harvard Univ. Library
  for Library of Congress   ₍a48e1₎†

NN   0051959   MH NNUN DLC OrU DAU NN

National foreign trade council, inc. Cuban committee.
  Cuban sugar and U.S. exports; report of the Cuban committee
of the National foreign trade council, inc. New York, Nat.
foreign trade council, 1945. 8 p. 21cm.

1. Sugar—Trade and stat.—Cuba.
N. Y. P. L.   February 13, 1948

NN   0051960   NN

National Foreign Trade Council. European
Division.
  European export trade promotion; current
measures and the post-war record, a survey
report. New York, 1954.
    pts.in v. 28cm.

    Contents.— pt.1. General appraisal.—
pt.2. Country appraisal. 1. Austria.
2. Belgium. 3. Denmark. 4. France.
5. West Germany. 6. Italy. 7. Netherlands. 8. Norway. 9. Sweden. 10. Switzerland. 11. United Kingdom.

NN   0051961   OrU NNC

National foreign trade council. *Foreign trade education
committee.*
  The problem of foreign trade education; outline of a proposed program of the Foreign trade education committee of
the National foreign trade council, inc. ... New York, N. Y.,
1941-1942. ₍New York, N. Y., 1941₎
  cover-title, 1 p. l., 35 p. incl. tab. 23ᶜᵐ.
  James S. Carson, chairman.

    1. Business education—U. S. 2. Language and languages—Study and
teaching. 3. Intellectual cooperation. ₍3. International education₎ I.
Carson, James S. II. Title. III. Title: Foreign trade education.

                                        E 42-66
  U. S. Off. of educ. Library   HF1131.N3 '
  for Library of Congress   ₍3₎

NN   0051962   DHEW CU-B CoU OrU OU OCU ODW NN

National foreign trade council. *Foreign trade reconstruc-
tion committee.*
  Foreign trade reconstruction studies. no. 1-
New York, N. Y., 1942-
    nos. 22ᶜᵐ.
  Title varies: no. 1, Reconstruction studies.
    no. 2-   Foreign trade reconstruction studies.

    1. Commercial policy. 2. Reconstruction (1939-   ) 3. World war,
1939-   —Transportation. I. Title. II. Title: Reconstruction studies.
                                        43-14501
  Library of Congress   HF1411.N3
                                        ₍10₎   382.082

NN   0051963   DLC DNAL CU OCl OU NNC

National Foreign Trade Council. Foreign Trade
Reconstruction Committee.
  Reconstruction studies
      see its Foreign Trade Reconstruction
Studies.

National foreign trade council. *Foreign trade reconstruction committee.*
  What they say; the quality and scope of support for the Reciprocal trade agreements program, compiled on behalf of the
Foreign trade reconstruction committee of the National foreign
trade council, which is cooperating with the Carnegie endowment for international peace, Committee for economic reconstruction; the Foreign commerce department of the Chamber of
commerce of the United States ... New York city, 1943.
  v, 6-64 p. illus., diagr. 23½ᶜᵐ.
    1. U. S.—Commercial treaties. I. Carnegie endowment for inter-
national peace. Committee for economic reconstruction. II. Chamber
of commerce of the United   States of America. Foreign commerce dept. III. Title.   43-16020
  Library of Congress   HF1731.N285
                                        ₍3₎   337.91

NN   0051965   DLC NN

National Foreign Trade Council. *International Finance
Committee.*
  Sterling since the convertibility crisis; a survey. New
York, National Foreign Trade Council, 1949.
  85 p. 23 cm.
  Cover title.

    1. Currency question—Gt. Brit. 2. Gt. Brit.—Comm. I. Title.

  HG939.N26   332.4942   49-4458*

PPFRB
NN   0051966   DLC OrU NN TxU NIC ICU MB CU PU-W

National foreign trade council--Law committee.
  Protection of industrial and intellectual property in China. Report by Sub-committee on industrial property Law committee of National
foreign trade council, inc. New York, N.Y.,
National foreign trade council, inc., 1945.
  cover-title, 61p.

    1. Copyright--China. 2. Trade-marks--China.
3. Patent laws and legislation--China. I. Title.

NN   0051967   IU OrU NNC MiU-L MiD NcU-L ICU

JX
5326
N21   National foreign trade council, inc. Law committee.
  War claims. Report of the Law committee of
the National foreign trade council, inc, New
York, 1944.
  cover-title, 27 p.

    1. Indemnity. 2. European war, 1914-1918 -
Claims. 3. World war, 1939-1945 - Claims. I.
Title.

NN   0051968   NNC

National Foreign Trade Council, Inc. Middle
East committee.
  United States commercial position in the
Middle East, analysis and recommendations;
report. New York, National foreign trade
council, 1946.
  13 p. 21 cm.
  Cover title.
    1. Commerce--U. S. and the Levant.
    2. Commerce--Levant and the U. S.

NN   0051969   NN

National foreign trade council, inc. Spanish-American advisory
committee.
  ...Circular no. 1– to American creditors having blocked
funds in Spain.

New York, 1937–   nos. 28cm.

  Circulars no. 1–   published irregularly from March 22, 1937 – Dec. 9, 1942.
Nos. 1–10 (March 27, 1937 – Feb. 21, 1939) issued by the Council.
Title varies slightly.

  1. Commerce—U. S. and Spain.   2. Commerce—Spain and U. S.
I. National foreign trade council, inc.
N. Y. P. L.   August 10, 1945

NN   0051970   NN

National foreign trade council, inc. Tax committee.
  Report on regime of tax relief for domestic taxpayers operating
abroad. New York, Tax committee, National foreign trade
council ₍1947₎ 30 p. 23cm.

    1. Corporations—Taxation—U. S. 2. Corporations, Foreign.
N. Y. P. L.   July 13, 1948

NN   0051971   NN

National Foreign Trade Council. Tax Committee.
  War loss recoveries. Report of the Tax Committee ... New York, National Foreign Trade
Council, 1945.
  18 p.

  Cover-title.

NN   0051972   NNC NN

National Foreign Trade Council. Tax Committee.
  Western hemisphere trade corporations;
report. New York, 1944.
  12p. 23cm.

    1. U.S. Commercial policy. 2. Corp-
orations. Taxation. I. Title.

NN   0051973   OrU

VOLUME 407

National foreign trade council. United kingdom committee.
Anglo-American commercial relations; report. 1947.
cover-title, 30 p. tables.
1. Gt. Brit. - Commercial policy.
2. Gt. Brit. - Commerce - U.S. 3. U.S.-Commerce - Gt. Brit.

NN 0051974 NNC

National foreign trade council. Western hemisphere division.
Canadian-United States commercial relations, their development and improvement; report. New York, 1948.
cover-title, 28 l.

1. Canada - Economic conditions - 1945-
2. Canada - Commerce - U. S. 3. U. S. - Commerce - Canada.

NN 0051975 NNC NN

... National foreign trade week bulletin
see under Chamber of commerce of the U.S. of America. Foreign commerce dept.

National foremen's institute, inc.

Lane, Donald F
Analysis of machine shop operations; a manual for training apprentices and learners [by] Donald F. Lane ... New York, Deep River, Conn. [etc.] National foremen's institute, inc., 1943.

National foremen's institute, inc.

Benge, Eugene Jackson.
Breaking the skilled labor bottleneck; how to subdivide labor skills to gain maximum production [by] Eugene J. Benge ... New York, Chicago [etc.] The National foremen's institute, 1942.

National Foremen's Institute.
A chart for the rating of a foreman
see under Bundy, Roy Dalton, 1887-

National foremen's institute, inc.

Bundy, Roy Dalton, 1887- FOR OTHER EDITIONS SEE MAIN ENTRY
Collective bargaining ... by R. D. Bundy ... New York, Chicago [etc.] National foremen's institute, inc., 1942.

National foremen's institute, inc.
Conducting foremen's meetings ... Chicago, Ill., National foremen's institute, inc. [°1929]
2 v. 21ᵐ.
CONTENTS.—I. Leadership methods.—II. Discussion plans.

1. Foremen. 2. Factory management. 3. Efficiency, Industrial. I. Title.
Library of Congress TS155.N18
29–22026 Revised

NN 0052005 DLC NIC OC1

PN4193 **National foremen's institute, inc.**
.D5M35
Maclin, Edward Silver, 1885–
Conference leader training, by Edward S. Maclin ... and Paul T. McHenry ... Chicago, New York [etc.] National foremen's institute, inc. [1945]

National foremen's institute, inc.
Conference leader's source book, by Samuel N. Morrison and the staff of the National foremen's institute, inc. New York, Deep River, Conn. [etc.] National foremen's institute, inc., 1946.
1 v. forms (2 fold.) diagr. 29 x 27ᵐ.
Loose-leaf.
"Slide films and motion pictures": p. 163–168.
Bibliography: p. 499–530.
1. Employment management. 2. Foremen. I. Morrison, Samuel N. II. Title.
TS155.N185 658.3 47–1008

NN 0052007 DLC DNAL WaS ICJ CaBVa

q658.3 **NATIONAL FOREMEN'S INSTITUTE, INC.**
N213c Conference leader's source book, by Samuel
1948 N. Morrison and the staff of the National foremen's institute, inc. New York, Deep River, Conn. [etc.] National foremen's institute, inc., 1948.
1v. forms (2 fold.)diagr. 29 x 27cm.
Loose-leaf.
"Slide films and motion pictures": p.163–168.
Bibliography: p.499–530.
1. Employment management. 2. Foremen. I. Morrison, Samuel N. II. Title.

NN 0052008 TxU LU MB CoU IaU

HD4802 **National Foremen's Institute.**
.E53
Employee relations bulletin. Report
[New York, National Foremen's Institute]

National foremen's institute, inc.
Executive's labor letter
see under title

National Foremen's Institute.
Executive leadership
see under Bureau of Business Practice.

National Foremen's Institute.
The Federal labor laws, a manual for supervisors. [New rev. 1946/47 ed.] New York [1946–
1 v. (loose-leaf) 24 cm.

1. Labor laws and legislation—U. S.
HD7833.N24 331 47–6207*

ICU OC1
NN 0052012 DLC MH–IR MtBC OC1U Mi MiD NcD–L TU

National Foremen's Institute.
The Federal labor laws, a manual for supervisors; compiled and edited by the staff of Executive's labor letter. [New rev. 1950 ed.] New London, Conn. [1951, °1950–
1 v. (loose-leaf) 24 cm.

1. Labor laws and legislation—U. S. I. Executive's labor letter.
331 51–2380 rev

NN 0052013 DLC CU

National Foremen's Institute.

Law
The **Federal** labor laws; the Wagner act, the **Wages and** hours act, the Walsh-Healey act [by] Russell L. Greenman [and] Leslie L. Sanders. A manual for supervisors, foremen and department heads. [New York] National **Foremen's** Institute [1941]

National Foremen's Institute.

The Foreman's letter.
[New London, etc., Conn.] National Foremen's Institute.

National Foremen's Institute.
Foreman's management conferences. Chicago [1941–45]
26 v. 21 cm.
Cover title: Foremanship management conferences.
"Modern foremanship practice, developed from a survey of industry made by the staff of National foremen's institute, inc."
First published in 1929 under title: The foreman's management library.

1. Foremen. 2. Factory management. 3. Personnel management. I. Title. II. Title: Foremanship management conferences.
TS155.N22 658.31243 41–20896 rev 2*

NN 0052016 DLC TU OC1 KMK TxLT CaBVa AAP MiU NNC

National foremen's institute, inc. Foreman's management conferences.

National foremen's institute, inc.
Foremanship conference leader's manual ... New York, Chicago [etc.] National foremen's institute, inc. [°1941]

National foremen's institute, inc., *Chicago.*
The foreman's management library ... Chicago, Ill., National foremen's institute, inc. [°1929]
8 v. 1 illus., diagr. 21ᵐ.
Paged continuously.
"Advanced foremanship methods from a survey of industry, by the staff of the National foremen's institute."—v. 1, p. [3]

1. Foremen. 2. Factory management. 3. Efficiency, Industrial. 4. Psychology, Applied. I. Title.

Library of Congress TS155.N2
29–21000

NN 0052018 DLC OC1

National foremen's institute, inc., *Chicago.*
The foreman's management library ... Chicago, National foremen's institute, inc. [°1937]
8 v. 1 illus., diagr. 21ᵐ.
Paged continuously.
"Advanced foremanship methods from a survey of industry, by the staff of National foremen's institute, inc."—v. 1, p. [3]
CONTENTS.—I. Management.—II. Handling men.—III. Man problems.—IV. Human relations.—V. Increasing output.—VI. Quality maintenance.—VII. Cost control.—VIII. Representing management. Index.
1. Foremen. 2. Factory management. 3. Efficiency, Industrial. 4. Psychology, Applied. I. Title.
Library of Congress TS155.N2 1937
37–4569
———— Copy 2.
Copyright A 104333 [3] 658.31243

NN 0052019 DLC ICJ

658.3124 **National Foremen's Institute, inc.**
N2772f Foremanship conference leader's manual.
New York [c1937]
2pts. in 1v.(looseleaf) 29cm.

pt.1. Technique of conducting successful foremen's conferences.- pt.2. Outlines of foremanship management conferences.

NN 0052020 CLSU DNAL DLC

National foremen's institute, inc.
Foremanship conference leader's manual ... New York, Chicago [etc.] National foremen's institute, inc. [°1941]
1 v. pl. (5 plans) forms (1 mounted) 29 x 25ᵐ.
Loose-leaf; reproduced from type-written copy.
CONTENTS.—pt. I. The technique of conducting successful foremen's conferences. — pt. II. Outlines of twenty-four foremanship management conferences.

1. Foremen. 2. Employment management. 3. Factory management. I. National foremen's institute, inc. Foreman's management conferences. II. Title.
Library of Congress TS155.N225 41–22244
[2] 658.31243

NN 0052021 DLC OC1

658.31243 **National Foremen's Institute, Inc.**
N277f Foremanship conference leader's manual.
1952 New York [1952]
1 v. (loose-leaf)

FOREMEN
EMPLOYMENT MANAGEMENT
FACTORY MANAGEMENT
Foremanship conference leader's manual.

NN 0052022 KMK

VOLUME 407

National Foremen's Institute, inc.
Tho foremanship management service; an organized
plan of foremanship training by the conference
method. [New York, c1937]
cover-title, 24 p. 22cm.
Consists mainly of excerpts from other publications of the Institute.

1. Foremen. 2. Employment management.
3. Factory management.   I. Title.

NN   0052023   MB

National foremen's Institute, inc.
The forgotten stockholder ...
see under   Bureau of business practice,
Chicago.

National Foremen's Institute, Inc.
How the Taft-Hartley bill will affect your
employer-employee relations; an operating guide
for all employers. Prepared by the staff of the
Collective bargaining bulletin of National
Foremen's Institute. New York, N.Y., 1947.
1 fold.l.

Tipped in at end of Hotchkiss, Arthur S. Conference guide to basic management training. 1947.

NN   0052025   MH-BA ICJ Or NcU

HF5549   National Foremen's Institute.
.G5
        Gillett, Albert N
          How to evaluate supervisory jobs; an executive and super-
        visory appraisal manual. New York, National Foremen's
        Institute, 1945.

National foremen's institute, inc.

Farren, Harry Desmond.
  ... How to fight fires resulting from air attacks, by Harry
Desmond Farren ... ₍Deep River,.Conn.₎ National foremen's
institute, inc., ʿ1942.

₍National foremen's institute, inc.₎
How to handle collective bargaining negotiations. This is a
confidential manual for management prepared by "bargaining
experts" in collaboration with the editorial staff of Executive's
labor letter ... ₍New York, ʿ1944₎

1 v. 29½ᵐ.

Loose-leaf.
Reproduced from type-written copy.

1. Collective bargaining.   I. Executive's labor letter.   II. Title.

A 46–1441

Enoch Pratt free library
for Library of Congress   ₍⁷₎

NN   0052028   MdBE OCl MiHM

₍National foremen's institute, inc.₎
How to handle collective bargaining negotiations. This is a
confidential manual for management prepared by C. F. Mugridge ... in collaboration with the editorial staff of Executive's
labor letter ... ₍Deep River, Conn., New York, etc., 1946₎

2 p. l., 39 numb. l.   29½ x 24ᵐ.

"Copyright ... ₍by₎ National foremen's institute, inc."
1944 edition by "bargaining experts" in collaboration with the editorial
staff of Executive's labor letter.

1. Collective bargaining.   I. Mugridge, Clayton Franklin, 1897–
II. Executive's labor letter.

HD6483.N35 1946   331.116   47–22377

NN   0052029   DLC NcRS MB TU IU WaSpG

HD6483   National Foremen's Institute, inc.
.J3
1948   Jacobs, Arthur Theodore, 1912–
          How to handle collective bargaining negotiations under the
        Taft-Hartley act; a manual which tells employers what
        they should know and what they should do in dealing with
        employees who are unionized or are about to be organized.
        By Arthur T. Jacobs and the staff of the Executive's labor
        service. Deep River, Conn., National Foremen's Institute
        ₍1948₎

HD6971   National foremen's institute, inc.
.L3
        Lapp, John Augustus, 1880–
          How to handle labor grievances, plans and procedures, by
        John A. Lapp, LL. D. New York, Deep River, Conn. ₍etc.₎
        National foremen's institute, inc. ₍1945₎

National foremen's institute, inc.
How to keep physically fit
see under   Bonomo, Joe, 1901–

National foremen's institute, inc.

Benge, Eugene Jackson.
  How to make a morale survey; a manual of procedures, by
Eugene J. Benge ... New York, Chicago ₍etc.₎ National fore-
men's institute, inc. ₍ʿ1941₎

HD6483   National Foremen's Institute, inc.
.J3
1947   Jacobs, Arthur Theodore, 1912–
          How to negotiate with labor unions; a manual which tells
        employers what they should know and what they should do in
        dealing with employees who are unionized, or are about to be
        organized. By Arthur T. Jacobs and the staff of the Execu-
        tive's labor service ... Deep River, Conn., National Foremen's
        Institute ₍1947₎

National Foremen's Institute.
  How to operate under the new wage controls, prepared by
the staff of the Employee relations bulletin. New London,
Conn. ₍1951₎

79 p. 21 cm.

1. Wages—U. S.   I. Employee relations bulletin.   II. Title.

HD4935.U4N3   331.2973   51–3416

NN   0052035   DLC

TS155   National foremen's institute, inc.
.O 2
1944   Oberdahn, Richard Charles, 1904–   FOR OTHER EDITIONS
                                          SEE MAIN ENTRY
          How to prepare a foreman's policy manual, by R. C. Ober-
        dahn. New York, Deep River, Conn. ₍etc.₎ National foremen's
        institute, inc. ₍1944₎

National Foremen's Institute.
  How to prepare an employee's handbook, prepared by the
staff of the National Foremen's Institute under the direction
of Charles C. Mercer. Illus. by Michael V. Sintal. New
York, 1946.

1 v. (loose-leaf) illus. 26 cm.

Sample handbook, "You and your job," in pocket.
1. Employees' magazines, handbooks, etc.   I. Title.

HD6975.N3   658.314   49–2756*

NN   0052037   DLC WaS MiD TxU

HD6975   National foremen's institute, inc.
N3   How to prepare an employee's handbook,
        prepared by the staff of the National Fore-
        men's Institute under the direction of
        Charles C.Mercer. Illus. by Michael V.Sin-
        tal. New York, 1948.
          1v.(loose-leaf) illus. 27cm.

1. Employees' magazines, handbooks, etc.
I. Title.

NN   0052038   IaU MiD OrCS

National Foremen's Institute.
  How to prepare an employee's handbook, prepared
by the staff of the National Foremen's Institute
under the direction of Charles C. Mercer; illus.
by Michael V. Sintal. New London, Conn. ₍1954₎
  1 v. (loose-leaf) illus. 26cm.
Sample handbook, "You and your job" in pocket.

1. Employees' magazines, handbooks, etc.
I. Title.

NN   0052039   MB IU

TS155   National foremen's institute, inc.
.O 22
        Oberdahn, Richard Charles, 1904–
          How to select foremen and supervisors, by R. C. Oberdahn.
        Chicago, Deep River, Conn. ₍etc.₎ National foremen's institute,
        inc. ₍1944₎

TS155   National foremen's institute, inc.
.M27
        McHenry, Raymond B   1904–
          How to supervise, a control manual for use by the director
        of the "How to supervise" program ₍by₎ R. B. McHenry and
        Reed Clement. Chicago, Deep River, Conn. ₍etc.₎ National
        foremen's institute, inc., 1944.

T65   National foremen's institute, inc.
.B83   FOR OTHER EDITIONS
1946   SEE MAIN ENTRY
        Bundy, Roy Dalton, 1887–
          How to teach a job, by R. D. Bundy ... New York, Deep
        River, Conn. ₍etc.₎ National foremen's institute, inc. ₍1946₎

HD7255   National foremen's institute, inc.
.J3
        Jacobs, Arthur Theodore, 1912–
          How to use handicapped workers, by Arthur T. Jacobs.
        New York, Deep River, Conn. ₍etc.₎ National foremen's insti-
        tute, inc. ₍1946₎

National Foremen's Institute.
  Human relations casebook; a practical guide on how to
avoid grievances. ₍Prepared and edited by the staff of the
Employee relations bulletin₎ New London, Conn. ₍1953₎

112 p. 21 cm.

1. Master and servant—U. S.—Cases. 2. Collective labor agreements—U. S.—Cases. 3. Personnel management.   I. Employee
relations bulletin.   II. Title.

658.3   53–30442 ‡

OOxM NN NcD MB TU ViU Wa
NN   0052044   DLC CaBVa MtBuM Or OrU AAP PP OClJC

National foremen's institute, inc.
  If you paid the bills. Chicago ₍etc.₎ National foremen's inst.,
c1937. 4 p. 20cm.

1. Machinery—Depreciation.
N. Y. P. L.   May 16, 1945

NN   0052045   NN NNC

VOLUME 407

National foremen's institute, inc.

Rosenfeld, Milton A., 1886–
The industrial cafeteria and restaurant worker's manual, by Milton A. Rosenfeld ... New York, Chicago [etc.] National foremen's institute, inc. [1943]

HV8290
.F33
1943

National foremen's institute, inc.

FOR OTHER EDITIONS SEE MAIN ENTRY

Farren, Harry Desmond.
Industrial guard's manual; what an industrial guard should know, by Harry Desmond Farren ... New York, Chicago [etc.] National foremen's institute, inc., 1943.

TD895
.V5

National foremen's institute, inc.

Vincent, R   F
The industrial housekeeping manual, methods, schedules, and organization, by R. F. Vincent. New York, Deep River, Conn. [etc.] National foremen's institute, inc. [1945]

National foremen's institute, inc., *Chicago.*
Industrial relations conferences ... A report of actual conferences prepared by R. D. Bundy ... New York, Chicago, National foremen's institute, inc. [°1938]
20 no. in 1 v.   port. 29½°°.
On cover: Industrial relations conferences for supervisors.
CONTENTS.—no. 1. Responsibilities of the modern foreman.—no. 2. Handling men.—no. 3. Reasons for individual differences.—no. 4. Work environment as a control factor.—no. 5. The foreman as a leader.—no. 6. Individual self-analysis.—no. 7. Leadership and discipline.—no. 8. Discipline as a positive measure.—no. 9. Cooperation—an end in itself.—no. 10. The line foreman—then and now.—no. 11. The staff man and his place in industrial organization.—no. 12. Why collective bargaining is here.—no. 13. Purpose and use of collective bargaining.—no. 14. Charting

the way for collective bargaining.—no. 15. Procedure for handling complaints.—no. 16. Looking at the representative's job.—no. 17. Seniority as a determining factor.—no. 18. Problem of accurate measurement of human traits.—no. 19. Rating as a tool of management.—no. 20. Rating as a basis for diagnosis and treatment.

1. Efficiency, Industrial. 2. Foremen. 3. Employment management.
I. Bundy, Roy Dalton, 1887–   II. Title.

A 40–2023

Illinois. Univ. Library
for Library of Congress   [2]

NN 0052050   IU NcRS ViU TU ICJ OClW ICU InLP

NATIONAL FOREMEN'S INSTITUTE, INCORPORATED
Job handbook for supervisors. Author c1947.
32 p. illus.

NN 0052051   Or

National Foremen's Institute.
Job safety training manual
see under   Faist, Kenneth L.

National foremen's institute, inc.
Keeping men fit; a foreman's management supplement. Chicago [etc.] National foremen's inst. [c1937] 17 p. 20cm.

1. Industrial betterment.
N.Y.P.L.   February 27, 1945

NN 0052053   NN DLC NNC

National foremen's institute, inc.

Lapp, John Augustus, 1880–
Labor arbitration, principles and procedures, by John A. Lapp ... New York, Chicago [etc.] National foremen's institute, inc., 1942.

HF5549
.S8438

National Foremen's Institute.

Stessin, Lawrence, *ed.*
Labor relations work kit, edited by Lawrence Stessin and the staff of Employee relations bulletin. New London, Conn., National Foremen's Institute [°1950]

HD6483
.B25

National Foremen's Institute, inc.

Baade, William J
Management strategy in collective bargaining negotiations; how to negotiate and write a better union contract, by William J. Baade, Jr., with the assistance of Morris Stone. New London, Conn., National Foremen's Institute [1950]

National foremen's institute, inc.
Manual of industrial relations. Prepared by the staff of the Executive's labor letter, und[er] the direction of Bruno R. Neumann and Arthur T. Jacobs. New York, National foremen's institute inc., 1946.
x, 185 p.
1. Industrial relations. I. Neumann, Bruno R II. Jacobs, Arthur Theodore, 1912–   III. Title.

NN 0052057   NNC MiD NBC

HD
31
N3M3

National Foremen's Institute.
Manual of industrial relations, prepared by the staff of the Executive's Labor Letter under the direction of Bruno R. Neumann and Arthur T. Jacobs. New York, 1947.
x, 191 p.   29 cm.

1. Industrial organization. I. Neumann, Bruno R. II. Jacobs, Arthur Theodore, 1912–   III. Title.

NN 0052058   NBuU

658
qN277m

National foremen's institute, inc.
Manual of industrial relations, prepared by the staff of the Executive's labor letter, under the direction of Bruno R. Neumann and Arthur T. Jacobs. N.Y. [etc.] 1948.
191p. 29cm.

Loose-leaf.

1. Industrial Management. I. Executive's labor letter.

NN 0052059   N WaU MtBuM OrU

National foremen's institute, inc., Chicago.
[Miscellaneous publications. c1938–

Unbound pamphlets.

1. Efficiency, Industrial. 2. Foremen. 3. Employment management.

NN 0052060   NNC

National foremen's institute, inc.

Brannon, Jerald A   Foster
Modern industrial leadership ... a special program of ten lecture-conferences on "How foremen can meet today's challenge," by Dr. Jerald A. Foster Brannon ... Deep River, Conn., Chicago, Ill. [etc.] National foremen's institute, inc.
[1942–

National Foremen's Institute, inc.
NFI supplement to the federal labor laws. New York [1950]
1v.(various pagings) 30cm. [Bound with its Pitfalls to avoid in labor arbitration. New York, 1947]

1. Labor laws and legislation. U.S. I. Title.

NN 0052062   IEN

National foremen's institute, inc.
NFI wage rate and contract provisions. Report "C" ... [New York, 1948]
81 p. tables.

"[Prepared] under the supervision of Burton B. Bendiner and Edith M. Bergstrom, members of the Editorial board."
"Collective bargaining bulletin. Special report, 'C'."
1. Labor-management relations act, 1947. 2. Labor contract – U. S. 3. Wages – U. S.

NN 0052063   NNC

NATIONAL FOREMEN'S INSTITUTE, INCORPORATED
The National foremen's institute; what it is and how it works. [°527 Fifth Ave., New York]
Author, [1946?]
32 p. illus.

NN 0052064   Or

[NATIONAL FOREMEN'S INSTITUTE,
The 1950 social security act; what it means to you and your family. [Author] c1950.
24 p. illus.

NN 0052065   Or

National foremen's institute, inc.
Outlines of twenty four foremanship management conferences; designed to be used in conjunction with texts prepared for twenty-four conferences on modern foremanship practice. [Chicago]
Author, c1937.
99 p.

NN 0052066   WaS

National foremen's institute.
Pitfalls to avoid in labor arbitration; a practical guide for writing labor arbitration clauses and handling arbitration cases. This is a confidential manual for management prepared by "labor arbitration experts" in collaboration with the editorial staff of Executive's labor letter ... [Deep River, Conn., 1946]
2 p. l., 4–56 numb. l. 29½ x 24 cm.
On cover: National foremen's institute, inc.
1. Arbitration, Industrial. 2. Collective bargaining. I. Executive's labor letter. II. Title.

HD5481.N33   331.155   46–8298 rev

NN 0052067   DLC OrU TxU

331.1
N22p
1950

[National Foreman's Institute, inc.]
Pitfalls to avoid in labor arbitration; a practical guide for writing labor arbitration clauses and handling arbitration cases, including a detailed analysis of the Labor-management relations act of 1947. This is a confidential manual for management prepared by "labor arbitration experts" in collaboration with the editorial staff of Executive's labor letter. [Deep River, Conn., 1950]
56 l., 13p. 30cm.

"NFI supplement   to the Federal labor laws" (57p.) in-   serted.

NN 0052068   IU

T58
.B336

National foremen's institute, inc.

Benge, Eugene Jackson.
Postwar supervision ... by Eugene J. Benge ... New York, Deep River, Conn. [etc.] National foremen's institute, inc.
[1945]

VOLUME 407

National foremen's institute, inc.
    Protect yourself
        see under Bonomo, Joe, 1901-

National foremen's institute, inc.
  ⟨Publications⟩ ⟨Chicago. °1945⟩

  Library has
  Job handbook for supervisors. °1945.
  How to keep ahead of your job. °1945.
  What the foreman needs for success. °1945.
  How to train your assistants by Richard W.
  Wetherell. °1945.

NN 0052071   MiD

⟨NATIONAL FOREMEN'S INSTITUTE⟩
  Qualified for promotion? ⟨Author⟩ c1945.
  cover-title, ⟨10⟩ p. illus.

NN 0052072   Or

National foremen's institute, inc.
                  FOR OTHER EDITIONS
Farren, Harry Desmond. **SEE MAIN ENTRY**
  Sabotage, how to guard against it, by Harry Desmond Farren. New York, Deep River, Conn. ⟨etc.⟩ National foremen's institute, inc. ⟨1942⟩

National foremen's institute, inc.
  Self analysis. Chicago, New York, National foremen's institute ⟨1941⟩
  2 p. l., 3-18 p. illus., diagr. 21½ᵐ.

  1. Foremen. 2. Factory management. I. Title.
                                   41–28089
Library of Congress   TS155.N227 1941

NN 0052074   DLC

National foremen's institute, inc.
  Self analysis, a foreman's management supplement. Chicago, National foremen's institute ⟨°1937⟩
  cover-title, 3-17 p. illus., diagr. 20½ᵐ.

  1. Foremen. 2. Factory management. I. Title.
                                     41–28088
Library of Congress   TS155.N227 1937
                    ⟨2⟩   658.31243

NN 0052075   DLC NNC

National Foremen's Institute, inc.
  Self analysis for supervisors. Chicago, New York, National foremen's institute [c1941]
  18 p. illus., diagr. 22 cm.
  1. Foremen. 2. Factory management. I. Title.

NN 0052076   CU

National foremen's institute, inc.
  Selling the job to the home folks; a foremanship management supplement. Chicago ⟨etc.⟩ National foremen's inst. ⟨1937⟩
  18 p. illus. 20cm.

  1. Labor.
N. Y. P. L.   February 27, 1945

NN 0052077   NN DLC NNC

National foremen's institute, inc.
  The seven steps to success; a foreman's management supplement. Chicago ⟨etc.⟩ National foremen's inst. ⟨c1937⟩ 17 p.
  20cm.

  1. Success. 2. Labor—Ethics.
N. Y. P. L.   March 13, 1945

NN 0052078   NN NNC DLC

            National Foremen's Institute.
HF5549
.S844   **Stessin, Lawrence.**
        Source book of personnel forms, a manual for improving personnel administration. New York, National Foremen's Institute ⟨1948⟩

National foremen's institute, inc.
  Supervising the woman war worker. Deep River, Conn., National foremen's institute, inc. ⟨1942⟩
  34 p. 20ᵐ.

  1. Employment management. 2. Woman—Employment. 3. World war, 1939- —Women's work. I. Title.
                                          43—440
  Library of Congress   TS155.N228
               ⟨43r2⟩   658.3124

NN 0052080   DLC OrP WaS DAS OCl OU

658.059 **National Foremen's Institute, Inc.**
N277   Supervisor's almanac, 1952. ⟨Comp. by Whitney Williams and the editorial staff⟩ New London, Conn. ⟨1951⟩
     415 p. forms., tables. 24 cm.

    1. Almanacs. 2. Business. Forms, blanks, etc. I. Title.

NN 0052081   N

NATIONAL FOREMEN'S INSTITUTE, INCORPORATED
    The supervisor's guide to the Taft-Hartley act. How the Labor management relations act of 1947 affects relations between foremen supervisors, department heads and company employees. ⟨Rev. ed.⟩ Nat. Foremen c1948.
    23 p.

NN 0052082   Or

658.3   **National Foremen's Institute, Inc.**
N213S   Supervisor's human relations pamphlet library. New London, c1942-1952.
    15 pamphlets in box. illus.

    1. Employment management.
   I. Title.

NN 0052083   WaT OCl

HF5549 **National Foreman's Institute.**
N19   ⟨The supervisor's human relations pocket library. A collection of booklets written for supervisors and designed to help them develop their ability to supervise people. New London, Conn., °1947-51⟩
    15 pamphlets in 2 v. illus. 24cm.

    1. Personnel management. 2. Foremen.
  I. Title.

NN 0052084   OrCS

National foremen's institute, inc.
  Ten thousand dimes. Chicago ⟨etc.⟩ National foremen's inst., c1937. 4 p. 20cm.

  1. Labor—Ethics.
N. Y. P. L.   February 27, 1945

NN 0052085   NN NNC

National Foremen's Institute, Inc.
  Union contract clause finder. Prepared and Edited by the Staff of the Employee Relations Bulletin. New London, Conn. ⟨1953⟩
  1 v. (looseleaf) 30 cm.

    1. Collective labor agreements--U. S.
  2. Labor laws & legislation--U. S. I. Title.

NN 0052086   AkU MiD PP TU IU

National foremen's institute, inc.

Nevins, Arthur W
  Wage and salary stabilization; a manual of questions and answers for employers, executives, and employees, by Arthur W. Nevins ... New York, Deep River, Conn. ⟨etc.⟩ National foremen's institute, inc. ⟨°1942⟩

        National Foremen's Institute.
HD4975
.W3   **Wage rate report.**
    Deep River, Conn., National Foremen's Institute.

National foremen's institute, inc.
  "The Wagner act" and its effect on labor relations; one of a series of reports especially prepared for executives on federal laws affecting business; prepared by the editorial staff of the National foremen's institute ... New York, N.Y. ⟨New York, National foremen's institute, 1937?⟩
  2 p. l., 21 numb. l. 33½ᶜᵐ.
  Mimeographed.
  "Bibliography": leaf 21.

NN 0052089   MiU-L

        National foremen's institute, inc.
TS155
.B728 **Bundy, Roy Dalton**, 1887–
    What price supervision; how management can build a stronger supervisory force, by R. D. Bundy ... New York, Deep River, Conn. ⟨etc.⟩ National foremen's institute, inc. ⟨1946⟩

National foremen's institute, inc.
  What the foreman needs for success. ⟨Deep River, Conn.: National foremen's institute, 1942⟩ 4 l. 18cm.

  1. Foremanship and foremen.
N. Y. P. L.   February 9, 1944

NN 0052091   NN

⟨NATIONAL FOREMEN'S INSTITUTE, INCORPORATED⟩
  What the new labor management relations act means to you. ⟨Deep River, Conn., Author⟩ c1947.
  22 p.

NN 0052092   Or

VOLUME 407

National foremen's institute, inc.
When employees organize; what employers should know, and how they can utilize National labor relations board procedures... New York [etc., c1946] 35 p. 20cm.

1. Employer and employed. 2. Trade unions.

NN 0052093 NN

HD6488
.B8
National foremen's institute, inc.
Buswell, D   E
Who wants "union security?" By D. E. Buswell. [Deep River, Conn., National foremen's institute, inc., 1945]

National foremen's institute, inc.
Nevins, Arthur W
Your pay envelope; rates for overtime and holidays, wage increases, payroll taxes and deductions, benefits for workers, as provided for under the new federal laws, by Arthur W. Nevins. [Deep River, Conn., National foremen's institute, inc., 1943]

National forensic handbook
   see   National directory of speech associations.

National Forensic League.
   Bulletin
   see
   The Rostrum. Ripon, Wis.

National forensic league, Ripon, Wis.
Current contest readings, recommended by the National forensic league ... [1941–
New York, Dramatists play service [c1941–

National Forensic League.
National championship debate, 1933, Hutchinson, Kansas versus Altus, Oklahoma. Resolved: That at least fifty per cent of all State and local revenues should be derived from sources other than tangible property. Ripon, Wis. [c1933]
31 p. ports. 22 cm.
Broadcast over the Columbia network, May 11, 1933.

1. Taxation—U. S. 2. Revenue—U. S. I. Title.

HJ2377.N34   336.20973   33–30839 rev*

NN 0052099 DLC

PN4185
.R6
National Forensic League.
The Rostrum. v. [1]–
Sept. 1926–
[Ripon, Wis., etc.]

NATIONAL FORENSIC LEAGUE, RIPON, WIS.
The work of the National forensic league; training youth for leadership. Author [1953]
[16] p.

NN 0052101 Or

KB178
M6N3
National Forest Advisory Council.
Report on the problem of mining claims on the national forests. U.S. Forest Service. [Washington, U.S. Govt. Print. Off.] 1953. vi, 125 p. illus., map. 27 cm.

1. Mining law – U.S. 2. Forest reserves – U.S. I. U.S. Forest Service. II. Title: Mining claims on the national forests.

NN 0052102 DI DNAL

National forest park guides
   see under   Gt. Brit. Forestry Commission.

National Forest Products Association.
Forest products industry facts.
Washington.
   v. illus. 28 cm.

1. Forest products—U. S.—Statistics. 2. Wood-using industries—U. S.—Statistics. I. Title.

HD9754.N25   74–615554

NN 0052104 DLC OrU N ICJ

National Forest Products Association
   see also   National Lumber Manufacturers Association.

National forest reservation commission (U.S.)
   see   U.S. National forest reservation commission.

National forests.
(In U. S. Dept. of agriculture. Yearbook, 1915, p. 579-584; Washington, 1916-   )   23cm.

1. Forest reserves.

Agr 16–456
Library, U. S. Dept. of   Agriculture 1Ag84Y

NN 0052107 DNAL

... The national forests of New Mexico. Washington, Govt. print. off., 1922.
21 p. illus., fold. map. 23cm. (U. S. Dept. of agriculture. Department circular 240)
Contribution from the Forest service.

1. Forest reserves—New Mexico.

Agr 22–1208
Library, U. S. Dept. of   Agriculture 1Ag84D no. 240

NN 0052108 DNAL CU CaBVaU WaWW

Day-NW
SD
428
A2
I26
The National forests of southern Idaho: Industrial activities; recreation advantages. [n.p., 1917?]
29 p. 27cm.

Typewritten copy.

1. Forest reserves - Idaho. 2. Forests and forestry - Idaho.

NN 0052109 IdU

National forging talk
   see under   National Machinery Company, Tiffin, Ohio.

The National formulary. London
   see
   British national formulary.

The National formulary. 1st– ed.; 1888–
Washington [etc.] American Pharmaceutical Association [etc.]
   v. illus. 24 cm.
Title varies: 1888, The National formulary of unofficial preparations.—1896-1906, The National formulary of unofficial preparations.
Vols. for 1916–   prepared by the association's Committee on National Formulary.
Vols. for 1888-96 issued also with the association's Proceedings. Separately paged supplements accompany some volumes.

1. Medicine—Formulae, receipts, prescriptions. I. American Pharmaceutical Association. II. American Pharmaceutical Association. Committee on National Formulary.

RS141.2.N3   615.1373   55—4116

PLFM CoDR
MtU WaU DFT PU PPF MoKU FU DI NcGU IaU TU MiHM PPT-M IdU-M IU CU CoU CoFS ICRL OC1W-H WaSp WaE ICU WaTC WaT NjP NNC-M PP OrStbM PHC TxU NcD PPC OC1W MtBC Or OrP WaS ICJ OC1 NN CoCC CoDU ICRL OrCS N NbU MBCo LU MWA CaBVaU DNAL Wa WaS WaWW DSI MiU MB AzU WyU CSt ViU UU KU UPB OrU-M PU-V OrU-D NBuC TxDaM DNLM CtY-KS CLSU FTaSU CtY-M OU
NN 0052112 DLC OrU IdU MsU NcGU IdPI CaBVaU OrSaW

The National Formulary.
   Abstract of changes and additions
   see under   Mallinckrodt Chemical Works.

RS151
.2
.D5
The national formulary.
The Dispensatory of the United States of America. [1st]– ed. Philadelphia, Grigg, Elliot, and co. [etc.] 1833–49; J. B. Lippincott company [etc.] 1851–19

RS141
.2
.P53
1955
National formulary.   FOR OTHER EDITIONS SEE MAIN ENTRY
The pharmacopœia of the United States of America.
Epitome of the Pharmacopeia of the United States and the National formulary, with comments. Issued under the direction and supervision of the Council on Pharmacy and Chemistry of the American Medical Association. 10th ed. Philadelphia, Lippincott [c1955]

The national formulary.
[The Pharmaceutical era]   FOR OTHER EDITIONS SEE MAIN ENTRY
The Era key to the USP xi & NF vi. 5th ed. rev. by Lyman D. Fonda ... Newark, N. J., The Haynes & George co., inc. [c1939]

The national formulary.
The pharmacopoeia of the United States of America.
Formulary of U. S. pharmacopoeia, U. S. P. and National formulary, N. F., drugs and preparations. [Philadelphia] Philadelphia county medical society, 1934.

National formulary.
Wright, John Shepard, 1870–   comp.
A guide to the organic drugs of the ninth revision of the United States pharmacopoeia, 1916, the third revision of the National formulary, and a few of the more commonly used unofficial drugs ... Comp. and arranged by John S. Wright; revisions and additions by Francis A. Federer and Harry W. Tuft. 3d revision, with appendix. 70th thousand. Prepared for students of pharmacy. Indianapolis, The Botanical department [E. Lilly & company] 1917.

VOLUME 407

RS125
.A48

The National formulary.

American pharmaceutical association.
Materials and preparations for diagnostic use; a preprint of the tentative revision of the National formulary VI chapter as prepared by the special N. F. committee on clinical laboratory preparations, Louis Gershenfeld, chairman, A. B. Nichols, secretary. E. N. Gathercoal, chairman, National formulary committee ... Washington, D. C., American pharmaceutical association (·1939·)

The National formulary.   FOR OTHER EDITIONS
SEE MAIN ENTRY
The pharmacopœia of the United States of America.
Physicians' manual of the Pharmacopeia and the National formulary; an epitome of all the articles contained in the U. S. P. (eighth revision) and the National formulary (third revision) by C. S. N. Hallberg ... and J. H. Salisbury ... 2d ed.—rev. Chicago, American medical association, 1908.

The National formulary.

The pharmacopœia of the United States of America.
Revised Physician's pocket manual; useful drugs, chemicals and preparations. Abstracted from the latest editions of the U. S. pharmacopœia XI and the National formulary VI; prepared by the U. S. P. and N. F. committee of the N. Y. state pharmaceutical assn. New York, 1936.

RS141
.2
.P6F8

The National Formulary.
Fuller, Horace James.
A synopsis of the United States pharmacopeia and National formulary preparations, giving the Latin and English titles, synonyms, composition, method of preparation, strength and doses, by H. J. Fuller ... for pharmaceutical and medical students. Philadelphia, P. Blakiston's son & co., inc. (·1931·)

National formulary committee
see
American pharmaceutical association. *Committee on National formulary.*

The National formulary of unofficial preparations
see
The National formulary.

National Forum, *Chicago*
see
National Forum Foundation.

BF 724
N3

National Forum Foundation.
About growing up ... Chicago, Ill. (·1950, c1949·)
222 p. illus. 25 cm. (National Forum guidance series)

BF 724
N3
Guide

——— Teacher's guide. Chicago, Ill. (·1950·)
96 p. 22 cm. (National Forum guidance series)

NN   0052127   OU NcD CaBVa CaBViP

National Forum Foundation.
About growing up; prepared by the guidance staff of National Forum inc.: Fred R. Bellmar (and others) Chicago (·1954, ·1949·)
222 p. illus. 25 cm. (National Forum guidance series)

1. Adolescence.   I. Title.

BF724.N3   136.7354   55-2756 ‡

NN   0052128   DLC NcGU

National forum foundation.
The alcohol problem. Chicago, Ill., The National forum (·1940·)
96 p. illus. (part col.) diagrs. 25½ x 19 cm. (Its Publications. 8)
Cover-title: The alcohol problem visualized.
"Second edition 1940 enlarged, redesigned, and rewritten."
Published, 1938, under title: Alcohol problems visualized.
"Suggested reading": p. 94-96; bibliography at end of each chapter.

1. Liquor problem—U. S. 2. Alcohol—Physiological effect.
I. Title.

HV5060.N3 1940   178.10973   41-2118 rev

NN   0052129   DLC ICJ Or OrCS OU OCl

National forum foundation.
The alcohol problem. Chicago, Ill., The National forum (·1942·)
96 p. illus. (part col.) diagrs. 25½ cm.
Cover-title: The alcohol problem visualized.
"Third edition, 1942, revised."
Published, 1938, under title: Alcohol problems visualized.
"Suggested reading": p. 94-95. Bibliography at end of each chapter.

1. Liquor problem—U. S. 2. Alcohol—Physiological effect.
I. Title.

HV5060.N3 1942   178.1   43-17406 rev

NN   0052130   DLC

National Forum Foundation.
The alcohol problem. Prepared by the staff of National Forum, inc.: W. Russell Shull, president and managing editor; editorial committee: Chester M. Kearney, chairman (and others) Rev. 4th ed.) Chicago (·1948·)
96 p. illus. (part col.) 26 cm.
On cover: The alcohol problem visualized.
Published 1938, under title: Alcohol problems visualized.
"Suggested reading": p. 94-95.

1. Liquor problem—U. S. 2. Alcohol—Physiological effect.
I. Title.

HV5060.N3 1948   178.1   48-7658 rev*

CaBVa
NN   0052131   DLC WaT OrP Wa Or OrCS Mi MU NRU

National forum foundation.
Alcohol problems visualized. (·Chicago·) The National forum (·1938·)
cover-title, (45) p. illus. (part col.) diagrs. 27½ cm.
Bibliography: p. (45)

1. Liquor problem—U. S. 2. Alcohol—Physiological effect.
I. Title.

HV5060.N3 1938   178.10973   40-1064 rev

NN   0052132   DLC NcD NN OrU SdSpeT

HV
5060
N3
1950

National forum foundation.
The alcohol problem visualized. Prepared by the staff of National forum, inc. ... Chicago, Ill., National forum, inc. (·1950·)
96 p. illus. 26 cm.
"Revised fifth edition, 1950."
"Suggested reading": p. 94-95.

1. Liquor problem – U. S. 2. Alcohol – Physiological effect. I. Title.

NN   0052133   Vi OrPS CaBVa NcU WaE OrU-M OrCS WaT

National Forum Foundation.
The alcohol problem visualized. Prepared by the staff of National Forum inc.: W. Russell Shull, president and managing editor; editorial committee: Chester M. Kearney, chairman (and others). Rev. 5th ed.) Chicago (·1955, ·1950·)
96 p. illus. 26 cm.
First published in 1938 under title: Alcohol problems visualized.

1. Liquor problem—U. S. 2. Alcohol—Physiological effect.
I. Title.

HV5060.N3 1955   *616.86 178.1   55-2722 ‡

NN   0052134   DLC Or OrP OrStbM

National Forum Foundation.
Being teen-agers; prepared by the guidance staff of National Forum inc.: Bernice L. Neugarten (and others) Chicago (·1950·)
270 p. illus. 25 cm. (National Forum guidance series)

NN   0052135   LU OU NcD DCU WaS CaBViP

National Forum Foundation.
Being teen-agers; prepared by the guidance staff of National Forum inc.: Bernice L. Neugarten (and others) Chicago (·1955, ·1950·)
270 p. illus. 25 cm. (National Forum guidance series)

1. Adolescence.   I. Title.

BF724.N32   136.7354   55-2755 ‡

NN   0052136   DLC NcGU

NATIONAL FORUM Foundation
Cooperation visualized. Chicago, Author (·1937·)
(·44·) p.

NN   0052137   OrU Or

National forum Foundation
Discovering myself, prepared by the Guidance staff ... Chic. National forum inc. [c1946].
146 p. illus. O. (National forum guidance series)

NN   0052138   Wa CaBViP

National Forum, Foundation.
Discovering myself, prepared by the Guidance Staff of National Forum, Inc. Bernice L. Neugarten [and others] Chicago [1947]
146 p. illus. 25 cm. (National forum guidance series, Book II)

NN   0052139   PU

National forum Foundation.
... Discovering myself, prepared by the guidance staff of National forum inc ... Chicago [1950]
1 p.l., 5-146 p. illus. 24 cm. (National forum guidance series)
"Copyright 1946".

NN   0052140   NcD OU

National Forum Foundation.
Discovering myself; prepared by the guidance staff of National Forum Foundation: Bernice L. Neugarten (and others. 2d ed.) Chicago (·1955·)
286 p. illus. 25 cm. (National Forum guidance series)
Includes bibliographies.

1. Conduct of life.   I. Title.

BJ1661.N3 1955   *179 170   55-35830 ‡

NN   0052141   DLC ICRL AU NcGU IdRR

National forum Foundation
Farm problems visualized. Chicago (·1937·) 20p. illus.

NN   0052142   CaBVa

Film
1113
no. 25

NATIONAL Forum Foundation.
Health problems visualized by the National Forum. Chicago (·1937·)
1 v. (unpaged) illus.
Film copy.
1. Health education – U. S.

NN   0052143   DNLM

VOLUME 407

National forum Foundation
High school life, prepared by the Guidance staff of National forum. Chicago ₍cl946₎
145 p. illus. 27 cm. (National forum guidance series, 1)

NN   0052144   MtU CaBViP Wa OU

National forum Foundation.
... High school life, prepared by the guidance staff of National forum inc. ... Chicago, Ill. [1949]
1 p.l., 5-145 p. illus. 24 cm. (National forum guidance series)
"Copyright 1946".

NN   0052145   NcD

National Forum Foundation.
Our school life; prepared by the guidance staff of National Forum inc.: Bernice L. Neugarten ₍and others₎. 2d ed.₎ Chicago ₍cl954₎
227 p. illus. 25 cm. (National Forum guidance series)
First ed. published in 1946 under title: High school life.

1. Personnel service in secondary education.   I. Title.

LB1620.5.N3 1954   371.42   55-35362 ‡

NN   0052146   DLC AU NcGU ICRL

National forum Foundation
Planning my future, prepared by the Guidance staff ... Chic. National forum inc.[cl946].
146p. illus. O. (National forum guidance series)

NN   0052147   CaBViP

National forum Foundation.
... Planning my future, prepared by the guidance staff of National forum inc. ... Chicago [1948]
1 p.l., 5-146 p. illus. 24 cm. (National forum guidance series)
"Copyright 1946".

NN   0052148   NcD

National forum foundation.
Social problems visualized ... Chicago, Ill., The National forum, ₍1937₎
₍220₎ p. incl. illus., plates (part col.) diagrs. 29 cm.
Includes bibliographies.

1. Social problems. 2. Graphic methods. 3. U. S.—Econ. condit.—1918— 4. U. S.—Soc. condit. I. Title.

HN57.N35 1937   309.173   38-5894 rev

NN   0052149   DLC OrU NcD OCIW OO

National forum foundation.
Social problems visualized ... Chicago, Ill., The National forum, 1939.
₍225₎ p. incl. illus., col. plates, diagrs. 29 x 23 cm.
Reproduced from type-written copy.
Various pagings.
Includes bibliographies.

1. Social problems. 2. Graphic methods. 3. U. S.—Econ. condit.—1918— 4. U. S.—Soc. condit. I. Title.

HN57.N35 1939   309.173   43-48327 rev

NN   0052150   DLC OCI NcD

National Forum, Foundation.
...Social studies charts, visualized. no.

Chicago ₍19   nos.   28-57cm.
Each chart has explanatory text suppl. (28cm.)
The charts, each with special title, are numbered consecutively and form five sections, as follows:
Civics. no.
Economics. no.
International. no.
Sociology. no.
Welfare. no.

1. Statistics—Per. and soc. publ.   —U. S. 2. Social sciences—Per. and soc. publ.—U.S.
N. Y. L.   June 11, 1948

NN   0052151   NN

NATIONAL FORUM Foundation
Special problems visualized. Chicago, Author ₍1937₎
₍44₎ p.

NN   0052152   Or WaT

HQ796   National Forum Foundation
N32   Teacher's guide for National Forum Guidance series. Chicago ₍cl946-1950₎
6 v. 22cm.

1. Youth. 2. Adolescence. 3. Success. 4. Occupations.   I. Title: National Forum   Guidance series.

NN   0052153   OrCS

BF 724.5 National Forum Foundation.
N3   Teacher's guide for Toward adult living,
Guide   prepared by the staff of National Forum inc.;
1950   W. Russell Shull, managing editor. ₍2d ed.₎ Chicago ₍cl950₎
96 p. 22 cm. (National Forum guidance series)

1. Adulthood. I. Shull, William Russell, 1890-   ed. II. National Forum, Chicago. Toward adult living. III. Title: Toward adult living.

NN   0052154   OU

Pn 170   National Forum Foundation.
N215
Toward adult living. Prepared by the Guidance staff of National forum inc. ... Chicago ₍1946₎
₍3₎-146p. illus. 24cm. (National forum guidance series. Book IV.)

NN   0052155   PU OU Wa NcD

National forum Foundation
Toward adult living, prepared by the Guidance staff ... Chicago, National forum, inc.[1948].
146p. illus. O. (National forum guidance series)

NN   0052156   CaBViP

LB1620   National forum guidance series. Prepared by
.N27   the guidance staff of National Forum, Inc.
1946   Chicago, National Forum [1946]
4v. illus. 27cm.
Contents:--1. High school life.--2. Discovering myself.--3. Planning my future.--4. Toward adult living.

1. Personnel service in education. 2. Counseling. I. National Forum.

NN   0052157   IEG

National Forum guidance series, prepared by the Guidance staff of National Forum inc., Bernice L. Neugarten ₍and others₎   Chicago, Ill. ₍1947₎
4v. illus. 24cm.

Contents.— Book 1. High school life.— Book 2. Discovering myself.— Book 3. Planning my future.— Book 4. Toward adult living.

1. Student activities. 2. Personality.

NN   0052158   IU InU

National Forum guidance series. Prepared by the Guidance Staff ... Bernice L. Neugarten ₍and others₎ Chicago ₍cl946-1950₎
6 v. illus. 24cm.

Includes bibliographies.

1. Youth. 2. Adolescence. 3. Success. 4. Occupations.   I. Neugarten, Bernice Levin,   1916- II. Title.

NN   0052159   OrCS

National forum of labor, agriculture and industry
see under Wyoming, University.

National forum on bus fuels and lubricants
see under American Transit Association. Bus Division.

National Forum on Trucking Industrial Relations.
Proceedings. 1st-
1950-
Washington.
v. 28 cm. annual.

1. Industrial relations—U. S. 2. Highway transport workers—U. S.

HD6976.A76N33   *331.15 331.1856   52-32769

NN   0052162   DLC NN OU DAU LU

National Foundation.
Advancing the education of the hospitalized child
see under Conference on the Education of Hospitalized Children, Atlantic City, 1948.

National foundation.
A bibliography of infantile paralysis, 1789-1944, with selected abstracts and annotations, prepared under direction of the National foundation for infantile paralysis, inc., edited by Morris Fishbein ... compiled by Ludvig Hektoen ... and Ella M. Salmonsen. Philadelphia, London ₍etc.₎, J. B. Lippincott company, 1946.
5 p. l., 672 p. 26 cm.
"Includes the bibliography of the periodical literature covering the clinical and investigation work on infantile paralysis."—Pref.

1. Poliomyelitis.   I. Fishbein, Morris, 1889-

Z6664.P8N3 1946   016.61683   46-4199 rev

ViU TU CaBViP Wa OrU OrP WaS WaT OrU-M OrCS CaBVaU
NN   0052164   DLC WaSp NIC CU NcD ICJ MB OCIW OCU

National Foundation.
A bibliography of infantile paralysis, 1789-1949, with selected abstracts and annotations. Prepared under direction of the National Foundation of Infantile Paralysis, inc. Edited by Morris Fishbein and Ella M. Salmonsen with Ludvig Hektoen. 2d ed. Philadelphia, Lippincott ₍1951₎
809 p. 26 cm.

1. Poliomyelitis—Bibl.   I. Fishbein, Morris, 1889-   ed.

Z6664.P8N3 1951   016.61683   51-6788 rev

NBuG ViU ICJ DNLM NcU-H CU-M MBCo TxU CaBVaU
NN   0052165   DLC OrU-M CaBViP WaSp CtY-M MB FU-HC

VOLUME 407

National Foundation .

Bulletin: When polio strikes ... helpful hints for everyone. New York ₍1944?₎ broadside. 28cm. (Its Publication, no. 51)

1. Poliomyelitis. I. Title: When polio strikes. II. Ser.

NN　0052166　　ViU

National Foundation .

Careers in service to the handicapped, information for vocational guidance specialists on the professions of physical therapy, occupational therapy, speech and hearing therapy and special education. Prepared in cooperation with American Occupational Therapy Association ₍and others₎ ₍New York₎ National Foundation for Infantile Paralysis, National Society for Crippled Children and

Adults with the cooperation of Federal Security Agency, Office of Vocational Rehabilitation ₍1952₎ 53 p. illus.

I. American Occupational Therapy Association. 362.161　615.8　362.162

NN　0052168　　ICJ

National Foundation.

Collected reprints on research by grantees. v. 1– 1939–40— New York.

v. in　illus. 26 cm. annual.
Vols. for 1941–　issued as the foundation's Publication 33.
Title varies: 1939–40–1958, Collected reprints of the grantees.
Vols. 1–19 issued by the foundation under its earlier name: National Foundation for Infantile Paralysis.
INDEXES:
Vols. 1–12, 1939–40–1951. 1 v.
Vols. 13–17, 1952–56. 1 v.
1. Poliomyelitis—Collected works.　(Series: National Foundation. Publication 33)

RC180.A1N28　　　616.835　　　42–18976 rev 2*

CU PPiU-H NcD CaBViP
ICJ ICRL OU ICU NNC MiU IaU OC1W MnU NhD
NN　0052169　DLC CaBVaU NcD　　OC1W-H OrU-M

WC
555
qN277

National Foundation .
₍Collection of publications₎

The Library has a collection of miscellaneous publications of this organization kept as received. The publications are not listed nor bound separately.

1. Poliomyelitis

NN　0052170　　DNLM

RJ496
.P6C6

National Foundation .

Courage. v.　–5; 19 –44. ₍New York, National Foundation for Infantile Paralysis₎

National foundation

Docteur, que faut–il faire? Données précises sur la paralysie infantile. New York, The National foundation for infantile paralysis, inc. 1941.
14 p.　21½ cm. (Its Publication no. 34)
Signed: Don W. Gudakunst, M.D., directeur médical.
Issued also in English.

1. Paralysis, Anterior spinal. I. Gudakunst, Donald Welsh, 1894–　II. Title. III. Ser.

NN　0052172　　ViU

National Foundation.

Doctor, what can I do? Facts about infantile paralysis. 2d ed. New York, 1942.
15 p.　22 cm. (Its Publication no. 34A)
Signed: Don W. Gudakunst, medical director.
Published by the foundation under its earlier name: National Foundation for Infantile Paralysis.

1. Poliomyelitis.　I. Gudakunst, Donald Welsh, 1894–1946.
II. Title.　(Series)

RC180.2.N29　　　616.83　　　44–37339 rev*

NN　0052173　　DLC Or ViU

National foundation.

Facts and figures about infantile paralysis. ₍New York₎ The National foundation for infantile paralysis, inc. ₍1945₎
cover-title, 30 p., 1 l. illus. (incl. maps) diagrs. 21½ x 28 cm.
₍Its Publication no. 59₎

1. Poliomyelitis.

RC180.1.N29　　　616.83　　　46–48 rev

NN　0052174　　DLC OrU NN DNLM ViU OC1 OCU NNC NBuG

RJ496.P2
N2191
1952

National Foundation

Filmscript on nursing care in poliomyelitis. ₍New York, 1952₎
24 p. illus.

"Additional notes for the film series of the National Foundation for Infantile Paralysis and the National League for Nursing."

NN　0052175　　NNC DNLM

WC
555
N277G
1944

National Foundation .
A guide for nurses in the nursing care of patients with infantile paralysis; including nursing aspects of the Kenny method. 2d ed. New York, 1944.
29 p. illus. 21 cm.

Includes bibliography.

1. Poliomyelitis - nursing.　I. Title.

NN　0052176　　WU-M

National foundation

The International bulletin for economics, medical research and public hygiene.
... Infantile paralysis ... Brussels, New York ₍etc.₎ 1939/40.

National foundation.

Infantile paralysis; a symposium delivered at Vanderbilt university, April, 1941. New York city, The National foundation for infantile paralysis, inc. ₍1941₎
vii, 239 p. incl. illus., diagrs., forms. 23½ cm.
CONTENTS.—History of poliomyelitis up to the present time, by P. F. Clark.—The etiology of poliomyelitis, by Charles Armstrong.—Immunological and serological phenomena in poliomyelitis, by T. M. Rivers.—The pathology and pathogenesis of poliomyelitis, by E. W. Goodpasture.—The epidemiology of poliomyelitis, by J. R. Paul.—Treatment and rehabilitation of the poliomyelitis patient, by F. R. Ober.—Bibliography (p. ₍191₎–228)
1. Poliomyelitis.　I. Vanderbilt university, Nashville.

RC180.A1N316　1941　616.835　　41–15476 rev

OC1W NcD TxU CaBViP OrU-M OC1W-H WaT IdU DPAHO
NN　0052178　DLC WaTC OrP ICRL ViU ICJ PU OC1 OU

National foundation
Infantile paralysis fight magazine
see under title

National Foundation.

Information for physicians on the Salk poliomyelitis vaccine, edited by Hart E. Van Riper, medical director. New York, National Foundation for Infantile Paralysis, 1955.
34 p.　22 cm.

1. Poliomyelitis vaccine.　I. Van Riper, Hart E., ed.　II. Title: Salk poliomyelitis vaccine.

RC180.1.N3　　　　　　56–1603 rev †

NN　0052180　　DLC NcU DNLM MnU

RJ496.P2
N219
1952

National foundation

Isolation techniques and nursing care in poliomyelitis. Additional notes for the exhibit of the National foundation for infantile paralysis. New York ₍1952₎
cover-title, 16 p. illus.

1. Poliomyelitis. 2. Nurses and nursing. I. Title.

NN　0052181　　NNC-M ViU ICJ NNC

W 6
P3

NATIONAL Foundation .

Management of poliomyelitis patients with respiratory difficulty; additional notes for the exhibit prepared by the National Foundation for Infantile Paralysis. New York ₍195- ?₎
26 p.
Cover title.
"Digest ₍of₎ a manual, 'Management of poliomyelitis patients with respiratory difficulty,' to be published at a later date."

1. Poliomyelitis - Treatment
2. Respiration - Disorders

NN　0052183　　DNLM NNC-M ICJ ViU

National Foundation .
A manual of instruction for glossopharyngeal breathing...
see under Dail, Clarence Wilding, 1907-

National Foundation.
A message about polio. ₍New York, 1950₎
₍4₎ p. illus. 19 cm. (Its Publication no. 31)
Caption title.
Published by the foundation under its earlier name: National Foundation for Infantile Paralysis.

1. Poliomyelitis.　(Series)

RC180.2.N295　　　616.83　　　51–27126 rev

NN　0052185　　DLC

National foundation.
The miracle of Hickory. New York, N. Y., The National foundation for infantile paralysis, inc. ₍1944₎
₍24₎ p. illus. (incl. ports.) 22½ cm. ₍Its Publication no. 53₎

1. Hickory, N. C. Emergency infantile paralysis hospital.
I. Title.

RC180.1.N32　　　362.19683　　　45–2741 rev

NN　0052186　　DLC OC1 ViU

N215

National foundation

₍Miscellaneous publications₎

In pamphlet box.

1. Paralysis, Anterior spinal.

NN　0052187　　NNC

VOLUME 407

RC180
.8
.P6W436

National foundation .

West, Jessie (Stevenson) 1891–
Modo de cuidar a los pacientes de parálisis infantil, por Jessie L. Stevenson ... New York, N. Y., The National foundation for infantile paralysis, inc., 1940.

National Foundation .

The National Foundation for Infantile Paralysis, inc. Policies governing the making of grants and rules governing grants. New York, 1944.
6 p. 21cm. (Its Publication, no. 39)

1. Poliomyelitis—Prevention. I. Ser.

NN 0052189   ViU

RJ496
.P2N3322

National Foundation

National Foundation news. v. 1–
Nov. 1941–
[New York] National Foundation for Infantile Paralysis.

RR
RC180.5
S4N

National foundation .
New information for physicians on the Salk poliomyelitis vaccine, edited by Hart E. Van Ripen, M. D. New York.
v. 22cm.

1. Poliomyelitis vaccine. I. Van Ripen, Hart Edgar, 1904–   ed. I. Title.

NN 0052191   CtY-M

RC180
.8
.P6W43
1940

National foundation .

West, Jessie (Stevenson) 1891–
The nursing care of patients with infantile paralysis, by Jessie L. Stevenson ... New York, N. Y., The National foundation for infantile paralysis, inc. [1940]

WC
555
qN2771o
1945

NATIONAL Foundation .
Our fight against infantile paralysis, Rockford and Winnebago County, Illinois. [Rockford, Ill.] 1945.
61 p.   illus.
1. Poliomyelitis - Illinois - Rockford Co. 2. Poliomyelitis - Illinois - Winnebago Co.

NN 0052193   DNLM

National Foundation.
Poliomyelitis, a source book for high school students. New York [1946]
15 p. illus. 22 cm. (*Its* Publication no. 61)
Cover title.
Published by the foundation under its earlier name: National Foundation for Infantile Paralysis.
——— Teacher's guide in the use of a high school unit on poliomyelitis. [Rev.] New York [1946]
31, [1] p. illus. 22 cm. (*Its* Publication no. 62)
Cover title.
Published by the foundation under its earlier name: National Foundation for Infantile Paralysis.
"References": p. [32]
1. Poliomyelitis.   RC180.2.N3 Guide
                                         (Series)
RC180.2.N3   616.83   Med 48–235 rev*

NN 0052194   DLC ViU

WC
555
[N277p
1951

NATIONAL Foundation.
Poliomyelitis; a source book of facts about the disease and current efforts to combat it on a national scale. Prepared by staff of National Foundation for Infantile Paralysis and Federal Security Agency [and others. Washington] 1951.
1 v. (various pagings)
Cover title.
1. Poliomyelitis I. U. S. Federal Security Agency

NN 0052195   DNLM

National Foundation.
Poliomyelitis; annual statistical review. New York.
v. illus. 28 cm.

1. Poliomyelitis—U. S.—Stat. 2. U. S.—Statistics, Medical.

RC181.U5N3   67–1402

NN 0052196   DLC IU PPCPh

National Foundation .
Poliomyelitis research

see under

Weaver, Harry M

National Foundation.
Poliomyelitis vaccine *evaluation report, April 12, 1955*
see under title

National foundation.
Principles of the Kenny method of treatment of infantile paralysis. New York city, The National foundation for infantile paralysis [1942]
[4]p. illus. 22 cm. (Its Publication no.41)

Bound with Cole, W.H. The Kenny method of treatment for infantile paralysis. [1942]

NN 0052199   OrU

RD795
.C57

National Foundation.
Conference on Teaching of Rehabilitation.
The problem : discharged cured? [Proceedings] 1955–
[n. p.]

National Foundation.
Publications. New York [1947–
1 v. (loose-leaf) 30 cm.
Cover title.
A collection of pamphlets and leaflets inserted in mounted envelopes.
Published by the foundation under its earlier name: **National Foundation for Infantile Paralysis.**

1. Poliomyelitis.

RC180.1.N34   616.835   Med 47–3103 rev*

ICU CtY TxU ICJ
NN 0052201   DLC OrU-M Or AAP Vi MiU NhD OU NNC Vi

National Foundation.
Report. 1st–
1938/39–
New York.
v. illus., diagrs. 22 cm. annual.
Reports for   issued as the foundation's Publication.
Report year irregular.
Reports for 1938/39–   issued by the foundation under its earlier name : National Foundation for Infantile Paralysis.

(Series: National Foundation. Publication)

RJ496.P2N3   614.549   40–33753 rev*

TU ICJ NN Vi OU LNL CU WaS OrCS IdU MtU MiU
AU-M IU NN MB NcD FTaSU CaBVaU OrU-M MtBC P TxU TxLT
NN 0052202   DLC AAP DNLM CtNlC PPiU-H PU-Med-TS IU

National Foundation .
Research reference bulletin. no. [1]–
Mar. 9, 1949–   New York.

NN 0052203   ICJ

National foundation.
Respirators; locations and owners. New York, N. Y., The National foundation for infantile paralysis, inc. [1940]
19 p. 22 x 10 cm.
"Compiled from records available September 1, 1940."

1. Respirators. 2. Poliomyelitis.

RC180.5.R4N3   43–512 rev

NN 0052204   DLC DNLM MH

National Foundation

Respirators: locations and owners. New York [1942]
23 p. 22 x 19cm. (Its Publication, no. 24B)

1. Respirators. 2. Poliomyelitis. I. Ser.

NN 0052205   ViU

NATIONAL FOUNDATION ,

Speakers handbook. 1954–
New York.   no.   illus.
22 x 29cm.

1. Paralysis, Infantile--U.S.   2. Paralysis, Infantile--Stat. --
U.S.

NN 0052206   NN

National foundation.
Splints, their distribution and use. 1941. New York city, The National foundation for infantile paralysis, inc. [1941]
[12] p. illus. 9½ x 23 cm.
"No. 21A."
"To furnish prompt aid in the acute stages of infantile paralysis the Foundation has had manufactured a supply of Toronto splints and Bradford frames ... [and] makes this equipment available to any community for use during epidemics or by those indigent ... patients who may be in need of them."—p. [2]

1. Splints (Surgery) 2. Paralysis, Anterior spinal.
                                          A 41–3448 rev
Michigan. Univ. Libr.
for Library of Congress   [r56c8]

NN 0052207   MiU Or

The national foundation
The story behind the polio vaccine. [Rev.]   New York [1955]
11 p. illus. 22cm.

1. Paralysis, Infantile—Immunity   and vaccination.

NN 0052208   NN

National Foundation

The story of the Kenny method. New York, 1944.
10 p. illus. 21cm. (Its Publication, no. 50)

1. Poliomyelitis. I. Title: Kenny method. II. Ser.

NN 0052209   ViU CtY NNC MnU

VOLUME 407

National Foundation.
    The story of the National Foundation for Infantile Paralysis, incorporated. ₍New York₎ 1941.
    30 p.   22 cm.   ₍Its Publication no. 36₎
    Published by the foundation under its earlier name: National Foundation for Infantile Paralysis.

    1. Poliomyelitis.   (Series)

RC180.A1N3   614.549   42–18441 rev*

NN   0052210   DLC ICJ ICU ViU Or

RC180
.A1S9
1953

National Foundation .

A Symposium on poliomyelitis 1953: an analysis of recent advances and an outline of clinical management, prepared with the editorial assistance of the National Foundation for Infantile Paralysis. ₍Philadelphia₎ Saunders ₍1953₎

National foundation

                FOR OTHER EDITIONS
                SEE MAIN ENTRY

Wilson, James Leroy, 1898–
    The use of the respirator in poliomyelitis, by James L. Wilson ... ₍New York, The National foundation for infantile paralysis, inc., °1942₎

National Foundation.
    When you have polio; a handbook for the guidance of adolescent and adult patients with infantile paralysis (poliomyelitis) New York ₍1948₎
    21 p.   illus.   21 cm.   (Its Publication no. 32)
    Published by the foundation under its earlier name: National Foundation for Infantile Paralysis.

    1. Poliomyelitis.   I. Title.   (Series)

RC180.2.N32   616.83   49–3952 rev*

NN   0052213   DLC

National Foundation.
    When your child has infantile paralysis; suggestions for parents. New York ₍1947₎
    36 p.   illus.   22 cm.   (Its Publication no. 67)
    Published by the foundation under its earlier name: National Foundation for Infantile Paralysis.

    1. Poliomyelitis.   I. Title.   (Series)

RC180.2.N325   616.83   48–18654 rev*

NN   0052214   DLC

WC
555
qN278s
1954

NATIONAL Foundation .
    Advisory Committee on Vaccination
    Specifications and minimal requirements for poliomyelitis vaccine aqueous (polyvalent) as developed by Dr. Jonas E. Salk, Virus Research Laboratory, University of Pittsburgh, Pittsburgh, Pennsylvania; to be used in field studies to be conducted during 1954 under the auspices of the National Foundation for Infantile Paralysis. ₍Pittsburgh?₎ 1954.

    1 v. (various pagings) illus.
    Letter of transmittal from the Advisory Committee on Vaccination of the National Foundation for Infantile Paralysis to the editor of the Journal of the American Medical Association: 2 ℓ. tipped in.
    1. Poliomyelitis - Immunity

    2. Poliomyelitis virus 3. Salk, Jonas Edward, 1914-   Title

NN   0052217   DNLM

RJ496.P2
N211
1954

National Foundation -
    Advisory Committee on Vaccine.
    Poliomyelitis vaccine, types 1, 2, and 3; recommendations of Vaccine Advisory Committee of National Foundation for Infantile Paralysis, and statement of United States Public Health Service. ₍New York₎ 1954.
    ₍7₎ p.

    1. Poliomyelitis vaccine. I. U. S. Public Health Service.

NN   0052218   NNC

Z6664
.P8P6

National Foundation. Dept. of Professional Education.
    Current literature ₍on₎ poliomyelitis and related diseases.
    v. 1–   Oct. 1946–
    New York.

National Foundation. *District of Columbia Chapter.*
    Report.
    ₍n. p.₎
    v.   28 cm.   annual.
    Reports for   issued by the chapter under the foundation's earlier name: National Foundation for Infantile Paralysis.

RJ496.P2N337   614.549   49–37474 rev*‡

NN   0052220   DLC

National Foundation. *Division of Professional Education*
    see
National Foundation. *Dept. of Professional Education.*

W 1
NA455

NATIONAL Foundation .
    Hamilton County (Ohio) Chapter.
    Annual report.
    ₍Cincinnati?₎ 19
    v.
    1. Poliomyelitis - Ohio

NN   0052222   DNLM

Z6664
.P8P6

National Foundation. Library.

    Current literature ₍on₎ poliomyelitis and related diseases.
    v. 1–   Oct. 1946–
    New York.

NATIONAL FOUNDATION .
    MULTNOMAH COUNTY CHAPTER
    Annual report. 1945/46   c1008 S. W. 6th
    Ave., Portland 4, Author 1946₎
    1 v.

NN   0052224   Or OrP

National foundation .
Wayne County chapter.
    Report on the activities. ₍Detroit, Detroit league for the handicapped₎ 1941.
    12 p.

NN   0052225   MiDW

616.83
N21o

National foundation.
    Winnebago county (Ill.) chapter₎
    Our fight against infantile paralysis, Rockford and Winnebago county, Illinois. ₍Rockford, Ill.₎ 1945.
    61p.   illus.(incl.ports., maps) diagrs.

    1. Paralysis, Anterior spinal. I. Title.

NN   0052226   IU

National Foundation for Adult Education.
    Foundation papers; a bulletin of adult education
    see under title

National Foundation for Adult Education
    see also National Institute of Adult Education.

National Foundation for Cerebral Palsy
    see
    United Cerebral Palsy Associations.

HQ750
.A2Y6

National foundation for child care.
    You and your child.   v. 1–
    Oct. 1940–
    ₍New York, Conner publications, inc.; etc., etc.₎ 1940–

National Foundation for Consumer Credit.
    Consumer credit conference handbook; a reprint of the data book prepared for the seventh annual Consumer Credit Conference, University of North Carolina, Chapel Hill, North Carolina. April 3rd-5th, 1955.   [n.p., 1955]
    1 v. (unpaged)   illus.   30 cm.
    1. Consumer credit. U.S.

NN   0052231   MiU

HG3755
.N32

National Foundation for Consumer Credit.

National Consumer Credit Counseling Service Conference.
    Proceedings.
    Indianapolis, National Foundation for Consumer Credit.

National foundation for education in American citizenship.
    ... An action program in the making. ₍Indianapolis, 1943?₎
    cover-title, 16 p.   29 x 22ᶜᵐ.
    Text on p. ₍3₎ and ₍4₎ of cover.
    Bibliography: p. 16.

    I. Title.

Library of Congress   H62.N36   43–15215
                       ₍3₎   323.806273

NN   0052233   DLC

E183
.7
.B6

National foundation for education in American citizenship.

Borchard, Edwin Montefiore, 1884–
    American foreign policy, by Edwin Borchard ... Indianapolis, National foundation press, 1946.

VOLUME 407

National foundation for education in American citizenship.
The Bill of rights of the United States. ₍Indianapolis, 1944₎
20 p.   21cm.   (Fundamental American principles series.)

"Prepared and published by the National foundation for education in American citizenship."
CONTENTS.—Introd. by S. R. Harrell.—The historical basis of the Bill of rights, by Roscoe Pound.—The Bill of rights, the first ten amendments.

1. Liberty—U. S.   2. United
1st–10th.   I. Harrell, Samuel
Roscoe, 1870–   III. United
N. Y. P. L.

States. Constitution—Amendments,
Runnels, 1897–   II. Pound,
States. Constitution.
September 12, 1947

NN   0052235   NN

National foundation for education in American citizenship.

National council for the social studies.
Education for citizen responsibilities; papers on the rôle of social studies disciplines in citizenship education, prepared for a conference jointly presented by the National council for the social studies and the National foundation for education in American citizenship. Indianapolis, 1941.

National foundation for education in American citizenship.

Burdette, Franklin L   1911–   ed.
Education for citizen responsibilities; the roles of anthropology, economics, geography, history, philosophy, political science, psychology, sociology, edited by Franklin L. Burdette. ₍By₎ John M. Clark, Lloyd Allen Cook and Stuart A. Queen ₍and others₎ … with an introduction by Samuel R. Harrell. ₍Princeton₎ Princeton university press for National foundation for education in American citizenship ₍1942₎

H39
.H8

National Foundation for Education in American Citizenship.

The **Human** affairs pamphlets. no. 1–46; Dec. 1945–Sept. 1949. Chicago ₍etc.₎ H. Regnery Co. ₍etc.₎

D410
.H8

National Foundation for Education in American Citizenship.

Human events; a weekly analysis for the American citizen.
v. ₍1₎–
Feb. 2, 1944–
Washington, D. C.

H65
.N32

NATIONAL FOUNDATION FOR EDUCATION IN AMERICAN CITIZENSHIP.
₍Miscellaneous publications₎

NN   0052240   ICU

JC599
.U5C85

National foundation for education in American citizenship.

Cushman, Robert Eugene, 1889–
… Our constitutional freedoms; civil liberties: an American heritage, by Robert E. Cushman. ₍Indianapolis₎ National foundation for education in American citizenship; ₍New York₎ Public affairs committee inc. ₍1944₎

JK2288
.B89

National foundation for education in American citizenship.

Burdette, Franklin L   1911–
… Political parties: an American way, by Franklin L. Burdette. ₍New York₎ National foundation for education in American citizenship and Public affairs committee inc. ₍*1945₎

National Foundation for Educational Research in England and Wales.
Current researches in education and educational psychology
see under title

L18
N37

NATIONAL FOUNDATION FOR EDUCATIONAL RESEARCH IN ENGLAND AND WALES.
Notes on the work of the National Foundation for Educational Research in England and Wales.
19–
London.
v.

1. Educational research—Societies.

NN   0052244   CU-Riv

370.942
N213o

National Foundation for Educational Research in England and Wales.
Occasional publication series. no.1–

Slough, Bucks.
no.   23cm.

Includes bibliographies.

NN   0052245   TxU IU

NATIONAL FOUNDATION FOR EDUCATIONAL RESEARCH IN ENGLAND AND WALES.
PUBLICATION

NN   0052246   TxLT

National Foundation for Educational Research in England and Wales.
Report.
London.
v.   22 cm.   annual.
Report year ends Mar. 31.

L18.N473   57–40831

NN   0052247   DLC ICU NN

National Foundation for Educational Research in England and Wales.
Research reports. 2d ser, no.–

NN   0052248   OCl

National Foundation for Educational Research in England and Wales.
A second list of researches in education and educational psychology presented for higher degrees
see   Blackwell, Annie Margaret.
A list of researches …

LB1028
.N357
1953

NATIONAL FOUNDATION FOR EDUCATIONAL RESEARCH IN ENGLAND AND WALES.
Statement of policy. London, 1953.
16 p.

NN   0052250   ICU

National Foundation for Educational Research in England and Wales.
A survey of rewards and punishments in schools; a report based on researches carried out by M. E. Highfield and A. Pinsent. London, Published for the Foundation by Newnes Educational Pub. Co. ₍1952₎
xxiv, 432 p.   fold. col. map, diagrs.   23 cm.   (Its Publication no. 3)
Bibliography: p. 427–428.

1. School discipline.   I. Highfield, Miriam Ethel (Hill) 1904–
II. Title.   (Series)
LB3025.N38   -371.5   52–4825

InU NcD MH ICU CU
NN   0052251   DLC CaBVa CaBVaU MoU TU TxU OU PU

LB3056
.G7
N3
pam

National Foundation for Educational Research in England and Wales.
Tests for educational guidance and selection. London, Newnes Educational Pub. Co. ₍1953?₎
21 p.   22cm.

1. Examinations - Gt. Brit.   I. Title.

NN   0052252   OrCS

National Foundation for Infantile Paralysis
see
National Foundation.

National Foundation for Welsh Troops
see   National Fund for Welsh Troops.

National Foundation-March of Dimes
see
National Foundation.

National Foundation news. v. 1–
Nov. 1941₎ National Foundation for Infantile Paralysis.
v.   illus., ports.   29–32 cm.   monthly.

I. National Foundation for Infantile Paralysis.

RJ496.P2N3322   616.83   51–22567

DNLM
NN   0052256   DLC OrP PHi MiU MdBJ TxU NNC MnHi ViU

National Foundation of Political Sciences
see
Fondation nationale des sciences politiques.

National Founders' Association
see
National Foundry Association.

National Foundry & Machine Co., *Louisville.*
The Reilly steam pump and pumping machinery.   Manufactured by the National Foundry and Machine Co. … .   96 p. il. ₍ pl.
O.   Louisville pref. 1898.

NN   0052259   ICJ

National Foundry Association.
Constitution and by-laws of the National Founders' Association, organized, New York, January 26, 1898. ₍Detroit₎ Speaker Print. Co.₎ 1906.
38 p.   15 cm.

F7N66   1906   56–55518

NN   0052260   DLC

National Foundry Association.
Constitution and by-laws of the National Founders' Association, organized, New York, January 26, 1898. ₍Detroit₎ 1911.
32 p.   15 cm.

HD6515.F7N66   1911   331.881271   56–55517

NN   0052261   DLC

VOLUME 407

National Foundry Association.
Constitution and by-laws of the National
founders' association. Organized, New York,
January 26, 1898. Chicago, 1918.
29, (5) p. 15.5 cm.

NN 0052262 DL

NATIONAL FOUNDRY ASSOCIATION.
Constitution and by-laws of the National founders' association. Organized, New York, January 26, 1898. Chicago, 1929.
29, [5] p. 15cm.

703009A.1. Foundries—Assoc. and org.—U.S.

NN 0052263 NN

National foundry association.
Durban, Thomas Edward, 1863–
The Erie strike situation, by Thomas E. Durban ...
[New York? 1913?]

[National foundry association]
Food for thought. [Detroit, Speaker printing company,
1903?]
75 p. 22½ cm.
On cover: N. F. A. Agreements.
Letter of transmittal to the members of the National founders' association signed: Antonio C. Pessano, Wm. H. Peahler, special committee
on uniform agreements.

1. Pessano, Antonio C. I. Title.

HD4966.F82U5 11–32883 rev

NN 0052265 DLC

National Foundry Association.
A foundry manual for the man in the shop, by
Gottfried Olson ... A series of pamphlets
covering foundry operations. No. 1937 –
Chicago, Ill.

NN 0052266 OCl

[National Foundry Association
Harmony between capital and labor promoted
by union of manufacturers. [n.p., 1902.

NN 0052267 MH

National Foundry Association.
If government regulation take away profits.

NN 0052268 OrU

National Foundry Association.
Labor relations that work. Chicago, National
founders association [1945]
1. Labor and laboring classes - U.S. I. Title.

NN 0052269 NNC

National foundry association.
The labor secretary and labor questions.
(Buffalo, 1913)
7 p. 21½ cm.

NN 0052270 DL

National Foundry Association.
[Letter from the association concerning the Anti-Injunction
Bill.] n. t.-p. [Chicago, 1914.] 2 l. 4°.
With: The Anti-Injunction Bill ... Opinion of G. F. Monaghan, and a repr.:
Of a page of American Federation of Labor Weekly news letter.

1. Labor—Jurisprudence, U. S., 1914.
N. Y. P. L.   September 12, 1914.

NN 0052271 NN

National foundry association.
A pattern for strikes ... Address to Forty-
seventh annual meeting, National founders
association, November 16, 1944
see under Kelley, Nicholas, 1885–

National foundry association.
Plan of organization...(Chicago? 1918?]
19 p. chart. 22½ cm

NN 0052273 DL

National Foundry Association.
A policy of lawlessness; partial record of riot, assault,
murder, coercion, and intimidation occurring in strikes of the
Iron Moulders' Union during 1904, 1905, 1906, and 1907.
Supplement to Report of O. P. Briggs, president of National
Founders' Association, November, 1908. Detroit [1909?]
111 p. 23 cm.
Cover title.
Published by the association under its earlier name: National
Founders' Association.
1. International Molders' and Foundry Workers' Union of North
America. 2. Strikes and lockouts. I. Briggs, O. P. II. Title.

HD5325.I 49N3 57–50478

NN 0052274 DLC DL

National Foundry Association.
Report [at the] annual convention.

New York.
v. 23 cm.
Reports for   issued by the association under an earlier
name: National Founders' Association.

HD6515.F7N6 57–50473 rev

NN 0052275 DLC MdBJ DL NN

National Foundry Association.
... Report of committee on industrial education ...
[Chicago? 192–?]
cover-title, 3–12 p. 21½ᶜᵐ.
At head of title: National founders association, Chicago.

1. Factory management—Addresses, essays, lectures.

NN 0052276 MiU

National foundry association.
... Safety code for the protection of industrial workers
in foundries. National founders' association, American
foundrymen's association, sponsors. Tentative American
standard, approved June, 1922, by American engineering
standards committee, April, 1923. Washington, Govt. print.
off., 1923.
iv, 12 p. 23½ cm. (Bulletin of the United States Bureau of labor
statistics, no. 336. Safety code series)

At head of title: U. S. Dept. of labor. James J. Davis, secretary.
Bureau of labor statistics. Ethelbert Stewart, commissioner.

1. Founding.—Safety measures; 2. [Accidents—Prevention] 3.
Safety appliances. 4. [Foundry workers] I. American foundrymen's society. II. American standards association. III. Title.

HD8051.A62 no. 336 L 23–146 rev
——— Copy 3. TS233.N3,

U. S. Dept. of Labor. Library
for Library of Congress [r57k⅝]†

NN 0052278 DL WaU–L WaWW MiU OU OCU DLC

National Foundry Association.
...Safety code for the protection of industrial workers in
foundries; approved, American Standards Association, April 7,
1932. Sponsors: American Foundrymen's Association, National
Founders' Association. American engineering and industrial
standards. [New York: American Standards Assoc., 1932.]
24 p. illus. [new ed., rev.] 19½cm.

At head of title: American standard.

642181A. 1. Foundries—Accidents— Prevention—U. S. I. American
Standards Association. II. American Foundrymen's Association.
N. Y. P. L. June 24, 1933

NN 0052279 NN MiU CU PU IaAS

National foundry association.
Short term training in the foundry.
[Miscellaneous papers] Chic.,
1939– 1v.(loose-leaf)

Cover title.

NN 0052280 CaBVa

National Foundry Association.
Short term training in the foundry. Chicago,
National founders association, c1941.
119 p. illus., diagrs., form.
Loose-leaf.
Pages printed on one side only.

NN 0052281 OCl

National foundry association.
Short term training in the foundry. Chicago, Ill., National
founders association, ¹1942.
119 numb. l. illus., diagrs., form. 29 x 26ᵐ.
Loose-leaf.

1. Founding. I. Title.

Library of Congress TS230.N35 42–51017
[3] 621.74

NN 0052282 DLC

National foundry association.
Short term training in the foundry. Chicago, Ill., Na-
tional founders association, ¹1944.
172 (i. e. 174) p. illus., diagrs. 29 x 23 cm.
Loose-leaf.
Includes extra numbered pages 100a–100b.

1. Founding. I. Title.

TS230.N35 1944 621.74 45–13179

NN 0052283 DLC MtBC OCl

National foundry association.
Short term training in the foundry.
Chicago, Ill., National founders
association, c1946.
172 (i.e.174) p. 29 x 23 cm.

NN 0052284 MtBC

National Foundry Association.
The shorter work day. Extract from the report of President
O. P. Briggs to the fourteenth annual convention of the National
Founders' Association, November 16, 1910. [Detroit, 1911]
3 l. 8°.
Letter from secretary, inserted.

1. Labor.—Hours of : Foundry workers, U. S.
N. Y. P. L. April 1, 1911.

NN 0052285 NN

VOLUME 407

National Foundry Association.
Summary of apprenticeship practices in
foundries. [By L.A. Hartley] ... Chicago,
The Author [1925?]
v. p. charts.
Typewritten copy, duplicated.
Text runs parallel with back of cover.
I. Hartley, Lawrence Arthur, 1880–

NN 0052286 MiD IU

TS230 NATIONAL FOUNDRY ASSOCIATION.
.N3 Summary of apprenticeship practices in found-
ries(1941 revision) Chicago,National founders'
association,1941.
34 numb.l. 8 l. diagrs. 27½cm.

Reproduced from type-written copy.

1. Founding.

NN 0052287 ICU OC1

658 National foundry association.
N21t "This thing called grievances." [Chicago,
1938]
13 numb.l.

Caption title.
At head of title: National founders associa-
tion ... Chicago, Illinois.
Lithoprinted.
"Notes from a discussion at the annual meeting
of the National founders association, New York,
November 17, 1938."

NN 0052288 IU

National foundry association. Committee on
foundry methods
Service bureau methods.
illus. tables.

Library has
no.1– 1916– Open entry.

Accompanied by blank forms for use in the
foundry industry.

NN 0052289 MiD

275.28
N214 National 4-H club activities and awards for
Georgia.

Chicago, National Committee on Boys and Girls
Club Work.

NN 0052290 DNAL

A275.28
N21 National 4-H club camp bulletin.

Washington, Federal Extension Service.

1. National 4-H club camp. I. U.S. Extension Service. II. U.S. Extension Service.
Division of 4-H Club and YMW Programs.

NN 0052291 DNAL

National 4-H club congress.
Proceedings, National 4-H club
congress; addresses at meetings of state leaders,
other selected material ... 19 –
[Chicago, Ill., National committee on boys and
girls club work, 19 –
v. 29½cm.

Mimeographed.

NN 0052292 OrCS NcRS

National 4-H Club Foundation
see
National 4-H Club Foundation of America.

National 4-H Club Foundation of America.
Final report
see its
Report to the Ford Foundation on the regular program
of the international farm youth exchange.

275.29
N218 National 4-H Club Foundation of America.
For the youth of your land and mine, the
National 4-H Club Foundation; its program
and plans. [Washington, 1952]
[13] p.

1. National 4-H Club Foundation of America.

NN 0052295 DNAL

275.29
N218I National 4-H Club Foundation of America.
IFYE folder. no.1

Washington.

1. International Farm Youth Exchange
Project. I. Title.

NN 0052296 DNAL

National 4-H Club Foundation of America.
Mid-year progress report
see its
Report to the Ford Foundation on the regular program
of the international farm youth exchange.

369.4 National 4-H Club Foundation of America.
N213 Progress report.

Washington, D.C. [etc.,
v. illus., tables. 15–28cm.

Title varies: 1955–63, Report.
Some reports issued under a variant name:
National 4-H Foundation.

NN 0052298 IU

275.29
N218Pr National 4-H Club Foundation of America.
Puerto Rican farm youth exchange.

[Washington]

1. International Farm Youth Exchange
Project. I. Title.

NN 0052299 DNAL

National 4-H Club Foundation of America.
Report to the Ford Foundation on the regular program
of the international farm youth exchange.

Silver Spring, Md.
v. 29 cm.

Vols. for published by the foundation under a variant
name: National 4-H Club Foundation.
During 19 –55 two reports were issued annually: Mid-year
progress report and Final report.

58 – 29882 rev ‡

S533.N35

NN 0052300 DLC IU OrCS DNAL NIC

The National 4-H club magazine.
v. 1

Kansas City, Mo.[, etc.]: 4-H Pub. Co., 1929–   29cm.
v. illus.

Monthly.
Published in the interests of the 4-H Clubs of America.

1. No subject. I. Four-H-Clubs.
N. Y. P. L.   September 12, 1933

NN 0052301 NN OrCS

275.2
N213 National 4-H farm safety guidebook for loaders
and members. [n.p., 194–?]
26 p.

1. Agriculture. Safety measures. 2. Agriculture. Accidents. I. Title: Farm safety guide-
book.

NN 0052302 DNAL

National 4-H Foods and Nutrition Committee.
Report of meeting of delegates with 4-H
Foods and Nutrition Committee

see under

U.S. Federal Extension Service.

National 4-H Foundation
see
National 4-H Club Foundation of America.

National 4-H news.
[Chicago]
v. in. illus., ports. 29 cm. monthly.

Began publication in Mar. 1923. Cf. Union list of serials.
Vols. for published by the National 4-H Service Committee (called —May 1960, National Committee on Boys
and Girls Club Work)

1. 4-H clubs—Period. I. National 4-H Service Committee.

S1.N33   62–52645

NN 0052305 DLC ScCleU NMScS OC1 ICRL NN OrCS

S National 4-H Service Committee.
22
N26 Annual report.   Chicago, Ill.
v. 33 cm.

1. 4-H Clubs.

NN 0052306 NIC OU

S National 4-H Service Committee.
22 Charts and data on 4-H leaders. Chicago
N27C [1937]
1 v. (unpaged) diagrs. (part col.)
tables. 31 cm.

Cover title.
Issued by the organization under its
earlier name National Committee on Boys
and Girls Club Work.

1. 4-H clubs. I. Title.

NN 0052307 NIC DNAL

VOLUME 407

275.29
N213Fo   National 4-H Service Committee.
    4-H grain marketing awards program.
Chicago [1952]
    [4] p.

    1. 4-H clubs.

NN   0052308   DNAL

275.29
N213F   National 4-H Service Committee.

    4-H handy book.
    [Chicago]

    1. 4-H clubs.

NN   0052309   DNAL

Pam   National 4-H Service Committee.
71-   4-H HANDY BOOK.   Chicago, 1928?
2189   59 p.   illus.

4-H CLUBS

NN   0052310   WHi

S533   National 4-H Service Committee.
N22   Handbook for local leaders, national 4-H
    award programs.
    Chicago, Ill. [National 4-H Service Commit-
    tee,
        p. ports.   27½cm.

    Formerly issued by the National Committee
    on Boys and Girls Club Work, as its National
    4-H awards handbook.
    1.4-H clubs. I.   National Committee on
    Boys and Girls   Club Work. II.Title.
    III.Title: Nati   onal 4-H awards pro-

NN   0052311   OrCS DNAL

275.2   [National 4-H Service Committee]
N212L   Learn how to freeze foods. Enter the new national
    4-H frozen foods contest.   [Chicago? 1945]
    folder.
    1. Food, Frozen. I. U.S. Extension service.
    II. Title: 4-H frozen foods contest.

NN   0052312   DNAL

275.2
N212G   National 4-H Service Committee.

    Let's demonstrate. A guide in giving 4-H
    demonstrations on tractor maintenance.
    Chicago, 1948.
    12 p.

    1. Traction-engines. Maintenance and repair.
    2. Teaching. Demonstration method. I. Title:
    4-H club tractor-maintenance program. II. Ti-
    tle: 4-H demonstrations on tractor maintenance.

NN   0052313   DNAL

National 4-H Service Committee.
    National 4-H awards handbook for local leaders
        see its Handbook for local leaders.

National 4-H Service Committee.
    National 4-H club activities and awards for
Georgia
    see under title

275.2
N212N   National 4-H Service Committee.
    National 4-H club song book. [Edited by
    Committee on 4-H club music... Chicago,Ill.,
    National committee on boys and girls club work,
    1938]
        64 p.   22cm.

NN   0052316   DNAL OU

275.29
N217   National 4-H Service Committee.

    National 4-H dairy foods demonstration awards
    program. Regulations.
    Chicago,

    1. 4-H clubs.

NN   0052317   DNAL

275.29
N217N   National 4-H Service Committee.

    National 4-H farm and home electric
    awards program.
    [Chicago,

    1. 4-H clubs. I. Title.

NN   0052318   DNAL

S1   National 4-H Service Committee.
.N33
    National 4-H news.
    [Chicago]

275.2
N212Na   National 4-H Service Committee.

    The 1945 National 4-H club rural electrifi-
    cation contest starts now!   Chicago [1944]
    folder.

    Date in title supplied in manuscript over
    date originally printed (1944).

NN   0052320   DNAL

275.2
N212Nf   National 4-H Service Committee.

    1950 national 4-H farm and home electric
    awards program.   [Chicago, 1949]
    [4] p.

    1. 4-H clubs.

NN   0052321   DNAL

National 4-H Service Committee.
    Proceedings,   National 4-H club
congress
    see under   National 4-H club congress.

275.2
N212R   National 4-H Service Committee.

    Report folder for 4-H club members;
    National 4-H club Better farm-and-home
    methods electric contest.   [Chicago, 1949]
    [25] p.

    1. 4-H clubs. I. Title: Better farm-and-
    home methods electric contests.

NN   0052323   DNAL

309.137   National 4-H Service Committee]
N21fo   Serving the 4-H clubs.   Chicago, 1946?
    cover-title, 29p. illus.(incl.ports.)

    1. 4-H clubs. I. Title.

NN   0052324   IU

National 4-H Service Committee.
    The spirit of American music, a dramalogue; narration by
    Morris A. Epstein, musical arrangement by Louis Bachmann ...
    Chicago, Produced and pub. by the National committee on boys
    and girls club work [1934]
        24 p. 23ᵐ.

    I. Epstein, Morris A. The spirit of American music. II. Bachmann,
    Louis. III. Title.
                                        45-29112
    Library of Congress   M1921.F4N

NN   0052325   DLC

275.29
N213Su   National 4-H Service Committee.

    Summary of National 4-H awards.
    Chicago.

    1. 4-H clubs. I. Title: National 4-H
    awards.

NN   0052326   DNAL

S   National 4-H Service Committee.
531
Z99   This is the story of the National Committee
no. 16   on Boys and Girls Club Work. Chicago
    [1948?]
    [9] p. illus. 23 cm.

    1. 4-H clubs.   [I. Title]

NN   0052327   NIC

S   National 4-H Service Committee.
531
Z992   22nd anniversary annual Thos. E. Wilson
no.10   day. Pioneer ed. Given for the 4-H Club
    boys and girls, December 4, 1939. [n.p.,
    1939]
    [68] p.

    1. 4-H clu   bs. 2. Agricultural
    extension wor   k - History.

NN   0052328   NIC DNAL OrCS

National Foxhunters' Association.
    The foxhound stud book, published by
    authority of the National Foxhunters'
    Association ... Compiled by Roger D.
    Williams ... [Lexington, Ky.?, 1902?-
        v. illus. 21cm.

    1. Fox-hunting - U. S. 2. Hounds, American
    fox. 3. Dogs - Stud-books. I. Williams,
    Roger D., 1856   comp. II. Title.

NN   0052329   ViW

VOLUME 407

q658.87 National franchise reports.
N2133
        Chicago.
        v. 34cm. monthly.

NN 0052330   IU OrU

National Franklin Committee, Philadelphia.

[Pamphlets on Benjamin Franklin] Philadelphia
[1942?]

In portfolio.
Mimeographed.
Contents.- [no.1]Franklin and economics.- [no2]
Franklin and electricity.- [no.3]Franklin's associations in the field of medicine.- [no.4]Franklin and
aeronautics.- [no.5]Franklin and sports.-[no.6]
Franklin and fool.- [no.7]Franklin - Printed and
publisher.- [no.8]Franklin explains himself: quotable
quotes.- [no.9]   Franklin the patriot.-

[no.10]Franklin the well-doer.-[no.11]Franklin and
freedom of religion, speech and the press.- [no.12]
Franklin and education.- [no.13]Franklin and city
planning.- [no.14]Franklin and business.- [no.15]
Franklin and the negro question.- [no.16]Franklin
and music.- [no.17]Franklin and agriculture.- [no.
18]Franklin and insurance.- [no.19]College sports
in America originated by B.Franklin.- [no.20]Two
hundred year old advice ... for women today.- [no.
21]Franklin's rules   of living.- [no.22]

Franklin lives as a statesman today.- [no.23] Franklin's influence evident today in many fields.- [no.
24]"The people meet B.Franklin": a program of activities for leaders of business and industry ... [no.
25]"The people meet B.Franklin" a program of activities for patriotic and civic organizations.- [no.
26] "Collegiate America meets B.Franklin": a program
of activities for colleges and universitite.-[no.27]
It will go through; a fifteen minute dramatic sketch.
[no.28]Poor Richard   has a word to say; a ten

minute dramatic program to aid the sale of defense
bonds.- [no.29]Franklin upholds freedom of press,
speech and religion.

NN 0052334   PSt

National Franklin committee, Philadelphia.
[Papers concerning Benjamin Franklin's
continuing contribution to American civilization]
Philadelphia, Pa., The National Franklin committee [1943]
        1 v. fold. table. 30 cm.

NN 0052335   OrU

National Franklin committee, Philadelphia.
[Release] ([1937?-43?]) (Incomplete?)

Philadelphia [1937?-43?] 22 nos. 28cm.

Each issue has individual title.
Ceased publication?

1. Franklin, Benjamin, 1706-1790.

NN 0052336   NN

National Fraternal Committee for the Re-election
of President Roosevelt, New York.
        Security with FDR. Illustrations by
William Gropper
        see under   Marcantonio, Vito, 1902-
1954.

National fraternal congress.
        The International congress on tuberculosis; a report
of the delegation from the National fraternal congress,
by the chairman, Ira W. Porter ... twenty-third annual
meeting, Boston, Mass., August 16, 1909. [Omaha, Neb.,
Press of A. I. Root, inc., 1909]
        86 p. front. (port.) illus. 23ᶜᵐ.

1. International congress on tuberculosis. 6th, Washington, 1908.
2. Tuberculosis—Exhibitions.   I. Porter, Ira W.

                                                          9–22279
        Library of Congress   RC307.I6 1909

NN 0052338   DLC DNLM MH MiDW-M MiU NN OU WaU

National fraternal congress.
        Journal of proceedings
                see its
        Proceedings of the ... annual session.

National fraternal congress.
        President's address.
        [Chicago?]
        v. 23ᶜᵐ.

1. Insurance, Assessment — Congresses. 2. Friendly societies — Congresses.

                                                    CA 18–272 Unrev'd
        Library of Congress   HG9203.N4

NN 0052340   DLC

National fraternal congress.
        Proceedings of the ... annual session.
        1st-   1887-
        Buffalo, N. Y. [etc., 1889?]–
                v. in   ports., tables. 21½ᶜᵐ.
        Proceedings of organization session, held Nov. 16, 1886, with 1st and
        2d annual session, 1887–88, are issued together, with cover-title.
        Title varies: 1886–93, Journal of proceedings.
        1894–   Proceedings of the ... annual session (varies slightly)
        Ceased publication with v. 27, 1913. cf. Union list of serials.

1. Insurance, Fraternal — Congresses. 2. Friendly societies — Congresses.
                                                      7–7247 Revised
        Library of Congress   HG9203.N35

NN 0052341   DLC CaBViP NN ICJ Wa Or IU Nh OCl

National Fraternal Congress. Law section.
        Papers and addresses on the law of fraternal
insurance, read and delivered before the law
section of the National fraternal congress, 1901-
... Pub. under direction National fraternal
congress of America, 1907-
        v.

NN 0052342   WaU-L

National fraternal congress of America.
        Proceedings of the ... annual meeting.
        [Madison, Wis., 19
        v. ports., tables. 23ᶜᵐ.

1. Insurance, Fraternal — Congresses. 2. Friendly societies — Congresses.
                                                    23–93/93 Revised
        Library of Congress   HG9203.N4

NN 0052343   DLC OrU ICJ Wa WaS NcD IdU TU

334.3   National Fraternal Congress of America.
N214p   Report of the annual meeting. [28th–82nd]
        1914–68.
        Chicago.
        55v. 23cm.

        Vols. for 1914–41 called 1st–27th.
        Supersedes and continues the numbering of the
        National Fraternal Congress. Proceedings of
        the annual session.

        Title varies: 1914–45, Proceedings of the
        annual convention.
        Superseded in 1968 by its Report of the
        general sessions and in 1969 by its Report
        of the plenary sessions.

NN 0052345   IU

National fraternal congress of America.
        Uniform code for organization and supervision
        of fraternal benefit societies

        see under

        National association of insurance commissioners.

National Fraternal Congress of America.
        Committee on General Welfare.
        Report of the Committee on General Welfare to the ...
annual convention of the National Fraternal Congress of
America ... [Madison, Wis., 1938-   ]
        Library has 1938 to date. illus., tables. 24ᶜᵐ.

NN 0052347   ICJ Or

National fraternal congress of America.
Committee on thrift and savings.
        Report, [1926-
        [New York, 1925-
        1 v. 23 cm.
        Henry J. Hyman, chairman.

NN 0052348   DHEW DLC

National fraternal congress of America. *Educational committee.*
        Fraternal life insurance; prepared and published under the
official sponsorship of the Educational committee and the
approval of the Executive committee of the National fraternal congress of America. Indianapolis, Ind., The Insurance research and review service [¹1938]
        208 p. 21½ cm.
        Bibliography: p. 200.

1. Insurance, Fraternal. I. Title.
        HG9213.N3   368.3   39—2285

NcRS CU OrPR IdU-SB WaWW OrU OrPR WaS
NN 0052349   DLC OrCS IdU WaE ICJ OU OCU OLak NcD

National fraternal congress of America. *Educational committee.*
        Fraternal life insurance, prepared and published under the
official sponsorship of the Educational committee and the approval of the Executive committee of the National fraternal
congress of America. Indianapolis, Ind., The Insurance research and review service [1942]
        208 p. incl. tables. 21ᶜᵐ.
        "Second printing 1942."
        Bibliography: p. 200.
1. Insurance, Assessment.   I. Title.
                                                          42–14249
        Library of Congress   HG9213.N3 1942
                                        [2]   368.3

NN 0052350   DLC OU MB

National Fraternal Congress of America. *Presidents' Section.*
        Proceedings of the Presidents' Section of the National Fra-
ternal Congress of America ...   [Madison, Wis., 1938–   ]
        Library has no. 25, 1938, to date. 24ᶜᵐ.

NN 0052351   ICJ

National fraternal review.

        v. 1
        Chicago ·   illus. 29cm.
        v. 10, nos. 11–12 have title: Co-operation, formerly the National fraternal review.

1. Freemasons, Negro—Periodi-   cals.
N. Y. P. L.   November 30, 1943

NN 0052352   NN

National Fraternal Society of the Deaf.
        Convention [officers and delegates]
        [Oak Park? Ill.]
        v. illus. 27 cm. quadrennial.

        HV2522.N42   55–27466 ‡

NN 0052353   DLC

VOLUME 407

HV2522
.N424

National Fraternal Society of the Deaf.

The Frat.

[Oak Park, Ill.]

National free art league.
    Report of the work of the National free art
league.   n.p. [1891?]
    8 p.   16 cm.

NN   0052355   RPB

National Free Church Council
    see
National Council of the Evangelical Free Churches.

HV6925
.N33

National free labor association.
    ...Bulletin...
    New York, 1913–

NN   0052357   DLC

National Free Labor Association.
    The prison labor question in Rhode Island.   [New York:
Allied Prtg. Trades Council, 1909?]   5 l.   8°.

1. Prison labor, U. S.: R. I.
N. Y. P. L.

NN   0052358   NN

National free labor association.
    ... Road making by convict labor.   New York, National
free labor association, 1913.
    48 p.   22½ᶜᵐ.   (Series no. 1—Road work.   Bulletin no. 1)
    "A list of articles on convict road work": p. 48.

1. Convict labor—U. S.   2. Roads—U. S.   I. Title.

14–13118

Library of Congress   HV8925.N33

NN   0052359   DLC

National free labour association, London.
    The Free labour gazette
    see under title

National Free Labour Association, London.
    Proceedings of the annual congress.
[no.]
London [1   16°.
no.

1. Labor (Non-union), Gt. Br.—   Congresses.
N. Y. P. L.   August 15, 1921.

NN   0052361   NN

National Free-Soil Convention, Buffalo, 1848
    see   Free-Soil Party.   National Convention,
Buffalo, 1848.

National Free Trade Congress, Manchester, Eng., 1926.
    ...Addresses...delivered at the National Free Trade Con-
gress, held in Manchester, Wednesday & Thursday, Sept. 29 &
30, 1926...   [Manchester: North Western Free Trade Union,
1926.]   19 p.   12°.

    Contents: Cox, H.   Imperial preferences.   CLAY, H.   The ethics of imperial
free trade.

1. Free trade—Congresses—Gr. Br.
N. Y. P. L.   August 24, 1927

NN   0052363   NN

The **National** freedman ...

    New York, 1865–
        v.   23ᶜᵐ.   monthly.
    Organ of the National freedman's relief association (later the **American**
freedman's union commission.   New York branch)

1. Freedmen.   I. American freedman's union commission.   New York
branch.
                                        CA 16–565 Unrev'd

Library of Congress   E185.2.N25

NN   0052364   DLC DHU RP IChi PBL N ICN MB MiU

National freedman's relief association, *New
                                        York*
    see
American freedman's union commission. *New York branch.*

National freedman's relief association of the District of
Columbia.
    Annual report.
    Washington, D. C., 1863.
        v.   21½ᶜᵐ.
    Report year ends April (?)
    1st report has title: First annual report of the National freedman's
relief association of the District of Columbia.

                                        6–10229†

NN   0052366   DLC MB

Slavery
E
441
M46
v.242
no.8

National Freedmen's Relief Association of the
    District of Columbia.
    A circular [regarding the needs of freedmen.
    Washington, 18––]
    3 p.   21cm.

    May anti-slavery pamphlets, v. 242.

    1. Freedmen.

NN   0052367   NIC

National freedman's relief association of the District of
Columbia.
    Temporary aid for the freedmen.   [Washington, 1865]
    2 p.   20½ᶜᵐ.
    Caption title.
    Signed: Officers and executive committee of the National freedman's
relief association.

1. Freedmen.   I. Title.
                                        20–18260

Library of Congress   E185.93.D6N2

NN   0052368   DLC

National freedman's saving and trust company,
                                        Washington
    see
Freedman's savings and trust company, Washington,
                                        D. C.

Slavery
E
441
M46
v.286
no.40

National Freedmen's Aid Union of Great
    Britain and Ireland.
    Actual and impending famine, and dis-
    astrous destitution in the Southern states
    of America.   [London, 1867?]
    4 p.   27 x 21cm.

    May anti-slavery pamphlets, v. 286.
    In slavery broadside box.

        1. Southern   states--Economic con-
    ditions.   I. T   itle.

NN   0052370   NIC

Slavery
E
441
M46
v.286
no.12

National Freedmen's Aid Union of Great
    Britain and Ireland.
    Final appeal [and list of final sub-
    scriptions.   London, 1867?]
    4 p.   27 x 21cm.

    May anti-slavery pamphlets, v. 286.
    In slavery broadside box.

        1. Freedmen.   I. Title.

NN   0052371   NIC

E185
.2
.N26

National freedmen's aid union of Great Britain and
    Ireland.
    The final report ...
    London, 1868.

NN   0052372   DLC

M973.84
N19f

National Freedmen's Aid Union of Great Britain
    and Ireland.
    The final report of the National freedmen's
    Aid Union of Great Britian and Ireland; with the
    names of the newly elected committee of corre-
    spondence with American freedmen's aid associa-
    tions; and reports of proceedings on the presenta-
    tion of addresses to their excellencies the Hon.
    C. F. Adams and the Hon. R. Johnson.   London,
    R. Barrett and Sons, 1865.
    2 pts.   19 cm.

NN   0052373   DHU

National freedmen's aid union of Great Britain and
    The industry of the freedmen of America   Ireland.
    ... [Birmingham: The National freedmen's
aid union, c1867]
    cover-title, [3]–23 p.

NN   0052374   MiU

The national freedmen's-aid union of Great
    Britain and Ireland.
    A public meeting, to inaugurate the National
    freedmen's-aid union... April 24th, 1866.
    4 p.
    Announcement.

NN   0052375   OC1WHi

... National freedom day
    see under   [National freedom day associa-
tion]

[National freedom day association]
    ... National freedom day ...   [Philadelphia? 1943?]
    62 p.   illus. (ports.)   26½ x 20ᶜᵐ.
    At head of title: February 1st, 1865.
    "Contains the speeches and resolutions given at the celebration of
National freedom day, February 1st, 1942 and 1943."—Introd.

1. Negroes.   2. U. S.   Constitution.   13th amendment.   I. Title.
                                        44–28537

Library of Congress   E185.5.N29
                            [2]   325.260973

NN   0052377   DLC Or DHU

VOLUME 407

The **National** freeman. Devoted to the advocacy of the suppression of the liquor traffic, and kindred reforms.
v. 1
Chicago: Stone & Hall, 1881   8°.
v.

Editor: 1881–   J. Russell.

1. Temperance.—Per. and soc. publ.   2. Prohibition.
N. Y. P. L.
March 13, 1920.

NN   0052378   NN

National freemason. v. 1–
June, 1863–
Washington ₍etc.₎ 1863–
v. illus. (incl. ports.) 24 cm.
Monthly, June, 1863–   ; weekly.
Title varies: v. June, 1863–Apr. 18, 1868, National freemason.
Apr. 25, 1868–   National and freemason.
Editors: June 1863–
Robert McCurdy (with J. W. Simons

1. Freemasons—Period.   I. McCurdy, Robert, ed.   II. Simons,
John W., ed.
CA 8—2364 Unrev'd
Library of Congress   HS351.N3

NN   0052379   DLC NcU N OU

National freight rate service, *Dowagiac, Mich.*
National rate service: parcel post, express, freight rates and
routing; parcel post and express rates to every known town in
the United States, and express rates to all principal towns in
Canada; also, all countries with which the United States have
postal regulations ... Dowagiac, Mich., National freight rate
service ₍1931₎
1 v. forms. 32ᶜᵐ.
Loose-leaf.
1. Parcels-post—U. S.—Rates.   2. Postal service—U. S.—Rates.   3.
Express service—U. S.—Rates.   4. Railroads—U. S.—Rates.   5. Railroads—U. S.—Freight.   6. Shippers' guides—U. S.   7. Express service—Canada—Rates.   I. Title.
CA 31–747 Unrev'd
Library of Congress   HE6473.A3N3
Copyright A 39005   ₍2₎   385.10973

NN   0052380   DLC

National frieght traffic manual
see under   [Stufflebeam, George Teele]

National French draft horse association.
Evidence presented by the National French draft horse
association. Before the Illinois state board of agriculture at Springfield, Ill., Jan. 4, 1888, on the breed and
breeding of the draft horses of France. Fairfield, Ia.,
Tribune ₍1888₎
2 p. l., 60 p.   21½ᶜᵐ.

1. French draft horse.   2. Percheron horse.   I. Illinois—Agriculture,
Dept. of.
Agr 3–482
Library, U. S. Dept. of   Agriculture. 42N3r

NN   0052381   DNAL DLC

National French Draft Horse Association.
... The national register of French draft horses ... together
with ... proceedings ... and ... annual reports ... ₍Fairfield,
Iowa, etc.₎ National French Draft Horse Association, 1881–1917.
Library has v. 1–14. 24ᶜᵐ.
Organized in 1876, incorporated 1884 as National Norman Horse Association;
name changed to above form in 1885.
Title varies: v. 1, The national register of Norman horses, with a general
history of the horse-kind and a thorough history of the Norman horse,
by James M. Hiatt.
Vol. 2–3, The national register of Norman horses ...
Place of publication varies.

NN   0052382   ICJ NcRS CU DLC OU

372.06   National Froebel Foundation.
NATF   Bulletin. no.1–   Jan.1940–
London.
no.   illus.   25cm.

Supersedes Child life; a monthly magazine.

NN   0052383   IU CaBVaU OU NNU-W

372.08   National Froebel Foundation
N277p   Pamphlets.
London.
Dates lacking or irregular. Arranged alphabetically by
title.

1. Education, Elementary.   2. Froebel, Friedrich Wilhelm
August, 1782–1852.   3. Education—Gt. Brit.

NN   0052384   ICarbS

LB   National Froebel Foundation.
775   Some aspects of Piaget's work. London, 1955.
.P58   45 p.   22 cm.
N28   Cover title.
CONTENTS.—Children's ideas of number. (1) Sum-
mary, by Evelyn Lawrence. (ii) The teacher and
Piaget's work on number, by T.R.Theakston.—The
wider significance of Piaget's work, by N.Isaacs.
—Piaget and progressive education, by N.Isaacs.

1.Piaget,Jean,1896–   2.Number concept₍.₎
3.Child study.

NN   0052385   MiU

National Froebel Foundation
see also
Froebel Society of Great Britain and Ireland.
National Froebel Union.

National Froebel Foundation. Education Library.

Catalogue, 1947. London ₍1947?₎

175 p.   22 cm.

1. Library catalogs.   2. Education – Bibl.

NN   0052387   CaBVaU

National Froebel union.
... Syllabus of the examinations for kindergarten and
lower form mistresses conducted by the National Froebel
union. (Founded 1887.) ... London, Office of the National Froebel union ₍1907₎
2 p. l., ₍3₎–23 p.   20ᶜᵐ.
At head of title: Issued October, 1907.

1. ₍Teachers₎—Examinations—England.   2. Teachers, Training of—
England.   ₍2. Teachers—Training—Kindergarten₎
E 15–1636
Library, U. S. Bur. of   Education LB1765.G7N2 1907

NN   0052388   DHEW

National Froebel union. *Joint examination board.*
... Syllabus of the examination of the Joint examination board of the National Froebel union consisting of
representatives appointed by the Froebel society ... ₍and₎
the Kindergarten company (Bedford) ... London, Office
of the Joint board of examination ₍1890₎
21 p.   20½ᶜᵐ.
At head of title: Ed. issued July, 1890.
"Books recommended for study and reference": p. 17–21.

1. Teachers—Examinations—England.
E 10–235
Library, U. S. Bur. of   Education LB1765.G7N2

NN   0052389   DHEW

National Froebel Union
see also
National Froebel Foundation.

National front; India's independent weekly newsmagazine.
Cawnpore.
v. illus., ports. 32 cm.

AP8.N285   052   50–17327

NN   0052391   DLC

National Front in Czechoslovakia
see
Národní fronta.

National Front of Democratic Germany
see Nationale Front des Demokratischen Deutschland.

HD9001   National Frozen Food Distributors Association.
.F7
Frozen food factbook and directory.
₍New York₎

National Frozen Food Distributors Association.
Yearbook of distribution, 1949–
New York, 1949
v.   illus. (part col.) diagrs.   30.5 cm.
1. Food, Frozen – Yearbooks.   2. Food industry
and trade – Yearbooks.   I. Title.

NN   0052395   OrCS MH–BA NcRS

295   [National Frozen Food Locker Association]
N216   [Food is power.   Des Moines, 1941]
14 p.   illus.   28 cm.
Title on ₍p. 4₎ of cover.
In support of H.R. 5532, 77th Cong., 1st
sess. "A bill ... providing for the extension of the
stamp plan ... to include authorization for the
issuance to farmers of famers of frozen food
locker certificates".

NN   0052396   DNAL

TP490   National Frozen Food Locker Association.
.N377
Frozen food locker plants directory.
Des Moines, National Frozen Food Locker Assn., ₍19₎

TP490   National frozen food locker association.
.L6
The Locker operator.
₍Des Moines, 19₎

National Frozen Food Locker Association.
Proceedings of annual convention.
₍Des Moines?₎
v.   23 cm.

1. Cold-storage lockers—Congresses.
TP493.5.N26   664.85   49–42029*†

NN   0052399   DLC DNAL MiD CU

VOLUME 407

280.3
N2112   National Frozen Food Locker Institute,
         Elizabethtown, Pa.
         Consumer frozen food packaging survey.
         Elizabethtown, Pa. [1951?]
         [8] l.

         1. Food, Frozen. Packaging. I. Title.

NN   0052400   DNAL

Z5074
.P7N3   The National fruit and produce blue book:
         quarterly supplement. 19
         Wheaton, Ill., Produce Reporter Co.,
         19   -
         v. 27 cm.

         1. Fruit trade—Bibl. 2. Produce trade—
         Bibl. I. Produce   Reporter Co. Blue
         Book.

NN   0052401   TU

The National fruit and vegetable directory. 1944–
Chicago, Ill., Aberdeen press, inc. [1944–
v. 21½ᵐᵐ. annual.

         1. Fruit trade—U. S.—Direct. 2. Produce trade—U. S.—Direct.
                                                   45–12908
         Library of Congress   HD9243.N3
                                          [2]   338.1405

NN   0052402   DLC CU WM DNAL

The National fruit grower and gardener. v.   –14, v. 15,
no. 1–8;   –Aug. 1910. St. Joseph, Mich.
[The Fruit publishing co.; etc., etc.]   –1910.
v. illus. 30½–37½ᵐᵐ. monthly.
Title varies: –Apr. 1910, The National fruit grower.
May–Aug. 1910, The National fruit grower and gardener.
Published in Chicago, May–Aug 1910.
No more published.

         1. Fruit-culture—Period.
                                                   11–28516
         Library of Congress   SB354.N27

NN   0052403   DLC MBH

399.3
N219   National Fruit Product Company, inc.
Ed.5   White House preservers' manual.   5th ed.
         Winchester, Va., 1949.
         78 p.

         1. Fruit preservation. I. Title.

NN   0052404   DNAL

National Fuchsia Society of America.
    The Fuchsian
    see under title

HF5585
.C7C7   National Fuel Credit Association.

         The Coal buyers "blue book."

         Chicago, National Fuel Credit Association [etc.]

National Fulton County Bank, *Gloversville, N. Y.*
    see Fulton County National Bank and Trust Company
    of Gloversville.

National Fund for Medical Education.
    Medical education in the United States ...
    see under title

National Fund for Medical Education.
    Report to contributors.
    [New York]
    v. ports. 28 cm. annual.

R735.A1N3   58–15246

NN   0052409   DLC DNLM

National fund for promoting efficient municipal
    accounting and reporting. New York

    see

Bureau of municipal research, New York. Metz fund.

PB
2293   National Fund for Welsh Troops.
.G99   Gwlad fy Nhadau, rhodd Cymru i'w Byddin.
         London, New York, Hodder & Stoughton [c1915]
         xi, 127, [1] p. fronts., plates (part col.,
         part. mounted) 25 cm.
         Includes music.
         Edited by Sir John Morris Jones.
         1. Welsh literature - Anthologies. I. Title:
         Gwlad fy Nhadau.

NN   0052411   DCU MH IU MB

National fund library.
    no. 1

The Hague [1917?]   21cm.
    no.   illus.
"Published by the head office of the Jewish national fund, The Hague."
For German edition see its Nationalfonds-Bibliothek.
                                 CONTENTS.
* PWC p.v.11
no. 1. BÖHM, ADOLF. The Jewish national fund. [2d ed.] [1917?]

NN   0052412   NN

National Fundamental Education Centre,
    Klay, Liberia
    see
    Klay, Liberia. National Fundamental Education
    Centre.

National Funeral Directors Association of the United States.
    Funeral service as a vocation. [Chicago, 1945]
    24 p.

NN   0052414   ICJ

National funeral directors' association of the United States.
    Pharmaceutical, anatomical and chemical lexicon. The Na-
    tional funeral directors' official text book ... Pub. under the
    auspices of the Funeral directors' association of the United
    States and Canada ... Comp. from the most reliable sources
    by H. Samson ... O. N. Crane ... A. B. Perrigo ... committee.
    Assisted by Marcus P. Hatfield ... Chicago, Donohue & Hen-
    neberry, printers, 1886.
    575 p. illus., vi col. pl. (incl. front.) 23½ᵐᵐ.
    Bibliography : p. 570–575.
    1. Embalming. I. Samson, Hudson, comp. II. Crane, Oscar N.,
    joint comp. III. Perrigo, Artemus B., joint comp. IV. Hatfield, Marcus
    Patten, 1849–   V. Title.
                                                   8–8784 Revised
    Library of Congress   RA623.N2

NN   0052415   DLC OU ICJ

National Funeral Directors' Association of the
    United States.
    Pharmaceutical, anatomical and chemical lexicon.
    The national funeral directors' official text
    book. 2d ed., Chicago Donohue & Henneberry,
    1887.
    600p. illus.

NN   0052416   ICRL ICJ

National funeral directors' association of the United
    States.
    Proceedings of the ... annual convention.

    [Chicago,
    v. illus., pl., ports., tab. 23ᵐᵐ.

    1. Undertakers and undertaking—Societies. 2. Embalming—Societies.
                                        CA 7—7012 Unrev'd
    Library of Congress   RA622.A5N2

NN   0052417   DLC DNLM Nh

National funeral directors' association of the United   States.
    Reference book containing a complete list of
    names of the officers and members of the various
    state associations of funeral directors.
    Alliance, 1898.

NN   0052418   Nh

National funeral service journal.
    [Chicago, Trade Periodical Co.]
    v. in   illus., ports. 26–31 cm. monthly.
    Began publication with Apr. 1892 issue.
    Title varies: –June 1980, The Embalmers' monthly.—
    July 1980–Mar. 1959, The Embalmers' monthly and national funeral
    director.

    1. Undertakers and undertaking—Period. 2. Embalming—Period.
    RA622.A3   61–23201

NN   0052419   DLC IaU PPC DNLM ICRL ICJ

636.905   The National fur news. v.1–
NA   1928–
           Denver.
           v. illus. 31cm. monthly.
           Issues for   –Jan.1938 have confused
           vol. numbering, but constitute v.9a, no. –12.
           Other slight irregularities in numbering.
           Official publication of the Rocky Mountain
           National Fur Growers Association (variantly
           called Rocky Mountain Fur Growers Association)
           –Nov. 1934 and Mar.1938–
           In Aug.1959   absorbed Black fox maga-
           zine and modern   mink breeder.

NN   0052420   IU CaBVaU NcRS TxU NIC OU MnU-A NMScS

National Furniture Association.
    Blue-book of the furniture trade
    see under title

National furniture review.

    [Chicago, National Retail Furniture Association]
    v. in   illus., ports., maps. 29 cm. monthly.
    "Founded 1927."

    1. Furniture—Period. I. National Retail Furniture Association.
    TS840.N28   *684.105   58–22774

NN   0052422   DLC NN OC1

HD9773
.U5N25   National furniture review.

         The NRFA buyer. 1st–   ed.; 1946–
         [Chicago, National Furniture Review]

VOLUME 407

National Furniture Warehousemen's Association.
The Furniture warehouseman, serving the
household goods storage and moving industry
see under title

National furniture warehousemen's association.
Membership and agency list...₍by₎ National
furniture warehousemen's association and Allied
van lines, inc.

Library has
Aug. 1929, Dec. 1936.

I. Allied van lines, Inc.

NN 0052425   MiD

The **National** future farmer. v. 1–
fall 1952–
₍Alexandria, Va., etc.₎

v. in   illus. 30 cm.

Quarterly, 1952–55; bimonthly, 1956–
"Official magazine of the Future Farmers of America."

1. Agriculture—Period.   I. Future Farmers of America.

S1.F97   67–9074

NN 0052426   DLC P OrCS HU

YA
8409
The national gag-law, ₍Signed: Republican₎
₍n.p., n.d.₎
6p.

(Wide-awake papers, no. 3)

NN 0052427   DLC MH

National Galleries Company, Washington.
Halls of the ancients
see under   Chandler, Jefferson.

National Gallery, *Cape Town*
see
South African National Gallery, *Cape Town.*

National gallery, London
see   London. National gallery.

National Gallery, Melbourne
see   Victoria, Australia. Public Library,
museums and National Gallery, Melbourne.

National gallery, Millbank, London
see   Tate Gallery, London.

National gallery, Prague

See

Prague. Národní galerie.

National Gallery, *Salisbury, Rhodesia*
see
Rhodes National Gallery, *Salisbury, Rhodesia.*

The National gallery, ...   New York, 1906
see under   ₍La Sizeranne, Robert de₎
1866–1932.

---

fN1070
N22
1375
The National gallery; a selection from its
pictures. Engraved by George Doo, William Finden, John and Henry Le Keux, John Pye, Edward
Goodall, John Burnet, W. Bromley, George Cooke,
and others. With biographical and descriptive
letterpress. A new edition, from the original
plates. London, Chatto and Windus, publishers,
1875.
vi p., 1 l., [9]–120 p. front., plates, ports.
43cm. Green cloth.
1. Painters.   2. Paintings—London. I.
London. National   gallery.

NN 0052436   CSmH

N
1070
N3
The National Gallery: a series of twenty-nine
plates from the best pictures in that celebrated collection, by Correggio, Paul Vero-
nese, and Caracci; Murrillo, Rubens, and
Vandyck; Poussin and Wilson; Gainsborough,
Reynolds and Wilkie; Rembrandt, Cuyp, and
Canaletti, engraved in the finest line-
manner by Finden ₍and others₎ London, M.
A. Nattali, 1846.
1 v. (unpaged) illus. 47 cm.

I. London. National gallery. II. Finden.
William, 1787-   1852.

NN 0052437   CU-S

A national gallery, being a collection of English charac-
ters. compiled by C. C. & D. G. London, M. Secker, 1933.
viii. 535, ₍1₎ p. illus. 19ᶜᵐ.
Title within ornamental border.
Illustrated lining-papers.
Blank pages for additional selections (503–510)

1. Characters and characteristics in literature. 2. English literature
(Selections: Extracts, etc.)   I. C., C., comp. II. C. C., comp. III. G.,
D., joint comp. IV. D. G., joint comp.

Library of Congress   PR1111.C5N3   35–35387
                                          ₍3₎   820.822

NN 0052438   DLC WaWW CoU WaU

National Gallery, British Art, *London*
see Tate Gallery, *London.*

National gallery committee

see

London. National gallery, Trustees.

The National gallery— London: the central Italian
schools
see under   ₍Holroyd, Sir Charles₎ 1861–

The National gallery——London: the Dutch school
see under   ₍Geffroy, Gustave₎ 1855–1926.

The National gallery - London: the early British
School
see under   La Sizeranne, Robert de,
1866–1932.

The National gallery - London: *The Flemish school*
see under   ₍Wedmore, Frederick₎ 1844–

The National gallery-London: the later British
school
see under   ₍La Sizeranne, Robert de₎ 1866–
1932.

The National gallery— London: the northern
Italian schools
see under   ₍Holroyd, Sir Charles₎ 1861–

E162
f.N17
The **National** gallery of American landscape. New York,
W. Pate & co.; ₍etc., etc.,₎ ᶜ1869₎
₍54₎ p. 24 pl. 58ᶜᵐ.

1. U. S.—Descr. & trav.—Views. 2. Engravings, American.

NN 0052447   ICU MiD ViU CU

National gallery of art handbook
see under   U.S. National Gallery of Art.

National gallery of art (Mellon gallery) *Washington,
D. C.*

see

U.S. National gallery of art.

National gallery of art of the Smithsonian institution

see

Smithsonian institution. *National collection of fine arts.*

The National gallery of art, Washington, D.C.
₍New York, H.H. Saylor, 1941₎
see under   ₍Saylor, Henry Hodgman₎ 1880–

National gallery of British art at South Kensington

see

South Kensington museum, *London.*

National Gallery of British Sports and Pastimes,
London
see London. National Gallery of British
Sports and Pastimes.

National Gallery of Canada
see   Ottawa. National Gallery of Canada.

National Gallery of Ireland, *Dublin*
see
Dublin. National Gallery of Ireland.

VOLUME 407

... The **National** gallery of pictures by the great masters, presented by individuals or purchased by grant of Parliament ... London & New York, J. Tallis & company [184–?]

iv, [217] p. front., 107 pl. (incl. ports.) 27½ᶜᵐ.

Engr. t.-p.

1. Paintings—London. 2. Paintings, Reproductions of.   ɪ. London. National gallery.

9-11828†

Library of Congress   N1070.N2

NN   0052456   DLC MB PU OFH MiU NN

The **National** gallery of pictures by the great masters, presented by individuals, or purchased by grant of Parliament. London, Jones & co. [1840?]

2 v. front., 114 pl. (incl. ports.) 27½ᶜᵐ.

Engraved title-pages, with ornamental borders.

1. Paintings—London.   ɪ. London. National gallery.

2–27154

Library of Congress   N1070.N22

WaU OClW MiU IU MH NN
NN   0052457   DLC PU–FA MdBP CtY WaSpG CaBVaU ViU

... The **National** gallery of pictures by the great masters, presented by individuals or purchased by grant of Parliament ... [London] London printing and publishing company [1848]

1 p. l., [128] p. front., 63 pl. (incl. ports.) 28ᶜᵐ.

Engr. t.-p.

1. Paintings—London. 2. Paintings, Reproductions of.   ɪ. London. National gallery.

9-8280†

Library of Congress   N1070.N24

NN   0052458   DLC NjP

The **National** gallery of pictures by the great masters; presented by individuals, or purchased by grant of Parliament. In a series of upwards of one hundred steel engravings, by the first artists; with descriptive letter-press ... London and New York, J. Tallis and company [1848?]

2 v. in 1. fronts., plates. 27ᶜᵐ.

Added title-pages, engraved.

1. Paintings—London.   ɪ. London. National gallery.

44–13009

Library of Congress   N1070.N242

NN   0052459   DLC

JA36   **National gallery of practical science, London.**
.P8   Catalogue for 1833. 5th ed.   London,
         J. Holmes.
         44 p. (Political pamphlets, 75:1)

NN   0052460   DLC

National Gallery of Practical Science, *London.*
Catalogue for 1834. 7. ed. *London: J. Holmes, printer,* 1834. 44 pp. 8°.
In: *C. p. v. 513.

NN   0052461   NN

The **national** gallery of presidents, comprising twenty-five photo-gravure portraits on heavy French vellum of the chief executives of the United States from George Washington to Theodore Roosevelt, together with perfect fac-similes of their signatures and brief biographies; also a steel-plate engraving of the Declaration of independence... New York [etc.] The Colonial press [1902?]   2 l.   facsim., ports.   50cm.

"Congressional library edition, limited to 5,000 copies."
The copy of the Declaration of independence is a direct impression from the steel plate engraved in 1856. — *cf. l. 2.*

94183B. 1. United States. President—   Portraits, statues, medals, etc.
ɪ. United States. Declaration of   independence. II. United States.
Library of Congress
N.Y.P.L.   February 10, 1941

NN   0052462   NN MiU CU MH

National gallery of Scotland
see
Edinburgh.   National gallery of Scotland.

National Gallery of South Africa
see
South African National Gallery, *Cape Town.*

Mu970.1   NATIONAL GALLERY OF THE AMERICAN INDIAN.
N215
           The National gallery of the American
         Indian to honor the creative work of America's
         first artists and craftsmen.   [New York]
         The National gallery of the American Indian,
         1945?]
           21p. 1 illus. 24cm.

NN   0052465   PU

National Gallery Orchestra
see
U. S.   *National Gallery of Art. Orchestra.*

National gallery pictures ... London, "Pall Mall gazette" office, 1893.
cover-title, 96 p. of illus. (incl. ports), 111-x p. 24½ᶜᵐ.
"Pall Mall gazette 'Extra' —no. 65 ... October 1892."
Advertising matter: p. i[1]-viii and x at end.
Imperfect: p. 85–86 mutilated.

1. Paintings—London.   ɪ. London. National gallery.
II. Pall Mall gazette.

NN   0052467   ViU RPB MH

National gallery pictures. 2d ed. ... London, Office of the "Pall Mall magazine," 1903.
cover-title, 96 p. of illus. (incl. ports.), x (i. e. xii) p. 25½ᶜᵐ.
"Pall Mall gazette 'Extra,' no. 77."

1. Paintings—London.   ɪ. London. National gallery. II. Pall Mall gazette.

4-24647 Revised

Library of Congress   N1070.N26

NN   0052468   DLC WaS

The National Gallery. Two letters to the editor
of The Times
see under   [Ruskin, John] 1819-1900.

National Game Conference
see
American Game Conference.

National Garbage Fuel Co., *Chicago.*
"?" Fuel made from city garbage and refuse is cheaper and better than coal. It is smokeless and odorless and will burn any place where coal is used. National Garbage Fuel Co. Chicago, [1905].
14 p. illus. 16½ x 26ᶜᵐ.

NN   0052471   ICJ

National garden almanack and trade directory
for the years 1853-1858, [comp.] by J. Edwards.

NN   0052472   MBH

National garden association.
                                          FOR OTHER EDITIONS
SB405   SEE MAIN ENTRY
.B3   Barron, Leonard, 1868–   *ed.*
1928   ... Flower growing, revised and adapted from the text of
         I. D. Bennett's "The flower garden," by Leonard Barron and
         the staff of the Garden magazine. [Garden City, N. Y.] Pub.
         by Doubleday, Doran & company, inc., for the National garden
         association, 1928.

1.90   **National Garden Conference, Washington, D.C.,**
C3N215   **1946.**
           Recommendations of Committee no. 1[2 and
         3]   Washington [1946]
           [6] p.

1. Food for freedom program. 2. Food conservation. Congresses. I. U.S. Dept. of Agriculture. National Garden Program.

NN   0052474   DNAL

91.09   National garden conference, Washington, D.C.,
N21Re   1946.
           Report of National garden conference, March
         26-27-28, 1946, Washington, D.C. ... United
         States Department of agriculture, Jefferson
         auditorium.   [Washington? 1946]
           53 p.   26.5 cm.
           Processed.

NN   0052475   DNAL

---

728   National garden homes corporation.
N2132   [House plans] New York city, National
         garden homes corporation [193-?]
           9 plans. 23x35½cm. fold. to 23x19½cm.
         in cover.

         Text runs parallel to back of cover.

           1. Architecture, Domestic.   Designs and
         plans.

NN   0052476   OrU

National garden institute.
  Garden plans, for low-cost homes. [New York, 1946]
18 p. illus. 22 x 28ᶜᵐ.

1. Landscape gardening. ɪ. Title.
SB473.N3   712.642   47-20849
                                     Brief cataloging

NN   0052477   DLC Or OrP WaS DNAL OCl NN IU

National Garden Institute.
  Liberty gardengram
  see under title

National Garden Institute.
  School gardengram
  see under title

National garden supply merchandiser and
  power equipment dealer
    see   Home and garden supply merchandiser.

VOLUME 407

The **National** gardener.

₍Concord, N. H.₎

v. in   illus., ports. 23 cm.   bimonthly.
Began publication in 1960. Cf. Union list of serials.
Bulletin of the National Council of State Garden Clubs.

1. Gardening—Period. 2. Gardening—U. S.—Period.   ɪ. National
Council of State Garden Clubs.

SB1.N2947   635.905   57–41339

WvU

NN 0052481   DLC Or LNHT LNL CU ScCleU LU OrCS Or

National gardens guild, Edgware, Eng.
   The Guild gardener
      see under title

National Gardens Scheme
   see Joint Gardens Committee of the National Trust and
   the Royal Horticultural Society.

The national garment cutter and voice of
fashion. Chicago, /Goldsberry, Doran &
Nelson, 1867.
   ₍2₎ p.
P 17, 843.

NN 0052484   OClWHi

NATIONAL GARMENT RETAILERS' ASSOCIATION.
   Official program, second national merchandise fair;
ready-to-wear exhibit and fashion revue, New York
City, July 23rd to August 3rd 1923.   New York,
[1923] 256 p. illus., ports. 31cm.

1. Dress—Exhibitions—U. S.—N. Y.—New York, 1923. I. Title:
National merchandise fair.

NN 0052485   NN

National Gas Association of Australia.
   The New Zealand gas industry, statistical year book.

Melbourne.

   ₇. tables. 34 cm.
   Title varies: 19   -57, Statistical year book of the gas industry
in New Zealand.
   Earlier data in the association's Statistical year book of the gas
industry in Australia & New Zealand (later Statistical year book of
the gas industry in Australia)
   Compiled and issued by the association's Statistical Dept.

   1. Gas industry—New Zealand—Stat. 2. Gas industry—Australia—
Stat.

TP738.N28   338.476657   60–30669

NN 0052486   DLC

National Gas Association of Australia.
   Statistical year book of the gas industry in Australia.

₍Melbourne₎

   v. in   tables. 34 cm.
   Title varies: 19   -53, Statistical year book of the gas industry in
Australia & New Zealand.
   Compiled and issued by the association's Statistical Dept.

   1. Gas industry—Australia—Stat. 2. Gas industry—New Zealand—
Stat.

TP738.N3   338.476657   55–38347 rev ‡

NN 0052487   DLC NNC NN DI DS

National Gas Association of Australia.
   Statistical year book of the gas industry in Australia &
New Zealand
   see its
   Statistical year book of the gas industry in Australia.

National Gas Association of Australia.
   Statistical year book of the gas industry in New Zealand
   see its
   The New Zealand gas industry, statistical year book.

National gas bulletin
   see   Australian gas journal.

National Gas Engine Association.
   Bulletin.
Chicago.
   v. illus. monthly.
   Published 1915–Aug. 1920.
   Continues Business in farming bulletin and is
continued by Gas engine and farm power
Association. Bulletin.

NN 0052491   ICRL ICJ

National gas engine association.
   Proceedings of the ... annual convention.

Lakemont, N. Y.

   v. diagrs. 21ᶜᵐ.

   1. Gas and oil engines—Societies.

16–18181

Library of Congress   TJ751.N3

NN 0052492   DLC

National gas light and fuel co., *Chicago.*
   ₍Catalogue of₎ the National gas light and fuel co., contractors for gas works and water-gas apparatus ... ₍Chi-
cago₎ 1892.
   40 p. illus. 19½ x 28ᶜᵐ.

   1. Water-gas. 2. Gas manufacture and works—Apparatus—Catalogs.

8–33223†

Library of Congress   TP760.N27
                             (Copyright 1892: 26259)

NN 0052493   DLC

National Gastroenterological Association.

RC799
.N33

   The American journal of gastroenterology. v. 1–
Mar. 1934–
₍New York₎

National Gastrointestinal Cancer Conference,
   5th, Cincinnati, 1952.

RC261
A38
1952
   Proceedings. Submitted by Morris K. Barrett
₍Washington₎ National Institutes of Health,
Public Health Service, Federal Security agency
₍1953₎
   927–1095 p. 26 cm. (Journal of the National
Cancer Institute. Reprint no. 461)

   1. Digestive organs—Cancer. 2. Cancer—
Congresses. 3. Cancer—Diagnosis. I. U.S.—
National Cancer   Institute.

NN 0052495   RPB

National Gastrointestinal Cancer Conference
6th, 1955, New York.
   Proceedings. ₍Baltimore, Gastroenterology,
1955₎
   491–683 p. illus., plates (part col.)

   Conference held April 4–5, 1955, Hosack Hall,
New York Academy of Medicine. Sponsored by the
Gastrointestinal Cancer Committee of the Na-
tional Advisory Cancer Council, National Cancer
Institute.

   Reprinted from Gastroenterology, v. 29, no.
4, Oct. 1955.
   Includes bibliographies.

NN 0052497   NNC-M

National gazette and literary register. v. 1–
Apr. 5, 1820–
Philadelphia, 1820–
   v.   51 cm.   triweekly.
   Frequency varies: 1820–Nov. 1822, semi-
weekly.
   Founded by William Fry.
   Title varies: Oct. 4? 1841–Jan. 1842,
National gazette.
   After issues of Jan. 1842 merged with the
Inquirer to form the Pennsylvania inquirer and
independent gazette (Later the Philadelphia
inquirer)

   1. American newspapers, Early – 1801–
1850. I. Fry, William.

FU PPL PSt NNC ICN UU MBAt

NN 0052499   NNC NjP DLC TxU PU CtY NPV PPiU NcRS

NATIONAL GAZETTE AND LITERARY REGISTER.
   Preliminary address;principles and men.
Philadelphia,W.Fry,1820.

   Pamphlet.

NN 0052500   MH

DA640 The **National** gazetteer: a topographical dictionary of the
.N3   British Islands.   Comp. from the latest and best sources,
         and illustrated with a complete county atlas, and numer-
         ous maps ... London, Virtue and co., 1868.
         3 v. in 12. plates, double maps. 28ᵐ.
         Title-pages for v. 1–3 bound at end of v. 3.
         Edited by N. E. S. A. Hamilton.

   1. Gt. Brit.—Descr. & trav.—Gazetteers. 2. Ireland—Descr. & trav.—Gazetteers.

NN 0052501   ICU PBL NjP NcD

---

*7290.45.9

National Gem. [Monthly.] Vol. 1 (no. 3) September, 1877.
Boston, Mass. 1877. v. 14½ cm.
Published by a boy, J. C. McLean.

H716o — Periodicals. Juvenile. (Issued by young people.)

NN 0052502   MB

National Genealogical Society.
   ₍Circulars, documents, etc.₎

NN 0052503   MWA

National Genealogical Society.
   Constitution and By-laws.   Washington, D.C.,
1911.
   17 p. Oblong 16mo (4 1/4 x 5 11/16 inches)
With covers.

NN 0052504   GU-De

National **Genealogical** Society, Washington, D. C.
   Constitution and by-laws, National Genealogical Society...
Washington, 1914. 11(1) p. illus. 16°.

1. Genealogy.—Associations, U. S.
N. Y. P. L.

January 15, 1916.

NN 0052505   NN

National genealogical society.

Curry, Kate Singer.
   Frederick Schott of Derry township, Lancaster county,
Pennsylvania, and descendants, by Kate S. Curry. Washing-
ton, D. C., 1933.

VOLUME 407

National Genealogical Society.
Genealogical publications
see its
Special publications.

National genealogical society.
Historical bulletin...being the official
leaflets containing its rules, members, proceedings, and other matter for circulation...
Washington, D. C., Issued by the Committee on
publication, 1904.
12 p.

NN   0052508   MiD-B

National genealogical society, *Washington, D. C.*
Historical pamphlet of the National genealogical society being the official pamphlet containing its rules, members, proceedings, and other matter for circulation ... Issued by the committee on publication. Washington, D. C.,
1909.
16 p.   23½ᶜᵐ.

9–30700

NN   0052509   DLC

National Genealogical Society, Washington, D. C.
Index of Revolutionary War pension applications
see under   Hoyt, Max Ellsworth, 1898?–
1954.

National Genealogical Society.
Index to Revolutionary War pension records
see under title *Supplement*

CS42   National Genealogical Society.
.N4
National Genealogical Society quarterly. v. 1–
(no. ₁1₁–   ); Apr. 1912–
Washington.

National Genealogical Society.
Report of the president.
₁Washington₁
v. 28 cm. annual.

CS42.N442   929.106273   52–39726

NN   0052513   DLC Vi

National Genealogical Society, Washington, D. C.
Roster. National Genealogical Society.   Washington,
D. C.: ₁Carnahan Press,₁ 1914.   9(1) p.   12°.

1. Genealogy.—Associations, U. S.
N. Y. P. L.   November 11, 1915.

NN   0052514   NN

National Genealogical Society.
Special publications. no. 1–
Washington, 1933–
v. in   fold. maps. 26 cm.
Number 1 preceded by an issue called no. 0, Announcement and
dated 1932–33.
Title varies: no. 1–   Genealogical publications.

1. U. S.—Geneal.

CS42.N43   929.106273   33–12190 rev*

MH NcD IU OrU OrP WaS WaSp
NN   0052515   DLC Or TxLT PBL NN CaBVaU LU N IU WHi

National genealogical society.
U. S. *Census office.*
Tennessee census reports ... no. 1–
Washington, D. C., 1933–

National Genealogical Society quarterly. v. 1–
(no. ₁1₁–   ); Apr. 1912–
Washington.
v. in   27 cm.
Title varies slightly.
INDEXES:
Vols. 23–26, 1935–38 (Suppl. to v. 27) *with* v. 22–26.

1. U. S.—Geneal.—Period.   I. National Genealogical Society.

CS42.N4   17—12813*

MB PBL P GU NjP OY KyHi IU NNU
NN   0052517   DLC PHi NN DSI WaS WaE OrP Or MdBP FM

National Genealogical Society Quarterly (Indexes)
Index of Revolutionary War pension applications
see under   Hoyt, Max Ellsworth, 1898?–
1954.

National Genealogical Society Quarterly (*Indexes*)

Index to Revolutionary War pension records
see under title *₁Supplement₁*

The **National** genealogist. v. 1–2, no. 1; Apr. 1940–spring
1941. ₁Los Angeles, 1940–41₁
2 v. in 1. illus. (incl. ports.) 28ᶜᵐ. irregular.
Edited and published by Abbott Mason.
No more published. *cf.* Union list of serials.

1. Genealogy—Period. 2. U. S.—Geneal.—Period.   I. Mason, Abbott,
1906–   ed.

Library of Congress   CS42.N45   45–41867
₃₃₁   929.105

NN   0052520   DLC NN TxU Or

338.7   National General Corporation.
N2188   Report.
₁Los Angeles₁
v. illus. 28cm. annual.

Report year ends in September.
Issued 1954/55–1959/60 under its earlier
name: National Theatres, inc.

NN   0052521   IU

National general export merchants' group, London.
...Report on post war trade policy... ₁London, 1943₁   11 p.
illus. 21cm.

1. Commerce—Gt. Br., 1939–   2. World war, 1939–1945—Post-war
problems, Economic—Gt. Br.
N. Y. P. L.   January 10, 1946

NN   0052522   NN

National general ticket agents' association
see
American association of passenger traffic officers.

The **National** geographic magazine. v. 1–
1888–
Washington, National Geographic Society.
v. illus. (part col.) ports., maps (part fold., part col.) 26 cm.
Frequency varies.
Editors: Jan. 1896–Oct. 1901, J. Hyde.—Nov. 1901–Feb. 1903, H.
Gannett.—Mar. 1903–June 1954, G. H. Grosvenor.—July 1954–Jan.
1957, J. D. LaGorce.—Feb. 1957–   M. B. Grosvenor.
INDEXES:
Vols. 1–42, Jan. 1899–Dec. 1922. 1 v.
Vols. 1–49, Jan. 1899–Dec. 1925. 1 v.
Vols. 1–66, Jan. 1899–Dec. 1934. 1 v.
Vols. 1–70, Jan. 1899–Dec. 1936. 1 v.
Vols. 1–78, Jan. 1899–Dec. 1940. 1 v.
Vols. 1–100, Jan. 1899–Dec. 1951. 2 v.

Vols. 91–110, Jan. 1947–Dec. 1956. 1 v.
Indexes kept up to date by supplements.

1. Geography—Period.   I. Hyde, John, 1848–1929, ed. II. Gannett, Henry, 1846–1914, ed. III. Grosvenor, Gilbert Hovey, 1875–
ed. IV. LaGorce, John Oliver, 1880–   ed. V. Grosvenor, Melville
Bell, 1901–   ed. VI. National Geographic Society, Washington, D. C.

G1.N27   14—7038*

ICMe
NjN WvU CU DAL DSI CoU CSt MB KEmT DN DPU MeP
InU-D NBuH WHi OkTU NN MBdAF MoSC MdBP NNStJ PBL
WaTC OrAshS NjNbS NNH NcRS Az KT ICN MNS KyLoU
CaBVaU OrPS OrSaW IdB Wa MtBC WaS WaE MtHi Or WaT
UU GDS GEU FM InCW CoCa PV WaSp OrMonO CaBViPA
OC1h OEac OLak DSI OO OC1 OC1W LNL TxU MoU TxLT
OrStbM MB MH ICJ TU MiU OAkU OFH Nh NjP NNUN NIC
NN   0052525   DLC MoU CaBVa IdPI NcD MtU OrCS OrU

TL   The **National** geographic magazine.
545   Aeronautics; compiled articles from the National
.N28   geographic magazine, with full color plates and topical index. Berrien Springs, Mich., Distributed by
White Brothers' International Visual Education
Service ₁1937₁
1 v. (various pagings) illus., ports., maps.
26 cm.
Thirty-one articles detached from various issues,
1918 to 1936.
1. Aeronautics.

NN   0052526   MiU

629.13   National geographic *magazine.*
N21a   Aeronautics; articles from the National geographic magazine ₁1918–1940₁   Chicago, Edwin
Allen company ₁°1941?₁
v.p. illus., plates, maps. 26cm.

NN   0052527   LU

629.13   National geographic magazine.
N21a   Aeronautics; articles from the National geographic magazine. Compiled and bound to order
by Edwin Allen company.   Chicago ₁c1941₁
1v. illus. (part col.)
Various pagings.
Twenty-five articles detached from various
issues of the magazine from 1922 to 1940.

1. Aeronautics.

NN   0052528   IU

918.98   National geographic *magazine.*
N21a   Alaska; articles from the National geographic
magazine ₁1917–1940₁   Chicago, Edwin-Allen company ₁°1941₁
v.p. illus., plates (part col.) maps. 26cm.

NN   0052529   LU

917.98   National geographic magazine.
N21a   Alaska; articles from the National geographic
magazine. Compiled and bound to order by Edwin
Allen company.   Chicago ₁c1941₁
1v. illus. (part col.)
Various pagings.
Eight articles detached from various issues of
the magazine from 1921 to 1940.

1. Alaska--Desc. & trav.

NN   0052530   IU

VOLUME 407

599
N21a   National geographic *Magazine*.
       American animals; articles from the National
geographic magazine ₍1917-1941₎   Chicago, Edwin
Allen company ₍°1941?₎
       v.p. front. (fold.plate) plates(part col.) 26cm.

NN   0052531   LU

599
N21a   National geographic magazine.
       American animals; articles from the National
geographic magazine. Compiled and bound to order
by Edwin Allen company.   Chicago ₍c1941₎
       1v. illus.(part col.)

       Various pagings.
       Eight articles detached from various issues of
the magazine from 1923 to 1941.

       1. Animals.

NN   0052532   IU

598.2
N2131a American birds; articles from the National
geographic magazine. Compiled and bound to order
by Edwin Allen company.   Chicago ₍c1941₎
       1v. illus.(part col.)

       Various pagings.
       Twenty-three articles detached from various
issues of the magazine from 1932 to 1941.

       1. Birds--U.S.

NN   0052533   IU LU

629.13 National geographic magazine.
N213am American flights; articles from the National
geographic magazine. Compiled and bound to order
by Edwin Allen company.   Chicago ₍c1941₎
       1v. illus.

       Various pagings.
       Nine articles detached from various issues of
the magazine from 1924 to 1933.

       1. Aeronautics--Flights. I. Title.

NN   0052534   IU LU

973
N21a   National geographic *magazine*.
       American history; articles from the National
geographic magazine₍1917-1941₎   Chicago, Edwin
Allen company ₍°1941?₎
       v.p. illus.,plates (part col.) maps,diagrs. 26cm.

NN   0052535   LU

973
N213a American history; articles from the National
geographic magazine. Compiled and bound to order
by Edwin Allen company.   Chicago ₍c1941₎
       1v. illus.(part col.)

       Various pagings.
       Thirty-four articles detached from various
issues of the magazine from 1921 to 1941.

       1. U.S.--Hist. 2. U.S.--Descr. & trav. I. Ti-
tle.

NN   0052536   IU

598
N21an National geographic *magazine*.
       Animals and birds; articles from the National
geographic magazine ₍1917-1941₎   Chicago, Edwin
Allen company ₍°1941?₎
       v.p. illus.,plates (part col.) maps. 26cm.

NN   0052537   LU

599
N21an National geographic magazine.
       Animals and birds; articles from the National
geographic magazine. Compiled and bound to order
by Edwin Allen company.   Chicago ₍c1941₎
       1v. illus.(part col.)

       Various pagings.
       Twenty-one articles detached from various issues
of the magazine from 1922 to 1941.

       1. Animals. 2. Birds.

NN   0052538   IU

National Geographic Magazine.
[Articles relating to Washington, D.C.]
(*In* National Geographic Magazine. Washington. 1915-31.)

Contents.--Vol. 27, no. 3. March, 1915. Washington: its beginning, its
growth, and its future, by William Howard Taft. **Vol. 43, no. 6.** June,
1923. The transformation of Washington, by Charles Moore. -- The Lincoln Memorial, by William Howard Taft. -- The Capitol, wonder building
of the world, by Gilbert Grosvenor. -- Washington, the pride of the
nation, by Charles Martin. -- The sources of Washington's charm, by J.
R. Hildebrand. **Vol. 53, no. 5.** May, 1928. The home of the first farmer
of America, by Worth E. Shoults. **Vol. 60, no. 5.** Nov., 1931. Washing-

ton through the years, by Gilbert Grosvenor.
Each article is catalogued separately.
Same. (*Cut from* Same. 4 parts in 1 v.)   °4475.263

NN   0052540   MB

915.6
N21a   Asia Minor; articles from the National geo-
graphic magazine ₍1918-1941₎   Chicago, Edwin
Allen company ₍°1941?₎
       v.p. illus.,plates (part col.) maps. 26cm.

NN   0052541   LU

915.6
N21a   National geographic magazine.
       Asia Minor; articles from the National geo-
graphic magazine. Compiled and bound to order
by Edwin Allen company.   Chicago ₍c1941₎
       1v. illus.(part col.)

       Various pagings.
       Twenty-two articles detached from various
issues of the magazine from 1922 to 1941.

       1. Asia Minor--Descr. & trav.

NN   0052542   IU

The National geographic magazine.
Australia and New Zealand, a selection of descriptive articles which have appeared in recent years in the pages of the
National geographic magazine, edited by Melville Bell Grosvenor, assistant editor, National geographic magazine. With
30 plates in full natural color and 257 photographs ... Prepared at the request of the United States navy. Washington,
D. C., National geographic society ₍1943₎
       304 p. incl. illus. (incl. ports., maps) plates (part col.) 25½ᶜᵐ.

       1. Australia--Descr. & trav. 2. New Zealand--Descr. & trav.
ɪ. Grosvenor, Melville Bell, 1901-   ed.
                                                        43-5908
       Library of Congress   DU104.N3
                                    ₍15₎   919.4

NN   0052543   DLC CLSU

919.4
N21a   Australasia; articles from the National geo-
graphic magazine ₍1919-1941₎   Chicago, Edwin
Allen company ₍°1941?₎
       v.p. illus.,plates (part col.) maps. 26cm.

NN   0052544   LU

919
N21a   National geographic magazine.
       Australasia; articles from the National geogra-
phic magazine. Compiled and bound to order by
Edwin Allen company.   Chicago ₍c1941₎
       1v. illus.(part col.)
       Various pagings.
       Sixteen articles detached from various issues
of the magazine from 1924 to 1941.

       1. Australasia--Descr. & trav. 2. Australia--
Descr. & trav. 3. New Zealand--Descr. & trav.
4. Australasia--Soc. life & cust.

NN   0052545   IU

914.9
N21b   National geographic *magazine*.
       Balkan countries; articles from the National
geographic magazine ₍1918-1941₎   Chicago,
Edwin Allen company ₍°1941?₎
       v.p. illus., plates (part col.) maps. 26cm.

NN   0052546   LU

914.9
N21b   National geographic magazine.
       Balkan countries; articles from the National
geographic magazine. Compiled and bound to order
by Edwin Allen company.   Chicago ₍c1941₎
       1v. illus.(part col.)

       Various pagings.
       Sixteen articles detached from various issues
of the magazine from 1922 to 1941.

       1. Balkan peninsula--Descr. & trav. I. Title.

NN   0052547   IU

[National geographic magazine]
       The Black hills, once happy hunting grounds of
the red men.   [Wash. D.C., National geographic
society, 1927]
       p. 305-330. illus. plates. O.
       I. Title.

NN   0052548   CaBViP

F
1409   National geographic magazine.
.N3   Bonds between the Americas [selected from
the Geographic 1927-1933. Washington, 1927-
38]
       1 v. illus. (part col.) fold. col. map
in pocket. 25 cm.

       Typewritten title-page and contents.
       "Collected and bound for José Tercero,
1939."

NN   0052549   DPU

914.2
N21b   National geographic *magazine*.
       British islands; articles from the National
geographic magazine ₍1917-1940₎   Chicago, Edwin
Allen company ₍°1941?₎
       v.p. illus.,plates (part col.) maps. 26cm.

NN   0052550   LU

914.2
N21b   National geographic magazine.
       British islands; articles from the National
geographic magazine. Compiled and bound to
order by Edwin Allen company.   Chicago ₍c1941₎
       1v. illus.(part col.)

       Various pagings.
       Twenty-two articles detached from various
issues of the magazine from 1921 to 1940.

       1. Great Britain--Descr. & trav. I. Title.

NN   0052551   IU

917.1
N21c   National geographic *magazine*.
       Canada; articles from the National geographic
magazine ₍1920-1941₎   Chicago, Edwin Allen
company ₍°1941?₎
       v.p. illus.,plates (part col.) maps. 26cm.

NN   0052552   LU

917.1
N21c   National geographic magazine.
       Canada; articles from the National geographic
magazine. Compiled and bound to order by Edwin
Allen company.   Chicago ₍c1941₎
       1v. illus.(part col.)

       Various pagings.
       Nineteen articles detached from various issues
of the magazine from 1921 to 1941.

       1. Canada--Descr. & trav.

NN   0052553   IU

VOLUME 407

917.28　National geographic magazine.
N21c　　Central America; articles from the National
　　geographic magazine [1919-1941] Chicago, Edwin
　　Allen company [1941]
　　　v.p. illus.,plates (part col.) maps. 26cm.

NN　0052554　LU

917.2　National geographic magazine.
N213c　　Central America; articles from the National
　　geographic magazine. Compiled and bound to order
　　by Edwin Allen company. Chicago [c1941]
　　　1v. illus.(part col.)

　　Various pagings.
　　Twenty-one articles detached from various issues
　of the magazine from 1922 to 1941.

　　　1. Central America--Descr. & trav.

NN　0052555　IU

915　National geographic magazine.
N21c　　Central Asia; articles from the National geo-
　　graphic magazine. Compiled and bound to order
　　by Edwin Allen company. Chicago [c1941]
　　　1v. illus.(part col.)

　　Various pagings.
　　Twelve articles detached from various issues
　of the magazine from 1921 to 1936.

　　　1. Asia, Central--Descr. & trav.

NN　0052556　IU LU

National geographic magazine.
　　Central states; articles from the National
　geographic magazine [1919-1939] Chicago,
　Edwin Allen company [c1941?]
　　　v.p. illus., plates (part col.) maps.
　26 cm.

NN　0052557　LU IEN IU

915.1　National geographic magazine.
N21c　　China; articles from the National geographic
　　magazine [1919-1940] Chicago, Edwin Allen com-
　　pany [°1941]
　　　v.p. illus.,plates (part col.) maps. 26cm.

NN　0052558　LU

915.1　National geographic magazine.
N21c　　China; articles from the National geographic
　　magazine. Compiled and bound to order by Edwin
　　Allen company. Chicago [c1941]
　　　1v. illus.(part col.)

　　Various pagings.
　　Twenty-nine articles detached from various
　issues of the magazine from 1923 to 1940.

　　　1. China--Descr. & trav.

NN　0052559　IU

National geographic magazine.
　　Classic Greece and the Aegean ... Washington,
　D.C., 1944.
　　　cover-title, [257]-354, 593-622 p. illus.
　(part col., incl. maps) 25.5 cm.
　　"Reprinted from the National geographic
　magazines of March and May, 1944".
　　　Contents. - The Greek way [by] Edith Hamilton.-
　Greece, the birthplace of science and free speech
　[by] Richard Stillwell. - The glory that was
　Greece [by] H.M. Herget. - The isles of Greece
　[by] Richard Stillwell.

　　　1. Greece - Civilization. 2. Greece, Modern.
　3. Aegean islands. I. Title.

NN　0052561　CSt-H LU

National Geographic Magazine.
　　The countries of the Caribbean, including,
Central America, the West Indies, and the Panama
Canal
　　　see under　National Geographic Society,
Washington, D.C. Cartographic Division.

591.5　National geographic magazine.
N21d　　Domestic animals and fowls; articles from the
　　National geographic magazine [1919-1941]
　　Chicago, Edwin Allen company [1941]
　　　v.p. illus.,plates (part col.) 26cm.

NN　0052563　LU

636　National geographic magazine.
N2131d　　Domestic animals and fowls; articles from the
　　National geographic magazine. Compiled and
　　bound to order by Edwin Allen company. Chicago
　　[c1941]
　　　1v. illus.(part col.)

　　Various pagings.
　　Nine articles detached from various issues of
　the magazine from 1925 to 1941.

　　　1. Domestic animals. 2. Poultry.

NN　0052564　IU

914.7　National geographic magazine.
N21e　　Eastern Europe; articles from the National
　　geographic magazine [1917-1940] Chicago, Edwin
　　Allen company [°1941]
　　　v.p. illus.,plates (part col.) maps. 26cm.

NN　0052565　LU

914　National geographic magazine.
N213e　　Eastern Europe; articles from the National geo-
　　graphic magazine. Compiled and bound to order by
　　Edwin Allen company. Chicago [c1941]
　　　1v. illus.(part col.)

　　Various pagings.
　　Twenty-two articles detached from various is-
　sues of the magazine from 1923 to 1940.

　　　1. Europe--Descr. & trav. I. Title.

NN　0052566　IU MiD

917.3　National geographic magazine.
N213e　　Eastern states; articles from the National geo-
　　graphic magazine. Compiled and bound to order
　　by Edwin Allen company. Chicago [c1941]
　　　1v. illus.(part col.)

　　Various pagings.
　　Nineteen articles detached from various issues
　of the magazine from 1922 to 1941.

　　　1. U.S.--Descr. & trav. I. Title.

NN　0052567　IU LU

National Geographic Magazine.
　　[Egypt] [Several issues bound in one volume]
Washingtion, D.C., Author, 1913, 1923.
　　　v.p. illus., plates (many in color), map.
　　Contents: Resurrection of ancient Egypt;
Reconstructing Egypt's history; The sacred ibis
cemetery and jackal catacombs at Abydos; At the
tomb of Tutankhamen; Egypt, past and present
(plates)

NN　0052568　WaT

916　National geographic magazine.
N21e　　Egypt and Ethiopia; articles from the National
　　geographic magazine. Compiled and bound to order
　　by Edwin Allen company. Chicago [c1941]
　　　1v. illus.(part col.)

　　Various pagings.
　　Fifteen articles detached from various magazines
　from 1922 to 1941.

　　　1. Egypt--Descr. & trav. 2. Ethiopia--Descr.
　& trav.

NN　0052569　IU LU

914.2　National geographic magazine.
N21e　　England; articles from the National geographic
　　magazine. Compiled and bound to order by Edwin
　　Allen company. Chicago [c1941]
　　　1v. illus.(part col.)

　　Various pagings.
　　Thirty-one articles detached from various
　issues of the magazine from 1922 to 1941.

　　　1. England--Descr. and trav.

NN　0052570　IU LU

National geographic magazine.
　　Everyday life in ancient times; highlights of the be-
ginnings of Western civilization in Mesopotamia, Egypt,
Greece, and Rome. With 215 illus; 120 paintings by H. M.
Herget. [Washington, 1951]
　　　355 p. illus. (part col.) maps. 27 cm.
　　"Reprinted from the National geographic magazine issues of Oc-
tober, 1941; March, 1944; November, 1946; and January, 1951."
　　CONTENTS.—Foreword, by G. Grosvenor.—Mesopotamia: light that
did not fail, by E. A. Speiser.—Daily life in ancient Egypt, by W. C.
Hayes.—The Greek way, by E. Hamilton.—Greece, the birthplace of
science and free speech, by R. Stillwell.—The Roman way, by E.
Hamilton.—Ancient Rome brought to life, by R. Carpenter.
　　1. Civilization, Ancient.　I. Title.

CB311.N3　　　　　913.3　　　　　51—5388

MtBC ScCleU
OrAshS CSaT TxU Or IdB IdU IdPI CaBVaU Wa WaT WaS
NN　0052571　DLC OrSaW NjN AAP CU OrPS OrP KEmT

913.3
N213e
1953　　National geographic magazine.
　　　Everyday life in ancient times; highlights
　　of the beginnings of Western civilization in
　　Mesopotamia, Egypt, Greece, and Rome. With
　　215 illus.; 120 paintings by H.M. Herget.
　　[Washington, c1953]
　　　368p. illus.(part col.) maps. 27cm.
　　"Reprinted from the National geographic
　magazine issues of October, 1941; March,
　1944; November, 1946; and January, 1951."

CaBVa Or NcD CSt MBtS
NN　0052572　TxU OrCS MiU PSt NN OOxM NRU NcGU IU

La
976.3　National geographic magazine.
N21e　　Excerpts. Louisiana. [Washington.
　　National Geographic Society, 1937-53]
　　　1 v. (various pagings) illus. (part
　　col.) maps. 26 cm.

　　Contents:-The great Mississippi flood of
　1927, by F. Simpich.-Louisiana, land of per-
　petual romance, by R. A. Graves.-The delec-
　table shrimp, by H. Major.-Louisiana trades
　with the world, by F. Simpich.-New Orleans:

　　　　　　　　　　Jambalaya on the levee,
　by H. T. Kane.-Map marks 150th anniversary
　of Louisiana purchase, by E. Petersen.-
　Land of Louisiana sugar kings, by H. T.
　Kane.

　　　1. Louisiana. I. Simpich, Frederick.
　The great Mississippi flood of 1927. II.
　Graves, Ralph A　　　　　Louisiana,
　Land of perpert-　　　　　ual romance.

　　　III. Major, Harlan. The delectable shrimp.
　IV. Simpich, Frederick. Louisiana trades
　with the world. V.Kane, Harnett Thomas,
　1910-　　　New Orleans: Jambalaya on the
　levee. VI. Petersen, Evelyn. Map marks
　150th anniversary of Louisiana Purchase.
　VII. Kane, Har-　　　nett Thomas, 1910-
　Land of Louisiana　　sugar kings.

NN　0052575　LU

VOLUME 407

National geographic magazine.
　　Flag numbers, Oct.1917 ‹and› Sept.
1934.　Washington,National geographic
magazine,1917,1934.　2pts.in 1 vol.
illus.(part col.)

　　Binder;title.
　　Detached from National geographic
magazine, v.32 no.4, Oct.1917 and v.66
no.3, Sept.1934.
　　Contents: pt.1 Our flag number.- pt.2
Flags of the world.

NN　0052576　　CaBVa

National geographic magazine.
　[Flags and memorials]
　　see under　National geographic society,
Washington, D.C.

National Geographic magazine.
　Flags of the United Nations
　　see under　King, Elizabeth W.

National geographic magazine.
　Flags of the Americas
　　see under　King, Elizabeth W
　⟨Supplement⟩

914.4　National geographic magazine.
N21f　　France and Belgium; articles from the National
geographic magazine ₍1918-1940₎　Chicago, Edwin
Allen company ₍°1941?₎
v.p. illus., plates (part col.) maps. 26cm.

NN　0052580　　LU

914.4　National geographic magazine.
N21f　　France and Belgium; articles from the National
geographic magazine.　Compiled and bound to order
by Edwin Allen company.　Chicago ₍c1941₎
1v. illus.(part col.)

　　Various pagings.
　　Twenty articles detached from various issues of
the magazine from 1921 to 1940.

　　1. France--Descr. & trav.　2 Belgium--Descr. &
trav.

NN　0052581　　IU

National Geographic Magazine.
　Geographical articles.　Articles classified and rebound from Na-
tional Geographic Magazines.
— Lynn, Mass. Classified Geographic. Inc. [1916-36.] 45 v. Illus.,
some colored.　Portraits, some colored.　Plates, some colored.
Maps.　Charts.　Tables.　Facsimiles.　24.5 cm.

The National Geographic Magazine is published by the National Geo-
graphic Society.
　Namely:—
　Elementary school set.　[Set 2. Vol. 1, 2.]　2 v.　　　　*6260A.30
　　Contents.— [1.] British Isles.　[2.] Islands of the Atlantic.
　High school set.　[Vol. 1-10.]　10 v.　　　　　　　　　*6260A.31
　　Contents.— [1.] Aeronautics.　[2.] American history.　[3.] Cities of the
　New World.　[4.] Cities of the Old World.　[5.] European history.
　[6.] Industry.　[7.] Plants and flowers.　[8.] Races of people.　[9.]
　Science.　[10.] World War.

　Complete geography set.　[Vol. 1-16.]　16 v.　　　　　*6260A.32
　　Contents.— [1.] Africa.　[2.] Asia Minor.　[3.] Australia and islands of
　the Pacific.　[4.] Balkan States, Islands of the Mediterranean.　[5.]
　Canada, Mexico, Central America.　[6.] Central Europe.　[7.] China.
　[8.] Japan, Manchuria.　[9.] New England, Middle Atlantic, Washing-
　ton, D.C.　[10.] Northern Europe.　[11.] South America.　[12.] Southern
　Asia.　[13.] Southern and Central States.　[14.] Southern Europe.　[15.]
　Western States and Alaska.　[16.] Western Europe.
　Special subjects.　[Vol. 1-16.]　16 v.　　　　　　　　*6260A.33

　　Contents.— [1.] Archaeology.　[2.] Birds.　[3.] Domestic animals, In-
　sects.　[4.] Exploration.　[5.] Fish.　[6.] Flags and memorials.　[7.]
　Geography of English literature.　[8.] Lands and their people.　[9.]
　Mountains.　[10.] Religion.　[11.] Rivers.　[12.] Sea-faring.　[13.] See-
　ing the world from the air.　[14.] Travels.　[15.] Unusual journeys.
　[16.] Wild animals.
　Index volume.　　　　　　　　　　　　　　　　　*6260A.34

NN　0052585　　MB

The National geographic magazine.
　Geographical articles ... Flags and memorials
　　see　National Geographic Society,
Washington, D.C.
　Flags and memorials.

National geographic magazine.
　Geographical articles ... Religious cults and
customs
　　see　National Geographical Society,
Washington, D.C.
　Religious cults and customs.

The National geographic magazine.
　The Geographic's upper masses ... Washington, D. C., The
National geographic magazine, '1931.

　106 p. Illus., plates. 26ᵐ.

　A study of the standard of living of subscribers to the National geographic magazine, and of the advertising influence of the magazine.

　1. Cost and standard of living—U. S.　2. U. S.—Stat. 3. Advertising.
I. Title.

Library of Congress　　　　HC106.3.N17　　　　　31-33126
Copyright　A 43448　　　　　₍5₎　　　　　　　　　070.36

NN　0052588　　DLC

914.3　National geographic magazine.
N213g　　Germany and Holland; articles from the
National geographic magazine.　Compiled and
bound to order by Edwin Allen company.
Chicago ₍c1941₎
1v. illus.(part col.)

　　Various pagings.
　　Twenty-seven articles detached from various
issues of the magazine from 1922 to 1940.

　　1. Germany--Descr. & trav.　2. Netherlands--
Descr. & trav.

NN　0052589　　IU LU

National Geographic Magazine.
　The Great Wall of China near Nankow Pass
　　see under　National Geographic Society.
Washington, D.C.

National geographic magazine.
　Industry & commerce; a compiled unit... ₍The
Author₎ °1937.
v. p. illus.

NN　0052591　　MiD

380　National geographic magazine.
N21i　　Industry and commerce; articles from the National
geographic magazine ₍1917-1941₎　Chicago, Edwin
Allen company ₍°1941?₎
v.p. illus.,plates (part col.) maps. 26cm.

NN　0052592　　LU IU

The National geographic magazine.

Wilgus, Alva Curtis, 1897–
　Index of articles relating to Hispanic America in the National geographic magazine, volumes I-LXI inclusive (1888-
1932) by A. Curtis Wilgus ... ₍Durham, N. C., 1932₎

595.7　National geographic magazine.
N2131i　　Insects; articles from the National geographic
magazine.　Compiled and bound to order by Edwin
Allen company.　Chicago ₍c1941₎
1v. illus.(part col.)

　　Various pagings.
　　Ten articles detached from various issues of
the magazine from 1927 to 1941.

　　1. Insects.

NN　0052594　　IU LU

National Geographic Magazine.
　Insignia and decorations of the U.S. armed forces
　　see under　National Geographic Society,
Washington, D.C.

914.5　National geographic magazine.
N211　　Italy; articles from the National geographic
magazine ₍1918-1941₎　Chicago, Edwin Allen company ₍°1941?₎
v.p. illus.,plates (part col.) maps. 26cm.

NN　0052596　　LU

914.5　National geographic magazine.
N21i　　Italy; articles from the National geographic
magazine.　Compiled and bound by Edwin Allen company.　Chicago ₍c1941₎
1v. illus.(part col.)

　　Various pagings.
　　Twenty-one articles detached from various issues
of the magazine from 1922 to 1941.

　　1. Italy--Descr. & trav.

NN　0052597　　IU

F931　National geographic magazine.
N3　　Klondike number.　Washington, D.C., 1898.
192 p. Illus., port., fold. col. map. 25cm.

Cover title.
Vol. 9, no. 4 (Apr. 1898) of the National geographic magazine.
Includes bibliography.

NN　0052598　　CU-B

National Geographic Magazine.
　Map of Africa, 1922 ...
　　see under　title

National geographic magazine.
　Map of Europe and adjoining portions of Africa
and Asia ...
　　see under　Matthews-Northrup co.,
Buffalo, N. Y.

National Geographic Magazine.　　　　No. 88 in *Map 86.2
　Map, Europe showing countries as established by the Peace Con-
ference at Paris.
= Washington.　1920.　Size, 32¼ × 29½ inches.　Scale, 84 miles
to 1 inch.
　Submap. — Map of the Dardanelles.

M2613 — Europe. Geog. Maps. — E. pean War, 1914-1919. Boundaries after
the war.

NN　0052601　　MB

National geographic magazine.
　Map showing location of Panama Canal ...
　　see under　Harden, Oliver B

VOLUME 407

The National geographic magazine.
   Marine life; articles from the National geographic
magazine [1919-1941] Chicago, Edwin Allen
company [c1941?]
   v.p. illus., plates (part col.) maps. 26 cm.

NN   0052603   LU

597
N21m   National geographic magazine.
   Marine life; articles from the National geographic magazine. Compiled and bound to order
by Edwin Allen company. Chicago [c1941]
   1v. illus.(part col.)

   Various pagings.
   Thirty-three articles detached from various issues of the magazine from 1921 to 1941.

   1. Marine fauna. I. Title.

NN   0052604   IU

54861   National geographic magazine.
   Martinique number. 1902.

NN   0052605   DI-GS

National Geographic Magazine.
   Medicine and religion; compiled articles from the
National Geographic Magazine with full color plates
and topical index. Berrien Springs, Mich.,
White Brothers International Visual Education
Service [c1937]
   1 v. (various pagings) illus. 26 cm.
   1. Medicine. 2. Religion. I. Title.

NN   0052606   NcU

National geographic magazine.
   The National geographic magazine map of Central
America ...
   see under   National Geographic Society,
Washington, D.C.

National geographic magazine.
   Natural phenomena; a compiled unit... [The
Author] °1937.
   v. p. illus.

NN   0052608   MiD

500
N2131n   National geographic magazine.
   Natural phenomena; articles from the National
geographic magazine. Compiled and bound to order
by Edwin Allen company. Chicago [c1941]
   1v. illus.(part col.)

   Various pagings.
   Twenty-two articles detached from various
issues of the magazine from 1923 to 1940.

   1. Nature. 2. Natural history. I. Title.

NN   0052609   IU LU

500
N21n   National geographic magazine.
   Natural phenomena; articles from the National
geographic magazine [1936-1940] Chicago, Edwin
Allen company [°1941]
   v.p. illus.,plates (part col.) maps,diagrs. 26cm.

NN   0052610   LU

---

cF
866.2
N3   National geographic magazine.
   New rush to golden California. Washington,
D. C., National Geographic Society, 1954.
   723-867 p. illus. (part col.) 26cm.

   Constitutes articles from the National
geographic magazine, June 1954.
   Title from first article.

NN   0052611   C

National Geographic Magazine.   *Map 35.2.1924
   North America. [Map.]
= Washington. 1924. Size, 37 × 27 inches. Scale, 1 :10,000,000,
or (computed), 157.82 miles to 1 inch.
   Submaps: The Aleutian Islands; Eastern part of the West Indies.

D5146 — America, North. Geog. Maps.

NN   0052612   MB NIC

917.4
N21n   National geographic magazine.
   North Atlantic states; articles from the Natio-
nal geographic magazine [1918-1941] Chicago,
Edwin Allen company [°1941?]
   v.p. illus.,plates (part col.) maps. 26cm.

NN   0052613   LU

917.4
N21n   National geographic magazine.
   North Atlantic states; articles from the National georgaphic magazine. Compiled and bound to
order by Edwin Allen company. Chicago [c1941]
   1v. illus.(part col.)

   Various pagings.
   Thirteen articles detached from various issues
of the magazine from 1923 to 1941.

   1. U.S.--Descr. & trav. I. Title.

NN   0052614   IU

915
N21n   National geographic magazine.
   Northeast Asia; articles from the National
geographic magazine [1919-1938] Chicago, Edwin
Allen company [°1941?]
   v.p. illus.,plates (part col.) maps. 26cm.

NN   0052615   LU

915
N21n   National geographic magazine.
   Northeast Asia; articles from the National geographic magazine. Compiled and bound to order
by Edwin Allen company. Chicago [c1941]
   1v. illus.(part col.)

   Various pagings.
   Eighteen articles detached from various issues
of the magazine from 1921 to 1938.

   1. Asia--Descr. & trav. I. Title.

NN   0052616   IU LU

916
N21n   National geographic magazine.
   Northern Africa; articles from the National
geographic magazine. Compiled and bound to order
by Edwin Allen company. Chicago [c1941]
   1v. illus.(part col.)

   Various pagings.
   Eighteen articles detached from various issues
of the magazine from 1922 to 1941.

   1. Africa--Descr. & trav. I. Title.

NN   0052617   IU LU

National geographic magazine.
   Our flag number
     see under   McCandless, Byron, 1881-

National geographic magazine.
   Our state flowers; the floral emblems chosen by
the commonwealths by the editor.
   p. 481-517.
   t. p. w.
   An extract from the National geographic magazine.

NN   0052619   WaT

919
N21p   National geographic magazine.
   Pacific islands; articles from the National
geographic magazine [1919-1941] Chicago, Edwin
Allen company [°1941?]
   v.p. illus.,plates (part col.) maps. 26cm.

NN   0052620   LU

919
N21p   National geographic magazine.
   Pacific islands; articles from the National
geographic magazine. Compiled and bound to order
by Edwin Allen company. Chicago [c1941]
   1v. illus.(part col.)

   Various pagings.
   Nineteen aticles detached from various issues
of the magazine from 1921 to 1941.

   1. Oceanica--Descr. & trav. 2. Oceanica--Soc.
life & cust. I. Title.

NN   0052621   IU

TL
521
.N28   The National geographic magazine.
   Pan-American flights; compiled articles from
the National geographic magazine,with full
color plates and topical index. Berrien Springs,
Mich., Distributed by White Brothers' International Visual Education Service [1937]
   1 v. (various pagings) illus.,ports.,maps.
26 cm.
   Ten articles detached from various issues of
the magazine from 1921 to 1933.

   1.Aeronautics   --Flights. I.Title.

NN   0052622   MiU

National geographic magazine
   Parks and scenery; a compiled unit... [The
Author] °1937.
   v. p. illus.

NN   0052623   MiD

711
N2132p   National geographic magazine.
   Parks and scenery; articles from the National
geographic magazine. Compiled and bound to order
by Edwin Allen company. Chicago [c1941]
   1v. illus.(part col.)

   Various pagings.
   Twenty-four articles detached from various
issues of the magazine from 1921 to 1941.

   1. Parks.

NN   0052624   IU CStbS LU

---

j665.5   NATIONAL geographic magazine.
   [Petroleum]
     Nat'l geog.soc. |v. illus. maps.
(The Magazine...)

NN   0052625   WaS

National geographic magazine.
   Plants; a compiled unit... [The Author] n. d.
   v. p. illus.

NN   0052626   MiD

VOLUME 407

580
N21p National geographic magazine.
      Plants; articles from the National geographic
      magazine ₁1917-1939₎ Chicago, Edwin Allen com-
      pany ₁°1941?₎
      v.p. illus.,plates (part col.) maps. 26cm.

NN 0052627   LU

580
N21p National geographic magazine.
      Plants; articles from the National geographic
      magazine. Compiled and bound to order by Edwin
      Allen company.   Chicago ₁c1941₎
      1v. illus.(part col.)

      Various pagings.
      Ten articles detached from various issues of
      the magazine from 1922 to 1939.

      1. Flowers--North America. 2. Plants.

NN 0052628   IU

919.8
N21p National geographic magazine.
      Polar lands; articles from the National geo-
      graphic magazine ₁1920-1940₎ Chicago, Edwin
      Allen company ₁°1941?₎
      v.p. illus.,plates (part col.) maps. 26cm.

NN 0052629   LU

919.8
N21p National geographic magazine
      Polar lands; articles from the National geo-
      graphic magazine. Compiled and bound to order by
      Edwin Allen company.   Chicago ₁c1941₎
      1v. illus.(part col.)

      Various pagings.
      Nineteen articles detached from various issues
      of the magazine from 1922 to 1940.

      1. Arctic regions--Descr. & trav. 2. Antarc-
      tic regions--Descr. & trav. 3. Scientific expe-
      ditions. I. Title.

NN 0052630   IU

G
3791
S 1
1939
N27
Map   National geographic magazine.
          The reaches of New York City. Done in
      the studios of the National geographic
      magazine. Washington, c1939.
          col. map 74x67 cm.

          Scale ca. 1:497,000 or 8 miles to the inch.
      "Designed by C. E. Riddiford; research by
      J. M. Darley and W. Chamberlin; culture by

      A. E. Holdstock; relief by J. J. Brehm."
      Albert H. Bumstead, chief cartographer.
      Issued with the National geographic
      magazine, v. 75, no. 4, April 1939.

      1. Middle Atlantic States - Maps.
      2. New York   (City) - Maps. 3. Middle
      Atlantic States   - Historical geography -
      Maps. I. Riddiford, Charles E
      II. Bumstead, Albert H   III. Title.

NN 0052632   NIC RPB OC1 NIC CLSU

      National geographic magazine.
      [Religious cults and customs]
          see under   National geographic society,
      Washington, D. C.

387
N21s National geographic magazine.
      Seafaring; articles from the National geo-
      graphic magazine ₁1918-1941₎ Chicago, Edwin
      Allen company ₁°1941?₎
      v.p. illus.,plates (part col.) maps. 26cm.

NN 0052634   LU

910
N21s National geographic magazine.
      Seafaring; articles from the National geo-
      graphic magazine. Compiled and bound to order
      by Edwin Allen company.   Chicago ₁c1941₎
      1v. illus.(part col.)

      Various pagings.
      Twenty-two articles detached from various
      issues of the magazine from 1921 to 1941.

      1. Voyages and travels. 2. Ships. I. Title.

NN 0052635   IU

914.8
N21s National geographic magazine.
      Scandinavia; articles from the National geo-
      graphic magazine. Compiled and bound to order
      by Edwin Allen company.   Chicago ₁c1941₎
      1v. illus.(part col.)

      Various pagings.
      Seventeen articles detached from various
      issues of the magazine from 1922 to 1941.

      1. Scandinavia--Descr & trav. 2. Iceland--
      Descr. & trav. 3. Faroe islands--Descr. & trav.

NN 0052636   IU LU

      National geographic   magazine.

      Grosvenor, Gilbert Hovey, 1875-   *ed.*
          Scenes from every land; a collection of 250 illustrations from
      the National geographic magazine, picturing the people, nat-
      ural phenomena, and animal life in all parts of the world.
      With one map and a short bibliography of gazetteers, atlases,
      and books descriptive of foreign countries and natural history.
      Ed. by Gilbert H. Grosvenor ... Washington, D. C., The Na-
      tional geographic society. 1907.

291.3
N21s National geographic magazine.
      Societies and cults; articles from the National
      geographic magazine, 1917-1937. Chicago, Edwin
      Allen company ₁°1941?₎
      v.p. illus.,plates (part col.) maps. 26cm.

NN 0052638   LU

290
N21s National geographic magazine.
      Societies and cults; articles from the National
      geographic magazine. Compiled and bound to order
      by Edwin Allen company.   Chicago ₁c1941₎

      Various pagings.
      Ten articles detached from various issues of
      the magaazine from 1921 to 1937.

      1. Religion, Primitive. 2. Christianity and
      other religions. I. Title.

NN 0052639   IU

918
N21a National geographic magazine.
      South America; articles from the National geo-
      graphic magazine ₁1920-1941₎ Chicago, Edwin
      Allen company ₁°1941?₎
      v.p. illus.,plates (part col.) maps. 26cm.

NN 0052640   LU

918
N21s National geographic magazine.
      South America; articles from the National ge-
      ographic magazine. Compiled and bound to order
      by Edwin Allen company.   Chicago ₁c1941₎
      1v. illus.(part col.)

      Various pagings.
      Thirty-one articles detached from various is-
      sues of the magazine from 1921 to 1941.

      1. South America--Descr. & trav.

NN 0052641   IU

915
N21c National geographic magazine.
      Southeast Asia; articles from the National
      geographic magazine ₁1920-1941₎ Chicago, Edwin
      Allen company ₁°1941?₎
      v.p. illus.,plates (part col.) maps. 26cm.

NN 0052642   LU

915
N21s National geographic magazine.
      Southeast Asia; articles from the National geo-
      graphic magazine. Compiled and bound to order by
      Edwin Allen company.   Chicago ₁c1941₎
      1v. illus.(part col.)

      Various pagings.
      Nineteen articles detached from various issues
      of the magazine from 1921 to 1941.

      1. Asia--Descr. & trav. I. Title.

NN 0052643   IU

916.8
N21s National geographic magazine.
      Southern Africa; articles from the National
      geographic magazine ₁1919-1937₎ Chicago, Edwin
      Allen company ₁°1941?₎
      v.p. illus., plates (part col.) maps. 26cm.

NN 0052644   LU

916
N21s National geographic magazine.
      Southern Africa; articles from the National
      geographic magazine. Compiled and bound to or-
      der by Edwin Allen company.   Chicago ₁c1941₎
      1v. illus.(part col.)

      Various pagings.
      Eleven articles detached from various issues
      of the magazine from 1922 to 1937.

      1. Africa--Descr. & trav. I. Title.

NN 0052645   IU

917.6
N21s National geographic magazine.
      Southern states; articles from the National
      geographic magazine ₁1920-41₎ Chicago, Edwin
      Allen company ₁°1941?₎
      v.p. illus.,plates (part col.) maps. 26cm.

NN 0052646   LU

917.3
N213s National geographic magazine.
      Southern states; articles from the National
      geographic magazine. Compiled and bound to order
      by Edwin Allen company.   Chicago ₁c1941₎
      1v. illus.(part col.)

      Various pagings.
      Twenty articles detached from various issues of
      the magazine from 1924 to 1941.

      1. Southern states--Descr. & trav.

NN 0052647   IU

915
N21so National geographic magazine.
      Southwest Asia; articles from the National
      geographic magazine ₁1919-1939₎ Chicago, Edwin
      Allen company ₁°1941?₎
      v.p. illus.,plates (part col.) maps. 26cm.

NN 0052648   LU

915
N21so National geographic magazine.
      Southwest Asia; articles from the National geo-
      graphic magazine. Compiled and bound to order
      by Edwin Allen company.   Chicago ₁c1941₎
      1v. illus.(part col.)

      Various pagings.
      Fifteen articles detached from various issues
      of the magazine from 1921 to 1939.

      1. Asia--Descr. & trav. I. Title.

NN 0052649   IU

      National Geographic Magazine.
      ... Space buyers reference annual ... 1930-
      New York, 1930-
          v.

NN 0052650   MH-BA

VOLUME 407

914.6
N21s   National geographic *magazine*.
        Spain and Portugal; articles from the National
        geographic magazine ₍1918-1941₎   Chicago, Edwin
        Allen company ₍°1941?₎
        v.p. illus.,plates (part col.) maps. 26cm.

    NN 0052651   LU

914.6
N21s   National geographic magazine.
        Spain and Portugal; articles from the National
        geographic magazine. Compiled and bound to order
        by Edwin Allen company.   Chicago ₍c1941₎
        1v. illus.(part col.)

        Various pagings.
        Twenty articles detached from various issues
        of the magazine from 1922 to 1941.

        1. Spain--Descr. & trav. 2. Portugal--Descr.
        & trav.

    NN 0052652   IU

National Geographic Magazine. [Special dog number.] Vol. 35,
    no. 3.
    Washington. National Geographic Society. 1919. 185-280 pp.
    Illus. Plates, mostly colored. 25 cm.
    Contents.— Mankind's best friend. By Ernest Harold Baynes. — Our
    common dogs. By Louis Agassiz Fuertes and Ernest Harold Baynes. —
    The sagacity and courage of dogs. — Sheep-killers—the pariahs of dog-
    kind.
    The colored plates are by Fuertes.
    A reprint, entitled The book of dogs, may be found on shelf-number
    6004.119.

M3432 — Dogs. — Fuertes, Louis Agassiz, illus., 1874–

    NN 0052653   MB ViW

SF197
.N3   National Geographic Magazine.
        ₍Special number on cattle₎
        Washington, D. C., National Geographic
        Society, 1925.
        p. ₍591₎-710, illus. 25 cm. (National
        Geographic Magazine, v.48, no.6, December,
        1925.)
        Contents.—The taurine world, ₍by₎ Alvin
        Howard Sanders.—The cattle of the world,
        ₍by₎ Edward Herbert Miner.
        1. Cattle.

    NN 0052654   TU

SF283
.N3   National Geographic Magazine.
        ₍Special number on horses₎   Washington,
        D. C., National Geographic Society, 1923.
        p. ₍455₎-566. illus. 25 cm. (National
        geographic magazine, v.44, no.5, November,
        1923.)
        Contents.—The story of the horse, ₍by₎
        William Harding Carter.—Horses of the world,
        ₍by₎ Edward Herbert Miner.

        1. Horses.

    NN 0052655   TU

SF482
.N3   National Geographic Magazine.
        ₍Special number on poultry₎   Washington
        D.C., National Geographic Society, 1927.
        p. ₍379₎-500, illus. 25 cm.

        (National geographic magazine, v.LI, no.4,
        April, 1927)
        Contents.—The races of domestic fowl,
        ₍by₎ M.A. Jull.—Fowl of the old and new
        world, ₍by₎ Hashime Murayama.—America's
        debt to the hen, ₍by₎ H.B. Lewis.—The
        Chinese: Farmers   since the days of
        Noah, ₍by₎ Adam   Warwick.
        1. Poultry.

    NN 0052656   TU

D526.8
N21   National geographic magazine.
        The story of the map ... ₍1932₎
        759-774 p. illus., facsims. 25.cm.

        Caption title.
        From the National geographic magazine, Decem-
        ber, 1932.

        1. Maps.

    NN 0052657   NNC OClh

910
N21t   National geographic *magazine*.
        Travel and geography; articles from the
        National geographic magazine ₍1917-1940₎
        Chicago, Edwin Allen company ₍°1941?₎
        v.p. illus., plates (part col.) maps. 26cm.

    NN 0052658   LU

910
N21t   National geographic magazine.
        Travel and geography; articles from the National
        geographic magazine. Compiled and bound to order
        by Edwin Allen company.   Chicago ₍c1941₎
        1v. illus.(part col.)

        Various pagings.
        Thirteen articles detached from various issues
        of the magazine from 1921 to 1940.

        1. Voyages and travels. 2. Geography. I. Ti-
        tle.

    NN 0052659   IU

917.29
N21w   National geographic *magazine*.
        West Indies; articles from the National geo-
        graphic magazine ₍1920-1941₎   Chicago, Edwin
        Allen company ₍°1941?₎
        v.p. illus.,plates (part col.) maps. 26cm.

    NN 0052660   LU

917.29
N21w   National geographic magazine.
        West Indies; articles from the National geo-
        graphic magazine. Compiled and bound to order by
        Edwin Allen company. Chicago ₍c1941₎
        1v. illus.(part col.)

        Various pagings.
        Sixteen articles detached from various issues
        of the magazine from 1922 to 1941.

        1. West Indies--Descr. & trav.

    NN 0052661   IU

917.9
N21w   National geographic magazine.
        Western states; articles from the National
        geographic magazine. Compiled and bound to order
        by Edwin Allen company. Chicago ₍c1941₎
        1v. illus.(part col.)

        Various pagings.
        Seventeen articles detached from various issues
        of the magazine from 1923 to 1941.

        1. The West--Descr. & trav. I. Title.

    NN 0052662   IU LU

591.5
N21w   National geographic magazine.
        Wild life; articles from the National geograph-
        ic magazine. Compiled and bound to order by Ed-
        win Allen company.   Chicago ₍c1941₎
        1v. illus.(part col.)

        Various pagings.
        Thirteen articles detached from various issues
        of the magazine from 1921 to 1937.

        1. Animals, Habits and behavior of. 2. Wild
        life, Conservation of. 3. Birds.

    NN 0052663   IU

591.5
N21w   National geographic *magazine*.
        Wild life; articles from the National geo-
        graphic magazine ₍1917-1937₎ Chicago, Edwin
        Allen company ₍°1941?₎
        v.p. illus.,plates (part col.) 26cm.

    NN 0052664   LU

TL
531   The National geographic magazine.
.N28   World flights; compiled articles from the
        National geographic magazine,with full color
        plates and topical index. Berrien Springs,
        Mich., Distributed by White Brothers' Interna-
        tional Visual Education Service ₍1937₎
        1 v. (various pagings) illus.,col.plates,
        ports.,maps. 26 cm.
        Ten articles detached from various issues,
        1921 to 1933.

        1.Aeronautics   --Flights. I.World
        flights.

    NN 0052665   MiU

910
N21w   National geographic magazine.
        World flights; articles from the National geo-
        graphic magazine. Compiled and bound to order
        by Edwin Allen company.   Chicago ₍c1941₎
        1v. illus.(part col.)

        Various pagings.
        Eleven articles detached from various issues
        of the magazine from 1921 to 1939.

        1. Aeronautics--Flights. I. Title.

    NN 0052666   IU LU

909
N21w   National geographic *magazine*.
        World history; articles from the National geo-
        graphic magazine ₍1917-1941₎   Chicago, Edwin
        Allen company ₍°1941₎
        v.p. illus.,plates (part col.) maps. 26cm.

    NN 0052667   LU

909
N21w   National geographic magazine.
        World history; articles from the National geo-
        graphic magazine. Compiled and bound to order
        by Edwin Allen company.   Chicago ₍c1941₎
        1v. illus.(part col.)

        Various pagings.
        Sixteen articles detached from various issues
        of the magazine from 1922 to 1941.

        1. History, Universal.

    NN 0052668   IU

National Geographic Magazine.
    The world map. Washington, 1951
        see under   National Geographic Society.

The National geographic magazine. (*Indexes*)
    A guide to unit material in the National geographic mag-
    azine.

    Berrien Springs, Mich. ₍etc.₎ Berrien Bindery ₍etc.₎
        v. 26 cm. irregular.
    Vols. for: –Jan. 1917/June 1968, called   ed.
    Title varies: –Jan. 1917/June 1968, Topical index to the
    National geographic magazine (varies slightly)–Jan. 1917/Dec. 1968–
        Skadsheim topical index to the National geographic maga-
    zine.
    Compiler: H. Skadsheim.
    I. Skadsheim, Henry, comp. II. Title.

    G1.N2712   59–32783 rev 2

    NN 0052670   DLC

VOLUME 407

The National geographic magazine. (*Indexes*)
Handy key to your National geographics; subject and picture locater. ₁1st₁– ed.; 1954–
₁n. p.₁
v. 22–28 cm.
Vol. for 1954 cumulative from 1935; 1955– from 1925.
Compiler: 1954– C. S. Underhill.

ɪ. Underhill, Charles Sterling, 1913– comp. ɪɪ. Title.

G1.N272 910.5 56—1375

NN 0052671 MoSW LU MiU OrPR IdU NcGU WaT WaS
DLC C CaBViP IdPI TxU CoU MoU KEmT

The National geographic magazine. (*Indexes*)
Handy key to your National geographics: subject and picture locater, 1935–1954, compiled by Charles S. Underhill.
₁East Aurora? N. Y., 1955₁
6 l. 28 cm.
Cover title.

ɪ. Underhill, Charles Sterling, 1913– comp. ɪɪ. Title.

G1.N272 910.5 55–35143

NN 0052672 DLC Or Wa NN Or IU OC1 PPPL PBL

National geographic magazine (indexes)
Skadsheim topical index to the National
geographic magazine
see its Topical index.

National Geographic Magazine (Indexes)
Topical index- with alphabetical and analytical
section. Skadsheim, c1939.
O. Mic.

NN 0052674 KyLx

G NATIONAL GEOGRAPHIC MAGAZINE (Indexes)
1 Topical index to the National
N27 geographic magazine. Angwin, Calif., Angwin
TOPICAL book bindery [1943]
INDEX [42]p. 25cm.
1943 "Index supplement - 1948-49": p.[39]-[42].
REF

ɪ. Skadsheim, Henry, comp.

NN 0052675 TxU

A THE NATIONAL GEOGRAPHIC MAGAZINE (*Indexes*)
5 Topical index to the National geographic
.633 magazine. ₁1914-1936₁ Berrien Springs,Mich.,
c1936.
index 11p.
1914-
1936 Compiled by H.Skadsheim.

NN 0052676 ICN IEN

National geographic monographs ...
see under National Geographic Society,
Washington, D. C.

National geographic news bulletin
see under National geographic society,
Washington, D. C.

National geographic school bulletin
see Geographic school bulletins.

Flat case National Geographic Society, Washington,
N3+ D. C.
The Adoration of the Magi by Fra
Angelico (1387-1455) and Fra Filippo
Lippi (c. 1406-1469)
col. reproduction 49 x 46 cm.

Supplement to January 1952 issue of
National geographic magazine.

I. Title: Adoration of the Magi.

NN 0052680 NIC

National geographic society, Washington, D. C.
Aeronautics; articles from the National
geographic magazine
see under National geographic magazine.

National geographic society, Washington, D. C.
Alaska; articles from the National geographic
magazine
see under National geographic magazine.

National geographic society, Washington, D. C.

Tarr, Ralph Stockman, 1864-1912.
Alaskan glacier studies of the National geographic society in the Yakutat bay, Prince William sound and lower Copper river regions. by Ralph Stockman Tarr ... and Lawrence Martin ... based upon the field work in 1909, 1910, 1911 and 1913 by National geographic society expeditions. Washington, The National geographic society, 1914.

National geographic society, Washington, D. C.
American animals; articles from the National
geographic magazine
see under National geographic magazine.

National Geographic Society.
American berries ... 1919.

NN 0052685 MBH

National geographic society, Washington, D. C.
American birds; articles from the National
geographic magazine
see under National geographic magazine.

National geographic society, Washington, D. C.
American flights; articles from the National
geographic magazine
see under National geographic magazine.

National geographic society, Washington, D. C.
American history; articles from the National
geographic magazine
see under National geographic magazine.

National geographic society, Washington, D. C.
Animals and birds; articles from the National
geographic magazine
see under National geographic magazine.

National Geographic Society, Washington, D.C.
The Arctic Regions ... 1925
see under National Geographic Society,
Washington, D.C. Cartographic Division.

Flat case National Geographic Society, Washington,
N 31+ D. C.
The argosy of geography. A photograph
of an almost obsolete type of old square-
rigged sailing ship taken April 26th, 1920,
in mid-Gulf Stream between Florida and
the Bahama Islands. Washington, c.1920₁
photograph 43 x 59 cm.

Supplement to January 1921 issue of
National geographic magazine.

NN 0052691 NIC

National geographic society, Washington, D.C.
Asia Minor; articles from the National geographic magazine
see under National geographic magazine.

National geographic society, Washington, D.C.
Australasia; articles from the National
geographic magazine [1919-1941]
see under National geographic magazine.

National geographic society, Washington, D.C.
Balkan countries; articles from the National
geographic magazine
see under National geographic magazine.

National Geographic Society, Washington. No. 29 in *Map 87.3
Bird's-eye view of the Panama Canal.
= Washington. 1912. Size, 8¼ × 17⅞ inches. Scale, none.
Colored.
Supplement to the National Geographic Magazine, February, 1912.

L9602 — Panama Canal. — Bird's eye views.

NN 0052695 MB

National geographic society. Washington, D.C.
FOR OTHER EDITIONS
SEE MAIN ENTRY
Calderón, Ignacio, 1848-1927.
Bolivia; address delivered by the Bolivian minister, Mr. Ignacio Calderon. under the auspices of the National geographic society at Washington, D. C. ... Conferencia leida en la Sociedad geográfica de Washington, D. C., por el señor Ignacio Calderon. 2. ed. London ₁Unwin brothers, limited₁ 1907.

National geographic society, *Washington, D. C.*
The book of birds; birds of town and country, the warblers and American game birds, with 331 color portraits of North American birds and 994 illustrations in black and white ... Washington, D. C., The National geographic society, 1925.
4 p. l., 215 p. illus. (part col., incl. maps) 25½ᶜᵐ.
"Color plates from paintings from life by Louis Agassiz Fuertes."
"Articles ... published in the National geographic magazine during the last ten years."—Foreword.
Published in part in 1914 under title: Common birds of town and country.

CONTENTS.—Foreword by G. Grosvenor.—Common birds of town and country, by H. W. Henshaw.—Friends of our forests—the warblers, by H. W. Henshaw.—The world record for feathered friends.—How birds can take their own portraits, by G. Shiras, 3rd.—The game birds of North America, by H. W. Henshaw.—Encouraging birds around the home, by F. H. Kennard.—Our greatest travelers—migratory birds, by W. W. Cooke.
1. Birds. ɪ. Henshaw, Henry Wetherbee, 1850-1930. ɪɪ. Shiras, George, 1859– ɪɪɪ. Kennard, Frederic Hedge, 1865– ɪᴠ. Cooke, Wells Woodbridge, 1858-1916. ᴠ. Fuertes, Louis Agassiz, 1874-1927, illus. ᴠɪ. Title.

Library of Congress QL676.N28 1925
25—25982

NN 0052698 MtU
DLC CLSU DI CU ViU NIC IU OEac OC1

VOLUME 407

National geographic society, *Washington, D. C.*
The book of birds; birds of town and country, the warblers, and American game birds, with 331 color portraits of North American birds and 129 illustrations in black and white ... Washington, D. C., The National geographic society, 1927.
4 p. l., 252 p. illus. (part col., incl. maps) 25½cm.
"Color plates from paintings from life by Louis Agassiz Fuertes."
"Articles ... published in the National geographic magazine during the last thirteen years."—Foreword.
"Revised new edition."

CONTENTS.—Foreword, by G. Grosvenor.—Common birds of town and country, by H. W. Henshaw.—Friends of our forests—the warblers, by H. W. Henshaw.—The world record for feathered friends.—How birds can take their own portraits, by G. Shiras, 3rd.—The game birds of North America, by H. W. Henshaw.—Encouraging birds around the home, by F. H. Kennard.—Our greatest travelers—migratory birds, by W. W. Cooke.—Bird banding, the telltale of migratory flight, by E. W. Nelson.

1. Birds. I. Henshaw, Henry Wetherbee, 1850-1930. II. Shiras, George, 1859- III. Kennard, Frederic Hedge, 1865- IV. Cooke, Wells Woodbridge, 1858-1916. V. Nelson, Edward William, 1855- VI. Fuertes, Louis Agassiz, 1874-1927, illus. VII. Title.
28—8932
Library of Congress QL676.N28 1927

OrU OrCS ICJ OOxM CaBVaU
NN 0052700 DLC OU OCl ViU NB NcD CLSU CU NcC

National geographic society, *Washington, D. C.*
The book of birds; common birds of town and country and American game birds, by Henry W. Henshaw ... illustrated in natural colors with 250 paintings by Louis Agassiz Fuertes; with chapters of "Encouraging birds around the home", by F. H. Kennard: "The mysteries of bird migration", by Wells W. Cooke, and "How birds can take their own portraits", by George Shiras, 3rd, and 45 illustrations and 13 charts in black and white. Washington, D. C., National geographic society [1918]
viii, 195 p. illus. (part col. incl. maps) 25½cm.

"Published in the National geographic magazine during the last six years."
Published in part in 1914 under title: Common birds of town and country.

1. Birds. I. Henshaw, Henry Wetherbee, 1850-1930. II. Fuertes, Louis Agassiz, 1874-1927, illus. III. Kennard, Frederic Hedge, 1865- IV. Cooke, Wells Woodbridge, 1858-1916. V. Shiras, George, 1859- VI. Title.
18—5769
Library of Congress QL676.N28 1918

MiD OCU OO OCl MB OOxM WaS Or CaBVaU MtU
NN 0052702 DLC MtBC DDO NIC NcRS CU IU DSI MnU

QL
676
.N28
1921

National geographic society, Washington, D. C.
The book of birds; common birds of town and country and American game birds, by Henry W. Henshaw ... illustrated in natural colors with 250 paintings by Louis Agassiz Fuertes; with chapters of "Encouraging birds around the home", by F. H. Kennard: "The mysteries of bird migration", by Wells W. Cooke, and "How birds can take their own portraits", by George Shiras, 3rd, and 45 illustrations and 13 charts in black and white. Washington, D. C., National geographic society [1921]
viii, 195 p. illus. 26 cm.

1. Birds. I. Henshaw, Henry Wetherbee, 1850-1930. II. Fuertes, Louis Agassiz, 1874-1927, illus. III. Kennard, Frederic Hedge, 1865- IV. Cooke, Wells Woodbridge, 1858-1916. V. Shiras, George, 1859- VI. Title

NN 0052704 OKentU LU

National geographic society, *Washington, D. C.*
The book of birds, the first work presenting in full color all the major species of the United States and Canada, edited by Gilbert Grosvenor ... and Alexander Wetmore ... with 950 color portraits by Major Allan Brooks ... Washington, D. C., National geographic society [c1937]
2 v. illus. (part col.; incl. maps) 26½cm.
Maps on lining-papers.

CONTENTS.—v. 1. Diving birds, ocean birds, swimmers, wading birds, wild fowl, birds of prey, game birds, shore birds, marsh dwellers, birds of the northern seas.—v. 2. Owls, goatsuckers, swifts, woodpeckers, fly-catchers, crows, jays, blackbirds, orioles, chickadees, creepers, thrushes, swallows, tanagers, wrens, warblers, hummingbirds, finches, and sparrows.

1. Birds—U. S. 2. Birds—Canada. I. Grosvenor, Gilbert Hovey, 1875- ed. II. *Wetmore, Alexander, 1886- joint ed. III. *Brooks, Allan, 1869- illus. IV. Title.
37—27382
Library of Congress QL676.N285 1937
—— —— Copy 2.
Copyright A 107589 [39p²5] 598.297

CaBVa IdPI MtHi CaBVaU CaBViP
OCl Wa WaE WaT IdU WaS WaSp OrCS OrAshS OrLgE MtU
OCl OU OOxM ViU NIC MoU ICJ TU MiU OKentU KEmT NN
NN 0052706 DLC Or OrCS OrMonO NcRS FMU WaU CU ICU

National geographic society, *Washington, D. C.*
The book of birds; the first work presenting in full color all the major species of the United States and Canada, edited by Gilbert Grosvenor ... and Alexander Wetmore ... with 950 color portraits by Major Allan Brooks ... Washington, D. C., National geographic society [c1939]
2 v. illus. (part col.) 26cm.
Map on lining-papers.
"Second edition."—Foreword.
CONTENTS.—v. 1. Diving birds, ocean birds, swimmers, wading birds, wild fowl, birds of prey, game birds, shore birds, marsh dwellers, birds of the northern seas.—v. 2. Owls, goatsuckers, swifts, woodpeckers, fly-catchers, crows, jays, blackbirds, orioles, chickadees, creepers, thrushes, swallows, tanagers, wrens, warblers, hummingbirds, finches, and sparrows.

1. Birds—U. S. 2. Birds—Canada. I. Grosvenor, Gilbert Hovey, 1875- ed. II. *Wetmore, Alexander, 1886- joint ed. III. *Brooks, Allan, 1869- illus. IV. Title.
39-23274
Library of Congress QL676.N285 1939
—— —— Copy 2.
Copyright A 131878 [10] 598.297

NN 0052708 DLC OrCS WaS NIC IaU OClGC OO DNAL

National geographic society, *Washington, D. C.*
The book of dogs; an intimate study of mankind's best friend, by Louis Agassiz Fuertes [Ernest Harold Baynes] and others, illustrated with 73 natural color portraits from original paintings by Louis Agassiz Fuertes. Washington, D. C., The National geographic society [c1919]
1 p. l., 96 p. illus. (part col.) 25½cm. $2.00
Reprinted from the National geographic magazine, vol. XXXV, no. 3, March 1919.
1. Dogs. I. Fuertes, Louis Agassiz, 1874-1927. II. Baynes, Ernest Harold, 1868-1925. III. Title.
20-14137 Revised
Library of Congress SF427.N3 1919

PU PPSteph OKentU MeB ViW OCl OO NN MB
NN 0052709 DLC DNAL WaE MtBC OrU CU-A PNt ViU

National geographic society, Washington, D. C.
[The book of dogs. By Ernest Harold Baynes, Louis Agsssiz Fuertes and others] Washington, 1919.
[185]-280 p. illus. (part col.) 25½cm.
Special issue of the National geographic magazine, vol. XXXV, no. 3, March, 1919.

1. Dogs. I. Baynes, Ernest Harold, 1868-1925. II. Fuertes, Louis Agassiz, 1874-1927. III. Title.

NN 0052710 ViW MB

National geographic society, *Washington, D. C.*
The book of dogs; an intimate study of mankind's best friend, with natural color portraits of 76 types of dogs from paintings of Louis Agassiz Fuertes and Hashime Murayama. Washington, D. C., The National geographic society, 1927.
3 p. l., 109 p. illus. (part col.) 25½cm.

1. Dogs. I. Fuertes, Louis Agassiz, 1874-1927. II. Title.
28—8911
Library of Congress SF427.N3 1927
—— —— Copy 2.

OrAshS WaE CaBVa GU CaBVaU NIC MU NcRS OCU OClh
NN 0052711 DLC NN NcD ViW IaU NN ICJ IdU OrLgE

National Geographic Society, Washington, D.C.
The Book of Dogs. Washington, 1927.
8 vo.
2nd ed.
By Ernest Harold Baynes.

NN 0052712 ViW

National geographic society, *Washington, D. C.*
The book of fishes; game fishes, food fishes, shellfish and curious citizens of American ocean shores, lakes and rivers; witl 134 illustrations, color plates of 92 familiar salt and fresh-water fishes ... color plates from life by Hashime Murayama. Washington, D. C., The National geographic society, 1924.
4 p. l., 243 p. illus. (part col.) 25½cm.
CONTENTS.—Fishes and fisheries of our North Atlantic seaboard, by J. O. La Gorce.—Our heritage of the fresh waters, by C. H. Townsend.—Certain citizens of the warm sea, by L. L. Mowbray.—Curious inhabitants of the Gulf stream, by J. T. Nichols.—Devil-fishing in the Gulf stream, by

J. O. La Gorce.—Salmon: America's most valuable fish, by H. M. Smith.—Oysters: a leading fishery product, by H. M. Smith.—Life on the Grand banks, by F. W. Wallace.

1. Fishes—North America. 2. Shell-fish. 3. Fisheries—North America. 4. Fishing—North America. I. Murayama, Hashime, 1879- illus. II. Title.
24—27800
Library of Congress QL625.N3 1924

MB NBuU CU PPAN OU OCl OEac NcC ViU CaBVa CaBViP
NN 0052714 DLC MH WaE WaTC DLC IdU IaU DNAL NIC

National geographic society, *Washington, D. C.*
The book of fishes. Rev. and enl. ed., presenting the better known species of food and game fishes of the coastal and inland waters of the United States. Edited by John Oliver La Gorce ... With 443 color portraits, 102 biographies, and 162 photographs. Narrative by John Oliver La Gorce; Charles Haskins Townsend ... John T. Nichols ... [and others] Original paintings by Hashime Murayama and Else Bostelmann. Washington, D. C., National geographic society [c1939]
367 p. illus. (part col.) 26cm.

CONTENTS.—Fishes and fisheries of our eastern seaboard, by J. O. La Gorce. — Our heritage of the fresh waters, by C. H. Townsend. — Some curious inhabitants of the Gulf stream, by J. T. Nichols.—Devilfishing in the Gulf stream, by J. O. La Gorce.—Certain citizens of the warm seas, by L. L. Mowbray.—Treasures of the Pacific, by L. P. Schultz.—Fishing in Pacific coast streams, by L. P. Schultz.—Sea creatures of our Atlantic shores, by R. W. Miner.—The lordly tarpon, by Van Campen Heilner.—Market fish have many names, by Russell Maloney.—"Compleat angler" fishes for fossils, by Imogene Powell.

1. Fishes—U. S. 2. Fishing—U. S. 3. Fisheries—U. S. I. La Gorce, John Oliver, 1880- ed. II. Murayama, Hashime, 1879- illus. III. Bostelmann, Mrs. Else, illus. IV. Title.
40-27021
Library of Congress QL625.N3 1939
—— —— Copy 2.
Copyright A 137403 [25] 597.0973

OrStbM CaBVaU
OCl OrCS NcRS NN MB MiU CU IaU WaU Or OrMonO OrP
NN 0052716 DLC WaWW WaSp IdU OrU ICJ ViU ODW OO

National Geographic Society, *Washington, D. C.*
The book of fishes. 1952 ed., rev. and enl., presenting the better-known food and game fishes and the aquatic life of the coastal and inland waters of the United States. Edited by John Oliver La Gorce. With 236 species in color with biographies, 67 other color photos., and 170 monochrome photos. Washington [1952]
xi, 339 p. illus. (part col.) 27 cm.
CONTENTS.—America's rich harvest of the sea, by J. O. La Gorce.—Our heritage of fresh waters, by C. H. Townsend.—Fishing in Pacific coast streams, by L. P. Schultz.—Angling in the United States, by L. Marden.—Marineland, Florida's giant fish bowl, by G. G. La

Gorce.—Some curious inhabitants of the Gulf Stream, by J. T. Nichols.—Man-of-war fleet attacks Bimini, by P. A. Zahl.—Devilfishing in the Gulf Stream, by J. O. La Gorce.—Certain citizens of the warm seas, by L. L. Mowbray.—Portugal's captains courageous, by A. Villiers.—The lordly tarpon, angler's delight, by V. Heilner.—Sea creatures of our Atlantic shores, by R. W. Miner.—Men who go down to the sea in aqualungs, by J. Y. Cousteau.—Goggle fishing in California waters, by D. Hellyer.—Strange babies of the sea, by H. B. Moore.
1. Fishes—U. S. 2. Fishing—U. S. 3. Fisheries—U. S. I. La Gorce, John Oliver, 1880- ed. II. Title.

QL625.N3 1952 597.0973 52—14581

DNAL CaBViP
MB OrCS MtBC OrAshS IdB CaBVa CaBVaU WaS Or IdU
NN 0052718 DLC WaT Wa OU NN PPT PP DI N MiD NcC

National geographic society, *Washington, D. C.*
The book of wild flowers; an introduction to the ways of plant life, together with biographies of 250 representative species and chapters on our state flowers and familiar grasses: with color plates of 250 familiar wild flowers and grasses ... Washington, D. C.. The National geographic society, 1924.
3 p. l., 243 p. illus. (part col.) 25cm.
CONTENTS.—Exploring the mysteries of plant life, by W. J. Showalter.—Our state flowers, by G. Grosvenor.—Familiar grasses and their flowers, by E. J. Geske and W. J. Showalter.—Plant biographies, by W. J. Showalter.

1. Flowers—U. S. I. Title.
24—31492
Library of Congress QK115.N3

PPPM-I ViU
WaS OrCS OrU Or WaSpG PP CaBVa DAU MBH FMU TU OU
NN 0052719 DLC ICJ NcD OOxM CaBVaU CaBViP IdU

National geographic society, *Washington, D. C.*
The book of wild flowers; an introduction to the ways of plant life, together with biographies of 250 representative species and chapters on our state flowers and familiar grasses; with color plates of 250 familiar wild flowers and grasses ... color plates from life by Mary E. Eaton ... Washington, D. C., The National geographic society, 1933.
3 p. l., 243 p. front., illus. (part col.) 25cm.
"Copyright second edition 1933."
CONTENTS.—Exploring the mysteries of plant life, by W. J. Showalter.—Our state flowers, by G. Grosvenor.—Familiar grasses and their flowers, by E. J. Geske and W. J. Showalter.—Plant biographies, by W. J. Showalter.
1. Flowers—U. S. I. Title.
33—35674
Library of Congress QK115.N3 1933
—— —— Copy 2.
Copyright A 68299 [39k2] 581.973

OrStbM OCU WaS OEac OO MiU MeB MsU MU
NN 0052720 DLC WaTC IdU OrCS OrMonO OrAshS OrU

National geographic society, Washington, D.C.
British islands; articles from the National geographic magazine
see under National geographic magazine.

National geographic society, Washington, D.C.
Canada; articles from the National geographic magazine
see under National geographic magazine.

VOLUME 407

National geographic society, *Washington, D. C.*
 The capital of our country, with 136 illustrations, including
16 pages in full color. Washington, D. C., National geographic society, 1923.
 2 p. l., 154 p. incl. illus., 16 col. pl. 25ᶜᵐ.
 Plates printed on both sides.

 1. Washington, D. C. 2. Washington, D. C.—Descr.—Views.
I. Title.

 Library of Congress   F195.N27   23—17609

NN 0052723   OC1 OCU MiU NcRS TU GU
          DLC LU MB ICJ WaS OrMonO NN DI WHi

National Geographic Society, Washington, D. C.
 Catalogue of the Sella collection of Alpine and
Caucasian views
      see under   Appalachian Mountain Club.

National geographic society, Washington, D. C.

Sanders, Alvin Howard, 1860–
 The cattle of the world; their place in the human scheme—
wild types and modern breeds in many lands, by Alvin Howard
Sanders ... paintings by Edward Herbert Miner ... with 114
illustrations, including 20 pages in color. Washington, D. C.
The National geographic society, 1926.

National geographic society, Washington, D.C.
 Central America; articles from the National
geographic magazine
      see under   National geographic magazine.

National geographic society, Washington, D.C.
 Central Asia; articles from the National
geographic magazine
      see under National geographic magazine.

National geographic society, Washington, D.C.
 China; articles from the National geographic
magazine
      see under   National geographic magazine.

National geographic society, *Washington, D. C.*
 Common birds of town and country. With 114 illustrations
in color and 52 in black and white ... Washington,
D. C., National geographic society [*1914]
 1 p. l., [493]–531, [1], [667]–698, 315–344, [346]–365. illus. (part col.,
incl. maps) 25½ cm.
 "Reprints from the National geographic magazine."
 CONTENTS.—"Birds of town and country," by H. W. Henshaw.
May, 1914.—"Fifty common birds of farm and orchard," by H. W.
Henshaw. June, 1913."—"Encouraging birds around the home," by
F. H. Kennard. March, 1914.—"Our greatest travelers: birds that fly
from Pole to Pole; birds that make 2,500 miles in a single flight," by
W. W. Cooke. April, 1911.
 1. Birds. I. Henshaw, Henry Wetherbee, 1850– II. Cooke,
Wells Woodbridge, 1858–1916. III. Kennard, Frederic Hedge, 1865–
IV. Title.

 QL676.N275   14—20293

NN 0052729   WaT WaE
          DLC FU KMK MiHM OC1 DAU IU NIC OC1W

National geographic society, Washington, D. C.
 Common birds of town and country... Washington
[c1915] 1 v. illus.,maps. 25cm.

 Contents.—Birds of town and country, by Henry
W. Henshaw.—Fifty common birds of farm and
orchard, by Henry W. Henshaw.—Encouraging birds
around the home, by Frederick H. Kennard.—Our
greatest travelers: birds that fly from pole to
pole; birds that make 2,500 miles in a single
flight, by Wells W.   Cooke.
 1. Birds—U.S. 2.Birds   —Migration. I. Title.

NN 0052730   NN WaTC OKentU

National Geographic Society, Washington, D. C.
 Contributed technical papers. Katmai series.
no.

Washington, D. C., 192   4°.
(Carnegie Institution of Washington. Geophysical Laboratory.
Papers.)
  no.   illus.
  Cover-title.

 1. Volcanoes, Alaska: Katmai.
N. Y. P. L.   June 17, 1924

NN 0052731   CaBVaU TU IU CU NjP
          NN ViU DI-GS PBL NcU DLC ICJ ICU WaS

National Geographic Society, Washington, D.C.
 Contents of the box deposited in the corner stone of the Hubbard
Memorial Building, the future home of the National Geographic
Society, now being erected in Washington, D.C... 1902, April 26.
= [Washington.] Printed for private circulation. [1902.] (11)
pp. 8°.
 The title is on the cover.
 Printed on one side of the paper only.

NN 0052732   MB

NATIONAL GEOGRAPHIC SOCIETY, Washington, D.C.
 ... Contributed technical papers. Pueblo Bonito
series. no. 1–
Washington, 1935–
  v. illus.,map,diagrs. 24½cm.

 1.Pueblo Bonito,N.M. 2.Indians of North America—
New Mexico. 3.Pueblos. 4.New Mexico—Antiq.

NN 0052733   CtNlC AAP NcU MsU LNHT OrCS MB WaT WaTC
          ICU MtBC DI-GS NN ICJ ViU ICU NNC ICN

National geographic society, *Washington, D. C.*
 ...Contributed technical papers. Solar eclipse series.
no. 1

Washington, 1939   25½cm.
  no.   illus.

 1. Eclipses, Solar
N. Y. P. L.

NN 0052734   ICJ CU MBdAF ILS NcU MsU
          NN WaS OrCS MtBC MtU PBL TxU TU GU

NATIONAL GEOGRAPHIC SOCIETY, Washington, D. C.
 Contributed technical papers. Mexican archaeology
series. v. 1, no. 1. Washington, 1940. 15 p. illus.
26cm.

 No more published?

 1. Mexico—Archaeology. I. Title: Mexican archaeology series.
 II. National geographic society, Washington, D.C. Mexican archaeology
series.

NN 0052735   NN DPU CtY TxU CU NcU OrU

National Geographic Society.
 ...Contributed technical papers. Stratosphere series.
no. 1

Washington, D. C., 1935   25½cm.
  v.   illus. (incl. maps, ports.)

 1. Aeronautics. I. Title:
N. Y. P. L.   Stratosphere series.
                             March 27, 1936

NN 0052736   CU MBdAF MsU ILS TU
          NN DI-GS MtBC CaBVaU MtHi WaS UCL ICJ

National geographic society, Washington, D.C.
 Domestic animals and fowls; articles from the
National geographic magazine
      see under   National geographic magazine.

National Geographic Society, Washington, D.C.
 Early maps. Washington, 1893

 1 v.
  Contents: Ptolemy, ca. A.D. 150.–Toscanelli, 1474. –
Nuremberg Chronicle, 1493. –Juan de la Cosa, 1500. –
Rysch, 1508

NN 0052738   MH

National geographic society, Washington, D. C.
 Eastern Europe; articles from the National
geographic magazine
      see under   National geographic magazine.

National geographic society, Washington, D. C.
 Eastern states; articles from the National
geographic magazine
      see under   National geographic magazine.

National geographic society, Washington, D. C.
 Egypt and Ethiopia; articles from the National
geographic magazine ...
      see under   National geographic magazine.

National geographic society, Washington, D. C.
 England; articles from the National geographic
magazine
      see under   National geographic magazine.

National Geographic Society, Washington, D. C.
 Europe and the Mediterranean
      see under   National Geographic Society,
Washington, D. C. Cartographic Division

National geographic society, Washington, D. C.
 Europe and the Near East. Compiled and drawn in the Cartographic section of the National geographic society .. Executed by Albert H. Bumstead, Ralph A. Graves, James M.
Darley ... [and others] Washington, National geographic
society. ©1929.

National geographic society, *Washington, D. C.*
 Europe and the Near East, compiled and drawn in the Carto-
graphic section of the National geographic society for the
National geographic magazine ... May 1940. Washington,
D. C., The National geographic society, ©19

 col. map. 83 x 95½ᵐ.
 "Scale 1 : 6,000,000 or 94.7 miles to the inch."
 "Azimuthal equidistant projection (pole of projection at latitude 50°
north, longitude 22°30′ east)"
 "Culture by James M. Darley, physiography by Charles E. Riddiford."
 "Printed by A. Hoen & co., inc., Baltimore."
 Inset: The Middle East.
                                 G5700 1940.N3

——— Index to the new map of Europe and the Near East.
Washington, D. C., National geographic society, 1940.
 30 p. 25½ᵐ.

 1. Europe—Descr. & trav.—Maps. 2. Levant—Descr. & trav.—Maps.
                                               Map 45–214
 Library of Congress.   Div. of maps G5700 1940.N3 Index

NN 0052746   DLC

National Geographic Society, Washington, D. C.
 Exhibition of photographs taken by the Peruvian
expeditions...
      see under   Bingham, Hiram, 1875–

VOLUME 407

Map
G
4181
A4
1935
N3

National Geographic Society, Washington,
D.C.
The first photograph ever made showing
the division between the troposphere and
the stratosphere and also the actual
curvature of the earth - photographed
from an elevation of 72,395 feet, the
highest point ever reached by man.
Washington, 1936.
photograph 35 x 60cm.

1. Atmosphere, Upper--Maps.

NN 0052748   NIC OrU

National geographic society, Washington,
D.C.
₍Flags and memorials₎ Geographical
articles: articles classified and
rebound from National geographic magazines
n.p. Classified geographic, inc.,n.d.
Illus.)₍Serial no.363, v.no.27₎)

Contents:
t
Flags
Insignia
Classified geographic, inc.

NN 0052749   CaBVaU

National geographic society, Washington, D.C.

McCandless, Byron, 1881–
Flags of the world, by Byron McCandless ... and Gilbert
Grosvenor ... with 1197 flags in full colors. 300 additional
illustrations in black and white ... Washington, D. C., The
National geographic society ₍1917₎

National Geographic Society, Washington, D.C.
France and Belgium; articles from the National
geographic magazine
see under   National Geographic Magazine.

National geographic society, Washington, D. C.

Geographic news bulletin ... Prepared and issued by the
National geographic society
Washington, D. C.

National geographic society.
Geographic news bulletin on sulphur,Sicily and civ-
ilization. Prepared and issued by the National geog-
raphic society. Washington, 1924.
3 p.   28 cm.
Caption title.
Alternate paging.
Mimeographed.

NN 0052753   DI-GS CtY

National geographic society, Washington, D. C.

G1
.G323

Geographic school bulletins ... Oct. 6, 1919–May 9, 1921;
₍new ser.₎ v. 1–
Feb. 6, 1922–
₍Washington₎ National geographic society ₍etc.₎, 1919–

National geographic society, Washington, D.C.
Germany and Holland; articles from the National
geographic magazine
see under   National Geographic Magazine.

National geographic society, *Washington, D. C.*
Germany and its approaches, with international boundaries
as of September 1, 1939, the day Germany invaded Poland,
and, in red, boundaries as of January 1, 1938, before Germany
seized Austria and Czechoslovakia. Compiled and drawn in
the Cartographic section of the National geographic society
for the National geographic magazine ... July 1944. Washington, D. C., National geographic society, ₍1944₎

col. map. 64 x 81¾".

Scale 1 : 2,000,000; "31.57 miles to the inch."
"Albers conical equal-area projection."

"James M. Darley, chief cartographer ; culture by Apphia E. Holdstock, Donald G. Bouma, and Ralph E. McAleer ; physiography by John
J. Brehm, and Charles E. Riddiford."
"Printed by A. Hoen and co., lithographers, Baltimore, Md., U. S. A."
—— Index to the National geographic society's map of Germany and its approaches. Washington, D. C., National
geographic society, 1944.
31 p. 25½".
1. Germany—Descr. & trav.—Maps.   I. Darley, James Morrison.
Map 45–7
Library of Congress. °   Div. of maps   G6080 1944.N3

NN 0052757   DLC

Flat case   National Geographic Society. Washington,
N32+   D.C.
The Great Wall of China near Nankow
Pass. Washington, D. C.,₍c1923₎
photograph 18 x 112 cm.

Special supplement to the February
1923 issue of National geographic magazine

I. Great Wall of China.

NN 0052758   NIC

Map
G
3804
N4
1933
N3

National geographic Society, Washington, D.C.
Greater New York...Metropolis of
mankind. Washington, 1933.
photograph 45 x 57 cm.

Photograph taken from height of 26,000
feet; covers area of approx. 3000 sq. miles.
Supplement to November, 1933 issue of
National geographic magazine.

1. New York ₍City₎--Maps.

NN 0052759   NIC

National geographical society, Washington, D.C.

Carter, William Giles Harding, 1851–1925.
The horses of the world; the development of man's companion in war camp, on farm, in the marts of trade, and in the
field of sports, by Major General William Harding Carter,
U. S. A.; paintings by Edward Herbert Miner. With 95 illustrations, including 24 pages of color. Washington, The National geographic society, 1923.

National Geographic Society.
Illinois. ₍Map₎ Washington,1931
see under   National Geographic Society,
Washington, D.C. Cartographic Division.

National Geographic Society.
Index to the New map of Europe.
— Washington. [1929.] 32 pp. Folded map. [National Geo-
graphic Magazine. Vol. 56, supplement.] 25 cm.
The New map of Europe may be found on a separate call-number.

N7547 — T.r. — S.r.c. — Europe. Geog. Maps.

NN 0052762   MB MH-A

REF
970.1
N2771

National Geographic Society
Indians of the Americas. Washington,
Nat'l Geog.Soc., 1955.

NN 0052763   KyU-A

National Geographic Society, Washington, D.C.
Industry and commerce; articles from the
National geographic magazine [1917–1941]
see under   National Geographic Magazine.

National geographic society, Washington, D. C.
Insects; articles from the National geographic ...
magazine
see under   National geographic magazine.

National geographic society, *Washington, D. C.*
Insignia and decorations of the U. S. armed forces. 1701
color reproductions. ₍Washington, 1943₎

cover-title, ₍1₎ 652–714, 409–458, 715–748 p. incl. illus. (incl. ports.)
plates (part col.) col. plates. 25½".
Reprinted from the June, October and December, 1943, issues of the
National geographic magazine.

1. U. S. Army—Insignia. 2. U. S. Army—Medals, badges, decorations, etc. 3. U. S. Navy—Insignia. 4. U. S. Navy—Medals, badges,
decorations, etc.
44–3134 Revised
Library of Congress   UC533.N3 1943

NN 0052766   DLC DI-GS CSt-H OCl NcD NcRS MB OClMA
OCl ViU Mi WHi WaS WaT

National geographic society, *Washington, D. C.*
Insignia and decorations of the U. S. armed forces, by
Gilbert Grosvenor, J. R. Hildebrand, Arthur E. Du Bois
₍and others₎ ... 2,476 reproductions in color and 159 illus-
trations from photographs. Rev. ed., December 1, 1944.
Washington, D. C., National geographic society ₍1945₎
208 p. incl. illus. (incl. ports.) col. plates. 25½ cm.
"New 'five star' generals and admirals" : p. ₍3₎ of cover.

1. U. S. Army—Insignia. 2. U. S. Army—Medals, badges, decorations, etc. 3. U. S. Navy—Insignia. 4. U. S. Navy—Medals, badges,
decorations, etc.   I. Grosvenor, Gilbert Hovey, 1875–
UC533.N3 1945   355.14   45–5147

CaBVa OrStbM MtBC WaSp IdB OCl DNLM OCU ODW OrP
MnU NcRS NcC MiEM DSI WaWW WaT OrHi OrU Wa WaT
NN 0052767   DLC OrCS CLSU ViU FTaSU TU MH CSt-H

National geographic society, Washington, D. C.
Italy; articles from the National geographic
magazine ...
see under   National geographic magazine.

National Geographic Society, Washington, D.C.
Katmai series
see its   Contributed technical papers.
Katmai series.

Map
G
4010
1930
N3

National Geographic Society, Washington,
D.C.
Louisiana. Washington, 1930.
col. map 30 x 31cm.

Scale 1:1,750,000 or 27.62 miles to
1 inch.
Inset: New Orleans, ca. 1:47,520.

1. Louisiana--Maps.

NN 0052770   NIC

Map
G
8200
1909
N3

National Geographic Society, Washington,
D.C.
Map of Africa. Washington, 1909.
col. map 51 x 39cm.

Scale 1:19,008,000.

1. Africa--Maps.

NN 0052771   NIC

VOLUME 407

National Geographic Society, Washington, D. C.

G8300
1922
.M3
Matthews-Northrup Company, Buffalo, N. Y.
Map of Africa and adjoining portions of Europe and
Asia. Washington, National Geographic Society, °1922.

National Geographic Society, Washington.
Map of Asia and adjoining Europe with a portion of Africa.
— Washington. 1921. Size, 27 × 36¾ inches. Scale (computed),
222.22 miles to 1 inch. Colored.

N7708 — Asia. Geog. Maps.

NN 0052773   MB

---

*BROAD-
SIDE   National Geographic Society, Washington, D.C.
-1938
.N375   Map of Czechoslovakia and adjacent sections
of Germany, Poland, Romania, and Hungary.
[Washington? D. C., 1938]
broadside ([3] p.) 28 x 21cm.

1. Czechoslovakia—Maps.

NN 0052774   ViU

G5700
1920
.M3
National Geographic Society, Washington, D. C.
Matthews-Northrup Company, Buffalo, N. Y.
Map of Europe showing countries as established by the
Peace Conference at Paris. Prepared ... by the Matthews-
Northrup Works. Washington, National Geographic So-
ciety, °1920.

National Geographic Society, Washington, D. C.
Map of Mexico ... Buffalo, 1916
see under   Matthews-Northrup Company,
Buffalo, N. Y.

G4410
1916
.N3
National Geographic Society, Washington,
D.C.
Map of Mexico. Washington, 1916.
col.map 49x73cm.

Scale ca.1:4,300,000.
Issued with the National geographic magazine, v.30,
no.1, July, 1916.
Insets: [comparative size of Southern New England
on same scale].- Physical map of Mexico.- Central
portion of Mexico on twice the scale of the main map.

1.Mexico - Maps.

NN 0052777   CLSU

Map
G
3270
1907
N3
National Geographic Society, Washington,
D.C.
Map of the North Pole regions.
Washington, 1907.
col. map 45 x 45cm.

Scale approx. 1:12,672,000.

1. Arctic regions—Maps.

NN 0052778   NIC

Map
G
5200
1921
N3
National Geographic Society, Washington,
D.C.
Map of South America. Washington, 1921.
col. map 91 x 63 cm.

Scale 1 inch equals approx. 130 miles.

1. South America—Maps.

NN 0052779   NIC IU

G8060
1905
.N3
National Geographic Society, Washington,
D.C.
Map of the Philippines. Washington,
1905.
col.map 84x53cm.

Scale ca. 1:2,400,000.
"Prepared by reduction from the map of the Bureau of
Insular Affairs, War Department. Relief compiled
from maps of the Corps of Engineers, U.S. Army, and
from Spanish surveys."
"Published as a supplement to the National geographic
magazine, Washington, D.C., for Aug.1905."

NN 0052780   CLSU

National Geographic Society, Washington, D.C.
A map of the travels of George Washington ...
Washington, 1931
see under   National Geographic Society,
Washington, D.C. Cartographic Division.

National Geographic Society, Washington, D.C.
Map of the western theatre of war
see under   National Geographic Society,
Washington, D.C. Cartographic Division.

Map
G
4880
1905
N3
National Geographic Society, Washington,
D.C.
Map showing location of Panama Canal
as recommended by the Isthmian Canal
Commission of 1899-1902. Washington,
1905.
col. map 61 x 83cm.

Scale 1:100,000.

1. Panama Canal—Maps.

NN 0052783   NIC

G
912
N213m
National geographic society, Washington, D.C.
...Maps, eastern hemisphere. [Washington,
D.C., The Society, 1945]
cover-title, 17 fold. maps in 10 pockets.
27½cm.

Each map, with exception of British isles and
Indian ocean, accompanied by index with individ-
ual t.-p.
For contents note see author card.

NN 0052784   LU

G4371
.C3
1914
.T3
National Geographic Society, Washington, D. C.
Tarr, Ralph Stockman, 1864-1912.
[Maps to accompany Alaskan glacier studies of the
National Geographic Society in the Yukutat Bay, Prince
William Sound and lower Copper River regions, by Ralph
Stockman Tarr and Lawrence Martin, based upon the field
work in 1909, 1910, 1911 and 1913 by National Geographic
Society expeditions. Washington, National Geographic
Society, 1914]

G
3840
1925
N3
National Geographic Society, Washington, D.C.
Maryland, Delaware and District of
Columbia. Washington, 1925.
col. map 30 x 46cm.

Scale 1:900,000.

1. Maryland—Maps.

NN 0052786   NIC

National Geographic Society, Washington, D. C.
Mexico, Central America and the West Indies ...
see under   National Geographic Society,
Washington, D. C. Cartographic Division.

National Geographic Society, Washington, D. C.
Midsummer wild flowers. 1922.

NN 0052788   MBH

G1
.N27
National Geographic Society, Washington, D. C.
The National geographic magazine. v. 1–
1888–
Washington, National Geographic Society.

National geographic society, Washington, D. C.
National geographic monographs prepared under the auspices
of the National geographic society ... v. 1. New York, Chicago [etc.] American book company [1895]
cover-title, 336 p. Illus. (incl. maps) 28cm.
Issued in 10 nos., each with special (cover) title. No more published.
Reissued in 1896 under title: The physiography of the United States.
CONTENTS.—no. 1. Physiographic processes, by J. W. Powell.—no. 2.
Physiographic features, by J. W. Powell.—no. 3. Physiographic regions
of the United States, by J. W. Powell.—no. 4. Present and extinct lakes
of Nevada, by I. C. Russell.—no. 5. Beaches and tidal marshes of the At-
lantic coast, by N. S. Shaler.—no. 6. The northern Appalachians, by B.
Willis.—no. 7. Niagara falls and their history, by G. K. Gilbert.—no. 8.
Mount Shasta, a typical volcano, by J. S. Diller.—no. 9. The physical
geography of southern New England, by W. M. Davis.—no. 10. The southern Appalachians, by C. W.   Hayes.
1. Physical geography—   Societies. 2. Geography—Societies.
I. Title.
Library of Congress   GB121.N265   4—23335

NcRS FTaSU
NN 0052790   DLC OC1MN ICJ LU MB MMeT CLSU OC1 OO

M
N277n
National Geographic Society, Washington, D.C.
National Geographic news bulletin. 1946-
Washington, D.C., 1946-
1 v.   28 to 36 cm.
Press releases on the weather.
Mimeographed.

NN 0052791   DAS DNAL

National Geographic Society, Washington, D. C.
National Geographic on Indians of the Americas; a color-
illustrated record [by] Matthew W. Stirling, with contributions by Hiram Bingham [and others] Illustrated with full-
color reproductions of 149 paintings by W. Langdon Kihn
and H. M. Herget. Foreword by John Oliver La Gorce.
Washington, °1955.
481 p. illus. (part col.) maps. 27 cm.

1. Indians. 2. Indians—Pictures, illustrations, etc. I. Stirling,
Matthew Williams, 1896– II. Title: Indians of the Americas.

E58.N3   970.1   55—4531

WaSp OrPS PWcS WHi
IU DHUD MU Or IdB CaBVa CaBVaU UU ScU FU DI-GS
OrCS TU WaS MtBC MtU NcD FU PJB Wa MiU PP MH-P
CU C OO OC1JC NN DSI GU OEac CoDCC WaT OrP OrLgE
NN 0052792   DLC OrU OC1 DNAL PU-Mu PBL NjN DI TxU

National geographic society, Washington, D. C.
The National geographic society ... 1888–89. [Wash-
ington, D. C., 1888–89]
2 v. 23½cm.
Cover-title.
Certificate of incorporation, by-laws, members, etc.
Lists of members of the society are also included in the Directory of
scientific societies of Washington and in the National geographic magazine.

CA 18-1149 Unrev'd
Library of Congress   G3.N32

NN 0052794   DLC

National geographic society, Washington, D. C.
... National geographic society—National bureau of standards solar eclipse expedition of 1940 to Brazil. Washington,
1942.
cover-title, 97 p. incl. illus., tables, diagrs. 25½cm. (Its Contributed
technical papers. Solar eclipse series, no. 2)

1. Eclipses, Solar—1940. I. U. S. National bureau of standards.
II. Title.

Library of Congress   QB544.40.N3   42—14844

[20]   523.78

OrP OU
MoU ViU Wa OrPR MtU OrU NIC CaBVaU Wa WaSp WaWW
NN 0052795   DLC DAS Or IaU MU IaAS OOxM ODW OCU

VOLUME 407

National geographic society, *Washington, D. C.*
... The National geographic society.-U. S. Army Air corps stratosphere flight of 1934 in the balloon "Explorer". Washington, 1935.

cover-title, 32, ;397;-434, 71-122 p. illus. (incl. ports.) diagrs. 25½ᶜᵐ. (National geographic society. Contributed technical papers. Stratosphere series, no. 1)

Pages ;397;-434 from the National geographic magazine, vol. LXVI, no. 4, October, 1934.
Papers by various authors.

1. Balloon ascensions. 2. Atmosphere, Upper.   I. U. S. Office of chief of Air corps (War dept.)   II. Title.

Library of Congress   TL620.N3A3   35-14119
———— Copy 2.   ;5;   629.13322

AAP MoU DAU NcRS OU MiU ODW DCGS
NN 0052796   DLC MtU IdU DAL CaBVaU Wa WaWW Or

National geographic society, *Washington, D. C.*
... The National geographic society.-U. S. Army Air corps stratosphere flight of 1935 in the balloon "Explorer II". Washington, 1936.

cover-title, 277, ;1; p. illus., diagrs. 25½ᶜᵐ. (National geographic society. Contributed technical papers. Stratosphere series. no. 2)

Papers by various authors.
"Pictorial supplement showing lateral curvature of the earth's horizon as photographed from the stratosphere": folded plate laid in.
"References" at end of two of the papers.

1. Balloon ascensions. 2. Atmosphere, Upper. 3. Explorer II (Balloon)
I. U. S. Office of chief of Air corps (War dept.)   II. Title.

Library of Congress   TL620.N3A3 1935
———— Copy 2.
Copyright A 100275   37-3449
                                                    629.13322

Ok ViU WaWW OrMonO OrSaW
CaBVaU WaTC DAU MU CtY-M MoU IEN OCU OC1 OU NcRS
NN 0052797   DLC Or IdU Wa WaSp MtBuM OrPR WaS DNW

National geographic society, *Washington, D. C.*
... National geographic society.-U. S. Navy solar eclipse expedition of 1937 to Canton island. Washington, 1939.

cover-title, 08, 361-394 p. illus. (incl. ports.) 2 col. pl. on 1 l., diagrs. 25½ᶜᵐ. (National geographic society. Contributed technical papers. Solar eclipse series. no. 1)

Pages 361-394 reprinted from the National geographic magazine, September 1937.
Papers by various authors.

1. Eclipses, Solar—1937. 2. Sun—Corona.   I. U. S. Navy dept.
II. Title.

Library of Congress   QB544.37N3
Copyright AA 300352   ;40h5;   39—25293
                                                    523.78

OOxM IaAS ViU NIC
NN 0052798   DLC CaBVaU DAS MtU MB MoU GU OC1W OU

National geographic society, Washington, D. C.
Natural phenomena; articles from the National geographic magazine
    see under   National geographic magazine.

National Geographic Society, Washington, D. C.
A new rôle for Guam, our smallest possession.
[n.p., ; 1931]

3 l. broadside. 28 x 22 cm. (Its Geographic news bulletin. 2050)
Mimeographed.
1. Guam. 2. Chamorros. I. Title.

NN 0052800   ViU

National Geographic Society, Washington, D. C.
Mexican archaeology series
    see its Contributed technical papers.
Mexican archaeology series.

National geographic society
...Nitrates and where they come from. Prepared and issued by the National geographic society. Washington, D. C., 1924.
4 p. 23 cm. (Geographical news bulletin)
Mimeographed.

NN 0052802   DI-GS

National Geographic Society, Washington, D. C.
The National geographic magazine map of Central America, Cuba, Porto Rico, and the islands of the Caribbean Sea; prepared by the American Bank Note Co.; Gilbert H. Grosvenor, editor...
;Washington; Nat. Geogr. Soc.; 1913.

Scale: 1 : 9 000 000 (142 m.   1 in.)
Size within border: →18½ × ↑12 in.
Photo-process, in color.
Cop. 1913 by Amer. Bank Note Co.
1 map on 1 sheet of stiff paper; published as a suppl. to the Nat. geogr. mag., Feb., 1913.
Inset map of Panama Canal zone in upper right corner.

1. Central America.—Maps, 1913.   2. Cuba.—Maps, 1913. 3. Porto
Rico.—Maps, 1913. 4. Caribbean Sea.   Rico.—Maps, 1913. 5. Canals (Inter-
oceanic). America: Panama.   oceanic). America: Panama.
N. Y. P. L.   6. National geographic magazine.
                                                    October 11, 1915.

NN 0052803   NN MB

National geographic society, Washington, D. C.
North Atlantic states; articles from the National geographic magazine
    see under   National geographic magazine.

National Geographic Society, Washington, D. C.
North central United States
    see under   National Geographic Society,
Washington, D. C. Cartographic Division.

National geographic society, Washington, D. C.
Northeast Asia; articles from the National geographic magazine
    see under   National geographic magazine.

National geographic society, Washington, D. C.
Northern Africa; articles from the National geographic magazine
    see under   National geographic magazine.

National geographic society, *Washington, D. C.*
Our insect friends and foes and spiders; a series of fascinating stories of bee, ant, beetle, bug, fly, butterfly, moth, and spider life; with sixty-four pages reproducing over 500 insects and spiders and their habits in their natural colors; foreword by Dr. Gilbert Grosvenor ... Washington, D. C., The National geographic society, 1935.

3 p. l., 252 p. front., illus. (part col.) 25ᶜᵐ.
"Collected articles and color pages on insects and spiders that have appeared in the National geographic magazine during the past decade."—Foreword.

1. Insects. 2. Spiders. 3. Insects—Pictorial works.   I. Title.

Library of Congress   QL467.N25   35-13919
———— Copy 2.
Copyright A 86090   595.7

OrMonO CaBViP CaBVa
KEmT OO OU OC1h WaE WaS OrStbM Or WaTC WaT OrAshS
NN 0052808   DLC OrU OrCS OrLgE OC1W NcRS CU TU

RM   National Geographic Society.
523.89   Palomar Observatory sky atlas, July 16, 1954.
N277p   Pasadena, Calif.. Printed by the Graphic Arts
        Facilities of the California Institute of
        Technology, 1954-1958.
        10p. and atlas of 1618 plates in 9v.

RM   . ;Supplement;   Pasadena, Calif.,
523.89 Printed by the Graphic Arts Facilities of the
N277p   California Institute of Technology ;195- -
sup   Atlas of   in   v.

        Contents.- sup.1, Southern extension.

NN 0052809   FTaSU ViU OU NNC WaU MiU UU

National geographic society, Washington, D. C.
Peruvian expeditions, 1912-1915
    see   Peruvian expeditions, 1912-1915.

National geographic society, *Washington, D. C.*
... The physiography of the United States; ten monographs ... New York, Chicago ;etc., American book company, 1896.
v. 345 p. incl. illus., maps. 28½ᶜᵐ.

First issued in 10 parts in 1895 under title: National geographic monographs, prepared under the auspices of the National geographic society.

CONTENTS.—Physiographic processes, by J. W. Powell.—Physiographic features, by J. W. Powell.—Physiographic regions of the United States, by J. W. Powell.—Present and extinct lakes of Nevada, by I. C. Russell.—Benches and tidal marshes of the Atlantic coast, by N. S. Shaler.—The northern Appalachians, by B. Willis.—Niagara falls and their history, by G. K. Gilbert.—Mount Shasta, a typical volcano, by J. S. Diller.—The physical geography of southern New England, by W. M. Davis.—The southern Appalachians,   by C. W. Hayes.

1. Physical geography—   U. S.

Library of Congress   GB121.N27   4—23334

CaBVaU OrCS
NcU OCU OO OC1 MtBuM WaWW OrU FMU ViU MB ICJ NjP
NN 0052811   DLC MtU WaTC NIC NcD KEmT TU MU OU DSI

National Geographic Society, Washington, D. C.
Pictorial geography.
Group 1, section 1
Washington ;1919?   ob. 8°.
v.   illus. (part col'd.)

Editor : 1919?—   G. H. Grosvenor.

Contents: Group 1, section 1. Eskimo life. ;1919?;

1. Geography.—Per. and soc. publ.
N. Y. P. L.   October 20, 1920.

NN 0052812   NN

National geographic society, Washington, D. C.
Plants; article from the National geographic magazine
    see under   National geographic magazine.

National geographic society, Washington, D. C.
Polar lands; articles from the National geographic magazine
    see under   National geographic magazine.

National geographic society, *Washington. D. C.*
Program of meetings.
;Washington? 19
v. 15ᶜᵐ.

1. Geography—Societies.
                                             CA 13-859 Unrev'd

Library of Congress   G3.N3

NN 0052815   DLC

Map   National Geographic Society, Washing-
G   ton, D. C.
8060   Progress map of Signal Corps tele-
1902   graph lines and cables in the Military
N3   Division of the Philippines. Prepared
        under the direction of Brigadier Gene-
        ral A.W. Greely. ;Washington; 1902.
        col. map 82 x 86 cm.

        Scale 1 inch equals approx. 15
        miles.
        "Sheet 1"   (Northern Philippines)

NN 0052816   NIC

National geographic society, Washington
D. C. Pueblo Bonito series

    see

National geographic society, Washington, D.
C. Contributed technical papers.
Pueblo Bonito series.

National geographic society, Washington, D. C.

Griggs, Robert Fiske, 1881-
... 1. The recovery of vegetation at Kodiak, by Robert F. Griggs ... Columbus, 1918.

VOLUME 407

National Geographic Society, Washington, D.C.
  The reaches of New York City
    see under   National geographic magazine.

National geographic society, Washington, D.C.
  [Religious cults and customs] Geographical
  articles: articles classified and rebound from
  National geographic magazines. n. p., Classified
  geographic, inc., n.d.
    Illus. ([Serial no. 362, vol. no. 39])
    Contents: 1. Religions. 2. Classified geographic,
  inc. 3. Manners and customs.

NN   0052820   CaBVa

National Geographic Society, Washington, D. C.
  Research reports.
  Washington.
    v. illus., maps. 24 cm.
    "Abstracts and reviews of research and exploration authorized
  under grants from the National Geographic Society.

    1. Research—Societies, etc. 2. Science—Societies, etc.
    Q181.A1N254   68–26794

NN   0052821   DLC IU KyU

National geographic society, Washington, D.C.

Wyllie, Robert E   1873–
  ... The romance of military insignia; how the United States
  government recognizes deeds of heroism and devotion to duty
  ... by Col. Robert E. Wyllie ...
    (*In* The National geographic magazine. Washington, 1919. 24½ᶜᵐ.
  vol. XXXVI, no. 6 (Dec. 1919) p. [463,–526. illus. (part col.) incl. ports.))

National Geographic Society, *Washington, D. C.*
  The round earth on flat paper. Map projections used by
  cartographers, by Wellman Chamberlin, with drawings by
  Charles E. Riddiford. Map services of the National Geographic Society, by Gilbert Grosvenor. 107 illus. from photos. and
  drawings; 18 pages of maps from the National geographic
  magazine. Washington [1947]
    126 p. illus., ports., maps. 26 cm.
    1. Map-projection. 2. Cartography.   I. Chamberlin, Wellman.
  II. Grosvenor, Gilbert Hovey, 1875–   III. Title.
    GA110.N3   526.98   47–6708*

        TxU CaBVaU
NN   0052823   DLC OClU OClW LU NNBG RPJCB DI IdP

National Geographic Society, *Washington, D. C.*
  The round earth on flat paper. Map projections used by
  cartographers, by Wellman Chamberlin, with drawings by
  Charles E. Riddiford. Map services of the National Geographic Society, by Gilbert Grosvenor. 109 illus. from photographs and drawings; 16 pages of maps from the National
  geographic magazine. Washington [1950]
    126 p. illus., ports., maps. 26 cm.
    1. Map-projection. 2. Cartography.   I. Chamberlin, Wellman.
  II. Grosvenor, Gilbert Hovey, 1875–   III. Title.
    GA110.N3 1950   526.98   50–14357

NN   0052824   DLC CoU CU MH NBuU MiU IdU MtU

National geographic society, Washington, D.C.
  Scandinavia; articles from the National geographic
  magazine ...
    see under   National geographic magazine.

National geographic society. Washington, D.C.,
  pub.   FOR OTHER EDITIONS
           SEE MAIN ENTRY
  Grosvenor, Gilbert Hovey, 1875–   ed.
    Scenes from every land, picturing the people, natural phe-
  nomena and animal life of all parts of the world. Third series. Ed. by Gilbert H. Grosvenor ... Washington, D. C.,
  National geographic society [°1912]

National geographical society, Washington, D. C.

The Ziegler polar expedition, 1903–1905.
  ... Scientific results obtained under the direction of William
  J. Peters, representative of the National geographic society in
  charge of scientific work, ed. by John A. Fleming. Pub. under
  the auspices of the National geographic society by the estate
  of William Ziegler. Washington, D. C. [Press of Judd &
  Detweiler] 1907.

National geographic society, *Washington, D. C.*
  ... Scientific results of the Katmai expeditions of the National geographic society. I–x. By Robert F. Griggs, J. W.
  Shipley, Jasper D. Sayre, Paul R. Hagelbarger and James S.
  Hine ... [Columbus] The Ohio state university, 1920.
    [230] p. incl. illus., maps, diagrs. pl. 25 cm. (The Ohio state uni-
  versity bulletin. vol. XXIV, no. 15. Contributions in geographical
  exploration, no. 1)
    Various pagings.
    Reprinted from the Ohio Journal of science, vol. XIX.
                      CONTENTS.
    I. The recovery of vegetation at Kodiak, by Robert F. Griggs.—II.
  Are the Ten thousand smokes real volcanoes? By Robert F. Griggs.—
  III. The great hot mud flow of the Valley of ten thousand smokes, by
  Robert Griggs.

    IV. The character of the eruption as indicated by its effects on nearby
  vegetation, by Robert F. Griggs.—V. The nitrogen content of volcanic
  ash in the Katmai eruption of 1912, by J. W. Shipley.—VI. The water
  soluble content, the ferrous iron content and the acidity of Katmai volcanic ash, by J. W. Shipley.—VII. Ammonia and nitrous nitrogen in the
  rainwater of southwestern Alaska, by J. W. Shipley.—VIII. A study of
  temperatures in the Valley of ten thousand smokes, by Jasper D. Sayre
  and Paul R. Hagelbarger.—IX. The beginnings of revegetation in
  Katmai valley, by Robert R. Griggs.—X. Birds of the Katmai region,
  by James S. Hine.

    1. Katmai, Mount.   2. Valley of ten thousand smokes.   I. Griggs,
  Robert Fiske, 1881–   Jasper Dean, 1893–   II. Shipley, John Wesley, 1878–   III. Sayre,
  Stewart, 1866–1930.   IV. Hagelbarger, Paul Rarey.   V. Hine, James

    Q115.K3   A 21—295
  Ohio State Univ. Libr.
  for Library of Congress   [a55k1]

NN   0052830   OU MiU ViU ICJ MtU OrU CU DLC OO

National geographic society, Washington, D. C.
  Seafaring; articles from the National geographic
  magazine
    see under   National geographic magazine.

National geographic society, Washington, D. C.
  Societies and cults; articles from the National
  geographic magazine
    see under   National geographic magazine.

National Geographical Society, Washington, D. C.
  Solar eclipse series
    see its   Contributed technical papers. Solar
  eclipse series.

National geographic society, Washington, D. C.
  South America; articles from the National
  geographic magazine
    see under   National geographic magazine.

National geographic society, Washington, D. C.
  Southeast Asia; articles from the National
  geographic magazine.
    see under   National geographic magazine.

National geographic society, Washington, D. C.
  Southern Africa; articles from the National
  geographic magazine
    see under   National geographic magazine.

National geographic society, Washington, D. C.
  Southern states; articles from the National
  geographic magazine
    see under   National geographic magazine.

Map
G
9800   National Geographic Society, Washington,
1899   D.C.
N3   South polar regions showing routes
          of the proposed Antarctic expeditions.
          [Washington] 1899.
            map 25 x 22cm.

            Scale 110 miles to the inch.

            1. Antarctic regions—Maps.

NN   0052838   NIC

National geographic society, Washington, D. C.
  Southwest Asia; articles from the National
  geographic magazine
    see under   National geographic magazine.

[National geographic society, Washington, D. C.]
  Souvenir record of testimonial dinner given in honor
  of the Ambassador of France and Madame Jules Jean
  Jusserand by the people of the city of Washington, Janu-
  ary ten, nineteen twenty-five ... [Washington, Press of
  Judd & Detweiler, inc., 1925]
    72 p. incl. front., illus. (facsim.) 2 port. on 1 pl., col. coat of arms. 25½ᶜᵐ.
    Dinner given by the National geographic society.

    1. Jusserand, Jean Adrien Antoine Jules, 1855–   I. Title.

    Library of Congress   DC373.J8N3   26–4849

NN   0052840   DLC ViU DI

National geographic society, Washington, D. C.
  Spain and Portugal; articles from the National
  geographic magazine
    see under   National geographic magazine.

QL681
.A62   National Geographic Society, Washington, D. C.

  Allen, Arthur Augustus, 1885–
    Stalking birds with color camera; a presentation of 331
  illus. in natural color from Kodachrome and Ektachrome
  photos., showing 266 species of North American birds. Of
  these color illus., 264 are by the author. Freezing the flight
  of hummingbirds, by H. E. Edgerton, R. J. Niedrach, and
  W. Van Riper. Supplementary color illus. contributed by
  Alfred M. Bailey, and others. Edited by Gilbert Grosvenor.
  Washington, National Geographic Society [1951]

National Geographic Society, Washington, D. C.
  The story of the map
    see under   National geographic magazine.

National Geographical Society, Washington, D. C.
  Stratosphere series
    see its   Contributed technical papers.
  Stratosphere series.

National geographic society, *Washington, D. C.*
  To the sixth International geographical congress, London, greeting from the National geographic society,
  United States of America. [Washington, D. C., Printed
  for the National geographic society by W. F. Roberts,
  1895]
    14 numb. l., 2 l. 35½ᶜᵐ.

    I. International geographical congress. 6th, London, 1895.

                                CA 17–829 Unrev'd

    Library of Congress   G56 1895 d

NN   0052845   DLC

VOLUME 407

National geographic society, Washington, D.C.
Mindeleff, Cosmos.
Topographic models. By Cosmos Mindeleff... ₁Washington, 1888₎

National geographic society, Washington, D. C.

U. S. *Nautical almanac office.*
... Total eclipse of the sun, October 1, 1940. Issued by the Nautical almanac office, United States Naval observatory, under the authority of the secretary of the navy. Washington, U. S. Govt. print. off., 1939.

National geographic society, Washington, D.C.
Travel and geography; articles from the National geographic magazine
    see under   National geographic magazine.

National Geographic Society.
    U.S.Army air corps. stratosphere flight of 1934 in the balloon Explorer. Washington, 1935.   (stratosphere series #1)

    Stratosphere flight of 1935 in the balloon Explorer 11.

NN   0052849   DN

Mp
K128
1923
National Geographic Society, **Washington,** D. C.
    United States of America.   **Washington** 1923.
    col. map 67 x 93cm.

    Scale 1:5,250,000 or 82.86 miles to the inch.
    Polyconic projection.
    Insets: showing several cities on varying scales.
    Supplement to April 1923 issue of National geographic magazine.

NN   0052850   NIC MB IU

National geographic society, Washington, D.C.
    United States of America
    see also under   National Geographic Society, Washington, D.C. Cartographic Division.

National geographic society, Washington, D. C.
Griggs, Robert Fiske, 1881–
    The Valley of Ten Thousand Smokes, by Robert F. Griggs, ph. d.; with 9 maps and 233 illustrations. Washington, The National geographic society, 1922.

National geographic society, Washington, D.C.
    Western states; articles from the National geographic magazine
    see under   National geographic magazine.

National geographic society, Washington, D.C.
    West Indies; articles from the National geographic magazine
    see under   National geographic magazine.

National geographic society, Washington, D.C.
FOR OTHER EDITIONS
SEE MAIN ENTRY
Nelson, Edward William, 1855–
    Wild animals of North America; intimate studies of big and little creatures of the mammal kingdom, by E. W. Nelson ... with illustrations from paintings by Louis Agassiz Fuertes and drawings of tracks by Ernest Thompson Seton. Washington, D. C., The National geographic society, 1930.

National geographic society, Washington, D.C.
    Wild life; articles from the National geographic magazine
        see under   National geographic magazine.

National geographic society, Washington, D.C.
    World flights; articles from the National geographic magazine
        see under   National geographic magazine.

National geographic society, Washington, D.C.
    World history; articles from the National geographic magazine
        see under   National geographic magazine.

G3200
1922
.M3
National Geographic Society, Washington, D. C.
Matthews-Northrup Company, *Buffalo, N. Y.*
    The world, prepared especially for the National geographic magazine, showing the political divisions, including those established after the World War. Washington, National Geographic Society, ᶜ1922.

Mp
A910
1951
National Geographic Society.
    The world map.   Washington, 1951.
    col. map 54 x 108cm.

    Scale 1:40,000,000, or 632 miles to the inch at the Equator.
    Supplement to December 1951 issue of National geographic magazine.

    1. World maps.

NN   0052860   NIC

National Geographic Society, *Washington, D. C. Cartographic Dept.*
    see
National Geographic Society, *Washington, D. C. Cartographic Division.*

National Geographic Society, *Washington, D. C. Cartographic Division.*
    Africa. Compiled and drawn in the Cartographic Section of the National Geographic Society; Albert H. Bumstead, chief cartographer. Washington, 1935.
    col. map 77 x 72 cm.

    Scale 1 : 11,721,600 or 185 miles to 1 inch.
    "Azimuthal equal-area projection (pole of projection at latitude 15° north, longitude 20° east)"
    Issued with the National geographic magazine, v. 67, no. 6, June 1935.
    Insets: Airways and relief.—Cape Verde Islands.

——— Index to the new map of Africa including adjacent portions of Europe and Asia. Washington, 1935.
    35 p. 26 cm.
                        G8200 1935.N3 Index

    1. Africa—Maps.   i. Bumstead, Albert Holt, 1875–1940.
    G8200 1935.N3   *Map 62–75*

NN   0052863   DLC MB CLSU

National Geographic Society, *Washington, D. C. Cartographic Division.*
    Africa. Compiled and drawn in the Cartographic Section of the National Geographic Society. James M. Darley, chief cartographer. 1st ed., June 1935; rev. Sept. 1942. Washington ₁1942₎
    col. map 77 x 72 cm.
    Scale 1 : 11,721,600 or 185 miles to 1 inch.
    "Azimuthal equal-area projection (pole of projection at latitude 15° north, longitude 20° east)"
    Insets: Airways and relief, scale 662 miles to 1 inch.—Cape Verde Islands.
    1. Africa—Maps.   i. Darley, James Morrison.

    G8200 1942.N3   Map 58–112 rev

NN   0052864   DLC

National Geographic Society, *Washington, D. C. Cartographic Division.*
    Africa. Compiled and drawn in the Cartographic Section of the National Geographic Society. James M. Darley, chief cartographer. Washington, 1943.
    col. map 77 x 72 cm.
    Scale 1 : 11,721,600 or 185 miles to 1 inch.
    "Azimuthal equal-area projection."
    "International boundaries as of Sept. 1, 1939."
    Issued with the National geographic magazine, v. 83, no. 2, Feb. 1943.
    Insets: Relief, scale 562 miles to 1 inch.—Airline distances in statute miles ₁table₎

——— Index. Washington, 1943.
    31 p. 26 cm.
                        G8200 1943.N3 Index

    1. Africa—Maps.   i. Darley, James Morrison.

    G8200 1943.N3   Map 48–1016 rev*

NN   0052866   DLC OCl KyU FU NIC OrU IU

National Geographic Society, *Washington, D. C. Cartographic Division.*
    Africa and the Arabian Peninsula. Compiled and drawn in the Cartographic Section of the National Geographic Society. James M. Darley, chief cartographer. Washington, 1950.
    col. map 76 x 69 cm.
    Scale 1 : 12,000,000 or 189.4 miles to the inch.
    "Chamberlin trimetric projection."
    Shows political administration and United Nations trusteeship.
    Issued with the National geographic magazine, v. 97, no. 3, Mar. 1950.
    Insets: Cape Verde Islands.—Physical map of Africa. ₁Scale 1 : 38,016,000 or 600 miles to 1 inch₎

——— Index. With 7,179 place names. Washington, 1950.
    34 p. 26 cm.
                        G8200 1950.N3 Index

    1. Africa—Maps.   i. Darley, James Morrison.

    G8200 1950.N3   Map 50–597 rev

NN   0052868   DLC ScCleU OCl OrU FU

National Geographic Society, *Washington, D. C. Cartographic Division.*
    Africa and the Arabian Peninsula. Compiled and drawn in the Cartographic Section of the National Geographic Society. James M. Darley, chief cartographer. Washington, 1950.
    col. map 122 x 111 cm.
    Scale 1 : 7,500,000 or 118.4 miles to the inch.
    "Chamberlin trimetric projection."
    Shows political administration and United Nations trusteeship.
    Enlarged from map issued with the National geographic magazine, v. 97, no. 3, Mar. 1950.
    Insets: Cape Verde Islands.—Physical map of Africa. Scale ₁1 : 23,760,000₎; 375 miles to 1 inch.
    1. Africa—Maps.   i. Darley, James Morrison.
    G8200 1950.N31   Map 53–1042 rev

NN   0052869   DLC NIC

Map
G
9800
1932
N3
National Geographic Society, Washington, D.C. Cartographic Division.
    The Antarctic regions.   Washington, D.C., 1932.
    col. map 48 x 65 cm.

    Scale 1:16,000,000.
    Insets: Byrd's South Pole flight; Antarctic archipelago; King Edward VII Land and part of Marie Byrd land.
    Azimuthal equidistant projection.

    1. Antarctic regions—Maps.

NN   0052870   NIC MB CLSU

VOLUME 407

M919.8 National Geographic Society, Washington, D.C.
N277a Cartographic Division.
 The Arctic regions. Prepared in the Map
Department of the National Geographic Society
for the National geographic magazine. Washington, D.C., c1925.
 col. map 47 x 49cm.

 Scale 1:14,673,400 or 231.6 miles to 1 inch.
 "Azimuthal equidistant projection - pole of projection at
North Pole."
 Issued with the National geographic magazine, v.48,no.5,Nov.
1925.

 Insets: Spitsbergen and Franz Josef Land.- Ellesmere Island
region.

 ✓1.Arctic regions - Maps.

 NN 0052872 CLSU NIC

M919.8 National Geographic Society, Washington, D.C.
N277a Cartographic Division.
1943 The Arctic regions. Prepared in the Map
Department of the National Geographic Society
for the National geographic magazine.
 ₍Washington, D.C.₎ 1943,c1925.
 col.map 47 x 49cm.

 "Reprinted 1943." Includes overprinted information on dis-
coveries subsequent to 1925.
 Scale 1:14,673,400 or 231.6 miles to 1 inch.
 "Azimuthal equidistant projection - pole of projection at
North Pole."

 Insets: Spitsbergen and Franz Josef Land.- Ellesmere Island
region.

 ✓1.Arctic regions - Maps

 NN 0052874 CLSU

National Geographic Society, *Washington, D. C. Carto-
graphic Division.*
 Asia and adjacent areas. Compiled and drawn in the
Cartographic Section of the National Geographic Society.
James M. Darley, chief cartographer. Washington, °1942.
 col. map 64 x 99 cm.
 Scale 1: 17,500,000 or 276.2 miles to the inch.
 "Transverse polyconic projection."
 "International boundaries as of Sept. 1, 1939."
 Issued with the National geographic magazine, v. 82, no. 6, Dec. 1942.
 —— Index. Washington, 1942.
 26 p. 26 cm.
 G7400 1942.N3 Index
 1. Asia—Maps. I. Darley, James Morrison.

 G7400 1942.N3 Map 45–244 rev 2*

 NN 0052875 DLC OrU WaS WaT IU FU NIC

National Geographic Society, *Washington, D. C. Carto-
graphic Division.*
 Asia and adjacent areas. Compiled and drawn in the
Cartographic Section of the National Geographic Society.
James M. Darley, chief cartographer. Washington, 1951.
 col. map 71 x 91 cm.
 Scale 1: 15,000,000 or 236.7 miles to the inch.
 "Two point equidistant projection, poles at 85° N.–40° E. and
35° N.–140° E."
 Issued with the National geographic magazine, v. 90, no. 3, Mar. 1951.
 Inset: ₍Northern Hemisphere₎ All distances are true to the Rus-
sian industrial center of Sverdlovsk.

 —— Index. With 7,646 place names. Washington,
1951.
 34 p. 26 cm.
 G7400 1951.N3 Index

 1. Asia—Maps. I. Darley, James Morrison.

 G7400 1951.N3 Map 51–611 rev

 NN 0052877 DLC OrU MtU NIC GAT NIC FU

G5671 National Geographic Society, Washington, D. C.
.A2 Cartographic Section.
1952
.U5 U. S. *Aeronautical Chart and Information Service.*
 Asia and adjacent areas. Index of World aeronautical
charts. ₍Washington₎ ACIS, 1952.

National Geographic Society, *Washington, D. C. Carto-
graphic Division.*
 Asia and adjacent regions. Compiled and drawn in the
Cartographic Section of the National Geographic Society.
Albert H. Bumstead, chief cartographer. Washington,
°1933.
 col. map 76 x 94 cm.
 Scale 1: 15,000,000, or 237 miles to 1 inch.
 "Azimuthal equidistant projection, pole of projection at 40° north
latitude, 90° east longitude."
 Issued with the National geographic magazine, v. 64, no. 6, Dec.
1933.

 —— Index to the new map of Asia, including Europe,
portions of Africa, and adjacent regions. Washington, 1934.
 30 p. 26 cm.
 G7400 1933.N3 Index

 1. Asia—Maps. I. Bumstead, Albert Holt, 1875–1940.

 G7400 1933.N3 Map 57–206 rev

 NN 0052880 DLC FU NIC NBuG MB

National Geography Society, *Washington, D. C. Carto-
graphic Division.*
 Atlantic Ocean. Compiled and drawn in the Cartographic
Studios of the National Geographic Society. Albert H.
Bumstead, chief cartographer. Washington, °1939.
 col. map 76 x 60 cm.
 Scale 1: 20,000,000 or 316 miles to 1 inch.
 "Stereographic (azimuthal-conformal) projection."
 Shows depth curves in meters, shipping routes and ocean currents;
includes historical notes. Shows also a large part of North America,
all of South America, most of Europe, and the western part of Africa.
 Issued with the National geographic magazine, v. 76, no. 1, July,
1939."
 Inset: Isthmus of Panama, scale 1: 2,000,000.
 1. Atlantic Ocean— Maps. I. Bumstead, Albert Holt,
1875–1940.

 G9100 1939.N3 Map 50–117 rev

 NN 0052881 DLC NIC FU WaPS NIC OrU CaBVa

National Geographic Society, *Washington, D. C. Cartographic Division.*
 Atlantic Ocean. Compiled and drawn in the Cartogra-
phic Section of the National Geographic Society. James M.
Darley, chief cartographer. Washington, 1941.
 col. map 76 x 60 cm.
 Scale 1: 20,000,000 or 316 miles to the inch.
 "Stereographic (azimuthal-conformal) projection."
 Shows depth curves in meters, shipping routes and ocean currents;
includes historical notes. Shows also a large part of North America,
all of South America, most of Europe and the western part of Africa.
 "International boundaries as of Sept. 1, 1939."
 Issued with the National geographic magazine, v. 80, no. 3, Septem-
ber, 1941.
 Inset: Isthmus of Panama, scale 1: 2,000,000.
 1. Atlantic Ocean— Maps. I. Darley, James Morrison.

 G9100 1941.N3 Map 56–364 rev

 NN 0052882 DLC MtU OrU NIC

National Geographic Society, *Washington, D. C. Carto-
graphic Division.*
 Atlantic Ocean. Compiled and drawn in the Cartographic
Section of the National Geographic Society. James M.
Darley, chief cartographer. Washington, °1955.
 col. map 97 x 68 cm.
 Scale 1: 20,000,000 or 316 miles to the inch at the Equator.
 "Mercator projection."
 Issued with the National geographic magazine, v. 108, no. 6, Dec.
1955.
 Shows ocean depth, prevailing winds, ocean currents, etc. Includes
descriptive and historical notes.

 Insets: Distances across the Atlantic ₍table₎—Submarine topography of the Atlantic.
 —— Index. With 4,238 place names. Washington,
1955.
 23 p. 26 cm.
 G9100 1955.N3 Index

 1. Atlantic Ocean—Maps. I. Darley, James Morrison.

 G9100 1955.N3 Map 56–287 rev 2

 NN 0052884 DLC OrU NIC OCl ScCleU FU

National Geographic Society, *Washington, D. C. Carto-
graphic Division.*
 Australia. Compiled and drawn in the Cartographic
Section of the National Geographic Society. James M. Dar-
ley, chief cartographer. Washington, 1948.
 col. map 60 x 76 cm.
 Scale 1: 6,000,000 or 94.7 miles to the inch.
 "Chamberlin trimetric projection."
 Issued with the National geographic magazine, v. 93, no. 3, Mar.
1948.
 Insets: Melbourne.—Sydney.—Tasmania.
 —— Index … Washington, 1948.
 20 p. 26 cm.
 G8960 1948.N3 Index
 1. Australia—Maps. I. Darley, James Morrison.

 G8960 1948.N3 Map 48–701 rev 2*

 NN 0052885 DLC NIC MtU OrU CaBVa

National Geographic Society, *Washington, D. C. Cartographic Division.*
 Bible lands and the cradle of western civilization. Compiled and drawn in the Cartographic Section of the National
Geographic Society. Albert H. Bumstead, chief cartographer. Washington, 1938.
 col. map 60 x 85 cm.
 Scale 1: 3,000,000 or 47.35 miles to 1 inch.
 "Conical projection (standard parallels 28° and 40°)"
 Includes numerous historical notes, covering events from earliest
times to the present.
 Insets: Jerusalem.—The Holy Land from Dan to Beersheba, scale
1: 1,000,000.—Comparative areas and latitudes of the Bible lands and

 the United States.—Economic development.—Route of the Exodus.—
St. Paul's travels and the Seven Churches.—The Crusades.—Alexander the Great.
 —— Index. With ₍3,166 place names and₎ a special
index to historical and biblical references. Washington,
1938.
 16 p. 26 cm.
 G7421.S1 1938.N3 Index.
 1. Near East—Historical geography—Maps. 2. Bible—Geography—Maps. 3. Near East—Maps. I. Bumstead, Albert Holt,
1875–1940. II. Title.

 G7421.S1 1938.N3 Map 54–1259 rev

 CaBVa
 NN 0052887 DLC WaPS FU OCl IdU MtU OrU OrMonO NIC

National Geographic Society, *Washington, D. C. Cartographic Division.*
 Bible lands and the cradle of western civilization. Compiled and drawn in the Cartographic Section of the National Geographic Society. Washington, 1946.
 col. map 53 x 80 cm.
 Scale 1: 4,000,000 or 63.13 miles to the inch.
 "Conic projection, standard parallels 28° and 40°."
 Includes numerous historical notes covering events from earliest
times to the present.
 Issued with the National geographic magazine, v. 90, no. 6, Dec.
1946.

 Insets: Holy Land today.—Holy Land in Biblical times from Dan
to Beersheba.—Jerusalem.—Traditional route of the Exodus.—St.
Paul's travels and the seven churches.—The Crusades.
 —— Index. Washington, 1946.
 18 p. 26 cm.
 G7421.S1 1946.N3 Index
 1. Near East—Historical geography—Maps. 2. Near East—Maps.
3. Bible—Geography—Maps. I. Title.

 G7421.S1 1946.N3 Map 48–1021 rev*

 NN 0052889 DLC OrU Or MtU FU NIC

National Geographic Society, *Washington, D. C. Carto-
graphic Division.*
 Bible lands and the cradle of western civilization. Com-
piled and drawn in the Cartographic Section of the Na-
tional Geographic Society. Washington, °1946.
 col. map 107 x 156 cm.
 Scale 1: 2,000,000 or 31.57 miles to the inch.
 "Conic projection, standard parallels 28° and 40°."
 Includes numerous historical notes covering events from earliest
times to the present.
 Enlarged from map on the scale of 1: 4,000,000 issued with the
National geographic magazine, v. 90, no. 6, Dec. 1946.

 Insets: Holy Land today.—Holy Land in Biblical times from Dan
to Beersheba.—Jerusalem.—Traditional route of the Exodus.—St.
Paul's travels and the seven churches—The crusades.

 1. Near East—Historical geography—Maps. 2. Near East—Maps.
3. Bible—Geography—Maps. I. Title.

 G7421.S1 1946.N31 Map 48–1020 rev*

 NN 0052891 DLC NIC

National Geographic Society, *Washington, D. C. Cartographic Division.*
 The British Isles: England, Scotland, Ireland and Wales,
officially known as the United Kingdom of Great Britain
and Northern Ireland, and the Republic of Ireland. Made
in the Map Division of the National Geographic Society.
James M. Darley, chief cartographer. Washington, 1949.
 col. map 81 x 66 cm.
 Scale 1: 1,786,752; 28.2 miles to an inch.
 Shows places of interest and historic sites.
 Illus., ports., and seals of cities in margins.

 Issued with the National geographic magazine, v. 95, no. 4, Apr.
1949.
 Includes "A list of the counties with their abbreviations."
 —— Index. With 4,063 place names. Washington,
1949.
 21 p. 26 cm.
 G5740 1949.N3 Index
 1. Gt. Brit.—Maps. 2. Ireland—Maps. I. Darley, James Morrison.

 G5740 1949.N3 Map 49–666 rev*

 NN 0052893 DLC OrU MtU IdU ScCleU NIC FU

VOLUME 407

National Geographic Society, *Washington, D. C. Cartographic Division.*
Canada. Compiled and drawn in the Cartographic Section of the National Geographic Society. Albert H. Bumstead, chief cartographer. Washington, °1936.

col. map 66 x 98 cm.
Scale 1 : 5,892,480 or 93 miles to 1 inch.
"Conical equal-area projection."
Relief indicated by altitude tints.
Issued with the National geographic magazine, v. 69, no. 6, June 1936.
Insets: Dominion of Canada, main natural resources, routes of explorers ¡and¡ time zones.—Precipitation and temperature.—Natural regions.

——— Index to the map of Canada including Newfoundland and portions of the United States and Alaska; more than 5600 place names. Washington, 1936.

23 p. 26 cm.
                                G3400 1936.N3 Index

1. Canada—Maps.   I. Bumstead, Albert Holt, 1875-1940.

G3400 1936.N3   **Map 50-119 rev**

NN 0052895   DLC CaBVa OrU FU NIC

National Geographic Society, *Washington, D. C. Cartographic Division.*
Canada, Alaska & Greenland. Compiled and drawn in the Cartographic Section of the National Geographic Society. James M. Darley, chief cartographer. Washington, 1947.

col. map 65 x 85 cm.
Scale 1 : 8,000,000 or 126.3 miles to the inch.
"Chamberlin trimetric projection."
Issued with the National geographic magazine, v. 91, no. 6, June 1947.
Insets: Aleutian Islands—¡Arctic Ocean¡

——— Index. Washington, 1947.

24 p. 26 cm.
                                G3400 1947.N3 Index

1. Canada—Maps. 2. Alaska—Maps. 3. Greenland—Maps.
I. Darley, James Morrison.

G3400 1947.N3   **Map 48-1015 rev°**

NN 0052897   DLC Mi FU NIC MtU OrU

National Geographic Society, *Washington, D. C. Cartographic Division.*
Central Europe and the Mediterranean as of August 28, 1939. Compiled and drawn in the Cartographic Section of the National Geographic Society. Albert H. Bumstead, chief cartographer. Washington, °1939.

col. map 65 x 90 cm.
Scale 1 : 5,000,000 or 78.91 miles to the inch.
"Conic projection with standard parallels at 34° and 53°."
Issued with the National geographic magazine, v. 76, no. 4, Oct. 1939.

1. Europe—Maps. 2. Mediterranean region—Maps. I. Bumstead, Albert Holt, 1875-1940.

G5700 1939.N29   **Map 55-1071 rev**

NN 0052898   DLC NIC

National Geographic Society, *Washington, D. C. Cartographic Division.*
Central Europe and the Mediterranean as of September 1, 1939. Compiled and drawn in the Cartographic Section of the National Geographic Society. Albert H. Bumstead, chief cartographer. Washington, °1939.

col. map 65 x 90 cm.
Scale 1 : 5,000,000 or 78.91 miles to the inch.
"Conic projection with standard parallels at 34° and 53°."
Issued with the National geographic magazine, v. 76, no. 4, Oct. 1939.

——— Index. Washington, 1939.

25 p. 26 cm.
                                G5700 1939.N3 Index

1. Europe—Maps.   2. Mediterranean region—Maps.
I. Bumstead, Albert Holt,   1875-1940.
G5700 1939 N3   **Map 45-213 rev 3°**

NN 0052899   DLC RPB IU MtU OrU CaBVa FU

National Geographic Society, *Washington, D. C. Cartographic Division.*
Central Europe, including the Balkan States. Compiled and drawn in the Cartographic Section of the National Geographic Society. James M. Darley, chief cartographer. Washington, 1951.

col. map 95 x 70 cm.
Scale 1 : 2,500,000 or 39.46 miles to the inch.
"Albers conical equal-area projection."
Shows occupation zones in Germany and Austria. "Russian and Polish boundaries according to treaties and claims as of July 1, 1951."
Issued with the National geographic magazine, v. 100, no. 3, Sept. 1951.

Continued in next column

Continued from preceding column

——— Index ... with 10,378 place names. Washington, 1951.

36 p. 26 cm.
                                G6030 1951.N3 Index

1. Central Europe—Maps. 2. Balkan Peninsula—Maps.
I. Darley, James Morrison. II. Title.

G6030 1951.N3   **Map 51-1546 rev**

NN 0052901   DLC MtU NIC

National Geographic Society, *Washington, D. C. Cartographic Division.*
China. Compiled and drawn in the Cartographic Section of the National Geographic Society. James M. Darley, chief cartographer. Washington, °1945.

col. map 84 x 91 cm.
Scale 1 : 7,000,000 or 110.5 miles to the inch.
"Albers conical equal-area projection."
"Elevations and depths in feet; boundaries as of September 1, 1939."
Issued with the National geographic magazine, v. 87, no. 6, June 1945.

——— Index ¡with 7,986 place names¡ Washington, 1945.

35 p. 26 cm.
                                G7810 1945.N3 Index

1. China—Maps.   I. Darley, James Morrison.

G7810 1945.N3   **Map 46-68 rev 2°**

NN 0052903   DLC IdU OrU KyU NIC FU ViU

National Geographic Society, *Washington, D. C. Cartographic Division.*
China coast and Korea. Compiled and drawn in the Cartographic Section of the National Geographic Society. James M. Darley, chief cartographer. Washington, 1953.

col. map 102 x 60 cm.
Scale 1 : 3,500,000 or 55.24 miles to the inch.
"Oblique Mercator projection."
Issued with the National geographic magazine, v. 104, no. 4, Oct. 1953.

——— Index. With 6,234 place names. Washington, 1953.

23 p. 26 cm.
                                G7800 1953.N3 Index
1. China—Maps.   2. Korea—Maps.   I. Darley, James Morrison.
G7800 1953.N3   **Map 53-1503 rev**

NN 0052904   DLC FU NIC OCl OrU

National Geographic Society, *Washington, D. C. Cartographic Division.*
Classical lands of the Mediterranean. Compiled and drawn in the Cartographic Section of the National Geographic Society. Albert H. Bumstead, chief cartographer. Washington, °1940.

col. map 64 x 87 cm.
Scale 1 : 2,217,600 or 35 miles to the inch.
"Conic projection with standard parallels at 37° and 45°."
Includes historical notes.
Issued with the National geographic magazine, v. 77, no. 3, Mar. 1940.

Insets: a. Roman Empire at the time of Trajan, its greatest extent, 98-117 A. D.—b. Ancient Athens.—c. Ancient Rome.—The world of Homer.
——— Index. With a special index to historical and mythological references. Washington, 1940.

16 p. 26 cm.
                                G6531.S2 1940.N3 Index
1. Mediterranean region—Historical geography—Maps. 2. Classical geography—Maps.   I. Bumstead, Albert Holt, 1875-1940.

G6531.S2 1940.N3   **Map 50-201 rev**

NN 0052906   DLC CaBVa MtU OrU OrMonO NIC FU

National Geographic Society, *Washington, D. C. Cartographic Division.*
Classical lands of the Mediterranean. Compiled and drawn in the Cartographic Section of the National Geographic Society. James M. Darley, chief cartographer. Washington, 1949.

col. map 53 x 78 cm.
Scale 1 : 2,750,000 or 43.4 miles to the inch.
"Conic projection, standard parallels 37° and 45°."
Includes numerous historical notes covering events of ancient times.
Issued with the National geographic magazine, v. 96, no. 6, Dec. 1949.

Continued in next column

Continued from preceding column

Insets: The world of Homer.—The world of Herodotus.—The world of Strabo.—Ancient Athens.—Ancient Rome.—The Greco-Roman world. Scale 1 : 20,000,000 or 316 miles to the inch.
——— Index. With 3,201 place names. Washington, 1950.

18 p. 26 cm.
                                G6531.S2 1949.N3 Index
1. Classical geography—Maps.   I. Darley, James Morrison.
II. Title.

G6531.S2 1949.N3   *Map 50-202 rev.*

NN 0052908   DLC NIC ScCleU FU OCl OrU MtU

Map
G
4390
1922
N3

National Geographic Society, Washington, D.C. Cartographic Division.
The countries of the Caribbean including Mexico, Central America, the West Indies and the Panama Canal. Washington, 1922.
col. map 60 x 107 cm.

Scale 1: 5,500,000·
Insets: Porto Rico; Panama Canal.

1. Mexico—Maps. 2. Central America—Maps.

NN 0052909   NIC MB IU OCl ICN WaPS

National Geographic Society, *Washington, D. C. Cartographic Division.*
Countries of the Caribbean, including Mexico, Central America and the West Indies. Compiled and drawn in the Cartographic Section of the National Geographic Society. James M. Darley, chief cartographer. Washington, 1947.

col. map 80 x 101 cm.
Scale 1 : 6,000,000 or 94.7 miles to the inch.
"Transverse Mercator projection."
Issued with the National geographic magazine, v. 92, no. 4, Oct. 1947.
Includes 10 insets of various islands and one of the Canal Zone.

——— Index. Washington, 1947.

30 p. 26 cm.
                                G4390 1947.N3 Index

1. Caribbean area—Maps.   I. Darley, James Morrison. II. Title.

G4390 1947.N3   **Map 48-1018 rev°**

NN 0052911   DLC MtU OrU NIC

National Geographic Society, *Washington, D. C. Cartographic Division.*
Eastern South America: Brazil, Paraguay, Uruguay, and the Guianas. Compiled and drawn in the Cartographic Section of the National Geographic Society. James M. Darley, chief cartographer. Washington, 1955.

col. map 100 x 71 cm.
Scale 1 : 5,000,000 or 78.91 miles to the inch.
"Chamberlin trimetric projection."

Issued with the National geographic magazine, v. 107, no. 3, Mar. 1955.
Inset: Rio de Janeiro, scale 1 : 125,000 or 1.97 miles to the inch.
——— Index. With 5,847 place names. Washington, 1955.

30 p. 26 cm.
                                G5200 1955.N3 Index

1. South America—Maps.   I. Darley, James Morrison.

G5200 1955.N3   **Map 55-236 rev**

NN 0052913   DLC FU MtU OrU NIC CLSU

G
5700
1938
N27
Map

National Geographic Society, Washington, D. C. Cartographic Division.
Europe and the Mediterranean. Washington, 1938.
col. map 82x96 cm. fold. to 47x99 cm.

Scale 1:6,000,000 or 94.7 miles to 1 inch.
"Azimuthal equidistant projection."
"Albert H. Bumstead, chief cartographer. Culture by James M. Darley. Physiography by Charles E. Riddiford."
Inset: Air   ways and relief.

1. Europe - Maps. 2. Mediterranean region - Maps. I. Bumstead, Albert H.

NN 0052914   NIC KyU CLSU IU

VOLUME 407

National Geographic Society, *Washington, D. C. Cartographic Division.*
Europe and the Near East. Compiled and drawn in the Cartographic Section of the National Geographic Society. Executed by Albert H. Bumstead ₍and others₎ Washington, ᶜ1929.
col. map 83 x 96 cm.
Scale 1 : 6,000,000 or 94.7 miles to 1 inch.
"Azimuthal equidistant projection."
Issued with the National geographic magazine, v. 56, no. 6, Dec. 1929.
Inset: Airways.
———— Index. Washington ₍ᶜ1929₎
32 p. 26 cm.
1. Europe—Maps. 2. Airways—Europe—Maps.
ɪ. Bumstead, Albert Holt. 1875–1940.
G5700 1929 .N3   Map 30–10 rev 2*

NN   0052915   DLC NIC IU OrU IdU MB OO CU

National Geographic Society, *Washington, D. C. Cartographic Division.*
Europe and the Near East. Compiled and drawn in the Cartographic Section of the National Geographic Society. Washington, ᶜ1940.
col. map 83 x 96 cm.
Scale 1 : 6,000,000 or 94.7 miles to the inch.
"Azimuthal equidistant projection (pole of projection at latitude 50° north, longitude 22°30′ east)"
Inset: The Middle East.
———— Index. Washington, 1940.
30 p. 26 cm.
1. Europe—Maps. 2. Near East—Maps.   G5700 1940.N3 Index
G5700 1940.N3   Map 45–214 rev 2*

NN   0052916   DLC NIC FU DNAL OrU MtU CaBVa

National Geographic Society, *Washington, D. C. Cartographic Division.*
Europe and the Near East. Compiled and drawn in the Cartographic Section of the National Geographic Society. James M. Darley, chief cartographer. Washington, ᶜ1943.
col. map 83 x 96 cm.
Scale 1 : 6,000,000, or 94.7 miles to the inch.
"Azimuthal equidistant projection (pole of projection at latitude 50° north, longitude 20°30′ east)"
Issued with the National geographic magazine, v. 83, no. 6, June 1943.
Insets: ₍Table of₎ distances between European ports and other important world ports via shortest navigable routes.—The Middle East.

———— Index ₍with 9,133 place names₎ Washington, 1943.
30 p. 26 cm.   G5700 1943.N3 Index

1. Europe—Maps. 2. Near East—Maps.   ɪ. Darley, James Morrison.
G5700 1943.N3   Map 54–1098 rev

NN   0052918   DLC NIC

National Geographic Society, *Washington, D. C. Cartographic Division.*
Europe and the Near East. Compiled and drawn in the Cartographic Section of the National Geographic Society. James M. Darley, chief cartographer. Washington, 1949.
col. map 69 x 78 cm.
Scale 1 : 7,500,000 or 118.4 miles to the inch.
"Chamberlin trimetric projection."
"Russian and Polish boundaries according to treaties and claims as of April 1, 1949."
Shows "occupation zones in Germany and Austria, World War ɪɪ."
Issued with the National geographic magazine, v. 95, no. 6, June 1949.

Includes lists of "geographical equivalents" and abbreviations.
———— Index ... with 8,085 place names. Washington, 1949.
39 p. map. 26 cm.   G5700 1949.N3 Index

1. Europe—Maps. 2. Near East—Maps.   ɪ. Darley, James Morrison.
G5700 1949.N3   Map 49–701 rev*

NN   0052920   DLC OrU MtU IdU FU

National Geographic Society, *Washington, D. C. Cartographic Division.*
Europe and the Near East. Compiled and drawn in the Cartographic Section of the National Geographic Society. James M. Darley, chief cartographer. Washington, 1949.
col. map 116 x 130 cm.
Scale 1 : 4,500,000 or 71 miles to the inch.
"Chamberlin trimetric projection."
"Russian and Polish boundaries according to treaties and claims as of April 1, 1949."
Shows "occupation zones in Germany and Austria, World War ɪɪ."
Enlarged from map issued with the National geographic magazine, v. 95, no. 6, June 1949.
Includes lists of "geographical equivalents" and abbreviations.
1. Europe—Maps.   2. Near East—Maps.   ɪ. Darley, James Morrison.
G5700 1949.N31   Map 53–1141 rev

NN   0052921   DLC NIC

G5701
.A2
1952
.U5

National Geographic Society, Washington, D. C.
Cartographic *Division.* Europe and the Near East.

U. S. *Aeronautical Chart and Information Service.*
Europe and the Near East. Index to World aeronautical charts. ₍Washington₎ 1952.

D769
.A533
vol. 3,
pt. 4

National Geographic Society, Washington, D. C.
Cartographic Section. Europe and the Near East.

Pogue, Forrest C
The Supreme Command. Washington, Office of the Chief of Military History, Dept. of the Army, 1954.

National Geographic Society, *Washington, D. C. Cartographic Division.*
The Far East. Compiled and drawn in the Cartographic Section of the National Geographic Society. James M. Darley, chief cartographer. Washington, 1952.
col. map 99 x 71 cm.
Scale 1 : 7,500,000 or 118.4 miles to the inch.
"Transverse Mercator projection."
Issued with the National geographic magazine, v. 102, no. 3, Sept. 1952.
Inset: Korea. Scale 1 : 4,000,000.
———— Index. With 10,028 place names. Washington, 1952.
43 p. 26 cm.   G7800 1952.N3 Index.
1. East (Far East)—   Maps.   ɪ. Darley, James Morrison.
G7800 1952.N3   Map 52–1245 rev

NN   0052924   DLC NIC FU WaS OrU MtU

Map
G
3930
1930
N3

National Geographic Society, Washington, D.C. Cartographic *Division.* Florida. Washington, ᶜ1930.
col. map 29 x 31 cm.

Scale 1 : 2,700,000 or 42.61 miles to 1 inch.

1. Florida—Maps.

NN   0052925   NIC MB

National Geographic Society, *Washington, D. C. Cartographic Division.*
Germany and its approaches, with international boundaries as of September 1, 1939, the day Germany invaded Poland, and, in red, boundaries as of January 1, 1938, before Germany seized Austria and Czechoslovakia. Compiled and drawn in the Cartographic Section of the National Geographic Society. James M. Darley, chief cartographer. Washington, ᶜ1944.
col. map 64 x 82 cm.
Scale 1 : 2,000,000 ; 31.57 miles to the inch.
"Albers conical equal-area projection."

Issued with the National geographic magazine, v. 86, no. 1, July 1944.
———— Index. Washington, 1944.
31 p. 26 cm.   G6080 1944.N3 Index
1. Germany—Maps.   ɪ. Darley, James Morrison.

G6080 1944.N3   Map 45–7 rev 2

NN   0052927   DLC FU NIC KyU IU OrU CaBVa

National Geographic Society, *Washington, D. C. Cartographic Division.*
Germany and its approaches, with international boundaries as of September 1, 1939, the day Germany invaded Poland, and, in red, boundaries as of January 1, 1938, before Germany seized Austria and Czechoslovakia. Compiled and drawn in the Cartographic Section of the National Geographic Society. James M. Darley, chief cartographer. Washington, Army Map Service, 1946.
col. map 86 x 109 cm.
Scale 1 : 1,500,000 or 23.67 miles to the inch.

"Albers conical equal-area projection."
Enlarged from map on scale: 1 : 2,000,000 issued with the National geographic magazine, v. 86, no. 1, July 1944.

1. Germany—Maps.   ɪ. Darley, James Morrison. ɪɪ. U. S. Army Map Service.

G6080 1944.N3a   Map 48–975 rev*

NN   0052929   DLC

National Geographic Society, *Washington, D. C. Cartographic Division.*
The Great Lakes region of the United States and Canada. Compiled and drawn in the Cartographic Section of the National Geographic Society. James M. Darley, chief cartographer.
col. map 68 x 104 cm.
Scale 1 : 2,027,520 or 32 miles to the inch.
"Albers conical equal-area projection, standard parallels 33° and 48°."
Issued with the National geographic magazine, v. 104, no. 6, Dec. 1953.
Includes 4 insets.

———— Index. With 11,959 place names. Washington, 1953.
36 p. 26 cm.

G3312.G7 1953.N3 Index

1. Great Lakes region—Maps. 2. Northeastern States—Maps.
ɪ. Darley, James Morrison.

G3312.G7 1953.N3   Map 54–89 rev 2

NN   0052931   DLC OrU KyU ScCleU NIC OCl FU

National Geographic Society, *Washington, D. C. Cartographic Division.*
Historic and scenic reaches of the Nation's Capital. Done in the Map and Art Studios of the National Geographic Society. Designed by C. E. Riddiford. Washington, ᶜ1938.
col. map 65 x 77 cm.
Scale ca. 1 : 650,000.
Extends from Philadelphia to Norfolk, and west to the Allegheny Mountains.
Issued with the National geographic magazine, v. 74, no. 1, July 1938.
1. Middle States—Maps. 2. Middle States—Historical geography—Maps. ɪ. Riddiford, Charles E. ɪɪ. Title: Reaches of the Nation's Capital.
G3791.S1 1938.N3   Map 50–118 rev

NN   0052932   DLC OrMonO CaBVa OrU RPB NIC

National Geographic Society, *Washington, D. C. Cartographic Division.*
Historical map of the United States. Compiled and drawn in the Cartographic Section of the National Geographic Society. James M. Darley, chief cartographer. Washington, 1953.
col. map 65 x 102 cm.
Scale 1 : 5,000,000 or 78.91 miles to the inch.
Issued with the National geographic magazine, v. 103, no. 6, June 1953.
Insets: Growth of our country.—₍New England coastal area₎—₍Middle Atlantic coastal area₎

———— Index. With 3,508 place names. Washington, 1953.
27 p. 26 cm.   G3701.S1 1953.N3 Index

1. U. S.—Historical geography—Maps.   ɪ. Darley, James Morrison. ɪɪ. Title.
G3701.S1 1953.N3   Map 53–529 rev

NN   0052934   DLC OrU MtU ScCleU NIC FU OCl

G4100
1931
.N3

National Geographic Society, Washington, D.C.— Cartographic *Division.*
Illinois. Washington, ᶜ1931.
col. map 46x29 cm.

"Scale 1:1,500,000 or 23.67 miles to 1 inch."
Inset: Chicago and suburbs.

1. Illinois—1931.

NN   0052935   IU

National Geographic Society, Washington, D. C. Cartographic Division.
Illinois. [Map.]
= Washington. 1931. Size, 18 × 11¼ inches. Scale, 1:1,150,000, or, 33.67 miles to 1 inch.
Submap: Chicago.

D2814 — Illinois. Geog. Maps.

NN   0052936   MB

National geographic society, Washington, D.C. Cartographic **Division.**

Index to maps. Author, 1937– 45

NN   0052937   OrP

VOLUME 407

National Geographic Society, *Washington, D. C. Carto-graphic Division.*
India and Burma. Compiled and drawn in the Carto-graphic Section of the National Geographic Society. **James M. Darley,** chief cartographer. Washington, 1946.

col. map 61 x 73 cm.
Scale 1 : 6,000,000 or 94.7 miles to the inch.
"Albers conical equal-area projection."
Includes also Afghanistan, Tibet and border states, and Ceylon.
Issued with the National geographic magazine, v. 89, no. 4, Apr. 1946.
Insets: Bombay.—Calcutta.
On verso : Political subdivisions of India.

——— Index. Washington, 1946.
22 p. 26 cm.
G7650 1946.N3 Index

1. India—Maps. 2. Burma—Maps. 3. India—Administrative and political divisions—Maps. I. Darley, James Morrison.

G7650 1946.N3   Map 48–1022 rev*

NN 0052939   DLC CaBVa MiU OrU FU NIC

National Geographic Society, *Washington, D. C. Carto-graphic Division.*
Indian Ocean, including Australia, New Zealand and Malaysia. Compiled and drawn in the Cartographic Sec-tion of the National Geographic Society. **James M. Darley,** chief cartographer. Washington, °1941.

col. map 62 x 81 cm.
Scale 1 : 20,000,000 or 316 miles to 1 inch at the equator.
"Mercator projection."
Insets: Guam.—Suez canal.—Hong Kong.—Philippines.—New Zea-land.—Singapore.

1. Indian Ocean—Maps. I. Darley, James Morrison.

G9180 1941.N3   Map 45–215 rev 2*

NN 0052940   DLC OrU MtU OCl NIC FU

National Geographic Society, *Washington, D. C. Carto-graphic Division.*
Japan and adjacent regions of Asia and the Pacific Ocean. Compiled and drawn in the Cartographic Section of the Na-tional Geographic Society. James M. Darley, chief cartog-rapher. Washington, 1944.

col. map 85 x 65 cm.
Scale 1 : 8,000,000; 126 miles to the inch.
"Azimuthal equidistant projection centered on Tokyo."
Issued with the National geographic magazine, v. 85, no. 4, Apr. 1944.
Insets : Industrial centers of Japan (5 maps)—Marshall Islands.
——— Index. Washington, 1944.
21 p. 26 cm.
G7950 1944.N3 Index
1. Japan—Maps.   I. Darley, James Morrison.
G7950 1944.N3   Map 44–155 rev 2*

NN 0052941   DLC NIC FU ViU OCl OrU

National Geographic Society, *Washington, D. C. Carto-graphic Division.*
Japan and Korea. Compiled and drawn in the Carto-graphic Section of the National Geographic Society. **James M. Darley,** chief cartographer. Washington, 1945.

col. map 64 x 93 cm.
Scale 1 : 3,000,000 or 47.35 miles to the inch.
"Albers conical equal-area projection."
Includes glossary of geographical terms.
Issued with the National geographic magazine, v. 88, no. 6, Dec. 1945.
Insets: 1–2. Kuril Islands.—3. Pescadores.—4. Karafuto.—5–7. Ryukuyu Islands.—8. Formosa.—9. Tokyo.—10. Location of Japan in the Western Pacific.

——— Index. Washington, 1946.
33 p. 26 cm.
G7950 1945.N3 Index

1. Japan—Maps. 2. Korea—Maps. I. Darley, James Morrison.

G7950 1945.N3   Map 48–1017 rev*

NN 0052943   DLC MtU OrU CaBVa Mi NIC FU

National Geographic Society, *Washington, D. C. Carto-graphic Division.*
A map of California, with descriptive notes. Compiled and drawn in the Cartographic Section of the National Geo-graphic Society. James M. Darley, chief cartographer. Washington, 1954.

col. map 91 x 72 cm.
Scale 1 : 1,305,216; 20.6 miles to the inch.
"Oblique cylindrical projection."
Issued with the National geographic magazine, v. 105, no. 6, June 1954.

Continued in next column

Continued from preceding column

Insets: Los Angeles ₍1:380,160₎ — San Francisco Bay region ₍1:380,160₎—San Francisco ₍ca. 1:41,000₎—San Diego ₍1:190,080₎—Yosemite Valley, Yosemite National Park ₍1:63,360₎
——— Index. With 4,186 place names. Washington, 1954.
G4360 1954.N3 Index

1. California—Maps. 2. California—Historical geography—Maps. I. Darley, James Morrison.

G4360 1954.N3   Map 54–671 rev

NN 0052945   DLC NIC OCl CLSU CU FU

National Geographic Society, *Washington, D. C. Carto-graphic Division.*
A map of New England, with descriptive notes. Com-piled and drawn in the Cartographic Section of the National Geographic Society. James M. Darley, chief cartographer. Washington, 1955.

col. map 104 x 71 cm.
Scale 1 : 760,320 or 12 miles to the inch.
Oriented with north toward the upper left.
Issued with the National geographic magazine, v. 107, no. 6, June 1955.

Inset: Northern Maine, scale 1 : 1,013,760 or 16 miles to the inch.
——— Index. With 4,442 place names. Washington, 1955.
26 p. 26 cm.
G3720 1955.N3 Index

1. New England—Maps. I. Darley, James Morrison.

G3720 1955.N3   Map 55–561 rev

NN 0052947   DLC OrU MtU NIC FU

National Geographic Society, *Washington, D. C. Carto-graphic Division.*
A map of Northwestern United States and neighboring Canadian Provinces. Compiled and drawn in the Carto-graphic Section of the National Geographic Society. James M. Darley, chief cartographer. Washington, 1941.
col. map 59 x 89 cm.
Scale 1 : 2,500,000.
Shows routes of exploration and includes numerous notes on his-torical and notable sites.
Issued with the National geographic magazine, v. 79, no. 6, June 1941.
1. Northwest, Pacific—Historical geography—Maps. 2. Northwest, Pacific—Maps. I. Darley, James Morrison.

G4241.S1 1941.N3   Map 48–970 rev*

NN 0052948   DLC FU IdU MtU OrU

Ayer
p133
N272   NATIONAL GEOGRAPHIC SOCIETY, Washington, D.C.
1931   Cartographic section.
             A map of the travels of George Washington.
             Washington,D.C.,National geographic society,c1931.
             map. 70x48cm.

               Scale: 1:2,500,000 or 39.5 miles to 1 inch.
               Insets: New York and the lower Hudson; Mount
             Vernon; Tidewater Virginia; Boston and vicinity;
             Philadelphia and vicinity.

NN 0052949   ICN MB MiU-C

           National Geographic Society, Washington,
             D.C. Cartographic Division.
CAD-h   Map of the western theatre of war. Prepared
1918   in the Map department of the National geographic
N3   society for the National geographic magazine
          A. H. Bumstead, cartographer   Washington,
          D.C., National geographic society, c1918.
          col.map. 66x79cm.
             "Scale 1:459,124, approximately 7¼ miles to 1
          inch."
             "Inset showing relation of the western theatre
          of war to the surrounding region and the connec-
          tion of the two sections of the main map."

NN 0052950   IU KyU

National Geographic Society, *Washington, D. C. Carto-graphic Division.*
A map of the world. Compiled and drawn in the Carto-graphic Section of the National Geographic Society. James M. Darley, chief cartographer. Washington, °1941.
col. map 52 x 105 cm.
Scale 1 : 35,000,000.
"Azimuthal equal-area projection ₍Western and Eastern. Hemi-spheres₎"
"International boundaries as of Sept. 1, 1939."
Issued with the National geographic magazine, v. 80, no. 6, Dec. 1941.
Insets: Land hemisphere.—World mapping.—Water hemisphere.—Density of population ₍Western and Eastern Hemispheres₎—Time zones.
1. World maps. I. Darley, James Morrison.
G3200 1941.N3   Map 56–365 rev

NN 0052951   DLC NIC MtU OrU

National Geographic Society, *Washington, D. C. Carto-graphic Division.*
Mexico and Central America. Compiled and drawn in the Cartographic Section of the National Geographic So-ciety. James M. Darley, chief cartographer. Washington, 1953.

col. map 66 x 91 cm.
Scale 1 : 3,500,000 or 55.24 miles to the inch.
"Albers conical equal-area projection, standard parallels 11°20′ and 28°40′."
Issued with the National geographic magazine, v. 103, no. 3, Mar. 1953.

Insets: Canal Zone.—Guadalupe Island.—Revilla Gigedo Islands.
——— Index. With 5,967 place names. Washington, 1953.
29 p. 26 cm.
G4390 1953.N3 Index

1. Mexico—Maps. 2. Central America—Maps. I. Darley, James Morrison.

G4390 1953.N3   Map 53–695 rev

NN 0052953   DLC MtU OrU IU NIC FU OCl

National Geographic Society, *Washington, D. C. Carto-graphic Division.*
Mexico, Central America, and the West Indies. Compiled and drawn in the Cartographic Section of the National Geographic Society. Albert H. Bumstead, chief cartog-rapher. Washington, °1934.
col. map 59 x 102 cm.
Scale 1 : 5,702,400 or 90 miles to 1 inch.
"Conformal conic projection; standard parallels 10° and 30°."
Issued with the National geographic magazine, v. 66, no. 6, Dec. 1934.
Insets: a. Puerto Rico and the Virgin Islands.—b. Bermuda Is-lands.—c. Isthmus of Panama.—d. Jamaica.—e. Cuba.

——— Index to the new map of Mexico, Central America, and the West Indies, including adjacent portions of the United States and South America. Washington, 1934.
22 p. 26 cm.
G4390 1934.N3 Index

1. Caribbean area—Maps. I. Bumstead, Albert Holt, 1875–1940.

G4390 1934.N3   Map 50–291 rev

NN 0052955   DLC CaBVa MtU OrU IU NIC FU

National Geographic Society, *Washington, D. C. Carto-graphic Division.*
Mexico, Central America, and the West Indies. Compiled and drawn in the Cartographic Section of the National Geographic Society. Albert H. Bumstead, chief cartog-rapher. Washington, °1939.
col. map 59 x 102 cm.
Scale 1 : 5,702,400 or 90 miles to 1 inch.
"Conformal conic projection; standard parallels 10° and 30°."
Includes historical notes.
Issued with the National geographic magazine, v. 76, no. 6, Dec. 1939.

Insets: a. Puerto Rico and the Virgin Islands.—b. Saint Thomas.—c. Isthmus of Panama.—d. Jamaica.—e. Cuba.—f. Bermuda Islands.
——— Index to the new map of Mexico, Central America, and the West Indies, including adjacent portions of the United States and South America. ₍5,602 place names₎ Washing-ton, 1939.
23 p. 26 cm.
1. Caribbean area—Maps. I. Bumstead, Albert Holt, 1875–1940.

G4390 1939.N3   Map 50–293 rev

CaBVa
NN 0052957   DLC CSmH TxU NIC FU RPB DNAL MtU OrU

National Geographic Society, *Washington, D. C. Carto-graphic Division.*
Mexico, Central America, and the West Indies. Compiled and drawn in the Cartographic Section of the National Geographic Society. Albert H. Bumstead, chief cartog-rapher. Rev. Nov. 1942. Washington ₍1942₎
col. map 50 x 102 cm.
Scale 1 : 5,702,400 or 90 miles to 1 inch.
"Conformal conic projection; standard parallels 10° and 30°."
Includes historical notes.

Originally issued with the National geographic magazine, v. 76, no. 6, Dec. 1939.
An index to place names was issued to accompany the 1939 edition.
Insets: a. Puerto Rico and the Virgin Islands.—b. Saint Thomas.—c. Isthmus of Panama.—d. Jamaica.—e. Cuba.—f. Bermuda Islands.

1. Caribbean area—Maps. I. Bumstead, Albert Holt, 1879–1940.

G4390 1942.N3   Map 50–294 rev

NN 0052959   DLC IdU

VOLUME 407

National Geographic Society, *Washington, D. O. Cartographic Division.*
A modern pilgrim's map of the British Isles, or more precisely, the Kingdom of Great Britain and Northern Ireland and the Irish Free State. Designed by C. E. Riddiford. Drawn in the Map and Art Studios of the National geographic magazine. Washington, °1937.
col. map 81 x 66 cm.
Scale 1 : 1,622,000.
Includes illustrated border with portraits.
Issued with the National geographic magazine, v. 71, no. 6, June 1937.
1. Gt. Brit.—Maps. 2. Ireland—Maps. I. Riddiford, Charles E.

G5740 1937.N3   Map 50–114 rev

NN   0052960   DLC FU KyU NIC OrU IU

National Geographic Society, *Washington, D. O. Cartographic Division.*
North America. Washington, °1924.
col. map 94 x 69 cm.
Scale 1 : 10,000,000 or 157.82 miles to one inch.
"Azimuthal equidistant projection, pole of projection : latitude 45° longitude 100°."
Issued with the National geographic magazine, v. 45, no. 5, May 1924.
Insets : The Aleutian Islands.—Eastern part of the West Indies.
1. North America—Maps.

G3300 1924.N3

NN   0052961   DLC KyU NIC

National Geographic Society, *Washington, D. O. Cartographic Division.*
North America. Compiled and drawn in the Cartographic Section of the National Geographic Society. James M. Darley, chief cartographer. Washington, °1942.
col. map 81 x 65 cm.
Scale 1 : 12,000,000, or 189.4 miles to the inch.
"Azimuthal equidistant projection, pole of projection latitude 45° longitude 92° 30'."
Issued with the National geographic magazine, v. 81, no. 5, May 1942.
Inset : Aleutian Islands.
——— Index. Washington, 1942.
19 p. 26 cm.
                                   G3300 1942.N3 Index
1. North America—   Maps. I. Darley, James Morrison.
G3300 1942.N3   Map 46–95 rev 2°

NN   0052962   DLC FU NIC MtU OCl CaBVa OrU

National Geographic Society, *Washington, D. O. Cartographic Division.*
North America. Compiled and drawn in the Cartographic Section of the National Geographic Society. James M. Darley, chief cartographer. Washington, 1952.
col. map 86 x 68 cm.
Scale 1 : 11,000,000 or 173.6 miles to the inch.
"Chamberlin trimetric projection."
Issued with the National geographic magazine, v. 101, no. 3, Mar. 1952.
Insets: Bering Sea and the Aleutian Islands—Diomede Islands.
——— Index ... with 5,204 place names. Washington, 1952.
21 p. 26 cm.
                                   G3300 1952.N3 Index
1. North America—   Maps. I. Darley, James Morrison.
G3300 1952.N3   Map 52–466 rev

NN   0052963   DLC NIC DPU MtU

National Geographic Society, *Washington, D. O. Cartographic Division.*
North Central United States. Compiled and drawn in the Cartographic Section of the National Geographic Society. James M. Darley, chief cartographer. Washington, 1948.
col. map 64 x 67 cm.
Scale 1 : 2,500,000 or 39.46 miles to the inch.
"Albers conical equal-area projection, standard parallels 38° 30' and 47° 30'."
Issued with the National geographic magazine, v. 93, no. 6, June 1948.
——— Index. Washington, 1948.
27 p. 26 cm.
                                   G4060 1948.N3 Index
1. Northwestern States—Maps.   I. Darley, James Morrison.
II. Title.
G4060 1948.N3   Map 48–954 rev°

NN   0052965   DLC OCl MtU OrU NIC FU MiU

National Geographic Society, *Washington, D. O. Cartographic Division.*
Northeastern United States. Compiled and drawn in the Cartographic Section of the National Geographic Society. James M. Darley, chief cartographer. Washington, °1945.
col. map 64 x 101 cm.
Scale 1 : 1,750,000 or 27.6 miles to the inch.
"Albers conical equal-area projection."
Issued with the National geographic magazine, v. 88, no. 3, Sept. 1945.
Inset : ₍Eastern Massachusetts, eastern Connecticut and Rhode Island₎

——— Index. Washington, 1945.
32 p. 26 cm.
                                   G3710 1945.N3 Index

1. Northeastern States—Maps.   I. Darley, James Morrison.
II. Title.

G3710 1945.N3   Map 46–358 rev 2°

NN   0052967   DLC OrU MtU CaBVa NIC FU

National Geographic Society, *Washington, D. O. Cartographic Division.*
Northern Africa. Compiled and drawn in the Cartographic Section of the National Geographic Society. James M. Darley, chief cartographer. Washington, 1954.
col. map 71 x 101 cm.
Scale 1 : 7,500,000 or 118.4 miles to the inch.
"Oblique Mercator projection."
Shows all of Africa north of the Equator.
Issued with the National geographic magazine, v. 106, no. 6, Dec. 1954.

Insets (a, b, and d, scale 1 : 2,500,000) : a. Eastern Mediterranean, Dead Sea to Damascus.—b. Eastern Mediterranean, Damascus to Antioch.—c. The Great Rift Valley.—d. Nile Delta and the Suez Canal.
——— Index, with 9,019 place names. Washington, 1954.
36 p. 26 cm.
                                   G8200 1954.N3 Index
1. Africa—Maps.   I. Darley, James Morrison. II. Title.
G8200 1954.N3   Map 55–156 rev

NN   0052969   DLC OrU FU NIC ScCleU

National Geographic Society, *Washington, D. O. Cartographic Division.*
Northern and Southern Hemispheres. Compiled and drawn in the Cartographic Section of the National Geographic Society. James Darley, chief cartographer. Washington, °1943.
col. map 52 x 103 cm.
Scale 1 : 40,000,000; 632 miles to the inch along the meridians.
"Azimuthal equidistant projections."
Issued with the National geographic magazine, v. 83, no. 4, Apr. 1943.
Insets: World terrain.—Time zones.—Airline distances ₍4 tables₎
——— Index ₍with 4,262 place names₎ Washington, 1943.
19 p. 26 cm.
                                   G3200 1943.N3 Index

1. World maps.   I. Darley, James Morrison.

G3200 1943.N3   Map 50–340 rev

NN   0052971   DLC IU KyU NIC FU OrU

National Geographic Society, *Washington, D. O. Cartographic Division.*
Northern and Southern Hemispheres. Compiled and drawn in the Cartographic Section of the National Geographic Society. James Darley, chief cartographer. Washington ₍1944, °1943.
col. map 83 x 163 cm.
Scale 1 : 25,000,000; 395 miles to the inch along the meridians.
"Azimuthal equidistant projection."
Enlarged from map issued with the National geographic magazine, v. 83, no. 4, Apr. 1943.
Insets: World terrain.—Time zones.—Airline distances ₍4 tables₎
1. World maps.   I. Darley, James Morrison.

G3200 1943.N3a   Map 50–339 rev

NN   0052972   DLC

National Geographic Society, *Washington, D. O. Cartographic Division.*
Northern Europe. Compiled and drawn in the Cartographic Section of the National Geographic Society. James M. Darley, chief cartographer. Washington, 1954.
col. map 89 x 71 cm.
Scale 1 : 2,500,000 or 39.46 miles to the inch.
"Albers conical equal-area projection."
Shows occupation zones in Germany. "Russian and Polish boundaries as of June 1, 1954 according to treaties and claims."
Issued with the National geographic magazine, v. 106, no. 2, Aug. 1954.
Includes 4 insets.

——— Index. With 9,155 place names. Washington, 1954.
36 p. 26 cm.
                                   G6905 1954.N3 Index

1. Europe, Northern—Maps.   I. Darley, James Morrison.
II. Title.

G6905 1954.N3   Map 54–1271 rev

NN   0052974   DLC FU OrU MtU GAT NIC

National Geographic Society, *Washington, D. O. Cartographic Division.*
Northern Hemisphere. Drawn in the Map Department of the National Geographic Society. Washington, 1946.
col. map 53 x 52 cm.
Scale 1 : 40,000,000; scale true along the meridians, 632 miles to the inch.
"Azimuthal equidistant projection."
Includes "Airline distances" (4 tables)
Issued with the National geographic magazine, v. 89, no. 2, Feb. 1946.
1. Northern Hemisphere—Maps.

G3210 1946.N3   Map 48–1019 rev°

NN   0052975   DLC OrU NIC FU

G   **National Geographic Society, Washington,**
4240   **D. C. Cartographic Section.**
1941   Northwestern United States and neighboring
N27   Canadian provinces. Washington, c1941.
Map   col. map 59x89 cm.

         Scale 1:2,500,000 or 39.46 miles to the
       inch.
       James M. Darley, chief cartographer.
       Culture by Apphia E. Holdstock. Research

       by Wellman Chamberlin. Physiography by
       John J. Brehm. Issued with the National geographic
       magazine, v. 80, no. 6, June 1941.

         l. Northwes   t, Pacific - Maps.
       I. Darley, Jam   es Morrison.

NN   0052977   NIC

National Geographic Society, *Washington, D. O. Cartographic Division.*
Northwestern United States and neighboring Canadian Provinces. Compiled and drawn in the Cartographic Section of the National Geographic Society. James M. Darley, chief cartographer. Washington, 1950.
col. map 61 x 89 cm.
Scale 1 : 2,500,000 or 39.46 miles to the inch.
"Albers conical equal-area projection, standard parallels 43° and 51°30'."
Issued with the National geographic magazine, v. 97, no. 6, June 1950.
Inset : Puget Sound region. Scale 1 : 1,000,000 or 15.8 miles to the inch.
——— Index. With 7,317 place names. Washington, °1950.
24 p. 26 cm.
                                   G4240 1950.N3 Index
1. Northwest, Pacific—Maps.   I. Darley, James Morrison.

G4240 1950.N3   Map 50–770 rev

NN   0052979   DLC OrU IU NIC

National Geographic Society, *Washington, D. O. Cartographic Division.*
Pacific Ocean. Compiled and drawn in the Cartographic Section of the National Geographic Society. Albert H. Bumstead, chief cartographer. Washington, °1936.
col. map 77 x 96 cm.
Scale 1 : 35,000,000 or 552.4 miles to 1 inch at the Equator.
"Mercator projection."
Shows depth curves and main shipping routes.
Issued with the National geographic magazine, v. 70, no. 6, Dec. 1936.
Includes 73 insets.

Continued in next column

VOLUME 407

Continued from preceding column

—————— Another issue.
Includes table, "Airline distances in statute miles."
G9230 1936.N3a

—————— Index to the map of the Pacific, with 73 insets showing in detail archipelagoes and islands. Washington, 1937.
24 p. 26 cm.
G9230 1936.N3 Index
1. Pacific Ocean—Maps. 2. Islands of the Pacific—Maps.
I. Bumstead, Albert Holt, 1875–1940.

G9230 1936.N3   Map 50–116 rev

NN 0052981   DLC FU NIC WaSp IU RPB CaBVa OrU OCl

National Geographic Society, *Washington, D. C.* Carto-
graphic Division.
Pacific Ocean. Compiled and drawn in the Cartographic
Section of the National Geographic Society. James M. Dar-
ley, chief cartographer. Washington, 1952.
col. map 71 x 93 cm.
Scale 1 : 27,500,000 or 434 miles to the inch at the Equator.
"Mercator projection."
Issued with the National geographic magazine, v. 102, no. 6, Dec.
1952.
Includes 60 insets, on enlarged scales, of islands in the area.

—————— Index ... with 5,958 place names. **Washington,**
1952.
29 p. 26 cm.
G9230 1952.N3. Index.

1. Pacific Ocean—Maps. 2. Islands of the Pacific—Maps.
I. Darley, James Morrison.

G9230 1952.N3   Map 53–532 rev

NN 0052983   DLC ScCleU OrU MtU FU

National Geographic Society, *Washington, D. C.* Carto-
graphic Division.
Pacific Ocean and the Bay of Bengal. **Compiled and**
drawn in the Cartographic Section of the National Geo-
graphic Society. James M. Darley, **chief cartographer.**
Washington, °1943.
col. map 65 x 90 cm.
Scale 1 : 27,500,000, or 434 miles to the inch and the Equator.
"Mercator projection."
Shows depth curves and ocean currents.
"International boundaries as of September 1, 1939."
Issued with the National geographic magazine, v. 84, no. 3, Sept.
1943.
Includes 59 insets and table of distances.

—————— Index. Washington, 1943.
29 p. 26 cm.
G9230 1943.N3 Index

1. Pacific Ocean—Maps. I. Darley, James Morrison.

G9230 1943.N3   Map 56–328 rev

NN 0052985   DLC OrU WaS IU NIC FU

National geographic society, Washington, D. C. *Cartographic Div.*
Path of total eclipse of the sun, 1 Oct., 1940. Compiled and
drawn in the Cartographic section of the National geographic
society for the National geographic magazine. Washington,
D. C.: The National geographic soc., c1935–37.   2 maps in 1 v.
49cm.

Both maps "Africa" (74 x 80cm.) and "South America" (68 x 95cm.) have inset
map "Airways and relief."

1. Eclipses, Solar, 1940. 2. Aero-   nautics—Routes—Africa. 3. Aeronautics—Routes—South America.   I. National geographic magazine.
N. Y. P. L.   March 25, 1941

NN 0052986   NN

Map
G
8060
1945
N3
National Geographic Society, **Washington,**
D. C., Cartographic *Division*
The Philippines. Washington, 1945.
col. map 44 x 66 cm.

Scale 1:3,000,000 or 47,35 miles to the
inch.
* Insets: Lingayen Gulf; Location map of
the Philippines; Manila.
Supplement to the March 1945 issue of
the National geographic magazine.

NN 0052987   NIC

Mann
G
8060
1945
N27
Map
National Geographic Society, **Washington,**
D. C. Cartographic *Division*.
The Philippines. Washington, 1945.
col. map 64x42 cm.

Scale 1:3,000,000 or 47.35 miles to the
inch.
"Polyconic projection."
"James M. Darley, chief cartographer.
Compilation by Apphia E. Holdstock and
Donald G. Bc   uma. Relief by John J.
Brehm."

NN 0052988   NIC CLSU

National Geographic Society, *Washington, D. C.* Cartographic Division.
A pocket map of central Washington, District of Columbia. Made in the Map Division of the National Geographic
Society. James M. Darley, chief cartographer. Washington, 1948.
col. map 58 x 67 cm. fold. to 21 x 9 cm.
Scale 1 : 15,840 or 4 inches to the mile.
Issued with the National geographic magazine, v. 94, no. 3, Sept.
1948.
Index in margin.
On verso: A pocket map of suburban Washington, D. C., Maryland & Virginia (scale 1 : 63,360 or 1 inch to the mile).
2. Washington, D. C.—Maps. 2. Washington, D. C.—Suburbs and
environs—Maps. I. Darley, James Morrison.

G3850 1948.N3   Map 49–122 rev*

NN 0052989   DLC OrU KyU NIC

National Geographic Society, *Washington, D. C.* Carto-
graphic Division.
South America. Compiled and drawn in the Cartographic
Section of the National Geographic Society. Albert H.
Bumstead, chief cartographer. Washington, °1937.
col. map 92 x 65 cm.
Scale 1 : 8,500,000, or 134.2 miles to 1 inch.
"Equal-area polyconic projection."
Issued with the National geographic magazine, v. 72, no. 6, Dec. 1937.
Insets: Galapagos Islands.—Chief natural resources.—Airways and
relief.—Precipitation and temperature.

—————— Index. Washington, 1938.
23 p. 26 cm.   G5200 1937.N3 Index
1. South America—   Maps. I. Bumstead, Albert Holt,
1875–1940.
G5200 1937.N3   Map 45–219 rev 2*

NN 0052990   DLC FU NIC OCl OrU OrMonO CaBVa

National Geographic Society, *Washington, D. C.* Carto-
graphic Division.
South America. Compiled and drawn in the Cartographic
Section of the National Geographic Society. James M. Dar-
ley, chief cartographer. Washington, °1942.
col. map 92 x 65 cm.
Scale 1 : 8,500,000 or 134.2 miles to the inch.
"Equal-area polyconic projection."
Issued with the National geographic magazine, v. 82, no. 4, Oct. 1942.
Insets: Galapagos Islands.—Chief natural resources.—Airways and
relief.—Precipitation and temperature.—Air line distances [table]
—————— Index. Washington, 1942.
22 p. 26 cm.   G5200 1942.N3 Index
1. South America—   Maps. I. Darley, James Morrison.
G5200 1942.N3   Map 45–220 rev 2*

NN 0052991   DLC DAS NIC IU OrU

National Geographic Society, *Washington, D. C.* Carto-
graphic Division.
South America. Compiled and drawn in the Cartographic
Section of the National Geographic Society. James M.
Darley, chief cartographer. Washington, 1950.
col. map 97 x 68 cm.
Scale 1 : 8,000,000 or 126.3 miles to the inch.
"Chamberlin trimetric projection."
Issued with the National geographic magazine, v. 98, no. 4, Oct.
1950.

Insets: Easter Island.—Sala y Gómez.—Galapagos Islands.—Canal
Zone.—St. Peter and St. Paul Rocks.—Fernando de Noronha.—Trinidad. — Martin Vez. — Location of South America in the Western
World.—Physical map of South America. Scale [1 : 25,344,000 or, 400
miles to the inch.

—————— Index ... with 6,942 place names. Washington,
1950.
30 p. 26 cm.
1. South America—Maps. I. Darley, James Morrison.

G5200 1950.N3   Map 51–557 rev

NN 0052993   DLC OrU NIC NcU FU IU

National Geographic Society, *Washington, D. C.* Carto-
graphic Division.
South America. Compiled and drawn in the Carto-
graphic Section of the National Geographic Society. James
M. Darley, chief cartographer. Washington, 1950.
col. map 155 x 108 cm.
Scale 1 : 5,000,000 or 78.9 miles to the inch.
"Chamberlin trimetric projection."
Enlarged from map issued with the National geographic magazine,
v. 98, no. 4, Oct. 1950.
Insets: Easter Island. — Sala y Gómez. — Galapagos Islands.—
Canal Zone.—St. Peter and St. Paul Rocks.—Fernando de Noronha.—
Trinidad.—Martin Vaz.—Location of South America in the Western
World.—Physical map of South America. Scale 1 : 15,840,000, 250
miles to the inch.
1. South America   Maps. I. Darley, James Morrison.
G5200 1950.N31   Map 53–1040 rev

NN 0052994   DLC NIC

National Geographic Society, *Washington, D. C.* Cartographic Division.
South Central United States. Compiled and drawn in the
Cartographic Section of the National Geographic Society.
James M. Darley, chief cartographer. **Washington, 1947.**
col. map 57 x 71 cm.
Scale 1 : 2,500,000 or 39.46 miles to the inch, standard parallels 28° and
36°."
Issued with the National geographic magazine, v. 92, no. 6, Dec.
1947.
—————— Index. Washington, 1947.
21 p. 26 cm.   G3990 1947.N3 Index
1. Southwest, Old—   Maps. I. Darley, James Morrison.
II. Title.
G3990 1947.N3   Map 48–958 rev*

NN 0052995   DLC NIC OrU MtU CaBVa

National Geographic Society, *Washington, D. C.* Carto-
graphic Division.
Southeast Asia. Compiled and drawn in the Cartographic
Section of the National Geographic Society. James M.
Darley, chief cartographer. Washington, 1955.
col. map 71 x 84 cm.
Scale 1 : 6,000,000 or 94.7 miles to the inch.
"Oblique Mercator projection."
"Depth curves and soundings in fathoms; elevations in feet." Gen-
eral relief indicated by shading.
Insets: a. Formosa and the Pescadores, scale 1 : 2,000,000.—b. Re-
lation of Australia and New Zealand to Southeast Asia.

Issued with the National geographic magazine, v. 108, no. 3, Sept.
1955.

—————— Index. With 5,944 place names. **Washington,**
1955.
27 p. 26 cm.   G8000 1955.N3 Index

1. Asia, Southeastern—Maps. I. Darley, James Morrison.

G8000 1955.N3   Map 55–775 rev

NN 0052997   DLC OCl MtU OrU ScCleU

National Geographic Society, *Washington, D. C.* Cartographic Division.
Southeast Asia and Pacific Islands from the Indies and
the Philippines to the Solomons. Compiled and drawn in
the Cartographic Section of the National Geographic Society. James M. Darley, chief cartographer. Washington,
°1944.
col. map 64 x 101 cm.
Scale 1 : 8,000,000 or 126 miles to the inch.
"Transverse Mercator projection."
Issued with the National geographic magazine, v. 86, no. 4, Oct. 1944.
Includes 22 insets.

—————— Index. Washington, 1944.
34 p. 26 cm.   G8000 1944.N3 Index

1. Asia, Southeastern—Maps. 2. Islands of the Pacific—Maps.
I. Darley, James Morrison. II. Title.

G8000 1944.N3   Map 45–222 rev 2*

NN 0052999   DLC CaBVa OrU IU OCl FU NIC

National Geographic Society, *Washington, D. C.* Carto-
graphic Division.
Southeastern United States. Compiled and drawn in the
Cartographic Section of the National Geographic Society.
Washington, 1947.
col. map 75 x 64 cm.
Scale 1 : 2,500,000 or 39.46 miles to the inch.
"Albers conical equal-area projection."
Issued with the National geographic magazine, v. 91, no. 2, Feb.
1947.
Insets (scale 1 : 1,250,000) : Littoral of Cape Hatteras and Nor-
folk.—The lower Mississippi.—South Carolina and Georgia coasts.
—————— Index. Washington, 1947.
22 p. 26 cm.   G3860 1947.N3 Index
1. Southern States—   Maps. I. Title.
G3860 1947.N3   Map 48–1024 rev*

OrU
NN 0053000   DLC ScCleU NIC KyU Mi FU CaBVa MtU

National Geographic Society, *Washington, D. C.* Carto-
graphic Division.
Southwest Asia, India, Pakistan, and northeast Africa.
Washington, 1952.
col. map 65 x 92 cm.
Scale 1 : 7,500,000 or 118.4 miles to the inch.
"Albers conical equal area projection."
Relief shown by hachures.
Issued with the National geographic magazine, v. 101, no. 6, June
1952.
Inset: The Moslem world.

—————— Index. With 7,790 place names. Washington,
1952.
82 p. 26 cm.
G7420 1952.N3 Index

1. Near East—Maps. 2. India—Maps. I. Darley, James Morrison. II. Title.

G7420 1952.N3   Map 55–240 rev

NN 0053002   DLC FU NIC DS OrU MtU ScCleU

VOLUME 407

National Geographic Society, *Washington, D. C. Cartographic Division.*
The southwestern United States. Executed in the Cartographic Section of the National geographic magazine. James M. Darley, chief cartographer. Washington, 1940.
col. map 63 x 87 cm.
Scale 1 : 2,500,000.
Shows routes of exploration, and includes numerous notes on historical and notable sites.
Issued with the National geographic magazine, v. 77, no. 6, June 1940.
1. Southwest, New—Historical geography—Maps. 2. Southwest, New—Maps. I. Darley, James Morrison.

G4301.S1 1940.N3 Map 48–967 rev*

NN 0053003 DLC NIC FU CaBVa MtU OrU

National Geographic Society, *Washington, D. C. Cartographic Division.*
Southwestern United States. Compiled and drawn in the Cartographic Section of the National Geographic Society. James M. Darley, chief cartographer. Washington, 1948.
col. map 56 x 84 cm.
Scale 1 : 2,500,000 or 39.46 miles to the inch.
"Albers conical equal-area projection, standard parallels 33° and
Issued with the National geographic magazine, v. 94, no. 6, Dec. 1948.
————— Index. ¡With 4,527 place names. Washington, 1948.
23 p. 26 cm. G4300 1948.N3 Index
1. Southwest, New—Maps. I. Darley, James Morrison.

G4300 1948.N3 Map 50–603 rev

NN 0053005 DLC OCl IU ScCleU FU NIC OrU MtU

National Geographic Society, *Washington, D. C. Cartographic Division.*
Sovereignty and mandate boundary lines in 1921 of the islands of the Pacific. Prepared in the Map Dept. of the National Geographic Society. Drawn by Albert H. Bumstead and James M. Darley. Washington, ©1921.
col. map 46 x 61 cm.
Scale 1 : 22,375,000.
"Sanson-Flamsteed equal area projection."
Issued with the National geographic magazine, v. 40, no. 6, Dec. 1921.
1. Islands of the Pacific—Maps. 2. Mandates — Islands of the Pacific—Maps. I. Bumstead, Albert Hoit, 1875–1940. II. Darley, James Morrison. III. Title.

G9231.F2 1921.N3 Map 54–175 rev

NN 0053006 DLC ODW NIC

National Geographic Society, *Washington, D. C. Cartographic Division.*
Theater of war in Europe, Africa and western Asia. Compiled and drawn in the Cartographic Section of the National Geographic Society. James M. Darley, chief cartographer. Washington, ©1942.
col. map 76 x 64 cm.
Scale 1 : 15,000 or 236.7 miles to the inch.
"Azimuthal equidistant projection, pole of projection latitude 40° longitude 20° E."
Relief shown by layer tints.
"International boundaries as of Sept. 1, 1939."
Issued with the National geographic magazine, v. 82, no. 1, July, 1942.
————— Index. Washington, 1942.
15 p. 26 cm. G5670 1942.N3 Index
1. Europe—Maps. 2. Africa—Maps. 3. Near East—Maps. I. Darley, James Morrison. II. Title.

G5670 1942.N3 Map 45–260 rev 2*

NN 0053008 DLC NIC OCl IU FU OrU CaBVa MtU

National Geographic Society, *Washington, D. C. Cartographic Division.*
Theater of war in the Pacific Ocean. Compiled and drawn in the Cartographic Section of the National Geographic Society. Washington, ©1942.
col. map 51 x 66 cm.
Scale 1 : 35,000,000, or 552.4 miles to 1 inch at the Equator.
"Mercator projection."
Issued also as main map of an issue of the society's map, "Pacific Ocean, ©1936."
Issued with the National geographic magazine, v. 81, no. 2, Feb. 1942.
————— Index. Washington, 1942.
11 p. 26 cm. G9230 1942.N3 Index
1. Pacific Ocean— Maps.
G9230 1942.N3 Map 54–174 rev

NN 0053009 DLC NIC OrU FU MtU

National Geographic Society, *Washington, D. C. Cartographic Division.*
The top of the world. Compiled and drawn in the Cartographic Section of the National Geographic Society. James M. Darley, chief cartographer. Washington, 1949.
col. map 72 x 69 cm.
Scale 1 : 14,000,000 or 221 miles to the inch.
"Azimuthal equidistant projection centered on the North Pole."
"Russian and Polish boundaries according to treaties and claims as of August 1, 1949."
Includes historical notes on polar exploration.
Issued with the National geographic magazine, v. 96, no. 4, Oct. 1949.
————— Index ... With 5,057 place names. Washington, 1949.
28 p. 26 cm.
G3270 1949.N3 Index
1. Arctic regions—Maps. 2. Northern Hemisphere—Maps. I. Darley, James Morrison. II. Title.

G3270 1949.N3

NN 0053011 DLC FU NIC IU KyU MtU OrU

National Geographic Society, *Washington, D. C. Cartographic Division.*
Union of Soviet Socialist Republics. Compiled and drawn in the Cartographic Section of the National Geographic Society. James M. Darley, chief cartographer. Washington, ©1944.
col. map 61 x 100 cm.
Scale 1 : 9,000,000 or 142 miles to the inch.
"Transverse polyconic projection."
"International boundaries according to Russian treaties and claims as of October 1, 1944; boundaries of January 1, 1938, are shown in red."
Issued with the National geographic magazine, v. 86, no. 6, Dec. 1944.
————— Index. Washington, 1945.
G7000 1944.N3 Index
42 p. 26 cm.
1. Russia—Maps. I. Darley, James Morrison.

G7000 1944.N3 Map 45–223 rev 2*

NN 0053013 DLC MiU OCl FU NIC ViU OrU WaT IU

G7001
.A2
1953
.U5

National Geographic Society, Washington, D. C.
Cartographic Section. Union of Soviet
Socialist Republics.
U. S. *Aeronautical Chart and Information Center, St. Louis.*
Index of World aeronautical charts and Soviet economic
regions. ¡St. Louis¡ 1953

Map
G
3700
1933
N3

National Geographic Society, Washington,
D.C. Cartographic Division.
The United States and adjoining portions
of Canada and Mexico. Washington, 1933.
col. map 66 x 101cm.

Scale 1:5,195,520 or 82 miles to 1 inch.

1. U.S.--Maps.

NN 0053015 NIC CLSU ICN RPB

National Geographic Society, *Washington, D. C. Cartographic Division.*
The United States and adjoining portions of Canada and Mexico. Compiled and drawn in the Cartographic Section of the National Geographic Society. Washington, 1940.
col. map 65 x 102 cm.
Scale 1 : 5,195,520 or 82 miles to the inch.
"Albers conical equal-area projection (standard parallels 29°30' and 45°30')"
Issued with the National geographic magazine, v. 78, no. 6, Dec. 1940.
Insets: Population of the States, sixteenth census, 1940.—National defenses.
————— Index ¡with 8,838 place names, incorporating results of the 1940 U. S. census¡ Washington, 1940.
31 p. 26 cm. G3700 1940.N3 Index
————— Another issue.
Inset: Army service command areas and naval districts.
G3700 1940.N3a
1. U. S.—Maps.
G3700 1940.N3 Map 54–1379 rev

NN 0053017 DLC FU NIC KyU MtU OrU WaT CaBVaU

National Geographic Society, *Washington, D. C. Cartographic Division.*
The United States of America. Compiled and drawn in the Cartographic Section of the National Geographic Society. James M. Darley, chief cartographer. Washington, 1946.
col. map 104 x 162 cm.
Scale 1 : 3,125,000 or 49.5 miles to the inch.
"Albers conical equal-area projection."
Enlarged from map on scale of 1 : 5,000,000 issued with the National geographic magazine, v. 90, no. 1, July 1946.
1. U. S.—Maps. I. Darley, James Morrison.

G3700 1946.N31 Map 48–994 rev*

NN 0053018 DLC NIC

National Geographic Society, *Washington, D. C. Cartographic Division.*
The United States of America. Compiled and drawn in the Cartographic Section of the National Geographic Society. James M. Darley, chief cartographer. Washington, 1946.
col. map 64 x 102 cm.
Scale 1 : 5,000,000 or 78.91 miles to the inch.
"Albers conical equal-area projection."
Issued with the National geographic magazine, v. 90, no. 1, July 1946.
Insets: United Nations area.—East of Maine.
————— Index. Washington, 1946.
35 p. 26 cm. G3700 1946.N3 Index
1. U. S.—Maps. I. Darley, James Morrison.
G3700 1946.N3 Map 48–977 rev

NN 0053019 DLC MtU NIC OrU

National Geographic Society, *Washington, D. C. Cartographic Division.*
The United States of America. Compiled and drawn in the Cartographic Section of the National Geographic Society. James M. Darley, chief cartographer. Washington, 1951.
col. map 65 x 102 cm.
Scale 1 : 5,000,000, or 78.91 miles to the inch.
"Albers conical equal-area projection."
Issued with the National geographic magazine, v. 99, no. 6, June 1951.
Insets: New York area.—East of Maine.
————— Index ... with 11,025 place names. Washington, 1951.
35 p. 26 cm. G3700 1951.N3 Index
1. U. S.—Maps. I. Darley, James Morrison.

G3700 1951.N3 Map 51–812 rev

NN 0053021 DLC NIC OrU MtU

National Geographic Society, *Washington, D. C. Cartographic Division.*
West Indies. Compiled and drawn in the Cartographic Section of the National Geographic Society. James M. Darley, chief cartographer. Washington, 1954.
col. map 71 x 92 cm.
Scale 1 : 3,500,000 or 55.24 miles to the inch.
"Transverse Mercator projection."
Issued with the National geographic magazine, v. 105, no. 3, Mar. 1954.
————— Index. With 4,957 place names. Washington, 1954.
26 p. illus. 26 cm. G4900 1954.N3 Index
1. West Indies—Maps. I. Darley, James Morrison.
G4900 1954.N3 Map 54–460 rev

NN 0053022 DLC FU NIC MtU OrU

National Geographic Society, *Washington, D. C. Cartographic Division.*
Western Europe. Compiled and drawn in the Cartographic Section of the National Geographic Society. James M. Darley, chief cartographer. Washington, 1950.
col. map 92 x 70 cm.
Scale 1 : 2,500,000 or 39.46 miles to the inch.
"Albers conical equal-area projection."
Shows occupation zones in Western Germany and Austria.
Issued with the National geographic magazine, v. 98, no. 6, Dec. 1950.
————— Index ... with 8,683 place names. Washington, 1950.
28 p. 26 cm. G5720 1950.N3 Index
1. Europe—Maps. I. Darley, James Morrison.
G5720 1950.N3 Map 51–560 rev

NN 0053023 DLC IU NIC OrU MtU

VOLUME 407

Map
G
3742
W4
1937
N3

National Geographic Society, Washington, D.C.
    The White Mountains of New Hampshire.
    Washington, 1937.
    col. map 41 x 48 cm.

    Scale 1 inch to 3 miles.
    Supplement to July 1937 issue of the
National geographic magazine.

    1. White Mountains, N.H.—Maps.

NN 0053024   NIC KyU

G3744
1937
.N3

National Geographic Society, Washington,
    D.C.   Cartographic Section.
    The White Mountains of New Hampshire.
    Washington, 1937.
    col. map 41x48cm.

    Scale ca. 1:190,080; 3 miles to the inch.
    Relief shown by shading.
    Issued with the National geographic magazine, v.72,
no.1, July, 1937.
    Inset map of New Hampshire shows area covered by
main map.

NN 0053025   CLSU

G3200
1922
.M3

National Geographic Society, Washington, D. C.
Matthews-Northrup Company, *Buffalo, N. Y.*
    The world, prepared especially for the National geo-
graphic magazine, showing the political divisions, including
those established after the World War. Washington, National Geographic Society, ᶜ1922.

National Geographic Society, *Washington, D. C. Cartographic Division.*
    The world. Washington, ᶜ1932.
    col. map 64 x 96 cm.

    "Equatorial scale 1 : 43,084,800; 1 inch=680 miles."
    "Van der Grinten projection."
    Issued with the National geographic magazine, v. 62, no. 6, Dec.
1932.
    Insets: The Arctic regions.—The Antarctic regions.—Natural vege-
tation and ocean currents.—Density of population, and prevailing
winds.

    1. World maps.

G3200 1932.N3

                                    Map 57–207 rev

NN 0053027   DLC OrU IU

National Geographic Society, *Washington, D. C. Cartographic Division.*
    The world. Compiled and drawn in the Cartographic
Section of the National Geographic Society. Albert H.
Bumstead, chief cartographer. Washington, 1935.
    col. map 56 x 109 cm.
    "Mean scale in center of each hemisphere 1 : 33,390,720; 527 miles
to 1 inch."
    "Projection ₍in hemispheres₎: Azimuthal equal-area."
    Issued with the National geographic magazine, v. 68, no. 6, Dec.
1935.
    Insets: The land hemisphere.—The water hemisphere.—Time zones
₍Western and Eastern Hemispheres₎
    1. World maps.   I. Bumstead, Albert Holt, 1875–1940.

G3200 1935.N3

                                    Map 57–208 rev

NN 0053028   DLC NIC Or OrU FU

National Geographic Society, *Washington, D. C. Cartographic Division.*
    The world map. Made in the Cartographic Department of
the National Geographic Society. James M. Darley, chief
cartographer. Washington, ᶜ1943.
    col. map 64 x 102 cm.

    Scale 1 : 40,000,000 or 632 miles to the inch at the Equator.
    "Van der Grinten's projection."
    Issued with the National geographic magazine, v. 84, no. 6, Dec. 1943.
    Insets: ₍Antarctica₎—₍Arctic Ocean₎—The First World War, 1914–
1918 ₍world map₎—The Second World War, 1939–? ₍world map₎

──────── Index. ₍With 4,874 place names₎ Washington,
1943.
    26 p. 26 cm.

                        G3200 1943.N31 Index

    1. World maps.   I. Darley, James Morrison.

G3200 1943.N31

                                    Map 45–221 rev 2*

NN 0053030   DLC OrU IU

National Geographic Society, *Washington, D. C. Cartographic Division.*
    The world map. Made in the Cartographic Section of the
National Geographic Society. James M. Darley, chief cartographer. Washington, ᶜ1943.
    col. map 104 x 163 cm.
    Scale 1 : 25,000,000 or 395 miles to the inch at the Equator.
    "Van der Grinten's projection."
    "International boundaries as of September 1, 1939."
    Enlarged from map on scale 1 : 40,000,000 issued with the National
geographic magazine. v. 84, no. 6, Dec. 1943.
    Insets: ₍Antarctica₎—₍Arctic Ocean₎—The First World War, 1914–
1918 ₍world map₎—The Second World War, 1939–? ₍world map₎
    1. World maps.   I. Darley, James Morrison.

G3200 1943.N31a

                                    Map 48–972 rev*

NN 0053031   DLC

National Geographic Society, *Washington, D. C. Carto-
graphic Division.*
    The world map. Compiled and drawn in the Cartographic
Section of the National Geographic Society. James M.
Darley, chief cartographer. Washington, 1951.
    col. map 64 x 102 cm.

    Scale 1 : 40,000,000 or 632 miles to the inch at the Equator.
    "Van der Grinten's projection."
    Issued with the National geographic magazine, v. 100, no. 6, Dec.
1951.

    Insets: ₍Portion of Southern Hemisphere₎—₍Portion of Northern
Hemisphere₎—The United Nations, inaugurated 26 June 1945 ₍world
map₎—International time zones ₍world map₎

──────── Index. With 5,488 place names. Washington,
1951.
    27 p. 26 cm.   G3200 1951.N3 Index

    1. World maps.   I. Darley, James Morrison.

G3200 1951.N3

                                    Map 52–167 rev

NN 0053033   DLC MtU OrU CLSU

National Geographic Society, *Washington, D. C. Cartographic Division.*
    The world map. Compiled and drawn in the Cartographic
Section of the National Geographic Society. James M. Darley, chief cartographer. Washington, 1951.
    col. map 104 x 163 cm.
    Scale 1 : 25,000,000 or 395 miles to the inch at the Equator.
    "Van der Grinten's projection."
    Enlarged from map issued with the National geographic magazine,
v. 100, no. 6, Dec. 1951.
    Insets: ₍Antarctica₎ — ₍Arctic regions₎ — The United Nations, in-
augurated 26 June 1945.—International time zones.
    1. World maps.   I. Darley, James Morrison.

G3200 1951.N31

                                    Map 53–866 rev

NN 0053034   DLC NIC

National Geographic Society, *Washington, D. C. Cartographic Section*
    see
National Geographic Society, *Washington, D. C. Cartographic Division.*

National geographic society, *Washington, D. C. Division
of school service.*
    The National geographic society pictorial geogra-
phy, a new and distinctive series of separate pictures
for schoolroom use ... ₍Gilbert Grosvenor, director and
editor, Jessie Logan Burrall, chief of school service₎
₍Washington, D. C., The National geographic society, 19
    v. illus. (part col.) 22½ x 27¾ᶜᵐ.
    Cover-title.
    Each volume or set consists of 48 sheets, printed on one side only.
    The first series, consisting of v. 1–3, is for primary and intermediate
grades; the second series, consisting of v. 4–6, is for intermediate and
grammar grades, and for certain primary and Americanization applications.

    The volumes or sets thus far issued are numbered as follows: ₍v. 1₎
Group I, sec. 1, 2; ₍v. 2₎ Group I, sec. 3, 4; ₍v. 3₎ Group I, sec. 5, 6; ₍v. 4₎
Group II, sec. 1–₍III₎; ₍v. 5₎ Group V, sec. 3; ₍v. 6 or no. 6₎

    CONTENTS.—₍v. 1₎ Eskimo life. Sahara life.—₍v. 2₎ The Indian in Amer-
ica and The Negro in Africa.—₍v. 3₎ Life in China and The hill tribes of
the Philippines.—₍v. 4₎ The land, the water, the air.—₍v. 5₎ The United
States. General view.—₍v. 6₎ Italy.

    1. Geography — Pictorial works. 2. Geography — Juvenile literature.
I. Grosvenor, Gilbert, ed. II. Burrall, Jessie Logan. III. Title. IV. Title:
Pictorial geography.

                                            A 21–771

    Title from National   Geographic Society. Printed by L. C.

NN 0053037   DNG

National geographic society. Division of
    school service.
    The National geographic society pictorial
geography; a new and distinctive series of
separate pictures for schoolroom use. Group I,
sections 5 and 6. Washington, D.C., National
geographic society [192-]

    Contents: Group 1, section 5, Life in China;
section 6, The hill tribes of the Philippines.

NN 0053038   MH

National Geographic Society, *Washington, D. C. Map Division*
    see
National Geographic Society, *Washington, D. C. Cartographic Division.*

E51
.U6
no. 140

National geographic society-Smithsonian institu-
    tion archeological expeditions to southern
    Mexico, 1938–
Drucker, Philip, 1911–
    ... Ceramic sequences at Tres Zapotes, Veracruz, Mexico, by
Philip Drucker. Washington, U. S. Govt. print. off., 1943.

E51
.U6
no. 141

National geographic society-Smithsonian institu-
    tion archeological expeditions to southern
    Mexico, 1938–
Drucker, Philip, 1911–
    ... Ceramic stratigraphy at Cerro de las Mesas, Veracruz,
Mexico, by Philip Drucker. Washington, U. S. Govt. print.
off., 1943.

E51
.U6
no. 139

National geographic society-Smithsonian institu-
    tion archeological expeditions to southern
    Mexico, 1938–   FOR OTHER EDITIONS
                        SEE MAIN ENTRY
Weiant, Clarence Wolsey, 1897–
    ... An introduction to the ceramics of Tres Zapotes, Vera-
cruz, Mexico, by C. W. Weiant. Washington, U. S. Govt. print.
off., 1943.

The **National** geographical journal of India. v. 1–
    Sept. 1955–
    Varanasi ₍etc.₎ National Geographical Society of India.
    v. in   illus. maps (part fold.) 25 cm. quarterly.

    1. Geography—Period. 2. India—Descr. & trav.—Period.
I. National Geographical Society of India.

G1.N3   59–32766

NN 0053043   DLC KU TxU OrCS LU

National Geographical Society of India.
    Bulletin. no. 1–
    Sept. 1946–
    Banaras.
    no. in   v. illus. 25 cm. Irregular.

    1. Geography—Societies, etc.

G35.N322   910.6254   53–34929

NN 0053044   DLC ICU WaU MB OrCS

NATIONAL GEOGRAPHICAL SOCIETY OF INDIA.
    Bulletin. no. 1-3, 5-20; ₍ Sept. 1946₎-Apr., May,
1947-Jan. 1954
    Banaras (Benares).   no.   illus.,plates,maps.   25cm.

    Film reproduction. Negative.
    Irregular.
    No. 1-2, Sept. 1946 lack date.
    Ceased publication with no. 21.
    1. India--Geography--Per.   and soc. publ.

NN 0053045   NN

VOLUME 407

National Geographical Society of India.
The National geographical journal of India
see *under title*

National geological survey of China
see China. Chung yang ti chih tiao ch'a so.

1885   National geology. The new home of the United States
geological survey [Washington, D. C.]
Washington, National Republican, 1884.
2 l.   12°.   (From National Republican,
Oct. 25, 1884)
[Toner Excerpts]

NN 0053048   DLC

National Geophysical Research Institute, *Hyderabad, India*
see
Hyderabad, India. National Geophysical Research Institute.

National German American Alliance,

Anleitungen zur Erlangung des Bürgerrechts in den Ver.
Staaten... [Philadelphia?, 1912?] 4 l. 8°.

1. Naturalization, U. S.
N. Y. P. L.   July 24, 1912.

NN 0053050   NN

National German American Alliance.   2
Aufruf an unsere deutsch-amerikanischen Mitbürger. Appeal to our
American fellow-citizens of German descent.
= [Boston? 1915.] 12, (3) pp. 19½ cm.
The text is in English and German.

L7441 — European War, 1914- . 1. paganda. German. — Germans in the
United States.

NN 0053051   MB MH

National German American alliance,

[Heinrici, Max] *ed.*
Das buch der Deutschen in Amerika. Hrsg. unter den
auspicien des Deutsch-amerikanischen national-bundes. Philadelphia, Walther's buchdr., 1909.

National German American alliance,
German American annals ... devoted to the comparative study
of the historical, literary, linguistic, educational and commercial relations of Germany and America. v. 1–4, 1897–
1902; v. 5–21 (new ser., v. 1–17), Jan. 1903–Dec. 1919. New
York, The Macmillan co.; [etc., etc.] 1897–1902; Philadelphia, German American historical society, 1903–19.

National German American alliance.
Helbig, Richard Ernest, 1870–
The German American collection in the New York public library. By Richard E. Helbig. Report of the Committee on historical research to the fourth convention of
the National German American alliance, held in New
York, Oct. 4–7, 1907. (Translated for "German American annals" from the published proceedings of the convention by R. E. H.) [Philadelphia, The International
printing co. 1908]

National German American Alliance.
The German element in the United States.
Philadelphia, 1909
see under   Goebel, Julius, 1857–1931.

973
D48

National German American Alliance.
Grundsätze und Verfassung des Deutsch-
Amerikanischen National-Bundes der Ver,
Staaten von Amerika. Gegründet am 19. Juni
1900. Konstituirt am 6. Oktober 1901. Re-
vidierte Verfassung am 7. Oktober 1905 ange-
nommen. Philadelphia, Pa., 1905.
cover-title, 8 p.

German text with partial English translation.

NN 0053056   NNC MiD PPCS

National German American Alliance.
Mitteilungen. Bulletin. 1.–10. Jahrg., Nr. 2; 1909–Feb.
1918. Philadelphia.
10 v. illus. 32–38 cm.
Publication suspended June–Sept. 1916. Cf. Union list of serials.
L. C. set incomplete: scattered issues wanting.

1. Germans in the U. S.—Societies, etc.

E184.G3N2   19–731 rev*

NN 0053057   DLC WaU PPG NN MH

National German American Alliance,

An open letter to Major General McArthur from the executive council of the National German-American Alliance. [New
York? 191–?] 4 l. sq. 8°.

Also same, broadside, German and English text.

1. Germans in the U. S.
N. Y. P. L.   August 12, 1912.

NN 0053058   NN OC1h

973
D482

National German-American Alliance.
Protokoll der Konvention.

Washington [etc.]
v. 27cm.
issued by the association
under its earlier German name: Deutschameri-
kanischer National bund der Vereinigten
Staaten von Amerika. (varies slightly)

NN 0053059   NNC

National German-American Alliance.
Protokoll der vierten Konvention des Deutsch-Amerikanischen National-Bundes der Ver. Staaten von Amerika,
abgehalten vom 4. bis 7. Oktober 1907. New York, 1907.
156 p. 26 cm.
Cover title.

1. National German-American Alliance.   I. Title.

E183.8.G3N37   74–230056

NN 0053060   DLC

NATIONAL GERMAN AMERICAN ALLIANCE.
Vorschläge des Nationalbund-auschuses für
deutsche sprache und schule zwecks ausbreitung
und einführung des deutschunterrickts[!] in den
öffentlichen schulen. Philadelphia,Deutsch-
amerikanischer Nationalbund,1914.

pp.(8).
Cover-title.

NN 0053061   MH

National German American Alliance. Chicago Branch.
Der Deutsche Tag, 5te. October. [Fest
Programm] Chicago, 1906.
4 l. 8°.

NN 0053062   NN

National German-American Alliance. Chicago
branch.
Die Deutschen in Amerika. Fest-schrift
zum Deutschen Tage in Chicago gefeiert am 6.
Oktober 1907 im Auditorium vom Zweig-Verband
Chicago, Deutsch-Amerikanischer National-Bund.
[Edited by Emil Mannhardt]   Chicago [Ill.]
Druck von H. Loesicke [1907]
21 l. illus. 4°

NN 0053063   ICJ NN PPCS

National German-American Alliance. *Chicago branch.*
Die Deutschen in Amerika; fest-schrift zum deutschen
tage in Chicago, gefeiert am sonntag, den 4. oktober '08 im
Auditorium, vom Zweig-verband Chicago Deutsch-amerikanischer national-bund. [Chicago] H. Loesicke printing
co. [1908]
45 p. illus. (incl. ports., map) 27½ cm.

1. Germans in Illinois.

F550.G3N3   9–3563 rev

NN 0053064   DLC ICJ ICHi

National German-American Alliance. *Zweig-Verband Chi-*
cago
see
National German-American Alliance. *Chicago Branch.*

NATIONAL GERMAN AMERICAN ALLIANCE,
New England Branch.
The German element in the United States.
[Boston,The Society,191–?].

Pamphlet.

NN 0053066   MH

National German-American Teachers' Seminary, *Milwaukee*
see Milwaukee. National Teachers' Seminary.

National get-out-the-vote club.

Michelet, Simon.
Four primary elections in [1920–22–24–26] forty states, by
Simon Michelet ... Issued under the auspices of the Nationa[l]
get-out-the-vote club. Washington, D. C. [1927]

VOLUME 407

JK1986   NATIONAL GET-OUT-THE-VOTE CLUB.
.N3   ₍Miscellaneous publications₎

    Includes pamphlets by the president, Simon Michelet.

    1. Voting. 2. Elections--U.S.

NN   0053069   ICU

National Get Out the Vote Club.
    New York state in presidential elections ...
      see under   Michelet, Simon, 1871-

National get-out-the-vote club.

Michelet, Simon, 1871-
    Ohio in 1928, by Simon Michelet ... Issued under the auspices of the National get-out-the-vote club ... Washington, D. C. ₍1928₎

National get-out-the-vote club.

Michelet, Simon, 1871-
    Presidential primary, 1928, by Simon Michelet ... Issued under the auspices of the National get-out-the-vote club ... Washington, D. C. ₍1927₎

National get-out-the-vote club.

Michelet, Simon.
    Primary elections in 1928, by Simon Michelet ... Issued under the auspices of the National get-out-the-vote club ... Washington, D. C. ₍1927₎

National get-out-the-vote club.

Michelet, Simon.
    Primary elections of senators, 1926, by Simon Michelet ... Issued under the auspices of the National get-out-the-vote club. Washington, D. C. ₍1927?₎

National get-out-the-vote club.

₍Michelet, Simon₎ 1871-
    The vote in 1924; popular vote for president by states and political parties. Percentage of qualified vote actually cast is shown by states and geographic divisions. Analysis of the returns. Compiled by the National get-out-the-vote club ... Washington, D. C. ₍1925₎

National get-out-the-vote club.

Michelet, Simon, 1871-
    Women delegates at national conventions, by Simon Michelet ... In 1924 women had a ten per cent voice in the national party conventions. How about 1928? Issued under the auspices of the National get-out-the-vote club ... Washington, D. C. ₍1928₎

NATIONAL GIFT AND ART ASSOCIATION.
    New York gift show. [Directory of exhibits] 53d, 55th-56th, 59th, Aug. 1957, Aug. 1958-Feb. 1959, Aug. 1960.
    New York,   no.   illus.   22cm.

    Semiannual.
    Ceased publication with no. 59, Aug. 1960?

1. Art industries and trade   Exhibitions--New York. I. Title.

NN   0053077   NN NB

652.1   National Girls' Work Board.
N385   A guide to group leadership. To be
1927   used in conjunction with Canadian girls in training, a book for leaders. Toronto, c1927.
    72 p. 18 cm.
    Bibliography: p. 68-72.
    1. Christian leadership. I. Title.a.

NN   0053078   CaBVaU

National gladiolus society. Handbook for 1911[-1913], in which is included list of members, by-laws and regulations, notices to members, future arrangements, &c. 8°. ₍London. 1911-13₎.

NN   0053079   MBH

96.43   National Gladiolus Society.
N213   Newsletter.
    Washington.

    1. Gladiolus. Periodicals.

NN   0053080   DNAL

National glass budget; weekly review of the American glass industry.
    Pittsburg, 18
    v. illus. 41½ᶜᵐ.

Editor: 18   F. M. Gessner.

1. Glass manufacture—Period.

      CA 6-1295 Unrev'd

Library of Congress   TP785.N2

NN   0053081   DLC WvU ICRL ICJ MdBJ

National glass budget.
    Directory of glass factories in the United States and Canada
      see   Glass factory directory.

National Glass Budget.
    Glass factory directory
      see under title

National glass distributors association.
    Glass and glazing, issued by the National glass distributors ass'n. ₍Saint Louis, Press of Kutterer-Jansen, °1916₎
    46 p., 1 l. illus. 23ᶜᵐ.
    "Compiled ... for the National glass distributers association by Clarence Warner Condie."

1. Glass manufacture. ɪ. Condie, Clarence Warner, comp. ɪɪ. Title.
      16-6276 Revised

Library of Congress   TP868.N3

NN   0053084   DLC ICJ

National glass distributors association.
    Roster and constitution and by-laws.
    ₍n. p., 19
      nos. 16½ x 9ᶜᵐ.

      43-35687

Library of Congress   HD9623.U45N356

NN   0053085   DLC

The national glee book. A collection of glees, madrigals, catches, rounds, &c., patriotic, sentimental and humorous. Selected and arranged from German, English and American composers, and adapted for the use of singing societies, social meetings, glee clubs, &c. Boston: Keith's Music Pub. House, 1846. 223(1) p. ob. 12°.

    Date on cover, 1847.
    Words with music for 3 and 4 voices.

      DOANE COLLECTION.

1. Glees.
N. Y. P. L.   November 13, 1919.

NN   0053086   NN

The National glee book. A collection of glees, madrigals, catches ... patriotic, sentimental humorous ... Boston, 1847.
    223 [1] p. 17 x 26 cm.

NN   0053087   RPB

7Q
216   The NATIONAL glee book. A collection of glees, madrigals, catches, rounds, &c., patriotic, sentimental and humorous. Selected and arranged from German, English and American composers, and adapted for the use of singing societies, social meetings, glee clubs, &c. Boston, Published by O.Ditson ₍c1849₎
    223,₍1₎p. 18x26cm.
    Imperfect: p.3-6,129-130,135-152,161-162, and 167-168 wanting.

NN   0053088   ICN

7Q
217   The NATIONAL glee book. A collection of glees, madrigals, catches, rounds, &c., patriotic, sentimental and humorous. Selected and arranged from German, English and American composers, and adapted for the use of singing societies, social meetings, glee clubs, &c. Boston, Published by O.Ditson ₍c1850₎
    223,₍1₎p. 16x26cm.

NN   0053089   ICN

National glider; the magazine of practical aviation
      see   National glider and airplane news.

National glider and airplane news. v. 1-
    Aug. 1930-   ₍New York, Dime publications, inc., 1930-32₎
    v. illus. 28-29½ᶜᵐ. monthly.
    Title varies: Aug. 1930, National glider; the magazine of practical aviation.
    Sept. 1930-Feb. 1931, National power glider; the magazine of practical aviation.
    Mar. 1931- 1932, National glider and airplane news.
    Emanuele Stieri, editor.

1. Gliders (Aeronautics) 2. Aeronautics—Period. 3. Aeronautics—U. S. ɪ. Stieri, Emanuele, 189?- ed.
      36-1957

Library of Congress   TL760.A1N3
      ₍2₎   629.1305

NN   0053091   DLC WaS NN OC1

VOLUME 407

629.172   National glider association.
.N26   By-laws of the National Glider association,
          approved February 6, 1929 and amended April 10,
          1929. [Detroit? 1929]
          cover-title, 7, [1]p.   14 1/2 cm.

          I. Gliders (Aeronautics)

NN   0053092   DSI

──────────────────────

329.172   National glider association.
.N27   Contest rules, the National glider association
          incorporated, approved February 6, 1929, amended
          October 15, 1929. [Detroit? 1929]
          cover-title, 20 p.   16 cm.

          1. Gliders (Aeronautics)

NN   0053093   DSI

──────────────────────

TL   National Glider Association.
760   Minutes ...
A1N27+   Detroit.
          v. 29cm.

          Includes minutes of the conferences and
          the meetings of the Board of Directors.

NN   0053094   NIC

──────────────────────

629.172   National glider association.
.N3   Wings for young America. Detroit, the National
          glider association, [1929?]
          cover-title, [16]p.   23 o/2 cm.

          1. Gliders (Aeronautics)   I. Title.

NN   0053095   DSI

──────────────────────

f657   National glove and mitten manufacturers'
N24c   association.
          Cost finding in the leather glove in-
          dustry; a report prepared for the Na-
          tional glove and mitten manufacturers'
          association. Comp. by Miller, Franklin,
          Basset and co.   New York [c1925]
          17p.   forms.

NN   0053096   IU

──────────────────────

[NATIONAL GOLDEN RULE COMMITTEE]
          Suggestions and meditations for golden rule
Sunday.   N.Y., Near East relief
[1924]
          46 p.
          I. Title.

NN   0053097   Or

──────────────────────

712.2   [National Golf Foundation]
N213g   Golf facilities; organization, construction,
1949   management, maintenance. [Enl. and rev.ed.
          Chicago, 1949]
          77p.   illus., plans, diagrs. 28cm.

          Originally published under title: Golf range
          operator's handbook.

          1. Golf-links. I. Graffis, Herbert Butler,
          1893- ed. II. Title.

NN   0053098   IU OU TU OCl WaS

──────────────────────

National Golf Foundation.
    Golf instructor's guide
    see under   Athletic Institute.

──────────────────────

National Golf Foundation.
    Golf lessons; the fundamentals as taught by
foremost professional instructors.   [Chicago, 1950]
    [28] p.   illus.   22 cm.
    1. Golf.

NN   0053100   NN

──────────────────────

National Golf Foundation.
    Golf lessons; the fundamentals as taught by
foremost professional instructors. [Chicago,
c1952]
    [32] p.   illus.

NN   0053101   Wa

──────────────────────

National Golf Foundation.
    Golf range operator's handbook. 2d rev.
printing.   Chicago [1949?]
    34 p.   illus. 28 cm.

NN   0053102   TU OCl Wa

──────────────────────

GV987   National Golf Foundation.
.N3   Miniature golf courses.   Chicago, 1949.
          24 p.   illus. 28 cm.

NN   0053103   TU Wa

──────────────────────

National Golf Foundation.
    Municipal golf course organizing and operating guide;
edited by Verne Wickham. Chicago, 1955.
    120 p. illus. 28 cm.

    1. Golf-links.   I. Title.

    GV975.N3   796.352   55-4451 ‡

NN   0053104   DLC IU PP MiD PSt NN Wa OrP Or CaBVa

──────────────────────

GV975   National Golf Foundation.
N28   Planning and building the golf course.
          Chicago, n.d.
          28 p. illus. 27cm.

          1.Golf-links - Construction and care.
          I.Title.

NN   0053105   NcRS

──────────────────────

796.4   National Golf Foundation.
N213   Planning and building the course.   Chicago
          [195-?]
          p.17-41. illus.,diagrs.,plans. 29cm.

          Cover title.
          "Course for 'typical golfer' popular at
          Pinehurst." folder [6]p. inserted.

          1. Golf-links   I. Title.

NN   0053106   OrU NcU CaBVaU

──────────────────────

NATIONAL GOLF LINKS OF AMERICA.
    Members.
[Southampton, N.Y.]   v.   15cm.

    1. Golf--Clubs and assoc.--U.S.

NN   0053107   NN

──────────────────────

National Golf Links of America.
19   [Yearbook.]

Southampton, L. I. [19   16°.
    v.

1. Golf.—Clubs, etc., U. S.
N.Y.P.L.   July 14, 1924

NN   0053108   NN

──────────────────────

The National golf review
    see   Golf (New York) 1936-

──────────────────────

GV961   The National golfer. v. 1-
G72   July 1949-
          [San Mateo, Calif., etc.], H. F. Lengfeld [etc.]
          v. illus., ports. 32 cm. monthly.
          Title varies: July-Aug. 1949, The California golfer.—Sept. 1949-
          July/Aug. 1957, The Golfer.
          Editor: July 1949-   H. F. Lengfeld.

          1. Golf—Period.   I. Lengfeld, Helen F., ed.
          GV961.G72   796.35205   52-30700 rev

NN   0053110   DLC

──────────────────────

          National good; or, The utility of the
          landed and commercial interests being united,
          for the welfare and happiness of British sub-
          jects. Addressed to the manufacturers, and
          those interested in the cotton and wool trade
          of Lancashire and Yorkshire. By a Manchester
          manufacturer. Manchester, Printed by W. Cow-
          droy, 1819.
          30 p. 22cm.

NN   0053111   NNC

──────────────────────

TE101   [National good roads association of China]
.N3   Foreigners and the good roads movement of China.
          The sixth annual canvass for new members.
          Shanghai, Printed at The sign of the willow pattern,
          1927.
          cover-title, 16 p.   diagrs. 22.5 cm.
          Verne Dyson, captain of foreign team.

NN   0053112   DLC

──────────────────────

National good roads convention, St. Louis, 1903.
    Official order of proceedings, the National and international
good roads convention, held at St. Louis, Mo. April 27th, 28th &
29th, 1903. [St. Louis, Mo., 1903]   [28] p.   illus., ports.
31cm.

    1. Roads—U. S. 1903.

NN   0053113   NN

VOLUME 407

National good roads convention, *St. Louis*, 1903.
... Proceedings of the National good roads convention held at St. Louis, Mo., April 27 to 29, 1903. Washington, Govt. print. off., 1903.

80 p. 23ᶜᵐ. (U. S. Dept. of agriculture. Office of public road inquiries. Bulletin no. 26)

1. Roads—Congresses.

Library, U. S. Dept. of   Agriculture 1R53B no. 26
Library of Congress   [TE1.U6 no. 26]   Agr 9-2445

NN 0053114   DNAL Or MB OO CU OC1

The **National** good templar.
v. 1–

Minneapolis, 1938–40.   30–38cm.
v.   illus. (incl. ports.)

Monthly.
"Published by the National grand lodge of the United States, I. O. G. T."

1. Temperance—Per. and soc.   publ. U.S. I. International order
of good templars. U.S. National   grand lodge.
N. Y. P. L.   November 25, 1940

NN 0053115   NN

... The **national** government and housing
    see under   [Hale, Dick]

... The **national** government and how to secure a position under it, both with and without civil service examination ... Washington, B. S. Adams, printer, 1885.

cover-title, 12 p. 16ᶜᵐ.

1. Civil service—U. S. 2. U. S.—Officials and employees—Salaries.

Library of Congress   JK716.N3   CA 10-3416 Unrev'd

NN 0053117   DLC

... The **national** government and subsidies
    see under [Fox, W   E   ]

National government journal, and register of official papers.
v. 1; Dec. 3, 1823–Nov. 20, 1824. [Washington, P. Force, 1823–24]

2 p. l., 574 (i. e. 580) col. 33ᶜᵐ. weekly.

Title varies: Dec. 3, 1823–June 5, 1824, National journal [extra]
June 9–Nov. 20, 1824, National government journal, and register of official papers.
Peter Force, editor.
No more published.

1. U. S.—Pol. & govt.—1817-1825. I. Force, Peter, 1790-1868, ed.

Library of Congress   E371.N27   5-5168

NN 0053119   DLC OCHP

National government journal. v. 1-2; Dec. 3, 1823–Nov. 29, 1825. [Washington, P. Force]

(American periodical series: 1800-1825. 149)

Microfilm copy (positive) made in 1950 by University Microfilms, Ann Arbor, Mich.
Collation of the original: 2 v.
Weekly.
Title varies: Dec. 3, 1823–June 5, 1824, National journal [extra]
Edited by P. Force.

1. U. S.—Pol. & govt.—1817-1825. I. Force, Peter, 1790-1868, ed.
II. Title: National journal [extra] (Series: American periodical series: 1800-1850. 149)

Microfilm 01104 no. 149 AP   Mic 57-5102

NN 0053120   DLC NN ICRL ViU

National government, law and practice
    see under   Hall, Ford Poulton

National government the Churchill way ...
    see under [Flanagan, J   ]

National governmental organizations, Chicago ...
    see under [Brownlow, Louis] 1879-

National Governors' Conference.
    Proceedings of the annual meeting. [1st]–   1908–
Chicago [etc.]

v. illus. 24 cm.

Title varies: 1908-25, Proceedings.—1926, 1930-31, Report of proceedings.
Other slight variations in title.
Proceedings for 1908-64 issued by the conference under its earlier name: Governors' Conference (1908 under a variant form of the name: Conference of Governors)
"Published by authority of Congress." 1908.

—————— Another issue. [1st] 1908.
Issued in the congressional series as House document.

HC101.C7 1908b

1. U. S.—Econ. condit. 2. U. S.—Pol. & govt. 3. Natural resources—U. S.   I. Governors' Conference. Proceedings of the annual meeting. II. Governor's Conference. Report of proceedings.

JK2403.G8   12-29056 rev

MiU-C FU P RP CtN1C InU PPFr NN INS
OrCS PHC FTaSU PBm NcD-L NcRS MH-L MB UU NcRS
IU PSt WHi KMK TxU OrU MtU DI ViU-L ICJ PPT NjP
NN 0053124   DLC KyU DSI MeB AAP GEU DNAL Vi OU

National graded course in seven grades for the pianoforte
    see under Hatch music company, pub.

National Graduated Tax Society.
    The Graduated taxer
    see under title

National Grain and Feed Dealers Association
    see Grain and Feed Dealers National Association.

National Grain Dealers Association
    see Grain and Feed Dealers National Association.

286.359
N21A   **National Grain Trade Council.**
          Analysis of the International wheat agreement.   Washington [1948]
          8 p.

NN 0053130   DNAL

286.359   National Grain Trade Council.
N21   The International wheat agreement, an analysis and comment. Washington, D.C., 1948.
          [2] p.

NN 0053131   DNAL

National Grain Trade Council.
    List, commodity exchanges of the United States
    see under   Grain and Feed Dealers National Association.

National Grain Trader.
    Grain: profitable grain trading. [Chicago, 1954?]

15 p.   28 cm.
Cover title.
To be use in conjunction with its twice-weekly trading letters.
"Wire service code list" inserted.
1. Grain trade. I. Title.

NN 0053133   MB

NATIONAL GRAMOPHONE COMPANY.
    Record catalogue.
New York.   no.   ports.   22cm.

1. Phonograph records--Catalogs, Publishers' 2. Catalogs, Publishers'.

NN 0053134   NN

National Gramophonic Society.   *4049a.606
    Catalogue of records. [1st.]   1927.
— London. [1927.] v. Portraits. 21 cm.

The 1927 issue has an introduction by Compton Mackenzie.
Inserted in the 1927 issue is an alphabetical list of works published by the Society, 1924-26.

N4096 — Phonograph. Records. Cats. — Mackenzie. Compton, pret., 1883-

NN 0053135   MB

National Gramophonic Society.   4049a.607
    A list of recorded chamber music. January, 1925.   [Also]
    Supplement, July, 1926.
= [London. 1925, 26.] 2 v. in 1. 21½ cm.

N4090 — Chamber music. Cats. — Phonograph. Records. Cats.

NN 0053136   MB NN ICRL

National Gramophonic Society.   *4049a.605
    [Prospectus. 1926.]
= London. Gramophone (Publications) Ltd. [1926.] v. 18½ cm.

NN 0053137   MB

National grand order of the United brothers of the African race of America
    see   United brothers of the African race of America. .

National grand tabernacle of Galilean fishermen, Baltimore, Md.
    see
Galilean fishermen, Baltimore, Md.

National Grand United Order of Brothers and Sisters of Love and Charity in America.
    Degree ritual of the N. G. U. O. of B. & S. of L. & C. in America; second or Ruth degree.
[n.p., n.d.]
24 p. 15cm.

NN 0053140   NcU

VOLUME 407

National Grand United Order of Brothers and
Sisters of Love and Charity in America.
Ritual, revised, compiled and issued under
the supervision of the Committee on Ritual, by
National Deputy Grand Worthy Superior J. P.
Butler. Weldon, Harrell's Printing House,
1921.
    19 p. 15cm.
--- -----[n.p., n.d.]
    9 p. 16cm.
No title-page.

NN 0053141   NcU

National Grange
    see Patrons of Husbandry. National
Grange.

284.6   National Grange Insurance Companies.
N213   Pennsylvania farm safety news. Harrisburg,
        [1948?]
        [8] p.

NN 0053143   DNAL

4   The National grange clip sheet [monthly,
N21831   January to October] no.
        Springfield, Mass.
        f°.
            1. Agriculture. Economic aspects. U.S.
        I. Patrons of husbandry. National grange.

NN 0053144   DNAL

HD1485
.P2A14 The National grange monthly.
        Springfield, Mass. [1907
            v. in   illus. 35-38cm.

            1. Patrons of husbandry--Period. I.
        Patrons of husbandry. National grange.

NN 0053145   DLC OC1 NcTS WrU ICRL NN

The NATIONAL grange monthly. v.1, no.25-v.5, no.24,
Apr. 22, 1908-Mar. 16, 1910 (incomplete); v.34, no.
11-v.59, no.9, Nov. 1937-Sept. 1962
Springfield, Mass. [etc.]   v.
illus.   28-50cm.

Vol.47-48, no.9, 1950-Sept. 1951, on film *ZAN-1730. Negative.
Weekly, Apr. 22, 1908-Mar. 16, 1910; monthly, Nov. 1937-Sept. 1962
Began publication Nov. 6,   1907, superseding the

American grange bulletin (not in the library).
    Official publication of the National grange, Patrons of husbandry.
    Title varies: v.1, no.25-v.5, no.24, Apr. 22, 1908-Mar. 16, 1910,
National grange.
    Ceased publication with v.59, no.9, Sept. 1962.

1. Periodicals--U.S. 2. Agriculture--Per. and soc. publ. I. Patrons
of husbandry. National   grange. II. The American
grange bulletin.

NN 0053146   NN DNAL MB ICU OU OC1 NIC CU

National Grange Mutual Liability Company.

    The National Grange Mutual Liability Company was founded in
1923. In 1959 it absorbed the National Grange Fire Insurance Company (founded 1932) and changed its name to National Grange
Mutual Insurance Company.

284.6   National Grange Mutual Liability Co.
N2122   The farmer's best friend. Keene, N. H.
1949   [1949]
        64 p.

            1. Agriculture. Accidents. 2. Accidents.
        Prevention. 3. Almanacs. 4. Insurance,
        Agricultural. U.S. I. National Grange Fire
        Insurance Co. II. Title.

NN 0053148   DNAL

National Grange of the Patrons of Husbandry
    see Patrons of Husbandry. National Grange.

National grange quarterly bulletin, ed. by N. J.
Bacheldor. Conc., 1900.

NN 0053150   Nh

QC119   National Granometer Co., Dayton, Ohio.
.N2   Tables and instructions for settling the
        granometer ... Dayton [c1913]

NN 0053151   DLC

280.29 National Grape Co-operative Association, inc.
N218   Annual report.

        Westfield, N.Y.,

            1. National Grape Co-operative Association,
        inc.

NN 0053152   DNAL

The National Graphic
    see The Graphic. London.

NATIONAL GRAPHIC ARTS EDUCATION ASSOCIATION.
    Annual conference [on] printing education.
[Proceedings]
Chicago, Ill.   no.   illus.   24cm.

1. Printing--Congresses--U.S.
and teaching--U.S. I. Title: 2. Printing, Practical--Study
education. [Proceedings]   Conference [on] printing

NN 0053154   NN

National graphic arts education association.
    Annual Graphic arts education guild yearbook.

Washington, D. C., 19
    v. 23ᶜᵐ.
    Issues for 19   published under the association's earlier name:
National graphic arts education guild.
Title varies:
    1937-38, Graphic arts education guild yearbook (on cover, 1938: An-
    nual Graphic arts education guild yearbook)
    1939-   Annual Graphic arts education guild yearbook
    1. Printing, Practical--Study and teaching. 2. Printers--U. S.
I. Title.
                                            45-25109
    Library of Congress   Z122.N3A3

NN 0053155   DLC ViU KyU MtU OC1 ViLxW CSmH NN CU

National graphic arts education association.

Gage, Harry Lawrence, 1887-
    An appraisal of graphic arts education, an informal evalua-
tion of the several educational activities in terms of their contribution to the graphic industries and to the current educational program of the United States, by Harry L. Gage ... Lexington, Va., Journalism laboratory press, Washington and Lee
university, 1938.

National graphic arts education association.
    The composite analysis of the printing trades; a research
project of the National graphic arts association. Fort Worth,
Tex., Department of printing, Masonic home and school, 1940.
    xii, 161 p. 23½ᶜᵐ.

    1. Printing as a trade. I. Title.

    Library of Congress   Z243.U5N3   41-25130
                               [2]   655.3

NN 0053157   DLC InU OC1

Z122
.N3A35 National Graphic Arts Education Association.
1950   Fifteenth anniversary Graphic arts educa-
        tion yearbook, 1935-1950. Washington, D. C.,
        1950.
            xxxix, 89 p. port. 24cm.
            "'Seen through the press' by C. Harold Lauck at
        the Journalism Laboratory Press of Washington and
        Lee University, Lexington, Virginia .... The edition
        consists of five hundred copies."
            Includes Who's who in Graphic arts education,
        1949-1950.
            1. Printing, Prac   tical--Study and teaching.
        2. Printers--U.S.

NN 0053158   ViU

DEPARTMENT
Z   National Graphic Arts Education Association.
239   Frederic W. Goudy issue. Annual Graphic Arts
G68   Education Guild yearbook for 1937. Washington,
N3   D.C., 1937.
            xvi, 147, [1] p. port. 23cm.
            "Edition limited to five hundred copies."
            Contributions about Goudy: p. [vi-vii], 45-46.

            1. Goudy, Frederic William, 1865-1947. 2.
        Printing, Practical--Study and teaching.
        3. Printers--U.S.

NN 0053159   NSyU

National Graphic Arts Education Association.

    Graphic arts education guild yearbook for 1936.
Washington, D. C., National Graphic Arts Education Guild [1936]
    x, 105, [1] p. port. 22½ᶜᵐ.
    Printed by the Journalism Laboratory Press, Washington
and Lee University, Lexington, Virginia.
    "Edition limited to three hundred copies."
    "This the first bound copy ... is presented to Edward
L. Stone ... [signed] C. Harold Lauck."

    1. Printing, Practical--study and teaching. 2.
Printers--U.S. I. Title.

NN 0053160   ViU

SCHOOL OF LIBRARY SERVICE
LS050
G75
        National Graphic Arts Education Association.
        Index issue.
1947-
        [Washington, D.C., National graphic arts
        education association, 1948-
            v. 23cm. annual.

            1947-   cumulative list of the monthly
        index lists that appeared in the Graphic arts
        summary issue of P.I.A. Management reports.

NN 0053161   NNC

VOLUME 407

National Graphic Arts Education Association.
The National Graphic Arts Education Guild.
The organization. The constitution and by-
laws. New York ₁1935₎
12 p. 19cm.

1. Printing - Societies. 2. National
Graphic Arts Education Guild.

NN   0053162   NNC

National graphic arts education association.
The National graphic arts education guild;
the organization, the constitution and by-
laws ... ₁Lexington, Virginia, Designed,
composed in lino-type Baskerville, and printed
by C. Harold Lauck at the Journalism laboratory
press of Washington and Lee university, 1936₎
12 p.

NN   0053163   ViU

Z1
N2131 National Graphic Arts Education Association.
       News bulletin. v. .
       Nov. 1937-ᵗ
       Washington₁₎
       v. in   illus. 28 cm.

       Frequency varies.
       Issues for Nov. 1937–June 1940 published by the association under
       an earlier name: National Graphic Arts Education Guild.
       Supplements accompany some numbers.

       1. Printing—Period.   I. Title.
       Z119.N13   655.05   52-28397

NN   0053164   DLC NNC CoU NN

Mann
LA   National Graphic Arts Education Associatio
5   The 1938 survey of printing education.
Z99   ₁New York, 1938?₎
no.117   ₁18₎ p.

           1. Printin₁   Practical - Study and
       teaching.

NN   0053165   NIC

National Graphic Arts Education Association.
A report on the symposia sessions ₁at the₎ annual conference on printing education.

₁n. p.₎
       v. ports. 23 cm.

1. Printing, Practical—Study and teaching.
Z122.N3A33   655.07   49-30793*‡
Library of Congress   ₁1₎

NN   0053166   DLC OC1

National graphic arts education guild
       see
National graphic arts education association.

---

f655.36 National graphic arts expositions, inc.
N27s   Souvenir of the fourth educational
         graphic arts exposition, Grand central
         palace, New York city, September 5th to
Springer 17th, 1927. ₁Brooklyn, Printed by
Coll.   the Brooklyn daily eagle commercial
         print. dept., 1927₎
         142p. illus.₁col.plates, ports. F.

         On cover: Official program of the 4th
         graphic arts exposition, New York, 1927.
         Issued by the Club of printing house
         craftsmen, New York.

NN   0053168   IaU

National Great Adventure for the Single Tax.
   Report of National conference of single taxers, held in Atlantic
City, April 13, 14, 15, 1917. Constitution of the National Great
Adventure for the Single Tax.   ₁n. p. 1917.₎   10 p.   nar. 16°.

   Leaflet entitled "Another inquisitive boy" inserted at end.

1. Single tax.—Congresses, U.S.:   N. J.: Atlantic City, 1917.
N. Y. P. L.   December 1, 1917.

NN   0053169   NN

RA622
A7N4   The National green book of funeral directors and embalmers.
       1954–55—
       ₁Chicago₎
       ₹. 29 cm.
       Editor: 1954–55—   R. H. Miller.

       1. Undertakers and undertaking—U. S.—Direct.   I. Miller, Robert
H., 1896—   ed.
       RA622.A7N4   55-15211

NN   0053170   DLC

National greenback labor party
       see
National greenback party.

National greenback party.
   Campaign documents, No. 1-V
n.p. n.d.
   v. O.

1. Political parties---U.S. 1. Nieuwland,
Edward J. 11. Title.

NN   0053172   00

National Greenback Party.
   Extracts from some of the communistic
inflammatory and treasonable documents, circulated by the National Greenback Party
       see under   Honest Money League of the
Northwest, Chicago.

JU83G National Greenback Party
.NA   Greenback Party history in brief, 1875 to
       1952. Indianapolis, Greenback Party ₁1952₎
       31 p. 20cm.

       Imprint covered by label: John Zahnd.
       P.O. Box 74, Beech Grove, Indiana.

NN   0053174   WHi

National Greenback Party.
   The greenbacker
   see under title

National Greenback Party.
   Legal tender. 3⁶⁵ bonds. Low interest. Let
us united stand in⁰⁰the Independent party greenback club. National legal tender money, inter-
changeable with government bonds, the only means
of restoring national prosperity ... Declaration of principles ...   ₁n.p., 1876?₎

   broadside. 25.4 x 21.2cm. (23 x 18cm.)

   1.Greenbacks.2.National Greenback Party.3.
Campaign lit.,1876-National Greenback Party.
I.Title.II.Title: ─National legal tender
money.

NN   0053176   MiU-C

National Greenback Party.
   The nomination to the presidency of Peter Cooper
see under   Cooper, Peter, 1791-1883.

National greenback party.
   Platform and address to the people and to the clergy.
Platform. We of the Greenback labor party welcome
to our ranks all who oppose class legislation, etc. ...
Chicago, Blakely, Brown & Marsh, printers ₁1880₎
18 p. 19¼ᶜᵐ.

On cover: "Money that is elastic, adequate, and just ..."
Signed: H. H. May, chairman of committee.

I. May, Harvey H., b. 1802.

₋ibrary of Congr   HG605.M3   12-23658

NN   0053178   DLC

National greenback party.
   The platform of the National greenback labor party
and the letter of acceptance of General J. B. Weaver.
₁n. p., 1880₎
8 p. 23ᶜᵐ.
Caption title.

                                            9-32976†

Library of Congress   JK2363 1880

NN   0053179   DLC

National Greenback Party
   see also   Independent Greenback Party of
Massachusetts. ₁*Supplement*₎

332.5 National greenback party. Delaware.
G829t   [Two articles]   n.p. [1878?]
         4p.

         Contents:- [no.1] To the voters and
       taxpayers of Delaware.- [no.2] Platform
       of the National greenback labor party of
       Delaware.

NN   0053181   IU

National Greenback Party. Missouri. Convention,
1877.
   Proceedings of the Missouri state greenback
convention ... The union of the Grangers and
Working-men with the Greenback-men
       see   Hill, Britton Armstrong, 1818-1888.
   The union of the Grangers and Working-men
with the Greenback-men.

Graff
2950   NATIONAL GREENBACK PARTY. Nebraska.
         Independent state convention... [Lincoln,
       Neb., Beach, printer, 1876]
         [4] p. 23cm.

         Signed: M. Warren, chairman.

NN   0053183   ICN

NATIONAL GREENBACK PARTY. *New York, New York County*
   Address of the New York County Committee of
the National Greenback-Labor Party. [New York,
1878?].

   18 cm. pp.7,(1).
   Without title-page. Caption title.

NN   0053184   MH

VOLUME 407

National Greenback party. New York. Queens
co.
The National greenback labor party of Queens
county, N. Y. Platform, constitution & by-
laws. [1880?]
[12] p. 12cm.

NN 0053185   NNC

JU830 National greenback party. Ohio.
.OH   To the independent citizens of Ohio.
[Cleveland? 187-?]
[1] ℓ. 22cm.

Caption title.
At head of title: Headquarters, Independent executive committee, State of Ohio.

NN 0053186   WHi

National greenbacker
see   The Greenbacker.

The **National** greenkeeper; the only trade paper in the world
on turf culture and golf course maintenance. v. 1–
Jan. 1927–
[Cleveland, The National greenkeeper, inc., 1927–
v. illus. 28½ᵐ. monthly.
"Official organ of the National association of greenkeepers of Amer-
ica."
Subtitle varies slightly.

1. Golf-links—Period. 2. Lawns. I. National association of greenkeepers of America. II. Title: Greenkeeper, The National.

29–20356

Library of Congress   GV961.N3

NN 0053188   DLC CU OC1

The **National** greenkeeper and turf culture.
v.

Cleveland, 192   29½cm.
v. illus. (incl. ports.)

Monthly.
Official organ of the National Association of Greenkeepers of America.
Title varies slightly.
Absorbed by the Greenkeepers' reporter,

1. Golf links—Per. and soc. publ.   I. National Association of Greenkeepers of America.
N.Y.P.L.   December 6, 1934

NN 0053189   NN

National Greenkeeping Superintendents Association
see
Golf Course Superintendents Association of America.

National Gregg Association.
The fortieth birthday of Gregg shorthand (published 28th
May, 1888). Report of proceedings of the annual conference of
the National Gregg Association, 1928, and of the banquet given
in honor of Mr. & Mrs. John Robert Gregg...edited by Ernest
W. Crockett. Liverpool, 1928. 57 p. illus. 8°.

544011A. 1. Shorthand—Systems,   Amer., 1928. I. Crockett, Ernest
W., editor.
N.Y.P.L.   October 5, 1931

NN 0053191   NN

National Gregg association.
Handbook, 1945. London, 1945. 25 p. 19cm.
Cover title.

1. Shorthand—Assoc. and org.—   John Robert Gregg Shorthand Coll.
Gt. Br.   Gt. Br. 2. Commerce—Education—

NN 0053192   NN

National Gregg Association.
The NGA news
see under title

National Gregg Shorthand Conference, London, 1923.
Proceedings of the National Gregg Shorthand Conference,
17th to 21st July, 1923. [London, 1923.] v, 69 p. illus.,
ports. 8°.

1. Shorthand—Conventions.
N.Y.P.L.   May 28, 1925

NN 0053194   NN

National grocer.
v.

Chicago: Byxbee Pub. Co., 19   4°.
v. illus.

Monthly.
Editor :   O. F. Byxbee.

1. Groceries—Per. and soc. publ.
N.Y.P.L.   May 14, 1923.

NN 0053195   NN

National grocer.
...Food administration number.
[Chicago, 1917]

HD9006
.A1N3

NN 0053196   DLC

National grocers bulletin
see   N.A.R.G.U.S. bulletin.

National grocers institute.
Getting started in the grocery business; a brief discussion
of the opportunities in the retail food field, and what is required for success ... Washington, D. C., National grocers
institute, °1946.
34 numb. l. 28½ x 21½ᵐ.
Reproduced from type-written copy.
"Reading list": leaf 34.

1. Grocery trade.   I. Title.

46–15176

Library of Congress   HF6201.G7N3
[2]   658.9414

NN 0053198   DLC Mi OC1 WaS

National Grocers Institute.
What consumers think about food and grocery
advertising. Washington, D.C., National Grocers
Institute, 1950.
49 p.

NN 0053199   PPCuP

National grocers institute
see also
National association of retail grocers of the United States.

The **National guaranteed bar; directory annual.**
Detroit, Mich., The National guaranteed bar (incorporated) [°1925–
v. 22ᵐ.

1. Lawyers—U. S.—Direct. [1. Legal directories—U. S.]

26–8658

NN 0053201   DLC

A national guard.
An historical and political account of the
events which took place at the Palace of the
Thuilleries
see under title

National guard.
The National guard of each state is entered under the name of
the state, e. g., Louisiana. National guard.

National guard, *District of Columbia*
see
District of Columbia. National guard.

20th.107.7
National Guard, The. Vol. 2 (no. 1). June 26, 1861. Captain Harmanus Neff, editor.
Camp Pennsylvania, Baltimore, Md. 1861. v. Vignette. 22
cm.
"Our 1st vol. was published while at Camp McLellan, near Lancaster, Pa.,
in July, 1856."

H4228 — Neff, Harmanus, ed. — Camp Pennsylvania. Baltimore, Md.

NN 0053205   MB DLC

The National guard, London
see   The National guard magazine, London.

The National guard, Feb. 21, 1891.
Washington, D. C. Polkinhorn, 1891.
vi. illus. ports 25 cm.

NN 0053207   DNW

National Guard Association.of *Pennsylvania*,
Proceedings of the Meeting of the
National Guard Association of Pennsylvania.

NN 0053208   DNW

VOLUME 407

National guard association of the state of New
York.
  Address and papers taken from the proceedings
of the convention of the National guard association of the state of New York held at Odd
fellows hall, Albany, N.Y., Thursday, February
8th, 1900. Albany, N.Y., Weed-Parsons printing
co., 1900.

  43 p. 23.5 cm.

NN   0053209   MH

National guard association of the state of New York.
  Annual convention.

  Buffalo, N. Y., 18
    v.   23ᶜᵐ.

  1. New York (State) Militia—Societies.

  Library of Congress   UA360.N2

                                        CA 7—23 Unrev'd

NN   0053210   DLC NN OFH

E457   NATIONAL GUARD ASSOCIATION OF THE STATE OF NEW
.52   YORK.
.N25   Veterans of the National guard. Head-quarters
Lincoln seventh regiment armory,New York,April 29,1865.
         ₍Resolutions on the death of President Lincoln
         adopted at a special meeting₎ N.Y.,Francis &
         Loutrel,printers₎1865₎
           ₍3₎ p. 27cm.

  1. Lincoln,Abraham,pres.U.S.--Memorial services,
1865.

NN   0053211   ICU

Wis.
Δ
Gu   National Guard Association of the State of
3:      Wisconsin.
          Proceedings of the ... [annual] convention
        of officers of the Wisconsin National Guard.
        2d-22d, 1883-1905. Madison, Democrat Print.
        co., state printer, 1883-1905.
          21 v. in 3. 23 cm.

  1st Proceedings not published.
  1. Wisconsin - Militia - Societies. I.
Wisconsin. National Guard.

NN   0053212   WHi NN

National Guard Association of the United States.
  Annual conference. 1st-
    see its   Official proceedings.

National Guard Association of the United States. Annual
  conference ₍Proceedings₎
  see its Official proceedings of the general conference.

National Guard Association of the United States. Annual
  convention report
  see its Official proceedings of the general conference.

National guard association of the United States.
  An appeal to the 74th Congress by the National guard association. Washington's lost plan revived. ₍Chicago? 1935₎
    cover-title, 23 p. 23ᵐᵐ.

  "Washington's lost plan revived ... by Professor James Weber Linn ...
Reprinted" (with special t.-p.) : p. ₍7₎-20.

    I. Linn, James Weber, 1876–   II. Title: Washington's lost plan
revived.
                                              35-25713

  Library of Congress   UA42.A6N35 1935
  ——— Copy 2.   ₍2₎   355.0973

NN   0053216   DLC

UA661   National guard association of the United States.
.M3   An appeal to the 74th Congress.
1745 a
         ₍Martin,   ₎ colonel. ·
           A plan for establishing and disciplining a national militia
         in Great Britain, Ireland, and in all the British dominions of
         America. London, A. Millar, 1745 ₍Chicago? 1936₎

National guard association of the
United States.
  Constitution and by-laws...adopted
at the convention held at Indianapolis,
Indiana, February, 1923.   (n.p.)
1923.
  cover-title, 4 p.   23 cm.

NN   0053218   DNW

UA42   **National Guard Association of the United States.**
.N24
           The **National** guardsman. v. 1–
         Mar. 1947–
         ₍Harrisburg, Pa.₎

WASP
National Guard Association of the United States.
  The Nation's National Guard. ₍Washington₎ 1954.
    119 p. illus. 24 cm.

  "Addresses delivered by Major General Ellard A. Walsh, president
of the National Guard Association of the United States, and Major
General Edgar C. Erickson, chief of the National Guard Bureau of
the Departments of the Army and the Air Force."

  1. U. S.—National Guard. 2. U. S.—Air National Guard.
  I. Walsh, Ellard A., 1887–   II. Title.

  UA42.N26   355   55-289 ‡

ScCleU
OOxM NN PSC MB TU ViU NcD ODW PBL MsSM ScU PV
OrHi WaSp IdPI MtBC OCU OO KyU KyLx OC1U OC1W IU
OrP OrPR OrSaW OrU Wa WaT WaTC WaWW FTaSU MiU
NN   0053220   DLC IdB IdU MtU Or OrAshS OrCS OrLgE

National Guard Association of the United States.
  Official proceedings of the general conference.

  ₍n. p.₎
    v. 24 cm.
  Title varies : 19   Annual convention report.—

  1946, Annual conference.—1947, Proceedings of the annual conference.
Other slight variations in title.

  1. U. S.—Militia—Societies.

  UA42.A6N25   355   51-37189 ‡

KyLoU WrU DNW CtY
NN   0053221   DLC DS ICJ NBuC NIC IdB OrU ICRL UU TU

National Guard Association of the United States.
  A plan for the permanent post-war military
establishment of the Army of the United States
revised 25 April, 1945, To the Congress of the
United States on behalf of the National guard
of the United States. Washington, D.C., 1945.

NN   0053222   MH

National Guard Association of the United States. Proceedings of the annual conference.
  see its Official proceedings of the general conference.

National guard association of the United States.
  Statement of policy adopted by the National guard association of the United States and the Adjutants general association of the United States, in joint convention at Baltimore,
Maryland May 4, 1944. ₍Baltimore? 1944₎
    cover-title, 4 p. 23½ᵐ.
    Signed : E. A. Walsh, president.

  1. U. S.—Militia. 2. U. S. Army.   I. Adjutants general association
of the United States. II. Walsh, Ellard A., 1887–
                                              46-12075

  Library of Congress   UA23.N245
                               ₍2₎   355

NN   0053224   DLC

National guard association of the United States.
  Statement of policy submitted to the House Select commit-
tee on post-war military organization, by Major General E. A.
Walsh ... on behalf of National guard association of the United
States and the Adjutants general association of the United
States, May 18, 1944. ₍Baltimore? 1944₎
    cover-title, 15 p. 23½ᵐ.

  1. U. S.—Militia. 2. U. S. Army.   I. Adjutants general association
of the United States. II. Walsh, Ellard A., 1887–
                                              46-12079

  Library of Congress   UA23.N246
                               ₍2₎   355

NN   0053225   DLC

National guard association of the United States.
  The volunteers of America. Proceedings of the con-
vention of national guards. St. Louis, Oct. 1st, 1879. St.
Louis, J. J. Daly & co., printers, 1879.
    cover-title, 18 p., 1 l. 22ᵐᵐ.

  1. U. S.—Militia.

  Library of Congress   U1.N17
                                              8-17141†

NN   0053226   DLC

National Guard Association of the United States. *Com-
  mittee on Legislation.*
  Report.
  ₍Washington?₎
      v. 28 cm.

  1. U. S.—Militia—Societies. 2. Military law—U. S.

  UA42.A6N33   355   51-40845 ‡

NN   0053227   DLC

The NATIONAL GUARD gazette. Devoted to the
  interests of national guardsmen of the United
States...Columbus, Ohio, 1897
  v. illus 21½ cm.

NN   0053228   DNW DNLM

VOLUME 407

The National guard in service
    see under   [Ordway, Albert] 1843-1897, comp.

The **National** guard magazine. v. 1–
    Jan. 1907–
    Columbus, O., E. T. Miller, 1907–
    v. illus., plates. 23½ᶜᵐ. monthly.
    Editor: Jan. 1907–   E. T. Miller.

1. U. S.—Militia—Period.   I. Miller, Edward T., ed.
                                                8-32061†

Library of Congress   U1.N175

NN   0053230   DLC NcD

The NATIONAL guard magazine. v. 1, no. 1-12;
    Apr. 1915-Mar. 1916.
    London. Terry, Herbert & co.   v.   illus., ports.
    25cm.

    Monthly.
    Title also as the National guard.

1. Militia—Gt. Br. —Per. and   soc. publ. I. Title: The
National guard.

NN   0053231   NN DNW NjP

National guard magazine. Special edition. v. 14.
    no. 3, 1917.   New York
        see   National Guard Association of the
    United States.
        Offical proceedings of the general conference.

National guard of industry.
    Platform and subordinate constitution of the National
guard of industry of the United States. Organized October, 1869. Washington, Powell, Gink and company, 1870.
    8 p. 18½ᶜᵐ.

1. Trade-unions—U. S.
                                    CA 9-5361 Unrev'd

Library of Congress   HD3136.W3N3

NN   0053233   DLC

NATIONAL guard of the United States. [Baton Rouge,
    La., Army and Navy pub. co., 1938-40] 29 v.
    illus. 31cm.

[Vols. 1-29]
    Cover-title.
    Title-pages vary: Historical and pictorial review, National guard;
Historical and pictorial review National guard, Naval militia and
Governor's guard; Historical annual, National guard. National guard,
Pictorial review.

CONTENTS. — [v. 1] Arizona. —[v. 2] Arkansas. —[v. 3]
Connecticut. —[v. 4] Delaware. —[v. 5] Florida. —[v. 6] Idaho. —[v. 7]
Indiana. — [v. 8] Iowa. —[v. 9] Maine. —[v. 10] Maryland. —[v. 11]
Massachusetts. —[v. 12] Mississippi. —[v. 13] Missouri. —[v. 14]
Montana. —[v. 15] Nebraska. —[v. 16] New Hampshire. —[v. 17] North
Carolina. —[v. 18] North Dakota. —[v. 19] Oklahoma. — [v. 20] Oregon.
— [v. 21] Rhode Island. —[v. 22] South Dakota. —[v. 23] Tennessee. —
[v. 24] Vermont. —[v. 25] Virginia. — [v. 26] Washington. —
[v. 27] Wisconsin. —[v. 28]   Wyoming. —[v. 29] New
Mexico.

1. Militia—U. S. I.Historical and pictorial review, National guard.
II. Historical annual, National guard. III. Pictorial review,
National guard.

NN   0053234   NN

National guardian; the progressive news-weekly. v. 1–
    Oct. 18, 1948–
    New York.
        v. illus., ports. 39 cm. weekly (Irregular)
    Subtitle varies slightly.
    Editor: Oct. 1948–   C. Belfrage.

I. Belfrage, Cedric, 1904–   ed.

A P2.N244   52-36925

NN   NN CU NcU PPT MiU MiDW InNd NcU CStbS
0053235   DLC PU FTaSU TxU MsSM InU NcD KU NcU

The **National guardian directory of the Scottish licensed
    trade.**
    [Glasgow, Munro-Barr Publications]
        v. 22 cm. annual.
    Continues The Scottish licensed trade directory.

1. Liquor traffic—Scotland—Directories.
HD9361.7.A3S35   381'.45'663102541   73-646758
                                              MARC-S

NN   0053236   DLC

The **National** guardsman. v. 1–
    Mar. 1947–
    [Harrisburg, Pa.]
        v. in   illus. 29 cm. monthly.
    Official publication of the National Guard Association of the
United States.

1. U. S.—Militia—Period.   I. National Guard Association of the
United States.
UA42.N24   56-33064

NN   0053237   DLC NjR NN MiU KMK CoCA N

The **National** guardsman.
    New York and Waterbury, Conn., 18
        v.   29ᶜᵐ. semimonthly.
    Editor: M. R. Pearsall.

1. Military art and science—Period. 2. U. S.—Militia—Period.
Pearsall, Marvin R., ed.
                                    CA 8-1875 Unrev'd

Library of Congress   I71 N19

NN   0053238   DLC

The **National** guardsman; [a journal devoted to the interests
    of the National guard of the U. S.] v. 1–
    Aug. 1877–
    New York, C. A. Coffin, 1877–
        v. illus., diagrs. 31ᶜᵐ. monthly.
    Ceased publication with Oct. 1878 issue.

1. U. S.—Militia—Period. 2. Military art and science—Period.
                                              43-43719

Library of Congress   UA42.A6N3

NN   0053239   DLC NN NjP

430
N212   **National Guidance Federation of Agricultural
        Co-operative Associations.**
        Rice stem borer control by parathion com-
        pounds in 1952.   Tokyo [1953]
        30 p.

        1. Chilo simplex.

NN   0053240   DNAL

National guide: attorneys and practitioners; counsel before
    Federal and State administrative tribunals, Interstate Com-
    merce Commission, Maritime Commission, United States
    Patent Office; biographical information; State aeronautical,
    motor carrier, and railroad law digests. 1942–
    Chicago, Traffic Service Corp.
        v. 26 cm. annual.
    Subtitle varies.

1. Lawyers—U. S.—Direct. 2. Law—U. S.—Digests. I. Traffic
Service Corporation.
                                        42-19520 rev*

NN   0053241   DLC WaU-L OC1

National guide of motorcycle dealers
    see under   [Beijen, Louis Karel Antoine]
    1914–

National Guild of Community Music Schools.
    National Guild of Community Music Schools, founded
1937. [n. p.] 1946.
    31 p. 22 cm.

ML27.U5N37   780.72973   49-41005*

NN   0053242   DLC

National guild of community music schools.
    Quarterly... v. 1–

Philadelphia, 1940–   v.   24cm.
    Irregular.

1. Music settlements, U. S.—Per.   and soc. publ.
N. Y. P. L.   February 9, 1949

NN   0053243   NN

National guild of piano teachers.
    The ... annual national directory of piano teachers, with
details pertaining to the National piano playing tournament.
1st–
    New York, N. Y., The National guild of piano teachers, inc.
[1937]–
        v. 27ᶜᵐ.
    On cover of 1st–   : National directory of piano teachers, United
States of America ... Yearbook of the National guild of piano teachers
inc.
    1. Pianists—Direct. 2. Music teachers—Direct.   I. Title. II. Title:
National directory of piano teachers. III. Title: Directory of piano
teachers. IV. Title: Piano teachers, National directory of.

Library of Congress   ML13.N24   38-9101
——— 2d set.   [8]   780.58

NN   0053244   DLC NcD OC1 MB

National guild of piano teachers.
    The guild syllabus. Streamlined ed. [Austin, Tex.] Na-
tional guild of piano teachers [*1944]
    19 p. 1 illus. 16ᶜᵐ.
    Edited by Irl Allison. cf. Foreword.

I. Allison, Irl, 1896–   ed.
                                            45-15233
Library of Congress   ML27.U5N38
                                            780.8

NN   0053245   DLC OrP

National Guild of Piano-Teachers.
    Roster...
    1936

[Hollywood, Cal., 1936   22½cm.
    no.
    Cover-title.
    At head of table of contents: National Guild of Piano-Teachers, Inc. National
Piano-Playing Tournament. Roster and bulletin.

1. Music—Assoc. and org.—U. S.   2. Music—Competitions, prizes, etc.
I. National Piano-Playing Tourna-   ment of the United States of America.
N. Y. P. L.   February 17, 1937

NN   0053246   NN

VOLUME 407

National guild of piano teachers.
Student's handbook for entrants in the national piano playing auditions, U. S. A. Sponsored by the National guild of piano teachers, U. S. A. ... ₍Austin, Tex., 1945₎
cover-title, 24 p. 15ᶜᵐ.

1. Music—Competitions.
                                                                    46–12181
Library of Congress   ML76.N28

NN   0053247   DLC

National guild of piano teachers.
Yearbook
        see its   The ... annual national directory of piano teachers.

National guilds, an inquiry into the wage system and the way out
        see under   Orage, Alfred Richard, 1873–

National Guilds League, London.
A catechism of national guilds.   [London, printed and published by the Victoria House Printing Co., Ltd., for the National Guilds League, 19––]
8 p.
Without title-page. Caption title.
At head of title: National Guilds League leaflets, 1.
"Reprinted, with revisions, from the New Age."

NN   0053250   MH

National guilds league, *London.*
Education and the guild idea. London, Pub. for the National guilds league by the Labour publishing company, limited, 1921.
cover-title, 19 p. diagr. 22ᶜᵐ.
Bibliography: p. 17–18.

1. Education—Addresses, essays, lectures. 2. Gild socialism.   I. Title.
Library of Congress   LC191.N3
                                                                    22–5097

NN   0053251   DLC MiU NN

HD
6479   **National Guilds League, London**
+N3   The guild idea; an appeal to the public. London, Printed and published by the Victoria House Printing Co., ltd., for the National Guilds League ₍19––₎
        19 p.   25 cm. (in binder, 27 cm.)   (*Its* Pamphlets, no. 2)

1. Gild socialism. I. Title.

NN   0053252   WU

National guilds league, *London.*
Guild socialism; a syllabus for class and study circles. London, The National guilds league, ₍192–?₎
cover-title, 20 p. 21½ᶜᵐ.

1. Gilds. 2. Trade-unions.   I. Title.

NN   0053253   MiU

National guilds league, London.
The Guild socialist; a journal of workers' control. no. 1–78; ₍Dec.?₎ 1916–Aug. 1923. ₍London, National guilds league; etc., etc.₎ 1916–23.

National guilds league, London.
Lloyd, J   Henry.
    ... Guilds and the salary earner, by J. Henry Lloyd. London, Published for the National guilds league by the Labour publishing company, limited, 1921.

National guilds league, London.
        National guilds league leaflets...
    London, ₍191– ₎

HD6661
.N25

NN   0053256   DLC

National guilds league, *London.*
National guilds or Whitley councils? Being a reprint, with a new introduction, of two pamphlets, entitled:— "Observations on the Whitley report," and "Notes for trade unionists on the Whitley report." London, The National guilds league ₍1918?₎
20 p. 21½ᶜᵐ.

1. Gild socialism. 2. Labor and laboring classes—Gt. Brit. 3. Gt. Brit. Ministry of reconstruction. Committee on relations between employers and employed. 4. Labor representation in regulation of industry.   I. Title : Whitley councils.
                                                                    19–10153
Library of Congress   HD5546.A3N3

NN   0053257   DLC MiU CaBVaU

National guilds league, London.
HD6661   Pamphlets ...
.N3   London, ₍1917?₎

NN   0053258   DLC DL MiD ICJ

National guilds league, *London.*
... The policy of guild socialism; a statement prepared and issued in accordance with the instructions of the annual conference of the National guilds league. London, Published for the National guilds league by the Labour publishing company, ltd., 1921.
cover-title, 23 p. 20½ᶜᵐ.

1. Gild socialism.

NN   0053259   MiU ICU WU CtY MH NN CaBVaU

National Guilds League, London.
Rules and constitution.   [Letchworth, England, Garden City Press, 191–?]
2 p.
Without title-page. Caption title.

NN   0053260   MH

HD6661   National guilds league, London.
.N38   A short statement of the principles and objects ...
        London [191–]

NN   0053261   DLC MH MiU

National guilds league, London.
Cole, George Douglas Howard, 1889–
    ... Unemployment and industrial maintenance, by G. D. H. Cole. London, Published for the National guilds league by the Labour publishing company, limited, 1921.

The National Guilds League, London.
Wage-slaves or free men: the building-workers choice.   [Keighley, Wadsworth & Co., The Rydal Press, 19––]
4 p.
Without title-page. Caption title.
Another issue, Type reset.

NN   0053263   MH

National guilds league, London.
Cole, George Douglas Howard, 1889–
    Workers' control series ... by G. D. H. Cole ... London, Published for the National guilds league by the Labour publishing company ltd. ₍1921–

National Guilds League, London.
Your part in control, an appeal to the rank and file. [London, National Guilds League, 191– ?]
11 p.
Without title-page. Caption title.

NN   0053265   MH

National gun association.
₍Union Pacific railroad company₎
    American rules for trap shooting adopted by the National gun association, and revised game laws for western states and territories. April 1, 1890 ... Omaha, Neb. ₍W. C. Gage & sons, printers, ʻ1890₎

GV1163
.N2A3
National gun association.
    History, constitution and by-laws, trap-shooting rules, tournament programmes of the National gun association ... ₍Cincinnati₎ ʻ1885.
77 p. 20½ᶜᵐ.

1. Trap shooting.
                                                        CA 5–1970 Unrev'd

NN   0053267   DLC

M2132
.W3N29   National gymanfa ganu association.

        Annual National gymanfa ganu ...
                ₍Chicago?₎ 19
        v.   illus. (ports.)   22cm.

1. Hymns, Welsh.

NN   0053268   DLC

National Gymanfa Ganu Association

Favorite Welsh and English hymns and melodies. [Warren, Ohio, Printing Service, Inc., 194– ?]
80 p. music.

NN   0053269   MH-Mu MH-AH

VOLUME 407

National Gymanfa Ganu Association.

M2132
.W3O6 **Old** and new Welsh and English hymns. ₁n. p., Gymanfa Ganu, 1939₎

National Gypsum Company.
Annual report.
₁Buffalo₎
v. illus. 28 cm.

HD9585.G9U583   49-37171*₁

NN   0053271   DLC OrCS

National gypsum company.
Employees' retirement plan. 4. ed.   [Buffalo]
1951.   16 p.   18cm.

1. Pensions, Old age—U.S.

NN   0053272   NN

National habits of providence
see under   Howard association, London.

National half-century exposition, Chicago. 1915

see

Chicago. Illinois national half-century exposition, 1915.

National ham and eggs. v. 1 (Dec. 3, 1938 – Nov. 4, 1939).   Los Angeles ₁etc.₎ 1938-39.   1 v.   illus. (incl. ports.)   43cm.

Weekly.
Vol. 1, no. 1 (Dec. 3, 1938) caption-title reads: Ham and eggs.
Published by the Retirement life payments association, Hollywood, Cal.
Ceased publication with v. 1, no. 49 (Nov. 4, 1939).

1. Pensions, Old age—Per. and age—U. S.—California. I. Retirewood, Cal. II. Title: Ham and N. Y. P. L.

soc. publ.—U. S. 2. Pensions, Old ment life payments association, Hollyeggs.

May 13, 1941

NN   0053275   NN CU-A

636.4   National Hampshire Meat Hog Conference.
H182   Conference program.

₁Peoria, Ill., Hampshire Swine Registry₎
v.   illus. 23cm.

Annual, 1948-
Issued
as the National Hampshire
Type Conference; other slight variations in
name of conference.

2 no. a year, 1964-

NN   0053276   IU

National Hampton Association
see Hampton Institute, Hampton, Va. National Hampton Association.

The National handbook of Australia's industries
see under   Pratt, Ambrose, 1874-

The **national** hand-book of facts and figures, historical, statistical, documentary, political, from the formation of the government to the present time. With a full chronology of the rebellion. New York, E. B. Treat & co.; Chicago, Ill., R. C. Treat & C. W. Lilley; ₁etc., etc.₎ 1868.

viii, ₁9₎-407 p. incl. front. 19½ᵐ.

1. U. S.—Pol. & govt.—Handbooks, manuals, etc. 2. U. S.—Pol. & govt.—Civil war.

9—21506

Library of Congress   JK8.N3

NN   0053279   DLC MB NjP NIC DI

JK8   The **national** hand-book of facts and figures, historical,
.N3   statistical, documentary, political, from the formation
1870   of the government to the present time. With a full chronology of the rebellion. New York, E. B. Treat & co.; Chicago, Ill., R. C. Treat & C. W. Lilley; ₁etc., etc.₎ 1870.

viii, ₁9₎-407 p. incl. front. 19½ᵐ.

1. U. S.—Pol. & govt.—Handbooks, manuals, etc. 2. U. S.—Pol. & govt.—Civil war.

NN   0053280   ViU OClWHi DNLM

National handbook of restaurant data
see under   [Dahl, Joseph Oliver] 1893-

NATIONAL handbooks.
no.1

Melbourne: Robertson & Mullens Ltd. [1934   12-18½cm.
nos.   illus.

NN   0053282   NN

National Hands off Russia Committee.
Japanese rule in Siberia
see under title

... The national handy dictionary of the English language
see under   [Lupton, Frank M   ]
1854-1910, comp.

National hardware association of the U. S.
Views of manufacturers of hardware and kindred lines concerning inflation of commodity price and wages. Extracts from letters received in response to an inquiry of the National hardward association of the United States.   Phila. [1923?]
29 p.

NN   0053285   OClFRB

The **National** hardware bulletin
see
Hardware retailer.

National hardwood lumber association.
Consumers' register ... containing the lumber requirements per annum of several hundred selected factory consumers of hardwoods of the United States and Canada ...   Chicago
v.   quarterly.
Cover title.

NN   0053287   OCl

National hardwood lumber association.
Members of the National hardwood lumber association, hardwood lumber & veneer manufacturers, wholesale dealers & consumers.

NN   0053288   OCl DLC

National hardwood lumber association.
Official report.
₁Chicago?₎
v. ports. 27ᶜᵐ.
Title varies: 19   Report of the ... annual meeting of the National hardwood lumber association.
19   Official report ...

Library of Congress   HD6515.L9N3   7-31609

NN   0053289   DLC ICRL CU DNAL

National hardwood lumber association.
Official year book
see its   Official report.

99.76   National Hardwood Lumber Association.
N211Re   Règles de classement pour le mesurage et l'inspection des bois francs.   [Québec?] 1941.
10, 9 p.

NN   0053291   DNAL

National hardwood lumber association.
Rules for the measurement and inspection of hardwood lumber, cypress, veneers, and thin lumber...adopted at annual meeting held in Chicago, Ill., Sept. 22-23, 1938, effective Jan. 1, 1939. ₁Chic.₎ The Author, °1939.
120 p.

NN   0053292   MiD WaU IU NN

R674   NATIONAL hardwood lumber association.
N2155R   Rules for the measurement and inspection of hardwood lumber, cypress, veneers, and thin lumber; and National hardwood lumber sales code. Includes revisions adopted at annual meeting...
1950- Chicago.   tabs.

NN   0053293   WaS OrP

National Hardwood Lumber Association.
Rules for the measurement and inspection of hardwood lumber, cypress, veneers, and thin lumber; and National hardwood lumber sales code. Includes revisions adopted at annual meeting held in Chicago, Illinois, September 27-29, 1949, effective January 1, 1950. Chicago, 1950.
102 p.

1. Lumber. 2. Grades and standards. 674.003

NN   0053294   ICJ

VOLUME 407

NATIONAL hardwood lumber association.
Standard specifications for grades of hardwoods and cypress lumber for freight cars and locomotives, in accordance with Association of American railroads recommended practice, rev. 1933 and conforming to American lumber standards.
Author. 1935. 31p.

With which are bound its Standard specifications for structural stress-grades of hardwoods and cypress, joist and plank, beams and stringers,

NN 0053295   WaS

99.76
N211N National hardwood lumber association.
Standard specifications for structural stress-grades of hardwoods and cypress; joist and plank beams and stringers, posts and timbers.
Chicago

NN 0053296   DNAL

99.76
N211N National hardwood lumber association.
1936 standard specifications for structural stress-grades of hardwoods and cypress; joist and plank, beams and stringers, posts and timbers.
Chicago, Ill., The National hardwood lumber association [1936]
48 p. 15cm.

NN 0053297   DNAL

99.76
N211S National hardwood lumber association.
1940 standard specifications for grades of hardwoods and cypress lumber for freight cars and locomotives, in accordance with Association of American railroads recommended practice revised 1933, and conforming to American lumber standards. Chicago, Ill.
[1940?]
31 p.

NN 0053298   DNAL

99.76
N211N National Hardwood Lumber Association.
1941   1941 standard specifications for structural stress-grades of hardwoods and cypress; joist and plank beams and stringers, posts and timbers. Chicago, 1941.
51 p.
1. Lumber. Grading and standardization.

NN 0053299   DNAL

National hardwood lumber association.
Year book and official report
see its   Official report.

99.81
N212 National hardwood magazine. v.

Memphis, Memphis lumberman co.,

1. Hard woods. Periodicals. 2. Lumber. Periodicals. I. Memphis lumberman co., Memphis, Tenn.

NN 0053301   DNAL NN CaOTU OU DI OkS

99.79
N215 National hardwood magazine.
How to specify and use hardwoods.   [Memphis, 1953?]
40 p.

1. Hard woods. 2. Wood. Properties and uses.

NN 0053302   DNAL OrU

TS825
N276h National hardwood magazine..
How to specify and use hardwoods.
[Memphis, n.d.]
39 p. 22cm.

"The entire content of this booklet appeared in a series over a period of more than two years in National hardwood magazine "

1. Hardwoods. I. Title.

NN 0053303   GU

National hardy plant society. Year book. 1912. 8°. 304
pp. 51. il. Burnley, [1912].

NN 0053304   MBH

The National harp of Zion and B. Y. P. U. hymnal. A choice selection of hymns and tunes, arr. by some of the most competent musical composers and hymnologists in this country. A volume of harmonious, soul-inspiring melodies. Designed for use in Baptist churches, Sunday schools, prayer meetings, and young people's societies throughout the world. Nashville, Tenn., National Baptist Publishing Board [c1893]

144 p. 21 cm.

1. Baptists—Hymns. 2. Hymns, English. 3. Negro songs.
I. Baptist Young People's Union.

M2122.N25   74-207029
[M1670]

NN 0053305   DLC

National Hat Makers' Association   331.06191 125
of the United States.
123824 Proceedings of the ... biennial convention of the National Hat Makers' Association of the United States. ... . 1883-1886.

Library has no. 1-2, 1883-1885; special convention, 1886. 17-22cm.
Title varies slightly.

NN 0053306   ICJ WHi

The National hay and grain reporter. Chicago, [etc.], 1903-1913.
Library has vol. 4-19, 1903-1913. illus. ports. 30-37cm.

Cover-title; no index.
Title varies: vol. 4-6, Hay and grain reporter.
Vol. 8, no. 1-8, The National hay and grain weekly.
Irregular.
In July 1906 absorbed Grain mans guide.
In 1914 united with the Cincinnati price current to form the Price current—grain reporter.
Vol. 8-10 published in Decatur, Ill.
Wanting: vol. 4, no. 20, 35; vol. 7; vol. 8, no. 3, 11-12, 16; vol. 9, no. 2-3, 11, 19-20; vol. 10, no. 14-vol. 11.

NN 0053307   ICJ

The National hay and grain reporter. Grain exchange number.
179842 [May 20, 1911. Chicago, Ill., 1911.]
cover-title, 164 p. illus. (incl. ports.) 31cm.
Extracted from the National hay and grain reporter, vol. 14.

NN 0053308   ICJ

National hay and grain weekly
see   The National hay and grain reporter.

National hay association.
Grades of hay and straw; inspection and weighing rules, revised July 8, 1915, established by the National hay association, incorporated. [Winchester, Ind., S. S. Watson of Herald printing co., c1915]
cover-title, [12] p. 14½cm.

1. Hay trade. 2. Straw.   I. Title.

Library of Congress   HD9049.H3U54   15—18942

NN 0053310   DLC

National Hay Association.   338.139 R700
Grades of hay and straw; inspection and weighing rules, revised June 25, 1917, established by the National Hay Association, incorporated. [1917.]
cover-title, [12] p. 17cm.

NN 0053311   ICJ

National Hay Association.
Hay trade journal, strictly devoted to, and an exponent of American hay trade interests.
Canajoharie, N. Y. [Hay trade journal publishing co.]

National hay association.
The National hay press
see under title

National hay association.
Report of the ... annual convention. The National hay association (incorporated)
[n. p.,
v. ports. 19cm.
Contains the Official directory.

1. Hay trade—Societies.

Library of Congress   HD9049.H3U5   CA 11—959 Unrev'd

NN 0053314   DLC ICJ

National hay association.

Daish, John B[roughton] 1867-   comp.
State demurrage rules with digest; compiled for the National hay association, by John B. Daish ... Chicago, Grain dealers journal, 1904.

National hay association.
Year book.
1939

[Indianapolis? 1939   20cm.
no. ports.

Cover-title: 1939   Year book and membership directory.
Includes a report of its annual convention, previously issued separately. See its Report of the annual convention.

1. Hay—Trade and stat.—Assoc.   and org.—U. S.
N. Y. P. L.   January 27, 1941

NN 0053316   NN PPi

VOLUME 407

The NATIONAL hay press. v. 4, no. 6-7, 9-v. 46, no. 8;
Mar.-Apr., June, 1921-Aug. 1963
Strasburg, Va. [etc.]   v.   illus.
23cm.

Monthly.
Issued by the National hay association.

1. Hay--Per. and soc. publ.   I. National hay association.

NN   0053317   NN

National health.
v.

London, 19   v.   illus.   8°.
Monthly.
Numbering continuous.
Official organ of the Association of Infant Welfare and Maternity Centers, the
National Association for the Prevention of Infant Mortality and for the Welfare of
Infancy and of various other organizations.
Superseded by Mother & child, April, 1930.

1. Children--Per. and soc. publ.   —Gt. Br. I. Infant Welfare
and Maternity Centers, London.   II. National Association for the Prevention of Infant Mortality and for the   Welfare of Infancy.
N. Y. P. L.   January 12, 1931

NN   0053318   NN DNLM

W 1   NATIONAL health; a monthly journal devoted
NA46H   to the interests of public health and hygiene,
sanitation and sewage purification, town
planning, housing, parks and gardens.
v. 1, no. 1-12; Mar. 1946-Feb. 1947.
Johannesburg.
1 v. illus., ports.

1. Hygiene - period. 2. Public health -
period.

NN   0053319   DNLM NN WaS

National health administration of China
see   China. National health administratio:.

National health agencies; a directory
see   National health council.
Directory of member organizations.

National health and food guardians, inc.
Denatured foods and their vital relation to health;
startling disclosures of the evils practiced with corrective
suggestions by a practical food expert, issued by the Publishing and printing bureau of the National health and
food guardians, inc. ... [Hartford] ᶜ1924.

60 p. 23ᶜᵐ.

1. Food adulteration and inspection.

Library of Congress   TX531.N3   24-21087

NN   0053322   DLC

National health and medical research council, *Australia*
see
Australia. *National health and medical research council.*

National health and welfare retirement association, inc., New York.
Constitution and by-laws, as amended February
5, 1946. [1946]

NN   0053324   PU-PSW

National Health and Welfare Retirement Association, Inc., New York
Constitution and by-laws as amended, April
25, 1951.   N.Y. [National Health and Welfare
Retirement Association, Inc., 1951]
65p.   illus.

NN   0053325   ScU PU-PSW

National Health and Welfare Retirement Association.
inc., New York.
A national retirement program...
see under   American Hospital Association.

National Health Assembly, *Washington, D. C.*, 1948.
America's health; a report to the Nation. Official report.
[1st ed.] New York, Harper [1949]
xiv, 395 p. 24 cm.

1. Hygiene, Public—U. S. 2. Medicine—U. S. I. Title.

RA445.N28 1948   614.0973   49-4679*

OrCS WaSpG
OClW PLF PSt PBm PP OO OU WaT Wa OrP CaBViP MtU
NN   TU MiU ICRL ViU PPLas NSyU OOxM PHC Or OrU OrU-M
0053327   DLC WaS OC1 PPT FU-HC DNLM ICU ICJ TxU

National Health Assembly, *Washington, D. C., 1948.*
Planning for health services; a guide for States and communities. Washington, Federal Security Agency, Public
Health Service [1949]
vii, 69 p. 24 cm. (Public health bulletin no. 304)

1. Hygiene, Public—U. S.   (Series: U. S. Public Health Service.
Public health bulletin no. 304)
RA445.N28 1948⁺   614.0973   49-47131*
———— Copy 2.   RA11.B177 no. 304

NN   0053328   DLC PP PPT OCU

WA   NATIONAL Health Assembly, Washington,
900   1948
AD6   [Reports] Washington, 1948.
qN2r   1 v. (various pagings)
1948   1. Public health - U. S.

NN   0053329   DNLM

National Health Assembly. Washington, D. C., 1948.
Dental health section.
A compilation of data, abstracts of articles and
references to the literature.   Washington, D. C.
[1949]
(Mimeographed, loose leaf)

NN   0053330   PPT-D

---

389   National Health Assembly, Washington, D.C.,
N2142   1948. Nutrition Section.
[Reports, etc. of subcommittees.   Washington? 1948]
1 v. (various pagings)

1. Nutrition.

NN   0053331   DNAL

National health bureau of America.
Perfect health exercise book ... scientific development
with exercises and basic food values, by the National
health bureau of America ... [La Fayette, Ind.] ᶜ1923.
cover-title, 80 p. incl. illus., ports. 24½ᶜᵐ.
Advertising matter: p. 76-80.

1. Hygiene. 2. Exercise. 3. Diet. I. Title.

Library of Congress   RA776.N3   CA 23-170 Unrev'd

NN   0053332   DLC

RM702   National health bureau of America.
.T4   FOR OTHER EDITIONS
1924   SEE MAIN ENTRY
[Thayer, Gilbert]
Perfect health, how to be young at sixty and live to be one
hundred. 45th ed. (rev.) Lafayette, Ind., The National
health bureau of America, 1924.

National Health Conference, Washington, D.C., 1938.
Addenda to report on expansion of the existing
federal-state cooperative program for maternal and
child health. Report of Technical Committee on
Medical Care. ... [Washington, 1938]
[51] p. illus.

NN   0053334   ICJ

National health conference, Washington, D. C.,
1938.
U. S. *Interdepartmental committee to coordinate health and
welfare activities.*
National health conference, July 18-19-20, 1938, called by
the Interdepartmental committee to coordinate health and
welfare activities. Mayflower hotel, Washington, D. C.
[Washington, 1938]

National health conference, *Washington, D. C., 1938.*
The nation's health. Discussion at the National health conference, July 18, 19, 20, 1938, Washington, D. C., called by the
Interdepartmental committee to coordinate health and welfare
activities, to consider a national health program proposed in
the report of the Technical committee on medical care. Washington, U. S. Govt. print. off., 1939.
1 p. l., 116 p. 23ᶜᵐ.

1. Hygiene, Public—Congresses. 2. Hygiene, Public—U. S. 3. Medical economics. 4. Health surveys. I. U. S. Interdepartmental committee to coordinate health and welfare activities. II. Title.
Library of Congress   RA422.N27 1938 b   39-26288
———— Copy 2.   [7]   614.06373

NcD OCU OO OC1 NN ICJ Or
NN   0053336   DLC MtBC CaBVaU WaWW WaTC OrCS OrU

National health conference, *Washington, D. C., 1938.*
Proceedings of the National health conference, July 18,
19, 20, 1938, Washington, D. C. Interdepartmental committee to coordinate health and welfare activities. Josephine Roche, chairman. Washington, U. S. Govt. print off.,
1938.
ix, 163 p. 28½ x 23 cm.

1. Hygiene, Public—Congresses. 2. Hygiene, Public—U. S. 3.
Medical economics. I. Roche, Josephine Aspinwall, 1886-   II.
U. S. Interdepartmental committee to coordinate health and wel-
fare activities.
RA422.N27 1938   614.06373   39—26244

Or WaTC WaWW MtBC MBCo CaBVaU
NN   0053337   DLC OrCS OrU NcU OCU OO ICJ NcD TU

WA   NATIONAL Health Council
546   Aids to community health planning.
AA1   [3d ed.] New York [1952]
N2a   1 v. (various pagings)
1952   Cover title.
Collection of pamphlets in folder.
1. Health boards - U. S. 2. Public
health - U. S.

NN   0053338   DNLM OrCS

VOLUME 407

W 1   National Health Council
NA4642   Annual report.

             New York, 1922?-
                v.

NN   0053339   DNLM IU NN OrU-M

National Health Council.
    Bibliography: local health units and health councils.
    ₍New York, 1950₎
    11 l.   28 cm.
    Caption title.

    1. Health boards—U. S.—Bibl.

    Z6672.B5N38   016.61406173   53–17399

NN   0053340   DLC DNLM NNC

National Health Council.
    The Children's Bureau of the U. S. Department of Labor; a
report prepared by the National Health Council.   Washington,
D. C., 1922.   16 f.   2. ed., rev.   4°.

    Cover-title.
    Typewritten copy.
    "Prepared by Mr. James A. Tobey."—*Foreword.*

    1. U. S.—Children's Bureau.   2. Tobey, James Alner, 1894–
    N.Y.P.L.   April 25, 1923.

NN   0053341   NN

WA   NATIONAL Health Council
1   ₍Collection of publications₎
qN277
        The library has a collection of miscel-
laneous publications of this organization
kept as received. These publications are
not listed nor bound separately.

NN   0053342   DNLM

HV688   National Health Council.
U5N3   Directory of community health planning
         councils.   New York, National Health
         Council, 1950.
             vi, 98 l.

             Cover title.
             "A list of 34 state and 1190 local com-
         munity health planning councils identified
         in the course of a nation-wide survey ...
         carried out by the National Health Council
         during the fall and winter of 1949-50."

NN   0053343   CU OrCS   MiU NNC DNLM

RA445   National Health Council.
N214   Directory of community health planning
1953   councils.   ₍2d ed.₎ New York, 1953.
             116 p.

             1. Public health - Societies - Directories.
             2. Community health - Societies - Directories.

NN   0053344   NNC LU NNC-M

RA421   National Health Council.
N29   Directory of member organizations.

             New York.
                v.

             Title varies: 19   National health
         agencies; a directory of member organizations.

        MoU CU DNLM IU MB NcU PU NNC
NN   0053345   CU CaBVaU OrCS ICJ MiU NNC-M NN PU

National Health Council.   *6257.596
    Film list including information on visual aids and their producers
    .and distributors. Edition 5. 1928. Prepared and printed by
    Welfare Division, Metropolitan Life Insurance Company.
    — ₍New York. 1928.₎ 178 pp. 19 cm.

D9455 — Moving pictures. Bibl. — Metropolitan Life Insurance Company. Welfare Division. Pubs. — Moving pictures. Direct.

NN   0053346   MB

National Health Council.
    Five State Regional Conference for Promotion
of Full Time Local Health Units, Mitchell, Ind.,
1948
        see under title

RA445   National Health Council.
qN292   Forecasting America's health, a condensed
pam   report of the public interest portion of the
         program at the 35th annual meeting of the
         National Health Council March 23-25, New
         York City. New York, The Council, 1955.
             64 p. 28cm.

         1.Hygiene, Public - U.S.   I.Title.

             MiU CaBVaU
NN   0053348   OrCS InU NcU NNC-M DNLM CU NIC NcD

National Health Council.
    Health careers guidebook. ₍Written and edited by Zilpha
    G. Franklin₎ New York, 1955.
        153 p. illus. 22 x 28 cm.

        1. Public health as a profession. 2. Medicine as a profession.
        I. Franklin, Zilpha (Carruthers) II. Title.

        RA440.9.N3   610.69   55—7825 ‡

        OrStbM OkU-M WaS CU IaU WaU WaT
        PPT PPWM MiU MsU MtBC OrU-M NcGU CU FMU OC1W-H
NN   0053349   DLC Or OrCS DNLM MB PPJ OC1W ViU MB

National Health Council.
    Highlights of the 1954 National Health Forum
on Changing Factors in Staffing America's
Health Services

    see under

    National Health Forum, New York, 1954.

National health council..
    List of health films prepared by the
national health council ... (New York city)
1923.
    (3) 49 numb. l.   28 cm.

NN   0053351   DHEW

National health council.
    Local health units for the nation
        see under title

WA   NATIONAL Health Council
1   Membership and program. Washington
N277m   ₍1921?₎
1921   31 p. (Its Publication no. 2)
         Mss. additions and corrections.
         Series

NN   0053353   DNLM DL

National Health Council.
    National health agencies, a directory of member
organizations ...
    see its   Directory of member organizations.

National health council.
    The National health council, January 1, 1921 – January 1, 1925
... ₍New York, 1925₎ 47 p. 23cm.

NN   0053356   NN

WA   NATIONAL Health Council
22   The National Health Council and its
AA1   member organizations.
N3n   ₍1921₎-
             New York.
                v.
             Directory for 1921 issued as
         Publication, no. 2 of the National Health
         Council.
             Issue for 1921 has title: The National
         Health Council; membership and program.

             Continued by the council's Directory
         of member organizations.
             1. Public health - Societies - U. S. -
         Direct.   Series: National Health
         Council. Publication, no. 2

NN   0053358   DNLM NNC-M NN

National Health Council.
    The National Health Council and its member
organizations
        see also its   Directory of member
organizations.

---

613   National Health Council.
N277n   National health series.   New York and
London, Funk & Wagnalls ₍1924₎
    20v.

    Contents.- v.₍1₎ Man and the microbe, by
C.-E.A. Winslow.- v.₍2₎ The baby's health,
by R.A. Bolt.- v.₍3₎ Personal hygiene, by
A.J. McLaughlin.- v.₍4₎ Community health, by
D.B. Armstrong.- ~~v.₍5₎ Cancer, by F.G. Wood~~
~~v.₍6₎ The human machine, by W.H. Howell~~.-

    v.₍7₎ The young child's health, by H.L.K.
Shaw.- v.₍8₎ The child in school, by T.D.
Wood.- ~~v.₍9₎ Tuberculosis, by L.R. Williams~~.-
v.₍10₎ The quest for health, by J.A. Tobey.-
~~v.₍11₎ Love and marriage, by T.W. Galloway~~.-
v.₍12₎ Food for health's sake, by L.H. Gil-
lett.- v.₍13₎ Health of the worker, by L.K.
Frankel.- v.₍14₎ Exercises for health, by

    L.L. Meanes.- v.₍15₎ Venereal diseases, by
W.F. Snow.- ~~v.₍16₎ Your mind and you, by F.E.~~
~~Williams~~.- v.₍17₎ Taking care of your heart,
by T.S. Hart.- v.₍18₎ The expectant mother,
by R.L. DeNormandie.- v.₍19₎ Home care of
the sick, by C.D. Noyes.- v.₍20₎ Adolescence,
by M.A. Bigelow.

    1.✓Hygiene. 2. ✓ Hygiene, Public.
3.✓Physiology.   I ✓Title. a anals
for contents.

NN   0053362   FTaSU

VOLUME 407

National Health Council.
The 1955 National health forum on forecasting
America's health

see under

National Health Forum, New York, 1955.

National Health Council.
Partners for health. ₁Written and edited by Zilpha C.
Franklin₁ New York, 1955.
40 p. illus. 22 x 28 cm.

1. Public health as a profession.   ɪ. Franklin, Zilpha (Caruthers) ɪɪ. Title.
RA440.9.N33   614.069   55–7826 ‡

ViU PPT–D CU OrU–M
NN   0053364   DLC OC1U NcGU PU-Med-TS OC1W DNLM

National health council.

National conference on college hygiene. *2d, Washington, D. C.,* 1936.
... Proceedings. New York city, National tuberculosis association. 1937.

W 1
NA4649   NATIONAL Health Council
Proceedings of the ... annual meeting.
New York ₁ 1921?₁ -
v.
Title varies slightly.
Each vol. has also a distinctive title:
1952, What's in the Health Council idea?—
1953, Advancing the nation's health.
1. Public health - Period.

NN   0053366   DNLM

National health council.

American health congress, *Atlantic City,* 1926.
... Proceedings of the general sessions, with an index of the
published papers ... ₁New York, National health council,
ᶜ1926₁

National health council.

National conference on college hygiene. *1st, Syracuse, N. Y.,* 1931.
Proceedings of the National conference on college hygiene,
Syracuse university, Syracuse, N. Y., May 5–9, 1931. Sponsored by the Presidents' Committee of fifty on college hygiene,
The National health council, the American student health association. New York city, National tuberculosis association,
1931.

W 6
P3   NATIONAL Health Council
The public health summer school as
an opportunity for a profitable vacation.
New York ₁1924₁
15 p. illus.
Title

NN   0053369   DNLM

RA421
.N25   National health council.
...Publication.
Washington, D. C. ₁and₁ New York, ₁192

NN   0053370   DLC

National Health Council.
Report.
₁New York₁
v. 21 cm. annual.

RA421.N263   55–24384
Library of Congress

NN   0053371   DLC MiU FTaSU NbU

National health council.
Report on The Bureau of animal industry, of the
U. S. Department of agriculture. 1922.
10 ₁i.e. 11₁ numb l.

NN   0053372   DNAL

National health council.
A selected bibliography of books on
public health, issued by the National
health council... 2d ed. rev. January 1,
1924. (New York city? 1924)
2 p. l., 12 numb. l. 28 cm.

NN   0053373   DL

National Health Council.
Signs of the health times seen at the 1955
National Health Forum on forecasting America's
health
see under   National Health Forum, New York,
1955.

National health council.
------Statement. 1927-1928, 1930/31.
New York (1927-31?)
3 v. 23 cm.

NN   0053375   DL ICU NN DHEW CU

National health council,
Statement of membership and activities, 1941-
1942. New York, 1941.

NN   0053376   OrU–M

National Health Council.
Stepping stones to a health council
see under   Lyon, Yolande.

National health council.
Teamwork in public health enterprises...
New York, The National health council, 1923.
36 p.   23 cm.

NN   0053378   DHEW DNLM

National Health Council.
Where do we stand on local health units?
see under   National Advisory Committee on
Local Health Units.

National Health Council
see also
National Conference on Chronic Disease: Preventive As-
pects, *Chicago,* 1951.
National Conference on Health in Colleges.
National Health Forum.

National health council. Committee for the
study of voluntary health agencies.
HV688
.U5G8   Gunn, Selskar Michael, 1883–1944.
Voluntary health agencies, an interpretive study, by Selskar
M. Gunn and Philip S. Platt, with a foreword by Louis I.
Dublin; under the auspices of the National health council.
New York, The Ronald press company ₁1945₁

National health council. *Library*

see ₁City₁
New York.   National health library.

National Health Council.   National
Advisory Committee on Local Health Units
see   National Advisory Committee on
Local Health Units.

National health council. *National health library*

see ₁City₁
New York.   National health library.

W
20.5   National Health Education Committee.
N273do   Does medical research pay off in lives and dollars?
1951   ₁New York, 1951?₁
1 v. (unpaged) illus.
1. Economics, Medical - U. S. 2. Research - U. S.
ɪ. Title

NN   0053385   DNLM

National Health Education Committee.
Facts on the major killing and crippling diseases in the
United States today; heart diseases, cancer, mental illness,
arthritis, blindness, neurological diseases, and other health
problems.
New York.
v. illus., col. diagrs., tables. 29 cm.
Includes bibliographies.

1. U. S.—Statistics, Medical. ɪ. Title.
RA407.3.N3   614.59   55–3279 rev

NbU NcU-H ICJ DNLM
NN   0053386   DLC DAU NcGU AAP CU MB MiU TxU NbU–M

WE
140   NATIONAL Health Education Committee
qN277s   Summary reports: research progress
1955   against arthritis and metabolic diseases,
aided by the National Institute of Arthritis
and Metabolic Diseases or conducted at
the Clinical Center in Bethesda.
New York ₁1955₁
1 v. (unpaged) illus.
1. Arthritis 2. Metabolism - Disorders 3. Rheumatism

NN   0053387   DNLM MBCo OU NcU NNC-M MiU NNC

RH
E393   National Health Federation.
Bulletin. v. 1-   1955-
Monorovia, Calif.
v. 20 cm. monthly (except July-August)

1. Nutrition. Periodicals. 2. Food.
Periodicals. 3. Pollution. Periodicals.

NN   0053388   KU

VOLUME 407

W
32
AA1
qN2

NATIONAL Health Federation
₁Collection of publications₁

The Library has a collection of
miscellaneous publications of this
organization kept as received. These
publications are not listed or bound
separately.
1. Medical legislation - U. S.

NN   0053389   DNLM

WA
300
N277

National Health Forum.
₁1st₁-   1954-
New York, National Health Council, 1954-
v. annual.

1. Public health - congresses. I.
National Health   Council.

NN   0053390   NcU-H IU

614
N2124m

National Health Forum.
Report.

New York, National Health Council.
v. 20-28cm. annual.

Title varies: 1962, Summary of discussions
and reports.
Some issues lack series title.
Each issue has also a distinctive title.
Some vols. issued in unnumbered sections.

NN   0053391   IU NNC-M N

National Health Forum.
Summary of discussions and reports
see its Report.

S
614.0973
qN27

National Health   Forum, New York, 1954
Highlights of the 1954 National Health
Forum on Changing Factors in Staffing
America's Health Services₁conducted by
National Health Council as part of its
34th annual meeting, March 24, 25, 26, 1954,
New York City₁ New York ₁1954₁
113 p. 29 cm.

1. Hygiene. Public. U.S. Congresses.
I. Title.

NN   0053393   N MiU NNC DNLM CtY-M MiU

W3
NA589
1955s

National Health Forum, New York, 1955.
Signs of the health times seen at the
1955 National Health Forum on forecasting
America's health. [New York] National
Health Council [1955?]
64 p. ports.

"A condensed report of the public
portion of the program of the 35th
meeting of the National Health Council,
March 23-25, New York."
Cover title.

NN   0053394   WaU

W
275
DC2
qN2
1943

The NATIONAL health insurance act; a
message of vital importance. ₁Ottawa?
1943?₁
8 l.
1. State medicine - Canada

NN   0053395   DNLM

National Health Insurance Commission (England)
see Gt. Brit. National Health Insurance
Commission (England)

National Health Insurance Commission (Ireland)
see Gt. Brit. National Health Insurance
Commission (Ireland); Irish Free State. National
Health Insurance Commission.

National Health Insurance Commission (Scotland)
see Gt. Brit. National Health Insurance
Commission (Scotland)

National Health Insurance Commission (Wales)
see Gt. Brit. National Health Insurance
Commission (Wales)

National health insurance, Proposals for an alternative to the government bill ...
see under [Sale, Charles V]

National health library
see
New York. National health library.

₁National health publications, inc., *Chicago*₁
Baby's first year; health, care and training. ₁Chicago, 1944₁
98, ₁3₁ p. illus. 25½ᵐ.
"A Stork corner guild publication."

1. Infants—Care and hygiene.   I. Title.
                                              S G 45-68
U. S. Surg.-gen. off. Libr.
for Library of Congress °   RJ61.N34
                                 ₁2₁†   649.1

NN   0053402   DNLM DLC

The National health review. La Revue de la santé nationale.
v. 1-   (no. 1-   ) ; Jan. 1933-
₁Ottawa₁ Published by authority of the Minister of pensions
and national health ₁etc.₁ 1933-
v. 25ᵐ. quarterly.

Vol. 1, no. 1 published by the National health division of the Depart
ment of pensions and national health.

1. Hygiene, Public—Period. 2. Hygiene, Public—Canada.   I. Canada. Dept. of pensions and national health.
                                              43-27871
Library of Congress   RA421.N28
                           ₁2₁   614.05

NN   0053403   DLC CaBVaU DL ICU CLU NN

National health service.   •
Book of health, written and compiled for the National
health service ... ₁1925-   ₁ New York, N. Y., The
National health service ₁ᶜ1925-
v. illus. 18ᶜᵐ.
Edition for 1926 has title: New book of health.

1. Hygiene. 2. Medicine, Popular.   I. Title.
                                              25-25955
Library of Congress   RA776.N35
                                              614.05

NN   0053404   DLC DHEW

National Health Service,
New book of health, written and compiled from data pro-
cured from the United States government and the principal physicians and dieticians of the world... New York₁, cop. 1927₁.
173 p. illus. 16°.

477412A. 1. Hygiene, Personal.   May 21, 1930
N. Y. P. L.

NN   0053405   NN

National health service. 4 pp. 8°. [San
Francisco, 1888.]
Repr. from : Pacific M. & S. J., San Fran., 1888, xxxi.

NN   0053406   DNLM

A National health service ₁by₁ Alice.Bush, J. McMurray Cole,
E. F. Fowler ₁and others₁ ... Wellington, N. Z., Progressive
publishing society, 1943.
4 p. l., 108 p. incl. front., diagrs. 18½ᵐ.
"2nd impression."

1. Hygiene, Public—New Zealand.   I. Bush, Alice.
New York. Public library   A 44-4869
for Library of Congress   RA555.N3
                                 ₁2₁†   614.09931

NN   0053407   NN DNLM NNC NNC-M CtY DLC

The National National Health Service act in Great
Britain
see under The Practitioner.

National Health Service acts: accounts
see under Gt. Brit. Exchequer and Audit
Dept.

A national health service for Great Britain.
(*In* International labour review. April-May, 1944. v. 49, p. ₁473₁-
481)

1. Hygiene, Public—Gt. Brit. 2. Medicine, State—Gt. Brit. 3. Gt. Brit.
Ministry of health. A national health service.
                                                        L 44-151
U. S. Dept. of labor. Libr.
for Library of Congress   [HD4811.I 65 vol. 49]
                                 ₁3₁   (331.05)

NN   0053410   DL

National health services commission (*South Africa*)
see
South Africa. *National health services commission.*

W 1
NA482

NATIONAL Health Society, London
Annual report.
1872/73-
London.
v.

NN   0053412   DNLM

National Health Society, London.

Facts concerning vaccination, for heads
of families. [Revised by the Local Government
Board, and issued with their sanction.] Vaccination and small-pox. 8 pp. 12°. [London, Allman & Son, 1880?]

NN   0053413   DNLM

VOLUME 407

Film 1069 no. 24

NATIONAL Health Society, London
How to prevent and oppose the cholera; plain instructions for heads of families and others. ₁London, Allman, 18--₎
8 p.
Film copy.
Caption title.
Imperfect: cover wanting.

NN 0053414 DNLM

National Health Society, London.
Lady Priestly memorial lectures.
no.
London: National Health Soc., 19   8°.

v.

Annual.

1. Hygiene (Public).
N. Y. P. L.   May 29, 1917.

NN 0053415 NN

National Health Society, London.
National Health Society's cookery for busy lives & small incomes; a handbook of practical instruction in plain cookery.
Liverpool: Literary Year Books Press, 1925. 97 p. 16°.

1. Cookery, English.
N. Y. P. L.   August 26, 1925

NN 0053416 NN

Film 1116 no. 31

NATIONAL Health Society, London
Synopsis of Prof. Metchnikoff's lecture on the warfare against tubercle.
London ₁1913?₎
4 p. (Priestley memorial lecture, 1912-13)
Film copy.
Caption title.
Series

NN 0053417 DNLM

National Health Survey
see under U.S. - Division of Public Health Methods.

W 1
NA485

NATIONAL hearing aid journal.

₁Sioux City, Iowa₎ 1947-
v.   illus., ports.
1. Hearing aids - Mechanical - Period.

NN 0053419 DNLM FTaSU KMK

M617.89025
qN274

National hearing aid journal.
Directory. 1947?-
Sioux City, Iowa.
v. in   illus. 29 cm. annual.

1. Hearing aids.   Mechanical   Direct.

NN 0053420 N

W 1
NA485A

NATIONAL Heart Foundation of Australia
Research in progress.

Canberra, 19
v.
1. Cardiology 2. Research

NN 0053421 DNLM

National Heart Institute
see U. S. *National Heart Institute.*

National (The) Heating and Ventilating Company operating the Timby system of heating, cooling, ventilating, and disinfecting. 8 pp., 2 pl. 8°. *Washington.* 1880.

NN 0053423 DNLM

National heating guide. Blue book of the industry
see under National radiator company.

National heirs protective league.
... Fisher's probate law directory ... Synopses of the laws of the various states in the United States and foreign countries relating to estates of deceased persons; copies of wills of prominent Americans; general forms of wills and citation of authorities; list of attorneys and counselors at law. ₁1st₎-
year; 1914-   St. Louis, Mo., Fisher's probate law directory ₁etc.₎ ₁°1913-

---

National Hells Canyon Association.
Before the Federal Power Commission in the matter of the Idaho Power Company

see under

Davidson & Nikoloric, Washington, D. C.

National Hells Canyon Association, Inc.
National Hells Canyon Association, Inc., et al., petitioners, v. Federal Power Commission, respondent, Idaho Power Company, intervener.
Washington ₁1955₎
13 pamphlets in 1 v.

Includes decision of hearing presiding examiner, briefs and petitions.

NN 0053427 NNC-L

627.1
N213

National Hells Canyon Association.
The people's fight to save Hells Canyon.
Portland, Ore., 1954.
11ℓ. 30cm.

Caption title.

1. Hells Canyon Dam (Proposed) 2. Water resources development. Northwest, Pacific.
I. Title.

NN 0053428 OrU

National helping fund "Dobroudja"

see

Dobroudja organisation in Bulgaria.

WH
1
N277

National Hemophilia Foundation.

[Collection of publications]

The Library has a collection of miscellaneous publications of this organization kept as received. These publications are not listed or bound separately.
1. Hemophilia

NN 0053430 DNLM

Micro-film 510

National Herald.
Lucknow, India. Washington, Library of Congress Photoduplication Service.

NN 0053431 KMK

National herald (New York)
see Ethnikos keryx.

National herb company, Washington, D.C.
Washington, nation's capitol ₁!₎ reproduced from the latest and best photographs; 70 new views ... Washington, D. C., The National herb company ₁192-₎

National herbarium and botanical museum, *Sydney*
see
Sydney. National herbarium and botanical museum.

National Herbart society
see
National society for the study of education.

National Hereford Hog Record Association.
Hereford swine journal
see under title

Special Collections

'SCG
.H916
.G12
no.2

The National Hibernian. Official Journal of the parent body of Ancient Order of Hibernians in Ireland in alliance with the A.O.H. in America. v.1,no.1-3; Mar.-May 1915. Dublin, 1915.
48p. 25cm. monthly.
Edited by F.S. Pollard.
No more published?

I. Ancient Order of Hibernians.

NN 0053437 MB DNLM

National Hide and Leather Bank, Boston.
Report of the hearing before Thos. Lamb, Geo. C. Richardson, Jas. H. Beal, referees, in the case of the National Hide and Leather Bank vs. George Homer, John G. Wetherell, Nathl. J. Bradlee, bondsmen for James D. Martin. Printed by the defendants. George O. Shattuck, attorney for the bank. John P. Healy, attorney for the bondsmen. Reported by James W. Perkins and George F. Walker.   Boston: A. Mudge & Son, law printers, 1870.   96 p. 23cm.

829016A. 1. Banks and bank-   ing—U. S.—Mass.—Boston, 1870.
2. Fraud—Trials—U. S.—Massachu-   setts.
N. Y. P. L.   July 1, 1936

NN 0053438 NN DLC

VOLUME 407

The **National** high school awards, 1930–1931. Best creative work. Edited by H. A. Berens. Continuing the series Literary leaves, 1928–1930 and Best creative work in American high schools, 1927. 1930. ₁Chicago₁ Quill and scroll, The International honorary society for high school journalists ₁ᶜ1931₁
160 p. illus. 20ᶜᵐ.
For later issues see Saplings.

1. American literature—20th cent. 2. School verse. 3. Children as authors. ɪ. Berens, H. A., ed. ɪɪ. Title : Best creative work.
ᴱ₁ 40–785

U. S. Off. of educ. Library   PS508.S4N2
for Library of Congress   ₁2₁

NN   0053439   DHEW InU IU

National High School Driver Education Award Program.
Report.

Sponsored by Accident Prevention Dept., Association of Casualty and Surety Companies.

National high school football annual.

Shelby, N. C., Universal Sports Press.
v. 27 cm.
Official publication of the N. H. S. F. C. Assn.

1. Foot-ball—Yearbooks.   ɪ. National High School Football Club.

GV951.A1N3   796.33   49–16590*‡

NN   0053441   DLC

GV951
.A1N3

National High School Football Club.

National high school football annual.

Shelby, N. C., Universal Sports Press.

National high school orchestra and band camp, Interlochen, Mich.
The overture. 1929-30   year book.

Interlochen, Mich., National high school orchestra camp associati on, 1929-30.
2 v.   illus.   23½ - 23 cm.
Opus   2-3
Editors: Gretchen Smoot:
            Edward Rhetts

NN   0053443   DHEW OU

National High-School Orchestra and Band Camp, Interlochen, Mich.
see also   National Music Camp.

National High School Orchestra Camp Association.
The overture. 1929-30 year book
see under   National High School Orchestra and Band Camp, Interlochen, Mich.

National High School Poetry Association.
Rhyming dictionary; a dictionary of rhymes, edited by Dennis Hartman. Los Angeles ₁ᶜ1949₁
224 p. 23 cm.

1. English language—Rime—Dictionaries.   ɪ. Hartman, Dennis, 1804–   ed. ɪɪ. Title.

PE1519.N3   *808.1 426.603   55–23778

NN   CaBVa
      0053446   DLC IdB MtBuM RPB Or WaSp WaU MB FU

PS59₁
.S3S6

National High School Poetry Association.

Songs of youth, a National anthology. Los Angeles, Poetry Society of America ₁1943₁

National High School Poetry Association.
Voice of **young** America.
see under   National Poetry Association.

National high school poetry association.

Young America sings ... anthology of private secondary school poetry. 1942–
Los Angeles, National high school poetry association ₁1942–

National high school poetry association.

The **young** Northwest sings ... anthology of Northwest high school poetry. 19   Los Angeles, Calif., National high school poetry association ₁ᶜ19

National high school poetry association.
The **young** West sings. 1938–   anthology of California high school poetry. Los Angeles, Calif., National high school poetry association ₁ᶜ1938–
v. 15½ᶜᵐ.

1. School verse. 2. High schools—California.   ɪ. Title.
38–15630

Library of Congress   PS591.S3N34
—— ——2d set.

Copyright   ₁3₁   811.50822

NN   0053451   DLC

National highway and airway carriers and routes. v. 1–
Mar. 1942–   Chicago, National Highway Carriers Directory.
v. in   maps. 30 cm. semiannual.
Title varies: 1942–   National highway carriers directory and routes, including air cargo transports (varies slightly)

1. Transportation, Automotive — U. S.—Direct. 2. Aeronautics, Commercial—U. S.—Direct.

HE5623.A45N3   388.3058   42–14688 rev*

NN   0053452   DLC OrP CoD OC1

National highway carriers directory and routes.
see **National** highway and airway carriers and routes.

HE6185
₁U5H18

National Highway Post Office Society.

H. P. O. notes.

₁Pleasantville, N. Y.₁

National highway stations, inc., *Washington, D. C.*
Tariff ... Containing list of cities, towns and villages located on highways and roads in the United States ... arranged in geographical order, segregated by road number, alphabetically indexed, with distance between points. no. 1–
Mar. 1, 1945–
Washington, D. C., ᶜ1945–
nos. 28ᶜᵐ.
Reproduced from type-written copy.

1. Transportation, Automotive—U. S. 2. U. S.—Distances, etc. 3. Roads—U. S.
45–20228

Library of Congress   HE5623.A1N28
₁2₁   388.3

NN   0053455   DLC

National highway traffic association.
Proceedings of the annual convention of the National highway traffic association and the Highway transport conference of the National automobile chamber of commerce ...
New York, National automobile chamber of commerce
v. 23ᶜᵐ.

1. Automobiles. 2. Motor trucks.   ɪ. National automobile chamber of commerce, inc. ɪɪ. Highway transport conference.

Library of Congress   HE5606.N3   ᴄᴀ 21–289 Unrev'd

NN   0053456   DLC OU OC1 ICJ CtY OrU

National Highway Users Conference.
The National Highway Users Conference (founded 1932), the Automotive Safety Foundation (founded 1937), and the Auto Industries Highway Safety Committee (founded 1946) merged in 1970 to form the Highway Users Federation for Safety and Mobility.
Works by these bodies are found under the name used at the time of publication.

388.1
N213a

National Highway Users Conference.
Acceleration of road improvements through bond issues; a report by NHUC'S Research Department.
Washington, 1955.
12ℓ. illus. 28cm.

Cover title.

1. Roads - U.S. - Finance. I. Title.

NN   0053458   TxU

National highway users conference.
Ahead with highway transportation; a statement of policies of the National highway users conference. ₁Washington, 1945₁
5 l. illus. 28cm.

1. Highway law—U.S. 2. High-   way finance—U.S.
N. Y. P. L.   March 18, 1948

NN   0053459   NN

National highway users conference.
Articles of organization, purposes and functions. Washington, Nat. highway users conference ₁1945₁ 12 p. 15cm.

1. Transportation—Assoc. and   org.—U. S.
N. Y. P. L.   November 20, 1947

NN   0053460   NN NNC

VOLUME 407

National highway users conference.
A bibliography dealing with highways and highway transportation. Prepared by National highway users conference ... August 1, 1935. Washington, D. C., 1935.
2 p. l., 46 numb. l. 28ᶜᵐ.
Planographed.
———— Supplements. Washington, D. C., 1935–
v. 28ᶜᵐ.
CONTENTS.—1st suppl. November 1, 1935.—2d suppl. March 1, 1936.—3d suppl. November 1, 1936.
1. Roads — Bibliography. 2. Transportation, Automotive — Bibliography. 3. ₍Highway transport—Bibliography₎

Bur. of railway econ. Libr.   Z7241.N2   A 37–300
for Library of Congress

NN   0053461   DBRE DNAL ICJ

S388.33   National Highway Users Conference.
qN274   Brief in opposition to Assembly, no. 96, State of New Jersey, entitled, "An act to create ports of entry to aid in the regulation of the use of the public highways of this state by commercial motor vehicles." Washington, D. C. [193–?]
8 l.   23 cm.

Cover title.

1. Motor-trucks. Law and legislation. New Jersey. I. Title.

NN   0053462   N

National highway users conference.
The case against restrictive regulation of highway transportation: abstract of testimony, in opposition to H. R. 6836, by authorities appearing before the House Committee on interstate and foreign commerce, 73rd Congress, 2nd session, January and February, 1934 ... Washington, D. C., National highway users conference, 1935.
31, ₍3₎ p. 28ᶜᵐ. (Highway user series, no. P1)

1. Highway law—U. S. 2. Automobiles—Law and regulations. I. U. S. Congress. House. Committee on interstate and foreign commerce

A 35–1245

Title from Univ. of Cin-   cinnati   HE5623.A5N3
₍3₎   Printed by L. C.

NN   0053463   OCU ViU MH-L

388.2   National Highway Users Conference.
N213c   The city traffic muddle--what exists? ₍Washington, 1954₎
23p. illus., ports. 21x28cm.

"From a panel of the Fifth Highway Transportation Congress, May 5, 1954."

1. City traffic—U.S. I. Title.

NN   0053464   IU

National highway users conference.
... Competition in transportation. ₍Washington, D. C., 1941?₎
15 p. 23 cm.

"A publication of the National highway users conference."
"An address by Chester H. Gray, director of the National highway users conference, delivered at the annual convention of the Mississippi valley association in St. Louis, Missouri, October 14, 1940."

"Highlights and summary": p. 3–4.

1. Transportation – U. S. 2. Roads – U. S. 3. Railroads – U. S. 4. Competition. ₍I, Gray, Chester Harold, 1897–   II. Title.

NN   0053466   Vi

National highway users conference.
Control of highway access; a summary of state legislation with 1955 legislative enactments. Wash.The Conference,1955.
6p.map,table,sq.4.

NN   0053467   CaBViP

National highway users conference.
Dedication of special highway revenues to highway purposes, an analysis of the desirability of protecting highway revenues through amendments to state constitutions. Washington, D. C., National highway users conference ₍1941₎
2 p. l., 10, ₍5₎ p. illus. (map) 28 cm.

1. Roads—U. S.—Finance. 2. Roads—U. S. I. Title.

HE355.N154   388.10973   42–18638 rev

NN   0053468   DLC OU NcU NNC Or

National highway users conference.
Diversion; an analysis of the practice of applying motor vehicle impost collections to other than highway purposes. Washington, Nat. highway users conference ₍1936₎ 32 p. illus. 27cm.

1. Finance—U. S.—States.   2. Automobiles—Taxation—U. S.
N. Y. P. L.   May 23, 1945

NN   0053469   NN DNAL

National highway users conference.
The Eastman report finds that highway users pay their way and more ... Washington, D. C., National highway users conference ₍1940₎
30 p. 23 cm.

Running title: Highway users pay their way and more.
Discussion of the report, "Public aids to transportation," published by the Office of federal coordinator of transportation, 1938–40.

1. U. S. Office of federal coordinator of transportation. Public aids to transportation. 2. Automobiles—Taxation. 3. Roads—U. S.—Finance. I. Title. II. Title: Highway users pay their way and more.

HE5623.N24   388.3   43–8450 rev

NN   0053470   DLC Or OrCS OrU OU NNC NN OC1FRB

HE5623.A1   **National highway users conference.**
N27   ...Economic and social values of the motor
no.R12   vehicle. Washington,D.C., National highway users conference ₍1937₎

63 p. incl.tables. 27½ᶜᵐ. (Highway user series: no.R 12)

1.Automobiles - Social aspects.2.Automobiles and economic development. I. Title.

NN   0053471   CSt PPT OU OC1 NBuG ViU

National Highway Users Conference.
The economic contribution of the motor vehicle. Washington [1933]
32 p. 27 cm. (Highway user series, no. R4)
Cover title.
1. Automobile industry and trade.

NN   0053472   ViU OCU PPT

National highway users conference.
Effects of weather and heavy loads on pavements ... Washington, D. C., National highway users conference ₍1941₎
31 p. illus. 28 x 21½ᶜᵐ.

"This bulletin is the work of Bertram H. Lindman of the National highway users staff."—Foreword.

1. Pavements. 2. Roads. 3. Automobiles. I. Lindman, Bertram Herman, 1906–   II. Title.

Library of Congress   TE250.N3   42–22605
₍3₎   625.8

NN   0053473   DLC NN OC1 OU MiD

National Highway Users Conference.
Equipment requirements for motor vehicles. 1940 ed. ... Washington, D.C. [ᶜ1940]
136 p. incl. tables. (Highway users series, no. L 3–B)

NN   0053474   MH-BA OC1

National highway users conference.
Equipment requirements for motor vehicles. 1942 ed. ... Washington, D.C. ₍c1941₎
140 p.incl.tables (1 double) illus. (Highway users series, no. L - 3)

NN   0053475   MH-BA OU

National highway users conference.
Equipment requirements for motor vehicles. 1946 ed. ... Washington, D.C. ₍c1946₎
153 p.incl.tables, diagr. (Highway users series: no. L 3)

NN   0053476   MH-BA

National Highway Users Conference.
Equipment requirements for motor vehicles. Washington ₍1947₎
1 v. (loose-leaf) 30 cm. (*Its* Motor vehicle law series. Service 3)

1. Automobiles—Laws and regulations—U. S. 2. Automobiles—Apparatus and supplies. I. Title.

HE5623.A5N32   629.2136   47–27141 rev*

NN   0053477   DLC

National Highway Users Conference.
The farmers' road problem; some suggestions for its solution, by Russell E. MacCleery, manager, State Services Dept. Washington ₍1950?₎
vi, 25 p. illus., ports. 23 cm.

1. Roads—U. S. I. MacCleery, Russell E. II. Title.

HE355.3.N3 1950?   388.1   51–18568

NN   0053478   DLC N DNAL Or

National highway users conference.
The farmer's taxes, new and old. Washington, D. C., National highway users conference ₍1941₎
51 p. illus. (maps) 23 cm.

"This survey was made ... by Myles W. English."—Foreword.

1. Agriculture—Taxation—U. S. 2. Motor fuels—Taxation—U. S. 3. Automobiles—Taxation—U. S. I. English, Myles Wesley, 1906–
II. Title.

HD9579.G4N28   336.27   42–12818 rev

NN   0053479   DLC Or OrU DNAL N OU NN

VOLUME 407

National highway users conference.

Federal aid - federal roads; a study of
federal highway legislation ... Washington,
D.C., 1936.
cover-title, 3 p.ℓ., 5-27 numb.ℓ.incl.tables.
([Highway user series, no. R8])

Manifold copy.

NN 0053480   MH-BA MH

NATIONAL HIGHWAY USERS CONFERENCE
Federal policy on toll roads ... Prepared by
J. Allyn Preston.   Author, 1954.
cover title, 4 ℓ.   (An NHUC research report)

NN 0053481   Or CaBViP PPCPC

N277   National highway users conference.
H6f   48 states - united! to achieve uniformity of
1951   motor vehicle laws. [Washington,D.C., National
highway users conference, 1951]
16 p.incl.illus.,ports.,maps.   16 x 23 ᶜᵐ.
Caption title.

1.Automobiles - Laws and regulations - U.S. 2.
Uniform laws - U.S. I.Title.

NN 0053482   MiU-L

HE5623
N37   National Highway Users Conference.

Gearing highway transportation to a
changing America.   [Washington, n.d.]
16 p.

1. Transportation, Automotive - U.S.
I. Title.

NN 0053483   HU

---

§
336.18   National highway users conference.
qN277
Highway development and financing; six
aspects of a vital problem.   [Wash.,D.C.]
1947.
18p. illus. 31cm.

1.Roads. U.S. 2.Roads. Finance. 3.Auto-
mobiles. Taxation. U.S. I.Title.

NN 0053484   N CSt

National Highway Users Conference, Washington,
D. C.
Highway facts of Alabama; a condensed
summary of state statistics, with some
comparable national totals.   Washington,
1945.
45-ℓ. 29cm.

1.Transportation, Automotive--Alabama.
2. Roads--Alabama.

NN 0053485   AAP

HE356   National Highway Users Conference, Washington,
C2N3   D.C.
Highway facts of California; a condensed
summary of state statistics, with some comparable national totals. Washington, National
Highway Users Conference, 1945.
45 ℓ. tables. 30cm.

Cover-title.

1. Roads - California. 2. Transportation,
Automotive - California.   I. Title.

NN 0053486   CU C

388.1   National highway users conference, Washington,
N218h   D.C.
Highway facts of Connecticut, a condensed summary of state statistics with some comparable
national totals.   Washington, D.C., National
highway users conference, 1945.
45 numb.l. incl.tables.

Reproduced from typewritten copy.

NN 0053487   IU

National Highway Users Conference.
Highway facts of Louisiana. A condensed
summary of state statistics, with some comparable national totals ... Washington, D.C.,
1945.
45 p. tables. 29 cm.
1. Roads - Louisiana. 2. Transportation,
Automotive - Louisiana. I. Title.

NN 0053488   LU

National highway user conference.
Highway facts of Massachusetts; a condensed summary of
state statistics, with some comparable national totals. Washington, National highway users conference, 1945.
45 numb. l. 28 cm.

1. Roads—Massachusetts. 2. Transportation, Automotive—Massachusetts.   I. Title.

A 45-3395 rev

Harvard Univ.   Library
for Library of Congress   [r50cⁱ]

NN 0053489   MH

National highway users conference.
Highway facts of Michigan; a condensed
summary of state statistics, with some comparable national totals.   Washington, 1946.
44 p. tables. 23 cm.

NN 0053490   Mi

HE356   National Highway Users Conference.
V8N2
Highway facts of Virginia; a condensed summary of state statistics, with some comparable national totals.   Washington, D.C., 1945.
45 ℓ. 29ᶜ.

1. Roads - Virginia. 2. Transportation,
Automotive - Virginia. I.Title.

NN 0053491   CSt

National Highway Users Conference.
Highway highlights
see   The highway user.

National highway users conference, Washington,
D. C.

Walker, John Earl, 1886–
Highway tax costs, by John E. Walker ... <1938 ed.> Washington, D. C., National highway users conference [1938]

National Highway Users Conference.
Highway taxation, finance and administration; an outline
of policies. Washington [1938?]
15 p. 28 cm.

1. Roads—U. S.—Finance. 2. Automobiles—Taxation—U. S.
3. Motor fuels—Taxation—U. S.

HE355.2.N3 1938   388.1   A 41-4707 rev*
Johns Hopkins Univ.   Library
for Library of Congress   [r60cⁱ]†

NN 0053494   MdBP OrU Or DLC NN OU

National Highway Users Conference.
Highway taxation, finance and administration; interpretations and definitions. Washington, 1945.
14 p. 23 cm.
"A special message to state and national highway user organizations": leaf inserted.

1. Roads—U. S.—Finance. 2. Automobiles—Taxation—U. S.
3. Motor fuels—Taxation—U. S.

HE355.2.N3 1945   388.1   45-20969 rev*

NN 0053495   DLC Or N IU NNC

National highway users conference.
The highway, the motor vehicle, and the community; a
study revealing how good roads and automotive equipment
meet the transportation needs of communities and help railroads to abandon unprofitable lines. Washington, D. C.,
National highway users conference [1938]
80 p. illus. (maps) 23 cm.
"The material in this study was prepared by Harold Gray and
Myles W. English."—p. 3.

1. Transporation, Automotive—U. S. 2. Railroads—U. S.   I.
Gray, Chester Harold, 1907–   II. English, Myles Wesley, 1909–
III. Title.

HE5623.N245   388.10973   39-25553 rev

NN 0053496   DLC Or OrU TU CoU NIC NN OU OC1 DNAL

National Highway Users Conference.
Highway transportation, presenting basic source material
for school activities; prepared by National Highway Users
Conference in cooperation with Association for Childhood
Education. [Washington, *1935]
52 p. illus. 23 cm.
Bibliography: p. 52.

1. Automobiles. 2. Roads. 3. Traffic engineering—U. S.   I. Association of Childhood Education (International) II. Title.

TL156.N3   388.3   36-454 rev*

NN 0053497   DLC Or OC1W DHEW

National Highway Users Conference.
Highway transportation feeds the nation in defense.
Washington [1941]
12 p. illus. 23 cm.
Cover title.

1. Transportation, Automotive—U. S.   I. Title.

HE5623.N246   388.30973   42-5786 rev*

NN 0053498   DLC NN DNAL

National Highway Users Conference.
Highway transportation in World War II. Washington
[1942]
59 l. 12 x 15 cm.
Cover title.

1. Transportation, Automotive—U. S. 2. Roads—U. S.   I. Title.

HE5623.N2466   388.3   43-4995 rev*

NN 0053499   DLC NN

National Highway Users Conference.
Highway transportation in World War II. Washington
[1942]
Microfilm (negative) made in 1943 by the Library of Congress.
Collation of the original, as determined from the film: 55 l.

1. Transportation, Automotive—U. S. 2. Roads—U. S.   I. Title.

Microfilm 361 HE   Mic 52-9 rev

NN 0053500   DLC

VOLUME 407

National Highway Users Conference.
Highway transportation legislation
see
National Highway Users Conference. *Legislative Reporting Dept.*
Highway transportation legislation.

National Highway Users Conference.
Highway transportation legislation ...
see also under   Highway Users Federation for Safety and Mobility. Governmental Activities Reporting Dept.

OrC₂
OrMonO
OrU

National Highway Users Conference.
Highway transportation re-makes America. Washington ₁1939₎
31 p. illus. 23 cm.

1. Transportation, Automotive—U. S. 2. Automobiles—Taxation—U. S. ɪ. Title.

HE5623.N247   388.10973   40–12843 rev*

NN 0053503   DLC Or OrCS OrMonO OrU NN OU

388.30973 National Highway Users Conference.
N274   The highway transportation story, in facts. [Washington, 1950]
32 p. illus. 21 cm.

ʟ. Transportation. Automotive. U. S. ɪ. Title.

NN 0053504   N

386.5   National Highway Users Conference.
N213
The highway transportation story in facts.
2d ed. ₁Washington, D.C.₎ 1954.
28p. illus. 23cm.

1. Transportation, Automotive. U.S. I. Title.

NN 0053505   OrU IEN OC1 AAP IU

National highway users conference.

... Highway user taxes. Washington, D. C.,
National highway users conference ₁1937₎
54 p. incl. tables, diagrs. 28ᶜᵐ. (Highway user series, no.R13)
Reproduced from typewritten copy.

1. Automobiles—Taxation. I. Title. II. Ser.

NN 0053506   ViU PPT NcU MH-BA N OCU

National Highway Users Conference.
Highway users series.
Washington, 1934–
v. illus. 28 cm.
Issued in three separately numbered parts: L, by the Legislative Reference Dept.; R, by the Research Dept.; P, by the Publicity Dept. Title varies slightly.
Most numbers in L series issued in rev. editions.

1. Automobiles—Laws and regulations—U. S. 2. Automobiles—Taxation—U. S. ɪ. Title.

HE5623.A1N3   36–160 rev*‡

NIC OrU OU
NN 0053507   DLC OrCS MB NN MiU OC1 OO ICU NNC OU

336.27 National highway users conference.
N21h   Highway users urge federal automotive excise tax repeal ... Prepared by the National highway users conference. Washington, D.C., 1947.
37p. incl. tables.

1. Automobiles--Taxation. 2. Gasoline--Taxation--U.S. I. Title.

NN 0053508   IU N NN Or OrU

National highway users conference.
Highways and motor transportation, a bibliography. Cumulative edition, December, 1, 1937. Washington, D. C., National highway users conference ₁1937₎
100 p. 28 x 21½ cm.

"₁Combines₎ books listed in the four previous issues ... as well as new and additional writings ... Compiled by C. Harold Gray." Photoprinted.

1. Transportation, Automotive—Bibl. 2. Roads—Bibl. 3. Traffic engineering—Bibl. ɪ. Gray, Chester Harold, 1907– ɪɪ. Title.

Z7164.T8N27   016.388   38–11761 rev

NN 0053509   DLC IaU CU CtY ICJ IaU NN OO OC1 OrU

National highway users conference.
Highways are war-time supply lines; a special study of communities dependent upon highway transportation. Washington, Nat. highway users conference, 1943. 19 p. 23cm.

ɪ. Automobiles—U. S. 2. Roads U. S. 3. World war, 1939– N. Y. P. L.   —Social and economic relations— —Transportation—U. S.   June 14, 1945

NN 0053510   NN DNAL

National highway users conference.
House trailers; a survey of all state legislative provisions which apply to their ownership and use
see its   State motor vehicle laws affecting mobile homes and travel trailers.

National Highway Users Conference.
House trailers; a survey of laws governing ownership and use.
see its   State motor vehicle laws affecting mobile homes and travel trailers.

National Highway Users Conference, Washington, D. C.
How should cities share in special motor taxes? A study of municipal participation in highway funds... Washington, D. C.: National Highway Users Conference, 1934. 15 p.   illus. 28cm. (Highway user series. no. R2.)

"Bibliography of references cited," p. 15.

1. Automobiles—Taxation—U. S., 1934. I. Ser. N. Y. P. L.   1934. 2. Municipal finance—U. S., September 20, 1935

NN 0053513   NN PPT OCU NBuG ViU IaDuL

NATIONAL HIGHWAY USERS CONFERENCE.
Information service.
Washington.   v.   28cm.
Irregular.

1. Roads--U.S. 2. Transportation, Automotive--U.S.

NN 0053514   NN

National highway users conference.

Stocker, Harry Ellis, 1889–
Inherent advantages of motor transportation, by Harry E. Stocker ... Washington, D. C., National highway users conference ₁pref. 1942₎

National highway users conference.
... The itinerant merchant; a memorandum surveying available information and analyzing legislative proposals. ₁Washington, D.C., 1939₎
27 numb. ℓ., 3 ℓ.

Caption title.
At head of title: For information only. Not for publication.
Manifold copy.

NN 0053516   MH-BA

S
388.31 National Highway Users Conference.
qN2694   The Kansas port of entry law; a study of the practical effect of its actual operation. Washington, D.C., 1934.
18 p. 29 cm. (Its Highway users series, no. R1)

Signed: Fred A. Eldean, research department.
Includes bibliography.

1. Transportation, Automotive. Laws and regulations.
2. Transportation,   Automotive, Taxation.
Kansas. ɪ. Title.   Series.

NN 0053517   N ViU CtY NBuG NN IaDuL MH-L PPT

HE5623 National Highway Users Conference.
.A5
qN22   Laws bulletin, v.1–
1947–
Washington, D.C., 1947–
v. illus. 28cm.

1. Automobiles - Laws and regulations.
2. Transportation - Laws and regulations.
I. Title.   ɪɪ. Title: Highway
transportation   law.

NN 0053518   OrCS CU

National highway users conference.
Military roads. A brief history of the construction of highways by the military establishment and a gazetteer of the military roads in continental United States. Prepared by National highway users conference ... Washington, D. C., 1935.
1 p. l., 20 numb. l. 28 cm.
Compiled by Chester Harold Gray.
Bibliography: leaves ₁19₎–20.

1. Military roads—U. S. ɪ. Gray, Chester Harold, 1907– comp.

HE355.N155   623.62   A 37–245 rev 2
Bureau of Railway   Economics. Library for Library of Congress   ₁59e₂₎†

NN 0053519   DBRE DNAL DNW DLC WHi MtHi

NATIONAL HIGHWAY USERS CONFERENCE.
The motor vehicle in disaster relief. Washington, [1939].

Manifold copy. ff.6.

NN 0053520   MH-PA

NATIONAL HIGHWAY USERS CONFERENCE.
Motor vehicle law reporting service.
Washington, D.C., 1947–
3v.
Looseleaf.

Contents:--v.1. State restrictions on motor vehicle sizes and weights.--v.2. Registration fees and special taxes for motor vehicles.--v.3. Equipment requirements for motor vehicles.

NN 0053521   WaU-L MiU

VOLUME 407

NATIONAL HIGHWAY USERS CONFERENCE.

Motor vehicle legislation, the 1935 trend; taxation, regulation, diversion, highways, safety. Washington, D.C.: National Highway Users Conference [1935] 12 p. table. 28cm.

843811A. 1. Automobiles—Jurisp.—U.S., 1935.

NN   0053522   NN Or DNAL IU MH OrU PPAuC

National highway users conference.

Motor vehicle taxes. Washington, D. C., 1947.
42 p. (Its Laws bulletin, v. 2)

1. Automobiles - Taxation.

NN   0053523   NNC

National Highway Users Conference.
NHUC reports
see its Reports.

National Highway Users Conference.
Our highways and the nation's defense. [Washington, 1941?]
15 p. illus. 23 cm.

1. Roads—U.S. 2. U.S.—Defenses.   I. Title.

TE23.N25   625.70973   41–25867 rev*

NN   0053525   DLC

TE183
.N3   National Highway Users Conference.

Planning and financing our highways; policies on highway planning, taxation, finance and administration. Washington, 1949.
15 p. 22 cm.

1. Roads—U.S. 2. Roads—Finance.

NN   0053526   TU Or CaBViP NN

National highway users conference
A positive program for highway transportation. Washington, Nat. highway users conference [1946] 8 l. illus. 23cm.

1. Transportation—U.S. 2. Auto-   mobiles—U.S. 3. Roads—U.S.
N.Y.P.L.   August 11, 1949

NN   0053527   NN

National highway users conference.
[Press release]

Washington, 19
v.   28cm.
Irregular.

1. Automobiles—Per. and soc.   publ. 2. Roads—Per. and soc. publ.
3. Automobiles—U.S. 4. Roads—   U.S.
N.Y.P.L.   April 15, 1943

NN   0053528   NN

National Highway Users Conference.
Proceedings
see Highway Transportation Congress.
Proceedings.

National Highway Users Conference.
Recent changes in state motor vehicle size and weight laws; special charts compiled pending biennial publication of size and weight limitations book. Washington, D. C., National highway users conference [1941]
[4] p. 28 cm.
"Corrected to August 15, 1941."—p. [3]

1. Automobiles—Laws and regulations—U. S. 2. Automobiles—Design and construction.

HE5623.A5N324   388.3   43–6845 rev 2

NN   0053530   DLC Or

National Highway Users Conference.
Registration fees and special taxes for motor vehicles.
1931

Washington, D. C., 1931–   28 – 29cm.
nos.

1931 in TB p.v.690.
Reproduced from typewritten copy.
Title varies: 1931   , State registration fees and special taxes for motor vehi-
cles; 193   , Registration fees and special taxes for motor vehicles.

1. Automobiles—Taxation—U. S.   I. Title.
N. Y. P. L.   December 6, 1934

NN   0053531   NN CU

National Highway Users Conference.
Registration fees and special taxes for motor vehicles
see also its State registration fees and special taxes for motor vehicles.

National highway users conference.
Registration fees and special taxes for motor vehicles. 1934 ed. Wash. [The Author] 1934.
35 p.

Earlier ed. has title: State registration fees and special taxes for motor vehicles.

NN   0053533   MiD

NATIONAL HIGHWAY USERS CONFERENCE.
Registration fees and special taxes for motor vehicles: a digest of license and taxation data incident to the purchase, registration and operation of motor vehicles as of January 1, 1936. Washington, D.C., Author c1936.
214 p. (its Highway users series no. L2)

NN   0053534   Or OrU IU MB

National highway users conference.
Registration fees and special taxes for motor vehicles. 1938 ed. Washington, D.C. [c1938]
202 p.incl.tables (1 double) forms. (Highway users series: no.L 2-A)

NN   0053535   MH-BA

National highway users conference.
Registration fees and special taxes for motor vehicles. 1940 ed. ... Washington, D.C. [c1940]
205 p.incl.tables, forms. (Highway users series: no.L-2-B)

NN   0053536   MH-BA RPB

National Highway Users Conference.
Registration fees and special taxes for motor vehicles. 1942 ed. ... Washington, D.C. [c1941]
202 p. incl. tables (Highway user series, no. L-2)
Manifold copy.

NN   0053537   MH-BA

National highway users conference.
Registration fees and special taxes for motor vehicles. 1946 ed. ... Washington, D.C. [c1946]
211 p.incl.tables. (Highway users series: no. L 2)

Manifold copy.

NN   0053538   MH-BA Or

National highway users conference.
Registration fees and special taxes for motor vehicles. 1944 ed. ... Washington, D.C. [c1944]
208 p.incl.tables. (Highway users series, no. L-2)

Manifold copy.

NN   0053539   MH-BA

National Highway Users Conference.
Registration fees and special taxes for motor vehicles. Washington [1947]
1 v. (loose-leaf) 30 cm. (Its Motor vehicle law series. Service 2)

1. Automobiles—Taxation—U. S. 2. Motor fuels—Taxation—U. S.
I. Title.

HE5623.A5N325   629.21342   47–27139 rev*

NN   0053540   DLC

388.205 National Highway Users Conference.
NA   Reports.

Washington.
v. 28cm.

Title varies: –May 1961, NHUC reports.

NN   0053541   IU N

625.703 National Highway Users Conference.
N216r
The right word, a glossary of highway terms. [Washington, D.C., 195–?]
18p. 23x10cm.

Cover title.

1. Roads—Dictionaries. I. Title.

NN   0053542   IU

HE5623
.A6N3   National Highway Users Conference.
1951
Roads to national security. Washington, 1951.
32 p. illus. 24 cm.

1. Roads—U.S. 2. Transportation, Automotive—U.S.   I. Title.

NN   0053543   TU NN

VOLUME 407

National highway users conference.
The rubber scarcity and what to do about it, a sample survey by the National highway users conference to ascertain present and prospective results of restricted highway transportation on American domestic economy and the war effort. ₍Washington, 1943?₎
1 p. l., 9 numb. l. 28 x 21½ cm.
Reproduced from type-written copy.

1. Transportation, Automotive—U. S. 2. Tires, Rubber. I. Title.

HE5623.N28   388.3   43–14253 rev

NN 0053544   DLC

336.2786292
N212s   National Highway Users Conference.

Sales and use taxes and similar taxes affecting motor vehicles: a tax study... Washington ₍1954?₎
53 l. 28cm.

Cover title.

1. Automobiles - Taxation. 2. Sales tax
I. T.

NN 0053545   MiDW

National highway users conference.

Save the federal aid highway principle; the story of what it is, how it operates and the attacks against it. [Washington, D.C.?] 1942.

37 numb. l. 28 cm.
Cover-title.

NN 0053546   MH

National highway users conference.
School buses; safety equipment and construction requirements, October 1, 1938. Washington, D. C., National highway users conference ₍1938₎
6 p. l., 96 numb. l. fold. tab. 29ᶜᵐ.
Mimeographed.

1. Motor buses. 2. Accidents—Prevention. 3. School children—Transportation. I. Title.
                                        E 40–636

U. S. Off. of educ. Library   TL232.N3
for Library of Congress   ₍2₎

NN 0053547   DHEW OrCS Or

NATIONAL HIGHWAY USERS CONFERENCE.
Shall the federal government "crack down" on highway transportation? Memorandum submitted to the Hon. Franklin D. Roosevelt, president of the United States, October 17, 1934. Washington, D.C.: National Highway Users Conference [1934]
8 p. 28cm.

783345A. 1. Transportation—U.S., 1934.

NN 0053548   NN IU

National highway users conference.
State barriers to highway transportation, a discussion of ports of entry, border inspection stations and restrictive regulations; a plea for reciprocity. Washington, D. C., National highway users conference ₍1938₎
24 p. illus. (incl. maps) 28 x 21½ cm.
Issued 1937 in its Highway user series. cf. p. ₍3₎ of cover.

1. Interstate commerce. 2. Transportation, Automotive—U. S.—Laws and regulations. I. Title.

HE5623.A5N328   388.30973   41–22331 rev

NN 0053549   DLC IU DNAL NN MH-BA Or

NATIONAL HIGHWAY USERS CONFERENCE.
State constitutional amendments dedicating special motor vehicle taxes to highway purposes. National press bldg., Washington 4, D.C. ₍1948₎
31 p. illus.

Earlier ed. has title: Text of state constitutional amendments dedicating special motor vehicle taxes to highway purposes.

NN 0053550   Or NIC NNC NN

625.7   National Highway Users Conference.
N216s
State constitutional limitations on borrowing. A report by NHUC's Research Department ... Washington, 1954.
4l. 28cm.

Cover title.
"First of a series of research reports on various phases of this general problem."

NN 0053551   IU

National Highway Users Conference
State motor vehicle laws affecting mobile homes and travel trailers. 1936–
Washington.
v. illus. 23–28 cm.
Title varies: 1936–   House trailers; a survey of laws governing ownership and use (varies slightly)
Vols. for   published in cooperation with Mobile Homes Manufacturers Association and Trailer Coach Association.
1. Automobiles—Trailers—Law and legislation—U. S. I. National Highway Users Conference. House trailers. II. Title. III. Title: House trailers.
                                        38–10489 rev 2*

NN 0053552   DLC Or OrP IU OCl NN ICU CaBViP

National highway users conference.
State registration fees and special taxes for motor vehicles. Washington, D. C., National highway users conference ₍1931₎
1 v. 29 x 23½ cm.
Cover-title.
Loose-leaf; reproduced from type-written copy.

1. Automobiles—Taxation—U. S. 2. Motor fuels—Taxation—U. S. I. Title.
HE5623.N284   629.21342   45–44883 rev

NN 0053553   DLC NN OU

National Highway Users Conference.
State registration fees and special taxes for motor vehicles
see also its Registration fees and special taxes for motor vehicles.

National Highway Users Conference.
State restrictions on motor vehicle sizes and weights ... Washington, D. C., National highway users conference.
v. tables, diagrs. 28 cm. ([National highway users conference] Highway users series: L–1)
1. Motor-trucks. 2. Transportation, Automotive - U. S. 3. Automobiles - Laws and regulations - U. S. I. Title.

NN 0053555   CU Or OrP

National highway users conference.

State restrictions on motor vehicle sizes and weights. 1940 ed. ... Washington, D.C. ₍c1939₎
120 p. incl. tables, diagrs., charts. (Highway users series, no. L 1–B)

Manifold copy.

NN 0053556   MH-BA MH OCl

National highway users conference.
D.C.
State restrictions on motor vehicles sizes and weights. 1944 ed. ... Washington, D.C. ₍1944₎
133 p. incl. tables, charts. (Highway users series, no. L–1)

Manifold copy.

NN 0053557   MH-BA WaS

National highway users conference.
State restrictions on motor vehicles sizes and weights. 1946 ed. ... Washington, D.C. ₍c1946₎
127 p. incl. charts, tables. (Highway users series: no. L 1)

Manifold copy.

NN 0053558   MH-BA

National Highway Users Conference.
State restrictions on motor vehicles, sizes and weights. Washington ₍1947₎
1 v. (loose-leaf) 30 cm. (Its Motor vehicle law series. Service 1)

1. Automobiles—Laws and regulations—U. S. 2. Automobiles—Design and construction. I. Title.

HE5623.A5N329   629.21342   47–27140 rev*

NN 0053559   DLC

National Highway Users Conference.
State restrictions on motor vehicle sizes and weights. Washington, ₍1952– ₎
1 v. (loose-leaf) illus., maps, tables. 30 cm. (Its Motor vehicle law series. Service no. 1)

1. Transportation, Automotive—U. S.—Laws and regulations. 2. Motor-trucks—Law and legislation—U. S. I. Title.

                        388.3173   63–20982

NN 0053560   DLC

National highway users conference.

The substitution of buses for street cars ... Washington, D.C., 1936.
cover-title, 23 numb. l. incl. tables. (₍Highway user series, no. R7₎)

Manifold copy.
Bibliography: l. 22–23.

NN 0053561   MH-BA

National Highway Users Conference.
Suggested reading for the study of highway transportation. ₍Washington₎ 1936.
11 l. 28 cm.

1. Transportation, Automotive—Bibl. 2. Roads—Bibl. I. Title.

Z7164.T8N3   60–56898

NN 0053562   DLC NN Or

National Highway Users Conference.
A taxation bibliography dealing with gasoline, highway, and motor vehicle taxes; supplementing A bibliography on highways and highway transportation. Washington, 1936.
19 l. 29 cm.

1. Gasoline—Taxation—Bibl. 2. Automobiles — Taxation — Bibl. I. National Highway Users Conference. A bibliography dealing with highways and highway transportation. II. Title.

Z7295.N27   60–56897

NN 0053563   DLC

VOLUME 407

National highway users conference.
Texas wipes out black spot! Legal rights of private truck owners are restored and 7,000-pound load limit is repealed. ₍Washington, D. C., National highway users conference, 1941₎
    folder (₍6₎ p.) 21½ x 10 cm.

    1. Automobiles—Laws and regulations—Texas. 2. Motor-trucks. I. Title.
HE5633.T4N3   42–5787 rev

NN   0053564   DLC NN Or

336.27   National Highway Users Conference.
N21t
    Texts of good roads amendments; State constitutional provisions safeguarding highway use taxes.   Washington ₍1955₎
    32p. map. 23x10cm.

    1. Motor vehicles—Taxation. 2. Roads—U.S.—Finances. 3. Highway law—U.S.—States. I. Title: Good roads amendments.

NN   0053565   IU

National highway users conference.
The ton-mile tax, a third-structure levy on motor carriers. Washington, D. C., National highway users conference ₍1936₎
    1 p. l., 30 p. 27½ cm.
    Text is autographic reproduction of type-written copy.

    1. Transportation, Automotive—Taxation—U. S. I. Title.
                      38–4712 rev

NN   0053566   DLC OrU Or OU MH–BA NN IU

HE5623   National Highway Users Conference
N2
1950   The ton-mile tax and related 'third structure' taxes, prepared by Dawes E. Brisbine and W. Yule Fisher. Washington, D.C., National Highway Users Conference ₍1950₎
    31 p. 28ᶜᵐ.
    Revision of The ton-mile tax, a third-structure levy on motor carriers, published 1936.—cf. Foreword.

    1.Automobiles - Taxation. 2.Automobiles - Laws and regulations - U.S. I.Brisbine, Dawes E II. Fisher, W Yule.

NN   0053567   CSt DBRE N

HE5623   National highway users conference.
.S655
    Stocker, Harry Ellis, 1889–
    Transportation and the public welfare in war and in peace, by Harry E. Stocker ... Washington, D. C., National highway users conference ₍1943₎

NATIONAL HIGHWAY USERS CONFERENCE.
A transportation catechism; current questions on land transport with answers by authorities. [Washington, D.C.: National Highway Users Conference, 1933] 20 p. 24cm.

872707A. 1. Transportation—U.S. 2. Railways and motor transportation—U.S.

NN   0053569   NN OU DNAL

National Highway Users Conference.
A transportation catechism; current questions on land transport, with answers by authorities. ₍Washington, 1936?₎
    20 p. 24 cm.

    1. Transportation, Automotive—U. S. 2. Railroads—U. S. I. Title.
HE5623.A5N34   43–30535 rev*

NN   0053570   DLC DNAL Or

National highway users conference.

Gray, Chester Harold, 1879–
    Transportation in 1950, by Chester H. Gray. Washington, D. C., National highway users conference ₍1940₎

National highway users conference.

Dillman, Grover Cleveland, 1889–
    Transportation in the public interest, by Grover C. Dillman ... Harry E. Stocker ... ₍and₎ John S. Worley ... Washington, D. C., National highway users conference ₍1942₎

National highway users conference.

Gilbert, Raymond V   H   1888–
    A treatise on irrational calculations of highway costs. Exposing the fallacies of theories which would have the states heap further highway taxes on motor vehicles and the general public, thereby impeding the present national war effort and threatening to interfere with economic recovery after the war. By R. V. H. Gilbert. Washington, D. C., National highway users conference ₍1942₎

National highway users conference.
Trends in state regulations of motor vehicles; sizes and weights. Greater freedom of highways needed in united war effort. Washington, D. C., National highway users conference ₍1942₎
    23 p. 23 cm.
    "Material for this study was prepared by Myles W. English of the Legislative department of the Conference staff."

    1. Automobiles—Laws and regulations—U. S. I. English, Myles Wesley, 1909– II. Title.

HE5623.A5N343   388.3   43–48039 rev

NN   0053574   DLC N

LB2864   National highway users conference.
.N62
    Noble, Marcus Cicero Stephens, 1899–
    War-time pupil transportation; the place of highway transportation in American education and its post-war possibilities, by M. C. S. Noble, jr., ᴇᴅ. ᴅ. Washington, D. C., The National highway users conference ₍1944₎

National highway users conference.
    Weighed - and found wanting

see under

    Fisher, Yule.

National highway users conference.
    The voice of the people, as heard through American automobile association, American farm bureau federation, National industrial traffic league, the National grange ₍and₎ the Farmers' union. ₍Washington, D. C., 1935₎ 17 p. 22cm.
    "Compiled by National highway users conference, Washington, D. C."

    1. Automobiles—Jurisp.—U. S.   I. American automobile association.
N. Y. P. L.   January 28, 1938

NN   0053577   NN

S   National highway users conference.
388.1
qN277   Why the toll method of financing roads is unsound. Washington, D. C. 1948?
    14 p. illus. maps. 22 x 28 cm.

    1. Roads. U.S. Finance. I. Title.

NN   0053578   N OrU NN Or

NATIONAL HIGHWAY USERS CONFERENCE.
Your highways; the facts down in front! [Washington, D.C.: National Highway Users Conference, 193–?] 8 l. illus. 23cm.

841848A. 1. Automobiles—U.S. 2. Automobiles—Taxation—U.S. I. Title.

NN   0053579   NN

National Highway Users Conference
    see also
Highway Transportation Congress.

National Highway Users Conference. *Legislative Reporting Dept.*
    Highway transportation legislation; a summary of Federal and State activity. Washington, National Highway Users Conference.
    v. illus. 28 cm.
    Subtitle varies slightly.
    Vols. for   issued by the National Highway Users Conference.

    1. Highway law—U. S. 2. Roads—U. S. 3. Transportation, Automotive—U. S.—Laws and regulations. I. Title.
                        59–17787 rev ‡

NN   0053581   DLC OU MiU NIC IU

HE   National Highway Users Conference. Research
331   Dept.
.N27   Report. 1954–
    Washington. National Highway Users Conference.

NN   0053582   MiU

National highways association.

Davis, Charles Henry, 1865–
    Arguments for and against national highways versus federal aid; a bill for Congress to create a National highways commission (3d ed.) by Charles Henry Davis, c. ᴇ. Washington, D. C., 1914.

National highways association.

₍**Davis, Charles Henry**₎ 1865–
    ... Arguments for the New England and middle Atlantic states to help the building of national highways. ₍Boston, The Everett press company, ʾ1914₎

National Highways Association.
    The bill-board nuisance in New York City. ₍Washington, D. C.: National Highways Assoc., cop. 1916.₎ 8p. illus. 4°. (National Highways Assoc. Municipal art division. Pamphlet no. 1.)
    Caption-title.
    In: VDG (Nat. H. Assoc.) p. v. 1, no. 31.

    1. New York City.—Signs and sign-   boards.
N. Y. P. L.   September 18, 1918.

NN   0053585   NN

VOLUME 407

National Highways Association.
A bill for Congress to create a National Highways Commission, proposed by the National Highways Association. ₍Washington?₎ 1913. 8 p. 2. ed. 12°.

Cover-title.
Signed: Charles Henry Davis.

1. Roads, U. S. 2. Davis, Charles Henry, 1865–
N. Y. P. L.   November 19, 1915.

NN 0053586   NN DLC

National highways association.
... A bill for Congress to create a National highways commission, proposed by the National highways association. What course shall the nation follow? 5th ed., January 1, 1915 ... ₍Boston, The Everett press company, ᶜ1915₎

8 p. illus. (incl. map) 25½ᶜᵐ.

1. Roads—U. S. I. Title.

Library of Congress   HE355.N18   15–3775

NN 0053587   DLC

National Highways Association.
A bill for Congress to create a national highways commission, proposed by the National Highways Association. What course shall the nation follow?... ₍Washington, D. C.,₎ 1916. 24 p. 6. ed. illus. 4°.

In: VDG (Nat. H. Assoc.) p. v. 1, no. 38.

1. Roads, U. S.
N. Y. P. L.   September 19, 1918.

NN 0053588   NN

National highways association.

Bruce, Robert, 1872–
Brandywine; a revolutionary battlefield on the main-traveled highway between New York, Philadelphia, Baltimore and Washington, by Robert Bruce ... in co-operation with American automobile association ... The Automobile club of America ... National highways association ... ₍Clinton, N. Y., R. Bruce, ᶜ1922₎

TE1 National highways association.
.N27 Certificate of federation of the ...
₍Washington, c1914₎

NN 0053590   DLC

National highways association.
...Certificate of incorporation, by-laws. 1st ed...
[n. p. 1914] *TE1*
1 pam. 8° *N34*

NN 0053591   DLC

National highways association.
Charles B. Dillingham presents Fred Stone in "Tip top", a musical extravaganza...
see under title

TE1 **National Highways Association.**
.N3   Charter of the ₍local division of the₎ National highways association. ₍Washington, D. C., c1914₎

NN 0053593   DLC

National Highways Association.   8010a.217
Competition for the design of membership certificates.
= ₍Washington. 1912.₎ 13 pp. Illus. Plate. Map. 29 cm.
Inserted are 3 leaflets and 2 maps.

₍3313 — United States. Roads.

NN 0053594   MB DLC

National highways association.
Copy of form of state charters and certificates of federation as issued by the National highways association and its various state divisions. Washington, D. C., 1914.

25 p. illus. 25ᶜᵐ.

Library of Congress   TE1.N33   14–11150

NN 0053595   DLC

National Highways Association.
Facts in the history of road-building... ₍Washington, D. C.: National Highways Assoc., cop. 1916.₎ 7(1) p. illus., maps, part col'd. 4°.

Caption-title.
In: VDG (Davis) p. v. 2, no. 19.

1. Roads, U. S. 2. Title.
N. Y. P. L.   August 16, 1918.

NN 0053596   NN

TE23   **National Highway Association.**
.N26   Fifty thousand miles of national highways ...
        4th ed. [Washington, D. C. , 1913]
        1 pam. 8°.

NN 0053597   DLC

National highways association.
... Fifty thousand miles of national highways, four fold system ... ₍Boston, The Everett press company, ᶜ1915₎

7, ₍1₎ p. illus. (incl. map) 25½ᶜᵐ.

Caption title.
At head of title: National highways association.
Signed: Charles Henry Davis, c. ᴇ., president.

1. Roads—U. S. I. Davis, Charles Henry, 1865– II. Title.

Library of Congress   HE355.N22 1915   15–4782
Copyright A 301565

NN 0053598   DLC

National Highways Association.
Fifty thousand miles of national highways; four fold system (three fold where the county is the smallest State unit); national highways, state highways, county roads, township or town roads. Washington, D. C.: National Highways Assoc., cop. 1916. 6 p., 1 l. illus. 8°.

Caption-title.
In: VDG (Nat. H. Assoc.) p. v. 1, no. 24.

1. Roads, U. S.
N. Y. P. L.   September 14, 1918.

NN 0053599   NN MiU

National Highways Association.
Fifty thousand miles of national highways, proposed by the National Highways Association. ₍Washington?₎ 1913. 7 p. 7. ed. 8°.

Cover-title.
Signed: Charles Henry Davis.

1. Roads, U. S. 2. Davis, Charles Henry, 1865– 3. Title.
N. Y. P. L.   December 10, 1915.

NN 0053600   NN

National highways association.
Fifty thousand miles of national highways proposed by the National highways association. ₍9th ed.₎ ₍Washington, D. C., 1914₎

7, ₍1₎ p. incl. map. 25½ᶜᵐ.

Caption title.
Signed: Charles Henry Davis, c. ᴇ., president.

1. Roads—U. S. I. Davis, Charles Henry, 1865– II. Title.

15–6805

Library of Congress   HE355.N22 1914

NN 0053601   DLC MiU NN

National highways association.
... Fifty thousand miles of national highways proposed by the National highways association, with a description of the Lincoln highway ... by Charles Henry Davis ... ₍Boston, The Everett press company₎ 1915.

₍7₎ p. illus., fold. map. 25½ᶜᵐ.

1. Roads—U. S. I. Davis, Charles Henry, 1865– II. Title.

Library of Congress   HE355.N22 1915 a   15–5540

NN 0053602   DLC NjP OC1

National highways association.
For national highways and good roads everywhere. ₍Boston,₎ The Everett press company, ᶜ1914₎

8 p. illus. (incl. map) 25½ᶜᵐ.
Folded map laid in.

1. Roads—U. S.

Library of Congress   TE23.N3   14–12160

NN 0053603   DLC

₍**National Highways Association.**₎
For national highways and good roads everywhere. Westgard rides again, 18000 miles in 1914. ₍Washington, cop. 1914.₎ 8 p., 1 fold. map. illus. 4°.

Cover-title.

1. Roads, U. S.
N. Y. P. L.   December 6, 1915.

NN 0053604   NN

National highways association.

Davis, Charles Henry, 1865–
Good roads everywhere, by Charles Henry Davis, c. ᴇ., with the assistance of Stanley E. Bates, s. ʙ. Washington, D. C., 1913.

National Highways Association.
..."Good roads everywhere." Co-operation — organization — distribution. ₍New York, 1915?₎ 4 l. illus. 4°.

Caption-title.
At head of title: National Highways Association... A membership corporation...
In: VDG (Nat. H. Assoc.) p. v. 1, no. 9.

1. Roads, U. S.
N. Y. P. L.   September 14, 1918.

NN 0053606   NN NjP

National Highways Association.
Good roads everywhere; four fold system of highways... Plan of organization of the National Highways Association... ₍Washington, D. C., 1912.₎ Chart →26 × ↑19½ in. fold. 4°.

In: VDG p. v. 36, no. 7.

1. Roads.—Associations, etc., U. S.
N. Y. P. L.   August 15, 1918.

NN 0053607   NN

VOLUME 407

National highways association.

Whitin, Ernest Stagg, 1881–
... Honor men and good roads everywhere, pub. jointly by National committee on prison labor, National highways association; reprinted with some additions, from Proceedings of the Academy of political science, January, 1914, under the title of "Good roads and convict labor," by E. Stagg Whitin, PH. D., and Charles Henry Davis, C. E. ... ₁Boston, The Everett press company₎ °1914.

National highways association.

Davis, Charles Henry, 1865-
Illustrated arguments for and against national highways versus federal aid; a bill for Congress to create a national highways commission. (4th ed.) By Charles Henry Davis, C. E. Washington, D. C., 1914.

National Highways Association.
... In the interest of good roads everywhere; 17,000 mile trip by motor car, 1913; Westgard — man of many miles. ₁Washington, D .C.₎ National Highways Assoc. ₁1914.₎ 4 l. illus. (incl. maps, ports.)   4°.

Caption-title.

1. Roads, U. S. 2. Westgard,   Anthon L., 1865–
N. Y. P. L.

NN   0053610   NN

National Highways Association.
An interview, by a journalist, for the Century magazine. ₁Washington, D. C.: National Highways Assoc., cop. 1916.₎   8 p. illus.   8°.

Caption-title.
In: VDG (Nat. H. Assoc.) p. v. 1, no. 27.

1. Roads, U. S.
N. Y. P. L.   September 14, 1918.

NN   0053611   NN

National Highways Association.
Iowa state roads, Iowa county roads...
see under   Beard, Henry Clay.

National highways association.

Lee, Emma D.
... A library of highway engineering founded by the National highways association, and located at Columbia university, in the city of New York. By Emma D. Lee ... Washington, D. C., 1914.

National highways association.

Davis, Charles Henry, 1865–
... Lincoln highway ... by Charles Henry Davis ... ₁Boston, The Everett press company₎ °1914.

912.78 National highways association.
919n   Map of the Albert Pike highway showing every city, town, village and hamlet thruout its entire length. Proposed by the Albert Pike highway association. Washington, 1919.
            61 x 38cm.

            Scale 4cm. = 50 statute mi.

NN   0053615   IU

National Highways Association.
Map of the Atlantic highway.   Washington. 1915.

NN   0053616   NjP

912.73 National highways association.
918n   Map of the Dixie overland highway showing every city, town, village and hamlet throughout its entire length, proposed by the Dixie overland highway association. Washington, 1918.
            83 x 17½cm.

            Scale: 3cm. = 100 statute mi.

NN   0053617   IU

National Highways Association.   *Map 60.2.S7.1921
Map of the Jefferson Davis National Highway proposed by the United Daughters of the Confederacy and Sons of Confederate Veterans.
· Washington, D. C. 1921. Size, 14½ × 36¼ inches. Scale (computed), 73 miles to 1 inch.

D6458 — United Daughters of the Con. .. racy. — Sons of Confederate Veterans. — United States. Geog. Maps. — Jefferson Davis National Highway. Proposed.

NN   0053618   MB

912.73 National highways association.
916n5   Map of the Pioneer way ...
            Washington, 1916.
            38 x 92cm.

            Scale: 80 mi.=1 in.

NN   0053619   IU WaS

912.79 National highways association.
915n3   Map of the Sunshine highway showing every city, town, village and hamlet throughout its entire length, proposed by the Sunshine highway association ... Washington, 1915.
            14½ x 57cm.

            Scale: 3cm. = 100 statute mi.

NN   0053620   IU

National Highways Association.   M656.0973 65
₁Maps and "Good roads everywhere" posters.₎
18140· Portfolio.

NN   0053621   ICJ

National Highways Association.
₁Maps showing proposed national highways in the United States₎   Washington, 1914–15.
            42 col. maps.   Sizes vary.   In envelope
            42 x 30 cm.
            Scales vary.
            1. Roads – U. S.   2. U.S. – Road maps.

NN   0053622   NIC

National Highways Association.
₁Membership, organization, proposed legislation, etc.₎   ₁Boston: Essco Sales Service.₎ 1912.   4 l.   Map.   4°.

No t.-p.

1. Roads, U. S.
N. Y. P. L.   November 19, 1915.

NN   0053623   NN

National highways association.
... National highways and good roads everywhere. ₁Washington† 1913†₎
cover-title, 3 p., 1 l., 5–49 p., 1 l.   plates, maps (1 fold.) fold. tab. 36½ᶜᵐ.

1. Roads—U. S.

                                                    14–11189
Library of Congress   TE1.N4

NN   0053624   DLC NcU

National Highways Association.
National highways and good roads everywhere.   New York: 1913.   1 p.l., xv, 3–49 p., 1 l., 2 fac., 2 maps (1 fold.), 13 pl. (incl. front.), 1 fold. table.   illus.   f°.

Cover-title.

1. Roads, U. S.
N. Y. P. L.   September 14, 1915.

NN   0053625   NN

National highways association.

Davis, Charles Henry, 1865–
... National highways and national drainage, by Charles Henry Davis ...   Washington, D. C., 1914.

National Highways Association.
National Highways Association.   ₁Washington, D. C., 1912.₎ 1 p.l., 26 p., 1 fold. map, 7 pl. (incl. front.)   4°.

Captions in red.
Prospectus of the association.
In: VDG p. v. 36, no. 6.

1. Roads.—Associations, etc., U. S.
N. Y. P. L.   August 15, 1918.

NN   0053627   NN

National Highways Association.
National Highways Association...   South Yarmouth, Massachusetts, March 1, 1913...   ₁Washington, D. C., 1913.₎   4 l. illus., map.   3. ed.   4°.

Caption-title.
Printed partly in red, blue and green.
In: VDG p. v. 36, no. 11.

1. Roads, U. S.
N. Y. P. L.   August 15, 1918.

NN   0053628   NN

National Highways Association.
The National Highways Association and amalgamated organizations; organization and list of officers, council members, etc. ₁Washington, D. C., 1914.₎   15(1) p.   1. ed.   8°.

1. Roads.—Assoc., &c., U. S.
N. Y. P. L.   October 28, 1919.

NN   0053629   NN MH DLC

812.099 National highways association.
S872n   ... The National highways association asks
f   you to attend the National theatre, Washington, D.C., during the week of April 16 to 22, 1922, the performance of Fred Stone and his company in "Tip top".   ₁Washington? D.C., 1922?₎

            ₁78 p.₎ illus.(incl.ports.)pl.   35½ᶜᵐ.
            Contains reproductions of invitation posters and special programs for various performances of Tip top.
            1. Stone, Fred Andrew, 1873–

NN   0053630   CSt NN

VOLUME 407

912.772 National highways association.
919n National highways map of the state of
Indiana showing three thousand miles of
national highways. Proposed by the
National highways association, Washington, D. C. Baltimore, 1919.
37½ x 25cm.

Scale: 2½cm.= 20 mi.

NN 0053631 IU

National Highways Association. No. 60 in *Map 117.6
National highways map of the State of Massachusetts showing one thousand miles of national highways proposed by the . . . Association.
= Washington. 1914. Size, 7⅜ × 13½ inches. Scale, 1:1000000 (or, 15.8 miles to 1 inch).

L-5933 — Massachusetts. Roads.

NN 0053632 MB

National Highways Association.
National highways map of the state of New Jersey showing 700 miles ...
Washington, 1914.

NN 0053633 NjP

912.748 National highways association.
915n National highways map of the state of
Pennsylvania showing three thousand
miles of national highways proposed by
the National highways association,
Washington, D.C. Pub. under direction
of General Coleman DuPont. New York,
c1915.
32 x 54½ cm.

Scale: 1 : 1,000,000.
John C. Mulford, cartographer.

NN 0053634 IU

912.73 National highways association.
917n National highways map of the United
States, showing one hundred fifty thousand miles of national highways proposed
by the National highways association.
Washington, 1917.
75 x 124cm.

Scale: 60 mi.=1 in.

NN 0053635 IU

National Highways Association. No. 58 in *Map 117.2
National highways map of the United States showing one hundred fifty thousand miles of national highways proposed by the . . . Association.
= Washington. [1918.] Size, 29½ × 48¾ inches. Scale (computed), 60 miles to 1 inch. Views. Vignettes. Folded.
Bordered by text describing the organization and work of the Association.

L-5933 — United States. Roads.

NN 0053636 MB IU

National Highways Association. No. 76 in *Map 117.2
National highways map of the United States, showing one hundred thousand miles of national highways proposed by the National Highways Association, Washington, D.C. Issued under joint auspices of the National Highways Association, National Old Trails Road Association [and 53 others].
= Washington, D.C. 1915. Size, 15¾ × 25⅞ inches. Scale (computed), 114.29 miles to 1 inch. Illus. Folded.

N3031 — United States. Roads. Maps.

NN 0053637 MB

National Highways Association. No. 77 in *Map 117.2
National highways map of the United States, showing principal transcontinental highways and connecting system of one hundred thousand miles of national highways proposed by the National Highways Association, Washington, D.C. Issued under the joint auspices of the National Highways Association, Pike's Peak Ocean to Ocean Highway Association, National Parks Transcontinental Highway Association [and 8 others]. 3d edition.
= Washington, D. C. 1915. Size, 30⅛ × 49¼ inches. Illus. Scale, none. Folded.

N3031 — United States. Roads. Maps.

NN 0053638 MB WaE IU NjP

912.73 National highways association.
919n National highways maps showing national
highways [for individual states] proposed
by the National highways association.
Washington, c1919.
47 sheets.

Scale varies.

NN 0053639 IU

912.73 National highways association.
913n3 National highways maps showing national
highways proposed by the National highways
association ... [Tentative locations for
a national highways system] Washington,
1913-15.
sheets.

Scale varies.

NN 0053640 IU

GDA-gmbd National highways association.
1913 National highways system – fifty thousand
N3n miles - main trunk and link lines. Proposed
by the National highways association, Washington, D.C. Washington, D.C., 1913.
col.map. 23x38cm.

Scale ca.1:3,000,000.
"Third edition, April 1,1913."

1. United States--1913. 2. Roads--U.S.--1913.

NN 0053641 IU

GDA-gmbd National highways association.
1913 National highways system – fifty thousand
N3 miles - main, trunk and link lines. Proposed
by the National highways association ... Washington, D.C., National highways association,
1913.
col.map. 44½x72cm.

"Scale 1:7,000,000."
"Fourth edition."

1. U. S.--1913. 2. Roads--U.S.--1913.

NN 0053642 IU

National highways association.

Davis, Charles Henry, 1865–
National highways to bring about good roads everywhere, by Charles Henry Davis, c. e., with the assistance of Stanley E. Bates, s. b. Washington, D. C., 1913.

National Highways Association.
National highway transcontinental tours. [Pawtucket, R. I.,
1915.] 8 p. illus., map. 4°

Caption-title.
"Reprinted with some additions from the Automobile journal. Issue of April 25, 1915."
In: VDG p. v. 36, no. 14.

1. Automobiles.—Touring.
N. Y. P. L. August 15, 1918.

NN 0053644 NN

National highways association.

Davis, Charles Henry, 1865–
National old trails road, ocean to ocean highway ...
By Charles Henry Davis ... [Boston, The Everett press company] 1914.

National highways association.
The National road ...
see under Bruce, Robert, 1873–

National highways association.

Stevens, Edwin Augustus, 1858–
On the necessity of the study of the problem of federal aid in highway work, by Edwin Augustus Stevens ...
[Boston, The Everett press company, °1914]

National Highways Association.
Pamphlets. v. 1– [Washington,
1913–
v. of pamphlets. illus. 28 cm.
Binder's title.
1. Roads - Collected works.

NN 0053648 CU

National highways association.
Panama canal vs. national highways ... Fifty thousand miles of national highways proposed by the National highways association ... Washington, D. C., Pub. under the direction of the National highways association, 1914.
1 sheet. illus. (map) 51 x 71¼ᵐᵐ.
Printed on both sides.

1. Roads—U. S. i. Title.

Library of Congress HE355.N26 14-20266

NN 0053649 DLC

National highways association.

Davis, Charles Henry, 1865–
... Permanent road improvement dependent upon national highways, by Charles Henry Davis, c. e., with the assistance of Stanley E. Bates, s. b. Washington, D. C., 1914.

[National Highways Association. Photographs. New York,
190–?] 4°.

Photographs in cloth-covered case.
Binder's title.

1. Roads—Machinery. 2. Roads.
N. Y. P. L. December 23, 1927

NN 0053651 NN

National Highways Association.
Program of National highways transcontinental tours, under the auspices of National Highways Association... National Old Trails Road Association... Lincoln Highway Association... [and] Automobile Club of Southern California... [New York, 1915.] [20] p. illus. nar. 8°.

Folder, one side printed in reverse.
In: VDG (Nat. H. Assoc.) p. v. 1, no. 11.

1. Automobiles.—Touring. 2. Lincoln Highway Association.
3. Automobile Club of Southern California.
N. Y. P. L. September 18, 1918.

NN 0053652 NN

VOLUME 407

National Highways Association.   L625.06161 20
¹⁰⁰¹⁰⁸ [Publications. Washington, D. C., 1913–.]
     Continued.

NN   0053653   ICJ

National highways association.

   ₍Davis, Charles Henry₎ 1865–
      ... Railroads and national highways. ₍Boston, Mass.,
   The Everett press company, °1914₎

National highways association.

   Lester, Francis Edward, 1868–
      ... Road building in Dona Ana County, New Mexico
   ... by Francis E. Lester ... ₍Boston, The Everett press
   company₎ 1914.

National highways association.

   ₍Davis, Charles Henry₎ 1865–
      ... Touring hotels, inns, road-houses, summer and win-
   ter resorts and national highways. ₍Boston, The Everett
   press company, 1914₎

National highways association.
   United States touring map showing 150,000 miles of
principal traveled highways...Baltimore Md., A. Hoen &
Co., 1925.
   1 large map fold 132 x 180 cm

NN   0053657   DNW

National Highways Association. Midland Trail Dept.
   Tour book. The midland trail. Compiled for the National
Midland Trail Association. A complete log of the trans-continental
highway, with much interesting information regarding com-
munities and scenery...   Grand Junction, Colo.: Midland Trail
Log Book Co. ₍1916₎ 192 p. illus., maps. nar. 8°.

   On cover: National midland trail tour book. 1916.

1. Automobiles.—Guides, maps, etc.   U. S. 2. Title: The midland trail.
N. Y. P. L.   March 29, 1918.

NN   0053658   NN

National Highways Association. Municipal Art Division.
   Pamphlet.
no. 1
₍Washington, D. C., cop. 1916.₎   8°.
1 v.   illus.

   Contents: no. 1. The bill-board nuisance in New York City. 1916.
   In: VDG (Nat. H. Assoc.) p. v. 1, no. 31.

1. New York City.—Signs and sign   boards.
N. Y. P. L.   September 12, 1918.

NN   0053659   NN

National Highways Association. National Old Trails Road Dept.
   Ocean to ocean over the National old trails road, 3000 miles
long... ₍Kansas City: Bishop Press. 1916.₎ 6 fold. l.   illus.,
map.   nar. 8°.

1. Roads, U. S. 2. Title: Old trails   road.
N. Y. P. L.   March 26, 1918.

NN   0053660   NN

National Highways Association. Physical Geography Division.
   Physiographic bulletin.
no. 1   (May, 1917)
₍Washington, D. C., 1917.₎   8°.
1 v.   illus.

   Contents: no. 1. Davis, W. M. Topographic maps of the United States. 1917.
   In: VDG (Nat. H. Assoc.) p. v. 1, no. 18.

1. U. S.—Maps.
N. Y. P. L.   September 12, 1918.

NN   0053661   NN CU

National highways protective society.
   Report in traffic accidents for the states of
New York and New Jersey for the year 1913.
[New York, 1914?]
          10 numb. l.   33cm.
HE355
.5   Typewritten.
.N3

NN   0053662   DLC

National highways sufficiency rating survey
   see
Devlet yolları yeterlik etüdü.

ML1   National Hillbilly Record Collectors' Exchange.
.D48
          Disc collector. no. ₍1₎–
             Jan./Mar. 1951–
          Cheswold, Del. ₍etc.₎

---

f   National Hillel Summer Institute, 5th,
BM   Camp High Point, N.Y., 1950.
727   Living as a Jew today: an
N2   exploration. [Washington, D.C.?] B'nai
             B'rith Hillel Foundations, 1950.
             59 l.   29 cm.

          1. Students, Jewish—Religious life.
          I. Title

NN   0053665   OCH

!M   National Hillel Summer Institute, 7th,
205   Camp High Point, N.Y., 1952.
N2.2   Goals for Jewish living: a collective
          inquiry. ₍Washington, D.C.₎ B'nai
          B'rith Hillel Foundations, 1952.
             104 l.   29 cm.

          1. Judaism—United States—Addresses,
          essays, lectures. I. Title

NN   0053666   OCH

---

f   National Hillel Summer Institute, 8th,
BM   Camp High Point, N.Y., 1953.
727   Toward a program of Jewish living.
N2.4   [Washington, D.C.] B'nai B'rith Hillel
          Foundations, 1953.
             85 l.   29 cm.

          1. Students, Jewish—Religious life.
          I. Title

NN   0053667   OCH NN

---

f   National Hillel Summer Institute, 9th,
BM   Camp High Point, N.Y., 1954.
205   American freedom and Jewish identity.
N2   An examination into the meaning of
          Jewish life on the occasion of the
          tercentenary. [Washington, D.C.] B'nai
          B'rith Hillel Foundations, 1954.
             94 l.   29 cm.

          1. Judaism—United States—Addresses,
          essays, lectures. I. Title

NN   0053668   OCH

F157   National Historical Association.
.J7H5
          A History of the Juniata Valley. Harrisburg ₍Pa.₎ Na-
          tional Historical Association, 1936.

National historical company, St. Joseph, Mo., pub.
   The history of Cass and Bates counties, Missouri, containing a history of these counties, their cities, towns,
etc., etc., biographical sketches of their citizens, general
and local statistics, history of Missouri ... St. Joseph,
Mo., National historical company, 1883.

National Historical Company, St. Joseph, Mo.,
   pub.
   The history of Clinton County, Missouri,
containing a history of the county, its cities,
towns, etc. ...
      see under title

National Historical Company, St. Joseph, Mo.
   The history of Gentry and Worth Counties,
Missouri ...
      see under title

National historical company, St. Joseph, Mo.,
   pub.
   The history of Henry and St. Clair counties, Missouri,
containing a history of these counties, their cities,
towns, etc., etc., biographical sketches of their citizens,
general and local statistics, history of Missouri ... St.
Joseph, Mo., National historical company, 1883.

National historical company, St. Joseph, Mo.
   The History of Holt and Atchison counties, Missouri,
containing a history of these counties, their cities,
towns, etc., etc., biographical sketches of their citizens,
general and local statistics ... history of Missouri ...
St. Joseph, Mo., National historical company, 1882.

National historical company, St. Joseph, Mo.
   The history of Nodaway county, Missouri, containing a history
of the county, its cities, towns, etc., biographical sketches of
its citizens, Nodaway county in the late war ... history of
Missouri, map of Nodaway county, etc., etc. ... St. Joseph,
Mo., National historical co., 1882.

National historical company, St. Louis, pub.
   History of Audrain County, Missouri, written and compiled from the most authentic official and private
sources, including a history of its townships, towns and
villages. Together with ... biographical sketches of
prominent citizens .... St. Louis, National historical
company, 1884.

VOLUME 407

National historical company, St. Louis, pub.
History of Caldwell and Livingston counties, Missouri ... including a history of their townships, towns, and villages, together with a condensed history of Missouri ... biographical sketches of prominent citizens; general and local statistics ... incidents and reminiscences. St. Louis, National historical company, 1886.

National historical company, St. Louis, pub.
History of Callaway County, Missouri, written and comp. from ... official and private sources, including a history of its townships, towns, and villages. Together with a condensed history of Missouri ... detailed history of Callaway County, its pioneer record, resources, biographical sketches of prominent citizens ... St. Louis, National historical company, 1884.

F472
.C5H5
National Historical Company, St. Louis.

History of Clay and Platte Counties, Missouri; written and compiled from the most authentic official and private sources, including a history of their townships, towns, and villages, together with a condensed history of Missouri; a reliable and detailed history of Clay and Platte Counties, their pioneer record, resources, biographical sketches of prominent citizens; general and local statistics of great value; incidents and reminiscences. St. Louis, National Historical Co., 1885.

National Historical Company, St. Louis.
History of Howard and Chariton counties, Missouri
see under title

National historical company, St. Louis, pub.
History of Howard and Cooper counties, Missouri, written and comp. from the most authentic official and private sources, including a history of its townships, towns, and villages. Together with a condensed history of Missouri ... detailed history of Howard and Cooper counties—its pioneer record, resources, biographical sketches of prominent citizens ... St. Louis, National historical company, 1883.

F472
.M76H5
National historical company, St. Louis.

History of Monroe and Shelby counties, Missouri, written and compiled from the most authentic official and private sources, including a history of their townships, towns and villages, together with a condensed history of Missouri; a reliable and detailed history of Monroe and Shelby counties, their pioneer record, resources, biographical sketches of prominent citizens; general and local statistics of great value; incidents and reminiscences ... St. Louis, National historical company, 1884.

F472
.R15H5
National historical company, St. Louis.

History of Randolph and Macon counties, Missouri, written and compiled from the most authentic official and private sources, including a history of their townships, towns and villages ... St. Louis, National historical company, 1884.

National historical company, St. Louis, pub.
History of St. Charles, Montgomery, and Warren counties, Missouri, written and comp. from the most authentic official and private sources, including a history of their townships, towns and villages, together with a condensed history of Missouri ... St. Louis, National historical company, 1885.

National historical magazine
see Daughters of the American Revolution magazine.

National Historical Museum, *Mexico*
see
Mexico (City) Museo Nacional de Historia.

National Historical Publications Commission
see
U. S. *National Historical Publications Commission.*

CS71
.L4854
1946
National historical society.

Gambill, Nellie Louise (McNish) 1875–
The kith and kin of Captain James Leeper and Susan Drake, his wife, by Nell McNish Gambill. New York, The National historical society [1946]

National historical society.

Miller, Charles Grant.
The poisoned loving-cup; United States histories falsified through pro-British propaganda in sweet name of amity, by Charles Grant Miller ... Chicago, National historical society, 1928.

National historical society.
The Progressive magazine. v. 1– Oct. 16, 1920–
Chicago, Steuben publishing company; [etc., etc.] 1920–

National historical society.

Mereto, Joseph J.
The red conspiracy, by Joseph J. Mereto. New York, The National historical society, 1920.

National Historical Society.
The Virginia Bailey genealogy together with related families
see under Bailey, Robert Gresham, 1874–

National historical society.

Wilcox, Reynold Webb, 1856–1931.
Wilcoxson-Wilcox, Webb and Meigs families, by Reynold Webb Wilcox ... New York, The National historical society, 1938.

National Historical Society. (Founded 1927.)
Unrolling the scroll.
v. 1

[New York, 1928 f°.
v. illus., ports.

Editor : 1928– , Helen E. Brenneman.
Compiler : 1928– , G. W. Angerstein.
v. 1 is no. 441 of a limited edition.

1. United States—Hist.—Addresses, essays, lectures.
N.Y. R L. June 11, 1929

NN 0053694 NN

The **National** history of France, edited by Fr. Funck-Brentano. [v. 1–10] London, W. Heinemann [etc., etc.] 1923–38, 10 v. in 11. 22cm.

Numbering supplied.

1. France—Hist. I. Funck- Brentano, Frantz, 1862–1947, ed.

CONTENTS.
[v. 1] FUNCK-BRENTANO, FRANTZ. The earliest times. [1927]
[v. 2] FUNCK-BRENTANO, FRANTZ. The Middle Ages. [1930]
[v. 3] BATIFFOL, LOUIS. The century of the Renaissance. 1935.
[v. 4] BOULENGER, J. R. The seventeenth century. 1933.
[v. 5] STRYIENSKI, CASIMIR. The eighteenth century. [1923]
[v. 6] MADELIN, LOUIS. The French Revolution. [1938]
———— Another ed. 1928.
[v. 7] MADELIN, LOUIS. The Consulate and the Empire. 2 v. [1934–36]
[v. 8] LUCAS-DUBRETON, JEAN. The Restoration and the July monarchy. [1929]
[v. 9] ARNAUD, RENÉ. The Second Republic and Napoleon III. [1930]
[v. 10] RECOULY, RAYMOND. The Third Republic. 1928.

NN 0053696 NN DAU DLC PPMoI

National Hockey League.
Guide.
[Montreal]
v. 17 cm. annual.

1. Hockey—Yearbooks. 2. National Hockey League—Yearbooks.
GV847.5.N38a 796.9'62'0973 74–640485
MARC-S

NN 0053697 DLC IU

GV1017
.H7 O 34
National hockey league.
The **Official** national hockey guide ... professional hockey's official rule and record book.

New York, A. S. Barnes and company, *19

National Hockey League.
Official rule book.
[Montreal]
v. illus. 17 cm.
Cover title : Rule book.

1. Hockey—Rules. 2. National Hockey League. I. National Hockey League. Rule book.
GV847.5.N38b 796.9'62 73–647902
MARC-S

NN 0053699 DLC NN

National hockey league.
Press and radio guide. «Montreal»
194–
Annual.

NN 0053700 CaBVa OrP OCl WaS NN CSf

16.8
I213
National hog farmer. v.1
Grundy Center, Iowa.

NN 0053701 DNAL

WH
28
H717
N213
National Holiness Association.
National Association for the Promotion of Holiness, 1932–1936. Chicago, Christian Witness [1937?]
59 p. 17 cm.

1. Holiness. I. Title.

NN 0053702 KyWAT

VOLUME 407

National Holiness Association.   3547.101
Proceedings of Holiness conferences held at Cincinnati, November 26th, and at New York, December 17th, 1877. [Philadelphia, 1878?] 225 pp. 12°.

NN 0053703   MB KyWAT

Microfilm
*BT767
.N3

National Holiness Association
Proceedings of Holiness Conference held at Cincinnati, November 26th, and at New York, December 7th, 1877. [Philadelphia, 1878?]
Microfilm copy (negative) made by Microreproduction Laboratory, Massachusetts Institute of Technology, 1964.
Collation of the original: 225 p.

1. Holiness.

NN 0053704   MB

National Holstein-Friesian Sale Company of New England.
The National Holstein-Friesian Sale Company of New England, at the Worcester Fair Grounds, Worcester, Mass., June 7–8, 1917. [Sandy Creek, N. Y.: Corse Press, 1917.] 125 l., 3 pl. illus. ob. 16°.

Cover-title.
"Catalog and publicity by E. M. Hastings Co., Lacona, N. Y."

1. Cattle.—Herdbooks: Holstein.   2. Hastings, E. M., Company, Lacona,
N. Y.
N. Y. P. L.   January 3, 1918.

NN 0053705   NN

National homage to Christ not disestablishment... By a ₑFree Church elder. [i. e., Wm. Mitchell]. *Glasgow: D. Bryce and Son*, 1875. 24 pp. 8°.
In: ZWGM D v. 2.

NN 0053706   NN

National home advisory association.
A portfolio of small house plans.   Seattle, Author, 1946?
unp.   illus., plans.

NN 0053707   WaS

National home and farm safety conference.
Transactions. 1st–   1942–   Chicago, National safety council inc. [1942–
v. 22½ᵐ.
Reproduced from type-written copy.

1. Accidents—Prevention—Congresses. 2. Agriculture—Accidents.
1. National safety council.
                                                        43-22867
Library of Congress   TX150.N3
                                   ₒ
                                                        614.8

NN 0053708   DLC

National Home Builders Association
see also National Association of Home Builders of the U. S.

National home building and loan association, *Bloomington, Ill.*
Charter and by-laws of the National home building and loan association ... [Bloomington, Ill., ᵉ1890]
15 p. 15ᶜᵐ.

                                                CA 8-946 Unrev'd

Library of Congress   HG2624.B6N3

NN 0053709   DLC

The national home budget system ...
see under   [Hyden, Edwin C   ]

Unclass.   National home cook book.   Chicago, National Clock & Mfg. Co. ₑn.d.,
191 p.   24 cm.

NN 0053710   DLC

275.29   National Home Demonstration Council.
N215S   Home demonstration work.   State reports.

            Amherst, Extension Service, University of Massachusetts,

            I. Massachusetts. University. Extension Service.

NN 0053711   DNAL

275.29   National home demonstration council.
N215   National notes, v.

            Loveland, Colo.,

            1. Home demonstration work. Periodicals.

NN 0053712   DNAL

National home estimator
see under   Cal Pacific Estimators, Los Angeles.

National Home for Disabled Volunteer Soldiers.
Annual report of an inspection of the several branches of the National Home for Disabled Volunteer Soldiers ...
see under   U.S. War Dept. Inspector General's Office.

UB   NATIONAL Home for Disabled Volunteer
360   Soldiers
N277   [Collection of publications]

          The Library has a collection of miscellaneous publications of this organization kept as received. These publications are not listed or bound separately.

NN 0053715   DNLM

National home for disabled volunteer soldiers.
Laws and regulations governing the National home for disabled volunteer soldiers. 1903. [New York, D. Taylor & co., 1903]
187 p. 24ᵐ.
M. T. McMahon, president Board of managers.

1. Soldiers' homes—U. S. I. U. S. Laws, statutes, etc.

Library of Congress   UB383.A45 1903

NN 0053716   DLC

National home for disabled volunteer soldiers.
Laws and regulations governing the National home for disabled volunteer soldiers, 1906. [New York, D. Taylor & co., 1906]
239 p. 24ᵐ.
M. T. McMahon, president Board of managers.

1. Soldiers' homes—U. S. I. U. S. Laws, statutes, etc. II. Title.
                                                        14-9749
Library of Congress   UB383.A45 1906

NN 0053717   DLC NcD

National home for disabled volunteer soldiers.
Laws and regulations governing the National home for disabled volunteer soldiers. 1908. [New York, D. Taylor & co., 1908]
247 p. 24ᵐ.
J. W. Wadsworth, president Board of managers.

1. Soldiers' homes—U. S. I. U. S. Laws, statutes, etc.
                                                        9-18613
Library of Congress   UB383.A45 1908

NN 0053718   DLC

National home for disabled volunteer soldiers.
Laws and regulations of the National home for disabled volunteer soldiers. 1912. [New York, D. Taylor & co., 1912]
339 p. 1 illus. 24ᵐ.
J. W. Wadsworth, president Board of managers.

1. Soldiers' homes—U. S. I. U. S. Laws, statutes, etc.
                                          [34b1]   12-34783
Library of Congress   UB383.A45 1912

NN 0053719   DLC WaU-L

National home for disabled volunteer soldiers.
Letter from George W. Houk, and others ...
see under   Houk, George W., et al.

National home for disabled volunteer soldiers.
National home for disabled volunteer soldiers. Post fund. Letter from the president of the Board of managers, National home for disabled volunteer soldiers, transmitting detailed report of receipts and disbursements and transfers in connection with the post fund from July 1, 1886, to March 2, 1911 ... Washington [Govt. print. off.] 1912.
138 p. 23½ᵐ. ([U. S.] 62d Cong. 2d sess. House. Doc. 474)
Referred to the Committee on military affairs and ordered printed January 23, 1912.
J. W. Wadsworth, president, Board of managers.
1. National home for disabled volunteer soldiers—Post fund. I. Wadsworth, James Wolcott, 1846–
                                                        12-35144
Library of Congress   UB383.A49 1912

NN 0053721   DLC MiU OO

VOLUME 407

National home for disabled volunteer soldiers.
Record of changes in membership of the National
Home for disabled volunteer soldiers showing gains,
losses, and transfers during the fiscal year ending
June 30, 1918. [Extract from House document 1500,
65th congress, third session)
Washington, 1919.

UB283
.A46

NN 0053722 DLC

NATIONAL Home for Disabled Volunteer Soldiers.
Record of disabled volunteer soldiers, who
now are, and have been, members of the National
Home for Disabled Volunteer Soldiers, from its
commencement to June 30, 1881.
Wash. [D.C.] Govt.Print.Off. 1883.
334p.

NN 0053723 WaS WaU

4E   National Home for Disabled Volunteer
553   Soldiers.
Record of disabled volunteer soldiers,
who now are and have been, members of
the National Home for Disabled Volunteer
Soldiers, from its commencement to June
30, 1881. Washington, Government
Printing Office, 1883.
334 p.

NN 0053724 DLC-P4 DI

National home for disabled volunteer soldiers.
Record of disabled volunteer soldiers who
now are and have been members of the National
home for disabled volunteer soldiers from July 1,
1894, to June 30, 1895. Washington, Govt. ptg.
off., 1896.
179 p.

NN 0053725 MiD-B

*"20th".68.2
National Home for Disabled Volunteer Soldiers.
Regulations. 1900.
= [New York. 1900.] 191 pp. 21 cm.

H 6

NN 0053726 MB

UB   NATIONAL Home for Disabled Volunteer
360   Soldiers
N277r   Regulations. [National Military Home,
1918   Ohio, 1918]
99 p.

NN 0053727 DNLM

National home for disabled volunteer soldiers.
Regulations of the National home for disabled volunteer
soldiers. 1910. [New York, D. Taylor & co., 1910]
239 p. 24ᵐᵐ.

1. Soldiers' homes—U. S.   I. U. S. Laws, statutes, etc.

10-36019

Library of Congress   UB383.A45 1910

NN 0053728 DLC DNLM ICRL ICJ

National home for disabled volunteer soldiers.
Regulations of the National home for disabled volunteer soldiers. 1915. [New York, D. Taylor & co., 1915]
184 p. 24ᵐᵐ.

1. Soldiers' homes—U. S.   I. U. S. Laws, statutes, etc.   II. Title.

16-12829

Library of Congress   UB383.A45 1915

NN 0053729 DLC

National Home for Disabled Volunteer Soldiers.
Regulations of the National Home for Disabled Volunteer
Soldiers, 1918.   [Dayton? 1918.]   99 p.   8°.

General orders, no. 1...Paragraphs 12, 19, 20, 21, 53, 91, 120, 240 and 259 Home regulations amended: 2 l. inserted.

73667A.   1. Soldiers.—Home for,   U. S.: Ohio.
N. Y. P. L.   December 1, 1923.

NN 0053730 NN

National home for disabled volunteer soldiers.
Report of inspection of state soldiers' and sailors
homes ...   [Washington, Govt. print. off.,
v. 23ᵐᵐ.
Report year ends June 30.

1. Soldiers' homes—U. S.

9-8224†

Library of Congress   UB384.A15

NN 0053731 DLC NcD Mi

National home for disabled volunteer soldiers.
Report of the Board of managers ...

Washington, Govt. print. off., 18   –19
v. plan. 23ᵐᵐ.
Report year ends June 30.
Contains reports from the various branches, and Proceedings of the Board of managers.
Continued by the Annual report of the administrator of veterans' affairs (U. S. Veterans' administration)

1. Soldiers' homes—U. S.

9-35259

Library of Congress   UB383.A2

NN 0053732 DLC OrCS OrU ICJ CSmH NjP OFH PHi PU

National home for disabled volunteer soldiers.
Statutes of the United States affecting the
National home for disabled volunteer soldiers.
By-laws of the National home for disabled
volunteer soldiers. Index to proceedings of
the Board of Managers from the organization to
end of the fiscal year ending June 30, 1884.
Hartford, Conn., The Case, Lockwood & Brainard
co., 1884.
44, xcivp.

NN 0053733 OC1

National Home for Disabled Volunteer Soldiers,
Central Branch. Dayton, Ohio.
[A collection of views of the home, with a
description.   Dayton, 187–?]
15 p.   14 photogrs.   ob. 32°.

NN 0053734 MH

National Home for Disabled Volunteer Soldiers.
Central Branch, Dayton, Ohio.
History of the National Home for Disabled
Volunteer Soldiers: with a complete guide-book
to the Central home, at Dayton, Ohio
see under   Gobrecht, J. G.

National home for disabled volunteer soldiers.
Central branch, Dayton, Ohio.
National soldiers' home near Dayton, Ohio.
[Dayton, 1881?]
cover-title, 15, [1] p.   plates.   9 x 13 cn
Plates are on folded strip.

NN 0053736 CtY

National home for disabled volunteer soldiers. *Central
branch, Dayton, O. Putnam library.*
Catalogue of the Putnam library. National asylum for
disabled volunteer soldiers, (Central branch.) ... Dayton,
O., National asylum printing office, 1872.
iv, [5]–64 p. 21½ᵐᵐ.

15-9395

Library of Congress   Z881.D2⁶

NN 0053737 DLC

National home for disabled volunteer soldiers.
Eastern branch, Togus, Me.
Eastern branch, National home D.V.S., Togus,
Maine. [Descriptive booklet, views] [Augusta,
1906]
36p.   plates, ports.

DLC:YA18760

NN 0053738 DLC

National Home for Disabled Volunteer Soldiers.
Eastern Branch, Togus, Me.
Souvenir views.
= [Togus, Me.? 19—?] Illus. Portraits. 32 plates. Decorated
cover. 21 cm.
The title is on the cover.

NN 0053739 MB

National home for disabled volunteer soldiers. *Eastern
branch, Togus, Me. Library.*
Catalogue of the library of the National home for disabled volunteer soldiers, (Eastern branch) Togus, (near) Augusta, Maine, May 1st, 1872. Sprague, Owen & Nash, printers, 1872.
100 p. 23ᵐᵐ.

2-7218

Library of Congress, no.   Z881.N276

NN 0053740 DLC

National home for disabled volunteer soldiers. *Marion
branch, Marion, Ind.*
Souvenir photographs: National home for disabled volunteer soldiers, Indiana. Twenty-first anniversary, Marion, Indiana. [Marion, W. S. Wright. 1911]
4 l., 12 pl. 27ᶜᵐ.
Issued in portfolio.

12-9097

Library of Congress   UB383.M3A4

NN 0053741 DLC

National home for disabled volunteer soldiers. *Mountain
branch, Johnson City, Tenn.*
Souvenir book. National soldiers home, Tennessee ...
[Knoxville, Knoxville printing & box company, 1910]
cover-title, [44] p. illus. (incl. ports.) 17 x 25½ᶜᵐ.

10-34313

Library of Congress   UB383.M8A4

NN 0053742 DLC DI

VOLUME 407

I
314
.611
NATIONAL HOME FOR DISABLED VOLUNTEER SOLDIERS.
Northwestern branch, Milwaukee.
Annual report.   Milwaukee, Wis.,
National home job printing office[18]
v.

NN 0053743   ICN PHi RPB OFH CU DLC MWA CSmH

Pam   National home for disabled volunteer soldiers.
70-623   Northwestern branch, Milwaukee.
NATIONAL SOLDIERS' HOME NEAR MILWAUKEE. New
York, The Albertype Co., c1889.
[16] l. (chiefly illus.)
NATIONAL HOME FOR DISABLED VOLUNTEER SOLDIERS. NORTH-
WESTERN BRANCH, MILWAUKEE.
MILWAUKEE, WIS.: HOMES: (FOR) SOLDIERS
SOLDIERS: HOMES (FOR): WISCONSIN: MILWAUKEE
WISCONSIN: SOLDIERS: HOMES (FOR): MILWAUKEE
HOMES: (FOR) SOLDIERS: WISCONSIN: MILWAUKEE
WISCONSIN: HOMES: (FOR) SOLDIERS: MILWAUKEE
title

NN 0053744   WHi DLC

National home for disabled volunteer soldiers. *Northwestern branch, Milwaukee.*
Souvenir history, Northwestern branch, National home
for disabled volunteer soldiers. Milwaukee, Wis., 1924.
87, [1] p. illus. (incl. ports.) 17 x 25½ᶜᵐ.
Includes advertising matter.
Tom L. Johnson, editor.

I. Johnson, Tom Lazenby, 1846-   ed.

Library of Congress   UB383.N8A215   24-27717

NN 0053745   DLC

National home for disabled volunteer soldiers. *Northwestern branch, Milwaukee. Library.*
Catalogue of library, belonging to the National home
for disabled volunteer soldiers, (Northwestern branch)
near Milwaukee, Wisconsin. Near Milwaukee, Wis., National soldiers' home printing office, 1875.
103, [1] p., 1 l. 23ᶜᵐ.
p. 33-36, blank, for additions.

Library of Congress   Z881.M659 '75   10-3051

NN 0053746   DLC OO MiU

National home for disabled volunteer soldiers. *Northwestern branch, Milwaukee. Library.*
Catalogue of the library of the National home for disabled volunteer soldiers, Northwestern branch, near Milwaukee, Wis. Near Milwaukee, Wis., National home
printing office, 1882.
120, 31 p. 24ᶜᵐ.

Library of Congress   Z881.M659 '82   10-3050

NN 0053747   DLC

Pam   National Home for Disabled Volunteer Soldiers.
71-844   Pacific Branch, Los Angeles.
PACIFIC BRANCH, NATIONAL HOME FOR DISABLED
VOLUNTEER SOLDIERS, LOS ANGELES COUNTY,
CALIFORNIA. Los Angeles, Calif., Ed. C.
Gird, c1906.
1 v. (unpaged) illus.

LOS ANGELES, CALIF.: HOMES: (for) SOLDIERS
CALIFORNIA: CITIES AND TOWNS: LOS ANGELES
HOMES: (for) SOLDIERS: LOS ANGELES
SOLDIERS: HOMES (for)
title

NN 0053748   WHi CU-B

National home for disabled volunteer soldiers.
Southern branch, Hampton, Va.
National home, D. V. S., Hampton, Va. Photo-
gravures ... C. E. Cheyne, photographer ...
Brooklyn, N. Y., The Albertype co., ©1900.
1 p.l., 15 plates. (1 fold.) 13.5 x 18 cm.

Illustration on cover.
"Copyright, 1900, by C. E. Cheyne, photographer,
Hampton, Va."
1. National home for disabled volunteer soldiers.
Southern branch, Hampton, Va. - Views. I. Cheyne,
C. E. II. Title.

NN 0053749   Vi

UB383.S7   National home for disabled volunteer soldiers.
N61   Southern branch, *Hampton, Va.*
Rules and regulations of the Southern
branch National home for disabled volunteer
soldiers. [N.p.] National soldiers' home,
Va., 1909.
32p. 15cm. in 18cm.

1. Soldiers' homes.

NN 0053750   NBuG

National home for disabled volunteer soldiers. *Southern
branch, Hampton, Va. Library.*
Catalogue of books belonging to the library, Southern
branch, National home disabled volunteer soldiers,
Hampton Roads, Virginia ... 1883. Hampton, Va., Normal school steam press print [1883]
158 p. 22½ᶜᵐ.

CA 17-3650 Unrev'd

Library of Congress   Z881.H24 1883

NN 0053751   DLC

National home for disabled volunteer soldiers. *Southern
branch, Hampton, Va. Library.*
Catalogue of the library at the Southern branch, National home for disabled volunteer soldiers, Virginia.
Comp. and classified by Julius Briesen, librarian. Hampton, Va., Normal school steam press print, 1894.
2 p. l., 213 p. 23ᶜᵐ.
13 blank pages included in numbering.

I. Briesen, Julius.

10-3049

Library of Congress   Z881.H24

NN 0053752   DLC

National home for lepers, Carville, La.
see   Louisiana. Leper home, Carville.

DS   A national home for the Jewish people;
149   the British Government's recognition of
Z79   the Zionist movement.   London, R.
Clay, 1917.
16 p. 21cm.

Reprinted from "The Jewish chronicle."
No. 2 in vol. lettered: Zionism.
Pamphlets.

1. Zionism.

NN 0053754   NIC NN PU

National Home Furnishings Association.
NHFA reports to the home furnishings
industry
see under title

---

q334.321   National Home Furnishings Association
N2132r   Operating experiences. 1946-
Chicago, Ill.

Cover title.
Title varies: -1946, Annual retail
furniture store operating experiences and
departmental activities. - Annual
report, store operating experiences.
1946-1970 issued under earlier name of the
association,   National Retail Furniture
Association.

NN 0053756   OC1

National Home Furnishings Association.
Operating experiences
see also   National Retail Furniture
Association.
Furniture store operating experiences.

1.913
EhSy6   National Home Furnishings Conference, Chicago,
1953.
Symposium on the Relation of the House and
Its Furnishings to the Mental, Physical and
Emotional Development of the Family, papers
presented.   [Washington] 1953.
[26] p.

Issued May 1953.

NN 0053758   DNAL

National home grown timber council.
A report on the Scottish pit-prop experiment
1936-37. Methods & costs of pit-prop production.
London, National home grown timber council,
1937.

41 p. plates, map, tables, diagr.
Its Bulletin no.1.

NN 0053759   MH DNAL

A national home in the light of Jewish history
see under   British Association for the
Jewish National Home in Palestine.

The National home journal. v. 1-
Nov. 1906-
St. Louis, T. J. Goe [etc.] 1906-
v. illus. 35⁻41ᶜᵐ. monthly.
Editors: Nov. 1906-Nov. 1907, T. J. Goe and others.—Dec. 1907-
Anna C. White.
Absorbed the Pilgrim, a magazine for the home, in June 1907.

I. Goe, Theodore J., ed. II. White, Anna Cliff, ed.

8-20435†

Library of Congress   AP2.N26

NN 0053761   DLC

National home-keepers' service club.
Brown, William Garland, 1877-   *ed.*
The home-keeping book; text compilation and editing
by W. Garland Brown; illustrations by Edgar Keller,
Rachel Robinson Elmer; art make-up and supervision by
Gauthier. New York, The Home-keeping press [c1918]

National Home Laundry Conference.
Proceedings...
see under   American Home Laundry
Manufacturers Association.

VOLUME 407

National home-making conference, Minneapolis, 1932.

National congress of parents and teachers.
Homemaking. The proceedings of a National homemaking conference, held at Minneapolis, Minnesota, under the auspices of the United States Office of education and the National congress of parents and teachers, May 16, 1932 ... Washington, D. C., The National congress of parents and teachers ₁1932₎

National Home Missions Council
see Home Missions Council of North America.

₁National home owner's plan, inc.₎
A home for life ... ₁Detroit, Mich.: The Donnelly foundation, c1935₎ 24 p. illus. (incl. ports.) 28cm.

Cover-title.
"An appreciation," p. 4, signed: J. Calvin Newman, executive secretary of National home owner's plan, inc.

1. Habitations for the working class —U. S. I. Donnelly foundation, Detroit. II. Title.
N. Y. P. L.   November 24, 1937

NN 0053766   NN NNC

National Home Planning Service.
America's most popular home plans

see under

Chirgotis, William G   1910–

National home planting bureau. How to plant the home grounds. / Edited by E. H. Wilson. Davenport, Ia. ₁cop. 1929.₎ nar. sm. 8°. pp. 23. Illustr.

NN 0053768   MH-A

National Home Reading Union, London.
 ...Annual report.
₁no.₎

London₁, 19   12°.
no.
Caption-title.

1. Books and reading—Per. and soc.   publ.
N. Y. P. L.   July 25, 1930

NN 0053769   NN

National Home-Reading Union, London.
Book list.
₁no.

₁London, 19   8°.
no.

1. Bibliography—Selected lists.
N. Y. P. L.   April 13, 1928

NN 0053770   NN

National homereading union, London.

The Readers' review; a monthly guide to books and reading
London, Sherratt & Hughes, 19   –10.

National home service conference.
 Proceedings
  see under National electric light association. Public relations national section. Women's committee. Home service subcommittee.

National Home Study Council.
Home study blue book. ₁1st₎–   ed.
Washington, 1928–

v. illus. 23 cm.

Cover title, 1st–   : Home study blue book and directory of private home study schools and courses (varies)
Compiler: 1st–   J. S. Noffsinger.

1. Correspondence schools and courses. I. Noffsinger, John Samuel, 1886–   comp. II. Title.

LC5951.N3   374.4   29-5889 rev

DNAL PU OCU PSt MBU MdBJ OU IEdS NNC CSf CStbS
NN   P NN Vi InLP ViU PPD NBuG DHEW OCIMN MH ViU MB PHi
0053773   DLC IdPI ICJ Or OrU IdU OrCS OrP OrSaW

National Home Study Council.
The manual of standards and directory of private home study schools and courses; J. S. Noffsinger, editor. Washington, 1947.

48 p. 21 cm.

1. Correspondence schools and courses. I. Noffsinger, John Samuel, 1886–   ed.

LC5919.N35 1947   374.4   47-6789 rev*

NN 0053774   DLC OrCS OrU ICU ICJ NN NNC TxU OU IdP₎

National Home Study Council.
The manual of standards for private home study schools; J. S. Noffsinger, editor. Washington, 1942.

64 p. 22 cm.

"Schools approved by, and members of, the council": p. 45–54.
"Bibliography of recommended reading": p. 61–63.

1. Correspondence schools and courses. I. Noffsinger, John Samuel, 1886–   ed.

LC5919.N35   374.4   42-15123 rev*
                                          ₁r60f₎

OrU CaBVaU MtU IdPI Or
NN 0053775   DLC ODW OCI OOxM CU NN ICJ OrP OrCS

National Home Study Council.
Orders and stipulations issued to home study schools by ₁the₎ Federal Trade Commission, 1925–1938. Compiled by J. S. Noffsinger, director. Washington, 1938.

172 p. 23 cm.

1. Correspondence schools and courses. 2. Educational law and legislation—U. S. I. Noffsinger, John Samuel, 1886–   comp. II. U. S. Federal Trade Commission. III. Title.

LC5951.N33   374.473   41-35069 rev*

NN 0053776   DLC DFT

NA7100   National Homebuilders Bureau, inc.
.S63
         Home guide. v. ₁1₎–   1937–
         ₁New York, etc.₎

National small homes bureau, inc., New York.
Small home builders' year book ...
 see Home guide.

NA7100   National homebuilders bureau, inc.
.S625
         Small homes data book.

         New York, N. Y., National home builders bureau, inc. ₁19

₁National homebuilder's society₎
The homebuilder. ₁Chicago, Printed by B. L. White & co., ₁1923₎

1 p. l., 5–188, ₁2₎ p. illus. (incl. plans) 28½ᵐ.

1. Architecture, Domestic—Designs and plans.   I. Title.

Library of Congress   NA7127.N43   23-13234

NN 0053780   DLC OCI

National Homemaking Conference, Minneapolis, 1932.
Homemaking
 see under National Congress of Parents and Teachers.

National homoeopathic hospital association of the District of Columbia, *Washington, D. C.*
Annual report.

Washington, 18

v. 22½–23½ᵐ.

In the first fifteen reports, the report year ends Dec. 31st; the 16th–17th were issued with combined cover-title and cover the years ending December 31, 1897, and June 30, 1898. In later reports, the report year ends June 30th.

1. Washington, D. C. National homeopathic hospital.

Library of Congress   RX1.N3   CA 11–228 Unrev'd

NN 0053782   DLC DNLM

National Homoeopathic Hospital Association of the District of Columbia, Washington, D.C.
——. Appeal to homoeopathic physicians and friends of homoeopathy in the United States in behalf of the National Homoeopathic Hospital, Washington, D.C. Including first report of Ladies' Aid Association of ..., the constitution, and a list of officers, members, and subscribers. 16 pp. 12°. ₁Washington, B. S. Adams, ₁1887₎.

NN 0053783   DNLM

National Homoeopathic Hospital Association of Washington, D.C. By-laws, rules, and regulations. 19 pp. 8°. Washington, T. McGill & Co., 1886.

NN 0053784   DNLM

National Homoeopathic Hospital Association of the District of Columbia, Washington, D.C.
——. By-laws, rules, and regulations. Adopted Jan. 21, 1889. 27 pp. 8°. ₁Washington₎, Gibson Bros., ₁1889₎.

NN 0053785   DNLM

NA7127   National Homes Corporation.
Y59
         Your national home magazine. ₁1st₎–   ed.
         ₁Muncie, Ind., National Homes Corp., 1951–

---

296   National Homes Foundation.
N216   Engineered low-cost farm and village homes. [Washington, D. C., 1941]
             23 p.
             1. Architecture, Domestic. Designs and plans. 2. Farm houses. U. S. I. Title: Low-cost farm and village homes. II. Title: Village homes.

NN 0053787   DNAL

VOLUME 407

National homes incorporated.
   Your home horizons and building
guide ... St.Petersburg,Fla.The Company
c1945.
   Illus.(incl.plans)ob.O.

NN   0053788   CaBViP Mi

F868
L8N2
National homestead association, Los Angeles, Cal.
   A home in southern california ... our new plan
secures a home, a life income. health. wealth,
happiness and independence
[Los Angeles; c1908]

NN   0053789   DLC

National honesty bureau.
   The honesty book; a handbook for teachers, parents and
other friends of children. Preliminary ed. New York, National honesty bureau [*1923]
   3 p. l., 56 p. illus. 28½ᵐ.

   1. Honesty.   I. Title.

   Library of Congress   BJ1533.H7N3   1923   23—7052

NN   DHEW DL
0053790   DLC OrCS Or KEmT MH NcD OC1 OLak OO

National honor society of secondary schools.
   Handbook.

Washington, D. C., National association of secondary-school
principals of the National education association; [etc., etc., 19
   v. 23ᵐ.
   The 2d, 4th–5th issued as Bulletins no. 31, 42, 67 of the Dept. of
secondary-school principals of the National education association (later
called National association of secondary-school principals)
Publication began in 1924.

   1. Students' societies—U. S.

U. S. Off. of educ. Library   E 37–239 Revised †
for Library of Congress   LJ151.N3
        [r45c2]†   371.852

NN   OU ViU WaS Or MtU
0053791   DHEW CU Wa DLC KEmT OU MiU MB NB PU

378.34   National Honor Society of Secondary Schools.
N214s   Scholarship program.

   Washington.
      v. 23cm.

      Sponsored by the National Association of
   Secondary School Principals.

NN   0053792   IU

National honor society of secondary schools.

Student life. v. 1, no. 1, Oct. 1937; v. 4, no. 2–
Nov. 1937–
[Fulton, Mo., The Ovid Bell press, inc., etc., etc., 1937–40;
Washington, D. C., 1941–

National honorary beta club
   see National beta club.

National honorary society for high school
journalists, Iowa City.
   Best creative work in American high schools, 1926/27–

   ... Iowa City, The National honorary society for high
schools journalists [*1927–

42.9   National horse association of Great Britain.
N213H   Horse owners' news sheet. no.
   London,

NN   0053796   DNAL

National horse association of Great Britain.
   ... Lists of the principal acts and orders which concern horse
owners. [London, 1937?]
   16 p. 21½ᵐ.
   Caption title.

   1. Horses—Law.

            43–28785

NN   0053797   DLC

National Horse Show Association of America.
   Judges' awards...

New York [1   8°.
      v.
   No horse show was held in 1914.

   1. Horseshows, U. S.: New York.
N. Y. P. L.   January 26, 1916.

NN   0053798   NN IaAS

National Horse Shoe Association of America.
   National horse show official catalogue
      see its Official catalogue ... annual
exhibition of horses.

National horse show association of America.
   Official catalogue
annual exhibition of horses ... New York [F. T. Alden]
   ⌒. 23ᵐ.

   1. Horse shows.

          CA 15–441 Unrev'd

   Library of Congress   SF295.N

NN   0053800   DLC IaAS Nh NN

SF295
N34
   National Horse Show Association of
      America.
      Prize list.
   New York, The Association.
      v. 23cm.

NN   0053801   IaAS

The National horseman.
   [Louisville, Ky.
      v. in   illus. (incl. ports.) 35½ᵐ.   monthly.
   Originally the Horse department of the Kentucky farmer's home
journal (established 1865) Became separate publication in July 1935.
In Nov. 1937 assumed numbering of Kentucky farmer's home journal.

   1. Horses—Period. 2. Horsemanship—Period.

   SF277.N3   636.105   47–21988

NN   0053802   DLC OrCS OU MoU AAP KyU ScCleU

National Horseshoe Pitchers Association of
   America.
   Horseshoe compendium
      see under Rose, Lee.

National Horseshoe Pitchers Association of
   America.
   The Horseshoe pitcher
      see under title

National horticultural and kindred societies.
   (*In* U. S. Dept. of agriculture. Yearbook, 1898, p. 621–624; 1899, p. 704–
708; 1900, p. 658–562; 1901, p. 632–633; 1902, p. 584–585; 1903, p. 525; 1904,
p. 555; 1905, p. 579; 1906, p. 470; 1907, p. 520; 1908, p. 512–513. 23½ᵐ.
Washington, 1899–1909)
   1898–1901, title reads: Secretaries of horticultural and kindred societies.
1902, title reads: Horticultural and kindred societies.

   1. Gardening—Societies. [1. Horticulture—Societies]

          Agr 6–1117 Revised

   Library, U. S. Dept. of   Agriculture

NN   0053805   DNAL

The National horticultural magazine
      see The American horticultural magazine.

National Horticultural Society
   see
National Horticultural Society of America.

SB1   National Horticultural Society of America.
.N3
   The American horticultural magazine. v. 1–
   Aug. 1922–
   Washington.

National horticulturist; official publication of the National
horticultural congress. [monthly]. v. 1–
   [₂ Council Bluffs, Iowa. 19

NN   0053809   MBH

National Hospital for Diseases of the Heart and
   Paralysis
      see London. National Hospital for Diseases
of the Heart and Paralysis.

National Hospital for Speech Disorders, New York
   see
New York (City) National Hospital for Speech
Disorders.

W 1   NATIONAL hospital forum. v. 1–2, no. 1;
NA485H   Nov. 1943–Jan. 1944. New York.
      2 v. in 1.   W1 NA485H
      Sponsored by the Hospital Equipment
   Corporation.
      Continued by the Hospital opinion.
      1. Insurance, Health - U. S.
   I. Hospital Equipment Corporation,
   New York

NN   0053812   DNLM

W 1   NATIONAL hospital forum. v. 5, no. 5–v. 8,
NA485J   no. 9; Mar. 1934–July 1937. Portland, Or.
      4 v. in   illus., ports.
               W1 NA485J
      Continues Western hospital news.
      Issue for Mar. 1934 has title: Hospital
   forum.

NN   0053813   DNLM

VOLUME 407

National hospital record.
Detroit, Mich., The National hospital record publishing co. ₍etc.₎
v. illus. (incl. ports., plans) 26½ᵐ. monthly.
Editor: D. T. Sutton.
Official organ of the Association of hospital superintendents.
Continued as the International hospital record.

1. Hospitals—Period. I. Sutton, Del T., ed. II. Association of hospital superintendents.

Library of Congress   RA960.N2   CA 6—1296 Unrev'd

NN   0053814   DLC ICRL ICJ DNLM

National hostess house committee.
Report of Hostess house committee. New York, War work council, National board of the Young womens Christian associations ₍1919?₎
43 p. illus. 23½ᵐ.

1. European war, 1914-1918—Women's work.

19-28011

Library of Congress   D639.W7N25

NN   0053815   DLC

NATIONAL HOT ROD ASSOCIATION.
National championship drag races. Offical program.
Los Angeles.   no.   illus.   28cm.

Annual.

1. Automobile racing--U.S. I. Title.

NN   0053816   NN

National Hot Rod Association.
Nationals yearbook.
₍Paramount, Calif.₎
v. illus. 28 cm. annual.
"Official souvenir program, annual National Championship
Drag Races."

1. Drag racing. I. Title.

GV1029.3.N3   796.7'2'0977251   67-40568

NN   0053817   DLC

National Hotel, Detroit
        see   Detroit. National Hotel.

F869   National Hotel and Coffee Shop, Nevada City,
N4N3   Calif.
        In the pines, the queen city of the Sierras. [San Francisco,
Engraved and printed by Calkins Pub. House, 190-?]
[13] p. illus. 14x18cm.

Issued by the hotel under an earlier name: National Hotel and Annex.

1. Nevada City, Calif. I. Title.

NN   0053819   CU-B

National hotel and travel gazette.
Year

Washington, D. C.: L. Mills, 19   f°.
v. illus.

Monthly.
Numbering continuous.

1. Hotels—Per. and soc. publ.
N. Y. P. L.   May 7, 1928

NN   0053820   NN

National hotel blue book.
Chicago, National Hotel Pub. Co.
v. 24 cm. annual.

1. Hotels, taverns, etc.—U. S.—Direct. 2. Hotels, taverns, etc.—Canada—Direct. 3. Hotels, taverns, etc.—Mexico—Direct.

TX907.N27   647.94058   51-39393 ‡

NN   0053821   DLC WaT

25.9   The national hotel directory for use of traveling.
men, hotels, liveries, commercial attorneys,
etc. ...   Des Moines, 1898-

NN   0053822   DLC

National hotel management co., inc.

Hitz, Ralph.
Standard practice manuals for hotel operation ... by Ralph
Hitz, president, National hotel management co., inc. New
York and London, Harper & brothers ₍1936₎

The national house builders' association of Canada.
[A letter to the federal government regarding
housing]. Vancouver,The association,1948.
3p.F.4.

NN   0053824   CaBViP

National house furnishing manufacturers association
...Blue book; official directory...11th annual
national house furnishing exhibit...Chicago, 1938.

NN   0053825   OC1

National Household Economic Association.
Report of the annual meeting. v.1-   ;
1893-
Chicago.
v.
Published as Columbian Association of Housekeepers and Bureau of Information. Report, 1893.
Vols. 1, 7 bound with National Columbian Household Economic Association. Articles of
incorporation and by-laws.
        Rev. cd.

NN   0053826   ICRL

National housewares directory.

₍San Francisco₎
v. 29 cm.
"Established 1931."
Issued by the Associated Pot and Kettle Clubs of America.

1. Household appliances—Direct.   I. Associated Pot and Kettle
Clubs of America.

TX298.N3   55-40311 ‡

Or WaS CoDB
NN   0053827   DLC OrP MiD CSt NBuG NIC NN ICJ PP MB

The **National** housing act; its background, its provisions, its
possibilities. ₍New York₎ Time and The Architectural
forum ₍ᶜ1934₎
15 p. illus. (ports.) diagr. 29ᵐ.
"Fifth printing."

1. Housing—U. S. 2. Building—U. S.   I. Time, the weekly news-
magazine. II. The Architectural forum.
        CA 35—281 Unrev'd
Library of Congress   HD7293.A3A24 (.N3) 1934 d
—— Copy 2.
Copyright AA 165092   331.8330973

NN   0053828   DLC OU

National housing agency
        see
U. S. *National housing agency.*

**National housing and town planning council,
London.**
Aldridge, Henry R.
The administration of the town planning duties of local
authorities. A supplement to "The case for town planning". By Henry R. Aldridge ... London, National
housing and town planning council ₍1922₎

NA9000   **National Housing and Town Planning Council,**
.H67   **London.**
The British housing and planning review. v. ₍1₎–
July 1940–
London.

NA9185   **National Housing and Town Planning Council,**
.N356   **London.**
British housing & planning year book. 1950–
₍London₎ National Housing and Town Planning Council.

**National housing and town planning council,
London.**
Aldridge, Henry R.
The case for town planning. A practical manual for the
use of councillors, officers, and others engaged in the preparation of town planning schemes, by Henry R. Aldridge ... with
an appendix by Frank M. Elgood ... and Edmund R. Abbott
... London, The National housing and town planning council ₍1916₎

National Housing and Town Planning Council,
London.
Continental town planning tour, Easter 1909.
Leicester, 1909.
24 p.   illus.   32 cm.
Cover title.
1. Cities and towns - Planning - Germany.
I. Title.

NN   0053834   NcU MH

National housing and town planning council, London.
... Facts and figures regarding the present
housing situation and the progress of the anti-
slum campaign in England and Wales (Revised,
April, 1936) By John G. Martin, secretary of
the council ...   London, National housing and
town planning council [1936]
21 p.   33.5 cm.
I. Martin, John G   jt. auth. 1. Housing -
Gt. Brit.

NN   0053835   NNC

National housing and town planning council,
London.
... Facts and figures regarding the present
housing situation in England and Wales (revised, April, 1938) by John G. Martin ...
₍London, 1938₎
16 p. incl. tables. 33ᵐ.
1. Housing - Gt. Brit.
I. Martin, John G   jt. au.

NN   0053836   NNC DL

VOLUME 407

National housing and town planning council, London.
The Housing and planning news-bulletin
       see   The British housing and planning
review.

NATIONAL HOUSING AND TOWN PLANNING COUNCIL.
Housing and town planning after the war. Report of deputation received on behalf of His Majesty's government, Sept.20,1916, by the president of the Local government board(W.H. Long). London,1916.

4°. pp.23.

NN   0053838   MH

NATIONAL HOUSING AND TOWN PLANING COUNCIL
Housing and town planning after the war. Memorandum relative to the housing preparedness campaign of the council. London,1917.

4°. pp.12.

NN   0053839   MH

NATIONAL HOUSING AND TOWN PLANING COUNCIL.
Housing and town planning after the war. Memorandum containing a record of the resolutions passed at a series of district conferences, Nov.1916.-March,1917; a memorandum submitted to Lord Rhondda, president of the Local government board, a report of the proceedings of the deputation received by Lord Rhondda at the offices of the Local Government Board, May 7, 1917. London,1917.

4°. pp.27+.

NN   0053840   MH

National Housing and Town Planning Council, London.

Thompson, W   of Surrey.
   Housing up-to-date (companion volume to the Housing handbook) by Alderman W. Thompson ... A practical manual giving the latest facts and figures for the use of ... all social or municipal reformers, interested in the housing of the working classes. Pub. by the National housing reform council ... London, 1907.

NATIONAL HOUSING AND TOWN PLANNING COUNCIL,
LONDON.
How to town-plan the building and equipment of cottages in garden suburbs together with official illustrated catalogue of the South Wales cottage exhibition, Swansea, 1910.

4°. pp.55+. Plans and plates.

NN   0053842   MH

NATIONAL HOUSING AND TOWN PLANNING COUNCIL.
Interim report of Technical conference set up by the council to consider and report on various technical problems which are likely to present themselves for solution in regard to housing and town planning at the close of the war. [London,1917?].

6°. pp.(4).

NN   0053843   MH CSt-H

HD7333   National housing and town planning council,
.A3N27   London.
          Memorandum...   London,1918-
          v. 28ᶜᵐ.

NN   0053844   ICU CSt-H

National housing and town planning council.
...Memorandum on the provisions of the New towns act, 1946. London [1946]   2 l.   25cm.

Caption-title.

1. Cities—Gt. Br.
N. Y. P. L.   June 8, 1949

NN   0053845   NN

National housing and town planning council,
London.
       Memorandum upon rural housing
       see under   Cooper, J   Brian.

National housing and town planning council,
London.
   ... Memorandum upon town and country planning during the war, by Thomas Adams ... [London, His Majesty's Stationery office, 1939]
   8 p. 33ᵐ.

Caption-title.

1. Housing - Gt. Brit.
    Adams, Thomas, 1871-1940.

NN   0053847   NNC

National Housing and town planning council.
London.
   Midland conference on the better planning of new housing areas ...
       see under   Midland Conference on the Better Planning of New Housing Areas, Birmingham, Eng., 1906.

HD7333   National housing and town planning council,
.A3N31   London.
          Miscellaneous pamphlets not separately cataloged.

NN   0053849   ICU

National housing and town planning council,
London.
Aldridge, Henry R.
   The national housing manual. A guide to national housing policy and administration. By Henry R. Aldridge, secretary National housing and town planning council. London, The National housing and town planning council, 1923.

National Housing and Town Planning Council, London.
***** A national housing policy. Official report of the housing deputation to the Prime Minister (Sir Henry Campbell-Bannerman, M.P.), and to the President of the Local Government Board (The Right Hon. John Burns, M.P.). November 6th, 1906. Arranged by the National Housing Reform Council. ... . Leicester, London, National Housing Reform Council, [1906].
   cover-title, 8, [4] p. 33½ᶜᵐ.

NN   0053851   ICJ MiU

National Housing and Town Planning Council,
London.
   1900-1910, a record of ten years' work for housing and town planning reform. [Leicester, Eng., n.d.]
   23p. 27cm.

   1. Housing. 2. Cities and towns - Planning - Gt. Brit. I. Titl'

NN   0053852   NcU NNC

National housing and town planning council.
   ...Notes on the fixation of rents of Council houses.   London [194-?]   4 p.   31cm.

Caption-title.

1. Rent—Gt. Br.
N. Y. P. L.   June 8, 1949

NN   0053853   NN

National Housing and Town Planning Council, London.

International housing congress. 8th, London, 1907.
   ... Papers submitted to the 8th International housing congress, held in London, August, 1907. (Under the auspices of the Permanent international housing committee and the National housing reform council). London [etc.] National housing reform council [1907]

National housing and town planning council, London.
   A policy for the slums, being the report of a special committee appointed by the National housing and town planning council. London, P. S. King & son, ltd., 1929.
   67, [4] p. 19ᶜᵐ.

   1. Housing—Gt. Brit. 2. Labor and laboring classes—Dwellings. I. Title.

                                              30-14601
Library of Congress   HD7333.A3A5 1929 a
                               [3]   331.8330942

NN   0053855   DLC WU MiU MH

NA9185   National housing and town planning council,
.N3   London.
          Proceedings of the National advisory town planning committee. Report communicated by alderman Arthur Bennett [and others] [London,1912]
          18 pam. in portfolio. 33ᶜᵐ.

On cover: National conference,1912.

NN   0053856   ICU

National housing and town planning council,
London
   [Publications]

   [no.1] Memorandum upon the present housing situation in England and Wales (April, 1934).
   [no.2] Memorandum upon the provisions of the housing act, 1930. (Rev. April, 1934.)
   [no.3] Memorandum upon the rural housing problem (Rev. April, 1934)

   [no.4] The campaign against the slums [Rev. April 1934]
   [no.5] Memorandum upon the progress of the anti-slum campaign and the main features of the housing act, 1930. (Rev. Nov., 1934).

   [no.1-5] by John Martin, Secretary of the Council.

NN   0053858   MiD-B

National Housing and Town Planning Council,
London.
   A record of 10 years' work for housing and town planning reform
       see its   1900-1910, a record of ten years' work ...

VOLUME 407

National Housing and Town Planning Council, *London.*
Report.

London.
v. 26 cm. annual.
Report year ends Mar. 31.
Reports for 1940/41— planning news-bulletin, no. 6, issued as the Housing and 14

1. Cities and towns—Planning—Gt. Brit. 2. Dwellings—Gt. Brit.

NA9185.N354 711.06142 50–29522 ‡

NN 0053860 DLC MiD

National Housing and Town Planning Council, London.
International housing congress. *8th, London, 1907.*
Report of the vIIIme Congrès international des habitations à bon marché, held in London, August, 1907. (Under the auspices of the Permanent international housing committee and the National housing reform council).
London [etc.] National housing reform council [1907]

National Housing and Town Planning Council, London.
Year book
see **British** housing & planning year book.

National housing and town planning council, *London. Technical committee.*
... Report of Technical committee, 1st–
London, 1925–
v. 28 x 21½ᵐ.
At head of title of 1st report: National housing and town planning council. Memorandum no. 34. Series 2.

1. Labor and laboring classes—Dwellings. 2. Housing—Gt. Brit.

Library of Congress NA7532.N3
CA 27–153 Unrev'd

NN 0053863 DLC

[**National housing association**]
Brief list of books on housing and city planning. [New York, 1916]
[2] p. 23 cm. (National housing association publications, no. 32)

1. Housing—Bibl. 2. Cities and towns—Planning—Bibl.
HD7293.A1N26 no. 32 20—17213

NN 0053864 DLC MB NN IU

National housing association.
... Constitution and by-laws. January. 1910. [New York, 1910]
8 p. 15ᵐ.

Library of Congress HD7293.A3N35
17–12582

NN 0053865 DLC OO MiU MB IU DL

[**National Housing Association.**]
The fight for better homes. [New York, 1913.] 24 p. nar. 16°.

1. Habitations for working classes, U. S. 2. Title.
N. Y. P. L. May 11, 1914.

NN 0053866 NN OO MH

National Housing Association. *8093.159
Governmental housing projects in danger. Sudden stopping of government housing projects: S. J. resolution 194.
= *Typewritten manuscripts.* New York. 1918. 2 parts in 1 v. 28 cm.
Appended is, Calendar no. 564, 65th Congress, 3d session, S.J. res. 194. (Report no. 620.)
A resolution affecting the United States Housing Corporation.

L5957 — Housing problem. — United States. Department of Labor. Bureau of Industrial Housing and Transportation.

NN 0053867 MB

HD7293 **National housing association.**
.A1H6 Housing. v. 1–23, no. 3; Feb. 1912–Oct. 1935. New York city, National housing association [1912–35]

HN80 **National housing association.**
.S7S7 Ihlder, John, *1876–*
no. 3 Housing in Springfield, Illinois; a study by the National housing association [by] John Ihlder; the Springfield survey, Housing section. Springfield, Ill., Springfield survey committee, 1914.

331.83 **National housing association.**
N21ho Housing progress in Massachusetts. The law for towns and the law for cities, New York, 1913.
19p. (Housing betterment. v.2, no.2)

NN 0053870 IU

National Housing Association. 8093.135.29
Housing progress in 1914. Summarized annual report of the National Housing Association.
= New York City. 1915. 6 pp. [Publication. No. 29.] 23 cm.

K6217 — Housing problem. — S.r.c.

NN 0053871 MB

National housing association.
Atterbury, Grosvenor, *1869–*
Model towns in America, by Grosvenor Atterbury ... New York city, 1913.

National housing association.
The Morrill moulded concrete houses... [1919]

NN 0053873 MiU

331.83 **National housing association.**
N212p Officers and directors. [New York]
no.3 1910.
unp. (National housing association. Publications. no.3)

NN 0053874 IU

National Housing Association.
Publications. no. –62; –Oct. 1930.
New York City.
no. illus., maps. 14–28 cm.

1. Housing—U. S. 2. Labor and laboring classes—Dwellings. 3. Cities and towns—Planning—U. S.

HD7293.A1N26 15–24761 rev*

NN 0053875 DLC ICJ OrCS PU CU MB DL

National Housing Association. 8093.135.2
Purposes.
= [New York.] 1910. (4) pp. [Publications. No. 2.] 15 cm.

K4514 — Housing problem. — S.r.c.

NN 0053876 MB IU

National housing association.
Recent books and reports on housing, zoning and town planning. New York city, 1928–
v. 23ᵐ. (National housing association publications, no. 58, 59, 62)

1. Housing—Bibl. 2. Cities and towns—Planning—Bibl. 3. Cities and towns—Planning—Zone system—Bibl.

Library of Congress HD7293.A3N3
30–2185 Revised
—— —— 2d set. Z7164.H8N3]

NN 0053877 DLC ICJ OC1W MH NN

National housing association.
Passaic, N. J. *Board of trade. Housing committee.*
A survey of housing conditions in Passaic, New Jersey. Recommendations by the National housing association. Prepared for the Housing committee of Passaic board of trade, by Udetta D. Brown. [Passaic? 1915]

National housing association.
A symposium on war housing held under the auspices of the National housing association, February 25, 1918, Philadelphia. [New York, 1918]
4 p. l., [3]–141 p. 23½ᵐ.
On cover: War housing problems in America.

1. Housing—U. S. I. Title. II. Title: War housing problems in America.

Library of Congress HD7293.A3N37 18–11732

OC1 NN MB ICJ
NN 0053879 DLC WaS WaSp ICRL CU NcU NcU MiU OO

National Housing Association.
"There ain't no law." New York, National Housing Assn., 1913.
32 p. illus. 23ᶜᵐ. [Its Publications, no. 19.]

1. Housing—Law and legislation. 2. Hygiene, Public—U. S. I. Ser.

NN 0053880 ViU IU

National Housing Association.
A war emergency in housing. New York, 1917.
8 p. 23ᶜᵐ. [Its Publications, no. 42.]
"Letter to President Wilson."

1. Labor and laboring classes—Dwellings. I. Title. II. Ser.

NN 0053881 ViU

National Housing Association.
What our cities do not know. [New York, 1914?] 29 p. 8°.
"Results of the questionnaire sent out by the National Housing Association to 128 cities."

1. Habitations for working classes, U. S. 2. Habitations for working classes, Canada.
N. Y. P. L. July 10, 1916.

NN 0053882 NN ICU

VOLUME 407

National housing committee, London.
Housing and planning policy; interim report of the National housing committee. ₍London, 1936₎ 9 p. 25cm.

Cover-title.
"National housing committee. Addendum... May, 1936," 2 l. inserted.

1. Habitations for the working   class—Gt. Br.
N. Y. P. L.   December 6, 1937

NN 0053883   NN MiD IU NNC

National housing committee, *London.*
A national housing policy; report of the National housing committee. London, P. S. King & son, ltd., 1934.
85 p. 24½ᶜᵐ.

1. Housing—Gt. Brit. 2. Labor and laboring classes—Dwellings.
I. Title.
Library of Congress   HD7333.A3N3   35-17619
                                    ₍3₎   331.8330942

NN 0053884   DLC WU ViU NN CtY MB OCl NNC IU

National housing committee, Washington, D. C.
The housing market; a report by the National housing committee, December 3, 1937. ₍Washington₎ 1937. 32 p. illus. 28cm.

1. Housing—Stat.—U. S. 2. Real   estate business—U. S.
N. Y. P. L.   April 6, 1944

NN 0053885   NN DNAL MiD NNC

National Housing Committee for Congested Areas.
A review of the housing situation; a statement issued by the National Housing Committee for Congested Areas. December 1927. New York: Printed at the Heckscher Foundation for Children₍, 1928₎. 47 p. illus. (incl. plan, ports.) 8°.

388041A. 1. New york (city)—   Tenements.
N. Y. P. L.   December 13, 1928

NN 0053886   NN WHi MH OCU

National housing conference.
Broadening the base of public housing, addresses delivered at the ninth annual meeting of the National public housing conference, Washington, D. C., January 26 and 27, 1940 ... ₍New York, 1940₎
35 p. 28 cm.

1. Housing—Congresses. 2. Housing—U. S.—Congresses.
I. Title.
HD7286.N44   331.83306373   41-24172 rev

NN 0053887   DLC

National housing conference.
Building a citizens housing association

see under

Crosby, Alexander L

National Housing Conference.
The first Washington conference on public housing, held under the auspices of the National Public Housing Conference; speeches. Washington, January 27, 1934. ₍New York?₎ 1934₎
61 p. 27 cm.

1. Housing—U. S.—Congresses. 2. Hygiene, Public—U. S.
I. Title. II. Title: The Washington conference on public housing.
HD7293.A1N3 1934b   331.83306273   56-53824

NN 0053889   DLC ICJ OCl DL NN

National Housing Conference.
Housing policy and national defense; a statement by the Board of the National Housing Conference, adopted at December 11, 1950, meeting in New York City.   N. Y., Dec. 29, 1950.
4 p.

NN 0053890   PPCPC

National   Housing Conference.
A housing program for now and later.
February 1948. Washington, National Public Housing Conference ₍1948₎
1v, 60 p.

Bibliographical footnotes.

NN 0053891   CU NN MH-BA

National Housing Conference.

HD7293   The Housing yearbook. 195₄–
.II785   Washington, National Housing Conference.

National   housing conference.

Alfred, Helen L.
Municipal housing, by Helen Alfred ... New York, N. Y., National public housing conference ₍1935₎

National   Housing Conference.
National Public Housing Conference, January 25, 1936
    see under   Ihlder, John, 1876–

National   Housing Conference.

HD7293
.A1P8   Public housing. v. 1–
Nov. 15, 1934–
₍Washington, etc., National Public Housing Conference₎

National Housing Conference.
Public housing tour guide. 1st ed.₍ 1940. New York.
50 p. 28 cm.
Issued by the Conference under an earlier name: National Public Housing Conference.
No more published?

1. Housing—U. S.   I. Title.
HD7293.A1N28   331.833   42-21484 rev*‡

NN 0053896   DLC OClW

HD7293 NATIONAL   HOUSING CONFERENCE.
.N43   Speeches delivered at the ... annual meeting
... ₍New York?₎ 1934–
v.
Title varies slightly.

1. Housing—U. S.

NN 0053897   ICU

National housing conference.
Speeches delivered at the eighth annual meeting of the National public housing conference ... New York, January 27–28, 1939 ... ₍New York, 1939?₎
35, ₍1₎ p. 28 x 21½ cm.

1. Housing—U. S.
HD7293.A1N3 1939b   331.83306273   42-5252 rev

NN 0053898   DLC NNC OrU

National Housing Conference.
Speeches. The first Washington conference on public housing ...
    see its   The first Washington conference on public housing.

National Housing Conference.
The third Washington conference on slum clearance and low rent housing, held under the auspices of the National Public Housing Conference; speeches. Washington, January 24–25–26, 1936. ₍New York? 1936?₎
62 l. 28 cm.

1. Housing—Congresses. 2. Slums—U. S. 3. Hygiene, Public—U. S. 4. Cities and towns—U. S. I. Title. II. Title: Washington conference on slum clearance and low rent housing.
HD7293.A1N3 1936b   331.83306273   38-3009 rev*

NN 0053900   DLC

National Housing Conference.
The truth about public housing.   Washington, D. C., Apr. 1, 1950.
11 p.

NN 0053901   PPCPC

331.833 National Housing Conference.
N2135   The truth about public housing. ₍Washington, D.C., 1950?₎
22p. illus. 24cm.

1. Labor and laboring classes. Dwellings. 2. Housing. U.S. I. Title.

NN 0053902   OrU

Avery
AA
7545   National Housing Conference.
N2147   Winning the fight to clear slums by building low-rent public housing. ₍Washington, D. C., 1950₎
59 p. illus. 22cm.

NN 0053903   NNC NcD

National Housing Policy Conference, *St. Louis, 1951.*
Housing in peace and war; a report to the nation. ₍St. Louis, 1951₎
98 p. illus., ports. 28 cm.

Caption title.
"List of participants" (5 l.) inserted.

1. Housing—Congresses. 2. Housing—U. S.   I. Title.
HD7293.N37 1951   331.83306373   51-28909

NN 0053904   DLC MiD

National Housing Reform Council, London
    see National Housing and Town Planning Council, London.

VOLUME 407

HD
7286
N3
National Housing Workshop.
Proceedings.
Lincoln, Neb.

NN 0053906 KMK

National Hughes Alliance.—Women's Committee.
Hughes campaign service. Bulletin.
See
Hughes campaign service.
Bulletin.

National Hughes alliance. *Women's committee.*
Women in national politics. New York, Women's committee National Hughes alliance, 1916.
3⁰ p. 25½ᵐ.

1. Campaign literature, 1916—Republican. 2. Women in politics.
ɪ. Title.
17-14084

Library of Congress JK2357.1916.N3

NN 0053908 DLC MnHi

284.5
N274
National Huguenot Society.
Proceedings. v. 1– 1942– Washington, D.C.
v. in 23 cm.

Annual, 1942-58; biennial 1959–

1. Huguenots in the U.S. 2. Huguenots. Societies, etc.

NN 0053909 N ICN MiD

National Huguenot-Walloon New Netherland
tercentary commission,

See

Huguenot-Walloon New Netherland commission,
New York

The National humane journal.
Chicago, Ill.,
v. illus. 30½ᵐ. monthly.

1. Animals, Treatment of—Period.
CA 15-50 Unrev'd

Library of Congress HV4701.N2

NN 0053911 DLC ICHi

The National humane review, pub. by the American humane association. v. 1–
Jan. 1913–
Albany, N. Y., 1913–
v. in illus. (incl. ports.) 31ᵐ. monthly.

1. Animals, Treatment of—Period. 2. Children—Charities, protection,
etc.—Period. ɪ. American humane association.
15-7652

Library of Congress HV4701.N3

NIC OCl MiU ICJ CU
NN 0053912 DLC OrU WaS DNLM NjP DL ICRL Nh MoU

Case
.Y
194
.614
The NATIONAL humourist; being a choice selection
of the most modern jokes, wit, and repartee.
London, W. Houstoun, 1836.
224p. front. 12cm.

NN 0053913 ICN

The national hunger march in pictures...
see under National Committee. Unemployed
Councils.

National hunt season
see Chaseform; national hunt racing season.

National Hydraulic Company, *Windsor, Vt.*
see
Jones and Lamson Machine Company, *Springfield, Vt.*

National Hydraulic Laboratory, Washington, D.C.
see U.S. National Hydraulic Laboratory,
Washington, D.C.

National Hydraulic Power Committee.
Minutes of the meeting...
May, 1934

[Lancaster, Pa.?] 1934 28cm.
no.
Reproduced from typewritten copy.
May, 1934 called reunion meeting.
Continues the work of the Hydraulic Power Committee of the National Electric
Light Association which held its last meeting in April, 1933.
A further report of the 1934 meeting is included in the periodical Power.

1. Engineering, Hydraulic.
N.Y.P.L. July 15, 1936

NN 0053918 NN

National hygiene and public welfare
see
Canada lancet and practitioner.

National hymn and tune book, for congregations, schools and the nome
= Boston. Ditson & Co. 1875. 128 pp. 12°.

F7101 — Church music. Psalmodv

NN 0053920 MB PPiPT RPB DLC

The national hymn book of the American Churches
see under Thompson, Robert Ellis,
1844–

National hymns ... 1861
see under White, Richard Grant, 1821-
1885.

National hymns, original and selected ...
see under Kneeland, Abner, 1774-1844,
comp.

... National hymns... used at the meeting of the
Columbian liberty bell committee held in Independence Hall, in Philadelphia, Pennsylvania,
June 7th, 1893
see under [Coles, Abraham] 1813-1891.

f657
N2131c
National Ice Association.
Cost accounting system. [Chicago]
n.d.
10 sheets.
Issued under its earlier name: National associa-
tion of ice industries.

NN 0053925 IU

286.2
N212
National Ice Association.
How to display the iced method way.
Washington, D.C. [1946?]
[14] p.
Issued under its earlier name: National
association of ice industries.

NN 0053926 DNAL

389.3
N2157
National Ice Association.
How to get more for your money when
you market. [Washington, 194-]
7 p.
Issued under its earlier name: National
association of ice industries.

1. Vegetables. Preservation. 2. Ice.

NN 0053927 DNAL

621.5
N277i
National Ice Association.
Iced comfort cooling. [Chicago? 1932?]
12 ℓ. illus., pl., 2 fold. plans, tables.
29 x 22½ cm.
Title stamped on cover.
Gift of the National association of ice
industries.
On the use of iced cooling in business
buildings.

NN 0053928 MiU

286.2
N212I
National Ice Association.
The iced method of displaying vegetables.
Washington, D.C. [1946?]
[14] p.
Issued under its earlier name: National
association of ice industries.

NN 0053929 DNAL

TH
7687
.N28
National Ice Association.
... Increasing ice sales with comfort cooling.
Chicago, Ill., Technical department, National
association of ice industries, ©1932.
7 pt. illus., fold. diagrs. 28ᶜᵐ.
Cover-title.
Sections I-III, V-VI by Emerson Brandt and Lee Currey.
Section IV in loose-leaf folder with special title only.
Prospectus (3 ℓ.) inserted at end of section I.
CONTENTS.—section I. Iced comfort cooling.—section II.
Organizing to sell comfort cooling.—section III. Comfort
cooling sales manual.—section IV., Iced comfort cooling.
—section V. Comfort cooling with ice; proposal for Mr.
John Smith.—section VI. Manufacturers, installation or-

ganizations and engineering service.—section VII. The
engineer's manual.

1. Air conditioning. 2. Ice industry. I. Brandt, Emerson
Andre, 1903- II. Currey, Lee.

NN 0053931 MiU MiD

VOLUME 407

National Ice Association.
⸢Miscellaneous publications. Washington,
D. C., 194-

Unbound pamphlets.

1. Refrigeration and refrigerating
machinery.

NN   0053932   NNC

389.3
N2157M   **National Ice Association.**
Money saving tips on marketing! ⸢Washington, 195-?⸣
⸢2⸣ p.
issued under its earlier name: National
association of ice industries.

1. Vegetables. Preservation. 2. Ice.

NN   0053933   DNAL

National Ice Association.
Principal ice producing and distributing companies in the
United States.
Washington.
v. 36 cm.
Began publication in 1945.
Vols. for   issued by the association under an earlier
name: National Association of Ice Industries.

1. Ice industry—U. S.—Direct.   I. Title.

HD9481.U3N28   621.58058   47–20897 rev 2*

NN   00523934   DLC

National Ice Association. *Annual Convention*
see
National Ice Association. *Convention.*

National Ice Association. *Convention.*
Annual Convention, National Ice Association. ⸢Proceedings⸣
Washington ⸢etc.⸣
v. in   illus., ports. 21–24 cm.
Began publication in 1918. Cf. Union list of serials.
Title varies slightly.
Proceedings for   issued by the association under an earlier
name: National Association of Ice Industries.
Proceedings of the 2d convention, 1919, incorporates the Proceedings of the 11th Annual Convention of the National Ice Association of America (TP498.N3)
1. Refrigeration and refrigeration machinery—Societies, etc.

HD9481.U3N3   62–68095

NN   0053936   DLC MiU OU NcD NIC TxU OrP PBL KyU CoD

National Ice Association. *Convention.*
Official proceedings
see its
Annual Convention, National Ice Association.

National Ice Association. *Convention.*
Proceedings
see its
Annual Convention, National Ice Association.

National Ice Association. *Household Refrigeration Bureau.*
H. R. B. ⸢publication⸣
Chicago,
v. ⸢24 cm.
No.   issued by the bureau under an earlier name of the
association: National Association of Ice Industries.

1. Refrigeration and refrigerating machinery.   I. Title.

TP492.6.N3   62–56556

NN   0053939   DLC CU NBuG DL NN OCl OU ICJ Or IU

**National Ice Association. Household Refrigeration
Bureau.**
Publication
see its   H. R. B. [publication]

TP492.6   **National Ice Association.**
N3   Household refrigeration bureau.
no.3   ... The romance of ice ...   Chicago, The
National association of ice industries, ©1927.

cover-title⸢15⸣p.   illus.   23½cm.   (At
head of title: Household refrigeration bureau
of the National association of ice industries
...   ⸢Publication⸣ no. 3)

1. Refrigeration and refrigerating machinery.
2. Ice.—Hygienic aspects.   3. Ice industry.
I. Title.

NN   0053941   NBuG ViU OU

National Ice Association.
Technical dept.
Increasing ice sales with comfort cooling.
Sect. 1- ⸢Chicago⸣ c1932-

NN   0053942   OCl

National Ice Cream Retailers Association.
NICRA yearbook.
⸢Toledo⸣
v. in   26–28 cm.
Began with yearbook for 1941.
Title varies: 19 –48, Retail ice cream manufacturer; yearbook
(varies slightly)—1949–54, 1956—, N. A. R. I. C. M. yearbook
(on cover, 1951–52: Yearbook)—1955, Yearbook (on cover, N. A. R.
I. C. M. yearbook)
Vols. for   issued by the association under its earlier
name: National Association of Retail Ice Cream Manufacturers.
I. National Association of Retail Ice Cream Manufacturers. N. A.
R. I. C. M. yearbook.   II. National Association of Retail Ice Cream
Manufacturers. Yearbook. III. Title. IV. Title: Retail ice cream
manufacturer; yearbook. V. Title: N. A. R. I. C. M. yearbook.

TX795.A1N2   62–27622

NN   0053943   DLC NIC

The **National** ice skating guide
see
World ice skating guide.

National illiteracy conference committee.
... Elementary instruction of adults. Report of National
illiteracy conference committee. Charles M. Herlihy, chairman ... Washington, Govt. print. off., 1925.
vi, 33 p. 23cm. (⸢U. S.⸣ Bureau of education. Bulletin, 1925, no. 8)
At head of title: Department of the interior ...

1. Education of adults.   I. Herlihy, Charles Michael, 1891–
II. Title.
E 25—153

U. S. Off. of educ. Library   L111.A6
———Copy 2.   LC5251.N2
for Library of Congress   L111.A6 1925, no. 8
———Copy 2.   LC5251.N85
⸢a41k1⸣   (370.61) 379.2

OO OCU ICJ
NN   0053945   DLC CaBVaU WaWW OrU MB IJC MiU DLC OO

AP2   **National illustrated magazine.**
N245   ⸢Washington, D.C., 18

NN   0053946   DLC

National illustrating co., *New York.*
Automobile emergency and repair manual; a manual
of information to meet every conceivable automobile
emergency. New York, National illustrating co., ©1911.
vi, 61 p. illus. 19 × 9cm. $0.50

1. Automobiles—Handbooks, manuals, etc.   11–22767

Library of Congress   TL151.N3

NN   0053947   DLC ICJ

Avery
AA
735   **National Illustrating Company,** Kinderhook,
M58   N. Y.
N21   Middletown in 1907 illustrated; a city of
homes, industry and enterprise. ⸢Illustrated
and compiled by the National Illustrating Company. Kinderhook, N. Y., 1907?⸣
20 p. illus. 23x32cm.

Caption title.
On cover: Illustrated & descriptive, Middletown, N. Y.

1. Middletown,   N. Y – Description.
Title.

NN   0053948   NNC

National immigration conference, New York, 1920
see   National conference on immigration,
New York, 1920.

National immigration conference, *New York,* 1923.
Proceedings of the National immigration conference
held in New York city, December 13 and 14, 1923 ...
New York city, National industrial conference board
⸢1924⸣
viii, 272 p. diagrs. 23cm. (National industrial conference board. Special report no. 26)

1. U. S.—Emig. & immig.

Library of Congress   JV6405 1924   24–6470

NcD OU OCU MB ICJ Or OCl
NN   0053950   DLC NcRS MtBC DHEW OrU MtU WaS CU

National implement and vehicle association
see
Farm equipment institute, *Chicago.*

The national impolicy of the present high duty on tobacco, extracted, for the information of His Majesty's
government and the members of both houses of Parliament, from the evidence given before the commissioners of revenue enquiry; the select committee on the
growth and cultivation of tobacco; and the commissioners of excise inquiry ... Westminster ⸢Eng.⸣ Vacher
& sons, 1837.
ix, ⸢1⸣, 27 p. 25cm.

1. Tariff—Gt. Brit. 2. Tobacco manufacture and trade—Gt. Brit.

Library of Congress   HF2651.T643N3   6–17299†

NN   0053952   DLC MH-BA

VOLUME 407

... The **National** importance of scientific and industrial research, by George Ellery Hale, Elihu Root, Henry S. Pritchett, Theodore N. Vail, Ambrose Swasey, A. W. Mellon, George Eastman, Walter Douglas, James R. MacColl, H. E. Howe. Washington, D. C., Published by the National research council of the National academy of sciences, 1919.

cover-title, 43 p. 25ᵐ. (Bulletin of the National research council. no. 1 (v. 1, pt. 1) Oct. 1919)

CONTENTS.—The purpose of the National research council, by G. E. Hale.—The need for organization in scientific research, by E. Root.—The function of scientific research in a modern state, by H. S. Pritchett.—Relations of science to industry, by T. N. Vail.—Coöperation be-

tween science and industry, by A. Swasey.—The value of industrial research, by A. W. Melon.—Concerning the importance of industrial research, by G. Eastman.—The significance of research for mining and metallurgy, by W. Douglas.—The application of scientific research to one industry, by J. R. MacColl.—The organization of scientific and industrial research at home and abroad, by H. E. Howe.

1. Research. 2. Science. 3. Industry.   I. Hale, George Ellery, 1868–1938. II. Root, Elihu, 1845–1937. III. Pritchett, Henry Smith, 1857–1939. IV. Title: Scientific and industrial research.

Library of Congress   Q11N292 no. 1   21—26021

NN 0053954   00 OCl NcRS
              DLC CaBVaU IU OC1W WaTC OrU OU MiU

The National importance of the dissolution of the East India Company, and a free trade throughout the Indian sea.[By G. Monroe.?] *Edinburgh: J. Moir,* 1812. 2 p.l., 5-22 pp. 8°.

In: *C. p. v. 1108.

NN 0053955   NN

National improved Saxony sheep breeders
     association.
          Register, v. 1.   Washington, Pa.
H. F. Ward, 1884.
          8°.

14
9352

NN 0053956   DLC

National Improved Telephone Company, New Orleans, La.
A concise statement of facts, with admissions by A. G. Bell, showing that he did not invent the telephone, with proof that his different statements under oath contradict each other. Issued by the National Improved Telephone Company, of New Orleans, La.   New Orleans: A. W. Hyatt [1886?].   28 p., incl. diagrs. 8°.

Cover-title.

1. Telephone.—Jurisprudence, law   suits, etc., U. S. 2. Bell, Alexander
Graham, 1847–1922.
N. Y. P. L.   July 2, 1924

NN 0053957   NN

National Incinerator Company, New York.
     Story of the incinerator.

NN 0053958   DNW

National income, 1937-1940
     see under   [Deutsch, John J   ]

National income and audit system, inc.
     ... National income and audit system, inc.
[3d simplified business edition] /Ed. and rev. b]
Maury M. Tepper ... [New York] c1930.
[138] p.   forms.   30½ cm.

1. Income tax - U. S. 2. Accounting.   Topper,
Maury M.   ([jt.au.)

NN 0053960   NNC

National income and product accounts of the
     United States
          see under   U.S. Office of Business
Economics.

HC157
.J2A168   The National income and product of Jamaica.
          1954?-
               Kingston, Jamaica, Dept. of Statistics.
               v.

          Report year varies.
          Title varies slightly.
          Each issue preceded by an issue called
          National income and product of Jamaica;
          preliminary estimates.

          1. National income - Jamaica. I. Jamaica.
          Dept. of Statistics.

NN 0053962   NbU

National income by distributive shares ...
     see under   [Ritchie, John A   ]

The national income from the liquor traffic.   [Manchester: United Kingdom Alliance Offices, 187–?]   3 p.   8°.

Caption-title.
Repr.: Alliance news.
In: VTZ p. v. 186, no. 13.

1. Alcoholic drinks.—Taxation, Gt. Br.   BLACK TEMPERANCE COLL.
N. Y. P. L.   May 29, 1919.

NN 0053964   NN

The National income of Burma
     see under   Burma (Union) Ministry of
National Planning and Religious Affairs.

The national income of Poland
     see under   Birmingham, Eng. University.
Information Service on Slavonic countries.
Polish section.

National income of Sweden, 1861-1930. Pt. I-II
     see under   [Lindahl, Erik Robert] 1891-

The National income of the Philippines and its
     distribution ...
          see under   United Nations. Technical
Assistance Administration.

National income of the Republic of China
     see under   China. Chu chi ch'u.

HB601
1277   National income statistics, 1929-1943, inclusive]
f   [New York] 1944.

          4,[1] p.   tables(part fold.)   35½ᵐ.

          Based in part on data from the April, 1944,
          issue of the "Survey of current business" pub.
          by the U.S. Bureau of foreign and domestic
          commerce.

          1.Income - U.S. - Statistics. I.U.S. Bureau
          of foreign and domestic commerce (Dept. of
          commerce) Survey of current business.
          II.Title: Survey of current business.

NN 0053970   CSt-H MH

National income statistics, 1929-1947 inclusive.
     [n. p.] 1948.
          cover-title, [1], 11 l. incl. fold. tables. 36 x 22ᶜᵐ.

          1. Income—U. S. 2. Wages—Statistics. I. Title:
Income statistics.

NN 0053971   ViU

National income statistics of various countries
     see under   United Nations. Statistical
Office.

The **National** income tax magazine
     see
Taxes; the tax magazine.

National Incorporated Association for the Reclamation of Destitute Waif Children
     see   Dr. Barnardo's Homes, National
Incorporated Association.

National Incorporating Company.
     Corporation blue-book. A synopsis-digest of the corporation laws of eleven leading incorporating states, including incorporation, organization and management ... also list of local attorneys ... Issued by the National Incorporating Company. New York, The Company, cop. 1903.
          2 p.l., 66 p.   8°.
          Rev. ed.

NN 0053975   NN DLC

National incorporating company.
     Corporation blue-book, a synopsis-digest of the corporation laws of eleven leading incorporating states, including incorporation, organization and management with preliminary comments and suggestions, also list of local attorneys. [Rev. ed.] New York, Pierre, S. D., The National incorporating co., ᶜ1906.
          91, [2] p. 15 x 12ᶜᵐ.

          1. Corporation law—U. S.   I. Title.
          Library of Congress   HD2777.N3 1906   18-7675
          ————— Copy 2.

NN 0053976   DLC NN MB

National incorporating company.
     Corporation blue-book, a synopsis-digest of the corporation laws of eleven leading incorporating states, including incorporation, organization and management with preliminary comments and suggestions, also list of local attorneys. [Rev. ed.] Pierre, S. D., New York, The National incorporating co., ᶜ1907.
          91, [2] p. 15 x 12ᶜᵐ.

          1. Corporation law—U. S.   I. Title.
          Library of Congress   HD2777.N3 1907   18-7674

NN 0053977   DLC NN

National Incorporating Company.
     Corporation blue-book of the National Incorporating Company; a synopsis-digest of the corporation laws of six leading charter states including incorporation, organization and management with preliminary comments and suggestions; also list of local attorneys...   Pierre, S. D.: National Incorporating Co., cop. 1915.   50 p. incl. table.   rev. ed.   16°.

1. Corporations.—Jurisprudence,   U. S. 2. Title.
N. Y. P. L.   November 5, 1919

NN 0053978   NN

VOLUME 407

National incorporating company.
Corporation hand-book, a synopsis-digest of the corporation laws of the states and territories of the United States, District of Columbia and Canada, including incorporation, organization and management with preliminary comments and suggestions, also list of local attorneys. ₍Rev. ed.₎ New York, Pierre, S. D., The National incorporating company, ʻ1903.
2 p. l., 148 p. 23ᶜᵐ.

1. Corporation law—U. S.   I. Title.

18–7682

Library of Congress   HD2777.N4 1903

NN   0053979   DLC NN

National Incorporating Company.
Corporation hand-book. A synopsis-digest of the corporation laws of the states and territories of the United States, District of Columbia, and Canada ... Pierre, S. D., State Publ. Co. [pref. 1904]
2 p. l., 148 p.   8°.
Rev. ed.

NN   0053980   NN

National incorporations and trusts. ₍v.p., 1904–1911₎
v.p. 25cm.

Binders title.
A collection of articles detached from various periodicals and bound together.

NN   0053981   IdU

National independent. v. 1–   May 1941–
₍New York, G. J. Burger₎ 1941–
v. in   illus. (incl. ports.) 31 cm. monthly.

Caption title.
Issued in the interests of the independent tire dealers and tire rebuilders of America.

1. Tires, Rubber—Period.   I. Burger, George J.

HD9161.U5N3   338.476292486   47–40253

NN   0053982   DLC NN

NATIONAL independent labor journal. v. 9, no. 11–date₎
July, 1957–date
Chicago.   v.   39cm.

Film reproduction. Positive.

Monthly.

1. Labor --Per. and soc. publ. --U. S.

NN   0053983   NN

National Independent Meat Packers Association.

TS1970
.M42
Meat Science Institute.
Proceedings.
Athens, Ga.

50.9
N213
National Independent Meat Packers Association,
Washington, D. C.
Proceedings. 1942–
[Washington? D. C., 1942–
1942–   also Proceedings of the 2d-
Emergency conference of meat packers.

NN   0053985   DNAL

E185
.61
.N273
National Independent Political League, Washington, D. C.
... An appeal to thoughtful and intelligent colored Americans ... Washington, 1912.
[8] p.   23 cm.

NN   0053986   DLC OClWHi

E185
.61
.N276
National Independent Political League, Washington, D. C.
... The case against Taft and Roosevelt from the standpoint of the colored voters ... Washington [1912]
6 p.   14 cm.

NN   0053987   DLC

National Independent Political League, Washington, D. C.
A collection of booklets and circulars relating to the campaign of the National Independent Political League in national politics for the year 1912. Washington, D. C., 1912

1. United States.—Politics, 1912.   2. Negro, U. S., 1912.
N. Y. P. L.   March 29, 1913.

NN   0053988   NN

National Independent Political League, Washington, D. C.
Fifty years of physical freedom and political bondage, 1862–1912. This jubilee year is a good time to strike for political liberty! "Equal rights and opportunities for all American citizens." ₍Washington, 1912₎
₍8₎ p. 24 cm. (Its Pamphlet no. 3)
At head of title: Abraham Lincoln issued his Emancipation Proclamation, Sept. 22d, 1862.

1. Negroes—Politics and suffrage. 2. National Independent Political League, Washington, D. C.   I. Title. II. Series.

E185.6.N25 1912   323.1ʹ19ʹ6073   74–167452

NN   0053989   DLC

National independent political league, Washington, D. C.
Waldron, J   Milton.
The political situation in a nut-shell, some un-colored truths for colored voters, by Dr. J. Milton Waldron and Lieutenant J. D. Harkless. Issued by the National independent political league, Washington, D. C. ... Washington, Trades allied printing council ₍1912₎

E185
.61
.N278
National independent political league, Washington, D. C.
The second emancipation of the race; the colored man learning to use his ballot for his own protection, supporting men and measures rather than parties ... Washington, D. C., 1912.
[3] p.   28 x 21.5 cm.

NN   0053991   DLC OClWHi

National independent political league, Washington, D. C.
...Some questions and answers. Issued by the National independent political league (formerly the National Negro-American political league)
Washington, [1912]
[Pamphlet no. 4]
E185
.61   5, ₍1₎ p. I l. 23cm.

NN   0053992   DLC

National Negro American political league
see   National Independent Political League, Washington, D. C.

National Independent Political League, Washington, D. C.
"We stand for men and measure, rather than parties". An appeal ... colored Americans... Washington, D. C.
see its   An appeal to thoughtful and intelligent colored Americans.

National independent political union.
National independent political union.
Address to the colored people of this country.
Grantism the father of Belknapism, Schenckism and Babcockism₎ Colored men desirethe "unity of the republic with equal rights to all and reconciliation." ₍Washington, D. C., n.d.₎
4 p.
Caption title.
Signed: Rev. Garland H. White, President.
Daniel Lewis, Secretary.

NN   0053995   ViU

National Independent Political Union.
... Negro Declaration of Independence.
Republican faithlessness and corruptions exposed and scathingly denounced by colored men.
They are tired of party yoke, and will combine to reconcile the sections, and maintain local self government.   [Washington, 1876]
8 vo.   Unbound.
[Caption-title]
At head of title: National Independent Political Union.

NN   0053996   CSmH

371.8306
N213m
NATIONAL INDEPENDENT STUDENTS' ASSOCIATION.
Minutes of the 1st-national convention of the N.I.S.A., April, 1938–
v. 23–30½cm.

Mimeographed.

1. Students.

NN   0053997   TxU

National Independent Telephone Association.   654.051 N21
Bulletin no. 1–16. ... . Issued by National Independent Telephone Association. Chicago, Illinois, 1913–1915.
90377
b   16 nos. in 1 vol. 23½ᶜᵐ.
No more published.
. On Jan. 1, 1916 the National Independent Telephone Association united with the Independent Telephone Association to form the United States Independent Telephone Association.

NN   0054001   ICJ

QC
71
P57+
v.39
no.8
National Independent Telephone Association.
Iron and steel telephone wire specifications
Chicago, 1910.
12 p. 23cm.

1. Telephone wire.

NN   0054002   NIC

National Independent Telephone Association, *Chicago.*   L654.6 10
[Minor publications.] Chicago, National Independent Telephone Association, ₍1906–1912₎.
78056
a   11 pamphlets in 1 vol. 23½ᶜᵐ.
Previous to 1910?: International Independent Telephone Association. On Jan. 1, 1916 the National Independent Telephone Association united with the Independent Telephone Association to form the United States Independent Telephone Association.

NN   0054003   ICJ

VOLUME 407

National Independent Telephone Association.
Proceedings.
₍Chicago, etc.₎
v. 24 cm. annual.
Issued   by the association under earlier names:
–19₍ᵦ, National-Interstate Telephone Association.—1907–
International Independent Telephone Association of America.

1. Telephone—U. S.—Societies, etc.

TK6183.N3   60–57311

NN 0054004   DLC ICJ

National Independent Telephone Association.

Johnston, Gansey R.
    Some comments on the 1907 Annual report of American
telephone and telegraph company, by Gansey R. Johnston ... Published by the International independent telephone association, Chicago. September, 1908. Columbus, O., The Berlin printing company, 1908.

QC   National Independent Telephone Association.
71   Some considerations on telephone deprecia-
P57+   tion. Chicago, 1910.
v.39   23 p. 24cm.
no.9

1. Telephone—Accounting.

NN 0054006   NIC MH

National Independent Telephone Association
    see also
United States Independent Telephone Association.

National Independent Telephone Association of the United
States
    see also
National Independent Telephone Association.

HD8055   National Independent Union Council, Washington,
N36A3   D. C.
1953   Constitution and by laws, as amended at 1953 convention, St.
Social   Louis, Mo. [Washington, D.C., 1953]
Sciences   9 ℓ.

NN 0054009   CU

The National index.
    v. 1
Basil, O., 1916.
    v.   4°.
Weekly.

1. Periodicals, U.S.
N.Y.P.L.   August 9, 1917.

NN 0054010   NN

National Indian association.

    Organized in December, 1880, as the Central Indian committee.
Name changed in 1881 to Indian treaty-keeping and protective as-
sociation, and in 1882 to Women's national Indian association. In
December, 1901, the name was further changed to the National
Indian association.

19–19581

National Indian association.
    Annual report. 1883–
New York ₍1883₎–19

    y. in   illus. 20–22¼ᶜᵐ.

Title varies: 1883, Annual meeting and report of the Women's national In-
    dian association.
1884   –1901, ... Annual report of the Women's national Indian
    association.
1902–   Annual report of the National Indian association.
Imprint varies: 1883–1903, Philadelphia.—1904–   New York.

1. Indians of North America—Societies.
    •
Library of Congress   E93.N27   19–18710

CSmH DI Nh RPB CU
NN 0054012   DLC NN OrU WaS NcD N CU-B ICJ MB OFH

N970.1   National Indian Association.
N274   Christian civilization and missionary work of the Women's
1887   National Indian Association November 30, 1887. Philadelphia,
no.2   1887.
              13 p. 22 cm. (Its/ Publications, 1887 [no. 2])

           In a box.

           1. Indians of North America. Missions. I. Title.
(Series)

NN 0054013   N

Ayer
266   National Indian association.
N2
1909   ...A glimpse of our missions.   [New
York?1909]
    20p.

           Caption title.
           At head of title: Publications of the
National Indian association.

NN 0054014   ICN

NATIONAL INDIAN ASSOCIATION.
    How to organize an Indian association.   15
[Issued by Women's national Indian association.]
[Phil.], [1889?].

NN 0054015   MH-AH

N970.1   National Indian Association.
N274   Indian bills in Congress, November 1889, by Kate Foote.
1889   [Philadelphia] Women's National Indian Association [1889]
no.5   7 p. 22 cm. (Its Publications, 1889 [no.5])
           Caption title: Report of the Committee on Indian
Legislation.
           In a box.

           1. Indians of North America. Legal status, laws, etc.
I. Foote, Kate. II. Title. (Series)

NN 0054016   N

NATIONAL INDIAN ASSOCIATION.
[Miscellaneous reports and other papers.]

NN 0054017   MH

National Indian Association.
    Missionary work of the Women's National
Indian Association, and letters of missionaries
        see under   National Indian Association.
Missionary Committee.

National Indian association.
    The National Indian association to aid in civil-
ization, teach industry, and give religious instruction to the Indians of our country.
New York, [1907]

NN 0054019   DLC

National Indian Association.
    Official pamphlet ... with suggestions and
facts for its helpers.   Philadelphia, 1882.
    15 p. 16°.   [In v. 5 of "Tracts American
Indians."]

NN 0054020   CtY

NATIONAL INDIAN ASSOCIATION.
    The Omaha mission. March,1888. [Issued by 21
the Women's national Indian association.]
[Philadelphia][1888?].

NN 0054021   MH-AH

       NATIONAL INDIAN ASSOCIATION.
    Our missions, 1895.
=   [Phila., 1896.]   v. 24°.

NN 0054022   MB

N970.1   National Indian Association.
N274   Our work: what? how? why? [Philadelphia] National
1893   Indian Association, Executive Board, 1893.
no.1   43 p. 16 cm. (Its Publications, 1893 [no. 1])

           Cover title.
           Caption title: Work of the Women's National Indian
Association.
           In a box.

           1. Indians of North America. Societies, etc. I. Title.
II. Title: Work of the   Women's National Indian
Association. (Series)

NN 0054023   N Nh MH

National Indian Association.
    Past legislative work of the Women's National
Indian Association
        see under   Burke, Mrs. William Lanon.

       National Indian association.

    U. S. *47th Cong., 1st sess., 1881–1882. Senate.*
    Proceedings on the occasion of the presentation of the
petition of the Women's national Indian association, by
Hon. H. L. Dawes, of Massachusetts, in the Senate of the
United States, February 21, 1882. Washington, 1882.

N970.1   National Indian Association.
N274   The Ramona Mission and the Mission Indians. [Phila-
1889   delphia, 1889]
no.4   18 p. 21 cm. (Its/ Publications, 1889 [no. 4])

           Cover title.
           In a box.

           1. Indians of North America. Missions. I. Title. (Series)

NN 0054026   N CSmH

National Indian Association.
    Religious nature of the Indian
        see under   Gilman, Clarabel.

N970.1   National Indian Association.
N274   Report of Committee on Indian Libraries, November 1890,
1890   by Frances C. Sparhawk. [Philadelphia] Women's National
no.1   Indian Association, 1890.
              11 p. 15 cm. (Its/Publications, 1890 [no. I])

           In a box.

           1. Indians of North America. Education. ₍I₎ Sparhawk,
Frances Campbell, 1847–   (Series)

NN 0054028   N RPB Nh

VOLUME 407

N970.1   National Indian Association.
N274   Report of Committee on Indian Libraries, by Frances C.
1901   Sparhawk. [Philadelphia] 1901.
no. 1   7 p.   16 cm. (Its Publications, 1901 [no. 1])

     Cover title.
     In a box.

     1. Indians of North America. Education. I. Sparhawk,
Frances Campbell, 1847-   II. Series.

NN   0054029   N

N970.1   National Indian Association.
N274   Report of Committee on Indian Libraries and Industries, by
1892   Frances C. Sparhawk. Philadelphia, 1892.
no. 2   20 p.   15 cm. (Its Publications, 1892 [no. 2])

     Cover title.
     "Publishers' list for Indian library work," p. 11-20.
     In a box.

     1. Indians of North America. Education. 2. Indians of North
America. Industries. I. Sparhawk, Frances Campbell, 1847-
(Series)

NN   0054030   N

N970.1   National Indian Association.
N274   Report of Committee on Indian Libraries and Industries,
1893   by Frances C. Sparhawk. [Philadelphia] 1893.
no. 2   16 p.   15 cm. (Its Publications, 1893 [no. 2])

     Cover title.
     "Publishers' lists for Indian library work," p. 7-16.
     In a box.

     1. Indians of North America. Education. 2. Indians of
North America. Industries. I. Sparhawk, Frances Campbell,
1847-   (Series)

NN   0054031   N

N970.1   National Indian Association.
N274   Report of Committee on Indian Libraries and Industries,
1895   November 1894 and November 1895, by Frances C. Sparhawk.
no. 1   [Philadelphia, 1895]
     19 p.   15 cm. (Its Publications, 1895 [no. 1])

     Cover title.
     "Publishers' lists for Indian library work," p. 11-19.
     In a box.
     1. Indians of North America. Education. 2. Indians of North
America. Industries. I. Sparhawk, Frances Campbell, 1847-
(Series)

NN   0054032   N

     NATIONAL INDIAN ASSOCIATION.
   Report of memorials to government, Nov. 1885,
to 1886. Philadelphia, [1886?]

     pp. 15.

NN   0054033   MH Nh

N970.1   National Indian Association.
N274   Report of missionary work, November 1885 to November 1886.
1886   Philadelphia, [1886]
no. 3   31 p.   22 cm. (Its Publications, 1886 [no. 3])

     Cover title.
     Adopted at the annual meeting, Nov. 18, 1886.
     In a box.

     1. Indians of North America. Missions. (Series)

NN   0054034   N Nh

     National Indian Association.
     Report of missionary department
       see   National Indian Association.
Missionary Dept.
     Report ...

     National Indian Association.
     Report of missionary work. 1889
       see under   National Indian Association.
Missionary Committee.

N970.1   National Indian Association.
N274   Report on missionary work, November 1888. [Philadelphia,
1888   1888]
no. 1   11 p.   22 cm. (Its Publications, 1888 [no. 1]

     Report of the National Committee.
     In a box.

     1. Indians of North America. Missions. (Series)

NN   0054037   N

     National Indian Association.
     ... The report of missions. .... [New York,   361.06161 2
                               -1913.]
85591
s   Association.)   illus. 14ᶜᵐ.   (Publications of the National Indian
     Association.)
     Annual.
     1913 last published.

NN   0054038   ICJ N ICN

     National Indian Association.
     Report of the Home Building and Loan
Committee ...
       see   National Indian Association. Home
Building and Loan Committee..
     Report.

     National Indian Association.
     Report of the hospital department
       see   National Indian Association.
Hospital Dept.
     Report.

     National Indian Association.
     Report on Indian home-building
       see   National Indian Association. Home
Building and Loan Committee.
     Report.

     National Indian Association.
     Seven ways to help Indians. Annual address of
the president ...
       see under   Quinton, Amelia Stone.

     National Indian Association.
     Sketches and plans of the Indian treaty-keeping
and protective association with suggestions to
workers.   Philadelphia, 1881.
     12 p.   18 cm.

NN   0054043   RPB

     NATIONAL INDIAN ASSOCIATION.
   Sketches of delightful work.   January, 1893.
Women's national Indian assoc., n.d.

     Pamphlet.

NN   0054044   MH

N970.1   National Indian Association.
N274   Sunshine work. [Philadelphia] 1894.
1894   44 p.   15 cm. (Its Publications, 1894 [no. 1])
no. 1

     Cover title: Missions of the Women's National Indian
Association for 1893 and 1894.
     In a box.

     1. Indians of North America. Missions. I. Title.
II. Title: Missions of the Women's National Indian Association
for 1893 and 1894. III.   Series.

NN   0054045   N

     National Indian Association.
     What Congress did for the Indians, 1890.
[Indian legislation and work for it]   n.p., 1890.
     11 p.   14 cm.
     Caption title.

NN   0054046   RPB

     National Indian association.
     Work for Indians. [N.Y., n.d.]
     7 p.   O

NN   0054047   OO

N970.1   National Indian Association. Dept. of Industries.
N274   Our industrial work, by Mrs. N. DeG. Doubleday.
1902   [Philadelphia, 1902]
no. 1   12 p.   14 cm. (National Indian Association. Publications,
1902 [no. 1])

     Caption title.
     In a box.

     1. Indians of North America. Industries. I. Doubleday,
Nellie Blanchan   (DeGraff) 1865-1918.
II. Title. (Series)

NN   0054048   N

     National Indian Association. Home Building and Loan Commit-
tee.
     Report ...
188

[Philadelphia, 188   12 – 22½ cm.
   nos.
      188   report year ends in Nov.; 1   in Dec.

   1. Indians, N. A.—Assoc. and org.   *Revised*
N. Y. P. L.   July 8, 1933

     Title varies: 188   Report on Indian home building...; 18   Report
of the Home building and loan committee (other slight variations).
     At head of title: 188   The Women's National Indian Association.
1   are Publications of the Women's National Indian Association; 1902
Publications of National Indian Association.
     Ceased publication?

NN   0054050   NN Nh RPB N

N970.1   National Indian Association. Hospital Dept.
N274   Report, by Laura E. Tileston. [Philadelphia] Women's
1891   National Indian Association, 1891.
no. 3   8 p.   15 cm. (National Indian Association. Publications,
1891 [no. 3])
     Cover title.
     Report of Susan La Flesche, M.D., Medical missionary of
the Women's National Indian Associaton among the Omaha
Indians (p. 4-8)
     In a box.
     1. Indians of North America. Hospitals. I. Tileston,
Laura E. II. La   Flesche, Susan. (Series)

NN   0054051   N Nh

VOLUME 407

4BV 1322
National Indian Association. **Mission-ary Committee.**
Missionary work of the Women's National Indian Association and letters of missionaries. Philadephia, Grant & Faires, printers, 1885.
19 p.

NN 0054052 DLC-P4 MB ICN N

N970.1 N274 1889 no. 2
National Indian Association. **Missionary Committee.**
Report of missionary work. Philadelphia, 1889.
2l, [l] p. 22 cm. (Its Publications, 1889 [no. 2])

Cover title.
Report of the Missionary Committee of the Women's National Indian Association.
In a box.

1. Indians of North America. Missions. (Series)

NN 0054053 N Nh

N970.1 N274 1890 no. 3
National Indian Association. Missionary Dept.
Report... November 1890. Philadelphia, 1890.
21 p. 12 x 15 cm. (National Indian Association. Publications, 1890 [no. 3])

Cover title.
In a box.

1. Indians of North America. Missions. (Series)

NN 0054054 N RPB

N970.1 N274 1891 no. 2
National Indian Association. Missionary Dept.
Report... November, 1891. Philadelphia, Women's National Indian Association, 1891.
30 p. 16 cm. (National Indian Association. Publications, 1891 [no. 2])

Cover title.
In a box.

1. Indians of North America. Missions. (Series)

NN 0054055 N

[National Indian association. *Washington auxiliary]*
In memoriam. Harriet W. Foote Hawley ... [Washington, 1886]
22, [1] p. front. (port.) 23ᶜᵐ.

1. Hawley, Mrs. Harriet Ward (Foote) 1831-1886. I. Title.

26-5102

Library of Congress CT275.H478N3

NN 0054056 DLC RPB OClWHi

N970.1 N274 1890 no. 4
National Indian Association. Young People's Dept.
The Young People's Department [by] Marie E. Ives. [Philadelphia] Women's National Indian Association, 1890.
7 p. 15 cm. (National Indian Association. Publications, 1890 [no. 4])

Read at the annual convention of the Women's National Indian Association, Nov. 20, 1890.
In a box.

1. Indians of North America. Societies, etc. [I] Ives, Marie E. I. Title. (Series)

NN 0054057 N

N970.1 N274 1891 no. 4
National Indian Association. Young People's Dept.
Report of the Young People's Department, by Marie E. Ives. [Philadelphia] Women's National Indian Association, 1891.
8 p. 15 cm. (National Indian Association. Publications, 1891 [no. 4])

Cover title.
In a box.

1. Indians of North America. Societies, etc. I. Ives, Marie E (Series)

NN 0054058 N Nh

N970.1 N274 1894 no. 4
National Indian Association. Young People's Dept.
Report, by Marie E. Ives. [Philadelphia] Women's National Indian Association, 1894.
12 p. 15 cm. (National Indian Association. Publications, 1894 [no. 4])

Cover title.
In a box.

1. Indians of North America. Societies, etc. I. Ives, Marie E (Series)

NN 0054059 N Nh

National Indian association in aid of social progress and education in India, *London.*
Annual report.
Bristol, 18
v. 21ᶜᵐ.

CA 8-1835 Unrev'd

Library of Congress DS401.N27

NN 0054060 DLC DNLM

National Indian association in aid of social progress and education in India, London.
Handbook of information for Indian students relating to university & professional studies, etc., in the United Kingdom. Issued by the Committee of the National Indian association, in conjuction with the Advisory committee, India office. 12th ed. London, J. S. Phillips, 1909.
3 p.l., 112 p. 23 cm.
1. Universities and colleges - Gt. Brit. 2. Technical education - Gt. Brit. 3. Hindus in Gt. Brit. I. Gt. Brit. India office. Advisory committee.

NN 0054061 CU

National Indian Association in Aid of Social Progress and Education in India, London.
The Indian magazine and review. Issued by the National Indian association in aid of social progress and education in India. no. 1-180, 1871-85; no. 181-324 (new ser. no. 1-84) 1886-97; no. 325-524 (new [3d] ser. no. 1-200) 1898-Aug. 1914. London, W. H. Allen & co.; [etc., etc., 1871-1914]

National Indian association in aid of social progress and education in India, London.
Journal of the National Indian association in aid of social progress and education in India. v. 1-[15]; 1871-85; [no. 1-180] London [etc., 1871-85]
15 v. port. 21ᶜᵐ. monthly.
The name of the society varies slightly in the title.
Continued after 1885 as the Indian magazine.

1. India. 2. Education—India. I. Title.

8—15833

Library of Congress DS401.I 4

NN 0054063 DLC NN DNLM PU-SRS

National Indian association in aid of social progress and education in India, *London*

see also

Manchester Indian association, *Manchester, Eng.*

National Indian association in aid of social progress in India, Bristol, Eng.

see

National Indian association in aid of social progress and education in India, London.

Zc16 D1 891na
National Indian defence association.
The Sioux nation and the United States. A brief history of the treaties of 1868, 1876, and 1889, between that nation and the United States. Washington, D.C., National Indian defence association, 1891.
32p. 24cm.

NN 0054066 CtY MiU-L ICN

National Indian institute

see

U. S. National Indian institute.

National Indian war veterans

Winners of the West. v. 1– Dec. 1923–
St. Joseph, Mo. [G. W. Webb, 1923–

National Indoor Base Ball Association of the United States.
... Constitution, by-laws and playing rules
see its Official indoor base ball guide containing the constitution, by-laws and playing rules ...

National indoor base ball association of the United States.
... Official indoor base ball guide containing the constitution, by-laws and playing rules of the National indoor base ball association of the United States ... New York, American sports publishing company, 1903–
v. fronts. illus. (incl. ports.) diagrs. 17ᶜᵐ. (Spalding's athletic library)

1. Indoor base-ball.

5-42062 Revised

Library of Congress GV881.N27

NN 0054070 DLC CtY OCl

BV1620 .M5
National indoor game association, inc.

Milnes, Frank Jay, 1877–
The church and the young man's game, by F. J. Milnes, B. S. Published for the National indoor game association, incorporated. New York, George H. Doran company [1913]

National Industrial Advertisers Association.
An abstract-bibliography

see under

Industrial Advertising Research Institute.

VOLUME 407

National industrial advertisers association
Book of proceedings of the...annual convention and exhibit...

NN   0054073   MiD LU ICU

659.2
N211h   National Industrial Advertisers Association
Handbook of industrial direct mail advertising. ₍New York, °1954₎
64 p. illus.

Cover title.
Bibliography: p. 63.

1. Advertising, Mail I. Title II.Title:
Industrial direct mail advertising

NN   0054074   MiD AU NIC

National industrial advertisers association.
Industrial market determination. ₍Chicago, 1946?₎
32 p.incl.illus., charts, tables.

"Prepared by the Professional development committee."
"Statistical sources": p.17-21.

NN   0054075   MH-BA

National Industrial Advertisers' Association.
Locating and developing new construction leads...   Chicago: National Industrial Advertisers Association, 1933.   27 p. incl. facsims.   illus.   27½cm.

Cover-title.
Reproduced from typewritten copy; cover printed.
"A $440 campaign pulls $24,591 in orders, by H. S. Stollnitz, jr.," 2 l. at end.

783345A. 1. Contractors' operations.   2. Advertising—Market analysis—
U. S. I. Stollnitz, Henry Sandé,   1865-
N. Y. P. L.   October 24, 1935

NN   0054076   NN

National industrial advertisers association.
...Membership roster... ₍Chicago₎ Industrial marketing ₍1945₎ 43 p. 28cm.

1. Advertising—Assoc. and org.—   U. S. I. Industrial marketing.
N. Y. P. L.   January 8, 1948

NN   0054077   NN OC1 NNC

National Industrial Advertisers Association.
HF5813
.U6N3   **A National** survey of industrial advertising budgets.

New York, National Industrial Advertisers Association.

National industrial advertisers association.

Conference on industrial advertising and selling, *Washington, D. C.,* 1929.
Report of the Conference on industrial advertising and selling, under the auspices of the National industrial advertisers association and the Industrial committee of the Association of national advertisers, inc., in conjunction with United States Department of commerce ... Washington, D. C., May 10, 1929. ₍New York, Business publishers international corporation, 1929₎

380.2
N277   National industrial advertisers association.
A study of business and trade magazine reading habits...   Chicago,Ill.,National industrial advertisers association,inc., c1942.

7 p.   27ᵈ.

Reproduced from type-written copy.

1.Periodicals - Statistics. 2. Advertising.
I.Title. II. Title: Reading habits.

NN   0054080   CSt

National Industrial Advertisers Association.
Survey of industrial buying practices. ₍New York, 1949₎
68 p. 28 cm.
Cover title.

1. Industrial procurement.   I. Title.

HF5437.N43   658.72   50-744

NN   0054081   DLC CaBVa MU MiD OC1 TxU OrCS ICU

National industrial advertisers association.
A survey of 1934 industrial advertising budgets; a report sponsored by the National industrial advertisers association of a survey made by the Advertising budget committee of the Engineering advertisers association, December 5, 1934 ... Chicago, National industrial advertisers association, inc. ₍1934₎
₍8₎ p. tables. 20ᶜᵐ.
1.Advertising. I.Engineering advertisers association.II.Title: Industrial advertising budgets.

NN   0054082   NNC CtY

HF5816
.N3   National Industrial Advertisers Association.
10 industrial advertisers report; how industrial advertising helps make sales. 10 entries for the Putman awards of 19
₍Chicago₎ Putman.
v. 30cm.

NN   0054083   NNU-W

National Industrial Advertisers Association.
Visual presentations for industrial salesmen; the report of a research committee which investigated current practice relative to the use of visual material by industrial salesmen during interviews. Released April 10, 1933.   Chicago: National Industrial Advertisers Association ₍1933₎   22 p.   7 pl.   28cm.

Cover-title.
"This investigation...was conducted by a committee of three...acting jointly on behalf of the Engineering Advertisers Assn., Chicago, and the National Industrial Advertisers Assn."
Reproduced from typewritten copy.
"Partial bibliography," p. 22.

873812A. 1. Sampling. 2. Salesman-   ship and salesmen. I. Engineering
Advertisers Association, Chicago.   II. Title.
N. Y. P. L.   March 26, 1937

NN   0054084   NN OC1 IU WaU

HF
5801   National Industrial Advertisers Association.
N27+   Budget survey-summary report.
New York.
v. illus. 28cm.

Some reports issued with distinctive title.

NN   0054085   NIC

659.1
N211r   National industrial advertisers association--Catalog committee.
Report of N.I.A.A. committee on catalog practice and procedure ₋ ₍Chicago, Technical publicity association, inc.₎ 1936.
16p. incl.forms.

Multigraphed.

1. Catalogs, Commercial. 2. Advertising.

NN   0054086   IU OC1

National Industrial Advertisers Association. *Chapter 24 see* **Rochester Industrial Advertisers,** *Rochester, N. Y.*

National Industrial Advertisers Association. *Industrial Advertising Research Institute see* **Industrial Advertising Research Institute.**

National Industrial Advertising Conference.
Report of proceedings and program...
₍no.₎ 1–

₍Milwaukee:₎ National Industrial Advertisers' Assoc.₍,₎ 19   12°.
no.

no. 1–   are "held in conjunction with" the 8th-
conventions of the Associated Advertising Clubs of the World.

1. Advertisements and advertising—   Congresses—U. S.
N. Y. P. L.   October 20, 1926

NN   0054089   NN

NATIONAL INDUSTRIAL ADVISORY CORPORATION.
Industry's obligation and its opportunity. First, the foundation for a code—after the code—what? National industrial recovery act. Second edition. New York [etc.] National industrial advisory corporation [c1933]
22 p. 26½cm.

895889A. 1. National industrial recovery act, 1933.
2. Industrial codes of fair competition₎ I Title₎

NN   0054090   NN

National industrial alliance.
... The case for and against family allowances. Harrow [1939?]
cover-title, 24, [4] p. 18 cm.
At head of title: The National industrial alliance.
Blank pages at end for "Notes" ([3] p.)
Bibliography: p. 24-[25]
1. Family allowances. 2. Wages - Gt. Brit.

NN   0054091   CU

National industrial alliance.
... Rationalisation and displaced labour.
₍London₎ National industrial alliance ₍1931₎
cover-title, 20 p. 21 cm.

"Report of the Rationalisation sub-committee, adopted by the National executive committee, July 13th, 1931."

1.Unemployed - Gt. Brit. I.Title.

NN   0054092   NNC

VOLUME 407

National Industrial Alliance.
Report.
1925

London, 1926   8°.
no.

1. Employer and employed—Assoc. and   org.—Gt. Br.   2. Arbitration
and conciliation, Industrial—Gt. Br.
N. Y. P. L.   March 9, 1927

NN 0054093   NN ICU

National industrial alliance.

Unity; a monthly review of industrial affairs ...

₍London, 19

National industrial association, London.

Morgan, Benjamin Howell, 1873–
Report on the engineering trades of South Africa. By Ben. H. Morgan ... With numerous tables, appendices, and reproductions of special plans, drawings, and photographs. London, Published by P. S. King & son, for the National industrial association, 1902.

National Industrial Conference, London, 1919.
...Minutes of proceedings of the National Industrial Conference, Central hall, Westminster, S. W... February 27, 1919 ... London: H. M. Stationery Off.₍, 1919₎ 64 p. 8°.

At head of title: (Prepared by the Publicity Branch of the Ministry of Labour.)
Cover-title: Full report of the speeches. Appeal by the prime minister.

1. Labor—Congresses, 1919.   2. Great   Britain. Labour Ministry. Publicity
Branch.
N. Y. P. L.   January 28, 1930

NN 0054096   NN DL

National industrial conference, London, 1919. Provisional joint committee.
Industrial conference. Report of Provisional joint committee presented to meeting of industrial conference, Central Hall, Westminster, April 4, 1919 ... London, H. M. Stationery off., 1919.
20 p. 33ᶜᵐ. (₍Gt. Brit. Parliament. Papers by command₎ Cmd. 139)
Thos. Munro, chairman.
Appendix. Provisional scheme for trade union representation on the National industrial council: p. 17–20.

1. Labor and laboring classes—Gt. Brit.   2. Arbitration, Industrial—Gt. Brit.   3. Employees' representation in management.   4. Trade-unions—Gt. Brit.   I. Munro, Sir Thomas, 1866–   II. Title.

Library of Congress   HD8384.N4 1919   21—7757

NN 0054097   DLC MH-L MH-BA MiU NN MB

National industrial conference, London, 1919. Provisional joint committee.
Industrial conference. Report of Provisional joint committee presented to meeting of industrial conference, Central hall, Westminster, April 4th, 1919 ... London, H. M. Stationery off., 1920.
16, xiv p. 33½ᶜᵐ. (₍Gt. Brit. Parliament. Papers by command₎ Cmd. 501)
Thos. Munro, chairman.

Appendix I. Memorandum on the causes of and remedies for labour unrest, presented by the trade union representatives on the Joint committee appointed at the National industrial conference, held at the Central hall, London, on February 27th, 1919: p. iii–xii.
Appendix II. Provisional scheme for trade union representation on the National industrial council: p. ixiii–xiv.

1. Labor and laboring classes—Gt. Brit.   2. Arbitration, Industrial—Gt. Brit.   3. Employees' representation in management.   4. Trade-unions—Gt. Brit.   I. Munro, Sir Thomas, 1866–   II. Title.

Library of Congress   HD8384.N4 1920   21—9578

NN 0054099   DLC MH-BA ICJ

JX1907
.A8
no. 140

National industrial conference, London, 1919.
Provisional joint committee.
American association for international conciliation.
... I. Report of the Commission on international labor legislation of the Peace conference. II. The British national industrial conference: Report of the Provisional joint committee ... New York city, American association for international conciliation ₍1919₎

National industrial conference, Ottawa, 1919.
... Conférence industrielle nationale des gouvernements fédéral et provinciaux avec des patrons et ouvriers représentatifs, au sujet des relations industrielles et des lois concernant le travail, et pour l'étude des clauses ouvrières du traité de paix. Ottawa, 15–20 septembre 1919. Rapport officiel ... et le Rapport de la Commission royale sur les relations industrielles ... Ottawa, J. de L. Taché, imprimeur de Sa Très Excellente Majesté le roi, 1919.
111, 234 p., 2 ℓ., 3–30 p.   25ᶜᵐ.
At head of title: Canada.

1. Labor and laboring   classes—Congresses.
I. Canada. Royal co...   sion on industrial
relations.   HD8102.A54 1919

NN 0054101   MiU

National industrial conference, *Ottawa*, 1919.
... National industrial conference of Dominion and provincial governments with representative employers and labour men, on the subjects of industrial relations and labour laws, and for the consideration of the labour features of the treaty of peace. Ottawa, September 15–20, 1919. Official report of proceedings and discussions, together with various memoranda relating to the conference and the report of the Royal commission on industrial relations. Proceedings and discussions reported by the official reporters of the Senate of Canada.

Issued by the Department of labour of Canada. Ottawa, J. de L. Taché, printer to the King's Most Excellent Majesty, 1919.
liv, 234 p., 2 l., 3–28 p. 25ᶜᵐ.
At head of title: Canada.

1. Labor and laboring classes—Congresses.   2. Labor and laboring classes—Canada.   3. Canada—Econ. condit.—1918–   I. Canada. Royal commission on industrial relations.   II. Canada. Dept. of labour.

                             19—18668
Library of Congress   HD8102.A5 1919

NN 0054103   DLC ICJ MtU OCl OrU CtY MB IaU

National Industrial Conference, Ottawa, 1919.
Proposed agenda and various memoranda relating to the National Industrial Conference of Dominion and Provincial Governments of Canada, with representative employers and labour men, on the subjects of industrial relations and labour laws, and for the consideration of the labour features of the treaty of peace. Ottawa, 1919. 42 p. incl. tables. 8°.

1. Labor—Congresses, 1919.   2. Labor—Canada.   3. Economic history—Canada.
N. Y. P. L.   February 27, 1928

NN 0054104   NN

National industrial conference, *Washington, D. C.*, 1919.
Called by the President of the United States to consider the conduct of industry; held October 6–23, 1919; composed of representatives of employers, employees, and the public.

NATIONAL INDUSTRIAL CONFERENCE, Washington, D.C., 1919.
A comparison of propositions made by the Labor group and Employers' group. [Washington, D.C., 1919].

4°. ff°. 12.
"Propositions of Employers, no similar porpositions [!] by Labor group", ff. 8–12.

NN 0054106   MH

HD8057
.N3
1919b

National industrial conference, Washington, D. C., 1919.
Minutes of the meetings of the general committee of the Industrial conference held at Washington, D. C., beginning October 7th, 1919. [Washington, D. C., 1919]
1 p. l., 30 numb. l.   29cm.

Type-written.

NN 0054107   DLC

National Industrial Conference, Washington, D.C., 1919.
Young women's Christian associations. *U. S. National board. War work council. Industrial committee.*
National industrial conference, Washington, D. C., October 20–21–22, 1919. A handbook for delegates, prepared by Ruth Chivvis and Lucy R. Somerville, issued by Industrial committee, War work council, National board, Young women's Christian associations. ₍New York₎ 1919.

National Industrial Conference, Washington, D. C., 1919.
Preliminary statement of Industrial Conference called by the President. Washington: Gov. Prtg. Off., 1919. 12 p. 8°.

1. Arbitration and conciliation, In-   dustrial—U. S., 1919.
N. Y. P. L.   April 15, 1925

NN 0054109   NN

National industrial conference, *Washington, D. C.*, 1919.
... Proceedings of the first Industrial conference (called by the President) October 6 to 23, 1919. Chairman, Hon. Franklin K. Lane, secretary of the interior; adviser to the conference, Hon. William B. Wilson, secretary of labor; secretaries, Hon. Lathrop Brown, Mr. J. J. Cotter. Washington, Govt. print. off., 1920.
285 p. incl. plan. 24 cm.
At head of title: Department of labor, Office of the secretary, Washington.
1. Arbitration, Industrial—U. S.   2. Employees' representation in management.   3. Labor and laboring classes—U. S.—1914–   I. Lane, Franklin Knight, 1864–1921.   II. Wilson, William Bauchop, 1862–1934.   III. Brown, Lathrop, 1883–   IV. Cotter, J. J.

HD8057.N3 1919a

₍a5704₎
                             20—26694

     OrU OrCS WaWW CU NIC
NN 0054110   DLC Or OCl OClW OO MiU ICJ DL MB

NATIONAL INDUSTRIAL CONFERENCE, Washington, D.C., 1919.
[Report and minutes of the group representing the public. Washington, D.C., 1919].

4°.
Manifold copy.

NN 0054111   MH

ILR
HD
8057
N3
1920

National Industrial Conference, Washington, D. C., 1919–1920.
Report of industrial conference called by the President. March 6, 1920. ₍New York, M. B. Brown & Co., 1920₎
51 p. 23 cm.

1. Industrial relations - Congresses. 2. Industrial relations - United States. ₍3. Employee representation₎ ₍4. Collective bargaining - United States. ₍5. Labor disputes - Adjustment₎
x-ref₍: Industr ... ₎ial Conference, Washington, D. C., 1919 ... 1920

NN 0054112   NIC MB OOxM

National industrial conference, Washington, D. C., 1919.
National industrial conference board.
Statement of principles which should govern the employment relation in industry. Submitted by the employer group to the Industrial conference at Washington, D. C., October 10, 1919. Boston, Mass., National industrial conference board ₍1919?₎

VOLUME 407

National industrial conference, *Washington, D. C., 1919.*
... Stenographic transcript. Washington, D. C. [1919]

6 v. 28½ᶜᵐ.

At head of title: National industrial conference, Pan-American building, Washington, D. C.
Official stenographers: Galt & Williams.
Autographed type-written copy: the volume numbers are supplied in ms. on printed covers; in v. 1-5 the leaves are consecutively (irregularly) numbered, and these volumes contain transcript of proceedings for the sessions of Oct. 6-21, 1919; v. 6 contains resolutions 1, 3-38.

1. Arbitration, Industrial—U. S. 2. Employees' representation in management. 3. Labor and laboring classes—U. S.—1914—

20-227

Library of Congress   HD8057.N3 1919

NN   0054114   DLC

ᴺATIONAL INDUSTRIAL CONFERENCE, Washington, D.C.
1919.
[Stenographic transcript] Oct.6-23,1919.
Washington,D.C.,[1919].

Manifold copy. 14 vol. 4°.
At head of title: National Industrial Conference, Pan-American building, Washington, D.C.
Official stenographers: Galt & Williams.

NN   0054115   MH

National industrial conference, *Wellington, New Zealand,*
1928.
... Report of proceedings. Wellington, W. A. G. Skinner, government printer, 1928.

iv, 450 p. front. (ports.) diagrs. 25ᶜᵐ.

At head of title: National industrial conference.
Frontispiece accompanied by guard sheet with outline drawing and descriptive letterpress.

1. Labor and laboring classes—Congresses. 2. Labor and laboring classes—New Zealand. 3. Arbitration, Industrial—New Zealand. 4. Agricultural laborers—New Zealand.

36-5374

Library of Congress   HD8862.N3 1928
[3]   331.063931

NN   0054116   DLC WaU CU NN ICJ CaBVa DL

National industrial conference board.
The agricultural problem in the United States. New York, National industrial conference board, inc., 1926.

xiv, 157 p. incl. tables, diagrs. 23½ cm.

1. Agriculture—Economic aspects. 2. Agriculture—U. S. I. Title.

HD1761.N3   26-26560

WaWW OrCS OrU
TU NIC GAT WaTC Or WaS IdU MtU MB MtBC Wa OrPR
NN   0054117   DLC NcRS OO OU ODW ICJ ViU WaU CU

HC101
.N3
no.112
1927

National industrial conference board.
The agricultural problem in the United States. New York, National industrial conference board, inc., 1926. [i.e. 1927]

xiv, 157 p. incl. tables, diagrs. 23½ᶜᵐ. [Its Studies no.112]
"Second printing, February, 1927."

NN   0054118   ViU

HC101
.N3
no.112
1927a

National industrial conference board.
The agricultural problem in the United States. New York, National industrial conference board, inc., 1926. [i.e.1927]

xiv, 157 p. incl. tables, diagrs. 23½ᶜᵐ. [Its Studies no.112]
"Third printing, October, 1927."

NN   0054119   ViU

National industrial conference board.
... Amendments of the Agricultural adjustment act ... [New York] National industrial conference board, inc., 1935.

cover-title, 6 numb. l. 28½ᶜᵐ. (Conference board information service: Domestic affairs. Special memorandum no. 7)
Mimeographed.

1. Agricultural administration—U. S.   I. Title.   II. Title: Agricultural adjustment act.

35-7554

Library of Congress   HC106.3.N243 no. 7
————— Copy 2.
Copyright   AA 170418   [8]   (330.973) 338.10973

NN   0054120   DLC

HC101
.N317

National Industrial Conference Board.
American affairs; the economic record. v. 1–
June 21, 1939–
[New York, National Industrial Conference Board]

National Industrial Conference Board.
American affairs pamphlets
see under *title*

National industrial conference board.
... American agricultural conditions and remedies. Preliminary general review. New York, National industrial conference board, inc. [1936]

vi, 57 p. diagrs. 23ᶜᵐ. (*Its* Studies. No. 224)
A study made under the direction of Dr. Robert J. McFall.

1. Agriculture—Economic aspects—U. S. 2. Agriculture and state—U. S.   I. McFall, Robert James, 1887–   II. Title.

36-17064

Library of Congress   HD1765 1936.N3
[a44p1]   338.10973

NcD OO OC1 OCU ViU TU
NN   0054123   DLC DHEW ICJ Or OrU OrCS WaS MtU NcRS

National industrial conference board.
American economic and social progress. Twentieth annual meeting, May twenty-eighth, nineteen thirty-six. [New York] National industrial conference board [1936]

18 p. incl. diagrs. 20ᶜᵐ.
A "brochure of charts" prepared for the 20th annual meeting.

1. U. S.—Economic conditions.   I. Title.

A 40-2691

Cincinnati. Univ. Libr.   HC106.N32
for Library of Congress   [2]

NN   0054124   OCU

National industrial conference board.
American industry and economic progress. [New York] National industrial conference board, 1935.

1 p. l., 2-30 p. diagrs. 19½ᶜᵐ.
"Nineteenth annual meeting, May sixteenth, nineteen thirty-five."

1. U. S.—Indus.—Hist. 2. U. S.—Manuf. 3. U. S.—Econ. condit. I. Title.

36-8514

Library of Congress   HC103.5.N3
————— Copy 2.
Copyright   AA 175243   [5]   330.973

NN   0054125   DLC OCU OC1FRB

National industrial conference board.
The American merchant marine problem. New York, National industrial conference board, inc., 1929.

xiv, 167 p. incl. tables, diagrs. 23½ cm.

1. Merchant marine—U. S. 2. Shipping bounties and subsidies—U. S.   I. Title.

HE745.N27   29-13989

OC1 OO DN ICJ MB MsU CU NIC FMU DAL ViU
NN   0054126   DLC MtU WaTC OrCS Or WaS NcD PPT OU

National Industrial Conference Board.
America's resources for world leadership. Prepared for the thirty-first annual meeting of the Conference Board, May 28, 1947. New York [1947]

82 p. col. maps, col. diagrs. 26 cm.

1. U. S.—Econ. condit.—1945–   I. Title.

HC106.5.N25   330.973   47—30498*

OrU
NN   0054127   DLC OrCS Mi NNC MB TxU TU DNAL NN OrP

National industrial conference board.
... America's war effort; objectives, resources, progress. New York, National industrial conference board, inc. [1942]

cover-title, 28, [1] p. illus. (maps) diagrs. 28 x 22ᶜᵐ. (*Its* Conference board reports)

1. U. S.—Econ. condit.—1918– 1939— 2. U. S.—Indus. 3. World war, ——Economic aspects—U. S.   I. Title.

43-69

Library of Congress   HC106.4.N358 1942 a
[3]   330.973

NN   0054128   DLC OrU MB ICJ

National industrial conference board.
America's war effort, objectives, resources and progress, prepared for the twenty-sixth annual meeting of the Conference board, May 20, 1942, the Waldorf-Astoria, New York city. New York, National industrial conference board, inc. [1942]

cover-title, 28, [1] p. illus. (incl. maps) col. diagrs. 28 x 22 cm.

1. U. S.—Econ. condit.—1918– 2. World war, 1939-1945—Economic aspects—U. S.   I. Title.

HC106.4.N358   330.973   42—18097

NN   0054129   DLC OrCS OU OC1W OCU

National industrial conference board.
Analysis of British wartime reports on hours of work as related to output and fatigue ... Boston, Mass., National industrial conference board [1917]

iv, 57 p. incl. tables. 23ᶜᵐ. (*Its* [Research report] no. 2)
"Memoranda ... prepared by the [Health of munition workers] committee" : p. 56-57.

1. Hours of labor—Gt. Brit. 2. Munition workers. 3. European war, 1914-1918—Economic aspects—Gt. Brit.   I. Title: British wartime reports on hours of work.

18—13188

Library of Congress   HD5106.N3

OO OC1 MtBC ICJ MB ViU
NN   0054130   DLC WaTC WaS CaBVaU WaWW Or OrU CU OU

National Industrial Conference Board.
Analysis of electrical union contracts in manufacturing: United Electrical Workers (UE-Ind.) International Union of Electrical Workers (IUE-CIO) [and] International Brotherhood of Electrical Workers (IBEW-AFL) [By James J. Bambrick, Jr., and Hermine Zagat, Division of Personnel Administration] New York [1954]

55 p. diagrs. 28 x 44 cm.
Cover title.

1. Collective labor agreements—Electric industries—U. S.   I. Bambrick, James Joseph, 1917–   II. Zagat, Hermine.   III. Title.

54-4135

*331.891 331.18213

NN   0054131   DLC IEN OC1 NN WaS

National Industrial Conference Board.
An analysis of the proposal for an American free gold market. Special research memorandum. Prepared for the Committee for the Nation.
= *Reproduced typewriting.* New York. 1933. 33, ii ff. Charts. 28 cm.
Typed on one side only of the leaf.
Prepared by the board's Research Staff.

D4189 — Gold. As money. — Comm...e for the Nation to Rebuild Prices and Purchasing Power. Pubs.

NN   0054132   MB NN OC1FRB

VOLUME 407

National Industrial Conference Board.
Annual index to the Economic record
see its   List of current publications.

National Industrial Conference Board.
Annual report.

New York.
v. illus., maps (part fold.) 23 cm.
Began publication in 1917?
Title varies slightly.
Vols.   have also distinctive titles:

v. 8, 1923/24, The task of American industry and the ... board.

v. 10, 1925/26, The changing environment of American industry and the ... board.—v. 11, 1926/27, American industry at a turning point.—
v. 12, 1927/28, Mechanization of industry and economic and social progress.

v. 24, 1939/40, The world crisis and American business management.—
v. 26, 1941/42, National mobilization for victory.

1. U. S.—Indus. 2. U. S.—Econ. condit.

HC106.3.N18   330.973   24–17698 rev*

MiD DNAL DFT NcU TxLT TU OClU UU MiD MBU GEU LNL
MtBC IdU IdPI LU NcU DI WaS WaSp NN AAP CSt ViU DL
NN 0054135   DLC MsSM NRU NBuG NIC OrCS MtU ICJ

National industrial conference board.
... Annual review of the cost of living. 1940–
New York, 1941–
v. tables, diagrs. 28ᶜᵐ. (*Its* Conference board reports)

1. Cost and standard of living—U. S.

                                         44–29592
Library of Congress   HD6983.N27
                             ₍2₎   331.831

NBuG OrU ICJ Or OrCS
NN 0054136   DLC DNAL Or GU TxU NIC OClW OCU NNC

National industrial conference board.
... Annual wage and employment guarantee plans ... New York, N. Y., National industrial conference board, inc. ₍1946₎
cover-title, 55 p. 28 x 22ᶜᵐ. (*Its* Conference board reports)
Studies in personnel policy, no. 76.
"Selected bibliography": p. 36.

1. Wages—Annual wage.   I. Title.

HD4928.A5N3   331.23   46–8660

NN 0054137   DLC CoU IaU OClJC

National industrial conference board.
... The Appalachian coals case: a brief interpretation. ₍New York, National industrial conference board, 1933.
1 p. l., 7 numb. l. 28½ x 22ᶜᵐ. (Conference board information service: Domestic affairs. Memorandum no. 3)
Reproduced from type-written copy.

1. Coal trade—U. S. 2. Trusts, Industrial—U. S. 3. Appalachian coals, incorporated.   I. Title.

                                         42–2969
Library of Congress   HC106.3.N24 no. 3
                             ₍2₎   (330.973) 338.2

NN 0054138   DLC NN

National Industrial Conference Board.
Appraisal of job performance. ₍By Stephen Habbe, Division of Personnel Administration₎ New York ₍1951₎
56 p. forms. 28 cm. (*Its* Conference Board reports. Studies in personnel policy, no. 121)
Cover title.

1. Employees, Rating of.   I. Habbe, Stephen, 1903–   II. Title.
(Series: National Industrial Conference Board. Studies in personnel policy, no. 121)

HF5549.A2N27 no. 121   658.3125   51–8470

NN 0054139   DLC ViU MH CoU

National industrial conference board.
Arbitration and wage-fixing in Australia ... Boston, Mass., National industrial conference board ₍ᶜ1918₎
vii, 52 p. 23ᶜᵐ. (*Its* Research report, no. 10)

1. Arbitration, Industrial—Australia. 2. Wages—Australia.
I. Title.

Library of Congress   HD5630.A6N2   19–531

                    MB ICJ CaBVaU WaS OrU ViU OrPR WaTC MtBC CaBViP
NN 0054140   DLC Or WaWW CU NcD NcRS OU MiU OO NN

National industrial conference board.
Arbitration and wage-fixing in Australia ... Boston, Mass., National industrial conference board, 1920.
vii, 52 p. 23ᶜᵐ. (*Its* Research report, no. 10)

NN 0054141   TxU

National industrial conference board.
The arsenal of American enterprise. New York, National industrial conference board, 1941.
66p.

NN 0054142   DAL

National industrial conference board.
Aspects of anti-trust legislation in the United States; a discussion at meetings of the National industrial conference board in January and February, 1922. New York city, National industrial conference board ₍ᶜ1922₎
iii, 16 p. 22½ᶜᵐ.

1. Sherman antitrust law, 1890. 2. Trusts, Industrial.   I. Title.

Library of Congress   HD2778.N3   22–9940

NN 0054143   DLC

HF
5549   **National Industrial Conference Board.**
A2N27   Assuring employment or income to
no. 7+   wage earners - a case study.   New York
         ₍1938₎
         19 p. 28cm. (Its Studies in personnel
         policy, no.7)

             1. Insurance, Social. I. Series.
         II. Title.

NN 0054144   NIC IaU ViU

National Industrial Conference Board.
Atomic energy in industry; minutes of ₍the annual₎ conference. ₍1st₎–   1952–
New York.
v. illus. 28 cm.

Subtitle varies: 1952, Minutes of special conference.

1. Atomic energy—Congresses. 2. Atomic power—Congresses.
I. Title.

TK9006.N3   *539.76 541.2   53–695 rev

NN 0054145   DLC OAkU WaS CaBVa IdPI WaT DAU NN

National Industrial Conference Board.
Atomic energy primer for management ₍by₎ R. Maxil Ballinger, Division of Business Practices. New York ₍1955₎
71 p. illus. 29 cm.
"Prepared for ... the Conference Board's 'Atomic energy course for management.'"
Bibliography: p. 66–71.

II. Nuclear engineering. 2. Atomic energy.   I. Ballinger, R. Maxil.
II. Title.

TK9146.N3   *539.76   55–2095

NN 0054146   DLC ViU OU MB Wa DI

National Industrial Conference Board.   ₍By R. Maxil
Ballinger, Division of Business Practices₎ New York ₍1955₎
Atomic energy primer for management.
72 p. illus. 28 cm. (*Its* Conference Board reports. Studies in business policy, no. 74)
Cover title.
"Prepared for ... the Conference Board's 'Atomic energy course for management.'"
Bibliography: p. 67–70.

1. Nuclear engineering. 2. Atomic energy.   I. Ballinger, R. Maxil.
II. Title. (Series: National Industrial Conference Board. Studies in business policy, no. 74)

HF5006.N3 no. 74   *539.76   55–4758

NN 0054147   DLC

National Industrial Conference Board.
Automobile plans for salesmen ₍by George M. Umemura, Division of Business Practices₎ New York ₍1955₎
63 p. forms. 28 cm. (*Its* Conference Board reports. Studies in business policy, no. 76)
Cover title.

1. Automobiles, Company.   I. Umemura, George M. II. Title.
(Series: National Industrial Conference Board. Studies in business policy, no. 76)

HF5006.N3 no. 76   658.81   56–540

NN 0054148   DLC WaU NB IaU LU OU ViU MH-BA DI

National industrial conference board.
The availability of bank credit. New York, National industrial conference board, inc., 1932.
xiv, 146 p. illus. (map.) diagrs. 23ᶜᵐ.
Supplement and complement of the Board's "The banking situation in the United States" published in May, 1932. *cf.* Pref.

1. Banks and banking—U. S. 2. Credit—U. S.   I. Title.
Library of Congress   HG3729.U5N3   33–924
———— Copy 2.
Copyright A 57624   ₍5–5₎   332.70973

OrU CaBVaU NcD NcRS ICJ OClFRB
NN 0054149   DLC WaTC TU CU MB FMU MtU OrPR WaS

National industrial conference board.
... The availability of bank credit, 1933–1938, by Lewis H. Kimmel, the Conference board research staff. New York city, National industrial conference board, inc. ₍ᶜ1939₎
xvii, 146 p. incl. illus. (map) tables, diagrs. 23ᶜᵐ. (*Its* Studies, no. 242)

1. Banks and banking—U. S. 2. Credit—U. S.   I. Kimmel, Lewis Henry, 1899–   II. Title.
Library of Congress   HG1641.N3   39–17789
———— Copy 2.
Copyright A 131236   ₍39i5₎   332.70973

MiU TU NcD DNAL OCU ViU OCl
NN 0054150   DLC DFT MtU WaS OrCS OrU ICJ WaTC ScU

National industrial conference board.
... The banking bill of 1935 ... ₍New York₎ National industrial conference board, inc., 1935.
cover-title, 10 numb. l. 28½ᶜᵐ. (Conference board information service: Domestic affairs. Special memorandum no. 4)
Mimeographed.

1. Federal reserve banks. 2. Banks and banking—Government guaranty of deposits. 3. Federal deposit insurance corporation.   I. Title.
Library of Congress   HC106.3.N243 no. 4   35–7551
———— Copy 2.
Copyright AA 171211   ₍8₎   (330.973) 332.10973

NN 0054151   DLC OClFRB

National industrial conference board.
The banking situation in the United States. New York, National industrial conference board, inc., 1932.
xiv, 157 p. diagrs. 23½ᶜᵐ.

1. Banks and banking—U. S.   I. Title.
Library of Congress   HG2481.N35   32–17184
———— Copy 2.
Copyright A 51949   ₍5–3₎   332.10973

OU OCU OO Or ICJ DN OrU IdPI MtBC WaS MtU
NN 0054152   DLC CaBVaU KEmT CU FMU WHi OrCS NcD

VOLUME 407

National Industrial Conference Board.
 Basic business factors
  see its Selected business indicators.

National industrial conference board.
 Basic data on excess-profits tax relief, reprinted from the Conference board economic record, 1942-3. New York city, N. Y., National industrial conference board, inc. [*1943]
  1 p. l., iv, 53 p. incl. tables, diagrs. 28 x 21½ᶜᵐ.

  1. Excess profits tax—U. S. 2. Corporations—U. S.—Taxation.
                                                    44—19652
  Library of Congress   HJ4653.E8N3
                 [3]   336.243

NN 0054154   DLC

National Industrial Conference Board.
 Basic industrial data for investment analysis. New York, *1946-
  v. in   28 cm.
  Some volumes have title: Basic industrial data; v. 18 has special title only.
  The pamphlets are frequently revised. This set includes all editions in the Library.
  CONTENTS.—[1] Aircraft.—[2] Aluminum and bauxite.—[3] Antimony.—[4] Automobiles.—[5] Bituminous coal.—[7] Cement.—[8] Chemicals: Basic industrial chemicals. Coal-tar chemicals and plastics materials. Drugs, pharmaceuticals, and medicinals. Fats and oils used in inedible products. Soap, glycerin, and toilet preparations. Fertilizers and fertilizer materials. Paint and

 paint materials. Insecticides, fungicides and disinfectants, and cleaning and polishing preparations. Composite chemicals. 9 v.—[9] Construction and building materials.—[10] Copper.—[11] Dairy products.—[12] Furniture.—[13] Glass industry.—[14] Grain and grain products.—[15] Iron and steel.—[16] Lead.—[17] Lumber.—[18] Magnesium metal and magnesium compounds.—[19] Meat packing.—[20] Nickel.—[21] Railroad equipment.—[22] Rayon.—[24] Retail trade: Grocery stores, variety stores. Total retail trade, department stores, mail-order houses. 2 v.—[25] Sugar and related products.—[26] Tires and rubber.—[27] Tobacco:

 Tobacco products excepting cigarettes. v.—[28] Zinc.—[29] Motor vehicles.—[30] Tin.—[31] Cotton and cotton textiles.—[32] Wool and wool textiles.—[33] Machinery (except electrical)—[34] Paper.—[35] Electric power.—[36] Rubber and rubber products.

  1. U. S.—Indus.   I. Title.
  HC101.N3155   338   49—3659 rev 2*

       CU MoU
NN 0054157   DLC ViU IU ICU NNC MH-BA N OrCS IdU

National Industrial Conference Board.
 Basic issues in decontrol; an Economic Forum discussion, Edwin B. George, chairman, Gardner Ackley [and others] New York, [1952]
  62 p. 23 cm. (*Its* Studies in business economics, no. 35)
  Cover title.

  1. Price regulation—U. S. I. George, Edwin Black, 1896–
  II. Title.   (Series)
  HB31.N33 no. 35   338.526   52—4104

NN 0054158   DLC ViU IaU OOxM PSt NN IU TxU NcD

National industrial conference board.
 ... Basic report on the construction industry; the building industry in Great Britain, July, 1937. New York, N. Y., National industrial conference board, inc., *1937.
  2 p. l., 14 numb. l. 27½ x 21½ cm. (Conference board industry reports)
  Mimeographed.
  Bibliographical foot-notes.

  1. Construction industry—Gt. Brit. 2. Housing—G Brit.
  TH57.N3   690.942   37—1279

NN 0054159   DLC

National industrial conference board.
 The birthday of our constitution.
 (September 17.....) Boston, National industrial conference board, [1919]
  6 p. T.

NN 0054160   00

National Industrial Conference Board.
 Bituminous coal; basic industrial data. [New York, 1949] *1948.
  [20] p. of tables. 28 cm.
  Caption title.

  1. Bituminous coal—Stat. 2. Coal mines and mining—Stat.
  HD9540.4.N3   338.2724   49—3660*

NN 0054161   DLC

Pamphlet
HD
66+   **National Industrial Conference Board.**
       Bituminous coal industry; basic industrial
      data. [New York] 1954.
       53 p. tables. 28 cm.

      Caption title.

       1. Bituminous coal. 2. Coal trade.

NN 0054162   NIC

National Industrial Conference Board.
 Brief analysis of War Revenue Bill H. R. 12863 as affecting industry. [Boston:] National Industrial Conference Board, 1919. 15 p. 8°.
  Cover-title.

  1. Taxation, U. S., 1919. 2. European   war, 1914- .—Finance, U. S.
  N. Y. P. L.   May 15, 1919.

NN 0054163   NN PBL CU OU MB DL OO MiU

National industrial conference board.
 ... British post-war planning. New York, National industrial conference board, inc. [1943]
  cover-title, 71 p. diagr. 28 x 22ᵐ. (*Its* Conference board reports)

  1. Reconstruction (1939–) I. Title.
                                        43—7630
  Library of Congress   D825.N3
                     [18]   338.91

NN 0054164   DLC GU OClW OrCS OrU OCl OU OCU ICJ

National industrial conference board.
 Budgetary control in manufacturing industry. New York, National industrial conference board, inc., 1931.
  xiii, 180 p. diagrs. 23½ᵐ.

  1. Budget in business. 2. U. S.—Manuf. I. Title.
  Library of Congress   HF5550.N3   31—9641
  ——— Copy 2.
  Copyright A 36443   [8]   658.154

       OU OO CU DN DL ICJ MtU
NN 0054165   DLC WaS MB OrCS Or MtU NcRS NcD OCU

National Industrial Conference Board.
 Budgeting expenses in small companies [by Arthur W. Nevins] New York, N.Y. [1952]
 Cover title, 44 p. illus. (*Its* Studies in business policy, no. 58)

  At head of title: Conference Board reports.

NN 0054166   MH-BA NNU PPCuP ViU OCl

National industrial conference board.
 The building situation ... New York city, National industrial conference board [1924]
  vi, 31 p. diagrs. 23ᵐ. (*Its* Special report, no. 29)

  1. Building—U. S. 2. Housing—U. S.   I. Title.
                                        24—19476
  Library of Congress   TH23.N3

NN 0054167   DLC MtU DFT CU OU OCl MB DL OClFRB

National industrial conference board.
 Bulletin, no. 1
 New York, National industrial conference board, *1921-27.
  v. 23ᵐ.
  Continued as the Conference board bulletin.

  1. U. S.—Econ. condit.—1918-   2. U. S.—Indus.
  Library of Congress   HC106.3.N2   21—16213

NN 0054168   DLC OU ICJ MtU OrU

National Industrial Conference Board.
 Bulletin boards. New York [1953]
  32 p. illus. 28 cm. (*Its* Conference Board reports. Studies in personnel policy, no. 138)

  1. Bulletin boards.
  HF5549.A2N27 no. 138   658.385   53—3304 ‡

NN 0054169   DLC IaU CoU OCU ViU OOxM MH AAP IdPI

National Industrial Conference Board.
 The business outlook; an evening with the Economic Forum. 1947-
 [New York]
  v. illus. 23 cm. (*Its* Studies in business economics)
  Issues for 1947-48 have subtitle: An evening with the economists.

  1. U. S.—Econ. condit.—1945-   I. Title: The business outlook.   (Series)
  HB31.N33   330.973   48—10195 rev 2*

       MU NcRS AAP CaBVa CaBVaU MtBC Wa WaWW OU WaBeW
NN 0054170   DLC TxU IU OCU CLU IaU NN MoU NcU

National industrial conference board. Business record
 see its The conference board business record.

National industrial conference board.
 ... Canada's role in the American hemisphere. New York, National industrial conference board, inc. [1942]
  cover-title, 88 p. incl. tables. map, diagrs. 28 x 22 cm. (*Its* Conference board reports)
  Bibliography: p. 87-88.

  1. Canada—Econ. condit.—1918-   2. Canada—Economic policy.
  3. World war, 1939-1945—Canada.   I. Title.
  HC115.N3   330.971   42—51757

NN 0054172   DLC ICJ OCU OU DNAL NNC GU MB OrU

National industrial conference board.
 The Canadian industrial disputes investigation act ... Boston, Mass., National industrial conference board, *1918.
  28 p. 23ᵐ. (*Its* Research reports, no. 5:
  Appendix: Abridged text of the Canadian industrial disputes investigation act, 1907: p. 24-28.

  1. Arbitration, Industrial—Canada. I. Canada. Laws, statutes, etc.
                                        18—10844
  Library of Congress   HD5508.A3N3

NN 0054173   DLC WaWW CU NcD MiU OU OO ICJ ViU

VOLUME 407

National Industrial Conference Board.
The Canadian Industrial Disputes Investigation Act. Revised.
— Boston. 1920. 31 pp. Tables. [Research report. No. 5.] 22½ cm.

D792 — Canada. Labor. — Canada. . . .s and laws. Industrial Disputes Investigation Act. — Arbitration. Industrial.

NN 0054174   MB WaS

National industrial conference board.
Capital formation and its elements; a series of papers presented at a symposium conducted by the Conference board. New York city, National industrial conference board, inc. [°1939]
vii, 150 p. incl. tables, diagrs. 23ᶜᵐ.
Contents.—Some introductory observations, by A. H. Hansen.—Capital formation in the United States, 1919–1935, by Simon Kuznets.—Effects of public spending on capital formation, by J. M. Clark.—Tax policy and capital formation, by Gerhard Colm.—The growth of large corporations and the formation of capital, by R. S. Tucker.—Consumer credit and consumers' capital formation, by Rolf Nugent.—The interest rate and capital formation, by Gottfried Haberler.—War and capital formation, by C. O. Hardy.
1. Capital. 2. U. S.—   Econ. condit.—1918—   I. Title.
Library of Congress   HB501.N3   39–5594
——— Copy 2.
Copyright A 126185   [5]   330.15

NN 0054175   DLC OrU OKentU WaU CU MB OC1CC OO
  OC1U NcD

HF5006   National Industrial Conference Board.
.N3
no.4   Carry-back, carry-over and refund
1945   provisions. New York [1945]
        12 p.   28cm.   (Its Studies in business
        policy, no. 4)
        Cover title.

        1. Taxation—U. S.   2. Business tax—U. S.
        I. Title. II. Ser.

NN 0054176   ViU OU MH-BA Mi

National industrial conference board.
A case of federal propaganda in our public schools; some criticisms of "Lessons in community and national life" issued by the United States Bureau of education. Boston, Mass., National industrial conference board, 1919.
13 p. 23ᶜᵐ.

1. U. S. Bureau of education. Lessons in community and national life.
I. Title.
Library of Congress   HN51.A35   19–5917

NN 0054177   DLC OrPR DHEW NIC WaS Or OrU OU OO
  MiU NN MB

National industrial conference board.
... Cases arising under the new deal legislation now before the United States Supreme court ... [New York] National industrial conference board, 1936.
cover-title, 1 p. 1., 4 numb. l. 28½ᶜᵐ. (Its Conference board information service: Domestic affairs series. Memorandum no. 55)

1. U. S. Constitutional law.   I. U. S. Supreme court.
                        44–27009
Library of Congress   HC106l3.N24 no. 55
                [2]   (330.973) 342.730

NN 0054178   DLC

National industrial conference board.
Changes in the cost of living, July, 1914–July, 1919 ... Boston, Mass., National industrial conference board, °1919.
vii, [1], 31 p. incl. tables, diagr. 23ᶜᵐ. (Its Research report, no. 19)

1. Cost and standard of living—U. S. 2. European war, 1914–1918—Economic aspects—U. S.   I. Title.
Library of Congress   HD6983.N3 1919 b   19–16066

NN 0054179   DLC MtBC NcRS CaBVaU OrU WaS WaWW
  WaTC NcD MiU OU OCU MH ICJ Or ViU

National industrial conference board.
Changes in the cost of living, July, 1914–November, 1919 ... Boston, Mass., National industrial conference board, °1919.
vii, [1], 24 p. incl. tables, diagr. 23ᶜᵐ. (Its Research report, no. 25)

1. Cost and standard of living—U. S. 2. European war, 1914–1918—Economic aspects—U. S.   I. Title.
Library of Congress   HD6983.N3 1919 c   20–6070

NN 0054180   DLC OrU Or WaS WaTC WaWW NcD OU MiU
  OC1 DL MB ICJ ViU NcRS MtBC

National industrial conference board.
Changes in the cost of living, July, 1914–March, 1920 ... Boston, Mass., National industrial conference board, °1920.
viii, 24 p. incl. tables, diagr. 23ᶜᵐ. (Its Research report, no. 28)

1. Cost and standard of living—U. S. 2. European war, 1914–1918—Economic aspects—U. S.   I. Title.
Library of Congress   HD6983.N3 1920   20–12528
——— Copy 2.

NN 0054181   DLC ICJ WaTC WaS OrU Or WaWW MiU OU
  OO MB ViU

National industrial conference board.
Changes in the cost of living, July, 1914–July, 1920 ... New York, National industrial conference board, °1920.
viii, 28 p. incl. tables, diagrs. 23ᶜᵐ. (Its Research report, no. 30)

1. Cost and standard of living—U. S. 2. European war, 1914–1918—Economic aspects—U. S.   I. Title.
Library of Congress   HD6983.N3 1920 a   21–4327

NN 0054182   DLC WaTC WaWW WaS Or OrU NcRS MiU OU
  OC1 MB ICJ ViU CaBVaU

National industrial conference board.
Changes in the cost of living, July, 1914—November, 1920 ... New York, National industrial conference board [°1921]
viii, 29 p. incl. tables, diagr. 23ᶜᵐ. (Its Research report, no. 33)

1. Cost and standard of living—U. S. 2. European war, 1914–1918—Economic aspects—U. S.   I. Title.
Library of Congress   HD6983.N3 1920 f   21–2959

NN 0054183   DLC MtBC CaBVaU WaTC WaWW WaS OrU
  NcD NcRS MiU OU OCU Or DL ViU ICJ MB

National industrial conference board.
Changes in the cost of living, July, 1914–March, 1921 ... New York, National industrial conference board [1921]
viii, 28 p. incl. tables, diagr. 23ᶜᵐ. (Its Research report, no. 36. April 1921)

1. Cost and standard of living—U. S. 2. European war, 1914–1918—Economic aspects—U. S.   I. Title.
Library of Congress   HD6983.N3 1921   21–14787

NN 0054184   DLC MtBC WaTC WaS OrU WaWW KU OCU MiU
  OC1 ViU ICJ

National industrial conference board.
Changes in the cost of living, July, 1914–July, 1921 ... National industrial conference board. New York, The Century co. [1921]
viii, 25 p. incl. tables, diagr. 23ᶜᵐ. (Its Research report, no. 39)

1. Cost and standard of living—U. S. 2. European war, 1914–1918—Economic aspects—U. S.   I. Title.
Library of Congress   HD6983.N3 1921 a   21–22094

NN 0054185   DLC WaTC MtBC Or WaS OrU NcRS MiU OCU
  OC1 WaWW ViU CaBVaU

National industrial conference board.
Changes in the cost of living, July, 1914–November, 1921 ... National industrial conference board. New York, The Century co. [°1922]
viii, 30 p. incl. tables, diagr. 23ᶜᵐ. (Its Research report, no. 44)
$0.75

1. Cost and standard of living—U. S. 2. European war, 1914–1918—Economic aspects—U. S.   I. Title.
Library of Congress   HD6983.N3 1922   22–3546

NN 0054186   DLC WaTC CaBVaU CU WaWW WaS Or NcRS
  OCU OC1 OO OrU ICJ ViU

National industrial conference board.
Changes in the cost of living, July, 1914–March, 1922 ... National industrial conference board. New York, The Century co. [1922]
viii, 33 p. incl. tables, diagr. 23 cm. (Its Research report, no. 49)

1. Cost and standard of living—U. S. 2. European war, 1914–1918—Economic aspects—U. S.   I. Title.
        HD6983.N3 1922a   22–13235

NN 0054187   DLC CaBVaU MiU OU ViU OC1 ICJ DL WaS
  MtBC WaWW OrU WaTC

National industrial conference board.
Changes in the cost of living, July, 1914–July, 1922 ... National industrial conference board. New York, The Century co. [°1922]
viii, 34 p. incl. tables, diagrs. 23ᶜᵐ. (Its Research report no. 54) $0.75

1. Cost and standard of living—U. S. 2. European war, 1914–1918—Economic aspects—U. S.
Library of Congress   HD6983.N3 1922 b   22–18601

NN 0054188   DLC OrU WaS KU NcD MiU OU OO ViU ICJ
  MtBC CaBVaU WaWW

National industrial conference board.
Changes in the cost of living, July, 1914–November, 1922 ... New York, National industrial conference board [°1923]
viii, 37 p. incl. tables, diagr. 23ᶜᵐ. (Its Research report, no. 57)

1. Cost and standard of living—U. S. 2. European war, 1914–1918—Economic aspects—U. S.   I. Title.
Library of Congress   HD6983.N3 1923   23–7108

NN 0054189   DLC ICJ WaTC WaS OrU WaWW MtBC CaBVaU
  MiU OC1 OU ViU DL

National industrial conference board.
Changes in the cost of living, July, 1914–March, 1923 ... New York, National industrial conference board [°1923]
viii, 34 p. incl. tables, diagr. 23ᶜᵐ. (Its Research report, no. 60)

1. Cost and standard of living—U. S. 2. European war, 1914–1918—economic aspects—U. S.
Library of Congress   HD6983.N3 1923 a   23–9211

NN 0054190   DLC WaWW MtBC WaS OrU WaWW NcD OO MiU
  OC1 ICJ Or

National industrial conference board.
Changes in the cost of living, 1914–July, 1923 ... New York, National industrial conference board [1923]
viii, 36 p. diagr. 23ᶜᵐ. (Its Research report, no. 63)

1. Cost and standard of living—U. S. 2. European war, 1914–1918—Economic aspects—U. S.
        HD6983.N3 1923 b   24–4853

NN 0054191   DLC OrCS WaWW Or OrU WaS MtBC WaTC OO
  NIC NcRS OCU OC1 ViU DL ICJ MB

VOLUME 407

National industrial conference board.
　　... Changes in the cost of living, January, 1933, to March, 1934 ... ₍New York₎ National industrial conference board, 1934.
　　cover-title, ii, 11 numb. l. 19ᶜᵐ. (Conference board information service: Domestic affairs. Memorandum no. 31)

　　1. Cost and standard of living—U. S. 2. Index numbers (Economics)
ɪ. Title.
　　Library of Congress　　　　HC106.3.N24 no. 31
　　　　　　　　　　　　　　　　　　　　　　　34–15663
　　—— —— Copy 2.
　　Copyright A 71697　　　　₍5₎　　　　(330.973) 331.8310973

NN　0054192　　　DLC WaS

National industrial conference board.
　　Changes in wages during and since the war, September 1914–March, 1920 ... New York, National industrial conference board, °1920.
　　x, 53 p. incl. tables, diagrs. 23ᶜᵐ. (*Its* Research report. no. 31)

　　1. Wages—U. S. 2. European war, 1914–1918—Economic aspects—U. S. ɪ. Title.
　　Library of Congress　　　　HD4975.N3 1920
　　　　　　　　　　　　　　　　　　　　　　　21–5408

　　CaBViPA OO MiU MB ViU NcD NcRS OC1 OCU
NN　0054193　　　DLC ICJ WaTC OrU WaWW CU MtBC CaBVaU

National Industrial Conference Board.
　　Chartbook of current business trends.

New York,
　　v. diagrs. (part col.) 28 cm.

　　1. U. S.—Econ. condit.—1945–　　　ɪ. Title.
　　HC106.5.A2843　　　　330.973　　　　58–1208 rev

NN　0054194　　　DLC NN TxU MBU IU

National Industrial Conference Board.
　　Chartbook of weekly business indicators.

New York₎
　　v. diagrs. 28 cm.
　　Includes "Supplementary data on ₍the board's₎ Weekly desk sheet series."

　　1. U. S.—Econ. condit.—1945–　　　ɪ. Title.
　　HC106.5.A2845　　　　330.973　　　　58–24653 rev

　　OrP IdPI OCU NbU
NN　0054195　　　DLC NcD FTaSU OU MoU NBuC NcRS MsSM

National Industrial Conference Board.
　　Chemical and allied products; general statistics. Basic industrial data.
₍n. p.₎
　　v. tables. 28 cm.

　　1. Chemical industries—U. S.
　　HD9651.4.N3　　　　　　　56–32211

NN　0054196　　　DLC

338.4　　National Industrial Conference Board.
N213ch　　Chemicals: basic industrial data. ₍n.p.₎ 1951.
　　　　2v. in 1. of tables. 28cm.

　　　　Contents.– 1. Industrial chemicals.– 2. Coal-tar chemicals and plastics materials.

　　　　1. Chemicals—Stat. I. Title: Industrial chemicals. II. Title: Coal-tar chemicals and plastics materials.

NN　0054197　　　IU

National industrial conference board.
　　Clerical salaries in the United States, 1926. New York, National industrial conference board, inc., 1926.
　　ix p., 1 l., 59 p. incl. tables, diagrs. 23½ cm.

　　1. Wages—U. S. 2. Clerks—U. S.—Salaries, pensions, etc.
ɪ. Title.
　　HD4966.C42U65　　　　　　27–1049

　　TU CU OO DL ICJ DAU KMK MtU
NN　0054198　　　DLC WaT WaS OrCS Or MB NcD OC1 ViU OCU

National Industrial Conference Board.
　　Clerical salary survey. Apr. 1943–
New York.
　　　　no. tables. 28–31 cm. irregular. (*Its* Conference board reports)
　　　　Numbers for Apr. 1943–Apr. 1948 issued as the board's Studies in personnel policy (HF5549.A2N27) ;　　issued as the board's Studies in labor statistics, no.
　　　　Title varies: Apr. 1943–　　　Clerical salary survey of rates paid.
　　　　L. C. set includes numbers for Apr. and Oct. 1949 issued without series note and called "confidential, not for publication."
　　　　1. Clerks—U. S. 2. Wages—U. S. ɪ. Title. (Series. Series: National Industrial Conference Board. Studies in personnel policy. Series: National Industrial Conference Board. Studies in labor statistics. no.
　　　　HD8065.N3　　　　　331.2851374　　　43–11987*

　　Or NNC InU OC1JC
NN　0054199　　　DLC OOxM OC1U UU AAP IEdS ViU CaBVa

HF　　　**National Industrial Conference Board.**
5549　　　The closed shop. New York ₍1939₎
A2N27　　11 p. 28cm. (The Conference Board. Studies in personnel policy, no. 12)
no.12+

　　　　1. Open and closed shop. I. Series: National Industrial Conference Board. Studies in personnel policy, no. 12.

NN　0054200　　　NIC MiU-L InU OO ViU IaU

National Industrial Conference Board.
　　Collective bargaining; an analysis of union contracts ₍in 17 industries₎ New York, 1947₎
　　18 nos. in 1 v.

NN　0054201　　　MH-BA WaS

National industrial conference board.
　　... Collective bargaining developments and representative union agreements ... New York, N. Y., National industrial conference board, inc. ₍1944₎
　　cover-title, 84 p. diagrs. 28 x 22ᶜᵐ. (*Its* Conference board reports)
　　Studies in personnel policy, no. 60.
　　"Selected bibliography relating to collective bargaining": p. 82.

　　1. Collective bargaining—U. S. 2. Labor contract—U. S.
　　　　　　　　　　　　　　　　　　　　　　44–4845
　　Library of Congress　　　　HF5549.A2N27 no. 60
　　　　　　　　　　　　　　　₍6₎　　　　(658.3) 331.116

NN　0054202　　　DLC OC1JC IaU CoU

National Industrial Conference Board.
　　Collective bargaining in Canada. New York ₍1947₎
　　cover-title, 56 p. 28 cm. (*Its* Conference board reports)
　　Studies in personnel policy, no. 84.
　　"Selected bibliography": p. 53–54.

　　1. Collective bargaining—Canada. 2. Labor contract—Canada. ɪ. Series. ɪɪ. Series: National Industrial Conference Board. Studies in personnel policy, no. 84.
　　HF5549.A2N27 no. 84　　331.116　　　47–6206*

NN　0054203　　　DLC CaBViP CoU MH AAP OC1JC

National industrial conference board.
　　Collective bargaining through employee representation ... New York, National industrial conference board, inc., 1933.
　　viii, 81 p. diagrs. 23ᶜᵐ.

　　1. Employees' representation in management. 2. Labor contract—U. S. ɪ. Title.
　　Library of Congress　　　　HD5650.N25
　　　　　　　　　　　　　　　　　　　　　　　33–19213
　　—— —— Copy 2.
　　Copyright A 64325　　　　₍5-5₎　　　　331.1520973

　　IdU NcD OO OOxM DL ViU ICJ CaBVa OrCS OC1U Or MtU
NN　0054204　　　DLC OrU-L WaU-L MH-BA CU ICU OrU WaS

National Industrial Conference Board.
　　College graduates in industry: recruiting, selecting, training. ₍By Stephen Habbe, Division of Personnel Administration₎ New York ₍1948₎
　　32 p. illus. 28 cm. (*Its* Conference Board reports. Studies in personnel policy, no. 89)
　　Cover title.

　　1. Employees, Training of. 2. Employment management. ɪ. Habbe, Stephen, 1903– ɪɪ. Title. (Series: National Industrial Conference Board. Conference Board reports. Series: National Industrial Conference Board. Studies in personnel policy, no. 89)
　　HF5549.A2N27 no. 89　　331.86　　　48–3036*

NN　0054205　　　DLC CoU MiEM IaU AAP PHC PU OC1JC

National Industrial Conference Board.
　　Communicating with employees ... ₍By Stephen Habbe, Division of Personnel Administration₎ New York ₍1952₎
　　48 p. illus. 28 cm. (*Its* Conference Board reports. Studies in personnel policy, no. 129)
　　Cover title.
　　Bibliography: p. 44.

　　1. Employees, Reporting to. ɪ. Habbe, Stephen, 1903– ɪɪ. Title. (Series: National Industrial Conference Board. Studies in personnel policy, no. 129)
　　HF5549.A2N27 no. 129　　658.31　　　53–276

NN　0054206　　　DLC AAP CoU ViU IaU MoSU-C TxU OC1

National Industrial Conference Board.
　　Communication within the management group. New York ₍1947₎
　　cover-title, 36 p. illus. 28 cm. (*Its* Conference board reports)
　　Studies in personnel policy, no. 80.
　　"By William W. Mussmann, Management Research Division."

　　1. Communication in management. ɪ. Mussmann, William W. ɪɪ. Title. (Series. Series: National Industrial Conference Board. Studies in personnel policy, no. 80)
　　HF5549.A2N27 no. 80　　658.3　　　47–4838*

NN　0054207　　　DLC OC1JC AAP ViU CoU OCU

National industrial conference board.
　　... Company annual reports to employees ... New York, National industrial conference board, inc. ₍1942₎
　　cover-title, 32 p. incl. illus., diagrs. 28 cm. (*Its* Studies in personnel policy, no. 47)
　　At head of title: Conference board reports.

　　1. Employment management. 2. Industrial statistics. I. Title. II. Title: Annual reports to employees. III. Title: Employees, Company annual reports to.

NN　0054208　　　Vi IaU InU

National Industrial Conference Board.
　　Company contributions
　　　　see its　　Company policies on donations.

National Industrial Conference Board.
　　Company food services ₍by Ethel M. Spears, Division of Personnel Administration₎ New York ₍1950₎
　　52 p. illus. 28 cm. (*Its* Conference Board reports. Studies in personnel policy, no. 104)
　　Cover title.

　　1. Restaurants, lunch rooms, etc.—U. S. 2. Welfare work in industry—U. S. ɪ. Spears, Ethel M. ɪɪ. Title. (Series: National Industrial Conference Board. Conference Board reports. Series: National Industrial Conference Board. Studies in personnel policy, no. 104)
　　HF5549.A2N27 no. 104　　647.95　　　50–4408

NN　0054210　　　DLC PPD AAP CoU OOxM PPT

VOLUME 407

National industrial conference board.
... Company group insurance plans ... New York, N. Y.,
National industrial conference board, inc. ₁1945₎

cover-title, 27, ₁4₎ p. 28 x 22ᶜᵐ. (*Its* Conference board reports)
Studies in personnel policy, no. 70.
"By F. Beatrice Brower, Management research division."—p. 3.

1. Insurance, Group—U. S.   I. Brower, Frances Beatrice.   II. Title.
45-9242
Library of Congress   HF5549.A2N27 no. 70
₁4₎   (658.3) 368.4

NN   0054211   DLC CoU OC1JC OC1U

National Industrial Conference Board.
Company group insurance plans ₁by F. Beatrice Brower,
Division of Personnel Administration₎ New York ₁1951₎

70 p. illus. 28 cm. (*Its* Conference Board reports. Studies in
personnel policy, no. 112)
Cover title.

1. Insurance, Group—U. S.   I. Brower, Frances Beatrice.
II. Title.   (Series: National Industrial Conference Board. Studies
in personnel policy, no. 112)
HF5549.A2N27 no. 112   368.4   51-2052

NN   0054212   DLC MtBC ViU CoU AAP

National Industrial Conference Board.
Company health programs for executives. ₁By Doris M.
Thompson, Division of Personnel Administration₎ New
York ₁1955₎

96 p. illus. 28 cm. (*Its* Conference Board reports. Studies in
personnel policy, no. 147)

1. Executives—Health programs.   I. Thompson, Doris M.
II. Title.
HF5549.A2N27   no. 147 658.382 55-1094 ‡

PPCuP OCU AAP
NN   0054213   DLC CoU IaU ViU DI DNLM NIC OOxM NB

National Industrial Conference Board.
Company medical and health programs ₁by Ethel M.
Spears, Division of Personnel Administration₎ New York
₁1948₎

72 p. illus. 28 cm. (*Its* Conference Board reports. Studies in
personnel policy, no. 96)
Cover title.

1. Industrial hygiene. 2. Labor and laboring classes—Medical care.
I. Spears, Ethel M.   II. Title.   (Series: National Industrial Confer-
ence Board. Conference Board reports. Series: National Industrial
Conference Board. Studies in personnel policy, no. 96)
HF5549.A2N27 no. 96 331.822   48-11539*

NN   0054214   DLC IaU NNC-M PPT ViU OC1JC

National Industrial Conference Board.
Company military leave policies ₁by John J. Speed, Division of Personnel Administration₎ New York ₁1951₎

40 p. diagrs. 28 cm. (*Its* Conference Board reports. Studies
in personnel policy, no. 114)
Cover title.

1. Leave of absence.   I. Speed, John Joseph, 1923–   II. Title.
(Series: National Industrial Conference Board. Studies in personnel
policy, no. 114)
HF5549.A2N27 no. 114   658.3816   51-4907

NN   0054215   DLC IaU AAP CoU

National industrial conference board.
... Company organization charts ... New York, N. Y., National industrial conference board, inc. ₁1944₎

cover-title, 28 p. diagrs. 28 x 22 cm. (*Its* Conference board
reports)
Studies in personnel policy, no. 64.
Pages 18-28 folded.

1. Corporations—U. S.   I. Title.
HF5549.A2N27 no. 64 .   658.16   44—7252

NN   0054216   DLC ViU OC1U IaU

National Industrial Conference Board.
Company organization charts. ₁By Geneva Seybold, Division of Personnel Administration. New York, 1953₎

137 p. illus. 29 x 44 cm. (*Its* Conference Board reports. Studies
in personnel policy, no. 139)

1. Corporations—U. S.   I. Title.

HF5549.A2N27 no. 139   658.16   53–4524 ‡

OOxM NIC ViU
NN   0054217   DLC IaU CoU OCU CaBVa IdPI NBuG NIC

National Industrial Conference Board.
Company-paid sick leave and supplements to workmen's
compensation ₁by Harland Fox, Division of Personnel Ad-
ministration₎ New York ₁1954₎

27 p. tables. 28 cm. (*Its* Conference Board reports. Studies in
personnel policy, no. 146)
Cover title.

1. Sick leave—U. S.   I. Fox, Harland.   II. Title.   (Series:
National Industrial Conference Board. Studies in personnel policy,
no. 146)
HF5549.A2N27 no. 146   658.3252   55-208

NN   0054218   DLC OCU CoU ViU OOxM PPCuP DI AAP IaU

National industrial conference board.
... Company pension plans and the amended Social security
act, complete texts and digests. New York, National industrial
conference board, inc. ₁*1940₎

cover-title, 51 p. 28ᶜᵐ. (The Conference board management record
supplements. Research memorandum, no. 4, July 1940)

1. Old age pensions—U. S.   I. Title.
42-18037
Library of Congress   HD7106.U5N17
₁2₎   331.254430973

NN   0054219   DLC MB UU PSt ViU OU OO OrU LU

National Industrial Conference Board.
Company pension plans and the Social security act. New
York ₁1939₎

46 p. illus. 28 cm. (Studies in personnel policy, supplement to
the Conference Board Management record, no. 16)

1. Old age pensions—U. S.   I. Title.
HF5549.A2N27 no. 16   331.252   55-49251 ‡

NN   0054220   DLC InU IaU NIC

National Industrial Conference Board.
Company policies on donations. New York, ₁1945–

v. forms, tables. 28 cm. (*Its* Conference Board reports.
Studies in business policy, 7, 49, 89
Cover title.
Vol. 3 has title: Company contributions.
Vol. 1 by Helen A. Winselman ; v. 2–   by John H. Watson, III.

1. Corporations—Charitable contributions—U. S.   I. Winselman,
Helen A.   II. Watson, John H.   III. Title.   IV. Title: Company contributions.   (Series: National Industrial Conference Board. Studies
in business policy, no. 7 ₁etc.₎)
HF5006.N3 no. 7, etc.   658.15   58–3450

ViU InU INS NB LU
NN   0054221   DLC FMU AAP DAU OU MH-BA MiEM CoU

National industrial conference board.
... Company policies on military service and war jobs ...
New York, National industrial conference board, inc. ₁1943₎

cover-title, 28 p. 28 x 21½ᶜᵐ. (*Its* Conference board reports)
Studies in personnel policy, no. 52.

1. Employment management. 2. Labor and laboring classes—U. S.—
1914–   3. U. S.—Army—Recruiting, enlistment, etc.—World war,
1939–   I. Title.
43-6782
Library of Congress   HF5549.A2N27 no. 52
₁5₎   (658.3) 658.32

NN   0054222   DLC CoU IaU ViU

National Industrial Conference Board.
... Company policies regarding military ab-
sences. New York, N. Y., The Conference board
Management research division ₁1940?₎

4 p.   28 cm.   (*Its* Defense memorandum
no. 1)
Caption title.
Reproduced from type-written copy.
"Not for publication".
1. Employment management. 2. Wages - U. S.

NN   0054223   CU

HF5549
.A2N27   **National Industrial Conference Board.**
no.44   Company policies regarding military and
1942   civilian war service. New York ₁1942₎

24 p. 28cm. (*Its* Studies in personnel
policy, no. 44)
Cover title.

1. Employment management. 2. Labor and laboring
classes—U. S.—1914–   3. U. S.—Army—
Recruiting, enlistment, etc.—World War, 1939–
1945. I. Ser.

NN   0054224   ViU

National Industrial Conference Board.
Company programs of executive development ₁by Stephen
Habbe, Division of Personnel Administration₎ New York
₁1950₎

64 p. illus. 28 cm. (*Its* Conference Board reports. Studies in
personnel policy, no. 107)
Cover title.

1. Executives. 2. Employees, Training of.   I. Habbe, Stephen,
1903–   II. Title.   (Series: National Industrial Conference
Board. Studies in personnel policy, no. 107)
HF5549.A2N27 no. 107   658.3124   51–377

NN   0054225   DLC IaU AAP CoU

National Industrial Conference Board.
Company rules, aids to teamwork. ₁By Geneva Seybold,
Division of Personnel Administration₎ New York ₁1948₎

56 p. illus. 28 cm. (*Its* Conference Board reports. Studies in
personnel policy, no. 95)
Cover title.

1. Employment management.   I. Seybold, Geneva, 1900–   II.
Title.   (Series: National Industrial Conference Board. Conference
Board reports. Series: National Industrial Conference Board. Stud-
ies in personnel policy, no. 95)
HF5549.A2N27 no. 95 658.314   48–9987*

NN   0054226   DLC AAP PPT ViU OC1JC

National Industrial Conference Board.
Company-sponsored foundations ₁by John H. Watson III,
Division of Business Practices₎ New York ₁1955₎

80 p. forms. 28 cm. (*Its* Conference Board reports. Studies in
business policy, no. 73)
Cover title.

1. Endowments—U. S. 2. Corporations—Charitable contributions—
U. S.   I. Watson, John H.   II. Title.   (Series: National Industrial Conference Board. Studies in business policy, no. 73)

HF5006.N3 no. 73   361.7   55-2155

NN   0054227   DLC NIC LU NB AAP Wa DI OU

National Industrial Conference Board.
Company tax administration

see under

National Industrial Conference Board. Division
of Business Practices.

VOLUME 407

National industrial conference board.
  ... Company vacation plans. New York, National industrial conference board ₁1939₎

cover-title, 1 p. l., 18 p. 28ᶜᵐ. (*Its* Conference board management research memoranda. No. 1)

"The current vacation plans of 13 companies ... selected to supplement the six complete plans included in the appendix of the Conference board Studies in personnel policy, no. 13, 'Developments in company vacation plans,' published in April, 1939."—Foreword.

  1. Vacations, Employee—U. S.   2. Retail trade—U. S.   I. Title.
                                                     41–19042
Library of Congress   HD5261.N28
           ₍a44c1₎   331.8160073

  NN   0054229   DLC UU OrU OU

National industrial conference board.
  ... Company plans, 1940. New York, National industrial conference board, inc. ₁1940₎

cover-title, 11 p. 28 x 21½ᶜᵐ. (*Its* Research memorandum no. 5, July, 1940)

The Conference board management record supplements.
"Verbatim statements ... from representative companies, none of which had plans included in the Conference board management research memorandum no. 1, issued in May, 1939."—Foreword.

  1. Vacations, Employee—U. S.
                                                    43–16871
Library of Congress   HD5261.N28 1940
          ₍a44c1₎   331.816

  NN   0054230   DLC ViU MB OrU OU

National industrial conference board
Comparative expenditures for living in the United States. A statement of the method used in constructing the index numbers. ₁1926₎
4 l.

Typewritten.

  NN   0054231   OCl

National Industrial Conference Board.
  Compensating expatriates for the cost of living abroad. ₁By J. Frank Gaston, Division of Business Economics, and John Napier, Statistical Division₎ New York ₁1955₎

48 p. illus. 28 cm. (*Its* Conference Board reports. Studies in labor statistics, no. 14)

Cover title.

  1. Americans in foreign countries. 2. Wages. 3. Cost and standard of living. I. Gaston, J. Frank. II. Title. (Series: National Industrial Conference Board. Studies in labor statistics, no. 14)

  HD4906.N28   658.32   55–1897

  NN   0054232   DLC NB ViU NcD DI OOxM

National Industrial Conference Board.
  Compensation and duties of corporate directors
    see under Dickson, Paul W

National Industrial Conference Board.
  Compensation and pensions for executives. ₁By Thomas A. Fitzgerald, Statistical Division₎ New York ₁1950₎

52 p. tables. 28 cm. (*Its* Conference Board reports. Studies in personnel policy, no. 111)

Cover title.

  1. Executives—Salaries, pensions, etc.—U. S. 2. Old age pensions—U. S. I. Fitzgerald, Thomas A., 1907– II. Title. (Series: National Industrial Conference Board. Studies in personnel policy, no. 111)

  HF5549.A2N27 no. 111   331.2858   51—2150

  NN   0054234   DLC ViU CoU AAP

National Industrial Conference Board.
  Compensation of executives
    see under Fitzgerald, Thomas A., 1907–

National industrial conference board.
  The competitive position of coal in the United States. New York, National industrial conference board, inc., 1931.

xvi, 288 p. illus. (maps) diagrs. 23½ᶜᵐ.

"The present volume has been prepared by Walter H. Voskuil and A. G. White and assistants."—Pref.

  1. Coal trade—U. S.   I. Voskuil, Walter Henry, 1892–   II. White, Alfred G. III. Title.
                                                   32—26249
Library of Congress   HD5545.N3
——— Copy 2.
Copyright A 48875   ₍40n1₎   338.2

              DL OCl OO ViU CU MtBC FTaSU
  NN   0054236   DLC ICJ MtU IdU WaS OrCS OrU NcD MB

National industrial conference board.
  The competitive position of coal in the United States. New York, National industrial conference board, inc., 1931 ₋c1932₎

xvi, 288 p. illus. (maps) diagrs. 23½ᶜᵐ. (Studies of international economic problems)

"The present volume has been prepared by Walter H. Voskuil and A. G. White and assistants."—Pref.

  NN   0054237   OU FMU

National industrial conference board.
  Compulsory sickness compensation for New York state, proposals, alternatives, costs. Prepared for the Associated industries of New York state, inc. New York, National industrial conference board, inc. ₁1947₎

vi p., 1 l., 184 p. incl. tables, diagrs. 28½ x 22½ᶜᵐ.
Bibliographical foot-notes.

  1. Insurance, Health—New York (State)   I. Associated industries of New York state, inc. II. Title.
  HD7102.U5N65   331.25442   47–4240

              ICJ ICU MB MH
  NN   0054238   DLC WaSp CU TU WaS OrP IdU NcD N TxU

National Industrial Conference Board.
  Computing the cost of fringe benefits. ₁By Harold Stieglitz, Division of Personnel Administration₎ New York ₁1952₎

56 p. illus. 28 cm. (*Its* Conference Board reports. Studies in personnel policy, no. 128)

Cover title.

  1. Non-wage payments. I. Stieglitz, Harold. II. Title. III. Title: Fringe benefits. (Series: National Industrial Conference Board. Studies in personnel policy, no. 128)

  HF5549.A2N27 no. 128   658.32   53—280

  NN   0054239   DLC CoU IaU OCU AAP MoSU-C ViU

National industrial conference board.
  Conciliation and arbitration in New Zealand ... Boston, Mass., National industrial conference board, ᵒ1919.

vii, 46 p. 23ᶜᵐ. (*Its* Research report, no. 23)

  I. Arbitration, Industrial—New Zealand. I. Title.
  Library of Congress   HD5630.N61N3
                                         20—6071

              MiU ICJ MB ViU MtBC WaTC NcD
  NN   0054240   DLC WaWW WaS OrU Or CU NcRS NcD OO OCU

National industrial conference board.

Business men's commission on agriculture.
  The condition of agriculture in the United States and measures for its improvement; a report by the Business men's commission on agriculture. New York city, National industrial conference board, inc.; Washington, D. C., Chamber of commerce of the United States of America, 1927.

National industrial conference board.
  Conference board bulletin. v. ₁1₎–13, no. 10; Jan. 1927–May 24, 1939. New York, 1927–39.

13 v. in   maps, tables, diagrs. 28½ cm.
Monthly, 1927–Oct. 1936; irregular, Oct. 20, 1936–May 1939.
Caption title.
Issues for 1927–32 (no. 1–72) without volume numbers but they constitute v. 1–6.
Supersedes its Industrial-economic conditions in the United States. Bulletin.
Feb. 1930–Mar. 1933 accompanied by separately paged supplements which were later issued independently as Conference board business survey.
Continued in its Conference board economic record. Cf. Union list of serials.

  1. U. S.—Econ.   condit.—Period.   I. Title.
  HC106.3.N22   49—58760

              NN NBuG ICU GEU WaS OrU MtU NhD
  NN   0054242   DLC NNU-W NNC MB DFT MiU ICJ PPT OO

National industrial conference board.
  The conference board business record. v. 1–
Jan. 1944–   New York ₁1944–

v. illus. (diagrs.) 28 cm. monthly.

Vols. 1–2 called "Wartime edition."
Vol. 1, no. 1–5 prepared by the board's Division of industrial economics; v. 1, no. 6–   by the Division of business practices and other divisions of the board.

  1. U. S.—Econ. condit.—Period.   I. Title.
  HC101.N316   330.973   47— 2734

       KyU NcU GEU FM MnU MtU MH-BA
  FTaSU KPT GU TxDaM GAT OAkU KU IaU CU-Riv NjR
  MtBC ICJ NNC WaS OrP MB CU NBuG ICU TxHR IaU TxLT
  TxU NN ICJ MtU MH OrU OrCS WaSp CaBVa CaBVaU LNL
  NN   0054243   DLC IU OClW DNAL TxU Vi FTaSU TU NcD

National industrial conference board.
  Conference board business survey. no. 38–73, Feb. 25, 1930–Jan. 20, 1933; v. 7, no. 2–v. 13, no. 5, Feb. 20, 1933–May 24, 1939. New York, 1930–39.

36 nos. and 7 v. tables, diagrs. 28½ᶜᵐ. monthly.
1930–Mar. 1933 issued as supplements to Conference board bulletin no. 38–73, taking their numbering from the bulletin. Nos. 38–72 bound with the bulletin. HC 106.3.N22 no. 38–72.
Title varies: 1930–31, Conference board bulletin ... Supplement. 1932, The business survey.
1933–39, Conference board business survey.
Superseded by its Conference board economic record. cf. Union list of serials.
L. C. set incomplete: v. 11–13 wanting.

  1. U. S.—Econ. condit.—   2. U. S.—Indus. I. Title.
  II. Title: The business sur-   vey. III. National industrial conference board.   Conference   board bulletin. Supplement.
  1918.   44–51878
  Library of Congress   HC106.3.N222   330.973
                 ₍3₎

       MH-BA ICU OCU NN ICJ MiU PU-BZ NBuG
  NN   0054244   DLC IU PBL NhD NIC OO OCU OrU OCl

National Industrial Conference Board.
  The Conference Board Economic Forum presents: Defense economics—CEA model. Solomon Fabricant, discussion leader, Jules Backman ₁and others₎. New York, 1951₎

80 p. 23 cm. (*Its* Studies in business economics, no. 29)

Cover title.

  1. U. S.—Economic policy. 2. Inflation (Finance)—U. S. I. Fabricant, Solomon, 1906– II. Title: Defense economics—CEA model. (Series)

  HB31.N33 no. 29   338.973   51–6118

  NN   0054245   DLC IaU CoU NN DAU CLU TxU MoU

National Industrial Conference Board.
  The Conference Board Economic Forum presents: Price control in a defense economy. Richard B. Heflebower, discussion leader, Jules Backman ₁and others₎. New York, 1950₎

64 p. diagrs. 23 cm. (*Its* Studies in business economics, no. 26)

Cover title.

  1. Price regulation—U. S. I. Heflebower, Richard Brooks, 1903– II. Title: Price control in a defense economy. (Series)

  HB31.N33 no. 26   338.526   51–870

  NN   0054246   DLC CLU IaU TxU NN

VOLUME 407

National Industrial Conference Board.
The Conference Board Economic Forum presents: Pros and cons of Council of Economic Advisers' policies. A. D. H. Kaplan, discussion leader ₁and others₎ New York, 1950₎

95 p. 23 cm. (*Its* Studies in business economics, no. 25)

Cover title.
Bibliography: p. ₁8₎

1. U. S. Council of Economic Advisers. 2. U. S.—Economic policy. ɪ. Kaplan, Abraham David Hannath, 1893– ɪɪ. Title: Pros and cons of Council of Economic Advisers' policies. (Series)

HB31.N33 no. 25   338.973   51–414

NN   0054247   DLC IaU RPJCB TxU NN

National Industrial Conference Board.
The Conference Board Economic Forum presents: Shall we return to a gold standard—now? ₁By₎ Murray Shields ₁and others₎ New York, 1954₎

167 p. illus. 23 cm. (*Its* Studies in business economics, no. 43)

Cover title.

1. Currency question—U. S. 2. Gold standard. ɪ. Shields, Murray. ɪɪ. Title: Shall we return to a gold standard—now? (Series)

HB31.N33 no. 43   332.422   54–2634

PPCuP OOxM NcC ViU PV NN OU DI OrLgE
NN   0054248   DLC CaBVa IaU DAU Wa TxU NcD PSt OCU

National Industrial Conference Board.
The Conference Board Economic Forum presents: The Council of Economic Advisers, retrospect and prospect ₁by₎ Jules Blackman ₁and others₎ New York, 1953₎

64 p. 23 cm. (*Its* Studies in business economics, no. 38)

Cover title.

1. U. S. Council of Economic Advisers. 2. U. S.—Economic policy. ɪ. Backman, Jules, 1910– (Series)

HB31.N33 no. 38   338.973   53—2319

NN   0054249   DLC TxU NcD OOxM OCU MH–BA NIC OU IaU

National Industrial Conference Board.
The Conference Board Economic Forum presents: The economics of consumer debt ₁by₎ John M. Chapman ₁and others₎ New York, 1955₎

84 p. illus. 23 cm. (*Its* Studies in business economics, no. 50)

Cover title.
Bibliographical footnotes.

1. Loans, Personal—U. S. ɪ. Chapman, John Martin, 1887– ɪɪ. Title: The economics of consumer debt. (Series)

HB31.N33 no. 50   *332.35 332.743   56—507

OCU PPCuP DI OU MH–BA NcD PPT NN
NN   0054250   DLC CaBVaU WaTC OrPS IaU IU TxU OOxM

National Industrial Conference Board.
The Conference Board Economic Forum presents: The economics of tariffs ₁by₎ Jules Backman ₁and others₎ New York, 1953₎

107 p. diagrs. 23 cm. (*Its* Studies in business economics, no. 40)

Cover title.

1. Tariff. ɪ. Backman, Jules, 1910– ɪɪ. Title: The economics of tariffs. (Series)

HB31.N33 no. 40   337   53–3280

ViU PPD NcD TxU
NN   0054251   DLC CoU DAU IaU OU NN NcC PP PSt

National Industrial Conference Board.
The Conference Board Economic Forum presents: The fair trade question ₁by₎ Walter Adams ₁and others₎ New York, 1955₎

112 p. 23 cm. (*Its* Studies in business economics, no. 48)

Cover title.
Bibliographical footnotes.

1. Price maintenance—U. S.   ɪ. Title: The fair trade question. (Series)

HB31.N33 no. 48   *338.522   56–80

MH–BA NIC NcD CtY-L NN PSt ViU TxU OOxM OCU
NN   0054252   DLC IaU CaBVaU WaWW CaBVa Wa DI OU

National Industrial Conference Board. The Conference Board economic record
see **American affairs; the economic record.**

National Industrial Conference Board.
Conference board folder; graphic business trends; current business opinion, July, 1939 - August, 1939. New York, 1939.
1 v.

NN   0054254   DAL PU-BZ

National industrial conference board.
Conference board industry charts. Monthly supplement to quarterly industry reports. Automobiles, chemicals, construction, electricity and gas, fuels, iron and steel, machinery, non-ferrous metals, railroads, textiles.

New York, 19
v. 28¼ᶜᵐ.

Reproduced from type-written copy.

1. U. S.—Indus.   ɪ. Quarterly review of the automobile industry. Supplement. ɪɪ. Quarterly review of the chemical industry. Supplement. ɪɪɪ. Quarterly review of the construction industry. Supplement. ɪv. Quarterly review of the electricity and gas industries. Supplement. v. Quarterly review of the fuel industries. Supplement. vɪ. Quarterly review of the iron and steel industry. Supplement. vɪɪ. Quarterly review of the machinery industries. Supplement. vɪɪɪ. Quarterly review of the copper, lead and zinc industries. Supplement. ɪx. Quarterly review of the railroad industry. Supplement. x. Quarterly review of the textile industry. Supplement.

Library of Congress   HC101.N318   45–53626
          ₁3₎   338.05

NN   0054256   DLC PU-Z

National Industrial Conference Board.
The conference board industry record
see under   **National Industrial Conference Board. Division of Industrial Economics.**

National Industrial Conference Board.
Conference Board information service: Domestic affairs series.
Memorandum no. 1–

New York, 1933–
nos.   28½ cm.

Irregular.
Reproduced from typewritten copy (nos. 1–2, 4, 9–10, 14, 16, 18, 35, 37, 39–40 are photostat reproductions).
Title varies slightly.
Contents:
no. 1. Depreciated currencies and commodity imports.   March 3, 1933.
no. 2. The general price situation.   March 20, 1933.
no. 3. The Appalachian coals case: a brief interpretation.   April 7, 1933.
no. 4. Federal restriction of working hours as an unemployment remedy.   April 21, 1933.
no. 5. The gold standard: recent developments and present status.   May 5, 1933.
no. 6. Industry's attitude toward the price situation.   May 22, 1933.
no. 7. The National industrial recovery act: formulation of codes of fair competition.   June 21, 1933.
no. 8. The National industrial recovery act: organization of industry for the administration of the act in the light of German cartel experience.   July 7, 1933.
no. 9. The National industrial recovery act: the cost of living and the minimum wage.   July 14, 1933.
no. 10. The National industrial recovery act: tax provisions of the act.   Aug. 4, 1933.

Continued in next column

Continued from preceding column

no. 11. The National industrial recovery act: analysis of approved codes.   Aug. 28, 1933.
no. 12. Income taxes and the depression.   Sept. 15, 1933.
no. 13. National recovery and dollar depreciation.   Sept. 29, 1933.
no. 14. National industrial recovery act: supplementary analysis of approved codes.   Oct. 13, 1933.
no. 15. Some aspects of price adjustments.   Nov. 6, 1933.
no. 16. Statistical and reporting requirements of N. R. A.   1933.
no. 17, 19, 21, 23, 25–26. National reconstruction and recovery program: administration financing. Part 1–6.   Dec. 4, 1933–April 5, 1934.
no. 18. National industrial recovery act: production and price control under codes of fair competition.   1933.
no. 19. See no. 17.
no. 20. Wage differentials: analysis of prior conditions and code requirements.   Jan. 5, 1934.
no. 21. See no. 17.
no. 22. The present state of the federal finances.   Feb. 7, 1934.
no. 23. See no. 17.
no. 24. New capital issues, 1933.   March 23, 1934.
no. 25–26. See no. 17.
no. 27. Legal aspects of the N. R. A. code system.   April 12, 1934.
no. 28. National Recovery Administration: text of general orders.   April 14, 1934.
no. 29. Present status of unemployment insurance or reserves legislation.   April 24, 1934.
no. 30. Employees in government service.   May 11, 1934.
no. 31. Changes in the cost of living, January, 1933, to March, 1934.   May 16, 1934.
no. 32. Employment, hours, and earnings, January, 1933, to March, 1934.   May 28, 1934.
no. 33. The Revenue act of 1934.   June 8, 1934.
no. 34. Cost of code administration under the N. R. A.   June 11, 1934.
no. 35. Governmental debt of the United States and European countries.   July 12, 1934.
no. 36. Federal finances in the fiscal year 1934.   Sept. 27, 1934.
no. 37. Dollar values of production of goods and construction, 1914–1933.   ₁1934₎
no. 38. A digest of the economic security program. 1935.
no. 39. The federal debt and the banks.   1935.
no. 40. The Townsend old age pension plan.   ₁cop. 1935₎

NN   0054264   NN DL

National Industrial Conference Board.
Conference Board information service: Domestic affairs. Special memorandum no. ₁1₎–

New York, 1934–   28½ cm.
nos.

Nos. 1–3 lack series title and numbering.
Reproduced from typewritten copy.
Contents:
no. 1. When did recovery begin?   Oct. 24, 1934.
no. 2. Questions regarding application of Securities exchange act to industrial corporations, their officers, directors, and security holders.   Sept. 4, 1934.
no. 3. Special memorandum for members, councillors, and associates of the Conference Board: Federal governmental departments or agencies and number of federal employees.   1934₎
no. 4. The banking bill of 1935.   April 2, 1935.
no. 5. The proposed tax on "bigness."   April 2, 1935.
no. 6. The Public utility holding company bill.   April 2, 1935.
no. 7. Amendments of the Agricultural adjustment act.   April 2, 1935.
no. 8. The proposed revision of the N. I. R. A. and the Wagner National labor relations bill.   April 24, 1935.
no. 9. The revised Economic security bill.   April 24, 1935.
no. 10. Federal legislation in 1935.   Oct. 9, 1935.

NN   0054267   NN DL OCU

National industrial conference board.
Conference board information service: Foreign affairs. Memorandum.
no. 1

₁New York₎ 1933   28½ cm.
nos.

Irregular.
No. 1, (reproduction).   reproduced from typewritten copy (no.   photostat
Feb. 17,   has title: Foreign affairs information service. Memorandum.

1. Economic history—Per. and —Per. and soc. publ.—U. S.   soc. publ.—U. S. 2. World politics
N. Y. P. L.   July 31, 1939

NN   0054268   NN DL OCl

National Industrial Conference Board.
Conference board information service: Foreign affairs series
see its   **Notes on foreign conditions.**

331.05   **National Industrial Conference Board.**
NAI   Conference board management record. 1–25. Jan. 1939–Mar. 1963.
New York.
25v. illus., tables. 28cm. monthly.

Title varies: 1939–47, Feb. 1949–Aug. 1951, The Conference board management record.– 1948– Jan. 1949, The conference board personnel management record.

FMU MnU NcD ScU MtU DNAL DBB
NN   0054270   IU CoD OrCS KyU Vi FTaSU OAkU NjR

VOLUME 407

National Industrial Conference Board.
  Conference board management research memo-
randum
      see
National Industrial Conference Board.
  Management research memorandum.

National industrial conference board.
  The Conference board, 1916–1941; the fact-tool builder for
American business. New York, National industrial conference
board, inc. ₁1941₎
  64 p. incl. front., illus. (incl. ports., map; part col.) diagrs. 25½ x 21ᶜᵐ.

  1. National industrial conference board.

  Library of Congress   HC106.3.N244   42–51933
                         ₁₄₎   658.06273

NN   0054272   DLC OrP ICJ IU OU OCl OCU

National Industrial Conference Board.
  Conference board personnel management
record
      see its   Conference board management.
record.

National Industrial Conference Board.
  The Conference Board presents a symposium on America's
mineral resource position. Participants: chairman, Ralph J.
Watkins, Richard J. Lund ₁and others₎ New York ₁1948₎
  40 p. maps, diagrs. 23 cm. (*Its* Studies in business economics,
no. 18)
  Cover title.
  CONTENTS.—Chairman's remarks.—Aluminum and magnesium, by
I. W. Wilson.—Copper, lead and zinc, by S. D. Strauss.—Lesser-known
metals and minerals, by R. J. Lund.—Canada's resources, by G. C.
Monture.

  1. Mines and mineral resources—U. S.   I. Title: America's mineral resource position.   (Series)

    HB31.N33 no. 18   338.272   48–11038*

NN   0054274   DLC IaU MU CLU ICU ICJ OCl MH TxU

National Industrial Conference Board.
  The Conference Board presents a symposium on
Should we return to a gold standard? Panel
participants: chairman, Philip Cortney ₁and
others₎ ₁New York, 1948₎
  52 p.   (Its Studies in business economics,
no. 17)

  Cover-title.

NN   0054275   MH-BA NN

National Industrial Conference Board.
  The Conference Board presents Air raid
protection in industry (European experience
in World War II) a forum. Richard L. ⁿᵒDavies,
Chairman. ₁New York, 1951?₎
  61 l.

  Cover title.

NN   0054276   MiD

National Industrial Conference Board.
  The Conference Board presents An appraisal of official
economic reports; an evening with the economists. Around
the table: Rufus S. Tucker, discussion leader, Julius Backman ₁and others₎ New York, 1948₎
  70 p. diagr. 23 cm. (Its Studies in business economics, no. 16)
  Cover title.
  A review by the Conference Board Economic Forum of the economic content of the reports of the Council of Economic Advisers to
the President. cf. p. 5.
  1. U. S.—Economic policy. 2. U. S. Council of Economic Advisers.
I. Tucker, Rufus Stickney, 1890–   II. Title: An appraisal of official
economic reports.   (Series)

    HB31.N33 no. 16   338.973   48–7344*

NN   0054277   DLC MiEM NN MoU MiU IaU TxU MH

National Industrial Conference Board.
  The Conference Board presents Behavior of wages, by
Jules Backman and M. R. Gainsbrugh. ₁New York, 1948₎
  96 p. diagrs. 23 cm. (*Its* Studies in business economics, no. 15)
  Cover title.
  Bibliographical footnotes.

  1. Wages—U. S.   I. Backman, Jules, 1910–   II. Gainsbrugh,
Martin Reuben, 1908–   III. Title: Behavior of wages.   (Series)

    HB31.N33 no. 15   331.2973   48–6664*

NN   0054278   DLC MiEM IaU FMU TxU MH OU

National Industrial Conference Board.
  The Conference Board presents Britain's economic crisis,
by Donald F. Heatherington. ₁New York, 1947₎
  28 p. diagrs. 23 cm. (*Its* Studies in business economics, no. 12)
  Cover title.

  1. Gt. Brit.—Econ. condit.—1945–   I. Heatherington, Donald
F. II. Title: Britain's economic crisis. III. Series.

    HB31.N33 No. 12   330.942   48–2513*

NN   0054279   DLC MiEM IaU TxU MH

National Industrial Conference Board.
  The Conference Board presents Credit policy: recent
European experience, by Per Jacobsson. What monetary
policy for the United States? A round table discussion, John
S. Sinclair, chairman. ₁New York, 1952₎
  48 p. 23 cm. (*Its* Studies in business economics, no. 33)

  1. Credit—Europe. 2. Currency question—Europe. 3. Currency
question—U. S.   I. Jacobsson, Per, 1894–   II. Title: Credit
policy : recent European experience.   (Series)

    HB31.N33 no. 33   332   52–1702 ‡

        NcD MH–BA NN
NN   0054280   DLC DAU IaU CoU MoU PSt TxU NIC

National industrial conference board.
  The Conference board presents Deflation or inflation? By
Jules Backman and M. R. Gainsbrugh ... ₁New York, 1946₎
  cover-title, 79 p. incl. tables, diagrs. 23ᶜᵐ. (*Its* Studies in business
economics, no. 3)

  1. Inflation (Finance)—U. S.   I. Backman, Jules, 1910–   II.
Gainsbrugh, Martin Reuben, 1908–   III. Title: Deflation or inflation?

                                          46–4180
  Library of Congress   HB31.N33 no. 3
                         ₁₆₎   (330.82)   332.414

NN   0054281   DLC DAU IaU MB OOxM TxU MiEM ViU

National Industrial Conference Board.
  The Conference Board presents Dividend policy and tax
problems; a symposium on Section 102, Internal revenue
code. Participants, chairman: J. K. Lasser; Maurice Austin
₁and others₎ New York, 1947₎
  35 p. 23 cm. (*Its* Studies in business economics, no. 10)
  Cover title.

  1. Corporations—U. S.—Finance. 2. Corporations—U. S.—Taxation.   I. Lasser, Jacob Kay, 1896–   II. Title: Dividend policy
and tax problems. III. Title: Internal revenue code.   (Series)

    HB31.N33 no. 10   658.15   48–10032*

NN   0054282   DLC IaU MiEM ViU OOxM NN MH-BA TxU

National Industrial Conference Board.
  The Conference Board presents Effects of depreciation
policy, by J. Frank Gaston. ₁New York, 1950₎
  63 p. illus. 23 cm. (*Its* Studies in business economics, no. 22)
  Cover title.

  1. Depreciation.   I. Gaston, J. Frank. II. Title: Effects of depreciation policy.   (Series)

    HB31.N33 no. 22   657   50–7569

NN   0054283   DLC InU TxU NN

National industrial conference board.
  The Conference board presents Full employment and scarcity; an evening with the economists ... ₁New York, 1946₎
  cover-title, 44 p. 23ᶜᵐ. (Studies in business economics, no. 6)

  1. U. S.—Economic policy. 2. Unemployed—U. S.

  HB31.N33 no. 6   338.973   47–3407
                                     Brief cataloging

NN   0054284   DLC IaU NN MB TxU

National Industrial Conference Board.
  The Conference Board presents the business outlook for
1947; an evening with the economists. Around the table:
Milton Gilbert, discussion leader, O. Glenn Saxon ₁and
others. New York, 1946₎
  52 p. diagrs. 23 cm. (*Its* Studies in business economics, no. 7)
  Cover title.

  1. U. S.—Econ. condit.—1945–   I. Gilbert, Milton, 1900–
II. Title: The business outlook for 1947.   (Series)

    HB31.N33 No. 7   330.973   48–10195*

NN   0054285   DLC OOxM CtY MiEM PPLas NcD MB TxU

National Industrial Conference Board.
  The Conference Board presents The business outlook for
1948; an evening with the economists. Around the table:
Lionel D. Edie, discussion leader, Jules Backman ₁and others.
New York, 1947₎
  44 p. 23 cm. (*Its* Studies in business economics, no. 14)
  Cover title.

  1. U. S.—Econ. condit.—1945–   I. Edie, Lionel Danforth,
1893–   II. Title: The business outlook for 1948.   (Series)

    HB31.N33 no. 14   330.973   48–10034*

NN   0054286   DLC MiEM OrU MH-BA NN TxU OOxM

National industrial conference board.
  The Conference board presents The crisis of the free market, by F. A. Harper ... ₁New York, 1945₎
  cover-title, 83 p. diagrs. 23 cm. (*Its* Studies in business economics, no. 2)

  1. Price regulation—U. S.   I. Harper, Floyd Arthur, 1905–
II. Title: The crisis of the free market.

                                          46–4179
  Library of Congress   HB31.N33 no. 2
                         ₁a50h1₎   (330.82)   338.526

NN   0054287   DLC IaU WaS MtBC MB TxU

National Industrial Conference Board.
  The Conference Board presents The "miracle" of productivity; an evening with the economists. Around the table:
Solomon Fabricant, discussion leader, Jules Backman ₁and
others. New York, 1947₎
  cover-title, 48 p. 23 cm. (*Its* Studies in business economics, no. 9)
  Bibliography: p. 48.

  1. U. S.—Indus.   I. Fabricant, Solomon, 1906–   II. Title:
The "miracle" of productivity.   (Series)

    HB31.N33 no. 9   338   47—5689*

NN   0054288   DLC IaU NN MB TxU DAU

National Industrial Conference Board.
  The Conference Board presents The need for Federal tax
revision; an evening with the economists. Around the
table: Roswell Magill, discussion leader, Jules Backman ₁and
others. New York, 1947₎
  64 p. 23 cm. (*Its* Studies in business economics, no. 11)
  Cover title.

  1. Taxation—U. S.   I. Magill, Roswell Foster, 1895–   II. Title:
The need for Federal tax revision.   (Series)

    HB31.N33 no. 11   336.2   47–11665*

NN   0054289   DLC MiEM ViU CLU MU IaU MH-BA TxU NN

VOLUME 407

National Industrial Conference Board.
The Conference Board presents The price problem reexamined; an evening with the economists. Around the table: Martin R. Gainsbrugh, discussion leader, Jules Backman ₁and others₁ New York, 1947₁

48 p. diagrs. 23 cm. (*Its* Studies in business economics, no. 13)
Cover title.

1. Prices—U. S.   I. Gainsbrugh, Martin Reuben, 1908–   II. Title: The price problem reexamined.   (Series)

HB31.N33 no. 13   338.52   48–10031*

NN   0054290   DLC IaU MiEM MU MH NN TxU

National industrial conference board.
The Conference board presents Union health and welfare funds; a symposium on evolution and problems, operation and experience ... ₁New York, 1947₁

cover-title, 48 p. 23ᶜᵐ. (*Its* Studies in business economics, no. 8)
Half-title: Conference on union health and welfare funds, Waldorf-Astoria hotel, January 23, 1947.

1. Welfare work in industry.   I. Title: Union health and welfare funds.

HB31.N33 no. 8   331.2544   47–3646

NN   0054291   DLC IaU MU ViU RPB MH TxU

National Industrial Conference Board.
The Conference Board presents Wages during the transition period ₁by Jules Backman and M. R. Gainsbrugh. New York, 1945₁

76 p. illus. 23 cm. (*Its* Studies in business economics, no. 1)
Cover title.

1. Wages—U. S.   I. Backman, Jules, 1910–   II. Gainsbrugh, Martin Reuben, 1908–   III. Title: Wages during the transition period.   (Series)

HB31.N33 no. 1   331.2973   48–10033*

NN   0054292   DLC MH NN TxU RPB ViU IaU

National Industrial Conference Board.
The Conference Board presents What if prices were free? An evening with the economists. Around the table: Jules Backman ₁and others₁ New York, 1946₁

43 p. 23 cm. (*Its* Studies in business economics, no. 4)
Cover title.

1. Price regulation—U. S.   I. Backman, Jules, 1910–   II. Title: What if prices were free?   III. Series.

HB31.N33 no. 4   338.526   48–1867*

NN   0054293   DLC IaU NIC ViU MB NN TxU

National Industrial Conference Board.
The Conference Board presents When should wages be increased? An evening with the Economic Forum: Douglass V. Brown, discussion leader, Jules Backman ₁and others₁ New York, 1950₁

64 p. illus. 23 cm. (*Its* Studies in business economics, no. 23)
Cover title.

1. Wages. 2. Wages—U. S.   I. Brown, Douglass Vincent, 1904–   II. Title: When should wages be increased?   (Series)

HB31.N33 no. 23   331.215   51–413

NN   0054294   DLC MH–BA InU OrPR

National Industrial Conference Board.
The Conference Board presents Will the guaranteed annual wage work? An evening with the economists. Around the table: A. D. H. Kaplan, discussion leader, Joseph L. Snider ₁and others₁ New York, 1946₁

44 p. 23 cm. (*Its* Studies in business economics, no. 5)
Cover title.
"A short reading list": p. 42.

1. Wages—Annual wage.   I. Kaplan, Abraham David Hannath, 1893–   II. Title: Will the guaranteed annual wage work?   (Series)

HB31.N33 no. 5   331.23   49–3143*

NN   0054295   DLC IaU ScU MH NN RPB TxU PPT ViU

HC106.3
.N43

National Industrial Conference Board.
Conference board previews; weekly summary and announcement of Conference Board studies and discussions. ₁no.1₁–
19 –   New York, 19 –
v.   27 cm.

1. U.S.—Economic conditions—Periodicals
I. Title.

NN   0054296   TU NBuG PU–BZ DAL NNC

Z7164
.E2N28

National Industrial Conference Board. Conference Board publications, general index.

National Industrial Conference Board.
Cumulative index of NICB publications. 1950–54—
₁New York₁

National industrial conference board.
Conference board reports ... Jan. 16, 1941–
New York, National industrial conference board, inc., 1941–

v. illus. (maps) tables, diagrs. 28ᶜᵐ.
Cover-title.
Includes bibliographies.

1. U. S.—Econ. condit.—1918–   2. World war, 1939–   —Economic aspects—U. S.

Library of Congress   HC106.4.A1N3   42–14419
                                                    ₍2₎   330.973

NN   0054298   DLC WaS FTaSU NNC MB TU TxU DAL NcD NN

National industrial conference board.
Conference board service letter. no.   –409,
–Dec. 26, 1927; n. s., no. 1–96, Jan. 5, 1928–
Dec. 30, 1932; v. 6–   Jan. 30, 1933–
New York ₁19

v. in   28 cm.
Weekly,   –1927; semimonthly, 1928–30; monthly, 1931–
Publication began in 1920?
Caption title.
Title varies: –1927, Service letter.
1928–32, The service letter on industrial relations.
1933–   Conference board service letter.

Nos.   –409 "for the special information of board members and financial subscribers."
Ceased publication with n. s., v. 11 (Dec. 1938) Superseded by its Conference board management record.

1. U. S.—Econ. condit.—Period.   I. Title.   II. Title: The service letter on industrial relations.

HC106.2.N4   331   48–32540

ICJ WaS MiD OrU PBL NBuG NNU–W
NN   0054300   DLC NIC MB DL NhD OCU OCl OClFRB NN

National industrial conference board. *Conference board service letter.*
National industrial conference board.
... The cost of living in the United States in 1932, ₁New York₁ National industrial board, inc., 1933–

National industrial conference board. *Conference board service letter.*
National industrial conference board.
... Current wages in manufacturing industry in foreign countries ... New York, National industrial conference board, inc. ₁ᶜ1938₁

National industrial conference board. *Conference board service letter.*
National industrial conference board.
... Wages, hours, and employment in the United States, July, 1936–December, 1937 ... New York, National industrial conference board, inc. ₁ᶜ1938₁

National industrial conference board. *Conference board service letter.*
National industrial conference board.
Wages in the United States in 1934. ₁New York₁ National industrial conference board, inc., ᶜ1935.

National industrial conference board.
Conference board studies in enterprise and social progress; selected chapters in the story of the American enterprise system and its contribution to prosperity and public welfare, assembled from special reports of the Division of industrial economics of the Conference board. New York, National industrial conference board ₁ᶜ1939₁

xvi, 327 p. incl. tables. fold. col. front., diagrs. (part col.) 28½ cm.

CONTENTS.—Introduction: On studying the enterprise system.—I. Natural resources.—II. Population and working force.—III. Wealth and debt.—IV. National income and its distribution.—V. Consumption and standards of living.—VI. Taxation, public expenditure and debt.—VII. Prices, wages and profits. — VIII. Organization of American enterprise.—IX. Comparative economic conditions in the United States and other countries.

1. U. S.—Econ. condit.—1918–   2. U. S.—Indus. 3. Business. 4. Economic conditions—1918–1945.   I. National industrial conference board. Division of industrial economics.   II. Title.   III. Title: Studies in enterprise and social progress.   IV. Title: Enterprise and social progress.

HC106.3.N245   330.973   40–1709

CoU KMK AAP WaSp OrPR WaS MtU OrU OrCS CaBViP Wa
NN   0054306   DLC NcD OClFRB OCl OU ViU ICJ MH CU

National industrial conference board.
The consolidation of railroads in the United States ... New York, National industrial conference board ₁ᶜ1923₁

vii, 107 p. 23ᶜᵐ. (*Its* Research report, no. 56)

1. Railroads—U. S.   I. Title.

Library of Congress   HE2741.N3   23–7192

ICJ WaTC MtBC MH–BA ViU WaS OrU CaBVaU WaWW
NN   0054307   DLC CoU CU NN CtY NjP OCl OCU OU MB

690
N2134ℓ
1952

National Industrial Conference Board.
Construction and building materials: basic industrial data. ₁n.p.,₁ 1952.
1v. of tables. 28cm.

1. Construction industry—U.S. 2. Building materials industry—U.S. I. Title.

NN   0054308   IU GU

National Industrial Conference Board.
Consumer attitudes and buying plans
see under title

HB235
.U6S3

National Industrial Conference Board.
Sayre, Robert A
Consumers' prices, 1914–1948. New York, National Industrial Conference Board ₁1948₁

National Industrial Conference Board.
Consumption taxes and tax reform. ₁New York, 1953₁

88 p. 23 cm. (*Its* Studies in business economics, no. 41)

1. Taxation of articles of consumption—U. S.   I. Title.

HJ5715.U6N28   336.271   54–389 ‡

OOxM ViU NN
NN   0054311   DLC IdPI Or IaU OCU NcD TxU OU PSt

VOLUME 407

National Industrial Conference Board.
Controlling capital expenditures
see under   Watson, John H

National Industrial Conference Board.
Controls for absenteeism.   New York ₁1952₎
56 p. illus. 28 cm. (*Its* Conference Board reports. Studies in personnel policy, no. 126)
Cover title.

1. Absenteeism (Labor)   I. Title.   (Series: National Industrial Conference Board. Studies in personnel policy, no. 126)
HF5549.A2N27 no. 126   658.381   52-4051

NN   0054313   DLC CoU IaU PPT ViU OC1 MoSU-C NIC OCU

National Industrial Conference Board.
Convertibil₁i₎ty and foreign trade, by J. Frank Gaston ₁and others₎   New York, 1955, °1954₎
159 p. diagrs. 23 cm. (*Its* Studies in business economics, no. 45)

1. Commercial policy. 2. Currency convertibility.   I. Gaston, J. Frank. II. Title.   (Series)
HB31.N33 no. 45   382   55-1226

PPCuP OU NN IaU OKentU CaBVaU
NN   0054314   DLC DI OCU OEac NcD TxU OOxM MH-BA

National Industrial Conference Board.
Convertibil₁i₎ty and foreign trade, by J. Frank Gaston ₁and others₎   New York, 1955, °1954₎
159 p. diagrs. 23 cm. (*Its* Studies in business economics, no. 45)
——— Photocopy. Ann Arbor, Mich., University Microfilms, 1969. 20 cm.

HB31
.N33
no. 45
1955a

NN   0054315   OrPS

National Industrial Conference Board.
Cooperative medical programs, a new solution for small companies. ₁By Doris M. Thompson, Division of Personnel Administration₎   New York ₁1953₎
36 p. diagr. 28 cm. (*Its* Conference Board reports. Studies in personnel policy, no. 134)
Cover title.

1. Medical care, Prepaid—U. S.   I. Thompson, Doris M. II. Title.   (Series: National Industrial Conference Board. Studies in personnel policy, no. 134)
HF5549.A2N27 no. 134   658.3822   53-1885

ViU
NN   0054316   DLC AAP OCU CoU NIC OOxM OC1JC PPT

338.4
N213co   National Industrial Conference Board.
Copper: basic industrial data. ₁n.p.₎ 1951.
1 v. of tables. 28 cm.

1. Copper industry and trade. 2. Copper industry and trade—U.S.

NN   0054317   IU

National Industrial Conference Board.
The corporate directorship ₁by John H. Watson, III, Division of Business Practices₎   New York ₁1953₎
31 p. tables. 28 cm. (*Its* Conference Board reports. Studies in business policy, no. 63)
Cover title.

1. Directors of corporations—U. S.   I. Watson, John H. II. Title.   (Series: National Industrial Conference Board. Studies in business policy, no. 63)
HF5006.N3 no. 63   56-3570 rev

NN   0054318   DLC ViU MH OU LU AAP IaU CoU

National Industrial Conference Board.
Corporate legal departments.   New York ₁1950₎
31 p. diagrs., tables. 28 cm. (*Its* Conference Board reports. Studies in business policy, no. 39)
Cover title.

1: Corporate legal departments—U. S.   (Series: National Industrial Conference Board. Studies in business policy, no. 39)
HF5006.N3 no. 39   *658.16   58-45884

CoU CtY-L TxU
NN   0054319   DLC MiU-L ViU-L NNC IaU LU MH-BA PPT

National industrial conference board.
... Cost of code administration under the N. R. A. ... ₁New York₎ National industrial conference board, 1934.
cover-title, 5 numb. l. 28½ᶜᵐ. (Conference board information service: Domestic affairs series. Memorandum no. 34)
Mimeographed.

1. Budget in business. 2. U. S.—Indus.—Costs. 3. U. S. National recovery administration—Codes.   I. Title.
Library of Congress   HC106.3.N24 no. 34   34-34204
——— Copy 2.
Copyright A 72765   ₁5₎   (330.973) 330.973

NN   0054320   DLC Or NcD

National industrial conference board.
Cost of government, 1923-1934 ...   New York city, National industrial conference board, inc. ₁°1934₎
viii, 46 p. 23ᶜᵐ.

1. Finance—U. S. 2. Taxation—U. S. 3. Debts, Public—U. S. I. Title.
                                                      35-6169
Library of Congress   HJ257.N312 1923-1934
——— Copy 2.
Copyright A 78928   ₁5-5-3₎   336.73

NN   0054321   DLC CaBVaU WaS Or Wa NcD DL ViU

National industrial conference board.
Cost of government in the United States ... 1926 ₁1925₎44-1435/51. New York city, National industrial conference board, inc., 1926-33.
v. illus. (maps) tables, diagrs. 23½ cm. (*Its* Studies)
Editor: 19   L. H. Kimmel

1. Finance, Public—U. S.—1901-1933. 2. Finance, Public—U. S.—1933-   3. Taxation—U. S.   I. Kimmel, Lewis Henry, 1899-   ed. II. Title.
HJ257.N3   336.73   30-6654

NcC OO PU-PSW DAL OC1U MB NcRS CU MiU ODW MeB IU NN OC1 TU MH PPCuP DL ViU ICJ MH Wa CSt WaS CaBVaU KEmT
NN   0054322   DLC NSyU MsU NIC NcD DHEW OC1W MH-BA

National industrial conference board.
Cost of health service in industry ...   New York, National industrial conference board ₁1921₎
iii, 33 p. incl. tables, diagr. 23ᶜᵐ. (*Its* Research report, no. 37. May 1921)

1. Labor and laboring classes—Medical care. 2. Occupations—Diseases and hygiene.   I. Title.
                                                      21-14786
Library of Congress   HD7261.N34

NcD OO OC1 MiU ViU ICJ WaWW CU KU
NN   0054323   DLC WaWW WaTC WaS OrU CaBVaU CtY-M

National industrial conference board.
The cost of living among wage earners, anthracite region of Pennsylvania, February, 1922 ...   New York city, National industrial conference board ₁°1922₎
viii, 41 p. incl. map, tables. 23ᶜᵐ. (*Its* Special report, no. 21)

1. Cost of living—Pennsylvania. 2. Coal-miners—Pennsylvania.   I. Title.
                                                      22-13234
Library of Congress   HD6993.P4N3

MiU ViU MB CaBVaU WaWW PSt MtU IdU MtBC
NN   0054324   DLC PSt OrU CU NIC KMK NcRS OO OC1

National industrial conference board.
The cost of living among wage-earners, Cincinnati, Ohio, May, 1920 ...   New York, National industrial conference board, °1920.
v, 18 p. 23ᶜᵐ. (*Its* Special report, no. 13)

1. Cost and standard of living—Cincinnati.
Library of Congress   HD6994.C5N3   20-20007

OCU MiU ViU CaBVaU WaWW CU
NN   0054325   DLC MtU IdU OrPR WaS OrU NcRS OC1 OCU

National industrial conference board.
The cost of living among wage-earners, Detroit, Michigan, September, 1921 ...   New York, National industrial conference board ₁°1921₎
2 p. l., 22 p. 23ᶜᵐ. (*Its* Special report, no. 19)

1. Cost and standard of living—Detroit. 2. Labor and laboring classes—Detroit.
Library of Congress   HD6994.D6N3   22-1744

NN   0054326   DLC CU OU OC1 MiU MtU OrU

National industrial conference board.
The cost of living among wage-earners, Fall River, Massachusetts, October, 1919 ...   Boston, Mass., National industrial conference board, °1919.
v, 18 p. 23ᶜᵐ. (*Its* Research report, no. 22)

1. Cost and standard of living—Fall River, Mass.
Library of Congress   HD6994.F2N3   20-2733
——— Copy 2.

NN   0054327   DLC CU NcD MiU OCU OO MB ICJ ViU

National industrial conference board.
The cost of living among wage-earners, Greenville, South Carolina; Pelzer, South Carolina; Charlotte, North Carolina, January and February, 1920 ...   Boston, Mass., National industrial conference board, °1920.
v, 25 p. 23ᶜᵐ. (*Its* Special report, no. 8)

1. Cost and standard of living—Greenville, S. C. 2. Cost and standard of living—Pelzer, S. C. 3. Cost and standard of living—Charlotte, N. C.
Library of Congress   HD6993.S6N3   20-14765

NN   0054328   DLC MtU WaS OrU CU MiU OO ViU

National industrial conference board.
The cost of living among wage-earners, Lawrence, Massachusetts, November, 1919 ...   Boston, Mass., National industrial conference board, °1919.
vii, 21 p. incl. tables. 23ᶜᵐ. (*Its* Research report, no. 24)

1. Cost and standard of living—Lawrence, Mass.   I. Title.
Library of Congress   HD6994.L4N3   20-6069

MB ICJ Or OrU WaWW
NN   0054329   DLC WaTC MtBC WaS NcD CU OU OO OC1

National industrial conference board.
The cost of living among wage-earners, north Hudson County, New Jersey, January, 1920 ...   Boston, Mass., National industrial conference board, °1920.
iii, 20 p. 23ᶜᵐ. (*Its* Special report, no. 7)

1. Cost and standard of living—Hudson Co., N. J.   I. Title.
Library of Congress   HD6993.N5N3 1920   20-12893

OU ViU NcU WaS OrU CaBVaU Or WaWW
NN   0054330   DLC MtU NcRS IdU OrPR NIC CU MiU OC1

VOLUME 407

National industrial conference board.
  The cost of living among wage-earners, Worcester, Massachusetts, June, 1920 ... New York, National industrial conference board, ᶜ1920.
    1 p. l., 16 p. incl. tables. 23ᶜᵐ. (*Its* Special report, no. 16)

  1. Cost and standard of living—Worcester, Mass.
  Library of Congress   HD6994.W6N3   21–4194

NN 0054331   DLC MtU WaS OrU CU OU OC1 OC1W MiU

National industrial conference board.
  The cost of living in foreign countries. New York, National industrial conference board, inc., 1927.
    xv, 402 p. incl. tables. 23½ᶜᵐ.

  1. Cost and standard of living. 2. Index numbers (Economics)
  ɪ. Title.
  Library of Congress   HD6978.N3   27–14864

DL ICRL NIC MB MtU WaS OrCS Or
NN 0054332   DLC NcRS CLSU CU FMU NcD OU MiU OO ICJ

National industrial conference board.
  The cost of living in New York city, 1926. New York, National industrial conference board, inc., 1926.
    xiii p., 1 l., 129 p. incl. illus. (map) tables, diagrs. 23½ᶜᵐ.

  1. Cost and standard of living—New York (City) ɪ. Title.
  Library of Congress   HD6994.N5N3   27–2801

MB ICJ OKentU OrCS ViU Or
NN 0054333   DLC NcRS WaS MtU CU KMK NcD OCU OC1 OO

National industrial conference board.
  The cost of living in the United States. New York, National industrial conference board, inc., 1925.
    xvi, 201 p. incl. tables, diagrs. 23½ᶜᵐ.
    "Addendum": 1 leaf laid in.

  1. Cost-and standard of living—U. S. ɪ. Title.
  Library of Congress   HD6983.N33   25—9955

WaS TU NIC CU NN ICJ Or DAL
NN 0054334   DLC OKentU DL MB OrU OrCS WaWW MtU

National industrial conference board.
  The cost of living in the United States, 1914–1926. New York, National industrial conference board, inc., 1926.
    xviii, 233 p. incl. tables, diagrs. 23½ᶜᵐ.
                                    HD6983.N33 1926
    ———— Copy 2.
    Copyright A 987339
  —— The cost of living in the United States in 1926, supplementing "The cost of living in the United States, 1914–1926". New York, National industrial conference board, inc., 1927.
    vi, 33 p. incl. tables, diagr. 23ᶜᵐ.
    1. Cost and standard of living—U. S. ɪ. Title.
                                    26–13481 Revised
  Library of Congress   HD6983.N33 1926 Suppl.

OrCS WaS NIC NcD OC1U CU MH OO OU ICJ ViU
NN 0054335   DLC FMU Or CaBViP WaTC IdU WaSpG

NATIONAL INDUSTRIAL CONFERENCE BOARD.
  The cost of living in the United States, 1914–26, with supplement for 1926. New York, 1927.

  Tables.
  ᵃPublished March, 1926. Reprinted January, 1927.

NN 0054336   MH–PA

National industrial conference board.
  The cost of living in the United States, 1914–1927. New York, National industrial conference board, inc., 1928.
    xiv, 142 p. incl. tables, diagrs. 23½ᶜᵐ.
  —— The cost of living in the United States in 1928, supplementing "The cost of living in the United States, 1914–1927" ... New York, National industrial conference board, inc., 1929.
    vi, 34 p. incl. tables, diagr. 22½ cm.
                                    HD6983.N33 1928
  1. Cost and standard of living—U. S. 2. Index numbers (Economics) ɪ. Title.
  HD6983.N33 1927   28—16993

CU TU NcC FMU MU KMK ICJ DHEW ViU DAL
NN 0054337   DLC WaSp WaS OrCS OrU WaOB ICJ WaTC DN

National industrial conference board.
  The cost of living in the United States, 1914–1929. New York, National industrial conference board, inc., 1930.
    xvi, 190 p. incl. tables, diagrs. 23ᶜᵐ.

  1. Cost and standard of living—U. S. 2. Index numbers (Economics)
  ɪ. Title.
  Library of Congress   HD6983.N33 1929   30–14895
  ———— Copy 2.
  Copyright A 24228   ₅₋₅₎   331.8310973

MB OU OO OOxM DL MH ICJ WaT WaS OrCS WaTC PPSPPR
NN 0054338   DLC OKentU AAP CU CaBViP Or NcD TU

National industrial conference board.
  The cost of living in the United States, 1914–1930. New York, National industrial conference board, inc., 1931.
    x, 170 p. incl. tables, diagrs. 23½ᶜᵐ.

  1. Cost and standard of living—U. S. 2. Index numbers (Economics)
  ɪ. Title.
  Library of Congress   HD6983.N33 1930   31–21788
  ———— Copy 2.
  Copyright A 40775   ₅₋₅₎   331.8310973

OU OCU OO DL DN MH Wa WaSp WaS OrCS OrU Or
NN 0054339   DLC MH–BA AAP MB NcRS DHEW CU KEmT

National industrial conference board.
  ... Cost of living in the United States, 1914–1936, by M. Ada Beney, Conference board Research staff ... New York city, National industrial conference board, inc. (ᶜ1936₎
    ix, 99 p. incl. tables, diagrs. 23½ cm. (*Its* Studies. No. 228)
    "Prepared by Miss M. Ada Beney ... with the assistance of Miss Edith Turner and Miss Bertha Jacobson."—Foreword.

  1. Cost and standard of living—U. S. 2. Index numbers (Economics) ɪ. Beney, Margarete Ada, 1896– ɪɪ. Turner, Edith A.
  ɪɪɪ. Jacobson, Bertha. ɪᴠ. Title.

  HD6983.N33 1936   331.8310973   36—27418

Or WaTC Wa
WaS OrU DL OC1W OOxM OU NN ViU MeB MB PPULC NIC
NN 0054340   DLC WaT NcRS WaSp OrCS CaBViP OrPR

National industrial conference board.
  The cost of living in the United States in 1931. New York, National industrial conference board, inc., 1932.
    viii, 52 p. incl. tables, diagrs. 23ᶜᵐ.

  1. Cost and standard of living—U. S. 2. Index numbers (Economics)
  ɪ. Title.
  Library of Congress   HD6983.N33 1931   32–10176
  ———— Copy 2.
  Copyright A 49437   ₇₋₃₎   331.8310973

OrCS MH IaU MWelC ViU
NN 0054341   DLC NcRS OrU WaS WaSp CU DL OO OCU OC1

National industrial conference board.
  ... The cost of living in the United States in 1932, ₍New York₎ National industrial conference board, inc., 1933–
    v. diagr. 28ᶜᵐ.
    "Supplement to Conference board Service letter."
    Caption title.
    "Takes the place of the usual annual volume published by the National industrial conference board on the subject of the cost of living."—p. 1.

  1. Cost and standard of living—U. S. 2. Index numbers (Economics)
  ɪ. National industrial conference board. Service letters. Supplement.
  ɪɪ. Title.
  Library of Congress   HD6983.N332   34–22592 Revised
  ———— Copy 2.   ₍r35f2₎   331.8310973

NN 0054342   DLC OOxM OC1W OU CU WaS

National Industrial Conference Board.
  ... The cost of living in the United States in 1933. [New York] 1934.
    8 p. incl. tables, diagrs. 28 cm. (Supplement to Conference board service letter, May 1934)
    Caption title.

NN 0054343   CU

National Industrial Conference Board.
  The cost of living in the United States in 1934.
  — [New York. 1935.] 1 v. Charts. Tables. [National Industrial Conference Board, Inc. Conference Board Service letter. Supplement, March, 1935.] 27.5 cm.

E1513 — S.r. — United States. Pol. econ. — Cost of living. Period.

NN 0054344   MB CU OC1W

National industrial conference board.
  The cost of living in twelve industrial cities. New York, National industrial conference board, inc., 1928.
    x, 76 p. incl. tables. 23½ᶜᵐ.

  1. Cost and standard of living—U. S. ɪ. Title.
  Library of Congress   HD6983.N34   28–16148

OC1 OU OO DAL ICJ WaS MtU OrCS OrU
NN 0054345   DLC OKentU NIC MB CU OrU AAP NcC NcD

National Industrial Conference Board.
  Cost of living provisions in union contracts. ₍By James J. Bambrick, Jr., and Harold Stieglitz, Division of Personnel Administration₎ New York ₍*1951₎
    64 p. diagrs. 28 cm. (*Its* Conference Board reports. Studies in personnel policy, no. 113)
    Cover title.

  1. Wages—Cost-of-living adjustments—U. S. ɪ. Bambrick, James Joseph, 1917– ɪɪ. Stieglitz, Harold. ɪɪɪ. Title. (Series: National Industrial Conference Board. Studies in personnel policy, no. 113)
  HF5549.A2N27 no. 113   331.215   51–3045

NN 0054346   DLC AAP KMK CoU IaU

National industrial conference board.
  "The cost of living." What is it? How is it measured? How is it used? New York city, National industrial conference board, inc. ₍*1941₎
    cover-title, 40 p. diagrs. 23ᶜᵐ.

  1. Cost and standard of living. 2. Cost and standard of living—U. S.
  ɪ. Title.
  Library of Congress   HD6978.N28   42–8334
                            ₍5₎   331.831

NN 0054347   DLC OU OC1FRB

National industrial conference board.
  Costs and profits in manufacturing industry, 1914–193? New York city, National industrial conference board, inc. ₍*1935₎
    4 p. l., 15 p. diagrs. 23ᶜᵐ. (*Its* Studies. no. 213₎
    "This study was prepared by Mr. Leonard Kuvin, of the Conference board's research staff."—Foreword.

  1. Manufactures—Costs. 2. U. S.—Indus.—Stat. ɪ. Kuvin, Leonard.
  ɪɪ. Title.
  Library of Congress   HD9724.N28   35–6927
  ———— Copy 2.
  Copyright A 82423   ₍5–5₎   338.40973

ICJ ViU
NN 0054348   DLC OrU OrCS CaBViP MtU OU OC1W MiU

VOLUME 407

338.1　National Industrial Conference Board.
N2137c　　Cotton and cotton textiles, basic indus-
　　　trial data. ₁New York?₎ 1953.
　　　unpaged(chiefly tables) 28cm.

　　Caption title.

　　1. Cotton--Stat₁　Title.

NN　0054349　　　IU

National Industrial Conference Board.
　The Council of Economic Advisers, retrospect
　and prospect

　　see its

　The Conference Board Economic Forum presents:
　The Council of Economic Advisers.

National industrial conference board.
　... Creating good will for the "hidden
product" ... New York, N.Y. ₁1945₎
　cover-title, 32 p.incl.facsims. (Its Studies
in business policy, no. 11)

NN　0054351　　　MH-BA MiEM OU

National Industrial Conference Board.
　The crisis of the free market
　　see under　Harper, Floyd Arthur, 1905-

National industrial conference board.
　... A critical analysis of the Meany-Thomas report on the
cost of living. New York, N. Y., National industrial conference board, inc. ₁1944₎
　cover-title, 36 p. 27½ x 21½ᶜᵐ. (*Its* Conference board reports)

　1. Meany, George, 1894-　Recommended report for the presidential committee on the cost of living. 2. Cost and standard of living—
U. S.
　Library of Congress　　HD6083.M43N3　　44-5188
　　　　　　　　　₁15₎　　　　　　　331.831

　NRU OrOrCS OrU WaS
NN　0054353　　DLC DNAL OC1U GU OC1W CU ICJ OCU OU

National Industrial Conference Board.
　Cumulative index of NICB publications. 1950-54—
₁New York₎
　　v. 28 cm. annual.
　Vols. for　　-1961 non-cumulative.
　Period covered by cumulations vary.
　Title varies: 1950-54—61, Conference Board publications, general
Index.
　Other slight variations in title.

　1. Economics—Bibl. 2. National Industrial Conference Board—
Bibl.　I. National Industrial Conference Board. Conference Board
publications, general index. II. Title.
　Z7164.E2N28　　　016.331082　　　56-58754 rev 2

　OU NN NBuG ODW DI OAkU TxU KU NNC C ICarbS NIC OCU
NN　0054354　　DLC MiU CaBVa WaS KU NcRS MiU NcU

National industrial conference board.
　Current tax problems in New York state. New York, National industrial conference board, inc., 1931.
　x, 146 p. illus. (map) 23½ cm.

　1. Taxation—New York (State)　I. Title.

　HJ2424.N28　1931a　　　336.2709747
　　　　　　　　　　　　　　　　32—940

　OC1W ICJ OU NcU WaS MtU OrPR OrCS OrU Or
NN　0054355　　DLC NBuHi OKentU MB KMK ViU NcD MiU

National industrial conference board.
　... Current wages in manufacturing industry in foreign
countries ... New York, National industrial conference board,
inc. ₁ᶜ1938₎
　15 p. 28ᶜᵐ. (Supplement to Conference board service letter. March
7, 1938)
　"With the exception of a large table showing weekly earnings in
Great Britain in October 1935, the data here presented relate to the
years 1936 and 1937."—p. 3.

　1. Wages. 2. Labor and laboring classes—Stat. 3. Index numbers
(Economics)　I. National industrial conference board. Service let-
ter₁s₎ Supplement. II. Title.
　　　　　　　　　　　　　　　　38-20770
　Library of Congress　　HD4966.M3N35
———— Copy 2.
　Copyright AA 267566　　₁5₎　　　　331.287

NN　0054356　　DLC OrCS OC1W OU

HF5549　National Industrial Conference Board.
.A2N27　　Curtailment, layoff policy, and seniority.
no.5　　New York, 1938.
1938　　　11 p. 28cm. (Its Studies in personnel
　　　　policy, no. 5)
　　　Cover title.

　　1. Layoff systems. I. Title. II. Ser.

NN　0054357　　　ViU InU IaU NIC

HF5006　National Industrial Conference Board.
.N3　　　Damage control in wartime. ₁New York,
no.53　1951₎
1951　　　80 p. 28cm. (Its Studies in business
　　　policy no. 53)

　　　1. Reconstruction (1939-　)—U. S. I. Title.
　　II. Ser.

NN　0054358　　　ViU MiA1bC

National Industrial Conference Board.
　Dealer margins
　　see under　Higgins, Elliott F

T56　National Industrial Conference Board.
N37　　Decentralization in industry. New York
　　₁1948₎
　　　40 p. col.maps,diagrs.,tables. (Its
　　Conference Board reports. Studies in
　　business policy, no.30)

　　Cover title.

　　1. Industries, Location of. I. Title.

NN　0054360　　CU OU MH-BA CSt AAP PPCPC

National Industrial Conference Board.
　Defense economics: the first year. ₁A graphic analysis₎
prepared for the thirty-fifth annual meeting of the Conference Board, May 17-18, 1951. New York ₁1951₎
　32 p. col. map, col. diagrs. 26 cm.

　1. U. S.—Econ. condit.—1945-　I. Title.

　HC106.5.N295　　　330.973　　　51-5062

NN.　0054361　　DLC OrCS MtBC OrP NcGU OrU TU

HF　National Industrial Conference Board.
5549　　Deferment under the Selective Service
A2N27　Act, ₎with appendix covering the National
no. 28+　Guard and Reserve Corps. Supplement to
　　the Management record. New York ₁1940₎
　　　24 p. 28cm. (Conference board.
　　Studies in personnel policy, no. 28)

NN　0054362　　NIC IaU ViU

National industrial conference board.
　... Depreciated currencies and commodity imports. ₁New
York₎ National industrial conference board, 1933.
　1 p. l., 7 numb. l. 28½ x 22ᶜᵐ. (Conference board information service:
Domestic affairs. Memorandum no. 1)
　Reproduced from type-written copy.

　1. Currency question. 2. Commerce.　I. Title.　42-2968

　Library of Congress　　HC106.3.N24　no. 1
　　　　　　　　　₁2₎　　　(330.973) 332.4

NN　0054363　　DLC NN

HC256　National industrial conference board.
.3　　　... Depression and recovery in the United
.N3　　Kingdom and in the United States. (In conference
　　board bulletin. New York,1938. vol.XII,no.14,
　　p.113-126)

NN　0054364　　DLC

National industrial conference board.
　... Designing a company pension plan ... New York, N. Y.,
National industrial conference board, inc. ₁1944₎
　cover-title, 16 p. 28 x 21½ᶜᵐ. (*Its* Conference board reports)
　Studies in personnel policy, no. 67.
　The proceedings of a round-table meeting on company pension plans
held September 21, 1944, in New York, in connection with the 262nd
meeting of the Conference board. *cf.* Foreword.

　1. Old age pensions—U. S.　I. Title.　　45-3220

　Library of Congress °　　HF5549.A2N27　no. 67
　　　　　　　　　₁5₎　　　(658.3) 331.252

NN　0054365　　DLC IaU

National industrial conference board.
　... Determining damages upon cancellation of war contracts.
New York, National industrial conference board, inc. ₁1943₎
　cover-title, 32 p. 28 x 22ᶜᵐ. (*Its* Conference board reports)

　1. War contracts—U. S. 2. Damages—U. S.　I. Title.
　　　　　　　　　　　　　　　　43-16400
　Library of Congress　　HD3858.N3
　　　　　　　　　₁15₎　　　　351.71

　ICJ
NN　0054366　　DLC DNLM OrCS OrP OrU GU OCU OOxM OU

National Industrial Conference Board.
　Determining salesmen's base pay, a role of job evaluation
₁by Elmer W. Earl, Jr., Division of Personnel Administra-
tion₎ New York ₁1948₎
　36 p. 28 cm. (*Its* Conference Board reports. Studies in personnel
policy, no. 98)
　Cover title.
　Bibliography: p. 35-36.

　1. Salesmen and salesmanship—U. S. 2. Job analysis.　I. Earl,
Elmer W. II. Title.　(Series: National Industrial Conference
Board. Conference Board reports. Series: National Industrial Con-
ference Board. Studies in personnel policy, no. 98)
　HF5549.A2N27　no. 98　658.85　　49-3214*

NN　0054367　　DLC OC1JC CoU IaU PPT NIC ViU

National industrial conference board.
　The development of American enterprise and the challenge
to the enterprise principle, prepared for the twenty-fourth annual meeting, the Conference board, May 22, 1940 ... New
York, National industrial conference board ₁ᶜ1940₎
　cover-title, ₁28₎ p. diagrs. 28ᶜᵐ.
　Includes 12 "charts", with descriptive letterpress on each preceding
verso.

　1. U. S.—Econ. condit. 2. U. S.—Economic policy.　I. Title.
　II. Title: American enterprise, The development of.　40-13173
　Library of Congress　　HC108.5.N32
———— Copy 2.
　Copyright A 336105　　₁4₎　　　330.973

NN　0054368　　DLC NIC OC1FRB

VOLUME 407

HF
5549
A2N27
no.13+

National Industrial Conference Board.
Developments in company vacation plans.
New York ₁1939₎
23 p. 28cm. (The Conference Board.
Studies in personnel policy, no.13)

1. Vacations, Employee. I. Series:
National Industrial Conference Board.
Studies in personnel policy, no. 13.

NN   0054369   NIC IaU

National Industrial Conference Board.
Developments in supervisory training ₁by William W.
Mussmann, Division of Personnel Administration₎ New
York ₁1952₎
84 p. illus. 28 cm. (*Its* Conference Board reports. Studies in
personnel policy, no. 124)
Cover title.

1. Personnel management—Study and teaching.   I. Mussmann,
William W.   II. Title.   (Series: National Industrial Conference
Board. Studies in personnel policy, no. 124)
HF5549.A2N27 no. 124   658.386   52–1144

NN   0054370   DLC MoSU-C AAP ViU OCU OCl

National industrial conference board.
...Developments in the federal fiscal situation.

New York, 19   28cm.
v.
Monthly.
Reproduced from typewritten copy.

1. Finance—Per. and soc. publ.—   U. S.
N. Y. P. L.   September 23, 1937

NN   0054371   NN OCl

National industrial conference board.
... Differentials in industrial wages and hours in the
United States, by M. Ada Beney, Conference board research
staff. New York city, National industrial conference board,
inc. ₁1938₎
xviii, 203 p. incl. tables, diagrs. 23½ cm. (*Its* Studies. no. 238
₁i. e. 239₎)
"Presented by the author with the permission of the board in
partial fulfillment of the requirements for the degree of doctor of
philosophy at Columbia university ₁1938₎"—Foreword.
1. Wages—U. S.   2. Hours of labor—U. S.   I. Beney, Margarete Ada.   II. Title.
HD4975.N885   1938   331.2973   38–27352
———— Copy 3.   Thesis note on label mounted on t.-p.
"Vita" on leaf mounted   on end lining-paper.

Or WaT WaTC
DAL ViU NN OCl OCU OCIW NIC OrPR MtU WaS OrCS OrU
NN   0054372   DLC MB TU IEN OKentU CU ICJ PU DFT DU

National industrial conference board.
... A digest of the economic security program ... ₁New
York₎ National industrial conference board, 1935.
cover-title, 1 p. l., 12 numb. l. 28½ᶜᵐ. (Conference board information
service: Domestic affairs series. Memorandum no. 38)
Mimeographed.

1. Insurance, Unemployment — U. S.   2. Old age pensions—U. S.   3.
Children—Charities, protection, etc.—U. S.   I. Title.   II. Title: Eco-
nomic security program.
Library of Congress   HC106.3.N24 no. 38   35–3293
———— Copy 2.
Copyright AA 164915   ₁5₎   (330.973) 331.25440973

NN   0054373   DLC OClCC OCIFRB

National industrial conference board.
A digest of "The metric versus the English system of weights
and measures", from Research report no. 42 ... New York city,
National industrial conference board ₁*1921₎
1 p. l., 11 p. 23ᶜᵐ. (*Its* Special report no. 20)

1. Metric system. 2. Weights and measures—Gt. Brit.   I. Title: The
metric versus the English system of weights and measures.
                                                22—1360
Library of Congress   QC88.N32

NN   0054374   DLC MtU CU CoU NcD OCIW OU OCl MB

HF5549
A2N27
no.1

National Industrial Conference Board.
Dismissal compensation.   New York,
₁1937₎
18p. 28cm. (Its Studies in personnel
policy, no.1)

1. Wages – Dismissal wage.

NN   0054375   IaU OClW ODW InU

HF5549
A2N27
no.50

National Industrial Conference Board.
Dismissal compensation.   New York
₁1943₎
32p. 28cm. (Its Studies in personnel
policy, no.50)

1. Wages – Dismissal wage.

NN   0054376   IaU InU OClJC ViU AAP

National Industrial Conference Board.
Dividend policy and tax problems; a symposium on Sec-
tion 102, Internal revenue code. Participants, chairman:
J. K. Lasser; Maurice Austin ₁and others. New York, 1947₎
35 p. 23 cm. (*Its* Studies in business economics, no. 10)
Cover title.

1. Dividends—U. S.   2. Corporations—U. S.—Taxation.   I. Lasser,
Jacob Kay, 1896-   II. Title: Internal revenue code.   (Series)

HB31.N33   no. 10   658.15   48–10032 rev*

NN   0054377   DLC TxU

National industrial conference board.
... Dollar values of production of goods and construction,
1914–1923 ... ₁New York₎ National industrial conference
board, 1934.
cover-title, 1 p. l., 8 numb. l. 28½ᶜᵐ. (Conference board information
service: Domestic affairs series. Memorandum no. 37)
Mimeographed.

1. U. S.—Indus.—Stat. 2. U. S.—Econ. condit.—1918-   I. Title.
                                                37–35023
Library of Congress   HC106.3.N24 no. 37
                         ₁5₎   (330.973) 330.973

NN   0054378   DLC OClFRB

National Industrial Conference Board.
Domestic consumer markets. Prepared for the thirty-
second annual meeting of the Conference Board, May 26,
1948. New York ₁1948₎
32 p. col. diagrs. 26 cm.

1. Market surveys—U. S.   I. Title.

HF5343.N3   658.8   48–4457*

DNAL MB TxU ICU
NN   0054379   DLC OrCS OrP OrU NN TU OOxM Mi ICJ

National Industrial Conference Board.
The duties of financial executives

see under

Finley, James A

National industrial conference board.

The **Economic** almanac for 1940–   A handbook
of useful facts about business, labor and government in the
United States and other areas. New York city, The Conference board, National industrial conference board ₁1940-

---

National industrial conference board.
... Economic aspects of Sino-Japanese relations. ₁New
York₎ National industrial conference board, 1933.
1 p. l., 21 numb. l. incl. tables, diagrs. 28½ x 22ᶜᵐ. (Conference board
information service: Foreign affairs. Memorandum no. 3)
Reproduced from type-written copy.
CONTENTS.—I. Report of Mr. Li Ming, managing director, Chekiang
industrial bank, Shanghai.—II. Report of Mr. S. Ikeda, managing director, Mitsui bank, ltd., Tokio.
1. China—Comm.—Japan. 2. Japan—Comm.—China.   I. Li, Ming,
1880-   II. Ikeda, Seihin, 1867-   III. Title.
                                                42–3164
Library of Congress   HF3778.J3N3
                         ₁2₎   382.0951

NN   0054382   DLC

National industrial conference board.
... Economic background for postwar reconstruction. New
York, National industrial conference board, inc. ₁1943₎
cover-title, 34 p. diagrs. 28 x 22ᶜᵐ. (*Its* Conference board reports)

1. U. S.—Econ. condit.—1918-   2. Labor supply—U. S. 3. Reconstruction (1939-   )—U. S.   I. Title.
                                                43–10236
Library of Congress   HC106.4.N359 1943 a
                         ₁10₎   338.91

NN   0054383   DLC NBuG NIC OU OClCC GU ICJ

National industrial conference board.
Economic background for postwar reconstruction, prepared
for the twenty-seventh annual meeting of the Conference
board, May 26, 1943, the Waldorf-Astoria, New York city.
New York, National industrial conference board, inc. ₁1943₎
cover-title, 34 p. diagrs. 28 x 22ᶜᵐ.

1. U. S.—Econ. condit.—1918-   2. Labor supply—U. S. 3. Reconstruction (1939-   )—U. S.   I. Title.
                                                43–10061
Library of Congress   HC106.4.N359
                         ₁20₎   330.973

NN   0054384   DLC OrCS OrU DNAL OClW ICU

National industrial conference board.
... Economic conditions in foreign countries: Great Britain,
Germany, France, and Japan. ₁New York₎ National industrial conference board, 1933.
2 p. l., 14 numb. l. 28½ x 22ᶜᵐ. (Conference board information service: Foreign affairs. Memorandum no. 10)
Reproduced from type-written copy.
1. Gt. Brit.—Econ. condit.—1918-   2. Germany—Econ. condit.—
1918-   3. France—Econ. condit.—1918-   4. Japan—Econ.
condit.—1918-
                                                42–3337
Library of Congress   HC57.N2913
                         ₁2₎   330.94

NN   0054385   DLC KMK OO OU MiU

National industrial conference board.
Economic conditions in foreign countries, 1932–1933. New
York, National industrial conference board, inc., 1933.
x, 62 p. 23½ᶜᵐ.

1. Economic conditions—1918-   2. Economic policy. 3. Commerce.
4. Finance. 5. Currency question.   I. Title.
                                                33–27172
Library of Congress   HC57.N29
                         ———— Copy 2.
Copyright A 64101   ₁5-5₎   330.904

NN   0054386   DLC MtU WaS OrCS Or NcD TU ICJ NNC

National industrial conference board.
... Economic development of Germany under National
socialism, by Vasco Trivanovitch, Conference board research
staff. New York city, National industrial conference board,
inc. ₁1937₎
xvii, 141 p. diagrs. 23½ cm. (*Its* Studies. no. 236)

1. Germany—Econ. condit.—1918-1945. 2. Germany—Pol. & govt.—
1933-1945. 3. Finance—Germany. 4. Nationalsocialistische deutsche
arbeiter-partei.   I. Trianovitch, Vasco.   II. Title.

HC286.3.N245   330.943   37—15897

OrPR WaS OrU OrCS
OOxM DN DL OO OCU DAU CoU NIC FTaSU Or WaTC MtU IdU
NN   0054387   DLC CU ScU NBuG DFT TU ViU ICJ NcD MB

VOLUME 407

National industrial conference board.
Economic developments; a graphic record. New York,
National industrial conference board, inc., °1933.
2 p. l., 16 numb. l. of diagrs. 19ᶜᵐ.
Lithographed.

1. U. S.—Econ. condit.—1918– 2. Economic conditions—1918–
3. Economics—Graphic methods. I. Title.
Library of Congress HC106.3.N25 33–18257
——— Copy 2.
Copyright AA 125158 ₍₃₎ 330.973

NN 0054388 DLC

National industrial conference board. . .
The economic doctrines of John Maynard Keynes; a series
of papers presented at a symposium conducted by the Na-
tional industrial conference board. New York city, National
industrial conference board, inc. ₍°1938₎
vii, 78, ₍2₎ p. 23 cm.
CONTENTS.—Some practical effects of the doctrines suggested by Mr.
J. M. Keynes prior to 1930, by F. C. James.—Some theoretical and
practical implications of J. M. Keynes' general theory, by Lauchlin
Currie.—Mr. Keynes' theories considered in the light of experience, by
R. S. Tucker.—The rôle of the multiplier and the interest rate in
Keynes' general theory, by Fritz Lehmann.—The practical importance
of Keynes' doctrines, by L. D. Edie.
1. Keynes, John Maynard, 1883– 2. Economics. I. Title.
HB103.K47N3 330.1 38–18612

NN 0054389 DLC CoU OU OCl OClW CU OrU OrPS

National Industrial Conference Board.
Economic expansion; patterns, problems, potentials. ₍A
graphic analysis, prepared for the thirty-fourth annual
meeting of The Conference Board, May 18, 1950. New York
₍1950₎
32 p. col. diagrs. 26 cm.

1. U. S.—Econ. condit. I. Title.
HC103.N28 330.973 50–4434

TU NcD OCU DNAL NN TxU
NN 0054390 DLC OrU OrCS PPFRB FU OrP PPD ICU MB

National Industrial Conference Board.
Economic fact or fiction. no. 1, 3.
New York ₍1947?₎–
2 nos. in 1 v.

Contents: - no. 1. Do profits make prices
high?
no.3.Have prices run away from wages?

NN 0054391 MH-BA NN

National industrial conference board.
Economic reconstruction legislation of 1933–₍1934₎ New
York, National industrial conference board, inc., 1933–34.
2 v. 23ᶜᵐ.
Vol. II has title: The economic legislation of the seventy-third Con-
gress.

1. U. S.—Economic policy. 2. Industrial laws and legislation—U. S.
3. U. S.—Public works. 4. Law reports, digests, etc.—U. S. I. U. S.
Laws, statutes, etc. II. Title. III. Title: The economic legislation of
the seventy-third Congress.
33–23031 Revised
Library of Congress
——— Copy 2. HC106.3.N26
Copyright A 63868 ₍r35f²2₎ 330.973

CSt
ICJ OU OCl MiU ViU ICU OU OO MB DL PPT MiD NcD ICU
NN 0054392 DLC NBuU-L NIC KMK TU OOxM MH-BA NcD

National Industrial Conference Board. The economic record
see **American** affairs; the economic record.

National industrial conference board.
The economic status of the wage earner in New York and
other states. New York, National industrial conference
board, inc., 1928.
xi, ₍1₎, 125 p. incl. tables, diagrs. 23½ cm.
On cover: The wage earner in New York and other states.

1. Labor and laboring classes—U. S.—1914– 2. Wages—U. S.
3. Wages—New York (State) 4. Cost and standard of living—U. S.
5. New York (State)—Indus. I. Title.
HD8072.N283 28–16149

ICJ MsU DAL NcD OCl OU OO DL ViU MH
NN 0054394 DLC WaTC WaS MtU Wa OrCS CU NIC MsSM

National Industrial Conference Board.
The economics of consumer debt

see *its*

The Conference Board Economic Forum presents:
The economics of consumer debt.

National Industrial Conference Board.
The economics of tariffs

see *its*

The Conference Board Economic Forum presents:
The economics of tariffs.

HD9875
.B3
National industrial conference board.
Backman, Jules, 1910–
Economics of the cotton textile industry ₍by₎ Jules Backman
₍and₎ M. R. Gainsbrugh. New York, N. Y., National indus-
trial conference board ₍1946₎

National Industrial Conference Board.
Economics of the President's economists; an evening with
the economic forum: discussion leaders, Solomon Fabricant,
Henry Hazlitt ₍and₎, Malcolm P. McNair; Jules Backman
₍and others₎. New York, 1949₎
87 p. 23 cm. (*Its* Studies in business economics, no. 20)
Cover title.

1. U. S. Council of Economic Advisers. 2. U. S.—Economic policy.
I. Title. (Series)
HB31.N33 no. 20 338.973 49–4486*

Vi MH-BA
NN 0054398 DLC ViU NN DAU TxU CLU OU PPT PPFRB

National industrial conference board.
Effect of the depression on industrial relations programs ...
New York city, National industrial conference board, inc.
₍°1934₎
vii, 17 p. 23ᶜᵐ.
"This survey was conducted by the research staff of the Conference
board in collaboration with Dr. J. E. Walters."—Foreword.

1. Employees' representation in management. 2. Employment man-
agement. 3. Industry—Organization, control, etc. I. Walters, Jack
Edward, 1896– II. Title. III. Title: Industrial relations programs.
35–5474
Library of Congress HD45.N3
——— Copy 2.
Copyright A 78929 ₍10–5₎ 331.15

OCU ViU IU ICJ
NN 0054399 DLC CU OrU OrCS WaS IdU MtU NcD OU OCl

National Industrial Conference Board.
Effects of depreciation policy, by J. Frank Gaston. ₍New
York, 1950₎
63 p. illus. 23 cm. (*Its* Studies in business economics, no. 22)
Cover title.

1. Depreciation. I. Gaston, J. Frank. II. Title: Effects of depreciation policy. (Series)
HB31.N33 no. 22 657 50–7569 rev

NN 0054400 DLC TxU IaU OU CoU PPFRB

National industrial conference board.
... Effects of taxes upon corporate policy. New York, National industrial conference board, inc. ₍1943₎
cover-title, 136 p. diagrs. 28 x 21½ᶜᵐ. (*Its* Conference board reports)

1. Stock companies—U. S.—Taxation. 2. Stock companies—Finance.
I. Title.
Library of Congress HD2753.U6N27 43–12906
₍3₎ 658.1712

NN 0054401 DLC OrCS DNAL OC1W OU OCU ICJ NBuG ViU

National Industrial Conference Board.
Effects on taxes upon corporate policy
see aslo *under* Ellis, Paul Warren, 1903–

National industrial conference board.
The eight hour day defined ... Boston, Mass., National industrial conference board, °1918.
1 p. l., 8, ₍1₎ p. 23ᶜᵐ. (*Its* Research report, no. 11)

1. Eight-hour movement. I. Title. 18–23258
Library of Congress HD5124.N2

OO OCl ICJ
NN 0054403 DLC WaTC MtBC WaS OrU CaBVaU NcD OU

National industrial conference board.
The eight hour day defined ... Boston, Mass., National
industrial conference board, °1918.
1 p. l., 9 p. 23ᶜᵐ. (*Its* Research report, no. 11)
"December 1918 (superseding November edition)"

NN 0054404 NIC CU MB ViU

621.3 **National Industrial Conference Board.**
N2145e Electric power; basic industrial data. ₍New
York?₎ 1955.
86p. tables. 28cm.

Caption title.

1. Electric power.

NN 0054405 IU NIC

National industrial conference board.
Electric public utilities; a graphic record of development ...
New York city, National industrial conference board, inc.,
°1935.
2 p. l., 10 diagr. 19¼ᶜᵐ.
Note signed: Roland P. Falkner, director, Information division.

1. Electric industries—U. S.—Stat. 2. Public utilities—U. S.—Stat.
I. Falkner, Roland Post, 1866– II. Title.
Library of Congress TK23.N35 35–7755
——— Copy 2.
Copyright AA 173255 ₍5₎ 621.30973

NN 0054406 DLC OC1FRB

National industrial conference board.
Elements of an American program for social progress; a
series of addresses delivered at the twentieth annual meeting
of the National industrial conference board, held at the Waldorf-Astoria hotel, New York, May 28, 1936. New York, National industrial conference board, inc. ₍1936₎
cover-title, 1 p. l., 68 p. 23ᶜᵐ.
CONTENTS.—Introductory remarks, by Virgil Jordan.—The rôle of
science, by Karl T. Compton.—The rôle of religion, by Bishop Francis J.
McConnell.—The rôle of business, by Ralph E. Flanders.—The rôle of
government, by Charles Nagel.—The rôle of education, by Harry Wood-
burn Chase.
1. Social problems. I. Title. II. Title: Social progress, An American
program for.
Library of Congress HN64.N36 36–18520
——— Copy 2.
Copyright A 97292 ₍5₎ 301

NN 0054407 DLC OCU

VOLUME 407

National industrial conference board.
Elements of industrial pension plans. New York, National
industrial conference board, inc., 1931.
2 p. l., vii-ix, 48 p. 23ᶜᵐ.
Bibliography: p. 47-48.

TU NIC NcD ICJ DL DHEW OCU OC1
NN 0054408   DLC MtU CU MB ViU WaS OrCS Or CaBViP

National industrial conference board.
Elements of national welfare at home and abroad ... twenty-
first annual meeting, May twenty-seventh, nineteen thirty-
seven. ₍New York₎ National industrial conference board
₍ᶜ1937₎
cover-title, 16 p. diagrs. 20ᶜᵐ.
"This brochure ... presents examples of the graphic treatment of
economic information which is an important part of the scientific and
educational work of the board."—Foreword.

1. Economic conditions—1918–   I. Title. II. Title: National wel-
fare at home and abroad, Elements of.
Library of Congress   HC57.N292   38–17912
——— Copy 2.
Copyright AA 239015   ₍3₎   330.904

NN 0054409   DLC

National Industrial Conference Board.
Employee education ₍by Elmer W. Earl, Jr., Division of
Personnel Administration₎ New York ₍1951₎
68 p. illus. 28 cm. (*Its* Conference Board reports. Studies in
personnel policy, no. 119)
Cover title.
"Selected films used in employee education programs": p. 63–67.

1. Employees, Training of. 2. Employees, Reporting to.   I. Earl,
Elmer W. II. Title.   (Series: National Industrial Conference
Board. Studies in personnel policy, no. 119)
HF5549.A2N27 no. 119   658.386   51–8015

NN 0054410   DLC AAP CoU IaU

National Industrial Conference Board.
Employee induction ₍by William W. Mussmann, Division
of Personnel Administration₎ New York ₍1953₎
48 p. illus. 29 cm. (*Its* Conference Board reports. Studies in
personnel policy, no. 131)

1. Employee induction.   I. Mussmann, William W.
HF5549.A2N27 no. 131   658.386   53–1213 ‡

PPT DLC
NN 0054411   DLC DCU IaU AAP ViU MoSU-C OC1 NIC

National Industrial Conference Board.
Employee magazines and newspapers ₍by Geneva Seybold,
Division of Personnel Administration₎ New York ₍1953₎
68 p. illus., tables. 28 cm. (*Its* Conference Board reports. Studies
in personnel policy, no. 136)
Cover title.

1. Employees' magazines, handbooks, etc.   I. Seybold, Geneva,
1900–   II. Title.   (Series: National Industrial Conference
Board. Studies in personnel policy, no. 136)
HF5549.A2N27 no. 136   070.486   53–2553

NN 0054412   DLC Or ViU IaU OCU AAP TxU OOxM

National industrial conference board.
Employee magazines in the United States. New York,
National industrial conference board, inc., 1925.
x, 86 p. 23½ᶜᵐ.
"Appendix: Employee magazines published in the United States":
p. 65–86.

1. Labor and laboring classes—Period. 2. Journalism.   I. Title.
Library of Congress   HF5549.A2N3   26–868

ViU ICJ DL MtU OrU MH IdB OrCS
NN 0054413   DLC Or MB OO OC1 OCU ICRL CU NIC KEmT

NATIONAL INDUSTRIAL CONFERENCE BOARD.
  Employee magazines in the United States.
New York, National Industrial Conference Board,
Inc., 1925.
  "Studies in industrial relations problems,
110."

NN 0054414   MH

PN   National Industrial Conference Board.
4888   Employee magazines in the United
E55N27   States.   New York, 1925 ₍i. e. 1927₎
1927   x, 89 p. 24cm.

               1. Employees' magazines, handbooks,
             etc.

NN 0054415   NIC

National industrial conference board.
  ... Employee publications ... New York, National industrial conference board, inc. ₍1941₎
cover-title, 48 p. illus., tables, diagrs.
28 cm. (Its Studies in personnel policy, no. 31)
  At head of title: Conference board reports.
  By Charles E. Payne. Management research divi-

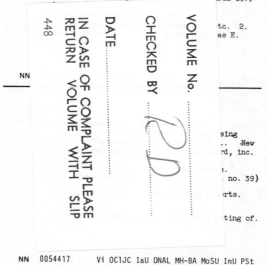

          tc. 2.
          es E.

NN ....

          sing
          ... New
          d, inc.
          ₎.
          no. 39)
          rts.
          ting of.

NN 0054417   Vi OC1JC IaU DNAL MH-BA MoSU InU PSt

National Industrial Conference Board.
Employee recreation activities, administration and cost.
₍By Geneva Seybold, Division of Personnel Administration₎
New York ₍1949₎
56 p. tables. 28 cm. (*Its* Conference Board reports. Studies in
personnel policy, no. 102)
Cover title.
1. Industrial recreation.   I. Seybold, Geneva, 1900–   (Series:
National Industrial Conference Board. Conference Board reports.
Series: National Industrial Conference Board. Studies in personnel
policy, no. 102)
HF5549.A2N27 no. 102   331.84   50–5495

NN 0054418   DLC AAP CoU IaU OC1JC OOxM

National Industrial Conference Board.
Employee salary plans in operation. ₍By Herbert S.
Briggs and Stephen Habbe, Division of Personnel Adminis-
tration₎ New York ₍1949₎
72 p. illus. 28 cm. (*Its* Conference Board reports. Studies in
personnel policy, no. 100)
Cover title.
1. Wages—U. S.   I. Briggs, Herbert S. II. Habbe, Stephen, 1906–
III. Title.   (Series: National Industrial Conference Board. Con-
ference Board reports. Series: National Industrial Conference Board.
Studies in personnel policy, no. 100)
HF5549.A2N27 no. 100   331.2973   49–48123*

NN 0054419   DLC AAP CoU PPT OC1JC OOxM

National Industrial Conference Board.
Employee savings and investment plans ₍by Lois E. Forde,
Division of Personnel Administration₎ New York ₍1953₎
31 p. 28 cm. (*Its* Conference Board reports. Studies in personnel
policy, no. 133)

1. Employee ownership.   I. Forde, Lois Elizabeth, 1922–
II. Title.
HF5549.A2N27 no. 133   *658.32 331.24   53–1277 ‡

NN 0054420   DLC AAP OCU ViU PPT PPD CoU

National industrial conference board.
Employee stock purchase plans and the stock market crisis
of 1929. A supplement to "Employee stock purchase plans in
the United States" published in January, 1928. New York,
National industrial conference board, inc. ₍ᶜ1930₎
vii, 37 p. 23ᶜᵐ.

1. Employee ownership. 2. Stocks. 3. Panics—1929.   I. Title.
Library of Congress   HD2781.S7N3 Suppl.   30–30282
——— Copy 2.
Copyright A 20649   ₍5-3₎   331.152

NcD DL
NN 0054421   DLC OrCS WaS MtU WaS MH CU OC1W OC1

National industrial conference board.
Employee stock purchase plans in the United States. New
York, National industrial conference board, inc., 1928.
xi, 245 p. 23½ cm.

1. Employee ownership. 2. Stocks—U. S.   I. Title.
Library of Congress   HD2781.S7N3   28–12534

NcD MtU WaS OrCS
NN 0054422   DLC TU CU MH NIC DL ICJ ViU OKentU KMK

National industrial conference board.
Employee thrift and investment plans. New York, National industrial conference board, inc., 1929.
xi, 114 p. incl. diagr., forms. 23ᶜᵐ.

1. Saving and thrift. 2. Investments.   I. Title.
Library of Congress   HG7920.N3   29–13391

MB DL ICJ ViU
NN 0054423   DLC OrCS OrU WaS MtU CU OC1 OOxM OU

National Industrial Conference Board.

  Employee thrift plans in wartime. New York
₍1942₎
  cover-title, 40 p. 28ᶜᵐ. (Its Studies in
personnel policy, no. 42)
  At head of title: Conference board reports.

  1. Saving and thrift. 2. Investments. I. Title.
II. Ser.

NN 0054424   ViU InU MoSU IaU OC1JC

National industrial conference board.
  ... Employees' handbooks ... New York, Nation-
al industrial conference board, inc. ₍ᶜ1942₎
  cover-title, 16 p. illus. (part col.) 28 cm.
(Its Studies in personnel policy, no. 45)
  At head of title: Conference board reports.

  1. Employees' magazines, handbooks, etc.

NN 0054425   Vi OC1 IaU

VOLUME 407

National industrial conference board.
... Employees in government service ... ₁New York₁ National industrial conference board, 1934.

cover-title, ii, 8 numb. l. 19ᶜᵐ. (Conference board information service: Domestic affairs. Memorandum no. 30)

Mimeographed.
Statistical data for the years 1929 and 1932.

1. U. S.—Officials and employees. I. Title.
Library of Congress   HC106.3.N24 no. 30   34–15664
——— Copy 2.

Copyright AA 147152   ₃₁   (330.973) 351.10973

NN   0054426   DLC

National industrial conference board.
... Employment, hours, and earnings, January, 1933, to March, 1934 ... ₁New York₁ National industrial conference board, 1934.

cover-title, ii, 16 numb. l. 28½ᶜᵐ. (Conference board information service: Domestic affairs. Memorandum no. 32)

Mimeographed.

1. U. S.—Indus.—Stat. 2. U. S.—Manuf.—Stat. 3. Unemployed—U. S. 4. Hours of labor—U. S. 5. Wages—U. S. I. Title.
Library of Congress   HC106.3.N24 no. 32   34–34205
——— Copy 2.

Copyright A 72567   ₅₁   (330.973) 330.973

NN   0054427   DLC Or TxU

HF5549
.A2N27   National Industrial Conference Board.
no.24
1940   Employment of aliens and plant protection. New York, 1940.

15 p. forms. 28cm. (Its Studies in personnel policy, no. 24)
Cover title.
Supplement to the Management record.

1. Aliens. I. Title. II. Ser.

NN   0054428   ViU IaU OClJC

National industrial conference board.
... Employment of handicapped persons ... New York, N. Y., National industrial conference board, inc. ₁1944₁

cover-title, 23 p. illus. 28 x 21½ cm. (Its Conference board reports)

Studies in personnel policy, no. 63.

1. Disabled—Rehabilitation, etc. I. Title.
HF5549.A2N27 no. 63   658.386   44—7251

NN   0054429   DLC AAP

National industrial conference board.
The employment of young persons in the United States. New York, National industrial conference board, inc., 1925.

2 p. l., iii-viii, 150 p. incl. tables, diagrs. 23½ᶜᵐ.

1. Children—Employment—U. S. I. Title.
Library of Congress   HD6250.U3N54   25–16325

NcU ICJ DHEW OrU MtBC MtU KMK WaS OrSaW OrCS
NN   0054430   DLC Or CU TU KEmT NcD OCl OU DL NN

National industrial conference board.
... Employment procedures and personnel records ... New York, National industrial conference board, inc. ₁ᶜ1941₁

cover-title, 84 p. plans, forms. 28 cm. (Its Studies in personnel policy, no. 38)
At head of title: Conference board reports.

1. Employment management - Forms, blanks, etc. I. Title. II. Title: Personnel records.

NN   0054431   Vi IaU InU MoSU PSt ViU OClU

National industrial conference board.
Engineering education and American industry ... New York city, National industrial conference board ₁1923₁

vii, 25 p. diagrs. 23ᶜᵐ. (Its Special report, no. 25)

1. Engineering—Study and teaching—U. S. I. Title.
Library of Congress   T73.N32   23–13157

ViU MB OrU CaBVaU WaWW DHEW
NN   0054432   DLC MtBC IdU MtU CU NcD OCU OCl MiU

National industrial conference board.
Enterprise and social progress; an audit and appraisal of private and public management of labor, investment and consumption in the United States and other countries... New York, Nat. industrial conference board ₁ᶜ1938₁   23 p.   19cm.

1. State control and ownership.   2. Laissez-faire.
N. Y. P. L.   September 17, 1945

NN   0054433   NN

National industrial conference board.
... Escalator protection in contracts. New York, National industrial conference board, inc., 1941.

cover-title, 16 p. incl. tables, diagrs. 28 x 21½ᶜᵐ. (Its Conference board reports)
"Selected bibliography on defense contracts": p. 16.

1. Contracts, Letting of. I. Title.
Library of Congress   HD2365.N3   43–5392
₃₁   658.721

OClW ICJ
NN   0054434   DLC OrCS DNAL OClU GU MB ICU OCU ICU

National Industrial Conference Board.
Escalators and the new BLS index ₁by Harold Stieglitz, Division of Personnel Administration₁ New York ₁1953₁

27 p. illus. 28 cm. (Its Conference Board reports. Studies in personnel policy, no. 137)
Cover title.

1. Wages—Cost-of-living adjustments—U. S. I. Stieglitz, Harold. II. Title. (Series: National Industrial Conference Board. Studies in personnel policy, no. 137)
HF5549.A2N27 no. 137   331.22   53–3499

NN   0054435   DLC OCU ViU CoU NIC OOxM

National industrial conference board.
... Essential facts for fiscal policy. New York, National industrial conference board, inc., 1941.

cover-title, 135 p. incl. tables. diagrs. 28 x 21½ᶜᵐ. (Its Conference board reports)
Bibliographical foot-notes.

1. Finance—U. S. 2. World war, 1939-   —Finance—U. S. I. Title.
Library of Congress   HJ257.N317   43–1711

MH–BA ICU
NN   0054436   DLC Or OrU MB DNAL GU ICJ OU OCU DFT

National industrial conference board.
Essentials of a program of unemployment reserves. New York, National industrial conference board, inc., 1933.

ix, 68 p. 23ᶜᵐ.
Supplementary to the Conference board's report on 'Unemployment benefits and insurance' published in October, 1931. cf. Foreword.

1. Unemployed—U. S. 2. Insurance, Unemployment—U. S. 3. U. S.—Indus. I. Title.
Library of Congress   HD5724.N26   33–4416
——— Copy 2.
Copyright A 60159   ₅-5₁   331.137973

DL MsU NIC ICJ ViU MH M
NN   0054437   DLC NcD OrCS WaS MtU CU NcD OO OCU OU

National Industrial Conference Board.
Evaluating managerial positions. ₁By Herbert S. Briggs, Division of Personnel Administration₁ New York ₁1951₁

112 p. forms. 28 cm. (Its Conference Board reports. Studies in personnel policy, no. 122)
Cover title.

1. Executives. I. Briggs, Herbert S. II. Title. (Series: National Industrial Conference Board. Studies in personnel policy, no. 122)
HF5549.A2N27 no. 122   658.3124   51–8469

NN   0054438   DLC ViU CoU

National industrial conference board.
... Evidences of world business recovery ... ₁New York₁ National industrial conference board, 1933.

2 p. l., 23 numb. l. incl. tables. diagrs. 28 x 22ᶜᵐ. (Conference board information service: Foreign affairs. Memorandum no. 12)
Reproduced from type-written copy.

1. Economic conditions—1918-   I. Title.
Library of Congress   HC57.N2923   42–3338
₂₁   330.904

NN   0054439   DLC

National Industrial Conference Board.
Executive compensation. New York ₁1954₁

44 p. 28 cm. (Its Conference Board reports. Studies in labor statistics, no. 12)

1. Executives—Salaries, pensions, etc.—U. S. I. Title.
HD4965.5.U6N26   331.2858   55–466 ‡

NN   0054440   DLC NB OOxM OCU NcD DI TxU ViU

National Industrial Conference Board.
Executive compensation in thirty-nine
    see under   Fitzgerald, Thomas A., 1907-

National Industrial Conference Board.
Executive development courses in universities. ₁By George V. Moser and Allison V. MacCullough₁ New York ₁1954₁

55 p. 28 cm. (Its Conference Board reports. Studies in personnel policy, no. 142)

1. Executives. 2. Industrial management—Study and teaching. I. Moser, George V. II. Title.
HF5549.A2N27 no. 142   658.3124   54–2901 ‡

ViU
NN   0054442   DLC OrPS OCU CoU NBuU PPT OOxM DI

National Industrial Conference Board.
Executive expense accounts ₁by Malcolm C. Neuhoff, Division of Business Practices₁ New York ₁1954₁

31 p. illus. 28 cm. (Its Conference Board reports. Studies in business policy, no. 67)

1. Executives—Salaries, pensions, etc.—U. S. I. Neuhoff, Malcolm C. II. Title.
HF5006.N3 no. 67   658.32   54–2164 ‡

NN   0054443   DLC ViU IaU LU

National Industrial Conference Board.
Executive planning if an A-bomb falls. ₁By R. Maxil Ballinger, Division of Business Practices₁ New York ₁1950₁

19 p. map, diagrs. 28 cm. (Its Conference Board reports. Studies in personnel policy, no. 108)
Cover title.
"Effects of atomic explosions": acetate overlay inserted.

1. Atomic bomb — Safety measures. I. Title. (Series: National Industrial Conference Board. Studies in personnel policy, no. 108)
HF5549.A2N27 no. 108   623.3   50–12820 rev

NN   0054444   DLC KMK MB AAP CoU IaU

VOLUME 407

National Industrial Conference Board.
Executive stock ownership plans; restricted stock option plan, executive stock purchase plan. ₍By F. Beatrice Brower, Division of Personnel Administration₎ New York ₍1951₎
72 p. 28 cm. (*Its* Conference Board reports. Studies in personnel policy, no. 120)
Cover title.

1. Employee ownership. I. Brower, Frances Beatrice. II. Title. (Series: National Industrial Conference Board. Studies in personnel policy, no. 120)
HF5549.A2N27 no. 120   331.17   51–8736

NN   0054445   DLC CoU AAP IaU ViU

National Industrial Conference Board.
Experience with employee attitude surveys ₍by S. Avery Raube, Division of Personnel Administration₎ New York ₍1951₎
120 p. illus. 28 cm. (*Its* Conference Board reports. Studies in personnel policy, no. 115)
Cover title.

1. Attitude (Psychology) 2. Personnel management. I. Raube, S. Avery. II. Title. (Series: National Industrial Conference Board. Studies in personnel policy, no. 115)
HF5549.A2N27 no. 115   658.3   51–4799

NN   0054446   DLC CaBVa CoU IaU ViU AAP

National industrial conference board.
... **Experience with employment tests** ... New York, National industrial conference board, inc. ₍1941₎
cover-title, 72 p. diagrs. 28 cm. (*Its* Studies in personnel policy, no. 32)
At head of title: Conference board reports.
"By Herbert Moore." – p. 1.
"Publishers and prices of tests mentioned in report": p. 70–72.

1. Employees, Rating of. 2. Ability – Testing. 3. Mental tests. I. Moore, Herbert, 1894– II. Title. III. Title: Employment tests, Experience with.

NN   0054448   Vi IU OCl InU IaU

National industrial conference board.
Experience with mutual benefit associations in the United States ... New York, National industrial conference board ₍°1923₎
viii, 155 p. 23 cm. (*Its* Research report no. 65)
"Industrial concerns which furnished data regarding mutual benefit associations": p. 147–155.

1. Friendly societies—U. S. 2. Insurance, Fraternal—U. S. I. Title.
HD7126.N3   24–891

OCU MiU ViU DL CaBVaU ICJ MB
NN   0054449   DLC OrPR OrU Or CU WaWW NcRS NcD OU

National Industrial Conference Board.
Experience with psychological tests. New York ₍1948₎
32 p. 28 cm. (*Its* Conference Board reports. Studies in personnel policy, no. 92)
Cover title.

1. Ability—Testing. 2. Personnel management. I. Title. (Series: National Industrial Conference Board. Conference Board reports. Series: National Industrial Conference Board. Studies in personnel policy, no. 92)
HF5549.A2N27 no. 92   658.01   48–3519*

NN   0054450   DLC AAP IaU OClJC Mi CoU

National industrial conference board.
Experience with trade union agreements—clothing industries. Research report, no. 38, by the National industrial conference board ... New York, The Century co. ₍°1921₎
iv, 134 p. 23ᶜᵐ.
Bibliographical foot-notes.

1. Trade-unions—U. S. 2. Arbitration, Industrial—U. S. 3. Clothing trade—U. S. I. Title.
Library of Congress   HD6515.C5N35   21–22095

WaTC UU CU MiU OU OO ViU ICJ MB
NN   0054451   DLC CaBVaU Or WaWW NcD OrU WaS MtBC

National industrial conference board.
Experience with works councils in the United States ... National industrial conference board. New York, The Century co. ₍1922₎
vi, 191 p. diagrs. 22½ cm. (*Its* Research report, no. 50)
"Industrial concerns having a form of employee representation": p. 185–191.

1. Works councils—U. S.
HD5650.N34   22–12909

ViU CU DL ICJ OrU WaWW CaBVaU
NN   0054452   DLC MtBC WaS WaTC NcRS OU OCU OO MB

National industrial conference board.
... Experiences with government contracts. New York, National industrial conference board, inc. ₍1942₎
cover-title, 28 p. diagrs. 28 x 22ᶜᵐ. (*Its* Conference board reports)

1. War contracts—U. S. I. Title.
42–52208
Library of Congress   UC267.N34
₍4₎   351.71

DNAL OClU ViU
NN   0054453   DLC OrU OrCS NBuG GU ICJ OClW OU OCU

National Industrial Conference Board.
Factors affecting employee morale ₍by S. Avery Raube, Management Research Division₎ New York ₍1947₎
cover-title, 35 p. tables. 28 cm. (*Its* Conference Board reports. Studies in personnel policy, no. 85)

1. Personnel management. I. Raube, S. Avery. II. Title. III. Series: National Industrial Conference Board. Conference Board reports. IV. Series: National Industrial Conference Board. Studies in personnel policy, no. 85.
HF5549.A2N27 no. 85   658.3   48–340*

NN   0054454   DLC CoU Mi AAP

National Industrial Conference Board.
The "fair trade" question

see its

The Conference Board Economic Forum presents:
The fair trade question.

National industry conference board.
Family budgets of American wage-earners, a critical analysis ... National industrial conference board. New York, The Century co. ₍°1921₎
viii, 97 p. tables (part fold.) diagrs. 23ᶜᵐ. (*Its* Research report, no. 41)
Bibliographical foot-notes.

1. Cost and standard of living—U. S. 2. Wages—U. S. I. Title.
21–22003
Library of Congress   HD6983.N35

NN   0054456   DLC ICJ WaTC WaS Or WaWW CU MtBC CaBVaU

National Industrial Conference Board.
February 12,1920. A Lincoln day message. [Boston, Mass. National Industrial Conference Board, copyright 1920]
6 p.   16 mo.   Unbound.
[caption title]
The Judd Stewart collection, May 1922.

NN   0054457   CSmH

National industrial conference board.
... The federal debt and the banks ... ₍New York₎ National industrial conference board, 1935.
cover-title, 9 numb. l. diagrs. 28½ᶜᵐ. (Conference board information service: Domestic affairs. Memorandum no. 39)
Mimeographed.

1. Debts, Public—U. S. 2. Bonds—U. S. 3. Banks and banking—U. S. I. Title.
Library of Congress   HC106.3.N24 no. 39   35–7549
———— Copy 2.
Copyright AA 166552   ₍8₎   (330.973) 336.30973

NN   0054458   DLC OC1FRB

National industrial conference board.
Federal finances, 1923–1932. New York, National industrial conference board, inc., 1933.
xvii, 124 p. diagrs. 23½ cm.
"The present study ₍was₎ prepared by Mr. Lewis H. Kimmel."—Foreword.

1. Finance, Public—U. S.—1901–1933. 2. Taxation—U. S. 3. Debts, Public—U. S. 4. U. S.—Executive departments. I. Kimmel, Lewis H. II. Title.
HJ257.N32   336.73   33–27173

MB FMU MtU WaS OrCS CaBVaU WaTC OrU Or
NN   0054459   DLC TU NIC NcD OU MiU OO DL ViU ICJ

National industrial conference board.
... Federal finances in the fiscal year 1934– ... ₍New York₎ National industrial conference board, 1934–
v. 28½ᶜᵐ. (Conference board information service. Domestic affairs series. Memorandum no. 36, 44, 49, 60.)
Mimeographed.
1936–   : By Lewis H. Kimmel.

1. Finance—U. S. I. Kimmel, Lewis Henry, 1899– II. Title.
34–38506 Revised
Library of Congress   HC106.3.N24 no. 36, 44, 49, 60,
———— 2d set.   ₍41₎₍42₎   (330.973) 336.73

NN   0054460   DLC OC1FRB MB

National industrial conference board.
The federal fiscal emergency. New York, National industrial conference board, inc., 1932.
xi, 84 p. diagrs. 23 cm.
"The present volume is the result of an investigation conducted by Roland P. Falkner and assistants."—Pref.

1. Finance, Public—U. S.—1901–1933. 2. Debts, Public—U. S. I. Falkner, Roland Post, 1866– II. Title.
HJ257.N33   336.73   32–7207

NN   0054461   DLC GU FMU MB ICJ MiU OCU OU TU NcD

National Industrial Conference Board.
...Federal governmental departments or agencies and number of federal employees... ₍New York, 1934₎ 4 f. incl. tables. 28cm. (*Its* ₍Conference Board information service: Domestic affairs₎ Special memorandum. ₍no. 3.₎)
Caption-title.
Reproduced from typewritten copy.

1. United States—Executive departments. 2. Civil service—Stat.—U. S., 1932–1934. I. Ser.
N. Y. P. L.   June 24, 1936

NN   0054462   NN

National industrial conference board.
Federal legislation in 1935 ... ₍New York₎ National industrial conference board, inc., 1935.
cover-title, 1 p. l. 20 numb. l. 28½ᶜᵐ. (*Its* Conference board information service: Domestic affairs. Special memorandum no. 10)
Reproduced from type-written copy.

1. Legislation—U. S. I. Title.
44–27008
Library of Congress   HC106.3.N243 no. 10
₍2₎   (330.973) 328.733

NN   0054463   DLC NN

VOLUME 407

National Industrial Conference Board.
　...Federal restriction of working hours as an unemployment remedy. ₍New York₎ National Industrial Conference Board, 1933. 6 f. 28cm. bd. 28 x 38cm. (*Its* Conference Board information service: Domestic affairs series. Memorandum no. 4.)

Photostatic reproduction, on 4 l.
Reproduced from typewritten copy.

1. Hours of labor—Day of 6 hours　　　—U. S. I. Ser.
N. Y. P. L.　　　　　　　　　　　　　　June 18, 1936

NN　0054464　　NN

NATIONAL INDUSTRIAL CONFERENCE BOARD.
A federation of American industries for study of industrial problems improvement of industrial relations promotion of industrial prosperity. [Boston, 1919].

19 cm.　pp. 24.
Paper cover serves as title-page.

NN　0054465　　MH-L

National industrial conference board.
Financial incentives; a study of methods for stimulating achievement in industry ... New York city, National industrial conference board, inc. ₍1935₎
ix, 47 p. 23ᶜᵐ.　(*Its* Studies. no. 217₎
"This report is based on an investigation conducted by Mr. Kenneth Stillman."—Foreword.

1. Wages. 2. Wages—U. S. 3. Piece-work. 4. Bonus system. 5. Profit-sharing.　I. Stillman, Kenneth.　II. Title.
　　　　　　　　　　　　　　　　　　　　35—13609
Library of Congress　　　HD4926.N25
————— Copy 2.
Copyright A 85412　　　₍5-5₎　　　　　331.21

NN　0054466　　OU NcD IEN
　　　　　　　DLC MtU WaS OrCS OrU ICJ ViU MiU OCU

National Industrial Conference Board.
　Financial management of pension trusts ₍by Egon von Mauchenheim, Division of Business Practices₎ New York ₍1954₎
43 p. 28 cm. (*Its* Conference Board reports. Studies in business policy, no. 66)

1. Pension trusts.　I. Von Mauchenheim, Egon.　II. Title.
HF5006.N3　no. 66،　　　658.3252　　　54—2088 ‡

NN　0054467　　DLC WaWW MH-BA ViU OU NBuU IaU LU

National industrial conference board.
　... The financial operations of the federal farm and shipping boards. New York, National industrial conference board, inc., 1933.
v, 93 numb. l. tables. 29 cm.

Multigraphed.
At head of title: For confidential use. Advance copy of a report.

1. U.S. Federal farm board. 2. U.S. Shipping board.

NN　0054468　　NNC

National industrial conference board.

New Orleans. *Tax revision commission.*
　A fiscal and administrative survey of the city of New Orleans ... Submitted to the Commission council of the city of New Orleans by the New Orleans Tax revision commission, December 5, 1933. ₍New Orleans, Press of Brandao printing co., inc., 1934₎

National industrial conference board.
　The fiscal problem in Delaware. New York, National industrial conference board, inc., 1927.
x, 150 p. incl. tables, diagrs. 23½ᵐ.

1. Finance—Delaware. 2. Taxation—Delaware.　I. Title.
　　　　　　　　　　　　　　　　　　27—13158
Library of Congress　　　HJ585.N3

NN　0054470　　OCU MiU OU ICJ WaTC MtU Wa WaS OrCS Or OrU CaBVaI
　　　　　　　DLC OKentU CU MsU MB AAP ViU DHEW

National industrial conference board.
　The fiscal problem in Illinois. New York, National industrial conference board, inc., 1927.
xiv, 219 p. incl. front., maps, diagrs. 23½ cm.

1. Finance—Illinois. 2. Taxation—Illinois.　I. Title.
HJ405.N3　　　　　　　　　　　　　27—23544

NN　0054471　　ICJ ICRL WaTC MtU WaS OrCS OrU FMU MB
　　　　　　　DLC NIC AAP MH-BA CoU ViU OO OU OCU

National industrial conference board.
　The fiscal problem in Massachusetts. New York, National industrial conference board, inc., 1931.
xv, 344 p. incl. tables, diagrs. 23½ cm.
"Sources and methods": p. ₍339₎–344.

1. Finance, Public—Massachusetts. 2. Taxation—Massachusetts. I. Title.
HJ495.N3　　　336.744　　　32—416

NN　0054472　　OCl OU DAL WaS OrCS Or WaTC OrU
　　　　　　　DLC MtU ICJ MB ScU ICRL MWelC NcD MiU

National industrial conference board.
　The fiscal problem in Missouri. New York, National industrial conference board, inc., 1930.
xvi, 359 p. incl. tables, diagrs. 23½ cm.
"Sources and methods": p. 356–359.

1. Finance, Public—Missouri. 2. Taxation—Missouri.　I. Title.
HJ535.N3　　　336.778　　　31—952

NN　0054473　　OO OCl OCU DAL
　　　　　　　DLC MH OrU WaTC Or OrCS WaS MtU MB NcD

National industrial conference board.
　The fiscal problem in New York state. New York, National industrial conference board, inc., 1928.
xx, 275 p. diagrs. 23½ cm.
"Sources of data": p. 3–4.

1. Finance—New York (State) 2. Taxation—New York (State) I. Title.
HJ605.N3　　　　　　　　　　　　　28—14390

NN　0054474　　OCl DL MB ICJ DAL MtU WaS OrCS OrU AAP
　　　　　　　DLC NBuHi TU ICRL CoU ViU NcD MiU OCU

National industrial conference board.
　The five-day week in manufacturing industries. New York, National industrial conference board, inc., 1929.
xi, 69 p. 23½ᵐ.

1. Hours of labor—U. S. 2. U. S.—Manuf. 3. U. S.—Indus. I. Title.
　　　　　　　　　　　　　　　　　　29—30188
Library of Congress　　　HD5123.N3

NN　0054475　　DAL MtU MtBC WaS OrCS CaBVa WaTC OrU MB MH ICJ ViU
　　　　　　　DLC KEmT CU OrU NcD MiU OOxM OCl DL

330.1
·N214f
National Industrial Conference *Board.*
Forecasting sales. New York ₍1947₎
47p. diagrs. 28cm. (*Its* Studies in business policy. no. 25)

Cover title.
"Conference Boards reports."
Bibliography: p. 47.

1. Business forecasting.　I. Title.　(Series)

NN　0054476　　IU MiEM MH-BA NIC

National industrial conference board.
　... Foreign trade and hemisphere unity ... New York, National industrial conference board, inc., 1941.
cover-title, 43 p. incl. illus. (map) tables, diagrs. 28 x 21½ᵐ. (*Its* Conference board reports)

1. U. S.—Comm.—Spanish America. 2. Spanish America—Comm.—U. S. 3. American republics.　I. Title.
　　　　　　　　　　　　　　　　　　43—5389
Library of Congress　　　HF3080.N45
　　　　　　　₍4₎　　　　　　　382

NN　0054477　　CtY MH-BA IaU DNAL ICJ ViU
　　　　　　　DLC OrCS OrU MB GU OClW OCU OU ICU

National industrial conference board.
　... Foreman compensation ... New York, National industrial conference board, inc. ₍1941₎
1 p. l., 16 p. tables, form. 28 cm. (*Its* Studies in personnel policy, no. 30)

At head of title: ... Conference board reports.
"Reprint".
By E. S. Horning, Management research division. cf. p. 16.
Bibliography: p. 16.
1. Foremen. 2. Wages.　I. Horning, Eugene S II. Title.

NN　0054478　　Vi InU IaU OClJC

National industrial conference board.
　... Foreman training in the anthracite industry ... New York, N. Y., National industrial conference board, inc. ₍1944₎
cover-title, 24 p. diagrs. 28 x 22ᵐ. (*Its* Conference board reports)
Studies in personnel policy, no. 68.
"Prepared ... by Mr. S. Avery Raube, associate director of the Board's Management research division."—Foreword.

1. Foremen. 2. Coal-miners.　I. Raube, S. Avery. II. Title.
　　　　　　　　　　　　　　　　　　44—41857
Library of Congress　　　HF5549.A2N27 no. 68
　　　　　　　₍5₎　　　　　(658.3)　658.3124

NN　0054479　　DLC CoU OClJC AAP OClU IaU

National Industrial Conference Board.
　Fringe benefit packages. ₍By Harold Stieglitz, Division of Personnel Administration. New York, 1954₎
198 p. 28 x 45 cm. (*Its* Conference Board reports. Studies in personnel policy, no. 143)
Cover title.

1. Non-wage payments—U. S.　I. Stieglitz, Harold. II. Title. (Series: National Industrial Conference Board. Studies in personnel policy, no. 143)
HF5549.A2N27 no. 143　　　658.32　　　54—3866

NN　0054480　　MH IaU CoU OCU
　　　　　　　DLC CaBVa DI NcD PPT PPCuP OOxM ViU

HB
31
.N33
no.6
National Industrial Conference Board.
　Full employment and scarcity: an evening with the economists. Around the table: Jules Backman, Discussion leader, D. H. Davenport ₍and others₎ New York, 1946.
44 p. (Studies in business economics, no. 6)

Cover title.

1. U.S. - Economic policy. 2. Unemployed - U.S. 3. U.S. - Full employment policies. I. Backman, Jules, 1910-　II. Title. (Series: National Industrial Conference Board. Studies in business economics, no. 6)

NN　0054481　　DAU ViU

VOLUME 407

National Industrial Conference Board.
... The general price situation. ₍New York₎ National Industrial Conference Board, 1933. 9 ₍i. e. 11₎ f. incl. tables. charts. 28cm. bd. 28 x 38cm. (Its: Conference Board information service: Domestic affairs series. Memorandum no. 2.)

Photostatic reproduction, on 10 l.
Reproduced from typewritten copy.

1. Prices—U. S., 1933. I. Ser.
N. Y. P. L.   June 18, 1936

NN 0054482   NN

National industrial conference board.
General sales or turnover taxation. New York, National industrial conference board, inc., 1929.
xv, 204 p. incl. tables, diagrs. 23½ᶜᵐ.

1. Taxation—U. S.   I. Title.   II. Title: Turnover taxation.
Library of Congress   HJ5715.U6N3   29—22653

FMU MB MH WaTC Wa Or OrCS
NN 0054483   DLC TxU CoU NcD OC1 OO MiU DL ICJ DAL

National Industrial Conference Board.
General wage adjustments in manufacturing, June 1950–March 1954. New York ₍1954₎
27 p. 28 cm. (Its Conference Board reports. Studies in labor statistics, no. 11)

1. Wages—U. S.   I. Title.
HD4975.N388 1954   331.2973   54—2714 ‡

NN 0054484   DLC OOxM ViU OCU NcD DI NBuU NB

National Industrial Conference Board.
General wage increases in manufacturing industries. New York ₍1949₎
40 p. 28 cm. (Its Conference Board reports. Studies in labor statistics, no. 1)
Cover title.
Foreword signed: Elizabeth M. Caselli.
CONTENTS.—Production workers, 1940-1948.—Clerical workers, 1945-1948.

1. Wages—U. S.   I. Caselli, Elizabeth M.   II. Title.   (Series: National Industrial Conference Board. Studies in labor statistics, no. 1)
HD4975.N388   331.2973   49—4653 rev*

NN 0054485   DLC OCU OOxM PPFRB

National Industrial Conference Board.
General wage increases in manufacturing, 1948–1950. I. Production workers. II. Clerical workers. ₍By Thomas A. Fitzgerald, Statistical Division₎ New York ₍1951₎
20 p. 28 cm. (Its Conference Board reports. Studies in labor statistics, no. 5)
Cover title.

1. Wages—U. S. 2. U. S.—Manuf.   I. Fitzgerald, Thomas A., 1907–   II. Title.   (Series: National Industrial Conference Board. Studies in labor statistics, no. 5)
HD5125.N28   331.2973   51—2666

NN 0054486   DLC NB ViU UU

National Industrial Conference Board.
Getting defense contracts ₍by Arthur W. Nevins, Division of Business Practices₎ New York ₍1951₎
47 p. map, diagrs. 28 cm. (Its Conference Board reports. Studies in business policy, no. 54)
Cover title.

1. Defense contracts—U. S. 2. U. S.—Armed Forces—Procurement. I. Nevins, Arthur W.   II. Title.   (Series: National Industrial Conference Board. Studies in business policy, no. 54)
HF5006.N3 no. 54   351.71   58—4141

NN 0054487   DLC MH-BA CoU LU IaU

666.1   National Industrial Conference Board.
N212g   Glass and glass products; basic industrial
          data. ₍New York?₎ 1955.
          30p. tables. 28cm.

          Caption title.

          1. Glass manufacture--U.S.   I. Title.

NN 0054488   IU NIC

National industrial conference board.
Glimpses of the labor situation; a series of reports on labor conditions from cooperating executives in representative industrial areas ...
New York, N. Y., National industrial conference board, ᶜ1937–

v. 28ᵐᵐ.
1. Labor and laboring classes—U. S.—1914–   2. Trade-unions—
U. S.   I. Title.   40–14434
Library of Congress   HD8072.N2835
———— 2d set.
Copyright   ₍2₎   331.870973

NN 0054489   DLC

National industrial conference board.
... The gold standard: recent developments and present status. ₍New York₎ National industrial conference board, 1933.
2 p. l., 21 numb. l. incl. tables, diagr. 28½ x 22ᶜᵐ. (Conference board information service: Domestic affairs. Memorandum no. 5)
Reproduced from type-written copy.

1. Gold. 2. Currency question.
                                                              42–2970
Library of Congress   HC106.3.N24 no. 5
                           ₍2₎   (330.973) 332.42

NN 0054490   DLC NN

National industrial conference board.
... Governmental debt of the United States and European countries ... ₍New York₎ National industrial conference board, 1934.
cover-title, 4 numb. l. 28½ᶜᵐ. (Conference board information service: Domestic affairs series. Memorandum no. 35)
Mimeographed.

1. Debts, Public—U. S. 2. Debts, Public—Gt. Brit. 3. Debts, Public—France. 4. Debts, Public—Germany.   I. Title.
                                                              34–34206
Library of Congress   HC106.3.N24 no. 35
———— Copy 2.
Copyright AA 150575   ₍5₎   (330.973) 336.3

NN 0054491   DLC OC1FRB NcD

National Industrial Conference Board.
Grain and grain products; basic industrial data. ₍New York, 1950₎
₍19₎ p. of tables. 28 cm.
Caption title.

1. Grain trade—U. S. 2. Flour and feed trade—U. S.   I. Title.
HD9034.N3   338.1731   50–3888

NN 0054492   DLC NNUN

National industrial conference board.
A graphic analysis of the census of manufactures of the United States, 1849 to 1919. New York, National industrial conference board ₍ᶜ1923₎
1 p. l., v–xx, 253 p. diagrs. 28½ᶜᵐ.

1. U. S.—Manuf. 2. U. S.—Indus.
                                                              23–11143
Library of Congress   HD9724.N3

ICJ MiHM MtU IdU WaS OrU
NN 0054493   DLC CoU CU MWA MiU OC1 OU DL DNW MB

National Industrial Conference Board.
A graphic analysis prepared for annual meeting
see its   The graphic record of American enterprise.

National Industrial Conference Board.
Graphic business news items.
New York,

NN 0054495   OC1

National industrial conference board, inc.
A Graphic guide to consumer markets
see under title

330.973 National Industrial Conference Board.
N215g   The graphic record of American enterprise.
           New York.
           v. col. diagrs. 26–29 cm.
           "Chart surveys prepared in connection with the annual meetings of the National Industrial Conference Board."
           Cover title.   : A graphic analysis prepared for the annual meeting.
           Some volumes lack   series title.
           Each volume has   also a distinctive title.

NN 0054497   IU OAkU CU OC1 MiD DBB

National Industrial Conference Board.
Grievance procedures in nonunionized companies ₍by James J. Bambrick, Jr., and John J. Speed, Division of Personnel Administration₎ New York ₍1950₎
47 p. illus. 28 cm. (Its Conference Board reports. Studies in personnel policy, no. 109)
Cover title.

1. Grievance procedures.   I. Bambrick, James Joseph, 1888– II. Speed, John Joseph, 1923–   (Series: National Industrial Conference Board. Studies in personnel policy, no. 109)
HF5549.A2N27 no. 109   658.315   51–1541 rev

NN 0054498   DLC CoU

National industrial conference board.
The growth of works councils in the United States, a statistical summary ... New York city, National industrial conference board, inc. ₍ᶜ1925₎
v, 15 p. incl. tables. 23 cm. (Its Special report, no. 32)

1. Work councils—U. S.

HD5650.N35   25—7449

NN 0054499   DLC CU Or IdU MtU DAL ICJ MB MiU OU OC1

National Industrial Conference Board.
Growth patterns in industry ₍prepared by Frederick W. Jones, assisted by Anita R. Beckerman, Division of Business Economics. New York, 1952₎
59 p. diagrs. 23 cm. (Its Studies in business economics. no. 32)
Cover title.

1. U. S.—Indus.   I. Jones, Frederick William, 1887– II. Title.   (Series)
HB31.N33 no. 32   338   52–2435

PSt ViU DAU NIC IaU
NN 0054500   DLC WaWW Wa OrLgE MoU NcD NN TxU PHC

VOLUME 407

National Industrial Conference Board.
Growth patterns of cities ₍prepared by Frederick W. Jones, assisted by Anita R. Beckerman, Division of Business Economics. New York, 1953₎

63 p. diagrs. 23 cm. (*Its* Studies in business economics, no. 39)

Cover title.

1. Cities and towns—Growth.   I. Jones, Frederick William, 1887–   II. Title.   (Series)

HB31.N33 no. 39   323.352   53–3466

OOxM NcD OU OCU CoU CaBVa Or OrLgE
NN   0054501   DLC DAU MiU   IaU ViU PPPH NN PSt TxU

National Industrial Conference Board.
Handbook of union government, structure and procedures. ₍By James J. Bambrick, Jr. and George H. Haas, Division of Personnel Administration₎ New York ₍1955₎

120 p. illus. 28 cm. (*Its* Conference Board reports. Studies in personnel policy, no. 150)

Cover title.
Bibliographical footnotes.

1. Trade-unions—U. S.   I. Bambrick, James Joseph, 1917–   II. Haas, George H.   III. Title.   (Series: National Industrial Conference Board. Studies in personnel policy, no. 150)

HF5549.A2N27   no. 150   331.880973   56–536

OOxM OC1FRB OU NcU AAP MH-L
NN   0054502   DLC NB CoU IaU OCU PPLas DI NIC ViU

National Industrial Conference Board.
Handbook on pensions. ₍Kinds, costs, planning and administration, texts of 48 union-negotiated and company plans, by F. Beatrice Brower, Division of Personnel Administration₎ ₍New York, 1950₎

164 p. illus. 28 cm. (*Its* Conference Board reports. Studies in personnel policy, no. 103)

Cover title.
1. Old age pensions—U. S.   I. Brower, Frances Beatrice.   (Series: National Industrial Conference Board. Conference Board reports. Series: National Industrial Conference Board. Studies in personnel policy, no. 103)

HF5549.A2N27   no. 103   331.252   50–3770

NN   0054503   DLC ViU IaU OOxM TxU PPT OU CoU

National Industrial Conference Board.
Handling higher replacement costs ₍by James A. Finley, Division of Business Practices₎ New York ₍°1950₎

32 p. illus. 28 cm. (*Its* Conference Board reports. Studies in business policy, no. 47)

Cover title.
Bibliography: p. 32.

1. Depreciation. 2. Capital investments—U. S.   I. Finley, James A.   II. Title.   (Series: National Industrial Conference Board. Studies in business policy, no. 47)

HF5006.N3   no. 47   58–47882

NN   0054504   DLC ViU LU CoU OU MH-BA IaU

National industrial conference board.
...Health insurance plans. A. Mutual benefit associations. New York, National industrial conference board, inc. ₍1938₎
34 p. incl. tables. 28ᶜᵐ. (*Its* Studies in personnel policy, no.9)

HD7102
U5N27W

1. Insurance, Health - U.S. 2. Insurance, Industrial - U.S. 3. Friendly societies - U.S. I. Title.

NN   0054505   CSt-H CaBVaU LU NIC ViU IaU InU

558.3
N21s
No.10

National industrial conference board.
...Health insurance plans. B.-Group health insurance plans. New York, National industrial conference board, inc. [c1939]
cover-title, 31p. tables. 28cm. (National industrial conference board. Studies in personnel policy. no.10)

1. Insurance, Health. I. Title.

NN   0054506   LU NIC ViU CaBVaU InU IaU

658.3
N21s
No.11

National industrial conference board.
...Health insurance plans. C.-Company non-contributory disability benefit plans. New York, National industrial conference board, inc. [c1939]
cover-title, 27p. tables. 28cm. (National industrial conference board. Studies in personnel policy. no.11)

1. Insurance, Health. I. Title.

NN   0054507   LU OC1JC IaU CaBVaU InU

National industrial conference board.
Health service in industry ... New York, National industrial conference board ₍1921₎

iv, 61 p. illus. 23ᶜᵐ. (*Its* Research report, no. 34)

1. Labor and laboring classes—Medical care. 2. Occupations—Diseases and hygiene.   I. Title.
Library of Congress   HD7263.N45   21–6422

NcD OC1 OO MiU ICJ ViU
NN   0054508   DLC CaBVaU WaWW CU OrU WaS MtBC WaTC

National Industrial Conference Board.
The Heller budget
see under   Backman, Jules, 1910–

National Industrial Conference Board.
Holiday practices ₍by John J. Speed, Division of Personnel Administration₎ New York ₍1948₎

36 p. illus. 28 cm. (*Its* Conference Board reports. Studies in personnel policy, no. 99)

1. Holidays—U. S.   (Series: National Industrial Conference Board. Conference Board reports. Series: National Industrial Conference Board. Studies in personnel policy, no. 99)

HF5549.A2N27   no. 99   331.817   49–1043*₎

NN   0054510   DLC OC1JC PPT CoU ViU AAP

National industrial conference board.
Hours of work as related to output and health of workers. Boot and shoe industry ... Boston, Mass., National industrial conference board, °1918.

vii, 76 p. incl. tables. 23ᶜᵐ. (*Its* Research reports, no. 7)

1. Hours of labor—U. S. 2. Boots and shoes—Trade and manufacture—U. S.   I. Title.
Library of Congress   HD5119.B7N3   18–14836

WaWW DHEW ICJ
NN   0054511   DLC CU NcD OU OO OC1 DL WaTC WaS Or

National industrial conference board.
Hours of work as related to output and health of workers; cotton manufacturing ... Boston, Mass., National industrial conference board, °1918.

vii, 64 p. 23 cm. (*Its* Research report, no. 4)

1. Textile workers—U. S. 2. Hours of labor—U. S. 3. Cotton manufacture—U. S.
HD5119.C7N3   18–9294

OC1W OU CU PPFML
NN   0054512   DLC CaBVaU WaWW WaS WaTC DL ICJ MiU

National industrial conference board.
Hours of work as related to output and health of workers; metal manufacturing industries ... Boston, Mass., National industrial conference board, °1919.

vii, 62 p. 23ᶜᵐ. (*Its* Research report, no. 18)

1. Hours of labor. 2. Metal-workers—U. S. 3. Metal trade—U. S.   I. Title.
Library of Congress   HD5119.M5N3   19–15298

OC1 OO ViU WaTC MtBC WaS CaBVaU Or WaWW
NN   0054513   DLC CtY-M OrU CU NcRS NNC MiU DL ICJ

National industrial conference board.
Hours of work as related to output and health of workers; silk manufacturing ... Boston, Mass., National industrial conference board, °1919.

vii, 54 p. 23ᶜᵐ. (*Its* Research report, no. 16)

1. Hours of labor. 2. Silk manufacture and trade—U. S.   I. Title.
Library of Congress   HD5119.S5N3   19–8983

MiU OC1 OO ICJ MB CaBVaU Or WaWW ViU
NN   0054514   DLC CtY-M OrU WaS MtBC WaTC NIC NcD

National industrial conference board.
Hours of work as related to output and health of workers; wool manufacturing ... Boston, Mass., National industrial conference board, °1918.

vii, 69 p. 23ᶜᵐ. (*Its* Research report, no. 12)

1. Hours of labor—U. S. 2. Woolen and worsted manufacture—U. S.   I. Title.
Library of Congress   HD5119.W6N3   19–5785

CtY-M CU MiU OC1 ICJ ViU MB WaWW OO OCU
NN   0054515   DLC WaTC MtBC WaS OrU CaBVaU Or NcD

National industrial conference board.
The hours of work problem in five major industries ... Boston, Mass., National industrial conference board, °1920.

x, 91 p. incl. tables, diagrs. 23ᶜᵐ. (*Its* Research report, no. 27)

1. Hours of labor.   I. Title.
Library of Congress   HD5125.N3   20–12529

OO OC1 OU ViU CU Or WaWW
NN   0054516   DLC CaBVaU OrU WaS WaTC ICJ MB NIC

National Industrial Conference Board.
How much government? Individual savings and how they increasingly funnel into government debt, 1910–1952. A graphic analysis prepared for the 36th annual meeting of the Conference Board. ₍New York, 1952₎

32 p. col. map, col. diagrs. 26 cm.

Cover title.

1. Finance, Public—U. S.—1933–   I. Title.

HJ258.N32   336.73   52–2603

OCU TxU OrP MsU Wa
NN   0054517   DLC OrCS IdU NcU ScCeIU OOxM PBL OC1W

National industrial conference board.
The immigration problem in the United States ... New York, National industrial conference board ₍°1923₎

viii, 130 p. illus. (maps) diagrs. 23ᶜᵐ. (*Its* Research report, no. 58)

1. U. S.—Emig. & immig. 2. Emigration and immigration law—U. S.   I. Title.
Library of Congress   JV6465.N3   23–17515

WaWW MB NN ICJ CaBVaU ViU OU OO OC1W
NN   0054518   DLC OKentU CU WaS MtBC WaSp WaTC NcD

National industrial conference board.
... Income in agriculture, 1929–1935, by Robert F. Martin, Conference board research staff ... New York city, National industrial conference board, inc. ₍°1936₎

xviii, 168 p. illus. (maps) diagrs. 23 cm. (*Its* Studies, no. 232)

1. Agriculture—Economic aspects—U. S. 2. Agriculture—U. S. 3. Income—U. S. 4. U. S.—Econ. condit.—1918–   I. Martin, Robert Fitz-Randolph.   II. Title.

HD1769.N3   338.10973   36–28571

ViU NcRS
NN   0054519   DLC FU WHi FMU OrU ICU OC1W OCU OU

VOLUME 407

National industrial conference board.
... Income received in the various states, 1929–1935, by John A. Slaughter, Conference board research staff. New York city, National industrial conference board, inc. [1937]

xv p., 1 l., 167 p. incl. illus. (maps) tables, diagrs. 23½ cm. (*Its* Studies. no. 234)

1. Income. 2. U. S.—Econ. condit.—1918–   I. Slaughter, John A. II. Title.

Library of Congress   HC106.3.N265   37–15898
——— Copy 2.
Copyright A 107712   [5]   339.20973

OC1W MB DL ICJ OCU OrCS WaTC WaSpG
WaTC WaSpG ICJ DFT ViU WaT MtU Or TU MiEM NcD OO
NN 0054520   DLC NcRS IdU MtBC WaS Wa OrPR OrU OrCS

National industrial conference board.
... Income taxes and the depression. New York city, National industrial conference board, 1933.

2 p. l., 11 numb. l. 28½ cm. (Conference board information service: Domestic affairs. Memorandum no. 12)

Mimeographed.

1. Income tax—U. S. 2. U. S.—Econ. condit.—1918–   I. Title.
40–14340

Library of Congress   HC106.3.N24 no. 12
[2]   (330.973) 336.240973

NN 0054521   DLC NN

National Industrial Conference Board.
Index of Conference Board publications, 1950–1954
        see its   Cumulative index of NICB
publications.

National industrial conference board.
Individual and collective bargaining in May, 1934. New York, National industrial conference board, inc. [1934]

x, 36 p. diagrs. 23 cm.

"This report supplements and brings up to date a similar survey conducted in November, 1933. It was conducted and this monograph was prepared by Mr. Harold F. Browne."—Foreword.

1. Labor contract—U. S. 2. Employees' representation in management. 3. National industrial recovery act, 1933. I. Browne, Harold Frederic, 1890–   II. Title. III. Title: Collective bargaining in May, 1934.

Library of Congress   HD7834.N3   35–1886
——— Copy 2.
Copyright A 73820   [5-5-3]   331.1520973

MiU NcD
NN 0054523   DLC MtU IdU WaS OrCS ICJ CU OU OC1

National industrial conference board.
Individual and collective bargaining in public utilities and on railroads, October, 1934 ... New York city, National industrial conference board, inc. [1934]

vii, 16 p. diagrs. 23 cm.

1. Trade-unions—U. S. 2. Labor contract—U. S. 3. Public utilities—U. S. 4. Railroads—U. S. I. Title.
35–2705

Library of Congress   HD6508.N3
——— Copy 2.
Copyright A 78640   [5-5]   331.880973

MiU
NN 0054524   DLC OrU Or OrCS WaS MtU CU OU OCU ICJ

National industrial conference board.
Individual and collective bargaining under the N. I. R. A.; a statistical study of present practice, November, 1933. New York, National industrial conference board, inc., 1933.

ix, 37 p. 23 cm.

"This monograph was prepared by Mr. Harold F. Browne ... under supervision of the staff Economic council."—Foreword.

1. Labor contract—U. S. 2. Employees' representation in management. 3. National industrial recovery act, 1933. I. Browne, Harold Frederic, 1890–   II. Title. III. Title: Collective bargaining under the N. I. R. A.

Library of Congress   HD5650.N27   34–877
——— Copy 2.
Copyright A 68606   [5-5]   331.1520973

ViU ICJ DL OrCS Or
NN 0054525   DLC WaS IdU MtU CU NcD MiU OC1 OU MB

National industrial conference board.
Industrial-economic conditions in the United States. Bulletin. no. 1–17; June 15, 1921–Jan. 1927. New York city, 1921–[27]

17 nos. tables. 23 cm.

Superseded by its Conference board bulletin.
L. C. set incomplete: no. 2–9, 11–16 wanting.

1. U. S.—Econ. condit.—1918–   2. U. S.—Indus.
21–16213 Revised

Library of Congress   HC106.3.N2

NN 0054526   DLC TU OO MH OC1FRB ICJ

National industrial conference board.
Industrial group insurance. New York, National industrial conference board, inc., 1927.

44 p. 23 cm.

1. Insurance, Group—U. S.   I. Title.
27–16110

Library of Congress   HG8830.N35

ViU DL
NN 0054527   DLC MB NcD MtU CU OC1W OC1 MiU ICJ NN

National industrial conference board.
Industrial group insurance. 2d ed., rev. New York, National industrial conference board, inc., 1929.

2 p. l., 3–46 p. 23 cm.

1. Insurance, Group—U. S.   I. Title.
29–24752

Library of Congress   HG8830.N35 1929

NN 0054528   DLC OrCS OOxM

National industrial conference board.
Industrial lunch rooms. New York, National industrial conference board, inc., 1928.

ix, 65 p. illus. (plans) 23 cm.

1. Restaurants, lunch rooms, etc. 2. Welfare institutions for laborers.   I. Title.
28–19302

Library of Congress   TX945.N3

NN 0054529   DLC MB DHEW OrCS MtU OC1 OU MiU ICJ

HF5549
.A2N27   National Industrial Conference Board.
no.48
1942   Industrial lunchrooms in wartime. New
        York [1942]
        28 p. illus. 28cm. (Its Studies in
        personnel policy, no. 48)
        Cover title.

        1. Restaurants, lunch rooms, etc.—U. S.
        I. Title. II.Ser.

NN 0054530   ViU IaU

National Industrial Conference Board.
Industrial mobilisation planning
        see under Dickson, Paul W

National industrial conference board.

Industrial news survey : a digest of industrial news and comment as published in reliable newspapers, magazines, reviews, special articles, and government documents. Boston, 19

National industrial conference board.
Industrial pensions in the United States. New York, National industrial conference board, inc., 1925.

xiii, 157 p. incl. tables. 23½ cm.

1. Old age pensions—U. S.   I. Title.
25–25961

Library of Congress   HD7106.U5N2

NcD MtU OrPR WaS OrCS OrU Or OrP IdU CU MH MB
NN 0054533   DLC DL MiU OU OO ICJ NN TU ViU OKentU

National industrial conference board.
Industrial progress and regulatory legislation in New York state. New York, National industrial conference board, inc., 1927.

xiv, 148 p. incl. tables, diagrs. 23½ cm.

1. Industrial laws and legislation—New York (State) 2. New York (State)—Indus.   I. Title.
27–24761

Library of Congress   HD3624.U5N7 1927

ICJ DL WaS OrCS Or WaTC FMU
NN 0054534   DLC MtU MsU KMK ViU-L NcD OCU MiU OO

National industrial conference board.
Industrial relations activities at Cheney brothers, South Manchester, Connecticut. New York, National industrial conference board, inc., 1929.

vii, 88 p. incl. diagrs., forms. 23 cm.

1. Cheney brothers. 2. Industry—Organization, control, etc. 3. Employment management.
29–13394

Library of Congress   HD7413.C5N3

MtU WaS OrU Or OrCS
NN 0054535   DLC OKentU TU NIC NcD OCU OO ODW ICJ

National industrial conference board.
Industrial relations: administration of policies and programs. New York, National industrial conference board, inc., 1931.

xii, 114 p. diagrs. 23½ cm.

1. Employment management. 2. Industry—Organization, control, etc. 3. Factory management.   I. Title.
31–21943

Library of Congress   HD6961.N3
——— Copy 2.
Copyright A 40776   [5-2]   331.1

NcD MtU OKentU WaS OrCS OrU DAL ViU ICJ
NN 0054536   DLC KMK MB Or CU TU NcRS OU MiU OO DL

National industrial conference board.
Industrial relations programs in small plants. New York, National industrial conference board, inc., 1929.

xi, 60 p. 23½ cm.

1. Employment management. 2. Factory management.   I. Title.
29–8427

Library of Congress   HF5549.N315

DL ICJ ViU
NN 0054537   DLC DAL WaS MtU CU NcD NIC OC1 OO OU

National Industrial Conference Board.
Industrial Russia : the new competitor. [New York, 1954]

88 p. 23 cm. (*Its* Studies in business economics, no. 44)

Cover title.
"A round table, held as part of the 346th meeting of the National Industrial Conference Board."

1. Russia—Econ. condit.—1945–   I. Title. (Series)

HB31.N33 no. 44   330.947   54–3009

NcD CoU IaU CaBVaU CaBVa OrLgE WaWW
NN 0054538   DLC ViU DI TxU OU OCU OOxM PSt NN AAP

VOLUME 407

National Industrial Conference Board.
Industrial security ₁by R. Maxil Ballinger₎ New York
₁*1952–
v. illus. 28 cm. (*Its* Studies in business policy, no. 60, 64,
70
Cover title.
CONTENTS.—1. Combating subversion and sabotage.—2. Plant guard
handbook.—3. Theft control procedures.
1. Factories—Protection. 2. Sabotage. 3. Police, Private. 4. Lar-
ceny. I. Ballinger, R. Maxil. II. Title. (Series)
[HF5006.N3 no. 60 ₁etc.₎] A 55–4538
Harvard Univ. Grad. Sch. Bus. Adm. Library
for Library of Congress ₁3₎

NN 0054539 MH-BA OU ViU OClU LU OCl IaU AAP WaU

National Industrial Conference Board.
The industrial situation. Jan. 1923.
New York, 1923–
monthly

NN 0054540 OClFRB

National industrial conference board.
Industrial standardization. New York, National industrial conference board, inc., 1929.
xiv, 306 p. diagrs. 23½ cm.
Thesis (PH. D.)—Columbia university, 1929.
Without thesis note.
"This present investigation was made, and this volume was prepared
... by Mr. Robert A. Brady."—Pref.
1. Standardization. 2. U. S.—Indus. I. Brady, Robert Alexander,
1901– II. Title.
HD62.N3 29–12513

DAL DHEW NcD MB WaS OrCS OrU Or WaTC
NN 0054541 DLC NcRS MtU CaBVaU GU NIC DL ICJ MiU

National industrial conference board.
... Industrial standardization (company
organization, practices and procedures) ...
New York, N.Y. ₁1947₎
cover-title, 64 p.incl.charts. (*Its*
Studies in business policy, no. 22)
At head of title: Conference board reports.

NN 0054542 MH-BA MiEM AAP

National Industrial Conference Board.
Industrial traffic departments ₁by Malcolm C. Neuhoff,
Division of Business Practices₎ New York ₁*1950₎
56 p. illus. 28 cm. (*Its* Conference Board reports. Studies in
business policy, no. 45)
Cover title.
1. Shipment of goods. I. Neuhoff, Malcolm C. II. Title. (Series: National Industrial Conference Board. Studies in business
policy, no. 45)
HF5006.N3 no. 45 58–47881

NN 0054543 DLC LU MH-BA OU CoU IaU

National Industrial Conference Board.
Industry cooperation with education
see under Watson, John H

National Industrial Conference Board.
Industry-sponsored research at universities
₁By Helen A.Winselman₎. New York ₁1946₎
cover-title, 12 p. (*Its* Studies in business
policy, no. 14)
At head of title: Conference Board reports.

NN 0054545 MH-BA Mi OU

National industrial conference board.
... Industry's attitude toward the price situation. ₁New
York₎ National industrial conference board, 1933.
1 p. l., 8 numb. l. 28½ x 22ᶜᵐ. (Conference board information service:
Domestic affairs. Memorandum no. 6)
Reproduced from type-written copy.
1. Prices—U. S. I. Title. 42–2971
Library of Congress HC106.3.N24 no. 6
₁2₎ (330.973) 338.50973

NN 0054546 DLC NN

National industrial conference board.
... Industry's community relations ...
New York, N.Y. ₁1946₎
cover-title, 16 p. (*Its* Studies in
business policy, no.20)
At head of title: Conference board reports.

NN 0054547 MH-BA MiEM FMU

National Industrial Conference Board.
Industry's terms and conditions of sale
see under Thompson, G Clark.

National industrial conference board.
The influence of public opinion and education upon economic progress in America; a series of addresses delivered at
the twenty-first annual meeting of the National industrial conference board, held at the Waldorf-Astoria hotel, New York,
May 27, 1937. New York, National industrial conference
board, inc. ₁1937₎
cover-title, 1 p. l., 53, ₁2₎ p. 23ᶜᵐ.
CONTENTS.—Introduction, by Virgil Jordan.—The rôle of the press as
a factor in public opinion and economic changes, by C. W. Ackerman.—
Education and political economics, by W. F. Russell.—Some aspects of
the relation between education and industry, by O. D. Young.—Radio
as a factor in economic progress, by Levering Tyson.—The problem of
public opinion in relation to the organization and control of business,
by Carl Byoir.
1. U. S.—Econ. condit.—1918– 2. Public opinion—U. S. 3. Education—U. S. I. Title. 38–8715
Library of Congress HC106.3.N267
———— Copy 2.
Copyright A 113918 ₁5₎ 330.973

NN 0054550 DLC OCU OU NcD ICJ

National Industrial Conference Board.
Information for the press
see its Press release.

National Industrial Conference Board.
Information racks, a new communications medium ₁by
Elmer W. Earl, Jr., Division of Personnel Administration₎
New York ₁1952₎
20 p. illus. 28 cm. (*Its* Conference Board reports. Studies in
personnel policy, no. 125)
Cover title.
1. Employees, Reporting to. I. Earl, Elmer W. II. Title.
(Series: National Industrial Conference Board. Studies in person-
nel policy, no. 125)
HF5549.A2N27 no. 125 658.385 52–1362

NN 0054552 DLC CoU AAP OCU MoSU-C ViU

National industrial conference board.
... The inter-ally debts and the United States. New York,
National industrial conference board, inc., 1925.
xvi, 290 p. diagrs. 23 cm.
At head of title: Preliminary study.
1. Debts, External. 2. U. S.—Econ. condit.—1918– 3. Euro-
pean war, 1914–1918—Finance. I. Title.
HJ8011.N35 25–11929

ViU NN ICJ DN
NN 0054553 DLC MB Or OrU OrCS WaS MtU MiU OO OCl

National industrial conference board.
The international financial position of the United States ...
₁by₎ Ralph A. Young (a study prepared for and printed by
the National industrial conference board, inc., New York city,
and used with their permission) Philadelphia, 1929.
1 p. l., v-xx, 276 p., 1 l. diagrs. 23ᶜᵐ.
Thesis (PH. D.)—University of Pennsylvania, 1929.
Published also without thesis note.
1. Finance—U. S. 2. Debts, Public. I. Young, Ralph Aubrey.
II. Title. 30–18572
Library of Congress HJ257.N35 1929
Univ. of Pennsylvania Libr.
———— Copy 2. ₁5₎ 336.73

NN 0054554 PU DLC CoU MB MH OCU MiU ViU DL

National industrial conference board.
The international financial position of the United States.
New York, National industrial conference board, inc., 1929.
xx, 276 p. incl. tables, diagrs. 23½ cm.
"This study was made and the present volume prepared by Mr.
Ralph A. Young."—Pref.
Published also as Mr. Young's thesis (PH. D.)—University of
Pennsylvania.
1. Finance, Public—U. S.—1901–1933. 2. Debts, Public. I. Young,
Ralph Aubrey. II. Title.
HJ257.N35 1929a 29–14162

CaBVaU OrCS OrU
ViU OCU NjN OU MiU DL ICJ DAL FMU OrU WaTC WaS MtU
NN 0054555 DLC WaTC WaS CaBVaU MtU OrCS OrU MB

National industrial conference board.
... The International labor organization in theory and practice: its structure and activities; class and national conflicts
that occur within it; its accomplishments; and theory underlying its work. ₁New York₎ National industrial conference
board, *1934.
cover-title, 1 p. l., 7 numb. l. 28½ᶜᵐ. (Conference board information
service: Foreign affairs series. Memorandum no. 14)
Mimeographed.
1. International labor organization. 2. Labor laws and legislation,
International. 34–40875
Library of Congress HD7809.N27
———— Copy 2.
Copyright AA 159751 ₁3₎ 331.0621

NN 0054556 DLC OClFRB

National industrial conference board.
The International labor organization of the League of
nations ... National industrial conference board. New
York, The Century co. ₁*1922₎
vi, 159 p. map, diagrs. 23ᶜᵐ. (*Its* Research report, no. 48)
Bibliographical foot-notes.
1. International labor organization. 2. Labor laws and legislation. 3. International labor office, Geneva.
Library of Congress HD7809.N3 22–12015

OKentU OU MiU MB ViU CU ICJ
NN 0054557 DLC WaTC MtBC WaS OrU CaBVaU WaWW OCl

National industrial conference board.
... International raw commodity price control, by Robert
F. Martin, Conference board research staff ... New York
city, National industrial conference board, inc. ₁1937₎
xvi, 166 p. incl. tables, diagrs. 23½ cm. (*Its* Studies. no. 238)
1. Prices. 2. Commercial products. I. Martin, Robert Fitz-
Randolph, 1900– II. Title.
HF5417.N3 338.5 38–27006

OClU MtU OrPR WaS OrCS OrU CaBVaU AAP
NN 0054558 DLC MB TU NN ICJ ViU DFT DL OU OCU

National industrial conference board.
International transactions of the United States; an audit
and interpretation of balance-of-payments estimates, by Ray
Ovid Hall, Conference board research staff ... New York
city, National industrial conference board, inc. ₁*1936₎
xv, 230 p. tables (1 fold.) 23½ cm.
The present report was prepared with the assistance of Miss Ruth
Jackendoff of the Conference board's research staff and edited for
publication by Mr. Vaso Trivanovitch, also of the board's staff. *cf.*
Foreword.

Continued in next column

VOLUME 407

Continued from preceding column

The present volume is a review and revision of the basic data recorded by the U. S. Dept. of commerce and issued since 1922 in its annual bulletins entitled, "The International balance of payments of the United States." *cf.* Foreword.

1. Balance of trade. 2. U. S.—Comm. 3. Commercial statistics. I. Hall, Ray Ovid, 1891– II. Jackendoff, Ruth, 1906– III. Trivanovitch, Vaso, ed. IV. Title. V. Title: Audit and interpretation of balance-of-payments estimates.

HF3031.N33   382.0973   36—19380

TU ODW MB ViU OCU DN Or OU OC1W FMU CU AAP
NN 0054560   DLC MtU IdU OrPR WaS OrU OrCS WaTC ICJ

National industrial conference board.
... Inventories, shipments, orders, 1929/40–
Revised indexes ... New York, National industrial conference board, inc. [*1940–

nos. diagrs. 28ᶜᵐ.

At head of title: The Conference board.
Supplement to the Conference board economic record, vol. II–Dec. 26, 1940–
"Indexes covering the period from 1929 through 1939 were first published about a year ago [in the Conference board economic record, vol. I, no. 18, December 16, 1939, and vol. II, no. 5, February 21, 1940]"

1. U. S.—Comm.   I. The Conference board economic record.

| Library of Congress | HF3001.N33 | 43–1155 |
| | [2] | 330.973 |

NN 0054561   DLC TxU NIC

National industrial conference board.
Is compulsory health insurance desirable? October, 1919 ... Boston, Mass., National industrial conference board, ᶜ1919.

2 p. l., 12 p. 23ᶜᵐ.

1. Insurance, Health—U. S. 2. Insurance, State and compulsory—. U. S.   I. Title.

| Library of Congress | HG9397.N3 | 21—2297 |

NN 0054562   DLC MtU WaS CU MB OU OO OC1

4DG
.632   National Industrial Conference Board.
        Italian Fascism as a political and
        economic system. New York, 1933.
        13 *l.*

        (*Its* Conference Board information service: foreign affairs, memorandum no. 11)

NN 0054563   DLC-P4

National industrial conference board.
... Job descriptions ... New York, N. Y., National industrial conference board, inc. [1946]

cover-title, 31 p. 28 x 21½ᶜᵐ. (*Its* Conference board reports)

Studies in personnel policy, no. 72.
"By E. S. Horning, Management research division."—p. 3.

1. Job analysis.   I. Horning, Eugene S.   II. Title.

| Library of Congress | T58.N27 | 46–2776 |
| | [20] | 658.3124 |

NN 0054564   DLC OC1U MiEM

HF5549
.A2N27 National Industrial Conference Board.
no.25
1940   Job evaluation; formal plans for determining basic pay differentials. New York, 1940.
        43 p. 28ᶜᵐ. (*Its* Studies in personnel policy, no. 25)
        Cover title.

        1. Job analysis. I. Title. II. Ser.

NN 0054565   ViU Vi OC1 MH MiU-L InU OC1JC IaU

National industrial conference board.
The Kansas Court of industrial relations ... New York, National industrial conference board [ᶜ1924]

iii p., 1 l., 103 p. 23ᶜᵐ.   (*Its* Research report, no. 67)
"The Kansas industrial court act": p. 95–103.

1. Kansas. Court of industrial relations. 2. Arbitration, Industrial—Kansas.   I. Kansas. Laws, statutes, etc.

| Library of Congress | HD5504.K2N3 | 24—5211 |

KEmT CU NcRS NcD-L MiU OU OCU OO OC1 DL MB ICJ ViU
NN 0054566   DLC CaBVaU WaS WaWW Or MtBC CU-AL

National Industrial Conference Board.
Keeping corporate directors informed.   [New York, 1947]
32 p.   28 cm.   (*Its* Studies in business policy, no. 24)
Cover title.
At head of title: Conference Board reports.
1. Directors of corporations. United States.
I. Title. (Series)

NN 0054567   AAP MiEM MH-BA PPT

National Industrial Conference Board.
Key materials: current supply and outlook, a round table discussion; George A. Renard, chairman, James Boyd [and others. New York, 1951]
47 p. diagrs. 23 cm. (*Its* Studies in business economics, no. 28)
Cover title.

1. Mines and mineral resources—U. S. 2. Chemicals—Manufacture and industry—U. S.   I. Title.   (Series)

| HB31.N33 | no. 28 | 338.2 | 51–3792 |

NN 0054568   DLC OrLgE TxU IaU CoU NN

National Industrial Conference Board.
Keys to efficient selling and lower marketing costs [by George M. Umemura, Division of Business Practices] New York [1954]
76 p. illus. 28 cm. (*Its* Conference Board reports. Studies in business policy, no. 71)

1. Marketing.   I. Umemura, George M.   II. Title.

| HF5006.N3 | no. 71 | 658.8 | 54–14566 ‡ |

NN 0054569   DLC NBuU IaU AAP LU ViU PPCuP OU

---

q331.0973
N213*l*
        NATIONAL INDUSTRIAL CONFERENCE BOARD.
        Labor problems under the Taft-Hartley Act.
        [A summary of the panel discussion at the 293rd
        meeting of the National Industrial Conference
        Board, January 22, 1948. New York, c1948]
        16p. 29cm.
        Cover title.
        "Supplement to The Conference Board Personnel
        management record, March 31, 1948."
        The act is officially known as the Labor-
        management Relations Act, 1947.
        1. Labor laws and legislation - U.S. I. Title.
        Labor-management   Relations Act, 1947. II.
        Title.

NN 0054570   TxU

National industrial conference board.
Lay-off and its prevention. New York, National industrial conference board, inc., 1930.
ix, 86 p. incl. forms. 23½ᶜᵐ.

1. Unemployed. 2. Labor and laboring classes.   I. Title.

Library of Congress	HD5724.N28	30–15719
——— Copy 2.		
Copyright A 24229	[5–5]	331.1352

ICJ DAL MiU OCU OC1 OU OO ViU MH MB
NN 0054571   DLC MtU WaS OrCS OKentU NcD TU CU DL

338.4   National Industrial Conference Board.
N213*l*   Lead: basic industrial data. [n.p.] 1951.
        1v. of tables. 28cm.

        1. Lead industry and trade. 2. Lead industry and trade—U.S.

NN 0054572   IU

---

675   National Industrial Conference Board.
N21*l*   Leather and leather products, basic industrial data. New York? 1953.
        1v.(unpaged) tables. 28cm.

        Caption title.

        1. Leather. 2. Leather industry and trade.

NN 0054573   IU

National industrial conference board.
... Legal aspects of mobilization for defense. New York, National industrial conference board, inc., 1941.

cover-title, 28 p. 28 x 21½ᶜᵐ.   (*Its* Conference board reports)

"Prepared jointly by the editors of the Columbia law review, the Harvard law review, and the Yale law journal, and ... originally published in these journals as a series of notes under the title of 'Mobilization for defense'."—p. 1.
Bibliographical foot-notes.

1. World war, 1939–   —Manpower—U. S. 2. Labor supply—U. S. 3. Excess profits tax—U. S.   I. Title.

| Library of Congress | HD5724.N282 | 43–3414 |

OO OCU CtY MH-BA
NN 0054574   DLC Or OrCS OrU GU OC1W DNAL ICJ MB

National industrial conference board.
... Legal aspects of the N. R. A. code system ... [New York] National industrial conference board, 1934.

cover-title, 11, 4 numb. l. 28½ᶜᵐ. (Conference board information service: Domestic affairs. Memorandum no. 27)
Mimeographed.

1. National industrial recovery act, 1933. 2. Industrial laws and legislation—U. S. 3. Trusts, Industrial—U. S.—Law.   I. Title.

Library of Congress	HC106.3.N24	no. 27	34–9843
——— Copy 2.			
Copyright AA 142696		[5]	(330.973) 338.973

NN 0054575   DLC NcD

National industrial conference board.
Legal restrictions on hours of work in the United States; a reference manual ... New York, National industrial conference board [ᶜ1924]

v, 125 p. incl. tables. 23ᶜᵐ. (*Its* Research report, no. 68)

1. Hours of labor—U. S. 2. Labor laws and legislation—U. S.   I. Title.

| Library of Congress | HD5118.U6N35 | 24—0717 |

OU OCU OC1 OO CU DL MB ICJ
NN 0054576   DLC MtBC OrPR Or WaS WaWW NcD ViU MiU

National Industrial Conference Board.
Letters to nonsupervisory employees. [By Elmer W. Earl, Jr., Division of Personnel Administration] New York [1951]
36 p. 28 cm. (*Its* Conference Board reports. Studies in personnel policy, no. 123)
Cover title.

1. Employees, Reporting to.   I. Earl, Elmer W.   II. Title. (Series: National Industrial Conference Board. Studies in personnel policy, no. 123)

| HF5549.A2N27 | no. 123 | 658.3 | 51–8468 |

NN 0054577   DLC MoSU-C AAP IaU

VOLUME 407

National industrial conference board.
Library source book. ₁New York, 1917?₁ 1 v. 28cm.

Loose-leaf.
Reproduced from typewritten copy.

42035B. 1. Social service—Organiza-
and org.—U. S. 3. United States—   tion. 2. Social sciences—Assoc.
N. Y. P. L.   Soc. condit., 1917—   **August 30, 1940**

NN   0054578   NN

National industrial conference board, inc.
...List of current publications. 1941–

New York, 1941–   nos.   28cm.

At head of title: The Conference board.
1941 has title: List of current publications and Annual index to the Economic
record, the Management record, Conference board reports, Road maps of industry.
1942 in two parts: part 1, List of current publications and list of special studies
and articles published in 1942; part 2, Annual index to the Economic record, the
Management record, the Industry record, Conference board reports, Road maps of
industry.

1. National industrial conference   board, inc.—Bibl. 2. Economic
history—U. S.—Bibl. 3. Management   —Bibl.
N. Y. P. L.   **January 8, 1948**

NN   0054579   NN NNC MB ICJ NBuG OCl DNAL CtY MiD

National Industrial Conference Board.
...List of publications. New York₁, 1927₁. 10 p. 8°.

402471A. 1. National Industrial   Conference Board—Bibl.
N. Y. P. L.   **February 20, 1929**

NN   0054580   NN

99.76
N218   **National Industrial Conference Board.**
     Lumber: basic industrial data.
[New York] 1950.
[25] p.

1. Lumber trade. Statistics. 2. Lumber trade. U.S. 3. U.S. Forestry.
Statistics.

NN   0054581   DNAL

338.4
N213mae   National Industrial Conference Board.
     Machinery, electrical. Basic industrial
data. ₁New York₁ 1953.
₁39₁p. tables. 28cm.

1. Electric machinery. 2. U.S.—Indus.

NN   0054582   IU

National industrial conference board.
Machinery, employment and purchasing power. New
York city, National industrial conference board, inc. ₁1935₁

xiii, 108 p. incl. tables, diagrs. 23½ cm.

Seal of National industrial conference board, inc., on t.-p.

1. U. S.—Econ. condit.—1918–   2. Unemployment, Technological. 3. Unemployed—U. S.   I. Title.

HC106.3.N27   338.4   35—31423

     OCl OO OCU ViU DL NcD MB
NN   0054583   DLC Or WaSpG ICJ OrU OrCS MtU WaS OU

National industrial conference board.
Machinery, employment, and purchasing power. New York
city, National industrial conference board, inc. ₁1936₁

xiii, 95 p. incl. tables, diagrs. 23ᶜᵐ. ₁Its Studies. no. 218R₁

"Published, October, 1935. Revised, May, 1936."

1. U. S.—Econ. condit.—1918–   2. Machinery in industry. 3. Unemployed—U. S.   I. Title.

                                      36—17065

Library of Congress   HC106.3.N27 1936
——— Copy 2.
Copyright A 96214   ₁5₁   338.4

NN   0054584   DLC IdU NcD ODW TU

338.4
N213ma   National Industrial Conference Board.
     Machinery (except electrical) Basic in-
dustrial data. ₁New York₁ 1953.
₁50₁p. tables. 28cm.

1. Machinery. 2. U.S.—Indus.

NN   0054585   IU

National industrial conference board.
Major forces in world business depression. New York, National industrial conference board, inc., 1931.

x, 52 p. tables (1 fold.) 23ᶜᵐ. $1.50

1. Economic conditions—1918–   2. Panics—1929.   I. Title.

                                  31—28524

Library of Congress   HB3717.1929.N32
——— Copy 2.
Copyright A 45569   ₁5–5₁   330.904

     CU OCl TU OO OU MiU ICJ MB PPAmP
NN   0054586   DLC MtU MtBC OrPR WaS OrCS Or OrU NcD

HD8059
.M3   National industrial conference board.

     The Management almanac ... A reference book of facts for
the personnel and labor relations executive. 1944–
New York, N. Y., National industrial conference board ₁1944–

National Industrial Conference Board.
Management development, a ten-year case study ₁by William W. Mussmann₁ New York ₁1953₁

54 p. illus. 28 cm. (Its Conference Board reports. Studies in
personnel policy, no. 140)

Cover title.

1. Armstrong Cork Company. 2. Factory management.   I. Mussmann, William W. II. Title.   (Series: National Industrial Conference Board. Studies in personnel policy, no. 140)

HF5549.A2N27 no. 140   658   53—4402

NN   0054588   DLC MH OOxM AAP OCU IaU ViU

National industrial conference board.   Management record
see its The conference board management record.

331.06
N211m   National Industrial Conference Board.
     Management research memorandum, no.1-13,
New York, 1939-43.
13 nos. 28cm.

No. 3-7 supplements to Conference board
management record.
No. 9-13 are also Its Conference board
reports.
Title varies: No.1-2, Conference board
     management   research memorandum.
No.3-6.   Research memorandum.

     DLC NN NjR TxU I OClW KyU OrP MiD
NN   0054590   LU LNL ICJ NcU ICU DBB CU DNAL OCl

National Industrial Conference Board.
Managing company airplanes ₁by Leonard R. Burgess and
Malcolm C. Neuhoff₁ Division of Business Practices₁ New
York ₁1954₁

47 p. 28 cm. (Its Conference Board reports. Studies in business
policy, no. 65)

1. Aeroplanes, Company.   I. Burgess, Leonard R.   II. Title.

HF5006.N3   no. 65   *629.18   629.138   54—2089 ‡

     LU WaWW
NN   0054591   DLC WaS MiU OU ViU MH-BA AAP IaU NBuU

National industrial conference board.
A manual for mutual benefit associations ... New York,
National industrial conference board ₁1924₁

iii p., 1 l., 48 p. 23ᶜᵐ. (Its Research report no. 66)

"Supplemental to Research report no. 65: 'Experience with mutual
benefit associations in the United States'."

1. Friendly societies—U. S. 2. Insurance, Industrial—U. S.
I. Title.

Library of Congress   HD7126.N35   24—3970

     ViU ICJ MB OU OCU OCl OO MiU
NN   0054592   DLC WaWW OrU Or CaBVaU MtBC CU NcRS DL

304
N213   **National industrial conference board.**
     The market for cotton textiles.   New York,
1946.
11 p. ₁Its The conference board industry
record. v.5,no.7. Aug. 14, 1946)

NN   0054593   DNAL

National Industrial Conference Board.
Marketing, business, and commercial research in industry.
₁By the Division of Business Practices₁ New York ₁1955₁

88 p. illus. 28 cm. (Its Conference Board reports. Studies in
business policy, no. 72)

1. Marketing research.   I. Title.

HF5006.N3   no. 72   *658.83   658.8072   55—1467 ‡

     OCl LU
NN   0054594   DLC CoU AAP UU ViU IaU NB DI PPCuP

National industrial conference board.
... Measuring and projecting national income
... New York, N.Y. ₁1945₁
cover-title, 27 p. tables, charts. (Its
Conference board reports)

Its Studies in business policy, no. 5.
"Bibliography of postwar estimates": p.22.

NN   0054595   MH-BA Mi OU

National Industrial Conference Board.
Measuring dealer and consumer inventories
see under   Higgins, Elliott F

HF5006
.N3   National Industrial Conference Board.
no.15   Measuring labor's productivity.   ₁New
York, 1946₁
20 p. 28 cm. (Its Studies in business
policy, no. 15)

Cover title.
At head of title: Conference Board reports.

1. Labor productivity. I. Title.   (Series)

NN   0054597   AAP Mi OU MH-BA

VOLUME 407

National Industrial Conference Board.
Measuring sales performance
see under Thompson, G   Clark.

338.1   National Industrial Conference Board.
N2137m   Meat packing, basic industrial data.
₍New York₎ 1955.
71p. ₍chiefly tables₎ 28cm.

1. Meat—Stat. I. Title.

NN   0054599   IU NIC

National industrial conference board.
... Medical and health programs in industry. New York,
National industrial conference board, inc. ₍1939₎
31 p. diagrs. 28 cm. (The Conference board management record
supplements)
Studies in personnel policy, no. 17.

1. Insurance, Health—U. S. 2. Labor and laboring classes—Medical
care.   i. Title.
HF5549.A2N27 no. 17   A 43—3628
(658.3) 658.3822

Wellesley College. Libr.
for Library of Congress   ₍a53d½₎†

NN   0054600   MWelC WaTC OrU OrCS WaS Wa MtU IaU DLC

National industrial conference board.
Medical care of industrial workers. New York, National
industrial conference board, inc., 1926.
ix, 112 p. incl. tables. 23½ cm.

1. Labor and laboring classes—Medical care. 2. Occupations—Diseases and hygiene.   i. Title.
RC963.N27   26—13648

TU DL ICJ DAL
NN   0054601   DLC CU DNLM CoU OO OCl OU MiU ViU NcD

National industrial conference board.
Medical supervision and service in industry. New York,
National industrial conference board, inc., 1931.
xi, 125 p. incl. tables. 23½ᶜᵐ.

1. Labor and laboring classes—Medical care. 2. Occupations—Diseases and hygiene.   i. Title.
                                             32—26100
Library of Congress   RC963.N28
                         ₍38k1₎   331.822

DAL ICJ MiU OU LU MB MH
NN   0054602   DLC OrCS WaS MtU TU OCU OCl OO NIC

WA   National Industrial Conference Board.
412   Medical supervision and service in industry.
N277M   New York, 1931 ₍c1932₎
1932   xi, 125 p. tables. 23 1/2 cm.

1. Industrial Medicine. 2. Occupational
Diseases. I. Title.

NN   0054603   WU-M

National industrial conference board.
Memorandum concerning national income by
industrial divisions and distributive shares,
1929-1942, inclusive. ₍New York? 1943₎
10, ₍6₎ l. of tables. 36cm.

NN   0054604   NNC

National industrial conference board.
Memorandum regarding national income statistics, 1929-1946 inclusive, 1947 partly estimated. ₍1948₎
11 l. tables. 36cm.

NN   0054605   NNC

National industrial conference board.
A memorandum to conference board associates. ₍New York
city, 1942?₎ 12 p. 22½cm.
Caption-title.

NN   0054606   NN

National industrial conference board.
Mergers and the law. New York, National industrial conference board, inc., 1929.
x, 153 p. 23½ cm.

1. Trusts, Industrial—U. S.—Law. 2. Sherman antitrust law, 1890.
3. Consolidation and merger of corporations—U. S.   i. Title.

HD2777.N45   29—6426

WaU-L CU-AL
OU ODW ViU NcD CU MB KMK NjR MtU IdU WaS OrU OrCS
NN   0054607   DLC FMU CU NIC ICJ MH MiU OCl OCU OO

National industrial conference board.
Mergers in industry; a study of certain economic aspects
of industrial consolidation. New York, National industrial
conference board, inc., 1929.
xiv, 205 p. incl. tables, diagrs. 23½ cm.
"Prepared by Mr. Myron W. Watkins of the conference board's
research staff."—Pref.

1. Consolidation and merger of corporations—U. S. 2. Trusts,
Industrial—U. S.   i. Watkins, Myron Webster, 1893-   ii. Title.

HD2795.N25   29—15743

FMU
OU NcD ViU ICJ DL MH MB MtU WaSp WaS OrCS Or WaTC
NN   0054608   DLC CU FTaSU KMK OO TU OCU MiU OCl

National industrial conference board.
The metric versus the English system of weights and meas-
ures ... National industrial conference board. New York,
The Century co. ₍c1921₎
xii, 261 p. incl. tables, diagrs. 23ᶜᵐ. (Its Research report, no. 42)
Bibliography: p. 252-254.

1. Metric system.   i. Title.
Library of Congress   QC91.N3   21—21778

ICJ MiU OO OCl WaTC WaSp MtBC WaS CaBVaU WaWW
NN   0054609   DLC UU KEmT CoU UU NIC CU NcRS ViU OCU

National Industrial Conference Board.
Military inspection in industry ₍by R. Maxil Ballinger₎
New York ₍c1951₎
76 p. illus. 28 cm. (Its Conference Board reports. Studies in
business policy, no. 50)
Cover title.
Bibliographical footnotes.

1. Engineering inspection. 2. U. S.—Armed Forces—Procurement.
i. Ballinger, R. Maxil. ii. Title.   (Series: National Industrial Conference Board. Studies in business policy, no. 50)

HF5006.N3 no. 50   62—43392

NN   0054610   DLC CoU LU MH-BA

National industrial conference board.
... Military service of employees ... New York, National
industrial conference board, inc. ₍1940₎
cover-title, 20 p. 28 x 21½ᶜᵐ. (Its Research memorandum no. 6, October, 1940)
Supplement to the Management record.
Supplements an article, entitled Company policies regarding military
absences, which appeared in the October 1940 issue of the Conference
board management record. cf. Foreword.

1. Labor and laboring classes—U. S.—1914-   2. U. S.—Army—
Recruiting, enlistment, etc.—World war, 1939-   3. Military service,
Compulsory—U. S.   Compulsory.
                                                 43—16932
Library of Congress   HD4905.5.N33 1940
                         ₍3₎   355.22

NN   0054611   DLC OrU MB ViU OU UU

National industrial conference board.
... Military service of employees, January, 1942 ... New
York, National industrial conference board, inc. ₍1942₎
cover-title, 32 p. 28 x 22ᶜᵐ. (Its Management research memorandum,
no. 10)
At head of title: Conference board reports.
Contents on p. ₍2₎ of cover.

1. Labor and laboring classes—U. S. 2. U. S.—Army—Recruiting, enlistment, etc. 3. Military service, Compulsory.   i. Title.
                                             42—13043
Library of Congress   HD4905.5.N33
                         ₍3₎   355.²2

NN   0054612   DLC OrU ViU OU UU

National industrial conference board.
Minimum wage legislation in Massachusetts. New York,
National industrial conference board, inc., 1927.
xiii, 243 p. incl. tables, diagrs. 23½ᶜᵐ.
"List of Massachusetts documents cited in text": p. 238-243.

1. Wages—Minimum wage—Massachusetts.   i. Title.
                                             27—18513
Library of Congress   HD4919.M4N3

OrCS OrU WaTC
NcD NcD-L ICJ MH DAL OU OCU MiU OO Or MtU Wa WaS
NN   0054613   DLC CU MH-BA xU MB NBuU-L TU KMK DL

NATIONAL INDUSTRIAL CONFERENCE BOARD,
₍MISCELLANEOUS PUBLICATIONS₎
BOSTON, 1917-
v.   23 CM.

NN   0054614   MdBJ

National industrial conference board.
₍Miscellaneous publications₎.
New York, The Board, 1934-35.

2 v.

NN   0054615   OCU

National Industrial Conference Board.
Mobilizing for atomic war ₍by R. Maxil Ballinger, Division of Business Practices₎ New York ₍c1950₎
64 p. illus. 28 cm. (Its Conference Board reports. Studies in
business policy, no. 46)
Cover title.
Bibliographical footnotes.

1. Industrial mobilization—U. S. 2. Atomic warfare.   i. Ballinger, R. Maxil. ii. Title.   (Series: National Industrial Conference Board. Studies in business policy, no. 46)

HF5006.N3 no. 46   62—43375

CoU LU
NN   0054616   DLC Wa AAP PPULC PPT OClU OU MH-BA

VOLUME 407

National industrial conference board.
... Monthly statement on foreign economic conditions.

New York, 19—   28½cm.
    v.   charts, tables.

Reproduced from typewritten copy.

1. Economic history—Per. and soc. economic conditions. 2. Economic N. Y. P. L.   publ.—U. S. I. Title: Foreign history, 1918–   October 5, 1937

NN   0054617   NN OU

National industrial conference board.
... The monthly survey of business practises.
Sept.1944–
New York, 1944–
    v.

Manifold copy.

NN   0054618   MH-BA

National industrial conference board.
... Morale factors in production ... New York, National industrial conference board, inc. ₁1943₎

cover-title, 12 p.   28 x 22ᶜᵐ.   (*Its* Conference board reports)
Studies in personnel policy, no. 54.

CONTENTS.—A sound compensation structure, the foundation of morale, by A. L. Kress.—Putting the labor-management committee to work, by C. J. Symington.

1. Employment management. 2. Wages—U. S. 3. Employees' representation in management. I. Title.
    :3–8840

Library of Congress   HF5549.A2N27 no. 54
    (858.8)   658.3

NN   0054619   DLC CoU ViU

HF5549
.A2N25
no.3   NATIONAL INDUSTRIAL CONFERENCE BOARD
    ...Multiple-shift operation. N.Y.,The
    Board ₁1937₎ 4p. Tables. (Its Studies
    in personnel policy, no.3)

    Cover-title.

NN   0054620   InU IaU ViU

National industrial conference board.
... Music in industry ... New York, N. Y., National industrial conference board, inc. ₁1947₎

cover-title, 32 p. illus., diagrs. 28ᶜᵐ.   (*Its* Conference board reports)
Studies in personnel policy, no. 78.

1. Music in industry.
    HF5549.A2N27 no. 78   780.13   47–3247

NN   0054621   DLC OClJC AAP CoU IaU

National industrial conference board.
National defense and economic reconstruction; a series of addresses delivered at the twenty-fifth annual meeting of the Conference board, New York, May 21, 1941. New York, National industrial conference board, inc. ₁1941₎

3 p. l., 38 p. 23ᶜᵐ.

Addresses by Virgil Jordan, Col. William J. Donovan, Sidney Hillman, and Philip D. Reed.

1. U. S.—Econ. condit.—1918– 2. U. S.—Defenses. I. Title.
    41–13978

Library of Congress   HC106.4.N36
    (6)   330.973

NN   0054622   DLC OrU ICJ OU DAL OClFRB

RA445
.N3   **National Industrial Conference Board.**
    National health and efficiency. Research
    report no. 6, April, 1918. Boston, Mass.,
    National Industrial Conference Board, c1918.
    20 p.   23 cm.

NN   0054623   DLC

₁330.973 **National industrial conference board.**
N215n   ... National income and its elements. │ New
    York, National industrial conference board, inc.,
    1934.
    p.33-40. tables, diagrs. (Conference board
    bulletin. vol.8, no.5)

    Caption title.
    "Prepared by Edward T. Frankel".

NN   0054624   IU

National industrial conference board.
... National income and its elements, by Robert F. Martin, Conference board research staff ... New York city, National industrial conference board, inc. ₁1936₎

xiii, 134 p. incl. tables, diagrs. 23½ᶜᵐ.

"Mr. Jack Slaughter ... prepared the section on state distribution of income."—p. vi.

1. Income. 2. U. S.—Econ. condit.—1918– I. Martin, Robert Fitz-Randolph. II. Slaughter, John A. III. Title.
    36–17967

Library of Congress   HC106.3.N28
    (a41r37d²)   330.973

    OU MB DN ICJ ViU MtU OClFRB OO OCU
NN   0054625   DLC WaT MtBC OrCS WaTC LU CU OrU AAP

National industrial conference board.
National income by distributive shares.
₁New York?₎ 1942.
7, ₁2₎ l. of tables. 36cm.

Bound with National industrial conference
board. Memorandum concerning national income
by industrial divisions ... 1943.

NN   0054626   NNC

National industrial conference board.
... National income in the United States, 1799–1938, by Robert F. Martin, director Economic research division, the Conference board. New York city, National industrial conference board, inc. ₁1939₎

xv, 146 p. incl. tables, diagrs. 23½ cm. (*Its* Studies, no. 241)

1. Income—U. S. 2. U. S.—Econ. condit. I. Martin, Robert Fitz-Randolph, 1900–

    HB601.N35   339.20973   39—27201

    CaBVaU WaSpG WaTC
    DFT NN ICJ ViU MB ScU MtU WaSp MtBC WaS OrCS OrU Or
NN   0054627   DLC NIC CoU DAL PPSOPR NcRS OOxM OU

HC101
.N32   National industrial conference board.
    National industrial conference board ...
    a co-operative body ...
    ₁Boston₎1917
    ₁7₎ p.   15.5 x 9 cm.

NN   0054628   DLC

HC101
.N33   National industrial conference board.
    National industrial conference board ...
    a federation of American industries for study
    of industrial problems.
    ₁Boston,1919₎
    24 p.   19cm.

NN   0054629   DLC MiD DL NN

National industrial conference board.
... The National industrial recovery act; analysis of approved codes. ₁New York₎ National industrial conference board, 1933.

1 p. l., 19 numb. l. 28½ x 22ᶜᵐ. (Conference board information service: Domestic affairs. Memorandum no. 11)

Reproduced from type-written copy.

1. National industrial recovery act, 1933. 2. Industry and state—U. S.
    42–3320

Library of Congress   HD3616.U456N3
    (2)   338.4

NN   0054630   DLC NN

National industrial conference board.
... The National industrial recovery act: formulation of codes of fair competition. ₁New York₎ National industrial conference board, 1933.

1 p. l., 7 numb. l. 28½ x 22ᶜᵐ. (Conference board information service: Domestic affairs. Memorandum no. 7)

Reproduced from type-written copy.

1. National industrial recovery act, 1933. 2. Industry and state—U. S.
    42–3867

Library of Congress   HC106.3.N24 no. 7
    (2)   (330.973) 330.973

NN   0054631   DLC NN

National industrial conference board.
... The National industrial recovery act: organization of industry for the administration of the act in the light of German cartel experience. ₁New York₎ National industrial conference board, 1933.

2 p. l., 14 numb. l. 28½ x 22ᶜᵐ. (Conference board information service: Domestic affairs. Memorandum no. 8)

Reproduced from type-written copy.

1. National industrial recovery act, 1933. 2. Employers' associations—U. S. 3. Trusts, Industrial—Germany.
    42–3868

Library of Congress   HC106.3.N24 no. 8
    (2)   (330.973) 330.973

NN   0054632   DLC NN Or

National industrial conference board.
... National industrial recovery act: production and price control under codes of fair competition ... ₁New York₎ National industrial conference board, 1933.

cover-title, 1 p. l., 22 numb. l. 28½ᶜᵐ. (Conference board information service: Domestic affairs. Memorandum no. 18)

Mimeographed.

1. National industrial recovery act, 1933. 2. Over-production. 3. Prices—U. S. 4. Competition. Unfair—U. S. 5. Industry and state—U. S. I. Title: Codes of fair competition.
    34–5517

Library of Congress   HC106.3.N24 no. 18
    —— Copy 2.
Copyright AA 134306   (5)   (330.973) 338.0973

NN   0054633   DLC

National Industrial Conference Board.
...National industrial recovery act: supplementary analysis of approved codes... ₁New York₎ National Industrial Conference Board, 1933. 25 f. 28cm. bd. 28 x 38cm. (Its: Conference Board information service: Domestic affairs series. Memorandum no. 14.)

Photostatic reproduction, on 14 l.
Reproduced from typewritten copy.

1. Industrial codes of fair competition. I. Ser.
N. Y. P. L.   June 18, 1936

NN   0054634   NN

National Industrial Conference Board.
...The National industrial recovery act: tax provisions of the act. ₁New York₎ National Industrial Conference Board, 1933. 5 f. 28cm. bd. 28 x 38cm. (Its: Conference Board information service: Domestic affairs series. Memorandum no. 10.)

Photostatic reproduction, on 3 l.
Reproduced from typewritten copy.

1. Corporations—Taxation—U. S., 1933. I. Ser.
N. Y. P. L.   June 24, 1936

NN   0054635   NN

VOLUME 407

National Industrial Conference Board.
...The National industrial recovery act: the cost of living and the minimum wage. ₁New York₎ National Industrial Conference Board, 1933. 9 f. incl. tables. 28cm. bd. 28 x 38cm. (Its: Conference Board information service: Domestic affairs series. Memorandum no. 9.)

Photostatic reproduction, on 5 l.
Reproduced from typewritten copy.

1. Prices and wages—U. S., 1933. I. Ser.
N. Y. P. L. June 18, 1936

NN 0054636 NN

National industrial conference board.
National mobilization for victory ... New York, National industrial conference board, inc. ₁1942₎
cover-title, vii p., 1 l., 230 p. fold. map, diagrs. 23ᶜᵐ. (Its Annual report. 26th. ₁1942₎)
Foreword signed: Virgil Jordan, president.

1. World war, 1939– — U. S. 2. World war, 1939– — Manpower—U. S. I. *Jordan, Virgil, 1892– II. Title.
Library of Congress HC106.3.N18 26th
42–19746 Revised
₁r43d3₎ (330.973) 330.6273

NN 0054637 DLC

National industrial conference board.
... National reconstruction and recovery program: administration and financing ... ₁New York₎ National industrial conference board, 1933–
v. 28½ᶜᵐ. (Conference board information service: Domestic affairs. Memorandum no.
Cover-title.
Mimeographed.
1. U. S. Federal emergency administration of public works. 2. U. S.—Public works. 3. U. S. Federal relief administration. 4. Unemployed—U. S. 5. U. S. Agricultural adjustment administration. 6. Agriculture—Economic aspects. 7. Prices—U. S. 8. Farm produce—Taxation. 9. Internal revenue—U. S. 10. Credit—U. S. I. Title.
34–5514
Library of Congress HC106.3.N24 nos. 17, 19, 21, 23
—— Copy 2.
Copyright ₁10₎ (330.973) 330.973

NN 0054638 DLC NcD

National industrial conference board.
... National recovery administration: text of general orders ... ₁New York₎ National industrial conference board, °1934.
cover-title, 7 numb. l. 28½ᶜᵐ. (Conference board information service: Domestic affairs. Memorandum no. 28)
Mimeographed.

1. U. S. National recovery administration—Codes. 2. Competition, Unfair—U. S. I. Title. II. Title: General orders.
34–9847
Library of Congress HC106.3.N24 no. 28
—— Copy 2.
Copyright AA 144342 ₁5₎ (330.973) 338.973

NN 0054639 DLC

National industrial conference board.
... National recovery and dollar depreciation. ₁New York₎ National industrial conference board, 1933.
2 p. l., 22 numb. l. charts. 28ᶜᵐ. (Conference board information service: Domestic affairs. Memorandum no. 13)
Mimeographed.

1. Dollar. 2. Currency question—U. S. 3. Prices—U. S. I. Title.
A 34–2934
Library, U. S. Interstate Commerce Commission
Library of Congress [HC106.3.N24 no. 13]

NN 0054640 DLC

National industrial conference board.
... New capital issues, 1933 ... ₁New York₎ National industrial conference board, 1934.
cover-title, ii, 11 numb. l. 28½ᶜᵐ. (Conference board information service: Domestic affairs. Memorandum no. 24)
Mimeographed.

1. Corporations—Finance. 2. Corporations—U. S. 3. Finance—U. S. 4. Investments—Tables, etc. I. Title. II. Title: Capital issues, 1933.
34–16129
Library of Congress HC106.3.N24 no. 24
—— Copy 2.
Copyright AA 143078 ₁5₎ (330.973) 332.630973

NN 0054641 DLC

National industrial conference board.
... New federal tax proposals ... ₁New York₎ National industrial conference board, 1935.
cover-title, 1 p. l., 29 numb. l. 28½ᶜᵐ. (Conference board information service: Domestic affairs series. Memorandum no. 43)
Mimeographed.

1. Taxation—U. S. 2. Income tax—U. S. I. Title.
Library of Congress HC106.N24 no. 43
35–17478
—— Copy 2.
Copyright AA 178971 ₁5₎ (330.973) 336.20973

NN 0054642 DLC

National industrial conference board.
The new monetary system of the United States ... New York, National industrial conference board, inc., 1934.
ix, 147 p. diagrs. (1 fold.) 23ᶜᵐ.

1. Currency question—U. S. 2. Gold. 3. Federal reserve banks. I. Title. II. Title: Monetary system of the United States.
Library of Congress HG538.N33
34–28401
—— Copy 2.
Copyright A 75769 ₁5–5₎ 332.40973

OkU CaBVaU CU TU
OCl OCU MiU OO ICJ MiHM MtU WaSp MtBC WaS OrCS
NN 0054643 DLC WaTC Or NIC GU NcRS NcD-L ScU OU

National Industrial Conference Board.
New product development. New York ₁1950–54₎
3 v. illus., tables. 28 cm. (Its Conference Board reports. Studies in business policy, no. 40, 57, 69)
Cover title.
CONTENTS.—I. Selection, coordination, financing, by E. F. Higgins.—2. Research and engineering, by E. F. Higgins.—3. Marketing new products, by S, Ethe and E. F. Higgins.
1. New products. I. Higgins, Elliott F. II. Ethe, Solomon. III. Title. (Series: National Industrial Conference Board. Studies in business policy, no. 40 ₁etc.₎)
HF5006.N3 no. 40, etc. 658.072 56–3466 rev

NN 0054644 DLC MH-BA IaU OU CoU LU AAP ViU

National Industrial Conference Board.
News release
see its Press release.

National Industrial Conference Board.
Nickel; basic industrial data. ₁New York, 1949₎ °1948.
₁18₎ p. of tables. 28 cm.
Caption title.

1. Nickel—Stat.
HD9539.N5N3 338.476697 49–3654

NN 0054646 DLC

338.2 National Industrial Conference Board.
N21n Nickel; basic industrial data. ₁New York₎ c1954.
28p. tables. 28cm.

1. Nickel industry--U.S. I. Title.

NN 0054647 TU NIC OCU

National industrial conference board.
Night work in industry. New York, National industrial conference board, inc., 1927.
ix, 45 p. incl. tables. 23ᶜᵐ.

1. Night labor. I. Title.
Library of Congress HD5113.N3 27–20579

OCl MB DL
NN 0054648 DLC ICJ MtU WaS OrCS CU NcD MiU OU

National Industrial Conference Board.
1954: recession, depression, recovery? A Conference Board round table. ₁New York, 1954₎
63 p. diagrs. 28 cm.
"Reprint of articles by Colin Clark in the Manchester guardian weekly of November 19 and 26, 1953, entitled 'Danger signs of an American slump'": p. 53–63.

1. U. S.—Econ. condit. —1945– 2. U. S.—Economic policy. I. Clark, Colin, 1905– Danger signs of an American slump. II. Title.
HC106.5.N27 330.973 54–1703

NN 0054649 DLC NBuG PPT PPSOPR

National industrial conference board.
... Notes on foreign conditions, no. 1–
₁New York₎ National industrial conference board, 1935–
v. diagrs. 28½ᶜᵐ. (Conference board information service: Foreign affairs series)
Mimeographed.
Number 3 has title: Notes on foreign conditions ... The situation in Germany and prospect of war; no. 4: Notes on foreign conditions ... The Spanish revolution, by Vaso Trivanovitch.

1. Economic conditions—1918– 2. World politics. I. Title.
Library of Congress HC57.N27
40–14339
—— 2d set.
Copyright ₁2₎ 330.904

NN 0054650 DLC NN OCl NRU

National industrial conference board.
Notes on personnel administration. New York City.
Autographed from typewritten copy.

NN 0054651 OCl

National Industrial Conference Board.
Obstacles to direct foreign investment
see under Gaston, J Frank.

National Industrial Conference Board.
Occupational wage rate survey. Apr. 1950–
New York.
v. 22–28 cm. annual.

1. Wages—U. S.
HD5124.N24 331.2973 52–26912

NN 0054653 DLC MH-BA

NATIONAL INDUSTRIAL CONFERENCE BOARD,
...Officers, members, councillors, foreign correspondents and affiliated organizations.

New York, 19 17cm.
no.

NN 0054654 NN OClFRB

National industrial conference board.
Oil conservation and fuel oil supply. New York, National industrial conference board, inc., 1930.
xiv p., 1 l., 165 p. incl. 1 illus., tables, diagrs. 2 fold. maps. 23ᶜᵐ.
"Prepared by Alfred G. White and assistants, of the Conference board's Research staff."—Pref.

1. Petroleum industry and trade. 2. Petroleum as fuel. 3. Natural resources. I. White, Alfred G. II. Title. III. Title: Fuel oil supply.
38–1377
Library of Congress TN870.N3 1930 a
₁3₎ 553.28

IdU-§B OKentU MH OrCS Or
MiU OCl OO OU NcD DAL MB ICJ OrU MWA PPSOPR FMU
NN 0054655 DLC MtU WaS MU NIC DI-GS KMK OCU TU

VOLUME 407

HF5006
.N3
no.23
1947

National Industrial Conference Board.
    Organization for exporting ʳby John H.
Watson₎ New York ₍1947₎
    47 p.   28cm. (National Industrial Conference
Board. Studies in business policy, no. 23)
Conference Board reports.

    1. U. S.—Comm. 2. U. S.—Commercial policy.
I. Title. II. Ser.

NN   0054656   ViU PPT MiEM CaBVaU MH-BA AAP

HF5006
.N3
no.29
1948

National Industrial Conference Board.
    Organization for importing ʳby John H.
Watson₎ New York ₍1948₎
    43 p. illus. 28cm. (Its Studies in
business policy no. 29)
Conference Board reports.

    1. U. S.—Comm. 2. U. S.—Commercial policy.
I. Title. II. Ser.

NN   0054657   ViU AAP CaBVaU MH-BA PPT

338
N214o

National industrial conference board, inc.
    … Organization for market research …   New
York, National industrial conference board, inc.
₍1945-46₎
    2v. incl.tables, diagrs. (Studies in business
policy, no.12, 19)

    "Conference board reports."
    "Contents.— pt. I. Industry experience.— pt.II.
Operating methods and company plans.

    1. Marketing. I. Title.

NN   0054658   IU MiEM OCl OU MH-BA

National industrial conference board.
    … Organization of personnel administration … New
York, N. Y., National industrial conference board, inc.
₍1946₎
    cover-title, 90 p. diagrs. (part fold.) 28 x 22 cm. (Its Confer-
ence board reports)

    Studies in personnel policy, no. 73.
    "By Geneva Seybold, Management research division."—p. 5.

    1. Personnel management.   I. Seybold, Geneva, 1900-
II. Title.
        HF5549.A2N27 no. 73   658.3   46—6345

NN   0054659   DLC ViU CoU IaU OClJC OClU OCl

National Industrial Conference Board.
    Organization standards and practices
    see under Fitzgerald, Thomas A., 1907-

National Industrial Conference Board.
    Paid vacation practices. ₍By Harold Stieglitz, Division
of Personnel Administration₎ New York ₍1951₎
    20 p. diagrs. 28 cm. (Its Conference Board reports. Studies in
personnel policy, no. 116)

    Cover title.

    1. Vacations, Employee—U. S.   I. Stieglitz, Harold. II. Title.
(Series: National Industrial Conference Board. Studies in personnel
policy, no. 116)
        HF5549.A2N27 no. 116   331.816   51—5898

NN   0054661   DLC CoU AAP

338.4
N213p

National Industrial Conference Board.
    Paint and paint materials, basic industrial
data. ₍New York₎ 1955.
    35p. (chiefly tables) 28cm.

    1. Paint—Stat. I. Title.

NN   0054662   IU NIC

National industrial conference board.
    Paper: basic industrial data. (New
York₎ 1955.
    80 p. of tables. 28cm.

NN   0054663   OCU

National industrial conference board.
    The pattern of inflation. Prepared for the twenty-ninth
annual meeting of the Conference board, May 17, 1945. ₍New
York, National industrial conference board, inc. ₍1945₎
    36 p. diagrs. (1 fold.) 25½ᶜᵐ.

    1. Inflation (Finance) 2. Inflation (Finance)—U. S.   I. Title.
                                                              45—5024
    Library of Congress °   HG233.N3
                                   ₍10₎   332.414

NN   0054664   DLC OrP OrU ICJ TU NNC OCU DNAL NBuG

National Industrial Conference Board.
    Pension plans and their administration. New York ₍1955₎
    53 p. illus. 28 cm. (Its Conference board reports. Studies in
personnel policy, no. 149)

    1. Old age pensions—U. S.   I. Title.

    HD7106.U5N24   55—4998 ‡

                  OCU IaU CoU NB
NN   0054665   DLC OOxM PPCuP NIC ViU ScU DI AAP

National Industrial Conference Board.
    Personnel activities in American business.
New York, 1940.
    36 p. 28 cm. (Its Studies in personnel
policy, no. 20)
    Cover title.
    Conference Board management record supple-
ments.
    1. Employment management. 2. Efficiency,
Industrial. I. Title. II. Ser.

NN   0054666   ViU InU NIC IaU OCl

National Industrial Conference Board.
    Personnel activities in American business. Rev. New
York ₍1947₎
    36 p. 28 cm. (Its Conference Board reports. Studies in per-
sonnel policy, no. 86)
    Cover title.

    1. Employment management.   I. Title. (Series: National In-
dustrial Conference Board. Conference Board reports. Series: National Industrial Conference Board. Studies in personnel policy, no.
86)
        HF5549.A2N27 no. 86   658.3   48—3037*

NN   0054667   DLC OClJC Mi AAP CoU ViU

National Industrial Conference Board.
    Personnel administration in the small company ₍by Geneva
Seybold, Division of Personnel Administration₎ New York
₍1951₎
    92 p. illus. 28 cm. (Its Conference Board reports. Studies in
personnel policy, no. 117)
    Cover title.

    1. Personnel management.   I. Seybold, Geneva, 1900- II.
Title. (Series: National Industrial Conference Board. Studies in
personnel policy, no. 117)
        HF5549.A2N27 no. 117   331.124   51—5897

NN   0054668   DLC IaU AAP MU CoU

National Industrial Conference Board.
    Personnel forms and records ₍by Thomas F. Dermody,
Division of Personnel Administration₎ New York ₍1948₎
    175 p. 29 cm. (Its Conference Board reports. Studies in person-
nel policy, no. 87)
    Cover title.

    1. Personnel records. I. Dermody, Thomas F. II. Title.   (Se-
ries: National Industrial Conference Board. Conference Board reports. Series: National Industrial Conference Board. Studies in
personnel policy, no. 87)
        HF5549.A2N27 no. 87   651.66   48—3309*

NN   0054669   DLC CoU OClJC Mi AAP IaU

National industrial conference board, inc.

HF5549
N3

    … Personnel policies affecting salesmen.
New York, National industrial conference board,
inc. ₍1938₎
    19 p. 27.8 cm. (National industrial conferenc
board, inc. Studies in personnel policy. no. 4)

    1. Salesmen and salesmanship. 2. Employment
management. I.   Title.

NN   0054670   CSmH InU IaU ViU IU

National industrial conference board.
    … Personnel practices governing factory and office adminis-
tration, by F. Beatrice Brower, Conference board research
staff … New York city, National industrial conference board,
inc. ₍1937₎
    xii, 134 p. incl. tables. 23½ᶜᵐ. (National industrial conference board
studies. no. 233)

    1. Factory management. 2. Office management. 3. Employment man-
agement. 4. Efficiency, Industrial.   I. Brower, Frances Beatrice. II.
Title.
    Library of Congress   HF5549.N32   37—27338
————— Copy 2.
    Copyright A 106635   ₍10-5₎   658.3

                  OOxM OCU OCl DL DN NN ICJ
NN   0054671   DLC OrCS DFT ViU MtU IdU WaS OKentU NcD

National industrial conference board.
    … Personnel practices in factory & office ₍I₎-II … New
York, National industrial conference board, inc. ₍1940-43₎
    2 v. tables, forms. 28 x 22ᶜᵐ. (Its Studies in personnel policy, no.
23, 59)
    Cover-title.
    Vol. 1: Supplement to the Management record; v. 2: Conference board
reports.

    1. Employment management.   I. Title.
                                                            44—2963
    Library of Congress   HF5549.A2N27 no. 23, 59
                                   ₍3₎   (658.3) 658.3

NN   0054672   DLC AAP CoU IaU MsU ViU OClU OClJC

National Industrial Conference Board.
    Personnel practices in factory and office. Rev. ₍By Geneva
Seybold, Division of Personnel Administration₎ New York
₍1948₎
    76 p. 28 cm. (Its Conference Board reports. Studies in personnel
policy, no. 88)
    Cover title.

    1. Employment management.   I. Seybold, Geneva, 1900-   II.
Title. (Series. Series: National Industrial Conference Board.
Studies in personnel policy, no. 88)
        HF5549.A2N27 no. 88 658.3   48—4006*

NN   0054673   DLC MB Mi OClJC IaU

National Industrial Conference Board.
    Personnel practices in factory and office. 5th ed. ₍by
Geneva Seybold, Division of Personnel Administration₎
New York ₍1954₎
    vii, 128 p. 29 cm. (Its Conference Board reports. Studies in
personnel policy, no. 145)
    Cover title.

    1. Personnel management.   I. Seybold, Geneva, 1900-   II.
Title. (Series: National Industrial Conference Board. Studies
in personnel policy, no. 145)
        HF5549.A2N27 no. 145   658.3   54—14491

                  PPCuP OOxM AAP
NN   0054674   DLC TxFTC CaBVa IaU CoU OCU DI ViU

VOLUME 407

National industrial conference board, inc.
Petition to the Committee on finance of the Senate of the United States respecting Revenue bill of 1918, H. R. 12863, National industrial conference board, October 16, 1918. ₍Boston, 1918₎ 7 p. 23cm.

Cover-title.

1. Taxation—U. S., 1918.
N. Y. P. L.   November 23, 1937

NN 0054675   NN DL

HD9560 .4 .P4

National industrial conference board.
The **Petroleum** almanac ... A statistical record of the petroleum industry in the United States and foreign countries ... ₍1946₎
New York, N. Y., National industrial conference board ₍*1946–

National industrial conference board.
The physician in industry : a symposium ... New York city, National industrial conference board ₍1922₎

viii, 98 p. 23ᶜᵐ. (*Its* Special report, no. 22)

1. Labor and laboring classes—Medical care. 2. Occupations—Diseases and hygiene. 3. Employers' liability. I. Title.
Library of Congress   RC963.N3   22–18407

CaBVaU WaWW MiU OU OCU OC1 OO ICJ ViU DL MB
NN 0054677   DLC CtY-M DNLM CU NcRS MtU MtBC IdU

National industrial conference board.
A picture of world economic conditions.
New York, National industrial conference board, inc., 1928–

v. 23½ cm.

"Sources of information": v. 1, p. 117–118.

1. Economic history—1918–   I. Title.
HC57.N28   28–30762

MH OC1JC KEmT
MeB KMK NcD ViU MiHM ICJ DAL DL Or MtBC CaBVaU OC1W
NN 0054678   DLC NN MB OU MBU CSt-H OCU WaS AAP MB

National industrial conference board.
A plan for rating factory and office jobs ... New York, N. Y., National industrial conference board, inc. ₍1944₎

8 p. diagrs. 28 x 21½ᶜᵐ. (Supplement to the Conference board management record)

1. Job analysis. I. Title.
                                                  44–9290
Library of Congress   T58.N3

NN 0054679   DLC ICJ

249.3 N213

National industrial conference board.
...Plans for rating employees. New York ₍1938₎
39 p. 28cm. (Its Studies in personnel policy. no.8)
Bibliography: p.19.

NN 0054680   DNAL IaU InU ViU

National industrial conference board.
... Plans for stimulating suggestions from employees, by F. Beatrice Brower ... New York city, National industrial conference board, inc. ₍*1936₎

viii, 51 p. incl. illus., tables, forms. 23 cm. (National industrial conference board studies, no. 231)

1. Suggestion systems. I. Brower, Frances Beatrice. II. Title.
III. Title: Suggestions from employees, Plans for stimulating.

T56.N35   658.3152   37—16

MtU OC1 ViU DL ICJ
NN 0054681   DLC Or OrCS WaTC WaS MtU OC1 OC1U OCU

National industrial conference board.
... The political situation in Germany. ₍New York₎ National industrial conference board, 1933.

1 p. l., 5 numb. l. 28½ x 22½ᶜ. (Foreign affairs information service. Memorandum no. 1)
Reproduced from type-written copy.

1. Germany — Pol. & govt. — 1918–   2. Germany — Pol. & govt.—1933–
                                                  42–5300
Library of Congress   DD251.N3
                             ₍2₎   943.085

NN 0054682   DLC

National Industrial Conference Board.
Post-defense outlook; a round table discussion, Heinz Luedicke, chairman, James Boyd ₍and others. New York, 1952₎

36 p. 23 cm. (*Its* Studies in business economics, no. 34)
Cover title.

1. U. S.—Econ. condit.—1945–   2. U. S.—Economic policy.
I. Luedicke, Heinz. II. Title.   (Series)

HB31.N33 no. 34   330.973   54–2090

MoU
NN 0054683   DLC ICU ViU DAU PSt MH TxU OCU OOxM

National industrial conference board.
Postwar employment opportunities, prepared for the twenty-eighth annual meeting of the Conference board, May 18, 1944, the Waldorf-Astoria. ₍New York₎ National industrial conference board, inc. ₍1944₎

32 p. diagrs. 19½ᵐ.

1. U. S.—Econ. condit.—1918–   I. Title.
                                                  44–5976
Library of Congress   HC106.4.N362
                             ₍4₎   330.973

NN 0054684   DLC

National industrial conference board.
Practical experience with profit sharing in industrial establishments ... Boston, Mass., National industrial conference board, *1920.

ix, 86 p. incl. tables. 23ᵐ. (*Its* Research report, no. 29)

1. Profit-sharing. I. Title.
Library of Congress   HD2984.N35   20—15562

OOxM OC1 OO MB ViU ICJ WaTC CaBVaU WaWW Or
NN 0054685   DLC WaS CU KU NIC UU NcRS MiU OU OCU

National industrial conference board.
Practical experience with the work week of forty-eight hours or less ... New York, National industrial conference board ₍*1921₎

ix, 88 p. diagrs. 23ᵐ. (*Its* Research report, no. 32)

1. Hours of labor—U. S. I. Title.
                                                  21—4085
Library of Congress   HD5125.N35

OC1 OO OCU MiU WaTC CU ICJ MB ViU DL
NN 0054686   DLC WaWW CaBVaU WaS MtBC NcD MiU OU

National industrial conference board.
A practical program for the coordination of government, labor and management; a series of addresses delivered at the twenty-second annual meeting of the National industrial conference board, New York, May 26, 1938. New York, National industrial conference board, inc. ₍1938₎

2 p. l., 81, ₍1₎ p. 23ᶜᵐ.

Addresses by Virgil Jordan, A. A. Berle, jr., O. S. Beyer, W. A. Harriman, G. H. Houston, Philip Murray and D. R. Richberg.

1. Industry—Organization, control, etc. 2. Industry and state.
3. U. S.—Economic policy. I. Title.
Library of Congress   HD45.N34   38–17795
——— Copy 2.
Copyright A 118534   ₍5₎   330.973

NN 0054687   DLC DNAL WaS DAL NcD OU OC1 OCU

National industrial conference board.
... Practices in renegotiation of war contracts. New York, National industrial conference board, inc. ₍1943₎

cover-title, 28 p. diagr. 28 x 22½ᵐ. (*Its* Conference board reports)

1. War contracts—U. S. I. Title: Renegotiation of war contracts.
                                                  43–13052
Library of Congress   HD8860.N28
                             ₍7₎   351.71

OU OC1W
NN 0054688   DLC OrCS OrU DNAL ICJ GU NBuG OC1U

HJ5715 .U6N32

National industrial conference board.
... Preliminary draft of a report on sales taxes: general, selective, and retail. New York city, National industrial conference board, inc., 1932.

2 p. l., II, 69 numb. l., 7 l. incl. tables. 29cm.

At head of title: For confidential use.
Mimeographed.

1. Sales tax—U.S. I. Title.

NN 0054689   DLC

National industrial conference board.
Preliminary study of major forces in world business depression. New York, National industrial conference board, inc., 1931.

viii, 46 p. tables (1 fold.) 23ᶜᵐ.

1. Economic conditions—1918–   2. Panics—1929. I. Title:
Major forces in world business depression.
Library of Congress   HB3717.1929.N3   31–13324
——— Copy 2.
Copyright A 37318   ₍7₎   330.9

NN 0054690   DLC OCU OC1

National industrial conference board.
Preparing for postwar reconstruction; addresses and round table discussions at the twenty-seventh annual meeting of the Conference board, May 26, 1943. ₍New York, 1943₎

3 p. l., 3–156 p. diagrs. 28 x 21½ᵐ. (*Its* Conference board reports)

1. U. S.—Economic policy. 2. Reconstruction (1939–   )—U. S.
I. Title.
Library of Congress   HC106.4.N364   43–15373
                             ₍15₎   330.973

OOxM
NN 0054691   DLC OrCS OrU MB GU DAU ICJ OU OCU

National industrial conference board.
The present railroad situation ... New York city, National industrial conference board ₍*1923₎

iv, 32 p. 23ᵐ. (*Its* Special report no. 23)

1. Railroads—U. S. I. Title.
                                                  24—2468
Library of Congress   HE2741.N35

OC1W OC1
NN 0054692   DLC CU Or MtBC MtU KU DBRE NjP MB OU

VOLUME 407

National industrial conference board.
... The present state of the federal finances ... ₍New York₎
National industrial conference board, 1934.
    cover-title, ii, 10 numb. l. diagr. 28½ᵐ.   (Conference board informa-
tion service: Domestic affairs. Memorandum no. 22)
    Mimeographed.

    1. Finance—U. S.   ɪ. Title.   ɪɪ. Title: Federal finances.
    Library of Congress   HC106.3.N24   34–40874
    ——— Copy 2.
    Copyright AA 138573   ₍3₎   (330.973) 336.73

NN 0054693   DLC

National industrial conference board.
    The present status of mutual benefit associations.   New
York, National industrial conference board, inc., 1931.
    xii, 104 p. 23 cm.

    1. Friendly societies.   ɪ. Title.   ɪɪ. Title: Mutual benefit associa-
tions, The present status of.
    HD7091.N3   334.7   31—13958

    OU ICJ DL MtU IdU Or
NN 0054694   DLC OrCS CU MB MH ViU MiU OC1W OC1

National industrial conference board.
    ... Present status of unemployment insurance or reserves
legislation ... ₍New York₎ National industrial conference
board, 1934.
    cover-title, ii, 13 numb. l. 29ᵐ.   (Conference board information serv-
ice: Domestic affairs. Memorandum no. 29)
    Mimeographed.

    1. Insurance, Unemployment—U. S.   ɪ. Title.   ɪɪ. Title: Unemploy-
ment insurance or reserves legislation.
    Library of Congress   HC106.3.N24 no. 29   34—16130
    ——— Copy 2.
    Copyright AA 145596   ₍5₎   (330.973) 331.254440973

NN 0054695   DLC Or

330.5 **National Industrial Conference Board.**
NATII   Press release; information for the press.

    New York.
    v. illus., tables. 28cm. irregular.
    Title varies: Jan.12, 1941-Feb.11, 1943,
    News release.—Feb.17, 1943-Sept.29, 1946,
    Information for the press.

NN 0054696   IU NjR NBuG OCU OC1 NN

National industrial conference board.
    ...Prevailing practices in inventory valua-
tion. New York, National conference board,
inc. ₍1938₎.
    15 p. (National industrial conference board.
Studies in administrative control, no. 1).

NN 0054697   OU

HB31 **National Industrial Conference Board.**
.N324
no.2   Prevailing practices regarding corporation
1939   directors. New York ₍1939₎
        27 p. tables. 28cm.   (Its Studies in adminis-
    trative control, no.2)

    The Conference Board Management record supplement.
    1. Directors of corporations—U. S.   I. Ser.

NN 0054698   ViU MH OU

National industrial conference board.
    ... Price protection in contracts.   New York
₍c1946₎
    cover-title, 16 p. 28cm. (Its Studies in
business policy, no. 17)

    At head of title: Conference board reports.

NN 0054699   ViU-L Mi MiEM OU MH-BA OC1U

National Industrial Conference Board.
    Prices, costs, wages. ₍A graphic analysis₎ prepared for
the 38th annual meeting of the Conference Board, May 20-21,
1954. New York ₍1954₎
    85 p. col. diagrs. 26 cm.

    1. Prices—U. S.   2. Costs, Industrial—U. S.   3. Wages—U. S.
ɪ. Title.
    HB235.U6N3 1954   338.52   54–3624

    MB NN DL DNAL NcD OrCS OrP OrU Wa
NN 0054700   DLC IdPI IdU CLSU TxU IU OCU ODW PU

HD3858 National industrial conference board.
N278   ... Pricing in war contracts ... New York, N.Y.,
    National industrial conference board, inc. ₍1944₎
        cover-title, 16 p. 27½ᵃ. (Its Studies in
    business policy, no.2)
        At head of title: Conference board reports.
        Contents. - General pricing policies of the
    War department, by Brigadier general A. J. Brown-
    ing. - Methods and technique used in pricing, by
    G.A. Lloyd. - Practical applications of pricing
    techniques, by Captain H. E. C. Hansen.
        1. War contracts   - U.S. 2.Prices - U. S.
    3.World war, 1939-   - Econ. aspects -
    U. S. I.Title.

NN 0054701   CSt-H OU ViU MiEM MH-BA

National industrial conference board.
    ... Principles and application of job evaluation ... New
York, N. Y., National industrial conference board, inc. ₍1944₎
    cover-title, 28 p. 28 x 21½ cm. (*Its* Conference board reports)
    Studies in personnel policy, no. 62.
    "A record of; two separate conferences on job evaluation ... held
on January 20, 1944, in connection with the 257th meeting of the National industrial conference board."—Introd.

    1. Job analysis.
    HF5549.A2N27 no. 62   658.322   44—5735

NN 0054702   DLC CoU OC1U OC1

National industrial conference board.
    ... Private long-term debt and interest in the United
States, by Leonard Kuvin, Conference board research staff
... New York city, National industrial conference board,
inc. ₍1936₎
    xiv, 138 p. diagrs. 23½ cm. (*Its* Studies, no. 230)

    1. Debts — U. S. 2. Interest and usury — U. S. 3. U. S. — Econ.
condit.—1918—   ɪ. Kuvin, Leonard, 1900—   ɪɪ. Title. ɪɪɪ.
Title: Debt and interest in the United States.
    HG181.N3   332.0973   36—28523

    MB CU DL ICJ PPCuP AAP WaTC WaS MtU OrPR OrCS WaSpG
NN 0054703   DLC NIC ViU OU OCU OO OC1W OC1FRB

National industrial conference board. Prize
essays, 1919-1920.
Hartman, Harleigh Holroyd, 1885-
    ... Should the state interfere in the determination of
wage rates? By Harleigh H. Hartman ... New York,
National industrial conference board, ᶜ1920.

National industrial conference board.
    ... Prize winning foreman essays (1941) ... New York, Na-
tional industrial conference board, inc. ₍1942₎
    cover-title, 28 p. 27½ x 21½ᵐ. (*Its* Management research memoran-
dum, no. 11)
    At head of title: Conference board reports.

    1. Foremen. 2. U. S.—Defenses.   ɪ. Title.
                                                42–14956
    Library of Congress   TS155.N229
                                    ₍a44e1₎   658.31243

NN 0054705   DLC ViU OU NIC MB OrU

National Industrial Conference Board.
    The probable impact of atomic energy
on the petroleum industry

    see under

    Wilson, Robert Erastus, 1892-

National industrial conference board.
    ... The problem of absenteeism ... New York, National in-
dustrial conference board, inc. ₍1943₎
    cover-title, 31 p. illus., diagrs. 28 x 21½ᵃ. (*Its* Conference board re-
ports)
    Studies in personnel policy, no. 53.

    1. Absenteeism (Labor)
                                                43–8759
    Library of Congress   HF5549.A2N27 no. 53
                                    ₍3₎   (658.3) 658.381

NN 0054707   DLC OC1JC CoU AAP IaU

HF5549 **National Industrial Conference Board.**
A2N27   Problems in wage adjustment.   New York
no.33   ₍1941₎
        27p. 28cm. (Its Studies in personnel
    policy, no. 33)

        1. Wages.

NN 0054708   IaU InU

National industrial conference board.
    Problems of economic reconstruction; a series of addresses
delivered at the twenty-third annual meeting of the Conference
board, New York, May 24, 1939. New York, National industrial conference board, inc. ₍ᶜ1939₎
    2 p. l., 58 p. 23ᵐ.

    1. U. S.—Economic policy.   ɪ. Title.   ɪɪ. Title: Economic reconstruc-
tion, Problems of.
    Library of Congress   HC106.3.N285   39–21433
    ——— Copy 2.
    Copyright AA 306515   ₍3₎   330.973

NN 0054709   DLC WaTC NcD ICJ OU OCU

National industrial conference board.
    ... Problems of industrial mobilization. New York, National
industrial conference board, inc., 1941.
    cover-title, 20 p. 28 x 22ᵐ. (*Its* Conference board reports)

    1. U. S.—Indus. 2. World war, 1939-   —Economic aspects—U. S.
ɪ. Title.
    Library of Congress   HC106.4.N365   43–1712
                                    ₍4₎

    ICJ ICU OU OO OCU OC1FRB
NN 0054710   DLC Or OrCS OrU GU MU CtY DNAL MH-BA

VOLUME 407

National industrial conference board.
　Problems of industrial readjustment in the United States ...
Boston, Mass., National industrial conference board, ᵉ1919.
　iv, 58 p. 23ᵐ. (*Its Research report, no. 15*)

　1. European war, 1914–　——Economic aspects—U. S. 2. Reconstruction (1914–　) 3. Labor and laboring classes—U. S.—1914. I.
Title. II. Title: Industrial readjustment in the United States.
　　　　　　　　　　　　　　　　　19—5625
　Library of Congress　　　HC106.3.N3

　　MiU ICJ DL OU OCU OO OC1 WaS OrPR OrU
NN　0054711　　DLC WaTC WaWW ViU ICJ CU NcD NcRS Or

National industrial conference board.
　Problems of labor and industry in Germany ... New York,
National industrial conference board, ᵉ1920.
　v, 65 p. 23ᵐ. (*Its Special report, no. 15*)

　1. Labor and laboring classes—Germany. 2. European war, 1914–
1918—Economic aspects—Germany. I. Title.
　　　　　　　　　　　　　　　20—20194
　Library of Congress　　　HD8450.N3

NN　0054712　　DLC OU OC1W OC1 CU MtU WaS OrU

National industrial conference board.

National industrial tax conference.
　Proceedings of the National industrial tax conference. Boston, Mass. ₍etc.₎ National industrial conference board, ᵉ1920–

National Industrial Conference Board.
　...Production of goods and construction, different kinds of
construction, consumers' goods and producers' goods, durable and
non-durable goods, method and definitions... ₍New York₎
National industrial Conference Board ₍1934?₎　8 f. incl. tables.
28cm. bd. 28 x 38cm. (*Its Conference Board information service:
Domestic affairs series. Memorandum no. 37.*)

Photostatic reproduction, on 5 l.
Reproduced from typewritten copy.

　1. Production—Stat.—U. S., 1914–　　1933. 2. Building trade—U. S.,
1914–1933. I. Ser.　　　　　　　　　1933.
N. Y. P. L.　　　　　　　　　　　June 24, 1936

NN　0054714　　NN

National industrial conference board.
　Productivity and progress, prepared for the thirtieth annual meeting of the Conference board, May 16, 1946. New
York, National industrial conference board, inc. ₍1946₎
　36 p. diagrs. (1 fold.) 26½ᵐ.

　1. Labor productivity—U. S. 2. Wages—U. S. 3. Cost and standard
of living—U. S. I. Title.
　HD57.N3　　　　　　338.016　　　46–7129 rev

　　OCU ICJ NBuG MB
NN　0054715　　DLC OrCS OrP OrU ScCleU TU NNC ICU TxU

National industrial conference board.
　Profit sharing; a management policy successful under certain conditions and for special purposes, but not universally
applicable or uniformly effective. New York city, National
industrial conference board, inc. ₍ᵉ1934₎
　vii, 29 p. 23ᵐ.
　"This volume was written by Mr. Harold F. Browne, of the conference board's research staff."—Foreword.

　1. Profit-sharing.　I. Browne, Harold Frederic, 1890–
　　　　　　　　　　　　　　　　35–3290
　Library of Congress　　　HD2971.N3
　Copyright　AA 167145　　　₍5₎　　　331.24

　　CU IEN
NN　0054716　　DLC MtU OrCS Or MiU OCU OU OC1 ICJ

HF5549
.A2N27　**National Industrial Conference Board.**
no.2
1937　　Profit-sharing and other supplementary—
compensation plans covering wage earners.
New York, 1937.
　　22 p.　28cm. (*Its Studies in personnel
policy, no. 2*)
　　Cover title.

　　1. Profit-sharing.　I. Ser.

NN　0054717　　ViU IaU

National Industrial Conference Board.
　Profit sharing for executives ₍by F. Beatrice Brower, Division of Personnel Administration₎ New York ₍1948₎
　39 p. 28 cm. (*Its Conference Board reports. Studies in personnel
policy, no. 90*)
　Cover title.

　1. Profit-sharing. 2. Executives — Salaries, pensions, etc. I.
Brower, Frances Beatrice. II. Title.　(Series: National Industrial
Conference Board. Conference Board reports. Series: National Industrial Conference Board. Studies in personnel policy, no. 90)
　HF5549.A2N27　no. 90　　　658.324　　48—4552*

NN　0054718　　DLC AAP CoU OC1JC Mi

National Industrial Conference Board.
　Profit sharing for workers. ₍By F. Beatrice Brower, Division of Personnel Administration₎ New York ₍1948₎
　56 p. illus. 29 cm. (*Its Conference Board reports. Studies in
personnel policy, no. 97*)
　Cover title.

　1. Profit-sharing.　I. Brower, Frances Beatrice.　(Series: National Industrial Conference Board. Conference Board reports. Series: National Industrial Conference Board. Studies in personnel
policy, no. 97)
　HF5549.A2N27　no. 97　　331.24　　　49—1015*

　　AAP MiEM
NN　0054719　　DLC ViU CU NIC CoU IaU PPT OC1JC

HF5549
.A2N25　NATIONAL INDUSTRIAL CONFERENCE BOARD
no.6　　...Profit-sharing plans for executives.
N.Y.,The Board ₍1938₎　15p.　Tables.
(Its Studies in personnel policy, no.6)

　　Cover-title.

NN　0054720　　InU IaU ViU

National Industrial Conference Board.
　Profits in perspective. ₍A graphic analysis₎ prepared for
the 37th annual meeting of the Conference Board, May 21–
22, 1953. New York ₍1953₎
　31 p. col. diagrs. 26 cm.

　1. Profit—U. S. 2. Corporations—U. S.—Finance. I. Title.
　HC110.P7N3　1953　　　339.23　　　53–2533

　　ViU CoU FU MsU IdU OrP WaU OrCS OrU
NN　0054721　　DLC WaU OC1JC NcU OOxM ODW NN MB TxU

HC106
.B16　**National industrial conference board.**

Backman, Jules, 1910–
　Profits in the national economy ₍by₎ Jules Backman and
Martin R. Gainsbrugh. New York, N. Y., National industrial conference board, inc. ₍1947₎

National industrial conference board.'
　Proposals for changes in federal income tax administration ... New York city, National industrial conference board ₍ᵉ1924₎
　iii, ₍1₎, 12 p. 23ᵐ. (*Its Special report, no. 27*)

　1. Income tax—U. S. I. Title.
　　　　　　　　　　　　　　24–5209
　Library of Congress　　　HJ4652.N295

　　ICJ NIC CU
NN　0054723　　DLC MtU MtBC Or NcD OU OC1W OC1 MB

National industrial conference board.
　Proposals for changes in the federal internal revenue system. New York, National industrial conference board, inc.,
1927.
　ix, 42 p. incl. tables. 23ᵐ.

　1. Taxation—U. S. 2. Income tax—U. S. I. Title.

　Library of Congress　　　HJ2379.N3435 1927　　28–859

NN　0054724　　DLC MiU MB ICJ OU OC1W OC1 MiU

National industrial conference board.
　Proposals for changes in the federal Revenue act of
1924 ... New York, National industrial conference
board, inc. ₍ᵉ1925₎
　vii, 44 p. incl. tables. 23½ᵐ. (*Its Special report, no. 33*)

　1. Taxation—U. S. 2. Income tax—U. S. I. Title. II. Title: Revenue
act of 1924.
　　　　　　　　　　　　　　25–23789
　Library of Congress　　　HJ2379.N3435

　　MB
NN　0054725　　DLC MtU CaBVaU Or CU MiU OU OC1 OC1W

National Industrial Conference Board.
　Proposed establishment of state labor
relations
　　　see under　　Murphey, Hermon K

National industrial conference board.
　... The proposed revision of the N. I. R. A. and the Wagner
National labor relations bill ... ₍New York₎ National industrial conference board, 1935.
　cover-title, 11 numb. l. 28½ᵐ. (*Conference board information service:
Domestic affairs. Special memorandum no. 8*)
　Mimeographed.

　1. National industrial recovery act, 1933. 2. Labor contract—U. S.
3. U. S. National labor relations board. I. Title. II. Title: Wagner
National labor relations bill.
　　　　　　　　　　　　　　35–7550
　Library of Congress　　　HC106.3.N243　no. 8
　———— Copy 2.
　Copyright　AA 173256　　　₍S₎　　(330.973) 330.973

NN　0054727　　DLC OC1FRB

National industrial conference board.
　... The proposed tax on "bigness" ... ₍New York₎ National
industrial conference board, inc., 1935.
　cover-title, 3 numb. l. 28½ᵐ. (*Conference board information service:
Domestic affairs. Special memorandum no. 5*)
　Mimeographed.

　1. Corporations—Taxation. 2. Corporations—U. S. I. Title.
II. Title: Tax on "bigness".
　　　　　　　　　　　　　　35–7552
　Library of Congress　　　HC106.3.N243　no. 5
　———— Copy 2.
　Copyright　AA 170416　　　₍S₎　　(330.973) [336.27] 658.171

NN　0054728　　DLC

National Industrial Conference Board.
　Protecting personnel in wartime

　　see under

　　Ballinger, R　　Maxil.

National Industrial Conference Board.
　Protecting records in wartime ₍by R. Maxil Ballinger,
Division of Business Practices₎ New York ₍1951₎
　40 p. forms. 28 cm. (*Its Conference Board reports. Studies in
business policy, no. 51*)
　Cover title.

　1. Records.　I. Title.　(Series: National Industrial Conference Board. Studies in business policy, no. 51)
　HF5006.N3　no. 51　　　651.5　　　54–3057

NN　0054730　　DLC DAU LU MH-BA IU IaU

VOLUME 407

National industrial conference board.
... Protection of plant and personnel ... New York, National industrial conference board, inc. ₍1942₎
cover-title, 16 p. 28 x 21½ cm. (*Its* Management research memorandum, no. 9)
At head of title: Conference board reports.

1. Civilian defense. 2. Factories—Protection.

UA926.N3   355.23   42–15477

NN 0054731   DLC MB ViU OU OrU

National industrial conference board.
Public education as affecting the adjustment of youth to life. New York, National industrial conference board, inc., 1929.
xi, 61 p. 23½ᵐ.

1. Education—U. S. 2. Research.   I. Title.

Library of Congress   LA210.N35.   29–29592

OrU OrMonO
         MH OCU MiU OC1 OO ViU DAL CaBVaU DHEW MB FMU OrCS
NN 0054732   DLC WaS IdU OrPR Or KMK NcD DL OU ICJ

National industrial conference board.
Public regulation of competitive practices. New York, National industrial conference board, inc., 1925.
xi, 281 p. 23½ cm.
"Documents, etc., issued by the Federal trade commission": p. 245–250.

1. Industry and state—U. S. 2. Trusts, Industrial—U. S.—Law. 3. Competition. 4. Competition, Unfair—U. S.   I. U. S. Federal trade commission.   II. Title.

HD3616.U47N3   25—25962

WaS
         OU NcD–L NcD NcRS AAP KMK MH OrPR OrCS MtU IdI NN
NN 0054733   DLC CU ViU MB NIC OOxM ICJ OC1 OO OC1W

National industrial conference board.
Public regulation of competitive practices. New York, National industrial conference board, inc., 1929.
xi, 320 p. 23½ᵐ.
"Bibliography of documents, etc., issued by the Federal trade commission": p. 279–285.

1. Industry and state—U. S. 2. Trusts, Industrial—U. S. 3. Competition.   I. Title.

Library of Congress   HD3616.U47N3 1929   29—24178

CU–AL OOxM MH–L OU OCU OC1 ViU
NN 0054734   DLC Or MB WaS OrCS OrU CaBVaU CU NBuU–L

National industrial conference board.
... Public regulation of competitive practices in business enterprise, by Myron W. Watkins and the Division of industrial economics of the Conference board. New York city, National industrial conference board, inc. ₍1940₎
xxi, 355 p. 23½ cm. (Conference board publications)
On cover: Third edition.
"Index of cases cited": p. 321–344.
"Bibliography of documents issued by the Federal trade commission since 1916": p. 300–317.
1. Industry and state—U. S. 2. Trusts, Industrial—U. S.—Law. 3. Competition. 4. Competition, Unfair—U. S.   I. Watkins, Myron Webster, 1893–   II. U. S. Federal trade commission.   III. National industrial conference board. Division of industrial economics. IV. Title.

HD3616.U47N3   1940   338.91   40—7945

CaBVaU NBuU–L
         WaTC ViU–L OrU–L MtU NNC WaSp OrU WaU–L PPCuP DFT
         OC1FRB OCU WaS OU OrCS ViU LU NcD NcD–L TU CoU
NN 0054735   DLC PPSOPR CU KEmT GU–L ScU ICJ ODW

National industrial conference board.
Public schools and the worker in New York; a survey of public educational opportunities for industrial workers in New York state. New York, National industrial conference board, inc., 1928.
xi, 80 p. 23½ᵐ.
Prepared by the Conference board for the New York state Industrial survey commission at the request of Associated Industries of New York state, inc. *cf* Pref.

1. Technical education—New York (State) 2. Vocational education—New York (State) 3. Education—New York (State) 4. Evening and continuation schools—New York (State)   I. Title.

Library of Congress   T74.N7N4   29–5685

OCU OC1 ICJ OU OC1W
NN 0054736   DLC FMU MB OrCS OrU GAT KMK CU NcD

National industrial conference board.
Public schools and the worker in New York; a survey of public educational opportunities for industrial workers in New York State, New York, National industrial conference board, inc., 1928, ₍c1929₎.

xi, 80 p. tables, D.

NN 0054737   OO

National industrial conference board.
... The Public utility holding company bill ... ₍New York₎ National industrial conference board, inc., 1935.
cover-title, 9 numb. l. 28½ᵐ. (Conference board information service: Domestic affairs. Special memorandum no. 6)
Mimeographed.

1. Public utilities—U. S. 2. U. S. Securities and exchange commission.   I. Title.

Library of Congress   HC106.3.N243 no. 6   35–7553

——— Copy 2.
Copyright AA 170417   ₍8₎   (330.973) 380.1682622

NN 0054738   DLC

National industrial conference board, inc.
... Public vs. private financing of transportation ... New York, N.Y., ₍c1945₎
cover-title, 16 p. (Its Studies in business policy, no. 10)

At head of title: Conference board reports.

NN 0054739   MH–BA MiEM OU OC1U

National industrial conference board.
... Public versus private housing; a review of the Washington slum clearance controversy ... New York, N.Y. ₍c1945₎
cover-title, 36 p. incl. tables. (Its Studies in business policy, no. 6)

At head of title: Conference board reports.

NN 0054740   MH–BA NNC MiEM OU

National industrial conference board.
Publications of the National industrial conference board. Boston, Mass., 1920.
cover-title, 36 p. 15ᵐ.
Membership list on inside of front cover.

1. National industrial conference board—Bibl. 2. Labor and laboring classes—Bibl.

Library of Congress   Z7164.L1N4   20–16866

NN 0054741   DLC MB

National Industrial Conference Board.
Purchasing for industry ₍by Francis R. Lusardi₎ New York ₍1946₎
40 p. illus. 28ᵐ. (Its Studies in business policy, no. 33)
Cover title.
Its Conference Board reports.

1. Buying.   I. Lusardi, Francis R   II. Ser. III. Ser.

NN 0054742   ViU MH–BA PPT

National Industrial Conference Board.
Purposes and by-laws.

New York₍, 192   16°.
no.

NN 0054743   NN MH

National industrial conference board.
Quality control: methods and company plans. New York, National industrial conference board, inc. ₍c1949₎
cover-title, 36 p. forms, diagrs. 28cm. (Its Studies in business policy, no. 36)

NN 0054744   ViU–L OU MH–BA

HD9710
.U5Q3
National industrial conference board.
Quarterly review of the automobile industry. no. 1– Mar 1937–   New York, N. Y., National industrial conference board, inc., 1937–

HD9651
.1
.Q3
National industrial conference board.
Quarterly review of the chemical industry. no. 1– June 1938–   New York, N. Y., National industrial conference board, inc., 1938–

HD9715
.U5Q3
National industrial conference board.
Quarterly review of the construction industry. no. 1– May 1937–   New York, N. Y., National industrial conference board, inc., 1937–

HD9539
.C5Q3
National industrial conference board.
Quarterly review of the copper, lead and zinc industries. no. 1–   Dec. 1936– New York, National industrial conference board ⁰1936–

HD9685
.U4Q3
National industrial conference board.
Quarterly review of the electricity and gas industries. no. 1–   Dec. 1937– New York, National industrial conference board, inc., ⁰1937–

HD9541
.Q35
National industrial conference board.
Quarterly review of the fuel industries. no. 1– Sept. 1937–   New York, N. Y., National industrial conference board, inc., 1937–

HD9705
.U6Q3
National industrial conference board.
Quarterly review of the machinery industries. no. 1– Dec. 1938–   New York, N. Y., National industrial conference board, inc., 1938–

VOLUME 407

National industrial conference board.
HE2714
.Q3   **Quarterly** review of the railroad industry. no. 1–
July 1937–   New York, N. Y., National indus-
trial conference board, inc., 1937–

National industrial conference board.

... **Quarterly** review of the textile industry ... no. 1–
Feb. 1938–
New York, N. Y., National industrial conference board, inc.,
*1938–

National Industrial Conference Board.
...Questions regarding application of Securities exchange act
to industrial corporations, their officers, directors, and security
holders. New York, 1934. 16 f. 28½cm. (Its ₍Con-
ference Board information service: Domestic affairs₎ Special memorandum. ₍no. 2.₎)

Cover-title.
Reproduced from typewritten copy.

1. Securities—Jurisp.—U. S., 1934.   2. Corporations—Finance—
U. S. I. Ser.   U. S.
N. Y. P. L.   June 24, 1936

NN   0054754   NN DL OCU OC1FRB

HF5549   National Industrial Conference Board.
A2N27   Quick-training procedures.   New York
no.26   ₍1940₎
40p. 28cm. (Its Studies in personnel
policy, no.26)

1. Employees, Training of.

NN   0054755   IaU OC1 InU ViU

338.4   National Industrial Conference Board.
N213rai   Railroad equipment: basic industrial data.
₍n.p.₎ 1952.
1v. of tables. 28cm.

1. Railroads—Equipment and supplies. 2.
Railroads—U.S.—Equipment and supplies.

NN   0054756   IU OrU

National industrial conference board.
Railroad performance ... New York, National industrial conference board ₍1924₎
vii, 60 p. incl. tables, diagrs. 23ᶜᵐ. (Its Research report, no. 71)
"Publications of the National industrial conference board": 4 p. at end.

1. Railroads—U. S.
Library of Congress   TF23.N3
                                          24–23033

OCU ICJ OC1 OO WaWW Or WaTC
NN   0054757   DLC CaBVaU MtBC CU NcD NcRS ViU MiU

National industrial conference board.
Railroad wages and working rules ... National industrial conference board. New York, The Century co.
₍1922₎
viii, 130 p. incl. tables (part fold.) diagrs. 23ᶜᵐ. (Its Research report, no.
46) $2.00

1. Railroads—U. S.—Salaries, pensions, etc. 2. Arbitration, Industrial—
U. S. 3. Railroads—U. S.—Employees. I. Title.
                                          22—9643
Library of Congress   HD4966.R12U67

NN   0054758   DLC NjR CU MiU OU OC1W OO OC1 MB ICJ

National industrial conference board.
Rationalization of German industry. New York, National
industrial conference board, inc., 1931.
xv, 182 p. diagrs. 28ᶜᵐ.

1. Germany—Indus. 2. Germany—Comm. I. Title.
Library of Congress   HC286.3.N25
                                          31–6607
———— Copy 2.
Copyright A 35043   ₍5-5₎   338.0943

MiU ViU DL DAL NSyU NIC TU CaBVaU WaS MB OrCS MtU
NN   0054759   DLC KMK GU CU ICJ NcD OU OC1 OO OCU

Pamphlet   National Industrial Conference Board.
TS   Rayon; basic industrial data. ₍New
7+   York₎ 1954.
38p. 28cm.

Cover title.

₍X.₎Rayon.

NN   0054760   NIC OCU IU

HF5006   National Industrial Conference Board.
.N3
no.3   Rebuilding industry's sales organization.
1944   New York ₍1944₎
19 p. 28cm. (Its Studies in business
policy, no. 3)
Cover title.

1. U. S.—Indus. 2. Sales management. 3.
Reconstruction ₍1939–   ₎—U. S. I. Title.
II. Ser.

NN   0054761   ViU MH-BA Mi

National industrial conference board.
... Recent agreements negotiated between company manage-
ments and organized labor ... New York, N. Y., National
industrial conference board, inc., *1937–
v. 28½ᶜᵐ. (Conference board information service: Domestic
affairs series. Memorandum no. 58, 61₎
Mimeographed.

1. Labor and laboring classes—U. S.—1914–   2. Trade-unions—
U. S. I. Title.
Library of Congress   HC106.3.N24 no. 58, 61₎
                                          40–14347
———— 2d set.
Copyright   ₍2₎   (330.973) 331.1540973

NN   0054762   DLC NcD

National industrial conference board.
Recent developments in industrial group insurance. New
York, National industrial conference board, inc., 1934.
ix, 46 p. 23½ᶜᵐ.
Revision and extension of a similar study, "Industrial group insurance," issued by the National industrial conference board in 1927 and
revised in 1929. cf. p. 4.

1. Insurance, Group—U. S. I. Title.
HG8830.N355   331.2530973
                                          34–39709

OC1W ViU
NN   0054763   DLC MtU OrCS NcD ICJ MiU OU OCU OC1

National industrial conference board.
... Recent plans providing security of income or employment
for wage earners, February, 1939 ... New York, N. Y., National industrial conference board, inc., *1939.
2 p. l., 22 numb. l. 28½ᶜᵐ. (Conference board information service:
Domestic affairs series. Memorandum no. 62₎
Mimeographed.

1. Insurance, Industrial—U. S. 2. Insurance, Unemployment—U. S.
I. Title.
Library of Congress   HC106.3.N24 no. 62
                                          40–14348
———— Copy 2.
Copyright AA 297285   ₍2₎   (330.973) 331.254440973

NN   0054764   DLC DFT

National industrial conference board.
... Recent state labor legislation ... ₍New York₎ National
industrial conference board, inc., 1935.
cover-title, 1 p. l., 10 numb. l. 28½ᶜᵐ. (Conference board information
service. Domestic affairs series. Memorandum no. 42)
Mimeographed.

1. Insurance, Unemployment—U. S. 2. Insurance, State and compul-
sory—U. S. 3. Labor laws and legislation—U. S. I. Title.
Library of Congress   HC106.3.N24 no. 42
                                          35–17479
———— Copy 2.
Copyright AA 84501   ₍5₎   (330.973) 331.254440973

NN   0054765   DLC OC1FRB

National Industrial Conference Board.
Recognition for long service; nonmonetary awards, extra
privileges, monetary awards, increased job security. ₍By
Harold Stieglitz, Division of Personnel Administration₎
New York ₍1950₎
36 p. illus. 28 cm. (Its Conference Board reports. Studies in personnel policy, no. 106)
Cover title.
1. Seniority, Employee. I. Stieglitz, Harold. II. Title. (Series: National Industrial Conference Board. Conference Board reports. Series: National Industrial Conference Board. Studies in
personnel policy, no. 106)
HF5549.A2N27 no. 106   331.125   50–13560

NN   0054766   DLC PPT AAP IaU

HF5549   National Industrial Conference Board.
A2N27   Recognizing long service.   New York
no.29   ₍1941₎
8p. 28cm. (Its Studies in personnel
policy, no.29)

NN   0054767   IaU InU

National industrial conference board.
A reconstruction program for American enterprise; a series
of addresses delivered at the twenty-fourth annual meeting of
the Conference board, New York, May 22, 1940 ... New York,
National industrial conference board inc. ₍*1940₎
3 p. l., 49 p. 23ᶜᵐ.
Contains addresses by Virgil Jordan, J. C. O'Mahoney, A. P. Sloan, jr.,
and W. L. Batt.

1. Industry and state—U. S. 2. U. S.—Economic policy. I. Title.
II. Title: American enterprise, A reconstruction program for.
Library of Congress   HC106.4.N37
                                          40–13791
———— Copy 2.
Copyright A 141980   ₍4₎   330.973

NN   0054768   DLC OrU OCU OU OC1 OC1FRB ICJ MB

National Industrial Conference Board.
Recruiting and selecting employees: employment policies,
employment interviewing, employment forms, employment
research. ₍By Stephen Habbe, Division of Personnel Ad-
ministration₎ New York ₍1954₎
80 p. illus. 28 cm. (Its Conference Board reports. Studies in
personnel policy, no. 144)
Cover title.
Bibliographical footnotes.
1. Recruiting of employees. I. Habbe, Stephen, 1903– (Series: National Industrial Conference Board. Studies in personnel
policy, no. 144)
HF5549.A2N27 no. 144   658.3115   54—4779

NN   0054769   DLC ViU AAP OCU PPCuP DI MiU OOxM CoU

HF5549   National Industrial Conference Board.
A2N27   Reducing absenteeism.   New York ₍1942₎
no.46   35p. 28cm. (Its Studies in personnel
policy, no.46)

1. Absenteeism.

NN   0054770   IaU

VOLUME 407

HF5549
.A2N25
no.27
NATIONAL INDUSTRIAL CONFERENCE BOARD
...Reducing fluctuations in employment, experience in 31 industries, N.Y., The Board [1940] 60p, Tables. Diagrs, (Its Studies in personnel policy, no.27)

Suppl. to the Management record.
Cover-title.

NN   0054771   InU ViU IaU

National industrial conference board.
... Reemployment of veterans ... New York, N. Y., National industrial conference board, inc. [1945]

cover-title, 43 p. incl. illus., forms, diagrs. 28 x 22cm. (*Its* Conference board reports)

Studies in personnel policy, no. 69.
"By Ethel M. Spears, Management research division."—p. 3.

1. Veterans—Employment—U. S.   I. Spears, Ethel M.
45–4077

Library of Congress °   HF5549.A2N27 no. 69
[10]   (658.3) 658.386

NN   0054772   DLC ViU IaU CoU

National Industrial Conference Board.
Renegotiation in peace and war [by R. Maxil Ballinger, Division of Business Practices] New York [*1950]

48 p. tables. 28 cm. (*Its* Conference Board reports. Studies in business policy, no. 44)

Cover title.
Bibliographical footnotes.

1. Renegotiation of government contracts—U. S.   I. Ballinger, R. Maxil. II. Title. (Series: National Industrial Conference Board. Studies in business policy, no. 44)

HF5006.N3   no. 44   58–47941

NN   0054773   DLC PPT PPULC OU MH-BA CoU AAP IaU LU

National industrial conference board.
... Renegotiation of government contracts. New York, National industrial conference board, inc. [1942]

cover-title, 12 p. 28 x 21½ cm. (*Its* Conference board reports)

1. Renegotiation of government contracts.

HD3860.N3   351.71   43—7463

OCU OC1U
NN   0054774   DLC OrU UU GU NBuG DNAL ICJ ICU OU

National Industrial Conference Board.
Replacement costs and depreciation policy. New York, N.Y. [1948]
cover-title, 30 p.   (Its Studies in business policy, no. 27)

At head of title: Conference Board reports.

NN   0054775   MH-BA PPT MiEM

National Industrial Conference Board.
Report [annual]
see its Annual report.

National Industrial Conference Board.
Report no. 112–210?
see its Studies.

331.06
N213m
no.2
NATIONAL INDUSTRIAL CONFERENCE BOARD.
... Representative union agreements. New York, National industrial conference board [c1939]
cover-title, 38p. 28cm. (Its Conference board management research memoranda, no.2, June, 1939)

1. Labor contract - U.S. 2. Trade-unions - U.S. I. Title. II. Series (contents)

NN   0054778   TxU

National Industrial Conference Board.
Representative union agreements. New York [1939–41]

2 v. 28 cm. (Management research memorandum no. 2, 7)

Vol. 2: Supplement to the Management record.

1. Collective labor agreements—U. S.   I. Title.   (Series: National Industrial Conference Board. Management research memoranda, no. 2, 7)

KF3408.Z9N3   331.1'16'0973   72–16026
MARC

NN   0054779   DLC

HD7811
.U6N322
National Industrial Conference Board.
Representative union agreements--II.
New York [1941]
63 p. 28cm. (Its Management research memorandum, no. 7)
Cover title.
Supplement to The Management record.

1. Labor contract--U.S. I. Management record. Supplement. II. Title.

NN   0054780   MB ViU

331.06
N213m
no.7
NATIONAL INDUSTRIAL CONFERENCE BOARD.
... Representative union agreements - II. New York, National industrial conference board, inc. [1941]
cover-title, 63p. 28cm. (Its Management research memorandum, no.8)

At head of title: The conference board.
"Supplement to The management record."

1. Labor contract - U.S. 2. Trade union - U.S. I. Title. II. Series (contents)

NN   0054781   TxU NBuG

HF5006
.N3
no.8
1945
National Industrial Conference Board.
Repricing war contracts under the company pricing program. New York [1945]
16 p. 28cm. (Its Studies in business policy, no. 8)
Cover title.

1. Prices—U. S. 2. World War, 1939–1945—Economic aspects. 3. Defense contracts—U. S. I. Title. II. Ser.

NN   0054782   ViU OC1U OU MH-BA

National Industrial Conference Board.
Research memorandum
see
National Industrial Conference Board.
Management research memorandum.

National Industrial Conference Board.
...The research organization of American industry in the field of industrial economics. New York, 1921. 26 p. 12°.
Cover-title.

NN   0054784   NN

National Industrial Conference Board.
...The research organization of American industry in the field of industrial economics. New York, 1922. 30 p. 12°.
Cover-title.

NN   0054785   NN

NATIONAL INDUSTRIAL CONFERENCE BOARD.
The research organization of American industry in the field of industrial economics. New York, [1923].

18 cm. pp. (4), 28.
Paper cover serves as title-page.

NN   0054786   NN

National Industrial Conference Board.
Research report
see its Studies.

National Industrial Conference Board.
Researching foreign markets. New York [1955]
72 p. illus. 29 cm. (*Its* Conference Board reports. Studies in business policy, no. 75)

1. Marketing research.   I. Title.

HF5415.N32   55–4999 ‡

NN   0054788   DLC LU DPU IaU NB WaU PPCuP DI ViU OU

National Industrial Conference Board.
Resources: from abundance to scarcity by 1975? A round table discussion, Felix E. Wormser, chairman, Eugene Ayres [and others. New York, 1952]
52 p. 23 cm. (*Its* Studies in business economics, no. 36)
Cover title.

1. U. S. President's Materials Policy Commission. Resources for freedom. 2. Natural resources—U. S.   I. Wormser, Felix Edgar, 1894– II. Title.   (Series)

HB31.N33 no. 36   333.7   54–2106

OCU OOxM PSt ViU PPCuP MoU CoU NN ICU
NN   0054789   DLC OrLgE IaU PBm DI MH-BA NIC TxU

National industrial conference board.
Rest periods for industrial workers ... Boston, Mass, National industrial conference board, °1919.
iv, 55 p. incl. tables. 23cm. (*Its* Research report, no. 13)

1. Hours of labor—U. S. 2. Fatigue.   I. Title.   19–5627
Library of Congress   HD5112.N3

NcRS MiU OU OCU OCl CU DL NjP ICJ MB ViU
NN   0054790   DLC Or CtY-M CaBVaU WaS OrPR MtBC NcD

658
N214r
National Industrial Conference Board.
Retail grocery and variety stores, basic industrial data. [New York] 1954.
unpaged. tables. 28cm.

Caption title.

1. Retail trade--U.S. I. Title.

NN   0054791   IU

VOLUME 407

HF5429
.B2
1945a

National industrial conference board.
⌐Backman, Jules⌐ 1910–
Retail price policy in the transition, a special study prepared for the OPA, Retail reconversion pricing committee. New York, N. Y., National industrial conference board, inc. ⌐1945⌐

658.87
N21r

National Industrial Conference Board.
Retail trade. Total retail trade: department stores, mail-order houses. ⌐n.p.⌐ 1952.
1v. of tables. 28cm.

1. Retail trade--U.S. 2. Department stores.
3. Mail-order business.

NN 0054793   IU NNC

National Industrial Conference Board.
Retirement of employees: policies, procedures, practices. ⌐By F. Beatrice Brower, Division of Personnel Administration⌐ New York ⌐1955⌐
48 p. illus. 28 cm. (*Its* Conference Board reports. Studies in personnel policy, no. 148)
Cover-title.
1. Retirement.   I. Brower, Frances Beatrice.   (Series: National Industrial Conference Board. Studies in personnel policy, no. 148)
HF5549.A2N27 no. 148   658.313   55–2601

NN 0054794   DLC NIC DI OOxM ViU OCU AAP CoU IaU

National industrial conference board.
⌐...⌐ The Revenue act of 1934 ... ⌐New York⌐ National industrial conference board, 1934.
cover-title, ii, 5 numb. l. 28½ᶜᵐ. (Conference board information service: Domestic affairs. Memorandum no. 33)
Mimeographed.
1. Taxation--U. S.--Law.   I. Title.
Library of Congress   HC106.3.N24 no. 33   34–34203
————— Copy 2.
Copyright A 72764   ⌐5⌐   (330.973) 336.20973

NN 0054795   DLC

National industrial conference board.
... The revised Economic security bill ... ⌐New York⌐ National industrial conference board, 1935.
cover-title, 10 numb. l. 28½ᶜᵐ. (Conference board information service: Domestic affairs. Special memorandum no. 9)
Mimeographed.
1. Insurance, Unemployment--U. S. 2. Old age pensions--U. S. 3. Children--Charities, protection, etc.--U. S.   I. Title.   II. Title: Economic security bill.
Library of Congress   HC106.3.N243 no. 9   35–7555
————— Copy 2.
Copyright AA 173237   ⌐8⌐   (330.973) 331.25440973

NN 0054796   DLC OC1FRB

National Industrial Conference Board.
∴ Road maps of industry. Chart⌐s⌐.
no.
New York, 192   f°.
v.   col'd charts.
Charts no.   also called series 192

1. Industries and mechanic arts--Stat.   --U. S. 2. Economic history--U. S.
N. Y. P. L.   March 20, 1930

OrCS NjR MdBJ ICJ NNU-W GAT
NN 0054797   NN NIC DL TU OU IC NcU DGW LU DI KyU

National industrial conference board.
... The Robinson-Patman act. ⌐New York⌐ National industrial conference board, inc., 1936.
cover-title, 1 p. l., 8 numb. l. 28½ᶜᵐ. (Conference board information service: Domestic affairs series. Memorandum no. 51)
Mimeographed.

1. Price discrimination--U. S.
                                                  40–14342
Library of Congress   HC106.3.N24 no. 51
⌐a44c1⌐   (330.973) 338.50973

NN 0054798   DLC OrCS

National Industrial Conference Board.
The Russian situation; addresses, by Count Ilya Tolstoy and V. Zenzinoff...delivered at the meeting of the National Industrial Conference Board, January 17, 1924. ⌐New York, 1924.⌐ 31 p. 8°.
Cover-title.
Contents: TOLSTOI, I. L., graf. The Soviet régime — its development and present situation. ZENZINOV, V. M. The possibilities of economic reconstruction in Russia.

1. Bolshevism. 2. Economic history   —Russia. 3. Tolstoi, Ilya Lvovich, graf, 1866–   4. Zenzinov, Vladi-   mir Mikhailovich.
N. Y. P. L.   May 10, 1927

NN 0054799   NN PBm

National industrial conference board.
Salary and wage policy in the depression. New York, National industrial conference board, inc., 1932.
viii, 67 p. diagrs. 23 cm.

1. Wages--U. S. 2. U. S.--Indus. 3. U. S.--Econ. condit.--1918–
I. Title.
HD4975.N25   331.2973   32–17803

OO ViU ICJ DL OrCS WaTC MtU IdU-SB WaS Or IEN
NN 0054800   DLC CU NcD NcRS OU OC1 OC1W MiU OCU

National industrial conference board.
... Salary and wage policy, 1933–1934 ... New York city, National industrial conference board, inc. ⌐1935⌐
vii, 23 p. 23ᶜᵐ. (*Its* Studies. no. 212)
"This report was prepared by Mr. Harold F. Browne of the Conference board's research staff."--Foreword.

1. Wages--U. S. 2. Industrial statistics.   I. Browne, Harold Frederic, 1890–   II. Title.
                                                  35–6928
Library of Congress   HD4975.N26
————— Copy 2.
Copyright A 82425   ⌐5–5⌐   331.2973

ViU NIC OC1 OCU OU
NN 0054801   DLC MtU WaS OrCS Or CU NcD MB MiU

National Industrial Conference Board.
Sales organization and compensation of sales executives. ⌐By Thomas A. Fitzgerald⌐ New York, N.Y. ⌐1948⌐
cover-title, 47 p. incl. charts, tables. (*Its* Studies in business policy, no. 28)
At head of title: Conference Board reports.

NN 0054802   MH-BA MiEM

National industrial conference board.
Sales taxes: general, selective, and retail. New York, National industrial conference board, inc., 1932.
ix, 79 p. 23½ cm.

1. Sales tax--U. S.

HJ5715.U6N33   336.27   32–14547

CaBVaU OrSaW Wa MB
OU OC1 OCU OO MiU IdU-SB Or MtU WaWW WaS OrCS
NN 0054803   DLC NcD DHEW ICJ ViU KMK CoU TU MH

National Industrial Conference Board.
Salesmen's compensation plans ⌐by Elmer W. Earl, Jr., Management Research Division⌐ New York ⌐1947⌐
39 p. 28 cm. (*Its* Conference Board reports. Studies in personnel policy, no. 81)
Bibliographical footnotes.
1. Salesmen and salesmanship. 2. Wages.   I. Earl, Elmer W.   II. Title.   III. Series: National Industrial Conference Board. Conference Board reports.   IV. Series: National Industrial Conference Board. Studies in personnel policy, no. 81.
HF5549.A2N27 no. 81   331.28588   48–17515*

NN 0054804   DLC OC1JC CoU AAP Mi IaU

HB 31
.N34
no.3

NATIONAL INDUSTRIAL CONFERENCE BOARD
Saving, liquid assets, and the consumer market; three articles reprinted from the Conference Board Business record, with additional introductory material by Bella Shapiro. N.Y. ⌐1954?⌐
19 p. tables, diagrs. (*Its* Technical paper, no.3)

1. Saving and investment.

NN 0054805   InU MiD NcD ViU NNC

National industrial conference board.
... Savings plans and credit unions in industry. New York city, National industrial conference board, inc. ⌐1936⌐
ix, 72 p. 23ᶜᵐ. (*Its* Studies. no. 225)
"This report was prepared by Miss F. Beatrice Brower, of the Department of industrial management of the Board's research staff."--Foreword.

1. Banks and banking, Cooperative. 2. Saving and thrift.
I. Brower, Frances Beatrice.   II. Title.
                                                  36–18249
Library of Congress   HG7920.N35
————— Copy 2.
Copyright A 96606   ⌐5–3⌐   334.2

ViU ICJ OC1W OC1 OU OCU
NN 0054806   DLC WaTC MtU IdU WaS OrCS Or NcD OO

National industrial conference board.
The scope of trade association activities in the light of recent decisions of the Supreme court of the United States. New York, National industrial conference board, inc., 1925.
8 p. 23ᶜᵐ.
"The National industrial conference board issues this brief analysis ... by way of supplementing its volume on 'Trade associations: their economic significance and legal status'."

1. Trade and professional associations--U. S.
                                                  26–3709
Library of Congress   HD2425.N3 1925 b

NN 0054807   DLC Or

National Indstrial Conference Board.
Selected business factors
see its   Selected business indicators.

National industrial conference board, inc.
Selected business indicators.

New York 1933–34.   28½ cm.
v.   charts, tables.
Monthly.
Reproduced from typewritten copy.
Jan., 1934, has title: Selected business factors; Feb.– March, 1934, Basic business factors.
193   included in its Conference board business survey (see that entry).

1. Index numbers--U. S.   2. Economic history--U. S., 1918–
I. Title.
N. Y. P. L.   January 21, 1938

NN 0054809   NN HU OCU

VOLUME 407

National industrial conference board.
    ... Selected company pension plans that take into account the federal Social security act ... New York, N. Y., National industrial conference board, inc., °1937.

    2 p. l., 54 numb. l. 28½ cm. (Conference board information service: Domestic affairs series. Memorandum no. 59)
    Mimeographed.

    1. Old age pensions—U. S.   I. Title.   II. Title: Social security act.

    HC106.3.N24 no. 59   331.2520973   37—17779

NN   0054810   DLC DFT

National industrial conference board.
    ... Selected company plans for granting supplementary compensation to employees. ₍New York₎ National industrial conference board, inc., 1936.

    cover-title, 1 p. l., 39 numb. l. 28½ᶜᵐ. (Conference board information service: Domestic affairs series. Memorandum no. 52)
    Mimeographed.

    1. Bonus system. 2. Profit-sharing.   I. Title.   II. Title: Supplementary compensation to employees.

                                       37—3902
    Library of Congress   HC106.3.N24 no. 52
    ———— Copy 2.
    Copyright AA 216531   ₍5₎   (330.973) 331.225

NN   0054811   DLC

National industrial conference board.
    ... Selected interpretations on the Fair labor standards act ... New York, National industrial conference board, inc. ₍1942₎

    cover-title, 40 p. diagrs. 28ᶜᵐ. (Its Management research memorandum, no. 8)
    At head of title: The Conference board.
    "Summary of interpretative bulletins and regulations used in this report": p. 40.

    1. Wages—U. S. 2. Hours of labor—U. S.   I. Title: Fair labor standards act.

                                    42—10452
    Library of Congress   HD4974.N3
                      ₍4₎   331.0973

NN   0054812   DLC OrU MB UU ViU OU

National industrial conference board.
    ... Selected plans of companies granting vacations with pay to wage earners ... ₍New York₎ National industrial conference board, inc., 1936.

    cover-title, 1 p. l., 25 numb. l. 28½ᶜᵐ. (Conference board information service: Domestic affairs series. Memorandum no. 48)
    Mimeographed.

    1. Vacations, Employee—U. S.

                                      40—1717
    Library of Congress   HC106.3.N24 no. 48
                      ₍a44e1₎   (330.973) 331.816

NN   0054813   DLC

249.3
N213S   National industrial conference board.
    ... Selecting, training and upgrading; supervisors, instructors, production workers. New York ₍1941₎
    cover-title, 72 p. 28cm. (Its Studies in personnel policy, no.37)

    At head of title: Conference board reports.

    1. Employment management. 2. Personnel training. ser. (2)

NN   0054814   DNAL MoSU InU ViU IaU

National industrial conference board.
    ... Seniority and reemployment of war veterans ... New York, N. Y., National industrial conference board, inc. ₍1944₎

    1 p. l., 12 p. 28 x 22ᶜᵐ. (Its Conference board reports)
    Studies in personnel policy, no. 65.

    1. Veterans—Employment—U. S.   I. Title.

                                      44—9662
    Library of Congress   HF5549.A2N27 no. 65
                      ₍4₎   (658.3) 355.115

NN   0054815   DLC OC1JC AAP ViU OC1 CoU OC1U

National industrial conference board.
    ... Seniority provisions in union contracts. New York, National industrial conference board, inc. ₍1939₎

    15 p. 28ᶜᵐ. (Its Conference board management record supplements. Research memorandum no. 3)

    1. Labor contract—U. S. 2. Trade-unions—U. S. 3. Employment management.   I. Title.

                                      41—19043
    Library of Congress   HD7811.U6N3
    ———— Copy 2.
    Copyright AA 323168   ₍2₎   331.1163

NN   0054816   DLC ViU OU OrU

National Industrial Conference Board.
    Seniority systems in nonunionized companies ₍by John J. Speed and James J. Bambrick, Jr., Division of Personnel Administration₎ New York ₍1950₎

    32 p. diagrs. 28 cm. (Its Conference Board reports. Studies in personnel policy, no. 110)
    Cover title.

    1. Seniority, Employee.   I. Speed, John Joseph, 1928–   II. Bambrick, James Joseph, 1888–   III. Title.   (Series: National Industrial Conference Board. Studies in personnel policy, no. 110)

    HF5549.N33   331.125   51—1010

NN   0054817   DLC AAP CoU

National industrial conference board.
    September 17, the birthday of our Constitution. ₍Boston, Nat. industrial conference board, c1919₎ folder of 7 p. 15cm.

    Caption-title.

    1. United States. Constitution—   Hist.
    N. Y. P. L.   August 11, 1949

NN   0054818   NN MB

National Industrial Conference Board. Service letter
    see its   Conference Board service letter.

National Industrial Conference Board. The service letter on industrial relations
    see its   Conference Board service letter.

National Industrial Conference Board.
    Severance pay plans. ₍By Lois E. Forde and F. Beatrice Brower₎ New York ₍1954₎

    47 p. 28 cm. (Its Conference Board reports. Studies in personnel policy, no. 141)

    1. Wages—Dismissal wage.   I. Forde, Lois Elizabeth, 1922–   II. Title.

    HF5549.A2N27 no. 141   658.313   54—2636 ‡

NN   0054821   DLC CoU AAP ViU OOxM PPT DI OCU

National Industrial Conference Board.
    Shall we return to a gold standard—now?

    see its

    The Conference Board Economic Forum presents: Shall we return to a gold standard—now?

HF5549
.A2N27   National Industrial Conference Board.
no.35
1941   Shift operation under defense conditions. New York ₍1941₎
    11 p. 28cm. (Its Studies in personnel policy, no. 35)
    Conference Board reports.

    1. Hours of labor. I. Title. II. Ser.

NN   0054823   ViU IaU OC1 MoSU

HF5549
A2N27   **National Industrial Conference Board.**
no.40   Shift practice in war industry. New York ₍1942₎
    20p. 28cm. (Its Studies in personnel policy, no.40)

    1. Shift system.

NN   0054824   IaU ViU OC1JC MoSU

National Industrial Conference Board.
    Shift problems and practices ₍by Herbert R. Northrup, Division of Personnel Administration₎ New York ₍1951₎

    23 p. diagrs. 28 cm. (Its Conference Board reports. Studies in personnel policy, no. 118)
    Cover title.

    1. Multiple-shift operation.   I. Northrup, Herbert Roof, 1918–   II. Title.   (Series: National Industrial Conference Board. Studies in personnel policy, no. 118)

    HF5549.A2N27 no. 118   658.3811   51—6260

NN   0054825   DLC MH AAP OCU CoU

National industrial conference board.
    The shifting and effects of the federal corporation income tax ... New York, National industrial conference board, inc., 1928–

    v. tables, diagrs. 23½ᶜᵐ.

    1. Corporations—U. S.—Taxation. 2. Income tax—U. S.   I. Title.

                                      28—25519
    Library of Congress   HD2753.U6N3

    MiU OO OOxM TU MB FMU MB KMK
NN   0054826   DLC MtU WaS OrU DAL NcD DL ICJ ViU

National industrial conference board.
    Shorter work periods in industry. New York, National industrial conference board, inc., 1932.

    x, 56 p. diagrs. 23ᶜᵐ.

    1. Hours of labor. 2. U. S.—Indus.   I. Title.

                                      32—35894
    Library of Congress   HD5125.N36
    ———— Copy 2.
    Copyright A 58093   ₍5-5₎   331.81973

    NNC DHEW OU OCU MiU OO OrU Or MB
NN   0054827   DLC OrCS WaS MtU ICJ CU NIC DL OC1

National Industrial Conference Board.
    Should we return to a gold standard? A round table contribution as part of the 293rd meeting of the conference board. ₍New York, 1948₎

    52 p. 23 cm. (Its Studies in business economics, no. 17)

    1. Gold standard. 2. Currency question—U. S.   I. Title. (Series)

    HB31.N33 no. 17   332.422   48—7323*

NN   0054828   DLC TxU PPT CLU IaU CoU Mi

National industrial conference board.
    Sickness insurance or sickness prevention? ... Boston, Mass., National industrial conference board °1918.

    24 p. 23ᶜᵐ. (Its Research report, no. 6) $0.50

    1. Occupations—Diseases and hygiene. 2. Hygiene, Public. 3. Insurance, Health.   I. Title.

    Library of Congress   HD7261.N35
                                      18—11385

    ICJ CaBVaU Or CaBViP WaWW DL OU OC1W MiU OC1
NN   0054829   DLC ViU WaS WaTC MtBC CtY-M CU NcD

VOLUME 407

National industrial conference board.
The situation in Germany at the beginning of 1933. New York, National industrial conference board, inc., 1933.

ix, 50 p. 23ᵉᵐ.

"The investigation ... was made by Mr. Vaso Trivanovitch ... and the text was prepared by him under the supervision of the staff economic council."—Foreword and summary.

1. Germany—Econ. condit.—1918-   2. Germany—Pol. & govt.—1918-   3. Finance—Germany. 4. Germany—Comm. I. Trivanovitch, Vaso. II. Title.

Library of Congress   HC286.3.N27   33—10555

———— Copy 2.

Copyright A 61426   [5-5]   330.943

NN   0054830   ViU DAU NcD DL OU OCU MiU OO ICJ
DLC MtU WaS OrCS GU KMK MH-BA OC1U

National Industrial Conference Board.
The small order, asset or liability?
see under   Thompson, G   Clark.

National industrial conference board.
Social adequacy 'of foreign nationals in the United States; a critical review of "Analysis of America's modern melting pot" ... New York city, National industrial conference board [1924]

v, 42 p. 23ᵐᵐ.   (*Its* Special report, no. 28)

1. U. S. Congress. House. Committee on immigration and naturalization. Analysis of America's modern melting pot. 2. U. S.—Emig. & immig. I. Title.

Library of Congress   JV6416.A3 1923 b   24—13700

NN   0054832   DLC MtU CU NcD OCU OU OC1 MB

National industrial conference board.
The soldiers' bonus; or, Adjusted compensation for soldiers ... New York city, National industrial conference board [1923]

v, 46 p. 23ᵐᵐ.   (*Its* Special report no. 24)

1. Pensions, Military—U. S.—European war, 1914-1918. I. U. S. Laws, statutes, etc. II. Title.

Library of Congress   UB373.N25   23—12071

NN   0054833   OU OC1W OC1 OC1FRB TU PSt IU KU WaWW
CU KyU MtU DL MsU PBL WvU IdU MtBC OrU CaBVaU Or
DLC LU TxLT MB ICJ NcD MiU GU ViU MB

National industrial conference board.
... Some aspects of price adjustments ... [New York] National industrial conference board, 1933.

cover-title, 5 numb. l. fold. diagr. 29ᵐᵐ.   (Conference board information service: Domestic affairs. Memorandum no. 15)

Mimeographed.
"Sources of data": leaf 5.

1. Prices—U. S. I. Title. II. Title: Price adjustments.

Library of Congress   HC106.3.N24 no. 15   34—5515

———— Copy 2.

Copyright AA 133102   [3]   (330.973) 338.50973

NN   0054834   DLC

National Industrial Conference Board.
... Special report number [1]-34. New York [etc.] National Industrial Conference Board, Inc. [1919-1926]

34 v. in 6. tables, diagrs. 23½ᵉᵐ.

No. 1-6 issued without series title or number (listed in no. 7 and later reports)
No more published.
No. 1-10 published in Boston.
Wanting: no. 18.

NN   0054835   ICJ OrU OrCS CaBVaU IdU

National industrial conference board.
State and local taxation of business corporations. New York, National industrial conference board, inc., 1931.

xii, 177 p. incl. tables. 23½ cm.

1. Corporations—U. S.—Taxation. 2. Taxation, State. I. Title.

HD2753.U6N35   31—12937

NN   0054836   ViU MB
MiU OU ICJ KMK Or MtU WaSp IdU-SB WaS OrCS Wa MH
DLC DL NBuU CoU TU NcD OC1U OO OC1 OCU

National industrial conference board.
State and local taxation of property. New York, National industrial conference board, inc., 1930.

xii, 245 p. illus. (maps) 23½ cm.

"This study has been made ... by Ralph Theodore Compton and assistants."—Pref.

1. Property tax—U. S. 2. Taxation, State. 3. Local taxation—U. S. I. Compton, Ralph Theodore.

HJ4120.N3   336.210973   31—308

NN   0054837   WaTC
ViU ICJ DAL WaS OrPR OrU MtU OrCS Or CaBVaU Wa MB
DLC TU OO OC1 NcD MH MiU OCU ODW OU

National industrial conference board.
State income taxes ... New York, National industrial conference board, inc., 1930.

2 v. 28½ᵐᵐ.

CONTENTS.—I. Historical development.—II. Analysis of income taxes in state fiscal systems.

1. Income tax—U. S. 2. Taxation, State. I. Title.

Library of Congress   HJ4655.A1N3   30—6441

NN   0054838   DL NcD ICJ ViU OC1 OCU OU MiU OO
DLC Or MB MH-L DAL WaS MtU Wa OrCS OrU

National industrial conference board.
... State sales taxes ... [New York] National industrial conference board, inc., 1935.

cover-title, 1 p. l., 25 numb. l. 28½ᵐᵐ.   (Conference board information service: Domestic affairs series. Memorandum no. 41)

Mimeographed.

1. Sales tax—U. S. I. Title.

Library of Congress   HC106.3.N24 no. 41   35—17480

———— Copy 2.

Copyright AA 178969   [5]   (330.973) 336.27

NN   0054839   DLC OC1FRB

National industrial conference board.
Statement of principles which should govern the employment relation in industry. Submitted by the employer group to the Industrial conference at Washington, D. C., October 10, 1919. Boston, Mass., National industrial conference board [1919?]

iii, 8 p. 23ᵐᵐ.

1. Labor and laboring classes—U. S.—1914-   2. Industry—Organization, control, etc. I. National industrial conference, Washington, D. C., 1919.

Library of Congress   HD6961.N32   40—38107

[2]   331.0973

NN   0054840   DLC MH OrCS

National industrial conference board.
Statement of purpose and rules... adopted unanimously at the regular meeting of the board on Dec. 16, 1920. [N.Y. 1920]

NN   0054841   InU

National industrial conference board.
... Statement ... respecting national labor situation and recommendation of means for preventing interruption by labor disputes of necessary war production... (Boston? 1917)
8 p. 27 cm.

NN   0054842   DL

National industrial conference board.
... Statistical and reporting requirements of N. R. A. ... [New York] National industrial conference board, 1933.

cover-title, 13 numb. l. 28½ᵐᵐ.   (Conference board information service: Domestic affairs. Memorandum no. 16)

Mimeographed.

1. Industrial statistics. 2. U. S.—Indus. 3. National industrial recovery act, 1933. I. Title.

HC106.3.N24 no. 16   34—5516

(330.973) 338.0973

NN   0054843   DLC TxU

HC 106   **National Industrial Conference Board.**
.3   Statistical charts ... National Ind. Conf.
.N33   Board. New York, c1929.
          1 v.   fol. 5 double diagrs.   46 cm.

NN   0054844   DLC

National industrial conference board.
... A statistical survey of public opinion regarding current economic and social problems as reported by newspaper editors in August and September, 1934. (Advance summary) New York city, National industrial conference board, inc. [1934]

vi, 8 p. incl. tables. 23ᵐᵐ.   (*Its* Studies. no. 205)

"The preliminary pages from the Conference board's full report are provided to furnish editors with necessary information regarding the purpose, method, scope, and general results of the survey."—p. [iii]

1. U. S.—Econ. condit.—1918-   2. U. S.—Soc. condit. 3. Public opinion. 4. Statistics. I. Title.

Library of Congress   HC106.3.N35   35—7470

———— Copy 2.

Copyright A 75768   [5]   330.973

NN   0054845   DLC MiU OU OC1 OCU

National industrial conference board.
... A statistical survey of public opinion regarding current economic and social problems, as reported by newspaper editors in August and September, 1934. Final report. New York city, National industrial conference board, inc. [1934]

viii, 40 p. incl. tables. 23ᵐᵐ.   (*Its* Studies, no. 205)

1. U. S.—Econ. condit.—1918-   2. U. S.—Soc. condit. 3. Public opinion. 4. Statistics. I. Title.

Library of Congress   HC106.3.N352   35—7255

———— Copy 2.

Copyright A 77797   [5-5]   330.973

NN   0054846   DLC MtU WaS OrCS ICJ ViU

National industrial conference board.
... A statistical survey of public opinion regarding current economic and social problems as reported by newspaper editors in the first quarter of 1936. New York city, National industrial conference board, inc. [1936]

viii, 56 p. incl. 53 tables. 23ᵐᵐ.   (*Its* Studies. no. 222)

1. U. S.—Economic policy. 2. U. S.—Soc. condit. 3. U. S.—Pol. & govt.—1933-   4. Public opinion—U. S.—Stat. 5. American newspapers. I. Title. II. Title: Economic and social problems as reported by newspaper editors.

Library of Congress   HC106.3.N353   36—11525

Copyright A 95241   [7-5]   330.973

NN   0054847   DL MB OC1 OC1W
DLC MtU WaS OrCS CU NcD ViU OU OCU

National Industrial Conference Board.
Stock ownership plans for workers. [By F. Beatrice Brower, Division of Personnel Administration] New York [1953]

68 p. illus. 28 cm.   (*Its* Conference Board reports. Studies in personnel policy, no. 132)

Cover title.

1. Employee ownership. 2. Stockholders—U. S. I. Brower, Frances Beatrice. II. Title. (Series: National Industrial Conference Board. Studies in personnel policy, no. 132)

HF5549.A2N27 no. 132   658.317   53—1791

NN   0054848   DLC IaU AAP OOxM PPD ViU PPT NIC OCU

VOLUME 407

fHF5006
.N3
no.43
National Industrial Conference Board.
Stockholder relations, by John H. Watson.
[New York, 1950]
56 p. 28 cm.   (Its Studies in business
policy, no. 43)

Cover title.
At head of title: Conference Board reports.

1. Stockholders. 2. Public relations--
Corporations. I. Title.   (Series)

NN 0054849   AAP MH-BA PPT

National Industrial Conference Board.
Strike controls in essential industries
see under   Northrup, Herbert Root, 1918-

National industrial conference board.
Strikes in American industry in wartime, April 6 to October 6, 1917 ... Boston, Mass., National industrial conference
board, °1918.
20 p. incl. tables. 23ᶜᵐ. (*Its* Research report, no. 3)

1. Strikes and lockouts--U. S. 2. Labor and laboring classes--U. S.--
1914-   3. European war, 1914-1918--Economic aspects--U. S.
I. Title.

Library of Congress   HD5234.N3
                                              18--8128

     MB MiU OU OCl OO
NN 0054851   DLC Or WaWW WaTC CU NcD ViU DL NN ICJ

330.973   National Industrial Conference Board.
N211s   Studies. no.1-
          1917-
          New York.
            v. tables, diagrs. 23cm.

          Title varies: no.1-71, Research report:
          no.112-210?, Report.
          No. 72-100 not issued. No. 106-111
          issued without series title or number.

          1. U.S. Indus   2. U.S. Econ. condit.

     DL
NN 0054852   KU NN KMK MtU CaBVaU UU MdBJ NjP IaGG

National industrial conference board.
Studies in administrative control ... New York, National
industrial conference board, inc. [1938-
     v. 27½ cm.

1. Industrial management.   I. Title. II. Title: Administrative
control, Studies in.
HB31.N3   658.04   38--34747

     ICJ CU MtU
NN 0054853   DLC OrCS OrU MnU NcD DFT OCl OCU DAL

National Industrial Conference Board.
Studies in business economics. no. 1-
[New York, 1945-
     no. in   v. 24 cm.

1. Economics--Collections.   I. Title.
HB31.N33   330.82   51--2519

     WaTC WaWW
Mi PBL NN WvU CoU CU TxHR IU PHC MBU NcU MiD GU-L
CtNIC MiD KMK UU NcGU ICU ICJ TU NcD LU NNC NIC
NN 0054854   DLC CtY NBuG Vi OCl CU-Riv INS MeB NBC

National industrial conference board.
... Studies in business policy. no. 1-
New York, N. Y. [1944-
     nos. 27½ᶜᵐ. (Conference board reports)

1. Business.   I. Title.

Library of Congress   HF5006.N3
                                              44--4986

     OClW MsU GEU OClJC ODW DBB
     ViU INS DAU KMK CU-Riv KyU P NcD CU TU DNAL OCl
NN 0054855   DLC OAkU NN LNL NBuC MB CoU NBPo1

National Industrial Conference Board.
Studies in individual and collective security.
no. 1-
New York, N. Y., National Industrial Conference
Board, inc. [c1947-
     v. tables. 21 1/2cm.

Library has:

no. 1.   Plumley, H. L. Budgeting the
             costs of illness. [c1947]

Library has:

no. 2.   Sulzbach, W. German experience
             with social insurance. [1947]

Library has:

no. 3.   Wilson, E. W. Compulsory
             health insurance. [1947]

Library has:

no. 4.   Steinhaus, H. W. Financing
             old age. [1948]

     GEU CU
NN 0054860   MB ICJ CtY MiD NcD ICU TxU Vi LU NRU

NATIONAL INDUSTRIAL CONFERENCE BOARD, INC.
Studies in labor statistics. no.1-18.   New York
[1949-57] 18 no. in 3 v. illus. (part col.) 28cm.

Irregular.
At head of title: Conference board reports.
1. Labor--Stat.--U.S. I. National industrial conference board, inc. Conference board reports. Studies in labor statistics. II. Title: Conference
board reports. Studies in labor   statistics. III. Title.

no. 1. General wage increases in manufacturing industries.   [1948]
no. 2. Clerical salary survey of rates paid, Apr. 1949. [1949]
no. 3. What an hour's work would buy, 1914-1948, by L.C. DeTrude and
        W. Nishimura.   [1950]
no. 4. Clerical salary survey, Oct. 1950. [1951]
no. 5. General wage increases in manufacturing, 1948-1950, by T. A.
        Fitzgerald. [1951]

no. 6. Trends in executive compensation, by T.A. Fitzgerald. [1951]
no. 7. Clerical salary survey, Oct. 1951. [1952]
no. 8. Top management compensation, by T. A. Fitzgerald. [1953]
no. 9. Clerical salary survey, Oct. 1952. [1953]
no. 10. Clerical salary survey, Sept. 1953. [1954]
no. 11. General wage adjustments in manufacturing, June, 1950-Mar. 1954.
        [1954]

no. 12. Executive compensation.   [1954]
no. 13. Clerical salary survey, Oct. 1954. [1955]
no. 14. Compensating expatriates for the cost of living abroad, by J. F.
        Gaston and J. Napier. [1955]
no. 15. Family expenditures for clothing. [1955]

     OCU
     CU LU WvU NBuG PU PPSOPR OU TU PBL FTaSU MtU MoSW
NN 0054864   NN NIC N CtY TxU ICU Vi NNC OCl MB

National Industrial Conference Board.
Studies in personnel policy. no. 1-
New York [1937-
     no. in   v. illus. 29 cm. (no. 139 and 143: 29 x 44 cm.)
No. 15-28 issued as supplements to the Conference Board manage-
ment record; no. 29-   issued as Conference Board reports.

1. Personnel management--Collections.   I. Title. II. Management record. Supplement.

HF5549.A2N27   38--5696*‡

     NmLcUCStbS CU-Riv NN OAkU OU LNL CoFS MtU GEU
     PU-W TxU UU GU-L TU CU FTaSU TxLT DBB MiU MsU WvU
NN 0054865   DLC NBuG DFT ICJ MB ICU OClU OCU DL

National industrial conference board.
... Studies in the economics of national defense, no. 5-   ...
Supplement to the Economic record. New York, National in-
dustrial conference board, inc. °1940-
     nos. tables, diagrs. 28ᶜᵐ.

At head of title: The Conference board.
Nos. 1-4 were published in the Conference board economic record,
v. 2, 1940.

1. U. S.--Econ. condit.--1918-   2. World war, 1939-   --Eco-
nomic aspects--U. S.   I. The Conference board economic record.
II. Title.

Library of Congress   HC106.4.A1N35
                                              42--6964
                           [3]   330.973

NN 0054866   DLC ICJ NIC ICU OCl OCU

National Industrial Conference Board.   L025.4933I N21
[Subject classification. 1917.]
118969   [17] leaves. 29ᵐᵐ.
          Typewritten.

NN 0054867   ICJ

National Industrial Conference Board.
Suggestion systems [by Herbert R. Northrup] New York
[1953]
     55 p. illus. 28 cm. (*Its* Conference Board reports. Studies in
personnel policy, no. 135)
     Cover title.

1. Suggestion systems.   I. Northrup, Herbert Root, 1918-
(Series: National Industrial Conference Board. Studies in personnel
policy, no. 135)
HF5549.A2N27 no. 135   53--2337
                *658.315   658.314

NN 0054868   DLC CaBViP ViU OCU IaU CoU AAP OOxM

National industrial conference board.
Summary of report on workmen's compensation acts
in the United States. The legal phase. National industrial conference board. [Boston] 1917.
     cover-title, 8 p. 23ᶜᵐ.

1. Employers' liability--U. S.
                                              18--5369
Library of Congress   HD7816.U6N25

NN 0054869   DLC NN MB MiU OU OO DL OrU Or MH-L

National industrial conference board.
Supplemental bonuses for wage earners, supervisors and
executives. New York, National industrial conference board,
inc., 1927.
     ix, 60 p. incl. tables. 23 cm.

1. Bonus system.   I. Title.

HD4928.B6N3   28--913

     MB ICJ
NN 0054870   DLC CU DL WaS OrCS NN MiU OU OCl OClW

National Industrial Conference Board.
Supplementary data on weekly desk sheet
series. New York [1954]
     21 ℓ.

NN 0054871   MH-BA

VOLUME 407

National industrial conference board.
The support of the aged: a review of conditions and proposals. New York, National industrial conference board, inc., 1931.

xi, 65 p. 23 cm.

1. Old age. 2. Old age pensions—U. S. 3. Old age pensions—New York (State) ɪ. Title.

HV1465.N3   331.2520973   31—12825

OC1U OC1W ViU MB CU TU MH
NN 0054872   DLC OrCS ICJ WaS MtU GU NcD DL MiU

HC106 .3 .N285
NATIONAL INDUSTRIAL CONFERENCE BOARD.
... Survey of business experience ...

New York ᵨ19
v.
Title varies: —Jan.1942, Survey of business opinion.

1. U.S.--Econ. condit.--1918-   2. U.S.--Indus.

NN 0054873   ICU MH-BA DAL

National Industrial Conference Board.
Symposium on electronics and automatic production, San Francisco, California, August 22-23, 1955; proceedings. Jointly sponsored by National Industrial Conference Board, inc. ᵨandᵧ Stanford Research Institute. New York, ᵨ195-ᵧ

1 v. (various pagings) illus. 29 cm.

1. Automation—Congresses.   ɪ. Stanford Research Institute, Stanford University. ɪɪ. Title. ɪɪɪ. Title: Electronics and automatic production.

HD45.N36 1955   621.8   58–1566

OC1W MiU MH-BA NIC
NN 0054874   DLC CU AU   TxU ICU ICJ OCU IU NN

National industrial conference board.
Systems of wage payment. New York, National industrial conference board, inc., 1930.

x, 131 p. 23½ᶜᵐ.

1. Wages. ɪ. Title.
Library of Congress   HD4926.N28   30–19588
—— Copy 2.
Copyright A 26348   ᵨ5-5ᵧ   331.2

OO OC1 MtU OrCS OrU Or WaS MH-L NIC IU
NN 0054875   DLC PU-W CU NcD MiU ICJ MB DL OU OOxM

NATIONAL INDUSTRIAL CONFERENCE BOARD.
...Tables relating to wages in the United States, 1932-   [New York] National industrial conference board,inc.c1933-
v. 28cm. (Supplement to Conference board service letter.
Continues its Wages in the United States.

1. Wages--U.S. 2. U.S.--Indus.

NN 0054876   ICU OO OC1W OC1 CU MoU

National industrial conference board.
Tax burdens and exemptions ... New York, National industrial conference board ᵨ*1923ᵧ

viii, 159 p. incl. tables, diagrs. 23 cm. (*Its* Research report, no. 64)

1. Taxation—U. S. 2. Taxation, Exemption from—U. S. ɪ. Title.
Library of Congress   HJ2377.N3   23—16836

ViU NcD NcRS OrU CaBVaU Wa WaWW Or
NN 0054877   DLC WaS MtBC CU ICJ MiU OC1 OCU OO OU

National industrial conference board.
Tax burdens and public expenditures. New York, National industrial conference board, inc., 1925.

2 p. l., iii–vii, 70 p. incl. tables, diagrs. 23 cm.

1. Taxation—U. S. 2. Finance, Public—U. S.—1901-1933. ɪ. Title.

HJ2051.N3   25—4577

ICJ ViU MiU Wa WaTC MtU IdU WaS OrCS OrU Or Wa MB
NN 0054878   DLC OOxM TU OC1 OU OKentU ICRL DAL NN

National industrial conference board.
The tax problem in West Virginia. New York, National industrial conference board, inc., 1925.

2 p. l., iii–viii, 235 p. incl. tables. 23½ᶜᵐ.

1. Taxation—West Virginia. ɪ. Title.

Library of Congress   HJ2440.N3   25—9583

ICJ OU OC1W OC1 MiU OOxM OrU Or MB MH
NN 0054879   DLC WaS MtU OrCS TU NIC NcD DL DAL

National industrial conference board.
The tax problem in Wisconsin. New York, National industrial conference board, 1924.

2 p. l., iii–viii, 163 p. incl. tables. 23ᶜᵐ.

1. Taxation—Wisconsin. ɪ. Title.

Library of Congress   HJ2441.N3   24—19447

TU NcD MiU ICJ MB DL OU OC1OCU OOxM ViU OrU Or WaWW
NN 0054880   DLC MtU IdU OrPR WaS CaBVaU PSt NSyU

National industrial conference board, inc.
... Tax relief under section 722 ... New York, N.Y. ᵨ1945ᵧ
cover-title, 48 p.incl.tables, charts. (*Its* Studies in business policy, no. 9)

At head of title: Conference board reports.

NN 0054881   MH-BA MiEM OU

National industrial conference board.
Taxation and national income ... National industrial conference board. New York, The Century co. ᵨ*1922ᵧ
vii, 86 p. incl. tables, diagrs. 23ᶜᵐ. (*Its* Research report no. 55) $1.50

1. Taxation—U. S. ɪ. Title.
Library of Congress   HJ2379.N344   22—25182

DL MB ICJ ViU OCU OC1 OU OO OrU CaBVaU WaWW
NN 0054882   DLC NIC CU OrPR MtBC WaS NcD NcRS MiU

HG1768 .U5K5 1934a
National industrial conference board.

ᵨKimmel, Lewis Henryᵧ 1899–
The taxation of banks. New York, National industrial conference board, inc., 1934.

National industrial conference board.
Taxation of motor vehicle transportation. New York, National industrial conference board, inc., 1932.

xii, 196 p. incl. tables. 23 cm.

1. Transportation, Automotive—Taxation—U. S. 2. Motor fuels—Taxation—U. S. ɪ. Title.

HE5623.A5N35   336.27   33—3707

TU MH-B NcD MB
NN 0054884   DLC ViU-L ViU OU OC1 OC1W OCU MiU CU

National industrial conference board.
Technical education and the chemical industry; a summary report of an investigation by the National industrial conference board, inc. New York, 1925.

11 p. incl. tables. 23ᶜᵐ.

1. Technical education. 2. Chemistry, Technical.
Library of Congress   T73.N33   25–14936

NN 0054885   DLC CU DL NN

National industrial conference board.
Technical education and the electrical manufacturing industry; a summary report of an investigation by the National industrial conference board, inc. New York, 1925.

11 p. incl. tables. 23ᶜᵐ.

1. Technical education—U. S. ɪ. Title.
Library of Congress   T73.N34   26–6790

NN 0054886   DLC DHEW NN

National industrial conference board.
Technical education and the metal trades industries; a summary report of an investigation by the National industrial conference board, inc. New York, 1925.

10 p. 23ᶜᵐ.

1. Technical education. ɪ. Title.
Library of Congress   T61.N255   25–8441

NN 0054887   DLC DHEW NN ICJ MH DL

National industrial conference board.
Technical education and the paper and pulp industry; a summary report of an investigation by the National industrial conference board. New York, 1924.

10 p., 1 l. 23ᶜᵐ.

1. Technical education. ɪ. Title.
Library of Congress   T61.N26   25–8442

NN 0054888   DLC

National industrial conference board.
Technical education and the rubber industry; a summary report of an investigation by the National industrial conference board. New York, 1924.

10 p., 1 l. 23ᶜᵐ.

1. Technical education. ɪ. Title.
Library of Congress   T61.N265   25–8440

NN 0054889   DLC ICJ

National industrial conference board.
Technical education and the textile industry; a summary report of an investigation by the National industrial conference board, inc. New York, 1925.

13 p. incl. tables. 23ᶜᵐ.

1. Technical education. ɪ. Title.
Library of Congress   T61.N267   25–8439

NN 0054890   DLC DL ICJ NN

VOLUME 407

National Industrial Conference Board.
Technical papers.   no. 1–
Jan. 1951–
New York.
    no. in   v. 29 cm.

1. Economics—Collections.

HB31.N34   330.82   52–26085

OC1W OrPS
NN 0054891   DLC DAU NBuC MsSM KMK CaBVaU IdPI WaS

National Industrial Conference Board.
Techniques of conference leadership.   [By William W. Mussmann and Wilbur M. McFeely]   New York [1946]
    cover-title, 32 p. 28 cm. (*Its* Conference Board reports. Studies in personnel policy, no. 77)

1. Discussion.   I. Mussmann, William W.   II. McFeely, Wilbur M.
III. Title.   IV. Series: National Industrial Conference Board. Conference Board reports.   V. Series: National Industrial Conference Board. Studies in personnel policy, no. 77.

HF5549.A2N27 no. 77   658.3124   47–7220*

NN 0054892   DLC IaU CoU OC1JC

National Industrial Conference Board.
Techniques of plant location

see under

Neuhoff, Malcolm C

National industrial conference board.
The thirty-hour week.   New York city, National industrial conference board, inc. [*1935]
    vii, 23 p. diagrs. 23 cm.   [*Its* Studies. no. 214]
    "This study was prepared by Mr. Fred S. Jahn, of the Conference board's research staff."—Foreword.

1. Hours of labor—U. S.   I. Jahn, Fred S.   II. Title.
                                                     35–6930
Library of Congress   HD5125.N363
—————— Copy 2.
Copyright A 82424   [5–5]   331.81973

OCU MiU OC1 OC1FRB
NN 0054894   DLC MtU OrCS OrU CU TU NcD OU ViU ICJ

National industrial conference board.
30 years of continuous research and education in behalf of the perpetuation and progress of America's productive enterprise.
New York, N. Y., The National industrial conference board, inc. [1946]
    82 p. illus. (incl. ports., facsims.) diagrs. 31½ x 25 cm.

HB1.N17   330.72   47–17320

NN 0054895   DLC CU CoU OrU MH MB ICU ICJ TxU

National Industrial Conference Board.
Time off with pay ...   [By Harold Stieglitz, Division of Personnel Administration]   New York [1952]
    16 p. illus. 28 cm. (*Its* Conference Board reports. Studies in personnel policy, no. 130)
    Cover title.

1. Vacations, Employee.   I. Stieglitz, Harold.   II. Title.   (Series: National Industrial Conference Board. Studies in personnel policy, no. 130)
    HF5549.A2N27 no. 130   658.3816   53–279

NN 0054896   DLC CoU IaU AAP Or ViU MoSU-C NIC

National industrial conference board.
... Time schedules in job training ...   New York, National industrial conference board, inc. [1943]
    cover-title, 16 p. 28 x 22½ cm. (*Its* Conference board reports)
    Studies in personnel policy, no. 55.

1. Technical education.   2. Vocational education.   I. Title.
                                                     43–13224
Library of Congress   HF5549.A2N27 no. 55
    [3]   (658.3) 331.86

NN 0054897   DLC OC1JC OCU OC1U CoU

338.2   **National Industrial Conference Board.**
N217t   Tin.   [New York] 1953.
            unpaged   tables. 28cm.

            Caption title.

            1. Tin--U.S.

NN 0054898   IU

338.4   **National Industrial Conference Board.**
N213t   Tires and rubber: basic industrial data.
            [n.p.] 1951.
            1v. of tables. 28cm.

            1. Rubber industry and trade.   2. Rubber industry and trade--U.S.   3. Tires, Rubber.

NN 0054899   IU

National Industrial Conference Board.
Top management compensation.   [By Thomas A. Fitzgerald, Statistical Division]   New York [1953]
    63 p. (chiefly tables) 28 cm. (*Its* Conference Board reports. Studies in labor statistics, no. 8)
    Cover title.

1. Executives—Salaries, pensions, etc.—U. S.   I. Fitzgerald, Thomas A., 1907–   II. Title.   (Series: National Industrial Conference Board. Studies in labor statistics, no. 8)

HD4965.5.U6N28   658.32   53–1836

NN 0054900   DLC MB UU ViU OCU NcD OOxM

National Industrial Conference Board.
Toward better government, prepared for the 39th annual meeting of the Conference Board, May 19–20, 1955. New York [1955]
    31 p. diagrs. 26 cm.

1. U. S.—Executive departments.   2. U. S.—Appropriations and expenditures.   I. Title.

JK681.N3 1955   353   55–2721 ‡

TxU NN DI ODW OCU IU
NN 0054901   DLC OrCS FU CaBViP MtU WaU MsSM PU

National industrial conference board.
... The Townsend old age pension plan ...   [New York] National industrial conference board, inc. [*1935]
    cover-title, 14 numb. l. 28½ cm. (Conference board information service: Domestic affairs. Memorandum no. 40)
    Mimeographed.

1. Old age pensions—U. S.   I. Title.
                                                     35–7556
Library of Congress   HC106.3.N24 no. 40
—————— Copy 2.
Copyright AA 166553   [8]   (330.973) 331.254430973

NN 0054902   DLC OC1FRB

National industrial conference board.
The Townsend scheme.   New York city, National industrial conference board, inc. [*1936]
    xi, 42 p. 23 cm.   [*Its* Studies. no. 219]

1. Old age pensions—U. S.   2. Townsend, Francis Everett, 1867–
I. Title.
                                                     36–8660
Library of Congress   HD7106.U5T758
—————— Copy 2.
Copyright A 92350   [5–5]   331.2520973

ViU OC1 WaS MtU MtBC WaTC OrCS WaSpG
NN 0054903   DLC NNC ICJ IU NcD OC1W MB DL OU OCU

National industrial conference board.
Trade associations, their economic significance and legal status. New York, National industrial conference board, inc., 1925.
    xiv, 388 p. 23½ cm.
                                 HD2425.N3 1925
—— Recent decisions affecting trade association statistical services; addendum of the 1st ed. of "Trade associations: their economic significance and legal status" ... New York, National industrial conference board, inc., 1925.
    8 p. 23½ cm.
    1. Trade and professional associations—U. S.   2. Efficiency, Industrial.   I. Title.
                                                     25—12032
Library of Congress   HD2425.N3 1925 Addendum
    [49d·1]   650.6273

NcRS OrU Or WaWW WaU-L IdU OrCS NBuU-L
NN 0054904   DLC MU ViU-L KEmT ScU NN NcD ICJ ViU

National industrial conference board.
Trade associations, their economic significance and legal status. New York, National industrial conference board, inc., 1925.
    xiv, 388 p. 23½ cm.
    "First edition published May, 1925; second, revised edition published July, 1925."

1. Trade and professional associations—U. S.   2. Efficiency, Industrial.
I. Title.
                                                     39—25631
Library of Congress   HD2425.N3 1925 a
—————— Copy 2.   [2]   650.6273

MiU WaS MtU WaSp CaBVaU
NN 0054905   DLC GU CU-AL NcD OU ODW DL DN OCU OO

National Industrial Conference Board.
Training dealers [by Elliott F. Higgins and James F. Fogarty, Jr., Division of Business Practices] New York [*1950]
    52 p. illus. 28 cm. (*Its* Conference Board reports. Studies in business policy, no. 48)
    Cover title.

1. Dealer aids.   I. Higgins, Elliott F.   II. Fogarty, James F.
III. Title.   (Series: National Industrial Conference Board. Studies in business policy, no. 48)

HF5006.N3 no. 48   59–20467

NN 0054906   DLC LU CoU MH-BA AAP IaU ViU

National industrial conference board.
... Training for industry. New York city, National industrial conference board, inc. [*1937]
    viii, 29 p. 23 cm. (*Its* Studies. no. 237)
    "Prepared in the Industrial management division of the Conference board's research staff."—Foreword.

1. Technical education—U. S.   2. U. S.—Indus.   I. Title.
                                                     38–4494
Library of Congress   LC1081.N25
—————— Copy 2.
Copyright A 111070   [5–5]   371.428973

DFT ICJ
NN 0054907   DLC OrU WaS OrCS OCU OC1 OU OOxM DL

HF5549   **National Industrial Conference Board.**
.A2N27
no.15   Training solutions of company problems. A-
1939   Programs giving special attention to development of executive and supervisory personnel.
            New York [1939]
            78 p. 28cm. (Its Studies in personnel policy, no. 15)
            Cover title.
            1. Employees, Training of.   2. Executives.
            I. Ser.

NN 0054908   ViU MH InU DNLM

VOLUME 407

HF5549
.A2N27
no.18
1940

National Industrial Conference Board.
Training solutions of company problems.
B. Programs giving special attention to
development of the skill of non-supervisory
production employees. New York, 1940.
71 p. 28cm. (Its Studies in personnel
policy, no. 18)
Cover title.
The Conference Board management record
supplements.
1. Employees, Training of. 2. Technical
education—U. S.   I. Title. II. Ser.

NN   0054909   ViU IdU DNLM InU

National industrial conference board.
... Training solutions of company problems. C.
—Programs designed for the development of sales
personnel. New York, National industrial conference board, inc. ₁1940₎
cover-title. 80 p. incl. forms. 27½ᶜᵐ. (Its Studies
in personnel policy ... no.22. June, 1940)
"Supplement to the Conference board management record."
1. Salesmen and salesmanship. I. National industrial
conference board. Conference board management record.
Supplement. II. Title. III. Title: Programs designed
for the development of sales personnel. IV. Ser.

NN   0054910   ViU IaU InU DNLM

HF5549
A2N27
no.36

National Industrial Conference Board.
Training white collar employees.   New
York ₁1941₎
59p. 28cm. (Its Studies in personnel
policy, no.36)

1. Clerks. 2. Employees, Training of.

NN   0054911   IaU MoSU InU ViU

National Industrial Conference Board.
... Treasurer's report...
1925/26

New York, 1926   8°.
no.
Caption-title.
For earlier years see its Annual report.

1. Economic history—U. S. 2. In-   dustries and mechanic arts—U. S.
N. Y. P. L.   May 15, 1928

NN   0054912   NN CtY ICJ

National industrial conference board.
... Trends in collective bargaining and union contracts ...
New York, N. Y., National industrial conference board, inc.
₁°1946₎
cover-title, 83 p. 28 x 22½ᶜᵐ. (Its Conference board reports)
Studies in personnel policy, no. 71.
"By Abraham A. Desser, Management research division."—p. 3.
"Selected bibliography relating to collective bargaining": p. 80.

1. Labor contract—U. S. 2. Collective bargaining—U. S.   I. Desser,
Abraham A. II. Title.
                                                    46–3476
Library of Congress   HF5549.A2N27 no. 71
                          ₁7₎   (658.3) 331.11

NN   0054913   DLC IaU CoU OC1U

National industrial conference board.
... Trends in company pension plans ... New York, N. Y.,
National industrial conference board, inc. ₁1944₎
cover-title, 52 p. 28 x 22 cm. (Its Conference board reports)
Studies in personnel policy, no. 61.

1. Pension trusts. 2. Old age pensions—U. S. 3. Profit-sharing.
I. Title.
HF5549.A2N27 no. 61   658.3252   44—5741

NN   0054914   DLC AAP OC1 OC1U PSC

HF
5549
A2N27
no.21+

National Industrial Conference Board.
Trends in company vacation policy.
New York ₁1940₎
19 p. 28cm. (Conference Board.
Management record supplements.
Studies in personnel policy, no. 21)

1. Vacations, Employee. I. Series:
National Industrial Conference Board.
Studies in personnel policy, no. 21.

NN   0054915   NIC InU IaU

National Industrial Conference Board.
Trends in executive compensation ₁by Thomas A. Fitzgerald, Statistical Division₎ New York ₁1951₎
24 p. 28 cm. (Its Conference Board reports. Studies in labor
statistics, no. 6)
Cover title.

1. Executives—U. S. 2. Wages—U. S.   I. Fitzgerald, Thomas A.,
1907–   II. Title.   (Series: National Industrial Conference
Board. Studies in labor statistics, no. 6)

HD4965.5.U6N3   331.2973   51–7472

NN   0054916   DLC ViU MB UU

National Industrial Conference Board.
Trends in industrial location ₁by Malcolm C. Neuhoff,
Division of Business Practices₎ New York ₁°1952₎
32 p. illus. 28 cm. (Its Conference Board reports. Studies in
business policy, no. 59)
Cover title.

1. Industries, Location of—U. S.   I. Neuhoff, Malcolm C. II.
Title.   (Series: National Industrial Conference Board. Studies in
business policy, no. 59)
HF5006.N3 no. 59   58–4503

NN   0054917   DLC MH–BA ViU DI DAU IaU CoU InU LU

National industrial conference board.
Trends in the foreign trade of the United States. New
York, National industrial conference board, inc., 1930.
xvi p., 1 l., 329 p. incl. tables. 23½ᶜᵐ.
"This volume is the result of an investigation conducted by Mr. Ar-
nold W. Lahee and assistants."—Pref.

1. U. S.—Comm.   I. Lahee, Arnold Warburton. II. Title.

Library of Congress   HF3031.N35   30—25374
                              ₁a42u1₎   382.0973

NN   0054918   DLC FMU CU KMK NNUN NcD ViU ICJ DL
OCU OU MiU OO MH DAL WaS MtU IdU–SB OrCS OrU Or

National industrial conference board.
Unemployment benefits and insurance. New York, National
industrial conference board, inc., 1931.
x, 127 p. 23½ᶜᵐ.

1. Insurance, Unemployment. 2. Insurance, Unemployment—U. S.
I. Title.
Library of Congress   HD7095.N3
—— Copy 2.   31–28607
Copyright A 45570   ₁5–5₎   331.25444

ODW MB MH
MH–L ViU WaS OrCS Or MtU CaBVaU WaTC OC1 OCU MiU
NN   0054919   DLC OKentU NcD CU KMK OO OU ICJ NN DL

National industrial conference board.
Unemployment insurance and relief in Germany. New York,
National industrial conference board, inc., 1932.
xvi, 107 p. incl. tables, diagrs. 23ᶜᵐ.

1. Insurance, Unemployment—Germany. 2. Unemployed—Germany.
3. Public welfare—Germany.   I. Title.
                                                    33–3917
Library of Congress   HD7096.G3N3
                              ₁a44u1₎   331.254440043

MiU OO WaS MtU OrCS OrU CaBVaU Or
NN   0054920   DLC CU KMK TU NcD ViU ICJ DL OU OOxM

National industrial conference board.
Unemployment insurance in theory and practice ..
National industrial conference board. New York, The
Century co. ₁°1922₎
vi, 127 p. 23ᶜᵐ. (Its Research report, no. 51)

1. Insurance, Unemployment. 2. Insurance, Unemployment—U. S.
I. Title.
Library of Congress   HD7096.U5N3   22—16625

ViU OU OC1 OrU CaBVaU Or WaWW
NN   0054921   DLC MtBC WaTC WaS CU NcRS MiU MB ICJ

National industrial conference board.
Unemployment insurance; lessons from British experience ...
New York, National industrial conference board, inc., 1934.
viii, 80 p. diagrs. 23ᶜᵐ.

1. Insurance, Unemployment—Gt. Brit.   I. Title.
                                                    34–39370
Library of Congress   HD7096.G7N3   331.25440042

ICJ WaS MtU OrPR OrCS OrU Or IEN
NN   0054922   DLC FMU CU NcD OU OCU OC1 MiU OOxM

National industrial conference board.
The unemployment problem ... National industrial conference board. New York, The Century co. ₁°1922₎
vii, 91 p. diagrs. 23ᶜᵐ. (Its Research report, no. 43)
Bibliographical foot-notes.

1. Unemployed—U. S.   I. Title.
                                                    22–3544
Library of Congress   HD5724.N3
—— Copy 2.

ICJ ViU OU OCU OO OC1
NN   0054923   DLC WaTC MtBC WaS OrU Or CU NcRS WaWW

National industrial conference board.
Uniform medical provisions for workmen's compensation
acts in the United States ... New York city, National industrial conference board, inc. ₁°1925₎
v, 28 p. 23ᶜᵐ. (Its Special report, no. 31)
"This report is the result of an investigation conducted by F. L.
Rector, M. D., and assistants, of the conference board's research staff,
under the supervision of the board's staff economic council."

1. Employers' liability—U. S.   I. Title.
                                                    25—9462
Library of Congress   HD7816.U6N28

MB ViU OU OC1 MiU DAL
NN   0054924   DLC WaS MtU IdU OrU Or CU NcD ICJ DL

National industrial conference board.
... Union agreements: I. Analysis of prevailing provisions.
II. Texts of representative agreements ... New York, National
industrial conference board, inc. ₁1942₎
cover-title, 52 p. incl. tables. 28 x 22ᶜᵐ. (Its Management research
memorandum, no. 12)
At head of title: Conference board reports.
Text on p. ₁2₎ of cover.

1. Labor contract—U. S.   I. Title.
                                                    42–11796
Library of Congress   HD7811.U6N33
                          ₁3₎   331.11630973

NN   0054925   DLC UU MB OrU ViU OU

National Industrial Conference Board.
Union contracts since the Taft-Hartley act ₁by James J.
Bambrick, Jr., Division of Personnel Administration₎ New
York ₁1948₎
88 p. illus. 28 cm. (Its Conference Board reports. Studies in
personnel policy, no. 94)
Cover title.
1. Labor contract—U. S. 2. Labor laws and legislation—U. S.   I.
Bambrick, James Joseph, 1888–   II. Title.   (Series: National
Industrial Conference Board. Conference Board reports. Series: Na-
tional Industrial Conference Board. Studies in personnel policy, no.
94)
HF5549.A2N27 no. 94   331.11   48–10334

NN   0054926   DLC CoU KMK AAP IaU OC1JC PPT ViU

VOLUME 407

National Industrial Conference Board.
Union security and checkoff provisions. [By James J. Bambrick, Jr., Division of Personnel Administration] New York [1952]
136 p. diagrs., tables. 28 cm. (*Its* Conference Board reports. Studies in personnel policy, no. 127)
Cover title.
1. Open and closed shop—U. S. 2. Checkoff—U. S. I. Bambrick, James Joseph, 1917- II. Title. (Series: National Industrial Conference Board. Studies in personnel policy, no. 127)
HF5549.A2N27 no. 127 331.889 53-587

NN 0054927 DLC CaBVa OCU AAP IaU MoSU-C ViU NIC

National industrial conference board.
... Unions of white collar employees ... New York, National industrial conference board, inc. [1943]
cover-title, 16 p. 28 x 21½cm. (*Its* Conference board reports)
Studies in personnel policy, no. 51.
1. Trade-unions—U. S. I. Title: White collar employees.
43-5208
Library of Congress HF5549.A2N27 no. 51
[5] (658.3) 331.88

NN 0054928 DLC IaU ViU CoU AAP PPT OClJC

382.0973
N213u National Industrial Conference Board.
The United States and its foreign trade position; a special study. New York, National Electrical Manufacturers Association [1954]
viii, 239 p. illus. 28cm.
Bibliographical footnotes.
1. Commerce. 2. U. S. - Foreign economic relations. 3. Balance of trade. I. T.

NN 0054929 MiDW OCl NN PPT NNC PU-W NIC TxU PBL

HD
9695
.U52N2
1953 National Industrial Conference Board.
The United States and its foreign trade position: the electrical manufacturing industry; a second draft of a confidential preliminary report prepared by the National Industrial Conference Board at the request of the National Electrical Manufacturers Association. New York, 1953.
1 v. (loose leaf)
1. Electric industries-U.S. 2. U.S.-Commerce-1945- I. Title.

NN 0054930 DAU DPU

National industrial conference board.
Unwarranted conclusions regarding the eight-hour and ten-hour workday; a critical review of a "Comparison of an eight-hour plant and a ten-hour plant". United States public health bulletin no. 106 ... New York, National industrial conference board, °1920.
v, 21 p. 23cm. (*Its* Special report, no. 14)
1. Goldmark, Josephine Clara. Comparison of an eight-hour plant and a ten-hour plant. 2. Fatigue. 3. Labor and laboring classes—Accidents. 4. Hours of labor. 5. Efficiency, Industrial. I. Title.
20-20012
Library of Congress RA787.G65

IdU NcRS NNC ViU MiU OU OCU OCl OO
NN 0054931 DLC WaWW OrU CaBVaU NIC CU MtU MtBC

HF5549
.A2N25
no.14 NATIONAL INDUSTRIAL CONFERENCE BOARD
...The use of tests in employment and promotion. N.Y.,The Board [1939. 23p. (Its Studies in personnel policy, no.14)
Cover-title.

NN 0054932 InU IaU

HF5006
.N3
no.1
1944 National Industrial Conference Board.
V-VT loans and conversion financing [by Charles C. Abbott and others] New York [1944]
20 p. col. diagr.. 28cm. (Its Studies in business policy, no. 1)
Cover title.
1. Credit—U. S. 2. U. S.—Indus. 3. World War, 1939-1945—Finance—U. S. I. Abbott, Charles Cortez, 1906- II. Title. III. Ser.

NN 0054933 ViU MiEM OU MH-PA

National industrial conference board.
... Vacation and holiday practices ... New York, N. Y., National industrial conference board, inc. [1946]
cover-title, 35 p. incl. tables. 28cm. (*Its* Conference board reports)
Studies in personnel policy, no. 75.
1. Vacations, Employee—U. S. I. Title.
HF5549.A2N27 no. 75 (658.3) 658.3816 46-8504

NN 0054934 DLC IaU CoU AAP OClJC OClU

HF5549
A2N27
no.34 **National Industrial Conference Board.**
Vacation policy and national defense.
New York [1941]
19p. 28cm. (Its Studies in personnel policy, no.34)
1. Vacation, Employee.

NN 0054935 IaU NIC ViU InU

National industrial conference board.
Vacation policy in 1944 ... New York, N. Y., National industrial conference board, inc. [1944]
7, [1] p. 28 x 21½cm. (Supplement to the Conference board management record)
1. Vacations, Employee—U. S. I. Title.
44-5967
Library of Congress HD5261.N285
[3] [illegible] 331.816

NN 0054936 DLC

National industrial conference board.
... Vacation-with-pay plans for wage earners effective in 1937 ... New York, National industrial conference board, inc., °1937.
2 p. l., 32 numb. l. 28½cm. (Conference board information service: Domestic affairs series. Memorandum no. 56)
Mimeographed.
1. Vacations. 2. Labor and laboring classes—U. S.—1914- I. Title. II. Title: Wage earners, Vacation-with-pay plans for.
40-14345
Library of Congress HC106.3.N24 no. 56
——— Copy 2.
Copyright AA 233898 [2] (330.973) 331.8160973

NN 0054937 DLC DFT MiU

National industrial conference board.
Vacations with pay for wage earners. New York city, National industrial conference board, inc. [°1935]
viii, 35 p. 23cm. [*Its* Studies. No. 215]
1. Vacations, Employee—U. S.
35-6929
Library of Congress HD5261.N3
[a44n2] 331.816

IEN
NN 0054938 DLC NcD ViU ICJ NN Or MtU OrU OrCS

National industrial conference board.
... Visual aids in industrial training ... New York, National industrial conference board, inc. [1943]
cover-title, 60 p. incl. illus., tables. 28 x 22 cm. (*Its* Conference board reports)
Studies in personnel policy, no. 49.
"List of films and slides used by 100 companies": p. 54-60.
1. Technical education—U. S. 2. Employees, Training of. 3. Moving-pictures in education. I. Title.
HF5549.A2N27 no. 49 371.33522 43-5201

NN 0054939 DLC CoU MiD AAP ViU IaU

National industrial conference board.
The vital issues in the Industrial conference at Washington, D. C., November, 1919 ... Boston, Mass., National industrial conference board, °1919.
iii, 15 p. 23cm.
1. National industrial conference, Washington, D. C., 1919. 2. Labor and laboring classes—U. S.—1914- I. Title.
21-2296
Library of Congress HD8057.N4

NN 0054940 DLC MtU WaS CU NIC OU OClW OO OCl

National industrial conference board.
... Wage and salary stabilization ... New York, National industrial conference board, inc. [1943]
cover-title, 27 p. 28 x 22cm. (*Its* Conference board reports)
Management research memorandum, no. 13.
1. Wages—U. S. I. Title.
43-5200
Library of Congress HD4975.N386 1943
[5] 331.2973

NN 0054941 DLC UU MB TU OrU OrCS NBuG OU

National industrial conference board.
Wage changes in industry, September, 1914-December, 1920 ... New York, National industrial conference board [°1921]
2 p. l., 50 p. incl. tables, diagrs. 23cm. (*Its* Research report, no. 35)
1. Wages—U. S. 2. European war, 1914-1918—Economic aspects—U. S. I. Title.
21-10623
Library of Congress HD4975.N3 1921

CaBVaU Or ICJ ViU OCU OCl OO MiU WaWW
NN 0054942 DLC NcRS NcD CU WaTC OrU MtBC WaS OU

National industrial conference board.
... Wage differentials: analysis of prior conditions and code requirements ... [New York, National industrial conference board, 1934.
cover-title, 21 numb. l. 28½cm. (Conference board information service: Domestic affairs. Memorandum no. 20)
Mimeographed.
1. National industrial recovery act, 1933. 2. Wages—Minimum wage—U. S. 3. Wages—Stat. 4. Industry and state—U. S. I. Title.
34-5518
Library of Congress HC106.3.N24 no. 20
——— Copy 2.
Copyright AA 136092 [5] (330.973) 331.2973

NN 0054943 DLC

National industrial conference board.
... Wage incentive practices ... New York, N. Y., National industrial conference board, inc. [1945]
cover-title, 44 p. incl. forms, diagrs. 27½ x 22cm. (*Its* Conference board reports)
Studies in personnel policy, no. 68.
"By E. S. Horning, Management research division."—p. 1.
1. Wages—U. S. 2. Job analysis. I. Horning, Eugene S. II. Title.
45-4076
Library of Congress * HF5549.A2N27 no. 68
[12] (658.3) 658.322

NN 0054944 DLC IaU CoU

VOLUME 407

National Industrial Conference Board.
Wage payment systems ₁by Herbert S. Briggs, Division of Personnel Administration₁ New York ₁1948₁

36 p. 28 cm. (*Its* Conference Board reports. Studies in personnel policy, no. 91)

Cover title.

1. Wages. ɪ. Briggs, Herbert S. ɪɪ. Title. (Series: National Industrial Conference Board. Conference Board reports. Series: National Industrial Conference Board. Studies in personnel policy, no. 91)

HF5549.A2N27 no. 91   658.32   48–4227*

NN   0054945   DLC ViU IaU AAP OC1JC UU Mi CoU

National industrial conference board.
... Wage problems of the northern cotton textile industry ... New York ₁1947₁

cover-title, 40 p. diagrs. 27 cm. (*Its* A Conference board industry report)

1. Wages—Textile workers—New England. 2. Cotton manufacture—New England. ɪ. Title.

HD4966.T4U515   331.28772   47–3167
                                   Brief cataloging

TU ICJ ICU NNC
NN   0054946   DLC OrCS OrU WaSp WaS MB CU UU Mi TxU

Law   **National Industrial Conference Board.**

U. S. *Wage Stabilization Board.*
Wage stabilization: orders, regulations, interpretations. New York, National Industrial Conference Board ₁1951–

National industrial conference board.
Wages and hours in American industry. New York, National industrial conference board, inc., 1925.

2 p. l., 7–199 p. incl. tables, diagrs. 23½ᵐ.

1. Wages—U. S. 2. Hours of labor—U. S. ɪ. Title.

Library of Congress   HD4975.N3 1925
                                   25–3563

DHEW ICJ MB DAL Or OCU MB OC1 OU MiU
NN   0054948   DLC OrU OrCS Wa MtU CU NIC KEmT NcD

National industrial conference board.
Wages and hours in American industry, July, 1914–July, 1921 ... National industrial conference board. New York, The Century co. ₁1922₁

viii, 202 p. tables (1 fold.) diagrs. 23ᵐ. (*Its* Research report, no. 45)

1. Wages—U. S. 2. Hours of labor—U. S. 3. European war, 1914–1918—Economic aspects—U. S. ɪ. Title.

Library of Congress   HD4975.N3₁ 1922₁
                                   22–3545

MiU OU OC1 OO
NN   0054949   DLC MtBC WaTC CaBVaU Or CU KEmT ICJ

National industrial conference board.
Wages and hours in American manufacturing industries July, 1914–January, 1922 ... National industrial conference board. New York, The Century co. ₁1922₁

vii, 235 p. incl. tables, diagrs. 22ᶜᵐ. (*Its* Research report, no. 52)

1. Wages—U. S. 2. Hours of labor.

Library of Congress   HD4975.N3 1922 a
                                   22–17764

ICJ MiU OCU OC1 00
NN   0054950   DLC MtBC WaTC WaS Or WaWW NcRS ViU

National industrial conference board.
Wages and hours in anthracite mining, June, 1914–October, 1921, inclusive ... National industrial conference board. New York, The Century co. ₁1922₁

vii, 67 p. incl. tables, diagrs. 23ᵐ. (*Its* Research report, no. 47)

1. Coal-miners—Pennsylvania. 2. Wages—Pennsylvania. 3. Cost and standard of living—Pennsylvania. 4. Hours of labor—Pennsylvania. ɪ. Title.

Library of Congress   HD4966.C72U58
                                   22–13232

ViU ICJ MB OU OCU OC1 00
NN   0054951   DLC WaTC MtBC WaS CaBVaU WaWW CU MiU

National industrial conference board.
Wages, hours and employment in American manufacturing industries July, 1914–January, 1923, with supplemental data up to April, 1923 ... New York, National industrial conference board ₁*1923₁

vii, 158 p. incl. tables, diagrs. 23ᵐ. (*Its* Research report, no. 59)

1. Wages—U. S. 2. Hours of labor.

Library of Congress   HD4975.N3 1923
                                   23–10539

CaBVaU WaWW OCU 00 OC1 OU MiU Or ViU ICJ
NN   0054952   DLC OKentU NcRS WaS WaTC MtBC Or NcD

National industrial conference board.
Wages, hours and employment in American manufacturing industries, July, 1914–July, 1923 ... New York, National industrial conference board ₁*1923₁

vii, 154 p. incl. tables, diagrs. 23ᵐ. (*Its* Research report, no. 62)

1. Wages—U. S. 2. Hours of labor—U. S. 3. U. S.—Manuf.

Library of Congress   HD4975.N3 1923 a
                                   23–14486

NN   0054953   DLC ViU NcRS NcD CU DL MB ICJ

National industrial conference board.
Wages, hours and employment in American manufacturing industries, July, 1914–January, 1924 ... New York, National industrial conference board ₁*1924₁

vii, 104 p. incl. tables, diagrs. 23 cm. (*Its* Research report, no. 69)

1. Wages—U. S. 2. Hours of labor—U. S. 3. U. S.—Manuf.

Library of Congress   HD4975.N3 1924
                                   24–9580

TU NcRS NcD ViU
NN   0054954   DLC MtBC OrPR Or WaS WaTC WaWW ICJ MB

National industrial conference board.
Wages, hours, and employment in the United States, 1914–1936, by M. Ada Beney, Conference board research staff ... New York city, National industrial conference board, inc. ₁*1936₁

x, 197 p. incl. tables, diagrs. 23½ cm. (*Its* Studies. no. 229)

1. Wages—U. S. 2. Hours of labor—U. S. 3. U. S.—Manuf. ɪ. Beney, Margarete Ada, 1896– ɪɪ. Title.

HD4975.N38 1936   331.2973   36–27456

OrCS WaU–L WaSpG WaTC NIC
OC1W ViU OO OCU OU WaS MtU Or WaT OrPR OrSaW OrU
NN   0054955   DLC MiU OOxM TU NIC MB WU ICJ OC1 NN

National industrial conference board.
... Wages, hours, and employment in the United States, July, 1936–December, 1937 ... New York, National industrial conference board, inc. ₁*1938₁

31 p. 28ᵐ. (Supplement to Conference board service letter. June, 1938)

1. Wages—U. S. 2. Hours of labor—U. S. 3. U. S.—Manuf.. 4. Index numbers (Economics) ɪ. National industrial conference board. Service letter₁s₁ Supplement. ɪɪ. Title.

Library of Congress   HD4975.N38 1937
                                   38–32430
——— Copy 2.
Copyright AA 270898   ₁5₁   331.2973

NN   0054956   DLC OrCS OU OC1W

National industrial conference board.
Wages, hours and employment of railroad workers ... New York, National industrial conference board ₁*1924₁

viii, 80 p. tables (1 fold.) diagrs. 23ᵐ. (*Its* Research report, no. 70)

1. Railroads—U. S.—Salaries, pensions, etc. 2. Railroads—U. S.—Employees—Hours of service.

Library of Congress   HD4966.R12U68
                                   24–16006

ViU ICJ MiU OO OC1 OC1FRB
NN   0054957   DLC CU WaTC Or CaBVaU WaWW NcD OU OCU

National industrial conference board.
Wages in foreign countries ... National industrial conference board. New York, The Century co. ₁*1922₁

viii, 181 p. incl. tables. 23ᵐ. (*Its* Research report, no. 53)

1. Wages—Europe.

Library of Congress   HD5014.N3
                                   23–3326

OU MiU ViU ICJ MB CU WaWW NIC
NN   0054958   DLC WaS WaTC MtBC CaBVaU NcRS OC1 OO

National industrial conference board.
Wages in Great Britain, France and Germany ... National industrial conference board. New York, The Century co. ₁*1921₁

vii, 110 p. incl. tables. 22½ᵐ. (*Its* Research report, no. 40)

Bibliographical foot-notes.

1. Wages—Gt. Brit. 2. Wages—France. 3. Wages—Germany.

Library of Congress   HD4906.N3
                                   21–22096

NcRS OU ICJ ViU OC1W MiU OOxM OCU
NN   0054959   DLC WaS WaTC MtBC Or CaBVaU WaWW CU

National industrial conference board.
Wages in the United States. New York, National industrial conference board, inc., 1926.

x, 153 p. incl. tables, diagrs. 28½ cm.

1. Wages—U. S. ɪ. Title.

HD4975.N35   26–14616

DL TU IdU OrCS Or OrU WaTC
NN   0054960   DLC NcD OU OO MiU OCU CU KMK ICJ ViU

National industrial conference board.
Wages in the United States, 1914–1926. New York, National industrial conference board, inc., 1927.

xi, 139 p. incl. tables, diagrs. 23½ cm.

"In the text of the present volume somewhat more attention than heretofore has been given to the relation of the wage situation during 1926 to the business and industrial conditions in the various fields during that year."—Foreword.

1. Wages—U. S. 2. Hours of labor—U. S. 3. U. S.—Indus. ɪ. Title.

HD4975.N36   27–14863

ICJ DL MiU CU KMK KEmT ViU NN IaU FMU MB
NN   0054961   DLC WaS WaTC OrCS Or OU OO NcD OC1W

National industrial conference board.
Wages in the United States, 1914–1927. New York, National industrial conference board, inc., 1928.
xiii, 168 p. incl. tables, diagrs. 23½ cm.
——— Wages in the United States in 1928, supplementing "Wages in the United States, 1914–1927" published in April, 1928. New York, National industrial conference board, inc., 1929.

x, 41 p. incl. tables, diagrs. 23 cm.

1. Wages—U. S. 2. Hours of labor—U. S. 3. U. S.—Indus. ɪ. Title.

HD4975.N36 1928   28–20894

DL ViU ICJ WaS OrCS Or FMU
NN   0054962   DLC NcC DAL TU OKentU CU KEmT KMK NcD

VOLUME 407

National industrial conference board.
   Wages in the United States, 1914–1929. New York, National industrial conference board, inc., 1930.
   xv, 223 p. incl. tables, diagrs. 23½ᶜᵐ.

   1. Wages—U. S.   2. U. S.—Indus.   ɪ. Title.
   Library of Congress   HD4975.N36 1929   30–22327
   —— Copy 2.
   Copyright A 27083   ₍7₎   331.2973

   OCU MiU OU ICJ OO CaBVaU
NN   0054963   DLC OrCS WaS OrU Or NIC CU MH NcD ViU

National industrial conference board.
   Wages in the United States, 1914–1930. New York, National industrial conference board, inc., 1931.
   xv, 226 p. incl. tables, diagrs. 23½ᶜᵐ.

   1. Wages—U. S.   2. U. S.—Indus.   ɪ. Title.
   Library of Congress   HD4975.N36 1930   31–13323
   —— Copy 2.
   Copyright A 38398   ₍8₎   331.2973

   ViU NcRS NcD DL OrCS WaSp OCU OO OOxM OC1W
NN   0054964   DLC Or Wa WaS WaT OKentU CU TU ICJ MiU

NATIONAL INDUSTRIAL CONFERENCY BOARD.
   Wages in the United States in 1928.
Supplementing "Wages in the United States,
1914–1927",published in April,1928. New York,
National Industrial Conference Board,Inc.,1929.

   pp.viii,41. Charts and tables.
"Studies of American wages."-verso of half-
title.

NN   0054965   MH OU DL

National industrial conference board.
   Wages in the United States in 1931. New York, National industrial conference board, inc., 1932.
   x, 78 p. incl. tables, diagrs. 23ᶜᵐ.

   1. Wages—U. S.   2. U. S.—Indus.   ɪ. Title.
   Library of Congress   HD4975.N36 1931   32–15175
   —— Copy 2.
   Copyright A 51674   ₍5-5₎   331.2973

   DL OCU MiU OO OU
NN   0054966   DLC OrCS WaS Or NN NcD NcRS CU ViU

National industrial conference board, inc.
   ... Wages in the United States in 1932–
1934, 1936.
New York, National industrial conference
board, inc., 1933-37.
   4 v.   tables.   28 cm.

NN   0054967   DL OU

National industrial conference board.
   Wages in the United States in 1934. ₍New York₎ National industrial conference board, inc., ᵉ1935.
   8 p. 28ᶜᵐ. (Supplement to Conference board service letter. April, 1935)

   Caption title.
   "The tables presented in this supplement ... contain the Conference board's regular series of figures pertaining to earnings, hours of work, employment, and payrolls for 1934."

   1. Wages—U. S.   2. U. S.—Indus.   3. Index numbers (Economics) ɪ. National industrial conference board. Service letter₍s₎ Supplement. ɪɪ. Title.
   Library of Congress   HD4975.N36 1934   35–7780
   —— Copy 2.
   Copyright AA 173392   ₍8₎   331.2973

NN   0054968   DLC OrCS Or OC1W CU

National Industrial Conference Board.
   Wages, prices, profits. ₍A graphic analysis₎ prepared for the thirty-third annual meeting of the Conference Board, May 25, 1949. New York ₍1949₎
   32 p. col. diagrs. 26 cm.

   1. Prices—U. S.   2. Profit—U. S.   3. Wages—U. S.   ɪ. Title.

   HB235.U6N32   338.52   49–4904*

   TU PPFRB OOxM OCU OC1 ODW OrCS OrP
NN   0054969   DLC NN ICU MB N DNAL OrU PBL MH-BA

National Industrial Conference Board.
   ... Wall chart service.
no. 1–

New York₍ 1922–   f°.
   v.   charts.

   Charts only.

   no. 8. Wholesale and retail prices, United States.   Feb., 1922.
   no. 9. Wholesale and retail prices, United States and foreign countries.   Feb., 1922.
   no. 10. War effects on commodity prices... 1810–1921.   Feb., 1922.
   no. 11. Wages in manufacturing industries ...   Feb., 1922.
   no. 12. "Money" earnings and "real" earnings, manufacturing industries .. Feb., 1922.
   no. 13. Average hourly earnings, manufacturing industries...   Feb., 1922.
   no. 14. Average weekly earnings, manufacturing industries...   Feb., 1922.
   no. 15. Employment, manufacturing industries...   Feb., 1922.

   no. 26. Changes in character of ownership, manufacturing industries...   May, 1922.
   no. 27. Wages—manufacturing industries ...   June, 1922.
   no. 28. Hourly and weekly earnings, manufacturing industries...   June, 1922.
   no. 29. Employment—Man-hours, manufacturing industries...   June, 1922.
   no. 30. Value of exports and imports... July, 1922.
   no. 31. Building activity—U. S.; value of construction contracts awarded. July, 1922.
   no. 32. Federal receipts and disbursements, U. S.—fiscal years, 1910–1922. July, 1922.

   no. 40. Average salary and wage cost, manufacturing industries—U. S., 1909, 1914 and 1919.   Oct., 1922.
   no. 41. Taxation...   Oct., 1922.
   no. 42. Per capita taxation, by states --U. S., 1919.   Oct., 1922.
   no. 43. Federal income tax returns...   Nov., 1922.
   no. 44. Sex and age—persons gainfully occupied, U. S., 1920.   Nov., 1922.
   no. 45. Sex and age of wage earners, manufacturing industries...   Nov., 1922.
   no. 46. 50 leading manufacturing cities, U. S., 1919.   Dec., 1922.
   no. 47. "Old" and "new" European immigration, U. S.   Dec., 1922.

   no. 55. Hourly and weekly earnings, manufacturing industries...   March, 1923.
   no. 56. Employment, manufacturing industries...   June, 1923.
   no. 57. Average hours of work, manufacturing industries...   July, 1923.
   no. 58. Raw materials...   July, 1923.
   no. 59. Character of imports and exports...   July, 1923.
   no. 60. Merchant tonnage, U. S. and foreign countries.   Aug., 1923.
   no. 61. National income, per capita, U. S.—1913 to 1922.   Aug., 1923.
   no. 62. Taxation and national income...   Aug., 1923.
   no. 63. Car loadings and car supply, railroads...   Sept., 1923.

   no. 74. Employment and industrial activity, manufacturing industries.   Dec., 1923.
   no. 75. Immigration and population...   Jan., 1924.
   no. 76. Nationality of foreign population...   Jan., 1924.
   no. 77. Immigration under per centum limit act...   Jan., 1924.
   no. 78. Federal receipts and expenditures...   Feb., 1924.
   no. 79. Cost of living changes...   Feb., 1924.
   no. 80. Wholesale and retail prices...   Feb., 1924.
   no. 81. Building costs...   March, 1924.
   no. 82. Building construction...   March, 1924.

   no. 93. Personal income tax returns.   Aug., 1924.
   no. 94. Mining and industrial activity...   Aug., 1924.
   no. 95. Cost of living changes...   Sept., 1924.
   no. 96. Wages—manufacturing industries...   Sept., 1924.
   no. 97. Hourly and weekly earnings, manufacturing industries...   Oct., 1924.
   no. 98. Employment and hours, manufacturing industries...   Oct., 1924.
   no. 99. Volume of production...   Nov., 1924.
   no. 100. Nationality of foreign labor supply.   Dec., 1924.
   no. 101. Expenditures and taxation.   Jan., 1925.
   no. 102. Employment of children...   Jan., 1925.
   no. 103. Economic position, U. S. and the world.   Feb., 1925.
   no. 104. American trade union membership, 1900 to 1923.   Feb., 1925.
   no. 105. Cost of living changes...   March, 1925.

NN   0054976   NN DLC

National industrial conference board.
   Wanted: skilled labor; an analysis of the causes and extent of the skilled labor shortage in the metal manufacturing industries and proposals for meeting the situation. New York city, National industrial conference board, inc. ₍ᵉ1935₎
   viii, 37 p. 23ᶜᵐ. ₍Its Studies. no. 216₎
   "This report was prepared by Mr. Harold F. Browne of the Conference board's research staff."—Foreword.

   1. Metal-workers—U. S.   2. Metal trade—U. S.   3. Labor and laboring classes—U. S.—1914–   4. Industrial statistics.   ɪ. Browne, Harold Frederic, 1890–   ɪɪ. Title.   ɪɪɪ. Title: Skilled labor.
   Library of Congress   HD8039.M52U65   35–16135
   —— Copy 2.
   Copyright A 83823   ₍5-5₎   331.7671

   MB DL OU MiU OC1 CU
NN   0054977   DLC MtU WaS OrCS NcD OCU ViU ICJ MB

National industrial conference board.
   War revenue act of 1918; a brief analysis, March 14, 1919. Boston, Mass., National industrial conference board ₍1919₎
   1 p. l., 18 p. 23ᶜᵐ. ₍Its Special report, no. 2₎

   1. War revenue law of 1918.

   Library of Congress   HJ2379.N345   21–7345

NN   0054978   DLC MtU WaS OrU OU OC1W OC1 OO

National industrial conference board.
   Wartime changes in the cost of living ... Boston, Mass., National industrial conference board, 1918.
   vii, 78, ₍3₎ p. incl. tables. diagrs. (1 fold.) 23ᶜᵐ. (Its Research report, no. 9) $1.00

   1. Cost and standard of living—U. S.   2. European war, 1914——Economic aspects—U. S.   ɪ. Title.
   Library of Congress   HD6983.N3   19—532

   ViU NcD OU OrU NN ICJ MB OCU OC1 WaWW
NN   0054979   DLC WaTC WaS MtBC OrPR MiU Or CaBVaU

National industrial conference board.
   Wartime changes in the cost of living, July, 1914–November, 1918 ... Boston, Mass., National industrial conference board, ᵉ1919.
   v, 33 p. incl. tables, diagr. 23ᶜᵐ. (Its Research report, no. 4)

   1. Cost and standard of living—U. S.   2. European war, 1914–1918—Economic aspects—U. S.   ɪ. Title.
   Library of Congress   HD6983.N3 1919   19—5626
   —— Copy 2.

   OU ICJ OCU MiU OO OC1 ViU
NN   0054980   DLC WaTC MtBC WaS OrU Or WaWW NcD

National industrial conference board.
   Wartime changes in the cost of living, July, 1914–March, 1919 ... Boston. Mass.. National industrial conference board, ᵉ1919.
   v. ₍1₎, 31 p. incl. tables. diagr. 23½ᶜᵐ. (Its Research report, no. 17)

   1. Cost and standard of living—U. S.   2. European war, 1914–1918—Economic aspects—U. S.   ɪ. Title.
   Library of Congress   HD6983.N3 1919 a   19—8985

   OU OCU OO OC1 MiU ICJ ViU NIC NcD
NN   0054981   DLC WaTC MtBC Or WaS OrU CaBVaU WaWW

National industrial conference board.
   Wartime changes in wages, September, 1914–March, 1919 ... Boston, Mass., National industrial conference board, ᵉ1919.
   xiii, 128 p. incl. tables, diagrs. 23ᶜᵐ. (Its Research report, no. 20)

   1. Wages—U. S.   2. European war, 1914–1918—Economic aspects—U. S.   ɪ. Title.
   Library of Congress   HD4975.N3   20—223

   NcD CU NcRS WaWW MiU OCU OC1 OU ViU ICJ MB
NN   0054982   DLC WaTC MtBC OrPR WaS OrU Or CaBVaU

National industrial conference board.
   Wartime employment of women in the metal trades ... Boston, Mass., National industrial conferene board, ᵉ1918.
   iv, 79 p. incl. tables. 23ᶜᵐ. (Its Research report, no. 8)

   1. Woman—Employment—U. S.   2. Metal-workers—U. S.   ɪ. Title.
   Library of Congress   HD6073.M4U6   18—23701

   NcD DHEW CU NN ICJ MiU OU OCU OO OC1 ViU
NN   0054983   DLC WaTC MtBC OrPR WaS CaBVaU Or WaWW

VOLUME 407

National industrial conference board.
... Wartime influences on vacation policies ... New York,
National industrial conference board, inc. ₁1943₎
cover-title, 16 p. 28 x 22ᶜᵐ. (*Its* Conference board reports)
Studies in personnel policy, no. 56.

1. Vacations, Employee—U. S.   ɪ. Title.
43–11830
Library of Congress   HF5549.A2N27 no. 56
₁a44e1₎   (658.3) 658.3816

NN 0054984   DLC ViU CoU IaU DAL

National industrial conference board.
... The wartime outlook for agriculture. New York, National industrial conference board, inc., 1941.
cover-title, 28 p. incl. illus. (map) tables. 28 x 21½ᵐ. (*Its* Conference
board reports)
Table of contents on p. ₁2₎ of cover.

1. Agriculture—U. S. 2. Agriculture—Economic aspects. 3. World
war, 1939-   —Food question.   ɪ. Title.
43–5209
Library of Congress   HD1765.1941.N3
₁5₎   338.1

MH ICU OU OCU OC1W OC1U
NN 0054985   DLC NBuG OrCS OrU IaU CtY DNAL GU ICJ

National industrial conference board.
... Wartime pay of women in industry ... New York,
N. Y., National industrial conference board, inc. ₁1943₎
cover-title, 31 p. 28 x 21½ cm. (*Its* Conference board reports)
Studies in personnel policy, no. 58.

1. Woman—Employment—U. S. 2. Wages—U. S.   ɪ. Title.
HF5549.A2N27 no. 58   331.42   44—625

NN 0054986   DLC CoU AAP OC1JC ViU OC1U

HC106 NATIONAL INDUSTRIAL CONFERENCE BOARD.
.3   Weekly chart service. no.1-   Jan.3,1936-
.N286   New York,National conference board,c1936-
v. 29½cm.

1.U.S.--Econ.condit.--1918-

NN 0054987   ICU

National industrial conference board, inc.
... Weekly desk sheet of current business indications.

New York, 19
v.
Reproduced from typewritten copy.

1. Commerce—Per. and soc. publ.   —U. S. ɪ. Title: Current business
indications.
N. Y. P. L.   October 4, 1937

NN 0054988   NN IU OCU OC1 NNC MH-BA TU LNL

National Industrial Conference Board.
Weekly report on current projects (publications)
New York, National industrial conference board,
1938.
1 v.

NN 0054989   DAL

National industrial conference board.
Weights and measures in the United States; arguments for
and against a change ... New York, National industrial conference board, inc. ₁1926₎
v, 30 p. 23½ᵐ. (*Its* Special report, no. 34)
"Publications of the National industrial conference board": p. 23–30.

1. Metric system. 2. Weights and measures—U. S.   ɪ. Title.
26—12709
Library of Congress   QC80.U5N3 †

CoU MtU WaS Or
NN 0054990   DLC ViU NcD OU OC1 MiU MB DAL KEmT

National industrial conference board.
What employers are doing for employees; a survey of voluntary activities for improvement of working conditions in
American business concerns. New York city, National industrial conference board, inc. ₁1936₎
xiv, 70 p. incl. 57 tables. 23ᵐ. (*Its* Studies. no. 221₎
"This report was prepared by Mr. Harold Browne ... of the Board's
research staff, with the assistance of Miss F. Beatrice Brower."—Foreword.

1. Welfare work in industry. 2. U. S.—Indus.—Stat. 3. Industrial
relations—U. S.   ɪ. Browne, Harold Frederic, 1890-   ɪɪ. Brower,
F. Beatrice. ɪɪɪ. Title. ɪᴠ. Title: Working conditions in American business concerns.
Library of Congress   HD7654.N3   36–10402
₁n45y1₎   331.0973

ViU MB DL ICJ OO MiU OC1 OCU OU
NN 0054991   DLC WaS MtU OrU OrCS IdU-SB Or NcD

National Industrial Conference Board.
What happened in 1949 wage negotiations. ₁By James J.
Bambrick, Jr., Division of Personnel Administration, and
Doris K. Lippman, Statistical Division₎ New York ₁1950₎
16 p. diagrs. 28 cm. (*Its* Conference Board reports. Studies in
personnel policy, no. 105)
Cover title.

1. Wages—U. S. 2. Collective bargaining—U. S.   ɪ. Bambrick,
James Joseph, 1917-   ɪɪ. Title.   (Series: National Industrial
Conference Board. Studies in personnel policy, no. 105)
HF5549.A2N27 no. 105   331.2973   50—4452

NN 0054992   DLC AAP CoU OOxM PPT

HD7811 **National Industrial Conference Board.**
.U6B35 Bambrick, James Joseph, 1917-
What's in UAW-CIO contracts. ₁By James J. Bambrick,
Jr. and Phyllis Syetta₎ New York, National Industrial
Conference Board ₁1952₎

NATIONAL INDUSTRIAL CONFERENCE BOARD.
...When did recovery begin?... [New York] 1934.
3 f. incl. tables. 2 charts. 28cm. (Its [Conference
Board information service: Domestic affairs] Special
memorandum. [no. 1.])

Reproduced from typewritten copy.

1. Crises and panics—U.S., 1929–1934. 2. Index numbers—
U.S. ɪ. Ser.

NN 0054994   NN

National Industrial Conference Board.
When should wages be increased? An evening with the
Economic Forum: Douglass V. Brown, discussion leader,
Jules Backman ₁and others. New York ₁1950₎
64 p. illus. 23 cm. (*Its* Studies in business economics, no. 23)
Cover title.

1. Wages. 2. Wages—U. S.   ɪ. Brown, Douglass Vincent, 1904-
ɪɪ. Title: When should wages be increased?   (Series)
HB31.N33 no. 23   331.215   51–413 rev

NN 0054995   DLC PPFRB OU NN CoU TxU NN IaU

National Industrial Conference Board.
White collar unionization; union strategy and tactics,
analysis of contracts, problems after unionization. ₁By
James J. Bambrick, Jr. and Harold Stieglitz, Division of
Personnel Administration₎ New York ₁1949₎
88 p. illus. 28 cm. (*Its* Conference Board reports. Studies in
personnel policy, no. 101)
Cover title.

1. Clerks—U. S. 2. Trade-unions—U. S.   ɪ. Bambrick, James
Joseph, 1917-   ɪɪ. Stieglitz, Harold. ɪɪɪ. Title.   (Series: National Industrial Conference Board. Studies in personnel policy, no.
101)
HF5549.A2N27 no. 101   331.88151   49–49034*

OOxM
NN 0054996   DLC OCU AAP KMK CoU OC1JC PPT ViU

HF 5549 NATIONAL INDUSTRIAL CONFERENCE BOARD
.A2 N25   Women in factory work. N.Y. ₁1942₎
no.41   52 p. illus. (Its Conference Board reports
Studies in personnel policy,no.41)

Cover title.

1. Woman—Employment. I. Title. Ser.ae:National
Industrial Conference Board. Studies in personne
policy,no.41.

NN 0054997   InU IaU MH-BA MoSU ViU MiU

National industrial conference board.
Women workers and labor supply. New
York City, National industrial conference
board, inc., (c1929)
xi, 42 p. tables, diagrs. 23 cm.

NN 0054998   DL

National industrial conference board.
Women workers and labor supply. New York city, National
industrial conference board, inc. ₁1936₎
xi, 42 p. diagrs. 23ᵐ. (*Its* Studies. no. 220₎

1. Woman—Employment—U. S. 2. Labor supply—U. S.   ɪ. Title.
36–8881
Library of Congress   HD6095.N25
₁a44n1₎   331.40973

ICJ DL OCU OU OC1W OC1
NN 0054999   DLC WaS MtU OrPR OrCS Or NcD TU ViU

338.4 **National Industrial Conference Board.**
N213w   Wool and wool textiles: basic industrial data.
₁n.p.₎ 1953.
1v. of tables. 28cm.

1. Wool trade and industry. 2. Wool trade
and industry--U.S. 3. Woolen and worsted manufacture. I. Title.

NN 0055000   IU

National industrial conference board.
The work of the International labor organization. New
York, National industrial conference board, inc., 1928.
xii, 197 p. incl. tables. 23½ cm.

1. International labor organization. 2. Labor laws and legislation,
International.
HD7809.N35   28—21540

IdU-SB WaTC NN MH GU-L
OC1 OO OCU ODW OOxM TU DL ICJ DAL MtU OrPR WaS OrCS
NN 0055001   DLC KEmT DAU ICRL NcD KMK AAP OU MiU

VOLUME 407

National industrial conference board.
Workmen's compensation acts in the United States, the legal phase ... Boston, Mass., National industrial conference board ₁1917₎

62 p. 22½ᶜᵐ. (*Its* ₁Research report₎ no. 1)

1. Employers' liability—U. S.   ₁. Title.

Library of Congress   HD7816.U6N24   18—13026

NN   0055002   DLC OrPR CaBVaU Or ICU MH-L MB ICJ NIC
MiU OCU OU OClW

National industrial conference board.
Workmen's compensation acts in the United States, the legal phase ... Boston, Mass., National industrial conference board, ₁1919₎

iii, 60 p. 23ᶜᵐ. (*Its* Research report no. 1)

1. Employers' liability—U. S   ₁. Title.
Library of Congress   HD7816.U6N24 1919   19—16455

NN   0055003   DLC WaWW WaTC WaS OrU MiU OCl NcD CU

National industrial conference board.
Workmen's compensation acts in the United States; the medical aspect ... New York, National industrial conference board ₁1923₎

ix, ₁1₎, 282 p. incl. tables. 23ᶜᵐ. (*Its* Research report, no. 61)

1. Employers' liability—U. S.
Library of Congress   HD7816.U6N27   23—13067

NN   0055004   NcD DL MB ICJ ViU OU OCU OCl MiU OO WaWW CaBVaU Or
DLC WaTC MtBC OrPR WaS OrU-M CU DNLM

National industrial conference board.
The workmen's compensation problem in New York state. New York, National industrial conference board, inc., 1927.

xx, 375 p. incl. tables, diagrs. 23½ᶜᵐ.

1. Employers' liability—New York (State)   ₁. Title.
Library of Congress   HD7816.U7N7 1927   27—16111

NN   0055005   MH WaS NcD OU MH-BA KMK NBuU NIC Or OrCS MtU TxU
DLC MB WATC ViU OO MiU OCU OCl DL ICJ

National industrial conference board.
Works councils in the United States ... Boston, Mass., National industrial conference board, ₁1919₎

vii, 135 p. 23ᶜᵐ. (*Its* Research report, no. 21)
Bibliography: p. 133–135.

1. Employees' representation in management.   ₁. Title.
Library of Congress   HD5650.   20—222

NN   0055006   NcD MiU OU OCU OO OCl ViU ICJ MB DL WaWW
DLC WaTC MtBC WaS OrU CaBVaU NIC CU Or

National industrial conference board.
A works council manual ... supplemental to Research report no. 21. Boston, Mass., National industrial conference board, ₁1920₎

v, 32 p. diagrs. 23ᶜᵐ. (*Its* Research report, no. 26)

1. Employees' representation in management.   ₁. Title.
Library of Congress   HD5650.N32   20—9492

NN   0055007   MiU OU OO OCl ViU MB ICJ DL
DLC WaTC MtBC WaS Or OrU WaWW CU NcD

National industrial conference board.
...World copper resources, comp. by the Department of business research, December, 1936. New York, National industrial conference board, c1936.

2 p. l., 10 numb. l., map.

NN   0055008   OCl

National industrial conference board.
The world crisis and American business management ... New York, National industrial conference board, inc. ₁1940₎

cover-title, ix p., 1 l., 258 p. diagrs. 23ᶜᵐ. (National industrial conference board. Annual report. 24th. ₁1940₎)
Foreword signed: Virgil Jordan, president.

1. U. S.—Econ. condit.—1918–   2. U. S.—Indus.   3. National industrial conference board.   ₁. *Jordan, Virgil, 1892–   ₁₁. Title.
Library of Congress   HC106.3.N18 24th   40—35646
——— Copy 2.   HC106.4.N38
Copyright   ₁5₎   (330.973) 330.973

NN   0055009   DLC OU

National industrial conference board.
... World economic conditions at the beginning of 1934 ... ₁New York₎ National industrial conference board, 1934.

cover-title, ii, 17 numb. l. 3 diagr. 28½ᶜᵐ. (Conference board information service: Foreign affairs. Memorandum no. 13)
Mimeographed.

1. Economic conditions—1918– (Economics)   4. Finance.   2. Prices.   3. Index numbers (Economics)   ₁. Title.
Library of Congress   HC57.N293   34—6285
——— Copy 2.
Copyright AA 140728   ₁3₎   330.904

NN   0055010   DLC

National industrial conference board.
World trade, prices, and money. New York city, National industrial conference board, inc., °1935.

12 numb. l. incl. diagrs. 19½ᶜᵐ.
Diagrams: leaves 2–12.

1. Economic conditions — 1918–   2. Index numbers (Economics)   3. Commerce.   4. Prices.   5. Finance.   ₁. Title.
Library of Congress   HC57.N295   38—8716
——— Copy 2.
Copyright AA 255428   ₁3₎   330.904

NN   0055011   DLC

National industrial conference board.
The world war veterans and the federal Treasury. New York, National industrial conference board, inc., 1932.

viii, 77 p. diagrs. 23ᶜᵐ.

1. Pensions, Military—U. S.—European war, 1914–1918.   ₁. Title.
Library of Congress   UB373.N27   33—27032
——— Copy 2.
Copyright A 60157   ₁a41m1₎   351.50973

NN   0055012   OrU MiU OU OCU OCl OO ViU NcD NIC KMK
DLC MB FMU WaS WaTC MtU OrPR OrCS Or

UB
373
.N27
1933

National industrial conference board.
The world war veterans and the
federal Treasury. New York, National
industrial conference board, inc.,
1933.
viii, 77 p. diagrs. 23 cm.

1. Pensions, military—U. S.—
European war, 1914–1918. I. Title

NN   0055013   OKentU

HJ257
.E4

National industrial conference board.

Ellis, Paul Warren, 1903–
The world's biggest business, American public spending, 1914–1944, by Paul W. Ellis ... New York, N. Y., National industrial conference board, inc. ₁1944₎

NN   0055008   OCl

National Industrial Conference Board.
Written statements of personnel policy ₁by Geneva Seybold, Management Research Division₎ New York ₁1947₎

36 p. 28 cm. (*Its* Conference Board reports. Studies in personnel policy, no. 79)

1. Employees' magazines, handbooks, etc.   ₁. Seybold, Geneva, 1900–   ₁₁. Title.   (Series: National Industrial Conference Board. Conference Board reports. Series: National Industrial Conference Board. Studies in personnel policy, no. 79)
HF5549.A2N27 no. 79   658.3   48—2207*

NN   0055015   DLC AAP ViU IaU CSt Mi CoU

National Industrial Conference Board. *Division of Business Economics.*
The social security almanac; a handbook of facts about voluntary and compulsory provision for social security in the United States and other countries. New York, National Industrial Conference Board ₁1949₎

vi, 112 p. 29 cm. (Studies in individual and collective security, no. 7)

1. Public welfare—U. S.—Stat.   2. Insurance, Social—U. S.—Stat.   3. Insurance, Social—Stat.   ₁. Title.   (Series: National Industrial Conference Board. Studies in individual and collective security, no. 7)
HV90.N3   331.2544   49—2754*

WaS OClU WaSpG WaSp
TxU ViU OOxM PPT PPLas NcGU CaBVaU OO MtBC PSC Wa
NN   0055016   DLC MB KEmT KMK DNAL NcD CaBVa CU ICU

National industrial conference board. *Division of business practices.*
Bibliography on research in industry: organization and management, prepared for Industrial research institute, July 20, 1945, by Division of business practices, National industrial conference board. New York, N. Y., °1945.

1 p. l., 31 numb. l. 29 x 22ᶜᵐ.
Reproduced from type-written copy.

1. Research, Industrial—Bibl.   ₁. Industrial research institute, New York.
Library of Congress   Z7914.R5N17   45—7916
        ₁4₎   016.5072

NN   0055017   DLC ICJ

National Industrial Conference Board. *Division of Business Practices.*
Company tax administration. New York, National Industrial Conference Board ₁1954₎

32 p. 28 cm. (National Industrial Conference Board. Conference Board reports. Studies in business policy, no. 68)

1. Corporations—Taxation.   ₁. Title.
HF5006.N3 no. 68   *658.15 658.171   54—2965 ‡

NN   0055018   DLC DI MH-BA OU ViU LU AAP IaU WaWW

National Industrial Conference Board. Division of Business Practices.
Controlling capital expenditures

see under

Watson, John H

National Industrial Conference Board. *Division of Business Practices.*
Cutting costs in industry. New York, National Industrial Conference Board ₁1949–

v. illus. (part col.) 28 cm. (Conference Board reports. Studies in business policy, no. 37)
Cover title.
CONTENTS.—1. Factory costs, by R. M. Ballinger and M. C. Neuhoff.

1. Costs, Industrial.   ₁. Title.   (Series: National Industrial Conference Board. Studies in business policy, no. 37)
HF5006.N3 no. 37, etc.   64—2748

NN   0055020   DLC ViU OU PPT MH-BA CoU DAU LU

VOLUME 407

National Industrial Conference Board. Division
of Industrial Economics.
The Conference board economic record
see   American affairs; the economic
record.

National industrial conference board. *Division of industrial
economics.*
The conference board economic record ... Special industry
reports ...

New York, National industrial conference board, inc. [19

v. diagrs. 28½ᵐ. monthly.

1. U. S.—Indus.   I. Title.

		44–13078
Library of Congress	HC101.N34	
	[2]	338.05

NN   0055022   DLC

National industrial conference board. *Division of industrial
economics.*
The conference board industry record. v. 1–
Jan. 1942–   New York, National industrial conference board, inc., 1942–

v. diagrs. 28ᵐ. monthly.
Dec. 1942 not published.

1. U. S.—Indus.   I. Title.

		44–12807
Library of Congress	HC101.N343	
	[3]	338.05

NcD WaSp MH-BA NhD PU-BZ
NN   0055023   DLC CU MoSW NBuG ICU ICJ OC1 OrU WaS

National industrial conference board. Division of industrial economics.

National industrial conference board.
Conference board studies in enterprise and social progress;
selected chapters in the story of the American enterprise system and its contribution to prosperity and public welfare,
assembled from special reports of the Division of industrial
economics of the Conference board. New York, National industrial conference board [°1939]

National industrial conference board. *Division of industrial
economics.*
Methods used by corporations in the selection of independent
auditors, a special report prepared by Division of industrial
economics, the Conference board, April 8, 1943. New York
city, National industrial conference board, inc., °1943.

2 p. l., 7, A–C numb. l. form. 28½ x 22½ᵐ.
Reproduced from type-written copy.

1. Auditing. 2. Stock companies—U. S.

		43–14222
Library of Congress	HG4028.A8N3	
	[2]	658.15

NN   0055025   DLC

National industrial conference board.
HD3616   Division of industrial economics.
.U47N3
1940   National industrial conference board.
... Public regulation of competitive practices in business
enterprise, by Myron W. Watkins and the Division of industrial economics of the Conference board. New York city, National industrial conference board, inc. [°1940]

National industrial conference board. *Division of industrial
economics.*
The shortened workday in the New York city building industry; report prepared by Division of industrial economics, the
Conference board, September 19, 1940, for the Building trades
employers association of the city of New York. New York
city [°1940]

3 p. l., 46 p. incl. tables, diagrs. 23ᵐ.
Seal of the Building trades employers' association on t.-p.
"Abstracts of economic discussion regarding the shorter work day
and work week": p. 43–46.
1. Hours of labor—U. S. 2. Building trades—New York (City)
I. Building trades employers' association of New York city. II. Title.

		40–29622
Library of Congress	HD5119.B5N3	
Copyright	[2]	331.8189
——— Copy 2.		

NN   0055027   DLC

National Industrial Conference Board. *Division of Labor
Statistics
see* **National Industrial Conference Board.** *Statistical
Division.*

National industrial conference board. *European commission.*
Interim report of the European commission of the National
industrial conference board, July 1919 ... Boston, Mass., National industrial conference board [°1919]

iii, 34 p. 23½ᵐ.

1. Labor and laboring classes—Gt. Brit. 2. Labor and laboring
classes—Italy. 3. Labor and laboring classes—France. 4. European
war, 1914–1918—Economic aspects. 5. Reconstruction (1914–1939)

19–19601

Library of Congress   HC57.N3

ICJ NN WaPS OU OC1W OC1 OO MiU NIC
NN   0055029   DLC Or MB PBL IdU WaS OrU MtU CaBViP

National industrial conference board. *European commission.*
Problems of labor and industry in Great Britain, France and
Italy; report of the European commission of the National industrial conference board ... Boston, Mass., National industrial conference board, °1919.

xv, 406 p. 23ᵐ.

1. Labor and laboring classes—Gt. Brit. 2. Labor and laboring
classes—France. 3. Labor and laboring classes—Italy. 4. European
war, 1914–1918—Economic aspects. 5. Reconstruction (1914–1939)

20—3721

Library of Congress   HD4851.N3

OC1 OOxM MA ICJ
NN   0055030   DLC WaS OrU MB CU CtY NIC MiU OC1W OO

017   National Industrial Conference Board. Library.
N213ℓ   Library bulletin.
Bus Ad
Eco RR   New York.
v. 28cm.

"A listing of books and reports recently
added to the Board's Library."

1. Business – Bibl.

NN   0055031   TxU IU

NATIONAL INDUSTRIAL CONFERENCE BOARD. Library.
List of references on instalment buying, compiled by
Library of National industrial conference board, October,
1937. [New York? 1937] 21 f. 28cm.

Caption–title.
Reproduced from typewritten copy.

1. Instalment business—Bibl.

NN   0055032   NN

National industrial conference board. Library.
Xn11   Selected list of references on business
+1   enterprise, the monopoly problem and related
subjects ... [Washington, D.C., 1938]
40 numb. ℓ. 28cm.
Caption title.
Mimeographed.

1. Business – Bibl.

NN   0055033   CtY

National industrial conference board. *Management research
division.*
Aircraft industry union contracts ... New York, N. Y.,
National industrial conference board, inc. [1944]

20 p. 28 x 21½ᵐ. (Supplement to the Conference board management
record)
"Prepared by the Conference board, Management research division."

1. Labor contract—U. S. 2. Aeroplane industry and trade—U. S.
I. Title.

		44–47370
Library of Congress	HD7811.U6N35	
	[5]	331.11

NN   0055034   DLC

National industrial conference board. **Management
research division.**
Nb10   ... Defense memorandum no. 1–
+N21g   New York, N. Y., The Conference board [1940?
28½cm.

Caption title.
Mimeographed.
"Not for publication".

NN   0055035   CtY

National Industrial Conference Board. *Management Research Division.*
Employee suggestion systems; formal plans for compensating employees for constructive ideas. New York, National Industrial Conference Board [1942]

92 p. facsims., forms. 28 cm. (Conference Board reports. Studies in personnel policy, no. 43)
Cover title.

1. Suggestion systems. I. Title. (Series: National Industrial
Conference Board. Studies in personnel policy, no. 43)

| HF5549..A2N27 no. 43 | *658.315   658.314 | 53–1003 |

NN   0055036   DLC ViU MoSU InU CoU

National Industrial Conference Board. Research
Staff.
An analysis of the proposal for an American
free gold market
see under   National Industrial Conference
Board.

National Industrial Conference Board. *Statistical Division.*
Family expenditures for clothing. New York [1955]

40 p. col. illus. 28 cm. (Conference Board reports. Studies in
labor statistics, no. 15)
Cover title.

1. Clothing trade—U. S. 2. Consumers—U. S. I. Title. (Series: National Industrial Conference Board. Studies in labor statistics, no. 15)

| HD9940.U4N43 | 646.3 | 56–872 |

NN   0055038   DLC OrLgE NB NcD OCU

National Industrial Conference Board. *Statistical Division.*
General wage increases to production workers, 1940–1948.
New York [1949]

30 p. 28 cm.
Foreword signed: Elizabeth M. Caselli.

1. Wages—U. S. I. Title.

| HD4975.N39 | 331.2973 | 49–3602* |

NN   0055039   DLC

VOLUME 407

National Industrial Conference Board. *Statistical Division.*
Indexes of change in retail prices of department stores.
Jan. 31, 1941/Jan. 31, 1942–

New York.
v. 28–31 cm.
"A special report prepared for National Retail Dry Goods Association."
Reports for Jan. 31, 1941/Jan. 31, 1942–
prepared by the board's Division of Industrial Economics;
by the Statistical Division under its earlier name: Division of Labor
Statistics.

———— Supplement: Indexes of change in retail prices
of department stores, including mail order chains and variety stores. Jan. 31/July 31, 1942–

New York.
v. 31 cm.
Reports for Jan. 31/July 31, 1942–
prepared by the board's Division of Industrial Economics;
by the Statistical Division under its earlier name: Division of Labor
Statistics.

1. Prices—U. S. 2. Retail trade—U. S. 3. Department stores.
I. National Industrial Conference Board. Division of Industrial Economics. II. National Retail Dry Goods Association. III. Title.

HB235.U6N33   338.5   42–15195 rev 2*

NN 0055042   DLC

National Industrial Conference Board. *Statistical Division.*
What an hour's work would buy, 1914–1948 ₍by Laurence
D. De Trude and Wistaria Nishimura, Statistical Division₎
New York ₍1950₎
19 p. illus. (part col.) 28 cm. (Conference Board reports.
Studies in labor statistics, no. 3)
Cover title.

1. Cost and standard of living—U. S. 2. Wages—U. S. I. Title.
(Series: National Industrial Conference Board. Conference Board
reports. Series: National Industrial Conference Board. Studies in
labor statistics, no. 3)

HD6983.N37   331.2154   50–7425

NN 0055043   DLC ViU WaT OCU OO UU KMK

National industrial conference board, inc. Tax committee.
Discussion of tentative report of Taxation committee of Na-
tional industrial conference board. November, 1920. New
York, N. Y.: Galey & Lord ₍1920?₎ 22 p. 23cm.

1. Sales and turnover tax—U. S.,   1920.
N. Y. P. L.   December 6, 1937

NN 0055044   NN

National industrial conference board. *Tax committee.*
Report of the Tax committee of the National industrial
conference board on the federal tax problem, for consideration of the third National industrial conference on
January 22 and 23, 1921 ... New York, National industrial conference board ₍1920₎
vii, 58 p. 23ᶜᵐ. (National industrial conference board. Special report, no. 18)

1. Taxation—U. S.
Library of Congress   HJ2379.N46   21–4397

NN 0055045   DLC OrU Or CU

National Industrial Conference Board. Tax Committee.
Tentative report of the tax committee of the National Indus-
trial Conference Board. Submitted for the consideration of the
Second National Industrial Tax Conference to be held in New
York City, October 22 and 23, 1920... New York: National
Industrial Conference Board, 1920. 52 p. 8°.

1. Taxation, U. S., 1920.
N. Y. P. L.   October 25, 1921.

NN 0055046   NN

National industrial congress.
...Constitutions of the Industrial congress and industrial
brotherhoods, and by-laws of "Young America," parent bower.
₍New York, 1845₎ 8 p. 22cm.

Caption-title.
At head of title: Young America.—Extra.

1. No subject. I. Industrial   brotherhood. (Founded 1845.)
II. Young America.   November 23, 1938
N. Y. P. L.

NN 0055047   NN

7th, 1852.
National industrial congress. ₍ Washington, D. C.
Proceedings of the 7th annual...congress.
June 2–7, 1852. ₍No pub., 1852₎
16 p.

NN 0055048   MiD

National Industrial Congress. 8th, 1853.
... Proceedings ...

Philadelphia, Rawlings & Zeising, Printers,
v. 21cm. annual.

Especially concerned with the distribution
of American public lands.

NN 0055049   NNC

4224.113
National Industrial Congress. 9th Congress. Trenton, 1854.
Proceedings.
= Philadelphia, 1854. 20 pp. 8°.
The Congress discussed current political issues.

F5038 — United States. Pol. hist.

NN 0055050   MB DLC

National Industrial Council.
Bulletin.
no.

New York, 191   4°.
v.
Title varies: Bulletin of the National Council for Industrial Defense;   Bulletin of the National Industrial Council.

1. Labor.
N. Y. P. L.   October 1, 1921.

NN 0055051   NN WHi ICJ

National industrial council.

**National association of manufacturers of the United States
of America.**
Congress of American industry and National association of
manufacturers. Platform and resolutions adopted December
5 and 6, 1934, also considered at annual meeting National industrial council. December 3–4. Supplementary analyses of
the several sections of the platform and resolutions ... Industry's record—a statistical and analytical digest ... New
York city, National association of manufacturers ₍1935?₎

National industrial council.
Digest of organization activities,
₍New York, 19
v. in   28ᶜᵐ. monthly.
Published by the National industrial council.

1. Industrial laws and legislation—U. S. 2. Labor laws and legislation—
U. S. 3. U. S.—Econ. condit.—1918–   I. Title.

CA 26–820 Unrev'd

Library of Congress   HD7833.N25

NN 0055053   DLC NN

NN 0055054   NN

National industrial council.
Fundamental principles of taxation; a basic program
for the necessary revision of our federal revenue laws,
formulated by a special committee representing organized industry. New York city, Washington, D. C., The
National industrial council, 1923.
31 p. 18⅟₂ᶜᵐ.
Text on p. 3 and 4 of cover.
"Fundamental principles of taxation. Final report of the Committee on
taxation of the National industrial council ₍C. R. Gow, chairman₎": p. ₍7₎–28.

1. Taxation—U. S.   I. Title.

Library of Congress   HJ2379.N37   24–7799

NN 0055055   DLC NN

National Industrial Council.
A letter to industrial shareholders
see under   National Association of Manufacturers of the United States of America₍.₎

National industrial council.
... Minimum wage legislation, its nature,
extent and validity. (New York, 1919?)
(13) p. 27 cm.

NN 0055057   DL

National industrial council

**Joint committee of the National association of manufactur-
ers and National industrial council.**
Public unemployment insurance; a factual analysis prepared by a Joint committee of the National association of
manufacturers and National industrial council. New York
city, 1930.

National industrial council.
A review of state legislation affecting industry in 1918
and 1919 ... New York city, Secretary's office National
industrial council ₍1919?₎
70 p. 23ᶜᵐ.

1. Labor laws and legislation. 2. Industrial laws and legislation.
I. Title.

Library of Congress   HD7833.N3   21–10876

NN 0055059   DLC

National industrial council.
...Statistical survey and review of legislation proposed and enacted in the state legislatures of 1929, together with a detailed report by
states. (Presented to the twenty-third Conference
of state manufacturers associations' presidents
and secretaries at the Hotel Roosevelt, New York
city, on Friday, October 11, 1929) Compiled by
Michael J. Hickey, executive secretary, October,
1929... ₍New York city, National industrial
council, 1929₎
1 p.l., 2–39 numb.l. 28x21½cm.

At head of title: Prepared and issued by the
National industrial council...

1. Legislation – U.S. I. Hickey, Michael J.
₍comp₎ II. Title.

NN 0055061   MdBJ

VOLUME 407

National industrial council.
...Summary and review of state industrial
legislation... 1925, 1927.

(New York, 1925-27)
2 v. 28 cm.

NN 0055062 DL

National industrial council.
Your community's share in national defense; an informative
manual on community pooling. Prepared by the National industrial council. New York city, 1941. 27, 8 p. incl. forms.
6 charts, illus. (incl. map, ports.) 28cm.

190572B. 1. Industrial mobilization
N. Y. P. L.   and conscription—U. S.
                               September 4, 1942

NN 0055063 NN

National Industrial Council. Advisory Committee.
Proceedings of the conference.
[no.]

New York [19
v.   8°.

1. Labor, U. S., 1914-18. 2. European   war, 1914-18.—Economic aspects.
U. S. 3. European war, 1914-18.—   Reconstruction (Economic), U. S.
N. Y. P. L.   September 21, 1923.

NN 0055064 NN

HD7951
Z7R45 National Industrial Council of the Mining
1955   Industry of Southern Rhodesia.
        Mining industry industrial agreement(officials)
[13th May, 1955 - 10th May, 1957. Salisbury,
Rhodesia, Printed by the Govt. Print. and
Stationery Dept., n.d.]
        21 p. tables. 24 cm. (Southern Rhodesia
Government notice no. 147 of 1955)
        Caption title.
        "Act 21/45."
        "Supplement to the Southern Rhodesia Govern-
ment gazette dated   13th May, 1955."
        1.Labor law and   legislation - Rhodesia,
Southern.2.Mineral   .ndustries - Rhodesia,
Southern. I. Title.

NN 0055065 DI

HD7951
Z7R45 National Industrial Council of the Mining
1955a   Industry of Southern Rhodesia.
        Mining industry industrial agreement (artisans)
[13th May, 1955 - 9th May, 1958. Salisbury,
Rhodesia, Printed by the Govt. Print. and
Stationery Dept., n.d.]
        33 p. table. 24 cm. (Southern Rhodesia
Government notice no. 148 of 1955)
        Caption title.
        "Act 21/45."
        "Supplement to the Southern Rhodesia Govern-
ment gazette dated   13th May, 1955."

NN 0055066 DI

NATIONAL INDUSTRIAL COUNCIL OF THE PRINTING
AND NEWSPAPER INDUSTRY OF SOUTH AFRICA.
Monthly record. no. 253-date; July, 1946-date
Cape Town.   v.   25cm.

1. Printing--Assoc. and org.--Union of South Africa.

NN 0055067 NN

National Industrial Council of the Printing and Newspaper
    Industry of South Africa.
    Report of proceedings.
)
    [Cape Town]
    (I) v. 25 cm.

1. Printing—Societies.

Z120.N255   655.06268   51-33534 ‡

NN 0055068 DLC DL NN

National Industrial Design Committee
        see
National Industrial Design Council.

[National Industrial Design Council]
    Award winners; design merit awards to industry
1953. [Ottawa] N.I.D.C. 1953.
    n.p.   illus.   Q.

NN 0055070 CaBViP

[National Industrial Design Council]
    Design award; N;I.D.C. Canada, 19-
19 ...   [Ottawa] N.I.D.C. 19 -19
    v.   illus.   Q.

NN 0055071 CABViP

National industrial design council.
    Design for Canadian living.
[Ottawa,1955] 12p.illus.

    Cover title.

NN 0055072 CABVa

National industrial design council.
    Good design is good business;
a booklet for retailers. [Ottawa,
1954] 1v.(chiefly illus.)

    Catalogue of Canadian design
awards for 1954.
    Cover title.

NN 0055073 CaBViP CaBVa

National industrial design council.

    How the industrial designer can help
you in your business: consultant designer,
design specialist, design group. [Ottawa,
National gallery,1949] 23p.illus.

NN 0055074 CaBViP CaBVa

National Industrial Design Council.

    The story of Canadian design ... n.p.,
n.d.
    [7] p. illus. O.
    By the National Industrial Design
Council, Ottawa, & the Canadian Association
of Consumers.

NN 0055075 CaBViP

National Industrial Development Corporation.
    Annual report.
    [New Delhi]
    v. in   25 cm.

1. Development credit corporations—India. 2. Industrial promotion—India.

HG3729.I 42N3   332.3   S A 68-10394

NN 0055076 DLC NN NSyU

National industrial development council of Wales and Mon-
    mouthshire, limited.
    Annual report. 1st-
1932/33–
[Cardiff, Wales, 1933?–
    v. illus. 22ᶜᵐ.

1. Wales—Indus. 2. Monmouthshire—Indus.

Library of Congress   HC257.W3N28   42-52129

NN 0055077 DLC NN DL

National Industrial Development Council of Wales and
    Monmouthshire.
    The happy holidayland of Wales; the comprehensive, fully
illustrated guide to the holiday haunts abounding in Wales
and Monmouthshire. 6th ed. Cardiff, National Industrial
Development Council of Wales and Monmouthshire (Tourist
and Holidays Section) [1952?]
    106 p. illus. 22 cm.

1. Wales—Descr. & trav.—Guide-books. 2. Monmouthshire—Descr.
& trav.—Guide-books. I. Title.

DA735.N3 1952   914.29   54-36871 ‡

NN 0055078 DLC CU NN

National industrial development council of Wales and Mon-
    mouthshire, limited.
    ... The industrial window of Wales ... [Cardiff, 1945]
    cover-title, 39 p. illus. (incl. ports.) 24½ x 19ᶜᵐ.

Text on p. [2] and [4] of cover.
Includes advertising matter.

1. Wales—Indus. 2. Monmouthshire—Indus. I. Title.

                                        45-18785
Library of Congress   HC257.W3N29
                            [2]   338.91

NN 0055079 DLC

National industrial development council of Wales and
    Monmouthshire.
    The second industrial survey of South Wales, published on
behalf of the National industrial development council of Wales
& Monmouthshire. Cardiff, University press board, 1937.
    3 v. fold. maps in pocket (v. [1]-2) 22½ᶜᵐ.

    "Survey was undertaken with the aid of a grant to the National
industrial development council of Wales and Monmouthshire from the
Commissioner for special areas (England and Wales)."—v. 1, p. 3.

    1. Wales, South—Industries. 2. Wales, South—Economic conditions.
[1, 2. Industrial surveys—Wales] I. Gt. Brit. Commissioner for the
special areas (England and Wales)

U. S. Dept. of agr. Library   281.171.N214
for Library of Congress   [HC257.W3]

                                        Agr 37-458

NN 0055080 DNAL IEN CU PPT NN OCU

National industrial development council of Wales and Mon-
    mouthshire limited.
    South Wales and Monmouthshire; an illustrated review of the
industrial and commercial potentialities of South Wales and Monmouthshire, with brief notes on its holiday resorts, by Councillor
George W[illia]ms, F. J. Hodson, David Evans, Marjorie W. Lloyd,
the editor, and other contributors. With a foreword by the Rt.
Hon. the Earl of Plymouth...Edited by H. E. O'Connor. Issued
by authority of the National industrial development council of
Wales and Monmouthshire... London: E. J. Burrow & co.,

ltd. [1937]   100 p. incl. tables.   illus. (incl. charts, map.)
25½cm.

Advertising matter interspersed.

1. Wales—Descr. and trav., 1900—   . 2. Monmouthshire, Eng.—
Descr. and trav. 3. Economic history   —Gt. Br.—Wales. 4. Economic
history—Gt. Br.—Eng.—Monmouth-   shire. I. O'Connor, H. E., ed.
II. Title.
N. Y. P. L.   April 17, 1939

NN 0055082 NN

VOLUME 407

National Industrial Development Council of Wales and Monmouthshire.
 This lovely land of Wales; the happy holidayland. ₈8th ed. Cardiff, 1954₎
 208 p. illus. 22 cm.
 Published in 1950? under title: Wales and Monmouthshire.

 1. Wales—Descr. & trav.—Guide-books. 2. Monmouthshire—Descr. & trav.—Guide-books.   I. Title.

 DA735.N3 1954   914.29   54–39774 ‡

NN   0055083   DLC

HC257 .W3W2   **National industrial development council of Wales and Monmouthshire.**
 Wales and Monmouthshire. v. 1–2, no. 6; spring 1935–Aug. 1939. ₍Cardiff, 1935–39₎

NN   0055084   N NN

914.29 N274   **National Industrial Development Council of Wales and Monmouthshire.**
 Wales and Monmouthshire; an illustrated review, ed. by D.J. Davies. The official handbook of the National Industrial Development Council of Wales & Monmouthshire, ltd. Cheltenham, E.J. Burrow ₍1951₎
 231 p. illus., ports., maps. 25 cm.

 On cover: Festival of Britain, 1951.
 1. Wales. Descr. & trav. 2. Monmouthshire. Descr. & trav.

NN   0055085   N NN

National Industrial Development Council of Wales and Monmouthshire.
 Wales and Monmouthshire, an illustrated review of industry, tourism and holidays; the official handbook, edited by D. J. Davies. Cheltenham, E. J. Burrow ₍1954₎
 232 p. illus. 25 cm.

 1. Wales—Industries. 2. Monmouthshire—Industries. I. Davies, David James. II. Title.

 HC257.W3N3 1954   338′.09429   74–191279
                                      MARC

NN   0055086   DLC

National Industrial Development Council of Wales and Monmouthshire.
 Wales and Monmouthshire; the happy holidayland. 4th ed. Cardiff ₍1950?₎
 128 p. (p. 119–128 advertisements) illus., maps (part fold.) 22 cm.

 1. Wales—Descr. & trav. 2. Monmouthshire—Descr. & trav.

 DA730.N3 1950   914.29   50–56865

NN   0055087   DLC

National Industrial Development Council of Wales and Monmouthshire
 Wales and Monmouthshire, the playground of Britain. Cardiff ₍1949?₎
 112 p. illus., maps (1 fold.)

NN   0055088   MiD

National Industrial Distributors' Association.
 Statement of overhead expenses. Philadelphia, 1924.
 annual.

NN   0055089   MH–BA

National Industrial Engineering and Management Clinic.
 Proceedings.
 Chicago.
   v. illus., ports., diagrs. 28 cm. annual.
   Clinic sponsored by the Industrial Management Society (19
 by its Research Division)
   Issued   by the clinic under its earlier name: Nationa
 Time and Motion Study Clinic.

 1. Industrial management—Congresses.

 T58.A2N33   658.5082   43–34042 rev*

 C NN
NN   0055090   DLC OrU AAP IU OU IaU MiU InU CL TxU

National Industrial Federation of Clothing Manufacturers. 3569a.455
 Articles of federation. July 18, 1919.
 = New York. 1919. (7) pp. 19½ cm.
   The Federation is authorized to make all labor arrangements in the men's clothing industry in Chicago, New York, Rochester and Baltimore, and also to make agreements with unions or other associations of employees.

 L8388 — Collective bargaining. — Clothing industry.

NN   0055091   MB

National Industrial Home for Crippled Boys and Refuge
      see   London.National Industrial Home for Crippled Boys and Refuge.

National industrial peace association. San Francisco branch.
 ... Industrial peace ... ₍San Francisco, Press of C. A. Murdock & co., 1910₎
 cover-title,32 p. 25cm.

 "Constitution": p. 31–32.

NN   0055093   CU–B

National Industrial Publishing Co.
 Industrial heating
      see under title

National industrial recovery act, 1933.

 U. S. *National recovery administration.*
   Charts on the operation of the National industrial recovery act. As prepared by Research and planning division, National recovery administration, Washington, D. C., February, 1935. ₍Washington, 1935?₎

National Industrial Recovery Administration
     see U. S. *National Recovery Administration.*

National Industrial Recreation Association.
 Industrial bands and orchestras, issued as a service to members. ₍Chicago, 1953₎
 32 p. illus. 28 cm.

 1. Music in industry.   I. Title.

 ML3922.N3   785   53–713 ‡

NN   0055097   DLC OU TxU IU Wa WaT

National Industrial Recreation Association.
 Standard sports areas for industrial recreation. Chicago, c1944.
 48p. illus. 21cm.

 On cover: Standard sports areas for industrial, school and public recreation.

 1. Sports. 2. Recreation. I. Title.

NN   0055098   FU WaS

National industrial register for interstate commerce and industry. 1950/51–
 Chicago, Manufacturers Directory Co.
   v. 28 cm.

 1. U. S.—Manuf.—Direct.

 T12.N27   51–36535

NN   0055099   DLC

HD8057 .N3 1953   **National Industrial Relations Conference, Cleveland, O., 1953.**
 Transcription of proceedings, January 14, 1953, Cleveland, Ohio. Sponsored by: Ohio Chamber of Commerce, Cleveland Chamber of Commerce, Chamber of Commerce of the United States. ₍n.p., 1953₎
 81p. 28cm.

NN   0055100   NNU–W NN

National industrial review; published in the interest of loyal, independent Americanism. v. 1–
 Apr. 4, 1921–
 Philadelphia, National industrial review publishing company ₍etc.₎ 1921–
   v. illus. 57ᶜᵐ. weekly.
 Caption title.

 1. Labor and laboring classes—Period. 2. Labor and laboring classes—U. S.—1914– 3. U. S.—Indus.

                                           27–14808

 Library of Congress   HD6500.N27

NN   0055101   DLC

National industrial safety conference, *Oxford*, 1936.
 Proceedings of the National industrial safety conference, 1936. Balliol college, Oxford, April 3rd,4th,5th and 6th. London, The National safety first association (1936)
 85. (1), p. illus. 22 cm.

NN   0055102   DL

National industrial safety conference, *Oxford*, 1937.
 Proceedings of the National industrial safety conference, 1937, Balliol college, Oxford, April 16th, 17th and 18th. London, The National safety first association (inc.) ₍1937₎
 159 p. illus., diagrs. 22ᶜᵐ.

 1. Accidents—Prevention—Congresses. 2. Safety appliances. I. National "safety first" association.

                                           38–37320
 Library of Congress   HD7260.N33 1937
                              ₍5₎   331.82306242

NN   0055103   DLC NN ICJ

VOLUME 407

National Industrial Salvage and Recovery Council.
Industrial salvage and recovery; a handbook. London,
H. M. Stationery Off., 1950.
39 p. 25 cm.
At head of title: Board of Trade.
Bibliography: p. 11-12.

1. Waste products.   I. Gt. Brit. Board of Trade.   II. Title.

TP995.N24   658.5671   50-37681

NN 0055104   DLC DNAL

National Industrial Sand Association
Safety in sandblasting, a manual prepared by
Industrial Hygiene Foundation of America, inc.,
for the National Industrial Sand Association. 2d
ed. Washington, D. C. [°1948]
32 p. illus.

I. Industrial Hygiene Foundation of America

NN 0055105   MiD WaS NNC

NATIONAL INDUSTRIAL SAND ASSOCIATION.
Safety in sandblasting; a manual prepared by
Industrial Hygiene Foundation of America, inc.,
Mellon Institute, Pittsburgh, for the National
Industrial Sand Association. 3d ed. Washington,
1954.
31 p. illus., diagrs.

1. Sand-blast. 2. Safety appliances. I.
Industrial Hygiene Foundation of America. II.
Title.

NN 0055106   GAT

National industrial stores association
NISA yearbook... Wash., D. C. [The Author]
Library has
1944/45-

NN 0055107   MiD

National industrial tax conference.
Proceedings of the National industrial tax conference
... Boston, Mass. [etc.] National industrial conference
board, °1920-
v. 23cm. (National industrial conference board. Special report,
no. 9, 17

1. Taxation—U. S. 2. Taxation—Congresses. 3. Excess profits tax—
U. S.   I. National industrial conference board.

20—12530
Library of Congress   HJ2360.N4

NcD NcRS ICJ MB OCU MiU OU OC1
NN 0055108   DLC WaS MtU IdU OrPR CaBVaU Or NNC CU

National Industrial Traffic League.
Before the Interstate Commerce Commission,
in re investigation of advances in rates by carriers in official classification territory
see under James, Francis Bacon, 1864-

National Industrial Traffic League.   L657.9656 S701
Before the Interstate Commerce Commission. In the matter
of depreciation charges on steam railroads. I. C. C. docket no.
15100. An alternative plan, submitted by the National Industrial Traffic League, November 9, 1927. John W. Roberts,
Earle D. Mudd, consulting accountants. [Chicago?, 1927.]
cover-title, [1], 79 leaves. tables (part fold.) 28½cm.
Multigraphed.

NN 0055110   ICJ CtY

National industrial traffic league.
Before the Interstate commerce commission. In
the matter of general revision of accounting
rules for steam railroads. Ex parte no.91. An
alternative plan. Submitted by the National
industrial traffic league, November 9, 1927.
John W.Roberts, Earle D.Mudd, consulting
accountants. [Chicago,1927]
cover-title,[1],48 leaves. fold. tables. 28½cm.

NN 0055111   CtY ICJ

National industrial traffic league.
Before the National association of railway commissioners, in the matter of proposed uniform code of demurrage
rules. Brief and argument in behalf of the National industrial traffic league ... St. Louis, J. W. Steele & co.,
prs. [1909]
cover-title, 31 p. 23cm.

1. Demurrage (Car service)   I. National association of railway commissioners.

10-25936†
Library of Congress   HE1826.N3

NN 0055112   DLC

National industrial traffic league.
Circular

NN 0055113   PU-W

National industrial traffic league.
Legislator.

NN 0055114   PU-W

National industrial traffic league.
The national industrial traffic league, its
organization and work...
[Chicago, 1913?]
26 p. 16. cm.
HE2715
.N47

NN 0055115   DLC

National Industrial Traffic League.
[Officers, standing committees, constitution, by-laws, members, etc.]
19
Chicago, 19   16°.
v.
DLC: HE2715.N45

1. Transportation.—Assoc. and or-
N. Y. P. L.   ganizations, U. S.
October 1, 1920.

NN 0055116   NN DLC MH-BA

National Industrial Traffic League.
[Officers, standing committees, preamble, constitution, by-
laws, members, etc.]   Chicago: Office of the secretary-treasurer,
1917. 87 p. 16°.
DLC: HE2715.N45 1917

1. Transportation.—Assoc. and
N. Y. P. L.   organizations, U. S.
August 20, 1917..

NN 0055117   NN DLC

National Industrial Traffic League.
Proceedings of the meeting.
[Chicago]
v. 28 cm.
Issued   as the league's Circular.

1. Shipment of goods—Societies, etc.

HF5780.U6N28   53-52516 ‡

NN 0055118   DLC OrU NN

National Industrial Traffic League.   656.06161 9
[Yearbook of] the National Industrial Traffic League. Head-
quarters ... Chicago, Illinois, ... [Chicago, 1919.]
Library has 1918/19. 17½cm.

NN 0055119   ICJ

---

*BROAD-
SIDE
1910
.N37
The National Industrial Traffic League.
Regional Committee. Richmond, Virginia.
You can help win the war by conserving
transportation facilities. Transporation
is the life blood of the nation. Make one
freight car do the work of two ...
Richmond, Va. [191-]
broadside. 28 x 22 cm.

1. European War, 1914-1918—U. S.—
Transportation. I. Title.

NN 0055120   ViU

**National Industrial Traffic League. Special Com-
mittee on Transportation Policy.**
Action of National Industrial Traffic League at
its annual meeting ... November 16-17, 1944.
[n.p., 1944?]
16p.

NN 0055121   ICRL

National Industrial Zoning Committee.
Characteristics of modern industrial plants

see under

Miller, Harold Vincent, 1909-

710.1
N213p
National Industrial Zoning Committee.
Principles of industrial zoning.
[Columbus, O., 1951]
[12]p. illus. 23cm.

Cover title.

1. Zoning. 2. Cities and towns—Planning. I. Title: Industrial zoning.

NN 0055123   IU ICU CoU

**National industries. v.1-   1917-
Charleston, W.Va.**
v.
Title varies: 1917-21, West Virginia mining
news; 1921-29, National coal mining news.

NN 0055124   DI-GS

HC
253
.N2
**National industries. v. 1-
London, K. Paul, Trench, Trübner, 1912-**

1. Gt. Brit.-Econ. condit.-Collections. 2.
Gt. Brit.-Indus.-Collections.

NN 0055125   DAU

**National industries and international trades report. v. 1,
no. 1; Sept. 1910. New York, 1910.**
32 p. illus. 38cm.
No more published.
Official organ of the Bureau of national industries.

1. U. S.—Comm. 2. Shipping bounties and subsidies—U. S.   I. Bureau of national industries, New York.

11-29435
Library of Congress   HF1.N3

NN 0055126   DLC

VOLUME 407

National industries, inc., *Washington, D. C.*
The National industrial recovery act; what it means ...
Washington, D. C., National industries, inc., 1933.
1 p. l., 8 p. 19¼ᶜᵐ.

1. National industrial recovery act, 1933.

Library of Congress   HC106.3.A52N3   33-24075

———— Copy 2.

Copyright AA 126579   ₃₁   330.973

NN   0055127   DLC

National industry.   New York, 1823.
8 p.   22 cm.
Caption title.
1. Free trade and protection - Protection.
2. Imprints - New York, 1823.

NN   0055128   MdBP

'8583
.A3
National Industry Convention.
Transcript of proceedings.
₍Sydney₎ Agricultural and Veterinary
Chemicals Association of Australia.

(05) 1. Chemicals, Agricultural. Congresses. 2. Chemicals, Agricultural.
Societies. I. Agricultural and Veterinary Chemicals Association of Australia.

NN   0055129   DNAL

National Industry-Government-Collegiate Conference on In-
strumentation.
Proceedings. 1953-
₍East Lansing, Mich.₎
v. illus. 28 cm.
Conferences sponsored by the Dept. of Electrical Engineering of
Michigan State University (called Michigan State College of Agri-
culture and Applied Science) and others.

1. Physical instruments—Congresses. 2. Engineering instruments—
Congresses.

QC53.N3   56-27390 rev

NN   0055130   DLC

1268   **National influence and the isthmian canal**
(reprint Engineering Magazine July, 1898)

NN   0055131   DPU

National Information Bureau, Inc., New York.   *55792.9ab
Annual report. [2d], 3d. 1919/20, 20/21.
New York. [1919, 21.]   v. 22½ cm., × 10 cm.

Devoted to civic and philanthropic work.
The first report cannot be supplied.

M6125 — Social service. Periodicals.

NN   0055132   MB

HV89
.N3
National information bureau, inc., New York.
... Bulletin ... no.
New York, [19

NN   0055133   DLC ICJ

National Information Bureau, inc., *New York.*
Giver's guide to national philanthropies.

₍New York₎
v. 21 cm.

1. Charities—U. S.—Direct.   ɪ. Title.

HV89.N32   360.58   53-36144 ‡

NN   0055134   DLC NN NNC TxU

F877
.1
N3
National Information Bureau, inc., New York.
Oregon & California Railroad grant lands.   Stop, look and
listen, watch out for your constituents.   [Washington? 1916?]
16 p. illus. 24cm.

Cover title.

1. Railroad land grants - Oregon.   2. Oregon and California
Railroad Company.   I. Title.

NN   0055135   CU-B

National information bureau, *New York.*
... Report.
₍New York₎
v. 22½ x 9½ᶜᵐ.
At head of title   : National information bureau.

CA 24-347 Unrev'd

Library of Congress   HV88.N69

NN   0055136   DLC DL NN OCl

National Information Bureau, Inc., New York.
Report of a study of the interrelation of the
work of national social agencies in fourteen
American communities ...
see under   Lee, Porter Raymond, 1879-1946

National information bureau, inc., *New York.   Commission*
on Russian relief.
The Russian famines, 1921-22, 1922-23; summary report,
Commission on Russian relief of the National information
bureau, inc.   New York ₍1923₎
40 p. maps (1 fold.) 23ᶜᵐ.
Signed: Allen Wardwell, Graham R. Taylor, Allen T. Burns, Commission on Russian relief.

1. Russia—Famines.   2. Russia—Econ. condit.—1918-   ɪ. Wardwell, Allen.   ɪɪ. Title.   23-8683
Library of Congress   HC335.N4

NN   0055138   DLC OrU NcD CtY PHC NNC OU NN

National Information Bureau directory ...
1
Indianapolis: National Information Bureau   8°.

1. Information bureaus.
N. Y. P. L.   December 10, 1915.

NN   0055139   NN

621.321   **National Information Committee on Lighting.**
N213l   Lighting and the nation's welfare.
₍Cleveland, O., 1951?₎
24p. 23cm.

1. Lighting.   I. Title.

NN   0055140   IU

National inheritance tax conference
see
National conference on inheritance and estate
taxation.

National inland waterways
see   National waterways; the magazine of
transportation ... Pittsburgh, 1919-

National Instalment Credit Conference.
Proceedings.
New York, Instalment Credit Committee, American Bankers
Association.
v. illus. 23 cm. annual.
First conference held in 1941.
Vols. for   issued by the committee under its earlier
name: Instalment Credit Commission.

1. Instalment plan—U. S.—Congresses.   ɪ. American Bankers
Association. Instalment Credit Committee.

HF5568.A58   57-36831 rev

NN   0055143   DLC MH NcU OU

National Institute for Agricultural Quality Research
see
Hungary. *Országos Mezőgazdasági Minőségvizsgáló Inté-*
zet.

National Institute for Architectural Education.
Annual report ...
see its   Report.

National Institute for Architectural Education.
Bulletin. v. 1-   Oct. 1924-
₍New York₎
v. in   illus., plans. 29 cm.
Frequency varies.
Issues for Oct. 1924-   1956 published by the organization
under its earlier name: Beaux-Arts Institute of Design.

1. Architecture — Societies, etc. 2. Architecture — Designs and
plans. 3. Architecture—Composition, proportions, etc. 4. Architectural drawing. 5. Decoration and ornament, Architectural. 6. Architecture—Competitions.

NA2300.N47   32-4807 rev

          OOxM ICRL ViU IC NIC ArU TxLT ICA NNC ViB1bV MtU
NN   0055146   DLC MiU PSt CoU MB KyU IU CSt NCsC NN

National Institute for Architectural Education.
Circular of information ...
19
₍New York, 19   4°.
no.

1. New York (city)—Art education.   2. Architecture—Education—U. S.
—N. Y.—New York.
N. Y. P. L.   September 20, 1929

NN   0055147   NN CU MB

NA2340   **National Institute for Architectural Education.**
N35   Circular of information, 1954-1955. Committee on architec-
Arch.   ture, Beaux-Arts Institute of Design, Lloyd Warren scholarship,
Library 42nd Paris prize in architecture.   [New York, The Institute,
1954]
14 p. plate

Cover title.

1. Architecture - Competitions.

NN   0055148   CU

VOLUME 407

National Institute for Architectural Education.
Class "B" V projet: "An island memorial". Class "A" V esquisse-esquisse: "A brewery". Class "A" V projet: "A community of low cost dwellings". Interior design VI: "A pent-house suite". New York, Beaux-arts institute of design, 1934.
22p. illus. 31cm. (In its Bulletin vol. X, no.10. August 1934)

NN   0055149   NNU-W

National Institute for Architectural Education.
A library and office building; a student competition conducted by Beaux-Arts Institute of Design. ₁New York, 1950₃
1 v. (unpaged) diagrs., photos., plans.

Cover title.
Prizes sponsored by Snead & Company, Orange, Va.

NN   0055150   MiD

National Institute for Architectural Education.
Meeting of the patrons of the ateliers with the trustees of the Beaux-arts Institute of Design, held at the Century Club, New York, N. Y., March 29, 1927. ₑNew York, 1927₃
53 l. 28cm.

1. Architecture - Study and teaching - U. S.

NN   0055151   NNC-A

National Institute for Architectural Education.
A memorial to Benjamin Franklin.
From the American architect and the Architectural review, v. 126, p. 461-463, Nov. 5, 1924.
Announcement of awards for a plan for a memorial to Benjamin Franklin to be erected by the city of Philadelphia.

NN   0055152   CtY

National Institute for Architectural Education.
₁Prospectus, charter, constitution, etc.₁
l
₁New York, 1   8°.
no.

1. New York City.—Art education.
N. Y. P. L.   March 10, 1922.

NN   0055153   NN

National Institute for Architectural Education.
Report.
₁New York₁
v. 27cm. annual.

Reports for   issued by the organization under its earlier name: Beaux-Arts Institute of Design.
Issues for   include also reports of the Society of Beaux-Arts Architects and the Société des architectes diplômés par le Gouvernement français, Groupe américaine.

1. Society of Beaux-Arts Architects, New York. II. Société des architectes diplômés par le Gouvernement. Groupe américaine.

NA2300.N473   44-17843 rev

NN   0055154   DLC NN NNC PP FMU

National Institute for Architectural Education.
27th Paris prize in architecture, Society of Beaux-arts architects: "An international athletic centre." New York, Beaux-arts institute of design, 1934.
p. 3-35. illus. 31cm. (In its Bulletin. vol. X, no.11. Sept.1934)

NN   0055155   NNU-W

National Institute for Architectural Education.
Year book of the Society of beaux-arts architects ... and of the Beaux-arts institute of design ... 19
New York city ₁19
v. illus., plates. 30½ᶜᵐ.
List of members in each volume.
Title varies.

1. New York. Beaux-arts institute of design. II. Title.

Library of Congress   NA11.86   c.a. 31-395 Unrev'd
                                   ₂₁

NN   0055156   DLC

National institute for commercial and trade organization executives.
Chamber of commerce administration; a text book prepared for use at the National school for commercial and trade organization executives, conducted under the auspices of Chamber of commerce of the United States, National association of commercial organization secretaries, American trade association executives, Northwestern university. 1927 ed. ₁Chicago, °1927₁
2 p. l., 303 p. diagrs. 23½ᶜᵐ.
"Publications": p. 300-303.
1. Boards of trade. I. Chamber of commerce of the United States of America. II. National association of commercial organization secretaries. III. American trade association executives. IV. Northwestern university, Evanston, Ill.   v. Title.
Library of Congress   HF294.N33 1927   27-15399 Revised
——— Copy 2.
Copyright A 909048   ₁31d2₁   381

NN   0055157   DLC OrCS WaS

National institute for commercial and trade organization executives.
Chamber of commerce administration; a textbook published by and for the National institute for commercial and trade organization executives ... conducted under the auspices of Chamber of commerce of the United States, National association of commercial organization secretaries, American trade association executives ₁and₁ Northwestern university ... Chicago, Ill., 1942.
x, 278 p. incl. diagr., forms. port. 23½ᶜᵐ.

"Revised edition ... by Marvin Hurley ... completed under supervision of Textbook advisory committee; D. Hodson Lewis, chairman."

1. Boards of trade. I. Chamber of commerce of the United States of America. II. National association of commercial organization secretaries. III. American trade association executives. IV. Northwestern university, Evanston, Ill.   v. Hurley, Marvin. VI. Lewis, D. Hodson. VII. Title.
Library of Congress   HF294.N33 1942   42-25738
                                   ₃₁   381

NN   0055159   DLC OkU ICJ OU CoU

National Institute for Commercial and Trade Organization Executives.
Chamber of Commerce administration, a textbook edited by S. G. Wennberg. 2d rev. ₁i. e. 3d₁ ed. ₁Chicago₁ 1951.
322 p. port. 24 cm.

1. Boards of trade. I. Wennberg, S. G., ed. II. Title.

HF294.N33 195'   381   51-2880

NN   0055160   DLC TxU CoU

NATIONAL INSTITUTE FOR COMMERCIAL AND TRADE ORGANIZATION EXECUTIVES.
Membership cases, National Institute for Commercial and Trade Organization Executives. Northwestern University, Evanston, Illinois, August 13-19,1939. [Evanston?,1939.]
Manifold copy. ff.11.
By Philip P.Gott.

Membership cases,references,procedures adopted,results obtained,suggestions;National

Institute for Commercial and Trade Organization Executives. Northwestern University,Evanston, Illinois,August 13-19,1939. [Evanston?,1939.]
Manifold copy. ff.11.
By Philip P.Gott.

NN   0055162   MH

National institute for commercial and trade organization executives.
... Series of text books on chamber of commerce administration prepared for the second National school for commercial secretaries, August 21 to September 2, 1922, at Northwestern university, Evanston, Illinois. ₁Chicago₁ National school for commercial secretaries, °1922.
10 v. diagrs. 23ᶜᵐ.
"Auspices Chamber of commerce of the United States, National association of commercial organization secretaries, Northwestern university."
CONTENTS.—I. The structure or organization of a chamber of commerce, by J. A. McKibben.—II. Program of work.—III. Meetings, their

purposes, objectives and procedure, the "how it is done" in chamber of commerce work, original text by J. M. Guild, revised by J. T. Daniels.—IV. Chamber of commerce membership.—V. Organization finances for chambers of commerce, by J. D. Larson.—VI. Publicity, by R. H. Faxon.—VII. Office organization for chambers of commerce, by S. C. Mead in collaboration with F. D. E. Babcock and G. W. Lemon.—VIII. Commercial activities of chambers of commerce.—IX. Industrial activities of chambers of commerce, by W. R. Jackson. References (p. 20)—X. Civic activities of a chamber of commerce. References (p. 24-28)
1. Boards of trade. I. Chamber of commerce of the United States of America. II. National association of commercial organization secretaries. III. Northwestern   university, Evanston, Ill.
Library of Congress   HF294.N35   31-23512
Copyright A 685106-   685115   381

NN   0055164   DLC

HF294 NATIONAL INSTITUTE FOR COMMERCIAL AND TRADE ORGAN-
.N3   IZATION EXECUTIVES.
            ...Series of text books on chamber of commerce administration prepared for the sixth National school for commercial and trade organization executives... ₁Chicago?c1926₃
            10 v.in 1.
            "1926 edition."

NN   0055165   ICU

National institute for commercial and trade organization executives.
Trade association management; a text book prepared for use at the National institute for commercial and trade organization executives, conducted under the auspices of Chamber of commerce of the United States, National association of commercial organization secretaries, American trade association executives, Northwestern university. 1930 ed. ₁Chicago, °1930₁
3 p. l., 187 p. illus. 23½ᶜᵐ.
1. Trade and professional associations. I. Chamber of commerce of the United States of America. II. National association of commercial organization secretaries. III. American trade association executives. IV. Northwestern univer-   sity, Evanston, Ill. v. Title.
Library of Congress   HD2421.N25 1930   31-12219
Copyright A 36807   ₁4₁   650.62

NN   0055166   DLC OrU WaS CoU GU MB MiU OC1 OC1W ICJ

L381.06
N2771.2 National Institute for Commercial and Trade
            Organization Executives.
            Trade association management; text book prepared in temporary for the use of students at the 1947 session. Editor: Delbert J. Duncan. Chicago, 1947.
            v,202p. tables. 26cm.

            1. Trade and professional associations. I. Duncan, Delbert J   II. Title.

NN   0055167   IEN

National Institute for Commercial and Trade Organization Executives.
Trade association management; textbook for trade association management curriculum. Editor: Delbert J. Duncan; assistant editors: Paul H. Sullivan ₁and₁ Minita Westcott. Rev. ed. ₁Chicago, 1948₁
ix, 190 p. 24 cm.

1. Trade and professional associations. I. Duncan, Delbert J., ed. II. Title.
HD2421.N25 1948'   650.62   48-4488*

      Mi
NN   0055168   DLC IEN WaE FMU CoU OU ICU TxU PP PPT

National Institute for Compilation and Translation, Tʻai-pei
see
Kuo li pien i kuan, Tʻai-pei.

VOLUME 407

National Institute for Education in Law and
Poverty.
Clearinghouse review.

Chicago.
v. 28cm. monthly.

NN 0055170   IU DLC

National Institute for Educational Research, *Tokyo*
see
Kokuritsu Kyōiku Kenkyūjo, *Tokyo*.

JK717
.C54S28

National Institute for Home Study, *New York*.
Clerk - grade 2, New York City. 1942 N.Y.C.
clerk exam and answer keys, complete summary
of municipal gov't., clerical aptitude test ...
₍New York, °1947₎
55 ℓ.

NN 0055172   MiD NFQC

National Institute for Home Study, *New York*.
Clerk - grades 3, 4, 5. New York City.
Two previous promotion exams and answer keys,
intensive review of municipal government, administrative and supervisory problems ...
₍New York, °1947₎
55 ℓ.

NN 0055173   MiD

JK717
.C54S28

National Institute for Home Study, New York.
Schwartz, William Harold, 1916–
Federal clerk (CAF 1–4) A carefully compiled civil serv-
ice course book designed to provide the applicant with the
materials essential to adequate preparation for these grades.
New York, National Institute for Home Study, °1948.

JK716
.S3

National Institute for Home Study, New York.
Schwartz, William Harold, 1916–
Investigator manual, a carefully compiled civil service
course book designed to provide the applicant with the
materials essential to adequate preparation for this exam.
New York, National Institute for Home Study, °1948.

Z665
.C56

National Institute for Home Study, New York.
Church, Eleanor Bradford, 1910–
Librarian, a carefully compiled civil service course book
designed to provide the applicant with the materials essential
for adequate preparation for this exam. New York, National Institute for Home Study, °1948.

TL152
S4

National Institute for Home Study, New York.
Schwartz, William Harold, 1916–
Motor vehicle license examiner, a carefully compiled civil
service course book designed to provide the applicant with
the materials essential to adequate preparation for this exam.
New York, National Institute for Home Study, °1948.

National Institute for Home Study, New York.
Schwartz, William Harold, 1916–
Office appliance operator, a carefully compiled civil service
course book designed to provide the applicant with the mate-
rials essential to adequate preparation for this exam. New
York, National Institute for Home Study, °1948.

HE6499
.S35

National Institute for Home Study, New York.
Schwartz, William Harold, 1916–
Post Office clerk, postal carrier, railway mail clerk; a
carefully compiled civil service course book designed to provide the applicant with the materials essential to adequate
preparation for this exam. New York, National Institute
for Home Study, °1948.

HV9278
.S35

National Institute for Home Study, New York.
Schwartz, William Harold, 1916–
Probation officer, a carefully compiled civil service course
book designed to provide the applicant with the materials
essential to adequate preparation for this exam. New York,
National Institute for Home Study, °1948.

JK717
.C54S3

National Institute for Home Study, New York.
Schwartz, William Harold, 1916–
U. S. typist-stenographer (CAF 2–3) A carefully compiled civil service course book designed to provide the applicant with the materials essential to adequate preparation for
this exam. New York, National Institute for Home Study,
°1948.

National Institute for Medical Research, London
   see   London. National Institute for Medical
Research.

National Institute for Moral Education
see
Character Education Institution, *Washington, D. C.*

National Institute for Occupational Safety and Health.
Division of Training.
Course announcement.
₍Cincinnati, Ohio₎
v. illus. 23 cm.
Period covered by announcement ends June 30.

1. Industrial hygiene—Study and teaching—United States. 2. In-
dustrial safety—Study and teaching—United States.
HD7654.N33a   614.8'52   74–641933
ISSN 0093–5093   MARC-S

NN 0055184   DLC

National Institute for Occupational Safety and Hygiene
see
ha-Mosad li-vetiḥut ule-gehut.

National Institute for Personnel Research.
Journal. Tydskrif
   see   Psychologia Africana.

HF5548
.8
.P76

National Institute for Personnel Research.
Psychologia Africana.
Johannesburg, National Institute for Personnel Research.

National institute for research in dairying, *Shinfield,
Eng.*
see
Reading, Eng. University. *National institute for research in
dairying, Shinfield.*

National Institute for Research in Nuclear Science, *Harwell, Eng.*
   see
Harwell, Eng. National Institute for Research in Nuclear Science.

National Institute for Social Work Training
     see   London. National Institute for Social
Work Training.

National Institute for the Blind
see
Royal National Institute for the Blind.

National Institute for the Deaf, London.
All about the deaf; how the deaf are helped and how they
may help themselves; a handbook of information on deafness, the
deaf and dumb and the deafened by disease. A revised edition of
The problem of the deaf, 1929; compiled and published by the
National Institute for the Deaf... London: Printed by Han-
bury, Tomsett & Co., Ltd.₍, 1934?₎   xiv, 122 p. incl. diagr., tables.
21cm.

731007A. 1. Deaf—Gt. Br.
N. Y. P. L.   October 30, 1934

NN 0055192   NN

National institute for the deaf, *London*.
All about the deaf: how the deaf are helped and how they
may help themselves; a handbook of information on deafness,
the deaf and dumb and the deafened by disease ... Compiled
and published by the National institute for the deaf ... London. ₍London, 1939₎
vl, 125, vii–xx p. 21ᶜᵐ.
"First issued as The problem of the deaf in 1929 ... Revised edition
1939."
"Publications": p. 122–125.
1. Deaf. 2. Deaf—Education and institutions—Gt. Brit.   ɪ. Title.
                                       46–36784
Library of Congress   HV2380.N35 1939
                      ₍2₎   362.4

NN 0055193   DLC DNLM

NATIONAL INSTITUTE FOR THE DEAF, London.
...Annual report of the executive committee.
     see its   Report of the executive committee ...

National Institute for the deaf, London.
Love, James Kerr, 1858–
The causes and prevention of deafness. Four lectures
delivered under the auspices of the National bureau for
promoting the general welfare of the deaf, by J. Kerr
Love ... London ₍Wayre & son, ltd., printers, 1913₎

WV
1
qN277

NATIONAL Institute for the Deaf, London
₍Collection of publications₎

The library has a collection of miscellaneous publications of this organization
kept as received. These publications are
not listed nor bound separately.
1. Deaf

NN 0055196   DNLM

VOLUME 407

National institute for the deaf, *London.*
The deaf; handbook containing information relating to
statistics, and schools, missions, hospitals, charities, and
other institutions for the deaf, compiled by the National
bureau for promoting the general welfare of the deaf ...
London. ₍London₎ Pub. for the Bureau by P. S. King &
son, 1913.

viii, 75 p. 21½ cm.

"Periodicals": p. 47.

1. Deaf—Education and institutions—Gt. Brit.

HV2716.N35   E 14–420 rev

U. S. Office of Education,   Library
for Library of Congress   ₍r49b1₎†

NN 0055197   DHEW ICJ DLC

617.8   National institute for the deaf,
N27p   London
...The prevention of deafness...
London, National institute for the
deaf ₍1934₎
cover-title, 16p. O. (N.I.D. booklets,
no.1)

Contributions: J. Kerr Love and A.G. Wells.

NN 0055198   IaU

National Institute for the Deaf, London.
The problem of the deaf; a handbook of information on deafness, the deaf and dumb, and the deafened through disease or
accident. Revised edition. Compiled by the National Institute
for the Deaf...   London: Printed by W. H. Taylor & Sons,
1929.   x, 96 p.   illus. (chart.)   21cm.

Cover imprint: London, Published by the National Institute for the Deaf.

81½18A. 1. Deaf.
N. Y. P. L.
                                            May 6, 1936

NN 0055199   NN OC1

National Institute for the Deaf, *London.*
Report of the executive committee to the council.
₍London₎
v. 22 cm.

Reports for the years ended Mar. 31, 1940, 1941, 1942 and the
period Apr. 1 to Dec. 31, 1942, were issued together.

HV2714.N3   371.912   48–44071*‡

NN 0055200   DLC NN DL

National Institute for the Deaf, London.
HV2350
.S62   The Silent world.
London.

**National Institute for the Promotion
of Science,** Washington, D.C.
Woodbury, Levi, 1789–1851.
The annual address delivered before the National institute in the hall of the House of representatives, January 15, 1845, by Levi Woodbury. Washington, J. & G. S.
Gideon, printers, 1845.

National institute for the promotion of science, *Washington,
D. C.*
Bulletin of the proceedings of the National institution for
the promotion of science. ₍vol. I, no. 1–4; 1840/41–1845/46₎
Washington, 1841–₍46₎.

1 v. pl., tab. 23ᶜᵐ.

For continuation see its Proceedings.
No. 3 of the Bulletin has half-title: Third bulletin of the proceedings
of the National institute for the promotion of science ...; no. 4: Fourth
bulletin of the National institute for the promotion of science ...

1. Natural history—Societies. 2. U. S.—Learned institutions and
societies. 3. Washington, D. C.—Learned institutions and societies.

Library of Congress   Q11.S61   2—17653

NN NcD DNLM DSI
NN 0055203   DLC OC1W DI–GS KyU NcRS MWA CSmH ICJ

National institute for the promotion of science,
Washington, D.C.
₍Circulars and papers₎
₍Washington, D.C., 18

Q11
.S638

NN 0055204   DLC

National institute for the promotion of science, *Washington,
D. C.*
Constitution and by-laws of the National institution for the
promotion of science, established at Washington, May, 1840.
Washington, Printed by Gales and Seaton, 1840.

14 p. 22½ᶜᵐ.

                                            2—17648

Library of Congress   Q11.S632 1840

NcD
NN 0055205   DLC MWA OKentU AU DeU Nh RPJCB OC1WHi

National institute for the promotion of science, *Washington, D. C.*
Constitution and by-laws of the National institute for
the promotion of science. Printed by order of the institute. Washington, J. and G. S. Gideon, printers, 1849.

18 p. 22ᶜᵐ.

                                            2–17649

Library of Congress, ₍etc.₎   Q11.S632.

NN 0055206   DLC OC1WHi OC1

National institute for the promotion of science, *Washington, D. C.*
Constitution of the National institution for the promotion of
science, established at Washington, May, 1840. Amended and
ordered to be printed, April, 1841. Washington, Printed by
P. Force, 1841.
19 p. 23ᶜᵐ.
"Officers and members": p. ₍7₎–19.
                                  Q11.S63
—————— Another issue. Washington, Printed by P. Force,
1841.
19 p. 23ᶜᵐ.
List of members differs slightly from that in preceding issue.
                                            2–18050–1 Revised
Library of Congress   Q11.S631

NN 0055207   DLC DNLM

National institute for the promotion of
science, Washington, D. C.
King, H₍enry₎ *M. D.*
Directions for making collections in natural history.
Prepared for the National institution for the promotion
of science, by H. King, M. D. Washington, Printed by
Gales and Seaton, 1840.

National Institute for the Promotion of Science
Washington, D.C.
Discourse on the objects and importance of
the national institution for the promotion of
science, established at Washington, 1840.
    see under   Poinsett, Joel Roberts,
1779–1851.

National Institute for the Promotion of Science.
Drafts of Letters, written by Francis Markoe,
Junior, Corresponding Secretary.
August 1840 to May 6, 1843.
One quarto volume, mss

NN 0055210   DSI

National Institute for the Promotion of Science,
Washington, D.C.
Extracts from the discourse of J.R.
Poinsett ...
    see under   Poinsett, Joel Roberts,
1779–1851.

National Institute for the Promotion of Science,
Washington, D.C.
Extracts from the proceedings of the National
institute for the promotion of science. At a
stated meeting of the National institute, held on
the 13th June, 1842, the Honorable John C. Spencer,
secretary of war, and one of the directors of the
National institute ... submitted the following
resolution ... ₍Washington, 1842₎

3 p.   25.5cm.

Concerns plans   for raising funds and

promoting the interests of science through the
Institute.
    Addressed on blank page at end to Honorable
Judge Story, Cambridge, Mass., from Col. John J. Abert
of the Bureau of Topographical Engineers.
    From the Story Papers, Manuscript Division.

NN 0055213   MiU–C

National institute for the promotion of science, *Washington, D. C.*
₍Form for announcement of election to membership,
accompanied by constitution and by-laws. Washington,
1842?₎
₍3₎ p. 32ᶜᵐ.
Caption: National institute for the promotion of science. Founded at
Washington, May, 1840. Incorporated by Congress, July, 1842.

                                  CA 17–3860 Unrev'd
Library of Congress   Q11.S632 1842

NN 0055214   DLC

National Institute for the Promotion of Science,
Washington, D.C.
Introductory address of the Hon. R.J. Walker
of Mississippi, delivered before the National
institute at its April meeting, 1844
    see under   Walker, Robert James,
1801–1869.

National Institute for the Promotion of Science.
Journal of Proceedings, May 7, 1840 to March
17, 1856. 3 vol. By Recording Secretaries,
Pishey Thompson, Garret Barry, and John
Townshend.
V.I, May 7, 1840 to Sept. 12, 1852; 357 pp
V.II, Oct. 10, 1842 to Dec. 17, 1849; 445 pp
V.III, May 21, 1849 to Mar. 17, 1856.
V.III are mostly rough minutes.
Being a mss record of its constitution, minutes,

resolutions, accessions, list of members
(resident and corresponding) and proceedings
of the ordinary, special, stated and adjourned
meetings.
24 x 21 x 4 cm.

NN 0055217   DSI

National Institute for the Promotion of Science.
Letters to the National Institute. Francis
Markoe, Jr., Corresponding Secretary. Washington,
1839 to 1845. 10 vol. mss. quarto V.I, to Apr. 21,
1841; V.II, Apr.22, 1841 to May 6, 1842; V.III,
Apr.22, 1841 to July 31, 1842; V.IV, Aug. 1, 1842
to Dec. 31, 1842; V.V, Jan. 5, 1843 to June 30,
1843; V.V, June 1, 1839 to Dec. 17, 1843; V.VI,
July 1, 1843 to Dec. 30, 1843; V.VII, Jan. 1,
1844 to Apr. 30, 1844; V.VIII, May 1, 1844 to

Continued in next column

VOLUME 407

Continued from preceding column

to Dec. 30, 1844; V.IX, Jan. 6, 1845 to Dec. 31,
1845.
Contains, besides correspondence relating to the
National Institute for the Promotion of Science,
many papers read before the National Inst. including those read at the scientific congress of Apr.
1844.

NN 0055219 DSI

National institute for the promotion of
science, Washington, D. C.
(Miscellaneous publications)
1841-(45)

NN 0055220 DI-GS

National Institute for the Promotion of Science,
Washington, D. C.
Totten, Joseph Gilbert, 1788-1863.
List of a cabinet of minerals presented to the National
institution in the city of Washington, by Col. Joseph G.
Totten ... [Washington, 1842?]

National Institute for the Promotion of Science,
Washington, D.C.
National institute. [Its early growth, and
History. Army and Science navy chronicle,
Feb. 8, and March 7, 1844. Also, Third circular
of the committee, dated April, 1844]

NN 0055222 MB

National institute for the promotion of science. *Wash-
ington, D. C.*
... National institute. Memorial of a committee of the
National institute, soliciting the aid of Congress in its be-
half. [Washington, Blair & Rives, print., 1845]
8 p. 24ᶜᵐ. ([U. S.] 28th Cong. 2d sess. House. Doc. no. 88)
February 3, 1845. Referred to a select committee, consisting of Messrs.
Barnard, Burt, Owen, H. Hamlin, and Marsh.

i. U. S. 28th Cong., 2d sess., 1844-1845. House.

Library of Congress Q11.S64N2

4-28277†

NN 0055223 DLC

NATIONAL INSTITUTE FOR THE PROMOTION OF SCIENCE,
WASHINGTON, D. C.
[Gibbes, Robert Wilson] 1809-1866.
National institute. [Review of first, second and third
Bulletins of the National institute, and of the address of
J. R. Poinsett, Jan. 4, 1841, and of Levi Woodbury, Jan.
15, 1845. Columbia, S. C., 1845]

National Institute for the Promotion of Science,
Washington, D.C.
National Institute. The Committee of the National Institute,...appointed to make arrangements for
the April meeting of the friends and members of
the Institute ... the following resolutions were
adopted ... Peter Force, vice-president. Francis
Markoe, Jr., corresponding secretary. Washington,
July 12, 1844. [Washington, 1844]
broadside, 25½ x 20½cm.

NN 0055225 MHi

National Institute for the Promotion of Science,
Washington, D.C.
[Ingersoll, Joseph Reed] 1786-1868.
National institute [Washington, D. C.] [New York,
1845]

National institute for the promotion of science, *Washington, D. C.*
Papers relative to the National institute, collected and
arranged by Francis Markoe, jr., corresponding secretary. v. 1. [Washington? D. C., 18—]
15 pamphlets in 1 v. 22½ᶜᵐ.
CONTENTS.—1. Constitution, with list of officers and members. April,
1841.—2. First bulletin. June to December, 1840. —3. Second bulletin.
March, 1841, to December, 1842.—4. Third bulletin. February, 1842, to
February, 1845.—5. Fourth bulletin. February, 1845 to November, 1846.—
6. Annual address, by Hon. Joel R. Poinsett. January 4, 1841.—7. Annual
address, by Hon. Levi Woodbury. January 15, 1845.—8. Review of third
Bulletin and Mr. Woodbury's address. By Hon. Jos. R. Ingersoll. Col-
ton's Whig review, September, 1845.—9. Review of first, second, and third
Bulletins, and of Mr. Poinsett's and Mr. Woodbury's addresses. Southern
quarterly review, October, 1845.—10. Memorial to Congress, soliciting aid
in behalf of the Institute. February 3, 1845.—11. Report of the Library
committee of the House of representatives on the above memorial. June
7, 1845.—12. Mr. Tappan's report to the Senate, on the National institute
and exploring expedition. February 28, 1843.—13. Reply of Col. Abert and
Mr. Markoe to Mr. Tappan. April 20, 1843.—14. Letters on the National
institute. Smithsonian legacy, the fine arts, and other matters. By John
Carroll Brent. June 1, 1844.—15. Directions for making collections in natural history. Prepared for the members of the National institution for
the promotion of science,   by H. King, M. D. 1840.
i. Markoe, Francis.

         CA 9-329 Unrev'd

Library of Congress Q11.S625

NN 0055228 DLC

Q
11
.S636
1854
  National institute for the promotion of
  science, Wasington, D. C.
  A popular catalogue of the
extraordinary curiosities in the
National institute, arranged in the
building belonging to the Patent
office. Curiosities collected from all
parts of the world, by the officers of
the army and navy of the United States.
Washington, A. Hunter, [1854]
 37 p. 22 cm.
 Prepared by Alfred Hunter.
 Cover-title: A catalogue of the
extraordinary curiosities of the
National institute ... also, a
catalogue of the botanical plants, to
be seen in th e government
conservatorie s...

NN 0055229 OKentU

National institute for the promotion of science, *Washington, D. C.*
A popular catalogue of the extraordinary curiosities in
the National institute, arranged in the building belonging to
the Patent office. Curiosities collected from all parts of the
world, by the officers of the Army and Navy of the United
States ... Washington, A. Hunter, 1855.
viii, [9]-72 p. 21½ cm.
Prepared by Alfred Hunter.
Cover-title: A catalogue of the extraordinary curiosities of the National institute ... also, a catalogue of the botanical plants, to be
seen in the government conservatories ...
i. Title.

Q11.S636 1855   4—23770

NN 0055230 DLC MWA DSI CSmH NjP NN ICRL

National institute for the promotion of science, *Washing-
ton, D. C.*
A popular catalogue of the extraordinary curiosities in the
National institute, arranged in the building belonging to the
Patent office. Curiosities collected from all parts of the
world, by the officers of the army and navy of the United
States ... 2d ed. Washington, A. Hunter, 1855.
viii, [9]-70 p. fold. plan. 22ᶜᵐ.
Prepared by Alfred Hunter.
Cover-title: A popular catalogue ... 6th ed. Improved with a dia-
gram of the floor of the great hall. Washington, 1856.
"A catalogue of plants in the National conservatories": p. 64-70.
i. Hunter, Alfred. ii. Title.

        4-23771

Library of Congress Q11.S636 1855 a

NN 0055231 DLC MH DSI PPAN

National institute for the promotion of science, *Washing-
ton, D. C.*
A popular catalogue of the extraordinary curiosities in the
National institute, arranged in the building belonging to the
Patent office. Curiosities collected from all parts of the
world, by the officers of the army and navy of the United
States ... 2d ed. Washington, A. Hunter, 1857.
viii, [9]-71 p. 20½ᶜᵐ.
Prepared by Alfred Hunter.
"A catalogue of plants in the National conservatories": p. 64-71.
i. Hunter, Alfred. ii. Title.

        4—23772

Library of Congress Q11.S636 1857

NN 0055232 DLC OKentU

National institute for the promotion of science, *Washington,
D. C.*
A popular catalogue of the extraordinary curiosities in the
National institute, arranged in the building belonging to the
Patent office. Curiosities collected from all parts of the world,
by the officers of the army and navy of the United States ...
2d ed. Washington, A. Hunter, 1857.
vii, [8]-71 p. 1 illus. 22½ᶜᵐ.
Pages iv and vi wrongly imposed.
Prepared by Alfred Hunter.
"A catalogue of plants in the National conservatories": p. 64-71.
i. Hunter, Alfred. ii. Title.

        30-17249

Library of Congress Q11.S636 1857 a

NN 0055233 DLC

National Institute for the Promotion of Science,
71718   *Washington, D. C.*
Proceedings of the National Institute for the Promotion of Science.
.... [Washington, 1842-1855.]
No. 2-3, new series, vol. i, no. i; March 1841–Feb. 1845, Jan. 1855. plates. 24ᶜᵐ.
No. 2 title reads: Second bulletin of the proceedings of the National Institution for
the Promotion of Science; no. 3, Third bulletin of the proceedings of the National Insti-
tute for the Promotion of Science.
Published irregularly.

NN 0055234 ICJ DLC NWM

National institute for the promotion of science, *Washington, D. C.*
Proceedings of the National institute, Washington,
D. C. new ser., v. 1, no. 1-3 [Jan. 1855-Jan. 1857] [Wash-
ington, 1855-57]
3 no. in 1 v. illus., pl. 24ᶜᵐ.
Cover-title.
The three numbers have signature dates as follows: no. 1, March, 1855;
no. 2, March, 1856; no. 3, May, 1857.
Designated "new series" in continuation of the Bulletin of the proceedings of the National institution for the promotion of science, v. 1,
nos. 1-4, 1840/41-1845/46.
No more published.
1. Science—Societies.

        17-30513

Library of Congress Q11.S62

NN 0055235 DLC DNLM NcD

National institute for the promotion of science, *Washington, D. C.*
Report of the recording secretary of the National institute for the year 1850. Rendered December 2, 1850.
Ordered to be printed for the use of the institute. Washington, Printed by R. A. Waters, 1850.
10 p. 23ᶜᵐ.   2-17639

Library of Congress, no. Q11.S634'

NN 0055236 DLC

National Institute for the Promotion of Science,
Washington, D.C. National gallery
  see Washington, D.C. National gallery.

National Institute news bulletin
  see under National institute of arts and
letters.

National institute of accountancy, *Chicago.*
Business and professional accountancy; an interesting
booklet describing the National institute business and
professional accountancy course and service. Chicago,
National institute of accountancy, inc. (formerly a department of Blackstone institute) [*1923]
50 p. plates. 19½ᶜᵐ.

1. Accounting. i. Title: Accountancy, Business and professional.

        CA 23-433 Unrev'd
Library of Congress HF5630.N3

NN 0055239 DLC

VOLUME 407

National Institute of Adult Education.

LC5201
.A35

Adult education. v. 1–   Sept. 1926–
London.

National Institute of Adult Education.
Adult education in Great Britain and the United
States of America
          see under   British Institute of Adult
Education.

National Institute of Adult Education.
Adult education in the United Kingdom; a directory of
organisations. ₍Rev. ed.₎ London ₍1952₎
     64 p. 22 cm.
     Cover title.

     1. Education of adults. 2. Education—Gt. Brit.—Direct.   ɪ. Title.

     L915.N38 1952   374.942   52–68217

NN   0055242   DLC NN

National Institute of Adult Education.

Z5814
.A21G8

Guide to studies in adult education. 1951–
London, National Institute of Adult Education.

National Institute of Adult Education.
Liberal education in a technical age; a survey of the relationship of vocational and non-vocational **further education**
and training. London, M. Parrish ₍1955₎
     128 p. tables. 22 cm.
     Bibliographical footnotes.

     1. Education, Humanistic. 2. Education of adults.   ɪ. Title.

     LC1011.N35   374   55–57447

CaBVaU Or
NN   0055244   DLC CaBViP CaBVa WaU ICU CU CtY LU IU

National Institute of Adult Education.
A select bibliography of adult education in
Great Britain

     see under

Kelly, Thomas, 1909–

LC5256
.G7N3

National Institute of Adult Education.
Social aspects of further education;
a survey of local education authority
action. London, 1952.
55p. 22cm.

NN   0055246   NNU-W

National Institute of Adult Education
see also British Institute of Adult Education.

59
N21D

                         Cambridge, Eng.
National Institute of Agricultural Botany.
Detailed descriptions of varieties of
wheat, barley and oats.   Cambridge
₍1954₎
1 v. (loose-leaf)

Kept up to date by revised and supplementary sheets.

     1. Wheat. Varieties. 2. Barley. . . .
Varieties.   3. Oats. Varieties.

NN   0055248   DNAL

SB
4
N271

National Institute of Agricultural Botany,
     Cambridge.
Farmers' leaflet no.1–
₍Cambridge₎ 1931–
     nos. 23 cm.

     1. Field crops.

NN   0055249   NIC NN IU

75.9
N216G

National Institute of Agricultural Botany.
Guide to plots of potatoes on headquarters
trialground.
Cambridge.

     1. Potatoes. Research.

NN   0055250   DNAL

SB
185
Z99
no. 8

National Institute of Agricultural Botany,
     Cambridge, England.
Guide to varieties of field and vegetable
crops under trial, observation and
propagation.   Cambridge, National
Institute of Agricultural Botany, 1952.
67 p.

     1. Field crops - Varieties. 2. Vege-
tables - Varieties. 3. Field crops.
4. Vegetables.   ɪ. Title.

NN   0055251   NIC IU

630.14
N21g
1955

National Institute of Agricultural Botany, Cam-
     bridge, Eng.
Guide to varieties of field and vegetable crops
under trial, observation and propagation.
Cambridge ₍Eng.₎ 1955.
79p. illus., tables. 24cm.

     Cover title.

     1. Seeds. I. Title.

NN   0055252   IU DNAL NIC

National Institute of Agricultural Botany, Cambridge, Eng.
The journal . . .
no. 1–

Cambridge₍, 1923–   8°.
     nos.   illus.
     Irregular.

1. Botany, Economic—Per. and soc. publ.
N. Y. P. L.   October 13, 1927

NN   0055253   NN

75.9
N216

National Institute of Agricultural Botany.
Key to the demonstration and training
collections, scheme for the inspection and
certification of growing crops of potatoes.

₍Cambridge, Eng.₎

NN   0055254   DNAL

National Institute of Agricultural Botany, Cambridge, Eng.
. . . Report and accounts.
₍no.

Cambridge, ₍19   8°.
     no.
     19   , cover-title.

1. Botany, Economic—Assoc. and org.—   Gt. Br.—Eng.
N. Y. P. L.   August 12, 1927

NN   0055255   NN

64.9
N21

National Institute of Agricultural Botany.
Summary of results of yield trials.

₍Cambridge? Eng.₎

     1. Crop yields. Statistics.

NN   0055256   DNAL

National Institute of Agricultural Botany, Cambridge, Eng.
Varieties of potatoes with their synonyms, immune from and
susceptible to wart disease . . . Revised edition . . . Issued by the
National Institute of Agricultural Botany.   Cambridge ₍Eng.₎
W. Heffer & Sons, Ltd., 1933.   35 p. incl. tables.   18½cm.

     Cover-title.

786808A. 1. Potato—Varieties.   2. Potato—Diseases and pests.
N. Y. P. L.   November 29, 1935

NN   0055257   NN NNC

National Institute of Agricultural Botany, Cam-
     bridge. Potato Synonym Committee.
Report of the Potato Synonym Committee . . .
and Resolutions of the Potato Industry Conference.
1920–1921   Cambridge.
     1 v.
Later reports of the Potato Synonym Committee are issued in the Institute's Journal after 1921.
     1. Potatoes - Societies, etc. 2. Potato
Industry Conference

NN   0055258   CU

National Institute of Agricultural Botany, *Cambridge, Eng.*
Seed Production Committee.
Report.
₍Cambridge, Eng.₎
     v. 25 cm.
     Report year ends May 31.

     1. Seed industry and trade.

     SB117.N174   631.52   52–38883

NN   0055259   DLC DNAL

61.9
N21S

National institute of agricultural botany, Seed
     production committee.
Seed notes. no.1–   Cambridge, Eng.
₍Cambridge, Eng., 1942?–

     1. Seeds. I. Title.

NN   0055260   DNAL

VOLUME 407

HD1970
.I59   The National institute of agricultural
economy (I.N.E.A.). Rome, 1951.
11 p.

Extract from the "Review of economic conditions in Italy" vol. V, no. 1, January 1951.

1. Italy - Agriculture - Economic aspects.
2. Agriculture - Economic aspects - Italy.
I. Istituto nazionale di economia agraria.

NN   0055261   DS

National Institute of Agricultural Engineering, *Silsoe, Eng.*
see
**Silsoe, Eng. National Institute of Agricultural Engi-
neering.**

National Institute of Agricultural Sciences, *Tokyo*
see
Nōgyō Gijutsu Kenkyūjo, *Tokyo.*

S 22
N29   National Institute of Animal Agriculture.
Proceedings. 1st-
1951-
ₙn.p.,ₙ
v. 22 cm.

1. Agriculture - Congresses.

NN   0055264   OU OrCS

National Institute of Animal Health, *Tokyo*
see
Kachiku Eisei Shikenjō, *Tokyo.*

National Institute of Animal Industry, *Chiba, Japan*
see
Chikusan Shikenjō, *Chiba, Japan.* (Supplement)

National Institute of Art Research
see
Bijutsu Kenkyūjo, Tokyo.

National Institute of Arthritis and Metabolic Diseases
see
U. S. *National Institute of Arthritis and Metabolic Diseases.*

National institute of arts and letters.
...An act incorporating the National institute of arts and letters.
₍Washington, D. C., 1910₎   8 p.   28cm.

Caption-title.
At head of title: 61st Congress, 2d session.   House calendar no. 92. S. 609. <Report
no. 475.> In the House of representatives.   January 19, 1910...

NN   0055269   NN

National institute of arts and letters.
... Aims and purposes of the institute, as
expressed by past and present members. Printed
for private distribution among the members, May
15, 1941.
37 p.   23cm.

NN   0055270   NNC

National institute of arts and letters.

American academy of arts and letters. *Museum.*
Catalogue, 1934-1935, of the Museum of the American academy of arts and letters and the National institute of arts and
letters, opened November 8, 1934, in the administration building of the academy, Broadway between 155th and 156th
streets, New York city. ₍New York₎ American academy of arts
and letters, 1934.

National institute of arts and letters.

American academy of arts and letters.
A catalogue of an exhibition of works by the living artist
members of the National institute of arts and letters, in connection with the opening of the art gallery of the new building
of the American academy of arts and letters, Broadway
between 155th and 156th streets, New York city. ₍New York₎
American academy of arts and letters, 1930.

National institute of arts and letters.

American academy of arts and letters.
... Comprehensive exhibition in the Art gallery and Museum
of works by members of the Departments of art, literature and
music, Broadway between 155th and 156th streets, New York
city ... ₍New York, 1942₎

National Institute of Arts and Letters.
Constitution and list of members
see its
National Institute of Arts and Letters, American Academy of Arts and Letters. ₍Members, by-laws, etc.₎

National Institute of Arts and Letters.
Exhibition of the development of Washington
from forest to national capital ...
see under   American Academy of Arts
and Letters.

NG512   National Institute of Arts and Letters.
.A568
American Academy of Arts and Letters.
Exhibition of work by newly elected members and re-
cipients of honors and awards.
New York.

Z1231   National Institute of Arts and Letters.
.P7A5
American Academy of Arts and Letters.
A festival of poetry; American poetry from 1912 to the
present. An exhibition of original manuscripts, books, and
magazines & a series of poetry readings, December 2-30, 1955.
New York, American Academy of Arts and Letters ₍and₎
National Institute of Arts and Letters ₍1955₎

National Institute of Arts and Letters.
First retrospective exhibition ... of
portrait busts .. by Jo Davidson
see under   American Academy of
Arts and Letters.

Z1225   National Institute of Arts and Letters.
.A6
American Academy of Arts and Letters.
The great decade in American writing, 1850-1860: Emerson, Hawthorne, Melville, Thoreau, Whitman; books and
manuscripts, with paintings by friends and contemporaries
of the authors. ₍Exhibition₎ Dec. 3-30, 1954. New York,
American Academy of Arts and Letters ₍and₎ National Institute of Arts and Letters ₍1954₎

National institute of arts and letters.
... Greetings to the new Russia; addresses at a meeting
held at the Hudson theater, New York, April 23, 1917, under
the auspices of the National institute of arts and letters.
Washington, D. C., The Endowment, 1917.
2 p. l., 14 p.   25 cm.   (Carnegie endowment for international peace.
Division of intercourse and education.   Publication no. 13)

CONTENTS.—Introduction by A. Thomas.—Addresses by G. Kennan.—Address by N. M. Butler.—Address to authors and artists of
Russia.

1. Russia—Hist.—Revolution, 1917-   I. Kennan, George,
1845-1924.   II. Butler, Nicholas Murray, 1862-   III. Title.

DK265.N3   17—28630

OrU CU DAU CaBVaU WaTC WaS MtU IdPI WaWW MtBC WaPS
NN   0055280   DLC MB ICJ NN OrCS ODW OCU OU OCl ViU

National institute of arts and letters.

Millay, Edna St. Vincent, 1892-
Invocation to the muses, by Edna St. Vincent Millay; read
at the public ceremonial of the National institute of arts and
letters at Carnegie hall, New York, January 18th, 1941 ⟨includ-
ing the words written for the Chorale by Deems Taylor⟩ New
York and London, Harper & brothers, 1941.

National Institute of Arts and Letters.
National Institute of Arts and Letters, American Academy of Arts and Letters. ₍Members, by-laws, etc.₎

New York.
v. 14-23 cm. annual.
Title varies: 19   Constitution and list of members.—19   -48,
National Institute of Arts and Letters.
Absorbed American Academy of Arts and Letters.   American
Academy of Arts and Letters. ₍Members, by-laws, etc.₎ in 1949.
Issues for 19   -48 include section: American Academy of Arts
and Letters.
I. American Academy of Arts and Letters.

AS36.N152   061   31—10098 rev 2*

NN   0055282   DLC PU FU ICU InU MB NN OCl MiU

AS36
.N1515

National institute of arts and letters.
National institute news bulletin...
New York city ₍1935-37₎
3 v. in 1   30.5 -31.5 cm.

NN   0055283   DLC NBuU IEN ViU

National Institute of Arts and Letters.
Proceedings
see
American Academy of Arts and Letters.
Proceedings of the American Academy of Arts and
Letters and the National Institute of Arts and Letters.

Ay
B435Cn   National Institute of Arts and Letters.
1941   Public ceremonial, Saturday evening, the
Rare   eighteenth of January, 1941, at 8:30. [New
Books   York? 1941?]
Col   [4]p.   25½cm. in envelope in folder 28cm.

"Ode to arts and letters, by Stephen Vincent Benét": p.[4]

I. Benét, Stephen Vincent, 1898-1943.

NN   0055285   TxU

VOLUME 407

National institute of arts and letters.

American academy of arts and letters.
Public meeting of the American academy and the National institute of arts and letters at the Fine arts society, New York, November 20, 1909, to confer upon the work of Augustus Saint-Gaudens the gold medal of the institute. ₍New York₎ American academy of arts and letters, 1922.

National institute of arts and letters.

American academy of arts and letters.
Public meeting of the American academy of the **National** institute of arts and letters in honor of John Burroughs, member of the academy from May thirteen, nineteen hundred and five, until his death, March twenty-nine, nineteen hundred and twenty-one; William Milligan Sloane, president of the academy, presiding. ₍New York₎ American academy of arts and letters, 1922.

National institute of arts and letters.
FOR OTHER EDITIONS
SEE MAIN ENTRY
American academy of arts and letters.
Public meeting of the American academy and the National institute of arts and letters in honor of William Dean Howells, president of the academy from its inception to the date of his death; William Milligan Sloane, president of the academy, presiding. ₍New York₎ American academy of arts and letters, 1922. **OTHER EDITIONS UNDER AUTHOR**

National institute of arts and letters.

American academy of arts and letters.
Public meeting under the auspices of the American academy and the National institute of arts and letters held at Carnegie hall, New York, November 3, 1910, in memory of Samuel Langhorne Clemens (Mark Twain) ₍New York₎ American academy of arts and letters, 1922.

National institute of arts and letters.
Report... May 15, 1914-
[n.p.,] 1914-

.AS36
.N15

NN   0055290   DLC

National Institute of Cleaning and Dyeing
see **National Institute of Drycleaning.**

Asia
PO
Ref.   National Institute of
Z7164   Community Development.
.H94   Land reforms in India—a select biblio-
graphy. Hyderabad, India, n. d.
11 l.

Photocopy of typescript.

1. Land   tenure — India —
Bibl.   I.   Title

NN   0055292   HU

National institute of community development.
N.I.C.D. studies series.
[New Delhi]   no.   25cm.

1. Community development--   India. I. Title.

NN   0055293   NN

HN682   National Institute of Community Development.
.5   Report.
N3
Hyderabad, etc.
v.

NN   0055294   CU NN

National Institute of Compilations and Translations, *Nanking*
see
Kuo li pien i kuan, *T'ai-pei.*

National Institute of Compilations and Translations, *T'ai-pei*
see
Kuo li pien i kuan, *T'ai-pei.*

National Institute of Culture, *Bangkok, Thailand*
see
Thailand. *National Institute of Culture.*

National Institute of Drycleaning.
Bookkeeping and costfinding for drycleaners
see under   Franks, Walter Hall, 1900-

National Institute of Drycleaning.
Bulletin service. Technical ₍bulletin₎
Silver Spring, Md.
no. in   v. illus. 28 cm. irregular.
Began in Feb. 1935. Cf. Michelsen, Edna M. Remembering the years 1907-1957, p. 105.
Title varies: —Aug. 21, 1950, Bulletin service.
Bulletins for   —Apr. 20, 1953 issued by the institute under an earlier name: National Institute of Cleaning and Dyeing.
Most bulletins prepared by the Research Dept.
1. Cleaning and dyeing industry—Period.   I. National Institute of Drycleaning. Technical bulletin.

TP932.N33   68-33253

NN   0055299   DLC IU DP CU-A

National Institute of Drycleaning.
Chemistry in drycleaning. [Silver Spring, Md.: National assoc. of dyers and cleaners, c1929] 34 p. incl. tables. illus. 23cm.

Cover-title.

1. Cleaning, Dry. I. Title

NN   0055300   NN MiD

National Institute of Drycleaning.
Convention report and year book. 1914-

Silver Spring, Md. ₍etc.₎
v. 23 cm. annual.
Ceased publication with 1931/32 issue; continued in the institute's Bulletin service. Cf. Union list of serials.
Issued under the institute's earlier name: National Association of Dyers and Cleaners of the United States and Canada.
L. C. set incomplete: 1915-1924/25, 1928/29-1930/31 wanting.

1. Dyes and dyeing—Societies, etc.

TP890.N2   667.1   15-857 rev 2*

NN   0055301   DLC

National Institute of Drycleaning.
The Drycleaner.   —v. 9, no. 10;
—Oct. 1932.
₍Silver Spring, Md., etc.₎

National Institute of Drycleaning.
FOR OTHER EDITIONS
SEE MAIN ENTRY
Randall, Clare Bert, 1901-
The drycleaning department; manual of cleaning room practice, by C. B. Randall ... Rev. ed. Silver Spring, Md., National association of dyers and cleaners of the United States and Canada ₍°1940₎

National Institute of Drycleaning.
[Miscellaneous publications.   Silver Spring₋, Md., 194-]
Unbound pamphlets.
1. Cleaning and dyeing industry.

NN   0055304   NNC

TP932   National Institute of Drycleaning.
.G3   **Gaubatz, George Godfrey,** 1900-   *ed.*
Modern methods in drycleaning, edited by George G. Gaubatz, jr. ... Silver Spring, Md., National association of dyers and cleaners ₍°1931₎

Egleston
DG46.G2
N2132   National Institute of Drycleaning.
‵NICD fellowship bulletin.
no.
Silver Spring, Md.,
v.   tables, diagrs. 28cm.

Title varies: —Feb. 20, 1947, Research fellowship; Dec. 1, 1947-
NICD fellowship bulletin.

1. Cleaning and   dyeing industry.

NN   0055306   NNC

---

657   National Institute of Drycleaning.
N212n   1934 ocst accounting forms. Set A, recommended for plants with an annual volume of business in excess of $150,000.00. Prepared by J. M. Matson. Silver Spring, Md., National association of dyers and cleaners ₍1934₎
36 l.

Mimeographed.

1. Dyes and dyeing--Accounting. 2. Cost--Accounting. I. Matson, J. M.

NN   0055307   IU

National Institute of Drycleaning.

Cooley, Warren K.
Practical science for the drycleaning industry, by Warren K. Cooley. ₍Washington, D. C., °1930₎

---

657   National Institute of Drycleaning.
N212p   Purchase order for accounting forms. Silver Spring, Md., National association of dyers & cleaners ₍193-₎
19 l. 19 forms (28x35½cm.)

1. Dyes and dying. 2. Accounting.

NN   0055309   IU

---

657   National Institute of Drycleaning.
N212p   Purchase order for accounting forms. Silver Spring, Md., National association of dyers & cleaners ₍193-₎
19 l. 19 forms (28x35½cm.)

1. Dyes and dying. 2. Accounting.

NN   0055309   IU

VOLUME 407

National Institute of Drycleaning.
Report of part-time course of instruction and training in the dry cleaning and dyeing industry ... St. Louis, Mo. National association of dryers & cleaners [1922]
76 p.

NN 0055310   OCU

National Institute of **Drycleaning.**
FOR OTHER EDITIONS
SEE MAIN ENTRY
Maher, Jennie Wisneski.
Silk finishing, by Jennie Wisneski Maher ... Rev. ed. Silver Spring, Md., National association of dryers and cleaners of the United States and Canada [1943]

National Institute of **Drycleaning.**

Covington, Clyde H.
The spotting department, by Clyde H. Covington ... Silver Spring, Md., National association of dyers and cleaners of the United States and Canada [*1940]

National **I**nstitute of Drycleaning.
Berg, Norbert J
Wetcleaning, by Norbert J. Berg ... Silver Spring, Md., National association of dyers and cleaners of the United States and Canada [1945]

TP932
.N33

National Institute of Drycleaning.
Technical bulletin.
National Institute of Drycleaning.
Bulletin service. Technical [bulletin]
Silver Spring, Md.

National Institute of Drycleaning.
Uniform cost accounting system. n.p., n.d.
2 v.
Accompanied by forms.
Vol. 2 and Forms are quarto size.

NN 0055315   IU

National Institute of Drycleaning. Year book
see its Convention report and year book.

HF5415
.S86

National institute of economic and social research.
Stone, Richard, 1913–
The analysis of market demand, by Richard Stone ... London, The National institute of economic and social research [1945]

National Institute of Economic and Social Research.
Annual report. 1940–41—
[London]
v. 19–22 cm.
Title varies: 1940–41, Report.

[*H11.N274   307.2   48–44069*

NNC CtY
NN 0055318   DLC CaBVaU NN NcD NcU CSt DNAL OU DS

National Institute of Economic and Social Research.
A classified list of large companies engaged in British industry. [London] 1955 [i. e. 1956]
39 p. illus. 28 cm.

Continued in next column

Continued from preceding column

1. Corporations—Gt. Brit.   I. Title.

HD2847.N3   56–57911 †

NN 0055319   DLC

H62
.C5848

National Institute of Economic and Social Research.
Commonwealth register of research in progress and in plan for the year in the social sciences.
London.

330.06
N278e

National Institute of Economic and Social Research.
Economic and social studies. [no.]1–
Cambridge, Univ. Press, 1942–

GEU   MiD PHC TNJ NcU NcD MB
NN 0055321   KMK MtU OO NcD KU PBL OU ICJ NN WvU

H
11
.N25

National Institute of Economic and Social Research.
Occasional papers, 1–
London, Cambridge University Press, 1942–

1. Economics—Collections.

PHC KyU MsU GFU NhD NcD OU PBL CaBVaU
NN 0055322   DAU   MiD NN ICJ OCI   CtNlC TU CU TNJ

National institute of economic and social research.
Publications & programmes of the National institute of economic and social research ... Westminster [London] 1944.
cover-title, 19, [1] p. 21½ᵐ.

1. Economics—Bibl.—Catalogs.
                                                       44–12265
Library of Congress   Z7164.E2N3
                           [2]   016.33

NN 0055323   DLC

H62
.R4

National institute of economic and social research.
Register of research in the social sciences in progress and in plan.
London [19

National Institute of Economic and Social Research. Report
see its Annual report.

HC260
.I5S8

National Institute of Economic and Social Research.
Studies in the national income and expenditure of the United Kingdom.
Cambridge, University Press, 1953–

National institute of economic and social research.
Trade regulations & commercial policy of the United Kingdom, by the research staff of the National institute of economic and social research. Cambridge [Eng.] The University press, 1943.
x, 275, [1] p. 22½ cm. (*Its* Economic and social studies. III)
In 1938 the Geneva research centre initiated a study of international trade regulations and commercial policy, and the National institute of economic and social research undertook the British section of this work. By 1939 the descriptive material had been largely assembled. It was revised and arranged by J. M. Sebag-Montefiore and is now published as a technical descriptive study. *cf.* Pref.
1. Free trade and protection. 2. Tariff—Gt. Brit. 3. Gt. Brit.—Commercial policy.   I. Geneva research center. II. Sebag-Montefiore, James Marcus, ed.   III. Title.
                                                       43—12788
Library of Congress   HF2046.N33
                           [48q2]   337

NcD ViU OCI DNAL CU PBL ScU
NN 0055327   DLC ICU OrU CU FU CaBVaU OrCS OrP MdU

FILM
16142
HF
SOCIAL
SCIENCE

National institute of economic and social research.
Trade regulations & commercial policy of the United Kingdom, by the research staff of the National institute of economic and social research. Cambridge [Eng.] The University press, 1943.
x, 275, [1] p. On film (positive) (Its Economic and social studies. III)
Microfilm. Original in University of Southern California library.

NN 0055328   CU

National Institute of Economic and Social Research
see also **Joint Exploratory Committee.**

National Institute of Economic Research, *Stockholm*
see
Sweden. *Konjunkturinstitutet.*

National Institute of Efficiency.
Monographs of efficiency
see under title

PM8208
.D8

National institute of Esperanto, Philadelphia.
Dubin, Joseph W
The green star [by] Joseph W. Dubin, A. M. Philadelphia, Pa., National institute of Esperanto [*1944]

National Institute of Farm and Land Brokers.
Roster.
[n. p.]
v. illus., ports. 15–23 cm. annual.
Issued by the institute under its earlier names: *1951 –1952,* Institute of Farm Brokers; 1953–62, National Institute of Farm Brokers.

1. Real estate business—Societies, etc. 2. Real estate business—U. S.

HD251.N27   *62–50461 rev*

NN 0055333   DLC IU

National Institute of Farm Brokers
see
National Institute of Farm and Land Brokers.

National Institute of General Medical Sciences
see   U.S. National Institute of General Medical Sciences.

W
N277R
1848

National Institute of General Practitioners in Medicine, Surgery and Midwifery.
Report of the council of the National Institute of General Practitioners in Medicine, Surgery and Midwifery, on the present state of the medical reform question... London, W. Davy, 1848.
84 p. 22 cm.

NN 0055336   WU-M DNLM

National Institute of Genetics, *Mishima, Japan*
see
Kokuritsu Idengaku Kenkyūjo, *Mishima, Japan.*

VOLUME 407

National institute of governmental purchasing.
... At your service. ₍Washington, 194–?₎
cover-title, 24 p.

NN 0055338   MH-BA

National Institute of Governmental Purchasing.
NIGP addresses and papers presented at annual conference and products exhibit.
₍Washington₎
(₎v. 28 cm.

1. Government purchasing—Societies, etc.

JF1525.P85N3   57–31963 ‡

NN 0055339   DLC

National Institute of Governmental Purchasing.

N. I. G. P. letter service.

Washington, National Institute of Governmental Purchasing.

National institute of government₍₎purchasing

National survey of public practices and procedures. (Report submitted by David Joseph...at the 2d annual conference... Sept.10,1947) 10p. ₍Author,1947₎

NN 0055341   OrP

National institute of graphic arts, *New York.*
How to make and print valuable etchings and dry points; practice plates and exercises. The Etchophane method ...
New York city, National institute of graphic arts ₍1938₎
16 p. illus. 23ᶜᵐ.

1. Etching. 2. Engravings—Printing. ɪ. Title.
                                        44–22313
Library of Congress   NE2130.N3
                         ₍2₎   767

NN 0055342   DLC

National Institute of Health, *Tokyo*
see
Kokuritsu Yobō Eisei Kenkyūjo, *Tokyo.*

National institute of industrial psychology, *London.*
An account of the research work carried out by the National institute of industrial psychology during the years 1921–34. London, The Institute ₍1934₎
1 p. l., 37 p. 25 cm. (On cover: The National institute of industrial psychology ... reports)
"Chronological table of the Institute's research work": p. 34–37.

1. Research, Industrial. 2. Psychology, Industrial.
T177.G7N3   [159.98] 150.13   36–31978

NN 0055344   DLC OrCS OCl OU WaU LU

151.2
N277a   National Institute of Industrial Psychology,
             London.
             Age and test performance ₍by D. F. Vincent.
             London, 1953?₎
             12p.   (Its N.I.I.P. occasional paper)
             Cover title.
             Contents.– The decline of intelligence test scores with age.– The linear relationship between age and score of adults in intelligence tests.
             Bibliography: p. 12.

             1. Mental tests.   I. Vincent, D. F. II. Title.

NN 0055345   ICarbS

National Institute of Industrial Psychology, London.
Annual report and statement of accounts.
₍no.₎

London₍₎, 19   8°.
no

1. Psychology, Applied—Assoc. and   org.—Gt. Br.
N.Y.P.L.   September 26, 192

NN 0055346   NN DL PPT ICJ OCl DLC OU NNU-W OO

National Institute of Industrial Psychology, *London.*
Bibliography of industrial supervision, compiled by the group carrying out a study of the selection, training and status of foremen, sponsored by the Human Factors Panel of the Committee on Industrial Productivity. London ₍1950₎
24 l. 35 cm.

1. Efficiency, Industrial—Bibl. 2. Foremen—Bibl. ɪ. Title.
Z7914.A2N27   53–19767 ‡
            *016.658386 016.6583124

NN 0055347   DLC NN

National institute of industrial psychology, *London.*
A Borstal experiment in vocational guidance: report of investigation by the National institute of industrial psychology ... Maidstone, Printed for private circulation at H. M. prison ₍1934₎
cover-title, 2 p. l., 7–44, xv (i. e. xxi) p. incl. fold. plates, fold. tab., diagrs. 23½ᶜᵐ.

1. Juvenile delinquency—Gt. Brit. 2. Vocational guidance. 3. Reformatories—Gt. Brit. ɪ. Title.
                                        44–1588
Library of Congress   HV9081.N3
                         ₍44c1₎   371.425

NN 0055348   DLC

301.155   National Institute of Industrial Psy-
N198c   chology, London.
            Conference leading.   London ₍1952?₎
            27 p. 21 cm.   (Its Paper, no. 4)

            1. Leadership. I. Title. II. Series.

NN 0055349   LU

National Institute of Industrial Psychology, *London.*
The foreman, a study of supervision in British industry.
London, New York, Staples Press ₍1951₎
158 p. 23 cm.
"Sponsored by the Human Factors Panel of the Committee on Industrial Productivity."
Bibliography: p. 152–154.

1. Foremen. ɪ. Title.
TS155.N2294   658.3124   51–8032

        ICU
NN 0055350   DLC OrU MtBC TxU NN NcU OCl AU CLSU

National Institute of Industrial Psychology, London.
The foreman, a study of supervision in British industry. London, New York [1951 repr. 1952]

NN 0055351   CU

National Institute of Industrial Psychology, *London.*
The future development of educational and vocational guidance; Conference, January 8th, 1944, report. London ₍1944₎
Microfilm copy made in 1946 by the Library of Congress. Negative. Collation of the original, as determined from the film: 31 l.

1. Personnel service in education—Congresses. 2. Vocational guidance—Congresses. ɪ. Title.

Microfilm Z–12   Mic 50–427

NN 0055352   DLC

National institute of industrial psychology,
London.
Seymour, W   Douglas.
    The heating, ventilation and lighting of school buildings, by W. Douglas Seymour. With a preface by Charles S. Myers ... Published on behalf of the Association of directors and secretaries for education. London, New York ₍etc.₎ Oxford university press, 1939.

National institute of industrial psychology.
London.
... How psychology enters into the institute's factory investigations... (London) The Institute, (1928?)
cover-title, 15 p.   24½ cm.

NN 0055354   DL

National institute of industrial psychology,
London.

The **Human** factor ... v. 1–
Jan. 1922–
London, National institute of industrial psychology, 1923–

National Institute of Industrial Psychology, London.
The human factor in industry.   London: Aldwych House₍₎,
192–?₎.   4 p.   8°.
Cover-title.

NN 0055356   NN

HF5548   National institute of industrial psychology,
.8   London.
.M9   **Myers, Charles Samuel,** 187?–   *ed.*
1929a   Industrial psychology, edited by Charles S. Myers ... New York, H. Holt and company; London, T. Butterworth ltd. ₍1929₎

658.311   National Institute of Industrial Psychology,
N211   London.
            Interviewing for selection.   London
            ₍1953₎
            20 p. 21 cm.   (Its Paper, no. 3)
            Prepared by Harold F. Lock in consultation with some of his colleagues.

            1. Interviewing. I. Lock, Harold F

NN 0055358   LU

VOLUME 407

National Institute of Industrial Psychology, *London.*
Joint consultation in British industry; a report of an inquiry undertaken by the National Institute of Industrial Psychology sponsored by the Human Factors Panel of the Committee on Industrial Productivity. London, New York, Staples Press ₁1952₎

276 p. illus. 22 cm.

Includes bibliography.

1. Industrial relations—Gt. Brit.   i. Title.

HD8390.N33   331.156   52–3019 ‡

AAP MU

NN   0055359   DLC MtBC PSt PU PPT CU IaAS MH–BA TxU

National Institute of Industrial Psychology, *London.*
Joint consultation in practice, a survey in British industry. ₁Paris, European Productivity Agency, 19–₎

43 p. illus. 19 cm. (European Productivity Agency. Industrial version no. 1)

First published in 1952 under title: Joint consultation in British industry.

1. Industrial relations—Gt. Brit.   i. Title.   (Series: Organization for European Economic Co-operation. European Productivity Agency. Industrial version no. 1)

HD8390.N332   63–507

NN   0055360   DLC

National institute of industrial psychology, *London.*
Journal
see
Occupational psychology.

National institute of industrial psychology, *London.*
Earle, Frank Maynard.
... The measurement of manual dexterities, by F. M. Earle ... assisted by F. Gaw, ph. d., and other members of the Institute's staff. London, The National institute of industrial psychology ₁1930₎

National institute of industrial psychology, *London.*
Earle, Frank Maynard.
Methods of choosing a career; a description of an experiment in vocational guidance conducted on twelve hundred London elementary school children, by F. M. Earle ... and other members of the staff of the National institute of industrial psychology, edited with a preface by Charles S. Myers ... with a foreword by the Right Honourable the Viscount D'Abernon ... London, Bombay ₁etc.₎ G. G. Harrap & company, ltd. ₁1931₎

National institute of industrial psychology, *London.*
Ndg14   Minutes of the ... annual general meeting ...
+N23a   ₁London,
                                      33cm.

Mimeographed,

NN   0055364   CtY

National Institute of Industrial Psychology, *London*
N.I.I.P. news ...
    see under title

National Institute of Industrial Psychology, *London.*
N. I. I. P. paper. no. 1–
₁London, 1952₎

no. 22 cm.

1. Psychology, Industrial—Collections.   i. Title.

HF5548.8.N3   66–98316

NN   0055366   DLC LU NBuU

National institute of industrial psychology, *London.*
The National institute of industrial psychology; its present position. ₁London₎ 1937. 7, 2, 2, 4 p. 23cm.

1. Psychology, Vocational—   Assoc. and org—Gt. Br.
N. Y. P. L.   March 6, 1940

NN   0055367   NN

National institute of industrial psychology, *London.*
... Occupation analysis. The study of aptitudes and attainments necessary for success in different kinds of employment ... London, Publ. at the offices of the Institute ₁1927?₎

cover-title, 2 p. l., 36 pl. incl. diagr. 24½ᵐ. (Institute report no. I)

At head of title: National institute of industrial psychology.

"The first of a series of special reports describing an experiment in vocational guidance carried out in London by a grant from the Carnegie United kingdom trust."

"The form and contents of this report are largely the work of Mr. F. M. Earle."—Pref.

1. Occupations. 2. Profession. Choice of. ₁2. Vocational guidance₎
3. Ability—Testing. i. Earle, Frank Maynard. ii. Title.

Library, U. S. Dept. of   Labor   L 27–403

NN   0055368   DL ICJ MiU OU NN OO CaBVaU

National institute of industrial psychology, *London.*
Bevington, Sheila.
Occupational misfits; a comparative study of north London boys employed and unemployed, by Sheila Bevington ... with a foreword by Charles S. Myers ... London, George Allen & Unwin ltd. ₁1933₎

National institute of industrial psychology, *London.*
Occupational psychology ... v. 1–
Jan. 1922–   London, National
institute of industrial psychology, 1923–

National institute of industrial psychology, *London.*
Practical methods for reducing accidents and transport costs. London, Issued by National institute of industrial psychology ₁1933₎

16 p. diagrs. 18¼ᵐ.

1. Accidents—Prevention. 2. Automobiles—Accidents. i. Title.

                                             CA 34–466 Unrev'd

Library of Congress   HE5614.N35   629.2136

NN   0055371   DLC CtY OU

BF56   NATIONAL INSTITUTE OF INDUSTRIAL PSYCHOLOGY,
.N3   London.
         Report. 1–   London ₁1926–

         Title varies: no.1, Institute report.
         Each report has special title.

         1. Psychology, Industrial.

         InLP MoSW
NN   0055372   ICU OO OU PBL CU OCl MiU ICJ CU OrU DL

National institute of industrial psychology, *London.*
Ramsay, J.
Rest-pauses and refreshments in industry; an inquiry into the operation of rest-pauses and mid-shift refreshments in factories in seven industrial areas in Great Britain (with an appendix on music in factories) by J. Ramsay, R. E. Rawson and others. London, The National institute of industrial psychology, 1939.

National Institute of Industrial Psychology, *London.*
The seven-point plan. London, National Institute of Industrial Psychology ₁1952₎

16 p. plate. 21½ cm. (*Its* N. I. I. P. paper, no. 1) 2/6
                                             (B 66–13373)

"Prepared by Alec Rodger."
Bibliography: p. 16.

1. Vocational qualifications.   i. Rodger, Alec. ii. Title.
(Series)

HF5548.8.N3 no. 1   66–67911

NN   0055374   DLC NIC CLSU

National Institute of Industrial Psychology, *London.*
Speed and precision in manual skill

see under

Vincent, D   F

National institute of industrial psychology, *London.*
... A study in vocational guidance carried out by
          see under   ₁Gaw, Frances₎ 1897.

National Institute of Industrial
Psychology, London.
Studying work for vocational guidance
and selection. London ₁195–?₎

21 p. 22 cm. (N. I. I. P. paper
no. 2)
1. Job descriptions. 2. Vocational guidance.

NN   0055377   MnU

LB1715   National institute of industrial psychology,
.S68   London.
          Stewart, Mary Elizabeth (Birkinshaw) 1905–
          The successful teacher; an occupational analysis based on an enquiry conducted among women teachers in secondary schools ₁by₎ Mary Birkinshaw. London, L. and Virginia Woolf at the Hogarth press, 1935.

National institute of industrial psychology, *London.*
... Training industrial workers. London, National institute of industrial psychology, 1940.

cover-title, 11, ₁1₎ p. 20½ᵐ. (War-time problems)

1. Technical education.   i. Title.

                                             42–10588

Library of Congress   T65.N3
                                      ₁5₎   658.386

NN   0055379   DLC

National institute of industrial psychology, *London.*
Training operatives for machine shops; a works instructor's handbook prepared by the National institute of industrial psychology. London, Sir I. Pitman & sons, ltd., 1944.

35 p. 21¼ᵐ.

1. Machine-shop practice. 2. Employees, Training of.   i. Title.
                                             44–5502

Library of Congress   TJ1167.N3
                                      ₁3₎   621.75

NN   0055380   DLC

VOLUME 407

658.3124
N213t
National Institute of Industrial Psychology,
London.
Two studies in supervision: Messrs. Exe &
Co., by Elizabeth Livingstone [and] Super-
vision in a cotton spinning firm, by John D.
Handyside. London, 1953.
59p. 25cm. (Its Report 10)

1. Supervision of employees. I. Livingstone, Elizabeth. II. Handyside, John D.
III. Title. IV. Series.

NN 0055381   TxU LU C NIC

National institute of industrial psychology.
London.
Earle, Frank Maynard.
... The use of performance tests of intelligence in vocational
guidance. An investigation conducted for the National institute of industrial psychology, by F. M. Earle ... M. Milner ...
and other members of its staff. London, H. M. Stationery
off., 1929.

HF5382
.5
.S34E3
National Institute of Industrial Psychology,
London. Report 6.
Earle, Frank Maynard, 1888–
... A vocational guidance research in Fife, by F. M. Earle ...
and J. Kilgour ... A. A comparison of urban and rural vocational conditions. B. The age at which vocational guidance
studies should begin. c. Minimal standards of ability and tem-
perament for various occupations. London, The National institute of industrial psychology [1935]

NATIONAL INSTITUTE OF INDUSTRIAL PSYCHOLOGY, *London.*
The work of the institute. London [194-?]
[7] p.

1. Great Britain
2. Industrial psychology- Gt.Brit.

NN 0055384   MH-IR

National institute of inventors.
... Constitution and by-laws of the National institute of
inventors. [New York, J. A. Cantor printing co.] *1917.
16 p. 15cm.

Library of Congress   T201.N3   17-23441

NN 0055385   DLC

National institute of inventors.
An outline of plans for the establishment and operation
of the National laboratory for invention and research by
the National institute of inventors, New York city, prepared, comp. and copyrighted ... by Ernest Gilmore Gardner, embodying the necessity, scope, organization, administration and comments of America's foremost men, en-
dorsing in principle such a philanthropic institution.
[New York, A. Straus printing co., *1918]

47 p. diagr. 23cm.

[I. Gardner, Ernest Gilmore, comp. II. Title: National Laboratory for
Invention and Research.

Library of Congress   T176.N3   18-15049

NN 0055386   DLC OrCS OrU IU ICJ MiU DSI OO

HD6511
.I45
National Institute of Labor Education.
Illinois. University. *Institute of Labor and Industrial Rela-
tions.*
An education program for union women; an experiment
conducted by the University of Illinois' Institute of Labor
and Industrial Relations as part of its Inter-university
Labor Education Committee program. [Champaign, 1954]

LC5051
.M5
National Institute of Labor Education.
Mire, Joseph.
Labor education, a study report on needs, programs, and
approaches, conducted on behalf of the Inter-university
Labor Education Committee. [Madison? Wis.] Inter-uni-
versity Labor Education Committee, *1956.

National institute of letters, arts, and sciences, *New York.*
Constitution of the National institute of letters, arts
and sciences. Founded 1868. New York, W. C. Bryant
& co., printers, 1868.
15 p. 23½cm.

Library of Congress   Q11.N33   5-11280

NN 0055389   DLC CU OClWHi

National institute of letters, arts, and sciences, *New York.*
Constitution of the National institute of letters, arts
and sciences. Founded 1868. New York, Moorhead, Bond
& co., 1868.
14 p. 23cm.

Library of Congress   Q11.N289   10-25779

NN 0055390   DLC MB NjR MWA

National Institute of Mental Health
see
U. S. *National Institute of Mental Health.*

Z7164
L8N37
National Institute of Municipal Clerks
A bibliography for municipal clerks;
key publications for a key official.
Chicago, 1952.
5p. 28cm.

Caption title.

1. Municipal government. Bibl

NN 0055392   IaU NRU N

National Institute of Municipal Clerks.
Proceedings [of the] annual conference.
[n. p.]
v. ports. 28 cm.

1. Municipal government—U. S.—Societies, etc.

JS302.N28   59-25406

NN 0055393   DLC N

JS
363
N27r
National Institute of Municipal Clerks.
Role of the municipal clerk in the
United States and Canada. Chicago, 1952.
15p. illus.,tables. 28cm.
Caption title.

1. Municipal officials and employees - U.S.
2. Municipal officials and employees - Canada. . I. Title. .

NN 0055394   NRU NBuG NcU IdU

R352
N194s
National Institute of Municipal Clerks
[Souvenir] program. Omaha, Neb. [etc.]

1. /Municipal officials and employees -
Congresses

NN 0055395   MiD

National Institute of Municipal Law Officers,
Washington, D.C.
Admission taxes
see under   Rhyne, Charles S., 1912–

SSTA
.N26r
no. 77
National Institute of Municipal Law Officers,
Washington, D. C.
Affidavits under soldiers' and sailors'
civil relief act of 1940 before default
judgments in suits to collect municipal
taxes—forms of affidavits now in use by
municipalities. Prepared by Charles S.
Rhyne. Washington, 1941.
23 p. (Its Report no. 77)
Cover title.
I. Rhyne, Charles S.

NN 0055397   ViU-L

629.144
N213a
National institute of municipal law officers,
Washington, D.C.
... Airport approach protection materials; model
statute and ordinance [by] John A. McIntire, executive director [and] Charles S. Rhyne, attorney ... [Washington, D.C., 1940]
cover-title, 39 l., 21 numb.l. (Its Report
no.59, February, 1940)

Mimeographed.
"Protection of airport approaches; transcript
of findings of fact and conclusions of law and

of decree in United airports company of Cal.,
ltd. v. Hinman, et al (U.S. Dist. ct., Southern
dist. of Cal., Central div., April 29,1939)": 21
leaves at end.

1. Airports--U.S. 2. Aeronautics--U.S.--Laws
and regulations. I. McIntire, John Albert, 1907–
II. Rhyne, Charles S. III. Title.

NN 0055399   IU IaU NjP NcD-L

National Institute of Municipal Law Officers,
Washington, D.C.
Airport lease and concession agreements
see under   Rhyne, Charles S., 1912–

National institute of municipal law officers, *Washington, D. C.*
... Airports and airplanes and the legal problems they create
for cities, prepared by John A. McIntire ... Charles S. Rhyne
... and associates. Printed in cooperation with the United
States conference of mayors. [Washington] 1939.
cover-title, v, 51 p. 28cm. (*Its* Report no. 42)

1. Aeronautics—U. S.—Laws and regulations. I. McIntire, John
Albert, 1907– II. Rhyne, Charles S. III. United States conference of
mayors. IV. Title.

Chicago. Univ. Law   library   A 41-1456
for Library of Congress   [5]

WaU-L MB ViU-L OClW OCU IaU
NN 0055401   ICU-L IdU OrU OrCS DAS CU NcRS NIC IU

TL726
.2
.R5
National institute of municipal law officers,
Washington, D. C.
Rhyne, Charles S., 1912–
Airports and the courts; a complete collection and analysis
of all reported court decisions involving acquisition, operation,
maintenance and zoning of airports, together with an analysis
of federal, state and local legislation in the airport field. The
air space rights of landowners, aviators and airport operators
are analyzed in the light of applicable legislation and legal
principles. By Charles S. Rhyne ... Washington, D. C., National institute of municipal law officers, 1944.

VOLUME 407

National institute of municipal law officers,
Washington, D.C.
... Ambulance regulation.   [Washington, D.C.]
1937.
cover-title, 21ℓ.   (Its Report no.18)
At head of title: Institute of municipal law
officers ... Washington, D.C.
Mimeographed.
Introduction signed: Sherwood L. Reeder, execu-
tive director.

1. Ambulances. I. Reeder, Sherwood Lewis, 1905-
II. Title.

NN 0055403   IU ViU N NcD-L

National institute of municipal law officers,
Washington, D. C.
American cities after the war - a plan for
the elimination of blighted areas. Preliminary
report no. 1 of the Committee on post-war
planning, prepared by Walter J. Mattison.
[Washington, D. C., 1943]
cover-title, 19 l.

1. Reconstruction (1939-   ) 2. Cities and
towns - Planning - U. S. I. Mattison, Walter J
ed. II. Title.

NN 0055404   NNC PPCPC NcU MiU-L IU NcD-L

National Institute of Municipal Law
Officers, Washington, D.C.
American cities after the war - A plan
for the elimination of blighted areas.
Preliminary report no. 1 of the Committee
on Post-War Planning prepared by Walter J.
Mattison, city attorney of Milwaukee,
Wisconsin, chairman. Washington, 1950.
19 p. 29cm.

NN 0055405   NIC NcD-L IU

National Institute of Municipal Law Officers, Washington, D.C.
Annual proceedings of the annual meeting ...
see NIMLO municipal law review ...

449.1   National Institute of Municipal Law Officers,
In7   Washington, D.C.
... Anti-noise ordinances ... [Washington,
D.C.] 1936.
18 numb. l.   27.5 cm. (Report no. 10)
Processed.

NN 0055407   DNAL

National institute of municipal law officers,
Washington, D.C.
Attorneys for municipalities, municipal agencies, officers and employees - their employment,
duties, powers, official status and compensation
as defined by court decisions. Prepared by
Charles S. Rhyne   Washington, D.C., National
institute of municipal law officers, 1942.
cover title, 33p.   (Its Report no.90. November 1942)
Bibliographical foot-notes.
1. Municipal government--U.S. 2. Lawyers--U.S.
I. Rhyne, Charles   S. II. Title.

NN 0055408   IU ICU ViU-L PSt N WaU-L

National institute of Municipal law officers,
Washington, D.C.
... Automobile trailer and tourist camps - legal
and administrative problems of municipal regulation with an annotated model ordinance, prepared
by Charles S. Rhyne ...   [Washington, D.C. National institute of municipal law officers, 1941]
cover-title, 34p.   (Its Report, no.75, July
1941)
1. Automobiles--Laws and regulations--U.S. 2.
Automobiles--Trailers. 3. Camps (Tourist) I.
Rhyne, Charles S . II. Title.

NN 0055409   IU OC1 ViU-L TxU N Or PU-L

National Institute of Municipal Law Officers,
Washington, D.C.
... Blackouts and air raids -model ordinance
annotated
see under Rhyne, Charles S., 1912-

National institute of municipal law officers,
Washington, D.C.
Charitable, religious, patriotic and philanthropic solicitations - city ordinances and court
decisions - model ordinance annotated. Prepared
by Charles S. Rhyne   [Washington, D.C.] 1942.
cover-title, 60p. tables, forms.   (Its Report
no.84. May, 1942)

1. Charity laws and legislation--U.S. 2. Peddlers and peddling. I. Rhyne, Charles S., ed.

NN 0055411   IU LU ICU CU WaU-L

National Institute of Municipal Law Officers,
Washington, D.C.
Circus regulation by municipalities
see under Burton, Charles H

National Institute of Municipal Law Officers, *Washington,
D.C.*
City smoke control and air pollution programs—model
ordinance, annotated, by Charles S. Rhyne [and] William G.
Van Meter. Washington, 1947.
23 p. 23 cm. (*Its* Report no. 120)
Cover title.

1. Smoke prevention.   ɪ. Rhyne, Charles S., 1912-   ɪɪ. Title.
ɪɪɪ. Series.
JS351.N3 No. 12   614.71   48-2737*

NN 0055413   DLC WaU-L TU NIC

National Institute of Municipal Law Officers,
Washington, D.C.
The Civil aeronautics act annotated
see under Rhyne, Charle S
1912-

---

q350   National Institute of Municipal Law Officers,
N277c   Washington, D. C.
Codification of municipal ordinances, pre-
pared by Charles S. Rhyne.   [Washington, D.C.
National institute of municipal law officers,
1943]
43p.   (Its Report no.95, April, 1943)
Cover-title.

1. International and municipal law.   I. Title.
II. Rhyne, Charles S   III. Series: National In-
stitute of Municipal   Law Officers, Washington,
D.C. Report 95.

NN 0055415   ICarbS ViU-L PSt NjR ICU WaU-L

National institute of municipal law officers,
Washington, D. C.
... Codification of municipal ordinances, by
Charles S. Rhyne ... Washington, National
institute of municipal law officers, 1950.
cover-title, 93 p. 23½cm.   (Its Report no.
132)

NN 0055416   ViU-L DLC TxU WaU-L CU PSt PPBMR

331.83   National institute of municipal law officers,
N2132d   Washington, D.C.
Demolition, vacation or repair of substandard
buildings in connection with housing programs;
summary of latest cases; model ordinance annotated. Prepared and edited by John A. McIntire,
executive director [and] Charles S. Rhyne, attorney   [Washington] 1938.
cover-title, 11p.   (Its Report no.39, August,
1938)
At head of title: National institute of municipal law officers

NN 0055417   IU NcD-L PPCPC

National institute of municipal law officers,
Washington, D.C.
... Emergency rent control and the national defense program [by] Charles S. Rhyne, executive
director. [Washington, D.C.] 1941.
cover-title, 20 numb.l.   (Its Report no.70)

Mimeographed.

1. Rent--U.S. I. Rhyne, Charles S. II. Title.

NN 0055418   IU CU NcD-L DNAL N

National Institute of Municipal Law Officers,
Washington, D. C.
Federal-city relations; a report to the
President of the United States presented at
the White House on March 27, 1953, by David
M. Proctor, president. Washington, D. C.,
[1953]
11 p.

1. Cities and towns - U. S. I. Title. II.
Proctor, David M

NN 0055419   NNC ViU-L IU NcU-L

National Institute of Municipal Law Officers,
Washington, D.C.
Firemen and the law
see under Bahme, Charles W

National Institute of Municipal Law Officers,
Washington, D.C.
Fluoridation of municipal water supply

see under

Rhyne, Charles S   1912-

National Institute of Municipal Law Officers, *Washington,
D. C.*
Labor unions and municipal employe law, by Charles S.
Rhyne. Washington [1946]
583 p. 24 cm. [Its Report no. 116]
"In 1941 the National Institute of Municipal Law Officers published
a study entitled 'Power of municipalities to enter into labor union
contracts—a survey of law and experience' ... The 1941 study is
herein revised, rewritten and expanded to cover the experience in this
field up through April 1, 1946."

——— A supplementary report by Charles S. Rhyne.
Washington, 1949.
63 p. 23 cm. (*Its* Report no. 129)
JS351.N3 no. 129

1. Municipal officials and employees—U. S. 2. Trade-unions—U. S.
3. Collective bargaining—U. S.   ɪ. Rhyne, Charles S., 1912-   ɪɪ.
Title: Municipal employe law.   (Series)
JS351.N3 no. 116   352.073   46-5649 rev 2*

OrU-L CaBVaU WaU-L
NN 0055423   DLC OU NIC TxU TU GU NcD NNC ViU-L

National Institute of Municipal Law Officers,
Washington, D.C.
Legal and statutory materials for city use
in meeting the veterans housing emergency
see under Rhyne, Charles S., 1912-

National Institute of Municipal Law Officers,
Washington, D.C.
Legal problems created for cities by the
national defense program. A report by the Com-
mittee on National Defense... Washington, Na-
tional Institute of Municipal Law Officers, 1941.
44p.
Cover title.
"Presented Dec.4, 1941, at the Annual
Meeting of the National Institute of Municipal
Law Officers..."

NN 0055425   NcD-L

VOLUME 407

National Institute of Municipal Law Officers,
Washington, D.C.
Legal problems incident to revenue bond
financing
see under Wood, David M 1892-

National Institute of Municipal Law Officers, Washington,
D. C.
The legal status of parking meters. Washington, 1936.
11 l. 29 cm. (Its Report no. 12)

Cover title.
At head of title: Institute of Municipal Law Officers.
"In cooperation with the United States Conference of Mayors."

1. Automobile parking—Law and legislation—United States.
I. United States Conference of Mayors. II. Title. III. Series.

KF5305.N3 no. 12   342'.73'09 s   74-187190
⟨KF2236⟩   [343'.73'0046]   MARC

NN 0055427 DLC

S
352.073   National institute of municipal law officers,
qN275r   Washington, D. C.
v.12   The legal status of parking meters. ⟨2d ed.⟩
         ⟨Washington⟩ 1936.
         11, 4 l. 28 p. (National institute of mu-
         nicipal law officers, Washington, D. C. Report
         no. 12)
         Cover title.

         1. Parking meters. I. Title.

NN 0055428 N

National Institute of Municipal Law Officers.
Lynbrook Gardens, inc., petitioner, vs.
Bernard C. Ullmann. Brief
see under   Lynbrook Gardens, inc.
petitioner.

National Institute of Municipal Law Officers,
Washington, D.C.
Mechanical amusement devices
see under   Rhyne, Charles S., 1912-

National Institute of Municipal Law Officers,
Washington, D.C.
Memorandum for attorneys

see under

Rhyne, Charles S   1912-

⟨National Institute of Municipal Law Officers,
Washington, D.C.⟩
Memorandum on local ordinances providing
for compensation and preservation of seniority
and other employment rights of persons employed
by a city who are drafted or who enlist for
Federal National defense service... ⟨Washington?
1939?⟩
8 numb.l.
Caption title.

NN 0055432 NcD-L

NATIONAL INSTITUTE OF MUNICIPAL LAW OFFICERS
Model comic book ordinance: ed. by
Charles S. ⟨Rhyne⟩ Author c1954.
⟨6⟩ p. ⟨⟩

At head of title: Nimlo model comic book
ordinance.

NN 0055433 Or

National institute of municipal law officers,
Washington, D. C.
Model ordinance creating and regulating municipal civil defense organization and operations
and model resolution establishing municipal civil defense organization, prepared by Charles S.
Rhyne ... Washington, National institute of municipal law officers, 1951.
cover-title, 42 p. 23cm. (Its Report, no.
136)

NN 0055434 ViU-L WaT

National Institute of Municipal Law Officers

Model ordinance service. ⟨Author, 1952?⟩-
⟨⟩v. (loose-leaf)

1. Municipal law. I. Title. II. Title:
Ordinance service

NN 0055435 OrP

National institute of municipal law officers,
Washington, D. C.
Model state airport zoning act (November 7,
1944) Washington, D. C., U. S. Dept. of
commerce, Civil aeronautics administration and
National institute of municipal law officers
⟨1945?⟩
15 p. 23cm.

NN 0055436 ViU WaU-L

National Institute of Municipal Law Officers.
Municipal curfew for minors—model ordinance
annotated; prepared by Charles S. Rhyne ...
Washington, D.C., 1943.
(Report no. 99)

NN 0055437 Mi

National institute of municipal law officers,
Washington, D.C.
Municipal law court decisions
see under title

National Institute of Municipal Law Officers,
Washington, D. C.
...Municipal law department organization and
administration. Part I. Prepared by John A.
McIntire...⟨and⟩ Charles S. Rhyne... Washington,
National Institute of Municipal Law Officers,
1940.
1p.l.,47 numb.l. (National Institute of
Municipal Law Officers. Report no.67)
Cover title.
Part II is Report no.90.
Bibliographical footnotes.

NN 0055439 NcD-L ViU OClW CLSU IU

National institute of municipal law officers,
Washington, D. C.
Municipal law journal. v. 1-
Jan. 1936-
Washington, D. C., Institute of municipal law officers ⟨1936-

---

National Institute of Municipal Law Officers,
Wash., D. C.
Municipal ordinance review
see under title

National institute of municipal law officers,
Washington, D. C.
Municipal regulation of dogs—model ordinance   annotated; prepared by Charles S.
Rhyne. Washington 1943.
18 l. 29 cm. (National institute of municipal law officers, Washington, D. C. Report no. 100)
Cover title.
1. Dogs. Laws and legislation. I. Rhyne,
Charles S   1912-   I. Title.

NN 0055442 N ViU-L

S
352.073   National institute of municipal law officers,
qN275r   Washington, D. C.
v.11   Municipal regulation of mechanical "amuse-
         ment devises." ⟨Washington⟩ 1936.
         8⟨6⟩ l. 28 cm. (National institute of mu-
         nicipal law officers, Washington, D. C. Re-
         port no. 11)
         Cover title.

         1. Vending machines. I. Title.

NN 0055443 N

National Institute of Municipal Law Officers,
Washington, D.C.
Municipal regulation of milk and milk products

see under

Rhyne, Charles S   1912-

National Institute of Municipal Law Officers, *Washington,
D. C.*
Municipal regulation of peddlers, solicitors, & itinerant
merchants, by Charles S. Rhyne, Charles H. Burton ⟨and⟩
Charlie O. Murphy. Washington, 1947.
165 p. 23 cm. (*Its* Report no. 118)

Cover title.

1. Peddlers and peddling—U. S.   I. Rhyne, Charles S., 1912-
II. Title.   (Series)

JS351.N3 no. 118   352.8   48-18873*

NN 0055445 DLC WaU-L NIC NBuU-L

S
352.073   National institute of municipal law officers,
qN275r   Washington, D. C.
v.115   Municipal regulation of refrigerated
         locker plants—model ordinance annotated, by
         Charles S. Rhyne. Washington, 1946.
         17 p. 23 cm. (National institute of mu-
         nicipal law officers, Washington, D. C. Re-
         port no. 115)
         Cover title.
         1. Refrigerators. Laws and regulations.
         I. Rhyne, Charles S   1912-   II.
         Title.

NN 0055446 N ViU-L

National Institute of Municipal Law Officers,
Washington, D.C.
Municipal regulation of signs, billboards,

see under

Rhyne, Charles S   1912-

National Institute of Municipal Law Officers,
Washington, D.C.
Municipal regulations, taxation and use of
radio and television

see under

Rhyne, Charles S   1912-

VOLUME 407

National Institute of Municipal Law Officers, *Washington,*
D. C.
Municipalities and the law in action
see
NIMLO municipal law review.

National Institute of Municipal Law Officers, *Washington,*
D. C.
Municipally owned parking lots and garages, by Charles
S. Rhyne. Washington, 1948.
54 p.   23 cm.   (*Its Report no. 121*)
Cover title.

1. Automobile parking—U. S. 2. Garages. 3. Municipal ownership—U. S.   I. Rhyne, Charles S., 1912–   II. Title.   (Series)

JS351.N3 no. 121   352.5   48–10685*

NN   0055450   DLC WaU-L NIC TxU N PPBMR

KB3811   NATIONAL INSTITUTE OF MUNICIPAL LAW
.N4N27   OFFICERS, Washington, D. C.

NIMLO codification computerization
project. Washington, D.C. ₍n.d.₎
1 v. illus.
Cover title.

1. Municipal government—U.S.
2. Automation—U.S. I. Title.

NN   0055451   ICU

KF   National Institute of Municipal Law Officers,
211   Washington, D. C.
P18   NIMLO model city income tax ordinance.
v.148   Ed. by Charles S. Rhyne. Washington
no.22   ₍1954?₎
         14 p. 24cm.

Cover title.
In Pamphlets 148.

1. Income tax. 2. Model ordinances.
I. Rhyne,   Charles S., 1912–
ed. II.   Title.

NN   0055452   NIC MiU Wa ICarbS MiU-L MiD

NAC   National Institute of Municipal Law Officers,
1472   Washington, D. C.
N27   NIMLO model municipal refuse collection sys-
         tem ordinance. ₍Washington, 195–₎
         ₍8₎ p. 24cm.

1. Refuse and refuse disposal.

NN   0055453   NIC

NAC   National Institute of Municipal Law Officers,
1451   Washington, D. C.
N27   *NIMLO model ordinance prohibiting unneces-
         sary noises. ₍Washington, 195–₎
         ₍4₎ p. 24cm.

1. Noise control—Law and legislation.

NN   0055454   NIC

National Institute of Municipal Law Officers, *Washington,*
D. C.
NIMLO model ordinance service. Rev. continuously to
reflect latest court decisions and current municipal problems.
Edited by Charles S. Rhyne, general counsel. Washington,
*1952–
v. 26 cm.

1. Model ordinances—U. S.   I. Rhyne, Charles S., 1912–   ed.
II. Title.

352.073   53—32403

IU PPCPC LU-L NBuU-L
NN   0055455   DLC CaBVaU OOxM NcD-L N OU TU NN FMU

JS   National Institute of Municipal Law Officers,
388   Washington, D.C.
.N28   NIMLO model purchasing ordinance annotated;
         edited by Charles S. Rhyne, general counsel.
         Washington ₍1954₎
         22 p.   23 cm.
         Cover title.

1. Government purchasing—U.S. 2. Model ordinances—U.S. I. Rhyne, Charles S., 1912– ed.

NN   0055456   MiU IU NNC NcU

KF   National Institute of Municipal Law Officers,
211   Washington, D. C.
P18   NIMLO model zoning ordinance. Ed. by
v.148   Charles S. Rhyne. Washington ₍1954?₎
no.23   43 p. 24cm.

Cover title.
In Pamphlets 148.

1. Zoning. 2. Model ordinances. I.
Rhyne, Charles   S., 1912–   ed.

ICarbS
NN   0055457   NIC IU PPPHA PPCPC PU-FA PPT MiU-L

Law   National Institute of Municipal Law Officers,
         Washington, D. C.
NIMLO municipal law review ... Proceedings of the annual
conference. v. ₍1₎–
1938–
Washington, National Institute of Municipal Law Officers.

National Institute of Municipal Law Officers,
Washington, D. C.
NIMLO's recommendations on the scope and
conduct of the President's proposed Commission
on Governmental Functions and Fiscal Resources. By David M. Proctor, president,
Denis M. Hurley, trustee ₍and₎ Charles S.
Rhyne, general counsel. Washington ₍1953₎
8 p.

NN   0055459   NNC ViU-L NcU-L

National Institute of Municipal Law Officers,
Washington, D.C.
National defense and municipal legal
problems
see under   Rhyne, Charles S., 1912–

National Institute of Municipal Law Officers
One city's legal experience in civil liberties
see under   Chicago. Dept. of law.

---

*HE370   National institute of municipal law officers,
N28   Washington, D. C.
         Parking meters as city legal problems ₍by₎
John A. McIntire, executive director ₍and₎
Charles S. Rhyne, attorney. ₍Washington,
D. C.₎ 1939.

cover-title, 26₍1₎ numb. ℓ.   29cm.   (Its
Report no. 47, September, 1939)

NN   0055462   NBuG CU MiU-L

National Institute of Municipal Law Officers, *Washington*
D. C.
Parking meters—legality—model ordinance, annotated, by
Charles S. Rhyne and Charlie O. Murphy. Washington,
1947.
29 p. 23 cm.   (*Its Report no. 119*)
Cover title.

1. Parking meters.   I. Rhyne, Charles S., 1912–   II. Series.

JS351.N3 No. 119   388.3   48–2736*

NN   0055463   DLC ViU-L NIC MnU-L WaU-L

National Institute of Municipal Law Officers,
Washington, D.C.
Pensions for death or disability incurred by
city employees while in armed forces, by
Charles S. Rhyne ... Washington, National
Institute of Municipal law Officers, 1946.
cover-title, 33 p. 23 cm.   (Its Report
no. 114)

NN   0055464   ViU-L

National institute of municipal law officers, *Washington,*
D. C.
... Power of municipalities to enter into labor union con-
tracts—a survey of law and experience, prepared by Charles
S. Rhyne ... ₍Washington₎ 1941.
cover-title, 78 p. 28ᵐ. (*Its Report no. 76*)

1. Municipal government—U. S. 2. Trade-unions—U. S. 3. Collective
bargaining—U. S.   I. Rhyne, Charles S. II. Title.

Princeton univ. Library   A 44–589
for Library of Congress   JS351.N3   no. 76
₍3₎†   (352.0006273) 352.073

ICU PU-L
NN   0055465   NjP OrU-L NIC N DI ViU-L DLC OC1 MH IU

National Institute of Municipal Law Officers, *Washington,*
D. C.
Proceedings of the annual conference
see
NIMLO municipal law review.

National institute of municipal law officers,
Washington, D.C.
... Radio and municipal regulations prepared by
John A. McIntire, executive director ₍and₎ Charles
S. Rhyne, attorney. ₍Washington, D.C.₎ 1940.
cover-title, 44p.   (Its Report no.62)
"Printed in cooperation with the United States
conference of mayors."

1. Radio—U.S.—Laws and regulations. I. McIntire, John Albert, 1907–   II. Rhyne, Charles
S. III. United States conference of mayors.

NN   0055467   IU TxU

National Institute of Municipal Law Officers, *Washington,*
D. C.
Report.

Washington.
no. 28–29 cm.
No.   Issued by the institute under its earlier name: **Institute of**
Municipal Law Officers.
INDEXES:

Subject index.
No. 1–133, 1935–50. (Issued as no. 134) 1 no.
1. Municipal government—U. S.

JS351.N3   352.073   48–27268 rev*

NcRS NcU
NN   0055468   DLC AAP MiU-L GU OrP Or MiD NN NcD LU

SSTA   National Institute of Municipal Law Officers.
.N26r   Reprint of brief filed before the National
no. 94   War Labor Board on December 2, 1942 ₍on₎ the
         law relating to collective bargaining between
         municipalities and their employees and the
         effect of the distinction between govern-
         mental and proprietary functions. Omaha
         ₍1943?₎
         157 p.   (₍Its Report no. 94₎)

NN   0055469   ViU-L

JS   National Institute of Municipal Law Officers,
351   Washington, D.C.
.N28   Subject matter index to NIMLO reports 1–133
Index   (with appendix listing titles and prices of each)
         By Charles S. Rhyne. Washington, 1950.
         60 p. 23 cm.   (Its Report no 134)
         Cover title.
         Text on p.₍2–4₎ of cover.

I. Rhyne, Charles Sylvanus, 1912–

NN   0055470   MiU NNC WaU-L ViU-L

VOLUME 407

National institute of municipal law officers,
Washington, D.C.
... Summary legal analysis and check list of ma-
terials on "bank night" schemes.   :Washington,
D.C.¡ 1937.
cover-title, 5 numb.l.   (Its Report no.22)
Mimeographed.
At head of title: Institute of municipal law
officers ... Washington, D.C.
Introduction signed: Paul V. Betters, executive
director.
"Check-list of recent materials": leaves 4-5.

NN   0055471   IU ViU-L NcD-L

S   National institute of municipal law officers,
352.073   Washington, D. C.
qN275r   Survey of exemption of state instrumental-
v.20   ities from federal taxation: McCullock v.
Maryland to Brush v. Helvering. Washington,
1937.
7 l. 28 cm. (National institute of municipal law officers, Washington, D. C. Report no. 20)
Cover title.
"Originally prepared by Mr. David Hotten-
stein."
1. Taxation.   Exemption from U.S. 2.
U.S. Taxation. I.Hottenstein,David.II.Title

NN   0055472   N

National institute of municipal law officers,
Washington, D.C.
... Tort notice of claim statutes, legal interpre-
tation and effect ¡by¡ John A. McIntire, executive
director ¡and¡ Charles S. Rhyne, attorney.
¡Washington, D.C.¡ 1940.
cover-title, 37 numb.l.   (Its Report no.60)
Mimeographed.
"The major research on this report was done by
Harry Kay".– Pref.
Bibliographical foot-notes.

NN   0055473   IU NcD-L

National institute of Municipal Law Officers,
Washington, D.C.
Traffic prosecutor's manual
see under Burton, Charles H

National institute of municipal law officers,
Washington, D.C.
... Use of confidential information by "adminis-
trative tribunals."   ¡Washington, D.C.¡ 1938.
3 p.l., 8 numb.l.   (Its Report no.35)
Mimeographed.
Caption title.
Signed: John A. McIntire and Charles S. Rhyne.

1. Evidence (Law)--U.S. I. McIntire, John Albert, 1907-   II. Rhyne, Charles S. III. Title.

NN   0055475   IU NcD-L ViU-L

National institute of municipal law officers,
Washington, D. C.
The United States municipal news; a bi-weekly record of
municipal progress. v. 1–   Apr. 10, 1934–
Chicago ¡etc.¡, 1934–

National institute of municipal law officers, *Washington,
D. C. Committee on wartime legal problems of cities.*
... One year's experience of American cities at war; a report
by the Committee on wartime legal problems of cities ...
Presented to the war conference of the National institute of
municipal law officers, hotel Commodore, New York city, December 2, 1942. ¡Washington, 1943?¡
cover-title, 104 p. 23ᶜᵐ.
Running title: The war and cities in 1942.
From the Institute's Municipalities and the law in action, 1943.
1. Municipal government– U. S. 2. U. S.–Civilian defense. ɪ. Title.
                                                A 44–2705 †
Enoch Pratt free library
for Library of Congress   JS331.N22
                              ¡a45d1¡†   355.23

WaU-L ViU-L
NN   0055477   MdBE IU NN MiU-L NIC NBuU DLC OrP

ML1   National Institute of Music and Arts.
.J92
           Junior musicians of America magazine.
           ¡Los Angeles, etc.¡ Junior Musicians of America¡

M1378   National institute of music and
.S656N5   arts.
           Stiska, Karl, *arr.*
           Nioma all grade concert album, piano ... Compiled by K.
           Stiska. Los Angeles, Seattle, National institute of music and
           arts, inc., ᶜ1939.

MT590   National institute of music and
.B3   arts.
           Baker, Leon I
           Nioma technical studies for Hawaiian guitar ... by Leon I.
           Baker ... to be used in conjunction with Nioma popular Ha-
           waiian guitar method ... Los Angeles, Seattle ¡National in-
           stitute of music & arts, 1940–

QU   NATIONAL Institute of Nutrition, London
1   ¡Collection of publications¡
N277
               The Library has a collection of miscel-
           laneous publications of this organization
           kept as received. These publications are
           not listed or bound separately.
               1. Nutrition

NN   0055481   DNLM

National Institute of Nutrition, *Los Angeles.*
A brief history of nutritional diseases. Los Angeles, 1952.
92 p. illus. 16 cm.

1. Deficiency diseases–Hist.

RC620.5.N3   *616.46   616.39   53–4 ‡

NN   0055482   DLC DNLM

RC813   National Institute of Nutrition, Los Angeles.
.N3   Nutritional obesity; its cause and correction;
           a new concept for the reduction of excess weight.
           [Los Angeles, National Institute of Nutrition]
           c1934.
               28 p.   19 cm.
               Arguments in favor of Min-amin.
               Bibliographical foot-notes.

NN   0055483   DLC

National Institute of Nutrition, *Tokyo*
                see
Kokuritsu Eiyō Kenkyūjo, *Tokyo.*

Q115   National Institute of Oceanography.
.D7
           Discovery reports. v. 1–
               Cambridge ¡Eng.¡ The University Press, 1929–

NATIONAL INSTITUTE OF OCEANOGRAPHY.
    Report. 1949/50–
Cambridge [Eng.] University press.   v.
illus.   26cm.

    Annual.
    Brief reports for 1950/51-1964/65 included in:
National oceanographic   council. Report.

Continued in next column

Continued from preceding column

    At head of title, 1965/66–   : Natural environ-
ment research council.

1. Ocean. I. Natural environment research council.

NN   0055487   NN CaBVaU PPAN DI

Q115
G7   National Institute of Oceanography.
v.28   Station list, 1950-1951.
p.299–   (In Discovery reports. Cambridge [Eng.]
398.   1957. 31 cm. v. 28, p. 299-398, plates (maps),
           tables)
               Cover title.
               Bibliography: p. 302.

           1. Oceanographic research. I. Title.

NN   0055488   DI

Q115
G7   National Institute of Oceanography.
v.26   Station list, R.R.S. 'William Scoresby',
p. 211-   p. 211-1950.
258.   (In Discovery reports. Cambridge [Eng.],
           1953. 31 cm. v. 26, p. 211-258, maps,
           tables)
               Cover title.

           1. Ocean. I. Title. (Series)

NN   0055489   DI

National Institute of Oceanography
see also Gt. Brit. *"Discovery" Committee.*

National Institute of Oceanography
see also National Oceanographic Council. (Gt. Brit.)

National Institue of Oceanography, *Wormley*
            see
Wormley, Eng. (Surrey) National Institue of Oceanography.

307
N214   National Institute of Oilseed Products.
Ed.2   Trading rules.   Rev.   San Francisco,
           1949.
               81 p.

           1. Oil-seed trade. U.S. 2. Fats and
oils.

NN   0055493   DNAL

NATIONAL INSTITUTE OF PACKAGING, HANDLING AND
    LOGISTIC ENGINEERS.
    Membership directory.
Washington.   v.   22cm.

    Annual.

1. Packing--Direct.--U.S. 2. Material handling--Direct.--U.S.

NN   0055494   NN

VOLUME 407

National Institute of Personnel Research
see
National Institute for Personnel Research.

W
19.5
AI3
C5N2   NATIONAL Institute of Pharmacy, Chicago
Catologs, announcements of courses,
requirements for admission and other
publications relating to the academic
program will be found under the above
call number. Included also are similar
publications of individual schools or
departments of instruction of the
institution.

NN   0055496   DNLM

Film
1435
no.7   National Institute of Pharmacy.
[Communications] Chicago, 1888.
12 p. illus.
Film copy.

NN   0055497   DNLM

615
N27   National institute of pharmacy, Chicago
Lectures, semi-monthly... term l-
lecture l-   Chicago, Engelhard,
n.d.
Q.   v. illus.,plates, tables (part fold.)

Term I, Term in pharmacy; term II: Botany
and materia medica. Term in chemistry.
C.S.N. Hallberg, director.
For list of vols. in this library see next
card.

NN   0055498   IaU DNLM OC1W

National Institute of Pharmacy, Chicago.
——. Semi-annual announcement for 1891-2
(2.). 16 pp. r°. Chicago, G. P. Engelhard &
Co., 1891.
A system of home study. Lectures semi-monthly by
mail.

NN   0055499   DNLM

National Institute of Pharmacy, Chicago.
Special announcement. October, 1888. 4°.
[Chicago, G. P. Engelhard & Co., 1888.]

NN   0055500   DNLM

Mann
SF
481
H29   National Institute of Poultry Husbandry,
Newport, Eng.
Bulletin. no. 1-
1928-   Reading.
nos. illus. 27 cm.

1. Poultry - Societies. 2. Poultry -
Gt. Brit. I. Harper Adams Agricultural College, Newport, Eng.

NN   0055501   NIC

National institute of practical mechanics, *Chicago.*
Complete practical rail-roading; a complete series of
text-books on modern railway transportation ... prepared by motive power superintendents, master mechanics, traveling engineers and mechanical experts, associated with the National institute of practical mechanics.
Standard brotherhood ed. Chicago, National institute
of practical mechanics [1911]
8 v. illus, plates (partly fold.) diagrs. (partly col, partly fold.) 18ᵐᵐ
(v. [8] 23ᵐᵐ)

Continued in next column

Continued from preceding column

Folded key to Portfolio of colored charts inserted in [v. 8]
"Authorities consulted" at beginning of each volume.
CONTENTS.—[v. 1] 1st, 2nd and 3rd year progressive examinations with
answers.—[v. 2] Locomotives, their operation, care and management.—
[v. 3] New York and straight air brake practice.—[v. 4] Practical electricity
for enginemen.—[v. 5] Practical repairing of everyday breakdowns.—[v. 6]
Standard rules, car heating and lighting.—[v. 7] Westinghouse air brake
practice.—[v. 8] Portfolio of colored charts.

1. Railroads. 2. Locomotives. 3. Air-brakes.

Library of Congress   TF7.N3   12-203

NN   0055503   DLC

FOR OTHER EDITIONS
SEE MAIN ENTRY
National institute of practical mechanics.
Horstmann, Henry Charles, 1858-   *ed.*
Electrical workers standard library; complete, practical, authoritative, comprehensive, up-to-date working
manuals for electrical workers ... Editors in chief:
Henry C. Horstmann, Victor H. Tousley ... assisted by
the instructors, Electrical department, National institute
of practical mechanics. Brotherhood ed. Chicago, National institute of practical mechanics [1915]

National institute of practical mechanics.
Modern American engineering; a complete series of
practical text books prepared especially for the use of
steam engineers, electricians, erecting engineers and
power users generally. Prepared by a corps of experts,
electrical engineers and designers connected with the National institute of practical mechanics ... Chicago, National institute of practical mechanics [1911]
5 v. illus, plates (partly fold.) tables, diagrs. 23ᵐᵐ. $30.00
Added t-p.
Editor-in-chief, C. F. Swingle.

CONTENTS.—v. 1. Steam boilers, steam engines, their construction, care
and operation.—v. 2. Marine engines, turbines, gas engines, air compres-
sors, elevators, refrigeration.—v. 3. Electricity for engineers, generators,
switchboards, armature winding.—v. 4. Millwrighting, shafting, mechanical
drawing, machine designing.—v. 5. Ventilating, plumbing, steam and hot
water heating, gas-fitting.

1. Mechanical engineering. I. Swingle, Calvin Franklin, 1846-   ed.

Library of Congress   TJ145.N2   11-17098

NN   0055506   DLC

National institute of practical mechanics.
FOR OTHER EDITIONS
SEE MAIN ENTRY
Swingle, Calvin Franklin, 1846-   *ed.*
Modern American railway practice; a complete sys-
tem of practical instruction in railway transportation ...
Calvin F. Swingle, editor in chief, assisted by a corps of
mechanical experts. Chicago. Ill., National institute of
practical mechanics [1913]

National institute of public administration
see
Institute of public administration, *New York.*

National Institute of Public Administration (*Indonesia*)
see
Indonesia. *Lembaga Administrasi Negara.*

National institute of public affairs, *Washington, D. C.*
... Annual report. 1936/37-
Washington, D. C., 1937-
v. 22½ᵐᵐ.

1. Civil service—U. S.

Library of Congress   JK716.A1N3   42-89140

NN   0055510   DLC OrCS

National institute of public affairs, *Washington, D. C.*
National institute of public affairs. Washington, D. C.
[1940]
cover-title, 28 p. 23ᵐ.

1. Political science—Study and teaching. 2. U. S.—Pol. & govt.—
Study and teaching. 3. Civil service—U. S.
43-29450

Library of Congress   JK716.N33   1940
[2]   350.714

NN   0055511   DLC NNC

National institute of public affairs, *Washington, D. C.*
National institute of public affairs. Washington, D. C.,
1941.
cover-title, 27 p. illus. (incl. port.) 23ᵐ.

1. Political science—Study and teaching. 2. U. S.—Pol. & govt.—Study
and teaching. 3. Civil service—U. S.
42-20456

Library of Congress   JK716.N33
[2]   350.714

NN   0055512   DLC

320.6
N213n
1945   NATIONAL INSTITUTE OF PUBLIC AFFAIRS,
Washington, D.C.
National institute of public affairs.
Washington, D.C., 1945.
32p. illus.(incl. ports) 23cm.

1. Political science - Study and teaching.
2. U.S. - Pol. & govt. - Study and teaching. 3.
Civil service -   U. S.

NN   0055513   TxU MH

National institute of public affairs, *Washington, D. C.*
The organization of basic courses in public administration
at 75 American colleges and universities, based upon a survey
made by the National institute of public affairs, Washington,
D. C., and the Committee on public administration, Social
science research council. New York, N. Y., 1937.
[8] p. 28ᵐ.
Planographed.
Frederick M. Davenport, chairman, National institute of public affairs; Louis Brownlow, chairman, Committee on public administration,
Social science research council.
1. Universities and colleges—U. S.—Curricula. I. Social science
research council. Committee on public administration. II. Davenport,
Frederick Morgan, 1866- III. Brownlow, Louis, 1879- IV. Title.
v. Title: Public administra- tion, The organization of basic
courses in.
E 40-314

U. S. Off. of educ. Library   LB2365.P85N2
for Library of Congress   [2]

NN   0055514   DHEW NNC

National Institute of Public Affairs, *Washington, D. C.*
The work of the National Institute of Public Affairs, 1934-
1949, a summary [by Karl E. Stromsen, educational director]
Washington [1949]
[v, 92 p. 24 cm.
"The background and present activities of the interns, 1936-1949":
p. 19-92.

1. Public administration—Study and teaching. 2. Political science—Study and teaching. I. Stromsen, Karl E.

JA88.U6N45   350.714   50-11567

DNAL
NN   0055515   DLC OrPR OrU DI ICU PBm TxU ViU PSt

National Institute of Public Health, Bilthoven,
Netherlands
see
Netherlands (Kingdom, 1815-). Rijks-
instituut voor de Volksgezondheid.

National Institute of Public Health, *Tokyo*
see
Kokuritsu Kōshū Eiseiin, *Tokyo.*

VOLUME 407

National Institute of Real Estate Brokers
see **National Association of Real Estate Boards.** *National Institute of Real Estate Brokers.*

National institute of research in colloid chemistry
see Wisconsin. University.
Proposed National institute for research in colloid chemistry.

National Institute of Rug Cleaners, inc., New York.
Carpets and their maintenance
see under American Hotel & Motel Association.

NATIONAL INSTITUTE OF RUG CLEANING.
Roster of active member firms.
Silver Spring, Md.?   no.   26cm.

1. Cleaning and dyeing industry   --Direct.

NN   0055521   NN

National Institute of Science.
Transactions. v. 1–   Apr. 1948–
₍n. p.₎
    v. 23 cm. annual.

1. Science—Societies, etc.
    Q11.N2894   506.273   53–33847

NN   0055522   DLC

National institute of science, Chicago.
    ... The key to mental and physical power...
    see under Anderson, Lewis H.

National Institute of Sciences of India.
Bulletin. v. 1–
Sept. 1952–
New Delhi.
    v. illus., maps, tables.
Includes bibliographies.

1. Science – Periodicals.

NN   0055524   MsSM NjP DNAL MH NcRS

Q1
.I53
    National Institute of Sciences of India.
Indian science abstracts. 1935–39. ₍Calcutta₎ National Institute of Sciences of India.

National Institute of Sciences of India.
Proceedings. v. 1–
New Delhi ₍etc.₎, 1935–
    v. in   illus., maps (part fold.) diagrs., tables. 25 cm.
Vols. 21–   issued in 2 parts: A. Physical sciences. B. Biological sciences.
Includes supplements.

1. Science—Societies, etc.
    Q73.N3   S A 64–6518

ICF CaOTU MiU CaBVaU OU ICRL DAS NNC
NN   0055526   DLC GU NN IU NSyU ICU DNLM KU ICJ NcRS

GB608
.71
.S95
1952
    National Institute of Sciences of India.
Symposium on the Rajputana Desert, *Delhi, 1952.*
    Proceedings. New Delhi, National Institute of Sciences of India, 1952.

TP326
.I5S9
1950
    National Institute of Sciences of India.
Symposium on Scientific Utilization of Coal in India, *Delhi, 1950.*
    Proceedings. New Delhi, National Institute of Sciences of India, 1953.

S590
.S9
1952
    National Institute of Sciences of India.
Symposium on Soil Research in India, *Calcutta, 1952.*
    Proceedings. New Delhi, National Institute of Sciences of India, 1954.

RS180
.I3S9
1955
    National Institute of Sciences of India.
Symposium on Indigenous Drugs and Insecticides, *Bangalore, 1955.*
    Proceedings. New Delhi, National Institute of Sciences of India, 1955.

TN103
.S9
1953
    National Institute of Sciences of India.
Symposium on Mineral Raw Materials and Their By-Products, *Delhi, 1953.*
    Proceedings. New Delhi, National Institute of Sciences of India, 1955.

QH366
.A1S9
1953
    National Institute of Sciences of India.
Symposium on Organic Evolution, *Delhi, 1953.*
    Proceedings. New Delhi, National Institute of Sciences of India, 1955.

TH153
.S9
1952
    National Institute of Sciences of India.
Symposium on Scientific Principles and Their Application in Tropical Building Design and Construction, *Delhi, 1952.*
    Proceedings. New Delhi, National Institute of Sciences of India, 1955.

QK867
.S94
1953
    National Institute of Sciences of India.
Symposium on Trace Elements in the Nutrition of Plants and Animals, *Lucknow, 1953.*
    Proceedings. New Delhi, National Institute of Sciences of India, 1955.

Q127
.I4P75
    National Institute of Sciences of India.
Progress of science in India. New Delhi, National Institute of Sciences of India ₍1953–

Y/1750
N277
    National institute of sciences of India, Calcutta.
    Symposium on weather prediction. Calcutta. 1939.
    p.43–165. tabs., diagrs. (part fold.) 25½cm.

    (Reprinted from Proceedings of the Institute of sciences of India, v.5, no.1.)

NN   0055536   DAS

National Institute of Sciences of India.
Transactions. v. 1–
New Delhi ₍etc.₎, 19,35–
    v. illus., maps (part fold.) diagrs., tables. 31 cm.

1. Science—Societies, etc.
    Q73.N32   S A 64–6517

NN   0055537   DLC NN OU CSt MiU

Z5853
.P8 I53
    Indian National Scientific Documentation Centre, Delhi.
    Utilization of solar energy; list of references, compiled by INSDOC for National Institute of Sciences of India ₍and₎ Unesco symposium on solar energy and wind power. ₍Delhi₎ 1954.

506
N212y
    National Institute of Sciences of India.
    Year book.

    New Delhi.
        v. tables. 21cm.

    1. Science – Societies.

NN   0055539   TxU DNAL NcU

National Institute of Social Relations.
    It pays to talk it over; some notes and suggestions for group discussion leaders. Washington ₍1947₎
    48 p. illus. 28 cm.
    Some of the material appeared serially in Talk it over, pub. by the institute.
    "Where to get recordings": p. 47.
    "For further reading": p. 48.
    CONTENTS.—It pays to talk it over, by Julius Schreiber.—But you have to sell the idea, by Ruth Green and E. I. Johnson.—And gather and organize your material, by W. L. Sturdevant, Jr.—However, discussions must be led, by H. M. Forstenzer.—And audio-visual aids are useful, by Stephen Kraft.
    1. Discussion.   I. Title.
    BF637.D5N3   374.24   48–523*

NN   0055540   DLC OrU-M CU Mi

National Institute of Social Relations.
    It pays to talk it over; some notes and suggestions for group discussion leaders. Washington ₍1948₎
    48 p. illus. 28 cm.

NN   0055541   NcD

National Institute of Social Relations
    It pays to talk it over; some notes and suggestions for group discussion leaders. [by Julius Schreiber and staff] NY, Community Relations Service [1951]

    40 p. illus.

NN   0055542   MH

HN51
.T3
    National Institute of Social Relations.

    Talk it over. ser.Y101, G101–
    1946–
    Washington, National Institute of Social Relations.

National Institute of Social Sciences.
    Annual meeting, containing an account of the proceedings
    see its
    Proceedings of the annual meeting.

VOLUME 407

H11   National institute of social sciences.
.N4   Bulletin...
          [New York?

NN 0055545   DLC

National institute of social sciences.
    Constitution and list of members of the National institute of
social sciences...   [New York, 1926]   23 p.   23cm.

NN 0055546   NN DPU OU DL

NATIONAL INSTITUTE OF SOCIAL SCIENCES. .
    Government versus private railroads..[New
York],1919.

    This volume also represents no.51 of the
Journal of the American social science association.

NN 0055547   MH-BA

National institute of social sciences.
    Journal of the National institute of social sciences ...
v. 1–   [New York] 1915–

    v. illus., plates, port. 23¾ cm.

    Vols. 16–19, 1931–34, combined in one issue.
    Editor: 1915–18, Lillie H. French.
    Vols. 1–11 also represent no. 47–57 of the Journal of the American
social science association.
    Vols. 4–   have each a special title at head of t.-p.: v. 4, 1918,
Reconstruction after the war; v. 5, 1919, Government versus private
railroads; v. 6, 1920, Leadership in democracy; v. 7, 1921, International obligations; v. 8, 1923, International questions; v. 9, 1924, Goodwill toward peoples in the development of international relations and

    promotion of peace; v. 10, 1925, World problems; v. 11, 1926, Current
discussions; v. 12, 1927, Wide influence of public service; v. 13, 1928,
Some present-day problems; v. 14, 1929, A widening outlook; v. 15,
1930/31, Science in social service; v. 16/19, 1931/34, Applied social
science.
    "Index to volumes of previous journals of the institute, vols.
I–XIII": v. 14, 1929, p. 196–204.
    List of members in v. 2–4, 6–7, 9–

    1. Social sciences—Societies, etc.   I. French, Lillie Hamilton, 1854–
1939, ed.   II. Title.   III. Title: Reconstruction after the war.   IV. Title:
Government versus private railroads.   v. Title: Leadership in a democracy.   VI. Title: International obligations.   VII. Title: International questions.   VIII. Title: Goodwill towards peoples in the development of international relations.   IX. Title: World problems.   x.
Title: Current discussions.   XI. Title: Wide influence of public service.
XII. Title: Some present-day problems.   XIII. Title: A widening outlook.   XIV. Title: Science in social service.   xv. Title: Applied social
service.

    H11.N43   306.273   16—3326

        OC1 OO ICJ MB MiU OCU OU MsU ViB1bV WvU
NN 0055550   DLC CU NjP MBCo IC ICRL Or OAkU NcD

National Institute of Social Sciences.
    Proceedings of the annual dinner. 1940–
[New York?]

    v. 23 cm.

    Report of the 1915 annual dinner pub. in the Report of the 1915
annual meeting; 1916–34 proceedings were pub. in v. 2–16/19 of the
institute's Journal; 1935–39 proceedings were not pub.

    H11.N295   306.273   49–40463*

NN 0055551   DLC TxU ICJ NN

National Institute of Social Sciences.
    Proceedings of the annual meeting.

    [New York]

    v. 24 cm.

    Title varies: Annual meeting, containing an account of
the proceedings and the report of the Medal Committee.
    Vol. for 1922 has also a distinctive title: Results of the Conference
on Limitation of Armaments.

    1. Social sciences—Societies, etc.

    H11.N3   17–12581 rev*‡

        MB
NN 0055552   DLC NBuG OC1 OU MiU NN DL MdBJ TxU DS

National Institute of Social Sciences.
    Report of the annual meeting.
New York.

    v. 23 cm.

    Most reports accompanied by the invitation to the annual meeting.

    1. Social sciences—Societies, etc.

    H11.N434   306.273   58–2058 ‡

NN 0055553   DLC

National institute of social science.

National liberty medal committee.
    Report ... of the Liberty medal committee; American
social science association ...   The National institute of
social sciences ...   1918/19–
[New York?] 1919–

National Institute of Social Sciences.
    Results of the Conference on Limitation of Armaments
    see its
    Proceedings of the annual meeting.

National Institute of Social Sciences
    see also
American Social Science Association.

National institute of social welfare and social
    reform, Havana
        see   Havana.   Instituto nacional de previsión
y reformas sociales.

National Institute of Statistics (Portugal)
    see
    Portugal.   Instituto Nacional de Estatística.

HF5549   National institute of vocational research,
.V27   Los Angeles.
            Van Allyn, Keith.
    Job placement reference, with introduction to the job place-
ment technique, by Keith Van Allyn ...   Los Angeles, National
institute of vocational research, inc., 1945.

National institute of vocational research, *Los Angeles.*
    The key to vocational guidance and occupational placement,
prepared for National institute of vocational research ...   For
educators, personnel directors, employment managers, vocational counselors.   [Los Angeles, National institute of vocational research, ᶜ1938]

    cover-title, sheet.   51 x 66ᶜᵐ fold. in cover 28 x 20ᶜᵐ.

    1. Occupations. 2. Profession. Choice of.   I. Title.
                                                        39–29701
    Library of Congress   HF5381.N33
    Copyright AA 292477   [3]   371.425

NN 0055560   DLC CU

HF5381   National institute of vocational research, Los
.V3   Angeles.

        Van Allyn, Keith.
    Van Allyn technique for vocational selection (tentative
manual) by Keith Van Allyn, PH. D. Prepared for National
institute of vocational research, Los Angeles, California [Los
Angeles, National institute of vocational research, 1940]

National Institute of Zoology and Botany, *Nanking*
    see
    Chung yang yen chiu yüan. *Tung chih wu yen chiu so,
    Nanking.*

The National institute on education and the war.

[National education association of the United States. *Educational research service]*
    The National institute on education and the war. [Wash-
ington] 1942.

National institute on education and the war, *Washington,
D. C.,* 1942.
    Handbook on education and the war, based on proceedings
of the National institute on education and the war, sponsored
by the U. S. Office of education Wartime commission at American university, Washington, D. C., August 28 through 31,
1942. Federal security agency ... U. S. Office of education ...
[Washington, U. S. Govt. print. off., 1943]
    xv, 344 p. diagrs. 26½ᶜᵐ.
    "Source materials": p. 312–313.
    1. Education—U. S. 2. World war, 1939–   —U. S.   I. U. S.
Office of education.
                                                        43–51852
    Library of Congress   D810.E3N35 1942
                                [10]   370.973

        WaS OrU OrP OrCS MtBC CABVaU
NN 0055564   DLC OOxM NcD TxU CtY ICJ OU OCU OC1

National institute on education and the war, *Washington,
D. C.,* 1942.
    National institute on education and the war. Sponsored by
the U. S. Office of education, Wartime commission, Washington, D. C., August 28 to August 31, 1942, American university
campus ...   [Washington, 1942]
    31, [1] p. illus. (map) 26½ᶜᵐ.

    1. Education—U. S. 2. World war, 1939–   —U. S.   I. U. S.
Office of education. Wartime commission.
                                                        42–38577
    Library of Congress   D810.E3N35
                                [3]   370.6373

NN 0055565   DLC CtY

National Institute on Girl Sports, Washington, D. C.
    Proceedings...
        see under   American Association for
Health, Physical Education, and Recreation.
Division for Girls and Women's Sports.

National Institute on Hospital Accounting and
    Finance, University of Chicago
        see   Institute on Hospital Finance,
Accounting, and Administration.

National institute on mercenary crime.

MacDougall, Ernest David, 1878–   *ed.*
    Crime for profit; a symposium on mercenary crime, edited
by Ernest D. MacDougall ... Boston, Mass., The Stratford
company [ᶜ1933]

HV   National Institute on Police and Community
8132   Relations,Michigan State University,East
.N32   Lansing.
                [Papers] 1st–   1954–
            East Lansing.

NN 0055569   MiU

VOLUME 407

National institute on war and postwar issues.
Proceedings. ₁1st–
1943–
Chicago, American library association, 1943–
v. 27½ᶜᵐ.
Issue for 1943 has also distinctive title: War and postwar issues.
Reproduced from type-written copy.

1. World war, 1939– —Congresses, conferences, etc.   ɪ. American
library association.   ɪɪ. Title: War and postwar issues.
43–8576
Library of Congress   D734.N3
₁30₁   940.5306373

NN   0055570   DLC CaBVa OrU OrCS OC1 NcD MB CU PSt

National institute on war and postwar issues
see also
Regional institute on war and peace for Arizona and Southern California, *Los Angeles,* 1943.

National Institutes of Health
see U. S. *National Institutes of Health.*

National institution, Washington, D.C.
see
National institute for the promotion of science, Washington, D.C.

National institution for massage by the blind.
see
Institute for massage by the blind, London.

National Institution for Moral Instruction
see
Character Education Institution, *Washington, D. C.*

National institution for promoting industry in the United States.
An address to the people of the United States, drawn up by order of the National institution for the promotion of industry, established in June, 1820, by delegates from New-York, New-Jersey, Pennsylvania, Connecticut, Massachusetts, Rhode-Island, Ohio, and Delaware. New-York: Printed by J. Seymour, 49 John-street. 1820.
1 p. l., 22 p. 23½ᶜᵐ.

1. Tariff—U. S.   2. Free trade and protection—Protection.
7–29606
Library of Congress   HF1754.N28

NN   0055576   DLC MnU MiU-C WHi MH MB OC1WHi

National Institution for Promoting Industry in the United States.
An address to the people of the United States, drawn up by order of the National Institution for the Promotion of Industry, established in June, 1820, by delegates from New-York, New-Jersey, Pennsylvania, Connecticut, Massachusetts, Rhode-Island, Ohio, and Delaware. Concord, Printed by Hill & Moore, 1821.
48 p. 24ᶜᵐ.
A plea to protect national industry through the increase of the tariff on certain imports.

NN   0055577   ICJ MH-BA OC1WHi Nh DLC

National institution for promoting industry in the United States.
Circular and address of the National institution for promoting industry in the United States, to their fellow-citizens. New-York, Printed by J. Seymour, 1820.
28 p. 21½ᶜᵐ.

1. Tariff—U. S.   2. Free trade and protection—Protection.
6–34108
Library of Congress   HF1754.N27

MB OO
NN   0055578   DLC PHC MU NIC CSt MdBP MWA MH-BA

National Institution for Promoting Industry in the United States.
Memorial of the National institute for the promotion of Industry, to the Hon. Senate and House or Representatives of the State of New York, Jan. 13, 1821.   New York.
8 p.
ɪ.Few, William.

NN   0055579   PHi

National Institution for Promoting Industry in the United States.
The Patron of industry.   Agricultural, manufacturing, commercial.   v. 1; June 28, 1820–June 27, 1821.   New-York, 1820–21.

HF1754   NATIONAL INSTITUTION FOR PROMOTING INDUSTRY IN
.N273   THE UNITED STATES.
The proceedings of a Convention of the friends of national industry...   ₁1st₁–   New York, Printed by C.S.Van Winkle,1819–
v.   22cm.

NN   0055581   ICU

National Institution for the Education of Deaf and Dumb Children of the Poor in Ireland
see **National Association for Promoting the Education of the Deaf and Dumb Children of the Poor of Ireland.**

National Institution for the Preservation of
Life from Shipwreck, London
see
Royal National Life-Boat Institution for the Preservation of Life from Shipwreck, London.

National Institution for the Promotion of Industry
see   **National Institution for Promoting Industry in the United States.**

National institution of the boot and shoe industry.
... Bibliographical index; boots and shoes, leather, rubber & other materials.   London ₁1936₁
2 p. l., vii–xv, 97, ₁1₁ p. 25ᶜᵐ.
Preface signed: Ruth Tomlinson.
"First edition, 1936."
"The present volume widens the scope of, and brings to date, an index which was started in the institution Journal ... some six years ago."—Pref.

1. Boots and shoes—Bibl.   2. Leather—Bibl.   ɪ. Tomlinson, Ruth, ed.
43–4544
Library of Congress   Z7914.B4N3
₁3₁   016.6853

NN   0055585   DLC CaBVaU OC1 DNAL NNC CtY NN

National institution pro south of Italy
see
Opera nazionale per il mezzogiorno d'Italia.

National institutional teacher placement association.
Current practices in institutional teacher placement, written by thirty-five members of the National institutional teacher placement association; editorial committee: Earl W. Anderson ... John Douglas Leith ... Ralph F. Strebel, chairman ... Published by National institutional teacher placement association, with the assistance of the Division on child development and teacher personnel, Commission on teacher education, American council on education. ₁Atlanta, J. M. Marbut co.₁ 1941.
xi, 186 p. 23½ᶜᵐ.
"This book has been prepared ... as a companion volume to Institutional teacher placement published ... in 1937."

1. Teachers—U. S.   2. Personnel service in education.   3. Universities and colleges—U. S.   ɪ. Strebel, Ralph Frederick, 1894–   ed.   ɪɪ. American council on education.   Commission on teacher education.   ɪɪɪ. Title.
41–9066 Revised
Library of Congress   LB1780.N3
₁2₁   371.142

ICU NcD ViU OC1 OU ICRL
NN   0055588   DLC KEmT WaWW WaTC OrCS MtU NcD NN AAP

National Institutional Teacher Placement Association.
The dynamics of teacher placement.   General editor: Robert C. Woellner.   ₁Eugene, Or.₁ 1955.
vii, 175 p.   24 cm.
Bibliography: p. 163–172.

1. Teachers—Selection and appointment.   ɪ. Woellner, Robert Carlton, 1894–   ed.   ɪɪ. Title.
A 56–4323
Louisiana.   State Univ.   Library
for Library of Congress   ₁3₁

NcU NcD CLSU PWcS NcGU MtBC OrPS
NN   0055589   LU CU MoU CoU NIC MiU OU LU IU ICU NIC

National institutional teacher placement
association.
Umstattd, James Greenleaf, 1896–   ed.
Institutional teacher placement, prepared under the auspices of the National institutional teacher placement association by J. G. Umstattd, Earl W. Anderson ₁and others₁ ... edited by J. G. Umstattd.   Detroit, Mich., Office of the editor. Institutional teacher placement, College of education, Wayne university ₁ᶜ1937₁

LB2835   National Institutional Teacher Placement
N35   Association.
Proceedings of the meetings.
[n.p.]
v.   23cm.   semiannual.

1. Teachers - Selection and appointment.
2. Education - Societies, etc.

NN   0055591   CoU PU ViU KEmT CLU NcD InLP

National Institutional Teacher Placement
Association
see also
Association for School, College and University
Staffing.

The National instructor.   v. 1–
May 25, 1850–
₁London, W. Rider₁ 1850–
v. 22ᶜᵐ.   weekly.

CA 15–146 Unrev'd
Library of Congress   DA559.7.A2N2

NN   0055593   DLC NNC WU

VOLUME 407

National Insulation Contractors Association.
NICA outlook.
₁Silver Spring, Md.₎
v. illus. 29 cm. monthly.
Continues IDCNA outlook.

1. Insulation (Heat)—Periodicals. I. Title.
TH1715.A1N37a   693.8'32'05   74–640947
ISSN 0047-8881   MARC-S

NN   0055594   DLC

National insurance: a lecture ...
see under ₁Jamieson, George Auldjo₎

National insurance act. A full explanatory digest, by
"An old parliamentary hand." London, W. MacDonald
& co. ₁1912₎
viii, 72 p. 18½ᶜᵐ.

1. Insurance, Industrial—Gt. Brit. 2. Insurance, State and compulsory—
Gt. Brit.
                               12–16150

Library of Congress   HD7166.N25

NN   0055596   DLC ICJ

National insurance and health services gazette.
₁London, Stone & Cox, etc.₎
v. illus., ports. 22–30 cm. weekly.
Began publication May 1912.
Title varies: –Dec. 19, 1931, The National insurance
gazette and sickness societies review.–Dec. 26, 1931–
The National insurance gazette.

1. Insurance, Social—Period. 2. Insurance, Social—Gt. Brit.
HD7165.N25   51–55353

NN   0055597   DLC

National Insurance Association
see   National Negro Insurance Association.

National Insurance Bill. Copy of a memorandum explanatory of the bill as passed by the House of Commons so far as
relates to national health insurance. London: Eyre & Spottiswoode, 1911. 16 p. f°. (Cd. 5995.)

1. Insurance (Workmen's), Gt. Br.,   1911.
N. Y. P. L.   June 13, 1913.

NN   0055599   NN

The **National** insurance buyer. v. 1, no. 1–2; June 1952–
Jan. 1953. ₁New York₎
1 v. illus., ports. 28 cm.
Published by the American Society of Insurance Management
under its earlier name: National Insurance Buyers Association.
Superseded in Mar. 1954 by a later publication with the same title.
No more published?
Bound with the National insurance buyer, v. 1–3, Mar./Apr. 1954–
Nov. 1956.

1. Business Insurance—Period. I. American Society of Insurance Management.
HG8059.C7N3   63–34691

NN   0055600   DLC OU

The **National** insurance buyer. v. 1–
Mar./Apr. 1954–
₁New York₎
v. in illus., ports. 28 cm.
Quarterly, 1954–55; bimonthly, 1956–
Supersedes an earlier publication with the same title, issued June
1952–Jan. 1953?
Official publication of the American Society of Insurance Management (called Mar. 1954–Sept. 1955 National Insurance Buyers Association)
Vols. 1–3 bound with the National insurance buyer, v. 1, June
1952–Jan. 1953.

1. Business Insurance—Period. I. American Society of Insurance
Management.
HG8059.C7N312   63–34690

NN   0055601   DLC MoU TxU MtBC Wa

National Insurance Buyers Association
see
American Society of Insurance Management.

National insurance convention of the United States
see   National Association of insurance
commissioners.

National insurance defence trust.

British medical association. *Insurance acts committee.*
National formulary for national health insurance purposes,
compiled by the Insurance acts committee of the British medical association, for the use of medical practitioners and phar-
macists in connection with the provision of medical benefit
under the national health insurance acts ... London, Issued by
the British medical association for the National insurance defence trust ₁1939₎

National Insurance Institute
see
ha-Mosad le-vituaḥ le'umi.

HG8011
.N3   National insurance journal; a journal of information and inspiration for insurance agents
and underwriters.

[Freeport, Ill., 19
v. illus. 29½cm. monthly.

1. Insurance—Period. 2. Insurance—U.S.

NN   0055606   DLC ICJ

K977
.I6N2   NATIONAL INSURANCE LAW SERVICE.
Vermont: regulations and bulletins, Vermont
Insurance Department. New York.
1 v. (loose-leaf)

1. Insurance law—Vermont. I. Vermont. Insurance Dept.

NN   0055607   ICU

The **National** insurance year book ...

London, The Insurance publishing company, ltd. ₁19
v. front. (port.) 18½ᶜᵐ.
Includes the National insurance acts.

1. Insurance, Industrial—Gt. Brit. 2. Insurance, Health—Gt. Brit. 3.
Insurance, State and compulsory—Gt. Brit.
                           18–19748

Library of Congress   HD7165.N3

NN   0055608   DLC ICU DL

National integration.
₁New Delhi, Gopal Singh₎
v. illus., ports. 28 cm. quarterly.

1. India. I. Singh, Gopal, writer on Sikhism.

DS401.N28   S A 65–3183 ‡

NN   0055609   DLC NN ViU MiU

RH   National intelligencer. v.1, no.1–
R26   1812?–   Washington, D.C., Gales
and Seaton.
v. 58–66ᵐ triweekly.

IU NNC
NN   0055610   KU OU CtY NN OOxM PU PHi ICRL OClW ICN

The National intelligencer, Washington, D. C.
v. 1, no. 1–v.7, no.? Oct. 31, 1800–1869?
Washington City, Printed by S. H. Smith, etc.
Some vols.   v. 61cm. tri-weekly and semi-weekly.
on microfilm.
MICRO   Title varies: Oct. 31, 1800–Nov. 24, 1810,
FILM   The National intelligencer and Washington
18   advertiser.
Microfilm. Washington, D. C., Library of
Congress Photoduplication Service. reels. 35mm.

I. The National intelligencer and Washington
advertiser.

NN   0055611   DGW NcRS CtY MH ICN NNC

National Intelligencer, Washington, D.C.
[Account of the assault of Preston S. Brooks
upon Charles Sumner, in the Senate chamber,
May 22, 1856] [Washington, 1856]
[9] p. 23 cm. [No. 6 in vol. lettered:
Charles Sumner. Speeches]
Mounted clippings from the National intelli-
gencer.

NN   0055612   CU

National intelligencer, Washington.

The **African** slave trade. The secret purpose of the in-
surgents to revive it. No treaty stipulations against
the slave trade to be entered into with the European
powers. Judah P. Benjamin's intercepted instructions
to L. Q. C. Lamar, styled commissioner, etc. Philadelphia, C. Sherman, son & co., printers, 1863.

National intelligencer, Washington.

Anticipation of marginal notes on the declaration of government of the 9th of January, 1813. In the American National
intelligencer ... London, Printed by A. J. Valpy, 1813.

National intelligencer, Washington, D.C.
Carriers' address to the patrons of the
National intelligencer
see under title

National intelligencer, Washington.

Fremont, John Charles, 1813–1890.
... Central railroad route to the Pacific. Letter of J. C.
Fremont to the editors of the National intelligencer, communicating some general results of a recent winter expedition
across the Rocky mountains, for a survey of a route for a railroad to the Pacific. ₁Washington, 1854₎

VOLUME 407

National intelligencer, Washington.

₁Woodward, Augustus Brevoort₁ d. 1827.
Considerations on the government of the territory of Columbia: as they recently appeared in the National intelligencer, under the signature of Epaminondas ₁pseud.₁ Washington, metropolis of the United States. Printed for the author, by Samuel Harrison Smith, New-Jersey avenue near the Capitol. M.D.CCC.I.

NN 0055618   CSmH

National Intelligencer, Washington, D.C.
Daily National Intelligencer. Washington, D.C. 1850- v. 38, no. 11572. March 30, 1850. Washington, 1850.
Lg. folio. 1 nos. In manila folder.
Began publication in 1814. Distinct from the National Intelligencer which was started in 1800 and was a tri-weekly.
No. 11572 contains, "California. Report of Hon. T. Butler King".

NN 0055619   DWP InU

National intelligencer, *Washington, D. C.*
Daily national intelligencer.
(*In* Columbia historical society. Records. Washington, 1940. 23½ᶜᵐ.
v. 40–41, p. 167–171)
Extracts from the issues of March 1 and 8, 1849, with titles, respectively, "Gen. Taylor's visit to Georgetown" and "Gen. Taylor at Georgetown."

1. Taylor, Zachary, pres. U. S., 1784–1850.

Washington, D.C. Public	library	W 41-16
for Library of Congress	[F191.C72 vol. 40–41]	
	₁2₁	(975.30062)

NN 0055619   DWP InU

National intelligencer, Washington, D. C.

Drake, Daniel, 1785–1852.
Dr. Daniel Drake's Letters on slavery to Dr. John C. Warren, of Boston. Reprinted from the National intelligencer, Washington, April 3, 5 and 7, 1851; with an introduction by Emmet Field Horine ... New York, Schuman's, 1940.

National Intelligencer, Washington, D.C.
Extracts of some of the marriages and deaths printed in the National Intelligencer, Washington, D.C., between the years 1806 and 1858.
80 ℓ. typescript (carbon copy)

NN 0055621   MiD-B

---

*H.90
.526   National Intelligencer, Washington, D. C.
The fate of war has befallen the city of Washington ... [Washington, August 30, 1814]
broadside. 34 2 26cm.

1. Broadsides—U. S. 2. Washington, D. C.— Capture by the British, 1814. I. Title.

NN 0055622   MB

National intelligencer, Washington, D.C.
First trip of the overland mail across our continent. ₁Washington, D. C., 1857₁
p.₁3₁, col. 2. 66 cm. fold to 44 cm.

Forms part of its vol. XLV, no. 14. 110, Oct. 21, 1857.
In folder. 45 cm.

1. Postal service – U. S.

NN 0055623   NjP

National intelligencer, Washington, D.C.
A fugitive slave case in court
see under title

National Intelligencer, Washington, D.C.
General Harrison in Congress
see under title

National Intelligencer, Washington.
Historical notes on the ancient and modern names ...
see under [Kohl, Johann Georg] 1808-1878.

National Intelligencer, Washington, D.C.
History and conditions of the tenure of the public lands of the United States
see under title

328.739   National intelligencer, Washington, D.C.
N21h   History of the last session of Congress, which commenced on the seventh of December, 1801. Washington, D.C., 1802.
196p.

NN 0055628   IU

AI21   National intelligencer, Washington, D.C.
N22   Index to the National intelligencer from 1816
Periodi-   inclusive to 1821 inclusive. [Washington? 18-?]
cal Div.   [324] p. 31.5 cm.
Office   Manuscript.

NN 0055629   DLC

The National intelligencer, Washington, D.C.
Loss of the "St. [!] Francisco" steamer in December and January, 1853/4.
Clippings. [Pamphlets on travel. v. 4 no. 13]
Binder's title.
1. San Francisco (Steamer)

NN 0055630   CU

The National intelligencer, Washington, D. C.
The Mexican boundary commission. [Clippings from the National intelligencer]
see under title

National Intelligencer, Washington, D. C.
Missouri compromise
see under title

National intelligencer, *Washington, D. C.*
Mr. Webster and his revilers. ₁Washington, National intelligencer, 1841₁
15 p. 22ᵐᵐ.
From the National intelligencer of April 24, 1841; principally copied from the New York express.

1. Webster, Daniel, 1782–1852. I. New York express.

| Library of Congress | E340.W4N2 | 14-19552 |

NN 0055633   DLC MH

National intelligencer, Washington, D.C.
The past, the present, and the future. ₁Washington? 1851₁
40 p. 23cm.

A series of articles from the National intelligencer.

1. U.S. - Pol. & govt. - 19th cent. 2. South Carolina - Pol. & govt. - 1775-1865.

NN 0055634   GU

The National intelligencer, *Washington, D. C.*
Rev. Andrew T. McCormick, minister of the first Episcopal congregation. (Reprint)
(*In* Columbia historical society. Records ... Washington, 1922. 23½ᵐ.
v. 24, p. 196-199)

1. McCormick, Andrew T., d. 1841.

| Washington, D. C. | Public Library | W 22-13 |

NN 0055635   DWP

National Intelligencer, Washington, D.C.
Secession neither a right nor a remedy
see under title

National intelligencer, Washington, D. C.

₁Rush, Richard₁ 1780–1859.
Sketch of the character of Mr. Canning. From the National intelligencer of Sept. 15, 1827. Washington, Printed by Gales & Seaton, 1828.

E423   National intelligencer, Washington, D. C.
.C613
Rare Bk.   Clay, Henry, 1777–1852.
Coll.   Speech of the Hon. Henry Clay, of Kentucky, on presenting his resolutions on the subject of slavery. Delivered in Senate, Feb. 5th & 6th, 1850. (As reported by the National intelligencer.) New York, Stringer & Townsend, 1850.

National Intelligencer, Washington, D.C.
A visit to Annapolis, Maryland
see under title

Z973.51   NATIONAL intelligencer extra. Aug. 10
fN213   ₁1809₁ Washington City ₁1809₁

broadside. 33 x 25cm.

Consists of President Madison's proclamation regarding the Embargo, and a "letter... addressed by the secretary of the Treasury to the respective collectors, in consequence of the above proclamation", signed: Albert Gallatin.

1. Broadsides, American. I. U.S. President, 1809-1817 (Madison) II. Gallatin, Albert 1761-1849. III. U.S. Treasury dept.

NN 0055641   MnU

National Interassociation committee on Interships
see National Intern Matching Program.

VOLUME 407

National intercollegiate Christian council.
Christians face war, by Paul Limbert ₁and others₁ ... New York, N. Y., Pub. for the National intercollegiate Christian council by Association press, 1944.
2 p. l., 43, ₁1₁ p. 21½ᵐ.
CONTENTS.—Introduction, by P. M. Limbert.—The Christian and war, by Kathleen W. MacArthur. (Bibliography: p. 23–24)—The Christian as soldier, by J. C. Bennett.—The power of non-violent good will, by Winnifred Wygal and W. T. Thomas. (Bibliography: p. 43)

1. War and religion. ɪ. Limbert, Paul Moyer, 1897–   ɪɪ. Title.
44–40284
Library of Congress   BR115.W2N35
₁4₁   261

NN 0055643   DLC ICU

National intercollegiate Christian council.
The **Intercollegian.** v. 1–8, Nov. 1878–Apr. 1886; **new ser.**, v. 9–13, Jan. 1887–June 1891; 4th ser., v. 21–35, Oct. 1898–Dec. 1912;
New York ₁etc.₁ 1878–₁19

HQ744
.H5
National intercollegiate Christian council.
Hill, Reuben.
Love and marriage in wartime and after, by Reuben Hill ... New York, N. Y., Pub. for the National intercollegiate Christian council by Association press ₁1944₁

National intercollegiate Christian council.
Babcock, Fern.
A new program book for student Christian associations, by Fern Babcock. New York, N. Y., Pub. for the National intercollegiate Christian council ₁by the₁ Association press ₁1943₁

BV970
.N3G7
1948
National Intercollegiate Christian Council.
Grant, Fern (Babcock) 1904–
A program book for student Christian associations. ₁3d ed., rev.₁ New York, Published for the National Intercollegiate Christian Council ₁by the₁ Association Press, 1948.

National intercollegiate Christian council. National assembly.
Miami University, Oxford, O., 1941–42.
...Assembly report. Pamphlet no. 1–   ₁New York, National intercollegiate Christian council, 1942₁   no. illus. 28cm.
CONTENTS. — no. 1. Actions of the National assembly of student Christian associations.

1. College societies, Religious—U. S.
N. Y. P. L.   November 12, 1946

NN 0055648   NN

National intercollegiate Christian council. *National assembly. Oxford, O.* 1937–38.
New direction for campus Christian action; report of the National assembly of Student Christian associations at Oxford, Ohio, December 27, 1937–January 2, 1938. New York, N. Y., The National intercollegiate Christian council ₁1938₁
181 p. 4 pl. on 2 l. 22ᵐ.

ɪ. Title.
40–14096
Library of Congress   BV970.N3A5 1937–38 a
₁2₁   267.61

NN 0055649   DLC NIC KEmT ViU

JC
599
.U5
N3
National Intercollegiate Christian Council.
National Commission on Ethnic Minorities.
A guide for those who would discover the civil rights practices of their community.
New York ₁1941₁
8ℓ. 29cm.

1. Civil rights. U.S. I. Title.
xNational Commission on Ethnic Minorities.

NN 0055650   OrU

National intercollegiate football, schedule, **rules, score**-card ...
Lebanon, Pa., Official football schedule publishing agency, ₁19
v. illus. 20½ᵐ.
Cover-title.
"Official score card and lineups" (4 p.) laid in.

1. Foot-ball.
                                CA 25–946 Unrev'd
Library of Congress   GV955.N35

NN 0055651   DLC

National interdenominational student conference, Evanston, Ill.
see   Interdenominational student conference, Evanston, Ill.

National interest in state and Congressional elections
see under   [Bishop, Putnam P.]

National interest photos, *Washington, D. C.*
Our air navy. Washington, D. C., **National interest photos,** ₁1928.
₁64₁ p. illus. 19½ x 27¼ᵐ.

1. U. S.—Navy—Illustrations. 2. Aeronautics, Military—U. S. 3. Aeroplanes. ɪ. Title.
29–6012
Library of Congress   VA59.N3

NN 0055654   DLC DN

National interests & domestic manufactures. Address of the Philadelphia society for the promotion of domestic industry
see under   [Carey, Mathew] 1760–1839.

National interests. By a member of the Labourer's Friend Society. ₁1820?₁
16 p. 22cm.

NN 0055656   NNC

371.85
N277a
National Interfraternity Conference.
The American college fraternity; its background and contribution to the American way of life. Philadelphia, 1948.
31,[23]p. 23cm.
Appendix: Letters of college administrators (facsimiles): p.[1–23]

1.Greek letter societies. I.Title.

NN 0055657   CLSU

National Interfraternity Conference.
Annual session.
New York.
v. 23 cm.
Title varies: 1909–25, Minutes.—1926–   Yearbook.
On cover, 19   Yearbook.
Issued 1909–30 by the conference under its earlier name: Interfraternity Conference.

1. Greek letter societies. ₁1. College fraternities—U. S.₁
LJ13.I 6   371.85506273   E 11–1559 rev 2*
U. S. Office of Education   Library
for Library of Congress   ₁r50c1₁†

MtU IU MeB   GEU NcD KyU PSt
OC1W NcD ODW NjP ICJ MB NIC TU ICU DLC WvU CL DAU
NN 0055658   DHEW IU OC1W MsU NN MB OrCS NcRS OO

LJ31
.N3
National Interfraternity Conference.
College fraternities; their origin, purpose and value. New York, 1935.
32 p. 18cm.

1. Greek letter societies.

NN 0055659   MB

NATIONAL INTER-FRATERNITY CONFERENCE.
The Inter-fraternity conference: what it is and what it does ... ₁New York? 1928₁
16 p.

NN 0055660   WaU MiEM CU MA

National Interfraternity Conference. Minutes
see its Annual session.

National interfraternity conference.
Projects for Interfraternity councils. New York, National interfraternity conference, 1939, 24p. 18cm.

NN 0055662   OrU

National interfraternity conference.
Report of the committee on the relation between colleges and fraternities to the 1912 inter-fraternity conference November 30, 1912. N. Y. City, Committee on relations between colleges and fraternities, 1912.
36 p.

NN 0055663   ODW MiEM IU MB MdBJ Mi

National Interfraternity Conference.
Reports. 1909–
₁v. p.₁
v. 23 cm. annual.
Title varies: 1909–23, 1925, Minutes.—1924, 19   –45, 19   –49, Session (cover title, 19   : Yearbook)—1926–   Yearbook.—1948, Program ₁of the₁ session.
Issued 1909–30 by the conference under its earlier name: Interfraternity Conference.
INDEXES:
1909–20. 1 v.
1909–38. 1 v.
1909–49. 1 v.
1. Greek letter societies. ₁1. College fraternities—U. S.₁
LJ13.N27   E 11–1559 rev 2*
371.85506273
U. S. Office of Education   Library
for Library of Congress   ₁r51d1₁†

NN 0055664   DHEW WaTC IdU PBL MiU–H OO OU CU DLC

National Interfraternity Conference. Session
see its Reports.

VOLUME 407

National Inter-fraternity conference.
... The **Sigma chi** quarterly; a journal of college and fraternity life and literature. Devoted to the interests of the Sigma chi fraternity. v. 1-
Apr. 1881-
Chicago, Ill. ₍etc.₎ 1882-₍19

National Interfraternity Conference. Yearbook
see its Annual session.

371.85   National interfraternity conference. Scholar-
N21in   ship committee.
            National interfraternity conference
         scholarship survey ... New York city, 1927-

            Title varies: Interfraternity scholarship
         survey.

NN   0055668   WaPS

National interfraternity conference. War committee.
    The college fraternity and the war; a special report of the War committee, April 1, 1942. ₍New York, 1942₎   16 p.
23½cm.

    At head of title: National interfraternity conference.

    1. College societies, Greek letter   —U.S. 2. World war, 1939-
      —Educational aspects—U.S.
N. Y. P. L.   September 15, 1942

NN   0055669   NN

National Intern Matching Program.
    Directory of approved hospitals partici-
pating in the matching program for intern-
ship appointment. ₍1954-
Chicago, Ill. N.I.M.P., 1954-

    Formerly: National Interassociation Commit-
tee on Internships.

NN   0055670   OrU-M

E
185.61 National Interracial Conference.
.N296x   Abstracts of the report of the research
         committee to the National Interracial Confer-
         ence. Charles S. Johnson, Secretary. 1928.
         1v. (various paging) mimeographed.

         Contents: I. Population., II. Health., III.
         Education., IV. Industry and agriculture.,
         V. Recreation., VI. Housing., VII. Law observ-
         ance and administration., VIII. Citizenship.,
         IX. Race relations.

         1. Race discrimination 2. Negroes - Civil rights
         I. Johnson,   Charles Spurgeon, 1893-
         ed.

NN   0055671   OYesA ICU

National Interracial Conference, 1st, Cincinnati, 1925.
    Toward interracial cooperation; what was said and done at the first National interracial conference held under the auspices of the Commission on the church and race relations of the Federal council of the churches and the Commission on interracial cooperation, Cincinnati, Ohio, March 25-27, 1925. Published by the Commission on the church and race relations, Federal council of the churches of Christ in America. Book number one. ₍New York, Printed by J. J. Little and Ives company, 1926₎

    vii, 5-192 p. 23 cm.

    1. United States—Race question—Congresses. 2. Negroes—Con-
gresses. I. Commission on Interracial Cooperation. II. Federal
Council of the Churches of Christ in America. Dept. of Race Relations. III. Title.

    E184.5.N28 1925   301.45'19'6073   26-23330

OCl PPT
NN   0055673   DLC NN OOxM DAU MU ICJ MH ViHaI OCU

National interracial conference, Washington,
1928.   FOR OTHER EDITIONS
                SEE MAIN ENTRY
Johnson, Charles Spurgeon, 1893–
    The Negro in American civilization: a study of Negro life and race relations in the light of social research, by Charles S. Johnson ...   New York. H. Holt and company ₍1930₎

National interracial conference, Washington, 1928.
    Report of the Committee on findings,
National interracial conference held
at Washington, D.C.
₍Washington? 1928?₎
    37 numb. l.   28 cm.
    Autographed from typewritten copy.

NN   0055675   DL

National interregional highway committee (*U. S.*)
            see
U. S. *National interregional highway committee.*

National interscholastic amateur athletic association of the United States.
    Constitution and by-laws of the National interscholas-
tic amateur athletic association of the United States ...
New York, American sports publishing company ₍1896₎

    17 p. 17ᶜᵐ. (*On cover:* Spalding's athletic library, v. 5, no. 49A)

    1. Athletics.

    Library of Congress   GV563.N28   5-24922†

NN   0055677   DLC

GV223   NATIONAL INTERSCHOLASTIC AMATEUR ATHLETIC ASSO-
.N3   CIATION OF THE UNITED STATES.
            Constitution of the National interscholastic
         association of amateur athletes of America. Bos-
         ton, A. G. Spalding & bros. ₍c1906₎
            10 p. 17cm.

NN   0055678   ICU

National Interscholastic Music Activities Commission.
    Instrumental ensembles: woodwind, brass, string ₍and₎
mixed; graded lists of recommended materials. Chicago
₍1948₎

    39 p. 23 cm.

    Published by the society under its earlier name: National School
Band, Orchestra and Vocal Association.

    1. Chamber music—Bibl.—Graded lists.   I. Title.

    ML132.C4N3   781.973   49-15439 rev*

NN   0055679   DLC TxU NcU OrSaW

National Interscholastic Music Activities
Commission.
    NSBOVA manual for interscholastic activities in
the field of music. Chicago [1951?]
    Chapters individually paged. 27 cm.

NN   0055680   OrSaW

Music   National Interscholastic Music Activities
MT 236   Commission.
N 213
            Organization, management and adjudication
         of sight reading contests for bands,
         orchestras and choruses. Washington, National
         Interscholastic Music Activities Commission
         ₍1954?₎

            14 p.

NN   0055681   MoSW

781.97   National Interscholastic Music Activities
N21se   Commission.
            Selective music lists; choral, string orches-
         tra, orchestra, band. 19 -
         Washington, 19 -
            v. 23 cm.
            Title varies: 19 -   Selective music lists;
         band, orchestra, string orchestra, choral
         groups.
            19 -   Selective music lists: choral
         groups, string orchestra, orchestra, band.

            1. Music—Bibl.—Graded lists. I. National
         Interscholastic Music Activities Commission.
         Selective music lists; choral groups, string
         orchestra, orchestra, band. II. National Interscho-
         lastic Music Activities Commission. Selective
         music lists; band, orchestra, string orchestra,
         choral groups. III. Title. IV. Title: Selective
         music lists; choral groups, string orchestra,
         orchestra, band. V. Title: Selective music lists;
         band, orchestra,   string orchestra, choral
         groups.

            OrSaW MoU CSt OU
NN   0055683   LU InU CU IEN CSt IaU OOxM TxU UU MoU

780.79   National Interscholastic Music Activities
N21s   Commission
            Standards of adjudication; a manual of sugges-
         tions regarding the adjudication of music
         competition-festivals.   Washington, D.C.,
         Music Educators National Conference, NEA
         Education Center ₍n.d.₎
            9 p.

NN   0055684   OrPS MtBC

National Interscholastic Music Activities Commission
            see also
National School Band Association.
National School Orchestra Association.
National School Vocal Association.

National interstate inheritance tax league.
    Prospectus.   Chicago, n.d.
    15 p.   15 cm.

NN   0055686   ICHi

GV710   National Intramural Association.
.N2   Proceedings. 1st-   1950-
         Dubuque, Iowa, W. C. Brown Book Co.
            v. 23cm.

            1. Intramural sports—Societies, etc.
            2. College sports—Societies, etc.

NN   0055687   ViU IdPI IaAS UU IU

T212   National inventors congress.
A1I6
         The Inventor.

            ₍Grand Rapids, Mich., The Inventor, inc., etc., 19

National inventors' council
            see
U. S. *National inventors' council.*

VOLUME 407

National investment and finance.
Delhi.
v. illus., ports. 31 cm. semimonthly.
Began publication in 1953. Cf. India (Republic) Office of the Registrar of Newspapers. Report, 1962.
Absorbed the Investment & finance.
Editor: May 1963—   G. K. Kapoor.

1. India—Indus.—Period.   2. Commerce—Period.   3. India—Comm.—Period.
HC431.N27   S A 63–3479

NN   0055690   DLC MiU NSyU ICRL MiU

National Investment Bank, Ghana.
NIB annual report.
₍Accra, Ghana₎
v. illus. (part col.) 28 cm.

1. National Investment Bank.   I. Title.
HG3399.G49N324a   332.6   73–644161
                                    MARC-S

NN   0055691   DLC

J
744   National Investment Bank, Ghana.
          Objectives and functions.   Accra,

9p.

1. Banks and banking - Ghana.

NN   0055692   MBU

J
744   National Investment Bank, Ghana.
B33   Report of the Directors.   Accra.

1. Banks and banking - Ghana.

NN   0055693   MBU NN

The national investor, published in the interest of American investments in mining, mortgages, stocks, government, state and municipal bonds. v. 1–
St. Paul, Chicago, 1900–

HG4811
.A3N2

NN   0055694   DLC

National Investor Relations Institute.
Proceedings of the annual national conference.

Washington.
v. illus. 28 cm.

1. Public relations—Corporations—Congresses. 2. Stockholders—United States—Congresses. 3. Securities—United States—Congresses.
HD59.N273a   332.6'32'0973   74–646003
ISSN 0094-1204   MARC-S

NN   0055695   DLC

Ng619   National investors corporation.
+N210d   Financial statements.
             [New York]   28cm.

NN   0055696   CtY

National Investors Corporation.
Report.

₍New York?₎
v. 21–23 cm. annual.

HG4530.N243   332.62   50–45570 ‡

NN   0055697   DLC NN

National Investors Corporation
see also National Investors Corporation (*1927–1937*); Second National Investors Corporation; Fourth National Investors Corporation.

National Investors Corporation (*1927–1937*)
Report.

₍New York?₎
v. 28 cm. annual.

HG4530.N253   332.63   50–43351 ‡

NN   0055699   DLC

National Investors Corporation (*1927–1937*)
see also National Investors Corporation.

National Iranian Oil Company.
The Iranian oil consortium, 1954; government agreement. ₍Tihran, 1954₎
71 p. 33 cm.

1. Petroleum law and legislation - Iran.
2. Concessions - Iran.   3. Iran - Treaties, etc.

NN   0055701   NNC

National Iranian Oil Company.
HD9576   A report on the history of the southern oil
I6A52   of Iran, presented by the National Oil Company
             of Iran to the Honourable Averell Harriman,
             special envoy of the President of the United
             States of America.   Tehran ₍Bank Melli Iran
             Press₎ 1951.
             21 p.   24cm.

1. National Iranian Oil Company. 2. Petroleum industry and trade - Iran. 3. Government owner-ship - Iran.   I. Harriman, William Averell, 1891–   II. Title.

NN   0055702   CSt-H

National iron and steel blue book. An authentic and con-cise list of firms, corporations, and individuals, engaged in the production of iron and steel, coal and coke, in the United States ... Ed. by B. H. Morwood ₍1902₎ Pittsburg, Pa., R. L. Polk & co. ₍1902₎
21½ᶜᵐ.

1902–16 have title: National iron and steel, coal and coke blue book.

1. Coal trade—Direct.   I. Morwood, B. H., ed.
                                                    2–13406
Library of Congress   TS301.N3

NN   0055703   DLC ICJ ICRL DI-GS

National iron and steel, coal and coke blue book. An authentic and concise list of firms, corporations and individuals, engaged in the production of iron and steel, coal and coke, in the United States. The plants or mines operated, their location, description, equip-ment, etc. 2d edition. Edited by B. H. Morwood.
— Pittsburg, Pa. Polk & Co. [1904.] 8vo pp. 8°.

F8667 — Morwood, B. H., ed. —   United States. Manuf. — United States. Direct. — Coal. Direct. — Coke. Direct. — Steel. Direct. — Iron. Direct. — Directories. Business. — Polk; R. L., & Co., publishers.

NN   0055704   MB

National iron bank of Morristown (*New Jersey*)
Historic Morris county, an informal story of men and events beginning with the discovery of iron in the colonial period. Printed here for the first time is a world war II honor roll of Morristown and vicinity ... ₍Morristown₎ The National iron bank of Morristown ₍1943₎
48 p. illus. 29 x 22ᶜᵐ.

1. Morris co., N. J.—Hist. 2. World war, 1939–   —Registers, lists, etc. I. Title.
Library of Congress   F142.M8N3   44–33979
                                    ₍2₎   974.974

NN   0055705   DLC PPCS CtY NNC

National Iron Bank of Morristown (New Jersey)
Historic Morris county; a brief account of some local happenings that have been of more than local significance. [Morristown, 1955] 39 p. illus., ports., map. 30cm.

1. Morris county, N.J.--Hist.

NN   0055706   NN KyU

National irrigation association.

American forests. v. 1–
₍Jan. ?₎ 1895–
Princeton, N. J. ₍etc.₎ J. Gifford. 1895–97; Washington, D. C. ₍etc.₎ The American forestry association, 1898–19

---

55   National irrigation commission(Mexico)
N212   ₍Irrigation in Mexico.   Mexico ₍D.F.,Editorial
             "Cvltvra"₎ 1936.
             unp. illus. 23cm.

NN   0055708   DNAL OCU

National irrigation congress
see
International irrigation congress.

National irrigation journal
see   National land and irrigation journal.

HV5090   The National issue; devoted to national
f.N2   prohibition to be secured and enforc-
             ed through honest and legitimate
             methods.
             St. Louis, W.G.Robinson.
             v. 31cm. monthly.

NN   0055710   MnHi

National issues; a survey of politics and legislation. v. 1–
Jan. 1939–
₍New York, National committee, Communist party, U. S. A., 1939₎
v. 28ᶜᵐ. monthly.

No more published.
L. C. set incomplete: no. 5–9 wanting.

1. U. S.—Pol. & govt.—Period. 2. U. S.—Pol. & govt.—1933   I. Communist party of the United States of America.
                                                    45–43326
Library of Congress   E806.N3

NN   0055711   DLC NNC PSt NIC DAU GU NN CoU

National Italian-American civic league.
Grand scholarship awards ...
    see its   Fourth annual convention,
June 14-15-16, 1935 ... Saint Paul, Minnesota.
Grand scholarship awards ...

VOLUME 407

LB2338
.N27
1935   National Italian-American civic league.
     Fourth annual convention, June 14-15-16,
1935 ... Saint Paul, Minnesota. Grand scholarship awards. Building American leadership for
tomorrow. National Italian-American civic
league. [Minneapolis, 1935]
     cover-title, 40 p. illus.(ports.) 27cm.

     Includes advertising matter.

     1. Scholarships--U.S.

NN 0055713   DLC

National Italian Association for the Assistance of Tourists
     see   Associazione Nazionale Italiana
Movimento Forestieri.

National jail association.
     ...A manual of jail administration to be issued by the National
jail association. The manual is being prepared for the Association
by Austin H. MacCormick...and Richard A. McGee... [New
York, 1938?] 1 v. 35cm.

     At head of title: Preliminary draft.
     Contains some chapters only.

     1. Prisons—Management and   discipline. I. MacCormick, Austin
Harbutt, 1893-   II. McGee,   Richard A.
N. Y. P. L.   August 24, 1948

NN 0056001   NN

NATIONAL jamboree. v.1, no.1, 3-4; June, Oct.-
Nov./Dec.1949
New York, L.K. Engel.   v.   illus.
28cm.

     Irregular.
     Ceased publication with v.1, no.4, Nov./Dec.1949?

     1.Amusements--Per. and soc. publ. 2. Theatre--Per.--U.S.

NN 0056002   NN

National Jamboree, Boy Scouts of America
     see
Boy Scouts of America. *National Jamboree.*

325.252| National Japanese American Student Relocation
P191   Council.
v.4   Activities and finances of the National
no.1   Japanese American Student Relocation Council.
     [Philadelphia, Pa.?] 1943.
     4 ℓ. 28cm. (In Pamphlets on the
Japanese in the U.S. v.4, no.1)

     Caption title.

     1. Japanese in the U.S. 2. Students.
U.S. I. Title.

NN 0056004   OrU

National Japanese American student relocation council.
     Directory of American students of Japanese ancestry in the
higher schools, colleges and universities of the United States
of America, including students currently working but intending
to enter college ... Philadelphia, Pa., Printed for private circulation by the National Japanese American student relocation
council with the collaboration of the National council of Christian associations, New York, N. Y., 1943.
     cover-title, 72 p. 22½ᵐ.
     "No. 258."

     1. Japanese in the U. S. 2. Students--U. S.   I. National council of
Christian associations.

Harvard univ. Library   A 44-4284
for Library of Congress

NN 0056005   MH OrU

NATIONAL JAPANESE AMERICAN STUDENT RELOCATION
COUNCIL
     Final composite report of the returned nisei
college leaders, summer of 1944. 1201 Chestnut
St. Philadelphia 7, Pa. Author [1944]
     11 p.

     Processed.

NN 0056006   Or

National Japanese American student relocation council.
     From camp to college; the story of Japanese American stu-
dent relocation ... Philadelphia, Pa., National Japanese American student relocation council [1945]
     [12] p. illus. 23ᵐ.

     1. U. S. War relocation authority. 2. World war, 1939-1945--Educa-
tion and the war. 3. Students--U. S.   I. Title.

                                                         46-1224
Library of Congress   D805.U5N3
                             [2]   940.547273

NN 0056007   DLC NN NNC CSt-H Or

325.252 National Japanese American Student Relocation
P191   Council.
v.4   How to help Japanese American student
no.3   relocation. Philadelphia, Pa., 1943.
     [8] p. 23cm. (In Pamphlets on the
Japanese in the U.S. v.4, no.3)

     Bibliography: p.[7]-[8]

     1. Japanese in the U.S. 2. Students.
U.S. I. Title.

NN 0056008   OrU

325.252 National Japanese American Student Relocation
P191   Council.
v.4   [Letter] to members of the Council.
no.4   Philadelphia, Pa., 1943.
     [3] p. 28cm. (In Pamphlets on the
Japanese in the U.S. v.4, no.4)

     1. Japanese in the U.S. 2. Students.
U.S

NN 0056009   OrU

325.252 National Japanese American Student Relocation
P191   Council.
v.4   Report of the Field Director, delivered at
no.5   the Council meeting, September 29, 1943.
     [Philadelphia, Pa.?, 1943]
     2 ℓ. 28cm. (In Pamphlets on the
Japanese in the U.S. v.4, no.5)

     Caption title.

     1. Japanese in the U.S. 2. Students.
U.S.

NN 0056010   OrU

SPECIAL
COLL.
BJ
N213   National Japanese American student relocation
         council.
     [Reports and literature of the National
Japanese American student relocation council;
correspondence of the Council with Karl W.
Onthank, University of Oregon] 1942-1946.
     3 folders.

     The University of Oregon had no official
connection with the Council.

NN 0056011   OrU

325.25 National Japanese American Student Relocation
P191   Council.
v.4   To the members of the Council of the
no.6   National Japanese American Student Relocation
     Council. New York, 1943.
     11 ℓ. 28cm. (In Pamphlets on the
Japanese in the U.S. v.4, no.6)

     Caption title.

     1. Japanese in the U.S. 2. Students.
U.S.

NN 0056012   OrU

BQX
4361
N277   The National Jesuit Institute on College
         Religion.
     Proceedings held at the College of the
Holy Cross, Worcester, Mass., Aug. 2-14,
1951. Ed. by Eugene B. Gallagher.   New
York, Fairfield University, 1952.
     ix, 381 p.

     1. Gallagher, Eugene B., ed.

NN 0056013   NSyL

TS720
.N3   ... National jeweler ...
     [Chicago, National jeweler, inc., etc., 1906-
     v. illus., diagrs. 20½-22½cm.
monthly.

     Beginning with Sept. 1940, title
reads: N J National jeweler.

     1. Jewelry trade--Period.

NN 0056014   DLC ICarbS ICJ NN KU ICRL

The National jeweler and optician
     see   National jeweler.

National jewelers board of trade.
     ... Reference book of the jewelry trade in the United
States and Canada.
Providence, Chicago [etc., Private press of National jew-
elers board of trade, 1912-
     v. 25½ᵐ.
     At head of title: Confidential.

     1. Jewelry trade—Credit guides.

Library of Congress   HF5585.J4N3   12-23186

NN 0056016   DLC NN

National jewelers board of trade.
     Report of proceedings, annual meeting,
1st-   annual convention, 1914-
Constitution and by-laws, officers, committees and members.
New York city,
     v. illus., ports. 22½ᵐ.

     Title varies: -1913, Report of proceedings, annual meeting ...
1914-   Report of proceedings, annual meeting ... annual convention ...

Library of Congress   HD9747.U5N3   43-34292
                             [2]   338.4773027

NN 0056017   DLC NN

National jewelers board of trade
     see also
Jewelers board of trade.

VOLUME 407

The **National** jeweler's directory of trade marks, manufacturers, wholesalers...of the jewelry trade. 1925

Chicago: The National Jeweler, cop. 1925   nar. 8°.
   v.
   Published by the National jeweler and optician.

1. Trade marks—U. S. 2. Jewelers   —Direct.
V V P L.   May 1, 1925

NN   0056019   NN MiD

NATIONAL JEWELERS PUBLICITY ASSOCIATION
   Diamonds. When buying diamonds.   Author, 1928.
   17 + 7 ℓ. (its Article no.8)

NN   0056020   Or

NATIONAL JEWELERS PUBLICITY ASSOCIATION
   Jewelry of the renaissance. Author, 1928.
   7 ℓ. (its Article no.1)

NN   0056021   Or

NATIONAL JEWELERS PUBLICITY ASSOCIATION
   The lore of precious stones. Author, 1930.
   6 ℓ. (its Article no.6)

NN   0056022   Or

NATIONAL JEWELERS PUBLICITY ASSOCIATION
   The pearl – the queen of gems. Author, n.d.
   10 ℓ. (its Article no.20)

NN   0056023   Or

NATIONAL JEWELERS PUBLICITY ASSOCIATION
   What do you know about diamonds? Author, n.d.
   8 ℓ. (its Article no.18)

NN   0056024   Or

NATIONAL JEWELERS PUBLICITY ASSOCIATION
   Where our knife, fork and spoon came from. Author ₍1929?₎
   6 ℓ. (its Article no.25)

NN   0056025   Or

The **National** Jewish blue book; an elite directory ... containing statistical data, names and addresses of officers and directors of local and national Jewish organizations, and of members of Greek letter fraternities and country clubs; general information; arranged geographically and alphabetically ... 1927–   Philadelphia, Pa., The Blue book publishing company ₍*1927–
   v. 24ᶜᵐ.

1. Jews in the U. S. 2. Jews—Societies. 3. Greek letter societies.
                           27–14924
Library of Congress   E184.J5N59

NN   0056026   DLC MH OCH OC1   MB NN WaS MiU

HS 3313
N3.85
1928
   National Jewish Committee on Scouting.
   Scouting and the Jewish boy. New York, Published by Boy Scouts of America [1928?]
   40 p. illus. 20 cm.

   1. Boy Scouts. I. Title

NN   0056027   OCH PPDrop

National Jewish Committee on Scouting.
   Scouting and the Jewish boy. Scouting, cubbing and senior scouting in synagogues, community centers and other Jewish organizations....
   N.Y., Jewish Committee on Scouting, cop. 1943.
   58 p. illus.

NN   0056028   OCH

National Jewish Committee on Scouting.
   Scouting and the Jewish boy; scouting, cubbing and senior scouting in synagogues and community centers and other Jewish organizations, developed and issued by the Jewish Committee on Scouting ... New York, Bloch publishing company, 1944.
   3 p. l., 58 p. illus. 21 cm.
   Bound with: Barcelo, L. P. Scouting for Catholics.
   1. Boy Scouts of America. I. Title.

NN   0056029   NNU-W

367.21
N213s
   NATIONAL JEWISH COMMITTEE ON SCOUTING.
   Scouting and the Jewish boy: the scout program in synagogues, community centers and other Jewish organizations. New York, c1949.
   3p ℓ.,66p. illus. 21cm.
   Bibliography: p.57–58.

   1. Boy Scouts of America. I. Title.

NN   0056030   TxU

HS 3313
N3.85
1954
   National Jewish Committee on Scouting.
   Scouting and the Jewish boy. The scout program in synagogues, community centers and other Jewish organizations, issued by Jewish Committee on scouting. New Brunswick, N.J., Boy Scouts of America c1954.
   54 p. illus. 20 cm.
   First published 1927?

   1. Boy Scouts. I. Title

NN   0056031   OCH

National Jewish hospital, *Denver*
   see
Denver. National Jewish hospital.

National Jewish Hospital for Consumptives, Denver
   see Denver. National Jewish Hospital.

National Jewish immigration council.
   ... Jewish immigrants. Report of a special committee of the National Jewish immigration council appointed to examine into the question of illiteracy among Jewish immigrants and its causes ... Washington, Govt. print. off., 1914.
   26 p. 23ᶜᵐ. ₍U. S.₎ 63d Cong. 2d sess. Senate. Doc. 611)
   Presented by Mr. O'Gorman. Referred to the Committee on printing March 24, 1914.
   Submitted to Mr. O'Gorman by Abram J. ₍₎ Elkus.
   Max J. Kohler, chairman of special committee.

   1. Jews in the United States. 2. Jews in Russia. 3. U. S.—Emig. & immig. I. Elkus, Abram Isaac, 1867– II. Kohler, Max James, 1871–1934. III. Title.
                          14–30849
Library of Congress   JV6805.J6N3

NN   0056034   DLC MiU OO OrU

National Jewish ledger; dedicated to united Jewish ideals.

Washington ₍Jewish ledger publishing co.₎ 19
   v. illus. (incl. ports.) 44ᶜᵐ. weekly.
   Caption title.
   Volume numbers irregular: v. 19, no. 2–   v. 29, no. 1 omitted.
   Editor: K. Cornell.
   Publication began in 1930. cf. American Jewish yearbook, v. 45, 1943/44, p. 555.

   1. Jews—Period. 2. Jews in the U. S. I. Cornell, Kay C., ed.
                            44–52978
Library of Congress   E184.J5N595
          ₍2₎   296

NN   0056035   DLC

National Jewish Mission.
   The Jew and Palestine news
   see under title

The **National** Jewish monthly.

₍Washington, etc.₎ B'nai B'rith, 19
   v. in   illus. (incl. ports.) 29½ᶜᵐ. monthly.
   Volume numbers irregular: v. 16 called v. 15; v. 15 ₍i. e. 16₎ no. 11–v. 38 omitted in numbering.
   Title varies: —June 1924, B'nai B'rith news.
   Oct. 1924–1938, B'nai B'rith magazine (cover-title, 1934–1938: B'nai B'rith national Jewish monthly)
   1939–   The National Jewish monthly.
   July–Sept. 1924 not published.
   Separately paged supplements accompany some numbers.

   1. Jews—Period. I. B'nai B'rith.
                             45–28687
Library of Congress   HS2228.B4N3
          ₍2₎   296.05

   OCU ICU AzU WvU
NN   0056037   DLC NcD NIC ICN OU MB NBuG Vi OO OC1

National Jewish monthly v. 1–date; Sept. 1908–date
   Washington [etc.]   v.   illus., ports. 29–40cm.

   Film reproduction. Positive.
   Vols. 1–7, 15–74, in *PYP.

   Monthly (irregular).

   Vol. 15 repeated in numbering.
   Issue for June, 1924, called v. 15, no. 10; for Oct. 1924, called v. 39, no. 1, the latter volume numbering computed from 1886, the year its predecessor, the Menorah began publication.
   Issued by B'nai B'rith (Sept. 1908–Sept. 1930, as Independent order of B'nai B'rith).   Sept. 1908–June 1924, B'nai B'rith news.
   Title varies: Oct. 1924–Sept. 1934, B'nai B'rith magazine; Oct. 1934–1938, B'nai B'rith national Jewish monthly (caption title: B'nai B'rith magazine); 1939–date, The   National Jewish monthly.

   Vol. 61, no. 6–v. 62, no. 7, Feb. 1947–Mar. 1948, most issues include the section: Washington news letter (formerly issued as a section of the A D L bulletin).
   Includes various supplements.

   1. Periodicals, Jewish, in English. 2. Periodicals, American. I. B'nai B'rith, Independent order of. II Title: B'nai B'rith magazine. III. Title: B'nai B'rith national Jewish monthly. IV. Title: The National Jewish monthly. V. Washington news   letter.

NN   0056040   NN

National Jewish Music Council.
   Bibliography of book and articles on Jewish music ...
     see National Jewish Music Council. Research Committee.
   Bibliography of articles and books on Jewish music.

VOLUME 407

National Jewish Music Council.
Bibliography of Jewish instrumental music ...
see under   National Jewish Music Council.
Bibliography Committee.

ML1
.J45

Jewish music notes.   -v. 4,
no. 4;   -Dec. 1949. ₁New York₎ National
Jewish Music Council.

ML
128
J4N3.9

National Jewish Music Council.
Music for the tercentenary: a
bibliography. New York, American
Jewish Tercentenary [1954]
27 p.   22 cm.

1. Instrumental music--Bibliography.
2. Vocal music, Jewish--Bibliography.
I. Title

NN 0056044   OCH

National Jewish Music Council.
The music of Ernest Bloch; a program manual.
Sponsored by the National Jewish Welfare Board.
[New York, 1955]
67 p.   illus., port., facsim.   29 cm.
Bibliography: p. 65-67.
1. Bloch, Ernest, 1880-1959. I. Title.

NN 0056045   OrU

National Jewish Music Council.
Our tenth year; a report of the activities
1953-1954. [New York,1954?.]
5 l.   29 cm.

Distributed to constituent members.
Alternate pages blank.

NN 0056046   OCH

National Jewish Music Council. *Bibliography Committee.*
Bibliography of instrumental and vocal music. ₁New
York₎ Jewish Music Council, 1946.
17 p. 28 cm.
Cover title.

1. Music, Jewish--Bibl. 2. Instrumental music--Bibl. 3. Vocal
music--Bibl.
ML120.J4N28   781.971   49-53292 rev*

NN 0056047   DLC NN NNC OrP

National Jewish Music Council. *Bibliography Committee.*
Bibliography of Jewish instrumental music. ₁New York₎
National Jewish Music Council ₁ᶜ1948₎
16 p. 28cm.
Cover title.
—— 1949-50 addenda. ₁New York₎ National Jewish Music
Council ₁1950?₎
7 l. 28cm.
Cover title.
                        ML120.J4N2822
1. Music, Jewish--Bibl. 2. Instrumental music--Bibl.
ML120.J4N282   781.971   51-26874

NN 0056048   DLC NcU MiD CU NN TU OrP

National Jewish Music Council. Bibliography
Committee.
Bibliography of Jewish instrumental music.
New York [1952]
19 [1] p.
Typewritten copy.
"Sponsored by National Jewish Welfare Board."
"... A reprint of the Bibliography prepared in
1949 ...".

NN 0056049   MiD NN OCH

National Jewish Music Council. *Bibliography Committee.*
Bibliography of Jewish vocal music. ₁New York₎ National Jewish Music Council ₁ᶜ1948₎
36 p. 28 cm.
—— 1949-50 addenda. ₁New York₎ National Jewish Music
Council ₁1950?₎
16 l. 28 cm.
Cover title.   ML120.J4N2842
1. Music, Jewish--Bibl. 2. Vocal music--Bibl.
ML120.J4N284   781.971   51-26873

NN 0056050   DLC NcU MB OrP MiD CU

National Jewish Music Council. Bibliography
committee.
List of collections of Jewish song
see under   National Jewish Welfare Board.

National Jewish Music Council. Bibliography Committee
Music for the tercentenary ...
see under   National Jewish Music Council.

National Jewish Music Council. *Committee on Recordings.*
Bibliography of Jewish recordings. ₁New York₎ National
Jewish Music Council ₁ᶜ1948₎
19 p. 28 cm.

1. Music, Jewish--Discography. 2. Vocal music--Discography.
3. Instrumental music--Discography.
ML156.4.J4N27   [789.9] 781.973   51-27535

NN 0056053   DLC NcU MiD CU OrP MB

National Jewish Music Council. *Committee on Recordings.*
List of instrumental and vocal recordings. ₁New York₎
Jewish Music Council, 1946.
7 p. 28 cm.
Cover title.

1. Music, Jewish--Discography. 2. Instrumental music--Discog-
raphy. 3. Vocal music--Discography.
ML156.4.J4N3   [789.9] 781.9734 49-53291 rev*

NN 0056054   DLC NBuG OrP

National Jewish Music Council. *Program
Committee.*
Oneg shabbat; a suggested program for Jewish
groups. [New York] National Jewish Music
Council [1949]
9 p. 28cm.
Cover title.

1. Jews--Social life and customs. 2.
Music, Jewish--Bibl. I. Title.

NN 0056055   MB

National Jewish Music Council. *Publications.
Committee.*
Annotated list of musico-dramatic scripts.
New York, National Jewish Music Council, 1949.
10 p. 28cm.
Cover title.

1. Music, Jewish--Bibl.

NN 0056056   MB

National Jewish Music Council. *Record Reviews Committee.*
Reviews of selected recordings of Jewish music. Editor:
Eric Werner. ₁New York₎ 1953.
70 p. 27 cm.

1. Phonorecords--Reviews. 2. Music, Jewish--Discography.
I. Title.
ML156.9.N3   *789.913   54-32390

NN 0056057   DLC NBuG OCH LU MB MiD NIC MB IU

National Jewish Music Council. *Research Committee.*
Bibliography of articles and books on Jewish music.
₁New York₎ Jewish Music Council, 1946.
4 p. 28 cm.
Cover title.

1. Music, Jewish--Bibl.
ML120.J4N3 19   016.78172   49-40884 rev*

NN 0056058   DLC NN InU NBuG

National Jewish Music Council. *Research Committee.*
Bibliography of articles and books on Jewish music.
₁New York₎ National Jewish Music Council, 1947.
7, 2 l. 28 cm.
Cover title.
"Addenda ... prepared by Joseph Yasser": 2 p. at end.

1. Music, Jewish--Bibl.
ML120.J4N3 1947   016.78172   51-27007

NN 0056059   DLC MB

National Jewish post
see   The National Jewish post and opinion.

The NATIONAL Jewish post and opinion. v.12, no.29-
v.23, no.7; Mar. 15, 1957-Nov.11, 1966. New
York. 11 v. illus., ports. 33-40cm.

Film reproduction. Positive.
Lacking: v.13, no.23-24, Jan. 31-Feb. 7, 1958; v.20, no.4, Oct.2,
1964.
Weekly.
Numbering irregular, sometimes omitted.

Formed by the union of the National Jewish post, and Opinion, continuing the v. numbering of the former.
Title varies slightly.
Called National edition; issued also in several local editions: Chicago
ed.; Indiana ed.: etc. (Library has only National ed.)
For later file, which continues its numbering, see the Jewish post and
opinion.

1. Periodicals, Jewish, in English.   2. Periodicals, American.

NN 0056062   NN

National Jewish Welfare Board.
Jews. *Liturgy and ritual.*
Abridged prayer book for Jews in the armed forces of the
United States. New York city, Jewish welfare board ₁ᶜ1941₎

VOLUME 407

National Jewish Welfare Board.
    Activities for the year
19

New York [19   28cm.
    no. illus. (incl. ports.)
    Cover-title.

1. Charities, Jewish—U.S.

NN   0056064   NN PHi

National
Jewish welfare board.
    Administrative and office system for Jewish centers...   **New**
York, Nat. Jewish welfare board, 1947.   62 p.   28cm.
    "Revised."

    1. Community centers—Admin-   istration. 2. Community centers,
Jewish.   Jewish.
N.Y.P.L.   December 13, 1948

NN   0056065   NN

National Jewish Welfare Board.
    The American Jewish adventure, an address at
the 1948 annual meeting of the National Jewish
Welfare Board, May 9, 1948, Chicago
        see under   Liebman, Joshua Loth, 1907–
1948.

National Jewish Welfare Board.
    Annual report. 1st–
    [1917/18,–
    New York.

        v. 23–27 cm.

    Reports for 1917/18–   issued under the board's earlier name:
    Jewish Welfare Board.

    1. Jews—Societies. 2. European War, 1914–1918—Jews. 3. World
War, 1939–1945—Jews.

    D639.J4J3   940.4776   19–12849 rev*

NN   0056067   DLC NN ICJ NNZ ICU

National Jewish welfare board.
    Baruch (Benedict de) Spinoza, 1632–1932; program ma-
terial for the observance of Spinoza tercentenary, November, 1932. New York, Jewish welfare board [1932]

    cover-title, 31 numb. l. 28 cm.

    "Selected bibliography": leaves 30–31.

    1. Spinoza, Benedictus de, 1632–1677. 2. Spinoza, Benedictus de,
1632–1677—Centennial celebrations, etc.
    B3997.J4   41–27759 rev
                                          Brief cataloging

NN   0056068   DLC NN OO MB

National
Jewish Welfare Board.
    Bibliography for workers in Jewish centers.   New York City:
Jewish Welfare Board, 1923.   22 f.   4°.
    Cover-title.
    Typewritten.

    1. Community centers, Jewish—   Bibl. 2. Jews—Bibl.
N.Y.P.L.   June 23, 1925

NN   0056069   NN PPYH

National Jewish Welfare Board.
    Bibliography of Jewish instrumental music
        see under   National Jewish Music Council.
Bibliography Committee.

National
JEWISH WELFARE BOARD.
    The book of trips, with places of Jewish interest;
complete, economical, self-guided tours of New York...
[New York] J. W. B. [c1939]   47 p.   illus.   18½:m.

    Cover-title.

    1. New York (City)—Guidebooks, 1939. 2. Jews in the
U.S.—N.Y.—New York.

NN   0056071   NN NNJ

National Jewish Welfare Board.
    Building operation and maintenance.   New York,
c1932.
    cover-title, 82 l.   28 cm.
    Bibliography: l. 78–79.

NN   0056072   NNC

National Jewish Welfare Board.
    Bulletin on the observance of Chanukah issued to
constituent societies, Nov. 1925.

NN   0056073   PPYH

National Jewish Welfare Board.   *3491.145
    Bulletin on the observance of Chanukah. 1931.
=   *Reproduced typewriting.* New York City. 1931. 1 v. 27½ cm.

    D2155 — Hanuccah. Plays., festival   ic. — Chanukah, Bulletin on the ob-
servance of.

NN   0056074   MB

National Jewish Welfare Board.
    Bulletin on the observance of Independence Day:
issued to constituent societies June 8, 1922.
New York, Jewish Welfare Board, 1922.

NN   0056075   PPYH

National Jewish Welfare Board.
    Bulletin on the observance of Lincoln's
birthday, January, 1932.   New York, 1932.
35 £ , multigraphed.   28 cm.

NN   0056076   RPB

National Jewish Welfare Board.
    Bulletin on the observance of Memorial Day;
issued to constituent societies May 15, 1922.
New York, Jewish Welfare Board, 1922.

NN   0056077   PPYH

National Jewish Welfare Board.
    Bulletin on the observance of passover issued to
constituent societies Feb. 26, 1923.   New York,
Jewish Welfare Board, 1923.

NN   0056078   PPYH

National
Jewish Welfare Board.   West End Branch (7481.48)
    Bulletin on the observance of Passover.
—   *Reproduced typewriting.* New York. 1932. 28 ff. Illus. 28 cm.
    Sources for references, ff. 6, 7.
    Typed on one side only of the paper.
    The title is on the cover.

    D3072 — Passover

NN   0056079   MB

National Jewish Welfare Board.
    Bulletin on the observance of Purim;
issued to constituent societies Jan. 1926.

NN   0056080   PPYH

BM695
.P9N3   National Jewish Welfare Board.
1938   Bulletin on the observance of **Purim**.
          New York, Jewish Welfare Board, 1938.
          46 l.   29cm.
          Cover title.
          "Selected references": leaves 25–26;
          "Plays and tableaux": leaves 29–36.

          1. Purim (Feast of Esther)

NN   0056081   MB

National
Jewish Welfare Board.
    Bulletin on the observance of Shevuoth. Issued to constituent
societies, May 10, 1922.   New York: Jewish Welfare Board
[1922].   14 f.   4°.
    Reproduced from typed copy written on one side of leaf only.

    1. Festivals, Jewish.
N.Y.P.L.   June 23, 1925

NN   0056082   NN

National Jewish Welfare Board, N. Y.
    Bulletin on the observation of She-
vuoth issued to constituent societies
April 1926.

NN   0056083   PPYH

National
Jewish Welfare Board.
    Bulletin on the observance of [special days]
issued to constituent societies.

    New York, 19   8°.
    nos.

    1. Festivals, Jewish.
N.Y.P.L.   June 14, 1927

NN   0056084   NN

National Jewish welfare board.
    Bulletin on the observance of [special days]...
    1930–1933.
        [v. 1–6]

NN   0056085   MiD

National Jewish Welfare Board, N. Y.
    Bulletin on the observance of
Succoth; issued to constitutent societies
Sept. 1925.

NN   0056086   PPYH

JUDAICA
BM693
.H5N3   National Jewish Welfare Board.
          Bulletin on the observance of the
          High Holy Days including twenty-five
          questions and answers on Rosh Hashonah
          and Yom Kippur.   New York, Jewish
          Welfare Board, 1931.
          22 l.   29cm.
          Cover title.
          Bibliography: leaves 10–10a.
          1. High Holy Days.

NN   0056087   MB

VOLUME 407

National Jewish Welfare Board.
Circle. v. 1– Oct. 1946–
₍New York₎ National Jewish Welfare Board.

National₎
^JEWISH MUSIC COUNCIL.
[Collection of pamphlets published by National
Jewish music council. New York, 1947-50]
7 pams. in 1 v. music. 28cm.

CONTENTS.—Jewish moods in music, by J. K. Eisenstein.—Of music
in modern Israel, by P. Gradenwitz.—Yiddish folksong of the eastern
European Jews, by R. Rubin.—Jewish center program aids.—Oneg Shabbat,
a suggested program for Jewish groups.—Suggested program of Israeli music.
—Suggested program for a Jewish music activity.
1. Jewish music. 2. Israel. 3. Music—Israel. 4. Music—
Jews. 5. Music.

NN 0056089 NN

National Jewish Welfare Board.
Combatting rumors
see under National Jewish Welfare Board.
Army and Navy Public Relations Comm.

D810
J4N273
Hoover
Library
National Jewish Welfare Board.
Compiling Jewish war records of World War
II. New York, 1946-5706.
28 p. 23ᶜᵐ.
Cover title.
"Reprinted from the American Jewish year
book, vol. 47."
Contents.- Jewish war records of World War
II, by S. C. Kohs. - Jews in the armed forces,
by Louis Kraft.

1.World War, 1939-1945 - Jews. I.Kohs,
Samuel Calmin, 1890-   II.Ameri-
can Jewish year   book. III.Title.

NN 0056091 CSt-H NN NIC MH

National Jewish Welfare Board.
Conference on Membership Problems arranged
by the Jewish Welfare Board, April 22-24, 1933.
New York, 1933.
35 p.

NN 0056092 PPDrop

National₎
^JEWISH WELFARE BOARD.
Direct by mail appeals for membership payments and
contributions. New York city: Jewish Welfare Board,
1935. 66 f. illus. 28cm.

Reproduced from typewritten copy.

867844A. 1. Money raising drives.

NN 0056093 NN

National Jewish Welfare Board.
Directory of Jewish community centers
see under title

National₎ Jewish Welfare Board
Discussion Groups in Jewish Centers.
Objectives, Technique and Materials.
N.Y. 1934.

39 p.

NN 0056095 PPDrop

National₎
^Jewish welfare board.
Expanding functions of the center; proceedings of the J. W. B.
Institute on public relations, budgeting, fund raising and refugee
adjustment. New York: National Jewish welfare board, 1940.
56, 4 f. diagr. 28cm.

"Bibliography," 4 f. at end.

1. Community centers.
N. Y. P. L.   March 18, 1943

NN 0056096 NN

940.9315296
N213f
1945
[National Jewish welfare board]
Fighting for America, a record of the participa-
tion of Jewish men and women in the armed forces
during 1944. [New York, 1945?]
3p.ℓ.,ix-x, 290p. illus.,plates. 19cm.
"Edited by L. Roy Blumenthal."
CONTENTS.--pt.1. The armed forces of the United
States.--pt.2. Honor roll.
1. World war, 1939-1945 - Jews. 2. World war,
1939-1945 - U.S. I. Blumenthal, L. Roy, ed. II.
Title.

NN 0056097 TxU NcD NRU ViU ICN NcD PP MiD NNC

₍National Jewish welfare board₎
Fighting for America, an account of Jewish men in the
armed forces, from Pearl harbor to the Italian campaign.
₍New York, 1944₎
1 p. l., ₍v₎-xiv p., 1 l., 176 p. 21¼ cm.
"Edited by Nathan C. Belth."
CONTENTS.—Statistics and surveys.—Facts on non-combatant serv-
ice.—For our kind of world, by Barney Ross.—Only five survived, by
Morton Deitz.—Crash landing in Java, by Harry Schreiber.—One
hundred days in Guadalcanal, by Louis Aronson.—Battle in the
Aleutians, by M. L. Chernow.—Night attack on hill 350, by Louis
Pickney.—Turn 'em over and roll out, by F. H. Sternberg.—Honors
and awards.
1. World war, 1939-   1945—Jews. 2. World war, 1939-
1945—U. S.   I. Belt'   Nathan C., ed. II. Title.
D810.J4J37   940.5315296   44-4365 rev

JU OCIW OCI ViU OrCS CBM IaU MH
NN 0056098 DLC WaSp ICU DSI WaT WaS WaE OrU PBm

940.9315296
N213f
1944rl
[National Jewish welfare board]
Fighting for America, an account of Jewish men
in the armed forces, from Pearl harbor to the
Italian campaign. [New York, c1944]
1p.ℓ.,₍v₎-xivp.,1ℓ.,169p. 20½cm.
"Second printing."
"Edited by Nathan C. Belth."
CONTENTS.--Statistics and surveys.--Facts on
non-combatant service.--For our kind of world, by
Barney Ross.--Only five survived, by Morton Deitz.
--Crash landing in Java, by Harry Schreiber. One
(Continued on

---

hundred days in Guadalcanal, by Louis Aronson.--
Battle in the Aleutians, by M.L. Chernow.--The day
we hit Palermo, by Schiller Cohen.--To Guadalcanal
and back, by S.A. Isquith.--Forced landing in China,
by Morton Sher.--Night attack on hill 350, by Louis
Pickney.--Last of the "Yankee Doodle", by Bernard
Leibowitz.--Honors and awards.
1. World war, 1939-1945 - Jews. 2. World war,
1939-1945 - U.S.   I. Belth, Nathan C., ed.

NN 0056100 TxU NBuG CtY NN MH NIC

National Jewish welfare board.
... Final report of war emergency activities. New York,
1920.
2 p. l., ₍7₎-127 p. incl. plates, ports. 21 cm.

1. European war, 1914-1918—Jews.

D639.J4J45 1921   21-18328 rev

TxU DNLM
NN 0056101 DLC Or ICJ PPDrop OO OCI OU DNW DN NcD

National₎
^Jewish Welfare Board.
The home camp; a summer project for juniors in the Jewish
center... New York city: Jewish Welfare Board, 1935. 50 f.
incl. table. 28cm.

Cover-title.
Reproduced from typewritten copy.
"Bibliography," f. 42-45; "Abridged Hebrew vocabulary for use in home camps,"
f. 46-50.

867844A. 1. Schools, Vacation.   I. Title.
N. Y. P. L.   February 9, 1937

NN 0056102 NN

E184
.J5C569
National Jewish Welfare Board.
In Jewish bookland. v. 1-6, no. 2; Mar. 1945–Nov./Dec. 1949.
₍New York₎ Jewish Book Council of America.

National Jewish Welfare Board.
In the nation's service, a compilation of facts concerning
Jewish men in the Armed Forces during the first year of the
war. ₍New York, 1942₎
47 p. illus., ports. 28 cm.
Cover title.

1. World War, 1939-1945—Jews. 2. Jews in the U. S.   I. Title.
D810.J4X3 1942   940.5315296   49-32441*

NN 0056104 DLC NN OCH OrU

₍National Jewish welfare board₎
In the nation's service, a compilation of facts concerning
Jewish men in the armed forces during the first year of the
war. ₍New York, 1943₎
cover-title, 55 p. illus. (incl. ports.) 28 x 21¼ cm.
"Second printing, February, 1943."

1. World war, 1939-1945—Jews. 2. Jews in the U. S.   I. Title.
D810.J4J4   940.5315296   43-5159 rev

NN 0056105 DLC ICRL PPT ODW OU NNC Or CaBVaU

E184
.J5C57
National Jewish Welfare Board.
JWB circle. v. 1-
₍New York₎ National Jewish Welfare Board.

National₎
^Jewish Welfare Board.
Jewish background; suggestive outlines for a basic course in
Jewish history, Jewish literature and current Jewish problems for
leaders in group work. New York City: Jewish Welfare Board,
1934. 48 f. 28cm.

Cover-title.
Reproduced from typewritten copy.

801658A. 1. Jews—Hist.—Outlines,   syllabi, etc. 2. Jewish literature—
Outlines, syllabi, etc. 3. Jews in   the U. S.
N. Y. P. L.   February 19, 1936

NN 0056107 NN OCU

National₎
^Jewish welfare board.
... Jewish calendar for soldiers and
sailors ... New York, N.Y., Jewish welfare
board (1935)
40 p. 12 cm.

NN 0056108 DNW

VOLUME 407

National Jewish Welfare Board.

E184
.J5J52

The Jewish Center. v. 1-24; Oct. 1922-Dec. 1946. **New** York, National Jewish Welfare Board.

National Jewish Welfare Board.
Jewish Center program aids
see under   Jewish Community Center
program aids.

National Jewish Welfare Board.
The Jewish center songster ...
see under   Carp, Bernard, 1908-   , ed.

National Jewish Welfare Board.
Jewish ceremonial articles and art objects, with
description of articles and explanatory notes.
New York, Jewish welfare board, 1934.
Autographed from typewritten copy.

NN 0056112   OC1

National Jewish Welfare Board.
Jewish children give thanks to America

see under

Serwer, Zachary.

National Jewish Welfare Board.

E184
.J5J535

Jewish Community Center program aids.

New York, National Jewish Welfare Board.

National Jewish Welfare Board.
Jewish community center self-study manual

see under

Picheny, Elias.

National Jewish welfare board.

Jewish information series, no. 1-
New York city, Jewish welfare board and American association for Jewish education ₁1942-

---

National Jewish Welfare Board.
(Jewish inspirational pamphlets for
personnel of the armed forces of the
United States)

1.History-U.S.

NN 0056117   NNJ

National Jewish welfare board.

*ML37
J3J3

Jewish music festival, February 7-March 6,
1947. New York, 1947.

2p.ℓ.,32p.   illus.   27 1/2cm.

Cover-title.

NN 0056118   NBuG

ML1
.J45

National Jewish Welfare Board.

Jewish music notes.
no. 4;   -v. 4,
Jewish Music Council.   -Dec. 1949. ₁New York₎ National

National
Jewish Welfare Board.
Jewish song book for soldiers and sailors.   New York City:
Jewish Welfare Board, United States Army and Navy ₁cop. 1918₎.
xii p., 1 l., 74 p.   24°.

Title in Yiddish at end of the volume.
Includes English, Yiddish and Hebrew songs.

1. Songs (Soldiers'), Jews. 2. Euro-   pean war, 1914- —Religious life,
etc.; Prayerbooks, hymnbooks, etc.   3. Title.
N. Y. P. L.   October 21, 1919.

NN 0056120   NN MB MH

BM
70
N2
1945

National Jewish Welfare Board.
Jewish themes for discussion. 2d
printing. New York [1945?]
45 l.   27 cm.

1. Religious education of adults,
Jewish--Outlines, syllabi, etc.
I. Title

NN 0056121   OCH

National Jewish Welfare Board.
Jewish war records of World War II,
by C. S. Kohs ...
see its   Compiling Jewish war records of
World War II.

National Jewish welfare board.
... The Jewish welfare board—purpose and program.
₁New York, 1918₎
9 numb. l.   28 x 21½ cm.
Caption title.

D639.J4J45 1918   19-16323 rev

NN 0056123   DLC MB

National Jewish welfare board.
Jewish welfare board, U. S. Army and Navy, its work,
purpose and scope ... New York, National executive offices
₁1918?₎
cover-title, 24 p. illus. 17½ cm.
"Prepared by Cromwell Childe ₁and₎ John W. Schmidt."—p. ₁3₎ of
cover.

I. Childe, Cromwell. II. Schmidt, John William, 1883-
D639.J4J45 1918b   19-16325 rev

NN 0056124   DLC OCH MB

National Jewish welfare board.
Jewish welfare board, United States Army and Navy,
co-operating with and under the supervision of the War
department, Commission on training camp activities; purpose, scope, achievements. N₁ew₎ Y₁ork₎ National headquarters ₁1918₎
cover-title, 16 p. illus. 17 cm.

D639.J4J45 1918c   19-16324 rev

NN 0056125   DLC OCH

National Jewish Welfare Board
Jewish Youth Night, Rally or Sympo-
sium. Outline of Objectives, Procedure
Suggestive Material and References.
N.Y. 1911.

11p.

NN 0056126   PPDrop

National Jewish Welfare Board.

The lamp of liberty; a patriotic pageant
depicting the struggle of democracy in America.
New York, National Jewish Welfare Board, 1945.

14p. 23cm.

"Originally produced.... July 31st, 1940
Re-issued 1946.

1. Pageants. I. Tilte.

NN 0056127   RPB

369.4
J55L

National
Jewish welfare board.
Leadership training in the Jewish center; a
manual of suggested course outlines, lectures, and
workshops, dealing with pre-service and in-service
training. New York City, Jewish welfare
board, c1943.
79p. 23cm.

Contains bibliographies.

1. Group work, Educational and social. 2.
Jews--Societies. .   3. Leadership. I. Title:
The Jewish center

NN 0056128   LU MiD

National Jewish Welfare Board.
List of collections of Jewish songs. ₁New York, 1934?₎
3 l. 28 cm.
Caption title.
Typescript.

1. Songs, Jewish—Bibl.

ML120.J4N34   51-49280

NN 0056129   DLC

National
Jewish Welfare Board.   No. 3 in 2299a.170
The Maccabaean spirit. A Chanuka greeting from home to our
Jewish boys in khaki and blue.
[New York, 1918.] (4) pp. 18½ cm.

NN 0056130   MB OCH

National Jewish welfare board.
Manual for speakers in the United war work campaign,
November 11th to 18th, 1918. N₁ew₎ Y₁ork₎ Jewish welfare board, United States Army and Navy ₁1918₎
24 p. 17 cm.

I. Title.
D639.J4J45 1918c   19-16327 rev

NN 0056131   DLC OCH NN MB

National Jewish welfare board.
A manual of program suggestions for Jewish music week,
May 20th-30th, sponsored by National Jewish welfare board.
New York, N. Y. ₁1945₎
cover-title, 1 p. l., 17 p. 27½ cm.
Prepared by Bernard Carp. cf. p. ₁3₎ of cover.
"Appendix: Some basic books on Jewish music ... Some available
vocal recordings ... Some available instrumental recordings": p.
15-17.
———— Supplementary list of some instrumental Jewish
music ... New York, N. Y. ₁1945₎
cover-title, 5 p. 28 cm.
Compiled by A. W. Binder.

ML200.5.N27 Suppl. 1

Continued in next column

VOLUME 407

Continued from preceding column

————— ————— Supplementary list of some vocal Jewish music: folk, art and liturgical ... New York, N. Y. ₁1945₎

cover-title, 20 p. 28 cm.

Compiled by Harry Coopersmith.

ML200.5.N27 Suppl. 2

1. Music week. 2. Music, Jewish. 3. Music, Jewish—Bibl. 4. Music, Jewish—Discography. I. Carp, Bernard, 1908– II. Binder, Abraham Wolf, 1895– III. Coopersmith, Harry, 1902–

ML200.5.N27   781.72   46–20088 rev 2

NN 0056133   DLC MB

National
Jewish Welfare Board.
∧ Mendelssohn sesquicentennial; Moses Mendelssohn, 1729–1786. Program material for the observance of the Mendelssohn sesquicentennial, 1936. New York city: Jewish Welfare Board ₁1936₎
34 f. port. 28cm.

Cover-title.
Reproduced from typewritten copy.
"Selected references," f. 33–34.

867844A. 1. Mendelssohn, Moses,   1729–1786.
N. Y. P. L.   February 4, 1937

NN 0056134   NN OCH

National Jewish welfare board.
Ministering to the Jews in the armed forces of the United States; prayers for the sick, military funeral service and memorial service. New York, N. Y., Jewish welfare board ₁°1942₎
iv, 60 p. 13½ cm.

Prepared by Aryeh Lev. cf. Foreword.

1. Soldiers—Prayer-books and devotions—Hebrew. 2. Soldiers—Prayer-books and devotions—English. I. Lev, Aryeh. II. Title.

BM667.S6N3   296   45–29871 rev

NN 0056135   DLC MH

BM
755
M6N3.8   National Jewish Welfare Board.
Moses Maimonides (Rambam); octocentennial celebration; 1135–1935. Program material for Jewish centers and religious schools. [New York, 1935]
59 l. 28 cm.

1. Moses ben Maimon, 1135–1204—Centennial celebrations, etc.

NN 0056136   OCH MB PPDrop

National Jewish Welfare Board.
Moses Mendelssohn, 1729–1786 ...
see its Mendelssohn sesquicentennial ...

National Jewish Welfare Board
Eisenstein, Judith (Kaplan)
Music for Jewish groups, by Judith Kaplan Eisenstein. New York, N. Y., Jewish welfare board, °1942.

National Jewish Welfare Board.

Newsletter... v. 1–4, no. 13 (April 23, 1945–March 3, 1947). New York, 1945–47. 4 v. illus. 27cm.

Weekly (biweekly Aug.–Sept. 1946).
Vol. 3, no. 19 incorrectly numbered no. 18.
Issued chiefly for the armed forces; v. 3, no. 2–v. 4, no. 13 (April 29, 1946–March 3, 1947) published by the board's Department of public information.
No more published.

1. World war, 1939–1945—War   work—Jewish welfare board.
2. Soldiers—Welfare work—U.S.   3. Seamen—Welfare work—U.S.
N. Y. P. L.   February 7, 1952

NN 0056139   NN

L016.812
N277o   National Jewish Welfare Board.
100 plays for Hanukah; an annotated bibliography, by Rose Zaltsman. New York, 1950.
18ℓ. 28cm.

1. Jewish plays. Bibl. 2. Hanukkah (Feast of Lights) I. Zaltsman, Rose, comp.

NN 0056140   IEN

National Jewish Welfare Board.
Organization of a Jewish community center
see under National Jewish Welfare Board. Jewish Community Center Division.

National Jewish welfare board.

Jews. *Liturgy and ritual.*
Prayer book; abridged for Jews in the armed forces of the United States ... New York city, National Jewish welfare board ₁°1943₎

National Jewish welfare board.
BM675   FOR OTHER EDITIONS
.N5A3   SEE MAIN ENTRY
1943 b   Jews. *Liturgy and ritual. High holy day prayers.*
Prayer book; New year and Day of atonement; abridged for Jews in the armed forces of the United States ... New York city, National Jewish welfare board ₁°1943₎

National
∧ Jewish Welfare Board.
Preliminary study for Philadelphia Y. M. H. A. building campaign, prepared by Jewish Welfare Board ... September 1921... ₁New York?, 1921.₎   53 p. incl. tables.   illus. 8°.

1. Young Men's Hebrew Associatie
N. Y. P. L.   Philadelphia.   April 30, 1927

NN 0056144   NN

HQ
799.7
N3.3   National Jewish Welfare Board.
Preliminary survey of guidance activities in New York City. New York, Jewish Welfare Board, 1939.
70,5 l. 28 cm.

1. Youth, Jewish—New York (City) 2. Social work with youth—New York (City) I. Title

NN 0056145   OCH

National
∧ Jewish Welfare Board.
Prize play.
192
New York, 192
nos.   8°.

At head of title: Jewish Welfare Board Publications.

1. Amateur theatricals. 2. Jews   in drama.
N. Y. P. L.   June 16, 1927

NN 0056146   NN

National Jewish Welfare Board
Program Bulletin on the observance of Lag Ba'Omer, April, 1932. N/y.

NN 0056147   PPDrop

BM695
.L3N3   National Jewish Welfare Board.
Program bulletin on the observance of Lag Ba'Omer. New York, Jewish Welfare Board, 1936.
35 l. 29cm.
Cover title.
Bibliography: leaves 34–35.

1. Sefirah period. I. Title: Lag Ba'Omer

NN 0056148   MB

BM690
.N36   National Jewish Welfare Board.
₁Program materials for Jewish holidays.₎ New York, 1945–55.
21 pamphlets in 1 v. illus., ports. 13–28cm.
Includes music.
Includes bibliographies.
CONTENTS.–Hanukkah, by S. Greenberg. 1954.–Passover, by D. I. Golovensky. 1954.–Purim, by G. Klaperman. 1954.–Rosh Hashanah, by E. J. Sack. 1954.–Shavuos, by S. M. Silver. 1954.–Sukkos (Season of gladness) by A. S. Goldstein.

1954.–Yom Kippur (the Day of atonement) by J. Nadich. 1955.–Jewish festival crafts, by T. N. Gezari. 1946.–Jewish folk dance book, by K. Delakova and F. Berk. 1948.–The Jewish holidays, by M. Soltes. 1952.–Lincoln's birthday, compiled and edited by P. Goodman. 1953.–Program material for youth and adults. compiled and edited by P.

Goodman: Hamishah Asar Bi-Shevat. 1950.–Hanukah. 1953.–Lag Ba-Omer. 1950.–New Year and Day of Atonement. 1955.–Passover. 1955.–Purim. 1955. –Sabbath. 1951.–Shavuot. 1953.–Sukkot and Simhat Torah. 1953.–Tishah B'ab. 1955.
1. Festivals—Jews.   I. National Jewish Welfare Board. Jewish Center Division.

NN 0056151   MB

National Jewish Welfare Board.
Programs: Mother's day, Father's day, joint celebrations. 1934.
48 ℓ.

Bibliography: ℓ.48.

NN 0056152   MiD

National
JEWISH WELFARE BOARD.
∧ Purpose, scope and achievement of the Jewish welfare board. [New York, 1918?] 16 p. 17cm.

Caption-title.

1. European war, 1914–1918—War work—Jewish welfare board.

NN 0056153   NN MB

BS1091
.J4
1942 a   National Jewish Welfare Board.
Bible. *O. T. English. Selections. 1942. Jewish publication society.*
Readings from the Holy Scriptures, for Jewish members of the armed forces of the United States. New York, National Jewish welfare board, 1942.

BS1091
.J4
1943   National Jewish Welfare Board.
Bible. *O. T. English. Selections. 1943. Jewish publication society.*
Readings from the Holy Scriptures, for Jewish sailors, soldiers and airmen. New York, Jewish welfare board, 1943.

VOLUME 407

National Jewish Welfare Board.
Report of biennial convention. 1st–
1922–
₍New York ₍etc.₎
v. 23–29 cm.
Reports for 1922– issued by the board under variant form of name: Jewish Welfare Board.

1. Community centers, Jewish—Congresses.

E184.J5N596   72–622534

NN 0056156   DLC DHEW OO OU PP ICU PU DL OCH

National
^ JEWISH WELFARE BOARD.
Report of conference on membership campaigns, September 27–28, 1934. New York City: Jewish Welfare Board [1934]
39 f. incl. table. 28cm.

Cover–title.
Reproduced from typewritten copy.

801658A. 1. Money raising drives. 2. Social service—Jews.

NN 0056157   NN

National
^ Jewish welfare board.
Report of the Commission on community organization...
New York: Jewish welfare board ₍1942₎ 15, v, 1 f. 28cm.

1. Jews in the U.S.—Communal organizations.
N. Y. P. L.   March 18, 1943

NN 0056158   NN

National
D639 ^ Jewish welfare board.
.J4J5   ...Report of war emergency activities.
New York
v. illus.,port. 21½ᶜᵐ.

Vol.2 has title:Final report...

1.Jews—Societies. 2.European war,1914–1918—Jews.

NN 0056159   ICU

National Jewish Welfare Board.
Report to Jewish centers transferring wartime gains to peacetime programs ...
   see under National Jewish Welfare Board.
Program reconversion committee.

National Jewish Welfare Board.
A resource for leadership training in the Jewish center; a manual of articles, suggested course outlines, lectures, and workshops, dealing with pre-service and in-service training. Revised, 1949.
New York, 1949 [c1943]
83 p. 27 cm.
"Resources and bibliography": p. 78–83.

NN 0056161   OU CaBVaU

National Jewish welfare board.
Selected Jewish songs for members of the armed forces, published by Jewish welfare board in cooperation with American association for Jewish education. New York city, Jewish welfare board ₍1943₎
96 p. 14 cm.
"Includes hymns and songs in English, Hebrew and Yiddish, suitable for Sabbath and festival days and other social and cultural group meetings."—Pref.
With music (unaccompanied melodies)
Compiled and edited by Harry Coopersmith. *cf.* Pref.
1. Songs, Jewish. 2. Jews—Hymns. 3. War-songs, American. I. American association for Jewish education. II. Coopersmith, Harry, 1902– ed. III. Title.

M1850.N3S4 1943   784.7   43–7585 rev*

NN 0056162   DLC

National Jewish welfare board.
Selected Jewish songs for members of the armed forces, published by the National Jewish welfare board in cooperation with American association for Jewish education. New York city, National Jewish welfare board ₍1943₎
96 p. 15½ cm.
"Includes hymns and songs in English, Hebrew and Yiddish, suitable for Sabbath and festival days and other social and cultural group meetings."—Pref.
With music (unaccompanied melodies)
Compiled and edited by Harry Coopersmith. *cf.* Pref.
1. Songs, Jewish. 2. Jews—Hymns. 3. War-songs, American. I. American association for Jewish education. II. Coopersmith, Harry, 1902– ed. III. Title.

M1850.N3S4 1943₎   46–13372 rev*

NN 0056163   DLC KyLxCB OCH

National Jewish welfare board.

The **Sentinel.** ₍Official magazine, Jewish welfare board, U. S. army and navy₎
₍New York, 19

National Jewish Welfare Board.

Serving Jewish religious needs in the United States armed forces. [New York, 194–?] 12 p. 22cm.

1. World war, 1939–1945—War work—Jewish welfare board. 2. World war, 1939–1945—Religious life, etc.

NN 0056165   NN

National
^ Jewish Welfare Board.   2299a.172
   Soldiers' and sailors' Jewish calendar. לוח תרע"מ.
= [New York.] 5679. 1918–1919. 56, (8) pp. 12½ cm.
Contents. — Calendar. — Notes on Jewish holidays. — The Jewish Welfare Board. — The Jews in the wars of the United States. — Principal events of the War. — Statistics of Jews. — Leading events in Jewry in 5678.
The calendar is in English and Hebrew; the rest of the text is in English.

M7989 — Transliterated title: Luah.— T.r. (2) — Calendars. — Hebrew lang. Works in Hebrew. — Jewish calendars.

NN 0056166   MB NN

E 184   NATIONAL JEWISH WELFARE BOARD
.J5 N28   The story of the Jews in the United States for Jews in the Armed Forces of the United States. New York,Jewis Welfare Board and American Association for Jewish Education,1943.
   32 p. (Jewish information series,No. 1)

1. Jews—U.S. I. Title.

NN 0056167   InU

National/Jewish Welfare Board.
Study of Community Center and informal educational, recreational activities, Portland, Oregon. [New York,1947].
   34 p. 28 cm.

1.Education. 2.U.S. – Oregon – Portland. I.ti.

NN 0056168   OCH

F
129   National Jewish Welfare Board.
S8N3   Study of the Jewish community of Syracuse, N.Y., with reference to social and recreational needs and facilities. New York, Jewish Welfare Board, 1922.
   34 l. 28 cm.

1. Jews in Syracuse, N.Y. I. Title

NN 0056169   OCH

National Jewish Welfare Boar
Study of the social and recreational resources of the Jewish community of Phila. with recommendations for a program of activities for the Young Men's and Young Women's Hebrew Ass'n of Phila.
N.Y., Jewish Welfare Board, March, 1924

NN 0056170   PPYH

---

xY3
– N59J
National Jewish Welfare Board.
A survey of recreation, group work, and informal education in the Jewish Community of New Orleans, Louisiana. [New York],1947.
82 p. 28 cm.

Cover title.

1. Education. 2.U.S. – Louisiana – New Orleans.

NN 0056171   OCH

National
^ JEWISH WELFARE BOARD.
Survey of recreational and cultural needs of the Jewish population of New York City, prepared by National Jewish welfare board for Federation of Jewish philanthropies of New York. [New York] 1946.
1 v. 28cm.

Part 2.
CONTENTS. —pt. 2. A study of the Jewish population of New York City.
1. Jews in the U.S.—N.Y.—   New York—Stat. 2. New
York (City)—Stat. I. Federa-   tion of Jewish philanthropies
of New York.

NN 0056172   NN

National
^ JEWISH WELFARE BOARD.
Survey report on informal educational and recreational activities of the Jewish community of Indianapolis. Prepared for Citizen's survey committee; sponsored by Jewish community center association and the Jewish welfare federation. [New York] National Jewish welfare board, 1948.
21, 35 l. 29cm.

1. Jews in the U.S.—Ind.—Indianapolis. 2. Education—Jews—U.S.—Ind.—Indianapolis. 3. Indianapolis—Stat. 4. Education—U.S.—Ind.—Indianapolis.

NN 0056174   NN

National
^ JEWISH WELFARE BOARD.
Training course for leaders in group work, including detailed outlines of lectures. New York City: Jewish Welfare Board, 1934. 73 f. incl. form. 28cm.

Cover–title.
Reproduced from typewritten copy.
"Bibliography," f. 57–59; "References," f. 69–73.

801658A. 1. Leadership. 2. Clubs.

NN 0056175   NN

National Jewish welfare board
Training course for leaders in group work, including detailed outlines of lectures. ₍The Author, 1936₎
88 l.

NN 0056176   MiD

VOLUME 407

HF
5382.5
U5N3
National Jewish Welfare Board.
Vocational guidance and employment
programs in Jewish centers. New York,
1940.
59 l. 28 cm.

1. Vocational guidance--United
States. 2. Community centers, Jewish.
I. Title

NN 0056177   OCH

National Jewish Welfare Board.
Weekly religious message for Jewish men in
the armed forces. New York, 1943-44.
v.1, no.1, Sept., 1943.

NN 0056178   OCH

National Jewish Welfare Board
What's What. Bulletin. Philadelphia,
1918-1919.

no. 6, 8-10.

NN 0056179   PPDrop

National Jewish Welfare Board.
Year book. 1950/51-
New York.
v. diagrs. 28 cm.

1. Jews in the U. S.—Charities—Yearbooks.

HV3191.N356   361.7   53-16996

NN 0056180   DLC MoSW NN

National Jewish Welfare Board
see also National Jewish Youth Conference.

LB
1044.7
N3
National Jewish Welfare Board. Adult
Services Dept.
Survey of the way in which Jewish
community centers in the United States
utilize local telecasting facilities.
New York, 1954.
11 l. 28 cm.
Caption title.
Cover title: Television... how Jewish
community centers use it to reach the
community.

1. Television in education.
2. Community centers, Jewish. I. Title

NN 0056182   OCH

National Jewish Welfare Board. Army and Navy
Public Relations Comm.
Combatting rumors: a positive public relations
program for community leaders. New York, Army
and Navy public relations comm., National Jewish
welfare board. 1942? 30 p. illus. 28cm.

1. World war, 1939-1945--Jews. 2. World war, 1939-
1945--Rumors, canards, etc. 3. Jews in the U.S.—
Anti-Semitism. 4. World war, 1939-1945--U.S.
5. United States—Anti-Semitism. I. Title.

NN 0056183   NN MnU

National Jewish Welfare Board, N. Y. Army and
Navy Service Department.
Report; summer training camp activities.
New York, Author, 1925.

NN 0056184   PPYH

National Jewish Welfare Board. Bureau of
Personnel and Training.
Conference on recruiting for Jewish
community center work. 1953.
On cover: Proceedings. Recruiting conference
PU-PSW

NN 0056185   PU-PSW

National Jewish Welfare Board. Bureau of War Records.
D810
.J4K3
Kaufman, Isidor.
American Jews in World War II; the story of 550,000
fighters for freedom. [New York] Dial Press [1947]

D
810
J4N3.3
National Jewish Welfare Board. Bureau
of War Records.
The war record of American Jewry in
the Second World War. [New York,
1943?]
10 p. 20 cm. (Its report no.2)

1. World War, 1939-1945--Jews.
2. Jews as soldiers. I. Title

NN 0056187   OCH NNJ

National
∧ Jewish welfare board. Building bureau.
...Postwar Jewish center building problems...
[New York?] 1948. 54 p. 28cm.

At head of title: Transcript of conference.

1. Community centers, Jewish. 2. Community centers.

NN 0056188   NN

National Jewish Welfare Board. CANRA.
see National Jewish Welfare Board.
Committee on Army and Navy Religious Activities.

National Jewish Welfare Board. Commission on
Jewish Chaplaincy.
Directory of chaplaincy service ...
see under National Jewish Welfare
Board. Division of Religious Activities.

National Jewish Welfare Board. Commission on
Jewish chaplaincy.
Responsa to chaplains (1948-1953). [New
York, 1953]
28 p. 30cm.
Cover title.
Typescript.
Rabbis Solomon B. Freehof, David Aronson and
Leo Jung served as members of the Responsa Com-
mittee; Aryeh Lev, Director, Commission on
Jewish chaplaincy.
1. Responsa -   1800--. 2. Jews as soldiers-
3. Responsa - Col-   lections. I. Title.

NN 0056191   NNJ

BM
522
A1N3.8
National Jewish Welfare Board.
Commission on Jewish Chaplaincy.
Responsa Committee.
Responsa to chaplains [(1948-1953)]
[New York, 1953]
50 p. 22 cm.
Cover title.
"...intended to
supplement...'Responsa in war time'."

1. Responsa--1800-   2. Chaplains,
Military--Judaism. I. Title

NN 0056192   OCH

DS113
.H44
National Jewish welfare board. Committee on
Army and Navy religious activities.
Hertz, Joseph Herman, 1872-1946.
A book of Jewish thoughts, selected and arranged by
Joseph Herman Hertz ... Abridged ed. for Jews in the
armed forces of the United States. New York, **National**
Jewish welfare board, 5703-1943.

BM512
.M3
National Jewish Welfare Board. Committee on Army
and Navy Religious Activities.
Maxims from the Midrash according to the weekly Scriptural
portion. New York, Committee on Army and Navy Religious Activities, National Jewish Welfare Board, 1944.

National Jewish Welfare Board. Division of
Religious Activities.
Directory of chaplaincy service. New York,
New York, Division of Religious Acitivities, National
Jewish Welfare Board [1949]
3 p.l., 42 p. sq. 4.

NN 0056195   OCH

NATIONAL Jewish Welfare Board. Division
of Religious Activities.
Directory of Chaplain Service. 1952.
New York, National Jewish Welfare Board,
1952. 65p. 28cm.
1. Chaplains. 2. Title.

NN 0056196   NNJ

National Jewish Welfare Board. Division of
Religious Activities.
Judaica
Mce27 Responsa in war time. New York, Published by
947n Division of Religious Activities, National
Jewish Welfare Board [1947]
v, 87p. 21cm.

1. She'elot u-teshubot

NN 0056197   CtY NNJ NN MH

National Jewish Welfare Board. Division of
Religious Activities
see also National Jewish Welfare Board.
Committee on Army and Navy Religious Activities.

National
∧ Jewish welfare board. Greater New York army and navy committee.
...In service for the services. [New York, 1943?] 12 l.
illus. 28cm.

1. World war, 1939-1945—War   work—Jewish welfare board.
N. Y. P. L.   November 7, 1947

NN 0056199   NN

VOLUME 407

National Jewish Welfare Board. *Jewish Center Division*
see
National Jewish Welfare Board. *Jewish Community Center Division.*

National
∧ Jewish welfare board. Jewish community center centennial committee.

See

Jewish community center centennial committee.

BM70
.A3

National Jewish Welfare Board.   Jewish ∧Center Division.
Community
Adult Jewish courses in the Jewish community center.

New York, Jewish Center Division, National Jewish Welfare Board.

National
∧ JEWISH WELFARE BOARD. Jewish∧center division.
Community
Games of all kinds for the Jewish club.   New York. [195-]
42 p.   29cm.

Cover-title.
Bibliography, p. 39-42.

1. Games.

NN 0056203   NN

National Jewish Welfare Board. Jewish ∧Center
Community
Division.
Hanukah

see under

Goodman, Philip, 1911-   comp. and ed.

National Jewish Welfare Board. Jewish ∧Center Division.
Community
(Goodman, Philip) comp.
Jewish ceremonial objects. New York, N. Y., Jewish center division, National Jewish welfare board, 1946.

E184
.J5J535

National Jewish Welfare Board. Jewish Community Center Division.

Jewish Community Center program aids.

New York, National Jewish Welfare Board.

National Jewish Welfare Board. Jewish∧Center Division.
Community
The lamp of liberty ; A patriotic pageant depicting the struggle of Democracy in America
see under title

National Jewish welfare board. *Jewish Community Center Division*
Organization of a Jewish community center.
N. Y., 1937.
30 p.

NN 0056208   MiD

BN
43
N4
1948

National Jewish Welfare Board. Jewish Community Center Division.
Organization of the Jewish community center. New York, 1948.
[55 p.   28 cm.
"Revised 1948."

1. Community centers, Jewish.

NN 0056209   OCH

National
∧Jewish Welfare Board. Jewish Community Center Division
Passover, program material for youth and adults
New York, Jewish center division, National Jewish welfare board, 1946.

NN 0056210   MH

FW40
pam

National Jewish Welfare Board. Jewish∧Center
Community
Division.
Teen agers in the Jewish Community Center; report of a consultation, October 5, 1954.
New York, N. Y. [1955]
33ℓ. 28cm.

NN 0056211   NNUT

National Jewish Welfare Board. Jewish∧Center
Community
Division.
We came to an island

see under

Kaufman, Theodore T

National
∧Jewish Welfare Board. Jewish∧Center Division. Dept. of
Community
Youth Service.
Survey of Jewish youth and young adult councils, 1947-48. Prepared by Meyer Bass. New York [1948]

NN 0056213   MH

National Jewish Welfare Board. Jewish Community Center Division. Dept. of Youth Service.
Survey of Jewish youth and young adult councils (1947-48) prepared by: Meyer Bass.   New York, Jewish welfare board [1949]
14 p.   28 cm.
1. Youth. U. S.

NN 0056214   NN

National Jewish Welfare Board. Jewish Community Center Lecture Bureau.
The lecturer and the Jewish community; preoceedings of the Lecturers' institute sponsored by the Advisory committee, Jewish center lecture bureau. [New York, 1944]
27 p.   21 cm.
"Reprinted from The Jewish center, September, 1944."
1. Education, Adult. Jews. U. S.
2. Education, Adult. U. S.

NN 0056215   NN

National Jewish welfare board. *Program reconversion committee.*
Report to Jewish centers transferring wartime gains to peacetime programs. Prepared by Program reconversion committee, National Jewish welfare board. New York, N. Y., 1946.
vi, 46 p. 23 cm.
"Written and edited by Reuben Bennett."--p. 45.

1. Community centers. 2. Jews in the U. S.   I. Bennett, Reuben.

HN43.J4   296   47-23132 rev

NN 0056216   DLC MH OCH

National Jewish Welfare Board. Recording Committee.
List of instrumental and vocal recordings
see under National Jewish Music Council.
Committee on Recordings.

National Jewish Welfare Board. *Survey Commission*
see Commission on Survey of the National Jewish Welfare Board.

National
∧ JEWISH WELFARE BOARD. Women's organizations'. division.
Women's division bulletin. v. 1-14; July, 1942-spring, 1956. New York. 14 v. 28cm.

Quarterly (irregular), July, 1942-spring, 1951; semiannual, fall, 1951-spring, 1956.
"Issued by Women's organizations' division, National Jewish welfare board" (July, 1942-Oct. 1947, as Women's division; Winter, 1948-Winter, 1949, as National Jewish Women's organization' division).

No more published?

1. World war, 1939-1945--War work--Jewish welfare board. 2. Soldiers--Welfare work--Jews. 3. Soldiers--Welfare work

NN 0056220   NN

National Jewish Welfare Conference.
A report: Midcentury White House Conference
see under Midcentury White House Conference on Children and Youth, Washington, D. C., 1950.

National Jewish Youth Conference.
Annual assembly workbook.
New York.
v. 28 cm.

1. Youth--Jews. 2. Jews in the U. S.--Societies, etc.

E184.J5N5967   55-25433

NN 0056222   DLC

National Jewish Youth Conference.

Proceedings, 1950-   New York
[1950-

v.

NN 0056223   CaBVaU

National Jewish Youth Conference. *Committee on National Jewish Youth Organizations.*
Directory, national Jewish youth organizations. New York [1950]
16 l. 28 cm.
Cover title.

1. Jews--Societies. 2. Jews in the U. S. 3. Youth--Jews.
I. Title: National Jewish youth organizations.

E184.J5N597   296   51-36120

NN 0056224   DLC

VOLUME 407

National Jewish Youth Conference. *Committee on National Jewish Youth Organizations.*
Directory of national Jewish youth organizations. New York ₁1952₎
26 l. 28 cm.

1. Jews in the U. S.—Societies. 2. Youth—Jews. ɪ. Title: National Jewish youth organizations.

E184.J5N5972 *296.6 52–33388 ‡

NN 0056225 DLC

National Jewish Youth Planning Commission
see National Jewish Youth Conference.

25L
N271

National Jobbing Confectioners' Association.
Official souvenir, 5th annual convention, Buffalo, N.Y., 1899.
₁unpaged₎ 26x20cm.

1. Confectionary—Buffalo.

NN 0056227 NBuHi

YA
9325

National Johnson Club.
[Document no. 1, and no. 2] Washington, D.C., 1866.
16, 32p.
Includes: Address of the National Johnson club, Testimony of Alexander H. Stephens, President's speech, Feb. 22, 1866, Freedmen's bureau bill, Freedmen's bureau bill veto message, civil rights bill, veto message of same, Speech to soldiers and sailors.

NN 0056228 DLC ICN

National Johnson Club.
Document no. 1, National Johnson club:
1. Address of the National Johnson club to the people of the United States. 2. Testimony of Alexander H. Stephens. [Washington, D.C., Intelligencer Printing House, 1866]
16 p. 8°.
Sabin 51993.
YA 14115

NN 0056229 NcU NN NNC OO CtY DLC

National Johnson Club.
Document. no. 2.
Washington, D. C., 1866. 8°.
In: IL p. v. 2.

1. United States.—History: Reconstruction.
N. Y. P. L.   August 29, 1912.

NN 0056230 NN CSmH OClWHi NcU OO

National Joint Action Committee for Genuine Social Insurance.
Genuine social insurance H.R. 2827 newsletter
see under title

National joint action committee for genuine social insurance.
Relief and work standards, containing H. R. 11186, the Marcantonio relief and work projects standards bill, and an introduction by Herbert Benjamin. ₁New York city: National joint action committee for genuine social insurance, 1936₎ 30 p.
18½cm.

1. Charities, Public—U. S.
N. Y. P. L. employed—U. S., 1929. ɪ. Title.
2. Public works—U. S. 3. Unemployed
November 22, 1938

NN 0056232 NN MH DLC MiEM

National joint apprenticeship and training committee for the electrical industry.
... National apprenticeship standards for the electrical construction industry ...
see its National apprenticeship and training standards for the electrical contracting industry ...

National Joint Apprenticeship and Training Committee for the Electrical Industry.
National apprenticeship and training standards for the electrical contracting industry. 1941–
₁Washington, U. S. Govt. Print. Off.₎
v. illus. 20–26 cm.
Vol. for 1941 issued as U. S. Bureau of Labor Standards. Bulletin no. 50.
Title varies: 1941, National apprenticeship standards for the electrical construction industry.—1945, National apprenticeship and training standards for the electrical industry.
Vol. for 1941 issued by the committee under its earlier name: National Joint Apprenticeship Committee for the Electrical Construction Industry.

Standards formulated by the National Electrical Contractors' Association and the International Brotherhood of Electrical Workers in cooperation with U. S. Dept. of Labor, Bureau of Apprenticeship and Training.

1. Apprentices—U. S. 2. Electricians—U. S. ɪ. Title. (Series: U. S. Bureau of Labor Standards. Bulletin no. 50)
HD4885.U5N26 *371.426 331.86 L 53–157 rev
U. S. Dept. of Labor. Library
for Library of Congress ₁r59d2₎†

NN 0056235 DL DLC WaWW NN MB OU

[**National joint apprenticeship and training committee for the electrical industry**]
National apprenticeship and training standards for the electrical industry ...
see its National apprenticeship and training standards for the electrical contracting industry.

National Joint Apprenticeship and Training Committee for the Sheet Metal Industry.
National apprenticeship and training standards for the sheet metal industry.
₁1949₎–
₁Washington₎
v. illus. 20–24 cm.
Developed and approved jointly by Sheet Metal & Air Conditioning Contractors' National Association (called in 1949– Sheet Metal Contractors' National Association) and the Sheet Metal Workers' International Association in cooperation with U. S. Dept. of Labor, Bureau of Apprenticeship and Training (called in 1949– Bureau of Apprenticeship)

1. Apprentices—U. S. 2. Metal workers—U. S. ɪ. Sheet Metal and Air Conditioning Contractors' National Association. ɪɪ. Sheet Metal Workers' International Association. ɪɪɪ. U. S. Bureau of Apprenticeship and Training.
HD4885.U5N2613 L 55–284 rev
U. S. Dept. of Labor. Library
for Library of Congress ₁r62c₎†

NN 0056238 DL NNC WaWW DLC

NATIONAL JOINT APPRENTICESHIP BOARD FOR THE BUILDING INDUSTRY
An opportunity for youth; apprenticeship in the building industry. By W.H. Forsdike. London
1st June 1947.

7 p.

ɪ. FORSDIKE, W H 1. Great Britain
2. Apprenticeship – Gt.Brit. 3. Building industry – Gt. Brit. 4. Building workers – Gt. Brit.

NN 0056239 MH-IR

National joint apprenticeship committee for the electrical construction industry
see
National joint apprenticeship and training committee for the electrical industry.

National Joint Apprenticeship Committee for the Stained Glass Industry
see
National Joint Glazier and Glassworker Apprenticeship Committee.

NATIONAL JOINT BOARD FOR SETTLEMENT OF JURISDICTIONAL DISPUTES, BUILDING AND CONSTRUCTION INDUSTRY.
Procedural rules and regulations.
Washington. v. 14cm.

Approved in 1949 and amended in later years.
1. Arbitration and conciliation, Industrial. Building trades'--U. S.

NN 0056242 NN MiD MH-IR

National Joint Bricklaying Apprenticeship Committee.
National bricklaying apprenticeship program and standards, prepared and approved in accordance with the recommended fundamentals of the Federal Committee on Apprenticeship. ₁1945₎–
₁Washington₎ U. S. Dept. of Labor, Bureau of Apprenticeship and Training.
v. illus. 20–23 cm.
Title varies slightly.
Vol. for 1945 issued by committee under a variant name: National Bricklaying Joint Apprenticeship Committee.
1. Apprentices—U. S. 2. Bricklayers. ₁2. Brick and tile laying₎ ɪ. U. S. Bureau of Apprenticeship and Training. ɪɪ. Title.
HD4885.U5N2614 L 54–162 rev
U. S. Dept. of Labor. *658.386 331.86
for Library of Congress Library ₁r59f1₎†

NN 0056243 DL MB DLC

National Joint Carpentry Apprenticeship Committee.
National standards for carpentry apprenticeship. 1942–
₁Washington₎ U. S. Dept. of Labor, Bureau of Apprenticeship.
v. illus. 20–27 cm.
Vol. for 1942 issued as U. S. Bureau of Labor Standards. Bulletin no. 54.
"Prepared and approved by the National Joint Carpentry Apprenticeship Committee, representing the Associated General Contractors of America, inc. and the United Brotherhood of Carpenters and Joiners of America in conformance with standards recommended by the Federal Committee on Apprenticeship."
1. Apprentices—U. S. 2. Carpenters—U. S. ɪ. U. S. Bureau of Apprenticeship. ɪɪ. Title. (Series: U. S. Bureau of Labor Standards. Bulletin no. 54)
HD4885.U5N262 L 42–148 rev
U. S. Dept. of Labor. Library
for Library of Congress ₁r55h2₎†

NN 0056244 DL DLC WaWW WaU-L Or OrU

National Joint Carpentry Apprenticeship Committee.
National standards for carpentry apprenticeship, prepared and approved by the National Joint Carpentry Apprenticeship Committee, representing the Associated General Contractors of America, inc., and the United Brotherhood of Carpenters and Joiners of America in conformance with standards recommended by the Federal Committee on Apprenticeship. Rev. ed., 1948. Washington ₁U. S. Govt. Print. Off., 1949₎
27 p. 20 cm.
Cover title.
Issued by Bureau of Apprenticeship.
1. Apprentices—U. S. 2. Carpenters – U. S. ɪ. U. S. Bureau of Apprenticeship. ɪɪ. Title.
HD4885.U5N262 1948 331.86 L 49–42*
U. S. Dept. of Labor. Library
for Library of Congress ₁3₎†

NN 0056245 DL Or OrU DLC

National Joint Cement, Asphalt and Composition Finishing Apprenticeship Committee
see
National Cement Masonry, Asphalt, and Composition Joint Apprenticeship Committee.

VOLUME 407

National Joint Cement Masonry, Asphalt, and Composition
    Apprenticeship Committee
        see
    National Cement Masonry, Asphalt, and Composition
    Joint Apprenticeship Committee.

National Joint Committee for Spanish Relief, London
    Famine faces a million in Spain. London,
    1937.
    14p.

NN 0056248   IEN

Pam.   **National Joint Committee for Spanish Relief,**
Coll.   **London.**
18277   Report ... London ₍1941₎
        15 p. 21½cm.

        1. Spain. History. Civil War, 1936-1939.
    Hospitals, charities, etc.

NN 0056249   NcD OC1

National joint committee of the South African trades and
    labour council and the Cape province federation of labour
    unions.
    The trade union movement in South Africa during the years
    following inception. Issued by the National joint committee.
    Johannesburg, 1939.
    cover-title, 16 p.; cover-title, 16 p. 21ᶜᵐ.
    English and Afrikaans, the latter inverted and with cover-title: Die
    suid-afrikaanse vakbond-beweging sedert die aanvangs-tydperk.
    1. Trade-unions—Africa, South.   I. Title. II. Title: Die suid-
    afrikaanse vakbond-beweging sedert die aanvangs-tydperk.
                                        A 41-3195
    Illinois. Univ. Library
        for Library of Congress

NN 0056250   IU WU

National joint committee on English
        see Joint committee on the reorganization
    of high school English.

S   **National Joint Committee on Fertilizer Ap-**
633   **plication.**
N29   Methods of applying fertilizer. Rev. ed.
        ₍Washington, D. C.₎ 1948.
        27 p. illus. 23 cm. (Its Pamphlet no.
        149)

        Cover title.

        1. Fertilizers and manures. I. Title.
    II. Series.

NN 0056252   DNAL

National joint committee on fertilizer application.
    Proceedings of the ... annual meeting of the National joint
    committee on fertilizer application ...
    ₍Washington, D. C.₎ The National fertilizer association ₍193
    v. illus., diagrs. 28ᶜᵐ.

        1. Fertilizers and manures—Societies.   I. National fertilizer asso-
    ciation (1925-   )
    Library of Congress   S631.N37   42-39149
                            ₍2₎   631.806273

    InLP NcRS ICJ IU MiU OU ICarbS
NN 0056253   DLC MtBC Or IdU OrCS CU NN TU DNAL Vi

National Joint Committee on Fertilizer
    Application.
        Proceedings
            see also under   Council on Fertilizer
    Application.

National joint committee on fertilizer application.
    Reports and proceedings of the Joint committee on fertilizer
    application, 1925-1928. Compiled by E. Truog and Ove F.
    Jensen ... Washington, D. C., The National fertilizer asso-
    ciation ₍1928₎
        cover-title, 55 p. illus. 23ᶜᵐ.
        "Annotated bibliography of works on methods of applying fertilizer,
    compiled by E. Truog" : p. 32-55.
        The Joint committee is composed of representatives from the Amer-
    ican society of agronomy, the American society of agricultural engi-
    neers, the National fertilizer association and the National association
    of farm equipment manufacturers.
        "Errata" slip mounted on back cover.
        1. Fertilizers and manures.   2. Fertilizers and manures—Bibl.   I.
    Truog, Emil, 1884-   comp.   II. Jensen, Ove F., comp.
    II. National fertilizer asso-   ciation (1925-
    U. S. Dept. of agr. Library   57.9N216R   Agr 30-665 Revised
    for Library of Congress   S633.N35
                            ₍r42c2₎   631.816

NN 0056255   DNAL DLC NN ICJ

57.7   **National Joint Committee on Fertilizer**
N21   **Application.**
        A survey of fertilizer application
    practices in connection with field crops.
    ₍Washington?₎ National Fertilizer Associa-
    tion, 1936.
        45 p.

        1. Fertilizers for field crops. I. Cum-
    ings, Glenn Arthur, 1894-   II. National
    Fertilizer Association.

NN 0056256   DNAL

---

58   **National Joint Committee on Fertilizer**
N212   **Application.**
        A survey of fertilizer distributing machines
    on the market. ₍n.p.₎ National Fertilizer
    Association, 1936.
        6 l.

        1. Fertilizers. Implements and machinery.
    Directories. 2. Fertilizer spreaders.

NN 0056257   DNAL

National Joint Committee on Fertilizer Application
    see also   Council on Fertilizer Application.

National Joint Committee on Nitrogen Utilization.
        Proceedings of the annual meeting. ₍1st -4th; 19₎42-45
    ₍n. p.₎
        v. diagrs. 28 cm.

        1. Fertilizers and manures—Societies, etc.

    S631.N4   631.8406273   53-34405

NN 0056259   DLC AAP

National Joint Committee on Nitrogen Utilization
    see also National Joint Committee on Fertilizer Appli-
    cation.

National joint committee on stamped envelopes.
    ... Special return cards on stamped envelopes. Letter
    from the National joint committee to Hon. Knute Nelson,
    replying to the postmaster general's letter of February 6,
    1911, relative to special return cards on stamped envel-
    opes ... Washington, Govt. print off., 1911.
        10 p. 23ᶜᵐ. (₍U. S.₎ 61st Cong., 3d sess. Senate. Doc. 814)
        Presented by Mr. Clapp. Ordered printed Feb. 8, 1911.
        Letter from a joint committee representing seven national associations
    of industries. R. P. Andrews, chairman.
        1. Postal service—U. S.   I. Andrews, R. P. II. U. S. Post-office dept.
    III. U. S. 61st Cong., 3d sess., 1910-1911. Senate.
                                        11-35139
    Library of Congress   HE6181.U6 1911 a

NN 0056261   DLC MiU OO

National joint committee on the reorganization of
    high school English
        see   Joint committee on the reorganization
    of high school English.

HE370   National Joint Committee on Uniform Traffic
.A498   Control Devices.
        Manual on uniform traffic control devices for
    streets and highways... Washington, D. C., U.S.
    Bureau of public roads, 1934.
        cover-title, ₍186₎p. illus., diagrs. 26½cm.
        Various pagings.
        Mimeographed.
        "This manual is a revision and consolidation
    of two previous manuals—that of the American
    Association of state highway officials for rural
    highways, and that prepared by the American en-
    gineering council for the National conference on
    street and highway   safety to apply to city
    streets."—Introd.

NN 0056263   ICU MiU DLC-P4

National Joint Committee on Uniform Traffic Control De-
    vices.
    Manual on uniform traffic control devices for streets and
    highways. Approved as an American standard, American
    Standards Association, Nov. 7, 1935. Washington, 1935.
        xii, 166 p. illus. (part col.) diagrs. 23 cm.
        Prepared by the committee under its earlier name: Joint Commit-
    tee on Uniform Traffic Control Devices.
        1. Traffic signs and signals.   I. Title. II. Title: Uniform traffic
    control devices.
        HE370.N32 1935   36-27533 rev 2*
    MH-L
    OU OC1W OC1 MiU CU N NcC CaBVaU Or WaS ICU PPT
NN 0056264   DLC PU-W OC1 NN ICJ MB TxU OC1WHi WaU

HE371   National Joint Committee on Uniform Traffic Control
A3A5   Devices.
1937   Manual on uniform traffic control devices for
    streets and highways. Approved as an American
    standard, American Standards Association,
    November 7, 1935. Washington, D. C., 1937.
        xii, 166 p. illus. (part. fold.) 23 cm.
        "Reprinted September, 1937."
        "Revisions approved by Joint Committee on
    Uniform Traffic Control Devices", Feb. 1939,
    laid in.
        1. Traffic regulations. U. S. I. Title.

NN 0056265   DI

National Joint Committee on Uniform Traffic Control De-
    vices.
    Manual on uniform traffic control devices for streets and
    highways. War emergency ed. Washington, 1942.
        xii, 186 p. illus. (part col.) diagrs. 23 cm.
        Prepared by the committee under its earlier name: Joint Commit-
    tee on Uniform Traffic Control Devices.
        1. Traffic signs and signals.   I. Title. II. Title: Uniform traffic
    control devices.
        HE370.N32 1942   43-46956 rev*

NN 0056266   DLC OrP

VOLUME 407

National Joint Committee on Uniform Traffic Control
Devices.
  Manual on uniform traffic control devices for
streets and highways, for approval of American
Association of State Highway Officials, Institute of
Traffic Engineers [and] National Conference on
Street and Highway Safety. [Washington] Public
Roads Administration, Federal Works Agency, 1947.
  1.v. (various pagings)   plates.   27 cm.
  Cover title.
  1. Traffic regulations. U.S. I. U.S. Bureau of
Public Roads. II. Title. III. Title: Uniform traffic
control devices.

NN 0056267   MiU

National Joint Committee on Uniform Traffic Control Devices.
  Manual on uniform traffic control devices for streets and
highways. Washington, Public Roads Administration, Federal Works Agency, 1948.
  xiii, 223 p. illus. (part col.) diagrs. 24 cm.
  Prepared by the committee under its earlier name: Joint Committee on Uniform Traffic Control Devices.

  1. Traffic signs and signals.   I. Title.   II. Title: Uniform traffic
control devices.

HE370.N32 1948   48-47045 rev*

OU PSt IEN IU PPULC IdU MtBC CaBVa WaTC OrCS
NN 0056268   DLC MiD TxU MH OrStbM CLL MB CU ICJ

---

388   National Joint Committee on Uniform Traffic
N278   Control Devices.
  Revisions to the Manual on uniform traffic
control devices for streets and highways.
Washington, Department of Commerce, Bureau
of Public Roads, 1954.
  iv, 15 p. illus. 24cm.

  "Approved by American Association of State
Highway Officials, Institute of Traffic Engineers, National Committee on Uniform Traffic Laws and   Ordinances."

NN 0056269   C IEN DHU NcU

National Joint Computer Committee
        see
American Federation of Information Processing Societies.

National joint conference board
  see also Joint national conference of the construction
industry of Canada, *Ottawa*, 1946.

National Joint Conference on Church Architecture.
  Proceedings.
  Joint meeting of the National Council of
Churches, Department of Church Building &
Architecture, and the Church Architectural Guild
of America.
  Mimeographed.

NN 0056272   MnSL

National Joint Council.
  Appeal from the Chinese Government British labour's
declaration on Far Eastern situation, issued by the National
Joint Council, London, on 23rd February, 1932. Geneva,
1932.
  3 l. 33 cm.
  Caption title.
  At head of title: League of Nations.
  Official no.: C.278.M.165.1932.vii.
  Branding Japan as aggressor in undeclared war on China and re-
questing withdrawal of diplomatic representation in Tokyo.

  1. China—Hist.—1912-1937. [1. China—Hist.—1931-1945,
2. Japan—For. rel.   I. League of Nations.

                                                    A 49-4985*

Woodrow Wilson   Memorial Library
for Library of Congress   [2]

NN 0056273   NNUN-W

National Joint Council.
  The Blind Persons' Act, 1920... Published by the National
Joint Council representing the General Council of the Trades
Union Congress, the Executive Committee of the Labour Party,
and the Parliamentary Labour Party.   [London, 1920.]   12 p.
8°.

  1. Blind.—Jurisprudence, Gt. Br.,   1920.
N. Y. P. L.
                                              August 29, 1923.

NN 0056274   NN

National joint council
  The Blind persons' act, 1920...London, National joint
council, 1922
  cover-title, 12 p. 24½ cm.

NN 0056275   DL CU

National Joint Council.
  The fair wages clause ... Westminster,
Published by the National joint council representing
the General council of the Trades union congress,
the Executive committee of the Labour party, and the
Parliamentary labour party [1922]

NN 0056276   CtY CU DL

National joint council.
  Labour and national "economy". I. The Geddes proposals and the government's policy. II. General observations on the Geddes reports. III. The national finances
and national policy. IV. "Economy" in education. V.
"Economy" in housing. VI. "Economy" in public health
... London, Pub. by the National joint council [1922]
  cover-title, 39 p. 25cm.

  1. Gt. Brit.—Appropriations and expenditures.   I. Gt. Brit. Committee
on national expenditure.   II. Title.   III. Title: Geddes proposals.

  Library, U. S. Dept. of   Labor   L 22-271

NN 0056277   DL

Pam.   National Joint Council.
Coll.
          Meerut: release the prisoners! A statement
32256   upon the Meerut trial and sentences, issued by
          the National Joint Council, representing the
          Trades Union Congress, the Labour Party and
          the Parliamentary Labour Party. London [1933]
          7 p. 25 cm.

          1. India. Politics and government. 1919-
          1947. 2. Trials (Sedition) Meerut, India. I.
          Title.

NN 0056278   NcD DL NN CtY CU

National joint council.
  ... Memorandum on unemployment insurance by industry. London [Labour party, 1922]
  31, [1] p. 25cm.
  At head of title: National joint council.

  I. Insurance, Unemployment—Gt. Brit.   I. Title.

  Library, U. S. Dept. of   Labor   L 22-340

NN 0056279   DL

National joint council. *Committee on inquiry into production.*
  The waste of capitalism. [Report] Foreword by
A. A. Purcell ... London, Labour joint publications dept.
[1924?]
  3 p. l., 118 p. 21½cm.
  A. Pugh, chairman; Sidney Webb, vice-chairman.

  1. Industry—Organization, control, etc. 2. Efficiency, Industrial. 3. [Out-
put] 4. Gt. Brit.—Industries. 5. Labor [and laboring classes]—Gt. Brit.
I. Pugh, Arthur.   II. Title.   III. Title: Capitalism, The waste of.

  Library, U. S. Dept. of   Labor   L 25-65

NN 0056280   DL WU IU ICJ TxU

National Joint Council for Local Authorities' Administrative, Professional, Technical and Clerical Services.
  A survey of the local government service. London [1950]
  189 p. 26 cm.
  The preparation of the statistical tables and assembling the results
of the survey were undertaken by H. Slater.

  1. Local government—Gt. Brit.   I. Slater, H., ed.   II. Title.

  JS3113.N38   352.042   52-27088

NN 0056281   DLC

TH1
N43
  National joint council for the building industry.
  Constitution, rules regulations, and national
working rules. Adopted...
London, 1928.   1pam. 12°

NN 0056282   DLC

NATIONAL JOINT COUNCIL FOR THE BUILDING INDUSTRY
  Introduction of a code of welfare conditions;
declaration by the council. [London, February 1948].
7p.
  Caption title.

  1. Great Britain 2. Building workers - Gt. Brit.

NN 0056283   MH-IR

            National Joint Council for the Port Transport
HD8039   Industry.
.82G69
            Gt. Brit. *National Dock Labour Board.*
            Report to the National Joint Council for the Port Trans-
          port Industry. 1st–   1947/48–
          [London]

HD8039   National Joint Council for the Port Transport
.L82G713   Industry.

            Gt. Brit. *National Dock Labour Board.*
            Review of the work, 1947-1949, as submitted to the Na-
          tional Joint Council for the Port Transport Industry. Lon-
          don, 1950.

351.1   National Joint Council of the Public Service
N2778   of Canada.
          The National Joint Council of the Public
          Service of Canada, 1944-1954. Ottawa,
          E. Cloutier, Queen's printer, 1954.
          31 p. 23 cm.

          Page 31 blank for "Notes".

          1. Canada. Officials and employees.

NN 0056286   N NN MiU NcD CaOTU

National Joint Educational Committee for Gravure.
  Technical guide for the gravure industry. [New York]
Gravure Technical Association [and] International Photo-
engravers' Union of North America [1955–
  1 v. (loose-leaf) illus. 19 cm.

  1. Photoengraving.   I. Title.

  TR970.N3   *655.32 777   55-37376

NN 0056287   DLC

VOLUME 407

National Joint Glazier and Glassworker Apprenticeship Committee.
National apprenticeship and training standards for glaziers & glassworkers adopted by the National Joint Glaziers and Glassworkers' Apprenticeship Committee, representing the employers in the glass and glazing industry and the Brotherhood of Painters, Decorators and Paperhangers of America, in conformance with the fundamentals recommended by the Federal Committee on Apprenticeship. 1956 ed. ₍Washington₎ U. S. Dept. of Labor, Bureau of Apprenticeship ₍1955₎

28 p. illus. 24 cm.
Cover title.

1. Apprentices—U. S. 2. Glass-workers—U. S.   I. Title.
HD4885.U5N265   L 56-162
U. S. Dept. of Labor.   -   Library
for Library of Congress   ₍2₎†

NN   0056288   DL DLC

National Joint Glazier and Glassworker Apprenticeship Committee.
National apprenticeship and training standards for the stained glass industry. 1946–
₍Washington₎ U. S. Dept. of Labor, Bureau of Apprenticeship and Training.
v. illus. 24 cm.
Title varies: 1946, Standards and organization for apprenticeship in the stained glass industry.

Issued under variant names of the committee: 1946, National Joint Apprenticeship Committee for the Stained Glass Industry; 1960– National Joint Glaziers and Glassworkers Apprenticeship Committee.

1. Apprentices—U. S. 2. Glass painting and staining—U. S. 3. Glass-workers—U. S.   I. U. S. Bureau of Apprenticeship and Training. II. Title. III. Title: Standards and organization for apprenticeship in the stained glass industry.
HD4885.U5N264   L 60-22
U. S. Dept. of Labor.   Library
for Library of Congress   ₍8₎†

NN   0056289   DL DLC

National Joint Glazier and Glassworker
    Apprenticeship Committee.
    Standards and orgazination for apprenticeship
in the stained glass industry
            see its   National apprenticeship and
training standards ...

National joint industrial council for retail pharmacy (*England and Wales*)
... Constitution (approved December, 1943) ₍London, 1943?₎
6, ₍1₎ p. 18½ᵐ.

                                     45-13354
    Library of Congress   HD9667.1.N3A5

NN   0056291   DLC

National joint industrial council for the
    asbestos industry (and other industries.)
    (Constitution and short history of joint
councils, established in Great Britain in
1918-19--.
    33 cm.
    Typewritten material.

NN   0056292   DL

National Joint Industrial Council for the Flour-Milling Industry,
    London.
    Annual report.
₍no.₎ 1–

₍London, 1920–
    v.

1925/26-1926/27 issued in one no.

1. Flour and grain—Mills and milling   —Gt. Br.
N. Y. P. L.   December 28, 1932

NN   0056293   NN

National joint industrial council for the flour
    milling industry.
    Group pension scheme, as finally approved by the
trustees, 1st January 1931...(London, 1931)
11,(1) p. 17 cm

NN   0056294   DL

283   National joint industrial council for the
N217   flour milling industry.
        ...Hours and security; report of speeches
    made on the occasion of the signing of the
    agreement on 12th March, 1937... ₍London,
    Printed by G. White, 1937₎
        18 p. 20 1/2cm.

        At head of title: National joint industrial
    council for the flour milling industry.

NN   0056295   DNAL

National Joint Industrial Council for the Flour-Milling Industry,
    London.
    Technical education series.
Pamphlet no 1

London₍, 1926   8°.
    no.   charts, tables.

    Contents:
    no. 1. Power.   1926.

1. Flour and grain—Mills and milling   —Gt. Br.
N. Y. P. L.   May 8, 1928

NN   0056296   NN ICJ CU

National Joint Painting and Decorating Apprenticeship and Training Committee.
    The National Joint Painting and Decorating Committee was established in 1949. In 1954 the name was changed to National Joint Painting and Decorating Apprenticeship and Training Committee and in 1971 to National Joint Painting and Decorating and Drywall Apprenticeship and Training Committee. Works by this body published before the change of name in 1971 are found under

    National Joint Painting and Decorating Apprenticeship and Training Committee.

National Joint Painting and Decorating Apprenticeship and Training Committee.
    National painting and decorating apprenticeship and training standards. 1939–
₍Washington₎ U. S. Dept. of Labor, Bureau of Apprenticeship and Training ₍etc.₎
    v. illus. 20-27 cm.
    Vol. for 1939 issued as Bulletin no. 23 of U. S. Bureau of Labor Standards under the Bureau's earlier name: Division of Labor Standards.
    Title varies: 1939, Building a national painting and decorating apprenticeship system.—19 –54, National painting, decorating, and paperhanging apprenticeship standards.

    Vol. for 1939 prepared by Federal Committee on Apprenticeship.—19 –54, by the committee under a variant name: National Joint Painting and Decorating Apprenticeship Committee.
    Standards adopted in conformance with the fundamentals recommended by the Federal Committee on Apprenticeship.

1. Apprentices—U. S. 2. Painting, Industrial. ₍2. Painters—U. S.₎ 3. Paper hanging. ₍3. Paper hangers₎   I. U. S. Bureau of Apprenticeship and Training. II. Title. (Series: U. S. Bureau of Labor Standards. Bulletin no. 23)
HD4885.U5N27   L 51-106 rev
U. S. Dept. of Labor.   Library
for Library of Congress   ₍r62c₎₁†

NN   0056299   DL NNC DLC

National Joint Sheet Metal Workers' Apprenticeship Committee
    see
National Joint Apprenticeship and Training Committee for the Sheet Metal Industry.

National joint steamfitting apprenticeship committee.
    ... National standards for steamfitting apprenticeship including suggestions for putting national standards into operation in local communities ...   Prepared by National joint steamfitting apprenticeship committee, in cooperation with Federal committee on apprenticeship, approved by Heating, piping, and air conditioning contractors' national association and the United association of journeymen plumbers and steamfitters. Washington, U. S. Govt. print. off., 1939.
    v. 11 p. incl. facsims. 27ᵐ. (₍U. S. Dept. of labor. Division of labor standards₎ Bulletin no. 28)

    At head of title: United States Dept. of labor ... Division of labor standards ...

    1. Apprentices—U. S. 2. Pipe-fitting.   I. U. S. Federal committee on apprenticeship. II. Title.
    U. S. Dept. of labor. Libr.   L 39-43
        for Library of Congress   HD4885.U5N28

NN   0056302   DL NN DLC WaU-L OCU OU OO WaWW

National joint steamfitting apprenticeship committee.
    ... Suggested local standards for training steamfitting apprentices, based on the National standards for steamfitting apprenticeship ...   Prepared by National joint steamfitting apprenticeship committee, in cooperation with Federal committee on apprenticeship, approved by Heating, piping, and air conditioning contractors' national association and the United association of journeymen plumbers and steamfitters. Washington, U. S. Govt. print. off., 1940.
    ix, 15 p. facsims. 27ᵐ. (₍U. S. Dept. of labor. Division of labor standards₎ Bulletin no. 28, part II)

    At head of title: United States Department of labor. Frances Perkins, secretary. Division of labor standards. V. A. Zimmer, director.
    Part I of Bulletin no. 28 has title: National standards for steamfitting apprenticeship.

    1. Apprentices—U. S. 2. Pipe-fitting.   I. U. S. Federal committee on apprenticeship. II. Heating, piping, and air conditioning contractors' national association. III. United association of journeymen plumbers and steamfitters of the United States and Canada. IV. Title.
                                                          L 40-102
    U. S. Dept. of labor. Libr.   HD8051.2.A2 no. 28, pt. 2
    ——— Copy 2.   HD4885.U5A4   1939 b pt. 2
        for Library of Congress   ₍4₎

NN   0056304   DL OO WaWW DLC

National Joint Steamfitting Apprenticeship Committee
    see also
Mechanical Contractors Association of America.

National Joint Stock Bank
    see Kansallis-Osake-Pankki.

HD5325
M62N2   National Joint Wage Conference of Mine Operators
            and United Mine Workers.
            [Proceedings]   Washington [Alderson Reporting
        Co.] 1943.
            39 l.   28 cm.
            At head of title: Department of the Interior.

            1. Collective labor agreements – Coal mining
        industry – U.S. 2. United Mine Workers. I. U.S.
        Dept. of the Interior. II. Alderson Reporting
        Company.

NN   0056307   DI

National Joseph Lee day committee.
    National Joseph Lee day; a tribute to a builder of the national recreation movement, July 28th...   New York, N. Y. ₍1938₎
16 f.   28cm.

    Cover-title.
    Reproduced from typewritten copy.

1. Recreation, Public—U. S.   2. Lee, Joseph, 1862-1937.
N. Y. P. L.   March 21, 1941

NN   0056308   NN

VOLUME 407

National Journal.
 Washington, D. C.
  v.
 Semiweekly; three times a week.
 Published Nov. 12, 1823–Jan. 23, 1832.

NN 0056309   ICRL

National journal, *Washington, D. C.*
 Prospectus of the National journal, a semi-weekly
newspaper, to be published in the city of Washington.
 ₍Washington, 1823₎
  8 p. 17ᶜᵐ.
  Caption title.

                               11–28074
 Library of Congress   PN4899.W31N3

NN 0056310   DLC

National journal. Washington, D.C.
 see also Daily national journal.

National journal - extra. Dec. 7, 1824. This day
 at 12 o'clock, the President ... communicated ..
 the following message
  see under U.S. President, 1817–1824.
 (Monroe)

The National journal—extra. July 20, 1831. Washington, 1831.
 24 p. 27½ᶜᵐ.
 Contains proceedings of the National Republican party in Washington,
May 3, 1831, etc.

 ɪ. National Republican party, Washington, D. C.

 Library of Congress   JK2313 1831 a   9-32458†
 —— Copy 2.   ₍Miscellaneous pamphlets, v. 792, no. 15₎
                          AC901.M5 vol. 792

NN 0056313   DLC

National journal - extra
 see also National government journal.

National journal of finance and Hodges' bank
 note reporter. v.12,no.6- Feb.2,1861-
 New York, D.M. Hodges, 1861-
  v.

 Published weekly, semimonthly and monthly.
 Title varies: Feb.1861–Nov.1,1865, Hodges'
journal of finance and bank note reporter; Jan.
1,1866— The National journal of finance and
Hodges' bank note reporter.
 Subtitle varies.
 Publisher varies.
 Discontinued   with v.24,no.1, Jan.1,1867.

NN 0056314   MH-BA

The National journal of legal education. v. 1–3; Feb. 1937–
 Apr. 1940. Chicago ₍etc.₎ National Association of Law
Schools.
 3 v. in 1. 23 cm. Irregular.
 No more published?

 1. Law—Study and teaching—U. S.   ɪ. National Association of
Law Schools.
                               65–80668

 CaBVaU
NN 0056315   DLC N IU NcU-L NjR GU MiU-L CU-AL

Y
144 NATIONAL JOURNAL, OR COUNTRY GAZETTE.
.612   A collection of political and humorous let-
     ters, poems, and articles of news, publish'd in
     an evening paper, intitled, the National journal,
     or, Country gazette. Which began to be supress'd
     on Saturday, March 22d, 1746, and was supress'd
     on Thursday, June 12th following, by the printer
     and author's being taken into custody, and the
     former confined in Newgate 'till the 26th day of
     February, 1746-7, when he was discharg'd by ha-
     beas corpus... London, J. Clark, 1748.
      122p. 20cm.

NN 0056316   ICN MiU-C CtY ICU MnU CU-A PU

National Journal, or Country Gazette.
Film A collection of political and humorous
     letters, poems and articles of news, pub-
     lish'd in an evening paper, intitled the
     National journal, or country gazette, which
     began to be publish'd on Saturday March 22,
     1746, and was suppress'd on Thursday June
     12th following, by the printer and author's
     being taken into custody and the former
     confined in Newgate 'till the 26th of Feb-
     ruary, 1746 7₍sic₎, when he was discharg'd
     by habeas corpus, the suspension of that
     act being then just expired. London,
     Printed for J. Clark, 1748.

       Microfilm copy, made by Yale University.
     Negative.
       With this is filmed: Old England; or the
     constitutional journal, Jan. 5, 1745 Jan. 3,
     1747.

NN 0056318   IEN InU DFo

National Journalism Conference, Lawrence, Kansas
  see National Journalism Conference,
University of Kansas, 1914.

National Journalism Conference, *University of Kansas, 1914*
 [Bulletin.] .... Proceedings of the National Journalism Con-
 ference held during Kansas newspaper week, under the auspices
 of the Department of Journalism, University of Kansas, ...
 Lawrence, Kansas, [1914].
  Library has no. 1, 3–7, 9, 12, 14. 25½ᶜᵐ. (University of Kansas news-
bulletin, vol. 14–15.)
  Title varies.

NN 0056321   ICJ OrCS OU OO IU OrU ICRL

PN4853 National Journalism Conference. *University of*
.K2   Discussions before the National Journalism
no.1-4   Conference. Lawrence, Kansas, University of
        Kansas, 1914.
          4v. (University of Kansas news-bulletin.
                              v.15, no.2)
        ₍Kansas. University. Dept. of Journalism.
        Kansas newspaper week bulletin, 1-4₎
          Proceedings of the National Journalism Confer-
        ence held during Kansas Newspaper Week. Under
        the auspices of the Dept. of Journalism, Univ-
        ersity of Kansas,   May 10 to 14, 1914.
          1. Journalism -   Congresses.

NN 0056322   NcU NN OU DLC Or

National journalist for editors
 see Mail order journal

---

*BROAD-
SIDE   National jubilee. Admission one dollar.
1858   Admit one. At Washington, D. C., May 1st,
.N37   1858. ₍Washington? D. C., 1858?₎
        broadside. illus. 7 x 12cm.
        Ticket of admission, no. 6659.

NN 0056325   ViU

The NATIONAL jubilee, celebrative of the fiftieth anniversary of the reign of George the
Third, politically and morally improved. By a
magistrate. L., 1809.

  pp. xviii, 74.

NN 0056326   MH

National jubilee melodies ... ₍10th ed.₎ Nashville, Tenn.,
 National Baptist publishing board ₍191 ₎
 ₍ 156, ₍3₎ p. 22ᶜᵐ.
  Running title: National Baptist jubilee melodies.

NN 0056327   ViU

National jubilee melodies...   Nashville, Tenn.: National Baptist
 Publishing Board ₍191-?₎. 156 p. ₍15. ed.₎ 12°.
  Words and music for 4 voices.
  "A collection of old plantation songs, the words and music of which were com-
posed and sung by the African slaves of the United States of America during the days
of slavery."—*Publisher's note.*
  Chiefly arranged by Phil V. S. Lindsley.
  Running title: National Baptist jubilee melodies.

 1. Negro songs. 2. Hymns.   JUILLIARD FOUNDATION FUND.
melodies.
N. Y. P. L.   3. Title: National Baptist jubilee
                          September 22, 1924

NN 0056328   NN

National jubilee melodies ... ₍16th ed.₎ Nashville, Tenn.,
 National Baptist publishing board ₍n. d.₎
 156, ₍3₎ p. 22ᶜᵐ.
  Running title: National Baptist jubilee melodies.

 ɪ. National Baptist publishing board. ɪɪ. Title: National Baptist jubilee melodies. ɪɪɪ. Title: Jubilee melodies.
                                    27–7076
 Library of Congress   M1670.N316

NN 0056329   DLC

M1670
.N316 National jubilee melody song book. Memorial
19—   ed. Nashville, Tenn., National Baptist
       Publishing Board, ₍19—?₎
       155 p. port., facsim. 23cm.
       Running title: National Baptist Jubilee melodies.
       "In memory of the late Richard Henry Boyd."

         I. National Baptist Publishing Board. II. Title:
       National Baptist jubi   lee melodies. III. Title:
       Jubilee melodies.

NN 0056330   ViU

National junior honor society of secondary schools.
 Handbook of the National junior honor society of secondary
schools. ₍Washington₎ National association of secondary-
school principals ₍1945₎
  cover-title, 183 p. incl. illus. (incl. facsims.) forms. 23ᶜᵐ.
  Bibliography: p. 181.

 1. Students' societies—U. S.   ɪ. National association of secondary-
school principals.
                               46–21313
 Library of Congress   LJ155.N34 1945
                          ₍3₎   371.857

NN 0056331   DLC PU-S

VOLUME 407

National **junior** personnel service, inc.

Charters, Werrett Wallace, 1875–
Analysis of secretarial duties and traits, by W. W. Charters and Isadore B. Whitley ... Baltimore, Md., Pub. by Williams & Wilkins company for the National junior personnel service, inc., 1924.

National Junior Personnel Service, Inc.
Service bulletin.
no. 1

New York, 1924.   8°.
no.
Cover-title.
Contents:
no. 1. CHARTERS, W. W., AND I. B. WHITLEY. Summary of report on analysis of secretarial duties and traits.   April, 1924.

1. Office organization and management.
N. Y. P. L.   April 29, 1930

NN 0056333   NN IU

National jurisdiction over murder of United States witnesses, &c. ...   The United States vs. Geo. Sanges et al. ...
see under   U.S.

The national justice vindicated: and the propriety of publick humiliation as a means of procuring publick blessings, shown, in a sermon, preached upon occasion of the late general fast...Dublin, Printed for the author by J.A. Husband, 1772.
1 p.l., 5-22 p. 24.7 cm.
Stevens 2d Addenda no. 204

NN 0056335   MiU-C

Law
National Juvenile Court Foundation.

National Council of Juvenile Court Judges.
Conference. ₁Papers₎

₁Pittsburgh?₎

National Juvenile Court Judges
see
National Council of Juvenile Court Judges.

Western
Americana   National Kansas Committee.
Broadsides   Information for emigrants to Kansas.
Zc39   [Chicago, 1857]
857na   broadside. 47 x 27 cm.

In four columns.
Signed: Edward Daniels, Agent Emigration Nat'nal Kansas Com.

1. Kansas - Descr. & trav. I. Daniels, Edward. II. Title.

NN 0056338   CtY

National Kansas Committee.
To the people of Kansas. The undersigned hereby announces that he has made arrangements to distribute, at once, under instructions from the National Kansas Committee, the balance of the relief clothing remaining on hand ... [Signed at end]: E. B. Whitman, Gen'l Agent K. N. Committee. Lawrence, October 22, 1857.
20.5 x 25.5 cm.   Broadside printed on blue paper.

NN 0056339   KHi

National kegler
see   American bowler and sportsman.

RC903   National Kidney Foundation.
.U56   U. S. Kidney Disease Control Program.
Kidney disease services, facilities, and programs in the United States.
Washington, For sale by the Supt. of Docs., U. S. Govt. Print. Off.

National kindergarten and elementary college, *Evanston, Ill.*
see
Evanston, Ill.   National college of education.

National kindergarten association.
Annual report. 1909–
₁New York, 1911–
v. illus. 23ᶜᵐ.
Reports for 1909-11 issued as one report.
Name changed in 1911 from National association for the promotion of kindergarten education.

E 15-102

Library, U. S. Bur. of   Education LB1141.N21

NN 0056343   DHEW OrU OO OCl

National kindergarten association.
The kindergarten in the United States, a report submitted by invitation to President Roosevelt's Advisory committee on education, by the National kindergarten association, Florence J. Ovens ... editor. New York, 1937.
1 p. l., 52 numb. l. 28½ x 23ᶜᵐ.
Reproduced from type-written copy.

1. Kindergarten. 2. Education—U. S.   I. Ovens, Florence Jane, ed. II. Title.
                                          41-24305
Library of Congress   LB1205.N3
                              ₂₎   372.20973

NN 0056344   DLC PPCS NN

National kindergarten association.

... Kindergarten training schools. Washington, Govt. print. off., 1916.

National Kindergarten Association
Setting up a kindergarten. New York, National Kindergarten Association, n.d.

NN 0056346   IdB

National Knitted outerwear *association.*

Group meetings on uniform cost finding. Cost bulletin.   Milwaukee, Wis., 1922- no.1-

NN 0056347   IU

National knitted outerwear association.

Knitted outerwear times ...

New York ₁National knitted outerwear association₎ 19

T695   National Knitted Outerwear Association.
K53
Knitting times buyers' guide directory.
₁New York₎

National knitted outerwear association.
Statement of National knitted outerwear association presented at hearing before Industry committee no. 7 for the knitted outerwear industry, Wage and hour division, United States department of labor. October 26, 1939. ₁New York₎ 1939.   20 f. 28cm.

1. Knit goods—Trade and stat.—   U. S. 2. Wages, Knit goods workers'—U. S.   ers'—U. S.
N. Y. P. L.   June 30, 1943

NN 0056350   NN

TT679   National Knitted Outerwear Association.
.K752
Knitted outerwear times.
Yearbook.
New York, National Knitted Outerwear Association.

338.405   National knitted outerwear bulletin. no.1-57,
NAT2   Jan.1926-Sept.1930; v.5,no.10-v.8,no.9, Oct.
             1930-Sept.1933. ₁New York, National knitted
             outerwear association, 1926-33₎
             8v. illus., ports., tables, diagrs.

Monthly.
No.7 omitted in numbering.
Supersedes an earlier publication with the same title.
Superseded by the Knitted outerwear times.
Wanting: no.3;v.8,no.6.

NN 0056352   IU NN

National komitee für ein "Freies Deutschland"
see
Nationalkomitee für ein "Freies Deutschland."

The **National** Kourier. Eastern and Middle West edition.
192

Washington, D. C.: The Empire Pub. Co., 192   f°.
v. illus.

Weekly.
Official organ of the Knights of the Ku-Klux Klan.
                  May 1, 1925, called North Central edition ; May 8
called Eastern and Middle West edition.
          Absorbed by The National Kourier.

1. Knights of the Ku-Klux Klan—Per.   and soc. publ. 2. Newspapers—U. S.
N. Y. P. L.   April 20, 1926

NN 0056354   NN

F902   National kourier; *Eastern and Middle West edition*
7BA512   v.3 no. 52-v.4 no. 15, Nov. 1924-Mar.
           1925. Washington. D. C., Empire Pub. Co.
           1 reel. negative.

Organ of the Knights of the Ku Klux Klan.
Frequency varies.
Title varies: Wisconsin kourier.
Microfilmed by W.H.S.
On same reel with Badger American.

NN 0056355   WHi

The **National** Kourier. North Atlantic edition.
192

Washington. D. C.: The Empire Pub. Co., 192   f°.
v. illus.
Weekly.

NN 0056356   NN

VOLUME 407

The National kourier. North Central edition
see The National kourier; Eastern and
Middle West edition.

The **National** Kourier. Southern edition.
192
Washington, D. C.₍, etc.₎: The Empire Pub. Co., 192   f°.
v. illus.

Weekly.
Official organ of the Knights of the Ku-Klux Klan.
– May 1, 1925, called the South Atlantic edition; May 8–22, 1925,
called the Southern edition.
Absorbed by The National Kourier.

1. Knights of the Ku-Klux Klan—Per.   and soc. publ. 2. Newspapers—U. S.
N. Y. P. L.   April 20, 1926

NN 0056358 NN

The **National** Kourier. Southwestern edition.
192
Washington, D. C.: The Empire Pub. Co., 192   f°.
v. illus.

Weekly.
Official organ of the Knights of the Ku-Klux Klan.
Absorbed by The National Kourier.

1. Knights of the Ku-Klux Klan—Per.   and soc. publ. 2. Newspapers—U. S.
N. Y. P. L.   April 20, 1926

NN 0056359 NN

The **National** Kourier. Western edition.
192
Washington, D. C.: The Empire Pub. Co., 192   f°.
v. illus.

Weekly.
Official organ of the Knights of the Ku-Klux Klan.
– May 1, 1925. called Western and Pacific edition; May 15–
called Western edition.
Absorbed by The National Kourier.

1. Knights of the Ku-Klux Klan—Per.   and soc. publ. 2. Newspapers—U. S.
N. Y. P. L.   April 20, 1926

NN 0056360 NN

National kraut packers association.
Cooking with kraut. ₍Oak Park, Ill., 1955?₎   39 p.   illus.
18cm.

1. Cookery—Vegetables—Cabbage.

NN 0056361 NN

National Kwangtung University, *Canton, China*
see
Chung-shan ta hsüeh, *Canton, China.*

National LP-gas Association.
NLPGA times
see under title

National Labor Committee against War.
Not labor's war ...
see under American People's Mobilization.

National Labor Committee for Organized
Jewish Labor in Palestine
see National Committee for Labor
Israel.

National Labor Committee for Palestine
see National Committee for Labor
Israel.

National labor conference on war aims, *London, 1917.*
... British labor's war aims; text of a statement adopted at
the Special national labor conference at Central hall, Westminster, on December 28, 1917.

₍*In* Association for international conciliation. **American branch.**
International conciliation. New York, 1918. 19½ᶜᵐ. no. 123, p. 23–34₎
Caption title.

1. European war. 1914–1918—Peace.   I. Title.

Library of Congress   JX1907.A8 ₊₋o. 123.   18—8793

CaBVaU
NN 0056367 DLC OrPR WaS WaU–L MiU OU OO OC1

National labor congress, Baltimore, Md.,
August 20, 1866.

Green, Benjamin Edwards, 1822–1907.
... Letter and remarks, by Ben. E. Green ... **New York,**
B. D. Benson, 1866.

NATIONAL LABOR CONGRESS. 2d, Chicago, 1867.
Address of the National labor congress to the workingmen of the
United States.   Chicago, Hazlitt & Quinton, printers, 1867.
20p. 22.5cm.

1. Labor and laboring classes. U. S.

Printed by Wesleyar   University Library

NN 0056369 CtW

331.87 National labor congress on the Mooney
N213p   case, Chicago, 1919.
Proceedings ... January 14th, 15th, 16th
and 17th 1919.   San Francisco [1919?]
cover-title, 71p.

NN 0056370 IU WaS

National labor council of Mexico
see
Consejo obrero nacional (*Mexico*)

National labor forum, New York.
Shall a labor party be formed?
see under Hillquit, Morris, 1869–

National labor health conference. 1st, Cleveland, 1927.
First National labor health conference, Cleveland, Ohio, June
18–19, 1927. Under the auspices of the Workers' health bureau
of America ... ₍New York, 1927₎   152 p.   23cm.

1. Hygiene, Industrial—Congresses   —U. S.—O.—Cleveland, 1927.
I. Workers' health bureau of America.
N. Y. P. L.   November 29, 1938

NN 0056373 NN DL

National labor journal. v. 1–18. Sept. 4, 1908 –
Mar. 7, 1924. Pittsburgh.
reels. 35mm. weekly.
First issue preceded by Advanced Issues
no. 1–4, Aug. 7–28, 1908.
"The National Labor Journal is published in
the interest of the American Federation of
Labor. "
Vol. 7, no. 16, vol. 8, no. 8 and vol. 17,
no. 26 repeated in numbering.
Title varies: Aug. 7, 1908 – Sept. 29, 1916,
Iron city trades journal.

Microfilm (positive) Madison, Wis., The
State Historical Society of Wisconsin, 1965.
1. Labor and laboring classes. U. S.
Period. I. American Federation of Labor.
II. Title: Iron city trades journal.

NN 0056375 PSt

HD6500 National Labor Journal.
.N28   ... Labor day issue
Pittsburgh, Pa.,
[National labor journal v. 13, no. 35;
August 29, 1919]

NN 0056376 DLC

National labor-management conference, *Washington,*
D. C., 1945
see
President's national labor-management conference, *Wash-*
ington, D. C., 1945.

HD4802   National Labor-Management Foundation.
.P₅
Partners; the magazine of labor and management. v. 1–
Jan. 1948–
₍Chicago₎

National labor review. v. 1, no. 1; Oct. 24, 1908. Wash-
ton ₍National labor review publishing co.₎ 1908.
8 p. illus. (ports.) 46ᶜᵐ.
R. G. M. Ross, editor.
No more published.

1. Trade-unions—Period.
                                                        9–12330
Library of Congress   HD6500.N3

NN 0056379 DLC

NATIONAL LABOR SERVICE
Labor looks at civil liberties. ₍N.Y., 1955₎.

₍5₎ p. (folded)

I. Title. 1. Civil liberty.

NN 0056380 MH–IR

National Labor Service.
Television – labor's new challenge; first
annual Labor Television Workshop, sponsored by
the National Labor Service in cooperation with
the Publicity Departments of the American Federation of Labor and the Congress of Industrial
Organizations September 7–8, 1954 at the Transport Workers Union ... and the DuMont Television Network Studios ... New York City.
₍1954₎
cover-title, 47, 13A l.

NN 0056381 NNC

VOLUME 407

KF   National Labor Service.
211   Your rights under state and local fair
P18   employment practice laws. ₍New York,
v.147   1955₎
no.13   32 p. illus. 23cm.

        In Pamphlets 147.

        1. Discrimination in employment.

NN   0056382   NIC NcD

                                        A331.051 11
National labor tribune. Pittsburg, Pa., [1897-].
    Continued from vol. 25, no. 22, May 20, 1897. illus. 56×44ᵐᵐ.
    Caption title; no index.
    Vol. 26, no. 2; 30, no. 14, 21, 29, wanting.

NN   0056383   ICJ MH

NATIONAL labor tribune. v.3, no.17-v.78, Apr. 24,
1875-Dec.1952 (incomplete); Jan., May, 1953-
Jan., May, Sept.1957-Nov.1958.
Pittsburgh   v.   illus.   58cm.

    Film reproduction. Positive.
    Weekly, Apr. 24, 1875-1938 (irregular); biweekly, 1939-Mar.1948;
monthly (irregular), May, 1948-1952; bimonthly (irregular), 1953-
Nov.1958.

    Numbering irregular.
    "Endorsed by the United mine workers of America as their official
organ."
    Ceased publication with Nov.1958?

1. Trade unions--Per. and soc. publ.--U.S. I. United mine workers
of America.

NN   0056385   NN

National Labor Union.
    Address of the executive committee of the
National labor union of the state of California.
June 15th, 1871 ...   San Francisco, Women's
co-operative printing union [1871]
    72 p. 19.5 cm. [Pamphlets on social
science. v. 2]
    1. Labor and laboring classes. 2. Land tenure.
3. Tariff. 4. Free trade and protection. Free
trade.

NN   0056386   CU

NATIONAL LABOR UNION.
    Address of the executive committee, June 15, 1871.
San Francisco, Women's co-operative printing union
[1871?] 72 p. 20cm.

    Film reproduction. Positive.

1. Labor, 1851-1900. 2. Labor--U.S.--Calif. i. Subs.for N-L-U-.
California.

NN   0056387   NN

National labor union
    Address of the National labor union to the people
of the United States, on money, land and other
subjects of national importance.
Chicago, Ill., Workingman's advocate, 1870.
    15 p.

NN   0056388   OClWHi

National labor union.
    Address of the National labor union to the
people of the United States, on money, land,
and other subjects of national importance.
Washington, D.C., McGill & Witherow, printers,
1870.

    22 p. 24 cm.
            YA18713

NN   0056389   MH DLC

HFA74   National Labor Union.
.M15   Platform, constitution, state constitution,
          local constitution. New York, Press of
          Rogers and Sherwood, 1872.
          18 p. 16½cm.

          Cover title.

NN   0056390   WHi

HFA74   National Labor Union.
.M15   Proceedings. 1-5, 1867-1871. [v.p.]
          1 v. (unpaged) mounted clippings;
          23cm.

          Taken from various newspapers.
          1871 incomplete.
          2, 1868, separately published: Philadel-
          phia, W. B. Selheimer print., 1868. (56
          p., 22cm.)

NN   0056391   WHi

NATIONAL LABOR UNION.
    Proceedings of the session in convention.
Philadelphia.   v.   8°.

    Microfilm (master negative)

1. Labor--Assoc. and org.--   U.S.

NN   0056392   NN

National Labor Union
    Ritual. n.p. [18- ?]

NN   0056393   MH

National Labor Union.   9331.8873a26
    To the colored workingmen of the United States, trades, labor, and
industrial unions.
    [Washington. 1871.] Broadside, 10 × 8 inches.

G8738 — Broadsides.

NN   0056394   MB

National Labor Union.   9331.8873a27
    To the workingmen of the United States:
[Norwich, Conn. 1867.] 4 pp. 8°.

NN   0056395   MB

National laboratory of psychical research, London
        see London. University. Council for
psychical investigation.

The National laborer. v. 1-
    Mar. 26, 1836-
    Philadelphia, 1836-
      , v. 65½ᵐ.
    Editor: Mar 26, 1837-   Thomas Hogan.
    Pub. by the Workingmen's national society for the diffusion of useful
knowledge.
    Absorbed the "Times and independent press" Sept. 17, 1836.

    1. Labor and laboring classes--U. S.--Period. 2. Trade-unions--U. S.--
Period. I. Hogan, Thomas, ed. II. Workingmen's national society for
the diffusion of useful knowledge, Philadelphia.

                                        CA 10-4258 Unrev'd

Library of Congress   11D4801.N3

NN   0056397   DLC

National Labour Federation. *Tel-Aviv.*
עֶעֱלוֹתינוּ: דין־וחשבון שנתי. תשרי תרצ"ו־תשרי תרצ"ז.
₍Tel-Aviv, 1936, 37₎
    100 p. illus. 24 cm. ₍ספרית הענבד הלאומי₎

    1. Tel-Aviv--Econ. condit. I. Title.
                        Title transliterated: Pe'ulotenu.

11C497.P2N35   61-57504 ‡

NN   0056398   DLC MH

NATIONAL labour journal. v. 6-date; 1953-date
Ottawa.   v.   illus., ports.   29-42cm.

    Film reproduction. Negative.

    Monthly (some issues in combined form).
    "Official magazine of the National council of Canadian labour."

1. National council of Canadian labour.

NN   0056399   NN

National Labour Press.
    Rapport de la deuxième Conférence interna-
tionale pour les états unis socialistes
d'Europe, Paris, 21 et 22 juin, 1947
        see under   International Conference
for the United Socialist States of Europe. 2d,
Paris, 1947.

National Labour Press.
    Report of the first International Conference
of the Peoples of Europe, Asia, Africa against
Imperialism, Paris, 18th to 21th June, 1948
        see under   International Conference
of the Peoples of Europe, Asia, Africa against
Imperialism, 1st, Paris, 1948.

National Lacrosse Association of Canada.
    The latest rules of lacrosse as revised and adopted by The
National Lacrosse Association of Canada.   New York: Peck
& Snyder, 1879. 8 p. illus. 16°.

                                SPALDING COLLECTION.
1. Lacrosse.
N. Y. P. L.   October 26, 1921.

NN   0056402   NN

636.305 The National lamb feeder. v.1-
NATL   Nov.1950-
         Denver ₍etc.₎
         v. illus. 28cm. monthly.

         Publication of the National Lamb Feeders
Association.

NN   0056403   IU

NATIONAL LAMP WORKS OF GENERAL ELECTRIC COM-
    PANY, Cleveland.

    See GENERAL ELECTRIC COMPANY. National
lamp works, Cleveland.

VOLUME 407

National Land & Improvement Company.
Report of the Board of Directors...to the
Stockholders. Colorado Springs, Colo, "Out West"
printing & publishing co., 1874.
8 p.   14 x 22 cm.

NN   0056405   CoHi

National Land and Improvement Company.
Report of the board of directors to the stock-
holders ...   1880.   Colorado Springs, 1881.
8°.
Contains also Report of Colorado Springs
Company, 1871-79.

NN   0056406   NN

National Land and Improvement Co.
Report to the stockholders.   1889.   Colorado
Springs, The Gazette Prtg. Co., 1890.
1 pmp.   8°.

NN   0056407   NN

National land and irrigation journal; devoted to reclama-
tion by irrigation, drainage, conservation. v. 1-6, v. 7,
no. 1; Dec. 1909-Jan. 1913.   Chicago, The H. O. Shep-
ard company ｛etc.｝ 1909-13.
7 v. in 3. illus. 35ᶜᵐ. monthly.
Dec. 1909-Nov. 1910, title reads: National irrigation journal.
Editors: Dec. 1909-Jan. 1911, C. A. Morrison.—Sept. 1912-Jan. 1913, J. W.
Shaw.
Absorbed the Irrigator in July 1911.
Merged into Irrigation age.

ɪ. Morrison, Clyde A., ed. ɪɪ. Shaw, James W., ed. ɪɪɪ. Title: National
irrigation journal.
14-21411
Library of Congress   TC801.N4

NN   0056408   DLC ICJ IChi OrCS

S.900 **National land bank.**
The humble offer of the National land-bank...[n.p.,
1696]
broadside. 31 × 19 cm.
An offer to exchange clipped or counterfeit money
for new coins.

NN   0056409   MH-BA

National Land Company.
Kansas and Colorado ...
see under   Pratt, C. N.

National land-draining company for England,
Ireland and Scotland.
Thoughts upon supplying food and employment
for the working population of the United Kingdom.
Published in connection with the prospectus of the
above company. London, 1845.
15 p.   22.5 cm.

NN   0056411   CtY

｛National land reform association, *New York*｝
Land and labor; their relations in nature—how vio-
lated by monopoly. ｛New York, 187-｝
16 p. illus. 23ᶜᵐ.
Caption title.

1. Land tenure—U. S. 2. Land, Nationalization of.   ɪ. Title.
CA 19-109 Unrev'd
Library of Congress   HD1306.U5N3

NN   0056412   DLC IU

National land-use planning committee.
... Annual report. 1st-   ; 1932/33-
Washington, D. C., 1933-
v. 26½ᶜᵐ. (*Its* Publication. no. v-   July 1933-   )
Mimeographed.

CA 34-629 Unrev'd
Library of Congress   HD189.N25

NN   0056413   DLC Or OCU

National Land-use Planning Committee.
｛Confidential minutes and reports, together
with miscellaneous source material.
｛n.p., n.d.｝
3 v. 29 cm.

NN   0056414   TU

National land-use planning committee.
The problems of "submarginal" areas and
desirable adjustments with particular reference to
public acquisition of land.   Washington, Govt.
print. off., 1933.
24 p.   O.   (National land-use planning
committee and national advisory and legislative
committee on land use. Publication No. 6)

NN   0056415   NcD

National land-use planning committee.
... Publication. no. 1-   ; June 1932-
Washington, U. S. Govt. print. off. ｛1932｝-
v. 23ᶜᵐ (no. 1-   : 27ᶜᵐ) irregular.
At head of title, no. 1, June 1932: U. S. Department of agriculture.
Office of information, Press service.—no. 3, Oct. 1932: National land-use
planning committee.—no. 3-   Mar. 1933—   National land-use
planning committee and National advisory and legislative committee on
land use.
Nos. 1 to   mimeographed.

1. Land tenure—U. S. 2. U. S.—Public lands. 3. Agriculture—U. S.
ɪ. National advisory and legislative committee on land use. ɪɪ. U. S.
Dept. of agriculture. Office of information. Press service.
33—16571
Library of Congress   HD189.N25
｛3741｝   333.0973

NN   0056416   DLC DL MB TU KMH CaBVaU Or ICJ MtBC

National land-use planning committee
see also   National advisory and legislative
committee on land use.

---

ffSB119   National Landscape Nurserymen's Association.
N3   15 sets of plans, details and reports from the competition for
Land-   the design of a nursery sales and display grounds, sponsored by
scape   the National Landscape Nurserymen's Association.   [Chicago?]
Arch.   1946.
Library   [35] p. 19 plans. 65x42cm.

Typewritten reports mounted facing most plans.

1. Nurseries (Horticulture) 2. Architecture - Designs and plans.
ɪ. Title: Competition for the design of a nursery sales and display
grounds.

NN   0056418   CU

90.1   **National Landscape Nurserymen's Associa-**
N21   **tion.**
For better care of your plantings; the
essentials of caring for your garden with
illustrations showing how: operations
briefly described.   West Hartford, Conn.,
Peter Cascio Nursery [1947]
｛8｝ p.

1. Gardening. I. Cascio (Peter) Nursery.

NN   0056419   DNAL

National language readers of Japan.

Ojima, Kikue.
Handbooks on the National language readers of Japan ...
By Mr. Kikue Ojima. Tokyo, San ko sha, 1929-

National Language Research Institute, *Tokyo*
see
Kokuritsu Kokugo Kenkyūjo, *Tokyo.*

｛**National Lanier centennial committee.** *Baltimore committee*｝
The centenary of Sidney Lanier, born February 3, 1842, died
September 7, 1881. ｛Baltimore？｝ 1942｝
｛4｝ p. illus. (incl. port.) 25½ᶜᵐ.
Caption title.
Announcement of exercises to be held at Peabody Institute and Johns
Hopkins university.

1. Lanier, Sidney, 1842-1881.   ɪ. Johns Hopkins university. ɪɪ. Peabody institute, Baltimore.
Library of Congress   PS2213.N35   42-25919

NN   0056422   DLC

National laundry & cleaning journal
see
Cleaning-laundry world.

National laundry and dry cleaner
see   Cleaning-laundry world.

National laundry journal
see
Cleaning-laundry world.

The **national** law finder for all states of the United States,
showing where the cases in the reports of the several
states have been exhaustively annotated in the selected
case, sets that cover the general field of law, also, where
any case decided in any state court has been affirmed,
reversed or distinguished by the United States Supreme court. Detroit, Mich., The Law stamps co., 1911.
421 p. 21½ᶜᵐ.
ɪɪ—885

NN   0056426   DLC WaU-L

The **national** law finder for all states of the United
States, showing where the cases in the reports of the
several states have been exhaustively annotated in
the selected case sets that cover the general field of
law; also, where any case decided in any state court
has been affirmed, reversed or dismissed by the United
States Supreme court. Pontiac, Mich., The National
law finder publishing co., 1912.
555 p. 21ᶜᵐ. $12.00

1. Law reports, digests, etc.—U. S. ｛1. Annotations and citations｝
12-29366

NN   0056427   DLC NjP

The **national** law finder for all states of the United States,
showing where the cases in the reports of the several
states have been exhaustively annotated in the selected
case sets that cover the general field of law. Also,
where any case decided in any state court has been
affirmed, reversed or dismissed by the United States
Supreme court. Pontiac, Mich., The National law
finder publishing co., 1914.
463 p. 20½ᶜᵐ. $10.00

1. Law reports, digests, etc.—U. S. 2. Annotations and citations (Law)—
U. S.
14-7085

NN   0056428   DLC NcD

Natural Law Institute, *University of Notre Dame.*
Proceedings. v. 1-5; 1947-51. Notre Dame.
5 v. 22 cm. annual.
Published by the university's Law School (called, 1947-51, College
of Law)

1. Natural law.   ɪ. Notre Dame, Ind. University. Law School.
A 52-8120 rev
Notre Dame Univ. Libr.

NN   0056429   InNd N TxU

VOLUME 407

The **National** law library ... New York, P. F. Collier & son corporation ₁*1939₎

6 v. 21 cm.

Half-title: An encyclopedia of law for the modern reader. The National law library; Roscoe Pound, supervising editor, Nathan Isaacs, editor, Wm. W. Beardsley, editorial director.
Bibliography: v. 1, p. 309-316.
"Bibliography of the common law of the family": v. 6, p. 255-263.
CONTENTS.—v. 1. The history and system of the common law, by Roscoe Pound.—v. 2. Crime and criminal law, by Morris Ploscowe.— v. 3. Public law, by H. L. Bevis.—v. 4. Business law, by Nathan

Isaacs.—v. 5. Property, by F. S. Philbrick.—v. 6. Legal relations: pt. 1. Contracts, torts and trusts, by Nathan Isaacs. pt. 2. The common law of the family, by Max Radin.

1. Law—U. S.   I. Pound, Roscoe, 1870-   ed. II. Isaacs, Nathan, 1886-   joint ed. III. Beardsley, William Waite, 1885- joint ed. IV. Ploscowe, Morris. v. Bevis, Howard Landis, 1885- VI. Philbrick, Francis Samuel, 1876-   VII. Radin, Max, 1880- VIII. Title: An encyclopedia of law for the modern reader.

39—8999

NBuU-L OOxM WaT IdPI PSt
NN   0056431   DLC WaU-L OrU IdU-L OU OCl NNC NcD-L

The **National** law review. v. 1 (no. 1–11); Jan.–Dec. 1888. ₁Philadelphia, 1888₎

568 p. illus. (ports.) 23ᶜᵐ. monthly (except August)

Caption title.
No more published.

1. Law—Period.—U. S. 2. Law—U. S. 3. Law reports, digests, etc.— U. S.

37–8056

NN   0056432   DLC MiU-L WaU-L

National law school, Washington, D.C.

see

Washington, D.C. National University. Law school.

National laws and regulations relating to the control of narcotic drugs. Cumulative index. 1947/56–
New York ₁etc.₎ United Nations, Commission on Narcotic Drugs.
v. in   28 cm. (United Nations. ₁Document₎ E/NL/ Index)
Indexes United Nations. Laws and regulations promulgated to give effect to the provisions of the international treaties on narcotic drugs.
Issued with United Nations publications sales numbers.
1. Narcotic laws.   I. United Nations. Commission on Narcotic Drugs. II. United Nations. Laws and regulations promulgated to give effect to the provisions of international treaties on narcotic drugs. (Indexes) (Series)

JX1977.A2   67–4393

NN   0056434   DLC UU TU GU NcD-L

National laws and rules committee.
The laws of duplicate contract bridge; duplicate movements and scoring, party contract bridge, progressive and pivot; effective December 2, 1935; approved and adopted by American bridge league, American whist league, United States bridge association. National laws and rules committee, William E. McKenney, chairman ... Philadelphia, Chicago, The John C. Winston company ₁*1935₎
xix, 91 p. 19ᶜᵐ.
On cover: New 1935 authorized laws.
1. Contract bridge. I. McKenney, William E. II. Title: Duplicate contract bridge, The laws of.

Library of Congress   GV1282.3.N33   36–291
—— Copy 2.
Copyright A 89735   ₁3₎   795.41

NN   0056435   DLC MB

National laws commission of the American contract bridge league

see

American contract bridge league. *National laws commission.*

National Lawyers Guild.
An appeal to reason; the proposal of the Attorney General to list the National Lawyers Guild as "subversive," its implications for the democratic process and the bar.   New York ₁1953?₎
19 p.   21 cm.
Cover title.
I. U.S. Dept. of Justice. II. Title.

NN   0056437   IU CU NNC NcU-L NN N

US **National lawyers guild**
962.4   ... The Bill of rights and the Mundt-Ferguson
NAT bills (S.1194 and S.1196); an analysis of
the provisions and opinion on their constitutionality ... Washington, D.C. ₁1949₎
1 p.l., 14 p. 21cm.
Stamp on t.-p.: From National Committee to defeat the Mundt Bill ...
Signed at end: National lawyers guild. Clifford J. Durr, president.

NN   0056438   MH-L

National Lawyers' Guild.
Brief on the unconstitutionality of the Mundt-Nixon bill
see under   **National lawyers guild.** Committee on constitutional rights and liberties.

National Lawyers Guild.
The case for the prosecution of "Social Justice" and Charles E. Coughlin under the Espionage Act of 1917
see its   The National Lawyers Guild presents the case ...

National Lawyers Guild.
Civil liberties docket
see under title

National Lawyers Guild.
The constitutional right to advocate political, social and economic change – an essential of American democracy; an analysis of proposed Federal legislation and executive order 9835. ₁Washington? 1947₎
24 p. 28 cm.

"Executive order 9835, issued on March 12, 1947, prescribes procedures for the administration of an employees' loyalty program in the executive   branch of the government." – p. 13.

NN   0056442   NNC ViU-L

National Lawyers Guild.
The Guild lawyer
see under title

Law
National Lawyers Guild.
The **Guild** practitioner. v. 1–
Oct. 1940–
₁Berkeley, Calif., etc.₎ National Lawyers Guild.

National Lawyers Guild.
In re order of February 3, 1941, appointing Alexander Holtzoff, secretary of Advisory Committee; memorial and petition. Washington ₁1941?₎
83 p. 24 cm.
Cover title.
At head of title: Supreme Court of the United States, October term, 1940.
Petition to the Supreme Court to terminate Alexander Holtzoff's membership in and secretaryship of the Supreme Court's Advisory Committee on Rules of Criminal Procedure, appointed by order of Feb. 3, 1941.
1. Holtzoff, Alexander, 1886-1969.   I. United States. Supreme Court. II. Title.

KF373.H62N3   72–191836
                                           MARC

NN   0056445   DLC CLL

National Lawyers Guild.
Judge J. Warren Madden, United States Court of claims. Addresses made by some of the distinguished guests who attended the National lawyers guild dinner in honor of Judge J. Warren Madden at Hotel Shoreham, Washington, D.C., on February 22, 1941. Printed in the Congressional records of February 24, 25, 26 and March 31, 1941. Wash., Govt. print. off., 1941.
14 p.   (Legal pamphlets, v. 31)
Contents: Preservation of democracy, by Elbert D. Thomas. Address by Edwin S. Smith. Address by J. Warren Madden and others.

NN   0056446   WaU-L

National Lawyers Guild.
Law in transition
see under title

National Lawyers Guild.
Lawyers referral directory. Detroit.
v. 23cm.

1. Lawyer referral service – U.S. – Direct.

NN   0056448   MiU-L

National lawyers guild.
...The legality of munitions shipments to Germany. ₁Washington, D.C.? 1938?₎
p.304–319. 25½cm.
Caption title.
"Reprinted from National lawyers guild quarterly, September 1938 issue"
Bibliographical foot-notes.

NN   0056449   DS NN

National Lawyers Guild.
BX4705   The National Lawyers Guild presents the case
C77N27   for the prosecution of "Social Justice" and Charles E. Coughlin under the Espionnage Act of 1917. ₁New York, 1942₎
88 p. 24ᶜᵐ
Cover title.
"A legal and factual study of the contents of the magazine Social Justice prior to and after Pearl Harbor."
1. Social Justice; Father Coughlin's Weekly Review. 2. Coughlin, Charles Edward, 1891 3. World War, 1939   --1945 - Propaganda. I. Title.

NN   0056450   CSt-H NN NcD

National lawyers guild.
Law
National lawyers guild quarterly. v. 1–3, no. 2; Dec. 1937– July 1940. ₁Washington, The National lawyers guild, 1937–40₎

National lawyers guild.
News-letter...   v. 1

Washington, 1937–   v. 30cm.
Irregular.
Vol. 1, no. 1 (June, 1937) lacks numbering.

1. Law—Assoc. and org.—U. S.
N. Y. P. L.   July 11, 1945

NN   0056452   NN CLL WaU-L

National lawyers guild.
Conference on contemporary problems in labor law and relations, *Washington, D. C.*, 1940.
Proceedings, Conference on contemporary problems in labor law and relations, January 12, 13, and 14, 1940, Carlton hotel, Washington, D. C. Washington, D. C., National lawyers guild ₁1940₎

VOLUME 407

Pam. National Lawyers Guild. Annual convention.
Coll. Washington, 1937.

23667   Resolutions. Washington, D. C., 1937.
    12 p. 22 cm.

    Cover title.

    1. Lawyers. Societies, etc.

NN   0056454   NcD

US   National lawyers guild. Committee on constitu-
962.4   tional rights and liberties
NAT   Brief on the unconstitutionality of the
   Mundt-Nixon bill (H.R. 5852), submitted by
   the National lawyers guild. Washington, D.C.
   ₁1948₎

    cover-title, ₍1₎ p.l., 27 p. 28cm.

NN   0056455   MH-L CU NN

76B   National lawyers guild. Committee on
9915.   international law and relations.
5   ... In the matter of the legality
   of the North Atlantic Treaty under
   the Charter of the United nations.
   Memorandum of law ... Washington,
   D.C. ₍1949?₎

    1 p.l., 21 p. 23½cm.
    At head of title: Before the Com-
   mittee on foreign relations, United
   States Senate.

NN   0056456   MH-L

DS   National Lawyers Guild. Committee on
126.4   International Law and Relations.
N3.8   Proposed amendments to the
   recommendations of the United Nations
   Special Committee on Palestine.
   Washington, D.C., 1947.
   17 p. 23 cm.

    1. Palestine—Politics and
   government. I. United Nations. General
   Assembly. Special Committee on
   Palestine. II. Title

NN   0056457   OCH

National lawyers guild. Detroit chapter.
   Brief for constitutionality. Fair employment
   practices ordinance. ₍Detroit, The Author₎
   1946.
    35, 3 ℓ.

    Cover title.

NN   0056458   MiD

National Lawyers Guild. Detroit Chapter.
   ... In re William Oliver on writ of certiorari
   to the Supreme court of Michigan. Brief for
   Detroit chapter, national lawyers guild, amicus
   curiae ... Erwin B. Ellmann, on the brief.
   Detroit, Mich., The Legal chronicle [1947]
    cover-title, v. 26 p. 25 cm.
    At head of title: In the Supreme court of the
   United States, October term, 1947. No. 215.
    I. Oliver, William, defendant. II. Ellmann,
   Erwin Barsook.

NN   0056459   MiU-H

KF309   National Lawyers Guild. Detroit Chapter.
.C7N3   Report of investigation by the Detroit Chapter,
   the National Lawyers Guild and Wolverine Bar
   Association of Michigan on the summary contempt
   citation against George W. Crockett, of the
   Michigan Bar, adopted at General Membership
   meeting of the Detroit Chapter of National
   Lawyers Guild..., and₎ the Wolverine Bar Association on November 16, 1949. ₍Detroit? 1949₎
    29, ₍1₎ ℓ. 35cm.

Continued in next column

Continued from preceding column

"On October 14, 1949, George W. Crockett
...was summarily found guilty of and sentenced
for contempt by...Harold R. Medina of the United
States District Court for the Southern District
of New York."

    1.Crockett, George W   1909-
   I.Wolverine Bar Association of Michigan.

NN   0056461   MiDW

N277   National lawyers guild. Detroit chapter.
L36dr   Report of investigation of summary contempt
1950   citation against George W.Crockett, jr. ...
   (defense counsel in the Foley square trial)
   Presented to the lawyers and judges of Michigan by National lawyers guild, Detroit chapter ..
   ₍Detroit, 1950₎
    31 p. 23 cm.
    Cover title.
    1.Crockett, George W   1909-   2.Contempt
   of court - U.S. I.Wolverine bar association.

NN   0056462   MiU-L

   National Lawyers Guild. International Law Com-
FT   mittee.
H8   American foreign policy and the rule of law; re
   port. Hollywood, Calif. [n. d.]
   ₍30₎ p.

    1. U. S. - Foreign relations. 2. Rule of law.
   I. Title.

NN   0056463   CSt-Law

HD7834
.N37   National Lawyers Guild. Labor Law Committee.
1840

    Conference on labor's rights and the
   defense program. Hotel Commodore December
   13 and 14, 1940. ₍Washington₎ 1940.
   166 p. 28cm.
   Cover title.

    1. Labor laws and legislation—U. S.
   2. U. S.—Defenses. I. Title.

NN   0056464   ViU

   National Lawyers Guild. Los Angeles Chapter.
   "Legal remedies available in the fight
   against smog"; a report by the National Lawyers' Guild, Los Angeles, Hollywood-Beverley
   Hills Chapters. ₍Los Angeles, 1954₎
   13 p.

    "Reprinted from the Los Angeles daily jour-
   nal, November, 1954."

NN   0056465   NNC

   National lawyers guild. National committee on
   social legislation.
    ...The new Wagner-Murray-Dingell social secur-
   ity bill, a new social security charter for America. A report by National committee on social
   legislation, national lawyers guild... ₍New
   York, The Guild, 1944₎
   cover-title, 27 p.

    "Reprinted from 'Lawyers guild review', vol.
   III, no.6".
    Bibliographical foot-notes.

NN   0056466   MiDW-M

National lawyers guild ₍Social legislation₎ National committee on₎
   A post-war low-rent public housing program. ₍New York,
   1944?₎ 19 p. 24cm.

    ¹ Housing—U.S.

NN   0056467   NN

National lawyers guild. *National committee on taxation.*
   ... A democratic tax program for the American people ₍by₎
   National committee on taxation of the National lawyers guild.
   May 9, 1941, Washington, D. C. New York, Appeal printing
   co., inc. ₍1941₎

    cover-title, 1 p. l., 13, ₍1₎ p. 23ᶜᵐ.

    At head of title: Revenue revision of 1941.

    1. Taxation—U. S.   I. Title.

                                      A 41-4878
   Wesleyan univ. Library
     for Library of Congress   ₍2₎

NN   0056468   CtW

National lawyers guild. New York city chapter.
   Analysis of the report of the New York state bar association
   for implementing the American bar association's proposal relative
   to loyalty among lawyers. ₍New York, 1954₎ 46 p. 22cm.

    Cover title.
   "Analysis prepared under the auspices of the Constitutional liberties committee and
   approved by the Board of directors, November 3, 1954."
   Bibliographical footnotes.

    1. Loyalty—U. S.   2. Lawyers   —U.S.

NN   0056469   NN IU ICU NNC CU MiU-L

National lawyers guild. New York city chapter.
   The Guild lawyer
   see under title

National Lawyers Guild. New York City Chapter.
   Memorandum on the implications of Sacher, et
   al. v. U. S., and of the decision ordering the
   disbarment of Harry Sacher, and the suspension
   for two years of Abraham J. Isserman from
   practice in the southern district of New York.
   New York [1952]
    11 p. 22 cm.
    Bibliographical footnotes.
    Cover title.
    1. Legal ethics. U. S. 2. Sacher, Harry.
   3. Isserman, Abraham J. I. Title.

NN   0056471   NcD

National Lawyers Guild. New York City Chapter.
   New York guild lawyer
   see under title

National lawyers guild. New York city chapter.
   Report on proposed changes in the manner of taxation of employers under the state Unemployment insurance law, otherwise
   known as merit rating. Submitted by the Committee on social
   legislation, National lawyers guild, New York chapter... ₍New
   York, 1940₎ 20 p. 23cm.

    1. Insurance, Unemployment—   Finance—U. S.
   N. Y. P. L.   May 24, 1945

NN   0056473   NN

JX
1416
N21   National lawyers guild. New York city chapter.
   Report submitted by the New York city chapter
   of the National lawyers guild in connection with
   the role of the United States in the Far eastern
   and Spanish crises. ₍New York city, 1937₎
   cover-title, 24 p. 26½ cm.

NN   0056474   NNC

VOLUME 407

National Lawyers Guild. New York City Chapter.
Shall the organized bar establish legal clinics? A round table discussion under the auspices of the New York city chapter of the National Lawyers Guild, broadcast over station WMCA, Tuesday, March 7, 1939, from 9:15 to 9:45 P. M. [New York, 1939]
11 p.

Prof. Karl N. Llewellyn among participants.
The thirteenth in a new series of broadcasts on The lawyer in   modern society.

NN   0056475   NNC

National Lawyers Guild. New York City Chapter.
Committee on Constitutional Liberties.
Analysis and appraisal of the report of the Rapp-Coudert committee. [New York, 1942]
8 numb. l.   36 cm.
Mimeographed.
1. New York (State) Legislature. Joint committee to investigate procedures and methods of allocating state moneys for public school purposes and subversive activities. 2. Communism — New York (City) 3. Education and state — New York (State)

NN   0056476   NNC

National lawyers guild. New York city chapter.
Committee on labor law and industrial relations.
Collective bargaining by public employees in New York state. A report prepared by the Subcommittee on municipal affairs, of the Committee on labor law and industrial relations, of the National lawyers guild. Written by: Saram Amerling. [New York, 1946]
12 l.

Bibliographical footnotes.

NN   0056477   NNC

National lawyers guild. *New York city chapter. Committee on social legislation.*
Unemployment insurance law, New York state; information about unemployment insurance benefit payments under the law as amended by the Legislature on July 1, 1939. [New York] National lawyers guild, New York city chapter, ⁹1939.
cover-title, 1 p. l., 14 p., 1 l.   22½ᵐ.
"Prepared by the Committee on social legislation of the National lawyers guild, New York city chapter."—1st prelim. leaf.

1. Insurance, Unemployment—New York (State)
                                        43–1055
Library of Congress   HD7096.U6N78
                       [2]   331.25444

NN   0056478   DLC NN

323.47   National Lawyers Guild, Oregon Chapter.
N277c   Report of the civil liberties committee.
           Portland, 1938.
           53 p.

1. American Legion—Oregon. 2. Civil Rights —Oregon. 3. Communism, Oregon. 4. Portland— Police. 5. Steiner, Richard M. I. Hart, C. Allan. II. Title.

NN   0056479   OrHi OrU OrPR

K83K   National Lawyers Guild. San Francisco chapter.
.NA   In the court of public opinion; people of the United States of American vs. the Dies Committee, indictment. San Francisco, 1939.
         48 p.   24cm.

1. U.S. Congress. House. Special committee on un-American activities (1938-1944)

NN   0056480   WHi MiEM

TX1971.6   National lawyers guild. Special committee to
¶277   study the United nations world court.
            The Permanent court of international justice; proposals of the National lawyers guild. Submitted on behalf of Special committee to study the United nations world court. New York, N. Y., National lawyers guild [1945]

cover-title, 16 p.   23ᵐ.

1. Hague. International court of justice (Proposed)

NN   0056481   CSt-H

National lawyers guild. Student division.
The Guild law student
see under title

The **National** Lawyers Guild practitioner
see
The **Guild** practitioner.

National lawyers guild quarterly. v. 1-3, no. 2; Dec. 1937-July 1940. [Washington, The National lawyers guild, 1937-40]
3 v.   25½ᵐ.
Includes section "Current books."
Superseded by Lawyers guild review.

[1. Law—Period.—U. S. 2. Law—U. S.   I. National lawyers guild.
                                        40-8504 Revised

       P OU NBuU-L
NN   0056484   DLC NdU GU-L WaU-L IdU-L GEU ViU-L

NATIONAL lead & oil co., *New York.*   **8018**
Concerning the preservation of iron and steel structures.
        [N. Y. 1891?] 24 pp. Facsimile. 8°.
On the value of red lead for painting these structures.

NN   0056485   MB

National lead company.
Annual report.
[New York]
    v. 17½ᵐ.
Report year ends Dec. 31.
Full title: Annual report, National lead company.

1. Lead mines and mining—U. S.
                               CA 12-333 Unrev'd
Library of Congress   HD9539.L42U55

NN   0056486   DLC

National lead company.
Cinch anchoring system; an economical and sure way of securing fixtures to masonry ... New York, Cincinnati, National lead company; [etc., etc., ⁹1915]
76 p. illus. 23ᶜᵐ.

1. Bolts and nuts.   I. Title. II. Title: Anchoring system, Cinch.
                                        15-19404
Library of Congress   TJ1330.N3

NN   0056487   DLC

National lead company.
Color in colonial times, by M. Rea Paul and K. J. Bowman... New York [n. d.]   4 l.   illus. 27cm.

1. Interior decoration, U. S.,   Colonial. 2. Paint—Manufacture.
I. Paul, Morris Rea, 1895–   II. Bowman, K. J. III. Title.

NN   0056488   NN IU

National Lead Company.
Commemorating the one-hundredth anniversary of the incorporation of the Brooklyn White Lead Company; the first corporation to enter the lead industry in the United States... [New York: National Lead Co., cop. 1925.]   39 p.   illus. (incl. ports.) 23cm.

On cover: The first hundred years; Brooklyn White Lead Company, National Lead Company, 1825, 1925.

667960A. 1. Lead—Trade and stat.—   U. S.
N.Y.P.L.   September 25, 1933

NN   0056489   NN NBHi NNC

National lead company
Cyclopedia of paint information.
N.Y., Boston, Author, c1926.
27, [3] p.

NN   0056490   PC1S

National Lead Company.
Die-castings.   New York: National Lead Co. [cop. 1913.]
19(1) p.   illus.   8°.

1. Die-sinking and dies. 2. Moulding   and casting.
N. Y. P. L.   May 21, 1918.

NN   0056491   NN

National Lead Company.
Distinctive wall effects ...
see under   National Lead Company.
Department of Decoration.

TP934   National Lead Company.
.D83
         The **Dutch** boy quarterly.

         New York, National Lead Co.

National Lead Company.
Early American architecture; selected sketches and measured drawings, showing colonial and Georgian design. [New York: National Lead Co., 192-?]   [43] f. incl. plans, plates.   4°.

In eight sections, paged separately.
Cover-title.
Contents: Section I. The old Royall house. Section 2. Trinity Church, Newport, R. I. Section 3. Mount Vernon, Va. Section 4. Mt. Pleasant Mansion, Philadelphia. Section 5. Bull-Pringle house, Charleston, S. C. Section 6. Thomas Cowles house, Farmington, Conn. Section 7. City Hall, New York. Section 8. Edgewood, S. C.

461221A. 1. Architecture—U. S.,   Colonial.
N. Y. P. L.   March 28, 1930

NN   0056494   NN IU UU NBuG CU NjP RPD

National Lead Co.
George Washington as a Mason
see under title

National Lead Company.
The handbook on painting.   New York, Author [c1926]
138 p.

NN   0056496   OC1

698.1   National Lead Company.
N21h   The handbook on painting.   New York [c1931]
1931   ii, 152p. illus. 14cm.

"Memoranda": p.146-152.

1. House painting. 2. Painting, Structural.

NN   0056497   IU

VOLUME 407

National Lead Company.   698
The handbook on painting. New York, National Lead Com- T200
pany; ₍etc., etc.₎ °1932₎
₍2₎, ii, 152 p. illus. 14ᶜᵐ. *bound* 16½ᶜᵐ.
Blank pages for "Memoranda" (148-152)

NN 0056498   ICJ

National lead co.
Handbook on painting. N. Y. ₍The Author₎
°1935.
156 p. illus.

NN 0056499   MiD

698.1   National lead company.
N21h   The handbook on painting.   New York, National
lead company; ₍etc., etc.₎ c1937₎
156p. illus.

Blank pages for "Memoranda" (144-148)

1. House painting.   2. Painting, Structural.

NN 0056500   IU MiD

National lead co.
Handbook on painting. N. Y. ₍The Author₎
°1938.
156 p. illus.

NN 0056501   MiD

National lead company.
The handbook on painting.   New York ₍etc.₎ National lead co.
₍1942?₎ 90 p.   illus.   18cm.

1. Painting, Industrial.
N. Y. P. L.   July 31, 1944

NN 0056502   NN WaS

National Lead Company.
The handbook on painting.   New York [etc.,
c1946]
90 p.   illus.   18.5 cm.
1. House painting. 2. Painting, Industrial.

NN 0056503   MiEM

National Lead Company.
Handling white lead ...   New York, 1914.
3 p.   28 cm.

NN 0056504   DL

National lead company
Handy book on painting.
N.Y., National lead co., c1924.
124 p.

NN 0056505   OC1

National lead company.

₍Harn, Orlando Clentom₎ 1871–
How to protect structural metal; a practical hand book upon
the mixing and application of paint to iron or steel, tin, and
galvanized iron, together with a brief explanatory discussion of
the causes of corrosion and remedies for it. New York,
Boston ₍etc.₎ National lead co. ₍°1909₎

₍ʟNational lead company₎
Kirksite "A", a zinc-base alloy, used (1) as
sand-cast for forming and trimming dies, (2) in
rolled form for blanking dies for sheet metal
and other sheet materials, (3) for plastic molds
made in sand or in casting plaster; a handbook
of shop and foundry practice ... ₍Rev. ed. New
York, National lead co., 1945₎
72 p. illus., diagrs.

Cover-title: Kirksite "A" handbook. Revised
1945.
Bibliography: p   71-72.
1. Zinc alloys.   I. Title: Kirksite "A"
handbook.

NN 0056507   NNC

National Lead Company.
Mixing directions for combining Dutch Boy white lead with
pure linseed oil and colors, to obtain any desired shade used in
house painting and decorating. ₍New York, 1914?₎   14 p.
nar. 8°.

Folder; p. 4-8 contain samples of paint.

1. Paint.
N. Y. P. L.   March 22, 1918.

NN 0056508   NN

National Lead Company.
Painting, protective and decorative; an attempt to help the
house-owner solve frequent and vexing problems.   New York:
National Lead Co. ₍cop. 1913.₎   1 p.l., 5–48 p., col'd front.   illus.
4°.

1. Painting (House, sign, etc.).
N. Y. P. L.   March 21, 1916.

NN 0056509   NN OO ICJ

National lead co.
Painting, protective & decorative; designed to
help the house-owner solve frequent and vexing
problems. N. Y., The Author, °1915.
48 p. illus. (part col.)

NN 0056510   MiD WaU

National lead company.
Price-list of drawn lead traps, bends, etc. National
lead company, Chicago branch. Manufacturers of lead
pipe, sheet lead, etc., combination ferrules, adjustable
lead sewer caps, etc. ... ₍Chicago, °1895₎
₍36₎ p. illus. 16ᶜᵐ.

1. Plumbing—Traps.
                                                CA 9-5121 Unrev'd
Library of Congress   TH6631.N3

NN 0056511   DLC

National lead company.
Private code, National lead company. New York,
N. Y., National lead company, °1924.
iv. 334 p. fold. tab. 17ᶜᵐ.

1. Cipher and telegraph codes—Lead.

                                                24-7921
Library of Congress   HE7677.L38N3

NN 0056512   DLC

National Lead Company.
The protection of structural metal; a practical handbook upon
the mixing and application of paint to iron or steel, tin and galvanized iron, together with a brief explanatory discussion of the
causes of corrosion and remedies for it.   New York: National
Lead Co. ₍cop. 1912.₎   48 p.   front., illus.   4°.

1. Metals.—Corrosion. 2. Red lead.
N. Y. P. L.   May 18, 1922.

NN 0056513   NN

National lead company.
Red lead in corrosion resistant paints. ₍New York₎ National
lead company ₍1944₎
cover-title, 25 p., 1 l.   illus., diagr.   28 x 22ᶜᵐ.

1. Red lead. 2. Paint.   I. Title : Corrosion resistant paints.

Library of Congress   TP936.N3   45-13711
                                       ₍2₎   667.6

NN 0056514   DLC DNAL ICJ

May37   National Lead Company.
UC   Report[quarterly]
N21e   [New York]
                               23cm.

NN 0056515   CtY

NATIONAL LEAD COMPANY.
...Retirement annuity plan and plan of past service and
minimum pensions. Effective January 1, 1937. [New York:
Metropolitan life insurance co. press, 1936] 18 p. 20cm.

1. Pensions, Lead workers'—U.S.

NN 0056516   NN

National Lead Company.
Solving the paint problem...   New York: National Lead
Co. ₍1914?₎   1 p.l., 14 p.   illus.   8°.

1. Paint. 2. White lead.
N. Y. P. L.   May 21, 1918.

NN 0056517   NN

National Lead Company.   L698
Specifications for the use of white-lead paint. New York, T100
National Lead Company; ₍etc., etc.₎ °1931₎
₍4₎, 31 p. 29¼ᶜᵐ.

Supplement: A. S. T. M. and government specifications, p. 22-31.

NN 0056518   ICJ

National lead company
Specifications for the use of white-lead
paint.
New York, Cincinnati, National lead company
₍1934₎
29 p.

NN 0056519   OC1

National Lead Company.
Standard specification for the use of red-lead paint.   New
York₍, 1926₎.   ₍31₎ p.   4°.
p. 1-8 paged in duplicate.

1. Red lead—Specifications.
N. Y. P. L.   January 19, 1927

NN 0056520   NN OC1

National Lead Company.
Standard specification for the use of white-lead paint.   New
York₍, 1926₎.   ₍51₎ p.   4°.
p. 1-18 paged in duplicate.

1. White lead—Specifications.
N. Y. P. L.   January 19, 1927

NN 0056521   NN

VOLUME 407

National lead company.
The story of white-lead; a description of the process by which lead ore is prepared for paint, by the manufacturers of Dutch boy products. New York, National lead company (c1932)
cover-title, 12 p. 19 cm.

NN   0056522   DL

National Lead Company.
Structural metal painting
   see under   Sabin, Alvah Horton, 1851–

National Lead Company.
Structural metal painting; literature review
   see under   National Lead Company.
Research Laboratories, Brooklyn.

National Lead Company.
A talk on paint. New York: National Lead Co., 1906.
39(1) p. illus. 8°.

I. Paint.
N. Y. P. L.   December 26, 1913.

NN   0056525   NN

NATIONAL lead company. Acid recovery division.
Recovery and concentration of sulphuric acid; Simonson-Mantius vacuum process.
N.Y. Author. c1929. 25p. illus. tab. diagrs.
(its Bulletin no.4)

NN   0056526   WaS

665.5
N214b
Engin
Lib'y   National Lead Company. Baroid Sales Division.
Baroid drilling mud data book. Houston, Tex. [c1953–
2v. (loose-leaf) illus., tables. 26cm.
Vol. 2 has no title-page; cover title: Drilling mud reference manual.
"Copy no.3688."
Includes bibliographies.
1. Petroleum – Well-boring. I. Title. II. Title: Drilling mud data book. III. Title: Drilling mud reference manual.

NN   0056527   TxU PSt IU TxHU

National lead company. Baroid sales division.

Drilling mud.

[Los Angeles, Houston, Tex., Baroid sales division, National lead co.; etc., etc., 19

National Lead Company. *Dept. of Decoration*
Distinctive wall effects, with directions for their production
...submitted by National Lead Company, Department of Decoration. New York [1926] 14 l. 7 col'd pl. 4°.

Typewritten.
Plates are mounted samples.

1. Wall decoration.
N. Y. P. L.   March 18, 1927

NN   0056529   NN

[National lead company. *Research laboratories, Brooklyn*]
Corrosion and preservation of iron and steel, a bibliography, 1936–1945 ... [Brooklyn, 1946]
4 p. l., 135 numb. l. 27 x 21 cm. (*Its* Laboratory publication, no. 126–46)
"Confined to that material which was covered in 'Chemical abstracts.'"—Pref.

1. Iron—Corrosion—Bibl. 2. Steel—Corrosion—Bibl.   I. Title.

Z6679.C7N3   016.6201122   47–4171

NN   0056530   DLC CU MB

National lead company. Research laboratories, Brooklyn.
Laboratory publications [a collection of articles written in] 1946 [by the technical staff] Brooklyn, National lead co., Research laboratories [1946]
133 p. illus., fold. table. 28cm.

"All of the papers of outstanding interest, published by the laboratories or reprinted from technical journals, have been included."

NN   0056531   CU

TA
462
N27+   National Lead Company. *Research Laboratories, Brooklyn.*
Structural metal painting; literature review. Brooklyn [1946]
cover-title, 54 l. 27 cm.
Condensations of selected articles pub. during the period 1936 to 1945.

1. Corrosion and anti-corrosives. 2. Painting, Industrial. 3. Steel, Structural.   I. Title.

TA462.N3   620.1122   47–29342*

NN   0056532   DLC CU MB NIC

698.1
N211s   National Lead Company. Research Laboratories, Brooklyn.
Styling with paint, by M. Rea Paul and E. K. Roberts ... [Brooklyn, National lead company, Research laboratories, 193–]
7p. illus.

1. House painting. I. Paul, Morris Rea, 1895– II. Roberts, E. K.. joint author. III. Title.

NN   0056533   IU

National leader.   –v.2 no.31;   –Sept.28, 1889. Washington, D.C.
v. weekly.

Began Jan.1888.
Continued by Leader. Cf. Gregory
Microfilm, positive copy.

NN   0056534   MH-S

---

*JK
2391
f.N41N8   The National leader. v.1–16 (no.1–310); Sept. 23, 1915–July 1923. Minneapolis [etc.] National Nonpartisan League.
16 v. in 6. illus., ports. 36–44 cm.

Title varies: Sept. 1915–Oct. 1921, The Nonpartisan leader.
Frequency varies: weekly, Sept. 1915–July 1920; biweekly, Aug. 1920–Apr. 1922; monthly, May 1922–July 1923.
Vols. for 1915–1917 published in Fargo, N.D., for 1918–   1920 in St. Paul.

Issues for July 1917–Nov. 1921 are the "National edition" with minor exceptions.
Condition poor; use restricted.

MICROFILM
80
MICROFILM
STORAGE
30   ----- Microfilm copy. St. Paul, Minnesota Historical Society, 1970. 6 reels. 35 mm.
     ----- Microfilm copy (negative). St. Paul, Minnesota Historical Society, 1969. 6 reels. 35 mm.

NN   0056537   MnHi DLC

National Leadership Development Conference in Trade and Industrial Education.
Conference report. 1955–
[Washington, U. S. Dept. of Health, Education, and Welfare, Office of Education.
v. illus. 26 cm. ([U. S. Office of Education] Circular)

1. Technical education—Congresses. [2. Industrial education—Congresses] (Series)

L111.A72   371.426082   E 56–135
——— 2d set.   T62.N3
U. S. Office of Education.   Library
for Library of Congress   [9,]

NN   0056538   DHEW DLC

National League for American Citizenship, Inc.
   see   League for American Citizenship.

National League for Economic Stabilization.
The Clair plan for Federal market control through annual national domestic prorate and minimum price stabilization of the ... food and clothing crops of the United States to insure national prosperity. Chicago [c1932]
23 p. 25 cm. (In Pamphlets on economic problems and theory. v. 1, no. 8)
1. Agriculture. Economic aspects. I. Title.

NN   0056540   OrU

National League for Economic Stabilization.
For Clair plan to restore farm and national prosperity. Chicago, The National league for economic stabilization [1932?]
23 p. 23 cm.

NN   0056541   DL

National league for good roads.
... Proceedings of a convention of the National league for good roads held at Washington, D. C., January 17 and 18, 1893 and hearing by the Committee on agriculture of the House of representatives, January 19, 1893. Published by authority of the Secretary of agriculture. Washington. Govt. print. off., 1893.
101 p. 23ᶜᵐ. (U. S. Office of experiment stations. Bulletin no. 14)

1. Roads—Congresses.
U. S. Dept. of agr.   Library   1Ex6B   no. 14   Agr 9–2582 Revised
for Library of Congress   [S21.ET   no. 14]
                      [37b]

NN   0056542   DNAL MB MiU OCl OO

National league for good roads.
... Proceedings of the convention at Chicago, October 20–21, 1892. Constitution of the league and temporary organization. [Chicago? 1892]
cover-title, 55 p. plates. 22½ᶜᵐ.
"Vol. 1, no. 1, Nov. 1892."

1. Roads—Societies. 2. Roads—U. S.

Library of Congress   TE5.N2 1892   7–32234

NN   0056543   DLC MH

National league for good roads. New York (State).
New York state, National league for good roads. (Temporary organization.) [Rochester, N. Y., 1893?] 15 p. incl. table. 23½cm.

Caption-title.
Reprints of speeches, articles and notes from various newspapers on the improvement of state roads.

1. Roads—U. S.—New York.
N. Y. P. L.   June 4, 1940

NN   0056544   NN

VOLUME 407

National League for Health, Maternity and Child Welfare, *London.*   362.06261
... Annual report ... ₍London, 1920–1926₎   5
Library has 1919–1925. tables. 23ᶜᵐ.
Cover-title.
At head of title: The National League for Health, Maternity, and Child Welfare.

NN   0056545   ICJ DL

₍National league for good government, inc.₎
₍Collection of pamphlets, leaflets, etc. issued or distributed by the National league for good government₎ ₍New York, 1935–44₎ 55 pieces. 29cm.

1. Bolshevism—U.S. 2. Women in politics—U.S.

NN   0056546   NN

National League for Medical Freedom.
A brief history of federal health legislation. 1878–1911. New York ₍1911₎. 63 p. 8°. (National League for Medical Freedom. League library, no. 4.)

1. Hygiene (Public).—Jurisprudence,   U. S.
N. Y. P. L.   September 19, 1911.

NN   0056547   NN CU IU

National league for medical freedom.
The compulsory medical inspection of school children ...
see under   Flower, Benjamin Orange, 1858–1918.

614.09 National league for medical freedom.
'28d   Digest of news items and editorial comment relating to the national health department and questions of general interest concerning the public health. New York ₍1910?₎
59p.

Printed on only one side of leaf.

NN   0056549   IU

614.09 National league for medical freedom.
N28e   Evils of a health bureau.   New York ₍1909?₎
23p.

NN   0056550   IU

---

614 National league for medical freedom.
N21f
The facts about "Collier's" attack on the National league for medical freedom. New York ₍1912?₎
₍6₎p.

NN   0056551   IU

National League for Medical Freedom.
Medical medievalism in the twentieth century. An account of the ... transformation of the American Medical Association, from a typical academic body of limited membership ... into a huge political machine, undemocratic ... and wholly un-American in its aims and methods. New York ₍1911₎. 16 p. 8°. (National League for Medical Freedom. League library, no. 5.)

1. American Medical Association.—   History.
N. Y. P. L.   September 20, 1911.

NN   0056552   NN

National League for Medical Freedom.
Organization of the National League for Medical Freedom; embracing officers ... aim and purpose. Creating a nation wide panic: Why? Political medicine in the public school.   New York ₍1911₎.   14 p., 1 l.   8°.   (National League for Medical Freedom. League library, no. 1.)

1. Hygiene (Public), U. S. 2. School   children.—Medical inspection of.
N. Y. P. L.   September 27, 1911.

NN   0056553   NN

W 1   NATIONAL League for Medical Freedom
NA487   Report to its members. 1st; 1910.
New York.
23 p.

NN   0056554   DNLM DLC-P4

₍National League for Medical Freedom. Illinois Branch₎
Mrs. Coonley Ward writes Illinois club women about national health bureau. ₍Chicago, 1910?₎
₍8₎ p.

NN   0056555   IU

National League for Nursing.
Established 1952.

National League for Nursing.
Biennial reports. 1953/55–
see its Reports to the members. 1953/55

NATIONAL LEAGUE FOR NURSING.
Bylaws.
New York, N.Y.   v.   22–23cm.

1. Nurses and nursing—Assoc.   and org.—U.S.

NN   0056558   NN N

National League for Nursing.
Certificate of incorporation and bylaws. As amended June 1953. New York, N.L.N., 1953.
24 p.

NN   0056559   OrU-M

W Y   NATIONAL League for Nursing
1   ₍Collection of publications₎
qN277
The Library has a collection of miscellaneous publications of this organization kept as received. These publications are not listed or bound separately.

NN   0056560   DNLM

National League for Nursing.
Curriculum bulletin
see under   National League of Nursing Education. Dept. of Services to Schools of Nursing.

National League for Nursing.
Current issues in nursing education
see under   National League for Nursing Education.

National League for Nursing.
Educational programs for the preparation of public health nurses for beginning public health nurse positions, 1955.   New York, ₍1955₎
12 numb. l.   28 cm.   (Its publication no. 558)
Mimeographed.

NN   0056563   PU PU-Med-TS

National League for Nursing.
Facts about nursing, a statistical summary
see under   American Nurses' Association.

National League for Nursing.
Guide for the development of libraries in schools of nursing ...
see under   National League of Nursing Education. Committee on Guides for the Development of Libraries in Schools of Nursing.

W 6   NATIONAL League for Nursing
P3   Guiding principles for junior colleges participating in nursing education; Developed by the Committee of the National League for Nursing and the American Association of Junior Colleges. ₍New York, 1955₎
9 ℓ.
Caption title.
1. Nursing - Education I. American Association of Junior Colleges

NN   0056566   DNLM

National League for Nursing.
The head nurse at work
see under   National League for Nursing. Dept. of Hospital Nursing.

National League for Nursing.
Inservice education for hospital nursing personnel by Mary Annice Miller.   New York, N. Y. National League for Nursing, 1953.
73p.   charts.   29cm.

1. Nursing education. 2. Hospitals. I. Title: Inservice education for hospital nursing personnel.

NN   0056568   NcU

National League for Nursing.
The league exchange. no. 1–
1952–
New York.
v.   28 cm.

No. 1–3, 1952 issued by the League under its earlier name: National League of Nursing Education.

1. Nurses and nursing—Collected works. I. National League of Nursing Education. II. Title ₍anals.₎

NN   0056569   CU-M NBuU PSt UU

National League for Nursing.
A library handbook for schools of nursing, prepared by a committee of the National League of Nursing Education. 2d ed. New York, 1953.

265 p. 23 cm.

First ed. prepared by the Committee on the Nursing School Library, National League of Nursing Education.

1. Medical libraries. 2. Subject headings—Medicine. 3. Classification—Books—Medicine.   I. National League of Nursing Education. Committee on the Nursing School Library. A library handbook for schools of nursing. II. Title.

Z675.M4N18 1953   ₍026.61₎ 020   53–2472 ‡

NcD-N TxU AU
OKentU OU PU-Med-TS NcD PPJ PV OC1W KEmT NNC MiU
NN   0056570   DLC IaU CaBVaU OrU-M NcU Or DNLM TU

VOLUME 407

National League for Nursing.
   Manual for student nurse recruiters
      see under   National League for Nursing.
Committee on Careers.

National League for Nursing.
   The NLN graduate nurse qualifying examination

   see under

National League for Nursing. Division of Nursing
Education.

National League for Nursing.
   NLN news
      see under title

National League for Nursing.
   Nursing care for the poliomyelitis patent at home
      see under   National League for Nursing.
Dept. of Public Health Nursing.

RD09
.P7

National League for Nursing.

Prickett, Edna A
   The operating room supervisor at work. New York, Dept.
of Hospital Nursing, National League for Nursing [1955]

RT42
.O35

National League for Nursing.

Ogg, Elizabeth.
   Preparing tomorrow's nurses. 1st ed. [New York] Public
Affairs Committee, 1952.

National League for Nursing.
   Program guide for future nurses clubs
      see under   National League for Nursing.
Committee on Careers.

RT
97
.N24

National League for Nursing.
   Progress report on combination services in
public health nursing. N[ew] Y[ork] Dept.of
Public Health Nursing,National League for
Nursing [1955]
   vii,56 p.   23 cm.
   Prepared by Eleanor Kunitz and Dorothy Rusby,
this report grows out of the discussions and
decisions of the Chicago Conference on Combination Services,Nov.29-30 and Dec.1,1954.
   Bibliography: p.56.
   1.Public health nursing. I.Title: Combination services   in public health nursing.

NN 0056578   MiU NcU MU NcU-H CU DNLM InU OrU-M

RT1
.P8

National League for Nursing.

Public health nursing. v. -44;   -Dec. 1952.
   [New York, etc.]

National League for Nursing.
   Public health nursing care of the sick at
home. New York, N.L.N., 1953.
   57 p.

NN 0056580   OrU-M

National League for Nursing.
   Public health nursing service manuals: a guide
for their development
      see under   National League for Nursing.
Dept. of Public Health Nursing.

National League for Nursing.
   Report. 1953/55-
      see its   Reports to the members ...
1953/55

National League for Nursing.
   Report of the meeting of administrators of
graduate programs in nursing
      see under   National League for Nursing.
Dept. of Baccalaureate and Higher Degree Programs

National Leagur for Nursing.
   Report of work conference on graduate nurse
education
      see under   National League for Nursing.
Division of Nursing Education.

National League for Nursing.
   Reports to the members. 1953/55-
New York.
   v.   biennial.
   Continues Report and record of proceedings
of the convention (title varies slightly)
issued by the society under its earlier name:
National League of Nursing Education.
   Cover title: NLN reports.
   1. National League for Nursing. 2. Nurses and
nursing-Societies. I. Title. II. Title: NLN
reports.

NN 0056585   DAU MiU LU NcU-H CU N

NATIONAL LEAGUE FOR NURSING
   Schools of nursing in the United States,
Author, 1953.
   v.

NN 0056586   Or

National League for Nursing.
   Schools of professional nursing ...
      see under   National League for Nursing.
Committee on Careers.

National League for Nursing.
   Self-evaluation guide for collegiate schools
of nursing

   see under

National League for Nursing. Division of
Nursing Education.

National League for Nursing.
   Self-survey guides for public health nursing
service ...
      see under   National League for Nursing.
Dept. of Public Health Nursing.

National League for Nursing.
   Source materialsin nursing education
      see under   National League of Nursing
Education.

National League for Nursing.
   State approved schools of professional nursing; schools
meeting minimum requirements set by law and board rules
in the various states and territories.

New York.
   v. 21-23 cm. quadrennial (irregular)
   Title varies: -1943, A list of schools of nursing meeting
minimum requirements set by law and board rules in the various
states and territories (varies slightly)—1946, State-accredited schools
of nursing.—1950-54, State approved schools of nursing.
   Issued   -1950 by the National League of Nursing Education
(19   -46 by its Dept. of Studies)
   1. Nursing schools—U. S.

   RT81.U6N3   610.73071173   36-6470 rev 2*‡

   OrStbM WaWW
   WaTC OOxM OLak DHEW DNLM MtBuM OrU-M OrSaW NN TU
   MtU OrCS OrP OrPR OrU WaE WaPS WaS WaSp WaSpG WaT
   CU-M WaSpG ViU DI MB CaBVaU IdB IdPI IdU MtBC Wa
   MnU-B MiU CtY-M AzU P OU NN NcGU ICJ NcD TxU NcU
NN 0056591   DLC OrU-M WaS OClW LN OCl MnU ICU InU

National League for Nursing.
   Teaching rehabilitative aspects of nursing ...
nursing care of the elderly patient with a fractured
hip. New York, N. L. N., 1955.
   32 p.

NN 0056593   OrU-M

National League for Nursing.
   Trends in school nursing

   see under

National Organization for Public Health Nursing,
   School Nursing Section, Atlantic City, 1952.

National League for Nursing.
   The use of tests in schools of nursing
      see under   National League for Nursing.
Division of Nursing Education.

National League for Nursing
   see also
   Association of Collegiate Schools of Nursing.
   National League of Nursing Education.
   National Organization for Public Health Nursing.
   Nursing Advisory Service

National League for Nursing. Advisory Services
for Orthopedics and Poliomyelitis
   see
National League for Nursing. Nursing Advisory
services for orthopedics and poliomyelitis.

National League for Nursing. Committee on Careers.
Handbook for counselors

   see under

Lewis, Edith Patton.

National League for Nursing. Committee on
Careers.
   Manual for student nurse recruiters
N. Y., The League, 1953. 63p., illus.

NN 0056599   OClW OrU-M

VOLUME 407

National League for Nursing. Committee
on careers.
Program guide for future nurses clubs;
drawings by Elizabeth D. Logan. New York,
National League for Nursing, 1955.
80p. illus. 24cm.

1. Nursing as a profession. I. Title.

NN 0056600 NcU OrU-M

National League for Nursing. *Committee on Careers.*
Schools of professional nursing. New
York, N.L.N., 1952.

NN 0056601 OrU-M

WY NATIONAL League for Nursing. Committee
19 on Careers
N276s Schools of professional nursing, 1954.
1954 ₁New York, 1954₁
39 p.
Cover title.
1. Nursing schools - U. S. - Direct.

NN 0056602 DNLM

National League for Nursing. Council of Associate Degree
Programs.
Associate degree education for nursing—current issues.

New York, Dept. of Associate Degree Programs.
v. 28 cm.
Title varies slightly.
Papers presented at the   conference of the Council.

1. Nurses and nursing—Study and teaching—United States—Con-
gresses—Collected works.   I. Title.
RT81.U6N37a   610.73'07'1173   73-161932
ISSN 0077-5118   rev   MARC-S

NN 0056603 DLC N

RT71 National League for Nursing. Curriculum
N34 Committee.
The case for shorter hours in hospital
schools of nursing. New York City ₁n.d.₁
32p. 23cm. (Its Bulletin, no.1)

1. Nurses and nursing - Study and teaching. I. Title.

NN 0056604 IaU

WY NATIONAL League for Nursing. Dept. of
19 Baccalaureate and Higher Degree
qN277Je Programs
Educational programs accredited for
public nursing preparation.

New York, 19
v.
1. Public health nursing 2. Schools,
Nursing - direct.   Title

NN 0056605 DNLM

W 1 NATIONAL League for Nursing. Dept. of
NA494B Baccalaureate and Higher Degree Programs
Report of the biennial business meeting of the Council of Member Agencies.

New York, 19
v.
Reports for 19   include Speakers'
notes from the biennial program meeting.
1. Education, Nursing

NN 0056606 DNLM

W1 National League for Nursing. Dept. of Baccalaureate and
NA494BD Higher Degree Programs.
Report of the conference of the Council of Member
Agencies of the Dept. of Baccalaureate and Higher
Degree Programs

New York ₁195-₁
v.
Later reports with distinctive titles classed
separately in this Library.
1. Education, Nursing. Degree Programs - U. S.
I. Title: Conference of the Council of Member Agencies
of the Dept. of Baccalaureate and Higher Degree
Programs

NN 0056607 DNLM

RT National League for Nursing. Dept. of Baccalaureate
73 and Higher Degree Programs.
.N27 Report of the meeting of administrators of
R3 graduate programs in nursing. New York, National League for Nursing, Dept. of Baccalaureate and Higher Degree Programs ₁1954?₁
25 leaves. 28 cm.
Cover title.
Held at the University of Chicago, Dec. 6-8,
1954.

1. Nurses and nursing - Study and teaching -
Congresses. I. Title.

NN 0056608 DCU

National League for Nursing. Dept. of
Baccalaureate and Higher Degree Programs.
Self-evaluation guide for collegiate school of
nursing ...
see under National League for Nursing.
Division of Nursing Education.

National League for Nursing. Dept. of Diploma and
Association Degree Programs.
Self-evaluation guide for schools of nursing
see under National League for Nursing.
Division of Nursing Education.

National League for Nursing. *Dept. of Hospital Nursing.*
The head nurse at work. New York ₁1953₁
60 p. illus. 23 cm.

1. Nursing service administration. I. Title.
RT89.N3   610.73   53-2705 ‡

OC1W MiD ViU PU Wa CaBVaU OC1U
NN 0056611 DLC WaSpG OrU-M MtBC DNLM NIC OCU OU

RT97 National League for Nursing. *Dept. of Public*
N24 *Health Nursing.*
Public Nursing activities of public health nursing agencies; a statistical
Health analysis of the activities of 513 public health nursing agencies.
Library New York, 1955.
12 ℓ. tables, diagrs.

1. Public health nursing - Stat.

NN 0056612 CU OrU-M TxU-M

National League for Nursing. Dept. of Public
Health Nursing.
Nursing care for the poliomyelitis patient at
home. New York [1955]
69 p. illus.
Prepared by the Dept. of Public Health
Nursing and the Nursing Advisory Services for
Orthopedics and Poliomyelitis.

NN 0056613 IdPI ViU CU InU WaS

National League for Nursing. *Dept. of Public Health
Nursing.*
Public health nursing service manuals: a guide for their
development. New York ₁*1955₁
122 p. illus. 28 cm.

1. Public health nursing. I. Title.
RT97.N19   610.73'4   56-4211 ‡

CU Wa
NN 0056614 DLC CtY-M WaU MiD DNLM OC1W MBU MiU

National League for Nursing. Dept. of Public
Health Nursing.
Report of Conference on Public Health
Nursing Care of the Sick at Home
see under Conference on Public Health
Nursing Care of the Sick at Home, Harriman, N. Y.,
1952.

RT National League for Nursing. *Dept. of Public* (Nursing
29 *Health Nursing.*
N27 Self-survey guides for public health nursing
service. New York, Dept. of Public Health
Nursing of the National League for Nursing,
1953-
v. tables 22 x 28 cm.

1. Public health nursing. I. Title.

NN 0056616 DCU ViU CU ICU OC1W NcU DNLM

National League for Nursing. *Dept. of Public Health
Nursing.*
Staff education, a guide for public health nursing services. New York, 1955.
47 p. 23 cm.

1. Public health nursing—Study and teaching. I. Title.
RT97.N2   610.734   55-2118 ‡

NN 0056617 DLC NcU-H ScU DNLM OC1W

National League for Nursing. *Dept. of Public Health
Nursing.*
Statistical reporting and costs in public health nursing.
New York ₁1953₁
36 p. illus. 28 cm.
"Brings up to date, amplifies, and replaces the material presented
in the 1944 handbook 'Statistical reporting in public health nursing'"
by Margaret L. Shetland.

1. Public health nursing. I. Shetland, Margaret L. Statistical
reporting in public health nursing. II. Title.
RT97.N22   610.734   53-1152 ‡

NN 0056618 DLC Wa FU-HC DNLM PU

National League for Nursing. Division of Nursing
Education.
Bibliographies on nursing

see under

National League of Nursing Education.

National League for Nursing. Division of Nursing
Education.
Guide for the development of libraries

see under

National League of Nursing Education. Committee
on Guides for the Development of Libraries in
Schools of Nursing.

VOLUME 407

National League for Nursing. Division of Nursing
Education.
Imaginative teaching

see under

Nursing Outlook.

RT
71
.N24
no.2
National League for Nursing. Division of Nursing
Education.
The NLN achievement tests in professional
nursing. New York, National League for Nursing,
Division of Nursing Education,Evaluation and
Guidance Service, 1954.
   v,41 p. diagr.,tables. 23 cm. (The Use
of tests in schools of nursing. Pamphlet no.2)

   1.Nurses and nursing--Study and teaching.
I. Title.

NN 0056622   MiU NcU-H DCU

RT
71
.N24
no.3
National League for Nursing. Division of
Nursing Education.
The NLN graduate nurse qualifying examination.
New York, National League for Nursing,Division
of Nursing Education,Evaluation and Guidance
Service, 1954.
   v,39 p. diagr.,form,tables. 23 cm. (The
Use of tests in schools of nursing. Pamphlet
no.3)

   1.Nurses and nursing--Study and teaching.

NN 0056623   MiU ViU DCU NcU-H

National League for Nursing. *Division of Nursing Education.*
Objectives of educational programs in nursing. **New**
York, 1955.
  22 l. 28 cm.

   1. Nurses and nursing—Study and teaching.   I. Title.

RT73.N33   610.7307   57–145 ‡

   OC1W InU CU TxU-M NbU-M NcU
NN 0056624   DLC OrU-M NcD-N ScU PU-Med-TS DNLM PU

National League for Nursing. Division of Nursing
Education.
Report of a Work Conference on Graduate
Nurse Education ...
see under   Work Conference on
Graduate Nurse Education,University of Chicago,
1952.

National League for Nursing. Division of Nursing Education
RT71
N2775r
1952-
Report on the program of temporary accreditation of the National
Nursing Accrediting Service. [New York?] 1952-
  v. tables. (part fold.) 28 cm.

  Includes bibliography.
  Contents. -Pt. 1. Study of basic programs offered by schools of
nursing.

   1. Nurses and nursing--Study and teaching. I. National Nursing
Accrediting Service.   II. Title.

   MtBC
NN 0056626   CU-M MnU CaBVaU DCU CU OrU-M CaBVaU

RT
71
.N265
National League for Nursing. Division of Nursing
Education.
Self-evaluation guide for collegiate schools of
nursing. New York, Dept.of Baccalaureate and
Higher Degree Programs,Division of Nursing
Education,National League for Nursing, 1954.
   23 p. 22 x 28 cm.
   Cover title.

   1.Nurses and nursing--Study and teaching.

NN 0056627   MiU IdPI OrU-M IaU DCU OU CU OC1W

RT71
N244
Biology
Library
National League for Nursing. Division of Nursing Education.
Self-evaluation guide for schools of nursing. New York,
1952.
  20 l.

   [Issued by] Department of Diploma and Associate Degree
Programs.
   "Reprinted from: Report on the program of temporary ac-
creditation of the National Nursing Accrediting Service. Part I.
Study of basic programs offered by schools of nursing."

   1. Nurses and nursing - Study and teaching.

NN 0056628   CU OC1W OU DCU PU-Med-TS

National League for Nursing. Division of Nursing
Education.
A study of desirable functions and qualifications
for psychiatric nurses

see under

National League of Nursing Education.

RT90
.S3
National League for Nursing. Division of
Nursing Education.

Schwier, Mildred E
   Ten thousand nurse faculty members in basic professional schools of nursing, prepared by Mildred E. Schwier
[and others] New York, National League for Nursing,
1953.

National League for Nursing. Division of Nursing
Education.
Toward a regional program

see under

McGlothlin, William Joseph.

RT
55
.N272
National League for Nursing. Division of
Nursing Education.
The use of tests in schools of nursing.
New York, 1954-
   v. figs., tables. 23 cm.

   1. Nurses and nursing - Examinations,
questions, etc.

NN 0056632   DCU OrU-M

National League for Nursing. Division of Public
Health Nursing
  see   National League for Nursing. Dept. of
Public Health Nursing.

National League for Nursing. Nursing **Advisory**
Services for Orthopedics and Poliomyelitis.
Bibliography on poliomyelitis. **New York**
[1952]
   13 numb. L. 28cm.

   Caption title.
   Typewritten.

NN 0056634   PU-Med-TS

National League for Nursing. Nursing Advisory
Service for Orthopedics and Poliomyelitis.
Nursing care for the poliomyelitis patient at
home
   see under   National League for Nursing.
Dept. of Public Health Nursing.

National League for Nursing. Nursing **Advisory**
services for orthopedics and poliomyelitis.
Orient the nurse recruited for polio; a
plan to help you help her give better patient
care. New York, 1952.
   32p. 20cm.

NN 0056636   PU

National League for Nursing. Nursing Advisory
Service for Orthopedics and Poliomyelitis.
Suggested references and visual aids for
nursing on rehabilitation. New York, n. d.
   190 p.   28 cm.
   1. Orthopedic nursing - Bibliogr.
2. Rehabilitation-Bibliography. I. Title: Visual
aids for nurses on rehabilitation.

NN 0056637   NcU

RT 73
.N28
NATIONAL LEAGUE FOR NURSING—Nursing Advisory
Services for Orthopedics and Poliomyelitis
   Teaching rehabilitative aspects of nur-
sing; suggestions for a modified role-playing
technique in demonstrating the nursing care
of the elderly patient with a fractured hip.
New York [1955]
   32 p. diagr.

   1. Nurses and nursing. I. Title.

NN 0056638   InU

W 6
P3
NATIONAL League for Nursing. Nursing
Advisory Services for Orthopedics and
Poliomyelitis
   Work conferences really work; report
of 1953 regional work conferences on
poliomyelitis nursing. New York [1954?]
   40 p.
   1. Poliomyelitis - Congresses
   2. Poliomyelitis - Treatment

NN 0056639   DNLM

National League for Nursing. *Tuberculosis Advisory Nursing Service*
  see
National League for Nursing. *Tuberculosis Nursing Advisory Service.*

National League for Nursing. Tuberculosis
Nursing Advisory Service.
Abilities, basic concepts, content in
tuberculosis for public health nurses ...
   see under   Tuberculosis Conference for
Public Health Nurse Faculty Members, New York,
1955.

National League for Nursing. Tuberculosis
Nursing Advisory Service.
Bibliography on tuberculosis nursing

see under

National League of Nursing Education.

National League for Nursing. *Tuberculosis Nursing Advisory Service.*
   Cues to staffing tuberculosis units in hospitals; a guide for
the nursing department. Prepared by the Tuberculosis Advisory Nursing Service of the National League for Nursing.
[New York National Tuberculosis Association, 1952.
   28 p. 23 cm.

   1. Tuberculosis nursing. 2. Tuberculosis—Hospitals and sanato-
riums. I. Title.

RC311.8.N35   362.1'9'6246   52–4545 ‡

NN 0056643   DLC MnU-B PU OC1W DNLM CaBVaU

VOLUME 407

RC309
.A1D9
National League for Nursing. Tuberculosis
Nursing Advisory Service.
Dwyer, Sheila Maureen.
Guide for the evaluation of hospital facilities used as
instructional units for tuberculosis nursing. Prepared by
Sheila M. Dwyer ₍consultant, Tuberculosis Nursing Advisory Service of the National League for Nursing. New
York₎ 1955.

NN   0056645   DLC CU DNLM OClW PU-Med-TS NcU PV

National League for Nursing. *Tuberculosis Nursing Advisory Service.*
Safer ways in nursing to protect against tuberculosis; a
guide to precautions in the care of patients. ₍2d ed. New
York₎ National Tuberculosis Association, 1955.
86 p. 23 cm.

First ed. prepared by the Joint Tuberculosis Nursing Advisory
Service.

1. Nurses and nursing. 2. Tuberculosis—Prevention.   I. Joint
Tuberculosis Nursing Advisory Service. Safer ways in nursing to
protect against tuberculosis. II. Title.

RC311.8.N38 1955   610.7369   55–41695 ‡

NN   0056645   DLC CU DNLM OClW PU-Med-TS NcU PV

National League for Nursing. Tuberculosis
Nursing Advisory Service
    see also   Joint Tuberculosis Nursing
Advisory Service.

National league for physical education and improvement.
Annual report.
190
London ₍190
    v. 21½ᶜᵐ.

Report year ends Oct. 31.
An "Interim report" was publ. in 1906, extending to May 1st, 1906.
7th–   include reports of the Association of infant consultations
and schools for mothers.

1. Hygiene, Public—Societies. 2. Children—Care and hygiene.
I. Association of infant consultations and schools for mothers.

                                            14–6309

Library of Congress   GV204.G7N4

NN   0056647   DLC DL

Film
S723
NATIONAL League for Physical Education
and Improvement
    Annual report.
    London ₍1906?–17?₎
    12 v. in
    Film copy.
    Report year ends Oct. 31.

NN   0056648   DNLM

National league for physical education and improvement.
The care of the school child; a course of lectures delivered under the auspices of the National league for physical education and improvement, May to July 1916, ed.
by James Kerr ... with an introduction by Bishop Boyd
Carpenter ... London, The National league for physical
education and improvement, 1916.
viii, 230 p. illus. 19ᶜᵐ.

1. Children—Care ₍and hygiene₎   I. Kerr, James, M. D., ed. II. Title.
                                            E 18–116

Library, U. S. Bur. of   Education RJ101.N2

NN   0056649   DHEW MBCo CtY NIC DL ICJ DNLM CaBVaU

National league for physical education
and improvement.
    The heal th visitor...London, National league for physical education and
improvement, 1910.
    cover-title, 10, 22₎   p. 17 cm.
    ₍Pamphlet no. 2₎.

NN   0056650   DL CaBVaU

National League for Physical Education and
Improvement.
    Infant welfare centres
        see under   Gibbon, Ioan Gwilym.

National league for physical education and improvement.
    ... Interim report, 1906. ₍London, Harrison and sons,
printers, 1906₎
cover-title, 27 p. 21½ᶜᵐ.

A series of Annual reports was begun in 1906.
Includes final report of the Twentieth century league, which was amalgamated with the National league for physical education and improvement
in 1905–06.

1. Hygiene, Public—Societies. 2. Children—Care and hygiene.   I. Twentieth century league, London.
                                            14–8496

Library of Congress   GV204.G7N3

NN   0056652   DLC CtY

RA610
.P3
National league for physical education and
improvement .
Palmer, Mabel (Atkinson) 1876–
    Life-saving in war-time, a campaign handbook, by Mabel
Palmer, M. A., with an introduction by the Rt. Hon. Arthur
H. D. Acland ... Comp. for the Infant welfare propaganda
committee of the National league for physical education &
improvement ... London, C. A. Pearson limited, 1916.

National League for Physical Education and
Improvement.
    Mothercraft
        see under   National Association for
the Prevention of Infant Mortality and for the
Welfare of Infancy.

W 1
NA494C
NATIONAL League for Physical Education
and Improvement
    Pamphlet. no. 1–7; 1909–13. London.
    7 no. in

NN   0056655   DNLM DLC ICRL

National League for Physical Education and
Improvement.
    ... Physical education in foreign countries.
        see its   Report on replies to questions
circulated by The Joint Committee on Physical
education.

National League for Physical Education and Improvement.
    Report of the proceedings of the annual general meeting...
₍no.₎
London: P. S. King & Son ₍19   8°.
    v.
    no. 5   is 1.   Conference of Health-Promoting Institutions.

1. Hygiene (Public).—Per. and soc.   publ. 2. Children.—Care and
hygiene: Per. and soc. publ.
N. Y. P. L.   May 18, 1916.

NN   0056657   NN DL DHEW MiU ICJ ICRL

National League for Physical Education and
Improvement.
    Report on existing schools for mothers and
similar institutions
        see under   Gibbon, Sir Ioan Gwilym,
1874–

National league for physical education and improvement.
    ... Report on replies to questions circulated by the
Joint committee on physical education (organised by the
National league for physical education and improvement).
London, National league for physical education
and improvement, 1909.
11, ₍1₎ p. fold. tab. 22ᶜᵐ. (Pamphlet, no. 1)

1. Physical education—Europe.
                                            E 10–2145

Library, U. S. Bur. of   Education GV243.N2

NN   0056659   DHEW NNU-W DL ViU

National league for physical education and improvement.
    Reproduction of a printed report originally submitted
to the Bucks County council in the year 1892 containing
letters from Miss Florence Nightingale on health visiting
in rural districts. London, P. S. King & son, 1911.
61 p. 21½ᶜᵐ.

On cover: With a prefatory note by Sir Lauder Brunton ... Pub. for
the National league for physical education and improvement.

1. Hygiene, Public.   I. Nightingale, Florence, 1820–1910.
                                            14–21813
Library of Congress   RA485.N37

NN   0056660   DLC DNLM DL ICJ Or

RJ61
.A8
National league for physical education and
improvement.
Association of maternity and child welfare centres.
    To wives and mothers; how to keep yourselves and your children well and strong. Compiled by the Association of infant
welfare and maternity centres ... London, National league for
physical education and improvement, 1916.

National league for physical education and improvement. *Dept. of schools for mothers*
    see also
Association of maternity and child welfare centres.

Pam.
Coll.
44892
National League for the Independence of Poland.
    Sympathy and aid for Poland; address to the
people of Great Britain. ₍London, 1863₎
    4 p. 22 cm.
    Caption title.
    Signed: On behalf of the committee of the
National League for the Independence of Poland,
Edmond Beales, president.
    1. Poland. Hist. 1830–1866. I. Beales,
Edmond, 1803–1881. II. Title.

NN   0056663   NcD

W 1
NA494N
NATIONAL League for the Prevention of
Spinal Curvature
    Journal. v. 1–2; Dec. 1916–Nov. 1918.
Kirksville, Mo.
    2 v. illus.
    Title: Journal of the National League
for the Prevention of Spinal Curvature

NN   0056664   DNLM

National league for the protection of American institutions.
    Documents no. 1–
New York, 1890–
    v. 20½ᶜᵐ.

                                            CA 7–5805 Unrev'd

Library of Congress   LC111.N3

NN   0056665   DLC OO Nh CtY OFH

VOLUME 407

NATIONAL LEAGUE FOR THE PROTECTION OF AMERICAN
INSTITUTIONS.
A petition [to the Congress of the U.S.]
concerning sectarian appropriations for Indian
Education. New York, 1892.

pp. 8.

NN 0056666 MH NN

NATIONAL league for the protection of American institutio
Some questions and answers concerning the National league.
N. Y. [1893.] 24 pp. [Document No. 18.] 16°.

NN 0056667 MB

National league for the protection of the family.
Organized 1881 as the New England divorce reform league;
name changed in 1885 to the National divorce reform league,
legally incorporated in 1887; present form adopted in 1898.

NATIONAL LEAGUE FOR THE PROTECTION OF THE
FAMILY.
Abstract of its Annual Reports, Oct. 1885.
Montpelier, 1885.

(2)+8+(1) p.

NN 0056669 MH-L MB

NATIONAL LEAGUE FOR THE PROTECTION OF THE
FAMILY.
Its aims, its methods, etc. n.p., n.d.

NN 0056670 MH

National league for the protection of the family.

Methods and work.   [Bost. 1893.] 11, (1) pp. 24°.

NN 0056671 MB

National league for the protection of the family.

Publications, special issues for 1893. n.p.,
1893.
no. 1-5.

NN 0056672 Nh

National league for the protection of the family.
Report.
Boston,
v. 21 x 23½ᶜᵐ.

Report year ends Dec. 31.
Title varies: Report of the National divorce reform league.
1895, A review of fifteen years. Report of the National divorce reform league.
Report of the National league for the protection of the family.

5-31596

Library of Congress   HQ106.N27

NjP CU DL NjNbS ICRL
NN 0056673   DLC MB MH OClW ICJ IEG Nh MB MU WvU

National league for the protection of the
family.
arW   Report of the committee on marriage
37037   and divorce. [n. p. 1893]
no.4   14 p. 24cm. (National divorce
reform league. Publications. Special
issues of 1893. No. 2)
By Daniel Merriman

I. Series: National league for the
protection of the family. Publications.
Special issues of 1893. No. 2.

NN 0056674 NIC MH MB RPB

National League for the Protection of the Family. 173.06161 2
Special issues of the National League for the Protection of the
Family. .... Boston, Mass., The Fort Hill Press, 1909-.
Continued from 1909. 21ᶜᵐ.

NN 0056675   ICJ Ar CU OClW OU

National league for the protection of the family.

Statistics of divorce. n.p., [1889.]

NN 0056676   MH-AH

National league for woman's service.
Organized 1917.

National league for woman's service.
Annual report. 1918-
New York city [1919-
v. illus., plates. 22½ᶜᵐ.
At head of title: National league for woman's service.
Report for 1918 includes a summary for 1917.

1. Women in the U. S. 2. European war, 1914- —Women's work.

Library of Congress   D639.W7N3   19-19628

NN 0056678   DLC WaT WaS OrU OCl MB NN ICJ MiU OO

National League for Women's Service.
Bi-weekly news letter.
no.
New York, 1917   8°.
nos.
Caption-title.

1. European war, 1914- —Women's   work.
N. Y. P. L.   September 27, 1920.

NN 0056679   NN

National League for Woman's Service.
Bulletin.
v. 1–2, no. 7.   (Oct. 15, 1917 – June, 1919)
New York, 1917–19. 2 v. illus.   8°., 4°.

Monthly.
Title varies slightly.
v. 2, no. 1–4 omitted in numbering.
Supersedes its: Bi-weekly news letter.
No more published.

1. European war, 1914- —   Women's work.
N. Y. P. L.   November 19, 1921.

NN 0056680   NN

National League for Woman's Service.
Circular.
no. 1–
New York, 1917   8°, 4°, 16°.
v.

1. European war, 1914- Women's   work.
N. Y. P. L.   December 21, 1917.

NN 0056681   NN

National league for woman's service.

Wells, Helen M   comp.
Everywoman's cook book, recipes and food combinations for the household, comp. and arranged by Helen M.
Wells ... San Francisco, Calif., National league for
woman's service [1922]

[National league for woman's service] For
God, for country and for home; roll of honor,
dedicated Sept. 6th, 1920, Flushing, Long Island. [Flushing, Case, 1920] [28]p. Cover
title.

NN 0056683   NJQ

National League for Woman's Service.
When women pull together
see under   Bacon, Josephine Dodge (Daskam),
1876-

National league for woman's service. *Michigan state
committee.*
The National league for woman's service in Michigan
from March, 1917, to April, 1919. Comp. by Mrs. R. C.
Sherrill. [Detroit? 1919]
40 p. illus. 19ᶜᵐ.

1. European war, 1914-   —Michigan. 2. European war, 1914-
—Women's work.

CA 21-79 Unrev'd

Library of Congress   D639.W7N45

NN 0056685   DLC MiD-B

National league green book
see under   National League of Professional
Base-ball Clubs.

PN121   National League of American Pen Women.
.N35   By-Laws of the National League of American
penwomen.   [1926]
1 pam. 16°.

NN 0056687   DLC

PN121
.N35   National league of American penwomen,
1928   By-laws...
[Wash., D.C., 1928].
1 pam.   16°

NN 0056688   DLC

National
League of American Pen Women,
Constitution and by-laws of the League of American Pen
Women... Washington, D. C. [1897.] 19 p. 24°.

1. Woman—Authors—Assoc. and   org.
N. Y. P. L.   July 14, 1925

NN 0056689   NN

National League of American pen women.
Guide number ...
see its   Official bulletin ...

VOLUME 407

NATIONAL LEAGUE OF AMERICAN PEN WOMEN.
...Membership register.
see its Membership roster.

National League of American Pen Women.
Membership roster.
Washington.
v. 20 cm.

PN121.N355   706.273   50-18477

NN 0056692   DLC MB MiD NN

National League of American pen women.
Monthly bulletin...
see its   Official bulletin...

National legue of American pen women.
National bulletin...
see its   Official bulletin...

NATIONAL LEAGUE OF AMERICAN PEN WOMEN.
Official bulletin. June, 1927; v.10, no.9-v.21,
no.8, v.22, June, 1934-May, Oct. 1947-June, 1948;
Oct.-1948-Feb., Apr. 1953-Apr., Oct. 1955, Jan.-
Feb., Oct.-Dec. 1957, Apr., June, Dec. 1958-Jan.
1959
Washington.   v.   illus., ports.   20-27cm.

Monthly (except July-Sept.; irregular)
Issues for Oct. 1948-Jan. 1959 called v. 23-34, no.4 (v. numbering
very irregular), Other irregularities in numbering.
Title varies: June, 1927, National bulletin, League of American pen
women; June, 1944-Jan. 1959, The Pen woman.
Vol.13, no.1, Sept. 1936, called Guide number, 1936/37, and
includes its List of members. (For other years, see its Membership register.)
Ceased publication with Jan. 1959.

1. Women--Authors--Assoc. and org.--U.S. I. National league of
American pen women. National bulletin. II. Title: The Pen woman.
III. National league of American pen women. Guide number.

NN 0056697   NN DLC

National league of American pen women,
The owl; an anthology of verse by members of the League
of American penwomen, edited by Margarette Ball Dickson
... New York, Dean & company, 1928.
46 p. 20ᶜᵐ.

1. American poetry (Collections)   I. Dickson, Margarette Ball, ed.
II. Title.
                                        29-3202 Revised
Library of Congress   PS589.N3
———— Copy 2.
Copyright A 3688   ₍r30c2₎   811.508

NN 0056698   DLC MsU TxU PU NN

National League of American pen women,
The Penwoman. v. 1-2; Apr. 1920-Feb. 1923. ₍Washington,
D. C., League of American pen women, 1920-23₎

National League of American pen women.
... A resumé of the first year's work. Address delivered by Miss Belle Vane Sherwood, recording secretary
... on the occasion of its first annual meeting and election
of officers. ₍Washington, D. C., 1898?₎
₍4₎ p. 18¼ᵐ.
Caption title.

1. Sherwood, Belle Vane.
                                        CA 15-391 Unrev'd
Library of Congress   PN121.L4

NN 0056700   DLC

National
∧ League of American Pen Women,
     Year book...
1
Washington, D. C. ₍1   nar. 8°.
     no.
     1   cover-title.

1. Woman.—Authors: Assoc. and   organizations.
N.Y.P.L.   May 2, 1923.

NN 0056701   NN MiD

National league of American pen women,
Birmingham branch.
Historic homes of Alabama and their traditions, by Alabama members, National league of American pen women;
edited by the Birmingham branch. Birmingham, Ala., Birmingham publishing company, 1935.
xiii, ₍1₎, 314 p. incl. front. (map) illus. (incl. facsim.) pl. 27¼ᵐ.
"Of this edition seven hundred copies have been printed, of which this
is copy no. 160."

1. Alabama—Historic houses, etc. 2. Alabama—Soc. life & cust.
I. Title.
                                        36-2366
Library of Congress   F327.N27
———— Copy 2.
Copyright A 91466   ₍5₎   976.1

NN 0056702   DLC ViU AU ABH AAP MB NcD

National league of American pen women,
Butte county branch.
Here is my land; sketches of Butte county, California, by the
Butte county branch of the National league of American pen-
women. ₍Chico, Calif., Printed by Hurst & Moore₎ 1940.
7 p. l., 86 p., 1 l. incl. illus., 2 port. (incl. front.) map. 23¼ᵐ.
"Of this edition this copy is number 20."

1. Butte co., Calif.   I. Title.
                                        41-5331
Library of Congress   FS68.B8N3
———— Copy 2.
Copyright   ₍2₎   979.432

NN 0056703   DLC CLU CU WHi CU-B

PN121
N4   National league of American pen women,   Chevy
          Chase branch.
          Bulletin...Jan, 1930-
     Washington, D.C., 1930-₎
          1 v.   4°

NN 0056704   DLC

National league of American pen women. Delta branch.
Cotton bolls; an anthology, by Delta branch, N. L. A. P. W.
₍Delta scences by₎ Wynn Richards.   ₍Summit, Miss., 1955₎
37 p.   illus., port.   22cm.
Cover title.

1. American literature—Miss.—   Collections. I. Title.

NN 0056705   NN MsSM

PN121   National League of American Pen Women,
.N44   Los Angeles Branch.
               [Bulletin] [Los Angeles?,

NN 0056706   DLC

National league of American pen women,
Coll   Los Angeles branch.
NA872la l
     National league of American pen women
anthology. ₍Sundland, Calif., C. L.
Anderson₎ 1950.
     47 p. illus., front., plates. 24 cm.

NN 0056707   RPB

National league of American pen women.
Manhattan branch.
Manhattan memo
see under title

National league of American pen women,
New York city branch.
Anthology of modern poetry, by members of the League of
American pen women of New York. New York, Hogan-
Paulus corporation ₍ᶜ1926₎
144 p. 25¼ x 22¼ᵐ.

1. American poetry—20th cent. 2. Women as poets. I. Title.
                                        26-14148 Revised
Library of Congress   PS589.N32
———— Copy 2.
Copyright A 901231   ₍r30c2₎   811.508

NN 0056709   DLC NcD ViU MB

National League of American Pen Women,
New York City Branch.
The New York pen woman
see under title

National League of American Pen Women,
Ref   *Philadelphia branch*
NA8743w
          Who's who and what they do. Planned and
Harris   edited by Elizabeth J. Marshall and Harriet B.
Collection Cooper. [Philadelphia? 193-?]
          [48] p. ports. 22 cm.

I. Marshall, Elizabeth J., ed. II. Title.

NN 0056711   RPB

National League of American Pen Women. *San Diego
Branch.*
The rainbow trail, poems. Chicago, Folio Press ₍1952₎
32 p. 21 cm.

1. American poetry—California—San Diego. I. Title.

PS572.S3N3   811.5082   52-43282 ‡

NN 0056712   DLC NN

National League of American Pen Women. San
Diego Branch.
Wind in the palms; anthology of San Diego
verse, 1932. San Diego, Calif., Press of the
City Print. Co. ₍c1932₎
129 p. 22 cm.

NN 0056713   CU-S DLC

National League of American Pen Women. Western
New York branch.
White peonies, a collection of poetry, com-
piled by Helen M.Bunclark.   New York,The Paebar
Co., 1948. 63p. 21cm.

NN 0056714   MWelC

VOLUME 407

The National League of American Pen Women's anthology
of poems.　v. 1–
New York, Vantage Press [*1951–

　　v. 23 cm.

　　Compiler: v. 1–　　A. F. Di Castagnola.

　　1. American poetry—20th cent. 2. Women as poets.　I. Di Castagnola, Alice Fay.

　　PS589.A1N3　　　　811.5082　　　　52–543

NN　0056715　　DLC OrU

National League of Business Educators.
　　Constitution and by-laws of the National League of Business
Educators.　[New York? 1913?]　16 p.　nar. 12°.

　　　　　　　　　　　　HOWARD SHORTHAND COLL.
1. Commerce—Education—U. S.
N. Y. P. L.　　　　　　　　　　　　　June 5, 1926

NN　0056716　　NN

JS302
.N38
　　National League of Cities.
　　　Addresses delivered at the 18th annual conference of the
American Municipal Association, Stevens Hotel, Chicago,
October 23, 24, 25, 1941.　Chicago, Ill. [1941]

　　154 l.　28 x 22 cm.　(*Its* Series AM. Report 24)

　　1. Municipal government — Societies, etc.　2. Municipal government—U. S.　(Series)

　　JS302.N38　　　　352.0004　　　　42–15894

NN　0056717　　DLC PPULC CoU

National League of Cities.
　　American taxes shared and allocated, 1938. A joint report of the American Municipal Association and the Federation of Tax Administrators, by Sidney Merlin.　Chicago, 1939.

　　67 p.　28 cm.　(*Its* Report no. 133)
　　[Federation of Tax Administrators]　Research report no. 7.
　　Errata slip inserted.
　　1. Taxation—U. S.　2. Taxation, State.　3. Grants-in-aid — U. S.
I. Federation of Tax Administrators.　II. Merlin, Sidney Daniell,
1916–　III. Title.　(Series.　Series: Federation of Tax Ad-
ministrators.　Research report no. 7)
　　JS302.A66　　no. 133　　352.1　　48–34185
　　――――Copy 2.　Bound with American Municipal Association.
Reports 124–141.　Chi-　　cago, 1938–40.
　　　　　　　　　　　　HJ2360.F4　no. 7

NN　0056718　　DLC N OC1W NNC CU MA ViU Or CU

National League of Cities.
　　Bulletin no. 1–
Chicago, 1937–

　　no.　28 cm.

　　No. 1–　issued by the league under its earlier name: American
Municipal Association.

　　1. Municipal government—U. S.

　　JS302.A67　　　　352.073　　　　A 41–3714
　　Michigan.　Univ.　Law　　Library
for Library of Congress　　[r70c2]　rev

NN　0056719　　MiU-L OC1 CoU DLC

National League of Cities.
　　City purchasing methods, some details of
practice
　　　see under　American municipal association.

National League of Cities.
　　Emergency personnel policies; a check list of items which
might be considered by state and local governments ...　Chicago, Ill., 1940.

　　1 p. l., 10 p.　28 cm.　(*Its* Bulletin no. 142)
　　Civil Service Assembly of the United States and Canada.　Special
bulletin no. 14.
　　Published by the league under its earlier name: American Municipal Association.

　　1. State governments.　2. Local government — U. S.　3. Personnel
management.　I. Title.　(Series.　Series: Public Personnel Association.　Special bulletin no. 14)

　　　　　　　　　　　　　　　S D 41–32 rev
U. S. Dept. of State.　　　Library　JK2471
for Library of Congress　　[r66c2]

NN　0056721　　DS PPT NNC

National League of Cities.
　　Financial relationships between state
governments and municipalities ...
　　　see under　American Municipal Association.

National League of Cities.
　　Financing municipal airport operation.　Chicago, 1940.

　　53 l.　illus.　28 cm.　[(*Its* Report no. 143)]
　　Published by the league under its earlier name: American Municipal Association.

　　1. Airports—U. S.—Finance.　I. Title.　(Series)

　　JS302.A66　no. 143　　　　　　　54–54317

PPULC PPT
NN　0056723　　DLC OC1 OC1W ViU IaAS NcC MH-BA WaS

National League of Cities.
　　The house trailer: it's effect on state and local
government ...
　　　see under　American Municipal Association.

National League of Cites.
　　House trailer regulation ...
　　　see under　American Municipal Association.

National League of Cities.
　　How shall our cities be financed?
　　　see under　American municipal association.

National League of Cities.
　　Library bulletin.　v. 1–
Chicago, 1932–

　　v.　28 cm.

　　Issued 1932–　by the league under its earlier name: American
Municipal Association.

　　1. Local government—Bibliography.

　　Z7164.L8N35　　　　　　　　　76–212682

NN　0056727　　DLC

National League of Cities.
　　List of publications of State leagues of municipalities,
prepared by Paul V. Betters, executive secretary, American
Municipal Association.　Chicago, 1932.

　　39 p.　30 cm.　(*Its* Report no. 10)

　　1. Municipal government—U. S.—Bibliography.　2. Municipal government—Bibliography.　I. Betters, Paul Vernon, 1906–　II.
Title.　(Series)

　　JS302.A66　no. 10　　016.352073　　35–13441

NN　0056728　　DLC IU OU

National League of Cities.
　　List of publications of State leagues of municipalities
(revised).　Chicago, American Municipal Association,
1935.

　　54 l.　28 cm.　(*Its* Report, no. 108)
　　Cover title.
　　"Introductory statement" by Paul V. Betters.
　　Appendix: (1) Official periodical publications of State leagues of
municipalities.　(2) List of secretaries of State leagues of municipalities, May 23, 1935.　(3) Information reports.
　　1. Municipal government—U. S.—Bibliography.　2. Municipal government—Bibliography.　I. Betters, Paul Vernon, 1906–　II.
Title.　(Series)

　　JS302.A66　　　　016.352073　　　　35–20050

NN　0056729　　DLC NNC ICJ

National League of Cities.
　　Local government's share of State collected highway
funds and revenues; a 1955 resurvey based upon pertinent
portions of a U. S. Census Bureau report, edited, up-dated,
and amplified principally through the cooperation of executives of State leagues and associations of municipalities.
By John R. Kerstetter, associate director.　Washington,
1955.

　　56 p.　28 cm.
　　Published by the league under its earlier name: American Municipal Association.
　　1. Roads—U. S.—Finance.　I. Kerstetter, John Richard, 1912–
II. Title.

　　HE355.N273　　　　388.1　　　　55–1252 ‡

NN　0056730　　DLC NN PPT PSt NcD PPULC Or Wa MiU

National League of Cities.
　　Milk control; governmental regulation of the dairy industry in the United States, prepared by the American Municipal Association.　Chicago, Public Administration Service,
1937.

　　49 p.　27 cm.　([Public Administration Service] Publication no.
57)

　　1. Dairy laws—U. S.　I. Title.　(Series)

　　　　　　　　338.1　　　　　　38–485 rev

OrP OrPR OCU OO DFT ViU TxU WU
NN　0056731　　DLC PPULC CoU CoDU Wa WaU-L Or OrU

National League of Cities.
　　Motorized police patrol—one-man or two-man crews?
Chicago, American Municipal Association, 1940.

　　14 l.　28 cm.　(*Its* Report no. 140)

　　1. Police—U. S.　2. Police patrols.　I. Title.　[Series]

　　JS302.A66　no. 140　　352.20973　　41–26481

NN　0056732　　DLC

National League of Cities.
　　Motorized police patrol; one-man or two-man crews?
Montreal, Canadian Federation of Mayors and Municipali-
ties, 1940.

　　18, iii l.　27 cm.
　　Cover title.
　　A report of the American Municipal Association reproduced by the
Canadian Federation of Mayors and Municipalities.　*cf.* Foreword.

　　1. Police—U. S.　I. Canadian Federation of Mayors and Municipalities.　II. Title.

　　HV8018.N3　　　　352.20973　　　　41–26479

NN　0056733　　DLC PPT PPULC

National League of Cities.
　　The municipal charter problem in Florida, prepared for
the Florida joint legislative committee and the Florida
League of Municipalities, by the American Municipal Association.　Chicago, Public Administration Service [*1937]

　　vi, 21 p.　27 cm.

　　"The field work and the preparation of this report have been done
for the American Municipal Association, by Mr. Donald C. Stone,
director ... [and others]"—p. iii.

　　1. Municipal government—Florida.　I. Stone, Donald Crawford,
1903–　II. Florida.　Legislature.　III. Florida League of Municipalities.　IV. Public Administration Service.　V. Title.

　　JS451.F65N36　　　　352.002　　　　38–3941

NcD N PPULC OrPR OrP Or
NN　0056734　　DLC TxU ICJ NmU CoDU ICRL OU OC1W OCU

National League of Cities.
　　Municipal police radio systems ...
　　　see under　American municipal association.

JW
+AM3
CUTTER　National League of Cities
　　The municipal position on current issues
involving intergovernmental relations (as
expressed in resolutions adopted at annual conventions held during 1947 by the state leagues of
municipalities and their national federation, the
American municipal association)　Chicago, 1948.
　　iii, 46 p.　28cm.　(Its Report no.164)

　　1. Municipal government.

NN　0056736　　WU

VOLUME 407

National League of Cities.
Municipalities and airport zoning ... Chicago, Ill., The American municipal association, 1941.
4 p. l., 2–15 numb. l., 3 l. 28 cm. *(Its Report no. 145)*
Reproduced from type-written copy.
"Publications of the American municipal association", including bulletins and reports with prices: 3 l. at end and p. ₍8₎ of cover.
Bibliographical foot-notes.

1. Airport zoning. I. Title. (Series)
[JS302.A66 no. 145]   A 41–2247
Northwestern Univ.   Library
for Library of Congress   ₍r69c2₎ rev

NN   0056737   IEN CU OC1W MH MH-SD PPULC DLC

National League of Cities.
Municipalities and the post-war, a statement by the Special Committee on Planning of the American Municipal Association, the federation of the State leagues of municipalities. Chicago, Ill., American Municipal Association ₍1944?₎
11 p. 23 cm.

1. Cities and towns—Planning—U. S. I. Title.
NA9108.N34   352.073   45–13416 rev

NN   0056738   DLC OrU CaBViP

National league of cities.
National municipal policy
see under title

JS302
.A65
National League of Cities. Papers presented at the annual conference.
American Municipal Congress.
Proceedings. 1st/2d–
1924/25–
Washington ₍etc.₎

National League of Cities.
Parking—what cities are doing. ₍Prepared by Arnold A. Sio. Chicago, 1949₎
17 p. 28 cm.
Bibliography: p. 17.
Published by the league under its earlier name: American Municipal Association.

1. Automobile parking—U. S. I. Sio, Arnold Anthony. II. Title.
HE371.A3N28   388.3   50–14179

NN   0056741   DLC Or CU NIC MiU CU

JS302
.A65
National League of Cities. Proceedings of the annual conference.
American Municipal Congress.
Proceedings. 1st/2d–
1924/25–
Washington ₍etc.₎

National League of Cities.
Report. no. 1–
₍Chicago, 1932–
no. 23–28 cm.
No. 1– issued by the league under its earlier name: American Municipal Association.
Some numbers issued in rev. editions.

1. Municipal government—U. S. 2. Municipal research.
JS302.A66   68–39943

NN   0056743   DLC NBuU

National League of Cities.
Report, together with the report of the executive director.
Chicago.
v. 28 cm. annual. *(Its Series AM. Report)*
Report year ends Sept. 30.
Began in 1932. Cf. Union list of serials.
Vols. for   issued by the league under its earlier name:
American Municipal Association.

(Series)

JS302.A674   58–51832

     ICRL PBm PPULC
NN   0056744   DLC CoU NN NNU TU OO OC1 MB MiD CtNIC

National League of Cities.
Requirements for publication of municipal ordinances ...
see under American municipal association.

National League of Cities.
Resolutions of the annual convention.
₍Chicago₎
v. 28 cm. *(Its Series AM. Report)*
Vols. for   issued by the league under its earlier name:
American Municipal Association.

(Series)

JS302.A68   43–28997

NN   0056746   DLC CoU

National League of Cities.
Restrictions upon the interest of municipal and other public officials in government contracts ... Chicago, Ill., The American municipal association, 1940.
3 p. l., 41 numb. l., 2 l. 28 cm. *(Its Report no. 135)*
Reproduced from type-written copy.
Bibliographical foot-notes.

1. Contracts. I. Title. (Series)
[JS302.A66 no. 135]   A 41–4724
Temple Univ. Library
for Library of Congress   ₍r69c2₎ rev

NN   0056747   PPT OC1W PPULC

JS
302
.N384
National League of Cities. Dept. of Urban Studies.
Staff report. no. 1–
Washington, D.C., 19 –

1. Municipal government-U.S.-Collections. 2. Cities and towns-U.S.-Collections. 3. U.S.-Soc. condit.-1945- -Collections.

NN   0056748   DAU

National League of Cities.
State-collected municipally-shared taxes ₍by Roy H. Owsley, assistant director. 2d ed.₎ Chicago, 1946.
iv, 37 l. 28 cm. *(Its Report no. 161)*
Published by the league under its earlier name: American Municipal Association.
———— 1948 supplement. Chicago, 1948.
15 l. 28 cm. *(Its Report no. 165)*
Published by the league under its earlier name: American Municipal Association.
JS302.A66 no. 165
1. Taxation, State. 2. Municipal finance—U. S. I. Owsley, Roy Hamilton, 1908– II. Title. (Series. Series: National League of Cities. Report no. 165)

JS302.A66 no. 161   336.2   48–581

NN   0056749   DLC UU Or MH WU PSt

National League of Cities.
The State leagues and the American Municipal Association. September 1, 1941 to September 1, 1942 ... ₍Chicago, 1942₎
69 l. 28 cm. *(Its Series AM. Report 27)*
Published by the league under its earlier name: American Municipal Association.

1. National League of Cities. 2. Municipal government—Societies, etc. I. Title. (Series)
JS302.N382   352.073   47–36194

NN   0056750   DLC CoU

National League of Cities.
Tax-delinquent vacant urban land
see under American municipal association.

351.1
Am35t   National League of Cities.
Toward competent government; the need for training public employees, a review of present methods, and proposals for future development. A report prepared...in cooperation with the International City Managers' Association and the Civil Service Assembly. Chicago, 1936.
4 p., l, ii, 39, 10 l. 28 cm.

1. U.S. – Officials and employees. I. Title.

NN   0056752   TxU

National League of Cities.
When a soldier breaks the law; facts and suggested procedures for State and local authorities. Chicago, American Municipal Association, 1941.
iii, 20 p. 21 x 10 cm.

1. Military law—U. S. 2. Criminal law—U. S. 3. Jurisdiction—U. S. I. Title.
UB500.N3   41–25868

NN   0056753   DLC PPULC

National League of Cities
see also its earlier name:
American Municipal Association.

National League of Colored Women.
First annual convention of the National League of Colored Women at the Fifteenth Street Presbyterian Church, Washington, D. C., July 14th, 15th and 16th, 1896. ₍Washington, 1896₎
₍20₎ p. ports. 26 cm.
L. C. copy replaced by microfilm.

1. National League of Colored Women. I. Title.
[E185.5.N29523]   322.4'4'06273   74–170145
Microfilm 60049 E

NN   0056755   DLC

National league of commission merchants of the United States
see
National league of wholesale fresh fruit and vegetable distributors.

National League of Compulsory Education Officials
see National League to Promote School Attendance.

National League of Girls' Clubs.   5572.134
The Association of Working Girls' Societies. [Annual meeting, 3rd. Reports, regulation, by-laws.]
[New York. 1887.] 22 pp. 23 cm.

H4216 — Working girls' clubs.

NN   0056758   MB

VOLUME 407

National League of Girls Clubs.
A brief history of the first decade of the National League of
Women Workers, 1898 to 1908. ₍Philadelphia, 1908?₎   24 p.
8°.

Cover-title.

555256A.   1. Working women—Assoc.   and org.—U. S.
N. Y. P. L.   November 23, 1931

NN 0056759   NN

National league of girls' clubs.
₍By-laws, etc.₎ ₍New York, n.d.₎
18 p.

NN 0056760   OO

National League of Girls Clubs.
The Club worker ...
see under title

₍National League of Girls Clubs.₎
History of the National League of Women Workers, 1914.
₍Brooklyn: The Pearl Press, 1914.₎   37 p.   8°.

Bibliography, p. 37.

1. Working women.—Assoc. and   organizations, U. S.
N. Y. P. L.   August 14, 1922.

NN 0056762   NN DL

National league of girls' clubs.
Miscellaneous pamphlets.

NN 0056763   DL

National League of Girls' Clubs.   396.06161 2
The National League of Women Workers. Summary of its
⁵⁰⁰¹⁹ work from 1898 to 1904. [Oswego, New York, The Radcliffe
Press, 1904.]
22, [2] p. 24ᶜᵐ.

NN 0056764   ICJ

National League of Girls' Clubs.
331.406   Report of proceedings. 1st-10th; 1890-1918.
N277R   Boston, Everett Press Co.
10 v.   23 cm.

Issued by the league under variant names:
1st, 1890 as Associations of Working Girls'
Societies; 2d, 1894 as National Convention of
Working Girls' Clubs; 3d, 1897 as National
Convention of Working Women's Clubs.
Vol. for 1894 includes Sixth annual reunion

of the Massachusetts Association of Working
Girls' Clubs
No more published?

1. Working-women's clubs.

NN 0056766   NcD DL MB

National League of Girls' Clubs.
(Report)
2d. 1886 1 v.

NN 0056767   DL

National League of Girls' Clubs.
Reports, by-laws.

NN 0056768   MB

National League of Government Employees.
Official manual and register...
19

₍Washington, D. C.? 19   4°.
v.   illus., ports.

1. Civil service, U. S.—Per. and   soc. publ.
N. Y. P. L.   April 25, 1924.

NN 0056769   NN OC1

National league of handicraft societies.

Handicraft; representing the arts and crafts movement.
v. 1–4, v. 5, no. 1–7; Apr. 1902–Oct. 1912. Boston, Society of arts and crafts, 1902–04; Montague, Mass., The
Dyke mill ₍etc.₎ 1910–12.

National league of Huguenot societies in the United States of
America.
Constitution. The National league of Huguenot societies in
the United States of America. Adopted May 19, 1924. ₍New
York? 1924₎   8 p.   23½cm.

1. No subject.
N. Y. P. L.   June 30, 1942

NN 0056771   NN WaT

National league of improvement associations

see

American league for civic improvement.

National league of industrial art.

NK25
.D35   ₍Daughters of the revolution. *Illinois*₎
Rare Bk.   The new industrialism. Part I. Industrial art, by Prof. Oscar
Coll.   L. Triggs. Part II. The future school, by Wilbur S. Jackman.
Part III. The art and craft of the machine, by Frank Lloyd
Wright. Chicago, National league of industrial art, 1902.

National League of Insured Savings Associations.
Membership directory.

Washington, D. C.

NN 0056774   OC1

National League of Insured Savings Associations.
Personnel relations handbook
see under Winsor, Harry B

National League of Insured Savings Associations.
Publicity handbook ...
see under Winsor, Harry B

National League of Insured Savings Associations. *Advisory Committee on Compensation.*
Compensation of executives and employees of savings and
loan associations; recommendations of Advisory Committee
on Compensation of the National Savings and Loan League.
Washington ₍1952₎

17 p.   23 cm.

1. Building and loan associations—U. S. 2. Executives—Salaries,
pensions, etc.—U. S.   I. Title.

HG2126.N3   332.32   53–17867 rev ‡

NN 0056777   DLC

National league of Japanese university
professors.
Essay series. no. 5–
₍Tokyo, 1938–

NN 0056778   OCU

National league of Japanese university professors.
The Japan China conflict and the attitude of Japan ₍by₎ the
National league of Japanese university professors. ₍Tokyo₎
The Nippon press, ltd., 1937₎
3 p. l., 3–53, ₍1₎ p. 1 illus., plates. 22½ᶜᵐ. (*Its* Pamphlets. vol. VII,
Dec. 1, 1937)
CONTENTS.—pt. I. Report on the conference held between the manage-
ment of the National league university professors and foreign
news correspondents.—pt. II. Prologue. Japan China relations and the
spirit of Japan. The Japan China conflict and the pro-communistic policy of China. Boycott and anti-Japanese movement. The attitude of
Japan. Officers of the National league of Japanese university professors.
1. China—Foreign relations—Japan. 2. Japan — Foreign relations—
China. 3. China—History—1937–   I. Title.
A 39–1049
New York univ. Wash. sq.   library DS777.53.N25
for Library of Congress   ₍2₎

NN 0056779   NNU-W OrU CtY CaBVaU

Wason   National League of Japanese University
DS783   Professors.
.7   An outline of the Manchurian problem; a
Z1   report made by the special committee of the
National League of Japanese University
Professors. [Tokyo, 1932]
2, 20 p. 22cm.

In vol. lettered: Manchuria pamphlets.

1. Manchuria.   2. Japanese in Manchuria.

NN 0056780   NIC

National League of Japanese University Professors.
Pamphlet. 1, 1932–

NN 0056781   KyU

National League of Japanese University Professors.
The real nature of Japan and the Japanese
see under ₍Honaga, Mosuke₎

NATIONAL LEAGUE OF JAPANESE UNIVERSITY PRO-
FESSORS.
The relations between Japanese national traits
and Buddhism. Tokyo, Japan, 1933.

pp. (2), v1, (2), 17.
"Pamphlet, 3."

NN 0056783   MH

National league of Japanese university professors.
Studies in the sociology and economics in Japan ... ₍Tokyo₎
The National league of Japanese university professors ₍1940₎
3 p. l., 89, ₍1₎ p. 22ᶜᵐ. (*Its* Essay series, no. 5)
CONTENTS.—The biological basis of our country's existence, by Prof.
K. Nakazawa.—The guiding spirit of our foreign diplomacy, by the late
Dr. Ujiro Oyama.—The real import of the Ten-no government, by Prof.
Takehiko Murase.—Japan's financial and economic conditions in the
present China affair, by Prof. Masutaro Kimura.

1. Japan—Nationality. 2. Japan—For. rel. 3. Japan—Econ. condit.
I. Title.
Brown univ. Library   A 41–4206
for Library of Congress   ₍3₎

NN 0056784   RPB MH CtY ViU CaBVaU OOxM OrU

VOLUME 407

National League of Jewish Combatants
    see   Reichsbund jüdischer Frontsoldaten.

National League of Masonic Clubs.   *7560a.69
   [Souvenir programme.] Annual convention. 18th   June, 1923.
Boston. 1923. v. Illus. Portraits. Plates. 26 cm.

Contains a guide to the city in which the convention is held.

M6798 — Freemasonry. United States. Conventions.

NN   0056786   MB

National league of Masonic clubs
   Twenty-fourth national convention, Cleveland,
Ohio, June 6-7-8, 1929.
   72 p.

NN   0056787   OCl

National league of Masonic clubs. Educational foun-
HS499   dation.
.N3   [The Educational foundation] [1926?]

NN   0056788   DLC

National League of Mineral Painters.
   Monthly review. February, 1894.   New York,
Acton publishing company, 1894.
   pamphlet. illus.

NN   0056789   PPPM

**National league of musicians of the United
States.**
American music journal. Pub. under the auspices of the
Musical mutual protective union, of the city of New
York, and devoted to the interests of the musical pro-
fession of America. v. 1, v. 2, no. 1–15; Dec. 6, 1884–
Apr. 24, 1886. New York, 1884–86.

National league of musicians of the United
   tates.
The **American** musician and American music journal ...
   v. 1–
Dec. 6, 1884–
New York, 1884–

HFBM95   National League of Musicians of the United
.N213   States.
MIS   Constitution and by-laws. [n.p.]   –
      v. 14½cm.

   Library has:

      184–   issued under prior name of the
   organization: Musical Mutual Protective Union.
      Certain constitutions also contained in
the organizations   Proceedings.

NN   0056792   WHi

NATIONAL LEAGUE OF MUSICIANS OF THE UNITED STATES
   [MISCELLANEA: CONSTITUTIONS, REPORTS, ETC.]
I.–
PHILADELPHIA, ETC.,

      v.   35CM.

NN   0056793   MdBJ

National League of Musicians of the United
States
   Official souvenir, eighth annual conven-
tion, and report of the national secretary.
Russell House, Detroit, Mich., convening
May 9th, 10th, 11th, 12th, 1893. Phila-
delphia, General Secretary's Office [1893]
[44] p. illus., ports.

   Advertisements interspersed.

   1. Music – Societies

NN   0056794   MiD

HFBM95   National League of Musicians of the United
.N213   States.
MIS   Proceedings.   –   , 18   –
      v. 18-19cm.

   Library has:

      1. Musicians – U.S. – Societies.

NN   0056795   WHi MiD

HFBM95   National League of Musicans of the United
.N213   States. Local no. 24, Cleveland.
MIS   Constitution and by-laws. M[usical]
   M[utual] P[rotective] A[ssociation] of
C[leveland, Ohio. October, 1893. Local 24,
N[ational] L[eague] of M[usicians of the]
U[nited] S[tates].   [Cleveland? 1893?]
   32 p. 14½cm.

NN   0056796   WHi

National League of Nursing Education.
   Organized 1893 as American Society of
Superintendents of Training Schools for Nurses.
Name changed 1912 to National League of Nursing
Education.
   Merged 1952 with other organizations to form
National League for Nursing.

National league of nursing education.

Pfefferkorn, Blanche.
   Administrative cost analysis for nursing service and **nursing**
education; a study to develop methods for finding out the **costs**
of nursing service and nursing education, sponsored by the
American hospital association and the National league of nursing education in cooperation with the American nurses' association; Blanche Pfefferkorn ... director of study ... Charles A.
Rovetta ... associate director of study ... Chicago, Ill., American hospital association; New York, N. Y., National league of
nursing education [*1940]

National League of Nursing Education.

The **American** journal of nursing. v. 1–
Oct. 1900–
New York [etc.]

National League of Nursing Education.
   Annual report and record of proceedings of the
convention
      see its   Proceedings of the ... annual
convention.

National League of Nursing Education.
   Bibliographies on nursing: books, pamphlets, **articles,**
audio-visual aids. New York, National League of Nursing
Education, Dept. of Services to Schools of Nursing, 1952–

      v. 28 cm.

"Successor to the major bibliographies published by the National
League of Nursing Education between 1937 and 1948, the later editions
of which were entitled 'Books suggested for libraries in schools of
nursing.'"
   Vols. 2 and 10 published by the League; v. 5 published by its Division of Nursing Education.
   1. Nurses and nursing—Bibl.   I. Title.

Z6675.N7B5   016.61   53–2371

      NcD-N IdPI
NN   0056801   DLC DNLM ViU OU MiU NNC DNLM CU

ZWY   NATIONAL League of Nursing Education
160   Bibliography [of] psychiatric nursing
qN277b   and mental hygiene. New York, 1949.
1949   49 ℓ.   ZWY160 qN277b
      A by-product of the study of **advanced**
programs of study in psychiatric
nursing and mental hygiene made by the
National League of Nursing Education
and the National Organization for Public
Health Nursing.

      1. Mental hygiene – Bibl.
      2. Nursing - Psychiatric - Bibl.
   I. National Organization for Public
Health Nursing

NN   0056803   DNLM MiU OrU-M

National league of nursing education.
   Bibliography on curriculum. New York,
National league of nursing education, 1950.
   26 p. mimeos.

NN   0056804   OrU-M

RC311   National League of Nursing Education.
.8   Bibliography on tuberculosis nursing. New York, Distri-
A12N4 buted by National League for Nursing, inc., Tuberculosis
1952   Nursing Advisory Service [1952?]
Public   53-70 p. (Its Bibliographies on nursing, v. 6)
Health
Library   "Reprinted."

RC311   --- ------ Supplement. New York, National League for
.8   Nursing, Division of Nursing Education, 1955.
A12N4   70a - 70m p. (Bound with the above)

NN   0056805   CU PU-Med-TS

920   **National league of nursing education**
N213b   [Biographical sketches of 40 nurses.] **New**
   York. The national league of nursing education,
   [1939]
      160 p. ports.

NN   0056806   WaPS CU PPWM

National League of Nursing Education.
   Books suggested for libraries in schools of
nursing
      see under   National League of Nursing
Education. Committee on the Nursing School
Library.

WY   NATIONAL League of Nursing Education
19   Clinical nursing courses offered to
qN277c   graduate professional nurses. New York,
1951   1951.
      [19] ℓ.
      Caption title.
      1. Nursing schools - U. S. - Direct.

NN   0056808   DNLM OrU-M NcU

WY   NATIONAL League of Nursing Education
18   [Collection of publications]
qN277
      The Library has a collection of mis-
cellaneous publications of this **organization**
kept as received. These publications **are**
not listed nor bound separately.
      1. Nursing - Study and teaching

NN   0056809   DNLM

National League of Nursing Education.
   Communicable disease control

   see under

   Heidgerken, Loretta Elizabeth, 1908–

VOLUME 407

National League of Nursing Education.
The contribution of Physical therapy to
nursing education ...
see under   National League of Nursing
Education. Committee on Curriculum.

National league of nursing education.
Cumulative index to the annual reports, 1894-1939,
compiled by D. Maxine Bailey. ₍The Author₎
1940.
93 p.

I. Bailey, Dorothy Maxine, 1915-

NN   0056812   MiD MiDP MiDW

National League for Nursing Education.
Current issues in nursing education.   New York
[c1922]
illus.
Includes bibliography.
1. Nurses and nursing. Addresses, essays,
lectures. 2. Nursing as a profession. I. Title.

NN   0056813   ScU

National League of Nursing Education.
Descriptions of eight collegiate basic programs in nursing.
New York, 1952.
57 l. 28 cm.

1. Nurses and nursing—Study and teaching.   I. Title.

RT71.N243   610.7307   55-18772 ‡

NN   0056814   DLC CaBVaU DNLM MtBC

₍National league of nursing education₎
Early leaders of American nursing. ₍New York, The
National league of nursing education, ¹1922₎
cover-title, ₍25₎ p. illus. (ports.) 23ᶜᵐ.
"This little booklet preserves in more permanent form the photographs
and biographical sketches which originally appeared in the Nursing calendar
of 1922."—Foreword.

1. Nurses and nursing.   I. Title.

Library of Congress   RT34.N3

                                                    23-4521

                    OC1 OC1W
NN   0056815   DLC CaBVaU NcD KU-M OrCS WaT ICJ

National league of nursing education.
Early leaders of American nursing ... ₍New
York City, The National league of nursing education, 1922₎-24.
3 v.in 1. ports. 21ᶜᵐ.
Illustrated covers.
Vols.₍2-3₎ have title: Leaders of American nursing.
"Preserves in more permanent form the photographs
and biographical sketches which originally appeared
in the Nursing calendar."--Foreword,v.₍1₎
Prepared by the Publications committee of the National league of nursing education. cf.Foreword,v.₍2-3₎
1.Nurses and nursing--Biog. I.Title.

NN   0056816   MiU MiD NcD-MC OC1

National League of Nursing Education.
Essentials of a good school of nursing
see under   National league of nursing
education. Committee on standards.

920.61   National League of Nursing Education
N21f   ₍Famous nurses. New York, National League
of Nursing Education, n.d.₎
1 v. illus.

NN   0056818   MtBC

WY   NATIONAL League of Nursing Education
18   Guidance programs for schools of
qN277g   nursing.   New York, 1945.
1945   90 l.
1. Nursing - Study & teaching

NN   0056819   DNLM

RT71   National League of Nursing Education.
.N37
1946   **National Nursing Council.**
A guide for the organization of collegiate schools of nursing, prepared by National Nursing Council for War Service
and Association of Collegiate Schools of Nursing, 1942. Rev.
by National League of Nursing Education, 1946. New York,
National League of Nursing Education, 1946.

National League of Nursing Education.
Handbook for career counselors on the
profession of nursing
see under   National league of nursing
education. Committee on Vocational Guidance.

RT51   **National League of Nursing Education.**
.A63
1950   **American Hospital Association.**
Hospital nursing service manual, prepared by a committee
of the American Hospital Association and the National
League of Nursing Education, with the assistance of Stella
Goostray. New York, National League of Nursing Education, 1950.

National League of Nursing Education.
How the N. L. N. E. serves you.   New York,
National league of nursing education, 1937.
cover-title, 15 p.   25 cm.

NN   0056823   NcD

W 6   NATIONAL League of Nursing Education
P3   Inventory and qualifications of
psychiatric nurses: report on the questionnaire study of the Psychiatric
Nursing Project of the National League
of Nursing Education, April, 1950.
Prepared by Aurelie J. Nowakowski.
New York, 1950.
68 p.   W6 P3
1. Nursing - Psychiatric - Study &
teaching 2. Nursing - Statistics - U. S.
I. Nowakowski, Aurelie J

NN   0056824   DNLM OrU-M NcU

National league of nursing education.
Leaders of American nursing
see its   Early leaders of American
nursing.

National League of Nursing Education.
The league exchange ...
see under   National League for Nursing.

National League of Nursing Education.
A library handbook for schools of nursing ...
see under   National League for Nursing.

D610.73
N21
National league of nursing education.
.... List of accredited schools of nursing.
New York, 1943.
1 p. l., 9, ₍1₎ p. 15ᶜᵐ.

1. Nurses and nursing - Study and teaching.

NN   0056828   NNC

National league of nursing education.
List of accredited schools of nursing. ₍1944-
New York, 1944-
nos. 15½ᶜᵐ. annual.

1. Nurses and nursing—Study and teaching. 2. Nurses and nursing—
U. S.

Library of Congress   RT71.N245
                                                    44-53417
                            ₍2₎   610.73071173

NN   0056829   DLC

National League of Nursing Education.
A list of schools of nursing meeting minimum requirements set by law and board rules in the various states and
territories
see
National League for Nursing.
State approved schools of professional nursing.

TX551   **National League of Nursing Education.**
.A483
American Dietetic Association.
A manual for teaching dietetics to student nurses. Authors: Professional Education Committee; consultants: The
National League of Nursing Education. Philadelphia, W. B.
Saunders Co., 1949.

National League of Nursing Education.
Manual for the nursing school library
see under   National League of Nursing
Education. Committee on the Nursing School
Library.

National league of nursing education.

                                            FOR OTHER EDITIONS
                                            SEE MAIN ENTRY
American hospital association.
Manual of the essentials of good hospital nursing service,
prepared by Division on nursing of the Council of the American hospital association and Committee of the National league
of nursing education; revised by Joint committee of the American hospital association, National league of nursing education,
American college of surgeons, American nurses' association,
American medical association. Chicago, Ill., American hospital association; New York, N. Y., National league of nursing
education, 1942.   OTHER EDITIONS UNDER AUTHOR

National league of nursing education.
Nurse leaders. ₍Portraits and biographies of
forty leaders in nursing₎ ...
see its   ₍Biographical sketches of 40 nurses₎

National league of nursing education.

Nurse practice acts and board rules; a digest. New York,
N. Y., American nurses' association, National league of nursing education, 1940.

National league of nursing education.

RT71   **American nurses' association.** *Nursing information bureau.*
.A53   Nursing, a profession for college women, 1945. The Nursing
information bureau of the American nurses' association cooperating with the National league of nursing education and
the National organization for public health nursing ... New
York, N. Y. ₍1945₎

National league of nursing education.
Nursing and the registered nurse
see under   American nurses' association.
Nursing information bureau.

VOLUME 407

National League of Nursing Education.
Nursing during disaster...
see under   National League of Nursing
Education. Dept. of Services to Schools of Nursing.

National league of nursing education.

RT71
.N77

Nursing education in wartime.   Bulletin no. 1-14; Nov. 19,
1942–June 6, 1945.   New York, N. Y., National league of
nursing education ₁1942₁–45.

National league of nursing education.
Practical nurse education
see under   National League for Nursing
Education. Committee on Practical Nurse
Education.

TX551
.A484

National league of nursing education.

American dietetic association.
Preliminary test form manual for teaching nutrition and
dietetics to student nurses, 1943–1944.   Chicago, Ill., The
American dietetic association. ⁰1944.

National league of nursing education.
Procedure for establishing an affiliation...
see under   National League of Nursing
Education. Committee on Records.

National league of nursing education.
Proceedings of the ... annual convention

Springfield, Mass.,
v. 24½ cm.

1. Nurses and nursing—Soc. 2. Nurses and nursing—Study and
teaching.
RT1.N3   CA 13—1889 Unrev'd

    DHEW WU-M TU-M NcU-H OU ICRL WaSpG MtBC MB CaOTU
NN 0056843   DLC LNL OU DNLM NBuG MiU ICJ OCl ViU

National league of nursing education.

Spalding, *Mrs.* **Eugenia (Kennedy) 1896–**
Professional adjustments in nursing, for senior students and
graduates, by Eugenia Kennedy Spalding ... 21 illustrations.
Philadelphia ₁etc.₁ J. B. Lippincott company ₁1940₁

RT71
N26

National League of Nursing Education.
Programs leading to a degree for graduate
nurses in universities and colleges.   ₁New
York₁ 1951.
22 p.

Caption title.
"For administrators, teachers, supervisors,
and head nurses in professional schools of
nursing, nursing service, and public health
nursing, and for administrators and teachers
in schools of practical nursing."

NN 0056845   CU OrU-M ICU IU

RT51
N21

National league of nursing education.
The pupil nurse in the out-patient department;
a study of the nurse and nursing services in
the out-patient department. Committee in
charge: Amelia Grant, chairman, Janet M.
Geister, Mary B. Hulsizer ... ₁and others₁
New York₁ National league of nursing education,
1925.
30 p.   21½ᶜᵐ.

1. Hospitals – Staff – Nurses. 2. Hospitals –
Out-patient service. I. Title.

NN 0056846   NNC OClW NN ICJ

National League of Nursing Education.
Report, 1953-1955
see   National League for Nursing.
Reports to the members.

National League of Nursing Education.
Report and proceedings ...
see its   Proceedings of the ... annual
convention.

RT3
.A52

National League of Nursing Education.

American Nurses' Association.
Report of conference of State boards of nurse examiners.

New York ₁etc.₁

National League of Nursing Education.
Report of proceedings of conference,
December 3, 4, 5, 1949 ...
see under   Joint Nursing Curriculum
Conference, New York, 1950.

National League of Nursing Education.
Report of the conference on advanced programs
in psychiatric and mental health nursing ...
see under   Conference on Advanced
Programs in Psychiatric and Mental Health
Nursing, University of Cincinnati, 1951.

National league of nursing education.
Review. Michigan. ₁Author, 1924₁
88 p. illus., port.

Cover title.

NN 0056852   MiD

WY
19
qN277sh
1951

NATIONAL League of Nursing Education
Schools of nursing admitting men
students. New York, 1951.
5 p. ...
Caption title.
1. Nursing schools – U. S. – Direct.

NN 0056853   DNLM

WY
19
qN277so
1951

NATIONAL League of Nursing Education
Schools of nursing admitting Negro
students. New York, 1951.
8 p.
Caption title.
1. Nursing schools – U. S. – Direct.

NN 0056854   DNLM

610.73
N21s

National League of Nursing Education.
Schools of nursing offering undergraduate
programs leading to a degree.   New York,
1950.
55p. 22cm.

1. Nurses and nursing—Study and teaching—U.S.

NN 0056855   IU DNLM

A Ref 2
ZWT71
N33
1952

NATIONAL League of Nursing Education.
Source materials in nursing education.
No. 1. [New York] 1952.
57p. 23cm.
No more published?
Prepared by the Committee on Early
Nursing Source Materials; I.M. Stewart,
chairman.

1. Nurses and nursing – Study and
teaching – Bibliography I. Stewart,
Isabel Maitla   nd II. National
League of Nur   sing Education.

Committee on Early Nursing Source
Materials III. Title

NN 0056857   CtY-M CU-M WU-M DCU MtBC

National League of Nursing Education.
State-approved schools of nursing
see
National League for Nursing.
State approved schools of professional nursing; schools
meeting minimum requirements set by law and board
rules in the various states and territories.

National league of nursing education.
Statement of policy for the accreditation of schools of nursing. ₁New York₁ National league of nursing education, 1944.
1 p. l., 8 p. 23ᶜᵐ.
"National league of nursing education. Committee on the administration of the accrediting program. Statement of fees": leaf inserted.

1. Nurses and nursing—Study and teaching.   I. Title: Accreditation
of schools of nursing.

Library of Congress   RT71.N27   45–4594
                           ₁3₁   610.7307

NN 0056859   DLC

RT55
.M3

National league of nursing education.

McManus, Rachel Louise (Metcalfe)
Study guide on evaluation; suggestions for faculty commit-
tees and other groups studying evaluation in nursing, prepared
by R. Louise McManus ... Printed with the approval of the
Committee on measurement and educational guidance. New
York, N. Y., National league of nursing education, 1944.

WY
160
qN275s
1953

NATIONAL League of Nursing Education
A study of desirable functions and
qualifications for psychiatric nurses,
conducted by Claire Mintzer Fagin.
₁New York₁ National League for Nursing,
Division of Nursing Education, 1953.
104 ℓ.
A joint project, conducted by the
National League of Nursing Education and
the National Organization for Public Health
Nursing.

1. Nursing - Psychiatric I. Fagin,
Claire Mintzer II. National League for
Nursing. Division of Nursing Education
III. National Organization for Public
Health Nursing

NN 0056862   DNLM PU-Med-TS DCU NcU

National league of nursing education.

**Joint committee on the costs of nursing service and nursing
education.**
A study of the incidence and costs of illness among nurses
₁by₁ Joint committee on the costs of nursing service and nursing education of the American hospital association, National
league of nursing education, American nurses' association;
issued by the American hospital association, June, 1938. ₁New
York₁ 1939₁

National League of Nursing Education.
A study on the use of the graduate nurse for
bedside nursing in the hospital
see under   National league of nursing
education. Dept. of studies.

VOLUME 407

National League of Nursing Education.
    Suggested outline for the teaching of veneral
disease nursing ...
        see under   Veneral Disease Work
Conference, Alto Medical Center, Alto, Ga. , 1952

National League of Nursing Education.
    Visual aids for use in schools of nursing ...
        see under   National League of Nursing
Education. Committee on Audio-Visual Aids.

National League of Nursing Education.
    Withdrawal of students ...
        see under   Taylor, Ella A.

National League of Nursing Education
    see also
American Nurses' Association. *Nursing Information
Bureau.*
Committee of the Six National Nursing Organizations on
    Unification of Accrediting Activities.
Committee on the Structure of National Nursing Organi-
    zations.
Joint Committee of the American Nurses' Association and
    National League of Nursing Education.

National League of Nursing Education
    see also   Joint Committee of the National
League of Nursing Education and the National
Organization for Public Health Nursing and Inte-
gration of the Social and Health Aspects of
Nursing in the Basic Curriculum.

National League of Nursing Education.
    see also
Joint Orthopedic Nursing Advisory Service of the Na-
    tional Organization for Public Health Nursing and the
    National League of Nursing Education.
National League for Nursing.
Structure Steering Committee.

National league of nursing education. Com-
    mittee on audio-visual aids.
    Films, filmslides, and slides as visual-
teaching aids in schools of nursing; some
suggestions for their selection and use.
New York, National league of nursing education, 1946.
    18 ℓ.

    Loretta Heidgerken, chairman.
    "References on audio-visual instructions":
ℓ. 17-18.

NN   0056871   NNC

RT   National League of Nursing Education. Committee
71   on Audio-Visual Aids.
.N367
        Visual aids for use in schools of nursing;
    graphic aids, objects, models, specimens, and
    pamphlets, some suggestions for their selection
    and use. New York, National League of Nursing
    Education, 1947.

        16 p.   25 cm.

        Lists sources of audio-visual materials.

        1. Nurses and   nursing - Study and
    teaching. 2. Visual education. I. Title.

NN   0056872   NBuC OrU-M

National League of Nursing Education--Committee
    on Careers.
        Careers in nursing; handbook for counselors.
    ₍Text by Edith Patton Lewis.   New York,
    1954?₎
        22p. illus. 26cm.

NN   0056873   IU

National league of nursing education. Committee on
    curriculum.
    Bulletin no. 1-4-6, 8-7
(New York) Pub. by the Committee on education of the
National league of nursing education, 1920.
        6 v.   23 cm
For contents see main card.

NN   0056874   DL OrCS

National League of Nursing Education. *Committee on Cur-*
riculum.
    The contribution of physical therapy to nursing educa-
tion, prepared by the Subcommittee on the Utilization of
Special Therapists in the Teaching of Student Nurses. **New**
York, 1948.
        78 p.   16 x 23 cm.
        Bibliography: p. 65-73. "Visual aid materials": p. 74-78.

        1. Nurses and nursing—Study and teaching. 2. Physical therapy.
    I. Title.

        RT71.N277   610.7307   50-3922

NN   0056875   DLC DNLM NNU-M ViU OrU-M WaSpG

National league of nursing education. *Committee on curriculum.*
    A curriculum for schools of nursing, prepared by the Com-
mittee on education of the National league of nursing education. 6th ed., rev. 1927. New York, N. Y., National league of
nursing education, 1927.
        227 p.   23½ᶜᵐ.
        Previously issued under title: Standard curriculum for schools of
    nursing.
        Bibliography : p. 190-208.

        1. Nurses and nursing—Study and teaching.
                                            27-2496 Revised

        Library of Congress   RT71.N35 1927

NN   0056876   DLC IaU NcD WU-M ICRL CaBVaU IdPI
        ICJ TxU OU OC1W OCI MiU ICJ WaU

National league of nursing education. *Committee on curriculum*
    A curriculum for schools of nursing, prepared by the Com-
mittee on education of the National league of nursing education. 7th ed., rev. 1927, reprinted 1929. New York, N. Y.,
National league of nursing education, 1929.
        237 p.   24ᶜᵐ.
        Bibliography : p. 199-218.

        1. Nurses and nursing—Study and teaching.
                                            29-14320 Revised

        Library of Congress   RT71.N35 1929

NN   0056877   DLC TU ICJ OU OC1W OCI DNLM MCR

National league of nursing education. *Committee on curriculum.*
    A curriculum for schools of nursing, prepared by the Com-
mittee on education of the National league of nursing education. 7th ed., rev. 1927, reprinted ... 1932 New York, N. Y.,
National league of nursing education, 1932.
        236 p.   23½ cm.
        Bibliography : p. 195-218.
        Previously issued under title: Standard curricu-
    lum for schools of nursing.

NN   0056878   ViU MiU OU ICRL

National league of nursing education. *Committee on cur-*
riculum.
    A curriculum guide for schools of nursing, prepared by
the Committee on curriculum of the National league of nursing education ... Second revision, 1937. New York, N. Y.,
National league of nursing education, 1937.
        xiii, 689 p. diagrs. 21 cm.
        "Prepared ... under the immediate direction of ... Isabel M. Stew-
    art."—Foreword.
        First published in 1917 under title: Standard curriculum for
    schools of nursing.
        Includes bibliographies.

                    Continued in next column

                    Continued from preceding column

—— Illustrative materials for use in nursing schools; a supplement to A curriculum guide for nursing schools. Prepared by the Subcommittee on illustrative materials of the
Curriculum committee, National league of nursing education. New York, N. Y., 1937.
    61 p. 23 cm.
    Includes bibliographies.   RT71.N279 1937 Suppl.
    1. Nursing schools—U. S. I. Stewart, Isabel Maitland.

    RT71.N279 1937   38—38300

        OrLgE OrU-M MtU MiU
        NcD TU OC1W CU DNLM ICRL MCR CaBVaU MtBC Or OrCS
NN   0056880   DLC OC1W CtY-M OU MiHM DL ViU NcU PV

National league of nursing education. *Committee on curriculum.*

    A curriculum guide for schools of nursing, prepared by the
Committee on curriculum of the National league of nursing
education ... Second revision, 1937. New York, N. Y., National league of nursing education, 1937. ₍i. e. 1958₎
    xiii, 689 p. diagrs. 21ᶜᵐ.
        "Prepared ... under the immediate direction of ... Isabel M. Stew-
    art."—Foreword. "Third printing, October 1958."

NN   0056881   ViU

National League of Nursing Education. Committee
    on Curriculum.
    A curriculum guide for schools of nursing,
prepared by the Committee on curriculum of the
National league of nursing education ...   Second
revision, 1937.   New York, N. Y., National
league of nursing education, 1937 [i. e. 1943]
    xii, 689 p.   diagrs.   21 cm.
    "Prepared ... under the immediate direction
of ... Isabel M. Stewart." Foreword.
    Previously published under titles: Standard
curriculum for schools of nursing and A curriculum
for schools of nursing.

    Includes bibliographies.
    "Copyright 1937 ... fourth printing ... 1943.'

NN   0056883   NcD MiDP

WY   National League of Nursing Education.
163   Committee on Curriculum.
N2771   Instructional plan for basic tuberculosis
1949   nursing, prepared by the Subcommittee on
        Tuberculosis Nursing of the Committee on
        Curriculum, co-sponsored by the Joint
        Tuberculosis Nursing Advisory Service of
        the National League of Nursing Education
        [et al.] New York, 1949.
            58 p. 26 cm.
            Includes bibliography.
            1. Education.   Nursing. 2. Tuberculosis
            - nursing. I.   Joint Tuberculosis Nursing
        Advisory Service.   II. Title.

NN   0056884   WU-M DNLM NcU MiU NNC-M MtBC OrU-M

National league of nursing education. Committee
    on Curriculum.
    List of books suggested for libraries in
schools of nursing ...
        see under   National league of nursing
education. Committee on the nursing school
library.

National league of nursing education. *Committee on curriculum.*
    The nursing school faculty; duties, qualifications, and prep-
aration, prepared by the Education committee of the National
league of nursing education. New York city ₍1933₎
        123 p. 22½ᶜᵐ.
        "All members of the Education committee serving between 1927 and
    1933 shared in this study."—p. 3.
        Bibliography : p. 119-123.

        1. Nurses and nursing—Study and teaching.   I. Title.

        Library of Congress   RT71.N34   33-16081 Revised
        Copyright A 62931   ₍r39d2₎   610.73

NN   0056886   DLC NcD WU DNLM IaU MiU OU

VOLUME 407

National League of Nursing Education. Committee
on *curriculum.*
The out-patient department in the education
of the nurse ...
see under Knapp, Louise.

National league of nursing education. Committee,
on *curriculum.*
Preliminary report of university. Schools of
nursing... prepared by the Committee on education
of the National league of nursing education.
New York city, The Association ₍192₋₎
20 p. 22.5

NN 0056888 OU CaBVaU

National league of nursing education. *Committee on curriculum.*
Spalding, *Mrs.* Eugenia (Kennedy) 1896–
Professional adjustments in nursing; being Professional adjustments II, by Eugenia Kennedy Spalding ... Philadelphia
₍etc.₎ J. B. Lippincott company ₍c1939₎

National league of nursing education. *Committee on curriculum.*
Standard curriculum for schools of nursing, prepared by
the Committee on education of the National league of nursing education. M. Adelaide Nutting, chairman, Isabel M.
Stewart, secretary ... ₍etc.₎ Baltimore, The Waverly press
₍1918?₎
166 p. 24 cm.
"In sending out this curriculum, the Committee desires to emphasize afresh its hope that there will be no failure to understand its purpose. It is not offered as a "model" curriculum. There are many improvements which we would gladly introduce if we could see any

possibility of putting them into effect at the present time. Moreover,
the Committee is not urging the unqualified adoption of this curriculum in training schools generally ... There is little doubt that the next
few years will see many new developments along nursing lines. It is
the intention of the Committee to keep the curriculum up to date by
frequent revision, and so supplement the material in this first edition
from time to time."—Introd.
CONTENTS.—Introduction.—Relation of hospital and training school
organization and administration to the curriculum.— Course of
study.—Outline of subject.—Appendix I. List of inexpensive and free

bulletins, pamphlets, and reports for use in training schools.—Appendix II. List of firms supplying equipment and illustrative material for
training schools.—Appendix III. Suggestions for physical exercises for
nurses in training.—Appendix IV. Suggested basis of credit for nursing
schools.—Appendix V. Schemes of practical training for college students receiving credit of 8-12 months for satisfactory previous work
in science.—Appendix VI. Hour schedules for hospitals in which an
eight-hour day is in operation.
1. Nurses and nursing—Study and teaching.
S G 18–103 rev
U. S. Army Medical Libr.
for Library of Congress   ₍r50c₎₎

NN 0056892 DNLM TU CU ICRL ICJ WaS OrU-M

National league of nursing education. *Committee on curriculum.*
Standard curriculum for schools of nursing, prepared by
the Committee on education of the National league of nursing education. 1915 to 1918. M. Adelaide Nutting, chairman, Isabel M. Stewart, secretary ... ₍Baltimore, The Waverly press, 1919₎
177 p. 24 cm.
Bibliography : p. 157–168.
1. Nurses and nursing—Study and teaching.

RT71.N279 1919   19–4786 rev 3

OC1W DHEW
NN 0056893 DLC CaBVaU MtBC OrCS IaU DNLM NcD

NATIONAL LEAGUE OF NURSING EDUCATION. Committee on *curriculum.*
Standard curriculum for schools of nursing, prepared
by the Committee on education of the National league
of nursing education (1915 to 1918) M. Adelaide Nutting, Chairman... ₍Baltimore, 1920₎
178 p. 24cm.
"Third edition."
Bibliography: p.157–167.
1. Nurses and nursing—Study and teaching.

NN 0056894 ICU NcD Vi MB MiU

NATIONAL LEAGUE OF NURSING EDUCATION.
Committee *on curriculum.*
Standard curriculum for schools of nursing,
prepared by the Committee on education of the
National league of nursing education. 1915
to 1917. M. Adelaide Nutting, chairman ...
Isabel M. Stewart, secretary ... ₍New York,
1924, c1919₎
177p. 24cm.
Later published under titles: A curriculum
for schools of nursing; A curriculum guide
for schools of nursing.
Bibliography: p.157–168.
1. Nurses   and nursing - Study and
teaching.

NN 0056895 TxU NcD

National League of Nursing Education. *Committee on Curriculum.*
Suggestions for content and instruction in orthopedic
nursing. Prepared by the Subcommittee to Study Supplementary Courses in Orthopedic Nursing. New York, 1950.
55 p. 23 cm.
Bibliography: p. 34–42. "Visual aid materials": p. 43–46.

1. Orthopedic nursing.

RD737.N35   617.3073   50—4113

NN 0056896 DLC ICU WU-M NcU MtBC OrU OrU-M

National League of Nursing Education. *Committee on Curriculum. Subcommittee on the Library*
see National League of Nursing Education. *Committee on the Nursing School Library.*

National League of Nursing Education. Committee
on Early Nursing Source Materials.
Source materials in nursing education
see under National League of Nursing
Education.

National League of Nursing Education. *Committee on Education*
see National League of Nursing Education. *Committee on Curriculum.*

National league of nursing education. *Committee on educational problems in wartime.*
Problems of collegiate schools of nursing offering basic
professional programs ... Prepared by Committee on educational problems in wartime. New York, N. Y., National
league of nursing education, 1945.
viii, 55 p. illus. (diagrs.) 23 cm.
"A study based on discussions at the nine regional conferences on
nursing education in colleges and universities held in 1944, under the
sponsorship of the National league of nursing education and the Association of collegiate schools of nursing with the co-operation of the
American Council on education."

"Programs of regional conferences on nursing education in colleges
and universities" : p. ₍33₎–52.
"Selected references" : p. ₍53₎–55.

1. Nurses and nursing—Study and teaching.   I. Title.
RT71.N28   610.73   S G 46—301
U. S. National Library   of Medicine
for Library of Congress   ₍a60e₎₎†

NN 0056901 DNLM ViU DLC MtBC CaBVaU WU-M InU

National League of Nursing Education.
Committee on Guides for the Development
of Libraries in Schools of Nursing.
Guide for the development of libraries in
schools of nursing. ₍New York₎ National
League for Nursing, Division of Nursing
Education, 1952.
13 1. 30 1/2 cm.
Includes bibliography.
1. Libraries, Nursing. I. National League for
Nursing. Division of Nursing Education. II. Title.
₍1. Libraries, Nursing school₎

NN 0056902 WU-M NNC DCU TxU DNLM OrU-M Or CaBVaU

National league of nursing education. Committee on
mental hygiene and psychiatric nursing
see National league of nursing education.
Committee on psychiatric nursing.

National League of Nursing Education. Committee
on Nursing Curricula.
A check list on abilities needed by nurses,
with suggestions for continued curriculum study.
New York, 1951.
15 p. 22 x 28cm.
1. Nurses and nursing. I. Title. II. Title:
Abilities needed by nurses. III. Title: Nurses,
A check list on abilities needed by.

NN 0056904 DCU

National League of Nursing Education. Committee
on Postgraduate Clinical Nursing Courses.
Courses in clinical nursing for graduate
nurses. Pamphlet, no. 1-6. New York, 1945-48.
6 pts. in 1 v. 23 cm.
Contents: pt. 1. Basic assumptions and
guiding principles. Basic courses. Advanced
courses.– pt. 2. An advanced course in psychiatric
nursing. – pt. 3. Guide for an advanced clinical
course in pediatric nursing.– pt. 4. Guide for an
advanced clinical course in tuberculosis nursing.–
pt. 5. Guide for an advanced clinical course in
maternity nursing.– pt. 6. Guide for an advanced

clinical course in orthopedic nursing.

NN 0056906 NcU

National League of Nursing Education. Committee
on Postgraduate Clinical Nursing Courses.
Courses in clinical nursing for graduate
nurses: guide for an advanced clinical course
in tuberculosis nursing. Prepared by Subcommittee on Tuberculosis Nursing of the
Committee on Postgraduate Clinical Nursing
Courses. New York, 1947.
17 p. 23 cm.
1. Education, Nursing, Graduate. 2.
Tuberculosis - nursing. I. Title.

NN 0056907 WU-M NcU

NATIONAL League of Nursing Education.
Committee on Practical Nurse Education
Practical nurse education; manual for
state and local leagues. New York,
1949-
pts.
1. Nursing - Study & teaching

NN 0056908 DNLM OrU-M

National league of nursing education.
Committee on
psychiatric nursing
Psychiatry and allied subjects; a
bibliography. Prepared by a subcommitt₎
of the Committee on mental hygiene and
psychiatric nursing, National league o
nursing education. New York, N.Y.
₍The Committee₎ 1939.
cover-title, 54₎. Q.
Reproduced from typewritten copy.

NN 0056909 IaU MtBC

National league of nursing education. Committee on psychiatric nursing.
Psychiatry and allied subjects, an annotated bibliography, prepared by the Subcommittee on bibliography of the Committee on
psychiatric nursing. New York, N.Y., National league of nursing education, 1946.
1 p.₎., 28 p.   30½cm.
1. Mental physiology and hygiene--Bibl.
2. Psychiatry--Bibl.

NN 0056910 MiU

VOLUME 407

National League of Nursing Education. Committee on Psychiatric Nursing.
Suggested basic list of psychiatric books for library of school offering psychiatric affiliation; a bibliography. Prepared by a subcommittee of the Committee on psychiatric nursing. New York, N. Y., National league of nursing education, 1945.
cover-title, 6 numb. l.   30.5 cm.
Reproduced from type-written copy.
1. Psychiatry. Bibl.

NN   0056911   MiU NNC

National league of nursing education. *Committee on records.*
A guide for the use of the League records, prepared by Committee on records of the National league of nursing education. New York, N. Y., 1938.
62 p. incl. forms.   28 x 22 cm.

1. Nurses and nursing—Study and teaching.
RT71.N3   610.7307   A 41—3166
Catholic Univ. of   America. Library
for Library of Congress   ₍a51c₎

NN   0056912   DCU OU DLC CaBVaU

WY   NATIONAL League of Nursing Education.
20   Committee on Records
qN277g   A guide for the use of the league
1941   records. ₍Partially rev.₎ New York,
                1942 ₍c1941₎
                72 p.   illus.
                1. Nursing schools - Organization,
                administration, etc. 2. Nursing -
                Study & teaching

NN   0056913   DNLM

B614.907   NATIONAL LEAGUE OF NURSING EDUCATION.
qN216   Committee on records.
                A guide for the use of the League
                records. Supplement for procedures
                and conditions lists₃ prepared by
                Committee on records of the National
                league of nursing education.   New
                York, N.Y., 1943.
                20 p. incl. forms.   27cm.
                1.Nurses and nursing. Study and
                teaching. I. Title.

NN   0056914   MnU

National League of Nursing Education. *Committee on Records.*
A guide for the use of the League records. ₍Rev.₎ New York, 1945.
74 p. illus. 28 cm.

1. Nurses and nursing—Study and teaching.
RT71.N3 1945   610.7307   54-28062 ‡

NN   0056915   DLC InU ICU DCU ViU MiU DNLM CU

National League of Nursing Education. *Committee on Records.*
Procedure for establishing an affiliation ... New York, 1947.
20 p. 28 cm.
"Selected references": p. 9.

1. Nurses and nursing—Study and teaching. ₍1. Nursing—Study and teaching₎ 2. ₍Nursing schools—U. S.₎ I. Title.
RT71.N313   610.73071   Med 47—2640
© 9Apr47; National League of Nursing Education, New York; AA50542.
U. S. Army Medical Library   ₍W6P3₎
for Library of Congress   ₍2₎†

NN   0056916   DNLM MiDP NcU MtBC OrU-M DLC

National league of nursing education. *Committee on revision of the faculty pamphlet.*
Faculty positions in schools of nursing and how to prepare for them ... New York, 1946.
vii, 55 p. 22½ cm.
2d ed.; 1st ed., entitled The nursing school faculty, duties, qualifications, and preparation, issued by the Education committee of the National league of nursing education in 1933.

1. Nurses and nursing—Study and teaching. ₍1. Nursing schools₎ 2. ₍Nursing—Study and teaching₎ I. Title.
RT71.N315 1946   610.73   Med 47—150
U. S. National Library   of Medicine ₍W6P3₎
for Library of Congress   ₍a57½₎†

OCU
NN   0056917   DNLM MiDP ICRL TxU NcU DLC OrU-M MtBC

National league of nursing education. *Committee on standards.*
Essentials of a good school of nursing, prepared by Committee on standards, National league of nursing education ... New York, 1936.
1 p. l., 48 p. 23ᵐ.
Bibliography: p. 45–48.

1. Nurses and nursing—Study and teaching. ₍1. Nursing education₎ I. Title.
                                            A 37—587
Teachers college library,   Columbia univ.
for Library of Congress   ₍2₎

OU
NN   0056918   NNC-T DNLM OrCS CU CaBVaU OrU-M MiU

National league of nursing education. *Committee on standards.*
Essentials of a good school of nursing, prepared by Committee on standards, revised by a special committee. New York, N. Y., National league of nursing education, 1942.
xi, 75 p. 23ᵐ.
"Second edition."
"References": p. 73–75.

1. Nurses and nursing—Study and teaching. I. Title.
Library of Congress   RT71.N325   42-17268

OU
NN   0056919   DLC NcGU CaBVaU OrU-M MtBC NcU ViU

National league of nursing education. *Committee on standards.*
Essentials of a good school of nursing, prepared by Committee on standards, revised by a special committee. New York, N. Y., National league of nursing education, 1945.
xi, 75 p. 23ᵐ.
"Fourth printing, April 1945."
"References": p. 73–75.

NN   0056920   ViU NcD

National league of nursing education. Committee on Studies
see   National league of nursing education. Dept. of studies.

National league of nursing education. *Committee on the nursing school library.*
Basic book list; books suggested for purchase for libraries in schools of nursing, compiled by a subcommittee of the Curriculum committee. New York, N. Y., National league of nursing education, 1937.
69 p. 23ᵐ.
Classified, with author index.

1. Nurses and nursing—Bibl.
                                            38-9861 Revised
Library of Congress   Z6675.N7N17
                          ₍r45d2₎   016.61073

NN   0056922   DLC

National league of nursing education. *Committee on the nursing school library.*
Books suggested for libraries in schools of nursing, compiled by the Committee on the nursing school library. New York, N. Y., National league of nursing education, 1944.
139 p. 23ᵐ.
Classified, with author index.
"First edition, 1937 ₍has title: Basic book list₎ ... Third edition, revised 1944."

1. Nurses and nursing—Bibl.
                                            45-5520
Library of Congress °   Z6675.N7N17 1944
                          ₍5₎   016.61

NN   0056923   DLC NcGU ICU OU

National League of Nursing Education. *Committee on the Nursing School Library.*
Books suggested for libraries in schools of nursing. ₍4th ed., rev.₎ New York, 1948.
viii, 197 p. 23 cm.
First ed. published in 1937 under title: Basic book list.

1. Nurses and nursing—Bibl.
Z6675.N7N17 1948   016.61   48-7299*

MtBC OrU-M
NN   0056924   DLC OC1W DNLM TxU NNC CU OC1 ICU

National league of nursing education. *Committee on the nursing school library.*
A library handbook for schools of nursing, prepared by the subcommittee on the nursing school library of the Curriculum committee, National league of nursing education in collaboration with the Bellevue school of nursing, Bellevue hospital, New York city. New York, National league of nursing education ₍1936₎
264 p. 23½ cm.
"Report of work of the subcommittee on the nursing school library," signed: Marian Rottman Fleming, chairman.

CONTENTS.—pt. I. Administration of a nursing school library. A short reading list. A list of fifty periodicals, compiled by Ethel Wigmore. Lists of sources of free and inexpensive material, compiled by Ethel Wigmore. Some library supply houses.—pt. II. List of subject headings, Bellevue school of nursing library.—pt. III. Classification outline, Bellevue school of nursing library.

1. Medical libraries. 2. Subject headings—Medicine. 3. Classification—Books—Medicine. I. Bellevue hospital, New York. Training school for nurses. II. *Fleming, Marian ₍Rottman₎ III. Title.
Z675.M4N2   [026.61] 020   36—13712

MB NcGU WaU DNLM CaBVaU MtBC Wa WaT OrU WaS
NN   0056926   DLC NcU NcD-N CtY-M ViU OC1 OC1W

National League of Nursing Education. Committee on the Nursing School Library.
A library handbook for school of nursing, prepared by the subcommittee on the nursing school library of the Curriculum committee, National League of Nursing Education in collaboration with the Bellevue School of Nursing, Bellevue Hospital, New York City, New York, National League of Nursing Education ₍1941, c1936₎
258p.

NN   0056927   ICRL OC1W NcD ViU

Z675   National League of Nursing Education. Committee
.M4N18   on the Nursing School Library. A library
1953   handbook for schools of nursing.
              National League for Nursing.
                 A library handbook for schools of nursing, prepared by a committee of the National League of Nursing Education. 2d ed. New York, 1953.

National league of nursing education. *Committee on the nursing school library.*
List of books suggested for libraries in schools of nursing, compiled by a subcommittee on the library of the Curriculum committee. New York, N. Y., National league of nursing education, 1942.
91 p. 23ᵐ.
A revised edition of Basic book list; books suggested for purchase for libraries in schools of nursing, compiled by a subcommittee of the Curriculum committee.

1. Nurses and nursing—Bibl.
                                            42-15631 Revised
Library of Congress   Z6675.N7N17 1942

NN   0056929   DLC OrU-M OC1 TxU

VOLUME 407

National League of Nursing Education. *Committee on the Nursing School Library.*
Manual for the Nursing School Library, prepared under the direction of Stella Marie Bruun ... and Charlotte Studer. New York, 1947.
vii, 40 p. 23 cm.
Bibliography : p. 33-39.

1. Libraries, Nursing school.
Z675.N8N3   026.61073   47-7889*

WaT
NN   0056930   DLC OrU-M MiDP MtBC CaBVaU TxU NcU ICU

National league of nursing education. *Committee on university relations.*
Conference on nursing schools connected with colleges and universities, *New York, 1928.*
Proceedings of conference on nursing schools connected with colleges and universities, under the auspices of the Department of nursing education of Teachers college and the Committee on university relations of the National league of nursing education, held at Teachers college, Columbia university, New York city, January 21 to January 25, 1928. New York, N. Y., National league of nursing education, 1928.

WY   **NATIONAL** League of Nursing Education.
18   Committee on Vocational Guidance
qN277g   Guidance programs for schools of
1945   nursing. New York, 1945.
             90 L.
             1. Nursing - Study & teaching

NN   0056932   DNLM OClW

National league of nursing education. *Committee on vocational guidance.*
Guidance programs for schools of nursing, prepared by the Committee on vocational guidance of the National league of nursing education in co-operation with the Occupational information and guidance service of the Vocational division of the United States Office of education. New York, 1946.
ix, 114 p. illus. 23 cm.

1. Nurses and nursing—Study and teaching. [1. Nursing—Study and teaching] 2. Personnel service in education. I. U. S. Office of education. Vocational division. II. Title.
RT71.N327   610.730711   Med 46—327
U. S. National Library   of Medicine [WY18N277g 1946]
for Library of Congress   [a57m1]†

NN   0056933   DNLM OrU-M MiDP ViU TxU ICU NcU DLC

National League of Nursing Education. *Committee on Vocational Guidance.*
Handbook for career counselors on the profession of nursing. New York, National League of Nursing Education, 1948.
viii, 31 p. 23 cm.
Bibliography : p. 31.

1. Nursing as a profession.
RT71.N328   610.73069   50-14117

NN   0056934   DLC CU OEac OrU-M

National League of Nursing Education. **Committee to Develop a Guide for Instructors on Nursing during Disaster.**
Nursing during disaster ...
see under   National League of Nursing Education. Dept. of Services to Schools of Nursing.

National league of nursing education. *Committee to study administration in schools of nursing.*
Fundamentals of administration for schools of nursing; report of the Committee to study administration in schools of nursing. New York, N. Y., National league of nursing education [c1940]
xxi, 270 p. incl. tables, diagrs. 21 cm.
Foreword signed by Effie J. Taylor, chairman.
Bibliography: p. 257-263.

1. Nurses and nursing.   I. Taylor, Effie Jane, 1874-   II. Title.
RT71.N33   610.73   41—4311

OrU
NcD MiDP CtY-M WU-M NcU-H ICRL IaU NcD-N OrU-M
NN   0056936   DLC OrCS MtBC CaBVaU ViU PU OU OClW

National League of Nursing Education. *Curriculum Committee*
see National League of Nursing Education. *Committee on Curriculum.*

WY   National League of Nursing Education. Dept.
161   of Measurement and Guidance
qN277a   Achievement examination in surgical nursing,
1949   form 149. New York, c1949.
           18 p. 1 illus.

           1. Nursing - Examinations, questions, etc.
           2. Nursing, Surgical

NN   0056938   DNLM

N 6   **NATIONAL** League of Nursing Education.
P3   Dept. of Measurement and Guidance
          Medical nursing; graduate nurse
          examination. New York, 1949.
          13 p. illus.
          1. Nursing - Examinations, questions,
          etc.

NN   0056939   DNLM

National League of Nursing Education. Dept. of Measurement and Guidance.
Obstetric nursing, state board test pool examination, form 949. New York, c1949.
14 p.

1. Nursing, Obstetrical 2. Obstetrics - Examinations, questions, etc.   •

NN   0056940   DNLM

WY   **NATIONAL** League of Nursing Education.
18   Dept. of Measurement and Guidance
qN277r   Representative items booklet. New
1949   York, c1949.
           15 p.
           1. Nursing - Examinations, questions,
           etc.

NN   0056941   DNLM InU NBuCC

A610.73   National League of Nursing Education--Dept.
N213b   of Services to Schools of Nursing.
             Bibliography on curriculum. [New
             York] 1950.
             26 l. 28 cm.

             1. Nurses and nursing--Study and teaching--Bibl.

NN   0056942   IU DNLM MiU ScU UU CU NNC-M

National League of Nursing Education. Dept. of Services to Schools of Nursing.
Bibliography on poliomyelitis nursing. New York, 1952.
49 p. 28 cm.

"Reprinted from v. 6 of the Bibliographies on nursing published by National League of Nursing Education, 1952."
1. Poliomyelitis - Treatment. 2. Nursing. I. National League   of Nursing Education. Dept. of Services to   Schools of Nursing. Bibliographies on   nursing, v.6. I. Title.

NN   0056943   CaBVaU

RT1   NATIONAL LEAGUE OF NURSING EDUCATION. Dept. of
.N28   Services to Schools of Nursing.
          Curriculum bulletin. no.1-
          New York, 1950-

          1. Nurses and nursing--Period.

NN   0056944   ICU DCU ICarbS

RT73   National League of Nursing Education. Dept.
N3   of Services to Schools of Nursing.
Public   Nursing during disaster, a guide for in-
Health   structors in basic professional programs,
Library   practical nurse programs. New York [1951]
           47 p. fold.col.table.
           Bibliography: p.42-47.
           Prepared by Committee to Develop a Guide
           for Instructors on Nursing during Disaster.

           1. Nurses and nursing - Study and teaching.
           2. Disasters. I. Title.

MiD
NN   0056945   CU MiU PU-M OU UU NNC-M DNLM DCU ViU

National League of Nursing Education. Dept. of Services to Schools of Nursing.
Report of proceedings
see under   Joint Nursing Curriculum Conference, New York, 1950.

National league of nursing education. *Dept. of studies.*
Annual salaries and salary increases and allowances paid to general staff nurses, a study prepared by the Department of studies, National league of nursing education. New York, N. Y., The American nurses' association, 1943.
50 p. 23ᵐ.

1. Nurses and nursing.   I. American nurses' association.   II. Title.
                                                      43-8464
Library of Congress   RT71.N355
                              [2]   331.28161073

NN   0056947   DLC OCl

National League of Nursing Education. Department of Studies.
A list of schools of nursing meeting minimum requirements set by law
see   National League for Nursing.
State approved schools of professional nursing ...

National league of nursing education. *Dept. of studies.*
Personnel practices for general staff nurses; a study, sponsored by the American nurses' association, the National league of nursing education, and the American hospital association. Prepared by the Department of studies, National league of nursing education. New York, N. Y., The American nurses' association, 1944.
75 p. 23ᵐ.
"The first part of the study [Annual salaries and salary increases and allowances paid to general staff nurses] published in 1943."—Foreword.

1. Nurses and nursing. 2. Hospitals—Staff.   I. American nurses' association.   II. American hospital association.   III. Title.
                                                      S G 45-105
U. S. Surg.-gen. off. Libr.
for Library of Congress   RT51.N27
                                [4]†   362.1

NN   0056949   DNLM DLC ICJ

National league of nursing education. *Dept. of studies.*
State-accredited schools of nursing; schools meeting minimum requirements set by law, and board rules in the various states and territories. New York, 1946.
83 p. 21 x 28ᵐ.
13th list, correct to Jan. 1, 1946.

1. Nurses and nursing — Study and teaching — U. S. 1. [Nursing schools—U. S.—Direct.]
RT81.U6N3 1946   610.73071173   Med 47-574
U. S. Army medical library   [WY19N277s 1946]
for Library of Congress   [5]†

NN   0056950   DNLM OrU-M MtBC ICJ ICU DLC ViU

VOLUME 407

National league of nursing education. *Dept. of studies.*
A study of the nursing service in fifty selected hospitals, by the Committee on studies of the National league of nursing education ... ₍New York₎ United hospital fund of New York, 1937.

1 p. l., p. 355–429. tables, diagrs. 23ᶜᵐ.

"Reprinted from the Hospital survey for New York, vol. II, chap. V, pp. 355–429."

"Literature cited": p. 429.

1. Nurses and nursing. 2. Hospitals. I. Title: The nursing service in fifty selected hospitals.

New York univ. Wash. sq.   library RT51.N28   A 40–1879
for Library of Congress   ₍2₎

NN   0056951   NNU-W NcGU OClW MiD CaBVaU MtBC

National League of Nursing Education. *Dept. of Studies.*
A study of nursing service in one children's and twenty-one general hospitals. New York, National League of Nursing Education, 1948.

63 p. forms. 23 cm.

1. Nurses and nursing—U. S.

RT4.N28   610.73   48–22025*

NcU OrU-M MtBC IaU
NN   0056952   DLC MiU DNLM ICU ViU PU-Penn OClW

National League of Nursing Education. *Dept. of Studies.*
A study of pediatric nursing, sponsored by U. S. Children's Bureau and National League of Nursing Education in cooperation with New York Hospital. New York, 1947.

112 p. illus. 23 cm.

1. Nurses and nursing. ₍1. Nursing, Pediatric₎ 2. ₍Children—Care and hygiene₎ I. U. S. Children's Bureau. II. New York Hospital.

RT91.N3   618.92073   Med 48–1164
U. S. Army Medical Libr.   [WY159N277s 1947]
for Library of Congress   ₍3₎†

DLC
NN   0056953   DNLM MiU ICJ MtBC ICU OrU-M PU-Penn

National league of nursing education. *Dept. of studies.*
A study on the use of the graduate nurse for bedside nursing in the hospital ₍by₎ Department of studies of the National league of nursing education. ₍New York₎ 1933.

90 p. diagrs. 22½ cm.

Bibliography: p. 87–90.

1. Nurses and nursing. 2. Hospitals. I. Title. II. Title: Graduate nurse for bedside nursing in the hospital.

RT51.N3   610.73   33—14838

NN   0056954   DLC CaBVaU OrU-M OU MiU

National League of Nursing Education. *Education Committee*
see **National League of Nursing Education.** *Committee on Curriculum.*

National league of nursing education. Joint nursing curriculum conference.
    ... Proceedings ...
      see Joint nursing curriculum conference, New York, 1950.
    Report of proceedings.

National League of Nursing Education. Special Committee on Postgraduate Clinical Nursing Courses
      see National League of Nursing Education. Committee on Postgraduate Clinical Nursing Courses.

National league of professional base ball clubs.
Constitution and playing rules of the National league of professional base ball clubs. Official. ₍Chicago, A. G. Spalding & bros.₎ 1876–
    v. 15–18ᶜᵐ.
1876 published by Reach & Johnston at Philadelphia.

1. Base-ball.

         5—24063

Library of Congress   GV877.N27

NN   0056958   DLC OCl NN

National league of professional base ball clubs.
Little encyclopedia...
Cleveland, Morgan & Bingham,

NN   0056959   OCl

National League of Professional Base-ball Clubs
National league green book.
1935–

₍New York?₎ National league service bureau ₍1935–
    nos.   20½ x 27 – 26cm.
1936 is 60th birthday edition; 1939 is Centennial edition.
Published by the National league of professional base ball clubs.

1. Baseball—Yearbooks. I. National league of professional base
ball clubs.   ball clubs.
N. Y. P. L.   August 5, 1941

NN   0056960   NN MB WaT MiD DLC OrU WaS

National league of professional base-ball clubs.
... National league green book, 1839–1939. ₍n. p., 1939?₎
cover-title, 48 p. incl. tables. 20½ x 26½ᶜᵐ.
At head of title: Centennial edition.

1. Base-ball. I. Title.

         A 41–1121

Wesleyan univ. Library
for Library of Congress

NN   0056961   CtW OCl OU WU FU KAS

National League of Professional Base Ball Clubs.
... National League official score. ₍Chicago? 1891.₎   **16 l.**
illus. 8°.

Cover-title.
Advertising matter interspersed.

1. Baseball.—Score books.   SPALDING COLLECTION.
N. Y. P. L.   October 26, 1921.

NN   0056962   NN

National League of Professional Base Ball Clubs.
Official schedule.
18

₍Louisville, Ky.?₎ L. Laffan ₍18   **32°.**
no.   illus.

Title   1896, Official schedule of the National League and American Association of Professional Base Ball Clubs.

1. Baseball.—Yearbooks.   SPALDING COLLECTION.
N. Y. P. L.   October 27, 1921.

NN   0056963   NN

National league of professional base-ball clubs.
The official schedule of the National league of professional base ball clubs. 1881. New York, A. C. Stevens & co., °1881.

1 fold. sheet. 18½ x 8½ᶜᵐ.

1. Base-ball.

Library of Congress   GV879.N27   5–23428†

NN   0056964   DLC

National League of Professional Baseball Clubs.
Schedule and score of base ball games of the National League for 1880. Being an official list of league clubs, averages, umpires and the dates of all league games. Buffalo, Kenney, °1880.
₍8₎ p. 17 cm.
Cover title.

1. Baseball.

GV879.N275   50–51776

NN   0056965   DLC

National League of Professional Baseball Clubs.
75th anniversary of the National League. ₍Charles Segar, editor. New York, 1951?₎
82 p. illus. 31 cm.

1. Baseball—Hist. I. Title.

GV875.A3A44   796.35709   52—2613 ‡

NN   0056966   DLC ViU MU OU InU MB FU WaS

National league of professional basket ball teams of the United States.
... Official book of rules for the government and protection of the game of basket ball, together with a synopsis of last year's work ... Issued by the National league of professional basket ball teams of the United States. 1902–19   Philadelphia, Pa., Thomson printing company, °1902–
17¼ᶜᵐ.

1. Basket-ball.

Library of Congress   GV885.N27   5–24522†

NN   0056967   DLC

National League of Republican Clubs
    see
National Republican League of the United States.

National league of teachers' associations.

    see

League of teachers' associations

National league of University professors.
An outline of the Manchurian problem ... Tokyo, The National league of university professors, 1932.
cover-title, 1 p. l., 2 p., 1 l., 20 p. 22½ cm. (Its [Pamphlet] no. 1)

Bj9a
N21d
v. 1

1. Manchuria. I. Ser.

NN   0056970   CtY

National league of wholesale fresh fruit and vegetable distributors.
Annual convention.

₍Washington, etc., 189 ₎–19
    v. in   illus., plates, ports., diagrs. 23ᶜᵐ.
Title varies: 189 –191   Proceedings of the ... annual convention of the National league of commission merchants of the United States.
191   Annual convention of the National league of commission merchants of the United States.
19   Annual convention of the National league of wholesale fresh fruit and vegetable distributors.
Cover-title, 19   : Official proceedings ...
1. Commission merchants—Societies. 2. Produce trade—U. S.

         15–8747 Revised 2

Library of Congress   HD9001.N3
         ₍r43d2₎   338.12

ICJ NNC OCl
NN   0056971   DLC NIC NN WaS MH-BA OrCS DNAL NBuG

VOLUME 407

National league of wholesale fresh fruit and vegetable distributors.
Constitution and by-laws of the National league of commission merchants of the United States. Revised February, 1914. As amended at twenty-second annual convention. ₁East Orange, N. J., The Abbey printshop, 1914₎
28 p. 14½ᵐ.

43-33599

Library of Congress   HD9001.N3₁₁ 1914

NN   0056972   DLC

National League of Wholesale Fresh Fruit and
Vegetable distributors .
Fresh fruit and vegetable merchandising
see under title

National league of wholesale fresh fruit and
vegetable distributors.
HD9240
.1
.F9   **Fruit** trade journal and produce record.

New York, Fruit trade journal company

287
N214I   National league of wholesale fresh fruit and
vegetable distributors.
Information circular. no.

Washington, D.C.,

NN   0056975   DNAL

National league of wholesale fresh fruit and vegetable distributors.
Membership list of the National league of commission merchants of the United States.

₁New York, etc.,
v. 15-19ᵐ.

43-33600

Library of Congress   HD9001.N34

NN   0056976   DLC OU

National league of wholesale fresh fruit & vegetable distributers .
Official proceedings
see its   Annual convention.

National league of wholesale fresh fruit & vegetable distributers .
Proceedings
see its   Annual convention.

287
N214P   National league of wholesale fresh fruit and
vegetable distributors.
Program ... annual convention.

₁n.p.,

NN   0056979   DNAL

287
N214Re   National League of Wholesale Fresh Fruit and
Vegetable Distributors.
Report from Washington.

₁Washington₎

1. Commission merchants. Societies.
2. Produce   trade. U.S.

NN   0056980   DNAL

NATIONAL LEAGUE OF WHOLESALE FRESH FRUIT AND
VEGETABLE DISTRIBUTORS.
Report of the secretary to the annual convention.
Washington.   v.   24cm.

Annual.
Earlier reports included in its Proceedings of the annual convention.
1. Commission merchants, jobbers, etc. --U.S.

NN   0056981   NN OrCS

287
N214R   National league of wholesale fresh fruit and
vegetable distributors.
Report to members on ... advisory board
meeting.
Washington, D.C.,

1. Produce trade. U.S. 2. Commission-merchant
Societies.

NN   0056982   DNAL

287
N214S   National league of wholesale fresh fruit and
vegetable distributors.
Special bulletin.
Washington, D.C.,

First several nos. omit title.

NN   0056983   DNAL

National league of wholesale fresh fruit and vegetable distributors.
A study and treatise on wholesale perishable terminal markets and suggestions for essential future development, by John R. Van Arnum, secretary, with the approval of the officers and advisory board, National league of wholesale fresh fruit and vegetable distributors.   Washington, 1946.   50 p.   chart.   23cm.

1. Fruit—Trade and stat.   2. Freight—Terminals and depots.
I. Van Arnum, John R
N.Y.P.L.   February 17, 1948

NN   0056984   NN NIC DNAL NNC ICJ IU

National league of wholesale fresh fruit and
vegetable distributors.
HD9244
.P5   **Phillips, Raymond G**
Wholesale distribution of fresh fruits and vegetables, by R. G. Phillips, assisted by Samuel Fraser, for the Joint council of the National league of commission merchants of the United States ... the Western fruit jobbers' association of America ... ₁and₎ International apple shippers' association ...   Rochester, N. Y., Printed by the Fish-Lyman company, inc. ₁1922₎

National League of Women Voters
see League of Women Voters of the United States.

National League of Women Workers
see   National League of Girls Clubs.

National League of Young Democrats
see also   Joint Committee Appointed by
New York Young Democratic Club and National
League of Young Democrats.

JN1129   National league of young liberals.
.L4L42
The Liberal news; peace, liberty, social justice. no. 1-26, **Apr.**
1936–May 1938; new ser., no. 1-15, June 1938–Aug. 1939.
₁London, 1936–39₎

National league of young liberals.
Pamphlets.

see *its*

Young liberal pamphlets.

National league of young Liberals.
Young Liberal pamphlets. ₁London₎ National **league**
of young Liberals ₁19
v. 21½ᵐ.

1. Gt. Brit.—Pol. & govt. 2 Liberal party (Gt. Brit.) **3. Liberalism.**
₁. Title.
15-2131

Library of Congress   JN1129.L4N3

NN   0056991   DLC

NATIONAL LEAGUE OF YOUNG LIBERALS. Political Research Committee.
To plan or not to plan? A report of the Political **Research**
Committee of the National League of Young Liberals, April,
1935.   London: Published for the National League of Young
Liberals by the Liberal Publ. Dept. [1935]   23 p.   21cm.

877884A. 1. Economic planning—Gt.Br. I. Title.

NN   0056992   NN IU

National League on Urban Conditions Among Negroes
see
National Urban League.

371.52   National League to Promote School Attendance.
qN277   Newsletter.   Cumberland, Md.
v. in   28 cm.

Title varies.—June 1943, Newsletter;
Sept. 1943–v. 4, 1947, National leaguer;
Dec. 1947—   Newsletter.

1. School attendance. U.S.

NN   0056994   N CaBViP

371.52   National League to Promote School Attendance.
N277p   Proceedings. v. 13-   1923-
Toledo ₁etc.₎,
v. ports. 23-27 cm.

Vols. 1-12 never published separately.
Vol. 6, 1919 in Detroit Board of Education
Minutes.
1923–Oct. 15, 1936, published under an
earlier name: National League of Compulsory
Education Officials.

Or Wa MB OU
NN   0056995   N MiD NN GEU OCU NNU-W ICU DHEW MiU

National leaguer
see   National League to Promote School
Attendance.
Newsletter.

VOLUME 407

NATIONAL LEATHER AND SHOE FINDERS' ASSOCIATION.
Annual convention...
[no.]

[St. Paul? 19   8°.
v.

1. Boots and shoes—Assoc.   and org.—U.S.

NN 0056997   NN MH-BA OC1

T7
.U62   National leather and shoe finders'
no. 17   association.
          Schnitzer, Julius Gabriel.
          ... Establishing and operating a shoe repair business ... Pre-
          pared by J. G. Schnitzer and Charlotte R. Budd, under the di-
          rection of H. B. McCoy. Washington, D. C., The Bureau of
          foreign and domestic commerce, United States Dept. of com-
          merce, in co-operation with National leather and shoe finders'
          association and Tanners' council of America [1945]

National leather and shoe finders' association

Leather and findings; truth in advertising. v. 1–3; July
1928–June 1931. Saint Louis, Mo., Trade promotion bureau,
National leather & shoe finders association [1928–31]

National leather and shoe finders' association.
    Post war planning. Action.
[St. Louis, Mo? National leather & shoe finders
association, 1944?]
    36 p.

NN 0057000   OC1

National leather and shoe finders' association.
    Proceedings of the ... annual convention
    see its   Annual convention ...

National leather and shoe finders'
    association.
Shoe repair service; advocating shoe re-building. v. 1–
Mar. 1921–   [St. Louis, L. M. Davis, etc., 1921–

National leather and shoe finders' association.
    Trade promotion bureau.
An easy method of keeping accounts especially
adapted to the shoe repair shop. 7th ed. The
Association, n. d.
unp. forms.

    Cover title.

NN 0057003   MiD

National leather goods and saddlery manufac-
    turers' association.
    Moseley, G   C.
    Leather goods manufacture; a practical guide to modern
methods and processes, by G. C. Moseley, edited by Beresford
Worswick ... Published under the auspices of the National
leather goods and saddlery manufacturers' association. London, Sir I. Pitman & sons, ltd., 1939.

National leather goods and saddlery manu-
    facturers' association. Museum of
    leathercraft

        See

London. Museum of leathercraft.

National leather workers association
    see also
International fur and leather workers **union of the United
States and Canada.**

National Lebanese Bloc Party
    see Ḥizb al-Waṭan (*Lebanon*)

National Legal Aid and Defender Association.
    Brief in support of equitable enforcement of
foreign alimony and support orders.   Rochester,
N.Y., National Association of Legal Aid Organizations [1946?]
    15 p.   29 cm.

NN 0057008   CU

National Legal Aid and Defender Association.
    Chest and council responsibility for legal aid ...
[Rochester, N.Y., National association of legal
aid organizations, 193–?]
    6 p.

NN 0057009   ViU-L

National Legal Aid and Defender Association.
    Committee reports and proceedings.

[n. p.]
    v. 23–33 cm. annual.

    Title varies: Reports of committees for discussion
at the convention.
    Issued   by the association under an earlier name:
National Association of Legal Aid Organizations.

    1. Legal aid societies—U. S. 2. Legal aid—U. S. 3. Public defend-
ers—U. S.

                                     56–53839 rev ‡

NN 0057010   DLC MH-L MB NN CtY

National Legal Aid and Defender Association.
    Conference proceedings
    see its
Summary of proceedings of the annual conference.

National Legal Aid and Defender Association.
    Directory of legal aid and defender services
    see under title

National Legal Aid and Defender Association.
    Examples of certificates and articles
of incorporation and constitutions and
by-laws of legal aid organizations.
[Rochester, N.Y., 1955]
    89 l. forms. 29 cm.

    Cover title.
    Emery A. Brownell, executive director.
    1. Legal aid. U.S. Forms. Lw 1. Legal
aid. U.S. Lw 2. Forms. Legal aid. U.S.
I. & Lw I.   Brownell, Emery A.

NN 0057013   N-L MH-L

National Legal Aid and Defender Association,

    Final report on uniform legal aid records
including classification of nature of cases, classification of source of cases, classification of
disposition of cases, classification of data as to
clients, by the Special Committee on Classification
and Standardization of Records.   [Boston, 18–?]
    (2) i i, 90 p.

NN 0057014   MH

National Legal Aid and Defender Association.
    A handbook of the National Association of Legal Aid
Organizations. [Cleveland? 1931]
    96 p. 23 cm.

    1. Legal aid—U. S.

                                     56–53073 rev

NN 0057015   DLC NcD

National Legal Aid and Defender Association
    The Legal aid briefcase. v. 1–
Nov. 1942–
    see under title

National Legal Aid and Defender Association.
    Legal aid directory
    see under title

National Legal Aid and Defender Association.
    The legal aid news-letter
    see under title

National Legal Aid and Defender Association.
    Legal aid records and standards; a collection
of committee reports and deliberations ...
    see under   Bradway, John Saeger, 1890–
comp.

National Legal Aid and Defender Association.
    The legal aid-social work relationship ... two
papers delivered at the 26th annual legal aid conference, Portland, Ore., Sept. 2, 1948, and
appearing in the 1948 Reports and proceedings ...
Rochester, N.Y., Author, 1948.
    p. A-54-A66.
    Mimeographed.

NN 0057020   Or

Law   National legal aid and defender association.

Bradway, John Saeger, 1890–   comp.
    Legal aid work and the organized bar; a collection of the de-
liberations of the National association of legal aid organizations
gathered from the stenographic record of the conferences.
Compiled by John S. Bradway. [Durham, N. C.,] *1939.

National Legal Aid and Defender Association.
    Memorandum of proceedings of the annual conference
    see its
Summary of proceedings of the annual conference.

VOLUME 407

National Legal Aid and Defender Association.
NLADA briefcase.

₍Chicago₎
v. illus. 28 cm. bimonthly.
Continues Legal aid brief case.

1. Legal assistance to the poor—United States—Periodicals.
I. Title: Briefcase. II. Title: NLADA briefcase.

K14.A863   345′.73′01   70-618074

NN   0057023   DLC ViU-L IU NcD-L

National Legal Aid and Defender Association.
NLADA briefcase
see also   Legal aid briefcase.

National Legal Aid and Defender Association.
... National social welfare organizations and the National legal aid association work together in legal aid development. Rochester, N.Y. ₍1955₎

7 numb. l. 28cm.
Caption title.
Reproduced from typewritten copy.

NN   0057025   MH-L

National Legal Aid and Defender Association.

League of nations. *Advisory commission for the protection
and welfare of children and young people. Child welfare
committee.*
... Note by the secretary. Geneva, 1933.

National Legal Aid and Defender Association.
Obtaining justice for the indigent
defendant accused of crime ... ₍Pub-
lished by the National legal aid
association and the Standing committee
on legal aid work of the American bar
association. Chicago, American bar
center, 1954?₎

cover-title, 11 p. 20½cm.
"References": p. 10.

NN   0057027   MH-L

National Legal Aid and Defender Association.
Proceedings of the annual conference
see its
Summary of proceedings of the annual conference.

National Legal Aid and Defender Association.
Record of proceedings at the annual meeting
see its
Summary of proceedings of the annual conference.

National Legal Aid and Defender Association.
Reports of committees for discussion at the convention
see its
Committee reports and proceedings.

National Legal Aid and Defender Association.
Statistics of legal aid and defender work
in the United States and Canada. 1955-
Chicago, American Bar Center.
v. 22 x 29cm. irregular.

1. Legal aid societies - Stat. I. Title.

NN   0057031   GU-L

National Legal Aid and Defender Association.
A study of legal aid in Philadelphia; a report
of a survey of the legal aid society and the Voluntary defenders association
see under   Brownell, Emery A.

National Legal Aid and Defender Association.
Summary of proceedings of the annual conference.

Chicago ₍etc.₎
v. 23-28 cm. annual.
Title varies: 19 -39; Record of proceedings at the annual meet-
ing.—1940-   Memorandum of proceedings of the annual confer-
ence.—   : Proceedings of the annual conference.
Cover title   : Conference proceedings.
Issued by the association under earlier names:
National Association of Legal Aid Organizations;   National
Legal Aid Association.
Proceedings for 1941-   included in the association's Commit-
tee reports and proceedings.
1. Legal aid—U. S. 2. Public defenders—U. S.

49-32632 rev 2*‡

        NNU IU MiU ICJ OCl OrU IdU-L MiU-L NcD
NN   0057033   DLC KU-L FU NcD-L CtY-L ICJ CU-AL NN

National Legal Aid and Defender Association.
Tabulated digest: divorce, annulment &
separation. ₍1944₎
2 l. 28 x 43cm. fold. to 28 x 22cm.

1. Divorce - U. S. 2. Marriage - Annulment -
U. S. 3. Separation (Law) - U. S.

NN   0057034   NNC

National Legal Aid and Defender Association.
... Tulsa organizes legal aid service; a report of a joint community
project sponsored by the Bar with a
timely assist from the Council of
social agencies and the National legal
aid association. Rochester, N.Y.
₍1955?₎
₍1₎, 5 numb. l. 28cm.
Reproduced from typewritten copy.

NN   0057035   MH-L

289f   National Legal Aid and Defender Association.
N275   Twelve point brief for legal aid. New York [1955]
tw   17 l.
Law
Library   Cover title.
             Bibliography: leaves 15-17.

NN   0057036   CU MH-L NcU-L

Pam.   National Legal Aid and Defender Association.
2368   When your client needs a lawyer. ₍Roch-
         ester, N. Y.? 1943?₎
         cover-title, 7 p. 22 cm.

         Emery A. Brownell, secretary.

         1. Legal aid. I. Brownell, Emery A.
         II. Title.

NN   0057037   N ViU-L

National Legal Aid and Defender Association.
Wills for servicemen. ₍2d ed. Rochester,
N. Y., 1944₎
24 p. forms.

"The pamphlet ... was conceived and created
by Mr. ₍Jule E.₎ Stocker."

NN   0057038   NNC

National Legal Aid Association
see
National Legal Aid and Defender Association.

National legal bureau.
The directory of the National legal bureau, containing a list of members of the
National legal bureau and a brief compendium of the laws of the different states
upon business subjects in the form of
questions and answers. ₍Chicago, Ill.,
Hornstein bros.₎ 1893-
v. 28ᶜᵐ. annual.

NN   0057040   MiU-L NN ICJ MH

The National legal directory
see   Hubbell's legal directory, for the
service of the lawyer ...

National legal documents co., *New York.*
Forms in bankruptcy in proceedings under the acts of 1933
and 1934. New York, N. Y., National legal documents co.,
ᶜ1934.
cover-title, 24 p. 25ᵐ.

1. Bankruptcy—U. S.—Forms.   I. Title.   35-2513

NN   0057042   DLC

National legal register ...
Chicago, Ill., National credit corporation ₍ᶜ1933-
v. 19¼ᵐ.

1. Lawyers—U. S.—Direct. 2. Courts—U. S.—Direct.   I. National
credit corporation.   CA 33-264 Unrev'd

NN   0057043   DLC

NATIONAL LEGION OF DECENCY.
Feature motion pictures reviewed by the New York
office. 1936/37-
New York.   no.   21cm.

Annual cumulation of the biweekly (earlier, weekly) National
legion of decency list.
Cover title: 1936/37-   , Legion of decency. Films reviewed.
1. Moving pictures—Catalogues.   2. Moving pictures—Censorship—
U. S. 3. Censorship—Cinema—   U. S. I. National legion of
decency. Films reviewed.

NN   0057044   NN

792.94   National Legion of Decency.
N277m   Motion pictures classified.

         New York.
              v. 23cm.

              1. Moving-pictures - Moral and religious
         aspects. 2. Moving-pictures and Catholic
         Church. I.Title.

NN   0057045   CLSU OCl

VOLUME 407

PN National legion of decency.
1995 Motion pictures classified by National legion of
.N27 decency; a moral estimate of entertainment feature
motion pictures prepared under the direction of the
National office of the Legion of decency with the cooperation of the Motion picture department of the International federation of Catholic alumnae. New
York, National legion of decency [1948]

    x, 157, [1] p. 23cm.
    On cover: "Motion pictures classified by National
legion of decency February, 1936 - November, 1948."
    1.Moving pictures -   sorship. 2.Moving pictures
- Moral and religious   aspects. 3.Censorship. 4.
Catholic church - Dis   cipline.

  NN   0057046   DCU NBuCC CLSU N MBtS

National Legion of Decency.
    Motion pictures classified by National Legion
of Decency. 1951 ed. New York, [1951]
    x,184p. 23cm.

    4. Moving-pictures. I. Title.

  NN   0057047   IEN CaBVa

National Legion of decency.
    [Report on the National Legion of Decency...
    see under Catholic Church in the U.S.
    Episcopal Committee on Motion Pictures.

NATIONAL legion of decency list. v.1-17; Feb.1936-
Sept. 1952 (incomplete)
    New York.   v.   28-56cm.

    Weekly, Feb.6, 1936-Aug.28, 1947; biweekly, Sept.4, 1947-Sept.
1952.
    Also cumulated annually; see entry: National legion of decency.
Feature motion pictures reviewed by the New York office. After Sept.1952,

the National legion of decency list, CURRENT IN THEATRE COLLECTION,
is discarded when the annual cumulation is received.
    Sept. 1947-Sept. 1952 lack title (referred to as Biweekly list).
    "A moral estimate of current entertainment feature motion pictures
prepared under the direction of the New York office of the National legion
of decency with the cooperation of the Motion picture department of the
International federation of Catholic alumnae" (varies slightly).
    Vol. 1, no.1-44, Feb.6-Dec.3, 1936, include the section: Special
estimate of pictures reviewed Feb.-Nov.6, 1936. (Later replaced by

attached slips giving reasons for classification of objectionable pictures.)

    1. Moving pictures--Catalogues. 2. Moving pictures--Censorship--U.S.
3. Censorship--Cinema--U.S. I. International federation of Catholic
alumnae. II. National legion of   decency. List. III. National
legion of decency. Special   estimate of pictures reviewed.

  NN   0057051   NN

National Legion of the State of Ohio.
    Constitution and by-laws of the National
Legion of the State of Ohio. Instituted,
January, 1858. Cincinnati: Tagart & Co.,
printers, 1858.
    29[3]p.12cm.

    Original printed wrappers.

  NN   0057052   OC

The National legionnaire. v. 1-
    Jan. 1935-
    Indianapolis.
    v. in   illus., ports. 44 x 30 cm. monthly.
    Official publication of the American Legion.

    1. European War, 1914-1918--Period. 2. European War, 1914-
1918--Societies. I. American Legion.

    D570.A1A34   369.1861   48-39389*

  NN   0057053   DLC

F836 The National legionaire. v. 1-v. 14, no. 6;
8A51 Jan. 1935-Nov. 1948]
N25 Indianapolis.
    2 reels.
    Official publication of the American Legion.
    Microfilm copy (negative) made by the State
Historical Society of Wisconsin.
    Collation of original: 44x30 cm. monthly.
    Publication discontinued.

  NN   0057054   WHi

NATIONAL LEGISLATIVE AIR CONFERENCE
    Proceedings. 1st. 1930. Northwestern
univ. press c1930.
    1 v. (Journal of air law v.1, no.4, Oct.
1930)

  NN   0057055   Or

S National Legislative Conference.
328.73   Articles of organization [adopted October 25, 1948
qN277ao n. p., 1948]
1948   2 l. 29 cm.

    Caption title.

    I. Legislative reference bureaus. I. Title.

  NN   0057056   N

328.73 National Legislative Conference.
qN277ao   Articles of organization [adopted October
22, 1948, as amended September 30, 1953 and
September 11, 1954. n.p., 1954?]
    3, 3, 2 l. 29 cm.

    Caption title.

  NN   0057057   N

National legislative conference.
    [Resolutions adopted at the 8th
annual meeting, Oct. 16-19, 1955.
[n.p., 1955]
    [6], 1. 28cm.

    Reproduced from typewritten copy.

  NN   0057058   MH-L

National Legislative Conference.
    Summary [of the] annual meeting.
[Miami Beach?]
    v. 28 cm.

    1. State governments--Societies, etc.

    JK2403 N37   57--15141

    NNC IU CLSU NBuU-L GU
  NN   0057059   DLC OrU InU CLL ViU-L NcU Or FTaSU Vi

National Legislative Conference
    see also Legislative Service Conference.

**National Legislative Conference. Committee on
Interstate Exchange of Legislative Service.**
    Report; revised October 10, 1955. Miami
Beach, Fla., 1955.
    3 l. 28 cm.
    Cover title.
    1. Government publications.

  NN   0057061   N Or

National Legislative Conference. Special
    Committee on Organization of Legislative
    Services.
    Revised preliminary report to Legislative
Service Conference at the sixth annual meeting.
[New Orleans, on September 28,1953. Chicago]
1953.
    1 v. (various pagings) 28 cm.
    Cover title.

    1.Legislative reference bureaus.

  NN   0057062   MiU

National legislative reference committee of the
    Progressive party
        see Progressive party. (Founded 1912)
National legislative reference committee.

National Lehrerseminar
    see National Teachers' Seminary.

National leisure hours institution (Italy)
    see
Opera nazionale dopolavoro.

National leper home, Carville, La.
    see U.S. Public Health Service Hospital,
    Carville, La.

National leprosarium, Carville, La.
    see U.S. Public Health Service Hospital,
    Carville, La.

W 1 NATIONAL Leprosy Fund, London
NA501   Journal of the Leprosy Investigation
Committee, no. 1-4; Aug. 1890-Dec. 1891.
London.
    4 v. in 1. illus.
    Ed. by Phineas S. Abraham.
    I. Abraham, Phineas Simon, 1847-
1921, ed.

  NN   0057068   DNLM MH MBCo ICJ PPC

London.
National leprosy fund. Prize essays on
subjects connected with leprosy. 8°. *London,*
Adlard & Son, 1895.
    CONTENTS.
    No. 1. On the history of the decline and final extinction
of leprosy as an endemic disease in the British Islands.
By George Newman.
    No. 2. Conditions under which leprosy has declined in
Ireland. By Edward H. Ehlers.
    No. 3. Leprosy in South Africa. By S. P. Impey.
    No. 4. On spontaneous recovery from leprosy. By S. P.
Impey.

  NN   0057069   DNLM

AE5 National Lexicographic Board.
.I 32
    The Illustrated encyclopedia of knowledge. [Prepared and
edited by the National Lexicographic Board, Albert H.
Morehead, chairman and general editor. Deluxe ed.
Brooklyn] Premiumwares [1954-55]

AE5 National Lexicographic Board.
.I 33
    The Illustrated home library encyclopedia. [Prepared and
edited by the National Lexicographic Board; Guild ed.
[New York, Educational Book Guild, 1955]

VOLUME 407

AG5
.N55

National Lexicographic Board.

The New wonder book, cyclopedia of world knowledge; the thrilling stories of twentieth-century industry, science, nature, transportation, communication, and other marvels of the world. ₍Prepared and edited by the National Lexicographic Board₎ Philadelphia, International Press ₍1954₎

NN 0057073   NjP

[National Liberal Association]
... The duty of liberal electors in the present crisis. [Haddington], 1885?]
4 p.   (Its Tracts. no. 1)
No. 9 of a volume of pamphlets.

NN 0057073   NjP

[National Liberal Association]
... On religious equality.   [Haddington, 1885?]
4 p.   (Its Tracts. no. 2)
No. 10 of a volume of pamphlets.

NN 0057074   NjP

[National Liberal Association]
... The patrimony of the church.   [Haddington, 1885?]
4 p.   (Its Tracts. no. 3)
No. 11 of a volume of pamphlets.

NN 0057075   NjP

NATIONAL liberal cartoons. [New series]
London,etc.,₍1886₎

Vol.1. obl.f°. 13 cartoons.

NN 0057076   MH

National liberal club, *London.*
Dinner to Mr. F. W. Chesson, at the National liberal club, on Friday, July 16th, M.D.CCC.LXXXVI. ₍London, 1886₎
lii p. 23ᶜᵐ.
Title and text within ornamental border.

1. Chesson, Frederick William, 1833 or 4–1888.   I. Title.

22–18045

Library of Congress   DA565.C45N3

NN 0057077   DLC MB

National liberal club, *London.*
The Gladstone golden wedding album. Presented Friday, July 26, 1889, by the National liberal club. ₍London, Printed by Cassell and company, limited, 1889?₎
₍8₎ l. illus. (incl. facsims.) 32 x 25ᶜᵐ.

1. Gladstone, William Ewart, 1809–1898.   I. Title.

21–22294

Library of Congress   DA563.8.N3

NN 0057078   DLC MH

National liberal club, *London. Gladstone library.*
... Catalogue of books and pamphlets. London, Printed by Alexander & Shepheard, limited, 1908.
vii, ₍1₎, 953 p. 26ᶜᵐ.
The author and title catalogue is based on work done by the former librarian, A. W. Hutton, revised by his successor, F. G. Haley; subject catalogue by F. G. Haley. *cf.* Pref.
Collection of 24,460 volumes and 20,152 pamphlets.

1. Gt. Brit.—Pol. & govt.—Bibl. 2. Gt. Brit.—Hist.—Bibl. 3. Economics—Bibl.   I. Hutton, Arthur Wollaston, 1848–1912. II. Haley, Francis George, 1873–

12–16400

Library of Congress   Z921.L6377

NN 0057079   DLC ICJ

National liberal club, *London. Gladstone library.*
... Early railway pamphlets, 1825–1900. London, The Gladstone library, National liberal club, 1938.
1 p. l., 5–60 p. incl. facsim. 24ᶜᵐ. (Gladstone library, Pamphlet collection subject lists, no. 1)
Arranged by country with indexes of persons and railways.

1. Railroads—Bibl. 2. Railroads—Gt. Brit.—Bibl.   I. Title: Railway pamphlets, Early.

39–9964

Library of Congress   Z7236.N27

₍3₎   016.385

NN 0057080   DLC CU NN CSmH CtY ICJ

National liberal club political and economic circle.
Transactions. v. 1–

London, 1891–
v. 22ᶜᵐ.
Editor: J. H. Levy.

1. Economics—Societies.   I. Levy, Joseph Hiam, 1838–1913, ed.

5–31597 Revised

Library of Congress   .   HB1.N2

NN 0057081   DLC CU MH OU MiU ICJ

National liberal club political economy circle
see
National liberal club political and economic circle.

National Liberal Committee, Ottawa
see   Liberal Party (Canada) National Liberal Committee.

The National Liberal Convention, Ottawa, August 5, 6, 7, 1919
see under   Liberal Party (Canada)

National Liberal Federation.
Articles and speeches by Liberal leaders, 1885–1892, being certain publications issued by the Liberal publication department. [London 1885–92]

21 cm.
Various pagings.

NN 0057085   MH

Rare
DA   National Liberal Federation.
26   Catalogue of publications obtainable
E581   from the National Liberal Federation.
v.49   1883–4. [Birmingham? 1884?]
no.17   12 p. 23cm.

No. 17 in vol. lettered: English history pamphlets, 49.

1. Liberal   party (Gt. Brit.)

NN 0057086   NIC

National liberal federation.

HD593
.H6
Howard, James, 1821–1889.
The English land question: past and present. By James Howard, M. P. Birmingham, The National liberal federation ₍1881₎

National liberal federation.
The general objects and constitution of the National liberal federation.
London, National pressagency, ltd., 1890?
7, ₍1₎ p.

NN 0057088   MiU CtY MH

NATIONAL LIBERAL FEDERATION.
The government education bill. A verbatim report of the proceedings at the meeting of the general committee held at the Caxton Hall, Westminster on October 15th, 1902. London, 1902.

"Authorized edition."

NN 0057089   MH

National liberal federation.

DS479
.D5
Digby, William, 1849–1904.
Indian problems for English consideration. A letter to the Council of the National liberal federation. By William Digby ... ₍Plymouth₎ The National liberal federation, 1881.

[National liberal federation.]
Leaflets. London, Liberal publication department, 1855–1898?]

NN 0057091   MH

National liberal federation.
The liberal way. London, The National liberal federation ₍1934₎
iv, 80 p., p. v. 24½ᶜᵐ.
Cover included in paging.

1. Liberalism. 2. Gt. Brit.—Pol. & govt.—1910–   3. Gt. Brit.—Econ. condit.—1918–   4. Economic conditions—1918–   I. Title.

35–1149

Library of Congress   JN1129.L47 1934

₍3₎   329.942

NN 0057092   DLC

National liberal federation.
The liberal way; a survey of liberal policy, published by the authority of the National liberal federation; with a foreword by Ramsay Muir ... London, G. Allen & Unwin ltd. ₍1934₎
224 p. 19ᶜᵐ.

1. Liberal party (Gt. Brit.) 2. Gt. Brit. — Pol. & govt. — 1910–   3. Gt. Brit.—Econ. condit.—1918–   4. Economic conditions—1918–   I. Title.

35–12953

Library of Congress   JN1129.L47 1934 a

₍3₎   329.942

WaTC
NN 0057093   DLC CLSU CtY PBm NN NNC CtY WaU OrPR

VOLUME 407

National liberal federation.

The *Liberal* year book ...

    London, 19

O■
1892n

National liberal federation.
    National liberal federation. Welcome to
the north. Sept. 30th, Oct. 1st & 2nd, 1891.
Official programme. Newcastle-upon-Tyne,
[1892]

  NN   0057095   CtY

DA561
.C48

National liberal federation.

Chamberlain, Joseph, 1836–1914.
    The policy of the government since the general election. A
speech delivered to his constituents in the Town hall, Birmingham, on ... June 7th, 1881, by the Right Hon. Joseph Chamberlain, M. P. ... Birmingham, The National liberal federation [1881]

  NN   0057097   DLC MiU

National liberal federation.
    ... Proceedings in connection with the
annual meeting of the National liberal federation ...
with the annual report and the speeches ... London, The
Liberal publication department.
    v. 21 ^{cm.}

    1. Liberal party (Gt. Brit.)   ca 11–65 Unrev'd

Library of Congress   JN1129.L4N65

               [a36b1]   329.942

  NN   0057097   DLC MiU

National liberal federation.
    ... Proceedings in connection with the meeting of the
general committee of the National liberal federation, held
at Manchester, September 26th and 27th, 1918, with the
resolutions and the speeches, including that delivered by
the Right Hon. H. H. Asquith ... in the Free trade hall.
[London] The Liberal publication department, 1918.
    139 p. 21 ^{cm.}

    1. Gt. Brit.—Pol. & govt.—1910–   I. Asquith, Herbert Henry, 1852–

                                  21–2891

Library of Congress   JN1129.L5A5   1918

  NN   0057098   DLC

National liberal federation.
    ... Report of the special meeting of the Council on indus-
trial policy, held in the Kingsway hall, London, on ... March
27th, 28th and 29th, 1928. Including speeches by the Right
Hon. D. Lloyd George ... and the Right Hon. Sir Herbert
Samuel ... London, Liberal publication department, 1928.
    239 p., 1 l. 21¾ ^{cm.}

    1. Industry and state—Gt. Brit.   2. Gt. Brit.—Indus.

                              33–39138

Library of Congress   HD3616.G73N3   338.0942

  NN   0057099   DLC

National liberal federation
    see also
Liberal party *(Gt. Brit.)*

National liberal federation. Committee on unemploy-
    ment insurance.
    Report of the N.L.F. Committee on unemploy-
ment insurance, and the Report of the Liberal women's
unemployment enquiry group. London, National liberal
federation, 1933.
    20 p.   21 cm

  NN   0057101   DL

JL
197
L5A36

National Liberal Federation of Canada
    Bulletin.

    Ottawa.
        no.

    Most issues are unnumbered; some numbers
are undated.
    Includes special issues.

  NN   0057102   CaOTU

National liberal federation of Canada.

King, William Lyon Mackenzie, 1874–
    Canada and the war. Mackenzie King to the people of
Canada, 1940. A series of radio broadcasts by Prime Minister
Mackenzie King from Ottawa, February–March, 1940.
[Ottawa, National liberal federation of Canada, 1940]

National Liberal Federation of Canada.
    Canada looks ahead; a series of addresses and papers pre-
sented at the national summer conference of the Young Liberal Federation of Canada, McMaster University, Hamilton,
Ontario, September 1 to 5, 1947. [Ottawa] Tower Books,
1948.
    viii, 214 p. ports. 24 cm.

    1. Canada—Pol. & govt.—1914–   2. Canada—Soc. condit.
3. Canada—For. rel.   I. Title.

    F1034.N3   971.063   51–24197

  NN   0057104   DLC

[National Liberal federation of Canada.]
    The Canada-United States trade agree-
ments; a great Canadian ambition achieved
by the Mackenzie King government.
[Ottawa, ?adson-Merrill, 1939?].
    0.

  NN   0057105   CaBViP

National Liberal Federation of Canada.
    Liberal speaker's handbook, 1953. Ottawa.
1953.
    1 v. (various pagings) illus., ports., charts,
tables.
    Cover-title: Speaker's handbook.
    Loose-leaf.

  NN   0057106   CaOTU

[National Liberal federation of Canada]
    The Prime Minister and his times. n.p.,
The federation, 1944.
    illus. ports. sq. Q.

  NN   0057107   CaBViP

National liberal federation of Canada.
    The task of liberalism: resolutions approved by Advisory
council, National liberal federation, Ottawa, Sept. 27 and 28,
1943 ... Ottawa, National liberal federation [1943?]
    cover-title, 12 p. 23 ^{cm.}

    Text on p. [3] of cover.

    1. Liberal party (Canada)   I. Title.

                           44–33645

Library of Congress   JL197.L5N3

                 [2]   329.971

  NN   0057108   DLC

National liberal federation of India.

India. *Governor-general, 1936–* (*Marquis of Linlithgow*)
    India and the war. Statement issued by the governor-gen-
eral of India on 17th October, 1939 ... London, H. M. Stationery off., 1939.

National liberal federation of India.

Mitra, Hemendra Nath, 1866–   *comp.*
    National congress, Muslim league & other conferences, 1920.
Compiled by H. N. Mitra ... Sibpur, Calcutta, The Annual
register office, 1921.

954.03
qN277R

National Liberal Federation of India.
    Report of the proceedings of the 1st-
session.
    Poona.
        v. 33 cm.

  NN   0057111   NcD PU

National liberal immigration league.
    Activity of Junior order United American mechanics
in opposition to immigration. New York, National liberal
immigration league [19—]
    7 p. 23 ^{cm.}

    1. U. S.—Emig. & immig.   2. Junior order United American mechanics.
                                          10–23058

Library of Congress   JV6501.N2

  NN   0057112   DLC

National liberal immigration league.

    An appeal to American citizens... (For the proper regula-
tion and better distribution of immigration.) New York [1911?].
8 l. 8°.

    1. Emigration, etc., U. S.   July 24, 1912.
    N. Y. P. L.

  NN   0057113   NN

NATIONAL LIBERAL IMMIGRATION LEAGUE.
    An appeal to American citizens [in regard
to the Burnett bill] New York, National
liberal immigration league, 1914.
    3 p.

  NN   0057114   Or

National liberal immigration league.

U. S. *Laws, statutes, etc., 1909–1910 (61st Cong., 2d sess.)*
    ... A bill to further regulate the immigration of aliens into
the United States. [New York, 1909]

National liberal immigration league.

    [Circulars and copies of letters to the league, or issued by the
league, 1907-1912.]

    1. Emigration, etc., U. S., 1907-12.   July 24, 1912.
    N. Y. P. L.

  NN   0057116   NN

VOLUME 407

National liberal immigration league.
Constitution and by-laws of the Liberal
immigration league. New York [19--?]
13 p. 16½cm.

NN   0057117   NNC IU

National liberal immigration league.
Contrary views on immigration. Opinions of
Prof. L. C. Marshall, Philadelphia press,
Chas. W. Eliot, Samuel Gompers and others.
New York, Nat. lib. im. league, n.d.
8 p.

NN   0057118   OO Or

National Liberal Immigration League.
Correspondence between Rev. Dr. Charles H.
Parkhurst and the president of the National liberal
immigration league on the effects of present-day
immigration
        see under   Parkhurst, Charles Henry,
1842-1933.

National liberal immigration league.

Division of labor and distribution of immigrants. An appeal
for free transportation. Opinions of the press. New York: the
league [1910?]. 14 p., 1 l. 8°.

1. Emigrants, etc., U. S., 1909.
                                            July 24, 1912.

NN   0057120   NN Or

National liberal immigration league.

The educational test; its futility and harmfulness as a measure to regulate immigration. New York: the league [1912].
4 l. 8°.

1. Emigration, etc., U. S.
N. Y. P. L.   September 22, 1913.

NN   0057121   NN

National Liberal Immigration League.
The fear of post-war immigration. New York: the league
[1914]. 4 l. 8°. (National Liberal Immigration League.
Publ. no. 191.)

1. European war, 1914-   .—Eco-   nomic aspects, U. S. 2. Emigration and immigration, U. S., 1914-   3. Title. 4. Series.
N. Y. P. L.   June 18, 1918.

NN   0057122   NN Or

National liberal immigration league.
Figures on immigration ... New York, National liberal
immigration league [19-]
cover-title, 7, [1] p. 23cm.

1. U. S.—Emig. & immig.

Library of Congress   JV6507.N2
                                            10-18680

NN   0057123   DLC Or

National liberal immigration league.
The immigrant Jew in America, by Edmund J. James ...
Oscar R. Flynn ... Dr. J. R. Paulding, Mrs. Simon N. Patton
(Charlotte Kimball) ... Walter Scott Andrews, M. A. Issued
by the Liberal immigration league ... New York ... New
York, B. F. Buck & company, 1906.
403 p. front., illus., plates. 20½cm.
Plates printed on both sides.

1. Jews in the U. S.   I. James, Edmund Janes, 1855-1925.   II.
Flynn, Oscar R.   III. Paulding, J. R.   IV. Patton, Charlotte (Kimball)
"Mrs. S. N. Patton."   V. Andrews, Walter Scott.   VI. Title.

Library of Congress   E184.J5N27
                                            7—424

WaTC NNJ
NN   0057124   DLC MB OrPR CLSU MiU OClTem OO NN ICJ

National liberal immigration league.
The immigrant Jew in America, ed. by Edmund J. James
... with the collaboration of Oscar R. Flynn ... Dr. J. R.
Paulding ... and other writers. Issued by the National
liberal immigration league ... New York, B. F. Buck &
company, 1907.
403 p. front., illus., plates. 20cm.
Plates printed on both sides.

1. Jews in the U. S.   I. James, Edmund Janes, 1855-   ed. II. Title.

NN   0057125   ICU MH GU MiDW MB IEG Or NN NBuG OCl

National Liberal   Immigration League.
Immigration: address
        see under   Ellis, L. J.

NATIONAL LIBERAL IMMIGRATION LEAGUE, N.Y.
The immigration bills of senator Latimer
and congressmen Burnett and Gardner.
New York, [1908?].

NN   0057127   MH Or

NATIONAL LIBERAL IMMIGRATION LEAGUE
Immigration in Congress: speeches by representatives Bonnet, Bartholdt, Cockran, Steener-
son, Michalek, and Keliher. Author, n.d.
[18] p.

NN   0057128   Or CaBViP

National liberal immigration league.
Immigration in the Sixtieth congress. Extracts
from speeches delivered in January, 1908 ...
        see under   U.S. 60th cong., 1st sess.,
1907-1908. House.

National liberal immigration league.
JV6403   Literature and documents of the National
N26   liberal immigration league. [New York, National
         liberal immigration league] 1914.

[213] l. incl. 26 mount. pamphlets [290] p.   illus.
ports., facsims., tables, diagrs.   29cm.

"This collection includes the pamphlets, leaflets, and circulars issued by the National liberal
immigration league, with the exception of appeals
in foreign languages and some pamphlets which are
exhausted. The   collection includes also
pamphlets and docu-   ments showing the activity
of the restrictionists."

NN   0057130   NBuG

NATIONAL LIBERAL IMMIGRATION LEAGUE.
A new problem. New York, 1910.
pp. 14.   2 Illustr.
Concerning placing emigration.

NN   0057131   MH IU

National Liberal Immigration League.
A New-Year's bulletin to members and friends.   New York,
1915.   2 l.   8°.   (Publication. no. 194.)
Caption-title.

1. Emigration, etc., U. S.
N. Y. P. L.   July 7, 1916.

NN   0057132   NN

NATIONAL LIBERAL IMMIGRATION LEAGUE.
Our immigrants not prone to crime. [League,
1914]

NN   0057133   Or

NATIONAL LIBERAL IMMIGRATION LEAGUE.
The outlook in Washington.   Jan. 4, 1915.
New York, National liberal immigration league,
1915.
4 p.

NN   0057134   Or

National liberal immigration league.
President Taft's veto of the immigration bill. New
York [1913]
19 p. incl. illus., ports., facsims. 23cm.

1. Emigration and immigration law—U. S.   I. Taft, William Howard,
pres. U. S., 1857-
                                            CA 13-1540 Unrev'd

Library of Congress   JV6425 1913

NN   0057135   DLC NN

National liberal immigration league.

The press against the Dillingham-Burnett Bill with special
reference to the educational test, December, 1912, and January,
1913. New York [1913]. 29(1) p., 1 l. 8°.

1. Emigration, etc.—Jurisprudence,   U. S.
N. Y. P. L.   December 30, 1913.

NN   0057136   NN CaBViP

325.1   National liberal immigration league.
N21p   The press on the league; opinions of
        newspapers on the league's propositions
        to deport alien criminals and to require
        a ten year probationary period before
        citizenship ... 4th ed.   New York
        [1908?]
        24 p.

NN   0057137   IU

National Liberal Immigration League.
Proceedings of the general meeting.   1st-
1908-
New York.
v.   23 cm.

1. U. S.—Emig. & immig.—Societies.

JV6403.N28   325.73   50-49015

NN   0057138   DLC

VOLUME 407

National Liberal Immigration League.
Publications.
no.
New York, 1   8°.

v.

no.   are: Pamphlets, no.

1. Emigration and immigration,   U. S.
N. Y. P. L.   August 8, 1917.

NN 0057139   NN OrU Or ICJ

National liberal immigration league.

Race discrimination. Resolutions and laws passed by the
legislatures of Virginia, North Carolina and South Carolina, in
opposition to immigration from southern Europe.   New York:
the league ₁1908?₎   1 p.l., 3-7 p.   8°.

1. Emigration, etc.—Jurisprudence,   U. S.
N. Y. P. L.   July 24, 1912.

NN 0057140   NN NcU Or

NATIONAL LIBERAL IMMIGRATION LEAGUE.
Recent comments on immigration legislation,
with special reference to the pending Dillingham
bill (S.3175) ₁League₎ 1912.
2 sheets

NN 0057141   Or

National liberal immigration league.

₁Reprints from newspapers and copies of letters, 1912.₎   8 l.

1. Emigration, etc., U. S., 1912.
N. Y. P. L.

NN 0057142   NN

National liberal immigration league.

_____ ₁Reprints of newspaper articles, 1911-'12, circulars, reproduction of letter from F. Y. Anderson to Senator J. F. Johnson, dated
Dec. 12, 1910.₎

1. Emigration, etc., U. S.
N. Y. P. L.

NN 0057143   NN

National liberal immigration league.

Restrictive immigration bills.   New York: the league ₁1912₎.
7(1) p.   8°.

Inserted, 2 L.: Restrictive immigration bills introduced in the 59th and 60th
Congresses.

1. Emigration, etc., U. S.
N. Y. P. L.

NN 0057144   NN

National Liberal Immigration League.
₁A selection of pamphlets on immigration.
New York, 1917₎
1v. (various paging) front. (port.) 25cm.

1. U. S. - Emigration and immigration.

NN 0057145   FMU

NATIONAL LIBERAL IMMIGRATION LEAGUE.
Two aspects of the immigration problem: the
humorous and the pathetic. Author, n.d.
9 p.

NN 0057146   Or

NATIONAL LIBERAL IMMIGRATION LEAGUE.
Unread immigrants, well and strong,/they
ought not to be excluded, by Abram I. Elkus.
Illiteracy and its significance, ₁edit. from₎
New York times, Jan.10, 1912. — Author ₁1912₎
sheet

NN 0057147   Or

National Liberal League.
Circular to the auxiliary leagues for 1878 and
1879, containing address of the president and
directors of the National liberal league to the
people of the United States, Official report of the
proceedings ... October 26 and 27, 1878, ...
Constitution ... platform and proposed amendments,
list of officers of the N. L. L., miscellaneous.
New York, published by order of board of directors,
1879.
42 p.   18.5 cm.

NN 0057148   OFH NN

NATIONAL LIBERAL LEAGUE.
Constitution adopted July 1,1876;[Officers
elected;Charter members;Life members;Local
auxiliary,Annual members. 1876.]

Manuscript. 26 x 20 cm.

NN 0057149   MH

National liberal league.

Centennial congress of liberals, *Philadelphia*, 1876.
Equal rights in religion. Report of the Centennial congress of liberals, and organization of the National liberal
league, at Philadelphia, on the fourth of July, 1876. With an
introduction and appendix. Boston, Mass., Published by the
National liberal league, 1876.

NATIONAL LIBERAL LEAGUE.
[Membership roll;Lists of charters issued to
head auxiliaries;etc. 1876-1878.]

Manuscript. 7 notebooks,14 x 9 cm.to
18 1/2 x 12 cm.,in box 28 cm.

NN 0057151   MH

NATIONAL LIBERAL LEAGUE.
[Papers,conventions,especially 1876;D.M.
Bennett troubles;correspondence and miscellany.
1876-1878.]

Manuscript. Folded in 3 boxes,26 x 32 cm.
and 1 bundle 22 x 23 cm.
Most of the material was collected by the
League's president,Francis Ellingwood Abbot.

NN 0057152   MH

National liberal league.
Patriotic address to the people of the United States, adopted
at Philadelphia on the Fourth of July, 1876, by the National
liberal league. Together with the chief resolutions of the
league, its constitution and list of officers, and its protest against
the shutting of the international exhibition on Sundays. Boston, Mass., The National liberal league, 1876.

23 p. 22ᶜᵐ.

1. Religious liberty—U. S. 2. Church and state in the U. S.
44-25959
Library of Congress   BR516.N3

NN 0057153   DLC OFH MB MH ICN

National liberal league
... Platform of the National liberal league,
for the presidential election of 1880, adopted
at Rochester, N.Y., Oct. 26, 1877.
Boston, National liberal league, 1877.
17 p.

NN 0057154   OClWHi

National liberal league.
Privilege for none-justice for all; platform
adopted Oct. 26, 1877. Bost., 1878.

NN 0057155   Nh

NATIONAL LIBERAL LEAGUE.
[Records,1876-9;organization and minutes of
meetings of the Centennial Congress of Liberals
and National Liberal League. 1877-1880.]

Manuscript. 26 x 19 cm.
Minutes of directors meetings,Nov.16,1877-
Oct.27,1878,ff.26,partly duplicate,laid in.

NN 0057156   MH

National liberal league.
Report of the centennial congress of liber-
als and organization of the ... July 4, 1876....
Bost. 1876. O.

NN 0057157   CU NBuG

National Liberal League.
[Reports of the third annual congress,
Cincinnati] September 13 & 14, 1879.

NN 0057158   MH

National liberal league, London.
...Papers for the people.
no. 1

London ₁1879   20½cm.
no.

NN 0057159   NN

National Liberal Organization
see   National Liberal Party (Gt. Brit.)

National Liberal Party (Gt. Brit.)
HC256   Burgin, Edward Leslie, 1887–
.4   ... British industry, its problems and purpose; an address
.B8   at a conference of the Scottish liberal national association, at
Edinburgh, on 11th December, 1943, by the Rt. Hon. Leslie
Burgin ... ₁London, Liberal national organization, 1944₎

National Liberal Party (Gt. Brit.)
Coal — in war and peace. Report by the Liberal national coal
committee, adopted by the Liberal national parliamentary party,
June, 1942.   ₁London₎ Liberal national organization ₁1942₎
11 p.   21cm.

1. Coal—Trade and stat.—Gt. Br.
N. Y. P. L.   January 21, 1948.

NN 0057162   NN

VOLUME 407

National Liberal Party (Gt. Brit.)
The colonies and their future.   Westminister
Liberal national council, 1944.
15 p.   21.5 cm.   (Britain after the war,
no. 6)

NN 0057163   NNZI

National liberal party (Gt. Brit.)
Effective liberalism; speeches delivered at a
conference held at Hastings on February 24, 1951,
under the auspices of the National Liberal council,
by the Rt. Hon. Sir Geoffrey Shakespeare...John
S. Maclay...[and] J. A. L. Duncan... London
[1951] 28 p.   21cm.

I. Shakespeare, Sir Geoffrey Hithersay, 1893-
II. Title.

NN 0057164   NN

National Liberal *Party*   (Gt. Brit.)
Government under the law; protecting the
citizen's rights
see under   Hastings Group of National
Liberals.

National Liberal *Party*   (Gt. Brit.)
Is this the way? Towards a freer Britain
see under   Hastings Group of National
Liberals.

NATIONAL LIBERAL PARTY (Gt. Brit.)
J. P. pamphlet.
London.   no.   18-28cm.

Published jointly with the Conservative and unionist central office.

1. Great Britain--Politics--Per. and soc. publ. I. Conservative and
unionist central office, London.   II. Title.

NN 0057167   NN

National Liberal Party (*Gt. Brit.*)
The Labour Party's black record on rearmament, 1934 to
1939, compiled from official sources. [London, 1945]
31 p. 19 cm.
Published by the party under an earlier name: Liberal National
Organization.

1. Gt. Brit.--Defenses. 2. Labor Party (Gt. Brit.) I. Title.

UA647.N3   355   45-8714 rev*

NN 0057168   DLC NN

NATIONAL LIBERAL PARTY (Gt. Brit.)
Nationalization. no. 1-12. [London, 1949?]
12 v. in 1.   22cm.

Published by the National liberal organization.
No more published?

1. State control and ownership--Per. and soc. publ.--Gt. Br. 2. Industry
and state--Gt. Br. I. Title.

1. Did the people expect this?   [1949?]
2. The coal industry since nationalization.   [1949?]
3. Look at the losses!   [1949?]
4. Do workers really want it.   [1949?]
5. Why iron and steel?   [1949?]
6. Why pick on cement?   [1949?]
7. The cement industry: the facts.   [1949?]
8. Why sugar?   [1949?]

Continued in next column

Continued from preceding column

9. Sugar refining: the facts.   [1949?]
10. Do socialists keep their promises?   [1949?]
11. Why industrial insurance?   [1949?]
12. Industrial insurance: the facts.   [1949?]

NN 0057171   NN

NATIONAL LIBERAL PARTY (GT. BRIT.)
Nationalization, a factual survey.   [London,
National liberal organization, 1950?] 16 p. 22cm.

Cover-title.

1. State control and ownership-- Gt. Br.

NN 0057172   NN

National Liberal Party (*Gt. Brit.*)
Policy of the Liberal National Party, as set out in the
resolutions adopted at the party conference, April 26th and
27th, 1945. [London, 1945]
8 p. 22 cm.
Caption title.
Cover title: Liberal National Party. Liberty, prosperity, unity.
Published by the party under an earlier name: Liberal National
Organization.

1. Gt. Brit.--Pol. & govt.--1936-1945.

JN1129.L47 1945f   329.942   45-19891 rev*

NN 0057173   DLC NN

National Liberal Party (Gt. Brit.)
The role of liberalism to-day...   [London, Liberal nat. organization, 1946?]   23 p.   18cm.

1. Liberal party (Gt. Br.).
N.Y.P.L.   November 22, 1948

NN 0057174   NN

National Liberal *Party*   (Gt.Brit.)
Who are the National Liberals? What National Liberals
believe--a re-statement of National Liberal principles
and aims. 1952. L [1952?]

15 p. photos. (ports.)

NN 0057175   MH

National liberal reform league.

The **Iconoclast.** v. 1-2 (no. 1-18); Mar. 1870-Aug. 1871.
Washington, D. C., National liberal reform league, 1870-71.

The NATIONAL LIBERAL UNION.
Constitution and by-laws.   Toronto, Perry, 1882

pp.14.

NN 0057177   MH

National Liberation Committee of Venezia Giulia
see Comitato di liberazione nazionale della Venezia
Giulia.

National Liberation Front (*Greece*)
see Ethnikon Apeleutherōtikon Metōpon.

National liberation movement, Gold Coast.
Proposals for a federal constitution

see under *title*

National liberation movement, Gold Coast.
Why CMB/CPC probe!
see under title

National liberty congress of anti-imperialists,
Indianapolis, 1900.
Cd27   ... Address to the voters of the United
18   States, adopted by the National liberty
13   congress of anti-imperialists at Indianapolis,
Ind., August 15-16, 1900 ... Chicago,
American anti-imperialist league, 1900.
[4]p. 22½cm. (Liberty tracts, no.13)

NN 0057182   CtY MH NN CSmH

National Liberty Convention, Buffalo, 1843
see   Liberty Party. National Convention,
Buffalo, 1843.

National Liberty Convention, Buffalo, 1848
see   Liberty Party. National Convention,
1848.

National liberty medal committee.
Report ... of the Liberty medal committee; American
social science association ... The National institute of
social sciences ... 1918/19-
[New York?] 1919-
v. 22½cm.

1. Liberty service medal. 2. Patriotic service medal. I. American social science association. II. National institute of social sciences.

Library of Congress   CJ5817.E8N3   20-1939

NN 0057185   DLC MiU

National Liberty Party
see   Liberty Party.

National library. [v.] 1-
Philadelphia, E. Littell, 1830-
v. 17½cm.

44-26915

NN 0057187   DLC

National Library, *Bandra, India*
see
Bombay. National Library, *Bandra.*

National library, *Louisville, Ky.*
Catalogue of the National library co.'s circulating
library ... Louisville, Ky., National library company
[188-?]
1 p. l., v, [1], 24, [4] p. 13½cm.

8-25034†

Library of Congress   7881.L0052

NN 0057189   DLC

VOLUME 407

National library association, Chicago.
Catalog of the National library association.
1890.
191 p.

1. Catalogs, Booksellers' - U. S.

NN 0057190   NNC

A national library for Canada
   see under   Canadian Library Association.

National library for the blind, London
see
London. National library for the blind

National Library for the Blind, *Washington, D. C.*
   see Washington, D. C. National Library for the Blind.

A national library not a mausoleum
   see under   [Savary, John] d. 1910.

National Library of Canada
see
Ottawa. National Library.

National library of Ireland, Dublin
   see   Dublin. National library.

National Library of Medicine
see
U. S. *National Library of Medicine.*

National Library of Peiping
see
Pei-ching t'u shu kuan.

National library of Scotland, *Edinburgh*
see
Scotland. National library, *Edinburgh.*

National Library of Social Sciences, *Prague*
see
Prague. Státní knihovna společenských věd.

---

32   National library of standard and popular music
       for the violin.   Philadelphia [&] Chicago,
       J.W. Pepper [1888-9]
       v. 1-5.

NN 0057201   DLC

National Library of the People's Republic of Serbia, *Belgrad*
see
Belgrad. Narodna biblioteka.

4AG
38   The National library of universal
       entertainment & instruction, con-
       taining many hundred original arti-
       cles of interesting and improving
       information. London, Mayhew [18   ]
       465 p.

NN 0057203   DLC-P4

AG241
N3   The National library of universal entertain-
     ment & instruction. Illustrated with two
     hundred & thirty engravings, by first rate
     artists.   London, Mayhew & Co.[183-?]
     iv,352 p.   illus., ports.   28ᶜᵐ.
     Apparently originally issued in 8-page parts.

     1.Curiosities.   2.London.

NN 0057204   CSt IU

National Library of Wales, *Aberystwyth*
see **Wales. National Library,** *Aberystwyth.*

National library of Wales journal
see
Cylchgrawn llyfrgell genedlaethol cymru.

National life...
   v. 1-

London, 1929-   28cm.
   v.

   Five nos. a year, 1929-31; quarterly, 1932-
   "To combat the theory and practice of contraception."
   Official organ of the League of national life. Includes a report of its annual
meeting ; 1933- includes also its Annual report.
   Vol. 2, no. 18 (Dec., 1935) has suppl.

   1. Birth control—Per. and soc.   publ.—Gt. Br.   I. League of
national life, London.
N.Y.P.L.   September 8, 1938

NN 0057207   NN

National life and accident insurance company, incorporated,
Nashville.
   ... Agents' training course ... [Nashville, Tenn., The
National life and accident insurance company, *1941]
   3 v.   10½ᶜᵐ.

   "The National life and accident insurance company incorporated" on
device at head of title.

   1. Insurance, Life—Agents.   I. Title.
                                           41–7904

   Library of Congress   HG8876.N34
                                   [2]
                                      368.3

NN 0057208   DLC

The National life and accident insurance company, incorpo-
rated, *Nashville.*
   A guide book to ordinary production for old and new shield
men ...   Nashville, Tenn., The National life and accident insurance company, incorporated [*1932]
   3 p. l., 260 p.   illus. (incl. ports.) diagrs.   23½ᶜᵐ.

   1. Insurance, Life—Agents.   I. Title.
   Library of Congress   HG8876.N35   32–14546
   ———— Copy 2.
   Copyright A 51183   [2]   368.3

NN 0057209   DLC

HG8963   National life and accident insurance company,
.N87 O 8   inc., Nashville.
      Our shield.

      Nashville, Tenn. [National life and accident insurance com-
pany] 19

National life and accident insurance company, inc., Nashville.

   The story of the shield; a book of pictures to be hand colored
by boys and girls... [Nashville, Tenn.] National life & accident insurance co. [c1936]   8 l.   illus.   15 x 23cm.

   1. Juvenile literature—Picture   books.   2. Shields.
N.Y.P.L.   June 15, 1948

NN 0057211   NN

National life and thought of the various nations
     throughout the world
       see under   Magnusson, Eirikr, 1833–1919]

National life and travelers insurance co., N.Y.
       see   National life insurance company,
New York.

---

*K
.B68885   National Life Association, plaintiff in error.
v.20
no.13   National Life Association, plaintiff in
      error against Berkeley and others, defendants
      in error.   Record No. 955.   From Hustings
      Court of the City of Staunton. [Staunton?
      Va., 1899?]
        26 p.   23cm.   [Braxton legal pamphlets]
        Cover title.
        "In the Supreme Court of Appeals of Virginia,
      at Staunton, Va."
        [I. Berkeley, Francis B., plaintiff in error.
      II. Virginia. Supreme   Court of Appeals.

NN 0057214   ViU

National life association, *Hartford, Conn.*
   Life insurance manual, by D. S. Fletcher (general manager) of the National life association of Hartford, Conn.
Issue 1889. [Hartford, Conn., 1889]
   cover-title, 84 p.   14½ᶜᵐ.

   I. Fletcher, Dolphin S.

                                          8–8212†
   Library of Congress   HG8963.N4A3   1889

NN 0057215   DLC

National life association, *Hartford, Conn.*
   ... Manual for the use of agents ... Ed. of 1895. [Hart-
ford, Conn., National life association, *1896]
   60 p.   19 x 10½ᶜᵐ.
   Library of Congress   HG8881.N3   1896
   ———— Ed. of 1897. [Hartford, Conn., National life
association, *1897]
   44 p.   19 x 10½ᶜᵐ.

                                          7–8888–9†
   Library of Congress   HG8881.N3   1897

NN 0057216   DLC

VOLUME 407

The National life conservation society.

Browne, Anita, *ed.*
Golden jubilee poems of the statue of Liberty; Anita Browne, editor ... Compiled from the poetry contest sponsored by the National life conservation society in co-operation with the National park service of the United States. New York city, The Poets press [°1936]

NN   0057218   CSmH

The National Life: containing Biographical sketches of the Presidents of the United States, from Washington to Grant; with correct Portraits, engraved expressly for this work. With other interesting incidents relating to the Life of the Nation.   Boston, Published by H.R. Stevens, 1870.
cover-title, 36 p.   illus. (ports.)   12 mo.
In the original blue-gray, printed paper covers.
Sketch of the Life of George Washington, p. 2.
The Lewisson collection, September 1922.

NN   0057218   CSmH

The National Life: containing Biographical sketches of the Presidents of the United States, from Washington to Grant; with correct Portraits engraved expressly for this work. With other interesting incidents relating to the life fo the Nation.   Boston, Published by H.R. Stevens, 1871.
cover-title, 48 p.   illus. (ports.)   12 mo.
In the original brown pictorial paper covers.
Sketch of George Washington : p. 2.
The Lewisson collection, September 1922.

NN   0057219   CSmH

The National Life: containing Biographical sketches of the Presidents of the United States, from Washington to Grant: with correct Portraits, engraved expressly for this work ...
Boston, Published by H.R. Stevens, 1872. c1870,
cover-title.   12 mo.   Original salmon paper covers.
Issued by H.R. Stevens, Boston, as an advertising medium.
Lewisson Collection, April 1925.

NN   0057220   CSmH

The national life, containing biographical sketches of the presidents of the United States from Washington to Hayes...
Boston, Mass, [c1879]
72 p.

NN   0057221   OClWHi OFH

National Life Insurance Company, Chicago.
Answer of the National Life Insurance Company of Chicago, to the circular against co-operation in life insurance. With the circular to which it is an answer. Read, and judge between the two systems of life insurance.   Chicago: Evening Post Print, 1870.   16, 4 p.   25½cm.

"A monstrous swindle. The fallacies of co-operative life insurance. By Hon. Elizur Wright," 4 p. inserted between p. 14 and 15.

869637A. 1. Insurance, Life—U. S.   I. Wright, Elizur, 1804–1885. A
monstrous swindle.
N. Y. P. L.   February 25, 1937

NN   0057222   NN

National life insurance company, *Chicago.*
... [Circular. Chicago, 1870]
cover-title, 34, [2] p.   14½cm.
p. 31–32 wanting.

Library of Congress   HG8963.N52A4   CA 9–1876 Unrev'd

NN   0057223   DLC

National Life Insurance Company, [Montpelier,] Vt.
Abstract of the 3d annual report to the Legislature, showing the condition of the company Nov. 1, 1852.
Montpelier. 1852. 56 pp. 24°.

F7386 — Life insurance.

NN   0057224   MB

National Life Insurance Company, Montpelier, Vt.
... Annual report ...
see its   Report.

National life insurance company, *Montpelier, Vt.*
Condensed value tables for installment bonds. Issued by the National life ins. co., of Vermont. [Montpelier, °1883]
[2] p. 15 x 8½ᶜᵐ.
Caption title.

CA 9–1877 Unrev'd
Library of Congress   HG8963.N64A3

NN   0057226   DLC

NATIONAL LIFE INSURANCE COMPANY, Montpelier, Vt.
Federal taxes as affecting life insurance and annuities.
Revised August 1, 1934.   Montpelier, Vt.: National Life Insurance Co. [1934]   23 p. incl. tables.   28cm.

Cover-title.

874161A. 1. Insurance, Life—Taxation—U.S., 1934.

NN   0057227   NN WaU-L

National life insurance company, *Montpelier, Vt.*
National life insurance company; a history of its foundation and development 1850–1925. Montpelier, Vt., The Company, 1925.
4 p. l., 3–188, [1] p., 1 l. front., illus. (incl. ports., facsims.) 27ᶜᵐ.
Foreword signed : Arthur B. Bisbee.

I. Bisbee, Arthur Brown, 1858–

Library of Congress   HG8963.N63A3 1925   25–22071

NN   IdU OrU ICJ ViU Ok MtHi
0057228   DLC MH CoU MWA MiU CU ScU MsU MtU

National life insurance company, Montpelier, Vt.
The National messenger, a magazine for that which is good in all things ...
see under title

National life insurance company, Montpelier, Vt.
Out of the rut.
[New York] c1882.

HG8963
.N64A3

NN   0057230   DLC

National life insurance company, Montpelier, Vt.
Paid-up life policy and cash balances for option no. 4. Investment insurance trust bond.
Montpelier, Vt., National life insurance company, 1902.
34 p.

NN   0057231   MiU

National Life Insurance Company, Montpelier, Vt.
[Prospectus.]
Montpelier. 1850. 36 pp. 16°.   9368-3743
Montpelier.

F7386 — Life insurance.

NN   0057232   MB

National life insurance company, Montpelier, Vt.
Rates, values and miscellaneous tables.
Printed for the use of the company's agents.
January 1, 1901.
n.p.,n.d.
250 p.

NN   0057233   MiU

NATIONAL LIFE INSURANCE COMPANY,Montpelier,Vt.
Rates,values and miscellaneous tables.
Montpelier,Vt.,1908.
24°.

NN   0057234   MH-BA

National Life Insurance Company, *Montpelier, Vt.*
Report.
Montpelier.
v. illus., ports. 21 cm. annual.

HG8963.N54A3   51–36234 ‡

NN   0057235   DLC Nh NN

National life insurance company, *Montpelier, Vt.*
Selecting and recruiting the new agent. Montpelier, Vt., National life insurance company, °1944.
1 p. l., 2 numb. l., 1 l., 174 numb. l. 28½ x 22ᶜᵐ.
Reproduced from type-written copy.

1. Insurance, Life—Agents.   I. Title.
44–44110
Library of Congress   HG8876.N37
[2]   368.3

NN   0057236   DLC

National Life Insurance Company, Montpelier, Vt.
Selling national policies. Montpelier, Vt., 1931.
116 p. illus.

1. Insurance, Life. I. Title.

NN   0057237   WaU

W.C.L.   National Life Insurance Company, Montpelier, Vt.
J917.43   [The story of old Vermont in pictures. [Mont-
N277S   pelier, Vt., c1937]
1 v. (unpaged, chiefly illus.) 19 cm.
Cover title.

1. Vermont. History. Pictorial works.
2. Vermont. Description and travel. Views. I. Title.

NN   0057238   NcD

VOLUME 407

National life insurance company, Montpelier, Vt.
The story of old Vermont in pictures. (Second edition.)
₍Montpelier: National life insurance co., 1939₎   12 l.   illus.
19cm.

1. Vermont—Hist.—Pictorial   works. I. Title.
N. Y. P. L.   May 13, 1942

NN   0057239   NN

National life insurance company, New York.
[Circular. New York, 1865?]

HG8963
.N55A3

NN   0057240   DLC

National life insurance company of the United States of
America.
... Agent's rate book. ₍Philadelphia, Chandler, pr.,
1871₎
cover-title, 48 p.   19 x 10½ᶜᵐ.

Library of Congress   HG8853.N3 1871   7–2256†

NN   0057241   DLC

National life insurance company of the United States of
America.
... Agents' rate book and instructions. ₍Chicago₎ 1877.
62, ₍2₎ p.   16½ᶜᵐ.

Library of Congress   HG8853.N3 1877   7–2258†

NN   0057242   DLC

National life insurance company of the United States of
America.
... Annual statement of the National life insurance
company of the United States of America, Washington,
D. C. ...
₍Chicago,
v. 15½–20ᶜᵐ.

CA 11–1605 Unrev'd

Library of Congress   HG8963.N56A3

NN   0057243   DLC

NATIONAL LIFE INSURANCE COMPANY Of the United
States of America.
Centennial offering of the book of the signers
and continental curiosities,containing fac-
simile letters of the signers of the Declaration
of Independence. The only edition in existence.
Philadelphia,[National Life Insurance Company of
theUnited States of America],1875.

f°. Ports,fac-simile plates and other illustr
Consists of fac-simile "letters,documents,or
signatures from every one of the illustrious
fifty-six" who signed the Declaration of Independence.

Introduction.
Each facsimile manuscript has a mounted
protrait or illustration.
The plates are inserted.

NN   0057245   MH

National life insurance company of the United States of
America.
Life insurance explained and objections answered, by
the National life insurance company of the United States
of America. ₍Philadelphia?₎ Inquirer printing office
₍*1868₎

cover-title, 23, ₍1₎ p.   17½ᶜᵐ.

1. Insurance, Life.

CA 10–3395 Unrev'd

Library of Congress   HG8963.N58A3

NN   0057246   DLC

Pam   National Life Insurance Company of the United
73–   States of America.
1410   [Miscellaneous publications] Philadelphia,
1868.

1. National Life Insurance Company.
2. Insurance, Life–Philadelphia.

NN   0057247   WHi

National life magazine.
v. 1

New York: Independent Magazine Distributing Co., 1928–30.
v.   illus. (incl. ports.)
Irregular.
v. 1, no. 6 incorrectly called v. 1, no. 5.
Ceased publication with v. 1, no. 8, June, 1930.

1. Periodicals—U. S.
N. Y. P. L.   January 23, 1931

NN   0057248   NN

THE NATIONAL LIFE OF CHINA. [Edin-
burgh, 1854.] [16] p. 8.
From Blackwood's magazine, 1854, v. 75, p. 593–608

NN   0057249   MSaE

National life saving and ship ballasting company, *New
York.*
The National life saving & ship ballasting company of
the city of New York. Incorporated under the laws of
the state of New York ... New York, L. H. Frank & co.,
printers ₍1869₎
64 p. illus, fold. plates. 25½ᶜᵐ.

CONTENTS.—Organization of the National life saving and ship ballasting company of New York.—Description of life saving apparatus.—Ballasting of vessels.—Extracts from the press.

1. Life-saving apparatus.

CA 17–2646 Unrev'd

Library of Congress   VK1477.N27

NN   0057250   DLC NN

YA   National Light and Fuel company.
18789   Copy of an act to incorporate the national
light and fuel company, and accompanying documents relating to the same. W₈shington, 1886.
72p.

NN   0057251   DLC

... A national light and heat company, for providing our streets and houses with hydrocarbonic
gas-lights, on similar principles as they are
now supplied with water
see under [Winsor, Frederick Albert]
1763–1830.

National lime association.

Agricultural lime news bulletin, published by the Na-
tional lime association. v. 1–
Apr. 1920–
Washington, D. C., 1920–

National Lime Association.
Annual convention. ₍Minutes₎

₍n. p.₎
v. 28 cm.

1. Lime—Congresses.

TA434.N3   666.9   49–35349*‡

NN   0057254   DLC

National Lime Association.
Approximate consumption of liming materials
on United States farms ... (ton basis)

Washington.
1. Lime. Statistics. I. National lime association. Consumption of liming materials on United
States farms. II. Title: Liming materials.

NN   0057255   DNAL

National Lime Association.
Better pastures.   [Washington, 194–?]
folder ([5] p.)

1. Fertilizers for pastures. 2. Pastures.
3. Liming of soils.

NN   0057256   DNAL

NATIONAL lime association.
Bulletin. 1905–09; no.1, 1916+
Washington, D.C.

NN   0057257   DPR ViU OCl OCU TxLT

Egleston
D691.5
N21
National lime association.
Chemical lime facts. Washington ₍1951₎
42 p. illus. (part col.) tables. (Its
Bulletin 214)

1. Lime.

NN   0057258   NNC DI

National Lime   Association.
Constitution and by-laws of the National Lime Manufac-
turers' Association. ₍Chicago?₎ 1914. 4 l. 24°.
Caption-title.

1. Lime.—Manufacture: Associations.
N. Y. P. L.   March 9, 1917.

NN   0057259   NN

National Lime Association.
The Crossland lime kiln
see under title

VOLUME 407

National Lime   Association.
   The garden.   ₍Riverton, Va.?₎ The assoc., 1917.   8 p.
8°.
   Cover-title.
   At head of title: Agricultural bull. no. 2.

1. Gardening (Vegetable).
N. Y. P. L.   August 24, 1917.

NN   0057261   NN

National Lime Association.
   Lime and lime-cement brick mortar...   Washington, D. C.:
National Lime Assoc. ₍1922?₎   11 p. incl. diagr., tables.   8°.
(National Lime Assoc. Bull. 300 A.)
   Cover-title.

1. Lime. 2. Mortar. 3. Series.
N. Y. P. L.   February 16, 1924.

NN   0057262   NN

National lime association.
   Lime brief...
   Washington, D.C.

TP886
.N3

NN   0057263   DLC

SD643   National lime association.
N25   Lime in agriculture.   Washington, D. C.,
         National lime association ₍°1930₎

           53p. front.,illus.,tables.   23cm.
         (National lime association.   Bulletin 190)

           I. Title.   1. Lime.

NN   0057264   NBuG

National lime association.
   Lime in agriculture (revised May, 1936) ...   Washington,
D. C., National lime association ₍1936₎
   53 p. incl. illus., tables, diagr. front. 28ᵐ. (Its Bulletin 190)

   1. Lime.
                                                  36-18161
   Library of Congress   S643.N3 1936 a
   ——— Copy 2.
   Copyright AA 211034   ₍3₎   631.821

NN   0057265   DLC

National lime association.
   Lime in agriculture (revised May, 1939) ...   Washington,
D. C., National lime association ₍°1939₎
   53 p. front., illus., diagr. 23ᵐ. (Its Bulletin 190)

   1. Lime.
                                                  39-20081
   Library of Congress   S643.N3 1939 a
   ——— Copy 2.   TP875.N36 no. 190
   Copyright AA 303782   ₍2₎   (666.9) 631.821

NN   0057266   DLC

National Lime Association.
   Lime in concrete; its use as approved by engineers, architects,
and contractors...   Washington, D. C.: National Lime Assoc.
₍1922.₎ 23 p. illus. 8°. (National Lime Assoc. Bull.
308.)

1. Lime. 2. Cement and concrete.   3. Series.
N. Y. P. L.   February 16, 1924.

NN   0057267   NN

NATIONAL LIME ASSOCIATION.
   Lime, its use and value in the industrial and chemical
processes. Washington, D.C. [, 1930.] 88 p. 8°.

600283A. 1. Lime.

NN   0057268   NN MiD NBuG OU

National Lime Association.
   Lime stucco; its essential qualities, historical development
and use, description of modern properties, its application, and
specifications for the guidance of architects and builders...
Washington, D. C.: National Lime Assoc. ₍1922.₎   48 p. illus.
8°.   (National Lime Assoc. Bull. 307A.)

1. Lime. 2. Stucco. 3. Series.
N. Y. P. L.   February 16, 1924.

NN   0057269   NN

National lime association.
   Masonry mortar ...
   Washington, D.C., National lime association
₍c1934₎
   36 p.   (Its Bulletin 321)

NN   0057270   OU

National Lime Association.
   ₍Minor publications₎
   Washington, D.C.

NN   0057271   ICJ

National lime association.
   Minutes of ... annual meeting of the National
lime association
           see its   Proceedings.

D691.5
N21
         National lime association.
           ₍Miscellaneous publications. 1915-

         Unbound pamphlets.

           1. Lime.   2. Concrete.

NN   0057273   NNC WaS

57.52
N21   National Lime Association.
         Nitrogen from the air.   [Washington, 194-?]
       folder ([5] p.)

           1. Nitrification. 2. Nitrifying bacteria.
       I. Title.

NN   0057274   DNAL

National lime association.

Rudolfs, Willem, 1886–
   Principles of sewage treatment, by Dr. Willem Rudolfs ...
Washington, D. C., National lime association ₍°1941₎

National lime association.
   Proceedings, National lime association.
   ₍Washington? D. C., 19
   v. illus., plates, tables, diagrs. 23½ᵐ.
   Title varies: 1911, Transactions of the ... annual meeting of the Na-
      tional lime manufacturers' association.
      1912–   Minutes of ... annual meeting of the National lime
         manufacturers' association.
      19   Proceedings of the ... annual meeting of the Na-
         tional lime manufacturers' association.
      19   Proceedings of the ... annual convention of the Na-
         tional lime association (slight variations)
      19   Technical papers and addresses, National lime associa-
         tion.
      1926–   Proceedings, National lime association.
   1. Lime—Societies.
                                              .CA 17–1609 Unrev'd
   Library of Congress   TP875.N35

NN   0057276   DLC MB NN CU DNW DNLM MiU ICJ

National lime association.
   Publications of the National lime association; construction, agricultural, and chemical departments (correct to
March 1, 1922) Washington, National lime association
₍1922₎
   7, ₍1₎ p. 15ᵐ.

   1. Lime—Bibl. 2. National lime association—Bibl.
                                                  23-12
   Library of Congress   Z7914.L6N2

NN   0057277   DLC

National Lime Association.
   Standard specifications for lime plaster.   Washington, D. C.:
National Lime Assoc. ₍1922?₎   16 p. 4°. (National Lime
Assoc. Bull. 305A.)
   Cover-title.

1. Plaster and plastering. 2. Series.
N. Y. P. L.   April 1, 1924.

NN   0057278   NN

National lime association.
   Technical papers and addresses
           see its   Proceedings.

309.0   National Lime Association.
N31T   Trade waste bulletin. no. 1-
         Apr. 1948-   Washington.
           1. Lime. 2. Factory and trade waste.

NN   0057280   DNAL NNC

National lime association.
   Transactions of the ... annual meeting ...
           see its   Proceedings.

National Lime Association.
   The use of lime in industrial trade waste
treatment. Washington, 1948.
   32 p. 28ᶜᵐ. (Its Trade waste bulletin no.1)
   Cover-title.
   Bibliography: p. 25-32.

   1. Lime. 2. Factory and trade waste. I. Ser.

NN   0057282   ViU DI

National Lime Association.
   The use of lime versus caustic soda and soda
ash as acid neutralizing agents. Washington,
1948.
   15 p. 28ᶜᵐ. (Its Trade waste bulletin no.2)
   Cover-title.
   "Errata" slip tipped in.

   1. Lime. 2. Acids, Inorganic. 3. Factory and
trade waste. I. Ser.

NN   0057283   ViU

VOLUME 407

National lime association.
The value of hydrated lime as a filler in asphalt paving mixtures. Washington, D. C., National lime association ₍1926₎

cover-title, 16 p. incl. illus., tables, diagrs. 23½ᶜᵐ. (*Its* Bulletin 318)

1. Lime. 2. Pavements, Asphalt.   ɪ. Title.

Library of Congress   TE270.N3   26–21000

NN 0057284   DLC

National lime association
Water softening: municipal, railroads, raw water ice, industrial. Wash., D. C., National lime association, °1925.
48 p. illus. tables, diagrs.

Cover title.

NN 0057285   MiD

National Lime Association.
Whitewash and cold water paint...   Washington, D. C.: National Lime Assoc. ₍1922?₎   8 p.   8°.   (National Lime Assoc. Bull. 304 B.)

1. Lime. 2. Whitewashing. 3. Series.
N. Y. P. L.   February 16, 1924.

NN 0057286   NN

National Lime Association.
Whitewash & cold water paints. ₍Washington, 1950₎
11 p. illus. 23 cm. (*Its* Bulletin no. 304–F)

1. Paint.   ɪ. Title.   ɪɪ. Title: Cold water paints.   (Series)

TP936.N315   667.6   55–44570

NN 0057287   DLC

National Lime   Association. — Committee on Publicity and Sales Promotion.
Report of meeting of Committee on Publicity and Sales Promotion of the National Lime Manufacturers' Association ₍at₎ Marlborough-Blenheim. Atlantic City, N. J., 1914. 8 p. 8°.

Cover-title.

1. Lime.—Manufacture: Associations.
N. Y. P. L.   June 23, 1916.

NN 0057288   NN

National lime association.   Committee on uniform cost accounting.

Uniform cost accounting system for the lime industry ... Washington, D. C., Lime association ₍Richmond, Virginia, Everett Waddey company 1919?₎
4 v. forms. (part fold.) 27½ᶜᵐ.
"Chart of accounts" laid in, v.2.
"Prepared by the Lime association committee on uniform cost accounting assisted by the American audit company."
Vols. ₍III–IV₎, cover-title; have also special t.–p. CONTENTS.—v. I. Analysis sheet method for the small manufacturer.—v. II. Cost ledger method for the large manufacturer.—v. VII, Supplement I: Operations of Baltimore, Inc. ... company, inc. for the month of January 1919.—v. V, Supplement II, Operations of Washington ... me company, inc., for the month of January 1919.
1. Lime industry—Accounting. ɪ. American audit co. ɪɪ. Title

NN 0057289   ViU IU

National Lime   Association.—Hydrate Manufacturers' Section.
Proceedings of meeting...
₍no.₎ 1
₍Riverton, Va., 1914.₎   8°.

1914 full title reads Proceedings of the first meeting of the Hydrate Manufacturers of the United States.

1. Lime.—Manufacture: Associations.
N. Y. P. L.   March 15, 1917.

NN 0057290   NN

National lime   association.
Hydrated lime bureau·
Dependable concrete, hydrated lime and its effect on workability, segregation, uniformity, strength, permeability.
Pittsburgh, The bureau, n.d.
14 p.

NN 0057291   OU

National lime association. Hydrated lime bureau.
Modern methods in concrete construction.
Pittsburgh, The author, c1917.
14 p.
With which is bound its Watertight concrete.

NN 0057292   WaS

National Lime   Association. Traffic Committee.
Report...
₍Chicago, 19   8°.
v.

1. Lime.—Trade and statistics. U. S.
N. Y. P. L.   October 3, 1918.

NN 0057293   NN

National lime manufacturers' association

see

National lime association.

National Lincoln Monument Association.
Address of the National Lincoln Monument Association.
Springfield, Ill. ₍1865₎

4 p. 24 cm.

Cover title.
Contains the Articles of the Association, and a description of the monument.
Signed: Ricard J. Oglesby, president.

1. Lincoln, Abraham, Pres. U. S., 1809–1865—Tomb.   ɪ. Oglesby, Ricard James, 1824–1899.   ɪɪ. Title.

E457.52N26   65–59345

NN 0057295   DLC

National Lincoln monument association.
Annual reports of the custodian to the executive committee of the National Lincoln monument association. Reports for nine years. From 1875 to 1883, inclusive. Closing with a dissertation on Sunday opening of the monument. Also, remarks on sight-seeing in London; sketches, historical and descriptive of the methods of taking care of the Brock monument at Queenston, Canada; the Washington monument at Baltimore, Md.; Mount Vernon, on the Potomac ... Bunker Hill monument, at

Boston ... Mention of the Washington monument at the Capital ... now almost completed; and of the proposed Garfield monument at Cleveland ... By John Carroll Power ... Springfield, Ill., H. W. Rokker, printer, 1884.
85 p. 23ᶜᵐ.

1. Lincoln, Abraham, pres. U. S.—Tomb.   ɪ. Power, John Carroll, 1819–1894.

Library of Congress   F549.S7N3   9–11006

NN 0057297   DLC OClWHi IU

National Lincoln monument association.
Articles of association, and by-laws, rules and regulations of the National Lincoln monument association, organized at Springfield, Ill., May 11, 1865. Springfield, Press of Baker & Phillips, 1865.
11 p. 21½ᶜᵐ.
Cover-title: Memorial, articles of association ₍etc.₎

1. Lincoln, Abraham, pres. U. S., 1809–1865.

Library of Congress   E457.52.N27   5–18224

NN 0057298   DLC IU N IHi

National Lincoln monument association.
Celebration by the Colored people's educational monument association in memory of Abraham Lincoln, on the Fourth of July, 1865, in the presidential grounds, Washington, D. C. ... Washington, D. C., McGill & Witherow, printers, 1865.
33, ₍1₎ p. 22½ cm.

1. Lincoln, Abraham, pres. U. S., 1809–1865.   ɪ. Title.

E457.52.N28   12—30032

PPPrHi MB
NN 0057299   DLC OClWHi MH TxU IaU MiKW CtY PPL

NATIONAL LINCOLN MONUMENT ASSOCIATION.
The colored people's education monument to the memory of Abraham Lincoln. An appeal to a loyal public, etc. ₍Wash., 1865₎.

4°. pp. 2.

NN 0057300   MH CSmH

National Lincoln Monument Association.
Constitution of the educational monument association to the memory of Abraham Lincoln ... Washington, D.C., McGill & Witherow, printers, 1865.
9 p.   Octavo.   In ¾ green morocco and marbled boards; gilt top; padded with blank leaves. With orig. yellow paper covers bound in.
The Judd Stewart collection, May 1922; with ex-libris.

NN 0057301   CSmH

National Lincoln Monument Association.
Lincoln monument association. An appeal to the soldiers and sailors of the United States
see under   Lincoln's Soldiers' and Sailors' Monumental Association.

₍**National Lincoln monument association**₎
A memorial in regard to the Lincoln monument to be erected at Springfield, Illinois. Trenton, N. J., Printed at the office of the State gazette, 1867.
cover-title, 15 p. 23ᶜᵐ.

1. Lincoln, Abraham, pres. U. S.—Tomb.   ɪ. Title.

Library of Congress   E457.52.N29   12—18999

NN 0057303   DLC NN OClWHi

National Lincoln monument association.
The National Lincoln monument.
Washington, 1868.
22½ᶜᵐ.

Published by the National Lincoln monument association, and sent only to those authorized to receive donations.

1. Lincoln, Abraham, pres. U. S., 1809–1865—Tomb.   ɪ. Title.

Library of Congress   E457.52.N25   12–7426

NN 0057304   DLC

VOLUME 407

National Lincoln Monument Association.
National Lincoln monument. Address to the
public. [Springfield, Ill., 1868]
[3] p. 25.5 x 19.5 cm. fold. to
20.5 x 12.5 cm. [Memorials of Abraham
Lincoln, v.3]
Caption title.
1. Lincoln, Abraham, pres. U.S. - Tomb.

NN 0057305 CtY RPB DLC

National Lincoln monument association.
National Lincoln monument association, incorporated
by act of Congress, March 30th, 1867. Washington,
Printed at the Great republic office, 1867.
12 p. 18½ᶜᵐ.
Presidential address by James Harlan, proceedings, memoranda, etc.

2-17865

NN 0057306 DLC CSmH

National Lincoln Monument Association.
National Lincoln monument. Office State
Superintendent Public Instruction, Illinois,
Springfield, May 16, 1865
see under Illinois. Dept. of Public
Instruction.

E
5 NATIONAL LINCOLN MONUMENT ASSOCIATION.
.L 63595 Official programme of the order of exercises
connected with the unveiling of the statue of
Abraham Lincoln upon the national Lincoln monument, Springfield, Illinois, Thursday, October
15th, 1874; also, his remarks to his neighbors on
leaving Springfield, February 11, 1861. With his
inaugural addresses, messages to Congress, emancipation proclamation, and address at Gettysburg,
Pennsylvania. Springfield,Illinois state journal company,1874.
lxxviip. 24cm

NN 0057308 ICN OClWHi CSmH CStbT

National Lincoln monument association.
... Organization and design. Proceedings of the Board of
managers. Plan and prospects. Progress of the work. Representative men selected. Appeal to the public. Appendix.
Washington [Printed at the office of the New national era]
1870.
41, iii p. 22ᶜᵐ.

Library of Congress E457.52.N32

5—33829

NN 0057309 DLC ICN OClWHi OO

National Lincoln Sheep Breeders' Association. 636.3 30
National Lincoln sheep breeders' record. ... . [Charlotte,
115747 Michigan, National Lincoln Sheep Breeders' Association. ᶜ1899]–
1910.
Library has vol. 1–3. illus. 22½ᶜᵐ.

NN 0057310 ICJ OrCS CaBVaU GU ICRL OU

National Lines of Mexico
see Ferrocarriles Nacionales de Mexico.

National Liquor Conference
see National Conference of State Liquor Administrators.

National liquor league of the United States of America
see
National retail liquor dealers' association of America.

National liquor review.
[Chicago, Liquor review publishing co., inc., 19
v. in illus. 28½–30ᶜᵐ. monthly.
Began publication in 1935.
Title varies: –Aug. 1938, Illinois package liquor review.
Sept. 1938– National liquor review.

1. Liquor traffic—Period. 2. Liquor traffic—U. S. 3. Liquor traffic—
Illinois.
HD9350.1.N3 178.4 47–38164

NN 0057314 DLC

The National list; a directory of bonded attorneys ... New
York, National surety company
v. 29½ᶜᵐ.

1. Lawyers—U. S.—Direct. [1. Legal directories—U. S.] 2. Lawyers—Canada—Direct. [2. Legal directories—Canada]
2–11896

NN 0057315 DLC OCIFRB

The National list; a directory of bonded attorneys. Abridged
ed. ... New York, National surety co.
16¼ᶜᵐ.

1. Lawyers—U. S.—Direct.
2—11896

NN 0057316 DLC OCl

The National list; a list of selected attorneys.
Mt. Vernon, N. Y.
v. 23 cm. annual.
Vols for accompanied by updating supplements.

1. Lawyers—United States—Directories.
KF190.N365 340'.025'73 73–645191
ISSN 0091–7656 MARC-S

NN 0057317 DLC NIC

The NATIONAL list of advertisers.
Toronto, Maclean-Hunter [etc.] v.
23cm.

Title varies: 1951, The National list; national advertisers in Canada
with personnel and products.

1. Advertising--Direct.--Canada. 2. Commerce--Direct.--Canada.
I. Title: The National list.

NN 0057318 NN NB MiD

National literary monthly. Toledo, Ohio.

NN 0057319 OU

National literary society, *inc.*
Charter and by-laws. Washington, D. C., National literary society, incorporated [*1922]
24 p. 18ᶜᵐ.

Library of Congress PNJ2.N3 CA 22–713 Unrev'd

NN 0057320 DLC

National Literary Society of Ireland.
Journal. v. 1–2, pt. 1. Dublin, O'Donoghue, 1900–16.
v. 23 cm.
L. C. set incomplete: v. 2, pt. 1 wanting.

1. Irish literature—Period.
PR8700.N37 53–50677

NN 0057321 DLC MB NcU

The National ... Literature, art, science. v. 1, no. 1;
Feb. 1875. Washington, National publication company,
1875.
cover-title, 140 p. illus. 24¼ᶜᵐ.
No more published.

9–19692

Library of Congress AP2.N23

NN 0057322 DLC ViU

M912.77437
F623na National Lithograph Co., Detroit.
New National authentic map of Flint and
environs. [Grand Rapids, Distributed by
Michigan Map Co., 1934?]
map 72x54cm. fold.to 18x9cm.

On cover: New street map of City of Flint,
Michigan.

1.Flint, Mich.-Maps. I.Title. II.New street
map of City of F] int, Michigan.

NN 0057323 Mi

National Lithograph Company, Detroit.
G4114
.D48Q4
1948 Detroit news.
.D4 Salesmen's map of Detroit and suburbs, showing 75 merchandising routes, street numbering guides and relative income areas. Detroit, National Lithograph Co., ᶜ1948.

The National lithographer. Devoted to the interests of lithography and the graphic arts.
New York [National lithographer publishing company]
v. illus. 31ᶜᵐ. monthly.
Editor: W. C. Browne.

1. Lithography—Period. I. Browne, Warren Crittenden, 1858– ed.
CA 9—590 Unrev'd
Library of Congress NE2250.N3

OCl
NN 0057325 DLC ICJ PBL CtH ICN NN TxU DNW ICJ

GRAPHIC ARTS
NE
2860 The National Lithographer.
.N3 The National Lithographer's sample book of
offset lithography. New York, 1920.
[92] p. specimens (part col.) 30cm.

1. Lithographs - Printing - Specimens.
I. Title.

NN 0057326 NNC OCU

VOLUME 407

FOR OTHER EDITIONS
SEE MAIN ENTRY

National lithographer.

Browne, Warren Crittenden, 1858–
... Offset lithography; a treatise on printing in the lithographic manner from metal plates on rubber blanket offset presses. With which is incorporated a comprehensive digest on photo-lithography and also on tin plate decorating; compiled and edited in the office of the National lithographer, by Warren C. Browne. New York, The National lithographer, 1927.

National lithographer.

Trade directory of lithographers; names and addresses of all the lithographing establishments in the United States and Canada together with a selected list from foreign countries ... New York, The National lithographer, 1908.

National lithographers' association.
Annual report. 1st–
1889–

Buffalo, N. Y., 1890–

v. ports. 20ᶜᵐ.

Report year ends Oct. 1.
Full title of 1st report: National lithographers' association of the United States ... Annual report.
1st– reports include the proceedings of the 2d– conventions.
Constitution and by-laws included in each vol.
Editor: 1889– Herman T. Koerner.

1. Koerner, Herman T. 8–6762†

NN 0057329   DLC ICJ ICRL

The **National** lithographer's yearbook
see
Lithographer's supply catalog.

HFBL72   National Lithographic Artists' and Engravers'
.NA   Association of the United States.
Constitution of the General Association
and the Subordinate Associations. New York,
Concord Co-operative print., 1890.
32 p. 14½cm.

Cover title.

1. Lithographers – U.S. – Societies, etc.

NN 0057331   WHi

HFBL72   National Lithographic Artists' and Engravers' Association of the United States.
.NA   Members card [New York? 1890?]
[7] p. 11cm.

NN 0057332   WHi

National lithographic awards exhibition
see Lithographers National Association.
National competition of offset-lithography.

National lithographic printing code authority.
Cost manual for the lithographic printing industry. New York, N. Y., The National lithographic printing code authority [1934]
1 v. 21½ᵐ.
Loose-leaf; lithographed.

1. Lithography—Accounting. 2. Cost—Accounting. I. Title.
                                   34–41423
Library of Congress   HF5686.L5N3
Copyright AA 152328   [2]   763

NN 0057334   DLC

National lithographic printing code authority.
Raeber, Bernard J.
Principles of budgeting normal operating costs for pricing purposes, by Bernard J. Raeber ... declared July 7, 1934 by the National lithographic printing code authority for the lithographic printing industry (B–1) in accordance with the provisions of article III, section 26, paragraph (a) of the Code of fair competition for the graphic arts industries. New York, N. Y., The National lithographic printing code authority [1934]

National Lithuanian Society of America
see
Amerikos lietuvių tautinė sąjunga.

National Little League
see Little League Baseball, inc.

National Liturgical Congress
see
North American Liturgical Week.

National Liturgical Week
see
North American Liturgical Week.

National Live Stock and Meat Board.
Annual report
see its Report.

National Live Stock and Meat Board.
Baking manual for the army cook, including instructions on using lard as a shortening in baking and for deep-fat frying and panfrying ... Chicago, National Live Stock and Meat Board [1942]
96 p. illus. 33ᶜᵐ.
Prepared for the United States Army by the National Live Stock and Meat Board.

NN 0057341   ICJ

National live stock and meat board.
Baking manual for the army cook, including instructions on using lard as a shortening in baking and for deep-fat frying and panfrying ... Prepared for the United States army by the National live stock and meat board ... Chicago, Ill., National live stock and meat board [1943]
96 p. illus. 33ᵐ.
Text on p. [2] and [3] of cover.
"Revised printing March, 1943."

1. Baking. 2. Cookery, Military. 3. U. S. Army—Commissariat. I. U.S. Army.
                           44–38969
Library of Congress   UC733.N3 1943
                   [3]   641.631

NN 0057342   DLC

National live stock and meat board.
Beef chart identification; wholesale and retail cuts... [1930?]

NN 0057343   MiU

National live stock and meat board.
Better meals mean better health for home defense
see under Better meals cooking school, Birmingham, Ala.

National live stock and meat board.
Better nutrition for the nation ... A contribution to the national nutrition program ... Chicago, National live stock and meat board, c1941.
24 p. diagrs. 28ᶜᵐ.

1. Nutrition.

NN 0057345   NNC DNAL

National Live Stock and Meat Board.
Cashing in on beef; a manual of modern cutting methods. Chicago [1930]
61 p. illus. 23 cm.

1. Meat cutting. I. Title.

TS1962.N28   53–48172

NN 0057346   DLC OCl DNAL

National live stock and meat board.
Cashing in on beef; a modern merchandising manual
see under National live stock and meat board. Dept. of meat merchandising.

National livestock and meat board.
Cashing in on lamb; a modern merchandising manual
see under National live stock and meat board. Dept. of meat merchandising.

National live stock and meat board.
Cashing in on pork; a modern merchandising manual
see under National live stock and meat board. Dept. of meat merchandising.

National live stock and meat board.
Cashing in on pork; suggestions for merchandising fresh and cured pork cuts. Chicago, Ill., National live stock & meat board, c1932.
79 p. illus. 23ᵐ.

1. Pork industry and trade. I. Title.
                                32–31879
Library of Congress   TS1962.N3
Copyright AA 107018   [2]   658.9414

NN 0057350   DLC OCl

National live stock and meat board.
Factors affecting color in beef. 1939.
International l[ive] s[tock] exposition.
n.p., n.d.
1v. 23x29½cm.

NN 0057351   MoU

National Live Stock and Meat Board.
Food and nutrition news
see under title

VOLUME 407

389.1   National live stock and meat board.
N21F   Food nutrition in wartime; a series of twenty
         reference charts.   Chicago [194-?]
         [20] p.
           1. Food. 2. Nutrition. I. Title.

NN   0057353   DNAL

National live stock and meat board.
    Food values ... ₍1933?₎

NN   0057354   MiU

National live stock and meat board.
    Fresh pork chart, identification, wholesale
and retail cuts ... ₍1930?₎

NN   0057355   MiU

National live stock and meat board.
    Guide for cutting beef, prepared for the United States navy
by the National live stock and meat board. Chicago, Ill. ₍1942?₎
    cover-title, 43 p. illus. 26½ x 20½ᵐ.

    1. Carving (Meat, etc.) 2. Beef. 3. Cookery, Military.   I. U. S.
Navy.
    Library of Congress   TX885.N3   44-38867
                                 ₍3₎   641.362

NN   0057356   DLC

National live stock and meat board.
    Guide for cutting lamb chops, machine and hand cutting,
prepared for armed forces of the United States by the National live stock and meat board. Chicago, Ill. ₍1942?₎
    cover-title, 24 p. illus. 26½ x 20½ᵐ.

    1. Carving (Meat, etc.) 2. Lamb (Meat) 3. Cookery, Military.
                                             44-38866
    Library of Congress   TX885.N32
                                 ₍3₎   641.363

NN   0057357   DLC

National live stock and meat board.
    Handbook on cutting beef, prepared for the United States
army by the National live stock and meat board. Chicago, Ill.
₍1942?₎
    cover-title, 48 p. illus. 33ᵐ.

    1. Carving (Meat, etc.) 2. Beef. 3. Cookery, Military.   I. U. S.
Army.
    Library of Congress   TX885.N33   44-38865
                                 ₍3₎   641.362

NN   0057358   DLC TU DNAL PSt

National live stock and meat board.
    Handbook on cutting lamb, prepared for the United States
army by the National live stock and meat board. Chicago, Ill.
₍1942?₎
    cover-title, 32 p. illus. 33ᵐ.

    1. Carving (Meat, etc.) 2. Lamb (Meat) 3. Cookery, Military.
I. U. S. Army.
    Library of Congress   TX885.N34   44-38864
                                 ₍3₎   641.363

NN   0057359   DLC TU DNAL

National live stock and meat board.
    Issuing meat by the unit supply, prepared for the United
States army by the National live stock and meat board. Chicago, Ill. ₍1942?₎
    cover-title, 24 p. illus. 26½ x 20½ᵐ.

    1. U. S. Army—Commissariat. 2. Meat.   I. U. S. Army.
                                             44-39226
    Library of Congress   UC713.N36
                                 ₍3₎   355.63

NN   0057360   DLC

National live stock and meat board
    Lamb chart, identification, wholesale and
retail cuts... ₍193-₎

NN   0057361   MiU

National Live Stock and Meat Board.
    The lamb menu book; a collection of menus
featuring selected lamb recipes ... Chicago,
Ill., Author, n.d.
    23 p.

NN   0057362   WaPS

National live stock and meat board, *comp.*
    Meat and how I cook it, compiled and distributed by the
National live stock and meat board. Chicago, Ill., ₍1924.
    57, ₍5₎ p. illus. 19½ᵐ.

    1. Cookery (Meat)   I. Title.
                                             25-8001
    Library of Congress   TX749.N3

NN   0057363   DLC MU

National live stock and meat board.
    Meat and meat cookery... 1932.
    see under title

National live stock and meat board.

Conference on cooperative meat investigations.
    Meat and meat cookery, by the Committee on preparation
factors, National cooperative meat investigations. Chicago,
Ill., The National live stock and meat board, 1942.

Home Economics   ₍National Live Stock and Meat Board, Chicago₎
    TX   Meat carving made easy.   Chicago, ₍n.d.₎
    652   ₍14₎ p.
    .7
    Z99
    no.9

           1. Carving (Meat, etc.) I. Title.

NN   0057366   NIC

---

*TX373   National live stock and meat board.
N2   Meat charts, showing wholesale and retail
         cuts; a guide to a better knowledge of meat.
         Chicago, National live stock and meat board
         ₍1934?₎

           cover-title, 19p.   tables, diagrs.   28cm.

             1. Meat.   I. Title.

NN   0057367   NBuG

389.25
N21Meh   National Live Stock and Meat Board.

           Meat for health; a discussion of the food
         value and healthfulness of meat, with
         suggestions for the selection, preparation
         and cooking of the various cuts, and more
         than eighty recipes for appetizing and
         economical meat dishes.   Chicago ₍1923?₎
         30 p.

             1. Cookery   (Meat) 2. Meat as food.

NN   0057368   DNAL

641.5   National live stock and meat board.
N213m   Meat for the family, prepared by high-school
         girls of the United States and the National live
         stock and meat board _ Chicago, Ill., National
         live stock and meat board, c1925.
         48p. illus.

             1. Cookery (Meat) I. Title.

NN   0057369   IU

National Live Stock and Meat Board.
    Meat in menu planning
         see under   National Live Stock and
    Meat Board. Dept. of Home Economics.

National Livestock and Meat Board.
    Meat manual: identification, buying, cooking
         see under   National Live Stock and
    Meat Board. Dept. of home economics.

National live stock and meat board.
    Meat point pointers. Compliments ₍of₎ National live stock and
meat board. ₍Chicago, 1944?₎   40 p.   illus. 20cm.

    At head of title: Wartime meat recipe book.

       1. Cookery—Meat.
    N. Y. P. L.   January 21, 1946

NN   0057372   NN DNAL

National live stock and meat board.
    Meat reference manual for mess sergeants and cooks, pre-
pared for the United States army by the National live stock
and meat board. Chicago, Ill. ₍1943₎
    cover-title, 36 p. illus. 26½ x 20½ᵐ.
    Reproduced from type-written copy.
    "Revised printing March, 1943."

    1. Meat. 2. Cookery (Meat) 3. Cookery, Military.   I. U. S. Army.
                                             44-38863
    Library of Congress   TX373.N26 1943
                                 ₍3₎   641.36

NN   0057373   DLC

National Live Stock and Meat Board.
    ₍Minor publications₎

NN   0057374   ICJ

National live stock and meat board.
    National live stock and meat board reivew.
    see under title

VOLUME 407

National Live Stock and Meat Board.
   Newsletter.   Chicago, Ill.
      v.   illus.   41.5 cm.

NN   0057376   DNAL

389.1   National live stock and meat board.
N21N   The normal diet, with food value charts.
Ed.4   4th ed., rev.   Chicago, 1942.
             18 p.   illus.   21 cm.
             Bibliography: p.2.
             1. Food. 2. Nutrition. 3. Meat as food.
           I. Title. II. Title: Food value charts.

NN   0057377   DNAL

National live stock and meat board.
   Nutrition and the importance of meat.
   [Chicago, National live stock and meat board,
   c1936]

      44p.   illus.   24cm.

NN   0057378   DLC OU

National Live Stock and Meat Board.
   Nutrition lecture: eat the right food daily.
Chicago [194-]
   10 p.   illus. (part col.)   28 cm.
   1. Food. Nutritive value. 2. Nutrition.
I. National live stock and meat board.   Eat the
right food daily.

NN   0057379   DNAL

National live stock and meat board.
   Nutrition yardstick; a graphic calculator for
   measuring the food value and adequacy of daily
   diets.   Rev. ed.   Chicago, National Live Stock
   and Meat Board, 1954.
   28 p.   tables.

NN   0057380   Wa

National live stock and meat board.
   Questions and answers about meat, prepared for the United
   States army by the National live stock and meat board.   Chi-
   cago, Ill. [1942]
      cover-title, 82 p.   illus.   26½ x 20½ᵐ.

   1. Meat.   I. U.S. Army.
                                               44–38862
   Library of Congress   TX373.N27
                              [2]
                                               641.36

NN   0057381   DLC

National live stock and meat board.
   Recipes using kitchen fats...by National live stock and meat
   board.   Chicago [1944]   11 p.   illus.   22cm.

   1. Cookery, American.
N. Y. P. L.   August 13, 1947

NN   0057382   NN

National Live Stock and Meat Board.
   Report.   [1st]–
   1923/24–
   [Chicago]
      v.   illus., ports., maps.   23–27 cm.   annual.
   Report year ends June 30.

   1. Meat industry and trade—Societies, etc. 2. Stock and stock-
breeding—Societies, etc.
TS1950.N27   56–17413

NN   0057383   DLC TU IU KU-RH TxU KyU ICJ OU

NATIONAL LIVE STOCK AND MEAT BOARD.
   Tempting meat recipes...   Chicago, Ill.: National Live
Stock and Meat Board [1935]   21 p.   illus.   20cm.

   On cover: Compliments of Wyoming Stock Growers
Association and National Live Stock Meat Board.

845056A. 1. Cookery—Meat. I. Wyoming Stock Growers Association, Cheyenne, Wyo.

NN   0057384   NN

National live stock and meat board.
   Timely meat recipes for meal appeal.   Chicago, Nat. live stock
and meat board, 1945.   39 p.   illus.   20cm.

   1. Cookery—Meat.
N. Y. P. L.   January 21, 1946

NN   0057385   NN

National live stock and meat board.
   Veal chart, identification, wholesale
and retail cuts...   [193-?]

NN   0057386   MiU

National Live Stock and Meat Board.
   Victory meat extenders.   Chicago [194-]
   39 p.
      1. Cookery (Meat) I. National livestock
and meat board. Meat recipe book. II. Title.
III. Title: Meat extenders.

NN   0057387   DNAL

National Live Stock and Meat Board
see also **Reciprocal Meat Conference.**

National live stock and meat board.   *Dept. of home economics.*
   Cooking meat in quantity.   A handbook on practical meat
cookery, designed for use in restaurants, hotels, cafeterias, lunch
rooms, hospitals, clubs, dining halls and other institutions
where meat is cooked for quantity service.   Chicago, Ill., National live stock and meat board, Dept. of home economics,
ᶜ1944.
      64 p. incl. illus., tables.   26½ x 20½ᵐ.
      The results of a study launched in 1942 by the Institution administra-
tion division of the University of Texas, with the cooperation of the
residence halls and other self-supporting institutions of the university,
and sponsored by the National live stock and meat board.   *cf.* Introd.
      "Recipes for meat dishes": p. 43–64.
      1. Cookery (Meat) 2. Cookery for institutions, etc.
I. Title.
   Library of Congress   TX749.N312   44–31331
                              [2]   641.66

NN   0057389   DLC TxU

National live stock and meat board.   *Dept. of home economics.*
   Cooking meat in quantity.   2d ed., rev. and enl. ...   Chicago,
Ill., National live stock and meat board, Dept. of home economics, ᶜ1946.
      64 p. incl. illus., tables.   26½ x 20ᵐ.
      The results of a study launched in 1942 by the Institution administra-
tion division of the University of Texas, with the cooperation of the
residence halls and other self-supporting institutions of the university,
and sponsored by the National live stock and meat board.   *cf.* Introd.
      "Recipes for meat dishes": p. 43–64.
      1. Cookery (Meat) 2. Cookery for institutions, etc.   I. Title.
                                                 46–6890
   Library of Congress   TX749.N312 1946
                              [2]   641.66

NN   0057390   DLC NBuC NN

National Live Stock and Meat Board. Dept. of
   Home Economics.
      Meat in menu planning; a guide to good
   meals.   Chicago, Ill. [1937]
      31 p.
      1. Cookery (Meat) 2. Menus. 3. Nutrition.
   I. Title.

NN   0057391   DNAL

National live stock and meat board. *Dept. of home economics.*
   Meat in menu planning; a guide to good meals.   Chicago,
Nat. live stock and meat board, Dept. of home economics [1945?]
   31 p.   illus.   23cm.

   1. Cookery—Meat.
N. Y. P. L.   December 29, 1950

NN   0057392   NN

National live stock and meat board. *Dept. of home economics.*
   Meat in the meal for health defense...   Chicago: Nat. live
stock and meat board, Dept. of home economics, 1942.   39 p.
illus.   20cm.

   1. Cookery—Meat.
N. Y. P. L.   June 3, 1943

NN   0057393   NN

389.25   National Live Stock and Meat Board.
N215Mea   Dept. of Home Economics.
Ed.3   Meat manual; identification, buying,
           cooking.   3d ed.   [Chicago, 1949]
           40 p.

             1. Cookery (Meat) 2. Meat as food.
           3. Marketing (Home economics) I. National
           Live Stock and Meat Board. Dept. of
           Meat Mer-   chandising.

NN   0057394   DNAL

389.25   National Live Stock and Meat Board. Dept.
N215Mea   of Home Economics.
Ed.5   Meat manual; identification, buying,
           cooking.   5th ed.   [Chicago, 1952]
           40 p.

             1. Cookery (Meat) 2. Meat as food.
           3. Marketing (Home economics) I. National
           Live Stock and Meat Board. Dept. of Meat
           Merchandising.

NN   0057395   DNAL KMK MiD

National Live Stock and Meat Board. Dept.
   of home economics.
      Meat manual, judging and grading
      see under   Reciprocal Meat Conference.

National Live Stock and Meat Board.
   Dept. of Home Economics.
      Medley of meat recipes
      see under title

VOLUME 407

National live stock and meat board. *Department of home economics.*
Ten lessons on meat for use in high schools, prepared by the National live stock and meat board, Department of home economics. Chicago, National live stock and meat board, ᶜ1926.
2 p. l., 79 p. illus. 23ᶜᵐ.

1. Meat. I. Title.
A 26–222

Title from Kansas City, Mo., Pub. Libr. Printed by L. C.

NN 0057398   MoK DHEW NN

National live stock and meat board. *Dept. of home economics.*
Ten lessons on meat, for use in schools ... Rev. ed. Chicago, Ill., National live stock and meat board, Dept. of home economics, 1927.
2 p. l., 79 p. illus., 4 col. pl. on 2 l., diagr. 23ᶜᵐ.
"Reading list ...": at end of each lesson.

1. Meat. I. Title.
Agr 28–1629

Library, U. S. Dept. of   Agriculture 389N216

NN 0057399   DNAL

National live stock and meat board. *Dept. of home economics.*
Ten lessons on meat, for use in schools. 2d rev. ed. Chicago, Ill., National live stock and meat board, ᶜ1933.
2 p. l., 91 p. illus., col. plates, diagrs. 23ᶜᵐ.
"Reading list" at end of each lesson.

1. Cookery (Meat)   I. Title.
33–8132

Library of Congress   TX749.N32 1933
Copyright AA 115934   ₍2₎   641.66

NN 0057400   DLC OCU OClW ICJ IdU

Mann
TX   National Live Stock and Meat Board. Dept. of
749   Home Economics.
N32   Ten lessons on meat, for use in schools.
1939   4th ed. Chicago, c1939.
    124 p. illus., diagrs., tables. 23 cm.

Bibliography: p. 123-124.

1. Cookery   (Meat) I. Title.

NN 0057401   NIC KMK

National live stock and meat board. *Dept. of home economics.*
Ten lessons on meat, for use in schools. 5th ed. Chicago, Ill., National live stock and meat board, Dept. of home economics, ᶜ1940.
1 p. l., 124, ₍2₎ p. incl. illus., tables, diagrs. 22½ᶜᵐ.
Bibliography: p. 123-124.

1. Cookery (Meat)   I. Title.
42–13153

Library of Congress   TX749.N32 1940
    ₍2₎   641.66

NN 0057402   DLC KMK WaS DNAL

641.3   National Live Stock and Meat Board—Dept. of
N21t   Home Economics.
1943   Ten lessons on meat, for use in schools.
    6th ed.   Chicago, 1943.
    138p. illus. 23cm.

Bibliography: p.133-135.

1. Cookery (Meat) I. Title.

NN 0057403   IU OrCS MiEM MU DNAL DNLM

National Live Stock and Meat Board. *Dept. of Home Economics.*
Ten lessons on meat, for use in schools. 7th ed. Chicago, ᶜ1950.
138 p. illus. 23 cm.
Bibliography: p. 133-135.

1. Cookery (Meat)   I. Title.

TX749.N32 1950   641.66   50–11413

NN 0057404   DLC DNAL

National live stock and meat board. *Dept. of Meat merchandising.*
Cashing in on beef; a modern merchandising manual. Chic. ₍The Author₎ ᶜ1937.
62 p. illus.

NN 0057405   MiD

National live stock and meat board. *Dept. of Meat Merchandising.*
Cashing in on lamb; a modern merchandising manual. ₍Rev. ed.₎ Chic. ₍The Author₎ ᶜ1937.
47 p. illus.

Cover title.

NN 0057406   MiD

50
N2122P   National live stock and meat board. Dept. of meat merchandising.
    Cashing in on pork; a modern merchandising manual.   Chicago, Ill. ₍1937₎
    78 p.   illus.   23cm.

    An earlier ed. issued in 1932 by National live stock and meat board.

NN 0057407   DNAL

338.1   National live stock and meat board--Dept. of meat
N2136p   merchandising.
    Pricing retail cuts; a reference book covering concisely the twelve essential steps in accurate retail meat pricing ... Prepared by National live stock and meat board, Department of meat merchandising ...   Chicago, Ill., c1937.
    28p. tables, diagrs.

    1. Meat industry and trade--U.S. 2. Prices--U.S. I. Title.

NN 0057408   IU

389.1
N211C   National live stock and meat board. Dept. of nutrition and research.
    The child's diet. Food value charts.   Chicago ₍19--?₎
    folder (₍8₎ p.)

    1. Children. Nutrition. 2. Food. Analysis. I. Title: Food value charts.

NN 0057409   DNAL

389.1
N211Dd   National live stock and meat board. Dept. of nutrition and research.
    The diet and dental disease. Food value charts.   Chicago ₍19--?₎
    folder (₍8₎ p.)

    1. Diet. Effect on teeth. 2. Food. Analysis. I. Title. II. Title: Food value charts.

NN 0057410   DNAL

389.1
N211Dp   National live stock and meat board. Dept. of nutrition and research.
    The diet during pregnancy. Food value charts.   Chicago ₍19--?₎
    folder (₍8₎ p.)

    1. Diet. 2. Food. Analysis. I. Title. II. Title: Food value charts.

NN 0057411   DNAL

389.1
N211Wg   ₍National live stock and meat board. Dept. of nutrition and research₎
    Weight gaining.   ₍Chicago, 1937₎
    31 p.

    1. Diet. 2. Food. Analysis. I. Title.

NN 0057412   DNAL

389.1
N211Wr   ₍National live stock and meat board. Dept. of nutrition and research₎
    Weight reduction with safety and comfort.   ₍Chicago, 1934₎
    28 p.

    1. Corpulence. 2. Diet. 3. Food Analysis. I. Title.

NN 0057413   DNAL

50.8
N21   National live stock and meat board review.

    Chicago, National live stock and meat board

    1. Meat. Periodicals. 2. Meat industry and trade. Periodicals. 3. Meat industry and trade. U.S. I. National live stock and meat board. Review.

NN 0057414   DNAL

National live stock association.
General convention.
Ottawa, 19
v. 24½ᶜᵐ.

1. Stock and stock breeding—Societies. 2. Stock and stock breeding—Canada.
CA 15–435 Unrev'd

Library of Congress   SF1.N24

NN 0057415   DLC

C630.6
N213am   National Live Stock Association of the
CoD   United States of America
    Amended constitution and by-laws of the National Live Stock Association of the United States, adopted at Denver, January 13, 1905. Annual address of President Frank J. Hagenbarth. Sound advice of Frank J. Benton. Analysis and comparison of old and amended constitutions. A little poem. ₍Denver? 1905?₎
    20p. illus. 23cm.

NN 0057416   CoD

VOLUME 407

National Live Stock Association of the United
    States of America.
Zc10   Constitution and by-laws, National Live
899na   Stock Association of the United States ...
    [n.p., 1899?]
    2 l. 24 cm.
    Caption title.

    1. Stock and stock-breeding - U.S.

NN 0057417   CtY

National Live Stock Association of the United States of
America.
    Constitution and by-laws as finally adopted. [Denver?
1905]
    8 p. 23 cm.

    Caption title.

    SF1.N28   57–53534

NN 0057418   DLC

National Live Stock Association of the United States of
America.
    Proceedings of the annual convention. [1st]–8th; 1898–
1905. [Denver]
    8 v. illus., ports. 24 cm.
    Superseded by the American National Cattlemen's Association.
Proceedings of the annual convention.

    1. Stock and stock-breeding—Societies, etc. 2. Stock and stock-
breeding—U. S.—Societies, etc.
    SF1.N27   56–50844

NN 0057419   DLC CtY Nh KU-RH ICU ICRL UU CoU TxU

National live stock association of the
United States of America.
Prose and poetry of the live stock industry of the United
States. With outlines of the origin and ancient history of
our live stock animals. Volume I. Issued in three volumes.
Illustrated ... Prepared by authority of the National live
stock association. Denver and Kansas City, National live
stock historical association [1905]

National Live Stock Association of the United States of
America
    see also
American National Cattlemen's Association.
American Stock Growers Association.

National live stock bulletin.
    Boston, 18   -1907.

SF371
.N3

NN 0057422   DLC

428
N213   National livestock conservation program.
    Don't let cattle grubs cheat Uncle Sam's
    marching feet! [Chicago, 1943?]
    folder.

NN 0057423   DNAL

National Livestock Exchange.
    Address: Our livestock industry

    see under

    Riddell, Robert J

National live stock exchange.
    Brief and argument... [Complaint]   1916.
    5 v.

NN 0057425   DNAL

National Live Stock Exchange.

HD9415   Ashby, Robert Childers, 1882–
.A8   Essentials of marketing livestock; prepared for the Na-
tional Live Stock Exchange. [Chicago, National Live Stock
Exchange] °1953.

National live stock exchange.
    Proceedings.
    Chicago,
      v. 23^{cm}.

                                 CA 10—2762 Unrev'd
    Library of Congress   HD9433.U4N3

NN 0057427   DLC CU ICJ Nh

National live stock exchange. *Committee on federal ante-
mortem inspection.*
    ... Proceedings of the meetings of Committee on fed-
eral ante-mortem inspection. St. Paul, Minn., 1914.
    1 p. l., 5–30 p. 21½^{cm}.
    At head of title: National live stock exchange.

    1. Meat inspection. [1. Meat—Inspection]
                                Agr 15–1393
    Library, U. S. Dept. of   Agriculture 50N21

NN 0057428   DNAL

National livestock exposition, San Francisco
    see   San Francisco. Grand National
Livestock Exposition.

National Livestock Feeders Association.
    The Livestock feeder.
    see under title

National live stock journal. v.1–
    Sept. 1870–
    Chicago.
      v. illus. monthly.
    Ceased Feb. 1889?

NN 0057431   ICRL NN OU MiU DLC TxU NcRS ViBlbV

National live stock journal. Weekly ed.
    v.1–   ; Dec. 16, 1884–
    Chicago.
      v. illus.
    Ceased Apr. 16, 1889?
    Center has:
    F-513   v[1–5, no.12]
    Cat. C   Dec. 16, 1884–Mar. 19, 1889

NN 0057432   ICRL ICHi ICJ

428
N212C   [National livestock loss prevention board]
1945   [Cattle grubs must go]   [Chicago, 1945]
    23 p.

NN 0057433   DNAL

National live stock loss prevention board
    Conserving meat in marketing live
stock 1947 report. [Chicago], National
live stock loss prevention board, 1947.

NN 0057434   ScCleU

41
N213   National livestock loss prevention board.
    [Leaflets.   Chicago, 1942–43]
    6 nos.
      Contents: 1. Grubs dig into cattle profits.
    2. Prevent colds and shipping fever. 3. Internal
injuries to cattle. 4. Nodular worm. 5. Horn
damage. 6. Conserve the nation's meat supply.

NN 0057435   DNAL

National live stock loss prevention board
    Preventable losses in marketing live stock.
    Chicago? Author, 1936
    24 p.

NN 0057436   OU

338.1   National live stock loss prevention board.
N212r   The reduction of losses in marketing livestock;
1937 report to the National livestock loss prevention board, by H. R. Smith, general manager.
[Chicago? 1938?]
    24p. illus., tab.

    Caption title.

    1. Domestic animals--Transportation. 2. Mark-
eting of live stock. \I. Smith, Howard Remus,
1872–

NN 0057437   IU

HD9433   National Live Stock Loss Prevention Board.
.U4N3   Report. 19 -
    [Chicago?] 19 -
      nos. illus. 28 cm.

    Each no. has individual title.

    1. Domestic animals.

NN 0057438   IU

National live stock marketing association.
    ... Annual meeting ... 1st-   1931-

    Chicago
       v.
    Manifold copy.

NN 0057439   MH-BA OCl DNAL

National live stock marketing association.
    Cattle handbook for the grower and feeder [1935]
      see under   Conway, Herman M   , 1893-

National Live Stock Marketing Association.
    Comments on the live stock situation
      see under   National Live Stock Producers
Association.

VOLUME 407

National live stock marketing association.

National live stock producer, the stockman's journal; efficient production, profitable marketing. v. 1–
Sept. 21, 1922–
₁Chicago, National live stock publishing association; etc.,
etc., 1922–

National Live Stock Marketing Association
     see also   American National Live Stock
Marketing Association.

National Live Stock Marketing Association.
     Research Dept.
         National live stock sales service. Confidential hog letter.   Chicago.

NN   0057444   DNAL

National live stock market service
     see   National live stock producers association.
         Comments on the live stock situation.

National live stock producer, the stockman's journal; efficient production, profitable marketing. v. 1–
Sept. 21, 1922–
₁Chicago, National live stock publishing association; etc.,
etc., 1922–
     v. illus., diagrs. 35–37ᶜᵐ (v. 1, no. 1: 27ᶜᵐ) monthly.
Title varies: Sept. 1922–July 1924, The News (running title, Sept. 1922–May 1923: The NP news)
Aug. 1924–Dec. 1925, National live stock producer.
Jan. 1926–   National live stock producer, the stockman's journal; efficient production, profitable marketing (subtitle varies)
Published by the National live stock producers association, Sept. 1922–June 1930; by the National live stock publishing association, a subsidiary of the National live stock marketing association, July 1930–

1. Stock and stock-breeding—Period. 2. Stock and stock-breeding—U. S.   I. National live stock producers association.   II. National live stock marketing association.

		42–12894
Library of Congress	SF191.N3	
	₂₁	636.05

NN   0057447   DLC TU TxLT ICRL CU ICU NN LU

National live stock producers association.
     Cattle handbook for the grower and feeder ...
         see under   Conway, Herman M., 1893–

National Live Stock Producers Association.
     Comments on the live stock situation.
         – Apr. 1957. [Chicago]   –1957.
         – Apr. 27, 1936   omit volume numbering; May 11, 1936 – Apr. 1957. are v. 8, no. 10–
v. 29, no. 8.
     Ceased. cf. Letter from publisher dated
Sept. 23, 1957.
     Issuing office varies: National live stock producers association. Research dept.
         – Apr. 16, 1943 (v. 15, no. 8)
National live stock marketing association. Research dept. Apr. 30, 1943 – Apr. 1957.

v. 15, no. 9– v. 29, no. 8, National live stock producers association. Research dept.
     Title varies: – Apr. 1957,
National live stock market service.

NN   0057450   DNAL

National live stock producers association.
     Cooperative live stock field service manual. Chicago, Department of information, National live stock producers association, 1929.
     184 p. illus. diagrs. 22ᶜᵐ.
"Livestock references": p. 183–184.

1. Stock and stock-breeding—U. S. 2. Live stock associations.
3. Farm produce—Marketing. I. Title.

		31–6565
Library of Congress	SF65.N3	
Copyright A 33928	₃₁	636

NN   0057451   DLC IU OU CU ICRL OrCS

National live stock producers association.

National live stock producer, the stockman's journal; efficient production, profitable marketing. v. 1–
Sept. 21, 1922–
₁Chicago, National live stock publishing association; etc.,
etc., 1922–

National Live Stock Producers Association.
     Report.
         ₁Chicago₁
             v. illus., ports. 28 cm. annual.

1. Stock and stock-breeding—Societies.

SF1.N354	636.06273	52–42438 ‡

NN   0057453   DLC DNAL IU PSt CU MH NcRS MH-BA GU
     CU-A OrCS ICU

284.340   National Live Stock Producers Association.
N21   Statement presented to the special sub-committee of the Committe on Agriculture of the House of
Representatives, Washington, D.C., May 2, 1949.
Chicago, 1949.
         6 l.
         1. Price subsidies. 2. Domestic animals.
Prices. I. Wilson, P   O

NN   0057454   DNAL

SF203   National live stock producers association.
.N3   Research Department.
             ... Cattle feeding; what kind of cattle to
feed and when to market.   Chicago, Ill., 1929.
     cover-title, 1 p.l., 7 numb. l.   tables.
28.5 x 22 cm.
     At head of title: National live stock producers association. Research department.
     Mineographed.

NN   0057455   DLC

49.9   **National Live Stock Sanitary Convention.**
N211   **Proceedings.**

         ₁Washington?₁

1. Stock inspection. U.S.

NN   0057456   DNAL Nh

**National live stock shippers' protective
league.**
Cowan, Samuel Houston, 1858–
     Government control of railroads. S. 3752. H. R. 9615.
Brief of National live stock shippers' protective
league, Chicago, and constituent members ... S. H. Cowan
... Clifford Thorne ... Graddy Cary ... attorneys. Washington, February 8, 1918. Washington, D. C., Press of
B. S. Adams ₁1918₁

National livelihood association.
     America's response to "Prohibiting poverty".
A selection of comments from representative
persons in all walks of life... Winter Park
Fla., The National livelihood association
₁1935₁
     31 p. 18 1/2cm.

NN   0057458   DNAL DL

National loan collection trust.
     Catalogue of pictures in the National loan collection trust
London ₁Printed by Cassell & company, limited₁ 1928.
     3 p. l., 3–115 p., 1 l. illus. 17¼ᵐ.
"Prepared for the trustees by Mr. J. B. Manson."—Introd.

1. Paintings, Dutch. 2. Paintings, Flemish. 3. Paintings—Catalogs.
I. Manson, James Bolivar, 1879–

		44–15520
Library of Congress	ND636.N3	
	₃₁	759.9492

NN   0057459   DLC OC1MA

The national loan, embracing the appeal in its
     behalf and the laws authorizing it
         see under   [Chase, Salmon Portland] 1808–
1873.

National loan exhibition, London, 1909–10
     see   London. National loan exhibition,
1909–10.

National loan exhibition, *London*, 1913–1914
     see
London. National loan exhibition, 1913–1914.

National loan fund, life assurance, and reversionary interest society, London
     see
National loan fund life assurance society, London.

National loan fund life assurance society, *London.*
     Annual report.
         ₁London₁ 18
             v. tables. 21ᶜᵐ.
Full title of report: National loan fund life assurance
society ... Annual report of the directors at the meeting of proprietors ...

	CA 10–4705 Unrev'd
Library of Congress	HG9058.Z9N3

NN   0057464   DLC NN MB

National loan fund life assurance society, *London.*
     ... Deferred annuities. ₁London, Printed by A. H.
Baily & co., 1838₁
     15, ₁1₁ p. 21½ᵐ.
Caption title.

	CA 8–841 Unrev'd
Library of Congress	HG9058.Z9N32

NN   0057465   DLC

VOLUME 407

National loan fund life assurance society, *London.*
Life assurance ... ₍New York, G. F. Nesbitt, printer, 1848₎
32 p. 17ᶜᵐ.

CA 8-840 Unrev'd

Library of Congress   HG9058.Z9N33

NN   0057466   DLC

National loan fund life assurance society, *London.*
Life insurance. National loan fund life assurance society ... London, and ... New York ... New York, G. F. Nesbitt, printer ₍1846₎
cover-title, 32 p. 22ᶜᵐ.

CA 8-839 Unrev'd

Library of Congress   HG9058.Z9N31

NN   0057467   DLC ViU

YA   **National loan fund life assurance society,**
17383   London.
(Prospectus) New York, 1845
31p.

NN   0057468   DLC

National Loan Fund Life Assurance Society, *London.*
Prospectus₍ Boston Agency ₎
Boston. Chadwick. 1848. 32 pp. 16°.

F7385 — Life insurance.

NN   0057469   MB DLC

National Loan Fund Life Assurance Society, *London.*
[Prospectus, *Manchester Branch*]
London. [184-?] 24 pp. 8°.

F7385 — Life insurance.

NN   0057470   MB

National Loan Fund Life Assurance Society, London.   9368.342133
[Prospectuses.]
= New York. Nesbitt. 1845 [-47?] 3 pph. in 1 v. 8°.

F7258 — Life insurance.

NN   0057471   MB

National Loan Fund Life Assurance Society, London.   9368.342
Report and prospectuses of life assurances, deferred & immediate annuities.
London. [1844.] 24 pp. Tables. Sm. 8°.
Contains also Fifth annual report.

F7329 — Life insurance. — Annuities.

NN   0057472   MB

National locker interests.
A food preservation and distribution system for the United nations; military and civilian inter-flexibility. New York city, The National locker interests ₍1942₎
1 v. mounted illus., pl., plans, diagrs. (part mounted) 29 x 23ᶜᵐ.
Loose-leaf; reproduced from type-written copy.
"Fifty copies ... have been published."

1. Cold storage. 2. Food, Frozen. I. Title.

42-25566

Library of Congress   TP493.5.N3
₍2₎   664.8

NN   0057473   DLC

TS519
.N3A3   **The National locksmith.**
₍Denver, McLean Pub. Co.₎
v. illus., ports. 23 cm. monthly (irregular)
Founded 1929.
Vol.   published by S. A. McLean for the National Locksmith's Association.

1. Locks and keys—Period. I. McLean, Stanley Allen, 1896-
II. National Locksmith's Association.

TS519.N3A3   60-36845

NN   0057474   DLC

National locksmiths' association.
The National locksmith
see under title

National locksmiths' association.
The National locksmith hand-book. v. 1-
Denver, Col. ₍1932-
v. illus., diagrs. 19½-22½ᶜᵐ. annual.
Reproduced from type-written copy.

1. Locks and keys.   43-35164

Library of Congress   TS520.A1N3
₍2₎   683

NN   0057476   DLC ICJ

National longshoremen's association of the United States
see
International longshoremen's association.

National long white lop-eared pig society.
Herd book. v. 1-   1927-
Plymouth, 1927-

NN   0057478   OU

HFBT4   **National Loom Fixers Association of America.**
.N215   General laws. New Bedford, Mass., Eve-
MIS   ning journal press, 1894.
16 p. 14cm.

1. Textile workers - U.S. - Societies, etc.

NN   0057479   WHi

HFBT4   **National Loom Fixers Association of America.**
.N215   Official manual and reference book. Offi-
M   cers, constitution, by-laws, etc. [Boston?]
1901.
139 p. illus., ports. 18½cm.

NN   0057480   WHi

The National loose leaf directory of advertisers; to-gether with their advertising managers and advertising agents.
₍v. 1-2₎
New York: James McKittrick Co. ₍c. 1913.₎   4°.
2 v.
Compiler: James McKittrick Company.
Kept up-to-date by means of "pasters" with additions and corrections issued irregularly.

1. Commerce, U. S.—Directories.   2. Advertisements and advertising.—
Directories, U. S. 3. McKittrick,   James, Company, firm, compiler.
N. Y. P. L.   July 1, 1916.

NN   0057481   NN

UG90   **National Lord's day convention, Baltimore,**
N213a   **1844.**
Abstract of the proceedings of the National Lord's day convention, held in the city of Baltimore, on the 27th and 28th November, 1844. Baltimore, Printed at the publication rooms of the Evangelical Lutheran church, 1845.
82 p. 22 cm.

1. Sunday.

NN   0057482   CtY-D TxDaM NjP MiU OO NN MB CSmH

National Lubricating Grease Institute.
Determination of the flow characteristics of lubricating greases: the S.O.D. pressure-viscosimeter. Summary report, project C.L.L.G.- 20-43. [Kansas City, Mo.?] Author [1946]
43 p. tables, diagrs.
Reproduced from type-written copy.
Issued by Grease projects, General division coordinating lubricants research committee, of the Coordinating research council, inc.
"Literature references": p. 42-43.

NN   0057483   WaS

TJ1077   **National Lubricating Grease Institute.**
.A1N2
NLGI spokesman.
₍Kansas City, Mo.₎

National Lubricating Grease Institute.
Tentative method for determination of performance characteristics of lubricating grease in anti-friction bearings at elevated temperatures. Buffalo, N.Y., Author [1944]
7 p. folded diagrs. (Its Technical bulletin, no. 5)
"Prepared for the ABEC-NLGI cooperative committee on lubricating grease test methods by the subgroup on performance tests at elevated temperatures."

NN   0057485   WaS

National lubricating grease institute. Technical committee.
[Technical bulletin no. 1-4]
see under Anti-friction bearing manufacturers association, inc. Annular bearing engineers committee.

TA1   **National lubrication engineering meeting,**
.P36   **Pennsylvania state college.**
no. 5,   Oil power conference, *Pennsylvania state college.*
Proceedings. 1st/2d-
1927/28-
State College, Pa. ₍1929-

VOLUME 407

Tzz
658.092
L828n   NATIONAL LUMBER & CREOSOTING CO. Board of
Directors.
In memoriam, John Thomas Logan, 1865-1929.
[Texarkana? Tex., 1929?]
1p.ℓ.,5-15p. port. 24cm.

1. Logan, John Thomas, 1865-1929. I. Title.

NN 0057488   TxU

The **National** lumber bulletin. v. 1– [Aug.] 1920–
Washington, D. C., Chicago, Ill., The National lumber
manufacturers association, 1920–
v.   map, diagrs. 27½ᵐ. monthly.
Caption title.
No number was issued for May 1921.
Title varies: Aug. 1920–Apr. 1921, The Lumber bulletin.
June–1921–   The National lumber bulletin.
Vol. 1, no. 1–6 were published in Chicago.
                                          TS800.N3
——— Supplement ... v. 1–3; May 20, 1921–May 22, 1924.
Washington, D. C., Chicago, Ill., The National lumber man-
ufacturers association, 1921–24.
3 v. in 1. diagrs. 28ᵐ. irregular.
No more published.
1. Lumber trade—Period   I. National lumber manufacturers'
association.   association.
Library of Congress   TS800.N3 Suppl.   28-10746
                                              [2]

NN 0057489   DLC WaU ScCleU WaS OrU NN ICJ OU

National Lumber Buyer's Bureau, inc., *St. Petersburg, Fla.*
Buyer's guide of the National Lumber Buyer's Bureau,
inc. St. Petersburg [1948]
[64] p. 23 cm.
Cover title.

1. Lumber trade—U. S.—Direct. I. Title.

HD9753.N3   338.1749   49-25195*

NN 0057490   DLC

National lumber exporters association.
... Car service, storage, switching, and other terminal
rules and charges at principal ports of the United States
and Montreal, Canada. Also dock rules and charges at
foreign ports ... Comp. from special consular reports to
the National lumber exporters association. Issued under
authority of annual meeting held at Cincinnati, 1909, for
the information of the membership only. [Baltimore?]
1909.
127 p. 23ᵐ.
1. Lumber—Rate books.
Library of Congress   HE2116.L8N3   10-5885

NN 0057491   DLC

National lumber handbook.
Washington, D. C., Chicago, 19

HD9751
.N3

NN 0057492   DLC MH ICU

725.37 National lumber manufacturers association.
N213a   ... Airplane hangar construction. [Washington,
D.C.] National lumber manufacturers association
[1931]
cover-title, 40p. illus., diagrs.   (Its Construction information series, vol.IV, ch.8)

At head of title: Lumber and its utilization.
"Fifth edition, May, 1931."

1. Hangars. I. Title.

NN 0057493   IU MH DLC WaS

National Lumber Manufacturers Association.
... Analysis of state forestry legislation with special reference
to taxation ...   Chicago, 1925.   45 l.   4°.
Summary state forestry legislation, 1925, and summary state forest tax laws.
Mimeographed.
Cover-title.

1. Forestry—Jurisp.—U. S.
N. Y. P. L.   January 20, 1928

NN 0057494   NN WaS ICJ

National lumber manufacturers association.
Announcement of a correspondence course in
lumber and construction information, covering
fundamentals arranged to meet requirements of
the retail lumber dealer ... 4th ed., January, 1925.
Washington, D.C. [etc.] 1925.
16 no. in 1 v. illus., plans. 28 cm.
1. Lumber trade. 2. Retail trade.

NN 0057495   CU

National Lumber Manufacturers' Association.
... Annual report
see its Report of ... annual meeting ...

National lumber manufacturers association.
Architectural and engineering data on wood
construction, offered by National lumber
manufacturers association...
[Chicago, 1917?]
16 p.

NN 0057497   OU

National lumber manufacturers association.
The best way to achieve low-cost housing
is to build low-cost homes...
Author, c1939.
32 p.

NN 0057498   OEac OClW MiD Mi

National Lumber Manufacturers Association.
A bibliography of forest management resources,
and uses, with special reference to the Pacific
Northwest. Washington, D.C., 1941.
15 p.   23 x 10 cm.
1. Forestry. Bibliography. 2. Northwest,
Pacific. Forestry. Bibliography.

NN 0057499   DNAL

National lumber manufacturers' association.
... Brief on behalf of the National lumber manufac-
turers association ... Chicago, Ill., National lumber
manufacturers association [1916]
2 v. plates, fold. diagrs. 23ᵐ.
At head of title: Before the Federal trade commission.
On cover of v. 1: L. C. Boyle, Joseph N. Teal, Geo. L. Boyle, counsel,
Washington, D. C., May, 1916; on cover of v. 2: L. C. Boyle, counsel,
Washington, D. C., July, 1916.
CONTENTS.—I. Problems of the industry.—II. Present state of the law
and the remedy.
1. Lumber trade—U. S. 2. Lumbering.   I. U. S. Federal trade commission. II. Boyle, L. C.
                                                17-2199
Library of Congress   HD9756.N3* 1916 a

NN 0057500   DLC OrU CaBVaU ICJ OO

National lumber manufacturers' association.
... Brief on behalf of the National lumber manufacturers association. Joseph N. Teal, L. C. Boyle, Rogers
MacVeagh, counsel. Washington, January, 1916. Chicago, Ill., The National lumber manufacturers' association [1916]
vii, 251 p. plates, fold. diagrs. 23ᵐ.
At head of title: Before the Federal trade commission.

1. Lumber trade—U. S. 2. Lumbering.   I. U. S. Federal trade commission. II. Teal, Joseph N.
                                      Agr 16-1001 Revised
Library, U. S. Dept. of   Agriculture 99.76N2152B

NN 0057501   DNAL CU WU ICJ NN NjP WaU CaBVaU

National lumber manufacturers' association.
... Brown book of lists, 1935.   [Chicago,
Ill.?] 1935.
cover-title, 64 l.   29 cm.
Mimeographed.
1. Forests and forestry-Direct. 2. Lumber
trade-Direct. I. Title.

NN 0057502   CU

National lumber manufacturers association.
Building ordinance ...
see under National lumber manufacturers
association. Architectural and building Code
Service.

National lumber manufacturers' association.
...Bulletin.
Chicago,

TS801
.N35

NN 0057504   DLC WaU KyU

National lumber manufacturers association.
Charting the American lumber industry; a panorama of
essential facts. February 1937. Washington, D. C., National
lumber manufacturers association [1937]
cover-title, 48 p. diagrs. 27½ x 21½ᵐ.
Reproduced from type-written copy.
Diagrams: p. 2–48.
Text on p. [2] and table of contents on p. [3] of cover.

1. Lumber trade—U. S.   I. Title.
                                                43–2205
Library of Congress   HD9754.N28

NN 0057505   DLC NcRS DL NNC CU MH-BA WaT MtU OrCS

National Lumber Manufacturers Association.
Charting the lumber industry, prepared for
annual meeting April, 1936. [Washington]
1936.
16p.of charts. 28cm.

1. Lumber trade. U.S. I. Title.

NN 0057506   OrU

National lumber manufacturers association.
... Chimneys, flues and fireplaces. Washington, D.C. [etc.,] 1923.
12 p. illus., diagrs. 28 cm. (Lumber and
its utilization. Fire prevention series. vol. v,
chap. 3)
1. Chimneys. 2. Flues. 3. Fireplaces.
I. Title.

NN 0057507   MtU MiD

VOLUME 407

National lumber manufacturers association.
Commercial woods of the United States, prepared by National lumber manufacturers association, Washington, D. C.
48 samples in box. 29 x 19½ x 15ᶜᵐ.

NN 0057508   NNC

National Lumber Manufacturers Association.
Comparative costs of walls, partitions, roofs for school buildings. ₍Washington, 1954₎
27 p. illus. 28cm.

NN 0057509   NcD

National lumber manufacturers association.
Comprehensive account of the National lumber manufacturers association's first American lumber congress and seventeenth annual meeting, Congress Hotel, Chicago, April 14,15,16 and 17, 1919. [Chicago, 1919]
96 p. 23 cm.
Reprinted from Lumber world review, April 25, 1919.

NN 0057510   NcD MH-BA NjP

National lumber manufacturers' association.

U. S. *Federal trade commission.*
Conference with National lumber manufacturers association, Chicago, July 19-20, 1915. ₍Chicago, Ill., National lumber manufacturers association, 1915₎

National Lumber Manufacturers Association.
... Conservation news digest
see under title

TA666   National lumber manufacturers' association.
N3   ... Construction information series...no.1,3-6
8-18. Washington, D. C., 1923-31.
14 no. in 1 v. illus., tables, diagrs.(part.
fold.) 28cm.
Binder's title.
At head of title: The lumber industry; Miscellaneous publications on lumber and its utilization.
Construction information series is v.4 of its Lumber and its utilization.

1. Wood. 2. Lumber trade - U.S. I. Title.

NN 0057513   CU

National lumber manufacturers' association.
... The cost of comfort; a handbook on the economics of dwelling insulation ... Washington, D. C., National lumber manufacturers association ₍°1928₎
cover-title, ii, 80 p. incl. illus., tables, diagr. 27¼ᶜᵐ. (Lumber and its utilization. Construction information series, vol. IV, chap. 11)
"Prepared by Joseph P. Quinlan and J. E. Myer, under the direction of Frank P. Cartwright, chief engineer."
1. Insulation (Heat) 2. Building—Tables, calculations, etc. 3. Heating—Tables, calculations, etc. 4. Building materials. I. Quinlan, Joseph P. II. Myer, James Edson, 1897–   joint author. III. Cartwright, Frank Poole. IV. Title.

Library of Congress   TH1715.N3   28-28515

NN 0057514   DLC WaS OrCS OC1

National lumber manufacturers association.
... Credit rating book ...
see under The National lumber manufacturers' credit corporation.

National Lumber Manufacturers Association.
Document
no. 1
Chicago, 1915.   8°.

pm. fold. chart.
Cover-title.
no. 1   is also General series no. 20.
Contents: no. 1. A challenge of the... statements that fire losses are due to the... use of lumber for building...

1. Building construction (Wood).
N. Y. P. L.   August 14, 1917.

NN 0057516   NN

National lumber manufacturers association.
Economic aspects of state forests ...   Chicago, Bureau of economics, 1920.
19 p. D.

NN 0057517   NcD MH-A

National Lumber Manufacturers' Association.
Educational series ...
see under National Lumber Manufacturers Association. Trade Extension Dept.

T7   National lumber manufacturers association.
.U62
no. 20 **Muller, Joseph Leo,** 1910–
... Establishing and operating a small sawmill business ... Prepared by Joseph L. Muller, under the direction of H. B. McCoy, the Bureau of foreign and domestic commerce, United States Department of commerce ... with the assistance of N. C. Brown and Raymond J. Hoyle of the New York State college of forestry, and in cooperation with National lumber manufacturers association. Washington, D. C., U. S. Govt. print. off. ₍1945₎

NN 0057520   NN DNAL

National lumber manufacturers' association.
Exposing the termite.   Washington, D. C.: National lumber manufacturers assoc. ₍1937₎   11 p.   illus.   28cm.
"Reference publications," p. 11.

1. Termitidae.
N. Y. P. L.   December 12, 1939.

NN 0057520   NN DNAL

National lumber manufacturers association.
Exposing the termite. ₍Washington, 1940?₎
11 p. illus.

Bibliography: p. 11.

1. Termitidae.

NN 0057521   NNC

National lumber manufacturers association.
Fire-stopping in dwelling construction. Washington, D.C., Chicago, Ill., National lumber manufacturers association ₍c1923₎
12 p.

NN 0057522   OU

National Lumber Manufacturers' Association.
For home lovers. [Washington, D.C.]
National lumber manufacturers association. [c1929]
cover-title, XXXII pl. on 16 l.   28.5 cm.
"Prepared under the direction of Richard G. Kimbell, architectural advisor".
Architectural designs and renderings by Eldred Mowery.
1. Architecture, Domestic. U.S. 2. Architecture, Domestic. Designs and plans. I. Kimbell, Richard G. II. Mowery, Eldred. III. Title.

NN 0057523   ViU DLC NNC WaPS OC1 OEac

National lumber manufacturers association.
For ten years; report of Wilson Compton, secretary and manager, at 37th annual meeting of the Board of directors, National lumber manufacturers association, San Francisco, November 10, 1939. [1939]
1 p.l., 9, [1] p.   23 cm.
1. Lumber trade - U.S. I. Compton, Wilson Martindale, 1890–

NN 0057524   NNC DNAL

National lumber manufacturers association.
The forestry omnibus bill; an interpretive synopsis, by Harris Collingwood ... Washington, D. C., National lumber manufacturers association, 1941.
cover-title, xi, 80 p. 28cm.

NN 0057525   NcD

99.71   National Lumber Manufacturers Association.
N213F   Forest policy statement ... amended and approved November 10, 1954.   Washington ₍1954₎
₍13₎ p.

1. Forest policy. U.S.

NN 0057526   DNAL

634.9   National Lumber Manufacturers' Association.
F7625   Forest products research guide. 1st-   ed.;
1943–
Washington, National Lumber Manufacturers Association, Committee on Products and Research.
v. 28cm.

Issued   -1945, first printing, by American Forest Products Industries. 1945, second printing, issued by the association and called 1945a in this library.

NN 0057527   IU PP

National Lumber Manufacturers Association.
Forest products research guide. 3d ed. Washington, National Lumber Manufacturers Assn., Committee on Products and Research, 1948.
v, 261 p. 28 cm.
Cover title.
"The first edition was published in 1943 under the title 'Bibliography of fundamental and applied research in forest products.' The second edition published in 1945 was entitled 'Forest products research guide in fundamental and applied research.'"

1. Forest products. 2. Forestry research. 3. Wood-using industries.

SD433.N3 1948   634.98072   49–4760*

PSt OU OC1U
NN 0057528   DLC NNC MiHM TU MiD NNUN CU DI MtU

National Lumber Manufacturers Association.
Forest products research guide. 4th ed. Washington, National Lumber Manufacturers Association, Standing Committee on Products and Research, 1950.
v, 335 p. 28 cm.
Cover title.
First published under title: Bibliography of fundamental and applied research in forest products.

1. Forest products. 2. Forestry research. 3. Wood-using industries.

SD433.N3 1950   634.98072   51–7407

MtU WaS WaT PPF
NN 0057529   DLC NNBG TxU MiHM NIC ViU TU MtBC

VOLUME 407

National Lumber Manufacturers Association.
Forest products research guide. 5th ed. Washington, National Lumber Manufacturers Association, Standing Committee on Products and Research, 1952.

vi, 386 p. 28 cm.

Cover title.
First published under title: Bibliography of fundamental and applied research in forest products.

1. Forest products. 2. Forestry research. 3. Wood-using industries.
[SD433.N] A 54—3733
Michigan. Univ. Libr.
for Library of Congress [54d3]

NN 0057530   MiHM ICJ DCU NIC DI DNAL CaBVa IdU MtU Or OrU WaT MiU OU OC1 OC1W TxU NcD CU IU MB NIC

National lumber manufacturers association.
Forest products research guide in fundamental and applied research. 2d ed. December 1945 (2d printing, April 1946) Washington, D. C., National lumber manufacturers association, Committee on research and product development [1946]

cover-title, 1 p. l., v, 142 p. 28 x 21½cm.

1. Forest products. 2. Forestry research. 3. Wood-using industries.
46—6021
Library of Congress SD433.N3 1946
[4] 634.98072

NN 0057531   DLC CU OrCS TxU NcRS MiHM NN IU

National lumber manufacturers' association.
Frame construction details. Chicago, Ill., National lumber manufacturers association, ℅1920.

2 p. l., 28 pl., 1 l. 29cm.

Verso of each plate blank for "Memoranda".

1. House framing. I. Title.
Library of Congress TH2301.N3
22-10104

NN 0057532   DLC TxU CU MU OrU OrCS ViU OKentU

SD
2
.N2815

National Lumber Manufacturers Association.
Golden anniversary meeting; proceedings. St. Louis, Missouri, May 8-10, 1952. Official report. Washington, 1952.
211 p. group port.

1. Lumber trade--Societies, etc.

NN 0057533   MiU CaBVa WaT

National lumber manufacturers association.
High humidity tests on wood exterior refrigerators.
Washington, D.C., National lumber manufacturers association 1929.
40 p.

NN 0057534   OC1

National lumber manufacturers association.
High lights of a decade of achievement of the National lumber manufacturers association. [Columbus, O., The Hann & Adair printing co., 1929]

67 p. 2 diagr. (1 fold.) 23cm.

This summary was prepared, printed and distributed by John W. Blodgett and W. M. Ritter.

I. Blodgett, John Wood, 1860– II. Ritter, William M. III. Title.
34-30807
Library of Congress HD9751.N355
338.4

OO IdU OrCS
NN 0057535   DLC NcD WaU NN MH OCU IaU CU DL ODW

NA7100
.H37

National lumber manufacturers association.
Home.
[Washington, 19

National lumber manufacturers association.
The house for the growing income ... Washington, D.C., National lumber manufacturers association [1931]
cover-title, 23 p. illus. (incl. plans) 27.5 cm.
Folded plan laid in.
"Designed by Eldred Mowery".
1. Architecture, Domestic. U.S. 2. Architecture, Domestic. Designs and plans. I. Mowery, Eldre. II. Title.

NN 0057537   ViU DLC OC1 WaPS NNC

---

q694.2 National lumber manufacturers' associ-
N21h3 ation.
... House framing details. [3d ed.]
[Washington, c1929]
cover-title, 1 l., XXIV pl. (Lumber and its utilization. Construction information service, vol.IV, chapt.3)

Blank leaves for "Memoranda".
A revision of "Frame construction details".- Foreword.

NN 0057538   IU NNC

National Lumber Manufacturers Association.
House framing details. [6th ed. Rev. by R. G. Kimbell. Washington, ℅1929]

[8] p. 24 plates. 28 cm. (Lumber and its utilization. Construction information series, v. 4, ch. 3)

1. Framing (Building) I. Kimbell, R. G. II. Title. (Series)
TH2301.N33 1929 51–48165

NN 0057539   DLC Or

National lumber manufacturers association
...How to acquire a new home...at less than one-dollar-per day...1940-41. [The Author, 1940]
28 p., illus., plans.

Cover title.

NN 0057540   MiD Mi

National Lumber Manufacturers' Association.
John Smith's garage
see under [Kellogg, Royal Shaw]
1874–

HD9756
.C67
1927 a

National lumber manufacturers association.
FOR OTHER EDITIONS
SEE MAIN ENTRY
Compton, Wilson Martindale, 1890–
Looking ahead from behind, by Wilson Compton ... before the twenty-fifth annual convention of the National lumber manufacturers association, April 29, 1927, Chicago, Illinois. Chicago, Washington, Printed and distributed by National lumber manufacturers association [1927]

NATIONAL LUMBER MANUFACTURERS' ASSOCIATION.
Looking ahead in the lumber industry. [Chicago] National Lumber Manufacturers Assoc., 1934. 29 p. incl. tables. illus. (charts.) 22½cm.

Cover-title.

825707A. 1. Lumber—Trade and stat.—U.S., 1934.

NN 0057543   NN

National lumber manufacturers' association.
Looking at national problems and prospects of the lumber industry. Annual meeting, National lumber manufacturers' association, Chicago, Illinois, November 18, 19, 1940. [Chicago, 1940] 10 p. 23cm.

1. Lumber—Trade and stat. U.S., 1940.
N. Y. P. L. July 19, 1943

NN 0057544   NN

TS820
.B67

National Lumber Manufacturers Association.

Brooks, Robert Angus, 1920–
Lumber. Prepared by Robert A. Brooks in cooperation with the National Lumber Manufacturers Association. [Cambridge? Mass.] U. S. Naval Supply Corps Reserve [1950]

99.76
N215LT
1926

National lumber manufacturers association.
Lumber and timber information. Rev. June, 1926. Washington, 1926.
44 numb. l.

NN 0057546   DNAL OC1

National Lumber Manufacturers' Association.
Lumber and timber information revised, February, 1931; compiled by National Lumber Manufacturers Association. Washington, D. C. [, 1931.] 65 f. incl. tables. 4°.

Caption-title.
Typewritten.
Bibliographical note, 1 l. preceding text.

534188A. 1. Lumber—Trade and stat.—U. S., 1919-1929. 2. Forestry—U. S.
N. Y. P. L. May 7, 1931

NN 0057547   NN OO

National lumber manufacturers association
...Lumber distribution and production information, where the lumber is shipped and where it is produced... Chic., The Author, ℅1925.
16 p. table, map. (National lumber handbook, series 2, no.2, April, 1925.)

Caption title.

NN 0057548   MiD

National Lumber Manufacturers Association.
... Lumber facts. no.
Washington, D.C.
illus. 8°.
1. Building, Wooden. 2. Lumber. I. Title.

NN 0057549   DNAL

674
N275Lm

National Lumber Manufacturers Association

Lumber: from forest to you. Author ℅1952.
24 p.

1. Lumber trade. I. Title.

NN 0057550   OrP

VOLUME 407

TS
825
N33

National lumber manufacturers association.
Lumber grade-use guide for building and general
construction. Washington, D.C., National lumber
manufacturers association [1943]
1 v. illus., diagrs. 28 x 22 cm.
Loose-leaf.

1. Lumber - Inspection.   I. Title.

NN 0057551   WaSpG

National Lumber Manufacturers Association.
Lumber grade-use guide for building & general
construction.   Washington, D.C., 1948-49.
1 v. illus. 30 x 26 cm.
Loose-leaf.
"A. I. A. 19-A-1".

NN 0057552   PSt LU

National Lumber Manufacturers Association.
Lumber grade-use guide for building &
general construction: Industry practices,
lumber terminology, definitions, specification
aids, lumber abbreviations [and] index of
pamphlets.   Washington D.C., 1953-
1 vol. (loose leaf)

Cover Title.

1. Lumber--Grading. I. Title

NN 0057553   AAP DCU

National lumber manufacturers association
Lumber grade-use guide for softwood and hardwood lumber in building and general construction.
Washington, D.C., National lumber manufacturers
association, 1934.

NN 0057554   MiU

National lumber manufacturers association.
Lumber grade-use guide for softwood and hardwood lumber
in building and general construction. Washington, D. C., National lumber manufacturers association [1935]
1 v. illus., diagrs. 29 x 24ᶜᵐ.
Loose-leaf.
"A. I. A. 19-A-1."

1. Lumber—Inspection. I. Title.

Library of Congress   TS825.N3   35-23286

                        [2]   674

    OU MU
NN 0057555   DLC KMK CU PSt NcD TU IU IdU MtBC ViU

National lumber manufacturers association.
Lumber grade-use guide for softwood and hardwood lumber
in building and general construction.   Pamphlet 1   Washington, D. C.: National lumber manufacturers assoc., 1935-40.
pams. in 1 v.   illus., tables.   29cm.

Issued in loose-leaf binder.
"A. I. A. 19-A-1."

1. Lumber.
N. Y. P. L.   January 27, 1941

NN 0057556   NN

National lumber manufacturers association.
Lumber grade-use guide for softwood and hardwood lumber
in building and general construction. Washington, D. C., National lumber manufacturers association [1943-1949]
cover-title, 16 pamphlets in 1 v.   illus.,
diagrs.   29½ x 25½cm.
Loose-leaf.
Pamphlet I: "A. I. A. 19-A-." Pamphlets II-XVI:
"A. I. A. 19-A-I."

NN 0057557   NcD

National lumber manufacturers association
The lumber industry at the crossroads.
Washington, The Association, 1931.
27 p. diagrs. 23cm.

NN 0057558   NcD

National Lumber Manufacturers Association.
Lumber industry facts,

Washington,

v. 24 cm.

1. Lumber trade—U. S.   I. Title.

HD9754.N3   338.1749   40-4613 rev

        GU ICU DNAL MtU WaS OrCS OrU CaOOS
NN 0057559   DLC OCl DI WM NN IU ICU ICJ NcD NcD

National lumber manufacturers' association.
The lumber industry is at the front.   [Washington?] National
lumber manufacturers assoc., Amer. forest products industries,
inc., 1933.   24 p.   23cm.

Cover-title.
"Report of Wilson Compton, annual meeting, National lumber manufacturers
association and American forest products industries, inc., June 30, 1933."

1. Lumber—Trade and stat.—   U. S. I. Compton, Wilson Martindale, 1890-   . II. American   forest products industries, inc.
N. Y. P. L.   May 12, 1938

NN 0057560   NN

National lumber manufacturers' association.
The lumber industry is not defeated unless it quits.   Washington: National lumber manufacturers assoc., 1932.   23 p.   22½cm.

Cover-title.

1. Lumber—Trade and stat.—U. S.
N. Y. P. L.   September 29, 1938

NN 0057561   NN

National Lumber Manufacturers Association.
Lumber literature, a bibliography. Rev. Washington,
1947.

cover-title, 56 p. illus. 23 x 10 cm.

1. Lumber—Bibl.

Z7914.L8N3 1947   016.674   48-12316*

NN 0057562   DLC OrP DNAL

National Lumber Manufacturers Association.
The lumber movement, January 1, 1912 – June 30, 1916.   Chicago, 1916.   1 fold. leaf.   8°.

Chart.

1. Lumber—Trade and industry,   U. S., 1912-16.
N. Y. P. L.   January 25, 1917.

NN 0057563   NN

Mann
TH
1101
N27

National Lumber Manufacturers Association.
A manual on sheathing for buildings;
laboratory and service data.   [Washington,
c1941]
31 p. illus. 28 cm.

References: p. 31.

1. Framing   (Building) 2. House
framing. I. Title.   Sheathing for buildings. II. Title.

NN 0057564   NIC NNC

National lumber manufacturers association
Maximum spans for joists and rafters...
Washington, D.C., Chicago, Ill., National
lumber manufacturers association [1927]
1 p. l., 28 p.

NN 0057565   OU

National lumber manufacturers association
... Maximum spans for joists and rafters.
Washington, D.C., National lumber manufacturers
association, [c1930]
27 p.

NN 0057566   OU

National lumber manufacturers' association.
Memorial to the railroads of the United States by the lumber
industry.   Chicago [etc.] Nat. lumber manufacturers assoc. [1927]
28 p.   22cm.

1. Freight—Rates, Lumber—U. S.
N. Y. P. L.   August 25, 1947

NN 0057567   NN OrCS

National Lumber Manufacturers' Association.   L674.006161 2
[Minor publications.]

NN 0057568   ICJ

D691.
N2132

National lumber manufacturers association.
[Miscellaneous publications. 1916-

Unbound pamphlets.

NN 0057569   NNC MiEM

National Lumber Manufacturers' Association.
Modern home interiors.   [Washington, D.C.]
National lumber manufacturers association
[c1929]
cover-title, xxix pl. on 15 l.   28.5 cm.
"The illustrations are reproductions of
architectural renderings prepared by Eldred
Mowery, under the direction of Richard G. Kimball,
architectural advisor". Foreword.
1. Architecture, Domestic. U.S. 2. Architecture, Domestic. Designs and plans. I. Mowery,
Eldred. II. Kimbell, Richard G. III. Title.

NN 0057570   ViU WaPS MoU

National Lumber Manufacturers Association.
National defense developments
see under title

National lumber manufacturers association.
National design specification for stress-grade lumber and its
fastenings ... 1st ed. Washington, D. C., National lumber
manufacturers association, ᶜ1944.
64 p. incl. illus., tables, diagrs. 27½ x 21ᶜᵐ.
"References": p. 63-64.

1. Lumber—Specifications. 2. Woodwork. 3. Joinery.   I. Title:
Stress-grade lumber and its fastenings.

                                                 45-18300

Library of Congress   TS835.N3
                          [3]   674

NN 0057572   DLC DNAL TU IU ICJ

VOLUME 407

620.12 National Lumber Manufacturers Association.
N21n   National design specification for stress-
1948   grade lumber and its fastenings. 1st ed.,
         rev. 1948.   Washington, 1948.
         62p. tables, diagrs. 27cm.

"References": p.61-62.

1. Wood--Testing. 2. Strength of materials.
3. Strains and stresses. I. Title.

NN   0057573   IU

National Lumber Manufacturers Association.
National design specification for stress-grade lumber and
its fastenings. 1st ed., rev. Washington, 1950.
65 p. illus. 28 cm.
Bibliography: p. 64-65.

1. Lumber—Standards. 2. Woodwork. 3. Joinery. I. Title:
Stress-grade lumber and its fastenings.

TS835.N3 1950   674   50-14022

NN   0057574   DLC MsSM ViU

---

674   National Lumber Manufacturers Association.
N213n   National design specification for stress-
1955   grade lumber and its fastenings. Rev. 1954.
Engin   Washington, c1955.
Lib'y   66,[12]p. illus. 28cm.
        "[The specification was] established 1944;
        revised 1954."
        "1955 amendments" ([12]p.) inserted.
        Bibliography: p.65-66.
        1. Lumber - Specifications. 2. Woodwork.
        3. Joinery. I. Title: Stress-grade lumber
        and its fastenings.

NN   0057575   TxU AAP CU IU PU-FA

National lumber manufacturers' association.

The **National** lumber bulletin. v. 1– [Aug.] 1920–
Washington, D. C., Chicago, Ill., The National lumber
manufacturers association, 1920–

National Lumber Manufacturers Association.
National lumber news
        see under title

National lumber manufacturers association.
National lumber problems and prospects ...
        see under   Compton, Wilson Martindale,
1890–

National Lumber Manufacturers Association.
National lumber production register and
directory
        see under title

National lumber manufacturers' association.

National lumber survey; analysis of lumber demand and supply. v. 1–3; Jan. 1, 1926–Nov. 1, 1928. Washington, D. C.,
Chicago, Ill. [etc.] National lumber manufacturers association, 1926–28.

National Lumber Manufacturers Association.
National lumber trade barometer
        see under title

National lumber manufacturers association.

[Compton, Wilson Martindale] 1890–
   New frontiers in the forest industries. November 13, 1941,
at annual meetings of National lumber manufacturers association, American forest products industries, inc. [and] Timber
engineering co. [Chicago? 1941]

National lumber manufacturers' association.
   New problems and opportunities in the lumber industry.
Washington: National lumber manufacturers assoc., 1937.
15 p.   22cm.
   Cover-title.
   "Report of Wilson Compton, secretary and manager, to meeting of board of
directors."

1. Lumber—Trade and stat.—   U. S.
N. Y. P. L.   May 6, 1938

NN   0057583   NN

National lumber manufacturers' association.
Official report ... annual convention
        see its   Report of ... annual meeting ...

National lumber manufacturer's association.
   On the road to recovery. [Washington?] National lumber
manufacturers assoc., 1934. 21 p. incl. charts, table. 23cm.
   Cover-title.
   "Report of Wilson Compton, 32nd annual meeting, National lumber manufacturers
association and American forest products industries, inc., June 12, 1934."

1. Lumber—Trade and stat.—   U. S. I. Compton, Wilson Martindale, 1890–   dale, 1890–
N. Y. P. L.   May 9, 1938

NN   0057585   NN

National lumber manufacturers association
   Our American forests; their essential contribution through lumber, other forest products and
in general to the wealth, happiness and welfare
of the people. [Washington, D. C. National pub.
co. 1929?]
   31 p. illus. maps.

NN   0057586   MiD NcD WaS

National lumber manufacturers association.
   Pamphlets.
[1923-1936]
   2 v. of pamphlets. illus. 23-24 cm.
   Binder's title.
   Vol. 1 has title: Miscellaneous publications.

   Partial contents. v. 1 [1] Information on lumber
and where to find it. 2d ed., 1928. [2] Information on lumber and where to find it. 3d ed., 1930.
[3] A brief account of the trade development activities of the National lumber manufacturers association.

Chapter 1.- [4] Lumber and timber information.
Chapter 2.- [5] Lumber distribution and production
information. Apr. 1925 - [6-7] Annual report of
the National lumber manufacturers' association,
1929-1930. - [8] High humidity tests on wood
exterior refrigerators. - [9] The house for the
growing income. - [10] For home lovers. - [11]
Modern home interiors. - [12] The use of lumber
on the farm. - [13] Architecture's portfolio of
fences of wood.

NN   0057588   CU

National Lumber Manufacturers Association.
Pictorial review of hangar fire tests. [Washington, °1930]
15 p. illus. 28 cm. (Lumber and its utilization. Construction
information series, v. 4, ch. 8)
   "Supplement to 'Airplane hangar construction.' "

1. Hangars. 2. Fire-testing. I. Airplane hangar construction.
Supplement. II. Title.   (Series)

TH9445.H3N3   614.84   50-3181

NN   0057589   DLC DSI

National lumber manufacturers association.
   Poultry houses and equipment
        see under   Miller, Carl Frederick, 1891-
1918.

HD9751 National lumber manufacturers' association.
.N35   ...Preliminary report. Estimated softwood
         lumber consumption, 1929-
         Washington, D.C. 1929-
         1 v. 4°

NN   0057591   DLC

National lumber manufacturers association
   Proposed negotiation of foreign trade agreement
with Canada... submitted on behalf of the
timber owners and the lumber manufacturing
industry of the United States...
[Washington, 1935]

NN   0057592   OClFRB

---

225   National lumber manufacturers association.
N2196   Public foresters; directory by states.
         Jan.1,1945-
         [Washington, D.C.] 1945-

1. U.S. Forestry. Directories. I. Title.

NN   0057593   DNAL

National Lumber Manufacturers' Association.
   ...Reconstruction mass meeting; an account of the great
"Reconstruction Mass Meeting" for the lumber industry, convened by the National Lumber Manufacturers' Association at
the Congress Hotel, Chicago, November 22 and 23, 1918, in the
interest of its regional associations... [Chicago, 1918.]   16 p.
illus. (incl. ports.)   f°.

   "Reprinted from 'Lumber world review,' issue of November twenty-fifth,
nineteen hundred and eighteen."

1. Lumber.—Trade and industry,   U. S., 1918- . 2. European war,
1914- .—Reconstruction (Eco-   nomic), U. S.
N. Y. P. L.   May 16, 1919.

NN   0057594   NN MiU

National Lumber Manufacturers Association.
   Report; Forest Conservation Conference of
representatives of private forest industry and
ownership, state, federal and other public agencies
and organizations ...
        see under   Forest Conservation Conference,
Washington, D.C., 1937.

National lumber manufacturers association.
   Report of ... annual meeting ...

Chicago [etc.] 19
   v. plates (part col.) tab. diagrs. 24ᶜᵐ.
   The 19th, 21st– reports were published in Washington, D. C.
   Title varies: 19 ... Official report ...
   19   Second American lumber congress and eighteenth annual meet-
      ing of the National lumber manufacturers association ... Reports
      of the addresses ...
   1921, Third American lumber congress and nineteenth annual meeting
      of the National lumber manufacturers association ... Reports of
      the addresses ...

Continued in next column

VOLUME 407

Continued from preceding column

1922, Comprehensive account of the twentieth annual meeting of the National lumber manufacturers association ... and the fourth American lumber congress ... Reports of the addresses ... ₍Reprinted from Lumber world review₎
1923- Report of ... annual meeting of the National lumber manufacturers association ... Reports of the addresses ...
Some of the volumes have distinctive title in addition to title "Official report", used either as binder's title, half-title, or caption for t.-p. 8th report, 1910: The forest and the saw mill.—9th report, 1911: National problems affecting the lumber industry.—10th report, 1912: The American lumber industry.—12th report, 1914: The merchandising of lumber.—
14th report, 1916: Problems in lumber distribution.

Reports of the association and of the 1st-4th American lumber congress (1919-22) may be found also in Lumber world review.

1. Lumber trade—Societies. I. American lumber congress. II. Title: The forest and the saw mill. III. Title: National problems affecting the lumber industry. IV. Title: The American lumber industry. V. Title: The merchandising of lumber. VI. Title: Problems in lumber distribution.
10-18984 Revised

Library of Congress   TS801.N3

OC1WHi MoU CaBVaU MH NN MsU
WaSpG MH-A DI NcD OrCS MB ICJ OrU NjP Or NcRS
NN 0057598   DLC PBL NcRS KEmT DNAL ICRL WaT OU

National Lumber Manufacturers Association.
    Report of tests on timber joints ...
        see under ₍Myer, James Edson₎ 1897-

National lumber manufacturers' association.
    ... Salesmen's information series, no. 2,3 & suppᵗ, 4-5, 8-10; Nov. 10 1927 - July 26, 1928, Feb. 27, 1929- Sept. 1929.   Washington, D.C., 1927-29.
    8 no. in 1 v.   illus.   29 cm.
    At head of title: Lumber trade extension.
    Nos. 1, 6-7 not printed.

    1. Building materials. 2. Wood.

NN 0057600   CU

National Lumber Manufacturers Association.
    Standard Wood Mouldings ... 7000 Series
        see under   National lumber manufacturers association. Central Committee on lumber standards.

99.76   National lumber manufacturers association.
N215S   Statement in behalf of American lumber indus-
1931a   try before United States Timber conservation board.   Washington, 1931.
    ₍7₎ p.
    1. Lumber trade. U.S. 2. Timber. U.S.
    I. U.S. Timber conservation board.

NN 0057602   DNAL

280.12   National Lumber Manufacturers Association.
N2122   Statement of policies.   Washington, 1949.
    ₍4₎ p.
    1. U.S. Economic policy. I. Title.

NN 0057603   DNAL

99.76   National Lumber Manufacturers Association.
N215S   Statement presented to United States Timber conservation board in behalf of American lumber industry, by Wilson Compton ...   Washington, 1931.
    cover-title, 29 numb. l.   28 cm.
    Processed.
    1. Lumber trade. U.S. 2. Timber. U.S.
    I. Compton, Wilson Martindale, 1890-

NN 0057604   DNAL

National Lumber Manufacturers Association.
    Statistical summary of lumber ...
        see under   National Lumber Manufacturers Association. Statistical Dept.

National Lumber Manufacturers Association.
    The story of wood.   ₍Washington, D.C., 1927₎
    Pamphlet. illus.
    Without title-page. Caption title.

NN 0057606   MH NcD MH-A OO MiU Or

National Lumber Manufacturers Association.
    ₍Structural timbers₎   ₍Chicago, 1921₎
    9 p., 22 numb. l.   illus., tables.   30 cm.
    Contents. I. Build-up yellow pine timbers tested for strength. II. Maximum spans for joists and rafters.
    1. Wood-Testing. 2. Timber.

NN 0057607   CU

99.79   National Lumber Manufacturers Association.
N212S   Survey of current research of interest to the forest products industry of the United States.   Washington, 1955.
    63 p.

    1. Forest products. Research. I. Timber Engineering Company, inc., Washington, D.C.

NN 0057608   DNAL NcD

National Lumber Manufacturers' Association.
    Table for determining safe working load capacities of wood walking beams for use with oil pumping rigs ...   Washington, D.C. ₍etc.₎
    National lumber manufacturers association ₍n. d.₎
    1 p.l., 12 numb. l.   tables, diagr.   28 cm.
    ₍With its Construction information series. no. 1-18₎
    1. Strains and stresses. 2. Wood.

NN 0057609   CU

99.9   National Lumber Manufacturers Association.
N219   Total production, lumber and flooring industries.

    Washington.

    1. Lumber trade. Statistics.

NN 0057610   DNAL

National Lumber Manufacturers Association.
    Two typical wood frame houses

    see under

    Kimbell, Richard G

728.57   National lumber manufacturers association.
N213u   Use of lumber on the farm. Rev. ed.
    Washington, D. C., National lumber manufacturers association ₍1928₎
    38 p. illus., diagrs.

NN 0057612   WaPS FU

National lumber manufacturers association.
    What can we do to improve and support our association activities?
        see under   McNary, James G.

99.79   National Lumber Manufacturers Association.
N212W   What you should know about lumber.
    Washington ₍n.d.₎
    23 p.

    1. Wood. Properties and uses.

NN 0057614   DNAL

National lumber manufacturers association.

Compton, Wilson Martindale, 1890-
    Will the lumber industry settle down, or settle up? By Wilson Compton ... before the annual convention of the National lumber manufacturers association, April 29, 1925, Chicago, Illinois. Chicago, Washington, Printed by National lumber manufacturers association ₍1925₎

National lumber manufacturers association.

Compton, Wilson Martindale, 1890-
    Will the lumber industry talk about it, or do it? By Wilson Compton ... before the Board of directors of the National lumber manufacturers association, December 7, 1925, Jacksonville, Florida. Chicago, Washington, Printed by National lumber manufacturers association ₍1925₎

National lumber manufacturers association.

Compton, Wilson Martindale, 1890-
    Will the lumber manufacturers stand up and be counted! Report of Wilson Compton ... before the Board of directors of the National lumber manufacturers association, November 21, 1924, Washington, D. C. Washington, D. C., Printed by National lumber manufacturers association ₍1924₎

National lumber manufacturers association.
    Wood structural design data ... ₍Washington, D. C.₎ National lumber manufacturers association, 1934–
    v. illus., tables, diagrs. 27½ᶜᵐ.
    Loose-leaf.
    "Preliminary printing."

    1. Wood. 2. Building—Tables, calculations, etc. 3. Strains and stresses. I. Title.

Library of Congress   TA666.N3 1934   35-7617
Copyright AA 162704   ₍3₎   691.1

OU NcRS MB
NN 0057618   DLC NcD CU TU MoU IU ViU MiU OCU OC1

National Lumber Manufacturers Association.
    Wood structural design data. 2d ed.
    ₍Washington₎ 1939–
    v. illus., tables, diagrs. 29cm.
*4020B ———— —Supplement, no. 1–
.177R   ₍Washington₎ 1929–
Suppl.   v. in illus., tables, diagrs. 29cm.
    Bound with the above.
    1. Wood. 2. Building—Tables, calculations, etc.   3. Strains and stresses.   I.   Title.

NN 0057619   MB CU PU OC1W

VOLUME 407

National Lumber Manufacturers Association.
Wood structural design data. 2d ed. ₍Washington₎ 1941-

v. illus., tables. 28 cm.
Loose-leaf.

1. Wood. 2. Building—Tables, calculations, etc. 3. Strains and stresses. ɪ. Title.

TA666.N32   691.1   48-40937*

NNC TxU
NN 0057620   DLC VU ViU OC1 OU ICJ WaT DNAL CU

National Lumber Manufacturers Association.
Wood structural design data. 2d ed., rev. ₍Washington₎ 1950-

v. illus. 28 cm.
Bibliography : v. 1, p. 296.

1. Wood. 2. Building—Tables, calculations, etc. 3. Strains and stresses. ɪ. Title.

TA666.N322   691.1   52-16198

NN 0057621   DLC OkU MB PU-FA NN

National lumber manufacturers association.
Wood walls produce the best houses for the least money. ₍Washington, D.C., 1937₎

cover-title,24p. illus. 28½cm.

NN 0057622   MoU

National lumber manufacturers association.
Wood walls produce the best houses for the least money. [Washington, etc., 194-]

24 p. illus. 28 cm.

NN 0057623   MH

National Lumber Manufacturers Association
see also National Forest Products Association.

614.85 **National lumber manufacturers' associa-**
N21b   **tion--Architectural and building code**
          service.
          Building ordinance ... [Chicago,
191-]
          60p. illus., diagrs.

Half-title.

NN 0057625   IU

National Lumber Manufacturers Association.
Architectural and building Code Service.
Building ordinance . . . ₍Chicago, Ill.: Architectural and building code service, National lumber manufacturers assoc., 1920?₎   62 p. illus. 20cm.

154255B. 1. Building laws—U. S.
N. Y. P. L.   April 9, 1942

NN 0057626   NN CU

₍**National lumber manufacturers association**₎—
Central committee on lumber standards.
Standard wood mouldings, 7000 series - Revised 1931. To supersede previous issues of American standard moulding designs and sizes, first published July 1, 1925. Full-size designs of standard mouldings and examples of assembly prepared under authority of Central committee on lumber standards ... Washington, D.C., Caslon press, 1931.

24p. illus.,tables. 28½cm.

NN 0057627   MoU NcD

National lumber manufacturers association.
Committee on research and product development.
Forest products research guide in fundamental and applied research
see under National lumber manufacturers association.

National Lumber Manufacturers Association.
Engineering Bureau.
Engineering bulletin no. 1–3 ... Chicago, National Lumber Manufacturers Association, Engineering Bureau ₍1916–1918₎

3 no. in 1 v. illus., tables, diagrs. 23ᵐᵐ.

Cover-title.
No. 1–2, 2d ed.; no. 2 also in special edition.

NN 0057629   ICJ MoU NN MB MiU

National Lumber Manufacturers Association. Engineering Bureau.
General series. No. 25, 69.
Chicago. 1916–18. v. Illus. Plates. Plans. Diagrams. 22½ cm.

L5010 — Lumber.

NN 0057630   MB

National Lumber Manufacturers' Association.
Engineering Bureau.
... Technical letter no. 1–15, May 1916–April 1919 ... Chicago ₍1916–1919₎

17 no. in 1 v. illus. 28ᵐᵐ.

Caption title; no index.
At head of title: National Lumber Manufacturers Association. Engineering Bureau.
No. 8 is in 2d edition; no. 8, 12, have supplements.
No more published?

NN 0057631   ICJ NNC NN

National Lumber Manufacturers Association.
Statistical Dept.
Statistical summary of lumber and hardwood flooring, 1948–1953; production, shipments, orders and stocks. Washington, 1953.
cover-title, 2 p. l., 17 p. of tables
28cm.

NN 0057632   NcD

99.76
N215St   National lumber manufacturers association.
         Statistical dept.
         Statistical summary of lumber production, lumber shipments, new orders, unfilled orders, gross mill stocks, 1929–1944. Washington, D.C., 1945.
         13 numb. l.

NN 0057633   DNAL NNC

National lumber manufacturers association.
Statistical dept.
Statistical summary of lumber production, lumber shipments, new orders, unfilled orders, gross mill stocks, hardwood flooring, 1929–1946. Washington, D.C., Statistical dept., National lumber mfrs. association, 1946.
3 p. l., 14 numb. l.

NN 0057634   OC1

National Lumber Manufacturers' Association. Trade Extension Department.
Better buildings
no. 1
Chicago, 1916   8°.
v.   llus.
no. 1   is also General series no. 52
Contents: no. 1. Edgcumbe, C. R. W. Your garage. 1916.

1. Building construction (Wood).
N. Y. P. L.   April 27, 1917.

NN 0057635   NN

National Lumber Manufacturers Association.—Trade Extension Dept.
Educational series
no.
Chicago, Ill., 19   8°, 4°.
v.   illus.
no.   are also General series no.

1. Building construction (Wood).
N. Y. P. L.   August 14, 1917.

NN 0057636   NN ICJ OO

National Lumber Manufacturers' Association.
Trade Extension Dept.
Engineering bulletin
see under National Lumber Manufacturers' Association. Engineering Bureau.

National Lumber Manufacturers' Association. Trade Extension Department.
Farm bulletin
no. 1–
Chicago, 1916   8°.
(National Lumber Manufacturers' Assoc. General series, no. 15–16, 22, 37–38, 48
v.   illus.
no. 1– have on cover: Farm structures.

Contents: no. 1. Ekblaw, K. J. T. Implement sheds. 1916.

no. 2. Ekblaw, K. J. T. Grain storage buildings. 1916.
no. 3. Sterling, E. A. The preservative treatment of farm timbers. 1916.
no. 4. Ekblaw, K. J. T. Swine houses. 1916.
no. 5. Ekblaw, K. J. T. Poultry house construction. 1916.
no. 6. White, F. M., and C. I. Griffith. Ice houses and ice supply. 1916.

NN 0057639   NN

National Lumber Manufacturers Association.—Trade Extension Dept.
News letter
no. 1
Chicago, Ill., 1916   4°.
pm.
no. 1   is also: General series, no. 29.

1. Building construction (Wood).
N. Y. P. L.   August 14, 1917.

NN 0057640   NN

VOLUME 407

National Lumber Manufacturers' Association.—Trade Extension
    Dept.
    Opportunity
no.
Chicago, 1916   nar. 8°.
    pms., illus.

    no.   are General series no.

    Contents:
    no. 4. Exhibit and educational material.
    no. 5. Description and prices.
    no. 6. Lumber advertising by city yard dealers.

NN   0057642   NN

National lumber manufacturers' association
    reconstruction mass meeting; an account of
    the great "Reconstruction mass meeting" for
    the lumber industry
         see   National lumber manufacturers
    association.
         ... Reconstruction mass meeting; ...

The National lumber manufacturers' credit corporation.
    ... Credit rating book ...   St. Louis, The National
lumber manufacturers credit corporation ₍1904–
    v. 25½ x 20ᶜᵐ.

    "Published semi-annually (April and October)"
    Vol. 1 pub. by the National lumber manufacturers' association.

                               CA 5—895 Unrev'd
    Library of Congress   HF5585.L8N2

NN   0057644   DLC

The National lumber merchant. v. 62–70; July 1, 1918–Nov.
    3, 1922. St. Louis ₍Journal of commerce co.; etc., etc., 1918–
    21₎; Chicago ₍Commercial journal company, inc., 1921–22₎
    9 v. in 17. illus. 29½ᶜᵐ. weekly.

    Title varies: May 1918–Dec. 1921, Lumber. Dealers' edition.
    Jan.–Nov. 1922, The National lumber merchant.
    Preceded by the St. Louis lumberman (Jan. 1888–Jan. 1918) In Feb.
    1918 the title of this publication was changed to Lumber. It was issued
    in two editions (Dealers' edition and Manufacturers' edition) from May
    1918 to Nov. 3, 1922. Only the Dealers' edition (called later National
    lumber merchant) is included in this entry. It was merged with the
    other edition Nov. 10, 1922. (L. C. set incomplete: May–June 1918 want-
    ing)

    The Manufacturers' edition (as well as the earlier section entitled
    the St. Louis lumberman) is included under title: The Lumber manu-
    facturer and dealer (the publication was called "Manufacturers' edi-
    tion" from May 1918 to Dec. 1921. In 1922 it became Lumber; the
    journal of forest products, and in Aug. 1924 the Lumber manufacturer
    and dealer)

    1. Lumber trade—Period.

                               27–9006
    Library of Congress   HD9750.1.L6

NN   0057646   DLC ICRL

99.81
N215   **National lumber news.**

        **Washington, National Lumber Manufacturers
        Association.**

         1. Lumber trade. U.S.   2. Lumber trade.
     Periodicals. I. National Lumber Manufac-
     turers Association.

NN   0057647   DNAL DLC

National lumber production register and directory.
    ₍v. 1
Washington D. C.₍, 1928   8°.
    v.
    Published by the National Lumber Manufacturers' Association.

1. Lumber companies—U. S.
N. Y. P. L.   November 6, 1928

NN   0057648   NN

National lumber survey; analysis of lumber demand and sup
    ply. v. 1–3; Jan. 1, 1926–Nov. 1, 1928. Washington, D. C.,
    Chicago, Ill. ₍etc.₎ National lumber manufacturers asso-
    ciation, 1926–28.
    3 v. in 1. 29ᶜᵐ. monthly.

    Caption title.
    No more published.

    1. Lumber trade—Period.   I. National lumber manufacturers' asso-
    ciation.
                                  29–9231
    Library of Congress   HD9750.1.N25

NN   0057649   DLC DNAL NN ICJ OCl OrU OrCS WaS CU

**National lumber trade association conference,
    Chicago, 1926.**
Compton, Wilson Martindale, 1890–
    Is the "future" of lumber ahead or behind? by Wilson
Compton, before the National lumber trade extension con-
ference, February 15, 1926, Chicago, Illinois. Chicago,
Washington, National lumber manufacturers association
₍1926₎

National lumber trade barometer.
    Washington, D. C., National Lumber Manufacturers'
    Association.
         v. illus.

    Weekly; monthly.
    Began 1916.
    Vol. 10 omitted.
    Published as Lumber movement, Jan. 24–June 13,
    1919.

    DNLM NN OrCS
NN   0057651   ICRL DLC OCl MiU OrP CU DNAL MH-BA

99.81
N218   **National lumber trade barometer. Quarterly
     supplement. v.1**

        **Washington, National Lumber Manufacturers
        Association.**

         1. Lumber trade. U.S.   2. Lumber trade.
     Statistics. I. National Lumber Manufacturers
     Association.

NN   0057652   DNAL OrCS

99.81
N214   National lumber trade barometer. Report
     of lumber movement. Statistical release.

                           Washington,
     National Lumber Manufacturers Association.
     Ceased; data later included in National
     Lumber Manufacturers Association. Finger
     tip facts and figures (99.9 N219F) cf. Letter
     from publisher, May 31, 1962.
        Title varies: 1955, no. 11–
     Mar. 12, 1955–   National
     lumber statistics. Statistical release.

NN   0057653   DNAL

National lumberman
         see   The Lumber manufacturer and dealer.

Newsp.   The **NATIONAL** Lutheran. New York, Division
1286   of Public Relations, National Lutheran
     Council, 1931–
        v.   28.5cm.

NN   0057655   MH-AH OSW

National Lutheran council.
    Annual report of the National Lutheran council ...

    New York, National Lutheran council ₍19
        v. front., plates, ports. 23ᶜᵐ.

    1. European war, 1914–1918—War work.

    Library of Congress   BX8041.A4   21—1944

NN   0057656   DLC PPLT MH-AH OCl WaS NN

National Lutheran council.
    The Bible in a thousand tongues, in commemoration of Lu-
ther's translation of the Bible in 1534, by Olaf Morgan Norlie,
compiled and issued under the auspices of the National Lutheran council. Minneapolis, Minn., Augsburg publishing house,
1935.
    2 p. l., 3–133 p. diagrs. 19ᶜᵐ.

    Photolithographed.
    "Supplement to ... 'The translated Bible' and ... 'Luther translates
the Bible', both by the same editor and author."—Pref.
    1. Bible—Versions.   I. Norlie, Olaf Morgan, 1876–   comp.
    II. Title.
    Library of Congress   BS450.N33   36–18432
    ——— Copy 2.
    Copyright AA 210099   ₍3₎   220.5

NN   0057657   DLC CU NIC MB IaU IU NcD OCl OrU

National Lutheran Council.
    By their side, a memorial; war service of the National
Lutheran Council, 1940–1948. ₍n. p., 1949₎
    112 p. illus., ports. 29 cm.

    1. World War, 1939–1945—Lutheran Church.   2. World War, 1939–
    1945—War work—Lutheran Church.   I. Title.

    D810.C66N3   940.5478   50–19597

    MtHi PPRETS
NN   0057658   DLC OOxM OU NN TxU NcD PPT Wa Or OrU

National Lutheran Council.
    Christ for the moving millions, a conference on mobility ...
held at the Sheraton-Cadillac Hotel, Detroit, Michigan,
December 14–15–16, 1954. Sponsored by National Lutheran
Council; arr. by Division of American Missions. Chicago
₍1955₎
    viii, 116 p. illus., maps 23 cm.

    Bibliographical footnotes.

    1. Migration, Internal—U. S.   2. Missions—U. S.   3. Social sur-
veys—U. S.   I. Title.
    BV2784.N3 1954   284.173   56–525

NN   0057659   DLC PPLT WaTC

National Lutheran Council.
    Four communities

    see under

    Protestant Council of the City of New York.
    Dept. of Church Planning and Research.

National Lutheran Council.
    The heart of Flatbush

    see under

    Protestant Council of the City of New York.
    Dept. of Church Planning and Research.

    National Lutheran Council.
BX8009
.L84   **Lutheran** church directory for the United States and Canada.

    New York, National Lutheran Council.

VOLUME 407

National Lutheran council.

... The **Lutheran** world almanac and annual encyclopedia for 1921–
New York city, N. Y., Issued by the Lutheran bureau, 1920–

BX8041
.H37

National Lutheran council.

Hauge, Osborne.
Lutherans working together; a history of the National Lutheran council, 1918–1943, by Osborne Hauge. Supplementary chapter, 1943–1945, by Dr. Ralph H. Long. New York city, N. Y., National Lutheran council ₁1945₎

National Lutheran council.
The National Lutheran council, 1918–1938.
see under Long, Ralph Herman, 1882–

National Lutheran Council.
A profile of the Lutheran church
see under Mueller, Elwin W., 1908–

National Lutheran Council.
The rural congregation and community health
see under National Lutheran Council.
Division of American missions.

BX8009 National Lutheran council.
.N27 A statistical bulletin for the Lutheran church in North America. New York, National Lutheran council, 1940.
cover-title, 60 p. 25cm.

NN 0057668 MnHi PPLT

AW6 National Lutheran council.
L9 A statistical bulletin for the Lutheran
N church in North America. New York, N.Y.,
1945 National Lutheran council, 1945.
cover-title, 64p. 24.5cm.
Photolithographed.

NN 0057669 NNUT

MGL1.5 National Lutheran council.
N277 A statistical handbook for the Lutheran
(1947) churches in North America. New York, N.Y.,
National Lutheran council, 1947.
₁1₎, 24, ₁1₎p. 24x34.5cm.

NN 0057670 NNUT

National Lutheran council.
The translated Bible, 1534–1934; commemorating the four hundredth anniversary of the translation of the Bible by Martin Luther; issued under the auspices of the National Lutheran council, O. M. Norlie, editor. Philadelphia, Pa., The United Lutheran publication house ₁*1934₎
222 p. 2 facsim. (incl. front.) 20ᶜᵐ.
Contents.—The life of Luther, by C. M. Jacobs.—Luther and the Bible; its origin and content, by W. H. B. Carney.—The original Bible text, by R. C. H. Lenski.—Bible criticism, by E. E. Flack.—Translations and revisions, by George Sverdrup, jr.—The early versions, by C. G. Erickson.—The printing press, by Grant Hultberg and C. R. Tappert.—German versions before 1534, by Theodore Graebner.—The September Testament, 1522, by L. F. Gruber.—The German Bible, 1534,

Continued in next column

Continued from preceding column

by J. M. Reu.—Luther, prince of translators, by L. F. Gruber.—German versions since 1534, by P. E. Kretzmann. Bibliography (p. 120–121).—The Bible in Danish, by A. T. Dorf.—The Bible in Swedish, by S. G. Youngert.—The Bible in Icelandic, by Runolfur Marteinsson.—The Bible in Norwegian, by J. O. Evjen.—The Bible in Finnish, by John Wargelin.—The Bible in Slavic languages, by John Body.—The Bible in English, by L. F. Gruber.—The Bible and missions, by M. J. Stolee.—Bible societies, by O. M. Norlie.—The Bible in a thousand tongues, by O. M. Norlie. A short bibliography (p. 213–215)
1. Bible—Hist. 2. Bible—Versions. 3. Bible. German—Versions—Luther. 4. Bible—Publication and distribution. 5. Bible—Bibl. 6. Luther, Martin, 1483–1546. ɪ. Norlie, Olaf Morgan, 1876– ed. ɪɪ. Title.

Library of Congress BS450.N3 34–30235
———— Copy 2.
Copyright A 75111 ₃₎ 220.5

PG1adM MH-AH PPPrHi
NN 0057672 DLC KyWAT WaS Or OrP ICN MB OCl NcC

National Lutheran Council
see also **Lutheran Evangelism Council.**

National Lutheran Council. Division of America Missions.
Adventuring in American missions
see under Lutheran home mission conference, 1955.

National Lutheran Council. Division of American missions.
American missions together
see under title

National Lutheran Council. Division of American Missions.
Evangelijos Zodis
see under title

BV
2766
L8
A22

National Lutheran Council. Division of American Missions.

The Lutheran church in the city. Prepared by C. P. Rasmussen. ₁Chicago₎ 1951–1952.
3v. illus., maps(part fold.)
CONTENTS: v.1. Des Moines, Ia.--v.2. Chicago.--v.3. Salt Lake City, Utah.
1. Lutheran Church - Missions. 2. Missions U. S. 3. Lutherans in the U. S. I. Rasmussen, Car l P., 1897- II. Title.

R
74547-9

NN 0057677 MoSCS

National Lutheran Council--Division of American missions.
Lutheran higher education in service to rural people. ₁Chic.Author,1949₎.
44p.Q.

NN 0057678 PPLT

National Lutheran Council. Division of American Missions.
Majas draugs
see under title

National Lutheran Council. Division of American Missions.
The open door in American missions
see under Lutheran Home Mission Conference, 1947.

National Lutheran Council. Division of American missions.
A profile of the Lutheran church in the United States
see under Mueller, Elwin W., 1908–

W 6
P3

National Lutheran Council. Division of American Missions.
The rural congregation and community health. ₁Prepared by Division of American Missions, National Lutheran Council₎ Chicago ₁1953₎
58 p. illus.
Outgrowth of a conference held in Dubuque, Iowa, June 24-26, 1952.
1. Rural hygiene Title

NN 0057682 DNLM

BV
637
N3

National Lutheran Council. Division of American Missions. Urban Church Planning.
Urban church planning; study director's manual. [Comp. by Walter Kloetzli. Chicago, 1955]
2v. illus.,maps.

NN 0057683 MoSCS IEG

National Lutheran Council. Division of Student Service.
Basic questions for the Christian scholar

see under

Brauer, Jerald Carl, 1921–

SEM
259
N277wi

National Lutheran Council. Division of Student Service.
Witness ! A manual of campus evangelism, by the National Lutheran Council, Division of Student Service and The Lutheran Student Association of America. Chicago, author, 1955.
1v. (unpaged)

1. Students - Religious life.
I. Lutheran Student Association of America.
II. Title.

NN 0057685 OkEG

National Lutheran Council. *Division of Welfare.*
Directory of Lutheran agencies and institutions. ₁New York?₎
v. 23 cm.

1. Lutheran Church—Charities—Direct. ɪ. Title.

BX8074.B4N3 64–4323

NN 0057686 DLC

National Lutheran Council. Division of Welfare.
Lutheran services for dependent children

see under

Lund, Henriette, 1829–1909.

National Lutheran Council. Division of Welfare.
Survey of Seamen's work in port of Philadelphia.
n.p., n.p., 1954.
[29] p. 29 cm.
Typescript.

NN 0057688 PPLT

VOLUME 407

National Lutheran council. Lutheran bureau.
A book of suggestions for the celebration of
the four hundredth anniversary, Luther at Worms,
1521–1921. New York, The Lutheran bureau of
the National Lutheran council [1921]
30 p. 23 cm.

Illustration on cover.
Bibliography: p. 28–29.

1. Luther, Martin, 1483–1546 – Anniversaries,
etc.

NN 0057689   Vi MiD MB NNUT OO OC1

National Lutheran Council. Lutheran Bureau.
... The Lutheran world almanac and annual
encyclopedia
see under title

National Lutheran Council. *Lutheran Refugee Service*
see
Lutheran Refugee Service.

National Lutheran Council. *Lutheran Resettlement Service*
see
Lutheran Refugee Service.

National Lutheran Education Conference.

Development of the Christian personality–
the major objective of Christian higher education.
The Roosevelt, N.Y. City, Jan. 13-14, 1936.
Proceedings of the N.Y. Convention. New York,
1936.
92 p. 22 cm.
1. Universities and colleges. Religious life.
2. Religious and moral education. I. Title.

NN 0057693   CBPL

L901   National Lutheran educational conference.
.N27   Directory of Lutheran teachers. 1924–
[Springfield,O.] National Lutheran educational
conference[1924–
v. 22½ᶜᵐ.

1.Teachers-Direct.

NN 0057694   ICU AzU

Period.   NATIONAL Lutheran Educational Conference.
1301.99   News bulletin. New York, Washington,
1932–
v. 28cm.

Monthly, Sept.-June.

NN 0057695   MH-AH

---

686   NATIONAL Lutheran Educational Conference.
Luth   Papers and proceedings. [Springfield,
N277p   Ohio, 1919–
v. 23cm.

NN 0057696   MH-AH DHEW OU CSt OCU

National Lutheran Inner Mission Conference
see
National Lutheran Social Welfare Conference.

WY   NATIONAL Lutheran Nurses Guild
87   Handbook for nurses; a pocket hand-
N277h   book designed for quick reference in
1953   giving spiritual care to patients.
Minneapolis, [c1953]
40 p.
1. Medicine - Pastoral 2. Nursing

NN 0057698   DNLM

National Lutheran Social Welfare Conference.
Index of papers in proceedings, 1922-1953.
New York, Author, n.d.
17 p. Q.
Typescript.

NN 0057699   PPLT

BX   **National Lutheran Social Welfare Conference**
8074   Proceedings [of national and regional]
.B4   meetings, 1922-1959.
L75   New York 1922-1959.
v. in v. 23cm.
1924-1954, Lutheran Welfare Conference in america;
Name of the conference varies: 1922-1928,
National Lutheran Inner Mission Conference.
National meetings at first annual: 1947-
-1959, biennial. Only regional meetings
held 1944, 1946.
Superseded   by Lutheran health and

welfare annual, later Lutheran health and
welfare directory, 1959–   issued by
Lutheran Council of the U.S.A., Division
of Welfare Services.

1. Church and social problems - Lutheran
church.

NN 0057701   MH-AH PU-PSW CBPL MoSCS

---

389   National macaroni institute.
N218   Americanized macaroni products; an interesting
story of the macaroni family, macaroni, spaghet-
ti, egg noodles. [Braidwood,Ill.,1939]
16 p. illus. 25½cm.

A reprint from the Macaroni journal, March,
1938.

NN 0057702   DNAL

664.7   National Macaroni Manufacturers Association.
N213m   Manual of system instructions for uniform accounting and cost system. System "A" and system
"B." [Braidwood, Ill., 1930]
24, 19p. 28cm.

1. Macaroni. 2. Cost--Accounting.

NN 0057703   IU MiU MiD

National macaroni manufacturers association
Portfolio of samples of stock forms for use
with uniform accounting and cost system. Chic.
Wolf and co. accountants, ©1930.
[34] p.

NN 0057704   MiD

National Macaroni Manufacturers Association.
Cost Accounting Committee.
System of cost accounting
see under   National cereal products
laboratories.

National Machine Accountants Association
see
Data Processing Management Association.

655.31 National machine company, Hartford,
N21d   Conn.
Descriptive catalogue of the gally
improved universal ... presses ...
Hartford, Conn., 1908.
16p. illus.

NN 0057707   IU

National Machine Tool Builders' Association.
Address[es]   Cleveland, O.

NN 0057708   OC1

National Machine Tool Builders Association.
Apprentice training standards, May, 1949.
Cleveland, O., 1951.
78 p.

NN 0057709   OC1

National machine tool builders' association.
The Association catalogue; machine tools made in
America; machines-utiles construites en Amérique; ma-
quinas de construcción americana; amerikanische werk-
zeug-maschinen ... [New York] National machine tool
builders' association [1921]–
v. illus. 31ᶜᵐ.
English, French, Spanish, German.

1. Machine-tools—Catalogs.   i. Title.

Library of Congress   TJ1190.N3   22–6728

NN 0057710   DLC ICJ MiD

National machine tool builders' association.
Can we win the battle for Asia

see under

Brines, Russell, 1911–

National Machine Tool Builders' Association.
Chip breaker studies
see under   Henriksen, Erik Karl, 1902–

National machine tool builders association.
... Constitution and by-laws. [n. p., 190–?]
cover-title, [8] p. 15ᶜᵐ.

CA 11–559 Unrev'd

Library of Congress   HD9703.U5N32

NN 0057713   DLC

National machine tool builders' association.
How to create jobs in a free economy; address by Joseph L.
Trecker, president, National machine tool builders' association...
before the 44th annual meeting of the association... Cleveland, Nat. machine tool builders' assoc. [1945]   15 p. 20cm.

1. Labor—U.S. I. Trecker,   Joseph L.
N. Y. P. L.   June 28, 1948

NN 0057714   NN

National machine tool builders' association
Index of machine tool orders.
Cincinnati, Ohio.

NN 0057715   OC1

VOLUME 407

National machine tool builders' association.
Index of new orders and shipments of machine tools. Apr.1949-   ₍Cleveland, 1949-
v. monthly.

NN   0057716   MH-BA

National machine tool builders' association
Machine age radio series.
Cleveland, O.

NN   0057717   OC1

National machine tool builders' association.
Machine tool electrical standards adopted by National machine tool builders' association September 5, 1941...   Cleveland, O.:
National machine tool builders' assoc. ₍1941₎   10 f. incl. plates.
28cm.

Reproduced from typewritten copy; cover printed.

J. Machine tools—Electric   driving.
N. Y. P. L.   December 31, 1942

NN   0057718   NN WaS

TJ1180   National machine tool builders association.
.A1M3
Machine tools.

Cleveland, National machine tool builders assn. ₍19

National machine tool builders' association.
Machine tools and related products. Jan. 1, 1940.   Cleveland, Ohio, 1940.
42 p.

NN   0057720   DAL

National machine tool builders association
Machine tools and related products, built by members of the National machine tool builders association (as of May 1, 1944) Cleveland, O.
₍The Author₎ 1944.
50 p.

Cover title.

NN   0057721   MiD

National machine tool builders' association
Machine tools and related products built by members of the National machine tool builders' association (as May 1, 1945) and (corrected to Dec. 1, 1945)
Cleveland, Ohio ₍1946?₎
50 p.

NN   0057722   OC1

National Machine Tool Builders' Association.
Machine tools made in America ...
see its   The Association catalogue ...

National machine tool builders' association.
Machines, prices, jobs.   Cleveland, Nat. machine tool builders' assoc. ₍1945₎   6 l.   illus.   28cm.

J. Machinery—Social and economic   aspects.
N. Y. P. L.   March 10, 1948

NN   0057724   NN

National machine tool builders' association.
Manual of cost procedure recommended by National machine tool builders' association ...   Cincinnati, O.,₎
National machine tool builders' association, 1931.
1 v.   forms, tables (part fold.) diagrs.   30ᶜᵐ.
Loose-leaf.
Autographed from type-written copy.
"The work of the Cost consultant, Mr. Albert E. Grover, assisted by the association staff, has been that of collection, analysis, presentation, discussion, planning, compilation, and production of the manual. ...   The final results were carefully reviewed by an Editing committee. ...   Chairman, Mr. Sterry H. Childs."
1. Machine-shops—Accounting.   2. Cost—Accounting.   I. Grover, Albert E.   II. Childs, Sterry H.

NN   0057725   MiU IU OC1

D621.9
N21
National machine tool builders association.
₍Miscellaneous publications. 1941-   ₎

Unbound pamphlets.

1. Machine-tools.

NN   0057726   NNC

National machine tool builders' association
Monthly review of economic conditions affecting the machine tool industry. Jan. 1932-Nov. 1933.
Cincinnati, Cleveland.

NN   0057727   OC1

338.4   National machine tool builders' association.
N215m   More goods for more people ... Mr. Walter P.
Chrysler's analysis of cost of an automobile extended to other products.   ₍Cleveland, Ohio₎
National machine tool builders' association
₍1936?₎
13p.

1. Machinery in industry.   2. Production.
I. Chrysler, Walter Percy, 1875-   II. Title.

NN   0057728   IU NN

National machine tool builders association.
Official report ... annual convention.

₍Springfield, O.,₎
v.   22½ᶜᵐ.
Full title: Official report.   The National machine tool builders association.   Annual convention.
Inserted in 7th report: List of members, 1 p.

1. Machine-tools.

                                            CA 11-36 Unrev'd
Library of Congress   HD9703.U5N3

NN   0057729   DLC DL MH-BA ICJ NN

National Machine Tool Builders' Association.
Quarterly shipments and net new orders of machine tools, 1942-
₍Cleveland₎
v.

1. Machine tool industry.   I. Title.

NN   0057730   MH-BA

National machine tool builders association.
Renegotiation. Cleveland, O., National machine tool builders association, 1943.
23 p. diagr. 23ᶜᵐ.

1. Machine-tools—Trade and manufacture—U. S.   2. War contracts—U. S.   I. Title.
                                            45-1058
Library of Congress °   HD9703.U5N34
                        ₍2₎   338.476219

NN   0057731   DLC MiU-L NN OC1FRB

National Machine Tool Builders' Association.
Survey of foreign sales, December 7, 1946.
Cleveland, 1946.
46 l.

NN   0057732   MH-BA

National machine tool builders' association.
Ten great inventions.   Cleveland ₍194-₎
30 p.   illus.

Contents.--Edmund Cartwright.--Elias Howe, jr.--Eli Whitney.--Thomas Blanchard.--Robert Fulton.--George Stephenson.--Francis M. Lechner.--Christopher Sholes.--Ottmar Mergenthaler.--John Butler Tytus.--

1. Inventions.   I. Title.

NN   0057733   NNC TxU

National machine tool builders' association.
Terminology and definitions for single-point cutting tools...
        see under   American Standards Association.
Sectional Committee on the Standardization of Small Tools and Machine Tool Elements, B5.

National machine tool builders' association.

Kearney, Edward J.
Transportation—the master key to progress, by Edward J. Kearney, delivered at Lenox, Mass., by its retiring president, before the National machine tool builders' association, Oct. 3, 1923. ₍Cincinnati? 1923₎

National machine tool builders' association.
Uniform cost methods ... cost bulletin no.1-Mar.12,1929-   Cincinnati, O.,
1929-
v.

Manifold copy.

NN   0057736   MH-BA

National machine tool builders' association.

Miller, Franklin, Basset & company.
Uniform cost system, designed for the National machine tool builders' association by Miller, Franklin, Basset & company ... ₍Worcester?₎ 1920.

National machine tool builders association.
The world's best investment...   Cleveland [1949]
11 p.   28cm.

1. Machine-tools—Trade and stat.—U.S.   I. Title.

NN   0057738   NN

National Machinery Company, Tiffin, Ohio.
₍National forging talk. no.1-
Tiffin, Ohio, 19 -

NN   0057739   ICJ

VOLUME 407

National Machinery Company, *Tiffin, O.*

What is a modern forging machine? Why does it produce accurate, close-limit forgings? ... booklet describing the National high duty forging machine ... Tiffin, O., The National Machinery Company ₁1934₎

cover-title, 27 p. illus. 28½ᶜᵐ. **bound** 30ᶜᵐ.

NN 0057740   ICJ

National McKinley birthplace memorial association.

The National McKinley birthplace memorial, erected by the National McKinley birthplace memorial association. Corner stone laid November twentieth, nineteen fifteen, dedicated October fifth, nineteen seventeen. ₁Cleveland, Penton press, ᶜ1918₎

2 p. l., 9–126 p. front., illus., ports., facsim. 27ᶜᵐ.

1. McKinley, William, pres. U. S., 1843–1901. 2. Niles, O. National McKinley birthplace memorial. I. Title.

Library of Congress   E711.6.N26   19–870

NN 0057741   DLC ViU OCU MB OO OC1

National McKinley birthplace memorial association.

... Proposal to build a monument and memorial to William McKinley at Niles, Ohio, the place of his birth. Pub. by the Association. ₁Cleveland, The Penton press company, 1911?₎

1 p. l., 7–37 p., 1 l. front. (mounted port.) mounted facsims. 23½ᶜᵐ.

1. McKinley, William, pres. U. S., 1843–1901. I. Title.

13–10891

Library of Congress   E711.6.N27

NN 0057742   DLC IEN PMA OFH OC1 OO

National magazine ... v. 1–60, v. 61, no. 1–2; Oct. 1894–May/June 1933. Boston, The Bostonian publishing company ₁etc.₎ 1894–1903₎; Chapple publishing company, limited ₁1903–33₎

61 v. in 60. illus., plates (part col.) facsims. 24–34ᶜᵐ. monthly.

Title varies: Oct. 1894–July 1896, The Bostonian, an illustrated monthly magazine.

Aug. 1896–June 1933, National magazine (cover-title, Sept. 1919–June 1933, Joe Mitchell Chapple's national magazine)

Editors: Oct. 1894–June 1897, A. W. Brayley.—July 1897–Apr. 1899, A. W. Tarbell.—May 1899–June 1933, J. M. Chapple.

Absorbed Good cheer in Aug. 1901.

No more published.

I. Brayley, Arthur Wellington, 1863– ed. II. Tarbell, Arthur Wilson, 1872– ed. III. Chapple, Joseph Mitchell, 1867– ed.

9–14043 Revised

Library of Congress   AP2.N34

     ₁r39e2₎   051

     WaT CtH

NN 0057743   DLC MB MiU OO N IaU NBuHi WaS WaSp

National magazine. ₍Boston₎

Florida, the land of enchantment; 40 face-to-face interviews ... [Boston, Mass.] 1925.

63p. illus. 32cm.

Special issue of Sept. 1925 (v.54, n.s., no.1)

1. Florida - Descrip. & travel. I. Title.

NN 0057744   FU

M1629   The National magazine ₍Boston₎
.H51   FOR OTHER EDITIONS
1909   SEE MAIN ENTRY

... **Heart** songs dear to the American people, and by them contributed in the search for treasured songs initiated by the National magazine. Boston, Mass., The Chapple publishing company, ltd., 1909.

PN6014   The National magazine ₍Boston₎
.C35
1905   ₁Chapple, Joseph Mitchell₎ 1867–   *comp.*

... Heart throbs in prose and verse dear to the American people ... Boston, Mass., The Chapple publishing company, ltd., ᶜ1905–11₎

National magazine ₍Boston₎

Little helps for home-makers; a wealth of personal practical knowledge in home-making, chosen from contributions made by ten thousand women of America to the National magazine. Boston, The Chapple publishing company, ltd. ₁1909₎

2 p. l., 341, 10 p. 23½ᶜᵐ. $2.00

1. Domestic economy. 2. Receipts.

Library of Congress   TX153.N25   10–1966

NN 0057747   DLC PP ICJ

National magazine. ₍Boston₎

Little helps for home-makers; a wealth of personal practical knowledge in home-making, chosen from contributions made by ten thousand women of America. Boston, Chapple publishing company, limited ₁1909₎

1 p. l., iii, 359, ₁12₎ p., 3 blank l. 23½ᶜᵐ.

Blank pages at end for "Your own favorites."

1. Domestic economy. 2. Receipts. I. Title.

     E 12–1500

Library, U. S. Bur. of   Education TX153.N22

NN 0057748   DHEW

National Magazine ₍Boston₎

West Virginia, the land overlooked₍ Reprinted from the National Magazine for December, 1913. Published by the Department of Agriculture, state of West Virginia... ₁Charleston? 1913.₎ 64 p. illus. (incl. port.), map. 8°.

Cover-title.

A collection of articles.

1. West Virginia.—Description and   travel. 2. Economic history, U. S.:
West Virginia. 3. West Virginia.   Agriculture Department.
N. Y. P. L.   September 10, 1923.

NN 0057749   NN

The **National** magazine. v. 1, no. 1–6; Jan.–June, 1954. ₁Chicago, National Anti-Vivisection Society₎

1 v. illus., ports. 20 cm. monthly.

No more published?

1. Vivisection—Period.   I. National Anti-vivisection Society (U. S.)

HV4925.N3   58–25390

Library of Congress

NN 0057750   DLC

B 3   The **National** magazine. v.1–15, Oct. 4,
N27   1856–1864. London, 1857–64.
        15 v. illus. 28cm.

NN 0057751   NIC IU KyLoU OU NBuHi NbU WaS NcD NN

The **National** magazine. v. 1–15; Nov. 1856–May 1864. London, W. Tweedie ₁etc.₎

4 reels. (English literary periodical series, 104E)

Microfilm copy, made in 1954 by University Microfilms, Ann Arbor, Mich. Positive.

Collation of the original, as determined from the film: 15 v. illus. Monthly.

Issues for Nov. 1856–Oct. 1858 called pt. 1–24; Nov. 1863–May 1864, pt. 85–91.

Edited Nov. 1856–Sept. 1857 by J. Saunders and W. Marston.

I. Saunders, John, 1810–1895, ed. II. Marston, John Westland, 1819–1890, ed. (Series)

Microfilm 01105 no. 104E AP   Mic 56–4405

NN 0057752   DLC NcU MiU N CSt PSt NB AAP CaBVaU

The **National** magazine. A journal devoted to
     American history
        see The National magazine; a monthly
     journal of American history.

The **National** magazine; a monthly journal of American history. v. 1–18, v. 19, no. 1–8/9; Nov. 1884–Sept./Oct. 1894. Cleveland ₁1884–88₎; New York, Magazine of western history publishing co. ₁etc.₎ 1888–94₎

19 v. illus., plates, ports. 25–26ᶜᵐ.

Title varies: Nov. 1884–Oct. 1891, Magazine of western history.

Nov. 1891–Oct. 1892, The National magazine. A journal devoted to American history.

Nov. 1892–Oct. 1894, The National magazine; a monthly journal of American history.

Editors: Nov. 1884–Apr. 1887, W. W. Williams.—Nov. 1887–Oct. 1891, J. H. Kennedy.

"Copies of this magazine exist in 1895, '96 and '97, but were probably never sold."—Boston book company, Check list of American and English periodicals.

L. C. set incomplete: v. 19, nos. 8/9, Sept./Oct. 1894, wanting.

1. U. S.—Hist.—Period.   I. Williams, William W., ed. II. Kennedy, James Harrison, ed. III. Magazine of western history.

5–16196

Library of Congress   E171.N27

     NjP
     WaT WaSp OrU WaS ICJ OC1CC MH MtHi WaSpG OU ICRL
NN 0057755   DLC MNS AzU MB CoU OC1 ICRL OAkU NIC

The **National** magazine ... A monthly review.

Calcutta, Printed at the New arya mission press

v. 25ᶜᵐ.

CA 7—6301 Unrev'd

Library of Congress   DS401.N3

NN 0057756   DLC

The **National** magazine: devoted to literature, art, and religion. v. 1–13; July 1852–Dec. 1858. New-York, Carlton & Phillips ₁etc.₎ 1852–₁58₎

13 v. illus., ports. 25½ᶜᵐ. monthly.

Editors: 1852–June 1856, Abel Stevens.—July 1856–1858. James Floy.

No more published.

I. Stevens, Abel, 1815–1897, ed. II. Floy, James, 1806–1863, ed.

5–14352

Library of Congress   AP2.N33

     NjP NN ICJ Nh OC1W OC1 OO MiU NcU OOxM N WaSp KyU
NN 0057757   DLC WaS NIC NcD NcA-S WvU MsU NNC AAP

FILM   The National magazine: devoted to
       literature, art, and religion.
       v. 1–13; July 1852–Dec. 1858.
       New York, Carlton & Phillips
       [etc.]
       13 v. (American periodical
       series: 1800–1850)
       Microfilm copy. Ann Arbor,
       Mich., University Microfilms.

NN 0057758   MoU IaAS

National magazine; or, A political, historical, biographical, and literary repository... v. 1–2 (no. 1–8); June 1, 1799–₁1800₎ By James Lyon. Richmond, Va. ₁etc.₎ Printed by and for the editor, 1799–₁1800₎

2 v. 23ᶜᵐ. semiquarterly.

No. 7 has imprint: District of Columbia, Printed by the editor, 1800. The National magazine and the Cabinet were united in 1801 to form the National magazine, or Cabinet of the United States.

1. U. S.—Pol. & govt.—1789–1809.   I. Lyon, James, ed.

4–23256

Library of Congress   E321.N27

     OC1WHi NcD MB MiU
NN 0057759   DLC PPL NN NjP RPJCB TxLT ViW NcU Vi

The **National** magazine; or, A political, historical, biographical, and literary repository. v. 1–2 (no. 1–8); June 1, 1799–₁n. d.₎ Richmond ₁etc.₎

(American periodical series: eighteenth century, 18)

Microfilm copy, made by University Microfilms, Ann Arbor, Mich. Positive.

Collation of the original, as determined from the film: 8 no. Issued in 3 v., June 1, 1799–Dec. 22, 1800. Cf. Union list of serials.

Edited by J. Lyon.

United with the Cabinet in 1801 to form the National magazine; or, Cabinet of the United States.

I. Lyon, James, ed.   (Series)

Microfilm 01103 no. 18 AP   Mic 56–4432

NN 0057760   DLC ViU ICRL OrU MiU NN

VOLUME 407

973.405
N21
▼
The National magazine; or, Cabinet of the
United States. no. 1-8, Oct. 1801-Jan. 11,
1802. Washington, 1801-02.
2 v. 23cm.
Supersedes National magazine; or, A political, historical, biographical and literary
repository (Richmond, 1799-1800)

1. U. S. - Pol. & govt. - Constitutional
period, 1789-1809.

NN   0057761   ViW

The National magazine; or, Cabinet of the United States.
no. 1-8; Oct. 22, 1801-Jan. 11, 1802. Washington, Washing-
ton Print. and Bookselling Co.
(American periodical series: 1800-1825. 34)
Microfilm copy, made in 1946 by University Microfilms, Ann Arbor,
Mich. Positive.
Collation of the original: 1 v. (various pagings)
Weekly.
Formed by the union of the National magazine (Richmond, 1799-
1800) and the Cabinet.
Edited by R. Dinmore.
I. Dinmore, Richard, 1765-1811, ed.   (Series: American periodical
series: 1800-1830. 34)
Microfilm 01104 no. 34 AP   Mic 56-4940

NN   0057762   DLC ICRL NcU NN OrU ViU

AP2
.N345
The national magazine; or lady's emporium. v. 1
Baltimore, 1830-

NN   0057763   DLC NcGU

AP2
Am358
Reel
799
National magazine; or Lady's empor-
ium. v. 1-2; Nov. 1830-July 1831.//
Baltimore, Printed by Sands &
Neilson, 1830-31.
(American periodical series: 1800-
1830, reel 799, APS 1037)
Microfilm copy made by University
Microfilms, Ann Arbor, Mich. Positive.
Edited and published by Mrs. Mary
Barney.
Monthly.

NN   0057764   IaAS MoU

AP2
.N28
The National magazine and Dublin literary gazette.
v. 1-   July, 1830-
Dublin, W. F. Wakeman; [etc., etc.] 1830-
v. 22cm. monthly.
Vol. 1 title reads: The National magazine; individual numbers have title: The
Dublin literary gazette and National magazine.
Editors: v. 1, C. Lover; v. 2, P. D. Hardy.

1. Periodicals.

NN   0057765   ICU NcU OU

Micro
Film
F163
The national magazine, and general review. v.1
(no. 1-7), Nov. 1826-May 1827. London.
1 reel. 35mm. (English literary periodicals,
105E)
Merged with Inspector, literary magazine and
review to form Inspector and national magazine.
Pages 391-392 omitted in numbering.
Microfilm (positive). Ann Arbor, Mich.,
University Microfilms, 1965.

NN   0057766   PSt NB

The National magazine and industrial record
see

Fisher's national magazine and industrial record.

The **National** magazine and republican review ... v. 1-
Jan. 1839.
Washington, D. C., Fulton & Smith, 1839-
v. 23½cm. monthly.
Editor: Jan.-Mar. 1839, H. J. Brent.

I. Brent, Henry Johnson, 1811-1880, ed.

Library of Congress   AP2.N346   CA 9—1167 Unrev'd

NN   0057768   DLC LU ICN OOxM

FILM
The National magazine and republican
review. v. 1-2, no. 2; Jan.-
Jun. 1839. Washington, Fulton
& Smith.
2 v. (American periodical
series: 1800-1850)
Microfilm copy. Ann Arbor,
Mich., University Microfilms.

NN   0057769   MoU IaAS

The National magazine of American history.
Vol. 1, no. 1-6. Jan.-June, 1920.
Bowling Green, O., Historical publications co.,
1920.
1 v.

NN   0057770   OClWHi MnHi ICHi

National magazine of home economics student clubs. v. [1]-
Nov. 1936-
Washington, D. C., American home economics association,
1936-
v. in   illus. (incl. ports.) 28½cm. 4 nos. a yr.

1. Domestic economy—Period.   I. American home economics association.

Library of Congress   TX1.N8   44-52895

(2)   640.5

NN   0057771   DLC

National magic company, Chicago.
...Catalog.
no.

Chicago [c19   23cm.
v.   illus.
Cover-title.

1. Legerdemain—Apparatus.
N. Y. P. L.   April 13, 1942

NN   0057772   NN

National mah jongg league.

GV1299
.M3M45
1945
Meyerson, Dorothy Sklarew.
"That's it," the authentic system of playing Chinese tiles, by
Dorothy S. Meyerson.
[Forest Hills, N. Y., 19

RH
C1150
National Mail Company.
Mail service performed by the National
Mail Company of Atchison, Kansas,
January 1st, 1880. New York, Press
of John A Gray, 1879.
321 p. 24 cm.

1. Postal service. I. Title.

NN   0057774   KU-RH

National malaria committee
see
National malaria society.

National Malaria Society.
Journal. v. 1-10; 1942-Dec. 1951. Savannah, Ga. [etc.]
10 v. in 7. illus., maps (part fold.) diagrs., tables. 26 cm.
Frequency varies.
Includes Minutes (sometimes called Proceedings) of the 24th-33rd
annual meeting of the Society.
Vol. 2 accompanied by supplement: A. Malarial study of Trinidad
and Tobago, British West Indies.
United with the American journal of tropical medicine to form the
American journal of tropical medicine and hygiene.

1. Malarial fever—Societies, etc.   I. National Malaria Society.
Minutes.

RA644.M2N28   43-4903 rev*

OrU-M ICJ CaBVaU TU-M
NN   0057776   DLC DNLM ICRL NcD MnU NIC TxU NNR LNL

WC
399.2
qN277m
1939
National Malaria Society
Malaria and its control; some papers
read at the 21st meeting of the National
Malaria Committee, Oklahoma City, Okla.,
Nov. 15-18, 1938.
Tallahassee, Florida, 1939.
111 p. illus.

"Supplement to the Symposium on malaria
appearing in the July and August, 1939,
issues of the Southern Medical Journal."

NN   0057777   DNLM

National malaria society.
Malaria control for engineers; report of National malaria
committee prepared by Subcommittee on engineering in cooperation with the United States Public health service. [Wash-
ington, 1936]
cover-title, 2 p. l., 81 p. incl. illus., forms, diagrs. plates. 26½cm.
Mimeographed by United States Public health service.
"A series of papers to serve as a basis for lecture courses in engineering schools throughout the country."—Foreword.
Bibliography at end of each paper.
CONTENTS.—Introduction.—Anopheline mosquitoes and malaria transmission.—Malaria and impounded water.—Malaria and transportation.—
The control of malaria.—Drainage for mosquito elimination.
1. Malarial fever—Prevention. 2. Mosquitoes. 3. Sanitary engineering. 4. Mosquitoes—Exter-   mination.   I. U. S. Public health
service.   II. Title.
36-18828 Revised
Library of Congress   RA644.M2N8
[r48d2]   614.53

NN   0057778   DLC MtBC TU MiU

National Malaria Society.
Malaria control for engineers, report.
[New York? 1939?]
46 p. illus.   WC765 J74m
Reprinted from Proceedings, Feb.
1939, of the American Society of Civil
Engineers.
1. Malaria - prevention & control

NN   0057779   DNLM

RA644
.M2N28
National Malaria Society. Minutes.

National Malaria Society.
Journal. v. 1-10; 1942-Dec. 1951. Savannah, Ga. [etc.]

WC
1
qN279n
1932
NATIONAL Malaria Society
National Malaria Committee, 1932.
[New York, 1932?]
[9] ℓ.

NN   0057781   DNLM

National Malaria Society.
Symposium on malaria
see under title

VOLUME 407

National malaria society.
... Treatment of malaria. Report of Subcommittee on medical research, National malaria committee, November, 1919. (With supplementary notes on quinine administration) ... Washington, Govt. print. off., 1920.

4 p. 24½ᶜᵐ.

At head of title: Treasury department. United States Public health service. Hugh S. Cumming, surgeon general.
Reprint no. 578 from the Public health reports, v. 34, no. 52, December 26, 1919 (p. 2959-2960)
C. C. Bass, chairman of subcommittee.

The notes on quinine administration "were prepared by Asst. Surg. Gen. H. R. Carter, secretary of the National malaria committee." *cf.* p. 4.

1. Malarial fever.   ɪ. Carter, Henry Rose, 1852-1925.   ɪɪ. Bass, Charles Cassedy, 1875-   ɪɪɪ. U. S. Public health service. Public health reports. Reprint 578.

20-26738 Revised

Library of Congress   RC156.N3

NN   0057784   DLC CaBVaU MiU

National Malaria society. Committee on Sanitary Engineering.
Malaria and the engineer; a treatise for technical students, prepared by the Committee on Sanitary Engineering of the National Malaria Committee. ₍Texarkana, Ark.₎ St. Louis Southwestern Railway lines, 1922. 20 p. illus. 8°.

1. Malaria.
N. Y. P. L.   September 6, 1923.

NN   0057785   NN OU ViU IU

428
N214   **National Malaria society.** Subcommittee on Entomology.
The work of state board of health entomologists on malaria control. [Birmingham? Ala., 1940?] 5 p.

NN   0057786   DNAL

National Malleable and Steel Castings Company.
Annual report.

₍Cleveland?₎
v. 24 cm.

HD9519.N3A3   48-35658*‡

NN   0057787   DLC NN

National malleable and steel castings company.
Conversion tables for finding elongation in 2 inches, per cent yield point, pounds per square inch tensile strength, pounds per square inch on malleable iron or similar unmachined tension test specimens nominally 5/8 inch diameter. ₍c1944₎
₍53₎ p. (Its Circular no. 344)

NN   0057788   NNC

HD9519
.N3C6   **National Malleable and Steel Castings Company.**
The conveyor. v. 1-
June 1943-
Melrose Park, Ill., National Malleable and Steel Castings Co.

National Malleable and Steel Castings Company.
Naco news ...
see under title

National malleable and steel castings company.
National malleable and steel castings company, 1868-1943 ... Cleveland, O., National malleable and steel castings company ₍1943₎

34 p. illus. (part col.; incl. ports., facsims.) 28½ x 22¾ᶜᵐ.
On cover: 75th anniversary.

                 45-16188

Library of Congress   TS229.5.U6N3
           ₍2₎   672.065

NN   0057791   DLC NN ICU OEac OCl

National malleable and steel castings company
see also
National malleable castings company.

National malleable castings company.
Catalogue of castings used in railway equipment and construction, manufactured by the Cleveland malleable iron co. ₍Cleveland, O., 1888₎

3 p. l., 82 pl. front. 24 x 32ᶜᵐ.

1. Railroads—Equipment and supplies.

Library of Congress   TF357.C63   6-30517†

NN   0057793   DLC

National malleable castings company.
The Tower coupler, manufactured only by the National malleable castings company, Cleveland, Chicago, Indianapolis, Toledo. Steel casting works, Sharon, Pa. ₍Cleveland, etc.₎, The National malleable castings company, 1901₎

19, ₍1₎ p. illus., diagrs. 10 x 21ᶜᵐ.
Title vignette.

1. Car-couplings.
                 CA 7-1234   Unrev'd

Library of Congress   TF410.N27 1901

NN   0057794   DLC

National malleable castings company.
... The Tower coupler, manufactured only by the National malleable castings company, Cleveland, Indianapolis, Chicago, Toledo, Sharon. ₍12th ed. Cleveland, etc., The National malleable castings company, 1904₎

20 p. illus., diagrs. 23ᶜᵐ.
Title vignette.

1. Car-couplings.
                 CA 7-1235   Unrev'd

Library of Congress   TF410.N27

NN   0057795   DLC

National malleable castings company
see also
National malleable and steel castings company.

A National man,
Life and times of Andrew Johnson ...
see under Rayner, Kenneth, 1808-1884.

National Management Association of Japan
see
Nippon Nōritsu Rengōkai.

National Management Council of the U. S. A.
see
Council for International Progress in Management (USA)

National Manpower Council.
Improving the work skills of the Nation; proceedings of a conference on skilled manpower, held April 27-May 1, 1955, at Arden House, Harriman Campus of Columbia University. New York, Columbia University Press, 1955.

x, 208 p. 24 cm.
Bibliographical footnotes.

1. Technical education—U. S. 2. Vocational guidance. 3. Labor supply—U. S. ɪ. Title. ɪɪ. Title: Conference on skilled manpower.

T73.N337 1955   607   56—5878

OOxM OClW OU NN_ICJ MU MtU GAT OrLgE KEmT OrCS OrU PBL PP PSt PPT PU-W MtBC AU Wa WaS MoU Wa OCl MB
NN   0057800   DLC PPPL ScU FMU TxU IU NcD CU TU

Egleston
D620.7
N2131   **National manpower council.**
A policy for scientific and professional manpower; a statement and recommendations. ₍New York, Columbia university press, 1953₎ 28 p.

"Reprint from National manpower council: A policy for scientific and professional manpower."

NN   0057801   NNC NcD

National Manpower Council.
A policy for scientific and professional manpower; a statement by the Council, with facts and issues prepared by the research staff. New York, Columbia University Press, 1953.

xix, 263 p. map, diagrs. 24 cm.
Bibliography: p. ₍259₎-263.

1. Professions—U. S. 2. Professional education—U. S. ɪ. Title.

HD8038.U5N3   331.7   53—9750

OClW MB CSt AU DS FMU KEmT NcU OrCS IdPI TOU GAT OCl OCU OO OU OrP OrCS Or MtU MtBC IdU CaBVaU ICJ ViU DNLM PPC PPT WaS WaTC Wa OrU PPD PBL PSt
NN   0057802   DLC OClW DAU PU-W NcD TxU OOxM NN TU

HD 5724
N2726   **National Manpower Council.**
A policy for skilled manpower: a statement and recommendations. [New York, Columbia University Press, 1954] 33 p. 23 cm.
"Reprinted from National Manpower Council: A Policy for skilled manpower; a statement by the Council with facts and issues prepared by the research staff."

1. Labor supply—U.S. 2. Vocational education—U.S. I. Title

NN   0057803   OU IU ODW NcD PPD

National Manpower Council.
A policy for skilled manpower: a statement by the Council with facts and issues prepared by the research staff. New York, Columbia University Press, 1954.

xxv, 299 p. 24 cm.
Bibliography: p. ₍293₎-299.

1. Labor supply—U. S. 2. Vocational education—U. S. ɪ. Title.

HD5724.N33   331.112   54—12810

TxU MiU ScU OrU Wa AAP IdPI IU KEmT MB OCl OU PBL PBm OrP OrLgE OrCS MtU IdU Or NcG ViU FU NIC LU TU CaBVa OrPR NcD OOxM OO OClW
NN   0057804   DLC MeB PPPL PPT PPCuP OCU NN FMU

VOLUME 407

National Manpower Council.
    Proceedings of a conference on the utilization of scientific and professional manpower, held October 7-11, 1953, at Arden House, Harriman Campus of Columbia University. New York, Columbia University Press, 1954.

xii, 197 p. 24 cm.

Bibliographical footnotes.

1. Professions—U. S.—Congresses. I. Title: Conference on the utilization of scientific and professional manpower. II. Title: Utilization of scientific and professional manpower.

HD8038.U5N33 1953   331.7   54—8065

OrLgE NIC IdPI OrU IdU MiHM
PBL PU-W PPD PU-E1 ScU KEmT Or MtBC CSt OrCS GAT
TxU MB WU-M MU NNC NBuG OC1 OOxM DNLM OO OC1U NcRS
NN 0057805   DLC PP PSt DI PPT TU ViU NcD NN ICJ

National Manpower Council.
    A report on the National Manpower Council. With an appendix on the Conservation of Human Resources Project. New York, Graduate School of Business, Columbia University, 1954.

x, 48, [3] p. 28 cm.

Bibliography : p. [51]

1. Manpower—U. S.

HD5724.N34   331.112   55—1010

PSC PPD IU AU MtU MtBC OrP CLSU NN OOxM
NN 0057806   DLC CU OrU ViU NcD PSt PBm OC1 OU OC1W

National Manpower Council.
    Student deferment and national manpower policy; a statement of policy by the council, with facts and issues prepared by the research staff. New York, Columbia University Press, 1952.

102 p. 24 cm.

1. Military service, Compulsory—U. S. 2. Students—U. S. I. Title.

UB343.N357 1952   355.22   52—1833 ‡

OrU WaS WaTC MtBC OKentU TU
MB NN NNU-W NNC NIC IdPI IdU ViU DAU Or OrCS
NN 0057807   DLC DS CtY-M MsU PBL OC1CC OC1W PSt

National Manufacture of the Gobelins
    see Paris. Manufacture nationale de tapisseries des Gobelins.

National manufacturers' association (U.S.A.)
    see National association of manufacturers of the U.S. of America.

National manufacturers directory ; registry of American manufacturers & industries. New York, National Directory Company.

v. 28 cm.

1. U. S.—Manuf.—Direct.

T12.N28   55—3913 ‡

NN 0057810   DLC

National Manufacturing Company.
    Standard wire goods ... Catalog no. 10 ... Worcester, Mass., National m'f'g company, c1916.

272 p. illus. 29.5 cm.

1. Hardware - Catalogs. 2. Wire.

NN 0057811   DP

National Map Company.
    Auto trails and commercial survey of the United States. ... Highway information and statistics by courtesy of the National Highway Association.
— Indianapolis, Ind. [1924.] 144 pp. Maps. 38 cm.
Includes Hints on driving. Highway pole markers. Motor vehicle laws and taxation. National parks and monuments, etc.

B9672 — T.-r. — Automobiles. — United States. Geog. Maps. — Road-books. United States.

NN 0057812   MB IU NjHi

National Map Company.
    Latest official survey, Kansas, showing counties in different colors, townships, cities, villages, post offices, steam and electric railways. Ed. 1266. Indianapolis [1928]

col. map 71 x 124 cm.

Scale 1 : 570,250; 9 miles, 1 inch.
Marginal map: Congressional, senatorial and representative districts.
Indexed.
Same map on verso without county coloring, and with main roads overprinted in red.

1. Kansas—Maps. 2. Kansas—Road maps. I. Title.

G4200 1928 .N3   Map 65—851
——— Copy 2.   G4201 .P2 1928 .N3

NN 0057813   DLC

National Map Company.
    National map company's map and street guide of Indianapolis
        see under title

National Map Company.   No. 27 in *Map 118.2
    National map of New England States: Vermont, New Hampshire, Massachusetts, Connecticut, Rhode Island and Maine, showing counties in different colors, towns, cities, villages and post offices, steam and electric railways ...
— Indianapolis, Ind. 1915. 4 sheets. Size, when joined, 58½ × 39⅝ inches. Scale (computed), 5.4 Miles to 1 inch.
Submaps.—1. United States. 2. Alaska. 3. Porto Rico. 4. Philippine Islands. 5. Hawaii. 6. Tutuila I. 7. Samoa. 8. Guam. 9. Wake I. 10. Howland I. and Baker I. 11. Map showing parcel post unit squares for New England and Middle Atlantic States.
The map of Maine and the submaps are on the back of the main map.

K5583 — New England. Geog. Maps.—United States. Geog. Maps.—Parcel post.

NN 0057815   MB

National Map Co., *publishers.*   *Map 1020.123
    [National street map of Indianapolis.
— Indianapolis. [1920?] Size, 24½ × 18½ inches. Scale (computed), 2778.9 feet to 1 inch. Folded.

M3417 — Indianapolis, Ind. Descr. Maps.

NN 0057816   MB

National Map Co., publishers.   No. 56 in *Map 117.6=*Map 1014.109
    [National topographic map of Massachusetts and Rhode Island, showing counties, townships, cities, villages and post offices, steam and electric railroads ...
— Indianapolis. [1918.] Size, 34¾ × 47½ inches. Scale, 4 miles to 1 inch.
Submap. — Congressional districts, Massachusetts and Rhode Island.
The copy on shelf-number *Map 1014.109 is folded.

L4198 — Massachusetts. Geog. Maps. — Rhode Island. Geog. Maps.

NN 0057817   MB

National map co.
    New standard atlas of the United States. A new series of over 50 maps in colors, based upon the latest official surveys, with a complete index showing location and population of all cities, towns and villages. The population figures are according to the latest official census. 1 p. l., 5-132 pp. incl. 50 col. maps. fol. Indianapolis, New York, National map co. ©1916.   4533
NOTE.—Contains 32 pp. of Statistics and information.

NN 0057818   DLC

National map co.
    New standard atlas of the United States. A new series of over 50 maps in colors, based upon the latest official surveys, with a complete index showing location and population of all cities, towns and villages. The population figures are according to the latest official census. 1 p. l., 5-100 pp. incl. 50 col. maps. fol. Indianapolis, New York, National map co. ©1916.   4533a
NOTE.—Without section of Statistics and information found in atlas of same title and date, published by National map co.

NN 0057819   DLC

National map co.
    New standard atlas of the United States. A new series of over 50 maps in colors, based upon the latest official surveys, with a complete index showing location and population of all cities, towns and villages. The population figures are according to the latest official census. 1 p. l., 5-100 pp. incl. 50 col. maps. fol. Indianapolis, New York, National map co. 1917.   4534

NN 0057820   DLC

National map co.
    [New standard atlas of the world. A new series of over 100 maps in colors, based upon the latest official surveys, with a complete index showing location and population of all cities and towns, including an encyclopedia of the states and foreign countries. The population figures are according to the latest official census. [3]-244 pp., incl. 102 col. maps, illus. fol. Indianapolis, New York, National map co. ©1916.   4430

NN 0057821   DLC

L912.773   National map company
N277   ...Official Illinois, showing counties in different colors, townships, cities, villages... Index with population according to 1930 federal census. Indianapolis, National map company[1931]
    fold.map. 138x121cm. fold.to 38x 30cm.

    At head of title: Illinois combination ed. no.1306.

    1. Illinois. Maps.

NN 0057822   IEN ODW OC1

G   **National Map Company.**
3800   Official New York, showing counties in
1930   different colors, townships, cities, villages,
N27   post offices, steam and electric railways
Map   with stations, and distances between stations
    Index with population according to 1930 Federal Census. 1930 census ed. Indianapolis, 1930.
    col. map 114x141 cm.

    Scale ca. 1 inch to 7 1/2 miles.
    Inset: Congressional districts.
    Wall map.

NN 0057823   NIC

National Map Company,
    Official paved road and commercial survey of the United States.

Indianapolis.

v. maps (part col.) 39 cm.

Sectional road maps cover also Lower Canada.

1. U. S.—Maps. 2. U. S.—Road maps. I. Title.

G1200.N37   Map 32—12 rev

NN 0057824   DLC OC1W OO T MC MnHi MiD

VOLUME 407

National map company's map and street guide of Indianapolis; a complete city map with index—location of streets and house numbers—travel distance table to cities and resorts—street railways—general information. Indianapolis, Chicago [etc.] National map co. [1921]–

v. fold. map. 18 x 9¼ᶜᵐ.

1. Indianapolis—Streets. 2. Indianapolis—Descr.—Guide-books.

Library of Congress   F534.I 3N27   21–19420

NN 0057825   DLC

---

32   The national march folio.   Chicago, National
    Music Co., [1889]
    80 p.

NN 0057826   DLC

National Marian Congress, Cap-de-la-Madeleine, 1954.
    National Marian Congress, August 5-15, 1954.
    Cap-de-laMadeleine, Canada, 1954.
    157, 151 p.

NN 0057827   ODaU-M

BT   National Marian Congress, Bombay, 1954.
1002   National Marian Congress, Bombay, India,
.N27   December 1954. Edited by Rev. T. Mascaren-
1954   has. [Bombay, J.S. Pereira, 1955]
        232 p. illus. (part col.) ports. 28 cm.

    1. Mary, Blessed Virgin - Congresses.
    I. Mascarenhas, Tarcy, ed.

NN 0057828   DCU ODaU-M IMunS

The **National** marine. v. 1–
    Jan. 1917–
    [Washington, D. C., The Navy press; etc., etc.] 1917–
    v. illus., col. plates, ports. 26½ᵐ. monthly.
    Volume numbering irregular; v. 12, no. 4 (Apr. 1918) follows v. 2, no. 3 (Mar. 1918)
    Official organ of the National marine league of the U. S. A.
    Title varies: Jan. 1917–Feb. 1918, The Navy and merchant marine. Mar. 1918–Aug. 1922, The National marine.
    Sept. 1922–   The National marine and foreign marketing.
    Published in Washington, D. C., from Jan. 1917 to Jan. 1918; in New York from Feb. 1918 to Apr. 1919; in Cooperstown, N. Y., from May 1919 to   (Editorial office: New York)
    Supersedes the Navy (1907-16)
    1. Merchant marine—   Period. 2. U. S.—Navy—Period.
    I. National marine league of   the United States of America.
                20–19487 Revised
    Library of Congress   VK1.N25

NN 0057829   DLC ICHi DNW OrU ICJ MB OCl

National marine and foreign marketing
    see   The National marine.

VM1   National marine engineers' beneficial associa-
.A45   tion of the United States.
    The **American** marine engineer. v. 1–
    Jan. 1906–
    [Washington, etc.] 1906–

NATIONAL MARINE ENGINEERS' BENEFICIAL ASSOCIA-
    TION OF THE UNITED STATES OF AMERICA.
    Constitution.
[n. p.]   no.   15cm.

    1906 ed. in B-10-140.
    Includes the "Constitution of the subordinate associations acknowledging the jurisdiction of the national association and general laws."
    1. Trade unions, Marine   engineers'--U.S.

NN 0057832   NN MH-PA MH-BA MdBJ IU

**National Marine Engineers' Beneficial Association of the
United States.**
    Journal of proceedings.   Record of the convention.
[n. p.]
    v. 22 cm.

    1. Marine engineers—Societies.

HD6515.E55N3   331.88156   40–27570*‡

NN 0057833   DLC TxU WHi MH-BA DL MdBJ IU

HFBE55   National Marine Engineers Beneficial As-
.N213   sociation of the United States.
MIS   Minimum wage scale, classification, crew
    list, etc., adopted by the Lake Conference,
    February, 1931 for steamers operating in
    the Great Lakes district. [n.p., 1931?]
    8 p. 18½ cm.

    Cover title.

NN 0057834   WHi

HFBE55   National Marine Engineers Beneficial As-
.N213   sociation of the United States.
MIS   Minutes of Atlantic and Gulf Coast con-
    ference, National executive committee,
    National officers' meeting; Buffalo, N.Y.,
    May, 1919. [Buffalo, F.J. Offermann print.,
    1919?]
    38 p. 21½ cm.

    Cover title.

NN 0057835   WHi

HFBE55   National Marine Engineers Beneficial Associa-
.N213   tion of the United States.
MIS   [Miscellaneous ephemeral materials not
    fully catalogued.]

    Shelved in three different sizes.

NN 0057836   WHi

National Marine Engineers Beneficial Association
    of the United States.
    Proceedings
        see its   Journal of Proceedings.

HFBE55   National Marine Engineers Beneficial As-
.N213   sociation of the United States.
MIS   Propositions to amend the national con-
    stitution. [Buffalo, 1919]
    12 p. 20 cm.

    Cover title.

NN 0057838   WHi

NATIONAL MARINE ENGINEERS' BENEFICIAL
    ASSOCIATION OF THE UNITED STATES OF
    AMERICA. District 1.
    Agreement: Dry cargo vessels.
[New York]   v.   16cm.

    Agreement for 1958/61 includes tanker vessel agreement. Later years issued separately; see: National   marine engineers' beneficial
    association of the United States of America. District 1. Agreement: Tanker vessels.
    On cover, 1958/61: National marine engineers' beneficial association (Atlantic and gulf district)

    1. Labor contracts, Seamen's--   U.S.

NN 0057840   NN

NATIONAL MARINE ENGINEERS' BENEFICIAL
    ASSOCIATION OF THE UNITED STATES OF
    AMERICA. District 1.
    Agreement: Tanker vessels.
[New York]   v.   16cm.

    Earlier years issued with its: Agreement: Cargo vessels.

    1. Labor contracts, Seamen's--   U.S.

NN 0057841   NN

HFBE55   National Marine Engineers Beneficial As-
.N213L   sociation of the United States.   No. 2,
C599   Cleveland.
    Manual and directory.   Cleveland, 18 -
    v. illus., ports. 15½ cm.

NN 0057842   WHi

RA331.88116   National Marine Engineers' Beneficial Asso-
N277   ciation of the United States. No. 30,
1900   Pittsburgh.
    Marine engineers' annual directory, 1900.
    ... [Pittsburgh, 1900?]
    86p.19cm.

NN 0057843   OC

National marine engineers' beneficial association of the
    United States. No. 33, New York (City)
    ... The 1899 year book of the Consolidated marine engineers' beneficial association no. 33 of the National marine engineers' beneficial association of the United States, by Henry B. Lister ... New York, Marine engineers' hall, 1899.
    257 p. fold. col. front., illus. 23½ᵐ.
    Advertising matter precedes and follows the text, and is also interspersed throughout the book; all included in the pagination.
    1. Marine engineering—Year-books.   I. Lister, Henry Bertram, comp.
                99—5813
    Library of Congress   VM605.N3

NN 0057844   DLC NN

National Marine Engineers' Beneficial Association
    of the U.S. No.35, San Francisco, Calif.
    ... Souvenir manual and directory of members. 1895.
    San Francisco, 1895.
    1 v. (unpaged) illus. 12x18 cm.

NN 0057845   CU-B

National Marine Engineers' Beneficial Association of
    the U.S. No. 38, Seattle, Wash.
    The 1901 annual. Seattle, Wash., Denny-Coryell Co.,
    1901.
    232 p. illus.

NN 0057846   Wa

National marine engineers' beneficial
    association of the United States. No. 101,
    Norfolk, Va.
    Constitution and by-laws... Norfolk,
    Va., n.d. 23 p. 13½cm.

NN 0057847   DL

National Marine Fisheries Service
    see   United States. National Marine
    Fisheries Service.

VOLUME 407

National marine league of the United States
of America.
Randolph, Carman Fitz, 1856–
  A brief on the shipping bill, by Carman F. Randolph ...
Washington, D. C. New York, The National marine
league of the U. S. A. ₍1916₎

National marine league of the United States of America.
  Charter and by-laws of the National marine league of
the United States of America, Aug. 7, 1913. Washington, New York ₍etc., 1913₎

  cover-title, ₍8₎ p. 23 x 10 ᶜ.

  1. Merchant marine—U. S.   ᵢ. Title.
                                                  15–16052
  Library of Congress   HE745.N3

  NN   0057850   DLC

₍National marine league of the United States of America₎
  Keep the flag flying. ₍New York, Charles Francis
press, ᶜ1915₎

  cover-title, 32 p. illus. 23ᶜᵐ.

  1. Merchant marine—U. S.   ᵢ. Title.

  Library of Congress   HE745.N3₍1₎   15–25240

  NN   0057851   DLC

National marine league of the United States
of America.
Ross, Patrick Hore Warriner, 1858–
  Why the subject of an American merchant marine is
vital to the individual business man; address delivered
by P. H. W. Ross, president, the National marine league
of the United States, before the Efficiency society of New
York, November 19, 1915. ₍New York, Charles Francis
press, 1915₎

National maritime board.
  ... Report on the work of the National maritime board,
1917–1919 ... London, H. M. Stationery off. ₍printed by
Eyre and Spottiswoode, ltd.₎ 1920.

  42 p. 24½ᶜᵐ. (Gt. Brit. Parliament. Papers by command₎ Cmd. 545)
  At head of title: National maritime board.
  "Constitution. (As agreed at a meeting on 19th December 1919 of the
Joint industrial council for the shipping industry)": p. 38–42.

  1. Arbitration, Industrial. 2. Seamen. 3. Merchant marine—Gt. Brit.
ᵢ. Title.

  Library of Congress   HD5545.A7 1919   21–19842

  NN   0057854   DLC MiU

National maritime board.

Shipping federation, ltd.
  The shipmasters' manual of information concerning
the Shipping federation, the law relating to seamen, and
the rates of pay and conditions of employment of seamen,
including the decisions of the National maritime board,
issued by the Shipping federation, ltd., Cuthbert Laws,
general manager, Michael Brett, secretary. London,
1925.

National maritime board.
  ... Standard rates of pay, hours of labour
and other determinations
    see its   Year book.

National maritime board.
  ... Year book ...
London, The National maritime board ₍19

  v. 18½ᶜᵐ.
  Cover-title.
  At head of title: The National maritime board.
  Title varies: Standard rates of pay, hours of labour and
    other determinations.
  19   Year book ...

  1. Merchant marine—Gt. Brit. 2. Seamen.

                                          ᶜᴬ 31–537 Unrev'd

  Library of Congress   HD4966.84G74   331.1856

  NN   0057857   DLC CtY

National Maritime Museum, *Greenwich, Eng.*
    see
    Greenwich, Eng. National Maritime Museum.

National Maritime Museum, *London*
    see
    Greenwich, Eng. National Maritime Museum.

National maritime union of America.
  Agreement between Lake tankers corporation and
National maritime union of America, CIO... ₍n.p.₎
1952. 23 f. 28cm.

  1. Labor contracts, Seamen's—U.S. I.₍ Lake tankers
corporation.

  NN   0057860   NN

NATIONAL MARITIME UNION OF AMERICA.
  Agreement between various tanker companies and
the National maritime union of America.
₍n.p.₎   v.   16cm.

  Agreement by the union "in its own behalf and in behalf of the
unlicensed personnel."

  1. Labor contracts, Seamen's--   U.S.

  NN   0057861   NN

NATIONAL MARITIME UNION OF AMERICA.
  Agreement between various tanker companies and
the National maritime union of America.
₍n.p.₎   v.   16cm.

  Film reproduction. Positive.

  Agreement by the union "in its own behalf and in behalf of the
unlicensed personnel."

  Beginning 1946/47, period covered by agreements ends June 15.
Includes suppl.

  1. Labor contracts, Seamen's--U.S.

  NN   0057863   NN

Pam.   National Maritime Union of America.
Coll.
          ₍Agreement between various steamship com-
24176   panies and the National Maritime Union of
        America ... in its own behalf and in behalf of
        the unlicensed personnel for whom the National
        Maritime Union has been certified by the National
        Labor Relations Board as the agent for collective
        bargaining, employed on the various companies'
        vessels registered under the American flag.
        Expiration date: September 30, 1941. ₍New

Continued in next column

Continued from preceding column

York? 1940?₎
    64 p. 17 cm.

    Cover title.
    1. Collective labor agreements. Merchant
marine. U. S.

  NN   0057865   NcD CU

FILM   National Maritime Union of America.
3189   Constitution.
HD
Social   New York.
Sciences   v.on   reels. On film (Negative)

        Microfilm. Original in U.S. Dept. of Labor Library.

  NN   0057866   CU

Pam.   National Maritime union of America.
Coll.
          Constitution of the National Maritime
17155   union of America affiliated with the Con-
        gress of industrial organizations ... As
        adopted by the sixth national convention
        held in the city of New York, from Sept. 22
        to Oct. 15, 1947 ... and ratified ...
        between Dec. 1, 1947, and Jan. 31, 1948.
        ₍New York, 1948₎
          94 p. 13½cm.

  NN   0057867   NcD NN PLF MB NcU NNC OrCS

NATIONAL MARITIME UNION OF AMERICA.
  Democracy for all; NMU manual on parliamentary procedure for ship and shore meetings. ₍Rev. by the NMU
research dept.; cartoons by Frank Hanley. Rev. ed.
New York, 1953] 32 p. illus. 21cm.

  Cover title: Democracy...

  1. TRADE UNIONS, SEAMEN'S--U.S.
  2. TRADE UNIONS--ORGANIZATION AND MANAGE-
     MENT--U.S.

  NN   0057868   NN

HX15   National Maritime Union of America.
Y3   Do you know that...₍n.p.₎ 1943₎
v. 48:3   ₍8₎ p. illus. 19cm. (Its Educational pamphlet no. 1)
x
           Cover title.
           Yates collection, v. 48, no. 3.

           1. Merchant seamen - Salaries, pensions, etc. I. Title.
(Series: National Maritime Union of America. Educational
pamphlets, no. 1)

  NN   0057869   CU-B

Pam.   National Maritime Union of America.
Coll.
           The enemy at home! ₍New York? 1943₎
24588   15 p. illus. 22 cm.

           1. Merchant seamen. U. S. 2. World
War, 1939–1945. U. S. I. Title.

  NN   0057870   NcD NN MiEM WHi

HD   National Maritime Union of America.
6515   Financial Report.
84N3.1

           1. Merchant seamen - Societies. 2. Merchant
seamen - U.S.

  NN   0057871   CtMyMHi NN MiD

VOLUME 407

Pam.
Coll.
24301

National Maritime Union of America.

Here's a program! Smash Hitler, vote NMU! ₁New York? 1942₃
30 p. illus. 20 cm.

1. National Maritime Union of America. 2. World War, 1939-1945. Naval operations. I. Title.

NN 0057872   NcD

₁National maritime union of America₃
`Heroes today, tramps tomorrow? ₁New York? 1944₃
₁16₃ p. illus. (National maritime union. Education dept. Publication no. 12)

"Based on a report by William L. Standard to the 1943 convention of the NMU."

1. Seamen. I. Title. II. Standard, William L

NN 0057873   NNC

National maritime union of America.
Hold that meeting! ₁New York, Nat. maritime union of America, 1943₃ 15 p. illus. 19cm.

1. Parliamentary practice—U.S., 1943. 2. Trade unions, Seamen's— U.S. 3. Trade unions—Organization and management.
N.Y.P.L.   September 17, 1945

NN 0057874   NN MiEM

Pam.
Coll.
24961

National Maritime Union of America.

How to get there; directory of piers, anchorages, and steamship companies in the New York-New Jersey harbor area ₁compiled by Madlyn Ford. Corr.₃ New York ₁1945₃
48 p. 14 cm.

1. New York (City) Description. Guide-books. I. Ford, Madlyn   II. Title.

NN 0057875   NcD

National maritime union of America.
In the back. NMU analysis of the Taft-Hartley law. ₁New York, Nat. maritime union of America, 1947₃ 19 p. illus. 20cm. (Publication. no. 17)

1. Labor—Jurisp.—U.S. 2. Trade unions, Seamen's—U.S.
N.Y.P.L.   April 30, 1951

NN 0057876   NN PPD

Pam.
Coll.
24965

National Maritime Union of America.

Instructions for new members. ₁New York? 1943₃
₁4₃ p. 13 cm.

Caption title.

1. National Maritime Union of America.

NN 0057877   NcD

HX15
Y3
v. 48:4
x

National Maritime Union of America.
Labor spies on the N.M.U.   New York ₁1938?₃
47 p. illus. 20cm. [Yates collection, 48, no. 4]

Cover title.

1. Trade-unions - U.S. 2. Spies. I. Title.

NN 0057878   CU-B NcD FU MH MiEM NN

National maritime union of America.
Merchant seamen and the law
see under   Standard, William L

National maritime union of America.
Minutes of constitutional convention, National maritime union of America, Manhattan opera house, New York, N. Y. ₁New York, 1937₃ ₁451₃ f. incl. tables. 35cm.

Caption-title.
Reproduced from typewritten copy.
Various paging.
Held July 19th – 30th, 1937.

915641A. 1. Trade unions, Seamen's   —U. S.
N.Y.P.L.   January 4, 1938

NN 0057880   NN

NATIONAL maritime union of America. N.Y.
₁Miscellaneous publications.₃

NN 0057881   NhD

Pam.
Coll.
24774

National Maritime Union of America.

The NMU fights Jim Crow. ₁New York, 1943₃
13 p. illus. 23 x 11 cm.

1. Discrimination in employment. U. S. 2. National Maritime Union of America. I. Title.

NN 0057882   NcD NNC NN

CPA
VF
1083.3

National Maritime Union of America.
○N.M.U. manual, political action. ₁New York, 1947₃
43 p. illus. (National Maritime Union of America. Pilot, Education and Publicity Department. Publication, no. 9)

"First printing."

1. Merchant seamen - U.S. 2. Trade-unions.   I. Title.

NN 0057883   MiEM

National maritime union of America.
○₁NMU pension and welfare plan; 2 year report, Jan. 1, 1951 to Dec. 31, 1952. ₁New York, 1953₃ ₁12₃ p. illus. 14 x 22cm.

Cover title; at head of title: N. M. U.

1. Trade unions—Benefits—U.S.   2. Trade unions, Seamen's—U.S.

NN 0057884   NN NcD

NATIONAL MARITIME UNION OF AMERICA.
₁NMU welfare plan. [New York, 1954] 16 p. illus. 20cm.

Cover title.

1. TRADE UNIONS--BENEFITS--U.S.
2. TRADE UNIONS, SEAMEN'S--U.S.

NN 0057885   NN

HD7812
S42U5
Social
Sciences

National Maritime Union of America.
Opening statement in contract negotiations for passenger and freighter vessels with the Committee for Companies and Agents, Atlantic and Gulf Coasts.   New York, 1949.
14, vi, 261 ℓ.

Title from caption and first paragraph of book.

1 Collective bargaining - U.S.   I. Committee for Companies and Agents, Atlantic and Gulf Coasts.

NN 0057886   CU

National Maritime Union of America.
Pamphlets.

v. of pamphlets. illus. 31 cm.
Binder's title.
Each volume has table of contents.
1. Merchant seamen. U.S. 2. National maritime union of America. 3. Seamen. Societies, etc.

NN 0057887   CU

HD6350
.S4P5

National maritime union of America.
The Pilot; a national paper for maritime workers.
₁New York₃ National maritime union of America, 19

National maritime union of America.
Pork chops and politics

see under

Curran, Joseph Edwin, 1906-

National Maritime Union of America.
President's report on the state of the union, submitted to the national convention.
₁n. p.₃
v. 28 cm.

HD6515.S4N28   62-27044 ‡

NN 0057890   DLC MiD NcD CU CtMyMHi

National maritime union of America.
Procedure for settling disputes under National maritime union agreements. ₁New York, National maritime union of America, 1950₃
cover-title, 22 p. 16cm.

NN 0057891   ViU NN NNC WaU-L

National Maritime Union of America.
Proceedings of the national convention.

₁n. p.₃

v. 23 cm.

1. Merchant seamen—Societies. 2. Merchant seamen—U. S.

HD6515.S4N3   331.88156   48-33946*‡

NN 0057892   DLC WaS CtY ICRL ICU MdBJ WrU NIC

VOLUME 407

HD
6515
S4N3.2
National Maritime Union of America.
    Report of National officers.

1. Merchant seamen - Societies. 2. Merchant seamen - U.S.

NN 0057893   CtMyMHi NcD

HD
6515
S4N3.4
National Maritime Union of America.
    Report of the National secretary.

1. Merchant seamen - Societies. 2. Merchant seamen - U.S.

NN 0057894   CtMyMHi

HD5325
.R2
1948
.G7
National Maritime Union of America.
    U. S. *Emergency Board (Grand Trunk Western Railroad Company, and other carriers, 1948)*
    Report to the President by the Emergency Board created June 23, 1948, by Executive order 9971 pursuant to section 10 of the Railway labor act, to investigate and report upon a dispute between the Grand Trunk Western Railroad Co., Chesapeake and Ohio Railway Co., Wabash Railroad and the Ann Arbor Railroad Co. and certain of its employees represented by the National Maritime Union of America. N. M. B. cases A-2801, A-2802, A-2803, A-2804. Detroit, Mich. July 20, 1948. No. 63. ₁Washington, U. S. Govt. Print. Off., 1948₁

HD5325
.R2
1947
.A6
National Maritime Union of America.
    U. S. *Emergency Board (Ann Arbor Railroad Company, and other carriers, 1947)*
    Report to the President by the Emergency Board ... to investigate and report upon certain disputes between the Ann Arbor Railroad Company, Grand Trunk Western Railroad Company, Pere Marquette Railway Company, Wabash Railroad Company and certain of their employees represented by the National Maritime Union (CIO) (NMB cases A-2455, 6, 7, and 8) Detroit, Mich., Apr. 21, 1947. No. 45. ₁Washington, U. S. Govt. Print. Off., 1947₁

National maritime union of America.
    The river rat murder case
        see under   Austin, Aleine.

NATIONAL MARITIME UNION OF AMERICA.
    Standard collier agreement signed between the ₁union₁ and...Collier owners' association...₁and₁ independent ₁companies₁
    ₁New York₁   v.   16cm.

    Agreement for 1949 in B-10-1270.
    Cover title: Agreement between various collier companies and the National maritime union of America,...in its own behalf and in behalf of the unlicensed personnel.
1. Labor contracts, Seamens'--U.S. I. Collier owners' association.

NN 0057898   NN

National maritime union of America.
    The story of the ship's committee. Prepared by ₁the₁ Pilot, education ₁and₁ publicity department. ₁New York, 1947₁
    illus.   20cm.   (ITS: Publication. no. 16)

Based on NMU filmstrip "Heart of the Union."

1. Trade unions. Seamen's--U.S.   I. Title: Heart of the union.

NN 0057899   NN

Pam.
Coll.
24112
National Maritime Union of America.
    Who are the hacks in the NMU? ₁New York?₁ 194-?₁
    15 p. 20 cm.

1. National Maritime Union of America.
I. Title.

NN 0057900   NcD

National maritime union of America.

Congress of industrial organizations. *Maritime committee.*
    Who's guilty? A record of certain activities of the United States Bureau of marine inspection and navigation, with regard to safety-at-sea and the collective bargaining rights of seamen. ₁Washington, New York, The CIO Maritime committee and the National maritime union of America ₁1940₁

NATIONAL MARITIME UNION OF AMERICA.
    Working agreement between various companies and agents (Atlantic and Gulf coasts) and the National maritime union of America.
    [n.p.]   v.   16cm.

    Agreement by the union "in its own behalf and in behalf of the unlicensed personnel on United States flag ocean-going dry cargo and passenger vessels."

1. Labor contracts, Seamen's--U.S.

NN 0057903   NN

Pam.
Coll.
24102
National Maritime Union of America.
    Your group insurance plan; elected officals ₁sic.₁ of National Maritime Union of America, C.I.O. ₁New York? 1952?₁
    19 p. illus. 21 cm.

    Cover title.
    1. National Maritime Union of America. Officials and employees. 2. Insurance, Group. I. Title.

NN 0057904   NcD

HD6350
.S4N3
no.21
1944
National Maritime Union of America. Education Dept.
    From kitchen to Congress. ₁New York, 1944₁
    28 p. illus. 15cm. (Its Publication, no. 21)
    Cover title.

1. Seamen--U.S. 2. Soldiers--Suffrage. I. Title. II. Ser.

NN 0057905   ViU

National Maritime Union of America. Education Dept.
    Publications, no. 1-   New York, 1942-

    Open entry.

NN 0057906   MiD WHi

---

f HD6515
S4N336
Social
Sciences
National Maritime Union of America. National Reorganization Committee.
    National reorganization; an outline, with methods of work for all officials, agents, organizers and patrolmen of the National Maritime Union of America. [n.p.] 1939.
    56, 10, 11 ℓ.   36cm.

1. National Maritime Union of America.

NN 0057907   CU

National Maritime Union of America. Pilot, Education and Publicity Dept.
    Publication no. 1-   New York, 1946-

    Open entry.

NN 0057908   MiD WHi

National Maritime Union of America. Pilot, Education and publicity department.
    The story of the ship's committee
        see under   National Maritime Union of America.

National Maritime Union of America. Research Dept.
    Democracy for all
        see under   National Maritime Union of America.

National market
    see under   Crowell Publishing Company.

National market letter. v. 1-
May 1946-
Chicago, Real Estate Research Corporation.
    v. in   illus. 29 cm.   monthly.

1. Real estate business—United States—Periodicals.   I. Real Estate Research Corporation.

HD251.N34   333.3'3   74-641369
                                                MARC-S

NN 0057912   DLC AzU NjR GU

NATIONAL MARKET REPORTS, INC.
    Blue book. Executives edition. v.43, no. 192, 196-v. 44, no. 200; Jan., July, 1954-Jan. 1955 Chicago.   v.   28cm.

    Quarterly.
    Issues are numbered continuously in an even sequence only and form the main issue of the Blue book. The odd sequence is an Auxiliary passenger car pricing edition. (Not in the ₁   ₁ library.)

    For earlier file, whose numbering it continues, see: National used car market report, inc., Chicago. Blue book. Executives edition.
    Contains Used car appraisals.
    Ceased publication.

1. Automobiles--Trade and stat.--U.S. 2. Automobiles--Used cars. 3. Prices, Automobiles--U.S.

NN 0057914   NN

National Market Reports, Inc.
    Blue book. Executives edition
        see also under   National Used Car Market Report, Inc., Chicago.

National Market Reports, inc.
    Illustrations of front end suspension grille and front bumper assembly, body parts of all 1954 model cars. For use in conjunction with the National auto parts & labor manual. Chicago, °1954.
    108 p. illus.

NN 0057916   MiD

National Market Reports, inc.
    National aircraft blue book.
        see under title

VOLUME 407

National Market Reports, Inc.
　National farm and tractor implement blue book
　　see　National farm tractor and implement
blue book.

National Market Reports, Inc.
　National tractor and farm implement blue
book ...
　　see　National farm tractor and implement
blue book.

National Market Reports, Inc.
　Red book⁻ national used car market report
　　see　Red book. Official used car valuations.

National Market Reports, Inc.
　Red book. Official used car valuations
　　see under title

NATIONAL MARKET REPORTS, INC.
　Truck blue book. Official used truck valuations.
1954-
Chicago.　　　　v.　　　　　14-28cm.

　　Quarterly, 1954-55; semiannual, 1956-

　　Continues　National used car market report, inc., Chicago.
Blue book truck appraisal guide. Truck edition.
　Vols. 45-40, 1956-61, numbered continuously, no. 176-187.
Title varies: 1954-July, 1955, Blue book truck appraisal guide. Truck
edition; 1956-58, Blue book national market report. Official used truck
appraisals; 1959-Jan./June, 1962, Blue book. Official used truck valuations.
(other variations).

　　Title also as: Blue book official used truck appraisal and data guide,
1956-Jan./June, 1960; official blue book used truck valuation guide
(varies), July/Dec. 1960-date.

1. Prices, Motor trucks--U.S.　2. Motor trucks--Trade and stat.--U.S.
I. Title: Blue book truck appraisal guide. Truck edition. II. Title: Blue
book national market report. Official used truck appraisals. III. Title:
Blue book. Official used truck　　　valuations. IV. Title:
Official blue book used truck　　　valuation guide. V. Title.

NN　0057924　　NN

National market reports, inc.

For publications before 1954, see

National used car market report, inc., Chicago.

National Marketing Research Workshop
　see
National Marketing Service Workshop.

The National marketing review. v. 1 (no. 1-4); summer
1935-spring 1936. ₁Chicago, Published for the National
association of marketing teachers by Business publications,
inc., 1935-36₁
cover-title, 379 p. illus. (maps) diagrs. 25½ᶜᵐ.
"Doctoral dissertations in marketing": p. 187-188.
Includes section "Book reviews and book notices, Edmund P. Learned,
editor".
United with the American marketing journal to form the Journal of
marketing.
　1. Marketing—Period.　　　I. National association of marketing
teachers.
　　　　　　　　　　　　　　　　　37-9975
Library of Congress　　HF5415.A2N15
　　　　　　　　　　　　　₂₁　　　　　658.805

NN　0057927　　DLC IU NN MiU ICU NNC NcD

National Marketing Service Workshop.
　Report.
　Washington ₁etc.₁
　　v. 27 cm. annual.
　　Vols. for　　　　issued as U. S. Agricultural Marketing Serv-
ice. AMS.
　First workshop held in 1949.
　Each report has also a distinctive title.
　Issued by the workshop under earlier names: 19　-51, Marketing
Research Workshop; 1952, National Marketing Research Workshop;
　　　National Marketing Workshop.
　1. Produce trade—U. S.—Congresses.　2. Farm produce—Market-
ing—Congresses.　(Series: U. S. Agricultural Marketing Service.
AMS)

HD9001.N38　　　　658.8072　　　51-60794 rev 3*

　　　　OrP OrU WaS NIC DNAL MH-BA NNC WaU-L MtBC OrU OU
NN　0057928　　DLC CU IU CLSU NIC CL InLP OrCS CaBVa

National marketing service workshop.
　A summary of proceedings including
recommendations for improving marketing
service programs under the Agricultural
marketing act.　Wash.,U.S.Agricultural
marketing service,19 -
　　Annual.
　　Title varies slightly.
　　Issued, 19　-1952 as Marketing
service workshop.

NN　0057929　　CaBVa

HF　　National Marketing Service Workshop,
5415　　University of Minnesota 1949.
M34　　　Marketing research; notes from National
1949　Workshop, held at Center for Continuation
　　Study, University of Minnesota, Minneapolis
　　Minnesota, August 29-September 8, 1949.
　₁n. p., ₁ 1949.
　　147 p. 27 cm.

　　Sponsored by the Land Grant College
Association,　　　　and the Agricultural Research Admin　　　istration.

NN　0057930　　NIC DNAL CU

National Marketing Workshop
　see
National Marketing Service Workshop.

National markets and national advertising
　　see under　Crowell publishing company.

HQ　　NATIONAL Marriage Guidance Council, London,
734　₁Collection of publications₁
qN277　　The library has a collection of
miscellaneous publications of this
organization kept as received. These
publications are not listed nor bound
separately.

NN　0057933　　DNLM

National Marriage Guidance Council, London.
　Marriage guidance
　　see under title

National Marriage Guidance Council.
　Marriage guidance in a local community.
London [1952?]
　17 p.　23 cm.
　1. Marriage counseling. I. Title.

NN　0057935　　OrU

National Mary Washington Memorial Association. Washington,
D. C.
　Certificate of incorporation and by-laws of the national Mary
Washington Memorial Association.　Washington: Gibson Bros.,
1890.　22 p.　12°

1. Societies (Patriotic), U. S.
N. Y. P. L.

NN　0057936　　NN

National Mary Washington memorial association,
Washington, D. C.
　List of hereditary life members of the National
Mary Washington memorial association.　Washington, D. C., Gibson bros., printers and bookbinders,
1898.
　1 p.l., 11 p.　21 cm.

　Additions and corrections in manuscript.

　1. Washington, Mrs. Mary (Ball) 1708-1789.

NN　0057937　　Vi

National Mary Washington memorial association,
Washington, D. C.
　List of hereditary life members of the National
Mary Washington memorial association.　Washington, D. C., Gibson bros., printers and bookbinders,
1900.
　1 p.l., 15 p.　21 cm.

　Two blank pages included in pagination.

　1. Washington, Mrs. Mary (Ball) 1708-1789.

NN　0057938　　Vi

National Mary Washington memorial association, Washington, D. C.
　To the women of the United States this appeal is addressed. ₁n. p., 1890₁
　4 p. 22½ᶜᵐ.
　Caption title.
　On cover: The National Mary Washington memorial association, Washington, D. C.
　Signed: Margaret Hetzel, secretary. Clifton Station, Va., Sept. 15,
1890.

　1. Washington, Mrs. Mary (Ball) 1708-1789.
　　　　　　　　　　　　　　　　　15-27862
Library of Congress　　　E312.19.N27

NN　0057939　　DLC NcD OFH

National Masonic Convention
　　see　Freemasons. U.S. National Convention.

National masonic research society.
　The Builder; the national magazine of freemasonry. v. 1-15,
v. 16, no. 1-5; Jan. 1915-May 1930. Anamosa, Ia. ₁etc.₁
1915-23; St. Louis, Mo. ₁1923-30₁

National masonic research society
　A catalog of books for the mason, prepared under the
supervision of the editor-in-chief of the National masonic research society, and of its official journal, the
Builder. St. Louis, Mo., Book department of the National masonic research society, ᵃ1924.
　72 p. 22ᶜᵐ.
　Contains advertising matter.

　1. Freemasons—Bibl.—Catalogs.
　　　　　　　　　　　　　　　　　26-11683
Library of Congress　　Z5993.N27

NN　0057942　　DLC

National masonic research society
Freemasons. Constitutions.
　The old constitutions of freemasonry; being a reprint
of the earliest printed edition, now in the library of the
Grand lodge of Iowa, which was published by J. Roberts
in 1722; together with a foreword by Joseph Fort Newton. Anamosa, Ia., Printed for and pub. by the National
masonic research society, 1917.

VOLUME 407

W 1   NATIONAL Mass-Radiography Association
NA507   (Ireland)
               Report.
               1st-   1951/54-
               Dublin.
                    v. illus.
               First report covers period Sept. 1951-
               Dec. 1954.
               1. Radiology - Period. 2. Tuberculosis
               - Ireland

NN   0057944   DNLM NNC-M

National Master Farriers' and Blacksmiths'
     Association
          see   National Master Farriers', Black-
     smiths' and Agricultural Engineers' Association.

331.88   National Master Farriers', Blacksmiths' and
F249g   Agricultural Engineers' Association.
             Income and expenditure accounts.

             Leeds ⟨Eng.⟩
                 v. tables. 22cm. annual.

             Title varies: General account showing
             expenditure and income.
             Issued 19 -48 by the association under an ear-
             lier name: National Master Farriers' and Black-
             smiths' Associa-   tion.

NN   0057946   IU

The national matches; the training of a national
     match rifle team
          see under   [National board for the pro-
     motion of rifle practice]

National Materials Handling Exposition, *Cleveland*, 1948
     see Cleveland. National Materials Handling Exposition,
     1948.

National maternal and child health council.
     Hidden hungers in a land of plenty. ⟨Washington⟩ National
     maternal and child health council ⟨1942?⟩
     1 v. 23ᶜᵐ.
     Cover-title.
     Consists of VIII sections, each separately paged, and 4 unnumbered
     pages (introduction and index) in folder.
     On p. ⟨2⟩ of cover: A handbook of nutrition projects for you and your
     group ... A cooperative venture of the American association of univer-
     sity women and the National maternal and child health council with
     special assistance rendered by the American Red cross and the American
     dietetic association in matters pertaining to nutrition. Prepared by
     Margaret Despard West in consultation with staffs of these and many
     other government and private agencies ... Second printing.
     1. Nutrition.   I. Ameri-   can association f university women,
     II. West, Margaret Despard.   III. Title.
                                                         43-4677
     Library of Congress   TX551.N37
                                    ⟨3⟩   613.2

NN   0057949   DLC MiU OU OO

National maternal and child health
     council.
     How can we help bring maternal and
     child health services to needy areas?
     ⟨A symposium⟩ Annual meeting of the
     National maternal and child health
     council. January 26, 1942.   Washington,
     1942.
          47 p., 28cm.

          Mimeographed.

NN   0057950   TU

National mathematics magazine
     see Mathematics magazine.

National mayonnaise machine co., inc.
     Sales manual, the National mayonnaise machine co.,
     inc. Brooklyn, N.Y... prepared by the Sales depart-
     ment.
     [Brooklyn, c1924]

HF5439
.M25N3

NN   0057952   DLC

R104   The national medical almanac...
.N3   Philadelphia, 18

NN   0057953   DLC

National Medical and Dental Association of America.
     Bulletin. v.1-   1929-   Chicago.

          Title varies: 1935-53, Medical and dental
     bulletin.
          1929-53 issued by the society under its former
     names: 1929-Aug. 1952, Polish Medical and Dental
     Association of America; Sept. 1952-1953, Medical
     and Dental Association of America.
          Articles chiefly in English.

     MiU OrU
NN   0057954   ICJ LNL InU-D GEU NNC-M CoU-M ICRL

National medical association.
     Journal.
     Tuskegee Institute, Ala., 19
          v. illus., ports. 26 cm. quarterly.

          1. Medicine—Societies, etc.   I. Title.

     R15.N3   CA 17—3598 Unrev'd

NN   0057955   DLC ICJ MiU CtWM ICRL CaBVaU

HV5035   NATIONAL Medical Association. Journal of the National
.R66   Medical Association.
          Roman, Charles Victor, 1864-
               The dethronement of a king, by C. V. Roman. ⟨n. p.⟩
          G. W. Hemphill Press ⟨1914?⟩

NATIONAL medical association for repeal of the contagious diseases' acts.
     Work accomplished and work still to be done. Communicated to the
     conference of the "British and continental federation" held Sept., 1882.
     [Liverpool. Brakell. 1882.] 12 pp. 8°.

     Contagious diseases acts.
          Sheet D 4672   Jan. 9, 1900

NN   0057957   MB

National Medical Association (Great Britain and
     Ireland) for the Abolition of State Regulation of
     Prostitution.
          An address to members of the American
     legislature and of the medical profession ...
          see under   International Abolitionist
     Federation.

National medical association of China.
     The Chinese medical directory ⟨1st⟩-   1928-
     Shanghai, The Chinese medical association, 1928-

National medical association of China.

Rakusen, Charlesworth Percival, 1894-
     History of optics in China, by C. P. Rakusen ... ⟨Shanghai?⟩
     The Committee on medical history of the National medical
     association of China, 1937.

NN   0057952   DLC

National Medical Association of China.
     Medical guide
          see   The Chinese medical directory.

The National Medical Association of China.
     The National medical journal of China ...
          see under title

National Medical Association of China. General
     Committee on Scientific Terminology
          see   K'o hsüeh ming tz'u shen ch'a hui.

National Medical Association of Physicians,
     Dentists and Pharmacists of the United States
     of America.
          Minutes of the National medical association of
     physicians, dentists and pharmacists of the United
     States of America.   Philadelphia, 1907-

NN   0057964   PPC

National Medical College, Washington, D.C.
          see   George Washington University,
     Washington, D.C. School of Medical.

W 3   NATIONAL Medical Convention
NA631   Proceedings.
               Philadelphia [etc.] 18 -47.
                    v.   W3 NA631
               Issue for 1846 called Minutes of pro-
          ceedings.
               Revised ed. of 1846 proceedings com-
          bined in one issue with those of 1847 con-
          vention and issued by the American Medi-
          cal Association.
               I. American Medical Association

NN   0057966   DNLM TxU

W 6   NATIONAL Medical Convention, Philadelphia,
P3   1847
               Address to the governments of the
          several States of the Union, recommending
          the adoption of a general registration of
          births, marriages & deaths. To which
          is appended a report on the "Nomenclature
          of diseases adapted to the United States,
          having reference to a general registration
          of deaths." New York, Langley, 1848.
               16 p.
          W6 P3

NN   0057967   DNLM

National medical convention, *Washington, D. C.*
     see
National medical convention, *Washington, D. C.*
United States pharmacopœial convention.

VOLUME 407

National Medical Exchange. [Monthly] No. 2,
v. 1, September, 1888. Pittsburgh, Pa.
fol.
An advertisement.

NN   0057969   DNLM PPC

R695
.N3   National Medical Fellowships
1953
Negroes in medicine. Chicago [1953?]
44 p.   24cm.

1. Scholarships.   2. Negroes in medicine.

ICJ
NN   0057970   ViU ICJ NNC PPC NN MiU IU DNLM MB Or

R378.3   National Medical Fellowships.
N217n   Negroes in medicine. Chicago [1955?]
42 p.

R378.3
N217n   ——Supplement. Chicago, 1955.
Suppl.   11 p.

1. Negroes in medicine   2. Scholarships

NN   0057971   MiD

W 1
NA521   The NATIONAL medical journal.

London [1914?]-
v. illus.
Issued by the National Medical Union.
1. Medicine - Period.
2. State medicine - Gt. Brit.
I. National Medical Union

NN   0057972   DNLM

National medical journal ... v. 1-2; Apr. 1870-Feb. 1872.
Washington, D. C., Judd & Detweiler, 1871-72.
2 v. illus, pl. 23ᶜᵐ.
Vol. 1, quarterly; v. 2, monthly.
Editors: Apr. 1870-Jan. 1871, C. C. Cox.—May 1871-Jan. 1872, S. C. Busey
and William Lee.
No more published.

1. Medicine—Period.   i. Cox, Christopher Christian, 1816-1882, ed.
ii. Busey, Samuel Clagett, 1828-1901, ed.   iii. Lee, William, 1841-   ed.

4—22409

Library of Congress   R11.N3

NN   0057973   DLC DNLM ICJ

The National medical journal of China ... v. 1-17, Nov.
1915-31. Shanghai [etc.] The National medical association
of China, 1915-31.
17 v. illus. (incl. ports.) plates (part col.) tables, diagrs. 24ᶜᵐ.
Quarterly, 1916-22; bimonthly, 1923-31.
Only one number of vol. 1 published?
Editors, English section: 1915-22, Wu Lien-teh.—1922-Jan., 1926, E. S.
Tyau.—Feb., 1926-31, Wu Lien-teh.
Editors, Chinese section : 1915-Jan., 1926, C. Voonping Yui.—Feb., 1926-
28, C. L. Kao.—1928-29, P. Z. King.—Jan.-Nov. (?) 1930, C. Fang.—
Dec. (?) 1930-31, Li Tao.
Chinese section published separately, 1929-31.

Imprint varies: 1930-31, Published in Peiping by The National medical
association of China, Shanghai. Merged into the China medical
journal.

1. Medicine—Periodicals.   2. Medicine, Chinese—Periodicals.   i. Wu,
Lien-teh, 1879-   ed.   ii. Tyau, E. S., ed.   iii. Yui, C. Voonping, ed.   iv.
Kao, C. L., ed.   v. King, P. Z., ed.   vi. Fang, C., ed.   vii. Li Tao, ed.

S G 16—68

U. S. Surg.-gen. off. Libr.
for Library of Congress   [a40r34g1]

NN   0057975   DNLM MnRM ICRL MBCo ICJ MiU

National Medical Library, *Prague*
see
Prague. Státní lékářská knihovna.

R15
.N325
National Medical Public Relations Conference.
Transcript of proceedings.

[Chicago, Public Relations Dept., American Medical Associa-
tion]
v. 28 cm. annual.
Issue for 1950 has also a distinctive title: County society p[ublic]
r[elations]

1. Medicine—Societies.   2. Public relations.

R15.N325   610.6373   51-40318 ‡

NN   0057977   DLC CU

W 1
NA528
NATIONAL medical review. v. 1, no. 1-6;
Dec. 1878-May 1879. Washington.
280 p. illus.
W1 NA528
Ed. by W. S. Wells.
I. Wells, Walter S   ed.

NN   0057978   DNLM

W 1
NA528A
The NATIONAL medical review. v. 1-11,
no. 1; Mar. 1892-June 1901. Washington.
11 v. in 9. illus.

The Military surgeon, v. 1-4, no. 3,
Mar. 1898-May 1901, is issued as a
supplement to the journal and is paged
continuously with it from Mar. 1898-
June 1901.
Issues for 1896-1901 contain the Transactions of the Medical Society of the

District of Columbia.
I. Medical Society of the District of
Columbia. Transactions   Title: The
Military surgeon

NN   0057980   DNLM NN ICJ Nh MiU ICRL

National Medical Society.
Journal. v. 1-
Jan. 1945-
[Chicago]
v. in   ports. 28 cm. quarterly (irregular)

1. Medicine—Societies.   2. Medicine—Period.

R15.N33   610.6273   48-9793*

NN   0057981   DLC DNLM

National Medical Union.
The National medical journal
see under title

National Medical University, Chicago.
... National Medical University, a corporation organized and
doing business under the laws of Illinois, appellant, vs. George
W. Webster, James A. Egan, R. E. Niedringhaus, Walter R.
Schussler, P. H. Wessel, Henry Richings and Charles J. Boswell,
appellees.   Appeal from Superior Court, Cook County ... Brief
and argument for appellant.   A. W. Brickwood, attorney for
appellant. Chicago, Barnard & Miller Print [1911]
cover-title, 24 p. 24ᶜᵐ.
At head of title: In the Appellate Court of Illinois, First district. March
term, A. D. 1911.

NN   0057983   ICJ

National Medical university journal
see Chicago Night University.
The Chicago Night University bulletin.

National Medicinal Chemistry Symposium
see under   American Chemistry Society.
Division of Medicinal Chemistry.

DS403
.I7C6   National Meerut Prisoners' Defence Committee.
v.1,
no.18   The Meerut trial; facts of the case. London, 1929.
15 p. 21cm. [Indian political pamphlets   CPI
v. 1, no. 18]

1. India—Pol. & govt.—1919-1947.   2. Prisons—
India.   3. Trade-unions—India.   4. Political crimes
and offenses—India.   5. Meerut, Conspiracy at.
I. Title. II. Ser.

NN   0057986   ViU

National Meeting of Franciscan Teaching Sisterhoods. 1st, Joliet, Ill., 1952.
Franciscan education; report of the First
National Meeting of Franciscan Teaching Sisterhoods
see under   Franciscan Educational
Conference. Sisters' Division.

National Meeting of Franciscan Teaching Sisterhoods. 2d, Milwaukee, Wis., 1953.
Theology in daily life; proceedings of the
Second National Meeting of Franciscan Teaching
Sisterhoods
see under   Franciscan Educational Conference. Sisters' Division.

National Meeting of Franciscan Teaching Sisterhoods. 3rd, 1954.
Mary in the Franciscan Order
see under   Franciscan Educational
Conference. Sisters' Division. [supplement]

National Meeting of State Officials for Aging, *Washington,
D. C.*
see
Conference of State Executives on Aging, *Washington,
D. C.*

National Meeting of the Wool Growers of the U.S.,
Washington, D.C., 1889.
Extract from the minutes ... held at
Washington, D.C., Dec. 3, 1889.   [n.p., n.d.]
18 p.

NN   0057991   DNAL

National melodies. Vocal. No. 1. Star-spangled
banner
see   The Star Spangled Banner.

VOLUME 407

National melodies and American war songs. A collection of national & patriotic songs for the post, the lodge, the school and the home ... Cincinnati, The John Church company [c1903] 94p. 30cm.

Title vignette
With music

NN 0057993 RPB

NATIONAL melodies,consisting of the most admired airs of England,Ireland,Scotland & Wales, arranged as rondos,or with variations for the piano forte,and an introductory movement to each composed by the most eminent authors. No.1-2,6,11. London,Chappell & co.,[181-?]

f°.
"This selection will consist of 24 numbers."

NN 0057994 MH

National melodies of Scotland, united to the songs of Burns, Ramsay [etc.] with symphonies and accompaniments for the pf. [etc.] by Haydn Pleyel [etc.] London, 1849. 4°.

NN 0057995 CtY

National Memorial Association. Constitution. 4 sheets, type-written. f°.

NN 0057996 NN

National memorial broadcast in honor of Stephen Tyng Mather, as sponsored by The Bohemian Club of San Francisco. Through the courtesy of The National Broadcasting Company. [n.p.] 1932. 19 p. illus. 22 cm. Cover title.

1. Mather, Stephen Tyng, 1867-1930. I. Bohemian Club of San Francisco.

NN 0057997 DI CU-B CU

National memorial co., Northfield, Vt.

... Catalog and price-list of fine memorial cards ... Northfield, Vt. [19-?] [2]p. (33x32cm.) fold to [8]p. (16x11cm.)

Includes "Selections of memorial poetry in English, French and German.

NN 0057998 RPB

The national memorial day: a record of ceremonies over the graves of the Union soldiers, May 29 and 30, 1869
see under [Faehtz, Ernest F M] comp.

National Memorial Parks Association
see
National Association of Cemeteries.

National memorial stadium commission for the District of Columbia
see
U. S. *National memorial stadium commission for the District of Columbia.*

The national memorial to His Royal Highness the Prince consort ... London, J. Murray, 1873.
4 p. l., [vii]-viii, 100 p. illus, 24 (i. e. 25) pl. (part col., incl. front.) 59⅟cm.

1. London. Albert memorial.

17-8765

Library of Congress NA9355.L6 [N6]

NN 0058003 DLC NjP CtY NN OO TxU PPD

National memory training institute, Springfield, Mass. Welham system of memory-mastery. Springfield, Mass. [c1916] 9 pams.

NN 0058004 IU MiU

National Mental Health Committee
see National Committee against Mental Illness.

Law National Mental Health Foundation.

Ehrlich, Leon. Admission to mental institutions; legal requirements for treatment, detention and release in Kentucky, by Leon Ehrlich and Mrs. Bernard Wolfman. [Philadelphia, Legal Division, National Mental Health Foundation, 1950]

Law National Mental Health Foundation.

Wolfman, *Mrs.* Bernard, 1928– Admission to mental institutions; legal requirements for treatment, detention and release in West Virginia. [Philadelphia, Legal Division, National Mental Health Foundation, 1949]

National Mental Health Foundation. Annual report. Philadelphia. v. 23 cm.

NN 0058008 NcU PU-PSW OrU-M

W 6 P3 NATIONAL Mental Health Foundation Forgotten children. [Philadelphia, 1948?] 24 p. illus. Cover title. 1. Mental deficiency

NN 0058009 DNLM Or

National Mental Health Foundation. Handbook for psychiatric aides. Philadelphia, 1946–
v. illus. 19 cm.
Includes bibliographies.
CONTENTS.—section 1. A general guide to work in mental hospitals.—section 2. Care of the overactive and disturbed patient.

1. Psychiatry. 2. Insane—Hospitals.

RC605.N3 362.2 Med 46–167 rev*

NN 0058010 DLC DNLM CaBVaU NN TxU ICJ Or Wa C

National Mental Health Foundation.

Thiermann, Stephen, 1916– Illinois: mental health laws in brief, by Stephen Thiermann and Willard C. Hetzel. Philadelphia [1949]

National Mental Health Foundation.

Law Fuson, William Meeker. Iowa: mental health laws in brief, by William Fuson and Willard C. Hetzel. [1st ed.] Philadelphia [1948]

RC445 .K3B7 National Mental Health Foundation.

Bruce, Dale. Kansas: mental health laws in brief, by Dale Bruce and Willard C. Hetzel. 1st ed. Philadelphia, 1946 [i. e. 1947]

WM 32 qN277m 1947 NATIONAL Mental Health Foundation Mental health laws in brief. Rev. outline in detail. Philadelphia, 1947. 45 ℓ. Outline to be followed in preparing briefs of state laws. Prepared and published cooperatively by the National Committee for Mental Hygiene and the National Mental Health Foundation, inc. 1. Insane - Laws & legislation I. National Committee for Mental Hygiene

NN 0058014 DNLM

National Mental Health Foundation.

Law Hetzel, Willard Charles, 1912– Mental health laws in brief; State of Nebraska, by Willard C. Hetzel and John Oyer. Philadelphia [1949]

National Mental Health Foundation.

Law Hetzel, Willard Charles, 1912– The mental health laws of Ohio; a brief of the statutes, by Willard C. Hetzel and C. Lloyd Bailey. Philadelphia [1949]

W 1 NA547 National Mental Health Foundation News-views; the National mental health program. ser. 1– Mar. 9, 1946– Philadelphia, Education Division. v.

1. Mental hygiene - Periodicals I. Title: National mental health program

NN 0058017 DNLM

National Mental Health Foundation.

Law Hetzel, Willard Charles, 1912– Oregon: mental health laws in brief, by Willard C. Hetzel and Stephen Thiermann. [1st ed.] Philadelphia, '1948.

RC443 .W7 National Mental Health Foundation.

Wright, Frank Leon, 1916– Out of sight, out of mind ... A graphic picture of present-day institutional care of the mentally ill in America, based on more than two thousand eye-witness reports. Philadelphia, National Mental Health Foundation [1947]

VOLUME 407

RC445
.P38L6

National Mental Health Foundation.

Loveland, George.
Pennsylvania: mental health laws in brief, by George Loveland and Stephen Thierman[!] 1st ed. Philadelphia, 1946 [i. e. 1947]

RC321
.P89

National Mental Health Foundation.

The Psychiatric aid. v. 1–
June 1944–
[Philadelphia]

RC605
.T45

National mental health foundation.

Thorman, George.
... Toward mental health, by George Thorman. [New York, Public affairs committee, inc., 1946]

Law

National Mental Health Foundation.

Underwood, Raymond Preston, 1920–
Utah: mental health laws in brief. Philadelphia [1949]

Law

National Mental Health Foundation.

Hetzel, Willard Charles, 1912–
Virginia: mental health laws in brief. Philadelphia [1949]

National Mental Health Foundation
see also
National Association for Mental Health (*U. S.*)

National Mental Health Materials Center, New York
see New York (City) Mental Health Materials Center.

W 2
A
qN22n

The NATIONAL Mental Health Program; progress report.
Washington, 194 –54.
v.
Issued, 194 –Mar. 1949, by the U. S. Public Health Service Division of Mental Hygiene; May 1949–Sept. 1954, by the U. S. National Institute of Mental Health
Superseded in part by a section of the NAMH reporter
1. Mental hygiene – Period. I. U. S. National Institute of Mental Health

II. U. S. Public Health Service. Division of Mental Hygiene

NN 0058028   DNLM NNC CLSU

National mercantile agency.
... [The "blue book" credits ... contains the names of merchants, manufacturers and dealers throughout the United States and ... Canada, together with the financial worth of each ...
New York, National mercantile agency [1900]–
v. fol.

1–21996

NN 0058029   DLC

National Mercantile Association.
Directory of the National Mercantile Association, a corporation under the laws of the state of Ohio. Being a complete list of responsible attorneys, real estate agents and hotels in all the principal cities and towns of the U.S. and Canadas.[etc.] Cincinnati, Elm St. printing co., 1879.
247 p.   12-

NN 0058030   DLC

National mercantile publishing co., *New York.*
... How and where to purchase anything in the crockery and glassware trade to the best advantage ... New York, The National mercantile publishing co. [1884]
cover-title, xl p. 22½ᶜᵐ.

1. Pottery—U. S.—Direct. 2. Glass manufacture—U. S.—Direct.

Library of Congress   TP789.N27   8-22840†

NN 0058031   DLC MB

National Merchandise Exchange, Los Angeles.
The California co-operator
see under title

The National merchandiser.
[Montreal, National drug and chemical company of Canada, limited, 19
v. illus. 31ᶜᵐ. monthly.
Title varies slightly.

1. Drug trade—Period. 2. Drug trade—Canada. ɪ. National drug and chemical company of Canada, ltd.
                                                    44-53096
Library of Congress   HD9670.C2N3   658.916154
                                     [2]

NN 0058033   DLC

National Merchant Marine Conference, Washington, D. C., 1925.
Government aid to shipping; report of Committee III, appointed by the President of the Chamber of Commerce of the United States... Washington, D. C., 1925. 48 p. 8°.

1. Shipping—Rates—U. S. 2. Shipping—Subsidies—U. S.
N. Y. P. L.   May 13, 1927

NN 0058034   NN

National Merchant Marine Conference, Washington, D. C., 1925.
Government regulatory and administrative relations to the shipping industry; report of Committee II, appointed by the President of the Chamber of Commerce of the United States... Washington, D. C., 1925. 37 p. 8°.

1. Shipping—Govt. control—U. S.
N. Y. P. L.

NN 0058035   NN

National Merchant Marine Conference, Washington, D. C., 1925.
National Merchant Marine Conference, held under the auspices of the Chamber of Commerce of the United States, composed of representatives of commerce, industry, agriculture, labor, finance, insurance, shipbuilding and ship operation, November 16–17, 1925. Washington, D. C., 1925. 192 p. incl. tables. chart. 8°.

1. Shipping—U. S., 1925.
N. Y. P. L.   October 16, 1926

        ViU OrU CtNlG
NN 0058036   NN MiD ICJ DLC IEN MiU OCl MA OU WaS

National Merchant Marine Conference, Washington, D. C., 1925.
Relation of merchant marine to American foreign trade and national defense; report of Committee I appointed by the president of the Chamber of Commerce of the United States... Washington, D. C., 1925. 33 p. incl. tables., map. 8°.

1. Shipping—U. S. 2. Commerce—U. S. 3. Defence—U. S.
N. Y. P. L.   October 21, 1926

NN 0058037   NN

The national merchant: or, Discourses on commerce and colonies
see under [Bennet, John] fl. 1736.

National Merit Scholarship Corporation, *Evanston, Ill.*
Report. 1st–   1955/56–
Evanston.
v. 27 cm. annual.
Report year ends June 30.

1. Scholarships—U. S.

LB2348.N26   61-43114

NN 0058039   DLC IEdS OrPS

The National message.
[Boston, National casket company, inc., 19
v. in illus. 23½ᶜᵐ. monthly.

1. Coffins—Period. 2. Undertakers and undertaking—Period.
ɪ. National casket company, inc.
                                                    44-15896
Library of Congress   TS2301.U5N35   614.6085

NN 0058040   DLC

The National message and banner.
v.
London, 19   4°.
v. illus., plates.
Weekly.
Numbering continuous.
Official journal of the British-Israel-World Federation.
Absorbed "The Banner of Israel" and "The Covenant People."
Various nos. have supplements.

1. Anglo-Israel—Per. and soc. publ.
N. Y. P. L.   September 6, 1927

NN 0058041   NN

National messenger. n.s. v.1–   Oct. 27, 1817–
Georgetown, D.C.
v. triweekly.

Ceased May 21, 1821.
Continues Messenger. Cf. Brigham, Gregory.

NN 0058042   MH

The National messenger, a magazine for that which is good in all things—including life insurance. v. 1–
Jan. 1904–
Montpelier, Vt., National life insurance co., 1904–
v. illus., plates, ports. 22½ᶜᵐ. quarterly.

1. Insurance, Life—Period. ɪ. National life insurance company, Montpelier, Vt.
                                                    9-19481†
Library of Congress   HG8963.N64

NN 0058043   DLC

VOLUME 407

National metal abrasive company, Cleveland, O.
The ABC and XYZ of cleaning, hardening, surfacing, relieving metal fatigue, strain, etc., etc., by controlled abrasives. Cleveland, O.: The National metal abrasive co. [1941] 20 p. illus. 21½ cm.

Cover-title.

1. Abrasives.
N. Y. P. L.   December 3, 1942

NN 0058044   NN

National Metal Congress and Exposition
see
American Society for Metals.

National Metal Exchange, Inc., New York.
... Annual report ... [1st]-   1929-
[New York] 1930-
v.

NN 0058046   MH-BA

National metal exchange, inc., *New York.*
Certificate of incorporation, and by-laws and rules of National metal exchange, inc. ... also commission law rules, arbitration rules, and the National metal clearing association, inc. by-laws and rules ... [New York] 1932-
v. 29 cm.
Loose-leaf.

I. National metal clearing association, inc., New York.
Library of Congress   HD9506.U6A53
Copyright A 58455   338.2

NN 0058047   DLC

National Metal Trades Association.
Annual report...
I

Chicago, 1
no.
I   presented at its   convention.
                                               nar. 8°.

I. Trades unions, Metal workers   —U. S.
N. Y. P. L.   February 27, 1930

NN 0058048   NN

National metal trades association.
Apprenticeship in the metal trades. Chicago, Ill., National metal trades association [1922]
38 p. forms (1 fold.) 23 cm.
"This book is registered and is no. 8."

1. Apprentices—U. S. 2. Metal-workers—U. S.   I. Title.
Library of Congress   HD4885.U5N3   22-13607

NN 0058049   DLC

National metal trades association.
Apprenticeship in the metal trades. Chicago, Ill., National metal trades association [1922]
42 p. forms (1 fold.) 23 cm.

1. Apprentices—U. S. 2. Metal-workers—U. S.   I. Title.
Library of Congress   HD4885.U5N3 1922 a   22-21505

NN 0058050   DLC

National metal trades association
Apprenticeship in the metal trades.
Chicago, Ill., National metal trades association, 1923.
42p.

NN 0058051   OC1

National Metal Trades Association.
Apprenticeship in the metal trades. Fourth edition. Chicago, Ill., National Metal Trades Association [1926]
44 p. forms (1 fold.) 24 cm.

NN 0058052   ICJ

[National metal trades association]
Apprenticeship plan of the metal trades industries. Cincinnati, O., 1926.
16 p. incl. forms. 23 cm.
"Copyright ... by the Cincinnati branch, National metal trades association."

1. Apprentices—Cincinnati. 2. Metal-workers—Cincinnati.   I. Title.
Library of Congress   HD4885.U5N3 1926   27-14334

NN 0058053   DLC

NATIONAL METAL TRADES ASSOCIATION
Arguments. Cincinnati, O., [n.d.]
nar. 24°.

NN 0058054   MH

National Metal Trades Association.   L331.06161 65
The bulletin of the National Metal Trades Association. ... .
Cincinnati, O., [1904].
Vol. 3, 1904. plates, ports. 26 cm.
With vol. 4, the scope of the Bulletin was enlarged, and its name changed to The Open shop; shelf number L331.051 57
Published monthly.

NN 0058055   ICJ MiD DLC

National metal trades association.
Bulletin... [Circular E-   ]
[Cleveland, 1910-   ]
1 no.   8°
TS200
.N27

NN 0058056   DLC

National Metal Trades Association.
Company practices regarding older workers and retirement. Chicago, 1952.
13 p.

Report of a survey of members, prepared by the staff of the Association in Cooperation with Edwin Shields Hewitt and Associates.

NN 0058057   MH-BA

National Metal Trades Association.
Conference leaders' manual. [Rev. by Committee on Industrial Relations] Chicago [1939]
xvi, 159 p. 21 cm.
"To assist ... in planning the presentation of the material contained in the National Metal Trades Association Foremanship course."
A thorough revision of the original manual developed by the Committee on Industrial Education in 1929 under title: Foremanship, conference leader's manual.
Bibliography: p. 157-159.

1. Foremen. 2. Factory management.   I. Title.
TS155.N23 1939   658.3124   39-24161 rev*

NN 0058058   DLC

National Metal Trades Association.
Conference leaders' manual. [2d ed., rev. by Committee on Foremanship] Chicago [1947]
xvi, 161 p. 21 cm.
"To assist ... in planning the presentation of the material contained in the National Metal Trades Association Foremanship course."
The 1929 ed., prepared by the Committee on Industrial Education, has title: Foremanship, conference leader's manual.
Bibliography: p. 159-161.

1. Foremen. 2. Factory management.   I. Title.
TS155.N23 1947   658.3124   47-27269*

NN 0058059   DLC

NATIONAL METAL TRADES ASSOCIATION.
Constitution, by-laws, declaration of principles, resolutions. Cincinnati, [1902].
Pamphlet.

NN 0058060   MH NjP

NATIONAL METAL TRADES ASSOCIATION.
Constitution, by-laws, declaration of principles, resolutions. Cincinnati.
1906.

NN 0058061   MH-PA

National metal trades association.
...Constitution, by-laws, declaration of principles. Adopted Jan. 19, 1909.
[Chicago? 1909?]
HD9506
.U64N35

NN 0058062   DLC

National Metal Trades Association.
Constitution, by-laws, declaration of principles.   Chicago, Ill.: Peoples Gas Building, 1916.   27(1) p.   12°.

1. Employers.—Assoc. (Metal   trades), U. S.
N. Y. P. L.   December 31, 1917.

NN 0058063   NN

National metal trades association.
Digest of industrial relations. v.1,pt.2-v ¿
Apr.1948-
Chicago,
v.

Weekly.   -Dec.29, 1948; monthly, Jan. -May 1949.
Publication discontinued May 1949.

NN 0058064   MH-BA MoSU

National Metal Trades Association.
Foremanship, conference leader's manual.
[Chicago, 1927]
2 v.   29.5 cm.
By the association's Committee on Industrial Education.

NN 0058065   DL OC1

National metal trades association.
Foremanship, conference leader's manual. Chicago, Ill., National metal trades association [1930]
96 p. 28¼ cm.
"Developed by the Committee on industrial education."
"To assist ... in planning the presentation of the material contained in the National metal trades association foremanship course."—Foreword.
"References": p. 93-94.

1. Foremen.   I. Title.
TS155.N23 1930   658.31243   30-32190 rev

NN 0058066   DLC ICJ

VOLUME 407

National Metal Trades Association.
How about accidents? A way to help...The universal
danger sign. Cleveland, O.: the association [1913]. 19(1) p.
illus. 16°.

1. Safety appliances, U. S., 1913.   2. Hygiene (Industrial), U. S.
N. Y. P. L.   January 10, 1914.

NN 0058067   NN

National Metal Trades Association.
Industrial betterment activities of the National Metal Trades
Association. Cleveland: R. Wuest [1912]. 18 p., 1 l. nar. 8°.

1. Industrial betterment, U. S.
N. Y. P. L.   September 5, 1913.

NN 0058068   NN DL

National metal trades association.
Industrial education bibliography, a list of texts and other
books for use in developing an effective training program. Revised and supplemented in 1946 by the Committee on industrial
training, C. H. Edgar, chairman ... Chicago, Ill., National
metal trades association [1946]

1 p. l., 22 p. 28 x 21½*.

1. Industrial arts—Bibl.

Z7911.N3 1946   016.6   47-17127

NN 0058069   DLC ICJ

National Metal Trades Association.
Industrial film bibliography
see   National Metal Trades Association.
Committee on Industrial Education.
Film guide for industrial training.

National metal trades association.
... Industrial practices survey ... Compiled by the Racine
branch, National metal trades association, in cooperation with
the Manufacturers association of Racine. [Chicago, °1947.

45 p. 28*.

1. Metal-workers—Racine, Wis.   I. Manufacturers association of
Racine. II. Title.
HD8039.M52U63   331.7671   47-3559
                                        Brief cataloging

NN 0058071   DLC

National metal trades association.
... Industrial practices survey, Rockford, Illinois ... [Chi-
cago] °1947.

40 p. 28 x 21½*.

1. Metal-workers—Rockford, Ill. 2. Metal trade—Rockford, Ill.
I. Title.
HD8039.M52U672   331.7671   47-22561

NN 0058072   DLC

National Metal Trades Association.
Industrial practices survey, Toledo Branch, relating to
I. Production, service and maintenance employes. II. Employes other than production, service and maintenance (office, etc.) III. Foremen. [Toledo] °1948.

19 p. 28 cm.

1. Labor and laboring classes—Toledo. 2. Industrial relations—
Toledo.   I. Title.
HD8085.T6N3   658.38   48-18348*

NN 0058073   DLC

National Metal Trades Association.
Industrial relations report.

Chicago [19

no. illus. 28 cm.

1. Industrial relations. 2. Metal trade.

HD6971.N25   658.3   49-14009*‡

NN 0058074   DLC OC1 TxU

National metal trades association.
Job rating; definitions of the factors used
in rating jobs, hourly rated occupations.
Chicago, National metal trades association
[1938?]
2 p. l., 22 numb. l. 16cm.

Text on verso of cover.

NN 0058075   NNC

National Metal Trades Association.
Labor-management relations act of 1947; 120 questions and
answers with topical index, prepared by David R. Clarke.
Chicago, °1947.

[19] p. 28 cm.
Cover title.

1. Labor laws and legislation—U. S.   I. Clarke, David R., 1892–
II. Title.
HD7834.N35   331.15   48-1706*

NN 0058076   DLC

National Metal Trades Association.
Labor-management relations act of 1947, as amended October 22, 1951; questions and answers with topical index,
prepared by general counsel. Chicago, °1952.

18 p. 28 cm.

1. U. S. Laws, statutes, etc. Labor management relations act,
1947.   I. Title.
                    331.15   52-27330 ‡

NN 0058077   DLC

National Metal Trades Association.
Machine shop instructor's manual; a manual of instruction
outlines.   Chicago, Ill., National Metal Trades Association
[°1934-1940]

cover-title, [157] p. illus. 29cm.
Various pagings.

NN 0058078   ICJ CaBVa MiD

National Metal Trades Association.
Machine shop technology [1934]
see under   National Metal Trades Association.
Committee on Industrial Education.

National metal trades association.
Machine shop technology ... Chicago, Ill., National metal
trades association, 1941–

v. illus. 28 x 22cm.

Loose-leaf; reproduced from type-written copy.
"Originally developed by the Committee on industrial education,
National metal trades association; revised and supplemented in 1941
by the sub-committee on Apprentice training ... approved by National
committee on apprentice training."

1. Machine-shop practice.   I. Title.

Library of Congress   TJ1160.N27   42-3681
                           [2]   621.75

NN 0058080   DLC

HD6951   National metal trades association.
.M4
          Metal trades digest. v. 1, no. 1-14; July 8, 1937–Apr. 1939.
          [Chicago, National metal trades association, 1937–39]

National Metal Trades Association.
N. M. T. A. plant management sectional conference minutes.

Chicago.

v. 23 cm.

1. Factory management—Congresses. 2. Employment management—
Congresses.
TS155.A1N3   658.506373   47-43026*

NN 0058082   DLC OC1

National metal trades association.
National metal trades association. History,
methods, facilites.
[Cleveland, 1909?]

HD9506
U64N37

NN 0058083   DLC

National metal trades association.
Officers and members.
Cleveland

v. 17cm.

                                        CA 16-612 Unrev'd

Library of Congress   TS200.N4

NN 0058084   DLC DL

National Metal Trades Association.
The open house in industry. Chicago
[°1948]
27 p. illus. 28cm. (Its Industrial
relations report, no. 2)

Processed.

1. Corporations. 2. Publicity. 3. Factories. 4. Good-   will (in business,
etc.) I. Title   Series.

NN 0058085   OrCS

National metal trades association.
The Open shop. v.   v. 7, no. 1-3;
                                  -Mar. 1908.
Cincinnati, O., National metal trades association [19
08]

National Metal Trades Association.
Reasons why the "closed shop" policy of organized labor is
detrimental to the country.   Cleveland: the association [1912].
14 p., 1 l. nar. 8°.

1. Closed shop.
N. Y. P. L.   August 19, 1913.

NN 0058087   NN

National Metal Trades Association.
Safety appliances. Cleveland, O., 1912. 35(1) p. illus.
4°.

1. Machinery.—Safety appliances.
N. Y. P. L.   July 22, 1912.

NN 0058088   NN

National metal trades association.
Synopsis of proceedings of the ... annual convention.

[Cleveland,

v. 22cm.

1. Labor and laboring classes—U. S.—Societies.

                                        CA 13-153 Unrev'd

Library of Congress   HD9506.U64N3

NN 0058089   DLC ICRL CU DL ICJ

VOLUME 407

National metal trades association
"Unemployment insurance"? What you can do.
(Chicago, Ill. ? 1933)
(4) p. 28 cm

NN 0058090 DL

National Metal Trades Association.
What it is, what it does, what it costs,
Cincinnati [n.d.]

NN 0058091 MH

National metal trades association. *Activities committee.*
Women in industry, a survey covering employment of women
in industry, 1943, prepared by Edward J. Kunze, industrial
engineer, N. M. T. A., adopted and approved by the Activities
committee, National metal trades association, H. Paul Nelligan,
chairman ... ₍and others₎ assisted by Clarence J. Uhlir ... ₍and₎
Charles L. Blatchford ... ₍Chicago, National metal trades
association, 1943₎
48 p. 21½ᵐ.
"Selected bibliography": p. 39–48.

1. Woman—Employment—U. S. I. Kunze, Edward J. II. Title.

43–17152

Library of Congress HD6068.N3

₍5₎ 331.4

NN 0058092 DLC ICJ OC1

NATIONAL METAL TRADES ASSOCIATION – Cleveland branch
Constitution and by-laws. [Cleveland, O., 194–?].
9 leaves.
Processed.
Caption title.

NN 0058093 MH-IR

---

q331.15
N2131m
NATIONAL METAL TRADES ASSOCIATION. Committee
on Employer-Employe Communications.
Manual of practical employer-employe com-
munications; prepared under direction of
Walter S. Roach. Chicago [c1949]
27p. 28cm.

On cover: Number 3.

1. Industrial relations. I. Title.

NN 0058094 TxU

National Metal Trades Association. Committee on
Employers' Liability
see National Metal Trades Association.
Committee on Employers' Liability Insurance.

National metal trades association. *Committee on employers' liability insurance.*
Proposed bill suggested by Committee on employers'
liability, presented before thirteenth annual convention,
National metal trades association, New York city, April
12 and 13, 1911. ₍n. p., 1911₎
cover-title, 15 p. 21½ᵐ.
Published also in Report of Committee on employers' liability insurance
to thirteenth annual convention, National metal trades association.

1. Insurance, Employers' liability. I. Title.

13–2894

Library of Congress HD7816.U6N3

NN 0058096 DLC OU

National metal trades association. *Committee on employers' liability insurance.*
Report of Committee on employers' liability insurance
to thirteenth annual convention, National metal trades
association, New York city, April 12 and 13, 1911.
₍Cleveland, The Denton press, 1911₎
97, 15 p. 22ᵐ.
William Butterworth, chairman.
Appendix: Proposed bill suggested by Committee on employers' liability. 15 p.

1. Insurance, Employers' liability. I. Butterworth, William, 1864–
II. Title.

12–23977

Library of Congress HG9964.E5N3

NN 0058097 DLC NcD CU NN OU

National metal trades association. *Committee on industrial
education.*
Elementary machine shop practice, by Committee on industrial education ... assisted by Philip C. Molter ... Robert J.
Spence ... Chicago, Ill., National metal trades
association ₍°1923–
v. illus., diagrs. 20ᵐ.

1. Machine-shop practice. I. Molter, Philip C. II. Spence, Robert J.
III. Title.

23–8795

Library of Congress TJ1160.N3

NN 0058098 DLC OU OC1 OCU NN ViU ICJ MH

National Metal Trades Association. *Committee on In-
dustrial Education.*
Film guide for industrial training. ₍1st₎– ed.;
1947–
Chicago.
v. in 28 cm.
Title varies: 1947– Industrial film bibliography.
First ed. has subtitle: A list of audio-visual aids for use in indus-
trial training.
Prepared in 1947 by the committee under a variant name: Commit-
tee on Industrial Training.
Supplements accompany some editions.

1. Industry—Film catalogs. I. Title.

T65.5.M6N3 48–12935 rev 3*

371.335230838

NN 0058099 DLC MtBC ICJ OrCS MiU MnU NIC PPD

National Metal Trades Association. Committee on
Industrial education.
Foremanship, conference leader's manual
see under National Metal Trades
Association.

National metal trades association. *Committee on industrial
education.*
Foremanship, presenting the fundamental principles of practical foremanship, developed by the Committee on industrial
education, National metal trades association ... ₍Chicago,
°1927₎
₍216₎ p. 29½ᵐ.
Various pagings.

1. Foremen. I. Title.

28–2505

Library of Congress TS155.N25

NN 0058101 DLC OC1 MiU CLSU

National metal trades association. *Committee on industrial
education.*
Foremanship, presenting the fundamental principles of practical foremanship, developed by the Committee on industrial
education, National metal trades association ... ₍Chicago,
°1927₎
1 v.

NN 0058102 ICJ

T379
.N35
National metal trades association. Committee
on industrial education.
National metal trades association. *Committee on specialist
training.*
How to read blueprints. Chicago, Ill., National metal trades
association ₍°1940₎

National Metal Trades Association. *Committee on Industrial Education.*
Industrial film bibliography
see its
Film guide for industrial training.

National metal trades association. *Committee on industrial
education.*
Machine shop technology ... Developed by the Committee
on industrial education, National metal trades association ...
Chicago, Ill., National metal trades association ₍°1934₎
6 v. in 2. illus., diagrs. 20ᵐ.
Harold S. Falk, chairman to 1933 ; Geo. A. Seyler, chairman, 1933.
Each part has various pagings.
CONTENTS.—pt. 1. A series of lesson units on the design, construction,
care and use of hand tools, measuring and recording instruments.—pt. 2.
A series of lesson units on the design, construction, care and operation of
the engine lathe.—pt. 3. A series of lesson units on the design, construc-

Continued in next column

Continued from preceding column

tion, care and operation of the milling machine.—pt. 4. A series of lesson
units on the design, construction, care and operation of the cylindrical
grinding machine.—pt. 5. A series of lesson units on the design, construction, care and operation of the shaper.—pt. 6. A series of lesson units on
the design, construction, care and operation of the turret lathe.

1. Machine-shop practice. I. Title.

A 40–2024

Illinois. Univ. Library
for Library of Congress ₍2₎

NN 0058106 IU RPD OC1

National Metal Trades Association. Committee on
Industrial Education.
Machine shop technology. 1941-
see under National Metal Trades
Association.

National Metal Trades Association.
Committee on Industrial Education.
A practical treatise on foremanship training ... developed by
the Committee on Industrial Education, National Metal Trades
Association ... Revised ... 1929 ... ₍Chicago, National Metal
Trades Association, °1929₎
14 p. 29ᵐ.
Cover-title: Foremanship, the introduction and administration of foremanship
training.

NN 0058108 ICJ

National metal trades association. Committee on industrial education.
A practical treatise on foreman training...developed by
the Committee on industrial education, National metal
trades association. Chicago, National metal trades association (c1936)
12 p. 28cm

NN 0058109 DL

National metal trades association. *Committee on industrial
relations.*
Conference leaders' manual. Chicago, Ill., National metal
trades association ₍°1939₎
xvi, 159 p. diagrs. 21ᵐ.
"To assist ... in planning the presentation of the material contained
in the National metal trades association foremanship course."—Foreword.
A thorough revision of the original manual developed by the Committee on industrial education in 1929 with many new and helpful suggestions. cf. Foreword.

1. Foremen. 2. Factory management. I. Title.

Library of Congress TS155.N23 1939 39–24161

———— Copy 2.
Copyright A 132119 ₍2₎ 658.31243

NN 0058110 DLC NN

National Metal Trades Association. Committee on Industrial
Relations.
Employe medical service, by Committee on Industrial Relations, National Metal Trades Association. Chicago, Ill.: Executive Office₍, 1929₎. 30 p. incl. tables. 8°.

507115A. 1. Hygiene, Industrial.
N. Y. P. L. December 30, 1930

NN 0058111 NN DL ICJ

NATIONAL METAL TRADES ASSOCIATION. Committee on Industrial Relations.
Experience with group insurance, by Committee on Industrial Relations, National Metal Trades Association...
Chicago, Ill.: Executive Off.[, cop. 1926.] 26 p. incl.
diagrs. 23cm.

740259A. 1. Insurance, Group—U.S.

NN 0058112 NN ICJ OC1 NIC DL

VOLUME 407

National Metal Trades Association.
Committee on Industrial Relations.
Industrial relations in the metal trades, by Committee on Industrial relations, National Metal Trades Association. Dr. Otto P. Geier, chairman ... assisted by Advisory Council on Industrial Relations ... Chicago, Ill., National Metal Trades Association ₍°1929₎
₍2₎ 16 p. diagrs. 24ᵐ.

NN   0058113   ICJ DL IaU NN

National metal trades association. *Committee on industrial relations.*
Meeting the cost of employe superannuation, by Committee on industrial relations, National metal trades association. Chicago, Ill. ₍National metal trades association, °1930₎
3 p. l., 53, ₍8₎ p. incl. tables, diagrs. 23ᵐ.
Dr. Otto P. Geier, chairman.

1. Old age pensions—U. S.   I. Title.
L 30—107
U. S. Dept. of labor Libr.   HD7106.U5N26
for Library of Congress   ₍a40c1₎

NN   0058114   DL NcD ICJ OC1

National metal trades association. *Committee on industrial relations.*
Methods of wage payment, by Committee on industrial relations, National metal trades association ... Chicago, Ill. ₍°1928₎
1 p. l., 57 p. diagrs. 23ᵐ. $0.50

1. Wages—U. S. 2. Efficiency, Industrial.   I. Title.
Library of Congress   HD4926.N⁹   28–13095

NN   0058115   DLC OC1 DL ICJ

HD5725 NATIONAL METAL TRADES ASSOCIATION. Committee
.N2915   on industrial relations.
Stabilizing metal trades employment, by Committee on industrial relations, National metal trades association, Dr. Otto P. Geier, chairman ... assisted by Advisory council on industrial relations ... research and manuscript by W. E. Odom ... Chicago, Dept. of industrial relations, National metal trades association ₍c1931₎
30 p. incl. tables, diagrs. 23cm.

1. Metal trade—U.S. 2. Unemployed—U.S.

NN   0058116   ICU OC1 NN DL ICJ

National metal trades association. *Committee on industrial relations.*
A study of employe pension plans, by Committee on industrial relations, National metal trades association ... Chicago, Ill., °1927.
16 p. diagrs. 23ᵐ.

1. Metal-workers—U. S.—Pensions.   I. Title.
CA 27–241 Unrev'd
Library of Congress   HD7116.M52U6

NN   0058117   DLC OrU NN OC1

National metal trades association. *Committee on industrial relations.*
Thrift and unemployment. By Committee on industrial relations, National metal trades association, G. E. Randles, chairman ... Otto P. Geier ... ₍and₎ H. A. Sedgwick ... Research and manuscript by the National office staff. Chicago, Ill., National metal trades association ₍°1932₎
21 p. tables, diagrs. 23ᵐ.
"This report ... is only preliminary to a more extensive treatment of this subject soon to be published."—p. ₍4₎
1. Saving and thrift. 2. Unemployed—U. S. 3. Labor laws and legislation—U. S.   I. Randles, George Earl, 1876–   II. Geier, Otto Philip, 1874–   III. Sedgwick, H. A.   IV. Title.
A 40–2394
Duke univ. Library
for Library of Congress   ₍2₎

NN   0058118   NcD

National metal trades association. *Committee on industrial relations.*
Unemployment benefit plans, by Committee on industrial relations, National metal trades association, G. E. Randles, chairman ... research and manuscript by W. E. Odom ... Chicago, Ill., Dept. of industrial relations, National metal trades association ₍°1932₎
14 p. fold. tab. 23ᵐ.

1. Insurance, Unemployment.   I. Odom, William Everette, 1894–
II. Randles, George Earl, 1876–   III. Title.
Library of Congress   HD7096.N35   33–12737

NN   0058119   DLC

National metal trades association. *Committee on Industrial Relations.*
"Unemployment insurance", by Committee on industrial relations, National metal trades association ...   Chicago ₍c1935₎
28 p. illus. 23cm.

1. Insurance, Unemployment—   U. S. 2. Insurance, Unemployment—Gt. Br.
N. Y. P. L.   March 3, 1943

NN   0058120   NN

National metal trades association. Committee
on job rating.
Job rating. Chicago, National metal trades
association ₍1938₎
11 p. tables, diagrs. 28ᶜᵐ.

1. Job analysis.

NN   0058121   NNC

National metal trades association. *Committee on specialist training.*
How to read blueprints. Chicago, Ill., National metal trades association ₍°1940₎
cover-title, 1 p. l., 22 p. illus., diagrs. 28 x 21½ᵐ.
"Developed by the Chicago branch, National metal trades association, Committee on specialist training ... Adopted and issued by the National committee on industrial training."

1. Blue-prints.   I. National metal trades association. National committee on industrial training. II. Title.
Library of Congress   T379.N35   41–12046
₍3₎   744

NN   0058122   DLC MiD

331.1 National metal trades association--Committee on
N217r   works councils.
Report of the Committee on works councils in
the metal trades. Chicago, Ill., National metal trades association ₍1920?₎
24p. tables(1 fold.)

1. Employees' representation in management. 2.
Industraial relations.

NN   0058123   IU NcD

National metal trades association. Foremanship committee.

Schappert, Joseph M
Foremanship; a practical guide, prepared by Joseph M.
Schappert ... adopted and approved by the Foremanship committee, National metal trades association ... Chicago, Ill., National metal trades association, °1942–

National metal trades association. Indianapolis
branch.
Synopsis of proceedings...(Inianapolis?)
1920–
1 v. 23 x 15 cm

NN   0058125   DL

National Metal Trades Association. *National Committee on Industrial Training*
see National Metal Trades Association. *Committee on Industrial Education.*

National Metallurgical Laboratory, *Jamshedpur*
see
Jamshedpur, India. National Metallurgical Laboratory.

National Meteorological Institute, Prague
see Prague. Státní Meteorologický Ustav.

National meter company, *New York.*
Nash gas and gasoline engines for electric lighting, pumping, fire protection and power purposes generally; manufactured by National meter company ... New York, Chicago ₍etc.₎ °1905.
56 p. illus. 15½ x 23½ᵐ.

1. Gas and oil engines—Catalogs.
CA 6—957 Unrev'd
Library of Congress   TJ776.N24 1905

NN   0058129   DLC

National Meter Company, New York.
National Meter Company of New York at the Panama-Pacific International Exposition, manufacturers of Crown, Empire, Nash, Gem, Empire-compound and premium water meters. [San
F869   Francisco, 1915]
S3   [16] p. illus.(part col.) 17cm. [With Union Oil Company
.95   of California. The Union Oil Company of California at the
U45   Panama-Pacific International Exposition. San Francisco? 1915]

NN   0058130   CU-B C

National meter company, *New York.*
Statistics, tables and water rates of cities and towns, together with facts about water meters. Comp. by the National meter company ... New York, D. H. Gildersleeve, printer, 1887.
82 p. illus., 4 fold. tab. 27½ᵐ.

1. Water-meters.
CA 7–6059 Unrev'd
Library of Congress   TD500.N2

NN   0058131   DLC

National Meter Company, New York.
Water meters. [New York, National Meter Company, c1908]
3 p. l., ₍9₎–94. illus., tables, diagrs.
Illus. t.-p.
2 forms laid in.
1. Water - meters.

NN   0058132   WaPS

National Meter Company, New York.
Water meters. Crown, Empire, Nash, Gem. ₍New York?₎
National Meter Co., cop. 1908. 42 p. front., illus. ob. 12°.

1. Water meters.—Catalogues.
N. Y. P. L.   August 29, 1923.

NN   0058133   NN

TG2   National Methodist educational conference, 1st,
N213f   Atlanta, 1936.
Forward together; addresses delivered at the
National Methodist educational conference,
Atlanta, Georgia, Dec. 13–15, 1936; a gathering
sponsored by: the Educational association,
Methodist Episcopal church; the College section,
Educational council, Methodist Episcopal church,
South; the Board of education, Methodist Episco-
pal church; the General board of Christian edu-
cation, Methodist Episcopal church, South;

the General board of Christian education,
Methodist Protestant church. ₍Nashville,
General board of Christian education, Methodist
Episcopal church, South, 1937₎
115 p. illus. 23 cm.

Cover title.

NN   0058135   CtY-D GEU

VOLUME 407

261.9 National Methodist rural life conference-Commit-
N21b tee on program and arrangements.
Both harvest and seed ... [n.p.] The Committee
on program and arrangements for the National
Methodist rural life conference [1946?]
cover-title, 127p.

Includes references.

1. Rural churches--U.S. I. Title.

NN 0058136 IU

National Methodist rural life conference. Committee on program and arrangements.
Opportunities for action in the rural church; a
study guide. [n. p.] The Committee on program
and arrangements for the National Methodist rural
life conference [1946?]
48 p. 18cm.

NN 0058137 ViU

National Methodist Rural Life Conference,
Lincoln, Neb., 1947.
Land policy and church stability; excerpts
from the final report of committee number 3.
[n.p., 1947?]
18 p.

NN 0058138 DNAL

National Methodist Rural Life Conference, *Lincoln, Neb.,*
1947.
Report of Commission Number   at the National
Methodist Rural Life Conference. New York, Dept. of
Town and Country Work, Division of Home Missions and
Church Extension of the Methodist Church [1948-

v. illus., maps. 23 cm.

Title varies slightly.
Includes bibliographies.
CONTENTS.

[2] The Methodist Church and the rural community, by D. E. Lind-

strom.—[3] Land policy and church stability, by Arthur Raper.

[6] A national rural policy for the Methodist Church, by J. B. Howes.—
[7] A program for the local rural church, by E. D. C. Brewer.—[8] The
Christian world view, by C. M. Julian.

1. Rural churches.

BV638.N4   261   48-2990*

NN 0058140 DLC NN

National Methodist Rural Pastors Conference,
Columbus, O., 1943.
The Methodist church in town and country;
proceedings. New York, Dept. of town and
country work, The Methodist church [1943?]
84 p.

NN 0058141 DNAL

National Methodist Student Conference.
Report.
[Nashville]
v. illus., ports. 22 cm.

BX8207.N43   287.673   51-30984 ‡

NN 0058142 DLC

National Methodist student leadership training **conference.**
Being a Christian on the campus; report of the [first] National Methodist student leadership training conference; students and counselors from Methodist colleges, universities,
Wesley foundations, theological seminaries representing 127
institutions and 35 states; edited by Nenien C. McPherson, jr.;
Berea college, Berea, Kentucky, June 12–17, 1939. [Nashville,
etc., 1939]
4 p., 1 l., 5–119 p. 27½ᶜᵐ.
Reproduced from type-written copy.
Published by the Board of education of the Methodist Episcopal
church, the General board of Christian education of the Methodist Episcopal church, South and the Board of Christian education of the Methodist
Protestant church.

No more national conferences held; superseded by the Regional
student leadership training conferences of the Methodist church.

1. Church work with students.   I. Methodist Episcopal church.
Board of education. II. Methodist Episcopal church, South. General
board of Christian education. III. Methodist Protestant church. Board
of Christian education. IV. Title.

45-31074
Library of Congress   BX8207.N45 1939

[2]   259

NN 0058144 DLC IEG

National Methodist Town & Country Conference,
Sioux City, Iowa, *1951.*
Methodists in town and country. A report
of the National Methodist Town and Country Conference, Sioux City, Iowa, July 21-24, 1951.
Mount Vernon, Iowa, Cornell College Press [1951]
139 p. front. 23 cm.

NN 0058145 IEG

National Methodist Town and Country Conference,
Sioux City, Iowa, 1951.
Study guide for the National Town and Country
Conference, Sioux City, Iowa July 21-24, 1951...
... Chairman, Bp. Charles W. Brashares, Secre-
tary, Glenn F. Sanford.   [n.p.]
32 p. 21.5 cm.
Cover-title.
1. Cities and town - U.S. 2. Rural churches -
U.S.

NN 0058146 MBU-T

National Methodist Town & Country conference,
July 22-25, 1955
Source book of Methodism in town & country
see under   Methodist Church (United States)
Division of National Missions. Section of National
Missions.

National Metropolitan Bank, Washington, D.C.
Banking made plain. General information
relating to modern banking transactions.
Cleveland, American Publishing Co. [1950]
45 p.

"Revised edition."

NN 0058148 MH-BA

National metropolitan bank, *Washington, D. C., plaintiff.*
... The National metropolitan bank of Washington, plaintiff,
vs. John F. Cook, collector of the District of Columbia, defendant, at law. No. 18, 241. [Washington? 1877?]
11 p. 24ᶜᵐ.
Caption title.
At head of title: In Supreme court of the United States.

I. District of Columbia. Collector of taxes, defendant. II. U. S.
Supreme court.

47-38642

NN 0058149 DLC

National metropolitan bank, *Washington, D. C.*
... The National metropolitan bank, Washington, D. C.
Oldest national bank in the District of Columbia. [Wash-
ington, D. C., Press of W. F. Roberts co., 1914]
48, [2] p. front. (port.) illus. (incl. ports., facsim.) 23½ᶜᵐ.
At head of title: 1814–1914.
Title vignette.
On cover: Organized January 11, 1814.

Library of Congress   HG2613.W34N5   14-1790

NN 0058150 DLC DAU ICJ

The National micro-news.
[Annapolis]
no. in   v. illus., ports., diagrs. 22 cm. bimonthly.
Began publication in Dec. 1953. Cf. New serial titles, 1950–1960.
Official journal of the National Microfilm Association.

1. Microfilms—Period.   I. National Microfilm Association.

TR835.N34   64-28157

NN 0058151 DLC NN DNAL MiD MoSW ICJ MB

National microbiological institute
See
United States. National microbiological institute.

National Microfilm Association.
Buyer's guide to microfilm equipment,
products and services.

1. Microphotography. Apparatus and
supplies. Catalogs. I. Title.

NN 0058153 OrU

NATIONAL MICROFILM ASSOCIATION.
Glossary of terms for microphotography and
reproductions made from micro-images.
Annapolis.   v.   24cm.
(ITS: Information monograph. no. 2)

1. Microphotography--Dictionaries.   I. Title.

NN 0058154 NN

National Microfilm Association.
Glossary of terms used in microreproduction [by] Hendrix
TenEyck. Hingham, Mass., 1955.
ii, 88 p. 22 cm.

1. Microphotography—Dictionaries. 2. Photocopying processes—
Dictionaries. I. TenEyck, Hendrix. II. Title.

TR835.N28 1955   66-48061

NN 0058155 DLC NNC

NATIONAL MICROFILM ASSOCIATION.
Handbook.
[n. p.]   no.   22cm.

1. Photography--Reproduc-   tion of books, manuscripts, etc.
--Assoc. and org.--U.S.

NN 0058156 NN

WR   National Microfilm Association.
8N277
MIS   [Miscellaneous ephemeral materials not
fully catalogued]

NN 0058157 WHi

VOLUME 407

TR835
.N34

National Microfilm Association.

The National micro-news.

₍Annapolis₎

1. Microfilms—

TR835.N3   55—34335 ‡

CSt-H TU DNAL DI DNLM IU UU
NN   0058159   DLC NBuT IdU CaBVaU OrPR IdPI CL LU

National Microfilm Association.
Proceedings ₍of the₎ annual meeting.

Hingham, Mass.
v. 28 cm.

1. Microfilms—
TR835.N3   55—34335 ‡

CSt-H TU DNAL DI DNLM IU UU
NN   0058159   DLC NBuT IdU CaBVaU OrPR IdPI CL LU

National microscopical congress, *Indianapolis, 1878.*
Proceedings of the National microscopical congress,
held at Indianapolis, Ind., August 14th to 19th, 1878. (*In*
American microscopical society. Transactions. 1879.
Indianapolis, 1880. 22¼ᶜᵐ. p. 11–15)

Library of Congress   QH201.A3   6–350

NN   0058160   DLC DNLM ICRL

National Midcentury Committee for Children
and Youth, inc.
Directory ₍of₎ state and territorial committees

see its

State and territorial committees.

R362.7   National Midcentury Committee for Children
N217p   and Youth, inc.
Proceedings ₍of the₎ two-year anniversary
conference ₍held at₎ Hotel Astor, New York,
November 30, December 1–2, 1952. ₍New York,
1952₎
61 p.

Cover title.

1. Children – U. S.   2. Youth

NN   0058162   MiD Wa

National Midcentury Committee for Children and
Youth, Inc.
Progress bulletin
see under   Mid-Century White House
Conference on Children & Youth, Washington,
D.C., 1950.

National Midcentury Committee for Children and Youth,
inc.
Report on children and youth, 1950–1952. ₍Written and
designed by Alexander L. Crosby. New York, 1952₎
46 p. 25 cm.
Bibliography: p. 44–46.

1. Child welfare—U. S. 2. Youth—U. S.   I. Crosby, Alexander L.
HV741.N32   362.7   A 54–2952 rev
Michigan. Univ. Libr.
for Library of Congress   ₍r54d3₎†

NcD OClCC MiD PLF PPC NIC DLC
NN   0058164   MiU Or OrCS OrU-M OrPS OU OCl OClW CU

National Midcentury Committee for Children and Youth,
inc.
State and territorial committees co-operating with the
National Midcentury Committee for Children and Youth,
inc. 1952–1953. New York ₍1952₎
₍62₎ p. 25 cm.

Cover title: Directory, state and territorial committees.

1. Child welfare—U. S.—Direct.

HV741.N33   369 7058   53–346

NN   0058165   DLC OrU IdPI Or NIC NN OU DCU

National Midcentury Committee for Children and Youth,
inc.
see also Mid-century White House Conference on Children and Youth, *Washington, D. C., 1950.*

National Military Establishment
see U. S. *Dept. of Defense.*

National Military-Industrial Conference.
Addresses and panel discussions.

New York, F. A. Praeger.
v. ports. 22–28 cm.
First conference held in 1955.
Title varies: 19 –57, Proceedings of the papers and discussions.
Issued 19 –57 by the conference under an earlier name: Military Industrial Conference.

1. U. S.—Military policy—Congresses.

UA23.A1N367   355.06373   59–7302₂

NN   0058168   DLC NIC IEN IU CU NN DI ICU

National Military-Industrial Conference.
Proceedings of the papers and discussions
see its
Addresses and panel discussions.

National Military Tournament, *Chicago.*   355.09773 R100
⁸⁴⁶³⁴ [Official program of the] National Military Tournament. Camp
Charles S.\Deneen, Major General Edward C. Young, Illinois National Guard, commanding. July 24th to 30th, 1911. Grant
Park, Chicago, Illinois, [1911].
160 p. illus. 24ᶜᵐ.
Advertising matter interspersed.
"Under the auspices of the Chicago Association of Commerce."

NN   0058170   ICJ

SF223   National milk conference, London, 1922.
N3   Report of the proceedings of the National
milk conference, ...
London, ₍1922₎]
222 p. 21 cm.

NN   0058171   DLC

National Milk Conference, London, 1923.
Report of the proceedings of the National Milk Conference,
subject: pasteurization, held in the council chamber of the Guildhall... Wednesday, Nov. 21st, 1923.   London: National Clean
Milk Soc., Inc.₍, 1923?₎ 85, xi–xv p.   8°.

171671A. 1. Milk—Pasteurization.
N. Y. P. L.   June 10, 1925

NN   0058172   NN CaBVaU IU

National Milk Conference, London, 1926.
Report of the proceedings of the National Milk Conference.
Subject: milk in relation to public health... ₍London: National
Clean Milk Soc., Inc., 1926₎ viii, 78, xi–xvi p. tables. 8°.
Includes advertising matter.
"Held in the King George's Hall...on Nov. 16, 1926."

302500A. 1. Milk supply—Gt. Br.
N. Y. P. L.   July 1, 1927

NN   0058173   NN

National Milk Producers Federation.
Address of the president
see its   President's address.

National Milk Producers Federation.
Annual report of the secretary
see its   Report of the secretary.

National Milk Producers Federation.
Background memorandum
see under   American Butter Institute,
Chicago.

National milk producers' federation.
Before the United States tariff commission.
In the matter of the hearing concerning the
cost of production of cassin. ... Washington,
D.C., 1923.
28 p. 23cm.

NN   0058177   DNAL

National Milk Producers Federation.
The Dairy director
see under title

National Milk Producers Federation.
Dairy Empire State; facts about the importance of dairying to the welfare of New York State residents. ₍New York,
1952₎
68 p. illus. 23 cm.

1. Milk trade—New York (State)   I. Title.
HD9282.U5N734   338.177   52–24421 †

NN   0058179   DLC

286.344   National Milk Producers' Federation.
N21   The dairy farmer's stake in retaining
Ed.3   import controls.   3d ed.   [Washington]
1952.
[4] p.

1. Dairy policies and programs. U.S.
2. Import control. U.S.

NN   0058180   DNAL

338.1   National Milk Producers Federation.
N214d   A dairy policy, 1935-   ; being the
resolutions passed by the 18th-   annual
convention, 1934-   Washington, 1935-
v. 23 cm.

1935-   published by the federation
under its earlier name: National Cooperative
Milk Producers Federation.
Vols. for 1935–1954 are Its Educational
series, no.3,   16, 18, 22–23, 25, 27,

Continued in next column

VOLUME 407

Continued from preceding column

29, 32, 34, 37, 39, 41, 43, 46 and 48, and
classed as such.
Title varies: -193 , The Program.

1. Dairy products--U.S. I. National Milk
Producers Federation. The Program. II. Title.
III. National Milk Producers Federation.
Educational series.

NN   0058182   LU NN

National Milk Producers Federation.
A dairy policy, 1947; being the resolutions passed by the
Thirtieth Annual Convention in St. Louis, Mo., Nov. 12, 13,
14, 15, 1946. ₍Washington, 1947?₎
13 p. map. 23 cm. (*Its* Educational series, no. 32)
Published by the federation under its earlier name: National Cooperative Milk Producers Federation.

1. Dairy products—U. S.   I. Title.   (Series)
HD9275.A1N3   no. 32   334.68371   48–655 rev*

NN   0058183   DLC

281.344
N213D   **National Milk Producers Federation.**
A dairy policy ... 1955; being the resolutions passed by the thirty-eighth annual convention in Washington, D.C., November 7 to 11,
1954. Washington ₍1955?₎
25 p.

1. Dairy policies and programs. U.S.

NN   0058184   DNAL NN NIC

HD9275
.U6N3   National Milk Producers Federation.
Dairy problems of 1938...
[Wash.,1938]
27p.   23 cm.
(Educational series. no.11)

NN   0058185   DLC

National Milk Producers Federation.
Educational series.
₍Washington, 19
v. 23 cm.
Began publication in 1934. Cf. Union list of serials.
No.   issued by the federation under its earlier name: Na-
tional Cooperative Milk Producers' Federation.

1. Dairy products.
HD9275.A1N3   338.177   45–40466 rev*

NN   0058186   DLC TU NN ICJ OrCS KyU DNAL IU

National Milk Producers Federation.
The farmer looks at the oleomargarine picture; being a discussion of the problems arising in the dairy industry through
the use of oleomargarine and suggestions for meeting them.
Issued by the National Cooperative Milk Producers' Federation. ₍Washington, 1935₎
105 p. illus., map. 23 cm. (*Its* Educational series, no. 5)
Cover title.

1. Oleomargarine. 2. Butter.   I. Title.   (Series)
HD9275.A1N3   no. 5   637.281   38–34749 rev*

NN   0058187   DLC OrCS WaS OrU IdU

National Milk Producers' Federation.
Here is what happens when you legalize yellow
oleo!
see under   American Butter Institute,
Chicago.

National Milk Producers Federation.
History and interpretation of the Capper-
Volstead act
see under   Miller, Seward A

National Milk Producers' Federation.
History series, no. 1-   [Washington, D.C.]
1932-
nos. in v.   maps, tables.   29 cm.
1. Milk trade - U.S.   2. Agriculture, Cooperative - U.S.

NN   0058190   CU

National Milk Producers' Federation.
Informal conference [of] executive committee ...
August 31, 1933.   [n.p.] 1933.
15 numb. l.
1. Milk. Marketing agreements. 2. Milk.
Prices. 3. Boston. Milk trade.

NN   0058191   DNAL

National Milk Producers Federation.
Informal conference ... U.S. Dept of agriculture ... December 29, 1933.   [Washington]
1933.
67 numb. l.
1. Milk. Marketing agreements. 2. Milk
control of production. 3. Milk trade. Congresses
4. Dairy industry and trade. U.S. 5. U.S. Agricultural adjustment administration.

NN   0058192   DNAL

284.341
N21   National Milk Producers Federation.
Necessary prices to maintain milk production
in 1944 at 1943 levels.   ₍n.p.₎ 1943.
6 numb. l.

1. Milk. Prices. 2. Milk. Cost of production.
3. Milk. Production.

NN   0058193   DNAL

National Milk Producers' Federation.
News for dairy co-ops. v.
Washington, D.C.

NN   0058194   DNAL

281.344
N21   National Milk Producers Federation.
Oleomargarine and the farmer.   Washington,
D.C., 1941.
31 p.   28cm.

1. Oleomargarine. 2. Farmers' income.

NN   0058195   DNAL

National Milk Producers Federation.
Oleomargarine —friend or foe of the South?
₍Washington, D. C., 1936?₎
35 p.   illus. (map) 23cm. (*Its* Educational series
no. 7)

1.Oleomargarine I. Ser.

NN   0058196   ViU

NATIONAL MILK PRODUCERS FEDERATION.
President's address.
[v. p.]   no.   21-23cm.

Annual.
Title varies: 1954-55, Address of the president.
Presented at the federation's annual convention.

1. Diaries and diarying--U.S.   I. National milk producers
federation. Address of the   president.

NN   0058197   NN

National Milk Producers' Federation.
Price report.   Washington, D.C.

Jan. 12-1941–Oct. 16, 1944 omit title.
Begins vol. and issue numbering with v. 23,
no. 1, Jan. 1945.
Ceased. Superseded by Dairy trends (44.8
D14342)
Title varies: —Aug. 12, 1940,
Statistical summary of data on manufactured dairy
products.
Sept. 12, 1940-   Statistical summary
of data on dairy products.

NN   0058198   DNAL

NATIONAL MILK PRODUCERS FEDERATION.
Report of the secretary.
[Washington]   no.   21cm.

Presented to the federation's annual convention.

1. Dairies and dairying--Assoc. and org.--U.S.

NN   0058199   NN NIC Or

National Milk Producers Federation.
Statistical summary of data on dairy
products
see its   Price report.

National Milk Producers Federation.
Statistical summary of data on manufactured
dairy products
see its   Price report.

National milk producers federation.
The tariff on dairy products; brief of the National cooperative milk producers' federation and its member
organizations, before the Committee on ways and means of
the United States House of representatives, in regard to
changes of rates of duties on products included in para-
graphs 19, 707, 708, 709, 710 and certain changes in administrative provisions of section 315, of title 3, of the Tariff act
of September 20, 1922. ₍Baltimore, The Lord Baltimore
press, 1929₎
4 p. l., 95 p. incl. illus. (maps) tables, diagrs. 23½ cm.
1. Tariff—U. S. 2. Dairy products—U. S. 3. Milk trade—U. S.
I. U. S. Congress.   House. Committee on ways and
means. II. Title.
HF2651.D303N3   29–12243 rev

NN   0058202   DLC OrCS

National Milk Producers' Federation.
What people really think about oleo and taxes.
[n.p., 1948]
[12] p.

NN   0058203   DNAL

National Milk Producers Federation.
What the AAA amendments will do to help farmers; being
a detailed explanation of the meaning and effect of the
amendments to the Agricultural adjustment act as approved
by the Committee on Agriculture of the United States House
of Representatives. Prepared and published by the National
Cooperative Milk Producers Federation. ₍Washington,
1935?₎
46 p. map. 23 cm. (*Its* Educational series, no. 4)
1. Agricultural laws and legislation—U. S. 2. U. S. Agricultural
Adjustment Administration.   I. U. S. Laws, statutes, etc. II. Title.
(Series)
HD9275.A1N3   no. 4   338.10973   36–10253 rev*

NN   0058204   DLC Or OrCS OrU ViU

VOLUME 407

NATIONAL MILK PRODUCERS FEDERATION
The why and the how of the self-help
program; dairy product price supports and
stabilization under a farmer-financed plan.
Author, 1955.
17 p

NN 0058205   Or

275.2
N214   National Milk Producers Federation. Youth
Committee.
Ideas for a youth program.   Washington
[1950]
39 p.

1. Youth in rural communities. 2. Recreation,
Rural. 3. Dairying, Cooperative.

NN 0058206   DNAL

National Milk Publishing Company.
Milk plant monthly
see under title

The national milk sales manual. 1930 edition
see under   Maughan, Merrill O.

TS   National miller.
2120   v.1-11 no.6 1911?-Sept.1921; v.26 no.10-v.35
N3   no.11 Oct. 1921-Nov. 1930.

Oct. 1921 absorbed Operative miller and
continued its volume numbering.
Merged into American miller.

NN 0058209   KMK ICRL NN ICJ DLC

National miller.
Feed trade manual; a reference work for all engaged in the
manufacture, mixing and handling of commercial feeds. 1st-
ed., 1930/31-   Chicago, Ill., National miller
[*1930-

National miller and American miller
see
American miller and processor.

National millers' association.
[Chicago meeting, May 12-15, 1879: miscellaneous
pamphlets.]

NN 0058212   IChi

National millinery company, *Cleveland.*
Home millinery course; a thorough, practical and complete series of lessons. [Cleveland, O.] National millinery
company [*1909]
69 p. illus. 26ᶜᵐ. $3.00

1. Millinery.
Library of Congress   TT655.N3   9-26968

NN 0058213   DLC ICJ

National Milling Corporation.
Annual report and accounts.
[Dar-es-Salaam]
v. illus. 26 cm.

Report year ends July 31.
English and Swahili, the latter inverted with title: **Taarifa ya
mwaka na maelezo ya hesabu.**

1. National Milling Corporation. 2. Food industry and trade—
Tanzania—Statistics.
HD9017.T34N376a   338.7'66'472009678   74-641684
MARC-S

NN 0058214   DLC

070.489 [National mimeograph paper association]
N21d   The duplicated school papers.   [Danville,
Ind., Commercial department, Central normal college, 1936]
cover-title, 44, [2]p.

"Third edition."
"Journalistic bibliography": p.[45-46]

1. College and school journalism. I. Danville,
Ind. Central normal college. II. Title.

NN 0058215   IU

622.8
N277q   National Mine Rescue Association.
Questions and answers on rescue and recovery
operations following mine fires and explosions.
Rev. Pittsburgh, Pa., Printed by Mine Safety
Appliances co., 1951.
26p.

Cover title.

1. Mine rescue work. 2. Mine fires.
3. Mine explosions. I. Title Rescue and
recovery operations following mine fires and
explosions.

NN 0058216   ICarbS

National mine safety demonstration, Pittsburgh

see

Pittsburgh. National mine safety demonstration.

National mine tax conference.
Proceedings of the 1st-   annual national mine
tax conference, at the 23d -   annual convention
...
Washington, 1921-
HJ4169
.N3

NN 0058218   DLC ICJ CU

National Mineral Wool Association, *New York.*
697.93
N277H   How to control moisture in homes; a manual
for home owners and builders. New York
[1953]
cover-title, 72 p. illus. 21½cm.

NN 0058219   NcD WaS

National mineral wool association, New York.
Insulation and your home... [New York, Nat. mineral wool
assoc., c1945] 23 p. illus. 25cm.

2. ed.

1. Heat—Insulation.
N. Y. P. L.   March 12, 1948

NN 0058220   NN NNC ICJ

National Miners' Minority Movement
see **National Minority Movement.**

National Mining and Industrial Exposition Association.
The mining industry; production of the precious metals from
the earliest time down to the present. How it effects the development of the country. The best methods for its promotion. Denver, Colo., 1881. 40 p. incl. tables. 8°.

498532A. 1. Mines and mining—U. S.,   1881. I. Title.
N. Y. P. L.

NN 0058222   NN

M622.343
N27a   National Mining Company.
Vault   Annual report.

Pittsburgh.
v. 23-24cm.

1860 report includes fold. map of mine.

NN 0058223   Mi

National mining company.
Report of the directors of the National mining company.
Also, reports of Wm. Webb, agent, and J. Chynoweth,
mine captain; together with statements from the books of
the treasurer. September 1st, 1860. Pittsburgh, Printed
by W. S. Haven, 1860.
25 p. fold. plan. 23ᶜᵐ.

CA 7-3658 Unrev'd
Library of Congress

NN 0058224   DLC OC1WHi

National Mining Company.
Report of the directors of the National Mining Company,
including reports of Wm. Webb, agent, and J. Chynoweth, mine
captain; together with statements from the books of the treasurer.
September 1st, 1861.   Pittsburgh: W. S. Haven, 1861.   18 p.
8°.

1. Copper.—Mines and mining: Com-   panies, U. S.
N. Y. P. L.   June 14, 1916.

NN 0058225   NN

National mining congress, *Denver,* 1891.
Report of the proceedings of the National mining congress
held in the People's theatre, in the city of Denver, Colorado,
on ... Nov. 18, 19 and 20, 1891. Denver, Col., News printing
company, 1892.
111 p. 23ᶜᵐ.

A second meeting of the congress was announced to take place at
Helena, Mont., in July 1892, but it was apparently not held.

46-39675
Library of Congress   TN5.N26 1891

NN 0058226   DLC ICRL MB ICJ

**National ministers' institute, Virginia union
university, Richmond.**
Hovey, George Rice, 1860-
The Bible, its origin and interpretation, by George Rice
Hovey ... Richmond, Va., National ministers' institute, Virginia union university; Richmond, Va., Brown print shop,
inc., 1930.

**National minister' institute, Virginia union
university, Richmond.**
Hovey, George Rice, 1860-
Christian ethics for daily life, by George Rice Hovey ...
New York, Association press, 1932.

**National ministers' institute, Virginia. Union
university, Richmond.**
Ransome, William Lee, 1879-
Christian stewardship and Negro Baptists, by W. L. Ransome ... Richmond, Virginia, National ministers' institute,
Virginia union university. Richmond, Va., Brown print
shop, inc., 1934.

VOLUME 407

National minorities in new China
    see   Hsin Chung-kuo shao shu min tsu ti
shêng huo.

National minorities institute, *Ljubljana*
        see
Manjšinski institut, *Ljubljana*.

The national minorities of central Europe and two
    world wars...
        see under [Echmalian, Dickran]

National Minority Conference.
    ...Report...
1924

London[, 1924
    no.   8°.
    1924 is the 1st issued.
    Published by the National Minority Movement.

1. Bolshevism—Gt. Br.
N.Y.P.L.

NN 0058233   NN NcD DL

National Minority Movement.
    British imperialism ...
        see under Labour Research Department.

HD   National Minority Movement.
8039   The British mineworkers' struggle. [Lon-
.M62   don, 1927?]
G7625   28 p.   22 cm. (in binder, 24 cm.)

        1. Trade-unions - Gt. Brit. 2. Coal-
    miners - Gt. Brit. 3. National Minority
    Movement. I. Ti-   tle.

NN 0058235   WU

National minority movement
    British mineworkers' union.
    (London, National minority movement, 1927?)
    cover-title, 47 (1) p. 16 cm.

NN 0058236   DL

HD   National Minority Movement
8039   Danger ahead! The railwaymen's conditions
.R12   and their next struggle. An examination of
G7   the policy of the companies and the financial
    situation of the railways.   London, 1928.
    16 p.   22 cm. (in binder, 24 cm.)

        1. Railroads - Gt. Brit. - Employees.
    2. Trade-unions -   Gt. Brit.
    3. National Mino.   ity Movement.
    I. Title.

NN 0058237   WU

National Minority Movement.
    International unity of the world's trade union movement.
London [192–?]
    40 p. illus., ports. 22 cm.

    1. Trade-unions. I. Title.

    HD6476.N3   331.88   48–38935*‡

NN 0058238   DLC MH CLU

HD   National Minority Movement.
6666   Is trade unionism played out? The Minority
.N353   Movement's answer.   London [1926?]
    15 p.   21 cm. (in binder, 24 cm.)

        1. Trade-unions - Gt. Brit. 2. Trade-
    unions and communism - Gt. Brit. 3. Nation-
    al Minority Move-   ment. I. Title.

NN 0058239   WU CLU

HD   National Minority Movement
6666   The militant trades council; a model constitu-
N354   tion for trades councils. 2d ed. London, 1926.
    22p.   16cm.

        1. Trade-unions - Gt. Brit. I. Title

NN 0058240   WU NcD CLU

National   Minority Movement.
    The miners' next task; an open letter to all
    miners on the next big step: one miners' union.
London, National Minority Movement [1926?]
    14 p.   21 cm.
    1. Miners. Gt. Brit. I. Title.

NN 0058241   NcD

HD   National Minority Movement.
6666   On strike! A word to all workers in dispute.   London,
N213o   1929.
    7 p.

    1. Strikes and lockouts.

NN 0058242   CLU

HD   National Minority Movement.
6666   Peace, but not with capitalism; the policy
.N355   of the Minority Movement versus the policy of
    the General Council.   London [1927?]
    31 p.   19 cm. (in binder, 24 cm.)

        1. Trade-unions - Gt. Brit. 2. Trade-
    unions and communism - Gt. Brit. 3. Nation-
    al Minority Move-   ment. I. Title.

NN 0058243   WU NN

National Minority Movement.
    Report of the annual conference
        see under   National Minority Conference.

HD   National Minority Movement.
6666   Strike strategy & tactics; the lessons of the industrial
N219s   struggles. Thesis adopted by the Strassburg conference
    held under the auspices of the Red International Labour
    Union. London, 193–?
    28 p.

    Foreword signed: Percy Glading.

    1. Strikes and lockouts. I. Glading, *Percy*.

NN 0058245   CLU

HD   National Minority Movement.
8039   The struggle of the Lancashire textile
.T42   workers. London, 1929.
G7   15 p.   22 cm. (in binder, 24 cm.)

        1. Textile workers - Lancashire. 2. Trade-
    unions - Gt. Brit. 3. National Minority
    Movement. I. Ti-   tle.

NN 0058246   WU

HX14   National Minority Movement.
R3N27   The 10th anniversary of the Russian Revolu-
    tion and the R.I.L.U.   London [1927]
    143 p.   21ᵐ.

    Articles by various authors.

        1. Russia - Hist. - Revolution, 1917-1921.
    2. Labor and laboring classes. 3. Red Interna-
    tional of Labor Unions. 4. Trade unions.
    I. Title.

NN 0058247   CSt-H CtY

HD   National Minority Movement.
45   What is rationalisation? The Minority
.N3   Movement's contribution to a wider under-
    standing in the Trade Union Movement of the
    meaning and effects of rationalisation.
    London, National Minority Movement, 1928.
    66 p.   22 cm.

        1. Industrial management - Gt. Brit.
    2. Gt. Brit. -   Indus. I. Title.

NN 0058248   WU

HD   National Minority Movement.
6666   What is this Minority Movement?   London,
.N358   1928.
    15 p.   22 cm. (in binder, 24 cm.)

        1. Trade-unions - Gt. Brit. 2. Trade-
    unions and commu-   nism - Gt. Brit.
    3. National Minori-   ty Movement. I. Ti-
    tle.

NN 0058249   WU CLU NcD

HD   National Minority Movement
8039   What's wrong in the textile industry? An
T42   analysis of the present state of the indus-
G72   try and of the unions. London [1926]
    23p.   22cm.
    Cover-title.

        1. Trade-unions - Gt. Brit. 2. Textile
    workers - Gt. Brit. I. Title

NN 0058250   WU

National Minority Movement.
    Workers' charter pamphlets.
no. 1–

London[, 1931   8°.
    nos.

    no. 1 lacks ser. title.
    no. 1   title of institution reads: Minority Movement.
    Title varies slightly.

    Contents:
    [no. 1.] DUTT, R. P. Fight for the workers' charter. [1931.]
    [no. 2.] WARD, B. The real scandal of the "dole." [1931.]
    [no. 3.] CAMPBELL, J. R. For the seven-hour day. [1931.]

    no. 5. DUTT, R. P. Free the colonies! [1931.]

NN 0058252   NN

The National minstrel: embracing a collection of
    the most popular and approved national,
    patriotic, moral, love, sentimental, comic and
    negro songs, compiled expressly for the
    publishers ...   Buffalo, N.Y., Phinney &
    company, 1858.
    vi, 250 p. front. 11.5 cm.

NN 0058253   NBuG RPB

VOLUME 407

The National minstrel folio. Containing a
splendid selection of ballads, comic and
sentimental songs, [etc.] Chicago,
National Music Co. [1889]
160 p. ill. cover. 4°.

NN 0058254   DLC

National minute men of America.
Constitution of the N. M. M. A. [Washington, 1882]
cover-title, vii, 21 p. 15ᶜᵐ.

Library of Congress   HS2330.N27A5 1882

19-4688

NN 0058255   DLC

The National miscellany ... A magazine of general literature. v. 1-4; 1853-55. London, 1853-55.
4 v. 22ᶜᵐ. monthly.
Merged into the Illustrated London magazine.

9-13396

Library of Congress   AP4.N2

NN 0058256   DLC MB NN

National Mission of Repentance and Hope.
Christianity and industrial problems
see under   Church of England. Archbishops'
fifth committee of inquiry.

National mission of repentance and hope.

Lyttelton, *Hon.* Edward, 1855-
The dedicated life; three addresses to schoolboys and
others on behalf of the National mission of repentance
and hope, by the Rev. the Hon. Edward Lyttelton ...
London, New York [etc.] Longmans, Green, and co., 1917.

National Mission of Repentance and Hope.
... Report of the Archbishops' committee of
inquiry
see under   Church of England. Archbishops' Committees of Inquiry.

National missionary congress. *1st, Chicago,* 1910.
Proceedings of the Men's national missionary congress of
the United States of America, Chicago, Illinois, May 3-6, 1910.
New York, Laymen's missionary movement, 1910.
xi, 620 p. incl. map. front. 20½ᶜᵐ.
"The official shorthand report."

1. Missions—Congresses. i. Laymen's missionary movement of the
United States and Canada.
13-12532 rev.

Library of Congress   BV2390.N3 1910

PPEB MnCS CtY-D IEG IU OO
NN 0058260   DLC NIC PPPrHi NRCR PPL IAurC NcD

National missionary congress. *2d, Washington, D. C.,* 1916.
Men and world service; addresses delivered at the National
missionary congress, Washington, D. C., April 26-30, 1916 ...
New York, Laymen's missionary movement, 1916.
v, 350 p. 20½ᶜᵐ.
The first congress, held in Chicago in 1910, was called the Men's
national missionary congress of the United States of America.

1. Missions—Congresses. i. Laymen's missionary movement of
the United States and Canada. ii. Title.
33-27686

Library of Congress   BV2390.N3 1916
———— Copy 2.
266.06373

NN 0058261   DLC CtY-D WaS Or IEG ViU OO IU ICU NN

National Missionary Council
see
National Christian Council of India.

National missionary council of Australia.

Needham, John Stafford, 1875-   *ed.*
White and black in Australia, by the Rev. J. S. Needham.
London, Published for the National missionary council of
Australia by the Society for promoting Christian knowledge,
1935.

Period.   The National missionary intelligencer.
1302   v.1, no.1-   1906-
           Madras.
           v. 21cm.

1. Christianity - India. 2. Missions -
India - Periodicals.

NN 0058264   MH-AH

The National missionary society of India.
Constitution, papers, etc. [Calcutta,
Baptist miss. pr.] n.d.
28 p.

NN 0058265   OO

National Missionary Society of India.
... The 1st sexennium of the N.M.S. 1905-11.
Rajahmundry [1911]
cover-title, 1 p.l., 49, [1] p. 19 cm.
(National missionary intelligencer. Supplement)

NN 0058266   CtY

National missionary society of India.
... The first ten years of the N. M. S., 1905-1916... [Salem]
The National missionary soc. of India [1917?]   136 p. illus.,
maps. 18cm.

1. Missions, Foreign—India.
N.Y.P.L.
May 6, 1941

NN 0058267   NN CtY MH-AH ODW

National Model Railroad Association.
N.M.R.A. bulletin
see under title

NATIONAL MODEL RAILROAD ASSOCIATION.
N. M. R. A. manual. [Detroit, 1946] 1 v. illus.
28cm.
Cover title.
Includes NMRA standards (1946 ed.): NMRA data sheets; Constitution and
by-laws.

1. Railways--Models.   t. 1946

NN 0058269   NN CaBVa

NATIONAL MODEL RAILROAD ASSOCIATION.
NMRA standards, 1949 edition. Canton, O.,
c1950. 1 v. (loose-leaf) illus. 28cm.

——NMRA data sheets. Supplements. Canton, O., 1951- v. illus.
28cm.
In loose-leaf binder with the above.

1. Railways--Models.   t. 1949

NN 0058270   NN

National Model Railroad Association.
Pike register
see its   Yearbook.

NATIONAL MODEL RAILROAD ASSOCIATION.
Yearbook.
Canton, O. [etc.]   v.   21-27cm.

Title varies: 1949, Pike register; 1951, Yearbook-Pike register.
On cover: N.M.R.A. yearbook (varies)
Lists clubs and individual members.

1. Railways--Models--Assoc. and org.--U.S. I. Title: N.M.R.A.
yearbook. II. Title: Pike   register.

NN 0058272   NN

National modern pioneers banquet, New York, 1940.
Our modern pioneers and the American patent system; a series
of addresses given at the National modern pioneers banquet,
sponsored by the National association of manufacturers, New
York, February 27, 1940. [New York, 1940] 30 p. illus.
23cm.

1. Inventions. 2. Patents.
N.Y.P.L.
September 22, 1943

NN 0058273   NN

HG538   National Monetary Association.
.N35   Money in the United States. N.Y.,
           n.d.
           1 pam. 8°.

NN 0058274   DLC

National Monetary Association.
Money in the United States... New York [1923?].   13 p.
8°. (National Monetary Assoc. Bull., no. 1.)

1. Money in the United States.   2. Series.
N.Y.P.L.
October 14, 1924

NN 0058275   NN OC1FRB

National Monetary Commission (U.S.)
see   U.S. National Monetary Commission.

National monetary conference.

Honest money year book and directory, 1940-
edited by the National monetary conference ... Chicago, Ill.,
Honest money founders, inc., 1939-

National monetary conference. *2d meeting, Washington,*
D. C., March 6, 1935.
Proceedings of National monetary conference, Washington,
D. C., March 6, 1935. Washington, T. O'Neal, general short-
hand reporting [1935]
cover-title, 3 p. l., 2-144 numb. l. 27½ᶜᵐ.
Mimeographed.

1. Money—Congresses. 2. Money—U. S. 3. Currency question—U. S.
38-3010
Library of Congress   HG538.N36 1935 f
———— Copy 2.   [3]   332.406373

NN 0058278   DLC

VOLUME 407

National money, or a simple system of finance; which **will** fully answer the demands of trade, equalize the value of **money,** and keep the government out of the hands of stock-jobbers. **In** three letters, addressed by a citizen of Washington to the Congress of the United States. Georgetown, Ca., Printed by **W. A.** Rind and co. ..... 1816.
18 p. 22½ᵐ.

1. Currency question—U. S.

Library of Congress   HG521.N2
6—18003

NN   0058279   DLC MH-BA PPAmP

National monitor of poultry and pets
   see   National poultry monitor.

National Montessori Promotion Fund.
Directory of Montessori classes and Montessori teachers in the United States. Rev. to May 10, 1916. New York city, The National Montessori promotion fund, 1916.
   cover-title, 24 p.   18.5 cm.

NN   0058281   DHEW

National monthly.
₍Buffalo, N. Y.₎ National monthly co., 19
      v.   illus. 36½ᵐ.
Editor: 19   Norman Mack.

ɪ. Mack, Norman Edward, 1858–   ed.
15–3188

Library of Congress   AP2.N348

NN   0058282   DLC N NBuHi OC1WHi

National monthly. A monthly **magazine devoted to the** interest and development of the undertaking **profession.**
New York city, The National **casket co.,** 19
      v. illus. 25ᵐ.

1. Undertakers and undertaking—Period.   ɪ. National casket co., **New York.**
CA 10–5483 Unrev'd

Library of Congress   RA622.A35

NN   0058283   DLC

The National monthly bond summary. v. 80–
July 1954–
New York, National Quotation Bureau.
      v. 24 cm. semiannual.
   Continues the National monthly corporation bond **summary.** Subtitle varies.

1. Bonds—United States—**Periodicals.**   ɪ. National Quotation Bureau, incorporated, New York.

HG4905.N3   332.6'323'0973   72–624151

NN   0058284   DLC NN IU

National monthly building survey, prepared by S. W. Straus & Co. ... ₍Chicago, 1929–1933₎

Caption title.
Ceased publication Feb. 1933.
July 1930–Feb. 1933 numbered v. 8, no. 7–₎, 11, no. 1.

NN   0058285   ICJ ICU MiD DL NN

The **National** monthly corporation bond summary (with foreign government edition ...
New York ₍etc.₎ The National quotation bureau incorporated, ᵃ19
      v. 23½ x 11½ᵐ.
   Cover-title, 19   : National corporation bond summary.
   Annual, 19 –24; semiannual, 1925–

1. Bonds—U. S. 2. Securities—U. S.   ɪ. National quotation bureau, incorporated, New York. ɪɪ. Title: National corporation bond **summary.**

Library of Congress   HG4905.N3
42–240

NN   0058286   DLC CSt NN OC1

The **National** monthly farm press, devoted to **the welfare of** the farmer and his family. An illustrated **agricultural** journal.
Chicago ₍Howard & Wilson publishing co., etc.₎ 18·
      v. illus. 30–40ᵐ.
   Weekly,   –Sept. 22, 1906; monthly, Oct. 1906–
   Title varies: –Nov. 5, 1892, Farm, field and stockman.
   Nov. 12, 1892–Sept. 22, 1906, Farm, field and fireside.
   Oct. 1906–   The National monthly farm press.
   Editors: –May 1905, C. H. Howard.—May 1905–   W. A. Radford.
   Absorbed Farm folks in Oct. 1906.

   1. Agriculture—Period. 2. Agriculture—U. S.   ɪ. Howard, Charles Henry, 1838–1908, ed. ɪɪ. Radford, William A., 1865–   ed.
CA 9—973 Unrev'd

Library of Congress   S1.N4

NN   0058287   DLC

National monthly farm press
   see also   Better farming.

National monthly merchandiser
         see
The **National** merchandiser.

The **National** monthly municipal bond summary ...
New York, The National quotation bureau, **incorporated,** ᵃ19
      v. 23½ x 11ᵐ.
   Cover-title,   : National municipal bond summary.
   Feb.–Dec. numbers cumulative from Jan. 20 of the same year; Jan. number cumulative from Jan. 20 of the previous year.

1. Municipal bonds.   ɪ. National quotation bureau, incorporated, New York.

Library of Congress   HG4951.N27
43–20611

NN   0058290   DLC NN

F1001   The National monthly of Canada.   Toronto, Can.,
.N37   J. Phillips.
                v.   illus.   26.5 cm.
                1. Canada.

NN   0058291   DLC

The **National** monthly stock summary ... Jan. 19
New York ₍etc.₎ The National quotation bureau incorporated, ᵃ19
      v. 23½ x 11ᵐ.
   Cover-title, 19   : National stock summary.
   Annual, 19 –25; semiannual, 1926–

1. Stocks—Tables, etc. 2. Securities—U. S.   ɪ. National quotation bureau, incorporated, New York. ɪɪ. Title: National stock summary.

Library of Congress   ᵃHG4905.N34
42–241
₍2₎   332.63

NN   0058292   DLC MB NN OC1 WM

F 191   National monument. v. 1–
.N23   May 10, 1851–   Washington, D. C., 1851–
                v.   31 cm.
                Caption title.
                Vol. 1 , no. 1, called "Prospectus of the National monument."
                Organ of the Washington national monument society.

NN   0058293   DLC

National Monument Society, Washington, D.C.
   see   Washington National Monument
   Society, Washington, D.C.

National Mooney-Billings committee.

Hunt, Henry Thomas, 1878–
   The case of Thomas J. Mooney and Warren K. Billings. Abstract and analysis of record before Governor Young of California. By Henry T. Hunt, March 25th, 1929. New York city, National Mooney-Billings committee ₍1929?₎

National Mooney-Billings committee, New York
   Copy of an open letter addressed to former Judge Matt. I. Sullivan ₌sent to Hon. James Ralph Jr. governor of California₌
   New York, Author, 1932.
   2, 13 numb. l.

NN   0058296   OC1

Nvp98   National Mooney-Billings committee.
S4   [Minor publications]   26cm.
M78n   Organized by the American civil liberties union.

NN   0058297   CtY

National Mooney-Billings committee
   An open letter to Judge Matt I. Sullivan ...
   New York, National Mooney-Billings committee, 1932.
   31 l.

NN   0058298   OU

National Mooney-Billings **Committee.**
   The scandal of Mooney and Billings; the decisions of the California Supreme Court, the Advisory Pardon Board, Governor Young, denying pardons to Mooney and Billings. All the facts up to date ... New York City, 1931. 62 p. illus. (ports.) 22½cm.

703734A. 1. Murder—Trials—U. S.   2. Mooney, Thomas J. 3. Billings, Warren K., 1894–
N. Y. P. L.   May 11, 1934

NN   0058299   NN MB InU InNd-L

NATIONAL MOONEY–BILLINGS COMMITTEE.
   The story of Mooney and Billings... New York City: National Mooney–Billings Committee₍, 1928?₎. 27 p. 22½cm.

710186A. 1. Mooney, Thomas J. 2. Billings, Warren K., 1894–

NN   0058300   NN

HD8073   National Mooney-Billings committee, New York.
M8N27   The story of Mooney and Billings... New York city, National Mooney-Billings committee, 1929.
                22, ₍2₎ p. 23ᵐ.

      1. Mooney, Thomas J   1882?–1942. 2. Billings, Warren K., 1894–   3. Trials – U. S.
1. Title.

NN   0058301   CSt-H MH CU-B

National Mooney-Billings committee.
   The story of Mooney and Billings at a glance.
   [N. Y., National Mooney-Billings committee, 1932?]

NN   0058302   InU NcD

VOLUME 407

National Moot Court competition
    see   Association of the Bar of the City of
New York. Young Lawyers Committee.
Report on the final rounds ...

National mortgage & agency company of New
Zealand limited.
        Produce circular [monthly] no.
London
    1. London. Commerce. 2. Prices.
London. I. Author. Produce markets.

NN   0058304   DNAL

National mortgage association of
Washington

    see

Federal national mortgage association.

National Mortgage Bank, Buenos Aires
        see   Banco Hipotecario Nacional, Buenos
Aires.

National mortgage bank of Estonia
        see
Pikalaenu pank, *Tallinn.*

National Mortgage Bank of Greece
        see
Ethnikē Ktēmatikē Trapeza tēs Hellados, *Athens.*
    [Supplement]

---

fF866   National Mortgage Company of California.
N142   California, nature's masterpiece. [Los
        Angeles, G. Rice & Sons, printers, c1925.
        47 p. illus. 32cm.

NN   0058309   CU-B

National mortician...
    v. 1-

Chicago: Standard Business Pub. Co., Inc., 1934-   22cm.
    v.   illus.
Monthly.

    1. Undertakers and undertaking—   Per. and soc. publ.
N. Y. P. L.   July 22, 1936

NN   0058310   NN

QX   National Mosquito Control - Fish and Wildlife
600   Management Coordination Committee.
N277
        [Collection of publications]

        The Library has a collection of miscellaneous
        publications of this organization kept as
        received. These publications are not listed or bound
        separately.
            1. Mosquito Control

NN   0058311   DNLM

National mosquito extermination society

        see

American mosquito extermination society.

National motel blue book.

Chicago, National Hotel Pub. Co.
        v. 24 cm. annual.
    Cover title, 19   : Motel blue book.

        1. Tourist camps, hostels, etc.—Direct.

    TX907.N29   647.97058   52-26669 †

NN   0058313   DLC OO OEac DI DNAL NN NNC OU TU

National motel directory; travelog, highway atlas, **United**
States, Canada, Mexico, coast to coast.
    [San Antonio, National Motel Directory Corporation]
        v. illus. 27 cm.

        1. Tourist camps, hostels, etc.—Direct. 2. North America—Descr.
    & trav.—Maps.
    TX907.N293   647.97058   54—27422 †

NN   0058314   DLC

National Motion Picture Council.
    Facts and opinions about the motion picture; a series of
    study outlines for motion picture councils and chairmen.
    Paper 1-8. [New York, 1941?-42?]
        no. in   v.   36 cm.
    L. C. set incomplete: no. 8 wanting.

        1. Moving-pictures.

    PN1994.N34   791.4   51-48208

NN   0058315   DLC NN

NATIONAL MOTOR BOAT SHOW.
    Official directory.
New York, National assocaition of engine & boat
manufacturers,   no.   22-28cm.

    Annual.
    Early years have title: Catalogue.
    1. Motor boats--Exhibitions. I. National association of engine and boat
manufacturers. II. National motor boat show. Catalogue.

NN   0058316   NN MiD

National motor travel guide.

Denver, United Motor Courts.
        v. col. illus. 22 cm.

        1. Tourist camps, hostels, etc.—Direct. I. United Motor Courts.
    TX907.N3   51-36418 †

NN   0058317   DLC

NATIONAL MOTOR TRUCK SHOW
    National transportation year book; official
program of the 5th annual national motor truck
show. New York, Author, 1938.
    1 v.

NN   0058318   Or

TL   National Motor Vehicle Company, Indianapolis,
215   Ind.
N3   National motor cars. Indianapolis, Inc.
N3   [19--]
            1 v. unpaged

        NATIONAL AUTOMOBILE--CATALOGS
        National motor cars

NN   0058319   KMK

TL   National Motor Vehicle Company, Indianapolis,
151   Ind.
N3   Operation and care: National motor cars. ...
        Six cylinder. Indiana, Ind. [19--].
        40 p. illus.

        NATIONAL AUTOMOBILE--HANDBOOKS, MANUALS, ETC.
        Operation and care

NN   0058320   KMK

National motorbus and taxicab journal
        see   Bus age.

National moulding book ... Adopted Apr. 15, 1896, by
    the wholesale sash, door, and blind manufacturers'
    association of the Northwest, and by the Eastern sash,
    door, and blind manufacturers' association. Chicago,
    Rand, McNally & co., 1899.
        2 p. l., 139 p. 4°. [With The national combined book of sash, doors,
    blinds, mouldings ... 1899]

                                                99—1455

NN   0058322   DLC

National Mount Wollaston bank, *Quincy, Mass.*
    National Mount Wollaston bank, a short history of the
    growth of the institution, 1853–1924. Quincy, Mass.
    [1924]
        2 p. l., 23, [1] p. illus. (incl. ports., 1 col.) 21½.
        "Prepared by Thomas Page Smith, Lincoln & Smith press, Boston."

        1. Smith, Thomas Page.
                                                CA 25-838 Unrev'd
    Library of Congress   HG2613.Q84N3

NN   0058323   DLC

National mouth hygiene association, Cleveland, O.
    Bulletin... March, 1914-   Cleveland, 1914-

Monthly: Oct.-Nov., Jan.-May.

NN   0058324   MiU OCl OClW-H

National mouth hygiene association, Cleveland, O.
    Preliminary announcement of the committees of
the National mouth hygiene association in cooperation with fourth International congress on school
hygiene, Buffalo, N.Y., Aug. 25-30, 1913.
[New York,]1913.

LB3455
.N3

NN   0058325   DLC NN

National mouth hygiene association, *Cleveland, O.*
    Report of the scientific experiments conducted in the Cleve-
land public schools for the purpose of ascertaining the value
of healthy conditions of the mouth. Experiments conducted
under the auspices of the National dental association, the Ohio
state dental society, the Cleveland dental society and the Cleveland board of education ... Cleveland, O. The National mouth
hygiene association, 1912.
        35 p. illus. (incl. ports.) 25½.
        1. Teeth—Care and hygiene. 2. Schools—Medical inspection. I.
    American dental association. II. Ohio state dental society. III. Cleve-
    land dental society. IV. Cleveland, O. Board of education.
                                                12—9534
        Library of Congress   LB3455.N2

NN   0058326   DLC DHEW OCl DL ICJ

VOLUME 407

Wason
Film
905

The National movement in Indonesia, its aim and tactics. ₍n. p., 2602? 1942?₎ 20 l.

Typewritten ms.
In ₍The Japanese occupation and the Indonesian revolution. Tokyo, 1964₎ Microfilm. Ithaca, N. Y., Photo Science Studios, 1964. 35mm. reel 3.

NN 0058327 NIC

A National movement to prevent crime and improve the condition of prisons and prisoners
    see under Mackie, G. W.

National Movement towards a Christian Order of Industry and Commerce.
    ...Cambridge Conference, January 12th to 15th, 1923. Papers by Sydney W. Pascall, Professor J. H. Jones, J. W. Madeley, Henry Atkinson...Theodore C. Taylor, Dr. T. R. Glover... York: National Movement towards a Christian Order of Industry and Commerce ₍1923₎. 62 p. 8°. (Christian Order of Industry series. ₍no.₎ 1.)

Cover-title.

1. Wages, Gt. Br. 2. Sociology (Christian). 3. Series.
N. Y. P. L.   June 5, 1924

NN 0058329 NN

National Movement towards a Christian Order of Industry and Commerce.
    ...Oxford conference; papers by John Hilton, Prof. Ernest Mahaim, John A. Todd... Dr. Gillett, Clarence H. Northcott... Joseph L. Cohen... New College, Oxford, July 20th to 23rd, 1923... ₍London, 1923.₎ 78 p. 8°. (Christian order of industry series. ₍no.₎ 3.)

Cover-title.
Papers on unemployment.

1. Labor (Unemployed). 2. Labor (Unemployed).—Insurance.
3. Series.
N. Y. P. L.   October 4, 1924

NN 0058330 NN

National Multiple Sclerosis Society.
    Annual report
        see its Report.

National Multiple Sclerosis Society.
    ₍Collected papers₎
    New York.

NN 0058332 ICJ

WL
1
qN277

NATIONAL Multiple Sclerosis Society
    ₍Collection of publications₎

    The library has a collection of miscellaneous publications of this organization kept as received. These publications are not listed nor bound separately.

NN 0058333 DNLM

National multiple sclerosis society.
    The course of disseminated sclerosis
        see under
    Thygesen, Paul.

National multiple sclerosis society.
    Home programs for multiple sclerosis patients
        see under
    Gordon, Edward E   1907-

National Multiple Sclerosis Society.
    MS keynotes
        see under title

National Multiple Sclerosis Society.
    Mental health and MS
        see under   Harrower, Mary Rachel, 1906-

ZWL
360
N277m
1955

NATIONAL Multiple Sclerosis Society
    Multiple sclerosis; a selected medical bibliography, June 1, 1955. New York, National Multiple Sclerosis Society, Medical Dept., 1955.
    12 l.
    Cover title.
    "No. 2."
    1. Sclerosis - Multiple - Bibl.

NN 0058338 DNLM

RC383
.S5G6

National Multiple Sclerosis Society.

Gordon, Edward E   1907-
    Multiple sclerosis; application of rehabilitation techniques. Prepared for the National Multiple Sclerosis Society. New York ₍1951₎

National Multiple Sclerosis Society.
    Report.
    ₍New York₎
        ₍v. illus. 28 cm. annual.

RC377.A1N3   614.59   60-42508

NN 0058340 DLC NN

National Municipal league.   3502.192
    Address to the public. Constitution and by-laws.
=   [Philadelphia.] 1896. (16) pp. [Publications. 2.] 8°.

Municipal reform.

NN 0058341 MB

S
353.9
qN279

National Municipal League.
    American intergovernmental relations, as of 1954; statement to the Commission on Intergovernmental Relations. New York, 1954.
    1 v. 29 cm.

    Includes bibliographies.

    1. Federal government. U.S. I. U. S. Intergovernmental Relations, Commission on. II. Title: Inter-   governmental relations, American.₎

NN 0058342 N

JS302
.N482

National municipal league.
    Annual meeting...
    [Philadelphia?]

NN 0058343 DLC

NATIONAL MUNICIPAL LEAGUE.
    Answers to your questions. [New York: National Municipal League, 1934?] 8 p. 14cm.

    Caption-title: About the manager plan.

867631A. 1. Municipal government by city manager—U.S.
I. Title.

NN 0058344 NN

NATIONAL MUNICIPAL LEAGUE.
    Answers to your questions [about the manager plan. New York City,1941].

    16 cm. pp.7,(1).

NN 0058345 MH-PA

National municipal league.
    Best practice under the manager plan ...
        see under Childs, Richard Spencer, 1882-

National Municipal League.
    A brief financial and administrative survey of the city of Winter Park, Florida
        see under National Municipal League. Municipal Consultant Service.

National Municipal League.
    A brief financial and administrative survey of the city of Yonkers, N. Y.
        see under National Municipal League. Municipal consultant service.

National Municipal League.
    A brief financial and administrative survey of the town of Greenburgh, N. Y.
        see under National Municipal League. Municipal consultant service.

National Municipal League.
    A brief financial and administrative survey of the town of Harrison, N. Y.
        see under National Municipal League. Municipal consultant service.

National Municipal League.
    A brief financial and administrative survey of the town of Mount Pleasant, N. Y.
        see under National Municipal League. Municipal consultant service.

National Municipal League.
    A brief financial survey of the borough of Dumont, New Jersey
        see under National Municipal League. Office of consultant service.

National Municipal League.   3569a.275
    Business bodies and municipal reform.
=   Philadelphia. [1904.] 8 pp. 16°.

F5279 — Municipal reform. — Business associations.

NN 0058353 MB

VOLUME 407

National municipal league.
₍Campaign pamphlets.₎
New York, 1948-
illus. unnumbered.

NN   0058354   PP

National Municipal League.
The citizen association; how to win civic campaigns.
₍Written and designed by Alexander L. Crosby. 1st ed.₎
New York ₍1953₎
64 p. illus. 23 cm.

1. Citizens' associations—U. S. 2. Local government—U. S.
I. Crosby, Alexander L. II. Title.

JS363.5.N33   352.073   54–29874 rev

OrCS
NN   MiD NBuG NcD WaT OCl OCU CU NN MiU Or OrP OrU Wa
0058355   DLC MiU CU PBL TxU ViU TU IU NIC CLSU

National municipal league.
Citizen organization for political activity
see under National municipal league.
Committee on citizens' charter organization.

National municipal league.
City growing pains, a series of discussions of metropolitan
area problems originally published in the National municipal
review. New York city, National municipal league, ᶜ1941.
116 p. 23ᵐ.
Bibliography: p. 106–116.

1. Cities and towns—Growth. 2. Local government—U. S.   I. Title.

Library of Congress   JS345.1941.N35
                                                          41–22492
                              ₍7₎   352.073

N OCl ViU NN
NN   0058357   DLC OU OClW MH NN NcD ICU Or OrP IdPI

National Municipal League.
The city manager plan at work; what
those who live in manager cities think
of their government. ₍c1930₎
(In Pamphlets, Vol. 28)

NN   0058358   NcD

National Municipal League.   352.006161 3
₇₈₈₇₆ .... Clipping sheet. .... [Philadelphia, 1907–.]
Continued from third series, no. 2, Oct. 1907. 24 x 104ᶜᵐ.
At head of title: National Municipal League.
Incomplete; continued irregularly by gift.

NN   0058359   ICJ MB DLC

National municipal league.
₍Collection of four pamphlets on municipal government.
Philadelphia, 1897–1906₎   4 pams. in 1 v.   15cm.

CONTENTS.—The National municipal league and the Committee of ten.—Address of
the Executive committee to the friends of good government throughout the United States.
—Public service by private citizens, by H. E. Deming.—The ignorance of good citizens,
by J. Horace McFarland.

1. Municipal government—U. S.   2. Municipal government—Assoc. and
org.—U. S.

NN   0058360   NN

National municipal league.

₍Waite, Henry Matson₎ 1869–
The commission-manager plan in actual operation; a
discussion. ₍Philadelphia₎ National municipal league,
1915.

National Municipal League.
The commission plan and commission-manager plan of muni-
cipal government; an analytical study by a committee of the
National Municipal League.   ₍Philadelphia: National Municipal
League, 1914.₎   24 p.   8°.
Cover-title.

1. Municipal government.—Com-   mission form. 2. Municipal government by city manager. 3. Title.
N. Y. P. L.   September 16, 1915.

OrU
NN   0058362   NN ODW NcD KyU ICU IU CaBViP MH-L WaS

National municipal league.
Competitive examinations for higher offices; report of
joint committee of the National municipal league and the
National civil service reform league, with supplemental
papers by Horace E. Deming and Richard Henry Dana.
New York, Pub. for the National civil service reform
league, 1916.
20 p. 20ᵐ.
"Commission government and efficiency, by Horace E. Deming": p. 7–9.
"Contracts in politics, by Richard Henry Dana": p. 9–17.
1. Municipal government—U. S. 2. Civil service—U. S.   I. National
civil service reform league. II. Deming, Horace Edward, 1850–
III. Dana, Richard Henry, 1851–   IV. Title.

Library of Congress   JS363.N3 1916
                                                          17–7220

NN   0058363   DLC NN Or OrU MB

National municipal league.
Constitutional amendment and municipal corporations
act, proposed by the National municipal league committee on municipal program, 1899. ₍Philadelphia? 1899?₎
cover-title, 37 p.   26½ᵐ.

1. Municipal government—U. S.   I. Title.
                                              CA 16–490 Unrev'd
Library of Congress   JS345.1899.N3

NN   0058364   DLC

352   National municipal league.
N21c   Constitutions and by-laws of leading
municipal reform organizations.
Phil. 1897.
31p.   (Publications of the National
municipal league. Pamphlet, no.4.)

NN   0058365   IU

NATIONAL municipal league.
Constitutions and by-laws of the Municipal league of Philadelphia; City
club of New York; Citizens' association of Boston [etc.].
[Phila.] 1895. 36 pp. [Publ. Pph. no. 4.] 8°.

NN   0058366   MB MH

National municipal league.
Constructive economy in government ... broadcasts ... presented by the Committee on civic education by radio of the
National advisory council on radio in education and the American political science association, in coöperation with the
National municipal league. New York city, National municipal league ₍ᶜ1934₎
₍124₎ p. 24½ᵐ. (You and your government. ser. v)
Various pagings.
"Delivered June 20–September 26, 1933, over a nation-wide network
of the National broadcasting company."
1. Local government—U. S. 2. Finance—U. S. 3. Budget—U. S.
I. National advisory council on radio in education. Committee on civic
education by radio. II. American political science association. III. Title.
Library of Congress   HJ257.N38   34–30376
——— Copy 2.   JS308.Y6 ser. v
Copyright   A 75496

NN   0058367   DLC NBuG OrCS WaS CU OU

KB88   National Municipal League.
C7N2   Coroners; a symposium of legal bases and actual
practices. 1st-   ed.; 1953-
New York.
v.

All but last volume superseded.

1. Coroners - U.S.   I. Title.

NN   0058368   CLL DNLM TU

347.96   National Municipal League.
N213c   Coroners; a symposium of legal bases
and actual practices. New York ₍1954?₎
1 v. (unpaged)

"How murderers beat the law," by Pete
Martin, reprinted from Saturday Evening
Post, Dec.10, 1949: ₍8₎ p. inserted.

1. Coroners - U. S. 2. Medical laws and
legislation. I.   Title.

NN   0058369   WaU IEN ViU-L PPC IU MiU-L

National Municipal League
Coroners in 1953; a symposium of legal bases
and actual practices. 3d ed. New York, National
Municipal League, ₍1955.
1 v.(various pagings)   29 cm.

1.Coroners - U.S. 2.Medical jurisprudence - U.S.

NN   0058370   MiU-L OrPR Wa ICU MH-L TU NcD NjR

National Municipal League.
Coroners in 1958 (sic). A symposium of
legal bases and actual practices. 3d ed.
New York, 1955.
1 v.   28 cm.

How murderers beat the law, by Pete
Martin, reprinted from the Saturday Evening
Post, Dec. 10, 1949. (8 p. at end)

NN   0058371   N-L

National municipal league.
... A correct public policy toward the street
railway problem ...
see under National Municipal League.
Committee on Public Utilities.

National municipal league.
Council-manager cities during the depression. New York
city, The National municipal league ₍ᶜ1935₎
32 p. 20ᵐ.

1. Municipal government by city manager. 2. Municipal finance—U. S.
I. Title.
                                                          36–9548
Library of Congress   JS344.C5N34
——— Copy 2.
Copyright A 83157   ₍3₎   352.008

NN   0058373   DLC PSt OU OO OClh

National Municipal League.
The county manager plan [1932]
see under Childs, Richard Spencer,
1882–

National municipal league.
The county manager plan. New York, National municipal
league, 1945.
cover-title, 22 p. 17ᵐ.

1. County government—U. S.
                                                          A 45–3367
Harvard univ. Library
for Library of Congress   JS414.N3
                              ₍3₎†   352.008

NN   0058375   MH N TxU DLC NN OrP Or

National municipal league.
The county manager plan. Rev. 1950.   New
York, 1950. 29 p. 17cm.

1. Government, Local—U.S.

NN   0058376   NN Or FMU NBuG

VOLUME 407

National municipal league.
The crisis in municipal finance ... broadcasts ... presented by the Committee on civic education by radio of the National advisory council on radio in education and the American political science association, in coöperation with the National municipal league. New York city, National municipal league ₁1934₎
₍163₎ p. 24½ᶜᵐ. (You and your government. ser. vi)
Various pagings.
"Delivered October 3, 1933–February 6, 1934, over a nation-wide network of the National broadcasting company."
1. Municipal finance—U. S. 2. Local government—U. S. i. National advisory council on radio in education. Committee on civic education by radio. ii. American political science association. iii. Title.

Library of Congress	HJ9145.N3	34–39373
——— Copy 2.	JS308.Y6 ser. vi	
Copyright A 75428	₍7₎	(352.073) 352.10973

NN 0058377   DLC OrCS WaS CU OU NBuG

National municipal league.
Democracy in the modern world
see under title

National municipal league.
Democracy must think; an informal round-table discussion on public opinion in a democracy at the National municipal league's forty-fourth annual conference on government. New York, Columbia university press, 1939.
xi, 65 p. 22½ᶜᵐ. (Half-title: National municipal league series)

1. Public opinion—U. S. 2. U. S.—Pol. & govt.   i. Title.

Library of Congress	HM261.N3	39–22232
——— Copy 2.		
Copyright A 129698	₍3₎	301.15

NN 0058379   DLC WaS IU CU WaT MiD OU

National Municipal League.
Digest of county manager charters and laws. New York, 1950.
61 l. fold. diagrs. 30 cm.

1. County government.
                                                            A 51–3510
Duke Univ. Library
for Library of Congress ₍5₎

TU
NN 0058380   NcD OrU OrP TxU ViU Or IU MiU CaBVaU

SF
7583   **National Municipal League.**
.07   Digest of county manager charters and
.674   laws. 2d ed. ₍New York, 1951₎
.11q   1 v. 30 cm.

1.County charters - U.S.

NN 0058381   NjP OrU

JS411 NATIONAL MUNICIPAL LEAGUE.
.N12   Digest of county manager charters and laws.
(Law) 3d ed. New York, 1954.
       1 v. (unpaged)

1. County government—U.S.

NN 0058382   ICU NNC

National Municipal League.
Directory, officers & council
see its
Report and directory.

National municipal league.
Draft of a proposed municipal nominating law submitted to the National municipal league at its annual meeting held April 27, 28 and 29th, 1904. ₍New York? 1904?₎
34 p. fold. diagrs.

1. Nominations for office.

NN 0058384   NNC OClWHi

National municipal league.
JF1601
.N3
National civil service league.
Draft of a state civil service law. Prepared by National civil service reform league ... and National municipal league ... ₍New York, 1939₎

National Municipal League.
Financial and administrative survey of the town of Cortlandt, New York
see under   National Municipal League.
Municipal Consultant Service.

National municipal league.
Financing a postwar public improvement program for greater Cleveland ...
see under   Reed, Thomas Harrison, 1881-

National municipal league.
Forms of municipal government; how have they worked? Prepared by National municipal league. New York city, ᶜ1939.
cover-title, 20 p. diagrs. 19¼ᶜᵐ.
Diagram on p. ₍2₎ of cover.

1. Municipal government—U. S.   i. Title.

Library of Congress	JS345.1939.N3	39–20843
——— Copy 2.		
Copyright AA 305307	₍3₎	352.073

NN 0058387   DLC ViU WaT WaWW Or PP OU MH

National municipal league.
Forms of municipal government. How have they worked? New York, 1944.

20 p. diagr. 19.5 cm.
Cover-title.

NN 0058388   MH-PA Or

National municipal league.
Forms of municipal government; how have they worked?   New York, National municipal league, 1947.
20 p. charts. 19.5 cm.
Cover-title.

NN 0058389   PSt

S
352.073 **National municipal league.**
N27f   Forms of municipal government; how have they worked? ₍N.Y.₎ 1949.
           cover-title, 20p. illus. 20cm.

1.Municipal government. U.S. I.Title.

NN 0058390   N

National Municipal League.
Forms of municipal government; how have they worked?
New York, 1951.
20 p. illus. 20 cm.

1. Municipal government—U. S.   i. Title.

JS345 1951.N3   352.073   51–36466 ‡

NN 0058391   DLC OrU OrP Or ViU

National Municipal League.
Forms of municipal government; how have they worked? New York, 1955.
19cm. illus. 20 cm.

Cover-title.

1. Municipal government - U. S. i. Title.

NN 0058392   FMU CaBVaU

National municipal league.
The 44 state legislatures of 1935 ... broadcasts ... presented by the Committee on civic education by radio of the National advisory council on radio in education and the American political science association, in coöperation with the National municipal league. New York city, National municipal league ₁1936₎
₍158₎ p. 24ᶜᵐ. (You and your government. ser. x)
Various pagings.
"Delivered February 5–June 11, 1935, over a nation-wide network of the National broadcasting company."
"References" at end of some of the broadcasts.
1. State governments. 2. Legislation—U. S. 3. Legislative bodies—U. S. i. National advisory council on radio in education. Committee on civic education by radio. ii. American political science association. iii. Title. iv. Title: State legislatures of 1935.

Library of Congress	JK2431.N35	37–247
——— Copy 2.	JS308.Y6 ser. 10	
Copyright A 95760	₍5₎	(352.073) 353.9

NN 0058393   DLC OrU WaS IU OClU

National municipal league.
The government of Hoboken ...
see under   Reed, Thomas Harrison, 1881-

National Municipal League.
The government of Nassau County ...
see under   National Municipal League.
Office of Consultant Service.

National municipal league.
Government of Wallingford ...
see under   Reed, Thomas Harrison, 1881-

National Municipal League.
The governments of Atlanta and Fulton County, Georgia; a report
see under   National Municipal League.
Office of consultant service.

National Municipal League.
A guide for charter commissions. New York ₍1947₎
iv, 34 p. 27 cm.

1. Municipal government—U. S.   i. Title.

JS335.N3   352.073   48–906*

NN 0058398   DLC MH-L NN OrP OrU N TU TxU PP

VOLUME 407

National Municipal League.
    A guide for charter commissions. 2d ed., rev. New York,
1952.
    44 p. 27 cm.

    1. Municipal government—U. S.   I. Title.

    JS335.N3 1952   352.073   53–31634 ‡

         NcD PSt
NN   0058399   DLC ViU-L NBuU-L OrP MiD IU ViU OCl

National municipal league.
    Handbook of the National municipal league, 1894–1904.
Philadelphia, National municipal league, 1904.
    70 p. 23ᶜᵐ.
    "Publications of the league" and "Authors of papers": p. 23–34.

                                5–13253

NN   0058400   DLC ICJ

National municipal league.
    Hand book National municipal league, 1914. Philadel-
phia, National municipal league, 1914.
    2 p. l., 127 p. 22½ᶜᵐ.

    I. Title.
                                14–13642
    Library of Congress   JS302.N53 1914

         ViU OO NjP
NN   0058401   DLC OrPR IdU WaS OrU Or MB ICJ OU OCU

National Municipal League.
    Have public employees the right to strike?
         see under title

National municipal league.
    How council-manager government is working as described
by newspapermen in 30 cities; a series originally published by
the Yonkers (N. Y.) Herald-statesman reproduced in pamphlet form by National municipal league. New York city,
1940.
    31, ₁1₎ p. 25½ᶜᵐ.
    "Constitutes a photographic reproduction of the articles exactly as
they appeared in the Herald-statesman."—p. 3.
    "Partial list of publications of National municipal league": p. 31.

    1. Municipal government by city manager. 2. Municipal government—
U. S.   I. The Herald statesman.   II. Title.   III. Title: Council-manager
government.
    Library of Congress   JS344.C5N316
                                                42–14289
                               ₍4₎   352.008

NN   0058403   DLC CSt OrP NN OO MH Vi OCU OC1W OU

National Municipal League.
    The influence of the National Municipal League.   ₁Phila-
delphia,₎ 1910. 12 p. 16°.

1. Municipal reform.—Associations,   U.S.
N. Y. P. L.   N. Y. PUBLIC LIBRARY   January 28, 1911.

NN   0058404   NN MH

National Municipal League.
    ...Information bulletin.
    v. ₁1₎

New York: National Municipal League, 1934–   28cm.
    v.
    Irregular.
    Reproduced from typewritten copy.
    Jan., 1934 lacks v. numbering.
    At head of title: National pay your taxes campaign.
    Suspended publication.

1. Municipal taxation—Per. and   soc. publ.—U. S.
N. Y. P. L.   November 10, 1936

NN   0058405   NN

National Municipal League.   352.006161 x
    ...Leaflets. Philadelphia, National Municipal League, 1901–
⁴²⁷⁸⁹ 1914.
ᵇ
    Cover-title.
    Various editions.

NN   0058406   ICJ NjR DLC Or

National municipal league.

Nunn, William Lee, 1902–
    Local progress in labor peace, by William L. Nunn ... a
series of articles originally published in the National municipal review; with an introduction by C. A. Dykstra ... New
York, National municipal league, °1941.

National municipal league.

Crane, Robert Treat, 1880–
    Loose leaf digest of city manager charters, by Robert Treat
Crane ... 1st ed., five hundred copies. New York, The National municipal league ₁1923₎

National Municipal League.
    Manager plan abandonments ...
         see under   Bromage, Arthur Watson,
1904–

National Municipal League.
    Membership. 1908.
    [Philadelphia.] 1908.   v. 16°.

NN   0058410   MB DLC

E
375.1721   National Municipal League.
qN278   Memorandum and proposals from President C.A.
             Dykstra outlining a plan of action for cooperating
             colleges and citizens' organizations. New York City
             [1940?]
                 1 v. 31 cm .
                 Caption title.
                 Proposals for implementing the recommendations of the
             Conference on American Self-Government held at Indiana
             University May 13   and 14, 1940.

                 1. Citizenship. U.S. Study and teaching.
             I. Conference on American Self-Government.
             Indiana University, 1940. II. Title.

NN   0058412   N

National Municipal League.
ᴹᴮ¹¹⁹ [Minor publications.]

NN   0058413   ICJ

National Municipal League.
    A model bond law ...
         see under
**National Municipal League. Committee on
Municipal Borrowings.**
**National Municipal League. Committee on
a Program of Model Fiscal Legislation
for Local Governments.**

National Municipal League.
    Model city charter ...
         see
**National Municipal League. Committee on
Municipal Program.**
**National Municipal League. Committee on
Revision of the Model City Charter.**

National Municipal League.
    Model investment of state funds law
         see under
**National Municipal League. Committee on a
Program of Model Fiscal Legislation for
Local Governments.**

National municipal league
    Model laws, prepared by committees of the
National municipal league.
New York, National municipal league ₑcl936₎
    270 p.

NN   0058417   OU OC1

National municipal league.
    Model laws ... Copyright by National municipal league.
    ₁New York, National municipal league, 1937?₎
    ₁278₎ p. 25ᶜᵐ.
    Reports by committees of the National municipal league issued 1928–
1936, each with special t.-p. and separate paging.
    CONTENTS.—A model municipal budget law.—A model bond law.—A
model registration system.—A model election administration system.—
A model real property tax collection law.—A model county manager
law.—Principles of a model county government.—A model state constitution.—Liquor control : principles, model law.

    1. Legislation—U. S. 2. Bill drafting. 3. Municipal corporations—
U. S.   I. Title.
                                                38–18394
    Library of Congress   ₁5–5₎   352.073

NN   0058418   DLC NcD Wa OOxM OC1W

NationalMunicipal League.
    Model municipal budget law
         see under   National Municipal League.
Committee on a model municipal budget law.

National Municipal League.
    Model real property tax collection law
         see under
**National Municipal League. Committee on a
Program of Model Fiscal Legislation for Local
Governments.**
*National Municipal League. Committee on a
Model Tax Collection Law.*

National Municipal League.
    A model registration system ...
         see under   National Municipal League.
Committee on election administration.

Law
    National Municipal League.
    Model State and regional planning law. Introd. by Cole-
man₍Woodbury. New York, 1955.
    vii, 66 p. 23 cm.

    1. Regional planning.   I. Title.
                                                A 55—6114
    Duke Univ. Library
    for Library of Congress   ₁56d3₎

         CaBViP WaU-L ODW FU TU NIC GU-L
         NN PU-FA Or OrP PPCPC PU NcU MtBC OrU CaBVaU Wa
NN   0058422   NcD PSt PPT NIC IU MiD TU ViU TxU OC1

Law
    National Municipal League.

    National Civil Service League.
    A model state civil service law; a model state merit sys-
tem constitutional provision, prepared by National Civil
Service League ₁and₎ National Municipal League. New
York, 1953.

VOLUME 407

National Municipal League.
A model state medico-legal investigative system

see under

Committee on a Model State Medico-legal Investigative System.

S
342
N27   National municipal league.
     Modernizing state constitutions ...
     N.Y.,1948.
       21 p. 23cm.

     "Reprinted from National municipal review, March,1948."

     1.Municipal government. U.S. I.Title.

NN   0058425   N NIC MiU IU

National Municipal League.
   ...Monograph series.
₁no.
New York, 1925
   no.   8°.

1. Municipal government.
N. Y. P. L.   September 21, 1925

NN   0058426   NN OC1

National municipal league.
   Municipal home rule and a model city charter ...
     see under   National Municipal League.
Committee on municipal program.

National Municipal League.
   Municipal problems. A few words for librarians ₁regarding proceedings of conferences, 1908-1909. List of libraries connected with the...League₁ Philadelphia: the League ₁1910?₁   8 p.
16°.

1. Municipal reform, U.S.
N. Y. P. L.   N. Y. PUBLIC LIBRARY   January 28, 1911.

NN   0058428   NN

National municipal league.
   A municipal program; report of a committee of the National municipal league, adopted by the league, November 17, 1899, together with explanatory and other papers. New York, London, Pub. for the National municipal league, the Macmillan company, 1900.
   xi, ₁1₁, 246 p. 21½ᶜᵐ.

     CONTENTS.—Municipal development in the United States ₁by₁ J. A. Fairlie.—The municipal problem in the United States ₁by₁ H. E. Deming.—The city in the United States, the proper scope of its activities ₁by₁ Albert Shaw.—The place of the council and of the mayor in the organization of municipal government, the necessity of distinguishing legislation from administration ₁by₁ F. J. Goodnow.—Public accounting under the proposed municipal program ₁by₁ L. S. Rowe.—The power to incur indebtedness under the proposed municipal program ₁by₁ Hon. B. S. Coler.—Municipal franchises ₁by₁ Charles Richardson.—Political parties and city government under the proposed municipal program ₁by₁ F. J. Goodnow.—Public opinion and city government under the proposed municipal program ₁by₁ H. E. Deming.—A summary of the program ₁by₁ L. S. Rowe.—Proposed constitutional amendments.— Proposed municipal corporations act.—An examination of the proposed municipal program ₁by₁ D. F. Wilcox.

     1. Municipal government—U.S.   I. Title.

Library of Congress   JS302.N6 1900   0—1488
—— Copy 2.
Copyright 1900 A 4301
352   ₁s26e1₁   Jw83

     ICJ ODW MB NjP MiU
NN   0058430   DLC ViU PSt NIC NBuU-L WaS OrU OU MB

National Municipal League.
   National municipal review
     see   National Civic review.

National Municipal League.
   National pay your taxes campaign. Information bulletin ...
     see its   Information bulletin.

National municipal league.
   A new deal in local government ... broadcasts ... presented by the Committee on civic education by radio of the National advisory council on radio in education and the American political science association, in coöperation with the National municipal league. New York city, National municipal league ₁*1936₁
     ₁102₁ p. 24½ᶜᵐ. (You and your government. ser. VIII)
     Various pagings.
     "Delivered June 26–September 25, 1934, over a nation-wide network of the National broadcasting company."
     1. Local government—U. S. 2. U. S.—Pol. & govt.—1933–   I. National advisory council on radio in education. Committee on civic education by radio. II. American political science association. III. Title.

Library of Congress   JS331.N25   37–168
—— Copy 2.   JS308.Y6 ser. 8
Copyright   A 95758   ₁5₁   (352.073)   352.073

NN   0058433   DLC WaS NN OrCS IU

JS
348
.N28   National Municipal League.
     New look at home rule,a symposium ₁by₁ Benjamin Baker ₁and others. New York, 1955₁
       32 p.   23 cm.
       "Reprinted from National municipal review, March and April,1955."

       1.Municipal home rule. I.Baker,Benjamin,1914-

NN   0058434   MiU OrU NcD

NATIONAL MUNICIPAL LEAGUE
   Outline of a model state presidential primary law. Author, 1955.
     9 ℓ.

     Mimeographed.

NN   0058435   Or

National Municipal League.
   Outlines of responsible government ...
     see under   Dawson, Edgar, 1872-

₁NATIONAL MUNICIPAL LEAGUE₁
   P.R. Proportional representation (P.R.) is the only voting method which guarantees real majority rule in the city council or legislature.
₁Author₁ 1948.
   ₁12₁ p. illus.

NN   0058437   Or

NATIONAL MUNICIPAL LEAGUE.
   Pamphlets

     See its "Publications".

National Municipal League.
   Panel session: Women as campaigners

     see under

     National Conference on Government, Richmond, 1953.

National municipal league.
   Planning ... broadcasts ... presented by the Committee on civic education by radio of the National advisory council on radio in education and the American political science association, in coöperation with the National municipal league. New York city, National municipal league ₁*1936₁
     ₁146₁ p. 24ᶜᵐ. (You and your government. ser. XII)
     Various pagings.
     "Delivered October 1, 1935–January 28, 1936, over a nation-wide network of the National broadcasting company."
     "Brief list of references" at end of each broadcast.
     1. U. S.—Economic policy. 2. U. S.—Public works. 3. Cities and towns—Planning. I. National advisory council on radio in education. Committee on civic education by radio. II. American political science association. III. Title.
                                         37–169

Library of Congress   HC106.3.N357
—— Copy 2.   JS308.Y6 ser. 12
Copyright   A 95762   ₁5₁   (352.073)   330.973

NN   0058440   DLC CU WaS

National Municipal League.
   Pocket civics series.
₁no.
New York ₁1922   16°.
   nos.

Contents:
   no. 2. The short ballot; a movement to simplify politics. ₁1922.₁
   no. 3. The story of the city-manager plan... ₁1922.₁
   no. 4. Childs, R. S. Ramshackle County government, the plague spot of American politics. ₁1922.₁

NN   0058442   NN Or

HD2766
.B33   National municipal league.
     Bauer, John, 1881–
       Postwar planning for metropolitan utilities ... by John Bauer ... New York, N. Y., National municipal league, 1945.

NATIONAL MUNICIPAL LEAGUE.
   Primer chart of typical city governments.

   Broadside 32 1/2 x 27 inches.

NN   0058444   MH NNU-W

NATIONAL MUNICIPAL LEAGUE.
   A primer in proportional representation. [New York City, 1934?]   4 f.   28½cm.

   Caption-title.
   Signed: National Municipal League.
   Reproduced from typewritten copy.
   Bibliography, f.4.

   785143A. 1. Representation, Proportional.

NN   0058445   NN

National Municipal League.
   Proceedings ... 1894-1910
     see under   Conference for Good City Government.

JS39
.N3   National Municipal League. Proceedings.
     1911-16.
     National civic review. v. 1–
     Jan. 1912–
     ₁Worcester, Mass., etc.₁

National Municipal League.
   Proceedings of the Buffalo conference for good government ...
     see   Conference for Good City Government. Proceedings.

VOLUME 407

National Municipal League.
　　Proceedings of the Louisville conference for
good city government
　　　　see　　　Conference for Good City
Government.
　　　　Proceedings.

National municipal league.
　　Program for the ... annual meeting of the National
municipal league and the ... National conference for good
city government ...
　　₍n. p.₎
　　　v. 18½ᶜᵐ.

　　Library of Congress　　　JS302.N485
　　　　　　　　　　　　　　　　　　　CA 11—251 Unrev'd

NN　0058450　　　DLC OrU MB

NATIONAL MUNICIPAL LEAGUE
　　Proportional representation.　12th ed.
Author c1951.
8 p.

NN　0058451　　　Or

National municipal league.
　　　　　　　　　　　FOR OTHER EDITIONS
Hallett, George Hervey, 1895-　　SEE MAIN ENTRY
　　Proportional representation — the key to democracy, by
George H. Hallett, jr., secretary of the Citizens union of the
city of New York and associate secretary of the National
municipal league, with the coöperation of Clarence Gilbert
Hoag ...　2d and rev. ed., 1940.　New York city, National
municipal league ₍1940₎

National Municipal League.
　　Public markets in the United States; second report of a committee of the National Municipal League, figures revised to March
15, 1917, by Clyde Lyndon King, chairman ...₍and others₎.　Philadelphia: National Municipal League, 1917.　32 p.　Tables.　8°.

1. Markets, U. S.　2. King, Clyde
N. Y. P. L.　　　　　　　　　Lyndon, 1879-
　　　　　　　　　　　　　　　　　　December 5, 1917.

NN　0058453　　　NN NIC MiD

National municipal league.
　　Publications of the National municipal league.　Pamphlet no. 1-
　　₍Philadelphia₎ 1895-
　　　v. 23ᶜᵐ.

1. Municipal government—Societies.　2. Municipal government—U. S.

　　Library of Congress　　　JS302.N5
　　　　　　　　　　　　　　　　　　8-23477†

NN　0058454　　　DLC Or WaS ICJ MiU Nh OO

National Municipal League.
　　Recent development in the use of the
constitutional convention in the States ...
　　　　see under　　Bebout, John Elber.

National municipal league.
　　The relation of the city to its food supply; report of a committee on the National municipal league, November 19, 1914,
by Clyde Lyndon King, chairman ₍and others₎ ...　Philadelphia, National municipal league, 1915.
　　75 p.　illus. (map) diagr.　23ᶜᵐ.

1. Food supply—U. S.　2. Markets—U. S.　3. Farm produce—Marketing.　I. King, Clyde Lyndon, 1879-1937.　II. Title.
　　　　　　　　　　　　　　　　　　17—21489

　　Library of Congress　　　HD9006.N3

　　IU ICJ Or OrU WaS CU NIC CaBViP KEmT
NN　0058456　　　DLC NjP DL OU OCU WaU MiU NN MdBJ MB

National municipal league.

Drellich, *Mrs.* Edith Berger.
　　Rent control in war and peace, by Edith Berger Drellich and
Andrée Emery.　A study prepared under the auspices of the
Laws and administration committee of the Citizens' housing
council of New York.　New York city, National municipal
league, 1939.

National Municipal League.
　　Report and directory.
　　₍New York₎
　　　v.　illus.　22 cm.
　　Title varies: 19　　　-53, Directory, officers & council.

　　JS302.N524　　　　　　　　　　54-34251 ‡

NN　0058458　　　DLC NN PLF NIC CLSU

National Municipal League.
　　Report of the Survey Committee to the National
Municipal League ...
　　　　see under　　National Municipal League.
Survey Committee.

National municipal league.
　　Report of the survey of the public schools of White Plains,
New York.　Made by the National municipal league.　How-
ard P. Jones, director, Consultant service, National municipal
league; John W. Withers, director of school survey.　₍White
Plains, N. Y., The Board of education, 1940₎
　　396 p.　tables, diagrs.　23ᶜᵐ.
　　"Publications and theses": p. 382-384.
　　"Unpublished research reports and term papers worthy of special at-
tention": p. 385-386.

1. Educational surveys.　2. White Plains, N. Y.—Public schools.
I. Jones, Howard Palfrey, 1899-　　II. Withers, John William, 1868-
　　　　　　　　　　　　　　　　　　A 41-2727

New York univ.　Wash. sq.　　　　library　LA339.W45N3
　for Library of Congress　　　　₍2₎

NN　0058460　　　NNU-W

National Municipal League.
　　Report on the financial condition of the city of
Yonkers, New York
　　　　see under　　National Municipal League.
Office of Consultant Service.

National municipal league.
　　Reviving local government ... broadcasts ... presented by
the Committee on civic education by radio of the National
advisory council on radio in education and the American
political science association, in coöperation with the National
municipal league.　New York city, National municipal league
₍1934₎
　　₍160₎ p.　illus. (map)　24½ᶜᵐ.　(You and your government.　ser. VII)
Various pagings.
　　"Delivered February 13-June 19, 1934, over a nation-wide network
of the National broadcasting company."

1. Local government—U. S.　I. National advisory council on radio
in education.　Committee on civic education by radio.　II. American
political science association.　III. Title.
　　　　　　　　　　　　　　　　　　34-39377

Library of Congress　　　JS323.N3
　　　　——— Copy 2.　　　JS308.Y6　ser. VII
　　Copyright A 75427　　₍7₎　　　　(352.073)　352.073

NN　0058462　　　DLC IU OrCS NBuG OU

355.23　National Municipal League.
N214s　　Save our cities, survival in the atomic age
　　depends on intensified planning now.　New
　　York ₍1954₎
　　　31p.　23cm.

　　"Reprinted from the National municipal review, June, July and September 1954."

1. Atomic bomb—Safety measures.　2. Civilian
defense.　I. Title.

NN　0058463　　　IU

National Municipal League.
　　The short ballot; a movement to simplify
politics ...
　　　　see under　　₍Childs, Richard Spencer₎
1882-

₍National municipal league₎
　　... The story of the city-manager plan, the most democratic
form of municipal government ...　₍New York, 1921₎
　　31, ₍1₎ p.　diagr.　16½ᶜᵐ.
　　At head of title: Supplement to the National municipal review, February, 1921.
　　"References": p. 31.

1. Municipal government by city manager.　I. National municipal
review.　Supplement.　II. Title.
　　　　　　　　　　　　　　　　　　44-25181

　　Library of Congress　　　JS344.C5N32 1921

NN　0058465　　　DLC OC1W MH MiU

National Municipal League.
　　The story of the city-manager plan; the most democratic
form of municipal government.　New York: National Municipal
League ₍1922₎.　31 p. incl. tables.　16°.　(National Municipal
League.　Pocket civics series.　no. 3.)

1. Municipal government by city man-　　ager.　2. Series.
N. Y. P. L.　　　　　　　　　　　　　　　October 14, 1924

NN　0058466　　　NN RPB

National municipal league
　　Story of the city manager plan; the most
democratic form of municipal government.
N.Y., 1928?
　　31 p.

NN　0058467　　　OC1W

National Municipal League.
　　The story of the city manager plan, the most
democratic and efficient form of municipal government.　c1931.
　　(In Pamphlets, Vol. 28)

NN　0058468　　　NcD

National municipal league.
　　The story of the city manager plan, the most democratic
and efficient form of municipal government.　New York city,
National municipal league, ᶜ1934.
　　47, ₍1₎ p.　illus., diagrs.　15½ᶜᵐ.
　　"Revised September, 1934."

1. Municipal government by city manager.　I. Title.
　　　　　　　　　　　　　　　　　　35-9225
Library of Congress　　　JS344.C5N32 1934 a
　　——— Copy 2.
Copyright A 77234　　₍3₎　　　　　352.008

NN　0058469　　　DLC

National municipal league.
　　The story of the council-manager
plan, most democratic and efficient
form of municipal government.　Revised.
New York city, National municipal league,
1921-
　　47 p. illus. diagrs.

　　Contains:"Directory of approved
council-manager cities and counties"

NN　0058470　　　PP

National municipal league.
　　The story of the council-manager plan, most democratic and
efficient form of municipal government.　Revised 1940.　New
York city, National municipal league, ᶜ1940.
　　47 p.　illus., diagrs.　17ᶜᵐ.
　　"Directory of approved council-manager cities and counties": p. 37-43.

1. Municipal government by city manager.　I. Title.
　　　　　　　　　　　　　　　　　　A 42-2906
Vassar college.　Library　　　₍JS344.C5N　₎
　for Library of Congress
　　　　　　　　　　　₍2₎　　　　　352.008

NN　0058471　　　NPV MiU FU ICRL N Or NN MH

VOLUME 407

National municipal league
The story of the council-manager plan; most democratic and efficient form of municipal government. Rev. 1944. N. Y. [The Author] 1944.
47 p., illus.

NN 0058472   MiD Or

JS National Municipal League.
344 The story of the council-manager plan;
C5N27 most democratic and efficient form of muni-
1948 cipal government. Revised 1948. New York, 1948.
45 p. illus. 15cm.

1. Municipal government--U.S. I. Title.

NN 0058473   NIC ViU OC1

National Municipal League.
The story of the council-manager plan, most democratic and efficient form of municipal government. Rev. 1949. N.Y. [1949]
45 p. illus. 15 cm.
1. Municipal government by city manager.
II. Title.

NN 0058474   N

352.073 National Municipal League.
N214s The story of the council-manager plan, most
1952 democratic and efficient form of municipal government. [Rev. 1952] New York, National Municipal League, 1952.
35p. illus. 17cm.

Cover title.

1. Municipal government by city manager.
I. Title: The council-manager plan.

NN 0058475   IU CaBViP OrU N ICU MiU-L ViU

National Municipal League
The story of the council-manager plan; most democratic and efficient form of municipal government. 25th ed. New York, 1954.
32 p. illus.

Cover title.

1. Municipal government by city manager
I. T.

NN 0058476   MiD MiU PBL ViU

S National Municipal League.
352.008 The story of the council-manager plan; most demo-
N277a cratic and efficient form of municipal government.
1955 26th ed. New York, 1955.
30 p. illus. 18 cm.

1. Municipal government by city manager. 1. Title.

NN 0058477   N FMU MiU

352.073 National municipal league
N277s ...Suggested procedure for selecting a city manager, to aid city councils in the process of selecting a
qualified manager; a report submitted
by a committee of the National municipal league composed of: Richard S.
Childs... [and others] New York,
National municipal league, 1933.
cover-title, 8p. forms. Q.
At head of title: Supplement to the National municipal review, Dec., 1933.

NN 0058478   IaU

National municipal league
Suggestions for a model railway franchise, by sub-committee of committee on franchises, of National municipal league. Presented at the Richmond conference, November 16, 1911... n.p., n.d.
13 p.

NN 0058479   00

352.06 National Municipal League
N2a Summary of proceedings of national conference on government. New York.

Complete text in National municipal review.

1. /Municipal government - Societies
2. /Municipal government - U. S. I. /National conference on government

NN 0058480   MiD

National Municipal League.
Survey of principal administrative departments of the city of White Plains, New York
see under   National Municipal League.
Office of Consultant Service.

National Municipal League.
Survey of the government or Bar Harbor, Maine, submitted January 1939
see under   National Municipal League.
Office of Consultant Service.

National Municipal League.
Taxation for prosperity... [New York] National Municipal League [1935] 89 p. 25½cm. (You and your government. ser. 11.)

Issued in 15 parts.
Addresses delivered June 18–Sept. 24, 1935, over the network of the National Broadcasting Company.
Bibliography at end of each part.

805463A. 1. Taxation—U. S., 1935.   I. Ser.
N. Y. P. L.   January 27, 1937

NN 0058483   NN IU

National municipal league.
Taxation for prosperity ... broadcasts ... presented by the Committee on civic education by radio of the National advisory council on radio in education, in coöperation with the National municipal league. New York city, National municipal league [*1936] [126] p. 24cm. (You and your government. ser. xi)
Various pagings.
"Delivered June 18–September 24, 1935, over a nation-wide network of the National broadcasting company."
"Brief list of references" at end of each broadcast.
1. Taxation—U. S. I. National advisory council on radio in edu-
cation. Committee on civic education by radio. II. American political
science association. III. Title.
Library of Congress   HJ2379.N4   37-167
———— Copy 2.   JS308.Y6 ser. 11
Copyright A 95761   [5]   (352.073) 336.20973

NN 0058484   DLC CU

National Municipal League.
Technical pamphlets.
[no.] 1–
New York [1920–
nos.   8°.

Contents:
no. 1. Purdy, Lawson. The assessment of real estate. 1923.
no. 2. Buck, A. E. Administrative consolidation in state governments. 1922.
no. 4. National Municipal League. Committee on Public Utilities. A correct public policy toward the street railway problem. 1920.
no. 5. Bassett, E. M. Zoning. 1922.

no. 8. Williams, F. B. The law of the city plan. 1922.

no. 9. Mathews, J. M. Administrative reorganization in Illinois. 1920.
no. 10. Service at cost for state railways; a symposium. 1921.
no. 11. Swan, H. S. The law of zoning. [1921.]
no. 12. Caparn, H. A. State parks. 1921.

no. 14. Merriam, C. E. Recent tendencies in primary election systems; Hughes, C. E. The fate of the direct primary. [1921.]
no. 15. National Municipal League. Committee on Sources of Revenue. Special assessments; a means of financing municipal improvements. [1923.]
no. 16. Adams, Thomas. Modern city planning; its meaning and methods. 1922.

no. 17. National Municipal League. Committee on Pensions. Pensions in public employment. 1922.
no. 18. Maxey, C. C. The political integration of metropolitan communities. 1922.
no. 19. National Municipal League. Committee on Sources of Revenue. Minor highway privileges as a source of city revenue. 1923.

NN 0058488   NN CtNIC ICJ MB OC1 DHEW NcD

National Municipal League.
Tentative outline: the commission manager plan, city government ...
see under   National Municipal League.
Committee on Municipal Program.

National municipal league.
Town management in New England ... New York city, National municipal league, *1940.
35 p. 23cm.
"A series of articles originally published in the National municipal review."
Contents.—Foreword by Norman MacDonald.—Manager plan in Con-
necticut towns, by C. W. Atkins.—Maine a pioneer in town management,
by O. C. Hormell.—The old and the new in Massachusetts towns, by
R. A. Atkins.—Town meeting vs. town management, by T. V. Kalijarvi.—
Twenty years of town management in Vermont, by K. R. B. Flint.
1. Municipal government—New England. 2. Municipal government
by city manager.   I. Title.
Library of Congress   JS344.C5N35   41-13681
                                           [2]   352.074

NN 0058490   DLC PSt IU

National Municipal League.
Training for citizenship. Philadelphia: the league, 1913.
19(1) p. 16°. (National Municipal League. Leaflets. Series 3, no. 2.)
"Embodies the principal part of the report of Mr. Arthur W. Dunn, chairman
of the...League's Committee on Civic Education, given at the Richmond meeting...
1911."
1. Citizenship.—Education for. U. S.   2. Dunn, Arthur William. 3. Series.
N. Y. P. L.   November 6, 1916.

NN 0058491   NN

National Municipal League.
Trends in government... [New York] National Municipal
League [1934–35] [83] p. 25½cm. (You and your
government. ser. 9.)
Cover-title.
Various paging.
Eighteen addresses delivered Oct. 2, 1934 – Jan. 29, 1935, over a nation-wide network
of the National Broadcasting Company.

865177A. 1. United States—Govt.,   1933– . I. Title. II. Ser.
N. Y. P. L.   January 11, 1937

NN 0058492   NN IU MH-BA WaS

National municipal league.
Trends of government ... broadcasts ... presented by the Committee on civic education by radio of the National advisory council on radio in education and the American polit-
ical science association, in coöperation with the National municipal league. New York city, National municipal league
[*1936] [150] p. 24½cm. (You and your government. ser. ix)
Various pagings.
"Delivered October 2, 1934–January 29, 1935, over a nation-wide network of the National broadcasting company."
1. U. S.—Pol. & govt.—Handbooks, manuals, etc. 2. Local government—U. S. 3. State governments.   1. National advisory council on
radio in education. Com-   mittee on civic education by radio.
II. American political   science association. III. Title.
Library of Congress   JK2408.N35   37-246
———— Copy 2.   JS308.Y6 ser. 9
Copyright A 95759   [5]   (352.073) 353.9

NN 0058493   DLC CLSU MtU OrU

NATIONAL MUNICIPAL LEAGUE
Wanted: municipal relief projects. Reprinted from National municipal review v.24, no.5,
May 1935.
p. 247-48.

NN 0058494   Or

NATIONAL MUNICIPAL LEAGUE.
What happens to city employees [under the council manager plan. New York City,1941].
19 cm. pp.(4).

NN 0058495   MH-PA

VOLUME 407

NATIONAL MUNICIPAL LEAGUE.
　What it is doing.　What other have to say
about it. n.p.,1899.

NN　0058496　MH

₍NATIONAL MUNICIPAL LEAGUE₎
　What the league is doing...report to members
for the months of Jan., Feb., March, April,
1940.　299 Broadway, Author, 1940.
　8 p.

NN　0058497　Or

National municipal league.
　Who's boss?　A story in pictures about the citizen and his
city government, by the National municipal league with Pictorial statistics, inc. ₍New York₎ National municipal league,
1940.
　₍24₎ p.　illus., diagrs.　12½ x 17½ᵐ.
　"Prepared by Miss Miriam Roher ... and Mr. Rudolf Modley."—p. ₍3₎
　"Data sources": p. ₍24₎

　1. Municipal government—U. S.　2. Municipal government by city
manager.　I. Pictorial statistics, inc.　II. Roher, Miriam.　III. Modley,
Rudolf.　IV. Title.
U. S. Off. of educ.　Library　　　　　　　　　　E 41-111
for Library of Congress　　　JS344.C5N36
　　　　　　　　　　　　　　　　₍3₎　　　　　　352.073

NN　0058498　DHEW

National Municipal League.
　Women as campaigners
　　see under　National Conference on Government, Richmond, 1953.

₍National municipal league₎
　The work of the league 1894-1904.　₍Philadelphia₎ National municipal league, 1904.
　20 p.　16ᵐ.

　　　　　　　　　　　　　　　　　5-17907

NN　0058500　DLC MB

JS345
N3
　　National municipal league.
　　　A year's disclosure and development...
　　Phil., 1904.
　　　1 pam.　8°

NN　0058501　DLC

National Municipal League
　see also **Conference for Good City Government.**

National municipal league. Committee on
　a model municipal budget law
　A model municipal budget law. Submit-
ted by the Committee on a model munici-
pal budget law of the National municipal
league: Carl H.Pforzheimer, chairman;
C.E.Rightor, secretary ... New York,
N.Y., National municipal league ₍1928₎
JS　　cover-title,2 p.ℓ.,p.437-445.　24½cm. (In
351　National municipal league. Model laws. ₍1₎)
N27m　"Supplement to the National municipal review,
　　　July, 1928. Vol.　　XVII,no.7."

NN　0058503　NRU OC1 IU OU MiU Or NcD ViU OC1W

National Municipal League. *Committee on a Model State
Medico-legal Investigative System*
　see **Committee on a Model State Medico-legal Investigative System.**

National municipal league. *Committee on a model tax collection law.*
　... A model real property tax collection law; report of the
Committee on a model tax collection law of the National
municipal league: Arnold Frye, chairman. New York, N. Y.,
Published by the National municipal league ₍1935₎
　cover-title, p. ₍289₎–305.　25ᵐ.
　At head of title: Supplement to the National municipal review, May,
1935, vol. XXIV, no. 5.

　1. Taxation—Law.　2. Real property.　I. Frye, Arnold.　II. National
municipal review. Supplement.　III. Title.
　　　　　　　　　　　　　　　　　　　A 35-1903
Title from Brown Univ.　　　HJ3247.N3　Printed by L. C.

NN　0058505　RB PP OC1

**National Municipal League.　Committee on a
Model Tax Collection Law.
　A model real property tax collection law
　　see also under　National Municipal
League.　Committee on a Program of Model Fiscal
Legislation for Local Governments.**

National Municipal League.　Committee on a
　Model Voter Registration System.
　Model voter registration system.　Prepared
by Joseph P. Harris, chairman, and the Committee on a Model Voter Registration System.
4th ed.　New York, National Municipal League,
1954.
　56 p.　tables.

　First ed. issued in 1927 by the League's
Committee on Election Administration.

　NIC OrP CaBViP OrU WaU-L WaU Wa NN
　NNU-W PP MiD ViU CU IU　CLSU ViU-L NBuG N NcD TxU
NN　0058507　NNC-L MtBC OC1 OU MiU IU NRU PPT OCU

National Municipal League. *Committee on a Program of
Model Fiscal Legislation for Local Governments.*
　Model accrual budget law.　A law relating to the administration of current finances of counties and municipalities
and the preparation of budgets.　New York, National Municipal League, 1946.
　xx, 20 p.　22 cm.

　1. Budget.　2. Municipal finance.　I. Title.
　　　　　　　　　　　　　　　　　A 50-2615
Chicago.　Univ. Lib₁.
for Library of Congress　　₍2₎

　MiD MiU IU N
NN　0058508　ICU WaU-L CaBVaU OrPR OrP DPAHO Or TxU

352.1
q₍₎275bo
　　National Municipal League.　Committee on
　　　a Program of Model Fiscal Legisla-
　　　tion for Local Governments.
　　Model bond law.　A law relating to the
incurring of indebtedness and the issuance
of bonds by counties and municipalities.
New York, 1939.
　　34 ℓ.　28 cm.
　　Cover title.
　　"This draft has been prepared by a drafting committee ... is entirely tentative and is

not for general distribution."
　　Vol. consists of mounted printed material.

　　1. Local finance. Law and legislation.
　　2. Municipal bonds.　I. Title.

NN　0058510　N

National Municipal League.　Committee on a
　Program of Model Fiscal Legislation for
　Local Governments.
　　Model bond law
　　　see also under　National Municipal
League.　Committee on Municipal Borrowings.

352.1
qN275
1939
　　National Municipal League.　Committee on a
　　　Program of Model Fiscal Legislation for
　　　Local Governments.
　　Model cash basis budget law.　A law relating
　　to the administration of current finances of
　　counties and municipalities and the preparation
　　of budgets on a cash basis.　₍Preliminary
　　draft₎ rev.₎ New York, National Municipal
　　League, 1939.
　　unpaged.　28 cm.

　　Consists of　　　typewritten and mounted
printed matter.

NN　0058512　N

National Municipal League. *Committee on a Program of
Model Fiscal Legislation for Local Governments.*
　Model cash basis budget law.　A law relating to the administration of current finances of counties and municipalities and the preparation of budgets on a cash basis.　New
York, National Municipal League, 1948.
　xx, 22 p.　22 cm.

　1. Budget.　2. Municipal finance.　I. Title.

HJ9111.N3　　　　352.1　　　　　49-4633*

　NIC IEdS Or OrP OrU WaU-L Wa
NN　0058513　DLC OU PP CU-AL TxU CaBVaU FMU IU MiU

Law
　　National Municipal League.　Committee on a
　　　Program of Model Fiscal Legislation for Local
　　　Governments.　Model cash basis budget law.
　　Kansas.　University.　*Governmental Research Center.*
　　A comparison of the Cash basis law and the Budget law of
Kansas with the Model cash basis budget law. ₍Lawrence₎
1952.

National Municipal League. *Committee on a Program of
Model Fiscal Legislation for Local Governments.*
　A model county and municipal bond law. New York,
National Municipal League, 1953.
　30 p.　22 cm.

　1. Municipal bonds.　I. Title.

　　　　　　　　　　352.1　　　　　54—2255 ‡

Wa
　TxU NIC NBuG NNC NN ViU TU CLSU CaBViP FMU Or OrP
NN　0058515　DLC WaU-L ViU-L CaBVaU PU-L NcD OC1 PPT

National Municipal League. *Committee on a Program of
Model Fiscal Legislation for Local Governments.*
　Model investment of state funds law. New York, National Municipal League, 1954.
　xvi, 22 p.　22 cm.

　1. Investment of public funds—Law and legislation—U. S.—States.
I. Title.
　　　　　　　　　　　　　　　　　58-38177

　NN MtBC CaBVaU Or OrU Wa WaU-L
　ICarbS NIC NcD NBuG TxU N PPT MiD IU CaBViP OC1 PP
NN　0058516　DLC TxU NIC NNC-L CLSU PPPHA NNU-W

National Municipal League. *Committee on a Program of
Model Fiscal Legislation for Local Governments.*
　Model real property tax collection law. 2d ed.　New
York, National Municipal League, 1954.
　xx, 40 p.　22 cm.
　First published in 1935.

　1. Land taxation—U. S.　2. Tax collection—U. S.　I. Title.
　　　　　　　　　　　　　　　　　A 55—3046
Grosvenor Library　　　HJ3247.N3 1954
for Library of Congress　　₍56e3₎

　NBuG CU-AL NNC-L
　TU IU N MiD NcD OCU PPT PSt PP MiU PPPHA OU FU
NN　0058517　NBuG WaU-L MtBC Wa NN DLC CaBVaU Or TxU

National Municipal League.　Committee on a
　Program of Model Fiscal Legislation for Local
　Governments.
　　Model real property tax collection law
　　　see also under　National Municipal
League.　Committee on a Model Tax Collection Law.

VOLUME 407

National municipal league. *Committee on citizens' charter organization.*

... The Cincinnati plan of citizen organization for political activity. New York, N. Y., National municipal league, 1934.

18, [1] p. 25½ᶜᵐ.

At head of title: Report of the Committee on citizens' charter organization of the National municipal league; Henry Bentley, chairman.

"Bibliography on the government of Cincinnati and the city charter movement": p. 18–[19].

1. Cincinnati—Pol. & govt.   I. Bentley, Henry, 1880–   II. Title. III. Title: Report of the Committee on citizens' charter organization of the National municipal league.

Library of Congress   JS740 1934   36–15238
———— Copy 2.
Copyright A 75425   [2]   352.077178

NN   0058519   DLC OC1h OU OEac

National municipal league. *Committee on citizens' charter organization.*

Citizen organization for political activity. 1st ed. 1934, rev. 1941. New York city, National municipal league, ᶜ1941.

48 p. diagr. 19½ᶜᵐ.

On cover: The Cincinnati plan.

"Originally prepared [under title: The Cincinnati plan of citizen organization for political activity] by the National municipal league's Committee on citizens' charter organization, composed of: Henry Bentley [and others]"—Introd.

1. Cincinnati—Pol. & govt.   I. Bentley, Henry, 1880–   II. Title.

Library of Congress   JS740.1941.N3   42–8894
[3]   352.077178

NN   0058520   DLC MiD NN OrP PP OOxM

National municipal league. *Committee on citizens' charter organization.*

Citizen organization for political activity. New York city, National municipal league, 1944.

47 p. diagr. 19½ᶜᵐ.

On cover: The Cincinnati plan.

"Originally prepared [under title: The Cincinnati plan of citizen organization for political activity ... this pamphlet was first published in 1934, revised in 1941 and republished in 1944."—Introd.

1. Cincinnati—Pol. & govt.   I. Title.

Library of Congress   JS740 1944.N3   45–20286

NN   0058521   DLC PP

National Municipal League. *Committee on Citizens' Charter Organization.*

Citizen organization for political activity. 3d ed. New York, ᶜ1949.

32 p. diagr. 20 cm.

On cover: The Cincinnati plan.
First published under title: The Cincinnati plan of citizen organization for political activity.

1. Cincinnati—Pol. & govt.   I. Title.

[JS740 1949.N   ]   352.0771   A 51–5127

Missouri. Univ. Libr.
for Library of Congress   [2]

NN   0058522   MoU IU TxU

National Municipal League. Committee on Citizens' Councils for Constructive Economy.

A citizens' council; why and how? A device to unite civic groups in their common aim to achieve economy in local government without sacrifice of essential services.

= New York. [1933.] (2), 5, (1) pp. 23 cm.

D3545 — T.r. — Municipal government.

NN   0058523   MB NBuG OrU Or

National Municipal League. Committee on Citizens' Councils for Constructive Economy.

Citizens' councils in action. Achievements and possibilities when civic groups unite for constructive economy in government and for the support of essential community services.

= New York. 1933. 20 pp. 23 cm.

D3545 — T.r. — Municipal government.

NN   0058524   MB NBuG Or

352.05 National municipal league--Committee on citizens'
NATM   councils for constructive economy.
        Citizens' councils news bulletin ... v.1, no.1-6;
        Oct.1,1933-June 1,1934.   [New York, 1933-34]
        1v.

        Irregular.
        Mimeographed.
        No more published.

        1. Municipal government--Period.   2. Municipal
        government--U.S.

NN   0058525   IU

National Municipal League. — Committee on Civic Education.

Plan for the promotion of civic education. Philadelphia: the league, 1913. folder. 16°. (National Municipal League. Leaflets. Series 3, no. 3.)

1. Citizenship.—Education for, U. S.   2. Series.
N. Y. P. L.   November 10, 1916.

NN   0058526   NN

JS
358   National Municipal League.   Committee
.N28   on Civil Service.
1923   Employment management in municipal civil
        service, a committee report with comment pro
        and con. Concord,N.H., National Municipal
        League [1923]
        441-513 p.   26 cm.   (National Municipal
        Review, v.xii, no.8, August, 1923)

        1. Municipal officials and employees--U.S.

NN   0058527   MiU

National Municipal League.   Committee on Civil
Service.
        Employment management in the municipal
civil service, a program; report.   [Philadelphia,
1922]
        Pamphlet.
        Cover serves as title-page.

NN   0058528   MH

National Municipal League.   Committee on County
Government.
        Constitutional barriers to improvement in
county government
        see under   Jones, Howard Palfrey.

S
352.008   National Municipal League.   Committee on
qN277c   County Government.
            Model county manager charter.   (Trial
        edition) New York, 1950.
        37ℓ.   28 cm.

        1. County government.   I. Title.

NN   0058530   N IU ViU-L MiU

National municipal league. *Committee on county government.*

A model county manager law submitted by the **Committee** on county government of the National municipal league ... New York, N. Y., National municipal league [ᶜ1930]

2 p. L. p. 565–579. diagrs. 25½ᶜᵐ.

"Supplement to the National municipal review, **August, 1930. vol. XIX, no. 8.**"

"Selected bibliography": p. 578–579.

1. County government.   I. National municipal review. **Supplement.** II. Title.

Library of Congress   JS411.N3   30–30405
———— Copy 2.
Copyright AA 49445   [3]   **352.008**

NN   0058531   DLC NcD OrPR Or OU OC1 ViU IU

National municipal league.   Committee on county government.

Atkinson, Raymond Cumings, 1895–

... Principles of a model county government [by] R. C. Atkinson. With a foreword by Professor John A. Fairlie ... New York, National municipal league, 1933.

National Municipal League. *Committee on Direct Primary.*

A model direct primary election system; report ... prepared by Joseph P. Harris and a committee of the National Municipal League. New York [1951]

46 p. 23 cm.

Bibliographical footnotes.

1. Primaries.   I. Harris, Joseph Pratt, 1896–   II. Title. III. Title: Direct primary election system.

JK2074.N3   324.237   51–4255

ICU TU ODW ViU OrCS OrP OrU Wa WaT WaU-L
NN   0058533   DLC NIC CU VtMiM FU CaBVaU MiD CU-AL

National municipal league. *Committee on election administration.*

A model election administration system, report of the Committee on election administration of the National municipal league, prepared by Joseph P. Harris, secretary ... New York, N. Y., National municipal league [ᶜ1930]

2 p. l., 629–671 p. 25½ᶜᵐ.

"Supplement to the National municipal review, September, 1930. Vol. XIX, no. 9."

1. Elections—U. S.   I. Harris, Joseph Pratt, 1896–   I. National municipal review. Supplement. III. Title.

Library of Congress   JK1080.N36   45–43274
[2]   324.73

N MA IEN IU RPB NRU NNU-W OC1 ODW OU
NN   0058534   DLC CaBVaU Or OrSaW MiU ViU NNC PSt MiD

National municipal league. Committee on election administration.

A model registration system; report of the Committee on election administration of the National municipal league ... New York, National municipal league [1927]

2 p. ℓ., 45–86 p. 24½ᶜᵐ.

"Supplement to the National municipal review January, 1927. Vol.XVI, no.1."
Revised by Dr.Joseph P.Harris. cf.Foreword.
Charles E.Merriam, chairman.

1.Election law--U.S.   I.Harris, Joseph Pratt.
II.Title.
JK2164.A2N27

NN   0058535   MiU IU NN NNU-W

National municipal league. Committee on election administration.

A model registration system; report of the Committee on election administration of the National municipal league, prepared by Joseph P.Harris ... New York, N.Y., National municipal league [1931]

47 p. illus.(forms)   25½ᶜᵐ.

"Supplement to the National municipal review January, 1927. Vol.XVI, no.1; revised and reprinted,February,1931. Charles E.Merriam, chairman.

1.Election law--U.S.   I.Harris, Joseph Pratt.   II. Title.

NN   0058536   MiU OU OC1 NN NRU Or MiD NcD

National municipal league. *Committee on election administration.*

A model registration system; report of the Committee on election administration, prepared by Joseph P. Harris ... for the National municipal league ... 3d rev. ed. ... New York city, National municipal league, ᶜ1939.

73 p. 21½ cm.

1. Voters, Registration of—U. S.   I. Harris, Joseph Pratt, 1896– II. Title.

JK2164.A2N3 1939   324.2420973   40—8758

NN   0058537   DLC PP ViU OU OC1 OrCS PPBMR

VOLUME 407

National Municipal League. Committee on Election Administration.
Model voter registration system

see under

National Municipal League. Committee on a Model Voter Registration System.

JS39 .N32 v.17, no.10
National municipal league. Committee on federal aid to the states.
Federal aid to the states. Report of the Committee on federal aid to the states of the National municipal league, prepared by Austin F. Macdonald ... New York, N.Y., National municipal league [1928.
cover-title. 1 p.l., p.619-659. tables. 25½cm. (Supplement to the National municipal review, October, 1928, vol. XVII, no.10)
1. Bounties. 2. U.S.--Pol. & govt. I. Macdonald, Austin Faulks, 1898- . II. Title. III. Ser.

NN 0058539 ViU MA OClW MH NcD DL LU IEN DHEW

National Municipal League. Committee on Franchises.
... Public regulation of wages, hours and conditions of labor of the employes of public service corporations. Concord, N.H., 1917.
p. 31-40. 25.5 cm.
Caption title.

NN 0058540 DL

National municipal league. Committee on franchises.
[Report of the subcommittee appointed to draft a model street railway franchise ordinance] [New York, 1911] 13 p. 23cm.
Report submitted to Robert Treat Paine, esq., chairman, Franchise committee, National municipal league. Signed and dated: James W. S. Peters, Delos F. Wilcox, subcommittee. New York city, November 9, 1911.

1. Railways, Street—Franchises—U. S.
N. Y. P. L. June 4, 1940

NN 0058541 NN

352.7 N21r
National municipal league. Committee on franchises.
Report ... submitted at the conference for good city government held at Toronto, November, 1913. [Toronto? 1913]
11 p.

1. Franchises. 2. Public utilities—Municipal control.

NN 0058542 IU

National Municipal League. Committee on Franchises.
Suggestions for a model railway franchise see under National Municipal League.

National municipal league. Committee on instruction in municipal government.
Report. Philadelphia, 1901.
32p. 23cm.

1. Municipal Goverement. Study and teaching.

NN 0058544 KAS

National Municipal League. Committee on Instruction in Municipal Government. 9352.073a3
Second report of the Committee on instruction in municipal government in American educational institutions.
= Philadelphia, 1902. (1), 24 pp. 8°.
The first report is out of print.

F2558 — Municipal government. Study and teaching.

NN 0058545 MB

National municipal league. Committee on liquor control legislation.
... Liquor control: principles, model law. A report of the Committee on liquor legislation of the National municipal league. Frank O. Lowden, chairman. Luther Gulick, secretary. New York, N. Y., National municipal league [1934]
34 p. 25½cm.
At head of title: Supplement to the National municipal review, January 1934, volume XXIII, no. 1.
"Selected references": p. 16.
1. Liquor problem—U. S. 2. Liquor laws—U. S. I. Lowden, Frank Orren, 1861- II. National municipal review. Supplement. III. Title.
40-21581

NN 0058546 DLC Or OrU OU OCl

National municipal league. Committee on liquor control legislation.
... Liquor taxes and the bootlegger [by] Paul Studenski ... A report prepared for the Committee on liquor control legislation of the National municipal league; Frank O. Lowden, chairman, Luther Gulick, secretary. New York, N. Y., National municipal league [©1935]
cover-title, 63-79, [1] p. tables, facsim. 25½cm. (Supplement to the National municipal review, January 1935, vol. XXIV, no. 1)
1. Liquor traffic—Taxation. 2. Liquor laws. I. Studensky, Paul, 1887- II. Title.
A 35-860
Title from Iowa State College. Printed by L. C.

NN 0058547 IaAS

National municipal league. Committee on metropolitan government.
... The government of metropolitan areas in the United States, prepared by Paul Studenski with the assistance of the Committee on metropolitan government ... New York, National municipal league [©1930]
403, [1] p. tables (part fold.) 23½ cm.
1. Local government—U. S. 2. Cities and towns—U. S. I. Studensky, Paul, 1887- II. Title. III. Title: Metropolitan areas in the United States.
JS331.N3 352.073 30—31097

OrPR CaBVaU OrU OrCS
NjP Wa NN WaU MH ViU ViU-L OOxM OO MiU OU NcD MH-L
NN 0058548 DLC OrPS WaS GU MB ICRL NIC ICU NBuU-L

National municipal league - Committee on municipal borrowings.
A model bond law ... N.Y. The League, 1927.
pp.135-150,tables,c.

NN 0058549 CaBViP

National Municipal League. Committee on Municipal Borrowings.
A model bond law, submitted by the Committee on Municipal Borrowings of the National Municipal League, Mr. Carl H. Pforzheimer, chairman. New York: National Municipal League[, 1928?]. p. 135-150. 8°.

388733A. 1. Municipal bonds.
N. Y. P. L. December 28, 1928

NN 0058550 NN MH

National Municipal League. Committee on Municipal Borrowings.
A model bond law, submitted by the Committee on Municipal Borrowings of the National Municipal League, Mr. Carl H. Pforzheimer, chairman. Second edition. New York, N. Y.: National Municipal League, 1929. 20 p. incl. tables. 25½cm.

827154A. 1. Bonds, Government—Jurisp.—U. S.
N. Y. P. L. June 25, 1936

NN 0058551 NN ViU-L MH IU OCl OU NcD N DHEW NRU

National Municipal League. Committee on Municipal Borrowings.
A model bond law
see also under National Municipal League. Committee on a Program of Model Fiscal Legislation for Local Governments.

NATIONAL MUNICIPAL LEAGUE - Committee on Municipal Budgets and Accounting.
Report. Springfield,Mass.,1916.
pp.(8). Tables (2 folded).

NN 0058553 MH-PA

National municipal league. Committee on municipal program.
The commission manager plan, city government, prepared by Committee on municipal program, National municipal league, March 15, 1916; constructed by Ralph D. Kern ... Cleveland, Distributed by Committee of fifteen, investigating the city manager plan for Cleveland, ©1917.
sheet. 37 x 24½cm.
1. Municipal government by city manager. I. Kern, Ralph Donald. II. Title.
Library of Congress JS344.C5N3 17-7542

NN 0058554 DLC OrU OCl NN

National Municipal League. Committee on Municipal Program.
Model city charter & municipal home rule; tentative drafts of the sections dealing with the council, city manager, civil service and efficiency, initiative, referendum, recall, electoral provisions and constitutional amendments, as prepared by the Committee on Municipal Program of the National Municipal League and presented at the twentieth annual meeting of the National Municipal League held at Baltimore, November 20, 1914, and revised at the meeting of the committee held in New York, April 8 and 9, 1915. [Philadelphia?] 1915. 31 p. 8°.
Cover-title.

1. Municipal government.
N. Y. P. L. August 27, 1926

NN 0058555 NN

National municipal league. Committee on municipal program.
A model city charter and municipal home rule as prepared by the Committee on municipal program of the National municipal league. Philadelphia, 1916.
59 p. 23 cm.
On cover: Final edition, March 15, 1916.

1. Municipal charters—U. S. I. Title.
JS354.N3 1916 16—21830

ODW NcD OrU WaS Or
NN 0058556 DLC CaBViP NN KEmT ICJ MB OO MiU OU

JS345 1921 .N27
NATIONAL MUNICIPAL LEAGUE. Committee on municipal program.
A model city charter,with home rule provisions recommended for state constitutions;prepared by the Committee on municipal programme of the National municipal league. Final edition,January, 1921. New York,National municipal league,[1921,
62 p. 23cm.

1.Municipal government--U.S. 2.Charters.

NN 0058557 ICU NcD

National municipal league. Committee on municipal program.
A model city charter, with home rule provisions recommended for state constitutions; prepared by the Committee on municipal programme of the National municipal league. Final edition, March, 1922. New York, National municipal league [1922]
62 p. 23cm.

1. Municipal government—U. S. 2. Charters. I. Title.
23—14276
Library of Congress JS345.N3 1922

NN 0058558 DLC WaU OrPR MtU WaS OClW IU NN ODW MiU

VOLUME 407

National Municipal League. Committee on Municipal program.
A Model City Charter with Home Rule Provisions recommended for State Constitutions; prepared by the Committee on Municipal Programme. Final ed. New York,1923.
62 p.

NN 0058559 MH-L

National municipal league--Committee on municipal program.
A model city charter with home rule provisions recommended for state constitutions. Rev. ed., 1927. New York [1927]
77p.

NN 0058560 IU ODW OCl OClh Or IdU WaS PSt NcD ViU

National municipal league. *Committee on municipal program.*
A model city charter, with home rule provisions recommended for state constitutions, prepared by the Committee on municipal program of the National municipal league. Rev. ed., 1933. New York, National municipal league [1933]
1 p. l., 106 p. 23cm.

1. Municipal government—U. S. 2. Charters. I. Title.
Library of Congress JS354.N3 1933 33—18254
——— Copy 2.
Copyright A 62906 [3] 352.073

OClW IU WaU OCl
NN 0058561 DLC ViU NIC MoU NN NcD WaS OrPR OrU Or

352 N213m3 National municipal league--Committee on municipal program.
Municipal home rule and a model city charter. Tentative of the sections dealing with the constitutional provisions, the council, nominations and elections, preferential ballot, recall, initiative, referendum, proportional representation, city manager, administrative departments, civil service board, financial provisions and franchises ... Presented at the twentieth annual meeting of the National municipal league held at Baltimore, November 20, 1914, and rev. at the meeting of the Committee held in New York, April 8 and 9, 1915, and on Sept. 14, 1915. 3d ed. [New York] 1915.
cover-title, 59p.

NN 0058563 IU OCU MH OCl

National Municipal League. — Committee on Municipal Program.
Tentative outline. The commission manager plan, city government. Prepared by Committee on Municipal Program, National Municipal League, December 1st., 1914. Constructed by Le Roy Hodges... Philadelphia: National Municipal League, 1914. 1 chart, folded, 8°. (National Municipal League. City manager chart. no. 1.)
Size within border: →19⅝ × ↑13⅞ in.

1. Municipal government by city manager. 2. Hodges, Le Roy.
N. Y. P. L. June 20, 1916.

NN 0058564 NN Or

National municipal league. *Committee on municipal reference libraries.*
Report.
[Baltimore?
v. 23½cm.
: Reprinted from National municipal review.
Chairman of committee: H. E. Flack.

1. Municipal reference libraries. I. Flack, Horace Edgar, 1879–
CA 15-1306 Unrev'd
Library of Congress Z675.M9N2

NN 0058565 DLC

National municipal league. *Committee on pensions.*
... Pensions in public employment; report of the Committee on pensions, prepared by Paul Studensky ...
(*In* National municipal review. Concord, N. H., April 1922. 25½cm. vol. XI, no. 4, total no. 70, p. 97–124)
Cover-title.
Caption title: ... Report of the Pension committee of the National municipal league, prepared by Paul Studensky, director of the Bureau of state research of the New Jersey state Chamber of commerce.
Brief bibliography on pensions: p. 124.

1. Civil service pensions—U. S. I. Studenski, Paul, 1887–
22—15943
Library of Congress JS39.N3 vol. XI, no. 4
——— 2d set. [a41b1]
Exception

NN 0058566 DLC NN MiU

National Municipal League. Committee on Play and Recreation Administration.
Standards of play and recreation administration; report of the Committee on Play and Recreation Administration of the National Municipal League, prepared by Professor Jay B. Nash ... New York[, 1931]. 485–506 p. diagrs., tables. 4°.
Cover-title.
"Supplement to the National Municipal review, July, 1931. v. xx, no. 7."

1. Parks—U. S. 2. Playgrounds—U. S. I. Nash, Jay Bryan, 1886–
N. Y. P. L. December 23, 1931

NN 0058567 NN ViU NNU-W NcD Or IU

National Municipal League. Committee on Public Utilities.
...A correct public policy toward the street railway problem; a report of the National Municipal League Committee on Public Utilities, in which all previous reports are summarized and the unsolved elements of the problems listed. Concord, N. H. [1920.] p. 251–267. 4°. (National Municipal League. Technical pamphlets. no. 4.)
Suppl. National municipal review. v. 9, no. 4.

1. Railways (Street).—Government control, U. S. 2. Series.
N. Y. P. L. October 6, 1924

NN 0058568 NN CtY MH NcU IU OO

National municipal league. *Committee on revision of the Model city charter.*
Model city charter, prepared by Committee on revision of the Model city charter. 5th ed. (complete revision) New York city, National municipal league, 1941.
xxxi, 141 p. 21½ cm.
Introduction signed: Committee on style and draft, Arnold Frye, chairman.
"First printing."
Previous editions by Committee on municipal program.

1. Municipal government—U. S. 2. Charters. I. Title.
JS354.N3 1941 352.002 43—3051

CaBViP NcD MiD TU
ViU MH PWcS MtU NcD CaBVaU TxU N OU WaU-L OCl ViU-L
NN 0058569 DLC FTaSU TxU GU-L CU OrP Wa WaS OrPR

National municipal league. *Committee on revision of the Model city charter.*
Model city charter, prepared by Committee on revision of the Model city charter. 5th ed. (complete revision) *New York city, National municipal league[1944]
xxxi, 141 p. 21½cm.
*2d printing 1944.
Introduction signed: Committee on style and draft, Arnold Frye, chairman.
Previous editions by Committee on municipal program

NN 0058570 ViU

S 352.002 N277 National municipal league. Committee on revision of the Model city charter.
Model city charter ... 5th ed. ... (complete revision) ... N.Y. [1947]
141 p. 22cm.
Introduction signed: Committee on style and draft, Arnold Frye, chairman.

1. Municipal government. U.S. 2. Charters. I. Title.

NN 0058571 N TxU

S 352.002 N277a2 National municipal league. Committee on revision of the Model city charter.
Model city charter ... 5th ed. ... (Complete revision) ... N. Y. [1948]
141 p. 22 cm.
Introd. signed: Committee on style and draft, Arnold Frye, chairman.

1. Municipal government. U.S. 2. Charters. I. Title.

NN 0058572 N OU MtBC

National Municipal League. Committee on Sources of Revenue.
Minor highway privileges as a source of city revenue; a report of the National Municipal League, Committee on Sources of Revenue... New York [1923]. p. 273–282. 4°. (National Municipal League. Technical pamphlets.)
Suppl. National municipal review, v. 12, no. 5.

1. Easements. 2. Municipal finance. 3. Series.
N. Y. P. L. August 30, 1924

NN 0058573 NN MH IU N NcD-L

National municipal league. Committee on sources of revenue.
... Special assessments. New York, 1922.
1. p. l., p. 43-58.. 26 cm. (National municipal review, v. 11, no. 2)
Bibliography: p. 58.
1. Special assessments.

NN 0058574 CU

National Municipal League. Committee on Sources of Revenue.
Special assessments; a means of financing municipal improvements, by the Committee on Sources of Revenue, National Municipal League... New York [1923]. 21 p. incl. plans. 2. ed. 4°. (National Municipal League. Technical pamphlets. no. 15.)

1. Special assessments. 2. Series.
N. Y. P. L. August 30, 1924

NN 0058575 NN OClW MH IU

National Municipal League. Committee on Sources of Revenue.
Special assessments; a means of financing municipal improvements, by the Committee on Sources of Revenue, National Municipal League. Third edition. New York City, 1929. 20 p. illus. (plans.) 25cm. (National Municipal League. Technical pamphlets. [no. 15])
"Brief bibliography and references on special assessments," p. 20.

1. Special assessments—U. S., 1929. I. Ser.
N. Y. P. L. August 26, 1935

NN 0058576 NN NRU NcD PSt MH LU ViU-L

National Municipal League. Committee on State Government.
A model state constitution, prepared by the Committee on State Government of the National Municipal League. Reprinted with explanatory articles. New York [192–?]. 43 p. 4°.

1. Constitutions, U. S.: Indiv. states.
N. Y. P. L. August 30, 1924

NN 0058577 NN NcD OU NcU

National Municipal League. Committee on state government.
A model state constitution; prepared by the Committee on State Government of the National Municipal League. New York City: National Municipal League[, 1921]. 16 p. 25½cm.

734781A. 1. Constitutions, State.
N. Y. P. L. November 7, 1934

NN 0058578 NN

VOLUME 407

National municipal league. *Committee on state government.*
A model state constitution, prepared by the Committee on state government of the National municipal league. Reprinted with explanatory articles. New York, National municipal league ₍1924₎
43 p. 25½ᶜᵐ.
CONTENTS.— The model state constitution.— Explanatory articles: The legislature, by H. W. Dodds. The executive, by J. A. Fairlie. The budget, by A. E. Buck. The judiciary, by W. F. Dodd. Counties, by R. S. Childs.

1. Constitutions, State. 2. State governments. I. Title.

A 26–713

Title from Vassar College.   Printed by L. C.

NN   0058579   NPV MH MeB PP MtU IdU OrU OrPR OO OClW

National municipal league. *Committee on state government.*
A model state constitution, prepared by the Committee on state government of the National municipal league. Rev. ed., March, 1933, with explanatory articles. New York city, National municipal league ₍ᶜ1933₎
43 p. 25½ᶜᵐ.
CONTENTS.—I. The model state constitution.—II. Explanatory articles: The legislature, by H. W. Dodds. The executive, by J. A. Fairlie. The budget, by A. E. Buck. The judiciary by W. F. Dodd. Counties, by R. S. Childs.

1. Constitutions, State—U. S. 2. State governments.   I. Title.
                    33–11571
Library of Congress   JK2417.N33 1933
—— Copy 2.
Copyright A 61343   ₍3₎   342

     TU OOxM OCl
NN   0058580   DLC Or OrU OrCS IdU WaS NcD PP NcD-L

National municipal league. Committee on state government.
A model state constitution, prepared by the committee on state government of the National municipal league.
New York, National municipal league, ₍ᶜ1936₎
43, ₍1₎ p.

NN   0058581   OU

---

342   National Municipal League. Committee on
qN277a   State Government.
Model state constitution; **first complete
preliminary draft of the fourth rev. ed.**
₍New York, National Municipal League₎ 1940.
45 p. 29 cm.
Reproduced from typewritten copy.

1. Constitutions. State. U.S. 2. State
governments. I. Title.

NN   0058582   N

National municipal league. *Committee on state government.*
Model state constitution, with explanatory articles. Prepared by Committee on state government. 4th ed. (complete revision) New York city, National municipal league, 1941.
viii, 53 p. 22½ᶜᵐ.

1. Constitutions, State—U. S. 2. State governments.   I. Title.
                    42–8077
Library of Congress   JK2417.N33 1941
            ₍4₎   342

    ICU ViU Or OU OClW OOxM IdU
NN   0058583   DLC NcD NIC TU IU OrP OrPR WaS MH NN

**National municipal league. Committee on state
government.**
Model state constitution, with explanatory
articles. 4th ed., complete revision—1941,
partial revision—1946. N. Y. ₍The Author₎
1946.
51 p., illus.

NN   0058584   MiD N MH

National Municipal League. *Committee on State Government.*
Model state constitution, with explanatory articles. 5th ed., rev. New York, 1948.
vi, 57 p. 23 cm.

1. Constitutions, State—U. S. 2. State governments.   I. Title.

JK2417.N33 1948   342   49–4928*

    OCl CaBVaU MoSW CU MtBC OrPR WaT MiU   KU-L
    NcD N NNC NIC ViU TxU ICU PPT PU PWcS Mi WaS PU-L
NN   0058585   DLC NcU FMU TU NN CLSU MH-L Or NcRS MsU

National municipal league. *Committee on state government.*
Progress report on a model state constitution presented by the Committee on state government for the approval of members of the National municipal league at Chicago, November 18, 1921. Subject to further amendment and improvement in draftsmanship. New York, National municipal league ₍1921?₎
16 p. 24½ᶜᵐ.
1. Constitutions, State.

NN   0058586   MiU

**National municipal league. Committee on
state government.
Proposals for model state constitution.**
N.p. 1920.
p. 711–716. 26cm.

Article taken from National Municipal
Review, November 1920.

NN   0058587   OU

National municipal league. *Committee on the Model
city charter*
      see
National municipal league. *Committee on revision of the
Model city charter.*

National Municipal League. Committee on Uniform Municipal Accounting and Statistics.
Report. Edward M. Hartwell, Chairman.
  — Philadelphia. 1901. 18 pp. 8°.
     Reprinted from Uniform municipal accounting and statistics ₍9352.1a3₎.
                         5568.133

H358 — Municipal statistics. — Municipal finance.

NN   0058589   MB ICJ DLC

National municipal league. *Committee on uniform municipal accounting and statistics.*
... Uniform municipal accounting and statistics; read at the Detroit Conference for good city government, by Dr. Edward M. Hartwell ... chairman ... Philadelphia, Office of the secretary, 1903.
cover-title, 21 p. 23ᶜᵐ. (National municipal league. Publications; pamphlet no. 10)
Caption title: Report of the Committee ...

1. Statistics. 2. Municipal finance—U. S.—Accounting.   I. Hartwell, Edward Mussey, 1850–
                       8–16789
Library of Congress   HJ9771.N3

NN   0058590   DLC ICJ OClWHi NN MB

National Municipal League. Conference Committee
on the Merit System
    see   Conference Committee on the Merit
System.

National municipal league. *Consultant service*
      see
National municipal league. *Office of consultant service.*

NATIONAL MUNICIPAL LEAGUE – Executive committee.
   Address. n.p., 1897.

NN   0058593   MH

National municipal league. *Executive committee.*
Report of Horace E. Deming, chairman of the Executive committee of the National municipal league, presented at Pittsburgh, November 16, 1908 ... ₍Pittsburgh?₎ 1909₎
cover-title, 7 p. 23ᶜᵐ.
Reprinted from the Proceedings of the Pittsburgh meeting.

1. Deming, Horace Edward, 1850–
                      10–7356
Library of Congress   JS302.N6 1908

NN   0058594   DLC

National Municipal League. Franchise Committee
   see   National Municipal League. Committee
on Franchises.

National municipal league. *Model city charter committee*
      see
National municipal league. *Committee on revision of the
Model city charter.*

352.1   National municipal league--Municipal consultant
N212bw   service.
     A brief financial and administrative survey of
     the city of Winter Park, Florida ... ₍New York,
     1934₎
     24 l.

     Caption title.
     Mimeographed.

NN   0058597   IU MH

National Municipal League. Municipal Consultant service.
   A brief financial and administrative survey
of the city of Yonkers, New York, November and
December, 1933. By the Municipal Consultant
Service of the National Municipal League.
New York City, ₍1933?₎.

   Manifold copy. 28 cm. ff.18, (1),7,7,(1).
Folded tables.
   Paper cover serves as title-page.

NN   0058598   MH

352.1   National municipal league--Municipal consultant
N212bg   service.
     A brief financial and administrative survey of
     the town of Greenburgh, N.Y. ... ₍New York, 1934₎
     12 numb.l. tables.

     Caption title.
     Mimeographed.

     1. Finance--Greenburgh, N.Y.

NN   0058599   IU MiU

352.1   National municipal league--Municipal consultant
N212bh   service.
     A brief financial and administrative survey of
     the town of Harrison, N.Y.   ₍New York, 1934₎
     11 numb.l. tables.
     Thomas H. Reed, Director.
     Caption title.
     Mimeographed.

NN   0058600   IU MH MiU

VOLUME 407

National Municipal League. Municipal consultant service
A brief financial and administrative survey
of the town of Kearny, New Jersey. New York
City, National Municipal League, Municipal Consultant Service, 1934.

Manifold copy. 28 cm. ff. (1), 20, (2).
Folded tables.
At head of title: Town council, town of Kearny.

NN 0058601 MH MiU

352.1   National municipal league--Municipal consultant
N212bm   service.
A brief financial and administrative survey of
the town of Mount Pleasant, N.Y. ₍New York,
1934₎
14 numb.l. tables.

Caption title.
Mimeographed.

NN 0058602 IU MH

352.1   National municipal league--Municial consultant
N212bn   service.
A brief financial and administrative survey of
the township of North Bergen, New Jersey …
₍New York, 1934₎
38 numb.l., 2 l., tables (part fold.)

Caption title.
Mimeographed.

1. Finance--North Bergen, N.J.   2. North Bergen,
N.J.--Pol. and govt.

NN 0058603 IU

HJ   National Municipal League. Municipal consultant
9289   Service.
.C83   Financial and administrative survey of the
N28   town of Cortlandt, New York. ₍New York, 1934₎
9 l.   29 cm.
Caption title.
Thomas H. Reed, Director.

1. Finance, Local--Cortlandt, N.Y.

NN 0058604 MiU MH IU

National Municipal League. Municipal Consultant
Service.
The government of Nassau County
see under   National Municipal League.
Office of Consultant Service.

National Municipal League. Municipal Consultant Service.
₍Reports.
no. 1–

New York, 1934   29cm.
nos.
Reproduced from typewritten copy.

Contents:
₍no. 1₎ Financial and administrative survey of the town of Cortlandt, New York. ₍1934₎
₍no. 2₎ A brief financial and administrative survey of the town of Greenburgh, N. Y.
₍1934₎
₍no. 3₎ A brief financial and administrative survey of the town of Harrison, N. Y.
₍1934₎
₍no. 4₎ …A brief financial and administrative survey of the town of Kearny, New
Jersey. ₍1934₎
₍no. 5₎ The fiscal affairs of Lehigh County; a report of the committee of fifty on
taxation of the Allentown Chamber of Commerce. ₍1934₎

₍no. 6₎ A brief financial and administrative survey of the town of Mount Pleasant, N. Y.
₍1934₎
₍no. 7₎ A survey of the financial condition of the city of Mount Vernon, N. Y. ...
₍1934₎
₍no. 8₎ A brief financial and administrative survey of the township of North Bergen,
New Jersey. ₍1934₎
₍no. 9₎ A brief financial and administrative survey of the city of Winter Park, Florida.
₍1934₎
₍no. 10₎ A brief financial and administrative survey of the city of Yonkers, November
and December, 1933. ₍1934₎
₍no. 11₎ Report on the financial condition of the city of Yonkers, New York. ₍1934₎

NN 0058608   NN IU

352.1   National municipal league--Municipal consultant
N212sm   service.
A survey of the financial condition of the city
of Mount Vernon, N.Y., including the Board of edu-
cation …   ₍New York, 1934₎
21, 4 numb.l. tables.
Thomas H. Reed, Director.
Caption title.
Mimeographed.
"Supplementary report …": 4 leaves at end.

1. Finance--Mount Vernon, N.Y.

NN 0058609   IU MiU

National Municipal League. Municipal Consultant
Service
see also   National Municipal League.
Office of Consultant Service.

National municipal league. New York state
committee.
Constitutional history of New York state
see under title

National municipal league. *New York state committee.*
What's in the proposed constitution? A summary of the
amendments submitted by the New York state constitutional
convention of 1938. This summary has been prepared by a
technical committee of the Special committee on the New York
state constitution. The Special committee was created by the
New York state committee of the National municipal league.
New York, N. Y., National municipal league ₍1938₎
34, ₍2₎ p. 25½ᶜᵐ.
1. New York (State) Constitution.   ɪ. New York (State) Constitutional convention, 1938.   ɪɪ. Title.
                                                              38–35759
Library of Congress   JK3425.1938.N3
——— ——— Copy 2.
Copyright A 122763   ₍5₎   342.747

NN 0058612   DLC

National Municipal League. Office of Consultant
Service.
A brief financial and administrative survey
of the town of Greenburgh, N. Y.
see under   National Municipal League.
Municipal Service.
   Consultant

National Municipal League. Office of Consultant
Service.
A brief financial and administrative survey
of the town of Harrison, N. Y.
see under   National Municipal League.
Municipal Consultant Service.

National Municipal League. Office of Consultant
Service.
A brief financial and administrative survey
of the town of Kearny, New Jersey
see under   National Municipal League.
Municipal Consultant Service.

National Municipal League. Office of consultant
service.
A brief financial survey of the borough of
Dumont, New Jersey. By the Consultant Service of
the National Municipal League. New York City,
1935.

Manifold copy. 28 cm. ff. 16. Tables
(part folded).
Paper cover serves as title-page.

NN 0058616   MH

National Municipal League. Office of consultant
service.
A brief financial survey of the township of
Teaneck, New Jersey. By the Consultant Service
of the National Municipal League. New York
City, 1935.

Manifold copy. 28.5 cm. ff. 16. Tables
(part folded).
Paper cover serves as title-page.

NN 0058617   MH

National Municipal League. Office of Consultant
Service.
Financial and administrative survey of the
town of Cortlandt, N. Y.
see under   National Municipal League.
Municipal Consultant Service.

JS738   National municipal league. Office of
.R4   consultant service.
Reed, Thomas Harrison, 1881–
The government of Cincinnati, 1924–1944, an appraisal, by
Thomas H. Reed and Doris D. Reed for the Consultant service
of the National municipal league, New York. A report to the
Stephen H. Wilder foundation, Public affairs division, Cincin-
nati. Cincinnati, O., The Stephen H. Wilder foundation, 1944.

National Municipal League. Office of Consultant
Service.
The government of Hoboken
see under   Reed, Thomas Harrison,
1881–

S352.0747245
N277   National municipal league. Office of consultant service.
The government of Nassau County, a report made to the Board of supervisors ...
Mineola, N.Y., 1934.
75 p. 4 fold. maps, diagrs, tables.
26 cm.

1. Nassau County, N.Y. Politics and
government.   ɪ. Title.

NN 0058621   N MiU NjP IU NcD NJQ

National municipal league. Office of consultant service
The governments of Atlanta and Fulton county, Georgia;
a report of a complete administrative and financial survey of
the several departments and activities of the city of Atlanta
and Fulton county, to the Board of commissioners of roads and
revenues of Fulton county, the mayor and general council of
the city of Atlanta, the Atlanta chamber of commerce, by the
Consultant service of the National municipal league, Thomas
H. Reed, director ... February 5, 1938. ₍Atlanta₎ The Atlanta
chamber of commerce ₍1938₎
2 v. in 1. illus. (maps) tables, diagrs. 27½ᶜᵐ.

Cover-title.
Reproduced from type-written copy.

1. Atlanta—Pol. & govt. 2. Fulton co., Ga.—Pol. & govt.   ɪ. Reed,
Thomas Harrison, 1881–   ɪɪ. Atlanta. Chamber of commerce. ɪɪɪ.
Title.
                                                              41–20092
Library of Congress   JS552.N3
                              ₍2₎   352.0758

NN 0058623   DLC CtY ViU

National municipal league. *Office of consultant service.*
The governments of Atlanta and Fulton county, Georgia; a
summary of the report of the administrative and financial survey of the several departments and activities of the city of
Atlanta and Fulton county to the Board of commissioners of
roads and revenues of Fulton county, the mayor and General
council of the city of Atlanta, the Atlanta chamber of commerce, by the Consultant service of the National municipal
league, Thomas H. Reed, director ... ₍Atlanta₎ The Atlanta
chamber of commerce, 1938.
cover-title, 4 p. l., 161 p. illus. (maps) diagrs. 27½ᶜᵐ.

Continued in next column

VOLUME 407

Continued from preceding column

Reproduced from type-written copy.
"Errata" slip attached to 3d prelim. leaf.

1. Atlanta—Pol. & govt. 2. Fulton co., Ga.—Pol. & govt. I. Reed,
Thomas Harrison, 1881– II. Atlanta. Chamber of commerce. III.
Title.

Library of Congress   JS552.N33   42–2562
     [2]   352.0758

NN   0058625   DLC WU NcD

National Municipal League. Office of Consultant
Service.
The organization of the Cleveland city hospital
    see under   Reed, Thomas Harrison,
1881–

Fine Arti
NAC   National Municipal League. Office of Consul-
7654   tant Service.
B87   A report of a brief survey of the park and
N27   recreation activities of the Town of Brookline,
     Massachusetts, by the Consultant Service of the
     National Municipal League. Prepared and pub-
     lished under the sponsorship of Brookline Tax-
     payers' Association. [New York?] 1937.
     12 p. 28cm.
     1. Recreation—Economic aspects—Brookline,
Mass. I. Brookline Taxpayers' Association.

NN   0058627   NIC MH

National Municipal League. Office of Consultant
Service.
Report of a survey of the town and borough
of Wallingford, Conn. ...
    see under   Reed, Thomas Harrison,
1881–

JJ   National Municipal League. Office of Consultant
9289   Service.
.Y6   Report on the financial condition of the city
N28   of Yonkers, New York. [New York, 1934]
     23,[7] ℓ. tables(part.fold.) 31 cm.
     Caption title.
     Thomas H. Reed, Director.

     1.Finance,Public—Yonkers,N.Y.

NN   0058629   MiU MH

JS565   National municipal league. Office of con-
.2   sultant service.
.A8R4   **Reed, Thomas Harrison,** 1881–
     ... Report to the citizens; a survey of the government of the
     city of Augusta, Georgia, by Thomas H. Reed and Doris D.
     Reed for the Consultant service of the National municipal
     league. Augusta, Ga., Augusta citizens union [1945]

National municipal league. Office of consultant
service
Special financial and operating report, 1946.
to 1951 [for Cleveland, Ohio]
n.p. [1945]
5 numb. l.

NN   0058631   OCl

National municipal league. Office of consultant
service.
Survey of principal administrative departments of the city of White Plains, New York;
field work completed 1939, report submitted February 28,1940. New York [1940]
1 v.(loose-leaf) diagrs.,tables. 28 cm.

    1.White Plains,N.Y.—Pol.& govt.

NN   0058632   MiU OrPR MH

National Municipal League. Office of Consultant
Service.
A survey of the financial condition of the city
of Mount Vernon, N. Y.
    see under   National Municipal League.
Municipal Consultant Service.

National municipal league. Office of consultant service.
Survey of the government of Bar Harbor, Maine, submitted
January 1939. New York city: National municipal league [1939]
79 p. incl. charts, tables. 29cm.

23599B.   1. Bar Harbor, Me.—   Govt.
N. Y. P. L.   December 15, 1939

NN   0058634   NN MiU MH MWelC

National Munucipal League. Office of Consultant
Service
    see also   National Municipal League.
Municipal Consultant Service.

National Municipal League. Special Committee on
Civil Service
    see   National Municipal League. Committee
on Civil Service.

National municipal league. *Survey committee.*
Report of the Survey committee to the National municipal league; a survey of the league's activities and
opportunities. Recommendations for extending its use-
fulness. Report made at the annual meeting in New
York, June 5, 1918. Philadelphia, Pa. [1918]
    1 p. l., 35 p. 23ᶜᵐ.
    Signed: The Survey committee, W. B. Munro, Richard S. Childs, Lent
D. Upson, George C. Sikes, Mayo Fesler, chairman.

    1. National municipal league.   I. Fesler, Mayo. II. Title.

Library of Congress   JS302.N62 1918   19–4353

NN   0058637   DLC DL OrU NN OU OO

The NATIONAL municipal league and the [commit]
tee of ten. n.p.,1897.

NN   0058638   MH

The **National** municipal policy.
Washington, American Municipal Association.
    v. 28 cm. annual.

    1. Municipal government—U. S.—Yearbooks.   I. American
Municipal Association.

    JS301.N33   60–41548 rev ‡

NN   0058639   DLC IU NBuG Or GU NIC PBL NN

National municipal review
    see
National civic review.

NN   0058641   MiD

National Munitions Control Board
    see   U.S. National Munitions Control
Board.

National museum, Athens
    see
Athens. Ethnikon archaiologikon mouseion.

National Museum, *Bangkok*
   see   **Bangkok, Thailand. National Museum.**

National museum, Copenhagen.
    SEE
Copenhagen. Nationalmuseet

National Museum (Denmark)
   see
Copenhagen. Nationalmuseet.

National museum, Dublin
    see   Dublin. National Museum of Ireland.

National Museum, *Ljubljana*
   see
Ljubljana. Narodni muzej.

National museum, Naples
    SEE
Naples. Museo nazionale

National museum, Rome
    SEE
Rome. Museo nazionale romano

National Museum, Washington, D.C.
    see   U.S. National Museum.

The **National** museum and weekly **gazette of discoveries,**
natural sciences, and the arts. v. 1, no. 1–16; Nov. 13, 1813–
Mar. 12, 1814. [Baltimore, C. M. Mann]
    (American periodical series: 1800–1825. 149)
    Microfilm copy (positive) made in 1950 by University Microfilms,
Ann Arbor, Mich.
    Collation of the original, as determined from the film: 8, 128 p.
    Title varies slightly.

    1. Science—Period.   (Series: American periodical series: 1800–
1850. 149)

Microfilm 01104 no. 149 AP   Mic 57–5101

NN   0058652   DLC ViU ICRL NN

VOLUME 407

National museum for Jewish ceremonial objects.
[n. p. , 19--]
   see under   National Federation of Temple
Sisterhoods.

National Museum of Anthropology, Mexico
      see   Mexico (City) **Museo Nacional de
Antropología.**

National Museum of Antiquities of Scotland, *Edinburgh*
         see
      **Edinburgh.   National Museum of Antiquities of Scot-
      land.**

National museum of Arab art, Cairo
   see   Cairo. Mathaf-al-Fann al-Islami.

National Museum of Archaeology, History, and
   Ethnology, Mexico
         see   Mexico (City) Museo Nacional de
Arqueología, Historia y Etnografía.

National Museum of Canada
      see   Canada. National Museum, Ottawa.

T180
.W45   National museum of engineering and industry.
1924   National museum of engineering and industry.
         To be under the direction of the Smithsonian
         institution, Washington, D. C. ...
         New York City, Engineering societies building,
         1924.
            24 p. incl. fold. pl. illus. 25½cm.

NN   0058659   DLC NN

T180
.W45   National museum of engineering and industry.
1925   National museum of engineering and industry
         (incorporated 1924) To be under the direction
         of the Smithsonian institution, Washington, D.C.
         ... New York City, Engineering societies build-
         ing, 1925.
            24 p. incl. fold. pl. illus. 25½cm.

            Date on cover: 1924.

NN   0058660   DLC NNC

T180   National museum of engineering and industry.
.W45
1930   **U. S.** *Congress. Senate. Committee on education and labor.*
            To establish a commission on a national museum of engineer-
         ing and industry. Hearing before a subcommittee of the Com-
         mittee on education and labor, United States Senate, Seventy-
         first Congress, second session, on S. 454, a bill to establish a
         commission to be known as a commission on a national museum
         of engineering and industry. May 27, 1930 ... Washington,
         U. S. Govt. print. off., 1930.

National museum of Ethnology, Leiden.
      see   Leyden. Rijksmuseum voor Volken-
kunde.

National Museum of History, Culture and Art,
   T'ai-pei
      see   Pei-ching li shih po wu huan.

National museum of Ireland, Dublin
      see   Dublin. National museum of Ireland.

National museum of Japan
      see   Tōkyō Kokuritsu Hakubutsukan.

National Museum of Korea, *Seoul*
         see
      Kungnip Pangmulgwan, *Seoul, Korea.*

National Museum of Modern Art, *Tokyo*
         see
      Kokuritsu Kindai Bijutsukan, *Tokyo.*

National museum of science and art, Dublin
      see   Dublin. National museum of Ireland.

National Museum of Southern Rhodesia, *Bulawayo*
         see
      **Bulawayo, Southern Rhodesia. National Museum of
      Southern Rhodesia.**

National museum of the history of science, *Leyden*
      see   Leyden. Rijksmuseum voor de
Geschiedenis der natuurwetenschappen.

National museum of Victoria.

         see

**Victoria, Australia. Public library, museums, and
   national gallery, Melbourne Museum.**

National museum of Wales, Cardiff

         see

Cardiff, Wales. National museum of Wales.

National Music Camp.
   Complete programs.

   Interlochen, Mich.
      v. illus. 23 cm.

      1. Concerts—Programs. 2. Concerts—Interlochen, Mich.

   ML42.I 7N39   780.79774   52–42310 ‡

NN   0058673   DLC MiU MB MiD IU

780.977 National Music Camp
N213f   The first twenty-five years. [n. p.,
         1952]
            [64] p., chiefly illus.

NN   0058674   MiD

*ML28
.I 5N37 National music camp,
KEPT IN   Interlochen bowl. Seasons programs. 1943-
BROWN MUSIC 45.
COLLECTION 16th-18th season. [Interlochen, Mich.,
         1943-44]
            v. illus., ports. 23 and 25cm.

      1. Concerts—Programs. 2. Concerts—
Interlochen, Mich. I. Title.

NN   0058675   MB

ML132   **National Music Camp.**
.C4 I 6   The **Interlochen** list of recommended materials for instru-
         mental ensembles. 3d ed. [Interlochen, Mich., 1953]

         National music camp,
            The scherzo; yearbook 1934- 35/36.
         Interlochen, Mich., 1934-36.
            2 v. illus.(incl.ports., map), forms,
         23 cm.
            On cover: 1934-35/36 Scherzo, Op. 7-8
         No. 1-2
            Includes advertising.

NN   0058677   DHEW

National music camp,
   Young America fights for constitutional rights; factual information, relating to the case of the school children of America versus
James C. Petrillo.   Interlochen, Nat. music camp, 1945.   34 p.
illus.   23cm.

NN   0058678   NN

National Music Camp
      see also   National High School Orchestra and
Band Camp, Interlochen, Mich.

Music
MT
4   National Music Camp. University of Michigan Divi-
.I6   sion.
N27   Announcement. 1942-
            [Ann Arbor]
                        (University of Michigan Offi-
         cial publication v.43, no.91

            Title varies: 1942, Courses offered at the Na-
         tional Music Camp, Interlochen, Michigan, by School
         of Music and Department of Speech, University of

         Michigan.- 1943, School of Music courses at the Na-
         tional Music Camp, Interlochen, Michigan.- 1944-56,
         University of Michigan courses at the National Mu-
         sic Camp, Interlochen, Michigan.

NN   0058681   MiU

National Music Company, publishers, Chicago.
      Excelsior violin and piano folio
         see under title

National Music Company, publishers, Chicago.
      The national march folio
   •   see under title

National Music Company, publishers, Chicago.
      The National minstrel folio.
         see under title

VOLUME 407

National Music Company, Chicago, publishers.   8053.863
National song folio. Vol. 4. [With accompaniments for pianoforte.]
= Chicago. [190–?]   v.   30½ cm., in 4s.
Contents. — Love's old sweet song, by J. L. Molloy. — Only to see thee,
darling, by F. Campana. — Calvary, by Paul Rodney. — The garden of
sleep, by Isidore de Lara. — If sighs had wings, by Ciro Pinsuti. — In
old Madrid, by H. Trotère. — Two hearts that beat as one, by J. E. Hartel.
— The star-spangled banner. — The rainy day, by I. Piaggio. — In thy
dreams, love, by Charles H. Perry. — Little Annie Rooney, by Michael
Nolan. — Little Katie Dooley . . . by Harry E. Bradt. — Full soon from

woe a sure relief, by Donizetti. — Honeymoon, by J. L. Molloy. — Mistress
Mary, by Cecile Tovey. — Lullaby. From "Erminie," by Ed. Jacobowski.
— An old faded picture, by H. E. Bradt. — The nightingale's song, by
H. S. Prescott. — Tell me of the old folks! By J. P. Skelly. — Song of
the helmet, by Charles Lecocq. — Our house was haunted, by Wm. C.
Walter. — A penny for your thoughts, by Cécile S. Hartog. — Gentle
faces, by Theodore Bonheur. — Love abides, by J. L. Roeckel. — Over
the summer sea. From . . . Rigoletto, by Verdi. — A vision of my
dream, by G. T. Meech. — Where is another sweet, by Arthur Sullivan.

— Staunch and true, by Theo. Bonheur. — Good bye, ye flow'rets fair.
Duet, by Franz Abt. — In the sweet of the year, by Ciro Pinsuti. —
My love is like a red, red rose. — Now was I wrong? By Louis Engel. —
I'll pray for thee, by Donizetti. — Just one year, by Carl Bohm. — Gently
draw near, by Chas. H. Collins. — Sweet Saturday night, by W. J. M. —
Two roses; Dreaming, by Milton Wellings. — Steering home, by Godfrey
Marks. — Night winds from the sea, by Herbert S. Prescott.

NN   0058687   MB

M30   National Music Compay, publishers, Chicago.
N27D1   [Dance music]
          Souvenir collection of American copyright
          dance music. Containing a choice selection
          of waltzes, polkas, marches, schottisches
          and other dance music by eminent American
          composers. Chicago, c1894.
          159 p.   31ᶜᵐ.

          1.Dance music.   I.Title.

NN   0058688   CSt

National music company, publishers, Chicago.

Standard songs for high voice ... Chicago, New York, National music co., c1901.

National music company, publishers, Chicago.

The **Windsor** popular two-steps and waltzes folio. Chicago
and New York, National mus. co., 1900.

National music council.
     Bulletin. v. 1–
     Nov. 1940–
     [New York, 1940–
         v. in   28 cm.   irregular.
         Reproduced from type-written copy.

     1. Music—Societies.

     ML27.U5N42   780.6273   44—9504

OC1W TNJ-P MsSM
OrU DAU CtY PSt KyU NcGU MtU PSC TxU NN MB NNC OrP
NN   0058691   DLC WvU C IU ScC1eU GU MnNC OC1 CoU CU

ML3795
.U5N3   National music council .
         ... State and municipal financial support of
         musical activities. A survey made by the
         National music council and published in its Bul-
         letin of December, 1943. [New York, 1943?]
         8 p. 28 1/2cm.
         Caption title.

         1. Music—U. S.—Economic aspects.   I. Title.

NN   0058692   MB

780.13
N213u   National Music Council.
         The use of music in hospitals for mental
         and nervous diseases; report on a survey.
         New York, 1944.
         8p. 28cm.
         "Prepared with the collaboration of Samuel
         W. Hamilton ... and Dr. Willem van de Wall."
         —p.2.
         1. Music, Physical effect of. 2. Music,
         Influence of. 3. Music therapy. I. Hamil-
         ton, Samuel Warren, 1879-   II. Van de Wall,
         Willem, 1887-

NN   0058693   TxU NcGU

National Music Council. *Committee on Music in Hospitals*
    see
National Music Council. *Hospital Music Committee.*

National Music Council. *Committee on the Use of Music in
Therapy*
    see
National Music Council. *Hospital Music Committee.*

ML1   National Music Council. Hospital Music
.H65   Committee.

         Hospital music newsletter. v. 1–3; May 1948–Sept. 1951.
         New York.

National Music Council. *Music in Hospitals Committee*
    see
National Music Council. *Hospital Music Committee.*

National Music League, Inc.
     Bulletin.
     v. 1

     New York, 1926–   8°.
         v.

         Monthly during the musical season.

     1. Music—Assoc. and org.—U. S.
     N. Y. P. L.   August 22, 1928

NN   0058698   NN

National music league, inc. Radio committee.
     "Music and you;" a study of audience reaction to programs of
serious music on the air. Report presented by Dr. Harold Vincent Milligan, chairman, Radio committee.   New York, N. Y.,
The Radio committee of the National music league, inc. [1937?]
75 p.   23cm.

     1. Music—Analysis, interpretation,   appreciation. 2. Radio and music.
     I. Milligan, Harold Vincent, 1886-   II. Title.
     N. Y. P. L.   September 16, 1947

NN   0058699   NN

National Music Meetings.
     An account of the Crystal Palace national
music meetings
         see under   Beale, Thomas Willert, 1828-
1894.

National Music Research Society of Korea.
     Korean folk songs
         see under   Lee, Kang Nyum.

The national music teacher... 1872
     see under   Mason, Luther Whiting, 1828-
1896.

780.79795   National music week, Portland, Ore.
N27c
         [Correspondence, and newspaper
         clippings relating to Portland's
         first music week] n.pub. [1921]

         Contains signed letters from out-
         standing American musicians.
         Manila envelope.

NN   0058703   OrP

º780.79795 National music week, Salem, Ore.
N28
         Official program.

         Library has
         1940

NN   0058704   OrP

NATIONAL MUSIC WEEK COMMITTEE
     Guide for the organization of local music
weeks in cooperation with national music week
[and other pamphlets on celebration of music
week] 45 W. 45th St. N.Y. Author [1925]
     8 pams in 1 cover.

NN   0058705   Or OC1

National Music Week Committee
     Guide for the organization of local music weeks in coopera-
tion with National Music Week...   Issued by National Music
Week Committee.   New York[, 1926].   32 p.   map.   8°.

     1. Community music.
     N. Y. P. L.   June 23, 1926

NN   0058706   NN

[NATIONAL MUSIC WEEK COMMITTEE]
     National music week proclamations and public
statements by governors issued for the 1938
observance. [Author, 1938]
     [56] p. illus. (facsims.)

NN   0058707   Or

NATIONAL MUSIC WEEK COMMITTEE
     Your participation in national music week,
May 1-7, 1938, fifteenth annual observance.
Author c1939.
     79 p.

NN   0058708   Or

                                        **M.446.103
National musical companion. A collection of vocal and instrumental
     music [arranged for pianoforte].
= Chicago. National Music Co. 1890. 159 pp. 30½ cm.

I.4781 — Songs. With music. Colls. — Pianoforte. Music. Colls.

NN   0058709   MB DLC

National
V   MUSICAL CONVENTION, Boston, 1838.
3844   Proceedings of the Musical convention assem-
.102   bled in Boston, August 16, 1838. Together with
         a brief view of the origin of the same. Printed
         by vote of the convention.   Boston, Kidder &
         Wright, 1838.
         48p.

NN   0058710   ICN

VOLUME 407

National musical convention, *Boston,* 1841.
Proceedings of the National musical convention, held at the Melodeon, Boston, August 25th to 28th, 1841, together with an exposition of the causes which led to the dissolution of the late National musical convention, and the origin of the present one. Boston, Manning & Hallworth, printers, 1841.
12 p. 20ᶜᵐ.

6-43124†

NN 0058711 DLC

368.363 **National Mutual Benefit Association,** Louisville, Ky.
N213 ₍Report and by-laws₎ Louisville, Ky. ₍1882?₎
31 p. 14 cm.

NN 0058712 KyU

National mutual building and loan association of New York.
Articles of association of the National mutual building and loan association of New York, as amended April 16, 1890 ... ₍New York, °1890₎
12 p. 18½ᶜᵐ.

CA 8—948 Unrev'd

Library of Congress HG2624.N7N3 1890

NN 0058713 DLC

National mutual building and loan association of New York.
Prospectus ... National mutual building and loan association of New York ... ₍New York, Press of J. J. Little & co., °1889₎
8 p. 19½ x 9ᶜᵐ.

CA 8—947 Unrev'd

Library of Congress HG2624.N7N5

NN 0058714 DLC

National mutual building and loan association of New York.
Receipt book of the National mutual building and loan association of New York. Articles of association ... etc. ... ₍New York, °1888₎
24 p. 18ᶜᵐ.
Blank leaves at end ruled for account.

CA 7—7444 Unrev'd

Library of Congress HG2624.N7N3 1888

NN 0058715 DLC

National mutual insurance bulletin
see Mutual insurance bulletin.

National Mutual Life Assurance Society.
The history of the National Mutual Life Assurance Society, 1830–1930; compiled by Robert Finch; assisted by Alfred Roberts; with a foreword by J. Maynard Keynes... London, 1930. 93 p. incl. front., tables. facsim., ports. 4°.

483481A. 1. No subject. I. Finch, Robert, compiler. II. Roberts, Alfred, jt. compiler.
N. Y. P. L. July 30. 1930

NN 0058717 NN MH-BA

GV1151 **National Muzzle Loading Rifle Association.**
.M88
Muzzle blasts. v. 1–
Sept. 1939–
Portsmouth, Ohio.

National narrow-guage railway convention.
Proceedings of the National narrow-gauge railway convention, held at St. Louis, Mo., June 19, 1872. St. Louis, Mo., By the "Industrial age" printing co., 1872.
96 p. 22ᶜᵐ.

1. Railroads, Narrow-gage.

Bur. of railway econ. Libr. A 13—1556
for Library of Congress ₍a40b1₎

NN 0058719 DBRE CtY MiU

National nature news.
v. 1
Washington, D. C., 1937 27½cm.
v. illus. (incl. ports.)
Weekly (no issues June 14–21, 1937).
Editor : March, 1937– L. C. Athey.

1. Natural history—Per. and soc. publ. I. Athey, Lillian Cox, ed.
N. Y. P. L. June 10, 1938

NN 0058720 NN

National Naval Aviation Meeting.
Proceedings
see under Institute of the Aerospace Sciences.

National naval medical center, *Bethesda, Md.*
see
U. S. *National naval medical center, Bethesda, Md.*

National navy league of the United States
see
Navy league of the United States.

TT515 **National Needlecraft Bureau, inc., New York.**
.W45
The Wise encyclopedia of modern sewing. 1943–
New York, W. H. Wise.

National needs and remedies ... 1890
see under Evangelical Alliance for the United States. General Christian Conference. 2d, Boston, 1889.

M310 The **National Negro Almanac and Year Book 1911**;
K13j a handbook of useful information compiled by H.N. Jenkins. Kansas City, Kansas, The Negro Almanac co., 1911.
31 p. illus. 22 cm.

NN 0058726 DHU

National Negro-American Political League
see
National Independent Political League, Washington, D. C.

National Negro business league.
... Annual observance under the auspices of the annual Tuskegee Negro conference and the National Negro business league
see under National Negro health week.

National Negro business league.
... National Negro business league in session at Philadelphia. Dr. Robert R. Moton, president, delivers notable address. ₍Philadelphia? 1922?₎
sheet. 63½ x 33ᶜᵐ fold. to 16½ x 9ᶜᵐ.
At head of title: Galley proof (for release morning papers August 19th)
Consists mainly of Robert R. Moton's address.

1. Negroes—Employment. I. Moton, Robert Russa, 1867–1940.
43–44089

Library of Congress E185.8.N259

NN 0058729 DLC

E184 **National Negro business league.**
.8 Official program of the 27th annual meeting of ...
.N262 [Cleveland? 1926]

NN 0058730 DLC

National Negro business league.
Official souvenir program ... sixteenth convention of the National Negro business league ..., August 18th, 19th, 20th, 1915, with a brief history of Negro business and professional men of Boston from 1846 to 1915, and other facts of the race. Boston, Boston Negro business league no. 1, 1915.
₍56₎ p. illus. 22½ᶜᵐ. $0.10
Contains advertising matter.

1. Negroes—Boston. I. Title.
15–19288

Library of Congress E185.5.N31

NN 0058731 DLC

National negro business league.
Proceedings of the ... annual meeting of the National negro business league ...
1st–
1900–
₍Nashville, Tenn., °1901–
v. fronts., ports. 21–23ᶜᵐ.
Title varies: 1st– Proceedings ...
... Annual report of the sixteenth session and the fifteenth anniversary convention.
... Report of the annual session.
Proceedings of the ... annual meeting.
1. Negroes—Employment.
1–31348 Revised

Library of Congress E185.8.N27

NN 0058732 DLC WaS CU ICJ MB CSt OWibfU

National Negro business league.
Report of the survey of Negro business conducted by the National negro business league, 1928, containing an introduction by Dr. Paul T. Cherington. ₍Tuskegee? Ala., National Negro business league, 1929₎
₍21₎ p. tables, diagrs. 28ᶜᵐ.

1. Negroes—Employment. I. Cherington, Paul Terry, 1876–
II. Title: Survey of Negro business.
CA 30–1253 Unrev'd

Library of Congress E185.8.N28 325.26

NN 0058733 DLC ICRL ICJ WaS TNF DL

301.45196073 **National Negro Conference,** New York, 1909.
N277p Proceedings. [New York? 1909?]
1909 229 p. illus. 20cm.

Bibliography: p. 64–66.

1. Negroes – Congresses.

NN 0058734 FU CU NjP TNF MH IaU MiU NN OO OClW

VOLUME 407

NATIONAL NEGRO CONFERENCE, New York, 1909.
Proceedings of the National Negro Conference,
1909, New York, May 31 and June 1.　[New York,
1909?]　229 p.　illus.　19cm.

Microfilm (Master negative)

NN　0058735　　NN IU

National Negro Congress.
Congress View
see under title

National Negro congress.

Kingston, Steve.
Frederick Douglass, abolitionist, liberator, statesman, by
Steve Kingston ...　[Brooklyn and New York, National Negro
congress, Brooklyn and Manhattan councils, 1941?]

National Negro congress.

E185
.61
.D35　Davis, John Preston, 1905–
Let us build a national Negro congress, by John P. Davis ...
[Washington, National sponsoring committee, National Negro
congress, 1935]

National Negro congress.
Negro people will defend America.　[Washington] National
Negro congress [1941]　23 p.　22cm.

1. Negro—U. S. 2. World war,　　　　　1939-　　—Negroes.
N. Y. P. L.　　　　　　　　　　　　　　　　　　　September 28, 1944

NN　0058739　　NN MiEM

National Negro congress.
Negro workers after the war.　[New York] National Negro
congress, 1945.　23 p.　18cm.

1. Negro—Employment—U. S.　　　2. World war, 1939-1945—Post-
war problems, Economic—U. S.
N. Y. P. L.　　　　　　　　　　　　　　　　　　　August 25, 1947

NN　0058740　　NN OCU IEN MiEM MH NNJ

M306
N21o　National Negro congress.
Offical proceedings... Washington, D.C.,
National Negro congress, 19
v　illus.　20cm.

NN　0058741　　DHU IU TNF MiEM NjP CU IEN NcD OCU OO

National Negro congress.
A petition to the United nations on behalf of 13 million op-
pressed Negro citizens of the United States of America.　[New
York, Nat. Negro congress, 1946]　15 p.　23cm.

1. Negro—U. S.
N. Y. P. L.　　　　　　　　　　　　　　　　　　　August 8, 1949

NN　0058742　　NN MiEM

National Negro congress.
Proceedings of the conference on postwar
employment. New York city, 1945.

31 p.　18 cm.

NN　0058743　　MH

National Negro congress.
Stop police brutality ! ! ! Washington's record of official murder and abuse; an account of "urban lynching."　[Washington
[1941]　iv, 22 l.　28cm.

Film reproduction. Positive.
Prepared by its Washington council.

1. Police—U. S.—D. C.—Wash-　　　　ington. 2. Negro—Legal status—
U. S.—D. C.—Washington.

NN　0058744　　NN

E185
.5
.N29
1940　National Negro Congress, 3d, 1940.
Third National Negro congress, April 26, 27,
28, 1940. Washington, U.S. Dept. of Labor [1940]
35 p. illus., ports. 30 cm.
Cover title.
A program.

1. Negroes—　　　　　　Congresses.

NN　0058745　　MB

CPA
VF
1088　National Negro Congress. Los Angeles Council.
Jim Crow in national defense.　[Los
Angeles, Calif., 1940?]
27 p.

1. Negroes - Employment. 2. World War,
1939-1945 - Negroes. I. Title.

NN　0058746　　MiEM CU-B

M975.3
N21p　National Negro Congress. Washington Council.
Public recreation. A report on the adequacy
of public recreational facilities for Negroes in
the District of Columbia.　Washington, 1939.
32 p.　29 cm.　(mimeographed)

NN　0058747　　DHU

National Negro health movement.
WPA and Negro health. In cooperation with the
United States Public health service.　National
Negro health week, April 4 to April 11, 1937 ...
[Washington, 1937]
12 f.　27 cm.
Reproduced from typewritten copy.
Seal of the National Negro health movement
on t.-p.
1. Negro - Charities - U.S. 2. Negro -
Hygiene. I. United States.　Public health services.
II. Title.

NN　0058748　　NN

National Negro health news. v. 1–
Jan./Mar. 1933–
Washington [1933]–
v. in　illus. (incl. ports.) plates, diagrs.　27½ᵐ.　quarterly.
No numbers were issued for July/Sept. 1933 and July/Sept. 1934.
Issued in the interest of the national Negro health movement by the
United States Public health service.

1. Negroes—Health and hygiene. 2. Negroes—Period.　I. U. S.
Public health service.
　　　　　　　　　　　　　　　　　　　46-32339
Library of Congress　　　E185.88.N3
　　　　　　　　　　　　　[2]　　　　　　013.05

NN　0058749　　DLC MiU ICRL DAU MoU NcRS

National negro health week.
... Annual observance under the auspices of the annual Tuskegee negro conference and the National negro business league,
in cooperation with the United States Public health service,
state health departments [etc.] ...
Washington, U. S. Govt. print. off., 19
v.　plates. 23½-25½ᵐ.
Issued by the United States Public health service.
Title varies slightly.

1. Negroes—Societies. 2. Hygiene—Societies.　I. Tuskegee negro
conference. II. National negro business league. III. U. S. Public
health service.
　　　　　　　　　　　　　　　　CA 31-413 Unrev'd
Library of Congress　　　RA448.5.N4N3
——— ——— 2d set.　　　[2]　　　　　614.062

NN　0058750　　DLC MB WaWW OOxM OCU OO

　NATIONAL Negro Health Week
[Collection of publications]

The library has a collection of miscellaneous publications of this organization
kept as received.　These publications are
not listed nor bound separately.
1. Negroes - Health and hygiene

NN　0058751　　DNLM

National Negro Insurance Association.
Biographies of presidents and secretaries of the National
Negro Insurance Association, 1921–1949; compiled and
edited by C. B. Gilpin, historian.　[n. p., 1949]
[42] l.　23 cm.
Cover title.

I. Gilpin, C. Bernard, 1881–　　ed.

HG8799.N3　　　　923.673　　　　49-52656*

NN　0058752　　DLC

National Negro Insurance Association.
Biographies of presidents and secretaries of the National
Negro Insurance Association, 1921–1949.　Compiled and
edited by C. B. Gilpin, historian.　[n. p., 1949?]
45 p. ports. 23 cm.

I. Gilpin, C. Bernard, 1881–　　ed.

HG8799.N3　1949r　　923.673　　　50-19039

NN　0058753　　DLC NcD

National Negro Insurance Association.
Proceedings of the annual session.

[Richmond]
v. illus. 24 cm.
Title varies: 1945, Proceedings of the Executive Committee sessions
in lieu of [the] annual convention.
*Vol for　issued by the association under
its later name: National Insurance Association.*

1. Insurance—Societies. 2. Insurance—U. S.

HG8522.N33　　　368.06273　　　51-35705 ‡

NN　0058754　　DLC TNF NNC MiD DHU NN ICU NSyU NNC OU

National Negro Labor Council.
Let freedom ride the rails
see under title

ML42
.W3L54　National Negro music centre.
"Three periods of Negro music and drama";
benefit, Saturday evening, May 6, 1922, under
the auspices of the National Negro music centre,
Lincoln Theatre, 1215 U St., N.W., Washington,
D.C.　[Washington, 1933]

NN　0058756　　DLC

National Negro printer and publisher.

Oxford, O. [etc.] NPP pub. co., 19
v.　illus.　20-23cm.
Irregular.
Caption and running title:　　　　　called v. 1　　Negro printer and publisher.
Each issue includes Directory, Negro newspapers and periodicals in the United
States.

1. Printing—Per. and soc. publ.　　　2. Journalism, Negro—U. S.
I. Title: Negro printer and publisher.
N. Y. P. L.　　　　　　　　　　　　　　　　　　　July 13, 1944

NN　0058757　　NN

VOLUME 407

The **National** Negro voice... v. 1, no. 1–11 (July 19 – Sept. 27, 1941). Kingston, Jamaica, 1941. 1 v. illus. (incl. ports.) 40cm.

Weekly.
"Official organ of the U. N. I. A. in the West Indies", July 19 – Sept. 13, 1941.
"Published by Z. Munroe Scarlett", July 19 – Sept. 13, 1941; "published by the Harmony div., U. N. I. A.", Sept. 20, 1941; "published by the Negro voice syndicate", Sept. 27, 1941.
Running title: Negro voice.
Superseded by the New Negro voice.

1. Negro—Per. and soc. publ.   —Jamaica. 2. Periodicals—Jamaica.
I. Universal Negro improvement   association. II. Negro voice.
N. Y. P. L.   April 16, 1943

NN   0058758   NN NcD AAP GU CLSU DAU NcRS

National Nephrosis Foundation
see
National Kidney Disease Foundation.

National network radio and television service.
  v.1–   ; Feb. 1951–
  Evanston, Ill.
  Standard Rate and Data Service.
  v. monthly.
  Ceased July 1956.
  Continued by Network rates and data.

NN   0058760   ICRL

WL
1
_3_N279
NATIONAL Neurological Research
   Foundation
   [Collection of publications]

   The Library has a collection of miscellaneous publications of this organization
   kept as received. These publications are
   not listed or bound separately.

NN   0058761   DNLM

National New Thought Alliance
  see **International New Thought Alliance.**

BF645
. N3
National new thought association (inc.)
   Field facts...
   [Lansing, Mich..[c1918.

NN   0058763   DLC

G3814
.N5
1955
.O6
National Newark and Essex Banking Company,
   Newark, N. J.
Opdyke Map Company, *Newark, N. J.*
   Map of Newark area, including west Essex from the
   Newark line, showing main bus lines and the Garden State
   Parkway, New Jersey. Newark, National Newark and
   Essex Banking Co. [1955]

G3814
.O7
1953
.O61
National Newark and Essex Banking Company,
   Newark, N. J.
Opdyke Map Company, *Newark, N. J.*
   Map of Orange, East Orange, South Orange, **West**
   Orange, including Livingston, Maplewood, Millburn, **Short**
   Hills, and Summit, New Jersey. Rev. Newark, **National**
   Newark & Essex Banking Co., c1953.

National Newark & Essex banking company, Newark, N.J.
   150th anniversary, 1804–1954. [Newark, 1954] 1 v. (unpaged) illus., ports., map. 29cm.
   Caption title.

1. Banks and banking—U. S.—   N. J.—Essex county. 2. Essex
county, N. J.—Hist.—Pictorial works.

NN   0058766   NN NjP

HG2613
.N64N32
National Newark and Essex Banking Company,
   Newark, N. J.
   One hundred and twenty-five years of service,
   1804–1929. Newark, N. J. [Printed by the Os-
   borne Co., 1929?]
   [16] p. illus. 31 cm.

1. Newark, N. J. - Hist.

NN   0058767   NjR

National Newark & Essex Banking Company,
   Newark, N. J.
   One hundred years. A record of the work of
   the oldest bank in the State of New Jersey
       see under   Rockwood, Charles Greene,
   1814–1904.

National Newark & Essex banking company, *Newark, N. J.*
Safeguarding your property in wartime and afterward.
[Newark] National Newark & Essex banking company [1943]
cover-title, 15, [1] p. 28 x 21½cm.
Text on p. [3] of cover.

1. Trusts and trustees.   I. Title.

Library of Congress   HG4485.N3   43–14656
                                                    332.14

NN   0058769   DLC

National Newman Apostolate.
   Directory.
   Washington.
   v. 24 cm.

1. Newman clubs—Direct.

BX810.N48N3   282.06273   67–840

NN   0058770   DLC NBuU CL CBGTU

BT
3653
.A21
N27
National Newman Club Federation of the U.S.
   Manual for initiation of members.
   Washington, D.C., [1952]
   [22] p. 23 cm.

1. Newman club. I. Title.

NN   0058771   DCU

BT
3532
S96
National Newman Club Federation of the U.S.
   A survey of Catholic students attending non-
   Catholic institutions of higher learning in the
   United States and territories, conducted by the
   National Newman Club Federation of the U.S.,
   1949–50. [n.p., 1950]
   1 v. (various pagings). 29cm.
   Mimeographed.
   1. Newman clubs. 2. Universities and colleges
   - U.S. 3. Students, Catholic. I. Title.

NN   0058772   DCU

NATIONAL news [Cape Town] no. 1–14; June 12, 1952–
   Apr. 7, 1953
   [Cape Town]   no.   illus.   45cm.
   Microfilm
   Published by the National party of the Cape.
   Ceased publication?

1. Union of South Africa—Hist. I. National party
(Union of South Africa).

NN   0058773   NN

National news letter (London)
   see   King-Hall news letter.

National news letter of Phi Delta Kappa
   see under   Phi Delta Kappa.

National news of the American Legion Auxiliary
   see under   American Legion. Auxiliary.

Z327
.B6
National Newsagent, Bookseller, Stationer.

Book trade handbook. [1st]–   ed.; 1944/45–
London, National Newsagent, Bookseller, Stationer.

National Newspaper Association.
   Portrait and data of John F. Dryden, United States
   Senator from New Jersey and president of the Prudential
   Insurance Company of America. New York [190–]
   [2] l. port. 31 cm. (*Its* National newspaper biographies)
   Cover title.

1. Dryden, John Fairfield, 1839–1911.   I. Title.

E664.D8N2   26–20245 rev

NN   0058778   DLC

National Newspaper Association.
   Portrait and data of Thomas C. Platt, thrice elected
   United States Senator, and a power in the business world.
   New York [190–]
   [1] l. port. 31 cm. (*Its* National newspaper biographies)
   Cover title.

1. Platt, Thomas Collier, 1833–1910.   I. Title.

E664.P72N2   26–20246 rev

NN   0058779   DLC

National newspaper conference
   ... Proceedings of the first–
National newspaper conference ... 1912–
Madison, The University, 1913–
   v. 23cm.
   At head of title, 1912–   : Extension division of the University of
Wisconsin. General information and welfare.
   1912–   Bulletin of the University of Wisconsin ... General series ...

1. Journalism—Congresses.   I. Wisconsin. University. University
extension division. Dept. of general information and welfare.

                                                    13–33157
Library of Congress   PN4848.N3

NN   0058780   DLC OU OrU ODW OO

National newspaper directory and gazeteer

   see under

Pettingill firm, newspaper advertising agents.

National Newspaper Promotion Association.
   How research works for newspapers

   see under

   Rosten, Harry, ed.

National newspaper promotion association.
   NNPA; 1943 convention, a summary. A digest
   of addresses, discussions and clinics presented
   at 14th annual convention, National newspaper
   promotion assn., New York, April 19–21, 1943.
   cover-title, 21 l.

1. Journalism - Congresses. 2. Newspaper
advertising.

NN   0058783   NNC

VOLUME 407

National Newspaper Promotion Association.
 Newspaper promotion primer. Authors: Clarence W.
Harding ₍and others₎ Edited by Clifford A. Shaw.
₍Charleston, W. Va., 1955?₎
 124 p. 22 cm.

 1. Public relations—Newspapers. 2. Journalism. ɪ. Shaw, Clifford A., ed. ɪɪ. Title.
 PN4734.N3   070.33   58–26807 ‡

NN 0058784   DLC LU CSt TxU PPCuP FTaSU IaU NcU

National Newspaper Promotion Association.
 Newspaper promotion year book and convention program.

 Washington.
    v. ports. 30 cm.

 1. Journalism—Societies. 2. Advertising, Newspaper—Societies.
ɪ. Title.
 PN4700.N37   070.348   52–68192 ‡

NN 0058785   DLC

659.132
N213s
Journ
Lib'y
 National Newspaper Promotion Association.
 "Selling retail advertising by plan." An
outline for the construction of effective
newspaper solicitations, together with an
illustration of its practical application.
Sponsored by: Newspaper Advertising Executives Association. Prepared by a committee
of the National Newspaper Promotion Association: Clarence W. Harding [and others]
Adopted and recommended by the Plans Board
of the Bureau of Advertising, ANPA. Produced and distributed by: Bureau of Advertising, ANPA.   [New York? 1952?]
 130p. illus., plates. 22½ x 30cm.

NN 0058786   TxU FTaSU

070.13 **National Newspaper Week Committee.**
qN277   How to observe National Newspaper Week,
October 1-8, 1952, a public relations kit.
₍n.p., 1952₎
 7 pieces in 1 v. 31 cm.
 Cover title.
 A planned public relations program with
the theme "Your right to know—a constitutional guarantee", sponsored by the Newspaper Association Managers, Inc.
 1. Liberty of the press. 2. Newspapers.
I. Title.

NN 0058787   N

RA772 National Noise Abatement Council.
.N7   Anti-noise ordinances and other measures for
N39   the elimination of unnecessary noise in 165 U.S.
Q   cities. Report of survey made by National noise
abatement council, June 1942. New York, National noise abatement council ₍1942?₎
 ₍12₎p., 10ℓ. forms. 31cm.

 1. City noise. I. Title.

NN 0058788   PSt CU OC1

National Noise Abatement Symposium.
 Proceedings.
 Chicago.
    v. illus. 23 cm. annual.

 1. Noise. 2. Hearing.
 RA772.N7N3   614.78   ℒ–36952

NN 0058789   DLC NN

HWT National Non-Partisan Committee to Defend
.NA   the rights of the 12 Communist Leaders.
 The big plot; proof of the Justice De-
partment's plan to jail 21,105 Americans.
[New York, 1950?]
 10 p. 19 cm.

 Cover title.

 1. Communism - U.S. - 1917.

NN 0058790   WHi NcD MiEM WU

**National Non-partisan Committee to Defend the Rights of
the 12 Communist Leaders.**
 Due process in a political trial; the record vs. the press.
₍New York, 1949₎
 64 p. 23 cm.
 Cover title.

 1. Communist Trial, New York, 1949. ɪ. Title.
                    347.9   51–32453

NN 0058791   DLC

**National Non-Partisan Committee to Defend the Rights of
the 12 Communist Leaders.**
 Due process in a political trial; the record vs. the press,
in the Foley Square trial of the 12 Communist leaders.
₍Rev. ed. New York, 1949?₎
 64 p. 24 cm.
 Cover title.

 1. Communist Trial, New York, 1949. ɪ. Title.
                    50–23795

NN 0058792   DLC WaU-L NcD WHi WU CU-B

National Non-Partisan Committee to Defend the
Rights of the 12 Communist Leaders.
 Freedom is everybody's job...
    see under Crockett, George W

National Nonpartisan League.
 The Articles of Association of the National Nonpartisan
League; together with a discussion of the democracy of the
League's purposes, the democracy of its form of organization, the
democracy of the measures supported by the League, and the
ending of the autocratic monopolies and the triumph of democracy,
by Walter Thomas Mills...   St. Paul, Minn., National Nonpartisan League₍, 1919₎. 26 p. nar. 8°.

 1. No subject. 2. Mills, Walter   Thomas, 1856–
N. Y. P. L.   September 10, 1926

NN 0058794   NN

National Nonpartisan League.
 [Collection of materials referring to the National
Non-Partisan League]
    see under title

National nonpartisan league.
 Facts for the farmer on conditions vitally important to
him as producer and to the wage worker as consumer.
(Minnesota handbook) Issued by the National nonpartisan league. (June 1917) St. Paul ₍1917?₎
 133, ₍3₎ p. illus. (incl. ports.) 19¼ᶜᵐ.

 1. Agriculture—Economic aspects. 2. U. S.—Econ. condit. 3. Minnesota—Pol. & govt. ɪ. Title. ɪɪ. Title: Minnesota handbook.
                    18–11754
 Library of Congress   HD1485.N4A3

NN 0058796   DLC WaSpG ICRL MnHi

---

*JK2391 National nonpartisan league.
.N41A3   Facts for the farmer on conditions
1918   vitally important to him as producer
and to the wage worker as consumer.
Issued by the National nonpartisan
league (April 1918) ₍St. Paul, 1918₎
 94 p. illus. 20cm.

NN 0058797   MnHi

National Nonpartisan League.   338.1 R900
 Facts for the farmer on conditions vitally important to him as
129106 producer and to the wage worker as consumer. (Minnesota
handbook.) St. Paul, The National Nonpartisan League, 1919.
 135 p. incl. illus., tables. 20½ᶜᵐ.

NN 0058798   ICJ NN

National nonpartisan league.
 Facts kept from the farmer; general handbook of the
National nonpartisan league, issued September, 1917. St.
Paul ₍1917?₎
 79 p. 20ᶜᵐ.
 CONTENTS.—Political campaign "investments."—Corporation "good will
campaigns."—Organization and "fighting funds."

 1. Elections—U. S.—Campaign funds. 2. U. S.—Econ. condit. ɪ. Title.
 Library of Congress   HD1485.N4A4   18–11755

NN 0058799   DLC

---

q784.4 National nonpartisan league.
N21f   Freedom for all forever, the spirit
that is fighting for democracy at home
and abroad, the spirit of 1776.
[St. Paul, Minn., 1918?]
 cover-title, 40p. illus., ports.
 1918 souvenir rally booklet, National
nonpartisan league.

 Contains music.

NN 0058800   IU

National Nonpartisan League.
 "Let's kick out both parties"

    see under

 Fisher, George H

National Nonpartisan League.
 Memorial to the Congress of the United States concerning
conditions in Minnesota, 1918. By the National and State Executive Committees of the National Nonpartisan League.   St. Paul₍,
1918₎. iii, 120 p. 8°.

 1. Minnesota—Politics, 1918.
N. Y. P. L.   January 19, 1926

NN 0058802   NN ICU DNW MiU MnHi

National nonpartisan league.

 The Nonpartisan leader. ₍Official magazine of the National nonpartisan league₎

 Fargo, N. D., 19

National Nonpartisan League.   ... Origin, purpose and
method of operation. ₍n. p., n. d.₎ 27 p. illus. (port.) 24°.
 At head of title: The National Nonpartisan League.

NN 0058804   NN

VOLUME 407

HGF
.NA
National Nonpartisan League.
Origin, purpose and method of operation; war program and statement of principles. [n.p., 1917?]
32 p.   16 x 9 cm.

Cover title.

NN   0058805   WHi

---

*E780
.N2
National Nonpartisan League.
Winning the War; nonpartisanship, the test; from the letters, messages and addresses of the President.   St. Paul ₍1918₎
24 p.   22cm.

NN   0058806   MnHi

National non-theatrical motion pictures, inc.
Burton Holmes catalog of films for school church & community. New York, National non-theatrical motion pictures, inc. (1923)
cover-title, 15 p. 18½ cm.

NN   0058807   DL

National non-theatrical motion pictures, inc.
Catalog of films, carefully selected for school, church & community. New York, National non-theatrical motion pictures, inc. (1923)
cover-title, 184 p. 18 cm.

NN   0058808   DL

The National normal; a monthly educational newspaper.
v. 1–
Oct. 1868–
Cincinnati, R. H. Holbrook ₍etc.₎ 1868–
v. pl., tab. 22ᶜᵐ.
Vol. 1-4 have title: The National normal; an educational monthly.
Editor: 1868–   R. H. Holbrook.

1. Education—Period.   I. Holbrook, Reginald Heber, 1845–   ed.

Library of Congress   L11.N23

CA 6-562 Unrev'd

NN   0058809   DLC DHEW OO OOxM

National Norman Horse Association
see   National French Draft Horse Association.

National note-book quarterly. v. 1–   ; 1919–
Augusta, Ga., National Association of Teachers in Colored Schools.
v. illus.
Ceased 1921?
Published as National note-book, Jan.–July 1919.

NN   0058811   ICRL

National notes. Kansas City, Mo.
see under   National Association of Colored Women.

National notion association.
Notion department manual... Ed. by Laura Van Doorn Harter ... New York, Nat. notion assoc. ₍c1936₎ 92 p.   23cm.

N. Y. P. L.   1. Notions—Trade and stat.   I. Harter, Laura Van Doorn, ed.
January 8, 1948

NN   0058813   NN OC1

National Notion Association.   5631.59
Notion Department Service book.   1927/28.
[New York. 1927.] 1 v. Illus. Plates. 25½ cm.

N6443 — T.r. — Small wares. Perio. - Department stores. Period. — Annuals and year-books.

NN   0058814   MB MiD OC1

Physics
DG21.329
N2131
National nuclear energy series. Manhattan technical section.
Division I: ₍Electromagnetic separation project₎
v.
New York, McGraw-Hill book co.,
v.   tables, diagrs. 24cm.

1. Electromagnetism.   2. Nuclear physics.

NN   0058815   NNC CtY NcD PP PHC

National nuclear energy series. Manhattan project technical section.
Division II: ₍Gaseous diffusion project₎
v.
New York, Toronto ₍etc.₎ McGraw-Hill book co.,
v.   illus., tables, diagrs. 24cm.

1. Diffusion.   2. Nuclear physics.

NN   0058816   NNC PP NcD

Physics
D621.329
N2133
National nuclear energy series. Manhattan project technical section.
Division III: ₍Special separations project₎
v.
New York, Toronto ₍etc.₎ McGraw-Hill book co.,
v.   illus., tables, diagrs. 24ᶜᵐ.
1. Isotopes.   2. Uranium.   3. Deuterium.
4. Deuterium compounds.   5. Spectrum analysis.
6. Nuclear physics.

NN   0058817   NNC NcD PHC

Physics
DG21.329
N2134
National nuclear energy series. Manhattan project technical section.
Division IV: Plutonium project record.
v.
New York, Toronto ₍etc.₎ McGraw-Hill book co.,
v.   plates (part col.) tables. 24ᶜᵐ.

1. Plutonium.   2. Nuclear physics.

NN   0058818   NNC ICarbS PHC NcD CtNlC

90.11
N21
National Nurseries.
Instructions for rooting cuttings in sand or vermiculite.   Biloxi, Miss. [1950?]
31 p.

1. Plant propagation.   I. Pickering, Spurgeon.   II. Title: Rooting cuttings in sand or vermiculite.

NN   0058819   DNAL

PW
6110
.C4
N3
The national nursery album.   New York, T. Nelson ₍1880?₎
1v. (unpaged) col. illus. 16cm.

1. Children's poetry.   2. Nursery rhymes.
3. Fairy tales.

NN   0058820   OrU

National nursery rhymes and nursery songs
see under   Elliott, James William, 1833–1915.

The National nurseryman. v. 1–47, no. 9; Feb. 1893–Sept. 1939. Hatboro, Pa., The National nurseryman publishing co., inc.; ₍etc., etc.₎, 1893–1939₎
v. in   illus. (incl. ports.) plates (part col.) 27½–30 cm.
Monthly, 1893–1928; semimonthly, 1929–Oct. 1933; monthly, Nov. 1933–Sept. 1939.
Official journal of the American association of nurserymen   1894–June 1916.
United with the American nurseryman to form the American nurseryman and the national nurseryman.

1. Trees—Period.   2. Shrubs—Period.   I. American association of nurserymen.
SB354.N29   47–43442

NN   0058822   DLC NcRS ICRL KMK OU TU

14
9254
The national nurseryman.   For growers and dealers in nursery stock.   Rochester,

NN   0058823   DLC MBH

W 6
P3
NATIONAL Nursing Accrediting Service
Is your nursing school accredited? How it is done step by step.   New York [1951?]
14 p.
1. Schools, Nursing - U. S.

NN   0058824   DNLM MiU

RT71
N46
National Nursing Accrediting Service.
Is your nursing school accredited? How it is done step by step.   New York ₍1952?₎
14p. 22cm.

Cover title.

1. Nursing schools - Accreditation.   2. Nurses and nursing - Study and teaching.   I. Title.

NN   0058825   IaU

RT71
.C67
National Nursing Accrediting Service.
Committee of the Six National Nursing Organizations on Unification of Accrediting Activities.
Manual of accrediting educational programs in nursing. New York, National League of Nursing Education ₍1949₎

National Nursing Accrediting Service.
Report on the program of temporary accreditation

see under

National League for Nursing. Division of Nursing Education.

VOLUME 407

WY
5
qN277

NATIONAL Nursing Council ₁,
  ₁ Collection of publications ₁

    The Library has a collection of mis-
cellaneous publications of this organization
kept as received. These publications are
not listed nor bound separately.
    1. Nursing - Collected works

NN 0058828   DNLM

W 6
P3

NATIONAL Nursing Council .
    Distribution of nursing service during
war. [New York] 1942.
    23 p.
    1. Nursing - U. S. - World War II

NN 0058829   DNLM MnU WU-M

National Nursing Council.
    Facts about war nursing needs and resources, January 16,
1945. Prepared by the National Nursing Council for War
Service in cooperation with Army Nurse Corps, Navy Nurse
Corps, Veterans Administration ₁and others₁ New York,
1945₁
    8 l. 28 cm.
    Caption title.

    1. Nurses and nursing—U. S.   I. Title: War nursing needs.

    RT4.N3   610.73   45–15613 rev*

NN 0058830   DLC

National Nursing Council.
    A guide for the organization of collegiate schools of nurs-
ing, prepared by the National Nursing Council for War
Service and the Association of Collegiate Schools of Nursing.
New York, 1942.
    35 p. 24 cm.
    Pub. by the council under its earlier name: National Nursing Coun-
cil for War Service.
    "Selected references": p. 35.

    1. Nurses and nursing—Study and teaching.   I. Association of
Collegiate Schools of Nursing.

    RT71.N37   610.7307   43–4514 rev*

NN 0058831   DLC MnU-B WU-M MtBC ICJ

National Nursing Council.
    A guide for the organization of collegiate schools of nurs-
ing, prepared by National Nursing Council for War Service
and Association of Collegiate Schools of Nursing, 1942. Rev.
by National League of Nursing Education, 1946. New York,
National League of Nursing Education, 1946.
    v, 32 p. 23 cm.
    Includes bibliographies.

    1. Nurses and nursing—Study and teaching.   I. Association of
Collegiate Schools of Nursing.   II. National League of Nursing Education.

    RT71.N37 1946   610.730711   S G 46–137 rev*
    U. S. Army Medical Libr.
    for Library of Congress   ₁r48d1₁†

NN 0058832   DNLM MsU IaU PU NcU ICU TxU MtBC DLC

National Nursing Council.
    The history of the National Nursing Council, by Hope
Newell, for the History Committee of the National Nursing
Council. ₁New York, National Organization for Public
Health Nursing, 1951₁
    118 p. 28 cm.

    I. Newell, Hope (Hockenberry) 1896–

    RT1.N348   610.73   53–24089 ‡

NN 0058833   DLC MtBC CaBVaU DCU MiU OrU-M N

National Nursing Council.
    The history of the National Nursing Council, by Hope
Newell, for the History Committee of the National Nursing
Council. ₁New York, National Organization for Public
Health Nursing, 1951₁
    118 p. 28 cm.
    Photocopy. Ann Arbor, Mich., University
Microfilms, 1971. 115 p. (on double leaves)

NN 0058834   MiU

610.7308₁ National Nursing Council .
P191   Information concerning scholarship and loan
v.1   funds available to students in schools of
no.3   nursing. ₁New York, 1943₁
            4p. illus. 19cm. (In Pamphlets on
         nurses and nursing. v.1, no.3)

            1. Professions, Choice of. Nursing.
         2. Nurses and nursing. Study and teaching.
         3. Scholarships and fellowships. I. Title.

NN 0058835   OrU

B614.9
qN212   NATIONAL NURSING COUNCIL .

            A manual for state nursing councils
         for war service. New York, N.Y.,
         National nursing council for war
         service ₁1943₁

            3 p.l., 2–19 numb. l.   29cm.

            Reproduced from type-written copy.
            1.Nurses and nursing. I.Title.

NN 0058836   MnU

RT71   National Nursing Council.
.B752
         Brown, Esther Lucile, 1898–
            Nursing for the future, a report prepared for the Na-
         tional Nursing Council. New York, Russell Sage Founda-
         tion, 1948.

RT4   National nursing council .
.A32
         U. S. *Public health service. Division of nurse education.*
            Schools of nursing approved by the respective state boards
         of nurse examiners and listing those with units of the U. S.
         Cadet nurse corps ...
         New York, N. Y. ₁19

National Nursing Council.
    A thousand think together. A report of three regional
conferences: Washington, October 23–25, San Francisco,
November 17–20, Chicago, December 4–6, 1947, held in con-
nection with the Study of Schools of Nursing, Esther Lucile
Brown, director, under the auspices of the National Nursing
Council ... New York, 1948.
    209 p. illus. 28 cm.

    1. Nurses and nursing—Congresses. 2. Nurses and nursing—Study
and teaching.   I. Title.

    RT3.N33   610.7307   50–1081

    DNLM OrU-M
NN 0058839   DLC NN OU PU OrCS CU ICU NcU MiDP DCU

National nursing council.
    You and professional nursing. Prepared jointly
by National nursing council for war service, inc.
... and Division of nurse education, U. S. Public
health service, Federal security agency ...
₁Washington, U. S. Govt. print. off., 1944₁
    11, ₁1₁ p. 22 x 9 cm.

    1. Nursing as a profession. 2. U. S. Cadet
nurse corps. I. U. S. Public health service.
Division of nurse education. II. Title.

NN 0058840   Vi NNC

National Nursing Council for War Service
    see National Nursing Council.

National nut growers' association
    see   National pecan association.

National nut news ...
    see   Modern school store.

National Nutrition Conference for Defense, *Washington,
D. C.*
    see
National Nutrition Conference, *Washington, D. C.*

JX1975   National nutrition policies, 1937/38.
.A25
1938   **League of Nations.** *Secretariat. Financial Section and Eco-*
.II.A.25   *nomic Intelligence Service.*
            Survey of national nutrition policies, 1937/38. ₁Geneva,
         1938₁

National nutrition society.
    ₁Food and health guides₁ no. 1–
N₁ew₁ Y₁ork₁ c₁ity₁ Journal of living publishing corp. ₁1943–
            nos. 19ᵐ. (National nutrition society library)
    Editor: 1943–   V. H. Lindlahr.

    1. Nutrition. 2. Diet.   I. Lindlahr, Victor H., 1895–   ed.
                                                    43–16124
    Library of Congress   RM216.N3

NN 0058845   DLC

National nutrition society.

Lindlahr, Victor H   1895–
    How to win and keep health with foods, by Victor H. Lind-
lahr ... New York, N. Y., National nutrition society, inc. ₁1942₁

National Nutrition Society.

RA773
.J83   **Journal** of lifetime living. v. 1–
         July 1935–
         ₁New York₁

National nutrition society.

Lindlahr, Victor H   1895–
    The Lindlahr vitamin cook book, by Victor H. Lindlahr.
New York city, National nutrition society, inc., *1941.

389.9   National nutrition society.
N212   National nutrition society library.

         New York,

            1. Diet. 2. Food. 3. Nutrition. I.
         Lindlahr, Victor H   1895–   ed.

NN 0058849   DNAL

National nutrition society.

Lindlahr, Victor H   1895–
    You are what you eat, by Victor H. Lindlahr ... New York,
National nutrition society, inc., 1940.

VOLUME 407

99.77
N214 National Oak Flooring Manufacturers Association.
Oak floors for your home; a home owner's
guide. Memphis, Tenn. [1955?]
31 p.

1. Floors. 2. Oak-wood.

NN 0058851   DNAL

59.9
N217R National Oat Conference.
Report.

[n. p.]

1. Oats. Congresses.

NN 0058852   DNAL

Ndx30   National oats company.
U2   Financial statement...
+N21b   [East St. Louis, Illinois
28cm.

NN 0058853   CtY

... A national observatory. [New York, 1899]
see under [Newcomb, Simon] 1835-1909.

National Observatory of Athens
see Athens. Ethnikon Asteroskopeion.

The National observer, Albany. Supplement.

Southwick, Solomon, 1773-1839.
... Speech of Solomon Southwick, at the opening of the
New-York anti-masonic state convention, at the Capitol,
in Albany, February 19th, 1829. Containing: 1. A concise statement of every important fact, relating to the
masonic outrages on William Morgan and David C. Miller. 2. A concise statement of every important fact,
amounting to a presumptive proof of the murder of William Morgan ... To which is added, the declaration of
independence, agreed upon and published by the Conven-

tion of seceding masons, at Le Roy, on the 4th of July,
1828, with the names of the signers. Albany, Printed by
B.-D. Packard & co., 1829.

The National observer.

Minneapolis, Minn. [H. E. Soule, etc.]
v. in illus. (incl. ports.) 40ᶜᵐ.
Weekly,   -Apr. 1, 1939; biweekly, Apr. 15, 1939-
Caption title.
Volume numbers irregular: v. 33, no. 1-23 repeated.

1. Freemasons—Period. 2. Freemasons. Minnesota.
45-43799
Library of Congress   HS351.N35
[2]   366.1

NN 0058858   DLC

The National observer, a record and review.
London [1892-93]
[v. 33ᶜᵐ. weekly.

CA 9-1166 Unrev'd
Library of Congress   AP4.N23

NN 0058859   DLC

The National observer, a record and review.
Twenty modern men, from the National observer. London,
E. Arnold, 1891.
iv, [2], 117 p. 18½ᶜᵐ.
On cover: Second series.
Includes advertising matter.

1. Biography—Addresses, essays, lectures. I. Title.
43-41616
Library of Congress   CT105.N3

NN 0058860   DLC NN CU

National observer, a record and review -
see also National observer and British review
of politics, economics, literature, science and art.

052
N2774 The National observer and British review of
politics, economics, literature, science
and art. v. 1-18 (no. 1-456); Nov. 24,
1888-Oct. 16, 1897. London [and] Edinburgh.
18v. 34cm. weekly.

Title varies: Nov. 24, 1888-Nov. 15, 1890,
The Scots observer, a record and reviews;
Nov. 22, 1890-Mar. 13, 1897, The national
observer, a record and review; Mar. 20-May

22, 1897, The national observer and British
review; May 29-Aug. 7, 1897, The British
review and national observer.

I. Title: The Scots observer. II. Title:
The British re-   view and national
observer.

NN 0058863   FU DLC ViU

9-83   National observer and British review of
no.117E   politics, literature, science and art.
v. 1-18; Nov. 24, 1888-Aug. 7, 1897. London.
18 v. on 6 reels. (English literary
periodicals, 117E)

Title varies: v. 1-4, Scots observer, a
record and review.—v. 5-17, National observer,
a record and review.
Microfilm. Ann Arbor, Mich., University
Microfilms.

I. Title: Scots observer, a record and
review. II. Title: National observer, a
record and review.

NN 0058865   ViU PSt MiU NBuU TxU WaPS

National observer and British review of politics,
economics, literature, science and art
see also National observer, a record
and review.

National observer & Washington mirror. v. 1-2, no. 4; July
1, 1933-Jan. 1, 1934. [New York] Capitol publishing corporation [1933-34]
2 v. in 1. illus. (incl. ports.) 30½ᶜᵐ.

Semimonthly, July-Nov. 1933; monthly, Dec. 1933-1934.
Supersedes the American Mayfair.
Vol. 1 has title: Washington mirror; politics, society, finance.
Edited by J. C. Schemm.
Superseded by the Tatler (later, American sketch; Washington mirror)
cf. Union list of serials.

I. Schemm, J. C., ed. II. Title: Washington mirror; politics, society,
finance.
46-38206
Library of Congress   AP2.N349
[2]

NN 0058867   DLC NN OOxM

The national obstacle to the national public style
considered
see under [Carey, William Paulet] 1759-
1839.

National Occupational Conference.
An appraisal and abstract of available literature
on banking as an occupation
see under Scott, Irving O.

National Occupational Conference.
An appraisal and abstract of available literature
on city and county management as an occupation
see under Pence, Edith E.

National occupational conference.

Gibson, Anson Wright.
An appraisal and abstract of available literature on farming
as an occupation, by A. W. Gibson. [New York, National occupational conference, ᶜ1937]

National occupational conference.
An appraisal and abstract of available literature on occupations
in journalism. [New York] National occupational conference
[1938]   12 p.   25cm.
"Reprinted from Occupations... April, 1938."
"Bibliography," p. 10-12.

1. Journalists—Bibl. I. National   occupational conference.
N. Y. P. L.   June 30, 1942

NN 0058872   NN

National occupational conference.
An appraisal and abstract of available literature on occupations
in music. [New York] Nat. occupational conference [ᶜ1938]
15 p.   25cm.
"Bibliography," p. 12-15.

1. Music as a profession—U. S.
N. Y. P. L.   August 25, 1947

NN 0058873   NN MH PU

National occupational conference.

Meyer, Herbert.
An appraisal and abstract of available literature on paint-
ing as an occupation, by Herbert Meyer and Lillian D. Allen.
[New York, National occupational conference, ᶜ1936]

National occupational conference.

Noall, Irvin Simon, 1891-
An appraisal and abstract of available literature on pharmacy as an occupation, by Irvin S. Noall. [New York, National occupational conference, ᶜ1937]

National occupational conference.

Sandell, Maynard L.
An appraisal and abstract of available literature on pho-
tography as an occupation, by Maynard L. Sandell. [New
York, National occupational conference, ᶜ1937]

National Occupational Conference.
An appraisal and abstract of available literature
on the occupation of insurance salesmen
see under Adler, Sigmund.

VOLUME 407

National occupational conference.

Schoettler, Arthur Edmund, 1888–
An appraisal and abstract of available literature on the occupation of the barber, by A. E. Schoettler. [New York] National occupational conference, ᶜ1937]

National occupational conference.

[Spiegler, Samuel]
An appraisal and abstract of available literature on the occupation of the blacksmith. [New York] National occupational conference [ᶜ1938]

National occupational conference.

[Spiegler, Samuel]
An appraisal and abstract of available literature on the occupation of the boilermaker. [New York] National occupational conference [ᶜ1938]

TH159
.S65   National occupational conference.

[Spiegler, Samuel]
An appraisal and abstract of available literature on the occupation of the building contractor. [New York] National occupational conference [ᶜ1938]

National occupational conference.
An appraisal and abstract of available literature on the occupation of the cabinetmaker
    see under   [Boardman, Martha T   ]

National Occupational Conference.
An appraisal and abstract of available literature on the occupation of the carpenter
    see under   Spiegler, Samuel.

National occupational conference.

[Spiegler, Samuel]
An appraisal and abstract of available literature on the occupation of the city fireman. [New York] National occupational conference [ᶜ1939]

National Occupational Conference.
An appraisal and abstract of available literature on the occupation of the dental mechanic
    see under   Spiegler, Samuel.

National occupational conference.

[Pavan, Ann]
An appraisal and abstract of available literature on the occupation of the detective. [New York] National occupational conference [ᶜ1938]

NATIONAL OCCUPATIONAL CONFERENCE.
An appraisal and abstract of available literature on the occupation of the free lance writer. New York, 1938.

pp.12.
"National Occupational Conference abstracts."

National occupational conference.

[Becht, Helen M   ]
An appraisal and abstract of available literature on the occupation of the general houseworker. [New York] National occupational conference [ᶜ1938]

National occupational conference.

[Spiegler, Samuel]
An appraisal and abstract of available literature on the occupation of the industrial chemist. [New York] National occupational conference [ᶜ1938]

National occupational conference.

Wells, Shirley.
An appraisal and abstract of available literature on the occupation of the motion picture actor, by Shirley Wells. [New York, National occupational conference, ᶜ1937]

National occupational conference.

[Tuxill, Virginia]
An appraisal and abstract of available literature on the occupation of the nurse. [New York] National occupational conference [ᶜ1938]

National occupational conference.

[Spiegler, Samuel]
An appraisal and abstract of available literature on the occupation of the office machine operator. [New York] National occupational conference [ᶜ1938]

National occupational conference.

[Spiegler, Samuel]
An appraisal and abstract of available literature on the occupation of the patternmaker. [New York] National occupational conference [ᶜ1938]

National occupational conference.

Hatcher, Orie Latham.
An appraisal and abstract of available literature on the occupation of the rural teacher, by O. Latham Hatcher. [New York, National occupational conference, ᶜ1936]

National Occupational Conference.
An appraisal and abstract of available literature on the occupation of the Stenographic worker
    see under   Spiegler, Samuel.

National occupational conference.

Hill, T   Arnold.
An appraisal and abstract of available literature on the occupation of the undertaker, by T. Arnold Hill. [New York, National occupational conference, ᶜ1936]

National Occupational Conference.
An appraisal and abstract of available literature on the occupation of the veterinarian
    see under   Spiegler, Samuel.

NATIONAL OCCUPATIONAL CONFERENCE.
An appraisal and abstract of available literature on the occupation of the vocational counselor. New York, Occupational Index, Inc., 1937.

pp.7.
"Occupational abstracts."

National occupational conference.

[Spiegler, Samuel]
An appraisal and abstract of available literature on the occupation of the welder. [New York] National occupational conference [ᶜ1938]

National occupational conference.

Murphy, John F.
An appraisal and abstract of available literature on waiters and waitresses, by John F. Murphy. [New York, National occupational conference, ᶜ1937]

HF5381   National occupational conference.
.B43   FOR OTHER EDITIONS
1942   Bingham, Walter Van Dyke, 1880–   SEE MAIN ENTRY
Aptitudes and aptitude testing, by Walter Van Dyke Bingham. New York and London, Pub. for the National occupational conference by Harper & brothers [1942]

National occupational conference.

Parker, Willard Eagleson, 1900–
Books about jobs; a bibliography of occupational literature, by Willard E. Parker. Preliminary ed. Chicago, Published for the National occupational conference by the American library association [ᶜ1936]

National occupational conference.

L111   Witmer, Marion H   comp.
.A6   Guidance bibliography; an annotated list of books, pam-
1937,   phlets and periodical references on guidance appearing dur-
no. 36–37 ing the calendar year 1935–1936. Compiled by Marion H.
Witmer and Maris M. Proffitt ... United States Department of the interior, Harold L. Ickes, secretary. Office of education, John W. Studebaker, commissioner. Washington, U. S. Govt. print. off., 1937–38.

National occupational conference.

Hoppock, Robert, 1901–
Job satisfaction, by Robert Hoppock ... photo-studies by Lewis W. Hine; aerial photography by Virgil Kauffman. A publication of the National occupational conference. New York and London, Harper & brothers, 1935.

National occupational conference.
Occupational adjustment; interim report, 1938. Occupational education tour for school superintendents. New York city, National occupational conference [ᶜ1938]

104 p. incl. diagr., forms. 23ᶜᵐ.

1. Occupations. 2. Profession. Choice of. 3. Vocational education. 4. Personnel service in education.   ı. Title.

Library of Congress   HF5381.N34 1938
                                                    39–20371
———— Copy 2.
Copyright AA 286504   [3]   371.425

National occupational conference.

Occupational index. v. 1–
Jan. 1936–
New York, National occupational conference [1936–

VOLUME 407

National occupational conference, New York
Occupational pamphlets. A series of appraisals and abstracts of available literature on a variety of occupations
New York, c1936-

NN   0058905   OC1

607
N2133o   National occupational conference.
¡Occupational studies¿ An appraisal and abstract of available literature ...   ¡New York, c1936¿
19v. in 1.

NN   0058906   IU DNAL

275
N217   National occupational conference.
¡Publications¿   New York, National occupational conference, 1936.
4 nos.   25cm.
Contents.- ¡no.1¿ An appraisal and abstract of available literature on beauty culture as an occupation.- ¡no.2¿ An appraisal and abstract of available literature on farming as an occupation. -¡no.3¿ An appraisal and abstract of available literature on landscape architecture as an occupation.- ¡no.4¿ What tests shall we use?.
¡No.4¿ is reprinted from Occupations, the vocational guidance maga   zine, March 1936.

NN   0058907   DNAL

National occupational conference.
The record of accomplishment; final report of the director, National occupational conference. 1933-1939. New York, N. Y., National occupational conference ¡1939¿
18, ¡2¿ p. illus. 26ᶜᵐ.
Signed: Edwin A. Lee, director.
"Reprinted, with additions as of September 30, 1939, from Occupations, the vocational guidance magazine, June, 1939, pp. 773-785."—p. ¡5¿

1. National occupational conference.   I. Lee, Edwin Augustus, 1888-   II. Title.

U. S. Off. of educ.   Library   HF5381.N31
for Library of Congress   ¡2¿
E 40-408

NN   0058908   DHEW NN RPB OC1

National occupational conference.
Regional conference on vocational guidance, Northeastern United States, New England, New York, New Jersey and Pennsylvania. New York [1933]

NN   0058909   MH NcD

National Occupational Conference.
...A report on the National occupational conference...
see under   Cartwright, Morse Adams, 1890-

National occupational conference.
Robert Irwin Rees, an appreciation. New York, National occupational conference, 1938.
3 p. l., 9-47, ¡1¿ p. incl. front. (mounted port.) 23½ᶜᵐ.
"Six hundred copies of this volume have been printed ... This is copy number 568."
"Preparation of this volume has been the responsibility of Raymond G. Fuller."

1. Rees, Robert Irwin, 1871-1936.   I. Fuller, Raymond Garfield, 1886-

Library of Congress   CT275.R36N3   38-38322
——— Copy 2.
Copyright A 122890   ¡3¿   923.573

NN   0058911   DLC NcRS NNC OCU

National occupational conference.
... Vocational guidance and education for Negroes. Edited by Franklin J. Keller. A conference at Atlanta university, December 9-14, 1935.
(In Occupations; the vocational guidance magazine. New York, N. Y. ¡1936¿ 25½ᶜᵐ. v. 14, no. 6. p. ¡481¿-576. plates)

1. Negroes — Education. 2. Vocational education — Southern states. ¡2. Negroes—Vocational education¿ 3. Negroes—Employment. 4. Occupations.   I. Keller, Franklin Jefferson, 1887-   II. Title.
E 40-915

U. S. Off. of educ.   Library   LC2703.N28
for Library of Congress   ¡2¿

NN   0058912   DHEW OCU

National occupational conference.

Campion, Howard Arthur, 1894-
The vocational schools of Essex county, New Jersey; a study made under direction of the National occupational conference, by Howard A. Campion. New York, National occupational conference, 1939.

449
N214   National Occupational Safety Association.
[Accidents and accident prevention of employers and workmen in industry]
Pretoria [1953?]
4 l.

1. Agriculture. Accidents. Statistics.

NN   0058914   DNAL

National Ocean Survey.
The U. S. Lake Survey (established in 1841) and the U. S. Coast and Geodetic Survey (established in 1878) were merged in 1970 to form the National Ocean Survey.
Works by these bodies are found under the following headings according to the name used at the time of publication:
U. S.   Lake Survey.
U. S.   Coast and Geodetic Survey.

National Oceanographic Council.
Proceedings of the Commonwealth oceanographic conference

see under

Wormley, Eng. (Surrey) National Institute of Oceanography.

National Oceanographic Council.
Report ¡on the National Institute of Oceanography¿ 1949/50-
Cambridge, University Press.
v. illus., maps. 25 cm. annual.
Report year ends Mar. 31.
Report for 1949/50 issued by the National Institute of Oceanography.

1. Wormley, Eng. (Surrey)   National Institute of Oceanography.

GC1.N294   551.4606142   53—22450

NN   0058917   DLC CaBVaU LU NcD KU NN MiU

National Oceanographic Council (Gt. Brit.)
see also
Wormley, Eng. (Surrey) National Institute of Oceanography.

The national ode.   July 4, 1876
see under   [Taylor, Bayard] 1825-1878.

National oeconomy recommended, as the only means of retrieving our trade and securing our liberties; occasioned by the perusal of the late Report of a committee of the House of commons relating to the army; by which, many gross and important abuses appear to have been committed in that article of the publick expence, for many years past, as proved by abstracts of the said report. In a letter to a member of the said committee. London, Printed for M.Cooper, 1746.
2 p.l., 51 p. tables. 18 cm.

NIC NN
NN   0058920   MH-BA ICU CtY PU MH CSmH NcD NNC PU

National office furniture association.
NOFA sales manual.   Chic.¡c1954¿
114p.illus.

Prepared by Anne Saum and associates.

NN   0058921   CaBVa

National Office Machine Dealers Association.
Vocational training program for office machine mechanics, in cooperation with the Veterans Administration.   [Cleveland, Ohio, c1945]
51 p. illus. 26 cm.
"A brief history of the American typewriter" by J. M. Dannenfelser, jr.: p. 27-48.
--- Instructor's manual for use with veterans training program.   Cleveland, Ohio [1945]
16 p. forms. 27 cm.
"Based on "The instructor and his job" prepared by the National Defense Curriculum Laboratory, Cornell University".

1. Mechanics (Persons) 2. Vocational education. U.S.   3. Type-writers. History. I. U.S. Veterans administration. II. Dannenfelser, John M. jr. III. Title.

NN   0058923   OrU

National office management association
Air raid protection for office personnel, property and records ...
Philadelphia, Pa., National office management association ¡1942¿
16 p.

NN   0058924   OC1

National Office Management Association. Bibliography for office managers.
see its The NOMA bibliography for office managers.

HF
5548
.N29   National Office Management Association.
Business equipment directory. Philadelphia ¡1948?-
1 v.(loose-leaf) illus. 29 cm.
Caption title.

1. Office equipment and supplies—Catalogs.

NN   0058926   MiU

HD6483
.N3   National Office Management Association.
Collective bargaining manual.
Philadelphia, c1948.
31p. 23cm. (Its Bulletin no.8)
Cover title.
Bibliography: p.30-31.

NN   0058927   NNU-W

VOLUME 407

National office management association.
Company policies regarding special benefits to employees entering military service; N. O. M. A. Research committee report of special survey, summarized by chairman E. H. Conarroe... ₍New York₎ 1941. 19 p. 28cm.

Caption-title.

1. Soldiers—Civil status, laws, etc. —U. S. 2. Seamen—Civil status, laws, etc.—U.S. I. Conarroe, E. H.
N. Y. P. L.   August 25, 1947

NN   0058928   NN

National Office Management Association.
Design and control of business forms

see under

Knox, Frank M

331.22   **National Office Management Association.**
N279   Employee security benefits. ₍Philadelphia, 1948₎

28 p. tables. 28ᶜᵐ. (Survey summary no.6)
Title on cover: Office benefits.

1.Insurance, Social. I.Title. II.Title: Security benefits.

NN   0058930   CSt NNC

National office management association.

Nyströmer, C   **Bertil.**
Four thousand years in the office, by C. Bertil Nyströmer ... ₍Philadelphia₎ National office management association, ᶜ1940.

National Office Management Association
A guide to job instruction. Philadelphia, 1950.
[19] p. illus.

NN   0058932   MiD

R
331.   **National Office Management Association.**
2851   Guide to salary rates, office salaries.
N2785   Survey summary. 1st-   19 -
[Willow Grove, Pa.] 19 -

v. tables.
Library has: 1962-
1st-14th, 19 -1960 issued in numbered series: National Office Management Association. Survey summary.

1. Clerks--U. S.--Salaries, pensions, etc. Title. Title: Salary rates, office salaries. x M.

NN   0058933   CL

650.7   National Office Management Association.
N213i   Information about national business entrance tests, sponsored by National Office Management Association and United Business Education Association. Philadelphia, 1950.
10 pts. in 1 v. 28cm.

1. Business   education—Study and teaching. I.   United Business Education Association.

NN   0058934   LU

National Office Management Association.
Manual of practical office short cuts, comp. from ideas sent in by members of the National Office Management Association. 1st ed. New York, McGraw-Hill Book Co., 1947.
xi, 272 p. illus. 24 cm.

1. Office procedures.   I. Title.

HF5547.N18   651   47—4190*

MtBC OrP OrSaW WaSp WaU-L
PSt NcGU KEmT CaBVa MtU Or WaS WaT CaBViP CaBVaU
NN   0058935   DLC GU CoU FU PPSKF TU OrU TxU ICU

National office management association.
...Membership roster...
19

Philadelphia, Pa., 19   28cm.
no.
Reproduced from typewritten copy, 19
Cover-title, 19

1. Management—Assoc. and org.   —U.S.
N. Y. P. L.   June 20, 1940

NN   0058936   NN OC1

National Office Management Association.
The NOMA bibliography for office managers; a classified compilation of selected references to articles and publications. 1938-44—   ed. ₍Philadelphia₎
v. 23 cm.
Annual, 1945-
Title varies: 1938-44—   **Bibliography for office man-**
agers ...   **agers.**
Issues for 1938-44—   comp. and pub. by the association's
Research Committee.

1. Office management—Bibl.

Z7914.A2N3   016.651   45—6291*

TNJ-P NcU IEN CL DNAL NN CU
TU ICJ MiD DNAL CU MnM OU MiEM OrCS N OU NcGU PPLas
NN   0058937   DLC IdU Or OrP WaSp WaS IdU MiU LU TxU

National office management association.
...NOMA bulletin; a service to members. no. 1-4 (Jan.-Aug. 1946). Philadelphia, 1946. 4 nos. 23cm. (no. 3: 21cm.)
Irregular.
Each issue has also individual title.
No more published?

1. Office organization and manage-   ment—Per. and soc. publ.—U. S.
I. Title.
N. Y. P. L.   June 28, 1950

NN   0058938   NN OC1

R
651.26   **National Office Management Association.**
N277   **NOMA glossary of automation terms**
[and] NOMA data processing exchange
index. 19 -   Willow Grove, Pa.,
c19 -

v.
Library has: 1961-

1. Electronic data processing--Terminology. 2. Electronic data processing--Direct. Tit   le. Title: **NOMA data** processing exch   ange index. x M.

NN   0058939   CL

HF5549   National Office Management Association.
,N3   The NOMA office customs survey; a tabular
1947   presentation of practices and facilities affecting more than 260,000 office employees of 836 companies in 75 principal cities of the United States and Canada. [Philadelphia] c1947.
[2] l., 26, v. p. 27cm. (National Office Management Association. Survey summary, no. 1)

1. Office management.   I. Title.

NN   0058940   MB

National Office Management Association.
National clerical ability tests
see under title

National office management association.
A new conception of office practice.

See under

Nichols, Frederick George, 1878-

National Office Management Association.
The Nomayear.
Philadelphia.
v. illus., ports. 23 cm.

I. Title.

HF5001.N265   651.06273   49-22090*

NN   0058943   DLC NNC NBuG OOxM NN MiU PPT

HF5547   National Office Management Association.
.A2N2   **Office** executive.
₍Philadelphia₎

National office management association.
Office salaries; the NOMA survey, 1947-48 ₍conducted under the direction of D. Lee Brennen. Philadelphia, 1948₎
80 p. tables. (Its Survey summary, no. 4)

1. Wages - U. S. - Statistics. I. National office management association. Survey summary. 4.

NN   0058945   NNC TxLT TxU OU

National office management association.
Office unions; the NOMA survey, 1947. ₍Philadelphia₎ 1947.
16 p. tables. 27ᶜᵐ. (Its Survey summary, no. 3)

1. Clerks - U. S. - Salaries, pensions, etc.

NN   0058946   NNC OrU

National office management association.
Proceedings of the ... annual conference ... 1st-
1920-   Dayton, O. ₍etc., 1920?-
v. illus. (part mounted) ports., diagrs. 28ᶜᵐ (1st, 24ᶜᵐ)
Title varies: 1920, First national conference, the National association of office managers.
1921-   Proceedings of the National association of office managers (Slight variations)
19   Proceedings of the ... annual conference, National office management association.

1. Office management—Societies.
                23-18519 (rev. '32)
Library of Congress   HF5547.A2N3
Copyright   ₍r32c2₎   651.062

CSt OU ICU DNAL TNJ-P IU NN ICJ GEU MB
NN   0058947   DLC MiU OCU OCT OC1FRB KyU TU CU KEmT

National office management association.
... Proceedings of the Office personnel conference, Des Moines, February 13 and 14, 1942. Your office personnel in the emergency. ₍Philadelphia, 1942₎
x, 101 p. illus. (NOMA forum. Conference proceedings number. Vol. XVII, no. 4, April, 1942)
1. Office management.
I. Title: Office personnel conference.

NN   0058948   NNC

VOLUME 407

National office management association.
Report of the national salary survey of the National office management association, 1940–41; a study by the National research committee summarized by E. H. Conarroe, chairman. Philadelphia, Pa.: W. H. Evans, 1941. 8 p. incl. tables. 23cm.

1. Wages, Clerical workers'— U. S., 1940-1941. I. Conarroe, E. H.
N. Y. P. L. October 13, 1942

NN 0058949 NN NNC

NATIONAL OFFICE MANAGEMENT ASSOCIATION.
Service bulletin. v.2, no.1-3; Jan.-May, 1925
[n.p.] v. 28cm.

Irregular.
Issued under the early name of the association: National association of office managers.
Vol. 2, no.1-3, Jan.-May, 1925, also called Bulletin.
Superseded by its Quarterly bulletin

1. Office organization and management--Per. and soc.
publ.--U. S. I. National office management association.
bulletin.

NN 0058950 NN

National office management association.
Special report the National association of office managers. Contents: Questionnaire summary, "Salary classification survey among member companies". Report prepared by Ray Noyes ... Fort Wayne, Ind., National association of office managers [1929?]
20 l. incl. tables. 23 x 32 cm.

NN 0058951 ICU

National office management association.
Subject index of technical articles appearing in the publications of the National office management association. [Philadelphia] 1942.
36 p. 23ᵐ.

1. Office management—Bibl.

43–4108
Library of Congress Z7164.C81N3
[3] 016.651

NN 0058952 DLC ICU NN OC1 OC1W

National office management association
see also
Joint committee on tests of the National office management association and the National council of business education.

HF5547 National office management association.
N2 Survey summary no. 1-

[New York] ⁰1947-
v. tables. 27cm.

1. Office management.

OrP
NN 0058953 OrCS PPT ICarbS NcGU TxU IU OU NN

National Office Management Association. *Boston Chapter.*
Clerical salary survey of rates paid in eastern Massachusetts and southern New Hampshire, January, 1947. Boston, National Off. Management Assn., Boston Chapter, Research Committee, ⁰1947.
cover-title, 11 p. 28 cm.

1. Clerks—Massachusetts. 2. Clerks—New Hampshire. 3. Wages—Massachusetts. 4. Wages—New Hampshire. I. Title.

HD4966.M44U47 331.2851374 47–28973*

NN 0058955 DLC MH-IR MH-BA

National Office Management Association. Boston Chapter.
Salary survey of rates paid in eastern Massachusetts and southern New Hampshire offices, October 1948. Boston [1949?]
12 p. tables.

NN 0058956 MH-BA NNC ICarbS

T National Office Management Association.
58 Detroit Chapter.
N27+ A plan for evaluating clerical jobs.
[Detroit, 1944]
17 l. forms. 29cm.

1. Job analysis.

NN 0058957 NIC

National Office Management Association. Greensboro Chapter.
Program and roster
[Library has]

1. N.C.--Directories

NN 0058958 NcU

HF5547 NATIONAL OFFICE MANAGEMENT ASSOCIATION—
.N18 National Research Committee
Communications in the office; a presentation of practices and facilities... 1953. Philadelphia, 1953.
27 p. illus. (National Office Management Association. Survey summary,15)

1. Office practice. I. Title.

NN 0058959 InU

HF5547 National Office Management Association.
N27 National Research Committee.
1951 The second Noma office customs survey, a presentation of practices and facilities affecting more than 464,000 office employees of over 2,100 companies in the principal cities of the United States and Canada, 1951. Philadelphia, National Office Management Association, 1951.
32 p. illus., tables. 28 cm. (Office customs no. 2. Survey summary no. 12)

1. Office management. I. Title: Office customs survey.

NN 0058960 DI

National Office Management Association. *New York Chapter*
see **Office Executives Association of New York.**

National office management association.
Philadelphia chapter.

Peirce school, *Philadelphia.*
A survey of personnel practices in the Philadelphia area, 1940; an interpretation of the results of a personnel survey covering 91 offices employing 31,852 persons, prepared for the Philadelphia chapter, National office management association, by Peirce school ... Philadelphia [1940]

Soc
HF National office management association.
1101 St. Louis chapter.
S64 Blueprint for business education, by a
no.65 Committee of St. Louis chapter of National Office management association and a Committee representing the St. Louis public schools. Cincinnati, South-western publishing co. 1946.
30p. (South-western publishing co. Monograph 65)

NN 0058963 FTaSU ViU InU

National Office Management Association. Seattle Chapter.
Better education. see under Joint Committee of the National Office Management Association, Seattle Chapter, the Seattle public schools, the University of Washington.

National Office Management Association. Tacoma Chapter.
Pathways to better business education, a report of a study of business education in Tacoma, Washington. Prepared by the Tacoma Chapter of the the National Office Management Association under the co-sponsorship of the Tacoma Chamber of Commerce. [Tacoma, 1949]
20 p. 28 cm.
1. Business education. Washington. Tacoma, I. Tacoma, Chamber of Commerce. II. Title.

NN 0058965 IEN OrCS

NATIONAL OFFICE MANAGEMENT ASSOCIATION.
Yakima Valley Chapter.
Business and the schools; education through cooperation; summary of a survey of business and business education in Yakima, Washington. September 1949. [Yakima? 1949?]
47 p.

NN 0058966 WaU

National Office of Vital Statistics
see **U. S.** *National Office of Vital Statistics.*

HF5001 National Office Products Association. Research
.N376A33 Department.
... Survey of operating results of NOPA dealers. [Washington, 1929?-
v. tables. 28 cm.

1. Office equipment and supplies. I. Title.

NN 0058968 NjR

HX1 The National office review.
.N12 v. 1, no. 1-8; Aug./Sept. 1917- May 1918. Chicago, 1917-18.
1 v. 43 cm. monthly.
Issued by the National office, Socialist Party.
. I. Socialist Party (U.S.) National office.

NN 0058969 DLC

National official hockey guide
see
The **Official** national hockey guide.

National official shippers guide, from Chicago to towns in Illinois ... Chicago, Des Moines, National shippers guide company
v. 15 x 28ᵐᵐ.

1. Shippers' guides—U. S.

CA 5—1499 Unrev'd
Library of Congress HE9.U5 I 3

NN 0058971 DLC

VOLUME 407

National official shippers guide, from Chicago to towns in Iowa ... Chicago, Des Moines, National shippers guide company
v. 15 x 28ᶜᵐ.

1. Shippers' guides—U. S.

Library of Congress HE9.U5 I 8
CA 5—1497 Unrev'd

NN 0058972 DLC

National official shippers guide, from Chicago to towns in Minnesota and North Dakota ... Chicago, Des Moines, National shippers guide company
v. 15 x 28ᶜᵐ.

1. Shippers' guides—U. S.

Library of Congress HE9.U5M66
CA 5—1495 Unrev'd

NN 0058973 DLC

National official shippers guide, from Chicago to towns in Montana, Wyoming and Idaho ... Chicago, Des Moines, National shippers guide company
v. 15 x 28ᶜᵐ.

1. Shippers' guides—U. S.

Library of Congress HE9.U5M85
CA 5—1496 Unrev'd

NN 0058974 DLC

National official shippers guide, from Chicago to towns in Nebraska and South Dakota ... Chicago, Des Moines, National shippers guide company
v. 15 x 28ᶜᵐ.

1. Shippers' guides—U. S.

Library of Congress HE9.U5N2
CA 5—1498 Unrev'd

NN 0058975 DLC

National official shippers guide, from Chicago to towns in Washington and Oregon ... Chicago, Des Moines, National shippers guide company
v. 15 x 28ᶜᵐ.

1. Shippers' guides—U. S.

Library of Congress HE9.U5W2
CA 5—1494 Unrev'd

NN 0058976 DLC

National official shippers guide, 1905; from Chicago to towns in Wisconsin ... Chicago, Des Moines, National shippers guide company ₁°1905–
v. 15 x 28ᶜᵐ.

1. Shippers' guides—U. S.

Library of Congress HE9.U5W6
CA 5—1493 Unrev'd

NN 0058977 DLC

National Oil and Gas Power Conference
see **American Society of Mechanical Engineers.** *Oil and Gas Power Division.*

T338.2
N213o

NATIONAL OIL AND PIPE LINE COMPANY, Beaumont, Tex.
The oil fields of the world; the Texas fields promise to be the greatest ever discovered - will revolutionize the fuel question. [Beaumont? Tex., 1901]
24p. 22 x 10cm.

Caption title.
Cover title: Speculation that beats gold mines or the New York Stock Exchange.

1. Petroleum - Texas - Beaumont.

NN 0058979 TxU

NATIONAL OIL BURNER AND EQUIPMENT COMPANY, St. Louis.
...Report of tests... [St.Louis, 1902] 14 p. incl. tables. pl. 20cm.

Caption-title.
Final result of the tests, made by the company, of the use of fuel oil in furnaces.

681217. 1. Oil burners.

NN 0058980 NN

National oil company.
Annaul report.
[Jersey City]
28 cm.
Incorporated in 1910 in New Jersey as the National oil company of Mexico. Name changed in August, 1910. To date (1919) it is essentially a holding company, its operations being conducted through several subsidiaries in U.S., Mexico and South America.

NN 0058981 CtY

665.5
N1994o
Engin
Lib'y

NATIONAL OIL CONSERVATION COMMITTEE.
Oil conservation, published by National oil conservation committee. Bristow, Okla., 1946.
27p. illus. 23cm.

1. Petroleum - U.S. 2. Natural resources.

NN 0058982 TxU

National Oil Creek oil company.
Prospectus of the National Oil Creek oil company ... Philadelphia, W. B. Selheimer, printer, 1864.
6 p. 20¼ᶜᵐ.

CA 7—3881 Unrev'd

Library of Congress TN872.Z6N2

NN 0058983 DLC

National Oil Mill Superintendents Association.
Proceedings of the annual convention.
[no.]
Houston, Tex.₁, 1
v.
8°.

1. Cotton seed and cotton seed oil.
N. Y. P. L. —Per. and soc. publ. January 27, 1921.

NN 0058984 NN MiD

National oil policy committee
see
Petroleum industry war council. *National oil policy committee.*

A national oil policy for the United States, a report
see under National Petroleum Council.

QV
772
₁N277

NATIONAL Oil Products Company
₁Collection of publications₁

The library has a collection of miscellaneous publications of this organization kept as received. These publications are not listed nor bound separately.
1. Drugs

NN 0058987 DNLM

SF494
.N3

National oil products co.
... A digest of vitamin D feeding facts. Harrison, N.J., Boston [etc.] National oil products co., inc., c1933.
1 v. 29 cm.
Cover-title.
Loose-leaf; variously paged.
Autographed from type-written copy on one side of leaf only.
Running title: Nutritional information and references, Nutritional laboratory, Farm feed department.

NN 0058988 DLC

National Oil Products Co.
Nopco bulletin.
v. 1–

Harrison, N. J., 1928– 4°.
v. illus.
Monthly (irregular).

1. Oils, Cod liver—Per. and soc. publ. 2. House organs. I. Title.
N. Y. P. L. November 25, 1931

NN 0058989 NN

TN871
.036
1950
A.10

National Oil Proprietary, Ltd., Glen Davis, New South Wales.
The development of the oil shale industry at Glen Davis, New South Wales, Australia, by the staff of National Oil Proprietary, Ltd., Glen Davis. [Bungay, Suffolk, 1950]
24 p. tables, diagrs. 23 cm. (Oil Shale and Cannel Coal Conference, 2d, Glasgow, 1950. [Papers] Preprint, A.10)
"References," p. 24.

1. Oil-shales - New South Wales.

NN 0058990 DI

National oil reporter; recognized petroleum authority of America. v. 1–4 (no. 1–39); June 20, 1901–1903. New York ₁The Bernier publishing co.₁ 1901–03.
4 v. illus., plates, ports., maps. 30ᶜᵐ. weekly.

Subtitle varies.
R. L. Bernier, editor.
No more published?
L. C. set consists of v. 1–3 (no. 1–26) June 20, 1901–Feb. 5, 1903; v. 4 wanting.

1. Petroleum—Period.

Library of Congress TN860.N4
5-35856 Revised

NN 0058991 DLC Nh

National Oil Scouts and Landmen's Association
see
International Oil Scouts Association.

National Oil Scouts Association of America
see
International Oil Scouts Association.

VOLUME 407

National Oil Shale Conference.
[Proceedings of] National Oil Shale Conference. .... .
Library has 1919 *to date.* (*In* Reports of Proceedings of the American Mining Congress .... Washington, D.C., 1919–. 24ᶜᵐ. Vol. 22–.)

NN   0058994   ICJ MoU

National Old People's Welfare Committee
see
National Old People's Welfare Council.

HV   National Old People's Welfare Council.
1481   Age is opportunity; a new guide to practical
.E58   work for the welfare of old people. London,
N27   National Council of Social Service, 1949.
             118 p. illus. diagrs., plates 22 cm.

          Bibliography: p. 108-115.

          1. Old age assistance. 2. Public welfare.

          CaBVaU
NN   0058996   DCU OU NIC CU CaOTP MiU DCU ICU MBCo

HV1481   National Old People's Welfare Council.
.G7   Age is opportunity: a new guide to prac-
N3   tical work for the welfare of old people.
1950   [3d ed.] London, National Council of
             Social Service, 1950.
                147 p. illus. 22cm.

             Pub. 1946 under title: Old people's wel-
          fare; 2d ed., 1947. 3d ed., with above
          title, first pub. in 1949; reprinted, with
          additions, 1950.
             The 1950 reprint also contains (Supplement
          to first impression. p.119-147.
             Includes bi[   ]liography.

NN   0058997   OrCS OrU NcD CU CaBVaU

NATIONAL OLD PEOPLE'S WELFARE Council.
   Age is opportunity; a new guide to practical work
for the welfare of old people. [3. ed., rev. impres-
sion] London, Published for the National old people's
welfare committee by the National council of social
service, 1954. 143 p. illus. 22cm.

   "The National old people's welfare committee first
published the handbook 'Old people's welfare: a guide
to practical work for the welfare of old people' in

February, 1946 (second edition, August, 1947). Increasing experience and the introduction of new legislation has made it necessary to issue a third edition
which has been considerably re-written and enlarged."
   Bibliography, p. 132-140.
   1. Aged—Charities—Gt.Br.   I. National council of
social service. II.   National old people's
welfare committee, Lon-   don. Old people's welfare.

NN   0058999   NN IaU LU

HV1481   National Old People's Welfare Council.
G72N4   The 1949 statement of work being carried out
             for old people by national and local voluntary
          organisations throughout the British Isles.
          [London] National Old People's Welfare Com-
          mittee (in association with the National
          Council of Social Service) [1949?]
             49 p.

             1. Old age. 2. Public welfare - Gt. Brit.

NN   0059000   CU

R367   NATIONAL old people's welfare council.
N2135o   Old people's clubs; a handbook for old
          and new clubs.
                London. National council of social
          service. 1952. 40p.

NN   0059001   WaS

339.42   National Old People's Welfare Council.
N2132o   Old people's clubs; a handbook for
          old and new clubs. Amended ed.
          London, Published by the National
          Council of Social Service for the
          National Old People's Welfare Commit-
          tee, 1954.

             39 p. 22cm.

             "Reference, no. 393"
          1. Aged. I. Title.

NN   0059002   MnU NN

National old people's welfare Council.
   Old people's welfare, a guide to practical
work for the welfare of old people. Lond.
National council of social service [1945]
63 [1] p.

   Bibliography: p. 58-62.

   I. National council of social service, pub.

NN   0059003   MiD

National old people's welfare council.
   Old people's welfare; a guide to practical work for the welfare of
old people.   London, Pub. for the National old people's welfare
committee by the National council of social service [1946]   63 p.
illus. 22cm.

   "Bibliography," p. 58-62.

   1. Aged—Charities—Gt. Br.   I. National council of social service.
N.Y.P.L.   October 11, 1948

NN   0059004   NN

362.6   National Old People's Welfare Council.
N21o2   Old people's welfare; a guide to practical work
         for the welfare of old people. New ed., rev. and
         enl. Published for the National Old People's Wel-
         fare Committee. London, National Council of
         Social Service, 1947.
            cover-title, 71p., 1 p. diagrs. 22cm.

            Bibliography: p.66-70.
            "First published 1946; new ed. 1947."
            Supplement... July. 1948 in pocket.

NN   0059005   LU MH-IR

National Old People's Welfare Council.
   Old people's welfare committee notes...   London, 1942-44.
7 pams.   33cm.

   CONTENTS.—Notes for the guidance of visitors.—Suggested programme of work for
local committees.—Clubs for old people.—Formation of housing societies for the aged.
—Setting up of voluntary homes for the aged.—Public utility societies.

   1. Aged—Charities—Gt. Br.
N.Y.P.L.   June 16, 1948

NN   0059006   NN

National old people's welfare council.
   Over seventy

   see under

   National Council of Social Service.

National Old People's Welfare Council.
   Progress report
   see its
   Report.

National Old People's Welfare Council.
   Report.
   [London, National Council of Social Service]
      v. 22 cm. annual.
   Report year ends Mar. 31.
   Title varies ·   Progress report

   1. Aged—Gt. Brit.   I. National Council of Social Service.
   HV1481.G52N33   63-4759 ‡

NN   0059009   DLC DNLM NN CU MnU

National old trails highway follows the
trail of the pioneers.
n.p., [c1931]

NN   0059010   OClWHi

National old trails road in Ohio
   see under [Galbreath, Charles Burleigh]
1858-1934.

The **National** omnibus; and general advertiser. A jour-
nal of literature, science, music, theatricals, and the
fine arts. v. [1]–
   Apr. 1, 1831–
   London, 1831–
      v. illus. 37ᶜᵐ.
   Biweekly, Apr. 1–Sept. 30, 1831; weekly, Oct. 1831–

   Library of Congress   AP4.N234   14-14029

NN   0059012   DLC OU MB MH

National Open Hearth and Basic Oxygen Steel Confer-
ence.
   Proceedings. v.1–   Apr.1925–
New York.

   Title varies: 192 -35,Minutes (varies slightly)—
1936-41,Open-hearth proceedings. Other slight vari-
ations.
   Sponsored by the National Open Hearth and Basic
Oxygen Steel Committee and,1925-1964,by the Blast
Furnace,Coke Oven and Raw Materials Committee.

NN   0059013   MiU IU ICRL PSt

National Open Hearth and Basic Oxygen Steel
Conference.
   Proceedings
      see also   Metallurgical Society of AIME.
   Iron and Steel Division. Blast Furnace, Coke Oven
   and Raw Materials Committee. Conference.
      Proceedings.

National open shop publicity bureau.
   Propaganda. New York, (1914)
3 pamphlets.

NN   0059015   DL

National Open Shop Publicity Bureau.   3569a.511
   The story of Duluth and the open shop: of common interest to the
owner, architect, builder and workman. By Walter [Drew,
Manager.
= New York. [1910.] (12) pp. 15½ cm.

M1588 — Open shop. — Duluth, Minn. Laboring classes.

NN   0059016   MB

National Opera Association.
   Annual meeting.
   [Flint, Mich.]
   (/) v. 28 cm.

   ML27.U5N475   66-34584/MN

NN   0059017   DLC

National Opera Association.
   Membership Directory. University, Mississippi,
University of Miss., 1955–
   v. 23cm.

   1. Opera—Directories.

NN   0059018   KyLoS

VOLUME 407

F869
S3P18
v. 20;11
x
    National Opera Company.
      American opera by the National Opera Company, the Grand
Opera House, San Francisco. Three weeks' season of grand
opera in English and grand ballet, second week, beginning
April 25, 1887; [program] San Francisco, Dodge Brothers, 1887.
    8 p. 25cm. [Pamphlets on San Francisco. v. 20, no. 11]

    1. Opera - San Francisco. 2. Ballet.. I. Title. (Series)

NN   0059019   CU-B

F869
S3P18
v. 21;18
x
    National Opera Company.
      Second season of grand opera in English sung by Americans
under the musical direction of Theodore Thomas. The first San
Francisco season at the Grand Opera House beginning Monday
evening, April 18, 1887. [San Francisco, C. A. Murdock &
Co., Printers, 1886?]
    10 p. 21cm. [Pamphlets on San Francisco. v. 21, no. 18]

    Cover title: American opera by the National Opera Company,
1886-87, Grand Opera House.

    1. Opera - San Francisco. I. Thomas, Theodore, 1835-1905.
II. Title. (Series)

NN   0059020   CU-B

ML21
.N27
    National Operatic and Dramatic Association, *London.*
      Directory.
      London.
      (l y. 19 cm.

    1. Music—Gt. Brit.—Direct. 2. Theater—Gt. Brit.—Direct.
3. Theater—Societies, etc.

    ML21.N27   5.-15944

NN   0059021   DLC NN

    National Operatic and Dramatic Association, London.
      NODA bulletin.

    London.
      v. illus. 25 cm. 3 no. a year.

    1. National Operatic and Dramatic Association, London.
I. Title.

    ML27.G7N44   782.8'1'06242   73-647551
                                              MARC-S

NN   0059022   DLC

    National operatic and dramatic association,
London.
    Page, Dudley Stuart.
      ... Operas—old and new, compiled by Dudley Stuart Page
and Bernard Richardson Billings. London, Simpkin, Marshall, ltd., 1929.

    National Operatic and Dramatic Association.
      ...Plays. A guide to the works in the Library of the National
Operatic and Dramatic Association... London: Noda, Ltd.,
1929. 167 p. 4°.
      Advertising matter, p. 155-167.

462677A. 1. Drama—Bibl. 2. Opera   —Bibl.
N. Y. P. L.   March 28, 1930

NN   0059024   NN MH

    National Operatic and Dramatic Association, *London.*
      Year book.
      London.
      v. 18 cm.

    1. Music—Almanacs, yearbooks, etc. 2. Theater—Yearbooks.
3. Opera—Gt. Brit. 4. Theater—Gt. Brit.

    ML21.N3   782.06242   53–34106 rev ‡

NN   0059025   DLC IU NIC

    National opinion...
      v. 1

    London, 1918-   4°, f°.
      v.

      Monthly.
      Numbering continuous.
      Published by the Grand Council of the National Party (Gt. Br.).

1. National party, Gt. Br. 2. Great   Britain.—Politics: Per. and soc. publ.
N. Y. P. L.   May 1, 1922.

NN   0059026   NN

HM
261
A1
N3
no. 39
    National Opinion Research Center.
      Animal experimentation; a survey of information, interest, and opinion on the question
among the general public, high school teachers
and practicing physicians. Chicago, 1949.
      81 l. (Its report no. 39)
      Cover title.

    1. Laboratory animals. 2. Medical research.

NN   0059027   UU

    National Opinion Research Center.
      Anti-inflation measures. [Report of a nation-wide sampling survey] [Denver, 1942]
      24 p. illus. (map) 23 cm.
      Cover title.

    1. Finance—U. S. 2. Public opinion—U. S. 3. World War, 1939-
1945—Finance—U. S. I. Title.

    HJ258.N33   332.414   45-15412 rev*

NN   0059028   DLC NN

    National Opinion Research Center.

      Are wars inevitable? [Denver, 1943]
      [3] p. diagr. 28cm. (Its Report, no. 16)
      1. War.

NN   0059029   ViU

HM
261
A1
N27+
no. 53
    National Opinion Research Center
      Attitudes of prominent citizens toward
problems of higher education in the Chicago
area. Chicago, National Opinion Research
Center, University of Chicago, 1954.
      x,71,34 l. 28cm. (Its Report no. 53)

      Its Survey 360.
      "Study director: Patricia Collette."
      Photocopy of typescript.

NN   0059030   NIC

    National opinion research center.
      Attitudes toward "the Japanese in our midst".
Denver, 1946.
      cover-title, 27 p. tables. 28 cm. (Its
Report no. 33)
      Mimeographed copy.

NN   0059031   Mi WaS Or

R
301.
5502
N277
    National Opinion Research Center.
      Bibliography of publications.
      1941-1960—   Chi., 1961-
      v.
      Library has: 1941-1967-
      1941-1960—   prepared by Charles
S. Mack.
      Kept up-to-date by frequent supplements,
which later are cumulated in one volume.

    1. Public opinion—U. S.—Bibl. Title.

NN   0059032   CL OrPS MoSW NN

Soc
JX
1977
N3
    National Opinion Research Center.
      Can the U.N.O. prevent wars? [Denver?]
      National Opinion Research Center, University
of Denver [1946]
      18 l. illus. (Its Report no. 29)

      Processed.

    1. United Nations. 2. War. I. Title.

NN   0059033   FTaSU UU

HM
261
A1
N3
no. 38
    National Opinion Research Center.
      Careers for medical men; some opinions
about medical practice in government services,
with special reference to the medical services
of the Armed Forces. Chicago, 1948.
      84 l. (Its report no. 38)
      Cover title.

    1. Medicine as a profession. 2. Medicine,
Military—United States. I. Title.

NN   0059034   UU

341.1
N213c
    National Opinion Research Center.
      Cincinnati looks again. A report of the
effects of a six months' information program
on behalf of the United Nations on interest,
information and opinion. [Chicago, 1948]
      38 l. 28cm. (Its Report no. 37A)

      Cover title.

    1. United Nations. 2. Public opinion—Cincinnati. I. Titl

NN   0059035   IU

HM
261
A1
N27+
no. 54
    National Opinion Research Center.
      Community aspects of aircraft annoyance.
[Chicago] 1954.
      xi, 127, 24, [42] p. illus. 28cm.
(Its Report no. 54)

      Photocopy (made in 1968?)

    1. Aeroplanes—Noise. I. Title.

NN   0059036   NIC

FILM
614.7
N2771c
    National Opinion Research Center.
      Community aspects of aircraft annoyance.
[Chicago] 1954.
      Microfilm copy made in 1957 by the Air
University Library. Positive.
      Collation of original: 1 v. (various
pagings) diagrs., forms, tables.
      "Report no.54."
      "Responsible for this project: Study director, Paul N. Borsky. Contract no. NAu 6276."
      1. Noises. 2. Sound—Physiological effect.
3. Airplanes. I.   Borsky, Paul N. II. Title.
III. Title: Air-   craft annoyance.

NN   0059037   AMAU

Map
G
3701
F9
1945
    National Opinion Research Center.
      Democratic and Republican governors—
1945. The area of each state is drawn
proportional to the popular vote cast
in 1944. Denver, 1945.
      map 20 x 26cm.

      "Distorted map G-7."

      1. U.S.—Maps.

NN   0059038   NIC

HM
261
A1
N3
no.7
    National Opinion Research Center.
      Detailed findings of an experiment to
test the reliability of opinion surveys.
[Denver] 1943.
      32p. illus. (Its report no. 7)

      "Page 5 to 12 of this report are reprinted
from The public opinion quarterly."

      1. Public opinion polls. I. Title.

NN   0059039   UU

VOLUME 407

National Opinion Research Center.
Distorted map, distribution of world population. Distorted map E showing countries of over 100,000 population as they would appear if their area were proportional to their population ... ₁Denver₎ °1943.
   map.   26 x 41 cm.
   Not true to scale.
   "Figures are shown to the nearest whole thousand and are population estimates from the Statistical yearbook of the League of Nations 1937–38."

   1. Population—Maps.
   G3200.E2 1943.N2   Map 44–5 rev*

NN 0059040   DLC NNC

Map
G
3701
F9
1944
N3
   National Opinion Research Center.
   Distribution of 1944 electoral votes by states. The area of each is drawn proportional to the popular vote cast in 1940.   Denver, 1944.
      map 18 x 25cm.

      "Distorted map F-10."

      1. U.S.—Maps.

NN 0059041   NIC

National opinion research center

   Do people use their public libraries? report prepared especially for Library association of Portland...Oregon;based on a survey ₁including 105 interviews₎ made for the American library association and seventeen cooperating city libraries. 25p. Author,1945.

NN 0059042   OrP

National Opinion Research Center.
The effects of television on college football attendance; report.
₁Chicago?₎
      v. diagrs. 27 cm. annual.
   Prepared for the National Collegiate Athletic Association.

   1. Football attendance. 2. Television audiences.   I. National Collegiate Athletic Association.
   GV959.N3   796.33   53–16712

NN 0059043   DLC OrU

---

fHM261 **National Opinion Research Center.**
.A1N3 For the record: public opinion misses on
no.27a Russia but scores on world organization.
   ₁Denver, 1945₎
      ₁4₎ 1. illus. 28cm. (Its Report no.27)

   Cover title.
   Photocopy.

   1. Public opinion polls. (Series)

NN 0059044   FMU

NATIONAL OPINION RESEARCH CENTER
   Germany and the post-war world.   Author
c1945.
      64 p. illus. (its Report no. 24)

NN 0059045   Or MH IEN Mi DAU

NATIONAL OPINION RESEARCH CENTER
   Has the United States any territorial ambitions? Trend report based on four nation-wide surveys. (10,142 interviews) University of Denver, 1943.
      ₁3₎ p. illus. (its Report no. 13)

NN 0059046   Or

Map
G
3701
F9
1932
   National Opinion Research Center.
   How each state voted in the 4 Roosevelt elections--1932-1944. The area of each state is drawn proportional to the popular vote cast in 1944. Denver, 1945.
      map 20 x 26cm.

      "Distorted map G-9."

      1. U.S.--Maps.

NN 0059047   NIC

HM
251
N277h
1954
   NATIONAL Opinion Research Center
   Human reactions in disaster situations. Chicago, 1954.
      3 v. in 2. illus. (Its Report, no. 52)
                          HM251 N277h
   Armed Services Technical Information Agency. [Document] AD 107-594.
   Research sponsored by the Chemical Corps Medical Laboratories under contracts no. DA-18-108-CML-762 and DA-18-108-CML-2275.

   Work carried out by the center's Disaster Project.
      Photocopy (positive)
      1. Disasters - psychology 2. Disasters - U. S. I. U. S. Chemical Corps. Medical Laboratories   Title

NN 0059049   DNLM

National Opinion Research Center.
Interviewing for NORC. ₁1st ed.₎ Denver, °1945.
      ix, 154 p. illus., forms. 24 cm.
   "Bibliography : public opinion polling": p. 147–148.

   1. Public opinion polls.   I. Title.

   HM261.N34   311.22   46–14116 rev*

NN 0059050   DLC OU OrU ODW MiEM CU TxU TU

National opinion research center
   Interviewing for NORC. Denver,Col.,National opinion research center,University of Denver, 1947.
      ix,154p.incl.illus.,forms. 23½cm.

      "Revised edition, January 1947."
      "Bibliography: public opinion polling": p.147–148.

NN 0059051   PSt ICU MtU NNC

H62
.H9
   National Opinion Research Center.

   Hyman, Herbert Hiram, 1918–
      Interviewing in social research, by Herbert H. Hyman with William J. Cobb ₁and others₎ Foreword by Samuel A. Stouffer. ₁Chicago₎ University of Chicago Press ₁1954₎

HM
261
A1
N3
no.32
   National Opinion Research Center.
   Japan and the post-war world. ₁Denver, 1946₎
      52p. illus. (Its report no. 32)

      Cover title.

      1. United States--Foreign relations--Japan. 2. Japan--Foreign relations--United States. I. Title.

NN 0059053   UU NNC MH PPT

National Opinion Research Center.
[NORC distorted maps] Denver, Col., 1945-1947.
      16 maps.   22 x 28 cm.

NN 0059054   OU

National opinion research
center.
   ... A nation-wide public opinion survey on post-war and current problems ... ₁Denver, 1942₎
      ₁1₎p. illus. (map) 22½cm. (Its Report no. 5)
   Title on cover: A nation-wide survey of post-war and current problems.

   1. Reconstruction (1939-   ). I. Title. II. Title: Post-war and current problems. III. Ser.

NN 0059055   ViU MH

National Opinion Research Center.
   National consumer survey of medical costs and voluntary health insurance
      see under   Health Information Foundation, New York.

National Opinion Research Center.
   National family survey of medical costs and voluntary health insurance

      see under

      Anderson, Odin Waldemar, 1914-

---

qC374.8
N213na
   National Opinion Research Center
   National Opinion Research Center, University of Denver, Denver, Colorado, presents the findings of a survey on night school education in the City of Denver. ₁Denver?₎ 1941.
      18ℓ. tables'. 30cm. (Its Report, no.101)

      1.Denver. Evening and continuation schools 2.Colorado imprints. Denver? 1941 Series

NN 0059058   CoD

National Opinion Research Center.
National survey, December, 1941. ₁Denver, 1941₎
      24 p. 23½ cm.
      Cover title.

      1. World War, 1939–1945—Public opinion—U. S.
      D810.P85U6 1941   940.5373   42–51506 rev*

NN 0059059   DLC

National Opinion Research Center.
National survey, March, 1942. ₁Denver, 1942₎
      32 p. 23 cm.
      Cover title.

      1. World War, 1939–1945—Public opinion—U. S.
      D810.P85U6 1942   940.5373   42–51508 rev*

NN 0059060   DLC OU MdBJ MH

National opinion research center.

      ———— News from N. O. R. C. surveys... Aug. 4–18,
   Dec. 8, 1946. [Denver, 1946] 3 nos. 28cm.

      1. Public opinion—Per. and soc. publ.—U.S.

NN 0059061   NN

National Opinion Research Center.

HM261
.A1O6
   Opinion news; a fortnightly digest of outstanding **polls and** surveys. v. 1-   Sept. 13, 1943-
   Denver, National Opinion Research Center.

VOLUME 407

HE8698
.C65
National opinion
research center.

Columbia university. *Bureau of applied social research.*
The people look at radio; report on a survey conducted by the National opinion research center, University of Denver, Harry Field, director, analyzed and interpreted by the Bureau of applied social research, Columbia university, Paul F. Lazarsfeld, director.   Chapel Hill, The University of North Carolina press ₁1946₎

Map
G
3701
F9
1944a
National Opinion Research Center.
Percentage of citizens voting in 1944 presidential election. The area of each state is drawn proportional to the popular vote cast in 1944. Denver, 1945.
map 20 x 26cm.

"Distorted map G-4."

1. U.S.--Maps.

NN   0059064   NIC

HM
261
A1
N27+
no.46
National Opinion Research Center.
Phonevision; a research report. Responsible for this project: Shirley A. Star ₍and₎ Jacob J. Feldman.   Chicago, National Opinion Research Center, University of Chicago, 1952.
iv,291 p. 28cm. (Its ₍Report no. 46,₎)

"This research was conducted for the Zenith Radio Corporation."

1. Subscription television. I. Star, Shirley Ann, 1918-   II. Zenith Radio Corporation. III. Fe   ldman, Jacob J IV. Title.   V. Series.

NN   0059065   NIC

Map
G
3701
E2
1940
National Opinion Research Center.
Population 21 years of age and over; in₎ 1940 showing states if area were proportional to the number of persons 21 years of age and over. Denver, 1945.
map 18 x 25cm.

"Distorted map A."

1. U.S.--Maps.

NN   0059066   NIC

HM261
.A1C4
1946
National Opinion
Research Center.

Central City Conference on Public Opinion Research, 1946.
Proceedings. Comp. by the National Opinion Research Center, Univ. of Denver. Denver ₍1946?₎

HM
261
A1
N3
no.17
National Opinion Research Center.
Public attitude toward subsidies... prices, wages and salaries; a special report of two telegraphic surveys. Denver, 1943.
5ℓ. (Its report no. 17)

Cover title.

1. Price regulation--United States.
2. Wage-price policy. I. Title.

NN   0059068   UU

W 6
P3
NATIONAL Opinion Research Center
Public attitudes toward prescription costs and the drug industry; a report based on preliminary tabulations from the summer 1955 survey. New York, Health Information Foundation, 1955.
27 p.
1. Drug industry - U. S.   2. Drugs - Prices   Title

NN   0059069   DNLM TxU NIC MiU

370.973
D41p
National opinion
research center
The public looks at education.
₍Denver₎ The Center ₍1944₎
cover-title, 40p. diagrs. Q. (Its Report, no.21)

NN   0059070   IaU CU

HM
261
.N28
National Opinion Research Center.
The public looks at politics and politicians.
[Denver?] University of Denver, 1944.
18 p.   (Its Report, no. 20)
Cover title.

1. Public opinion. I. Title. Series.

NN   0059071   NBuU

HM
261
A1
N3
no.36
National Opinion Research Center.
The public looks at trade and tariff problems. ₍Denver₎ 1947.
32p. illus. (Its report no. 36)

1. Foreign trade regulation--United States. 2. Tariff--United States. I. Title.

NN   0059072   UU OCICC ViU NNC

National Opinion Research Center.
The public looks at world organization.
Denver, 1944.

cover-title, 32p. illus. 28ᶜᵐ. (Its Report no. 19)

1. International organization. I. Title. II. Ser.

NN   0059073   ViU

National Opinion Research Center.
Public opinion in wartime Britain ... ₍Denver₎ 1943-
v. 28 x 22 cm. (Its Special report)
CONTENTS.—pt. I. Attitudes toward rationing and other restrictions.—pt. II. Attitudes toward the United States and Russia.

1. World War, 1939-1945—Public opinion—Gt. Brit.   I. Title.

D810.P85G77   940.5342   44-36050 rev*

NN   0059074   DLC

HM
261
A1
N3
no.25
National Opinion Research Center.
Public opinion on world organization up to the San Francisco Conference. [Denver] 1945?
29ℓ. illus. (Its report no.25)
Cover title.

1. International organization. 2. World politics. I. Title.

NN   0059075   UU NNC ViU

HE8698
.C654
National Opinion Research Center.

Columbia University. *Bureau of Applied Social Research.*
Radio listening in America; the people look at radio—again. Report on a survey conducted by the National Opinion Research Center of the Univ. of Chicago, Clyde Hart, director; analyzed and interpreted by Paul F. Lazarsfeld and Patricia L. Kendall of the Bureau of Applied Social Research, Columbia Univ. New York, Prentice-Hall, 1948.

National opinion research
center.

The reconversion period from war to peace.
₍Denver₎ National opinion research center, University of Denver, 1943.
cover-title, 24 p. incl. diagrs. 28ᶜᵐ. (Its Report no. 9)
1. U. S. - Economic policy. 2. Reconstruction (1939-   ) - U. S.

NN   0059077   NNC ViU

National Opinion Research Center.
Report. no. ₍1₎–   Dec. 1941–
₍Chicago₎
nos. in   illus., maps. 23-29 cm. irregular.
Nos. 1-4 issued without title and numbering.
No. 7 issued in cooperation with the University of Colorado.
Pub. in Denver, Dec. 1941–
Nos. 3-4 accompanied by suppl.

1. Public opinion—U. S. 2. Public opinion.   I. Colorado. University.
HM261.A1N3 ——— 301.154   43-9865 rev*

NN   0059078   DLC UU TxU NBuC MoU INS IU WU NN

330.904
P191
v.1
no.1
National Opinion Research Center.
Report of a nation-wide sampling survey on anti-inflation measures. June, 1942.
₍Denver₎ 1942.
24p. illus. 22cm. (In Pamphlets on business and money. v.1, no.1)

1. Inflation (Finance) U.S. 2. Public opinion. U.S.

NN   0059079   OrU

National Opinion Research Center.
Rocky Mountain survey, with national comparisons.
₍Denver₎ 1942.
24 p. map, diagrs. 23 cm.
Cover title.

1. U. S.—Commercial policy. 2. U. S.—For. rel—1933-1945.
3. Public opinion—The West.   I. Title.
HF1756.N36   337   48-31428 rev*

NN   0059080   DLC

331.25
N214r
National Opinion Research Center.
The role of unemployment compensation in maintaining family income and expenditure in an area of critical unemployment. Chicago, National Opinion Research Center, University of Chicago, 1951.
iv, 37p. tables. 28cm. (Its Survey no.274)

National Opinion Research Center Report no. 43.

NN   0059081   IU

D819
.G3D4
National opinion
research center.

Denver. University. *Social science foundation.*
Shall we try to collect reparations from Germany? Results of a limited public opinion survey in Colorado. ₍Denver₎ Social science foundation, University of Denver, and Carnegie endowment for international peace, in cooperation with National opinion research center, University of Denver, 1943.

HM
261
A1
N3
no.30
National Opinion Research Center.
Should price and rent control be continued? [Denver] 1946.
16ℓ. illus. (Its report no. 30)

Cover title.

1. Price regulation--United States.
2. Rent control. I. Title.

NN   0059083   UU

VOLUME 407

389
N2134 National Opinion Research Center.
Should we return to rationing? ₍Denver₎
1946₎
23 l. (Its Report. no.31)

NN 0059084 DNAL

D81C
.P85U53 National opinion research
center.
Special graphic supplement on current and post-
war problems. ₍Denver,Col.₎1942.
cover-title,16 p. diagrs. 28cm. (Report no.6)

1.World war,1939- Public opinion--U.S.

NN 0059085 ICU

National opinion research center.
...Special report. Jan.-Feb. 1943 [Oct. 1944]
[Denver, 1943-44] 3 nos. 28cm.

1. Public opinion—Per. and soc. publ.—U.S.

NN 0059086 NN

Map
G
3701 National Opinion Research Center.
F9 State-by-State majorities--1940
1940 Presidential election. The area of
each state is drawn proportional to
the popular vote cast in 1940.
Denver, 1944.
map 20 x 26cm.

"Distorted map F-11."

1. U.S.--Maps.

NN 0059087 NIC

National opinion
HF1756 research center.
.D27 Denver. University. *Social science foundation.*
Tariffs versus competitive trade; results of a limited public
opinion survey in Colorado. ₍Denver₎ Social science foundation, University of Denver, and Carnegie endowment for international peace, in cooperation with National opinion research center, University of Denver, 1943.

National opinion
D753 research center.
.D45 Denver. University. *Social science foundation.*
1943 To collect or not to collect for lend-lease; results of a limited
public opinion survey in Colorado. ₍Denver₎ Social science
foundation, University of Denver, and Carnegie endowment
for international peace, in cooperation with National opinion
research center, University of Denver, 1943.

Map
G
3701 National Opinion Research Center.
E2 Total United States population
1940 1940, showing states if area were
N3 proportional to population. Denver,
1945.
map 18 x 25cm.

"Distorted map B (Revised.)"

1. U.S.--Maps.

NN 0059090 NIC

NATIONAL OPINION RESEARCH CENTER
UNESCO and public opinion today. **Author**
c1947.
cover-title, 14 p. (its Report no. 35)

NN 0059091 Or

HM261
.A1D4 National Opinion Research Center.
no.35
1947 UNESCO and public opinion today. ₍Chicago₎
Univ. of Chicago ₍1947₎
74 p. diagrs. 28cm. (National Opinion
Research Center. Report, no. 35)
Cover title.

1. United Nations Educational, Scientific and
Cultural Organization. 2. Public opinion. I.
Ser.

NN 0059092 ViU NNC DCU UU MiU

Map
G
3701 National Opinion Research Center.
F9 U.S. House of Representatives.
1944 Party membership in the 79th Congress
House by states. The area of each state is
drawn proportional to the popular vote
cast in 1944. Denver, 1945.
map 20 x 26cm.

"Distorted map G-6."

1. U.S.--Maps.

NN 0059093 NIC

National Opinion Research Center.
What do the American people think about Federal health
insurance? Report of a nation-wide survey of civilian
adults, conducted for the Physicians' Committee on Research,
inc. ... Special report ... ₍Denver,1944₎
66 l. 28 x 21 cm.

1. Insurance, Health—U. S. 2. Medical care, Cost of—U. S.
I. Physicians' Committee on Research, inc. II. Title.
HD7102.U4N28 1944 331.25442 44-51344 rev*

NN 0059094 DLC CU DNLM

National Opinion Research Center.
What do the American people think about Federal health
insurance? Report of a national public opinion survey of
civilian adults, conducted in August 1944 for the Physicians'
Committee on Research, inc. ₍Denver₎ 1944.
66 l. 28 x 22 cm.

1. Insurance, Health—U. S. 2. Medical care, Cost of—U. S.
I. Physicians' Committee on Research, inc. II. Title.
HD7102.U4N28 1944a 331.25442 45-18407 rev*

NN 0059095 DLC OU

National Opinion Research Center.
What — where — why — do people read?
Highlights of a survey made for the American
Library Association and 17 cooperating city
libraries. [Denver, 1945]
32p. charts. 28cm. (Its Report no.28)

1. Books and reading. 2. Libraries. U.S.
3. Education of adults. I. American Library
Association. II. Title. III. Series.

PP
0059096 IEN UU NFQC TU OrU IU TxU LU Mi CU Or

HM
261 National Opinion Research Center.
A1 Where UNESCO begins; the climate of
N3 opinion in the United States and other
no.34 countries. [Denver, 1947]
66p. (Its report no. 34)

Cover title.

1. United Nations Educational, Scientific,
and Cultural Organization. I. Title.

NN 0059097 UU PPT NNC

National Opinion Research Center
see also Denver. University. Opinion
Research Center.

W 1
NA556 The NATIONAL optical journal.
Liverpool, 1929-₍52?₎
16 v. in illus.
Official organ of the National Association
of Opticians.
Superseded by the National Association
of Opticians (Gt. Brit.) Journal.
1. Optometry - Period. I. National
Association of Opticians (Gt. Brit.)

NN 0059099 DNLM

The National Orator.
Selections adapted for rhetorical recitation,
from parliamentary, forensic and pulpit eloquence
of Great Gritain.
New York, White, Gallaher, 1892.
pp. xi & 300 18 com.

NN 0059100 DCU-H

National Oratorical Contest.
₍Report₎
₍no.
Washington, D. C.₍, 192 12°.
no.
192 lack title.
1925 includes announcement of the 1st International Oratorical Contest... 1926.

1. Oratory—Per. and soc. publ.
N. Y. P. L. September 15, 1926

NN 0059101 NN

National Oratorical Contest.
Sixth national oratorical contest and Fourth
international oratorical contest for secondary
schools, 1929. Randolph Leigh, director,
Washington, D.C., 323 Star Bldg.
74 p.
Contents. - Coolidge, Calvin, Address at the
international finals in 1926. - Hoover, Herbert,
Address at National finals, May 25, 1928.
Ponthieu, Rene, French thought and the idea of
liberty. Tomaso, Jose de, The confraternity of
the Americas. Fox, jr., William, Canada's
future. Moore, James Rayborn, The development
of the Constitution of the United States.

Baker, Dudley Raymond, The English governmental
system. Barth, Heinz, Unity, justice and liberty
in the development of the German Constitution.
Rosado, Efrain Brito, The charater and future of
Spanish culture in America. Fernandez, Julio
Cesar, Cuba's future. Norquist, Elliot, The
present significance of the Constitution. Olson,
jr., Charles J., The present significance of the
Constitution. Johnson, Frederick, The present
significance of the Constitution. West, Joseph E.,
The present significance of the Constitution.
Zabludofsky, Ralph, The present significance of
the Constitution. Hinden, Benjamin E., The

development of the Constitution. Noyes,
Theodore W., Marvelous South America.

NN 0059104 WaU-L

National Oratorical Contest. *5599-206
3d National Oratorical Contest, and International Oratorical
Contest, 1st, for secondary schools. 1926.
= [Washington. 1926.] v. 19½ cm.

Each issue contains the prize winning speeches of the previous year.

N2991 — Double main card. —
— International Oratorical Contest. ₍2₎ — Orations. (1, 2) — Secondary
schools. United States. (1, 2)
National Oratorical Contest. (M1)

NN 0059105 MB OC1

The National oratorical contest news. Washington, D.C.]1928-29]
3 v. in 1. illus. (incl. ports.) 33-35 cm.
(In binder: 41 cm.)
"Published in the interest of the contest
in its national and international phases".
"Bibliography to aid contestants prepared by
special committee of American bar association":
v.3, no. 1, p. 5.: 3 v. in 1 v. 2, no. 2-3;
Mar. 1-Nov. 1, 1929: 3 v. in 1., v. 3, no. 1-
3; Feb. 22-Apr. 29, 1929: 3 v. in 1., v. 4,
no. 1; Nov. 13, 1929.

NN 0059106 WaU

VOLUME 407

National Orchard Heater Co.
Frost protection; how market crops are safeguarded from frost damage. [1927?]
61 p. illus., diagrs. 23.5 cm.

NN   0059107   PSt DAS

National orchard heater Co.
Frost protection. How market
crops are safeguarded from frost
damage. (Covina. 1928.)
68 p. illus. 23 1/2 cm.

NN   0059108   DAS

NATIONAL ORCHESTRAL ASSOCIATION, London.
Constitution, objects, and rules. London, [1913].
16p.
Date in pencil on cover.
Cover-title.
Tipped in inside back cover: Temporary branch rules
1 leaf, folded.

NN   0059109   MH-IR

NATIONAL ORCHESTRAL ASSOCIATION, London
Directory of members, August, 1914. London [1914?].
168p.

NN   0059110   MH-IR

NATIONAL ORCHESTRAL ASSOCIATION, London
Memorandum and articles of association of the
orchestral association (founded June, 1893)... revise
articles registered May 4th, 1898. [London?, 1898?].
22p.
Date, 1898, in pencil on front cover.
"Founded June, 1893"

1.Great Britain - Union publications
2.Musicians -Gt.Brit.   Brit. Lib. of Pol. & Econ.
Sc., 1948.

NN   0059111   MH-IR

National orchestral association, New York.
So practical a contribution, 1930-1940. New York, The
National orchestral association, incorporated [1940]
86 p., 1 l. illus. (incl. map) diagr. 27ᶜᵐ.

"In this association (young musicians) ... have the opportunity, without cost, to secure training in symphonic repertoire, in the technique of
playing in an orchestra, and to obtain experience in public concerts."—
p. 3.
Appendix: Programs, 1930-1940.—Soloists of regular series, 1930-
1940.—Saturday afternoon series; concertos played from 1934-1935 to
1939-1940.—"How many a tale their music tells"; repertoire, 1930-1940.
I. Title.

Library of Congress   ML28.N5N22
Copyright   40-29674
Copy 2.

OCl OC1W
NN   0059112   DLC PPT MiU OkU WaU FTaSU NIC OU WaS

ML410
.M9W45
National Orchestral Association, New York.
[Wheaton, Eliot Barculo]
The story of the MS. of Mozart's Haffner symphony.
[New York, National Orchestral Association, 1941?]

NN   0059113

National orchestral survey.
Grant, Margaret.
America's symphony orchestras, and how they are supported,
by Margaret Grant and Herman S. Hettinger. New York,
W. W. Norton & company, inc. [1940]

National order of cowboy rangers.
Official ritual, National order of cowboy rangers, written by A. U. Mayfield, supreme boss. Officially adopted
by the Supreme ranch, National order of cowboy rangers,
Denver, Colorado, A. D. 1914. [Denver, Printed in secret
by J. A. Payne, ᶜ1915]
20 p. 17½ᶜᵐ. $0.25

I. Mayfield, Albert U.

Library of Congress   HS1510.C892 1915   16-4103

NN   0059115   DLC

National order of the true aid society of america
see
True aid society of America.

National Organic Chemistry symposium
see under   American Chemical Society.
Division of Organic Chemistry.

National Organization Committee of the Ladies' Garment Work-
ers.
Report of the National Organization Committee of the Ladies'
Garment Workers to the first convention for the establishment of
our new union. New York, N. Y., 1930. 50 f. f°.
Cover-title.
Typewritten.

556503A. 1. Trades unions, Garment   workers'—U. S.
N. Y. P. L.   November 23, 1931

NN   0059118   NN

National organization for decent literature.
The drive for decency in print; report of the bishops' committee sponsoring the National organization for decent literature. Huntington, Ind., Our Sunday visitor press [1939?]
218 p. illus. (incl. port.) 19ᶜᵐ.

1. Literature, Immoral. 2. Censorship—U. S. 3. Publishers and publishing—U. S.   I. Catholic church in the U. S. Bishops. Committee
on obscene literature. II. Title.
                                              A 40-2518

Catholic univ. of America.   Library
for Library of Congress   [2]

NN   0059119   DCU WaSpG ICU

National Organization for Decent Literature.
Manual of the National Organization for Decent
Literature
see under   Noll, John Francis, bp. 1875-

National Organization for Decent Literature.
Report of Bishops' Committee on Obscene
Literature. Huntington, Ind., Our Sunday
Visitor Press [1939?].
15p. 19cm.

1. Literature, Immoral 2. Censorship - U.S.
3. Publishers and publishing - U.S. I. Catholic
Church in the U.S. Bishops' Committee on
Obscene Literature.

BT3495.N35

NN   0059121   KAS

W
1
NA558
National Organization for Public Health
Nursing
Annual report to member agencies ...

New York [19
v. illus.

NN   0059122   DNLM

National Organization for Public Health Nursing.
Bibliography [of] psychiatric nursing and
mental hygiene
see under   National League of Nursing
Education.

National organization for public health nursing.
Bibliography on administration of public health nursing.
[New York, National organization for public health nursing,
1938]
4 numb. l. 28ᶜᵐ.
Caption title.
Mimeographed.

1. Hygiene, Public — Bibliography. 2. Nurses and nursing — Bibliography.   A 40-772

Catholic univ. of America.   Library
for Library of Congress   [2]

NN   0059123   DCU

RT97
A12N5
Public
Health
Lib.
National Organization for Public Health
Nursing.
Bibliography relating to administration of
public health nursing. [New York, 1951]
5 l.
Caption title.

I. Public health nursing - Bibl.

NN   0059124   CU DNLM

National organization for public health
nursing.
Biennial report.
New York
v.   20½ᶜᵐ.

1. Public health nursing - Societies.

NN   0059125   NNC

National organization for public health nursing.
Board members' manual, for board and committee members
of public health nursing services, prepared by the National
organization for public health nursing, inc. New York, The
Macmillan company, 1930.
xi p., 2 l., 3-127 p. diagrs. 19½ᶜᵐ.
"Suggested reference reading on public health nursing": p. 117-119.

1. Public health nursing.

Library of Congress   RT97.N25   30—15542
                          [a45f1]   610.73

NN   0059126   DLC MiU OC1W OCl CaBVaU

National organization for public health nursing.
Board members' manual, for board and committee members
of public health nursing services, by the National organization
for public health nursing. 2d ed., rev. and reset. New York,
The Macmillan company, 1937.
xii p., 1 l., 173 p. 19½ᶜᵐ.
Bibliography: p. 158-161.

1. Public health nursing.

Library of Congress   RT97.N25 1937   37—21942
                          [a44d1]   610.73

NN   0059127   DLC NcD-MC CtY-M Or OrU-M MiDP NN

WY
108
N277b
1937
NATIONAL Organization for Public Health
Nursing
Board members' manual, for board
and committee members of public health
nursing services. 2d ed., rev. and reset.
New York, Macmillan, 1938 [c1937]
xii, 173 p.

1. Nursing - Public health

NN   0059128   DNLM OU OC1W NcD CaBViP

VOLUME 407

National organization for public health nursing.
... Bookkeeping guide ...   New York, N.Y.
[1937?]
9 numb. l.   table.   29 cm.
Caption title.
Mimeographed.
1. Nurses and nursing - Accounting.

NN   0059129   CU

RT97
.W4
National Organization for Public Health **Nursing.**

Wensley, Edith Elizabeth, 1906–
Building sound public relations. New York, **National
Organization for Public Health Nursing, 1949.**

W 1
NA558C
NATIONAL Organization for Public Health
Nursing
Bulletin. no. 1-12; Nov. 1913-Dec.
1916.   New York.
12 no. in   W1 NA558C
No more published?
Title: Bulletin of the National
Organization for Public Health Nursing

NN   0059131   DNLM

National organization for public health nursing.
Census of public health nursing in the United States
prepared by the National organization for public health
nursing (byLouise M. Tattershall. Albany, N.Y., 1926)
cover-title, p. 247-313. 24½ cm (The Public health
nurse, vol. XVIII, no. 5 May 1926)
A detached copy

NN   0059132   DL

National organization for public health nursing.
Census of public health nursing in the United States
1931. Prepared by the National organization for public
health nursing, by Louise M. Tattershall. (New York,
1934)
cover-title, 2 p.l., 71 p. maps, tables, 25 cm

NN   0059133   DL OC1W

[National Organization for Public Health Nursing.
Collection of pamphlets relating to public health nursing.
New York: National Organization for Public Health Nursing,
1914-20.] 71 pamphlets in 1 v.   diagrs., illus. (part col'd.)   8°.

1. Nurses and nursing (Public
N. Y. P. L.   health).
                                      August 16, 1920.

NN   0059134   NN

WY
108
qN277
NATIONAL Organization for Public Health
Nursing
[Collection of publications]

The Library has a collection of miscellaneous publications of this organization
kept as received. These publications are
not listed nor bound separately.
1. Public health nursing - U. S.

NN   0059135   DNLM

RT97
.W42
National Organization for Public Health **Nursing.**

Wensley, Edith Elizabeth, 1906–
The community and public health nursing; a handbook
for and about boards and citizens committees, by Edith
Wensley for the National Organization for Public Health
Nursing. New York, Macmillan, 1950.

National organization for public health nursing.
...Constitution and by-laws. Adopted April 29th,
1914; revised April 26th, 1917. (New York? 1917?)
cover-title, 19 p.   15½ cm
"Supplement to Bulletin, vol. 2, no. 3."

NN   0059137   DL

National Organization for Public Health Nursing.
Cost analysis for public health nursing services. New
York [1950?]
vii, 104 p. 28 cm.

1. Public health nursing—Costs.

RT97.N26   614.073   51-4373

NN   0059138   DLC NcD AU DNLM OrU-M Wa CU

National Organization for Public Health Nursing.
Cost study manual (temporary draft). New
York, N.O.P.H.N., n.d.

117 p.

NN   0059139   OrU-M

RN
440
.N62
National organization for public health nursing.
Descriptive criteria for evaluation of advanced programs of study in psychiatric nursing and mental hygiene. [n.p., 1949]
4 p.l., 54 (i.e. 55) numb. l.   28 x 21½ cm.
Reproduced from type-written copy; includes
extra numbered leaf 12a.
Stamped at foot of t.p.: Headquarters, National league of nursing education, New York, N.Y.
"The National organization for public health
nursing and the National league of nursing
education cooperated in ... [this] study."--
Pref.
1.Psychiatric nursing.   I.National league of
nursing educa-   tion. 2.Nurses and nurs-
ing--Study and   teaching.

NN   0059140   MiU DNLM NcU

WY
1
qN281h
1940
NATIONAL Organization for Public Health
Nursing
Handbook of information for board
members of the National Organization for
Public Health Nursing.   [New York] 1940.
36 l.   illus.   WY1 qN281h

NN   0059141   D NLM

National organization for public health nursing.
... A handbook on records and statistics in the field of public-
health nursing, prepared by a joint committee of the National
organization for public health nursing, and the Advisory committee on social statistics in child welfare and related fields
of the United States Children's bureau. June 1932. Washington, U. S. Govt. print. off., 1932.
vi, 30 p. incl. forms. 23ᶜᵐ.
At head of title: United States Department of labor, W. N. Doak,
secretary. Children's bureau. Grace Abbott, chief.
1. Nurses and nursing—Statistics.   I. U. S. Children's bureau.
Advisory committee on social statistics in child welfare and related
fields. II. Title.
                                               L 33–56
Library. U. S. Dept. of   Labor RT45.N24

NN   0059142   DL MB NN WaWW OrCS Or OU OCU MiU OO

RT97
.D3
National organization for public health nursing.

Davis, Evelyn K
Handbook on volunteer services in public health nursing
organizations, prepared by Evelyn K. Davis, assistant director,
National organization for public health nursing, inc., New
York, N. Y. [New York] 1941.

National organization for public health
nursing.
Health insurance; a brief study guide
see under American nurses'
association.

National Organization for Public Health Nursing.
History of the National nursing council
see under National Nursing Council.

National organization for public health nursing.
Learning through experience in family health
work, a report of student participation in the
East Harlem nursing service program, 1928-1941.
New York, National organization for public health
nursing, 1944.
102 p.   23 cm.
1. Public health nursing. I. East Harlem
nursing and health service program. II. Title.

NN   0059146   NcU

RC180
.8
.P6W436
National organization for public health nursing.

West, Jessie (Stevenson) 1891–
Modo de cuidar a los pacientes de parálisis infantil, por
Jessie L. Stevenson ... New York, N. Y., The National
foundation for infantile paralysis, inc., 1940.

National organization for public health
nursing.
The nurse in the industrial field. [New
York, 1947?]
7 p.

Bibliography: p. [8]

1. Industrial nursing.   I. Title.

NN   0059148   NNC

National organization for public health nursing.

Joint committee on health problems in education.
The nurse in the school, an interpretation. A report of the
Joint committee on health problems in education of the National education association and the American medical association. Cooperating agency: Education committee of the
School nursing section of the National organization for public
health nursing. Washington, D. C., National education association [1942?]

RT71
.A53
National organization for public health nursing.

American nurses' association. *Nursing information bureau.*
Nursing, a profession for college women, 1945. The Nursing
information bureau of the American nurses' association co-
operating with the National league of nursing education and
the National organization for public health nursing ... New
York, N. Y. [1945]

National organization for public health nursing.
Nursing and the registered nurse
see under American nurses' association.
Nursing information bureau.

RC180
8
P6W43
940n
National organization for public health nursing.
FOR OTHER EDITIONS
SEE MAIN ENTRY
West, Jessie (Stevenson) 1891–
The nursing care of patients with infantile paralysis, by
Jessie L. Stevenson ... [New York] 1940.

RT99
.M33
National organization for public health nursing.

McGrath, Bethel J
Nursing in commerce and industry, by Bethel J. McGrath,
R. N., for the National organization for public health nursing.
New York, The Commonwealth fund, 1946.

National organization for public
health nursing.
The nursing profession and the
maternity and infancy act... (Washington,
Govt. print. off., 1923.
6 p.   22 x 10 cm.

Folder.

NN   0059154   DL

VOLUME 407

RT97
.R3

National organization for public health
    nursing.
Randall, Marian G
    Personnel policies in public health nursing; a report of current practice in a sample of official health agencies in the United States, prepared for the Committee on personnel practices in official agencies of the National organization for public health nursing by Marian G. Randall. New York, The Macmillan company, 1937.

National organization for public health nursing.
    Principles and practices in public health nursing, including cost analysis, prepared by the National organization for public health nursing ... New York, The Macmillan company, 1932.
    ix, 129 p. forms (1 fold.) 20½ᶜᵐ.
    "The National organization for public health nursing, through its Service evaluation committee, has prepared this handbook ... which is to be used in connection with the Board members' manual and the Manual of public health nursing."—Introd.

    1. Nurses and nursing. 2. Hygiene, Public.   I. Title: Public health nursing.
                                                            32-5475
    Library of Congress   RT97.N34
    Copyright A 48608   ₍3₎   610.73

    CaBViP OU OCl MiU WaU DHEW
NN 0059156   DLC NcD NcD-MC DSI ViU MtBC WaS OrU-M

National organization for public health
    nursing.
    Programs of study for the preparation of
public health nurses. New York, 1946.
    11 p.

    1. Public health nursing. I. Title.

NN 0059157   NNC

National Organization for Public Health Nursing.   3769a.88
    The public health nurse.
= New York City. [1919.] 8 pp. 23 cm.
    In the form of a folder.

L.7531 — T.r. — Nursing. Public.

NN 0059158   MB

RT1
.P8

National Organization for Public Health Nursing.

    Public health nursing. v.   -44;   -Dec. 1952.
    ₍New York, etc.₎

National organization for public health nursing.
    Public health nursing, care of the sick; a survey of needs and resources for nursing care of the sick in their homes in 16 communities, by the National organization for public health nursing. Hortense Hilbert, associate director; Sybil Palmer Bellos, staff associate for the survey. New York, N. Y., National organization for public health nursing, inc., 1943.
    56 p. 23ᶜᵐ.

    1. Public health nursing.   I. Hilbert, Hortense. II. Bellos, Sybil Palmer.
                                                            43-18360
    Library of Congress   RT97.N343
                               ₍a44d2₎   614.073

NN 0059160   DLC DNLM

RT99
.H6

National organization for public health
    nursing.
    Hodgson, Violet (Hoffman) 1888–
    Public health nursing in industry, prepared for the National organization for public health nursing by Violet H. Hodgson ... New York, The Macmillan company, 1933.

National Organization for Public Health Nursing.
    Report of conference on graduate education in
public health nursing
        see under   Conference on Graduate Education for Public Health Nurses, New York, 1951.

National organization for public health nursing.
    Manual of public health nursing, prepared by the National organization for public health nursing ... **New York, The Macmillan company, 1926.**
    viii, 169 p. 17ᶜᵐ.
    Bibliography: p. 165-166.

    1. Nurses and nursing. 2. Hygiene, Public.

    Library of Congress   RT97.N3   26-11430

NN 0059163   DLC OrU-M DNLM OEac

National organization for public health nursing.
    Manual of public health nursing, prepared by the National organization for public health nursing ... New York, The Macmillan company, 1927.
    viii, 169 p. 17ᶜᵐ.
    Bibliography: p. 165-166.

NN 0059164   ICJ MiU OU

National organization for public health nursing.
    Manual of public health nursing, prepared by the National organization for public health nursing ... 2d ed. New York, The Macmillan company, 1932.
    x, 253 p. 20½ᶜᵐ.
    Bibliography: p. 239-244.

    1. Nurses and nursing. 2. Hygiene, Public.
                                                            32-9309
    Library of Congress   RT97.N3 1932
    ———— Copy 2.
    Copyright A 50548   ₍2₎   610.73

    DL NN MB
NN 0059165   DLC TxU NIC DSI MtBC IdB OrU-M OClW

National organization for public health nursing
    Manual of public health nursing, prepared
by the National organization for public health
nursing... 2d ed.
New York, The Macmillan co., 1933.
    x, 253 p.

NN 0059166   OU MiU OCl

National Organization for Public Nursing.
    Manual of public health nursing. 2d ed. New
York, Macmillan, 1935.
    253p.

NN 0059167   ICRL

National Organization for Public Health Nursing.

    Manual of public health nursing. 2d ed.
New York, Macmillan, 1936 [c1932]

    253 p. 21 cm.
    This ed. first published 1932.
    Bibliography: p. 239-244.

    1. Nurses and nursing 2. Public health
a. Public health nursing.

NN 0059168   CaBVaU

National organization for public health nursing.
    Manual of public health nursing, prepared by the **National** organization for public health nursing ... **3d ed. New York,** The Macmillan company, 1939.
    xvi, 529 p. 19¼ᶜᵐ.
    "Revised and reset."
    "References" at end of some of the chapters.

    1. Public health nursing.
                                                            40-3049
    Library of Congress   RT97.N3 1939
                               ₍a44p1₎   614.073

    OrU-M PU OCl OU OLak Or CaBVaU
NN 0059169   DLC MiDP NcD PU TU PPPL PPWM IdU MtBC

National organization for public health nursing

    Manual of public health nursing, prepared by the
National organization for public health nursing ...
3d ed. New York, The Macmillan company ₍1941₎
xvi, 529 p. 19½cm
    "Revised and reset."
    "References" at end of some of the chapters.
    "Reprinted November 1941."

    1. Public health nursing

NN 0059170   ViU MiDP CaBViP

National organization for public health
    nursing.
    Selected reading on the history of public
health nursing. ₍New York, 1947₎
    3 v.
    1. Public health nursing - History -
Bibliography.

NN 0059171   NNC

National organization for public health nursing.
    Serving you nationally ... New York, National
organization for public health nursing, inc. [1938]
    23 p. 25 cm.

NN 0059172   NcD-MC

RT97
.S53

National organization for public health nursing.

Shetland, Margaret L
    Statistical reporting in public health nursing, by Margaret L. Shetland ... written under the guidance of the Records committee and the Cost analyses committee of the National organization for public health nursing. New York, N. Y. ₍1944₎

National Organization for Public Health Nursing.
    A study of desirable functions and qualifications
for psychiatric nurses

    see under

    National League of Nursing Education.

National organization for public health nursing
    Suggestions for statistical reporting and cost
computation in public health nursing. N. Y.,
1937.
    48 p.

    References: p. 47-48.

    Later edition published as Statistical reporting in public health nursing, by Margaret L. Shetland.

NN 0059175   MiD MH WaU

National organization for public health nursing.
    Supervision in public health nursing ... New York, N. Y.,
National organization for public health nursing ₍1940₎
    cover-title, iv, 46 p. incl. tables, diagr. 24½ᶜᵐ.
    "Articles reprinted from Public health nursing magazine."
    "References" at end of two of the articles.

    1. Nurses and nursing. 2. Hygiene, Public.   I. Title.
                                                            A 41-2478
    Catholic univ. of America.   Library
    for Library of Congress   ₍2₎

NN 0059176   DCU

National Organization for Public Health Nursing.
    Supplement to Cost analysis

    see under

    Levenson, Goldie.

VOLUME 407

National organization for public health nursing.
Survey of public health nursing; administration and practice, by the National organization for public health nursing; Katharine Tucker, general director; Hortense Hilbert, assistant director for the survey. New York, The Commonwealth fund; London, H. Milford, Oxford university press, 1934.
xv, 262 p. 24ᵐ.
"Selected list of publications of the National organization for public health nursing": p. ₍223₎-225.

1. Nurses and nursing. 2. Hygiene, Public.   ɪ. Tucker, Katharine, 1884-   ɪɪ. Hilbert, Hortense. ɪɪɪ. Title: Public health nursing.

Library of Congress   RT97.N35   34–11237
Copyright A 71332   ₍3₎   614.073

MtBC OrU-M CaBVaU MB ViU OO WaU MiU
NN 0059178   DLC OrU Or OrCS ICRL IaU ICRL LU OU

National Organization for Public Health Nursing
see also
American Nurses' Association. *Nursing Information Bureau.*
Committee of the Six National Nursing Organizations on Unification of Accrediting Activities.
Committee on the Structure of National Nursing Organizations.
Joint Committee of the National Organization for Public Health Nursing and the United States Public Health Service.

Joint Orthopedic Nursing Advisory Service of the National Organization for Public Health Nursing and the National League of Nursing Education.
National League for Nursing.
Structure Steering Committee.

National Organization for Public Health Nursing
see also Joint Committee of the American Nurses' Association and the National Organization for Public Health Nursing.

National Organization for Public Health Nursing
see also Joint Committee of the National League of Nursing Education and the National Organization for Public Health Nursing on Integration of the Social and Health Aspects of Nursing in the Basic Curriculum.

National Organization for Public Health Nursing
see also Joint Tuberculosis Nursing Advisory Service.

RT
97
.N283
National Organization for Public Health Nursing. Collegiate Council of Public Health Nursing Education.
Proceedings of work conference, October 10-13, 1951, Haven Hill Lodge, Milford, Michigan. New York, National Organization for Public Health Nursing, 1951.
25 l.   28 cm.

1. Public health nursing--Study and teaching.

NN 0059184   MiU CU NcU

National Organization for Public Health Nursing. Committee on Auxiliary Workers in Public Health Nursing.
Volunteers and other auxiliary workers in public health nursing
see under ₍Carter, Dorothy J₎

W 6
P3
NATIONAL Organization for Public Health Nursing. Committee on Camp Nursing
The nurse in the camp program ₍prepared by the Committee on Camp Nursing of the School Nursing Section of the National Organization for Public Health Nursing in cooperation with the National Committee on Health and Safety of the American Camping Association₎ New York ₍1951₎
36 p. illus.

Continued in next column

Continued from preceding column

Cover title.
1951 revision of Suggested standards for camp nursing.
1. Camping 2. Nursing - Pediatric
I. American Camping Association.
National Committee on Health and Safety

NN 0059187   DNLM OrU-M Or NcU

National organization for public health nursing. Committee on camp nursing.
Suggested standards for camp nursing. New York, 1946.
cover-title, 19 p.

Bibliography: p. 16-19.

1. Medical jurisprudence. I. Kovács, Richárd, jt au.

NN 0059188   NNC TU TxU

National Organization for Public Health Nursing. *Committee on Nursing Administration.*
A study of combination services in public health nursing; a project. New York, National Organization for Public Health Nursing, 1950.
v, 55 p. 28 cm.
Bibliography: p. 55.

1. Public health nursing.   ɪ. Title.

RT97.N358   614.073   52–607

NN 0059189   DLC ViU NcU ViU CU CtY-M DNLM MU OrU-M

National organization for public health nursing. ₍
Committee on organization and administration.
Suggestions for constitutions and by-laws of nursing organizations, with notes, also suggestions in regard to nurses' salaries, promotions, etc., etc. Prepared by the chairman of the Committee on organization and administration...of the National organization for public health nursing... ₍New York? 1915?₎
9 ₍1₎ p. 23 cm.

NN 0059190   DL

National Organization for Public Health Nursing. *Committee on Part-time Nursing Service to Industry.*
Part-time nursing in industry as provided by visiting nurse associations in the United States; report. New York ₍1947?₎
68 p. forms, plans. 23 cm.
"Suggested reading": p. 35-36.

1. Industrial nursing.   ɪ. Title.

RT99.N3   610.73   Med 47–2665*

NN 0059191   DLC OrU-M

National Organization for Public Health Nursing. *Committee on Personnel Policies.*
Personnel policies for public health nursing agencies. New York ₍1946₎
1 v. (loose-leaf) 29 cm.

1. Public health nursing.   ɪ. Title.

RT97.N36   614.073   Med 47–2680*

NN 0059192   DLC CU DNLM OrU-M

National organization for public health nursing. Committee to study visiting nursing
Report₍ of the Committee to study visiting nursing instituted by the National organization for public health nursing at the request of the Metropolitan life insurance company. New York, 1924.
196 p.

NN 0059193   OC1 CU NN MiD ViU MB MiU DNLM DL

National Organization for Public Health Nursing. *Industrial Nursing Section. Committee on Part-time Nursing Service to Industry*
see **National Organization for Public Health Nursing.** *Committee on Part-time Nursing Service to Industry.*

National organization for public health nursing. *Library department.*
Reading lists on organization, administration and development of public health nursing, child welfare, school welfare, school nursing and health teaching, nutrition and school lunches, dental hygiene, community hygiene and sanitation, tuberculosis, industrial welfare, venereal disease problems and sex hygiene, mental hygiene, health centers, occupational therapy. Appendix, A list of bureaus and organizations publishing reports and bulletins

... Comp. by A. M. Carr and Florence Bradley. New York city, The Library department, National organization for public health nursing, 1920.
24 p. 23ᵐᵐ.

1. Nurses and nursing—Bibl. 2. Hygiene, Public—Bibl. 3. Children—Care and hygiene—Bibl.   ɪ. Carr, A. M. ɪɪ. Bradley, Florence.

Library of Congress   Z6675.N7N2   20–27472

NN 0059196   DLC NB OC1

National Organization for Public Health Nursing. School Nursing Section, Atlantic City, 1952.
Trends in school nursing as seen by ... John L. Miller ₍and others₎ New York, National League for Nursing ₍1952₎
₍14₎L. 28cm.
Cover title.
Mimiographed.
"Discussion at 1952 Biennial Meeting ... June 19, 1952..."

NN 0059197   PU

National Organization for the Rehabilitation of Cripples
see
Organización Nacional de Rehabilitación de Inválidos.

National organization, masters, mates and pilots of America.
Directory of the American association of masters and pilots of steam vessels of the Great lakes. 1899-
Buffalo, N. Y. ₍1899-
v. illus. 18ᵐ.

1. Pilots and pilotage—Great lakes—Direct. 2. Merchant seamen—Great lakes—Direct.

99–4351 Revised 2
Library of Congress   HD6515.S4N37⁹

NN 0059199   DLC

National Organization, Masters, Mates and Pilots of America. Log of the ... annual voyage
see its Report of proceedings of the ... convention.

HE561
.M4
National organization, masters, mates and pilots of America.
The Master, mate and pilot. v. 1-8, no. 9; June 1908–Feb 1916. New York ₍1908-16₎

National organization masters, mates and pilots of America. (Publication) 1928—

₍New York, 1928 -)
1v. 22cm.

NN 0059202   DL

National Organization, Masters, Mates and Pilots of America. Record of the ... convention
see its Report of proceedings of the ... convention.

VOLUME 407

National organization, masters, mates and pilots of America.
  Report of proceedings of the ... convention.

  ₍New York₎
    v. 22½–35½ cm.
    Annual,   ; biennial.
    First meeting held in 1887.
    Vols. for   –1942 mimeographed.
    Vols. for   issued by the organization under its earlier name:
    American association of masters, mates and pilots.
    Title varies: Log of the ... annual voyage.
    1944–   Report of the ... convention.
    1944–   Report of proceedings of the ... convention.
    1. Merchant seamen—U. S. ₍1. Seamen—U. S.₎

  VK1.N27   L 47–126
    U. S. Dept. of labor. Libr.
    for Library of Congress   ₍2₎†

NN   0059204   DL DLC MB NN WHi

  National organization masters, mates and
    pilots of America. Local union, no.88.
    New York harbor, no. 88 of masters and
    mates...Constitution and by-laws...
    (New York, 1918)
    16 p. 13cm.

NN   0059205   DL

  National Organisation of Catholic Action,
    Australia.
        Catholic action in Australia
        see under Catholic Church in Australia.
    Bishops.

National organization of sausage manufacturers.
  Sausage and ready-to-serve meats for every occasion. Chicago, Ill.: National organization of sausage manufacturers, 1935.
  32 p. illus. 18cm.

  On cover: 93 appetizing recipes.

  1. Cookery—Meat. I. Title.
  N. Y. P. L.   September 30, 1940

NN   0059207   NN MB

KF4119
A2N3   National Organization on Legal Problems of
          Education.
          Conference proceedings. 1st– 19 –
          Topeka.
          v. 27cm.

          Each vol. has also a distinctive title:

          15th, Upsurge and upheaval in school law;
          16th, Critical issues in school law;

NN   0059208   GU-L IU NbU NBuC NjR ViU-L ICarbS LU

VA   National organizations. Prepared for the N.E.
          Non-resistance society. Published by the
20941   executive committee. Boston, 1839.
          32p.

NN   0059209   DLC

  National Organizing Committee for the 20
    Year Plan.
    Preliminary prospectus of the 20 year
    plan. Wash.The Comm.[n.d.].
    15p.nar.D.

NN   0059210   CaBViP

National Organizing Committee for War Savings.
  Leaflet
no.

London: the Committee ₍191   12°.
    no.
    no.4. How to save and why.

  1. European war, 1914– .—Eco-   nomic aspects, Gt. Br. 2. Thrift,
  Gt. Br.
  N. Y. P. L.   December 1, 1916.

NN   0059211   NN

**National ornamental glass manufacturing association of
    the United States and Canada.**
    100% ; a computation table in which profits consistent with production can be found. Copyright ... by the National ornamental glass manufacturing association of the United States and Canada. St. Louis, Mo., For sale by the secretary, C. C. Jacoby, ₍1918.
    15 p. 35 x 10½ᶜᵐ.

    1. Ready-reckoners. 2. Glass trade—Tables and ready-reckoners.
    i. Title.

  Library of Congress   HF5699.N25   18–5894

NN   0059212   DLC

AR 748.5 N13
    National Ornamental Glass Manufacturing Association of the United States and Canada.
    Revised international stained glass catalog:
    church.
    [n.p.] National Ornamental Glass Manufacturing Association of the United States and Canada
    [n.d.]
    16 p. of col. illus.

    Cover title.
    Running title: Revised international art glass

    catalogue.
    Labels on covers: Manufactured by Colonial Art Glass Co., Ottawa.

    1. Glass painting and staining—Canada.
    I. Colonial Art Glass Co., Ottawa.

NN   0059214   CaOTP

  National Orphans' Homestead, Gettysburg, Pa.
    see Gettysburg, Pa. National Orphans'
    Homestead.

  National Orthopaedic Hospital for the Deformed,
    London
        see London. National Orthopaedic Hospital
    for the Deformed.

National outboard association.
    ... Year book for 1930–   ₍Chicago?₎ The Association
    ₍1930–
      v. illus. (incl. ports.) 20½ᵐ.
      At head of title, 1930–   : National outboard association. Organized January 21, 1929.

    1. Motor-boats—Societies. 2. Boats and boating—Societies.

  Library of Congress   GV835.A1N3   41–27496

NN   0059217   DLC

  National outdoor advertising bureau, inc.
    Manual of poster advertising coverage; 24 sheet poster advertising allotments and cost. New York, 1952. 251 p. 23 x 30cm.

    1. Advertising—Mediums, Outdoor.

NN   0059218   NN

659.134 National Outdoor Advertising Bureau, inc.
N214n   NOAB buyer's guide to poster advertising;
          poster markets, allotments and costs.

          v. illus. 29–30cm.

          Some years issued in parts.
          Subtitle varies slightly.

NN   0059219   IU

  National Outdoor Advertising Bureau.
    Outdoor advertising and the agency. ₍Chicago,
    1927₎
    61 p.

    This copy is numbered 787.

    1.Advertising, Outdoor.   I.Title.

NN   0059220   InNd

659.134 National Outdoor Advertising Bureau, inc.
N214po   Poster rate book.

          New York.
            v. illus., maps, tables. 29cm.

          Loose-leaf.
          Kept up to date between editions by replacement sheets.

NN   0059221   IU

659.134 National Outdoor Advertising Bureau, inc.
N214r   Report.

          New York.
            no. illus. 28cm.

NN   0059222   IU

  National Overseas and Grindlays Bank Limited
    see also
  National Bank of India, ltd.

  National overseas and Grindlays review
    see
  The **National** and Grindlays review.

  National PTA
    see
  National Congress of Parents and Teachers.

  ... The national pageant and dramatic events in the history of Connecticut. Testimonial to Mrs. Harriet Beecher Stowe. Opera house, Hartford, Conn., Tuesday afternoon, Sept. 24, 1889 ... Hartford, Clark & Smith, printers ₍1889₎
    cover-title, 8 p. 30 x 24ᶜᵐ.
    Includes advertising matter.

    1. Pageants—Hartford. 2. Stowe, Mrs. Harriet Elizabeth (Beecher)
    1811–1896.

                              CA 25–497 Unrev'd
  Library of Congress   F95.N26

NN   0059225   DLC

  The **National** pageant, and dramatic events in the history of New York. Testimonial to Mrs. Lillie Devereaux Blake ... 'Union-square-theater ... Nov. 25, 1889 ... Mrs. Mary A. Livermore, historian. ₍New York, 1889₎
    cover-title, 8 p. 30ᵐ.

    1. Blake, Mrs. Lillie (Devereux) 1835–

                              CA 11–2314 Unrev'd
  Library of Congress   PN3211.N4N3

NN   0059226   DLC

  National pageantry corporation.
    ... Grand patriotic pageant, The glory of Old glory, directed by the National pageantry corporation. ₍Cedar Rapids, Ia., The Torch press, ₍1917₎
    cover-title, ₍12₎ p. illus. (incl. ports.) 33½ x 17ᶜᵐ.
    Text on p. ₍2₎ and ₍3₎ of cover.

    1. Pageants. i. Title: The glory of Old glory.

                                              17–19153
  Library of Congress   PN3206.N3

NN   0059227   DLC

VOLUME 407

National Paint and Coatings Association.
Annual report — National Paint & Coatings Association.

₍Washington₎
v. illus. 30 cm.
ISSN 0095-2729

1. National Paint and Coatings Association.

TP934.N25a   667.9'06273   74-644349
                           MARC-S

NN   0059228   DLC

The **National** paint bulletin. v. 1–
Dec. 1936–
₍Alexandria, Va., etc.₎ J. R. Stewart, 1936–
v. in   illus., diagrs. 30½ᶜᵐ.   monthly.
Official organ of the Stewart research laboratory.
Oct. 1937–   include: Review of patents recently granted.

1. Paint—Period. 2. Varnish and varnishing—Period.   ɪ. Stewart research laboratory, Washington.
                              43-32371

Library of Congress   TP934.N27
             ₍2₎
                            667.605

NN   0059229   DLC CU ICJ NN OC1

National paint, oil and varnish association.
Proceedings of the ... annual convention.

New York
v. tab. 23ᶜᵐ.

                            CA 9-376 Unrev'd

Library of Congress   TP934.N3

NN   0059230   DLC ICJ

National paint, oil and varnish association.
... A revised list of the trade names registered with the
National paint, oil and varnish association
New York city
v. 27, 23ᶜᵐ.
Title varies: Trade mark book.
————— ... Supplement ...   **New York,**
N. Y., Trade mark bureau of the National paint, oil and **varnish**
association, inc., ₍19
     v. 23½ᶜᵐ.
1. Paint. 2. Oils and fats. 3. Varnish and varnishing.
                         14-18485 Revised
Library of Congress   TP934.5.N3
Copyright   ₍r40b2₎   667.6058

NN   0059231   DLC

National Paint, Oil and Varnish Association.
... Year book and report of the annual convention...
₍no.₎
₍New York, 1   8°.
   v.   ports.

1. Paint.—Per. and soc. publ.   2. Oils.—Per. and soc. publ.
3. Varnish.—Per. and soc. publ.
N. Y. P. L.   January 26, 1922.

NN   0059232   NN ICJ

National Paint, Oil and Varnish Association. Trade Mark Bureau.
₍Publications.₎
no.
New York₎ 19
   nos.   8°.

1. Trade marks—Per. and soc. publ.
N. Y. P. L.   November 27, 1925

NN   0059233   NN

National paint, oil and varnish association

   see also

National paint, varnish and lacquer association.

National paint, varnish & lacquer association, inc.
After war - what? ... Washington, 1944.
2 p.ℓ., ₍3₎-203 p.incl.tables. illus., diagrs.

"The material in this booklet has been reprinted from the issues of the 'Convention-at-home daily'."

NN   0059235   MH-BA NNC

TP934
A532   **National paint, varnish and lacquer association.**
American paint journal ...

St. Louis. American paint journal co., inc. ₍19

657
N2411b   **National paint, varnish and lacquer association.**
Brass tacks; a dramatic presentation in four scenes of current problems in the paint, varnish and lacquer industry ... Adaptation and dialogue by Burr Price. ₍Washington? 1935?₎
56p.

1. Paint manufacturers. 2. Cost--Accounting.
I. Price, Burr, 1888-   II. Title.

NN   0059237   IU

R667.6
N213c   **National Paint, Varnish and Lacquer Association**
Color survey. Washington.

   Library has

   1./Paint   2. /Paint industry and trade –
   Statistics   I. /T.

NN   0059238   MiD

TP934
.N32   NATIONAL PAINT, VARNISH & LACQUER ASSOCIATION.
₍Convention report₎
(In Paint, oil and chemical review

NN   0059239   ICU

National paint, varnish and lacquer association
Cost of distribution in the industrial field for the paint, varnish and lacquer industry
Report of special committee...
Washington, 1939.
52 p.

NN   0059240   OC1FRB

C
665
N21f   **National paint, varnish and lacquer association, inc.**
...Federation papers presented at the annual meeting of the Federation of paint and varnish production clubs, Washington, D.C., October 29 and 30, 1934. Washington, D.C., c1934.
   caption-title, pp.289-363. illus., plates, tables. 22½cm. (National paint, varnish and lacquer association, inc. Scientific section. Circular no. 471)

   1. Varnish and varnishing. 2. Paint. I. Title.

NN   0059241   LU

306
N213N
Ed.14   **National Paint, Varnish and Lacquer Association, inc.**
Guide to United States Government paint specifications. 14th ed. Washington, 1954-
   1 v. (loose-leaf)

   Supersedes National Paint, Varnish and Lacquer Association, inc. Scientific Section. Circular no. 751 (306.9 P162c)
Kept up-to-date by replacement pages which are in-   serted.

NN   0059242   DNAL

National paint, varnish and lacquer association.
Labeling laws and regulations. Washington, D. C., National paint, varnish and lacquer association, inc. ₍1941?₎
· 1 v. 24 cm.
Loose-leaf.

1. Paint industry and trade—U. S. 2. Oil industries—U. S. 3. Labels. ɪ. Title.
   HD9999.P153U737   338.4   42-22751

NN   0059243   DLC DFT

C
667.6
N21L   **National paint, varnish and lacquer association, inc.**
...Laboratory notes... Washington, D.C., c1935.
   caption-title, pp.153-171. illus. 23½cm. (National paint, varnish and lacquer association, inc. Scientific section. Circular no.481)

   1. Lacquer and lacquering. 2. Oils and fats. 3. Painting. I. Title.

NN   0059244   LU

National paint, varnish and lacquer association
Looking toward tomorrow. Bulletin no. 1-
Washington, D.C., c1945₎

NN   0059245   OC1

National Paint, Varnish and Lacquer Association, Inc.
Maintenance and painting
see under title

306
N213P   **National Paint, Varnish and Lacquer Association, inc.**
National consumer survey of painting habits. Washington ₍1954?₎
56 p.
Digest of survey made by Statistical Division, Sept.-Dec. 1953.

   1. House painting. Statistics. 2. Consumers' preference. I. Title. II. Title: Painting habits.

NN   0059247   DNAL

C
016.665
N21o   **National paint, varnish and lacquer association, inc.**
...Oil index... Washington, D.C., c1934.
   caption-title, pp.378-410. 23cm. (National paint, varnish and lacquer association, inc. Scientific section. Circular no.474)

   "Bulking value and other data on some oils, by Jeffrey R. Stewart."

NN   0059248   LU

TP934
.O 55   **National Paint, Varnish and Lacquer Association.**
The Open door. v. -14;   -Dec. 20, 1948. Washington.

306
N213   ₍National paint, varnish and lacquer association, inc.₎
Paint at war. ₍Washington, 1944?₎
₍16₎ p.

   1. Paint. 2. World war, 1939-   Economic aspects. U.S. I. Title.

NN   0059250   DNAL

VOLUME 407

306
N213Pa   National Paint, Varnish and Lacquer Association
         inc.
         Paint, varnish and lacquer statistical hand-
         book. ₍1st ed.₎ Washington, 1950.
         91 p.

         1. Paint. Statistics. 2. Varnish and
         varnishing. Statistics. 3. Lacquer and
         lacquering.   Statistics. I. Title.

NN   0059251   DNAL OC1

306
N213Pa   National Paint, Varnish and Lacquer Association,
Suppl.   inc.
         Paint, varnish and lacquer statistical
         handbook. 1953 supplement. Washington ₍1953₎
         71 l.

         1. Paint. Statistics. 2. Varnish and
         varnishing. Statistics. 3. Lacquer and
         lacquering. Statistics. I. Title.

NN   0059252   DNAL

306
N213R   National Paint, Varnish and Lacquer Associa-
         tion, inc.
         Raw materials index. Washington, 1955-
         1 v. (loose-leaf)

         Supersedes National Paint, Varnish and
         Lacquer Association, inc. Scientific Section.
         Circular no. 722 (306.9 P162C)
         Kept up-to-date by supplements and replace-
         ment pages.

         1. Paint materials. I. Scofield, Francis,
         1905-

NN   0059253   DNAL

HD9999
P15N27   National Paint, Varnish and Lacquer Association,
         Inc.
         Statistical survey, percentage by color paint
         sold by paint manufacturers, exterior, interior
         flats, latex emulsion, all purpose enamels.

         Washington.
             v. diagrs., tables. 28 cm. annual.

         1. Paint. 2. Paint industry and trade – U.S.

NN   0059254   DI

National paint, varnish and lacquer association

... Trade-mark directory ... Issued by Trade-mark bureau,
National paint, varnish and lacquer ass'n, inc. Washington,
D. C. ₍etc.₎ ⁺19

NATIONAL PAINT, VARNISH AND LACQUER ASSOCIATION.

A treatise on trade-marks. Issued by the Trade-mark
bureau, National paint, varnish and lacquer association,
inc. ... Washington, D.C., 1935. 16 p. 22½cm.

1. Trade-marks.

NN   0059256   NN MiD ICJ

National Paint, Varnish and Lacquer Association.
    Year book...
1933/35

Washington, D. C. ₍1935₎   24cm.
    v.   ports.
    Cover-title, 1933/35.
    1933/35   in 1 v.
    1933/35   includes Proceedings of its annual convention. ₍no.₎ 1
    1933/35 also includes Summary of proceedings of the organization meeting, Oct.
31 – Nov. 1, 1933.

1. Paint—Assoc. and org.—U. S.   2. Oils—Assoc. and org.—U. S.
3. Varnish—Assoc. and org.—U. S.
N. Y. P. L.   January 14, 1936

NN   0059257   NN OC1 DFT ICU MiU

National paint, varnish and lacquer
    association, inc.

    see also

National paint, oil and varnish association.

National paint, varnish and lacquer association. Cost accounting
    committee.
    ...Cost for the executive. Bulletin no. ₍1₎–

₍Washington, D. C.₎ 1944   nos.   28cm.
    Irregular.
    Includes supplementary material.

1. Accounting and bookkeeping   for paint and varnish industry. Cost.
N. Y. P. L.   October 5, 1949

NN   0059259   NN

                                                667.06161
National Paint, Varnish and Lacquer   8   1929?
    Association. *Scientific Section.*
    Abstract review ... ₍Washington, D. C., Institute of Paint
and Varnish Research, 1928– ₎
    Library has no. 1 to date. 23ᶜᵐ.
    No. 1–8 issued as its Circular no. 320, 324, 329, 340, 346, 350, 354, 357;
    no. 9– as unnumbered Special circulars; bound in its Proceedings, 1929–
    At head of title: ... Scientific Section ... National Paint, Varnish and Lac-
    quer Association, Inc. (no. 1–17, Scientific Section, Educational Bureau, Ameri-
    can Paint and Varnish Manufacturers' Association)
    No. 1–12 issued in cooperation with the Federation of Paint and Varnish
    Production Men's Clubs.
    Wanting: no. 18–22.

NN   0059260   ICJ OU DNAL WaS

National paint, varnish and lacquer association
inc. Scientific sertion
Circular no. 204
Washington, D.C., Scientific section, National
paint, varnish and lacquer association, inc., 1924–

NN   0059261   OU

National paint, varnish and lacquer association. *Scientific
    section.*
    ... Index of Scientific section publications ... ₍Washington₎
₍1938.
    201 p. 23ᶜᵐ. (*Its* Special circular. May, 1938)
    "This circular represents thousands of additional entries to the index
    issued in May, 1930" by the Scientific section, Educational bureau, Amer-
    ican paint and varnish manufacturers association.
    Includes a list of bulletins, circulars and books indexed.
    Compiled by A. W. Van Heuckeroth and M. L. Edwards.
    1. Paint—Bibl. 2. Varnish and varnishing—Bibl.   I. Van Heucke-
    roth, Arthur William, 1904–   comp.
                                                   42–50272
    Library of Congress   Z7914.P15A5 1938
                               ₍3₎   016.6676

NN   0059262   DLC IU ICJ

241.9
N213   National paint, varnish and lacquer associa-
        tion, inc. Scientific section.
        Key to publications abstracted in the
Abstract review.   Washington, D.C. ₍1943?₎
        8 p.

        1. Chemistry. Periodicals. Bibliography. 2.
Periodicals. Abbreviations of titles. I.
Title.

NN   0059263   DNAL

241.9
N213   National Paint, Varnish and Lacquer
1947   Association, inc. Scientific Section.
        Key to publications abstracted in the
        Abstract Review.   Washington, D.C., 1947.
        16 p.

NN   0059264   DNAL

National paint, varnish and lacquer association. *Scientific
section.*
    ... Proceedings of the Scientific section, National paint, var-
nish and lacquer association, inc. ...
Circulars, nos.   Abstract reviews,
    nos.   Washington, D. C., Scientific
    section, National paint, varnish and lacquer association, inc.
    ₍19
    v. illus., port., tables, diagrs. 22½ᶜᵐ.
    The Circulars and the Abstract reviews are first issued separately and
    are then reissued in the annual volume of Proceedings; the Abstract re-
    views are also called Special circulars.
    1. Paint. 2. Lacquer and lacquering. 3. Varnish and varnishing.
    4. Driers.
    Library of Congress   TP934.N35   42–16030
                               ₍2₎   667.096273

NN   0059265   DLC NN

National paint, varnish and lacquer association
Scientific section
    ...Publications... ₍Index₎

    Issue, May 1938   is its Special circular.

NN   0059266   MiD

306.9
N21S   National Paint, Varnish and Lacquer
        Association, inc. Scientific Section.
        Scientific Section notes. v.1

        Washington, D.C.

NN   0059267   DNAL OC1

National Paint, Varnish and Lacquer Association,
    Inc. Scientific Section.
    Subject classification system for information
on the paint industry, by Robert P. Ware.
Washington, D.C., November 1951.
    7 p. (Library Bulletin)

NN   0059268   OC1W

National Paint, Varnish and Lacquer Association.
    Trade-mark Bureau.
    A treatise on trade-marks
        see under National Paint, Varnish and
Lacquer Association.

National paint works, Williamsport, Pa.

Cheesman, Frank P   1864–
    A second review of technical paints for the protection of
metal surfaces, by Frank P. Cheesman of the National paint
works ... Williamsport, Pa. ₍1904 ed.₎ Williamsport, Pa.,
New York ₍etc.₎, National paint works ₍⁺1904₎

National painters magazine.

₍New York, Schnell publishing company, inc., etc.₎ 18 –19
    v. in illus., plates, ports., diagrs. (part fold.) 25–30½ᶜᵐ.
monthly (except July and Dec., 1942–   )
    Vol. 61, no. 10–v. called also v. 1–
    Title varies: 18 –July 1904, The Painters magazine and wall paper
       trade journal (varies slightly)
    Aug. 1904–1913, The Painters magazine ...
    1914–Sept. 1934, Painters magazine and paint and wall paper dealer,
       painting and decorating (varies)
    Oct. 1934–   National painters magazine.

    Absorbed the Coach painter and the Painters journal in Dec. 1884; the
Painter in Mar. 1886; Wall paper trade journal in Oct. 1888; Painting
and decorating in Jan. 1899; the Master painter in Jan. 1914.
    Includes proceedings of annual conventions of several painting and
decorating organizations, among them the Painting and decorating contractors of America, under its various forms of names.

    1. Painting, Industrial—Period. 2. House decoration—Period.
    r. Painting and decorating contractors of America.
                                                   46–33375
    Library of Congress   TT300.N3
                               ₍2₎   698.105

NN   0059272   DLC MB ICJ WaS OrP

VOLUME 407

National painters magazine.

Nineteen ninety five paint questions answered; a sequel to "1,000 more paint questions answered." A reference encyclopedia answering knotty problems that are met daily by painters, decorators and paint and varnish manufacturers ... New York, The Painters magazine

798 p. 23½ᶜᵐ. [ᶜ1919]

Advertising matter: p. 787–798.

NN 0059273 ICJ MB

National painters magazine.

Nineteen ninety five paint questions answered; a sequel to "1,000 more paint questions answered." A reference encyclopedia answering knotty problems that are met daily by painters, decorators and paint and varnish manufacturers ... New York, The Painters magazine [1920]

798 p. 23½ᶜᵐ.

1. Paint.

20–2857 Revised

Library of Congress TP936.N32

NN 0059274 DLC OrP OC1

National painters magazine.

Nineteen ninety five paint questions answered; a sequel to "1,000 more paint questions answered." A reference encyclopedia answering knotty problems that are met daily by painters, decorators and paint and varnish manufacturers. Arranged under topical heads for ready reference, with complete index, so that desired information may be readily found. ... . New York, Published by the Painters magazine, [1923].

792 p. illus. 24ᶜᵐ.

Two new chapters have been added, one on Automobile painting, the other on Railway equipment painting, both by M. C. Hillick. *cf.* Pref.

698 8300
155889

NN 0059275 ICJ

National painters magazine.

One thousand more paint questions answered; an entirely new book, a sequel to "739 paint questions answered." A reference encyclopedia answering knotty problems that are met by the painter, decorator and paint manufacturer in their daily work ... New York, The Painters magazine; [etc., etc., ᶜ1908]

630 p. illus. 26ᶜᵐ.

1. Paint.

9–8822 Revised

Library of Congress TP936.N325

NN 0059276 DLC OrCS ICJ

National painters magazine.

The Painters magazine directory of contracting painters and decorators ...
New York, The Painters magazine,

National painters magazine.

739 paint questions answered; a reference encyclopedia answering knotty problems that confront the painter, decorator, and paint manufacturer in their everyday work, with complete topical index. New York, The Painters magazine; London, The Trade papers publishing co., ltd. [1904]

383 p. 26ᶜᵐ.

1. Paint.

4–13292 Revised

Library of Congress TP936.N33

NN 0059278 DLC OC1 ICJ MB

National Palace Museum, *Peking*
see
Ku kung po wu yüan, *Peking.*

National Palace Museum, *T'ai-chung, Formosa*
see
Ku kung po wu yüan, *T'ai-chung, Formosa.*

National Palace Museum of Peiping
see
Ku kung po wu yüan, *Peking.*

371.85
N21r   **National panhellenic congress.**
[Report]   n.p., 1925.
16p.

NN 0059282 IU

National Panhellenic congress.
Report of the Congress.   21st – 1930.

(n.p., 1930 –   )
1 v.   23 cm.

NN 0059283 DHEW

371.856 National panhellenic congress
N213s   Survey on cost of fraternity life and fraternity housing, presented at the meeting of N. P. C. in February, 1928 ... [Author, 1928]
[41,37] l. tables.

NN 0059284 WaPS

371.85   **National panhellenic congress--Committee on college panhellenics.**
N213m   – Manual of information.   1929.
63p.

1. Greek letter societies.

NN 0059285 IU

National Panhellenic congress, 19th, Dallas, Texas, 1926
[Proceedings] Supplement to Alpha xi delta, vol. 23, no. 2, March issue [1926]

LJ13
.N3
1926

NN 0059286 DLC

National Panorama Company.
Panorama of the battle of Gettysburg
see under title

National paper and type company.

Z119
.A81

El Arte tipográfico.

[Nueva York, National paper & type company] 19

National Paper and Type Company,
Muestrario de tipos y catálogo ilustrado de maquinaria y materiales de imprenta.   New York [1908]
xxvii, 775 p.   illus., specimens.   28cm.

1. Printing – Specimens.   2. Type and typefounding.   3. Printing machinery and supplies – Catalogs.

NN 0059289 NNC

National Paper and Type Company.
Napatico
see under title

National paper and type company.

National paper and type company, a sketch of its formation, aims, ideals and progress, 1900–1920.   [New York, 1920?]

93 p., 1 l.   col. front., illus., ports. (1 double)   23ᶜᵐ.

Cover-title: A chapter in the romance of trade.

HD9829.N3A52   47–33718

NN 0059291 DLC NN NNC

National Paper Box Manufacturers Association.
Bulletin
see   Box-craft.

NATIONAL PAPER BOX MANUFACTURERS' ASSOCIATION.
Post war market, sales and industrial progress survey... First [-sixth] in a new series of six post war industrial surveys with special attention to packaging problems. Compiled for the Post war planning committee of the National paper box manufacturers association, Philadelphia, Pa. Edited by W. Clement Moore. Philadelphia, Moore and co., ᶜ1945-46.
6 pams. in 1 v. illus., maps. 28cm.

Cover title.

CONTENTS. —1. Textile industries. —2. Leather industries. —3. Drug, chemical, cosmetic and allied lines. —4. Paper products, stationery and allied lines. —5. Hardware, electrical and metal industries. —6. Department store and retail trade, and confectionery industry.

1. Industries--U. S.   I. Moore, Walter Clement, 1881-   , ed.

NN 0059294 NN ICU CSt MH-BA

National paper box manufacturers' association.
Post war market, sales and industrial progress survey of the department store and retail trade, and confectionery industry; sixth in a new series of six post war industrial surveys, with special attention to packaging problems, compiled for the Post war planning committee of the National paper box manufacturers association, Philadelphia, Pa. ... Edited by W. Clement Moore. Philadelphia, Pa., Moore and company, ᶜ1946.
cover-title, 24 p. illus., diagrs. 27½ x 21½ᶜᵐ.

1. Retail trade— U. S. 2. Department stores. 3. Confectionery — U. S. I. Moore, Walter Clement, 1881-   ed.

HF5429.N256   658.87   47–1095

NN 0059295 DLC NcRS NcGU

National paper box manufacturers' association.
Post war market, sales and industrial progress survey of the drug, chemical, cosmetic and allied lines; third in a new series of six post war industrial surveys, with special attention to packaging problems, compiled for the Post war planning committee of the National paper box manufacturers association, Philadelphia, Pa. ... Edited by W. Clement Moore. Philadelphia, Pa., Moore and company, ᶜ1945.
cover-title, 24 p. illus., diagrs. 27½ x 21½ᶜᵐ.
Reproduced from type-written copy.

1. Chemical industries— U. S. I. Moore, Walter Clement, 1881-   ed.

Library of Congress   HD9651.6.N35   46–1636
[5]   338.4766

NN 0059296 DLC NcGU CU OrP

National paper box manufacturers' association.
Post war market, sales and industrial progress survey of the hardware, electrical and metal industries; fifth in a new series of six post war industrial surveys, with special attention to packaging problems, compiled for the Post war planning committee of the National paper box manufacturers association, Philadelphia, Pa. ... Edited by W. Clement Moore. Philadelphia, Pa., Moore and company, ᶜ1946.
cover-title, 1 p. l., [2]–23 p. illus., diagrs. 27½ x 21½ᶜᵐ.

1. Metal trade— U. S. 2. Hardware— U. S. I. Moore, Walter Clement, 1881-   ed.

HD9724.N35   338.47671   47–16520

NN 0059297 DLC NcGU

VOLUME 407

National paper box manufacturers' association.
  Post war market, sales and industrial progress survey of the paper products, stationery and allied lines; fourth in a new series of six post war industrial surveys, with special attention to packaging problems, compiled for the Post war planning committee of the National paper box manufacturers association, Philadelphia, Pa. ... Edited by W. Clement Moore. Philadelphia, Pa., Moore and company, °1945.
    cover-title, 24 p. illus., diagrs. 27½ x 21⅜ᵐ.
    Reproduced from type-written copy.
    1. Paper making and trade—U. S.   I. Moore, Walter Clement, 1881- ed.
        Library of Congress   HD9826.N35   46–1637
                                        [5]   338.47676

NN   0059298   DLC ICJ N MB NcGU

National paper box manufacturers' association.
  Post war market, sales and industrial progress survey of the textile industries; first in a new series of six post war industrial surveys, with special attention to packaging problems, compiled for the Post war planning committee of the National paper box manufacturers association, Philadelphia, Pa. ... edited by W. Clement Moore ... Philadelphia, Pa., Moore and company, °1945.
    cover-title, 24 p. illus., diagrs. 27 x 21⅜ᵐ.
    Reproduced from type-written copy.
    1. Textile industry and fabrics—U. S.   I. Moore, Walter Clement, 1881- ed.
        Library of Congress   HD9855.N27   46–18879
                                        [3]   338.47677

NN   0059299   DLC NcGU

National Paper Box Manufacturers Association.
  Proceedings of national convention...

  [no.] 1–
  [Philadelphia, 1919–
    v.   8°.
    Title varies slightly.

  1. Paper boxes.—Per. and soc. publ.
  N. Y. P. L.   January 24, 1922.

NN   0059300   NN OU WaS

657.5 **National Paper Box Manufacturers' Association.**
N21r   Regulations governing accounting and costing for the set-up paper box manufacturing industry. [Philadelphia, 1949?]
          1v. (loose-leaf) fold. forms. 30cm.

          Caption title.

          1. Paper making and trade--Accounting. 2. Cost--Accounting. I. Title.

NN   0059301   IU

National Paper Box Manufacturers Association.
  Roster of membership, officers and directors, code of ethics, constitution and by-laws, terms and trade customs.
  19
  [Philadelphia, 19   12°.
    no.

  1. Paper boxes—Manufacture—Assoc. and org.—U. S.
  N. Y. P. L.   March 7, 1930

NN   0059302   NN

q657   **National paper box manufacturers associa-**
N2133u   **tion.**
          Uniform accounting, estimating and cost finding methods for the set-up paper box industry. Philadelphia [1922]
          2v. charts, and forms in envelope.

          Prepared under the direction of the Joint cost committee with the advice of the firm of Ernst and Ernst.

NN   0059303   IU PU-W

280.12 **National paper box manufacturers association,**
N2142   Post war planning committee.
          Post war industrial surveys. Philadelphia, Moore, 1945

NN   0059304   DNAL Mi

  National paper money, issued by government for internal and colonial circulation, a legal tender for debts and taxes. Showing the sophistry of "Mercator", in the "Times", who confounds money and capital. Being a reprint of articles taken from the "Sun" and the "Derbyshire courier", January 15th, 1856. Liverpool, 1856.
    7 p. 20 cm.

NN   0059305   CtY NjP

National Paper Trade Association.
  Annual survey of paper merchants' operations
  see its
  Paper merchant performance.

  National paper trade association
  Chart of accounts, the National paper trade association. A fundamental classification with index of accounts, providing for a sound analysis which will permit accurate comparison on a uniform basis. The National paper trade association primer, edited by Ernst & Ernst.
  n. p., n. d.
    11 p.

NN   0059307   OC1

  National Paper Trade Association
    Manual of accounting and costing for the paper distributing trade. 3d ed. New York, N. Y., 1949.
      21 p.

      Cover-title.

NN   0059308   MH-BA

  National Paper Trade Association,
    Manual of accounting and costing for the paper distributing trade; including a section on the compensating of outside salesmen.
    4th ed. New York, N. Y. [1955]
      29 p.

      Cover title.

NN   0059309   MH

  National Paper Trade Association
    Membership and by-laws...
  19

  New York [19   22½cm.
    nos.
    Title varies: 19   , Year book; 19   Membership and by-laws.
    Name appears as National Paper Trade Association.

  1. Paper—Assoc. and org.—U. S.
  N. Y. P. L.   December 26, 1935

NN   0059310   NN OC1

  National Paper Trade Association.
    Paper merchant performance.
    New York.
      v. illus. 30 cm. annual.
      Title varies: 19   Annual survey of paper merchants' operations.

    1. Paper making and trade—U. S.   I. Title.

    HD9824.N3   63–44727 ‡

NN   0059311   DLC OrPS MH-BA

ENV   **National Paper Trade Association.**
:49   Roster of membership.
N27   New York.

NN   0059312   MH-BA

  National paper trade association

    Standard classification of expense... adopted November 11th, 1920. No pub. 1920.
      28 p. tables

      Cover title.

NN   0059313   MiD IU

  National paper trade association
    Trends in fine paper merchandising and 1939 mid-year survey results.   Sept. 1939.
      15 p.

NN   0059314   OC1FRB

676.288 **National Paperboard Association.**
N213s   Paperboard industry statistics.

          Washington [etc.]
            v. col. diagrs., tables. 28cm. annual.

NN   0059315   IU NNC

  National paperboard association
    Paperboard industry statistics, 1928–1937
    Chicago, c1938.
      20 p.

NN   0059316   OC1FRB

  National paperboard association.
    Paperboard industry statistics, 1932–1941. Chicago, Ill., New York, N. Y., National paperboard association [1942]
      cover-title, 24 p. incl. tables, diagrs. 28ᵐ.
      Reproduced from type-written copy.

      1. Paper making and trade—U. S. 2. Paper box industry—U. S.
      I. Title.
        Library of Congress   HD9839.P33U55   42–14250
                                        [2]   338.4

NN   0059317   DLC OrU ICJ

  National paperboard association.
    Paperboard industry statistics, 1933–1942. Chicago, Ill., New York, N. Y., National paperboard association [1943]
      cover-title, 24 p. incl. tables, diagrs. 28 x 21⅜ᵐ.

      1. Paper making and trade—U. S. 2. Paper box industry—U. S.
      I. Title.
        Library of Congress   HD9839.P33U55 1943   43–8750
                                        [2]   338.47676

NN   0059318   DLC OC1

  National paperboard association.
    Paperboard industry statistics, 1934–1943. Chicago, Ill., New York, N. Y., National paperboard association [1944]
      cover-title, 24 p. incl. tables, diagrs. 28 x 21⅜ᵐ.
      Reproduced from type-written copy.

      1. Paperboard.
                                                            44–27526
        Library of Congress   HD9839.P33U55 1944
                                        [2]   338.47676

NN   0059319   DLC

VOLUME 407

National paperboard association.
Paperboard industry statistics, 1935–1944. Chicago, Ill.,
New York, N. Y., National paperboard association [1945]
cover-title, 24 p. incl. tables, diagrs. 28 x 21½ᶜᵐ.
Reproduced from type-written copy.

1. Paperboard.

Library of Congress   HD9839.P33U55 1945

    45–18196

    [2]   338.47676

NN   0059320   DLC

National paperboard association.
Paperboard industry statistics, 1936–1945. Chicago, Ill.,
New York, N. Y., National paperboard association [1946]
cover-title, 24 p. diagrs. 28 x 21½ᶜᵐ.
Reproduced from type-written copy.

1. Paperboard.

    46–17004

Library of Congress   HD9839.P33U55 1946

    [2]   338.47676

NN   0059321   DLC NNC

National Paperboard Association
Paperboard industry statistics, 1943–
1952. [Chicago, Ill., 1953]
32p., tables, charts.

Cover-title.

NN   0059322   OC1

National Paperboard Association.
Statistical history of the paperboard industry. [Alvin A.
Newburg, statistician. Chicago, 1952]
32 p. illus. 28 cm.

1. Paperboard.   I. Newburg, Alvin A., 1905–   II. Title.

HD9839.P33U545   338.47676   52–68259 ‡

NN   0059323   DLC CaBVaU NcD PU-W

National Paperboard Association.
Statistics, paperboard industry
   see its   Paperboard industry statistics.

The **National** parcel post news. v. 1–
Oct. 7, 1914–
Washington, D. C. [The National parcel post publishing company] 1914–
v. illus. 33½ᶜᵐ. monthly.

1. Parcels-post—Period. 2. Parcels-post—U. S.

    18–13938

Library of Congress   HE6471.A2N3

NN   0059325   DLC

HQ769
.D3   **National parent-child association.**

Davis, Marion Quinlan.
A plan for growing up; the blue book for building better
lives, by Marion Quinlan Davis ... with a foreword by John
Frederick Dashiell ... and contributions by Garry Cleveland
Myers ... and Dorothy E. Norris ... Kingsport, Tenn., J. A.
Richards, inc. [1939]

National parent-teacher. v. 1– Nov. 1906–

Washington, D. C., Child welfare co., inc.; [etc., etc.,] 1906–
v. illus., plates. 24–28½ᶜᵐ.
Monthly except July and August, 1906–11; monthly 1912–
(In 1928–34, omitting one or more summer issues)
Official organ of the National congress of mothers, Nov. 1906–Apr.
1915; National congress of mothers and parent-teacher associations, May
1915–May 1924; National congress of parents and teachers, June 1924–
Title varies: Nov. 1906–Nov. 1909, The National congress of mothers
magazine.
Dec. 1909–Aug. 1928, Child-welfare magazine.
Sept. 1928–July 1934, Child welfare, the national parent-teacher magazine.

Continued in next column

Continued from preceding column

Sept. 1934–Jan. 1937, The National parent-teacher magazine.
Feb. 1937–   National parent-teacher.
Published in Philadelphia, Nov. 1906–Nov. 1914; Lancaster, Pa., etc.,
Dec. 1914–Aug. 1922; Philadelphia, Sept. 1922–Sept. 1931; Washington,
D. C., Oct. 1931–   (editorial offices, 1929–34, Winchester,
Mass.; 1935–   New York)

1. Children—Management—Period. 2. Parent and child—Period.
I. National congress of parents and teachers.

    12–15373 (rev. '37)

Library of Congress   HQ750.A2N4

    649.105

     NN MiU OC1 OOxM ICJ MB PWcS PPC PSC PP
NN   0059328   DLC NBuG PPPL DL DHEW TU NcD CU NcD

[National parent-teacher]
Children who are exceptional. Chicago, Ill., National congress of parents and teachers, °1945.
63 p. illus. 21ᶜᵐ.
"Twelve articles ... reprinted from recent issues of the National parent-teacher, the P. T. A. magazine."—p. 58.
"Sources of material": p. 61.

1. Children, Abnormal and backward.   I. National congress of parents and teachers.   II. Title.

    46–7024

Library of Congress   LC3965.N35

    [5]   371.92

NN   0059329   DLC NN MU IaU

National parent-teacher.
Guiding the young child, selected readings on the infant and
preschool child. Chicago, Ill., National congress of parents
and teachers, 1941.
3 p. l., 57, [1] p. illus. 21ᶜᵐ.
"Articles selected from recent issues of the 'National parent-teacher'."—Foreword.
Bibliography: p. 56–57.

1. Children—Management.   I. National congress of parents and
teachers.   II. Title.

Library of Congress   HQ769.N33   42–11577

    [3]   649.1

NN   0059330   DLC WaPS OC1

National parent-teacher.
Purposes of education. Reprinted from National
parent-teacher ... Issued by National congress of
parents and teachers, Educational policies
commission National education association [1939?]
cover-title, 24 p. illus. 30.5 cm.
Contents.– What are schools for? by W.G.
Carr. Education for self-realization by G.D.
Stoddard. Education for human relationships by
J.K. Folsom. Education for economic efficiency
by E.A. Lee. Education for civic responsibility
by C.A. Dykstra. From purposes to results by
W.G. Carr.

NN   0059331   PSt

National Park Bank of New York.
The doorway
   see under   Clymer, Ernest Fletcher.

NATIONAL PARK BANK OF NEW YORK.
Reprints of advertisements of the National
Park Bank of New York. [New York, 1922].

Pamphlet.

NN   0059333   MH

The National Park Bank of New York.
The trust department of the National Park Bank of New
York. New York, 1919. 24 p. 12°.

12701A. I. New York City.—Banks   and banking: National Park Bank
of New York.   October 6, 1921.
N. Y. P. L.

NN   0059334   NN MH

National Park College, *Forest Glen, Md.*
   see
Forest Glen, Md. National Park College.

National park concessions, Inc.
Pictorial study of Mammoth cave and Mammoth
cave national park. Photography by W. Ray Scott.
n.p., National park concessions, inc., c1951.

NN   0059336   KyBgW

National Park Conference, *1911–1915*
   see
National Parks Conference.

National Park Conference, *1921*
   see
National Conference on State Parks.

A national park in the Great Smoky Mountains ...
   see under   [Kephart, Horace] 1862–

**National park seminary. General alumnae association.
Chicago chapter.**
National park seminary (alumnae) cook book, composed of favorite and tested recipes submitted by former National park seminary students. [Chicago] The
Chicago chapter, 1924.
4 p. l., iii, 1170 (i. e. 245) p. pl. 23ᶜᵐ.
"Arranged and compiled by Faette S. Toppan."
In binder.
Sold for the benefit of the National park seminary day nursery association,
Chicago.
Contains advertising matter.
1. Cookery, American.   I. Toppan, Faette S., ed.   II. National park
seminary day nursery association, Chicago.

Library of Congress   TX715.N33   24–22281

NN   0059340   DLC

National Park Seminary, *Forest Glen, Md.*
   see
Forest Glen, Md. National Park College.

**National park seminary day nursery
association, Chicago.**
National park seminary. General alumnae association.
Chicago chapter.
National park seminary (alumnae) cook book, composed of favorite and tested recipes submitted by former National park seminary students. [Chicago] The
Chicago chapter, 1924.

National Park Seminary for Young Women, Forest
Glen, Md.
   see   Forest Glen, Md. National Park College

SK601
N3   The National Park Service in the field of
organized camping. For the 1937 yearbook –
Park and Recreational Progress. [n.p.,n.d.]
10 l. 27 cm.
Cover title.

1. Camping. 2. U.S. National Park Service.

NN   0059344   DI

National park-to-park highway association, inc.
Official publication and guide of the National park-to-park highway association. [Denver, 1922] 64 p. illus. 19cm.

1. Parks, National—U. S.
N. Y. P. L.   January 27, 1944

NN   0059345   NN

VOLUME 407

National Parking Association.
    Panel discussions on parking ₍at the₎ annual convention.

Chicago.
    v. 27 cm.

    1. Automobile parking—Congresses.

HE370.N33   388.3   55–33806 ‡

NN   0059346   DLC

HE371
.A2P3
National Parking Association.

Parking. Oct. 1952–
₍Washington, National Parking Association₎

    ... National parks and monuments
       see under [Dorr, George Bucknam] 1853–
1944.

    National parks and reservations. [Washington. 1897.] 8°.
    From *Report of the secretary of the interior*, 1897, pp. 79–94.

NN   0059349   MH-A

National Parks Association, *Washington, D. C.* Bulletin
  see   **National** parks magazine.

National parks association, *Washington, D. C.*
    ... Essential facts concerning the war on our national
parks ... A concise statement of the moves in and out of
Congress, offensive and defensive, arranged in chronological order for quick reference ... Issued by the National parks association, Washington, D. C. ₍Washing-
ton, D. C., The National parks association, 1923₎
    ₍8₎ p. 22ᶜᵐ.
    Tenth series, to date, October, 1923.
    "Sixty-eighth Congress edition."

    1. National parks and reserves—U. S.

                             26–12064

Library of Congress   E160.N3

NN   0059351   DLC NN OO

    National parks association. Essential facts of the war on
    our national parks system and its effect on national policy.
    70th congress ed. Washington. [1927.] 8°. pp. [10].

NN   0059352   MH-A OO

E160
.B8
1949
    National Parks Association, Washington, D. C.
                         FOR OTHER EDITIONS
                         SEE MAIN ENTRY
Butcher, Devereux.
    Exploring our national parks and monuments. Art work
by the author. 2d ed. Boston, Houghton Mifflin, 1949.

F1011
.B8
    National Parks Association, Washington, D. C.

Butcher, Devereux.
    Exploring the national parks of Canada. **Washington,**
National Parks Association ₍1951₎

SB482   **National parks association, W₍ashington₎ D. C.**
.A467   ...Information for members, June 20, 1928–
Washington, D. C. 19–
    v. 4°

NN   0059355   DLC OC1

SB482   **National Parks Association, Washington, D. C.**
.A466
    National parks magazine.   v. ₍1₎–   (no. 1–   );
June 6, 1919–
₍Washington₎ National Parks Association.

National parks association, Washington, D.C.
    National parks newsservice. VD–17
Washington, D.C., 1929–35.

NN   0059357   OC1

National parks association, Washington, D. C.

    ... National parks situation critical: a re-
port to the system's defenders, November 7, 1928,
by Robert Sterling Yard ... ₍n.p., 1928?₎
    9 numb. l.   28ᶜᵐ.
    Caption title.
    Multigraphed.

    1. National parks and reserves—U.S.   I.
Yard, Robert Sterling, 1861–

NN   0059358   ViU OO

National parks association, Washington, D. C.
    The Nation's parks
    see under title

National Parks Association, *Washington, D. C.* News bulle-
    tin
  see   **National** parks magazine.

    National parks association.
    Osborne amendment a blow aimed at America.
    [Washington. 1922.] l. 8°. pp. [4]. (In its Bulletin,
28.)

NN   0059361   MH-A

National Parks Association, *Washington, D. C.*
    The proposed C and O Canal Parkway project; report to
the Board of Trustees. Washington ₍1953₎
    4, 8 l. maps. 28 cm.
    Caption title: Potomac Valley recreation project.

    1. Chesapeake and Ohio Canal Parkway (Projected)   I. Title.
II. Title: C and O Canal Parkway project.   III. Title: Potomac Valley
recreation project.
TE24.M3N27   56–46325

NN   0059362   DLC

National parks association, *Washington, D. C.*
    ... The proposed Everglades national park. Report of a
special committee of the National parks association appointed
to study all the features in connection with the proposed Everglades national park in the state of Florida ... Washington,
U. S. Govt. print. off., 1932.
    iii, 14 p. 23ᶜᵐ. (₍U. S.₎ 72d Cong., 1st sess. Doc. 54)
    Presented by Mr. Fletcher. Ordered to be printed January 22, 1932.
    Signed: Frederick Law Olmsted ... William P. Wharton.
    1. National parks and reserves—U S.   I. Fletcher, Duncan Upshaw,
1859–   II. Olmsted, Frederick Law, 1870–   III. Wharton, William Pickman, 1880–   IV. Title.   V. Title: Everglades national park.
                                   33–20807
Library of Congress   SB482.F6N3
—— Copy 2.   [917.593] 719

NN   0059363   DLC MiU ViU

National Parks Association, *Washington, D. C.*   711.73 13
     .... Publication. ... .. Washington, D. C., The National Parks
180278   Association, 1919–.
    Library has no. 1 to date. Illus. 24ᶜᵐ.

NN   0059364   ICJ NN ICRL DLC

National parks association, Washington, D. C.
    Publications on national parks and related topics, comp. by the
National parks association... ₍Washington, D. C., 1946₎ 7 p.
24cm.
    Caption-title.

    1. Parks, National—U. S.—Bibl.
N. Y. P. L.   June 28, 1948

NN   0059365   NN

National parks association, Washington, D. C.

Joint committee on recreational survey of federal lands.
    Recreation resources of federal lands. Report of the Joint
committee on recreational survey of federal lands of the American forestry association and the National parks association to
the National conference on outdoor recreation. Washington,
D. C., National conference on outdoor recreation, 1928.

National Parks Association of Japan
    see
    Kokuritsu Kōen Kyōkai.

DU260   **National Parks Association of Queensland.**
N3   The national parks of Queensland. [Brisbane,
Australia, n.d.]
    40 p.   illus.   25 cm.
    Cover title.

    1. National parks and reserves – Queensland.

NN   0059368   DI

National parks conference.
    ... Proceedings of the National parks conference ... 1911,
1912, 1915, 1917. Washington, Govt. print. off., 1912–17.
    4 v. 24½ᶜᵐ.
    The conferences were called by the Department of the Interior; the
first two were held in the Yellowstone national park, September 11–12,
1911 and October 14–16, 1912; the third at Berkeley, Calif., March 11–13,
1915 and the fourth at Washington, D. C., January 2–6, 1917.
    At head of title, 1917: Department of the interior ... The National
park service ...
    Title varies slightly.
    1. National parks and reserves—U. S. 2. Natural resources.
I. Title.
Library of Congress   E160.N27
                                   12—35713

    OC1WHi WvU TU PPAN NcD ICJ MtBC OrCS MH-A OrU
NN   0059369   DLC OU PBL NN NjP MB ICJ MiU CU-B DI

    National parks forum; official pub-
lication Friends of our national
parks ... Los Angeles, California,
1923.

    1 v. illus.,maps. 30cm.

    Issued January to December 1923.

NN   0059370   CLSU

National Parks Highway Association.   No. 53 in*Map 117.2
    Map of the National Parks Transcontinental Highway: northwest
trail, the red trail. Showing every city, town, village and hamlet
throughout its entire length, proposed by the National Parks
Highway Association and also advocated by the National Highways Association ...
=   Washington. 1915. Size, 10⅞ × 39¼ inches. Scale (computed),
75 miles to 1 inch.

    K9727 — Double main card. —   National Parks Highway Asso-
ciation. (M1) — National Highway Association. (M2) — National Parks
Transcontinental Highway. (1)

NN   0059371   MB

    NATIONAL PARKS HIGHWAY ASSOCIATION
    Minutes of executive committee meeting...
held in...Spokane, Washington...April 9th, 1921.
    n.p. ₍1921?₎
    ₍14₎ p.

NN   0059372   Or

VOLUME 407

National parks magazine. v. ⌊1⌋– (no. 1-); June 6, 1919–
⌊Washington⌋ National Parks Association.

v. in illus., ports., maps. 25–28 cm. irregular.

Issues for June 6, 1919 to Nov. 1925 (no. 1–46) have no vol. numbering but constitute v. 1–6.
Title varies: June 6–Oct. 19, 1919, Sept. 30, 1920, Dec. 22, 1920–Oct. 9, 1923, Bulletin.—Dec. 30, 1919–June 25, 1920, Oct. 2–Nov. 20, 1920, News bulletin.—Dec. 1, 1923–Nov. 1939, National parks bulletin.

1. Parks—U. S.—Period. I. National Parks Association, Washington, D. C.

SB482.A466 719.32 50–26021

NcRS CSmH CoCA
MiU NcD INS OCU CSt ScCleU CaBVaU OrCS MtU KyU
MBtS OU WHi CU DI AAP OOxM NNC OrCS ICRL CtY
NN 0059373 DLC NcU MsSM PSt KU NBuG WaS WvU

National Parks of Kenya. Board of Trustees
see
Kenya National Parks' Trustees.

E160
N36
x

National parks reports and publications. [Washington, 1893-1919]
115 v. in 7. illus., fold. maps. 24cm.

Binder's title.
A collection of publications and reports of the national parks.

1. National parks and reserves - U. S.

NN 0059376 CU-B

The **National** parliamentarian. v. 1– Jan. 1938–
Kansas City, Mo. ⌊National Association of Parliamentarians⌋
v. in illus., ports. 24 cm. quarterly (irregular)
Title varies: Jan.–May 1938, Parliamentary pickles.

1. Parliamentary practice—Period. I. National Association of Parliamentarians. II. Title: Parliamentary pickles.

JF515.N33 64–58341

NN 0059377 DLC

JN558
.N3

National Parliamentary and Financial Reform Association.
National reform tracts. No. 1-24.
[London, B. D. Cousins 1850-1851]
12 pt. in 1 v. 21½cm.

Binder's title.
Bound with these is The speech of Richard Cobden ... at the fourth monthly soirée of the National parliamentary and financial reform association ... on ... May 26, 1851.

1. Gt. Brit.--Pol. & Govt.--1837-1901.

NN 0059378 DLC

National Parliamentary and Financial Reform Association.
National reform tracts - no. 1-30. [London, 1850-52]
15 v. 20.5 cm. [Bound with National parliamentary and financial reform association, London. Speeches of Joseph Hume ... and Sir Joshua Walmsley ... London, 1850]

NN 0059379 CtY

National Parliamentary and Financial Reform Association.
... Speeches of Joseph Hume ... and Sir Joshua Walmsley ... on moving and seconding the motion for parlimentary reform in the House of commons... 1850 ... [London, 1850]
16 p. 20.5 cm.
At head of title: National reform association.
Binder's title: National reform tracts.

NN 0059380 CtY

942.08
N213

National Parliamentary and Financial Reform Association.
To the members of the National Reform Association. ⌊London, Society, 1854⌋
4 p. 21cm.

A letter, "signed on behalf of the Council, Joshua Walmsley, President."

1. Gt. Brit. Politics and government. 1837-1867. 2. Gt. Brit. Parliament. Reform.

NN 0059381 MnU

National Parole Conference
see
National Conference on Parole.

4JS
138

The National Parties; their platforms and the speeches of acceptance of their presidential candidates, Republican, Democratic and Socialist New York State platforms. Brooklyn -New York, Brooklyn Daily Eagle, 1908.
38 p.

(Eagle library, no. 140. V. 23, no. 14)

NN 0059383 DLC-P4

National party (Australia).
Facts about the Bruce-Page government; a positive constructive policy now carried on continuously for nearly six years; sane finance and progressive legislation; authorised by Neville R. Howse, campaign director. 1928. ⌊Sydney: Printed by Deaton and Spencer⌋ 1928. 160 p. incl. tables. 21½cm.

On cover: Commonwealth of Australia. General election, 1928.

1. Economic history—Australia. 2. Industry and state—Australia. I. Howse, Sir Neville Reginald, 1864–
N. Y. P. L. December 21, 1937

NN 0059384 NN

National Party (*Egypt*)
see
al-Ḥizb al-Waṭanī (*Egypt*)

National Party (Great Britain)
National opinion. London
see under title

National Party (Great Britain). L331.0994 S001

188863 Report of the Industrial Committee of the National Party on industrial unrest and labor policy. ... . London, [1920].
24 p. 34cm.
Sir M. E. Manningham-Buller, chairman.
Presented to the Grand Council of the National Party on June 9th, 1920, and unanimously adopted.

NN 0059387 ICJ NN DLC MiD

National party (Gt. Brit.) Industrial committee
see
National party (Gt. Brit.)

Pam.
Coll.
20852

National Party (New Zealand)
Constitution and rules of the New Zealand National Party. ⌊Wellington, Printed by G. Deslandes⌋ 1951.
cover title, v, 32 p. 14 cm.

NN 0059389 NcD

Pam.
Coll.
30793

National Party (New Zealand)
Handbook on organization; a guide to party officials. Wellington, Dominion Headquarters, New Zealand National Party ⌊introd. 1949⌋
127 p. illus. 22 cm.

1. National party (New Zealand)

NN 0059390 NcD

National Party (*New Zealand*)
The National Government, 1949–1954; five years of progress and prosperity. Wellington ⌊1954?⌋
153 p. illus. 19 cm.

1. New Zealand—Pol. & govt. I. Title.

JQ5815 1954.N3 58–19443 ‡

NN 0059391 DLC MH NcD

National Party (New Zealand)
The work of the National government, December, 1949-August, 1952. 2d ed. Wellington, N.Z. [1952]
63 p.
At head of title: Record of Achievement

NN 0059392 MH-PA

National Party (New Zealand)
The work of the national government. December, 1949 - May, 1953. 3rd ed. Wellington, N.Z. [1953]
104 p.

NN 0059393 MH-PA

National Party (South Africa)
National news [Cape Town]
see under title

National Party (South Africa) Federal council.
The fruits of four years; a short resumé of the work of the Hertzog-government
see under Conradie, J H comp.

NATIONAL PARTY (U.S)
The golden link and National Party for the salvation of a nation, by Ernest H. Woolard. [Indianapolis, Ind., 1934] 73 p. 22cm.

Cover-title.

871586A. 1. Money—U.S., 1933- . I. Woolard, Ernest H.

NN 0059396 NN

National party (U.S.)
The national party of America; declaration, principles, analysis of platform and principles. Chicago ⌊c1937⌋
28 p. 20½ cm.

NN 0059397 NjP

VOLUME 407

National Party.(U.S)
...Platform and history, as condensed by Martin Hemmy...
New York: Allied Prtg. Trades Council [1918?].　4 p.　16°.
Caption-title.

1. U. S.—Politics, 1918.
N. Y. P. L.　　　　　　　　　August 7, 1922.

NN　0059398　　NN

National party (U. S.)
JK2391　Platform spirit and aims of the National party,
N3　founded Oct. 4th, 1917.　Chicago, 1917.
1917　14 p.　15cm.

Cover title.

NN　0059399　　OrPR CSt-H

National Party(U.S)
Program for constructive democracy.　Message and war pro-
gram of the National Party.　An appeal to the heart and brain of
America.　Adopted Chicago, March 6-7-8, 1918.　New York:
Allied Prtg. Trades Council [1918?].　19 p.　16°.
Caption-title.

1. U. S.—Politics, 1918.
N. Y. P. L.　　　　　　　　　August 7, 1922.

NN　0059400　　NN

National party, inc.
Loog, Sidney.
The end of an economic era and the needs of the future, by
Sidney Loog.　Philadelphia, Pa., National party, °1936.

The National party native Americans.
N.O.,Democrat office,1878

NN　0059402　　LNHT

National Party of America
　　see　National Party (U.S.)

National Party of the Cherokee Nation.
Zc16　Platform of the National Party of the
C5　Cherokee Nation, adopted in convention at
887kna　Tahlequah, November 23d, 1874. [Tahlequah,
　Okla., 1874]
　broadside.　30 x 22 cm.

Dated and signed: November 23d, 1874. S.H.
Benge, President of Convention.

NN　0059404　　CtY

National Party of the Cherokee Nation.
Beinecke
Library　Resolution of the National Party and Honor-
Zc16　able Samuel Smith's answer.　[Tahlequah, C.N.,
C5　1887]
887na　broadside.　25 x 16 cm.

The answer signed: Samuel Smith, ass't and
acting principal chief.
I. Cherokee Nation. Principal chief.
II. Smith, Samuel, 1817?-1897. III. Title.

NN　0059405　　CtY

National Party of the Muskogee Nation.
Platform of the National Party of Muskogee Nation, In-
dian Territory.　[n. p., 1899]
4 p.　port.　22 cm.
Cover title.
English and Creek.

1. Creek Indians—Tribal government.

E99.C9N38　　　　　　　　　　49-42640*

NN　0059406　　DLC KHi

National Party of the Transvaal.
JQ2698　The National Party of the Transvaal.
N2A3　[Pretoria? 195-?]
　100 p.　17cm.

NN　0059407　　CSt-H

National Pasteur Centenary Celebration, Philadelphia, 1922.
National celebration of the centenary of the birth of Louis
Pasteur.　Philadelphia, Pa., December 27, 1922.　[Philadelphia,
1923?]
1 p. l., 68 p., 1 l.　ports.　28mm.
Dr. Wm. Duffield Robinson, chairman.
Addresses by R. H. Chittenden, V. Kellogg, J. B. Deaver, H. S. Cumming,
J. Jusserand, E. Burnet, R. Abbe, L. S. McMurtrie, H. A. Hare, H. S. Pritchett.

NN　0059408　　ICJ PPAN

The National pastorals of the American Hierachy
　　(1792-1919)
　　　　see under　Catholic church in the U.S.
Bishops.

National Patent Copy Service, Cleveland.
Alphabetical patent subject index of United States letters
patent.　Cleveland, °1947.
18 l.　28 cm.

1. Patents—U. S.—Indexes.
T223.D7N3　　　　　608　　　　47-7086*

NN　0059410　　DLC

National patent council.
Invention news and views
　　see under title

National patent council.
What feeds free enterprise?
　　see under　Anderson, John William, 1883-

National patent planning commission
　　　see
U.S.　National patent planning commission.

NATIONAL PATENT WOOD PRESERVING COMPANY.
Important invention! The Robbins' process
for preserving wood and lumber from mould, decay and destruction by worms.　N.Y.,1868.
(2), 101 p.
Front.　　　　　　　　Chem 8005.68.3

NN　0059414　　MH NjR MH-A NjP

National Patent Wood Preserving Company.
The preservation of wood by coal-tar and its products,
as applied by John Bethell, of England, and Louis S.
Robbins, of America.　New York, 1869.
30 p.　23 cm.

1. Wood—Preservation.　I. Title.

　　　　　　　　　　　　　　　72-218560

NN　0059415　　DLC DBRE

National Patent Wood Preserving Company.
The preservation of wood by coal-tar and its products,
as applied by John Bethell, of England, and Louis S. Robbins, of America.　New York, 1869.
31 p.　23 cm.

1. Wood—Preservation.　2. Bethell, John, 1804-1867.　3. Robbins,
Louis S.　4. Coal-tar.　I. Title.

TA424.N26　1869　　　　　　　4-34355

NN　0059416　　DLC

National Patent Wood Preserving Company.
A treatise on the Robbins process for seasoning wood,
and preserving it from decay, mould, attacks of land and
water insects, and molluscs ...　Cincinnati, O., R. Clarke
& co., printers, 1869.
1 p. l., 91 p.　front.　23 cm.

1. Wood—Preservation.

TA424.4.N37　　　　　　　　7-41264

NN　0059417　　DLC

National pathfinder.　v. 1, no. 1-8; Nov. 1935-Aug. 31, 1936.
[Manila, 1935-36]
1 v.　illus.　26mm.　irregular.
Editors: Nov. 1935-　　　　N. N. Jaramillo.—
July 1936, Juan Santos.—Aug. 1936, Faustino Bugante.
No more published.
L. C. set incomplete: v. 1, no. 2-3 wanting.

1. Philippine islands.　I. Jaramillo, Narciso N., ed.　II. Santos, Juan,
ed.　III. Bugante, Faustino, ed.

　　　　　　　　　　　　　　　　43-27826
Library of Congress　　DS651.N26

NN　0059418　　DLC

616.07　National pathological laboratories, Chicago.
N277d　Diagnostic aids.　Chicago, The National pathological laboratories [1928]
63p.　illus.

1. Diagnosis.　2. Diagnosis, Laboratory.

NN　0059419　　IU-M ICRL

National patriotic instructors' institute
Journal of proceedings of the first National
patriotic instructors' institute. Under the
auspices of the Grand Army of the Republic...
Minneapolis, Minn. January 18, 1913.
n.p., n.d.
80 p.

NN　0059420　　OClWHi ICU

HG106　National patriots of America.
.3　What America needs to restore prosperity and
P33　save it and its people from national bankruptcy,
vol 7,　by a patriot ...　[Minneapolis, Minn.] c1932.
no. 12　cover-title, 19 p., 2 l.　19.5 cm.
Pamphlets on the economic crisis of 1929.
v. 7, no. 12.

NN　0059421　　DLC

National pattern for local apprenticeship
standards in the roofing industry
　　see under [National Roofing Contractors' Association]

VOLUME 407

625.8　National Pavements.
N27　　National pavement pays for itself.
　　　［New York City, °1921］
　　　20 p. illus. 25 cm.

　　　Cover title.

　　　1. Pavements. I. Title.

NN　0059423　　N

625.82
N277bp　National paving brick association.
　　　Brick pavements: city streets, country high-
Science ways. ［Cleveland, O., n.d.］
　　　16p. illus. 23cm.
　　　Cover-title.

　　　1. Pavements, Brick. I. Title.

NN　0059424　TxDaM NIC

National Paving Brick Association.
Proceedings ［of the］ general sessions ［of the］ annual meet-
ing. 23d-26th, 29th, 1929-32, 1935,
Washington.
　v. illus., maps, ports. 24 cm.
　Proceedings for 1st-22d, 27th-28th, 30th annual meetings not pub-
lished.
　Vols. for 1929-30 issued by the association under its earlier name:
National Paving Brick Manufacturers Association.

　1. Pavements, Brick—Congresses. 2. Bricks—Congresses. I.
National Paving Brick Manufacturers Association. Proceedings of
the general sessions of the annual meeting.

　　TE255.A1N33　　625.8′2　　71-17587

NN　0059425　DLC DL OU TU MiU OU ICJ NN OrCS WaS

National paving brick association.
　... Standard specifications for vitrified brick
pavement and brick parking strips and gutters
　　see under American society of municipal
engineers.

National Paving Brick Association.
Work scenes, progressive steps ...
　　see under National Paving Brick
Manufacturers Association.

National paving brick manufacturers association.
The ABC of good paving. ［Cleveland, Ohio,
n.d.］
　16p. illus. 23cm.
　Cover title.

　　1. Pavements, Brick.

NN　0059428　TxDaM

National paving brick manufacturers association.
Brick roads outlast the bonds. ［Cleveland,
Ohio, n.d.］
　24p. illus. 23cm.
　Cover title.

　　1. Pavements, Brick.

NN　0059429　TxDaM

National paving brick manufacturers association.

U. S. *Bureau of mines.*
　The burning problems of industrial kilns; an investigation
by the Ceramic experiment station and the Fuel division of the
U. S. Bureau of mines in co-operation with the four heavy clay
products associations composed jointly of the National paving
brick manufacturers association, the Common brick manufacturers association, the American face brick association and the
Hollow building tile association. ［Washington？ 1924］

National Paving Brick Manufacturers Association.　625.8 S401
The construction of vitrified brick pavements including recom-
147017 mended specifications. Cleveland, O., National Paving Brick
Manufacturers Association, ［1924］.
　92 p. illus. 23½ᶜᵐ.

　　OrCS WaS IdB
NN　0059431　ICJ OCl OO NN MiU CU IEN MH MiD InU

TE255　**National Paving Brick Manufacturers Association.**
A1N3
　Dependable highways.
　　［Washington］

National Paving Brick Manufacturers' Association.
Directions for laying vitrified brick street pavements. ［In-
dianapolis？］ National Paving Brick Manufacturers' Association
［1911］. 1 p.l., 16 p., 1 pl. illus. 8°.

　Title from cover.

　1. Pavements (Brick).
N. Y. P. L.　　　　　　　　　　　　February 27, 1912.

NN　0059433　NN OO

National Paving Brick Manufacturers' Association.　625.8 Q800
Directions for laying vitrified brick street pavements. .... Speci-
09113 fication. [Indianapolis], Published by the National Paving Brick
ᵃ Manufacturers' Association, ［1908?-1911?］.

　Library has nos. 1-3. illus. 23½ᶜᵐ.
　No. 1 in four editions.

NN　0059434　ICJ NN

National Paving Brick Manufacturers' Association.
Forms for special assessments, Illinois
　　see under Baer, August H., comp.

National Paving Brick Manufacturers' Association.
Good roads at the home of Indiana University. ［Indianapo-
lis：National Paving Brick Manufacturers' Association, 1911］ 4 l.
illus. nar. 4°.

　Repr.: Clay-Worker. Title from cover.

　1. Pavements (Brick), U. S.: Indiana.
N. Y. P. L.　　　　　　　　　　　　February 27, 1912.

NN　0059436　NN

［National Paving Brick Manufacturers Association.］
　The Indianapolis motor speedway. ［Indianapolis：National
Paving Brick Manufacturers Association, 1911］ 8 l. illus.
ob. 32°.

　1. Pavements, U. S.: Ind: Indian-　　apolis. 2. Pavements (Brick).
3. Title.
N. Y. P. L.　　　　　　　　　　　　August 31, 1912.

NN　0059437　NN

National Paving Brick Manufacturers Association.
　A model paving program for a city of twenty thousand, with
special reference to vitrified brick pavements, by Maurice B.
Greenough... A paper written for presentation to the City Managers Association, meeting at Cincinnati, November 15, 1920.
(Preprint.) ［Cincinnati？ 1920？］ 19 p. incl. diagrs., tables.
4°.

　1. Pavements (Brick). 2. Pave-　　ments, U. S. 3. Greenough, Maurice B.
N. Y. P. L.　　　　　　　　　　　　November 2, 1921.

NN　0059438　NN

[National Paving Brick Manufacturers' Association]
The permanent roadway. [Indianapolis, Ind.,
　　see under ［Blair, Will P］

NN　0059439　NN

TE255　　　National Paving Brick Manufacturers Association.
.A1N33　　Proceedings of the general sessions
　National Paving Brick Association.
　　Proceedings ［of the］ general sessions ［of the］ annual meet-
ing. 23d-26th, 29th, 1929-32, 1935,
Washington.

National Paving Brick Manufacturers' Association.
　Report of a variety survey in the vitrified paving brick industry for the year 1926; made at the request of the Department
of Commerce of the United States by the National Paving Brick
Manufacturers Association; submitted to the Permanent Committee on Simplification of Variety and Standards for Vitrified
Paving Brick of the Department of Commerce, Washington, D. C.,
March 31st, 1927... ［Cleveland, O., 1927.］ 9 l. diagrs.,
table. 4°.

　Cover-title.

　Typewritten.
　Includes tabulations of reports of variety surveys made in 1921, 1923, 1924, 1925,
1926 and 1927 for the years 1914 to 1926 inclusive.

　416569A. 1. Bricks, Paving—Trade　　and stat.—U. S. 2. United States.
Commerce Department.
N. Y. P. L.　　　　　　　　　　　　November 13, 1929

NN　0059442　NN

National paving brick manufacturers association.
　Report of a variety survey made in the
　vitrified paving brick industry made for the
Department of Commerce by the National paving
brick manufacturers association...［1921］
　p.13-36 (In Proceedings of the Conference on
simplification of variety and standards for
vitrified paving brick of the Department of
Commerce of the United States, Washington, D. C.,
Nov. 15, 1921).

NN　0059443　MiD

National Paving Brick Manufacturers Association.
　Report of the investigation of paving and general
highway conditions
　　see under National Paving Brick Manufacturers Association. Engineering Commission.

NATIONAL paving brick manufacturers'
association.
　Specifications... City streets and
country highways.
　　Cleveland. Author. 1920? unp.

NN　0059445　WaS

National Paving Brick Manufacturers' Association.
　Specifications for standard rattler test for paving brick, endorsed and recommended by the National Paving Brick Manufacturers' Association; being a report of the committee of that
association on technical investigation, adopted at Louisville, February 7, 1911. ［Cleveland，］ 1911. 7 p., 1 diagr. 8°.

　1. Pavements (Brick).
N. Y. P. L.　　　　　　　　　　　　February 29, 1912

NN　0059446　NN

VOLUME 407

National paving brick manufacturers association.
Specifications for the construction of vitrified brick street pavements and vitrified brick highways. National paving brick manufacturers association. ₁Cleveland, F. H. Kimball co., 1914₁

cover-title, 45, ₁2₁ p. illus. 23ᵐᵐ.

1. Pavements, Brick.

CA 16-655 Unrev'd

Library of Congress   TE255.N3

NN   0059447   DLC CU WaS NN OO

National Paving Brick Manufacturers' Association.
Specifications for the construction of vitrified brick street pavements and country roads... ₁Cleveland:₁ National Paving Brick Manufacturers' Assoc. ₁1916₁   2 p.l., 46 p., 2 l., 46 p., 2 l., 46 p. incl. pl.   illus.   8°.

Cover-title.
Blank pages for memoranda included.
Contents: Sand-cement superfoundation type. Green concrete foundation type. Sand-cushion type.

1. Pavements (Brick). 2. Roads   (Paved).
N. Y. P. L.   April 1, 1918.

NN   0059448   NN OU

National Paving Brick Manufacturers Association.
Specifications of the National Paving Brick Manufacturers Association... Cleveland ₁1920₁.   84 l. diagrs., illus. 8°.

20767A. 1. Pavements (Brick).
N. Y. P. L.   October 4, 1921.

NN   0059449   NN IU OC1

National paving brick manufacturers association.
Two-sided value. Cleveland, Ohio ₁n.d.₁
14p. illus. 23cm.

1. Pavements, Brick.

NN   0059450   TxDaM

₁625.8   National paving brick manufacturers
N21v   association.
     Vitrified brick pavements for city
streets and country highways. Cleveland [191-?]
     [29]p. illus.

NN   0059451   IU

National paving brick manufacturers association.
   Work scenes, progressive steps in proper methods
of construction, easy - economic -accurate.
Vitrified brick roadway.
Cleveland, O., National paving brick manufacturers'
association, n.d.
   10 p.

NN   0059452   OU

National paving brick manufacturers association. *Committee on uniform cost finding.*
A system of uniform cost finding for paving brick manufacturers, prepared by the Committee on uniform cost finding of the National paving brick manufacturers association ... Cleveland, O., National paving brick manufacturers association, ᶜ1921.

1 p. l., 7-44 p. incl. tables. 25½ᶜᵐ.

1. Brick trade—Accounting.

21-18258

Library of Congress   HF5686.B6N3

NN   0059453   DLC WaS OC1FRB ICJ NN

National paving brick manufacturers association. *Engineering commission.*
Report of the investigation of paving and general highway conditions by the Engineering commission appointed by the National paving brick manufacturers association. Washington ₁1928?₁

66 p. illus. 23ᵐᵐ.

1. Pavements, Brick. 2. Roads—U. S. ₁2. U. S.—Roads₁

Agr 29-940

U. S. Dept. of agr. Library   288N216
for Library of Congress   ₁a38c1₁

NN   0059454   DNAL OrCS WaS NN OC1 ICJ OU IU

National Paving Brick Manufacturers' Association. *Engineering Commission.*
Report of the investigation of paving and general highway conditions by the Engineering Commission appointed by the National Paving Brick Manufacturers Association. ₁Washington? D. C., 1929?₁   86, 24 f.   4°.

Cover-title.
Typewritten.

482634A. 1. Pavements, Brick—U. S.   2. Roads—U. S.   3. Pavements—U. S.
N. Y. P. L.   July 19, 1930

NN   0059455   NN

---

182   **National peace action conference.** 1st,
673   Durham, N.C., 1934.
     Report of the first National peace
action conference held in connection
with the Institute of international
relations at Duke university, Durham,
N.C., June 11-23, 1934 ₁n.p., 1934₁

1 p.l., 18 numb. l. 35½cm.

Reproduced from typewritten copy.

NN   0059456   MH-L

National Peace Conference.
   Bricks for building world government to win
the peace. Issued by the Commission On the
World Community, National Peace Conference.
New York City, 1942.

NN   0059457   MH

National peace conference.
   Bulletin.
   v.

New York, 19   28cm.
   v.

Monthly (irregular).
Full title: 17   – Feb., 1941), National peace conference bulletin;
v. 2, no. 18–   NPC bulletin.
Reproduced from typewritten copy.

1. War and peace—Per. and soc.   publ.—U.S.
N. Y. P. L.   September 17, 1942

NN   0059458   NN

National peace conference.
   Conference on world economic cooperation, *Washington, D. C.,* 1938.
   Conference on world economic cooperation, Washington, D. C., March 24–26, 1938. New York, N. Y., National peace conference ₁1938₁

National peace conference.
   Directory. National peace conference. Personnel, aims, activities, 1937. New York, National peace conference ₁1937₁

32 p. 23ᵐᵐ.

A 38-1447
Provisional

Carnegie endow. int. peace.   Library JX1932.N273 1937
for Library of Congress   ₁2₁

NN   0059460   NNCE NN OCU NNC OO

National peace conference.

Economics and peace; a primer and a program; the primer by Marc A. Rose ... the program by a group of thirty-four economists ... New York, National peace conference, 1937.

National peace conference.
   Geneva information service of National peace conference.
   see under title

National Peace Conference.
   NPC American newsletter
   see under title

National peace conference.
   The National peace conference and the European crisis; an American peace program. ₁New York: National peace conference, 1941₁   1 l.   21½cm.

Caption-title.

1. World war, 1939–   —   Neutrality of the U. S.
N. Y. P. L.   June 30, 1942

NN   0059464   NN

NATIONAL PEACE CONFERENCE.
   The National peace conference, clearing house and council board of the peace movement in the United States, coordinates programs, policies and services. Statement of principles, plan of organization, list of members. New York, N.Y. [1939?]   16 p.   21½cm.

1. War and peace—Assoc. and org.—U.S.

NN   0059465   NN

National peace conference.
   The neutrality issue. New York, National peace conference ₁1939₁

15 p. 21¼ᵐ.

CONTENTS.—What the neutrality laws provide, by William T. Stone.—Should our neutrality act be repealed or revised? From the Town hall advisory service, no. 9, December 22, 1938.—The case for continuing and strengthening mandatory neutrality, by Harold E. Fey.—The case for applying the law to belligerents violating anti-war treaties, by Emily Hickman.—Questions—Sources for additional information (p. 14)—Suggested reading (p. 15)

1. U. S.—Neutrality.   I. Stone, William Treadwell, 1899–   II. Fey, Harold Edward, 1898–   III. Hickman, Emily Gregory, 1880– IV. Title.

U. S. Dept. of state. Libr.   JX5361.N3   S D 40-19
for Library of Congress   ₁2₁

NN   0059466   DS

National Peace Conference.
   Peace in the Pacific, by the Honorable Hirosi Saito... ₁and₁ Chester H. Rowell... Broadcast from New York city through the courtesy of the National Broadcasting Company over WJZ and associated stations, February 29, 1936. New York, N. Y.: The National Peace Conference ₁1936₁   7 p.   28cm.

Reproduced from typewritten copy.

860432A. 1. Pacific ocean—Political   and economic aspects. I. Saito, Hiroshi, 1886–   II. Rowell,   Chester Harvey, 1867– III. Title.
N. Y. P. L.   December 22, 1936

NN   0059467   NN

National peace conference.

Stone, William Treadwell, 1899–
   Peaceful change, the alternative to war; a survey prepared for the National peace conference campaign for world economic cooperation, by William T. Stone and Clark M. Eichelberger ... New York, The Foreign policy association, incorporated, ᶜ1937.

National peace conference.
   A primer on the trade agreements
   see under   [Hubbard, Ursula Phalla]
1904–

VOLUME 407

National peace conference.
Pros and cons of universal military training. New York, Commission on the world community, Nat. peace conference ₁1946₎ 11 p. 21cm.

Written largely by Helen Raebeck.

1. Military service—U. S. I. Raebeck, Helen.
N. Y. P. L. August 18, 1949

NN 0059470 NN

HD82
.S845

National peace conference.

Stone, William Treadwell, 1899–
... ¿ Puede evitarse la guerra? (Peaceful change) Estudio preparado para la campaña de la Conferencia nacional de la paz en pro de la cooperación económica mundial. Traducción de Inés Cané Fontecilla. Santiago de Chile, Ediciones Ercilla, 1939.

National peace conference.
Report of the committee of experts to the Conference on world economic cooperation, Washington, D. C., March 24–26, 1938. New York, N. Y., Campaign for world economic cooperation of the National peace conference, 1938.

31, ₁1₎ p. 20½ᵐ.

1. Economic policy. I. Conference on world economic cooperation, Washington, D. C., 1938.
Library of Congress HC57.N35 43–48629
₍2₎ 330.631

NN 0059472 DLC UU NN NNCE

National peace conference.
... Report of the director. 1935/37–
New York ₁1937–
v. 23½ᵐ.
The first report covers the period Dec. 1, 1935–Nov. 30, 1937.

A 38–1449
Provisional
Carnegie endow. int. peace. Library JX1932.N 3
for Library of Congress ₍2₎

NN 0059473 NNCE UU NN

National peace conference.
... A study of neutrality legislation; report of a committee of the National peace conference, with an introduction by James T. Shotwell ... New York city, Carnegie endowment for international peace, Division of intercourse and education ₁1936₎

3 p. l., 3–61 p. 19½ᵐ. (International conciliation ... January, 1936, no. 316)

1. U. S.—Neutrality. I. Shotwell, James Thomson, 1874–
II. Title. III. Title: Neutrality legislation, A study of.
36–745
Provisional
Library of Congress JX1907.A8 no. 316
—— —— Copy 2. ₍12₎ (341.6082) 341.3

NN 0059474 DLC OU MiU OCl OrPR CaBVaU WaU–L

HF1713
.V5

National peace conference.

Villard, Oswald Garrison, 1872–
Tariffs and economic disarmament, by Oswald Garrison Villard. ₁New York? 1937?₎

National peace conference.
To prevent a third world war — World government. Why? How? What kind? What must we do to get it? New York, Commission on the world community, National peace conference ₁1941?₎ 13 p. 21cm.

1. Federation, International, 1939–
N. Y. P. L. August 25, 1947

NN 0059476 NN

National peace conference.
Where to find it; a guide to popular education materials on international relations... Literature review... Compiled by James Rietmulder, secretary Literature committee. Section 1–
New York: National peace conference, 1938– parts. 28cm.

Caption-title.
Reproduced from typewritten copy.
CONTENTS.—Section 1. Pamphlets, posters, films.—Section 2. Books and periodicals.

1. World politics—Bibl. I. Rietmulder, James, comp.
N. Y. P. L. May 29, 1942

NN 0059477 NN

National peace conference.
World affairs pamphlets [New series]
see World affairs pamphlets. [New series]
New York, N. Y., Foreign policy association, incorporated, in cooperation with National peace conference.

National peace conference.
World government day kit. ₁19

New York ₁19 v. 20–28cm.
Annual
The kit comprises miscellaneous pamphlets, radio scripts, single issues of periodicals, etc.; title appears only on envelope used for mailing.

1. World war, 1939– —Peace. I. Title.
N. Y. P. L. April 23, 1945

NN 0059479 NN

National Peace Conference. Commission on the World Community.
The G.I.O., functions of a general international organization. New York ₁1944₎
8p. 21cm. (In Pamphlets on international federation. v.1, no.2)

National Peace Conference. Commission on the World Community. World government series.

NN 0059480 OrU

National peace conference. Committee on economics and peace.
Report. 1937.
29 p.

NN 0059481 MiD NN

National peace conference. *Committee on military training in schools and colleges.*
Report of the Committee on military training in schools and colleges. New York, N. Y., National peace conference ₁1936₎
cover-title, 16 p. 23ᵐ.
Daniel L. Marsh, chairman.
"Selected reading references on the military training problem": p. 16.

1. Military education—U. S. 2. Universities and colleges—U. S.
I. Marsh, Daniel Lash, 1880– II. Title.
E 40–315
U. S. Off. of educ. Library U435.N2
for Library of Congress ₍2₎

NN 0059482 DHEW NN

National peace conference ₁at Hague, 1899₎
see Hague. International peace conference, 1899.

National peace congress
see
American peace congress.

National Peace Congress of Catholic Clergy, *Prague, 1951.*
The Catholic priest in the fight for peace; addresses and resolutions from the National Peace Congress of Catholic Clergy held in Prague. Prague, Czech Catholic Charita, 1951.
61 p. illus., ports. 21 cm.

1. Catholic Church in the Czechoslovak Republic—Clergy. 2. Church and state in the Czechoslovak Republic. 3. Peace—Congresses.
I. Title.
BX1518.N3 1951a 282.437 53–22801

NN 0059485 DLC NN

National Peace Council, *Budapest*
see
Országos Béketanács.

National Peace Council, London.
Accept the General Act. An explanation of the General Act for the Pacific Settlement of International Disputes; a treaty prepared by the League of Nations and open to all countries to sign. ₁London₎ National Council for the Prevention of War, and the Women's Internat. League, 1929. 7 p. 8°.

516703A. 1. Arbitration, Internat.— Treaties, 1924. 2. Defence—Treaties, 1924.
N. Y. P. L. March 10, 1931

NN 0059487 NN

National peace council, London.
American newsletter
see N. P. C. American newsletter.

National Peace Council, London.
Annual report
see its Report.

National peace council, *London.*
... The Atlantic charter; the Roosevelt-Churchill declaration ... ₁London₎ N P C ₁1941?₎
cover-title, 15, ₁1₎ p. 21½ᵐ. (*Its* "Peace aims pamphlet" no. 9)
"Reference list": p. 12.
CONTENTS. — The Roosevelt-Churchill declaration. — A point-by-point commentary. — Resolution of the St. James's palace conference.—A discussion outline.—President Wilson's "fourteen points" of January, 1918.

1. Atlantic declaration, Aug. 14, 1941.
SD 42–72
U. S. Dept. of state. Libr.
for Library of Congress D735.N3
₍2₊₎ 940.531

NN 0059490 DS IaU DLC

National peace council, *London.*
Britain & Russia; the future. London, National peace council ₁1942₎
62 p. 21½ᵐ. (*On cover:* "Peace aims pamphlet" no. 12)
"Addresses given at a conference on the theme 'Britain and Russia in the new world order' held in London in April 1942."
"A selection of recent books on Russia," p. 62.

1. Gt. Brit.—Relations (general) with Russia. 2. Russia—Relations (general) with Gt. Brit. I. Title.
42–50473
Library of Congress DA47.65.N3
₍4₎ 327.4200947

NN 0059491 DLC NNU–W NN OU

4DA
207

National Peace Council, London.
Britain & Russia; the future. Rev. and reprinted. London, 1943.
64 p.
(Peace aims pamphlet, no. 12)

NN 0059492 DLC–P4

VOLUME 407

National peace council, *London.*
　　The British commonwealth and the U. S. A. in the post-war
world.　London, National peace council ₍1941₎
　　64 p.　21½ᶜᵐ.　(On cover: "Peace aims pamphlet" no. 10)
　　"Addresses given at a conference held under the auspices of the National peace council, at the Aeolian hall, London, in November 1941."
　　"A selected list of books and pamphlets": p. 64.
　　CONTENTS.—The cultural and psychological aspects, by Sir Arthur Eddington, Vera Brittain, Willard Connely and George Catlin.—The economic factors, by H. E. Elvin and Barbara Ward.—The political and constitutional issues, by Norman Bentwich, A. L. Goodhart and H. N. Brailsford.—The implications for the rest of the world, by Denis Saurat, S. de Madariaga and H. D. Liem.
　　1. U. S.—Relations (general) with Gt. Brit.　2. Gt. Brit.—Relations (general) with U. S.　3. Re-　　　construction (1939-　)　I. Title.
　　　　　　　　　　　　　　　　　　　　　　　42-21190
　　Library of Congress　　E183.8.G7N38
　　　　　　　　　　　　　　₍3₎　　　　327.420973

NN　0059493　　DLC ViU Or OCU

National Peace Council,　　　London.
　　Circular...

London, 1912–　　　　　　　　　　　　　　8°.
　　v.
　　Monthly, 1912–May, 1924; monthly (irregular), July, 1924–
　　Numbering continuous; v. 1 lacks v. numbering.
　　Title varies: 1912–May, 1924, National Peace Council.　Monthly circular;
July, 1924–　　National Council for the prevention of War.　Circular...

　　1. War and peace—Assoc. and org.　　　　　　Gt. Br.
N. Y. P. L.　　　　　　　　　　　　　　　August 21, 1929

NN　0059494　　NN

National peace council, *London.*
　　The conditions of a constructive peace.　₍Rochester, Eng.,₎
Printed by the Stanhope press ltd., 1944₎
　　₍8₎ p.　21ᶜᵐ.
　　Caption title.

　　1. World war, 1939-　　—Peace.　I. Title.
　　　　　　　　　　　　　　　　　　　　S D 45–52
　　U. S. Dept. of state.　Libr.　　　D816.5.N3
　　for Library of Congress　　　　　₍2₎

NN　0059495　　DS NN

National　Peace Council, London.
　　Disarmament; Britain must give a lead.　London, National
council for prevention of war ₍1926?₎
　　7, ₍1₎ p.　21½ᶜᵐ.

　　1. Disarmament.　I. Title.　II. Title: Britain must give a lead.
　　　　　　　　　　　　　　　　　　　　27–8340
　　Library of Congress　　　　JX1974.N3

NN　0059496　　DLC

National Peace Council, *London.*
　　.... ..　Educational series ... .　[London], National Peace
132675　Council, 1908–[1913?].
　　Library has no. 1–2, 4, 6, 8.　22ᵐᵐ.
　　Cover-title.
　　At head of title: National Peace Council.
　　No. 1–2 published without series title.

NN　0059497　　ICJ DLC ICRL NN DAU

National Peace Council, London
Ozd10　　Forum.　1/13–114/121, June 1944–July 1945.
+N22pf　London.
　　13 nos. in 1v.　33cm.　monthly.

　　Succeeds *its* Opinion.

NN　0059498　　CtY

National peace council, London.
　　Freedom for colonial peoples
　　　see under　Hinden, Rita.

HC286
.5　　National Peace Council, *London.*
.N3　　The German crisis.　London ₍1946₎
　　20 p.　18 cm.　(Peace aims pamphlet, 37)
　　"The articles ... appeared in the Economist of April 6, 1946."
　　CONTENTS.—The British approach.—Ruhr coal decline.—The reparations plan.—The new Luddites.—Policy for Germany.

　　1. Germany—Econ. condit.—1945-　　I. Title.　　(Series:
National Peace Council, London.　Publications, 37)
　　　　　　　　　　　　　　　　　　　A 51–8314
New York.　Public Libr.
for Library of Congress　　₍2₎

NN　0059500　　NN NIC MH DLC

National Peace Council, London.
　　H.G. Wells, S. de Madariaga, J. Middleton
　　Murry, C.E.M. Joad on the new world order
　　　see under　Wells, Herbert George, 1866-

National peace council, London.
D826
.C3　　Carter, Henry, 1874-
　　The human needs of Europe ₍by₎ Rev. Henry Carter, C. B. E.,
with a foreword by the Bishop of Chichester.　London, The
National peace council ₍1945₎

JX1974　National Peace Council, London.
.A1P3　　... The increasing burden of armaments.
no. 35　London, 1913.
　　[2] p.　[Pamphlets on disarmament.　No. 35]

NN　0059503　　DLC

National peace council, London.
　　India, 1939-1942
　　　see under　[Harrison, Agatha]

National Peace Council, *London.*
　　International declarations.　no 1-　　[London,
　　National Peace Council, 1945-　　no.
　　　see under title

National peace council, London.
Xo94　　[Lists of publications]
+N17l　　　　　　　　　　　　　　32cm.

NN　0059506　　CtY

National *Peace Council, London.*
Smith, Rennie, 1888-
　　Militarism in our educational institutions; the menace of
the Junior cadet corps and the O. T. C., by Rennie Smith ...
London, National council for prevention of war ₍1926?₎

National *Peace Council, London.*
Smith, Rennie, 1888-
　　Military service in the British Empire; do we want conscription?　By Rennie Smith ...　London, National council for
prevention of war ₍1927?₎

National Peace Council, *London.*
　　Military training in our educational institutions.　London,
1929.
　　10 p.　21 cm.　(₍Its₎ ₍Publication₎ no. 13)
　　Pub. by the council under its earlier name: National Council for
Prevention of War.

　　1. Military education—Gt. Brit.　I. Title.　　(Series)
　　　　　　　　　　　　　　　　　　　49–38017*
　　U549.N28

NN　0059509　　DLC

National peace council, *London.*
　　The military training of youth, a study of the Officers' training corps.　London, National council for prevention of war,
1930.
　　13 p.　21ᶜᵐ.　(₍Its₎ ₍Publication₎ no. 19)

　　1. Military education—Gt. Brit.　2. Gt. Brit.　Army.　Officers' training
corps.　I. Title.　　　　　　　　　45–43918
　　Library of Congress　　　　U549.N3

NN　0059510　　DLC CU

National Peace Council, London.
　　Monthly circular ...
　　　see its　Circular.

National Peace Council, London.
　　NPC papers
　　　see under title

National peace council, London.
　　National petition "for a new peace conference."　A call from a
million British citizens.　London: National peace council ₍1939₎
　　19 p.　25cm.

　　1. War and peace, 1914-
N. Y. P. L.　　　　　　　　　　　　　　March 6, 1940

NN　0059513　　NN

National　Peace Council,　　　London.
　　News bulletin.
　　v.

London, 19　　　　　　　　　　　　　　8°.
　　v.
　　Irregular.
　　Numbering continuous.
　　Superseded by The Peace review.

　　1. War and peace—Per. and soc.　　　publ—Gt. Br.
N. Y. P. L.　　　　　　　　　　　　　　March 16, 1932

NN　0059514　　NN

National Peace Council, London.
JX1901
.O6　　One world.　v. 1-
　　June 1946-
　　London, National Peace Council.

National Peace Council, *London.*
　　Our trust in Central Africa: The background to federation.　An analysis of the federal scheme.　Memorial to the
Prime Minister.　London ₍1953₎
　　26 p.　illus.　22 cm.　(Peace aims pamphlet no. 56)

　　1. Rhodesia and Nyasaland.　I. Title.
　　　　　　　　　　　　　　　　　　　53—2896 ‡
　　JQ2755.N3　　　　　　342.68909

NN　0059516　　DLC ViU MH TxU OU NN NIC

VOLUME 407

National Peace Council, London
₍Pamphlets₎
no.

London, 19   8°.
nos.

1. War and peace, 1914–
N. Y. P. L.   August 15, 1929

NN 0059517   NN

National peace council, London.

... **Peace** aims documents. no. 1–
₍London, The National peace council, 1942–

National peace council, London.
Peace aims leaflet
see under title

172.4   National Peace Council, London.
N277   Peace aims pamphlet no. 1–
        ₍1940₎–   London.
        v.   illus.   22 cm.

        1. Peace. Societies.

NN 0059520   N ICU MiU CtNIC RPB DLC WaS

National peace council, London.

Peace and the colonial problem. London, National peace council ₍1936?₎

National Peace Council, London.

Huntsman, M   H.
        Peace bibliography ... By M. H. Huntsman. London,
The National peace council ₍1910₎

National peace council, London.

The **Peace** review; the news bulletin of the National peace council. no. 1–11; Jan./Feb. 1931–Sept./Oct. 1932. ₍London, Caledonian press, ltd., 1931–1932₎

National Peace Council, London.

Smith, Rennie, 1888–
        Peace with China, by Rennie Smith ... London, National council for prevention of war ₍1927₎

National peace council, London.

Peace year book. 1910–18, 1921, 1927, 1929, 1931–

London, National peace council ₍1910–

National Peace Council, London.
        Planning for abundance ...
            see under   Peace Aims Conference, Oxford,
1943.

National Peace Council, London
        .... Political series .... Westminster, National Peace Council,
117735 [1908?–1912].
        Library has no. 1–7. 22cm.
        Cover-title.
        At head of title: National Peace Council.
        No. 1–3 published without series title.
        No. 5 wanting.

NN 0059527   ICJ ICRL

JX
1905
.N3   National Peace Council, London.
        Publications. no. 1–
        London, 19 –

        1. Peace–Collections. 2. International relations. 3. Arbitration, International. 4. World politics.

NN 0059528   DAU OCU

National Peace Council, London
Ozd10   Register; articles, declarations, pamphlets
+N22r   and books bearing on problems of peace and
        reconstruction. no.1–8; Oct.10,1944–June 30,
        1945. London.
        8 nos. in 1v. 33cm. monthly.

NN 0059529   CtY

National Peace Council, London.
        The renewal of civilisation
            see under   Dawson, Chritopher Henry, 1889–

NATIONAL PEACE COUNCIL, London
        Reasons for a reduction of expenditure on
        armaments. A report of a meeting at the Cannon Street Hotel, London, E.C., Jan.16,1914.
        Westminster, S.W., National Peace Council, [1914].

        Pamphlet.
        Cover serves as title-page.

NN 0059531   MH

JX 1908
.G8N33   National Peace Council, London.
        Report.

        ₍London₎
        v. 21cm. annual.
        Report year ends Apr. 30.

        JX1908.G8N33   172.406242   50–30442 ‡

NN 0059532   DLC NIC NNUN NN

National Peace Council, London.
        The road to security ...
            see under   Mitrany, David, 1888–

National Peace Council, London.
        Towards a world order
            see under   Peace Aims Conference, Oxford,
1943.

National Peace Council, London.
JX1954
.T65   **Towards** world government. no. 1–
        London, National Peace Council ₍1948₎–

D825
.C275   National peace council, London.

        Carter, Henry, 1874–
        Towards world recovery, plans and proposals for international functional co-operation ₍by₎ Rev. Henry Carter, c. B. E.
London, The National peace council ₍1945₎

National peace council, London.
        Unofficial British peace aims; a summary
            see under   Donington, Robert.

National Peace Council, London.
        The war and the peace, an appeal for a constructive policy. ₍London, 1941₎
        ₍2₎p. 28cm. (In Pamphlets on post-war planning. v.5, no.21)

        Caption title.

        1. World war, 1939–1945.   Peace.
I. Title.

NN 0059538   OrU

National peace council, London.
        What about Germany? An outline for discussion groups.   London, Nat. peace council ₍1944₎   8 p.   22cm.
        "Additional books and pamphlets," p. 8.

        1. World war, 1939–1945—Post-   war problems—Germany.
N. Y. P. L.   July 8, 1946

NN 0059539   NN CtY

National peace council, London.
        What is democracy?   London ₍1946₎   19 p.   21cm.
("Peace aims pamphlet." no. 38)

        1. Democracy.

NN 0059540   NN MH MiU-L NIC

National peace council, London.

        What kind of peace? London, National peace council ₍1940₎

National peace council, London, comp.
        The Wilson peace terms. ₍London₎ National peace council ₍1919?₎
        22 p., 1 l. 21ᶜᵐ.

        1. European war, 1914–   —Peace.   I. Wilson, Woodrow, pres. U. S., 1856–   II. Title.
                                                    A 20–845
        Title from Carnegie   Endow. Int. Peace. Printed by L. C

NN 0059542   NNCE NN

National Peace Council, London.
        Yugoslavia and peace, a study of Cominform accusations; report of the N. P. C. delegation to Yugoslavia, 1950. London ₍1950₎
        27 p. map (on cover) facsim. 22 cm. (Peace aims pamphlet 50)

        1. Yugoslavia—For. rel.—1945–   2. Yugoslavia—Pol. & govt.—1945–   I. Title.   (Series: National Peace Council, London. Publications, 50)
        DR370.N3   949.7   51–6654

NN 0059543   DLC MH TxU NIC

National Peace Council, London
        see also
        Peace Aims Conference.

VOLUME 407

National Peace Council, *London. Commission on Disarmament*
see
National Peace Council, *London. Disarmament Commission.*

National Peace Council, *London. Commission on East-West Relations.*
Christians and Communists; a study of relations between church and state in Eastern Europe. London ₁1953₎
36 p. 22 cm. (Peace aims pamphlet no. 55)
Prepared by the Sub-committee on Church and State Relations of the East-West Commission of the National Peace Council.

1. Church and state in Europe, Eastern.   I. Title.
BR738.6.N3   55-18766 ‡

NN   0059546   DLC N MH OU NN NIC CLSU

National Peace Council, London.   Commission on
HF3496   East-West Relations.
.5   **Barratt-Brown, Michael.**
.B35   East-West trade. London, National Peace Council ₁1950₎

National Peace Council, *London. Commission on East-West Relations.*
Two worlds in focus; studies of the Cold War. London, National Peace Council ₁1950₎
133 p. 22 cm.

1. World politics—1945–   I. Title.
D844.N3   940.55   50-11640

NN   0059548   DLC NIC

National Peace Council, *London. Disarmament Commission.*
World disarmament; report on the political, technical, and economic problems. London, National Peace Council ₁1953₎
78 p. 22 cm. (Peace aims pamphlet no. 58)

1. Disarmament.   I. Title.
JX1974.N39   341.67   54-27189 ‡

NN   0059549   DLC MH IU OU NIC NN

National Peace Council, *London. East-West Commission*
see
National Peace Council, *London. Commission on East-West Relations.*

KF   National Peace Council, London. Information
211   Office.
P18   For your information. London ₁1947₎
v.123   7 p. 21cm.
no.9
In Pamphlets 123.

1. Peace. 2. International relations.

NN   0059551   NIC

National Peace Council, London. Peace Aims
Conference
see   Peace Aims Conference.

National Peace Council of Hungary
see Országos Béketanács.

B166   National peace federation.
0806   The manifesto issued by envoys of the Inter-
1915n   national congress of women at the Hague to
        the governments of Europe, and the President
        of the United States₎and other material₎
        ₁Chicago,Ill.,1915₎

NN   0059554   CtY

Ozd10   National peace federation.
+N213m ₁Minor publications₎
                        31cm.
        Includes publications of the Emergency peace
        federation and of the National peace conference,
        Chicago, 1915.

NN   0059555   CtY

National peace jubilee, Washington, D.C., 1899
see
Washington, D.C. National peace jubilee, 1899.

NATIONAL peace jubilee and musical festival,
Boston,1869.

See BOSTON - National peace jubilee
and musical festival,1869.

... The **National** peace jubilee, and musical **reporter.**
May 15, 1869–July 24, 1869. Boston, J. M. Usher ₁1869₎
1 v. 24ᶜᵐ. weekly.
No issue for June 19; ceased publication with July 24.

1. Boston. National peace jubilee and musical festival, 1869.
Library of Congress   ML38.B7P3   5-27478

NN   0059558   DLC CLSU MoSW OU

281.3939
N21B   National peach council.
        ₁Bulletin₎ no.
        Martinsburg, W. Va.

        1. Peach industry. U.S.

NN   0059559   DNAL

National peach council.
It's peachtime U.S.A.
see under title

634.22 National Peach Council.
N21p   Proceedings ₁of the₎ annual convention.
        1st-
        1941-
        Martinsburg.
        v. 23-28cm. annual.

        Vol. for 1969 issued as Virginia fruit
        v.57, no.3.
        No convention held in 1943.
        Title varies: Proceedings of con-

Continued in next column

Continued from preceding column

ference.₎   -68, Proceedings ₁of
the₎ annual convention and trade show.
Cover title,   -51: Peach annual; 1952-
National Peach Council annual.
Vol. for 1969 includes the Proceedings ₁of
the₎ annual meeting of the Virginia State
Horticultural Society, and of the Woman's
Auxiliary; 1970 includes the Proceedings ₁of
the₎ annual convention of the Western Colorado
Horticultural   Society.

NN   0059562   IU NcD

National peanut council, inc.
Annual report.   1941-
₁Atlanta?₎ 1941-
v.

NN   0059563   MH-BA MiD

National Peanut Council.
Food & nutrition ideas
see under title

National Peanut Council.
N.P.C. newsletter
see under title

National peanut council.
The National peanut council, incorporated, in a war time program, 1942–1943 ... Atlanta, Ga. ₁1942?₎
cover-title, 16 numb. l. illus. 28ᶜᵐ.

1. ₁Peanuts as food₎ 2. Peanuts.   Agr 48-79
                                           Brief cataloging
U. S. Dept. of agr. Library   380.1N213
for Library of Congress   ₁2₎

NN   0059566   DNAL

National peanut council, inc.
Peanuts — their food values and interesting recipes.   Atlanta,
Nat. peanut council ₁1942₎ 83 p. illus. 22cm.
"References," p. 32.

1. Cookery—Peanut.
N. Y. P. L.   January 21, 1946

NN   0059567   NN

389.1   National peanut council.
N213P   Peanuts; their food values and interesting
        recipes ... Atlanta, Ga. ₁1943?₎
        64 p. illus. 22 cm.
        Contains bibliographies.
        1. Peanuts as food. 2. Cookery (Peanuts)

NN   0059568   DNAL WaS

₁National Peanut Council₎
The snack jar plan.   ₁n.p., c1946₎
₁16₎ p. illus. 23 cm.
1. Cookery (Peanuts) 2. Peanuts as food.
I. Title.

NN   0059569   DNAL

VOLUME 407

National Peanut Council.
Year book. 1st–   1941–
[Atlanta?]
v. illus., ports. 23 cm.
Title varies: 1941, Proceedings.

1. Peanuts.

HD9235.P32U48   338.4   42–21928 rev*

NN   0059570   DLC OrCS

National Pecan Association.
The **Nut-grower;** devoted to the interests of the National nut-
growers' association.
Poulan, Ga., The Nut-grower company [19

National Pecan Association.
Report of proceedings of the annual
convention. v.

19

Tifton, Ga. [etc.] 19
v. illus., plates, tables. 24cm.

v.27– 1928– also numbered as its
Bulletin, v.3 no.2.
1901–1921, known as National Nut Growers'
Association; 1922–1928, as National Pecan
Growers' Associa   tion; 1929–
as National Pecan   Association.

Cumulative index, 1921–   issued in
each volume, 1925–

1. Pecan - Societies. 2. Nuts - Societies.
x: National Nut Growers' Association.
x: National Pecan Growers' Association.
ser.: Its   Bulletin.

NN   0059573   OrCS MBH CU

National Pecan Growers' Association
see   National Pecan Association.

National pedagogic congress of Spain
see under   U. S. Office of Education.

National penmanship compendium; a complete guide to free-arm
or muscular movement writing... for self-instruction and for use
in schools and colleges...   New York City: The Business Jour.[,
190–?]   16 l.   obl. 16°.

Cover-title.
Contents: LESLIE, S. E. Lessons in business writing. COURTNEY, T. Lessons in
ornamental writing. MOORE, M. B. Lessons in flourishing. DAKIN, A. W. Lessons in
card writing. DENNIS, W. E. Lessons in Old English lettering.

I. Handwriting—Systems.
N. Y. P. L.   May 12, 1925

NN   0059576   NN

HD
7106   **National Pension Conference, Cleveland,**
.U5   **1950.**
N32   National Pension Conference, sponsored by
1950   the National Association of Life Underwriters
... Cleveland, June 28th, 1950. [Proceedings.
New York, National Association of Life
Underwriters, 1950.]
30 p.   28 cm.
Cover title.

1. Old age pensions--U.S.

NN   0059577   MiU IU

National pension insurance in Finland. [Helsinki,
Maalaiskuntien litton kirjapaino, 1950]

14 p.
Appendix, Sept.1952, 2 p., in pocket

NN   0059578   MH

NATIONAL PENSIONS.
...Cash, tax-less, debt-less national pensions for all
citizens 50 years of age; act simply and immediately...
Los Angeles, Cal.: National pensions, c1938. 31 p.
illus. (charts.) 23 x 10½cm.

"Books recommended," p. [32]

1. Pensions, Old age—U.S. 2. Economic history—U.S.,
1933–

NN   0059579   NN

National People's Congress
see
China (*People's Republic of China, 1949–   *) *Ch'üan
kuo jên min tai piao ta hui.*

NATIONAL PEOPLE'S PARTY, Germany

See DEUTSCHNATIONALE VOLKSPARTEI.

National perishable freight committee
Ice capacity of bunkers or tanks of refrigerator
cars of railroads and car lines operating in the
United States and Dominion of Canada.

NN   0059582   OC1

National perishable freight committee.
... Perishable protective tariff
Chicago, Ill., J. J. Quinn
v. 27 cm. with supplements.
1. Railroads. U. S. Freight. 2. Railroads.
U. S. Rates.

NN   0059583   CU

National personnel association
see
American management association.

423.9
N213   **National Pest Control Association.**
Annual report of the Executive Secretary.

Elizabeth, N.J.,

**Every issue has also individual title e.g.
1961/62 is Progress for people in pest control.**

1. **National Pest Control Association.**

NN   0059585   DNAL

National Pest Control Association.
Approved reference procedures for subterranean termite
control, by the Wood Destroying Organisms Committee,
1948–51. Edited by Ralph E. Heal, technical director. New
York, 1951.
250 p. illus. 30 cm.

1. Termites. I. Title.

QL513.T3N3   693   52–17887 ‡

NN   0059586   DLC MB

National Pest Control Association, Inc.
A complete set of 14 photographs relating to
termite attack and injury and standard corrective
measures
see under [Bender, Alva H   [Supplement]

National Pest Control Association.
Exterminators log ...
see under title

National Pest Control Association.
Membership roster.
New York.
v. 23 cm.

Continued by the Association's Roster of
members.

SB950.N3   58–47590

NN   0059589   DLC

National Pest Control Association.
Pest control technology
see under title

SB950
.N3
National Pest Control Association.
Roster of members.

Elizabeth, N. J.
v. 23 cm.
Continues the association's Membership roster.

SB950.N3   632'.9'06273   72–620936

NN   0059591   DLC

614.48   **National Pest Control Association.**
N212s   **Service letter. no.**

Brooklyn, N.Y.
no. 28cm. irregular.

Issued   by the
association under its earlier name: National
Association of Exterminators and Fumigators.
Incomplete: frequent numbers wanting.

NN   0059592   IU DNAL

632.4   National Pest Control Association.
N212s   Serviceman's manual, by the Serviceman's Selection and Training Subcommittee of the Manage-
ments Clinics Committee of the National Pest
Control Association, inc. Edited by Philip J.
Spear.   New York, 1955.
119p. illus. 24cm.

NN   0059593   IU NIC

423.9
N213T   **National Pest Control Association.**
Technical release.

Elizabeth, N.J.

1. **Entomology, Economic. Research.**

NN   0059594   DNAL

VOLUME 407

The National pet stock association of America.
Standard of perfection for rabbits, cavies, mice, rats
& skunks, by the National pet association of America.
₍Waukegan, Ill., Triangle press, ₍1915₎
cover-title, 32 p. illus. 17½ᶜᵐ. $0.50

1. Rabbit.

Library of Congress   SF453.N3   15-4972

NN 0059595   DLC ICJ

National Petro-Chemicals Company,
Community improvement program

see under

Bartholomew (Harland) and Associates.

TP248
H9N27 **National Petro-Chemicals Corporation.**
From cornfields to chemicals in two years; a
brief account of the creation of a great, new
industry in the heart of the Illinois prairie.
[n. p., c1953]
38 p. illus. 26 cm.

1. Chemicals - manufacture and industry.
I. Title.

NN 0059597   DI

National petroleum & water gas company.
Description and illustrations of the Hanlon process for making
illuminating gas from petroleum or any liquid hydro-carbon, with
a few references from parties using the same, and letters from
well-known insurance authorities and others. The National petroleum gas company, owners of the Hanlon process... Newark, Daily Advertiser steam prtg. house, 1880. 24 p. illus.
26cm.

1. Gas, Oil.
N. Y. P. L.   August 10, 1944

NN 0059598   NN

National petroleum association

Chamberlin, Charles Dudley, 1854-
Address of C. D. Chamberlin, secretary and counsel
general of the National petroleum association, Cleveland, Ohio, to the special committee of the German
Reichstag having under consideration a bill regulating
the sale of illuminating oil within the German empire.
₍New York, 1913₎

National petroleum association
Annual report of ... secretary and ... traffic manager
to the National petroleum association at its annual meeting.
₍Cleveland?₎
v. 27ᶜᵐ.

Report year ends October 1.

1. Petroleum industry and trade—Societies.
CA 16-777 Unrev'd
Library of Congress   HD9569.N3A4

NN 0059600   DLC NN

National petroleum association.
A digest of pipe line rates on crude petroleum oil on file with
the Interstate commerce commission.

Washington, D. C., ₍19
nos. 29ᶜᵐ.
Editor: 19   H. S. Elkins.
Nos.   have revisions called Memoranda.
Reproduced from type-written copy.
1. Petroleum—U. S.—Transportation.   I. Elkins, Harry S., ed.
II. U. S. Interstate commerce commission.
43-42535
Library of Congress   HD9580.U7N25

NN 0059601   DLC

National petroleum association.
A digest of pipe line rates on gasoline and other petroleum
products as named in specific items herein, on file with the
Interstate commerce commission.

Washington, D. C., ₍19
nos. 29ᶜᵐ.
Editor: 19   H. S. Elkins.
Nos.   have revisions called Memoranda.
Reproduced from type-written copy.
1. Petroleum—U. S.—Transportation.   I. Elkins, Harry S., ed.
II. U. S. Interstate commerce commission.
43-42534
Library of Congress   HD9580.U7N26
₍2₎   338.476055

NN 0059602   DLC

National petroleum association
A digest of state gasoline tax laws in effect
August 1, 1926...
Washington, 1926.
45 mimeo. l.

NN 0059603   OC1FRB

National petroleum association.
A digest of state gasoline tax laws in effect December 1,
1927, compiled by Washington office, National petroleum asso-
ciation, Western petroleum refiners association. Fayette B.
Dow. Horace L. Lohnes ... ₍Washington, D. C., ₍1927.
cover-title, 6 p. l., 47 (i. e. 65) numb. l. 28ᶜᵐ.
Extra numbered leaves inserted.
Autographed from type-written copy.
1. Gasoline—Taxation.   I. Western petroleum refiners association.
II. Dow, Fayette B., comp.   III. Lohnes, Horace L., joint comp.   IV. Title.
V. Title: Gasoline tax laws.
28-1554
Library of Congress   HD9579.G4N3

NN 0059604   DLC

HD9579
.G4N3 **National petroleum association.**
1928   A digest of state gasoline tax laws in effect
Dec. 1, 1928, ... [Washington] c1928.

NN 0059605   DLC

National petroleum association.
The National petroleum association, 1902–1927. ₍Washing-
ton, D. C., ₍1927₎
98 p., 1 l. incl. ports. 24ᶜᵐ.

1. Petroleum industry and trade—Societies.
Library of Congress   HD9569.N3A5 1927   27-20209
——— Copy 2.

NN 0059606   DLC CLU ICJ

National Petroleum Association.
The National Petroleum Association, 1902–1952

see under

Dow, Fayette Brown, 1881-

The National petroleum association
Objections to the proposed amendments to the
interstate commerce act. By C. D. Chamberlin,
Secretary.
Cleveland, Ohio, April 13, 1910.
9 p.

NN 0059608   OC1WHi

National Petroleum Association.
₍Papers of the₎ annual meeting.

₍Washington, D. C.?₎
v. illus. 28cm.

1. Petroleum industry and trade - societies.
2. Petroleum industry and trade - U.S.

NN 0059609   NNC

TN860
N3 National Petroleum Association.
Prepared papers presented at the
semi-annual meeting.
₍Cleveland, Ohio₎
v. plates   28 cm.

1. Petroleum - Congresses. 2. Petroleum -
Societies.

NN 0059610   DI

National petroleum association.
₍Speeches at₎ annual meeting at Atlantic City,
N.J., September 15,16,1937. Washington,D.C., 1937
7 pts. in 1 v. 28 cm.
Mimeographed.
Contents.- President's address, by Charles L.Suhr;
Thirty-five years of cooperation, by W.R.Boyd,Jr.;
Future regulation of business, by Donald R.Richberg;
Changing relations between government and business,
by Ernest G. Draper; Legislated merchandising, by
Edwin B. George; Recent Congress and the coming
session,by Julian D.Conover; National labor rela-
tions act, by Charles Fahy.
1.Industry and sta   U.S. 2. Price fixing. 3.
Petroleum industry   d trade - U.S. I.Analytic
for authors and title.

NN 0059611   DFT

HF5417
.15 **National petroleum association.**
... State fair trade acts. September 24, 1937.
Washington, D.C., 1937.
4 l. charts. 35½ cm. (Bulletin no. 1769)
Typed mss.

1.Resale price maintenance. 2. Prices - Laws and
regulations - U. S. I.Title. II.Title: Fair trade
acts.

NN 0059612   DFT

National petroleum congress
Official review.

Library has
7th-   1919-

Annual.
7th   1919   include information on American
petroleum league and American petroleum
institute.

I. American petroleum league. II. American
petroleum institute.

NN 0059613   MiD DLC

National Petroleum Convention, *Caracas, 1951*
see Convención Nacional de Petróleo, *Caracas, 1951.*

National Petroleum Council.
Directory.
Washington.
v. 28 cm.
Title varies: Membership lists.

I. National Petroleum Council. Membership lists.
TN867.N3   64-35721-*

NN 0059615   DLC

TN867
.N3   National Petroleum Council. Membership lists.

National Petroleum Council.
Directory.
Washington.

VOLUME 407

HD9564
N28   National Petroleum Council.
         Minutes of meeting.   Washington, 1949-
              v.   27 cm.

              Library has October 25, 1949, January 26,
         1950, July 25, 1950.

              1. Petroleum – Congresses. 2. Petroleum – U.S.

NN   0059617   DI

National Petroleum Council.
         A national oil policy for the United States, a report.
    ₍Washington₎ 1949.
         23 p.   27 cm.
         Prepared at the request of the Secretary of the Interior by the
    National Oil Policy Committee to supplement the report on A
    petroleum policy for the United States adopted on October 24, 1945
    by the Petroleum Industry War Council.

         1. Petroleum industry and trade—U. S.   ɪ. Petroleum Industry
    War Council. ɪɪ. U. S. Dept. of the Interior. ɪɪɪ. Title.

         HD9566.N25   338.2728   49–3225*

NN   0059618   DLC OU TxU OrCS Or MB ICJ ICU PPFRB OrU

HD9564
N25   National Petroleum Council.
         Report of the National Petroleum Council's
    Committee on Capital and Materials Requirements
    for Increasing Availability of Petroleum Prod-
    ucts (Million-barrel Committee) October 31, 1951.
    Robert E. Wilson, chairman. Washington [1951].
         10 [9] l.   diagrs.   28 cm.

         1. Petroleum industry and trade – U. S. 2.
    Petroleum – U. S.   I. Wilson, Robert E.

NN   0059619   DI

HD9564
N33   National Petroleum Council.   Agenda Committee.
         Report.   [Washington, 1950
              v.   27 cm.

              Library has April 26, 1950, July 24, 1950,
         September 28, 1950.

              1. Petroleum – U.S. 2. Petroleum industry
         and trade – U.S.

NN   0059620   DI

HD9564
N337   National Petroleum Council.   Committee on
              Federal Lands Oil and Gas Policy.
         Report.   December 3, 1953.   Washington
    [1953]
         14 [1] l.   28 cm.

         1. Petroleum – U.S. 2. Gas, Natural – U.S.

NN   0059621   DI

HD9564
N338   National Petroleum Council.   Committee on
              Government Oil and Gas Organization.
         Report.   December 3, 1953.   Washington
    [1953]
         10 [1] l.   28 cm.

         1. Petroleum – U.S. 2. Gas, Natural – U.S.

NN   0059622   DI

HD9564
N35   National Petroleum Council.   Committee on
              Liquified Petroleum Gas.
         Report ...   April 26, 1950.   [Washington,
    1950].
              v. (various pagings).   27 cm.

              1. Liquid fuels. 2. Petroleum as fuel.

NN   0059623   DI

National Petroleum Council. *Committee on National Petro-
    leum Emergency.*
         Report, Jan. 13, 1949.   ₍n. p., 1949₎
         9 l. 28 cm.

         1. Petroleum industry and trade—U. S.

         HD9566.N26   338.476655   50–686

NN   0059624   DLC DI

National Petroleum Council. *Committee on Oil and Gas
    Availability.*
         Petroleum productive capacity; a report on present and
    future supplies of oil and gas, presented on January 29,
    1952. ₍Washington, 1952₎
         xvi, 102 p. map, diagrs. 24 cm.

         1. Petroleum industry and trade—U. S.   ɪ. Title.

         TN872.A5N3   338.2728   52—2954

         MtBC
         MiHM PPFML PPF WaS Or OrCS Wa WaWW WaTC
         PU TxU TU ICU NN OrP OrU OCl NIC MB NcRS
         MtBuM MtU CU CoU ICJ ViU OClFRB PBL PHC PSt
    NN   0059625   DLC CStbS IdU WaE DI OrPR IdB

National Petroleum Council. *Committee on Oil and Gas
    Emergency Defense Organization.*
         Disaster planning for the oil and gas industries. ₍Wash-
    ington, National Petroleum Council₎ 1955.
         77 p. illus. 28 cm.

         1. Petroleum industry and trade—Defense measures. 2. Gas indus-
    try—Defense measures.   ɪ. Title.

         UA929.95.P4N3   *355.26 355.24   56–1325 ‡

NN   0059626   DLC Wa

HD9564
N325   National Petroleum Council.   Committee on Oil
              and Gas Exploration, Drilling and
              Production Requirements.
         Report, December 1953.   Washington [1953?]
         61, 11 l.   diagrs. (1 fold.), tables.   28cm.
         Cover title.

         1. Petroleum engineering. 2. Petroleum – U.S.
    3. Gas, Natural – U.S. 4. Drills and drilling.

NN   0059627   DI

HD9564
N319   National Petroleum Council.   Committee on Oil
              and Gas Industries Manpower.
         Interim report, October 20, 1955.   Washing-
    ton [1955]
         [9] l.   28 cm.

         1. Petroleum workers – U.S. 2. Gas industry –
    U.S. 3. Manpower – U.S.

NN   0059628   DI

HD9564
N31   National Petroleum Council.   Committee on Oil
              Country Tubular Goods.
         Report.
    Washington, D. C.,
              v.   tables.   28 cm.

         1. Pipe. 2. Tubes.

NN   0059629   DI

National Petroleum Council. *Committee on Petroleum Im-
    ports.*
         Petroleum imports; a report. ₍Washington₎ 1955.
         57 p. illus. 28 cm.

         1. Petroleum industry and trade—U. S.   ɪ. Title.

         HD9565.N3   62–43371 ‡

NN   0059630   DLC NjP

BUSINESS
         National Petroleum Council.   Committee on
         Petroleum Industry Steel Requirements.
              Report of the National petroleum council's
         committee on petroleum industry steel require-
         ments. 1948.
              cover-title, 1 v. tables, diagrs.

              1. Petroleum industry and trade – U. S.
         2. Petroleum industry – U. S. 3. Steel.

NN   0059631   NNC

HD9564
N3   National Petroleum Council.   Committee on
1950   Petroleum Industry Steel Requirements.
         Report ...   September 26, 1950.   [Washing-
    ton, 1950].
         13, 6 [1] l.   27 cm.
         Draft – not for release.   Committee use only.

         1. Steel – Production. 2. Petroleum industry
    and trade – U.S.

NN   0059632   DI

HD9564
N3   National Petroleum Council.   Committee on
1948   Petroleum Industry Steel Requirements.
         Report of Production Subcommittee ...
    [Washington, 1948].
         1 v. (various pagings).   fold. diagrs.,
    tables (part. fold.).   28 cm.
         Preceded by National Petroleum Council news
    release, March 18, 1948.   6 p.
         Contains Appendices A–F.

         1. Steel – Production. 2. Petroleum industry
    and trade – U.S.

NN   0059633   DI

HD9564
N344   National Petroleum Council.   Committee on
              Petroleum Productive Capacity.
         Report
    Washington,
              v.   28 cm.

         1. Petroleum – U.S. ". Petroleum – Production

NN   0059634   DI

HD9564
N343   National Petroleum Council.   Committee on
              Petroleum Storage Facilities.
         Report.

         Washington.
              v. tables. 28 cm.

         1. Petroleum – Storage.

NN   0059635   DI

VOLUME 407

HD9564
N352   National Petroleum Council.   Committee on
          Submerged Lands Productive Capacity.
          Interim report.
       Washington,
              v.   map   28 cm.

          1. Petroleum in submerged lands - U.S. 2.
       Continental shelf.

NN   0059636   DI PU-W InU

HD9565
.N33
       National Petroleum Council. *Committee on Synthetic Liquid
       Fuels Production Costs.*
          Interim report.
       Washington.
              v. 28 cm.

          1. Petroleum, Synthetic—Costs.

          HD9565.N33   58-37788

NN   0059637   DLC

       National Petroleum Council. Committee on
          Synthetic liquid fuels production costs.
          Report[s] of the Committee on synthetic
       liquid fuels production costs.   Washington,
       1951-53.
          3 v. in 1.   tables.
          Contents: Report, Oct. 31, 1951. Interim
       report, Jan. 29, 1952. Final report, Feb. 26,
       1953.
          W.S.S. Rodgers, chairman.

NN   0059638   MH-BA FMU

HD9565
.N276   NATIONAL Petroleum Council. Committee on
          Synthetic Liquid Fuels Production
          Cost.
       . Synthetic fuels production costs;
       subcommittee report,October 15,1951.
       [Washington,1952?]
          1v. (Loose-leaf) illus.,tables.
          Cover title.

          1.Petroleum,Synthetic - Costs. I.Title.

NN   0059639   MCM

HD9564
N354   National Petroleum Council. Committee on Tank
          Truck Transportation.
          Report.
       Washington.
              v. tables.   28cm.

          1.Petroleum - Transportation. I.Title: Tank
       truck transportat'

NN   0059640   DI

       National Petroleum Council. *Committee on the Impact of
       Oil Exports from the Soviet Bloc.*
          Impact of oil exports from the Soviet bloc; a report of the
       National Petroleum Council's Committee and Working Sub-
       committee on the Impact of Oil Exports from the Soviet
       Bloc. Adopted by the National Petroleum Council October
       4, 1962. Washington, [1952-
          v. fold. maps (part col.) diagrs. 28 cm.

       ——— Supplement. Adopted by the National Petroleum
       Council March 19, 1964. Washington, National Petroleum
       Council [1964]
          vi, 177, A-28 p. illus., fold. maps (part col.) 28 cm.
          "A revision of volume 1, issued October 4, 1962."
          Bibliographical footnotes.
                     HD9578.C6N3 Suppl.
          1. Petroleum industry and trade—Communist countries.   I. Title.

          HD9578.C6N3   62-53524 rev 2

NN   0059642   DLC

HD9564
N355   National Petroleum Council. Committee on
          the Use of Radio and Radar.
          Report
       Washington,
              v. map, diagrs. 28 cm.

          1. Petroleum - U.S. 2. Radio. 3. Radar.

NN   0059643   DI

       National petroleum gas company
          see   National petroleum and water gas
       company.

       National petroleum news.
          [New York, etc., McGraw-Hill Pub. Co., etc.,]
              v. in   illus., ports. 29-32 cm.
          Frequency varies.
          Began publication in 1909. Cf. Union list of serials.
          Issues for July 29, 1942-Aug. 7, 1946 include monthly Technical
       section devoted to refinery management and petroleum chemical tech-
       nology (later issued separately as Petroleum processing)

          1. Petroleum industry and trade—U. S.—Period.

          HD9560 1.N3   55-3942

       ICJ
       PSt TxLT PV ViB1bV CtH FM CSfSO IU ICRL KU CU OC1
NN   DLC ICU MB FTaSU NRU NBuU WaS OkTU KyU
       0059645

       National petroleum news.

          ...America's oil industry, what it means to
       the consumer, to the farmer, to the government,
       and to all industry a message to the American
       people. Cleveland, O., 1936.
          512 p. illus.
          Issue of Feb. 5, 1936 - v. 28, no. 6.

NN   0059646   MiD CoU CU OU OC1

---

q665.5 National petroleum news.
N21e   Engineering issue - Sept. 21, 1927.
          Cleveland, 1927.
          368p. illus.   (National petroleum
       news, vol.XIX, no.38)

NN   0059647   IU

HD 9560 National petroleum news.
.1   Factbook issue. 1955- New York,
.N272   McGraw Hill.
Lastv.   Annual.
RRA   Mid-May issue of National petroleum
       news.
          Called also NPN factbook issue.
          *Holdings under main entry in
       *serial record.

          1. Petroleum industry and trade--U.S.
       I. Title: NPN factbook issue.

NN   0059648   ICU

       National petroleum news.
          Multi-pump service stations today and
       tomorrow
          see under Wollstadt, Paul.

       National petroleum news.
          Oil code data book. Issue no. 4, corrected to
       Sept. 15, 1934. Cleveland, Ohio, National
       petroleum news [1934]
          cover-title, 96 p.

          Pages 91-96 blank for Memoranda.

          1.Petroleum industry and trade - U.S. I.
       Title.

NN   0059650   NNC IU OC1

       National petroleum news.
          Oil price handbook
          see   Platt's oil price handbook ...

       National petroleum news.

       Platt's oil price handbook for 1924–
          ... Compiled by the market reporting organization of Platt's
       oilgram and National petroleum news. Cleveland, O., The
       National petroleum publishing co. [°1925–

       National petroleum news.
          Refresher on wartime refining technology. Prepared by
       the editorial staff, Technical section, National petroleum news.
       [Cleveland, National petroleum publishing company, 1945]
          4 p. l., 135 p. 17½ᵐ.
          "Reading references": p. 111-118.

          1. Petroleum—Refining. 2. Petroleum industry and trade—U. S.
       I. Title.
                                                    45-4745
          Library of Congress °   TP690.N3

NN   0059653   DLC WaS

543.7   National petroleum news
N27s   Selected articles on...[developments
          in the field of refining]   Cleveland,
          Ohio, National petroleum news, 1945.
Chem.   4v. illus.,ports.,tables, diagrs.,forms.
          Bibliography at the end of some of the
          articles.
          Contents: [v.1] New refining processes.-
          [v.2] Refinery design and construction.-
          [v.3] Refinery operation and maintenance.-
          [v.4] Wartime and postwar petroleum products.

NN   0059654   IaU MiEM

       National petroleum news.

          Selected articles on new refining processes.
       Reprinted February 1945 from the wartime issues
       of Technical section, National petroleum news ...
       Cleveland, Ohio, National petroleum news [1945]
          cover-title, 64 p. illus. (incl. ports.) diagrs. 28ᶜᵐ.
          "One of a series of four booklets in which selected
       articles have been reprinted." Articles are from issues
       of 1943 and 1944.
          "Contents": p. [2] of cover.
          Bibliographies at end of most articles.

          1. Cracking process. 2. Gasoline. I. Title. II.Title:
       Refining processes.

NN   0059655   ViU MdBJ NNC

       National petroleum news.

          Selected articles on refinery design and con-
       struction. Reprinted February 1945 from the
       wartime issues of Technical section, National
       petroleum news ... Cleveland, Ohio, National
       petroleum news [1945]
          cover-title, 64 p. illus. (incl. ports., plans) diagrs.
       28ᶜᵐ.
          "One of a series of four booklets in which selected
       articles have been reprinted." Articles are from issues
       of 1943, 1944, and January 3, 1945.
          "Contents": p. [2] of cover.
          1. Petroleum industry and trade. 2. Petroleum industry
       and trade—Equipment   and supplies. I. Title. II.
       Title: Refinery desi   gn and construction.

NN   0059656   ViU MdBJ

       National petroleum news.

          Selected articles on refinery operation and
       maintenance. Reprinted February 1945 from the
       wartime issues of Technical section, National
       petroleum news ... Cleveland, Ohio, National
       petroleum news [1945]
          cover-title, 76 p. illus., diagrs. 28ᶜᵐ.
          "One of a series of four booklets in which selected
       articles have been reprinted." Articles are from issues
       of 1943 and 1944.
          "Contents": p. [2] of cover.
          Bibliographies at end of two articles: p. 11 and 24.
          1. Petroleum—Refining. 2. Petroleum industry and
       trade. I. Title. II   Title: Refinery operation and
       maintenance.

NN   0059657   ViU NNC MdBJ

VOLUME 407

National petroleum news.

Selected articles on wartime and postwar petroleum products. Reprinted February 1945 from the wartime issues of Technical section, National petroleum news ... Cleveland, Ohio, National petroleum news ₍1945₎
cover-title, 80 p. illus. (incl. ports., map) diagrs. 28cm.
"One of a series of four booklets in which selected articles have been reprinted." Articles are from issues of 1942, 1943, 1944, and 1945.
"Contents": p. ₍2₎ of cover
Bibliographies at end of articles on p. 13 and 45.
1. Petroleum. 2. Petroleum industry and trade.
I. Title. II. Title: Wartime and postwar petroleum products.

NN   0059658   ViU NNC MdBJ

National petroleum news.
Statistical desk sheet of the oil industry of the United States.
19
Cleveland₍, 19
no.   sq. f°.

1. Prices of petroleum—U. S.
N. Y. P. L.   August 28, 1929

NN   0059659   NN

National petroleum news.
TBA directory.
₍Cleveland₎
v. 21 cm.

1. Petroleum industry and trade—U. S.—Direct.

HD9563.N3   51–35810 ‡

NN   0059660   DLC OC1 CU

National petroleum news.
Weekly price service. **v. 1–**
Oct. 29, 1954
New York, McGraw-Hill.
v. in   29 cm.

1. Petroleum industry and trade—U. S.—Period.

HD9564.N3   56–3658

NN   0059661   DLC

National petroleum news
See also NPN; National petroleum news.

National petroleum schools, Chicago.
Dictionary of oil words, terms, and expressions, comp. by National petroleum schools...
[Chicago, c1920]

TN871
.N3

NN   0059663   DLC

National pharmaceutical convention, *Philadelphia*, 1852
see
American pharmaceutical association.

National Pharmaceutical Council.

QV
701
N277

[Collection of publications]

The Library has a collection of miscellaneous publications of this organization kept as received. These publications are not listed or bound separately.
1. Pharmacy

NN   0059665   DNLM

National pharmaceutical syllabus committee.

The **pharmaceutical** syllabus, outlining the course of instruction for the degree of bachelor of science in pharmacy (B. S. Pharm.) 4th ed. Prepared and published by the National pharmaceutical syllabus committee, representing the American pharmaceutical association, the American association of colleges of pharmacy, the National association of boards of pharmacy. ₍Chapel Hill, N. C.₎ 1932.

National Pharmaceutical Syllabus Committee.
The tentative pharmaceutical syllabus
see under title

National Philanthropic Association.₎ Employment of the poor. First report of the employment of the poor as street orderlies, in promoting the health and cleanliness of the parishes of St. James, St. Anne's, and St. Martin-in-the-Fields, by the council of the National Philanthropic Association. 16 pp. 8°. *London, T. R. Harrison,* 1848. [P., v. 38.]

London .

NN   0059668   DNLM

NATIONAL PHILANTHROPIC ASSOCIATION, London.
Report of progress in the employment of the poor; and in the promotion of health and cleanliness in the metropolis. January, 1853.
London, G. Nichols₍1853₎
26p. 22cm.

Binder's title: Pamphlets on the poor. England.

I
3045
.6535
v.4

NN   0059669   ICN

NATIONAL Philanthropic Association, London
Sanatory progress; being the fifth report of the National Philanthropic Association. 2d ed. London, Hatchard, 1850.
xvi, 251 p. illus.

WAA
N285s
1850

NN   0059670   DNLM CtY MH

National philanthropist and investigator and genius of temperance
see   Genius of temperance, philanthropist and people's advocate.

The national philatelic album, 1887.
see under   Bishop, Willis Fowler.

National philatelic museum, Philadelphia.
see   Philadelphia. National philatelic museum.

National philatielic news; in the interest of the National philatelic federation. **v. 1.**
Oct. 1, 1930–   Washington, D. C.
[1930–
v.   23 cm. (in binder 25.5 cm.)
semi—monthly.
Vol. 1, no. 5 has title: National philatelic news; an educational adjunct.
Editor: Oct. 1, 1930–   J. F. Du Hamel.

HE6187
.N3

NN   0059674   DLC

National Philatelic Society.
Annual year book.
v. 1–
Dover, N. H., 1914–   8°.
nos.
1914–   cover-title.

1. Postage stamps—Assoc. and org.—   Yearbooks.
N. Y. P. L.   June 16, 1927

NN   0059675   NN

National Philatelic Society.
The **Collector's** library table. v. 1–
Oct. 1881–
Waterloo ₍etc.₎ N. Y., H. F. Smith ₍etc.₎

HE6187
.C585

National Philatelic Society (*Founded 1949*)
Year book.
₍n. p.₎
v. ports. 23 cm.

HE6188.N34   383.2206273   59–23811

NN   0059677   DLC

National Philatelic War Funds.
National Philatelic War Funds auction; catalogue of a fine selection of British, foreign & colonial postage stamps and philatelic literature, to be sold in aid of the Society of the British Red Cross and the Order of St. John of Jerusalem...on... March 13th & 14th, 1916... ₍London: Women's Prtg. Soc.. Ltd.,₎ 1916.₎
57(1) p., 1 l., 4 pl. (incl. front.)   8°.

1. Postage stamps.—Catalogues.
N. Y. P. L.   December 24, 1917.

NN   0059678   NN

National philatelical society, New York.
The **American** journal of philately ... v. 1–
Mar. 1868–
2d ser., v. 1–   1888–
New York, New York philatelic society ₍etc.₎ 1868–

National philatelical society, *New York*.
A color chart. Designed to illustrate and identify the colors of postage stamps. New York, National philatelical society, 1884.
79 p. col. illus. 23ᶜᵐ.
English, French, German, and Spanish.

1. Postage-stamps. 2. Colors.   I. Title.

Library of Congress   HF6215.N3   11–34669

NN   0059680   DLC ICJ

National philatelical society, New York.
Bulletin. No. 1.   New York, 1878.

NN   0059681   Nh

National Philatelical Society, New York.
Constitution and by-laws of the National Philatelical Society. Organized 1874. Incorporated 1892. ₍New York, 1894?₎ 14 p. 12°.

1. Postage stamps.—Collections: Assoc. and organizations.
N. Y. P. L.   June 6, 1918.

NN   0059682   NN

VOLUME 407

National philatelical society, *New York.*

Tiffany, John Kerr, 1843–1897.
The stamped envelopes, wrappers and sheets of the
United States, by John K. Tiffany, R. R. Bogert and Joseph Rechert. A committee of the National philatelical
society. New York, The Scott stamp & coin co., limited,
1892.

National phonograph association.
Proceedings of the ... annual convention.
₍Milwaukee, 18

v. plates. 23½ᵐ.

1. Phonograph—Societies.

Library of Congress   TS2301.P3A26

42–51406

NN   0059684   DLC

FM
000
NY8
547
Micro-
form
edition

National phonograph association.
Proceedings of the ... annual convention.
₍Milwaukee, 1890?–

v. plates. 23½ᵐ.

1. Phonograph—Societies.

NN   0059685   N

National Phonograph Company
see   Edison (Thomas A.) Inc.

The **National** phonographer...
v. 1

London: R. Holmyard₍, etc., etc.₎, 1891   8°, 4°.
v. illus., plates.
Monthly (no issue for Oct., 1893 – Jan., 1894).
Text in shorthand.

1. Shorthand—Per. and soc. publ.
N. Y. P. L.

NN   0059687   NN

The **National Phonographic Society**
see   Incorporated Phonographic Society.

National Phosphorus Research Work Group.
Summary of phosphorus research in the United States relating to soils and fertilizers. ₍Beltsville, Md., National Soil
and Fertilizer Research Committee, Soils Divisions, Bureau
of Plant Industry, Soils and Agricultural Engineering₎ 1950.

iii, 114 p. 27 cm.

Cover title.
Bibliography: p. 57–108.

1. Phosphorus. 2. Fertilizers and manures. 3. Soils. 4. Agricultural research.   I. Title.

S647.N3   631.85   51–60174

MtBC
NN   0059689   DLC ICJ TU NN MsSM DI OrP OrU WaS OrCS

National photo dealer.

TR12
.D5

Directory of the photographic industry.

New York, National Photo Dealer.

The **National photographer.**
₍Milwaukee₎
v. illus. 28 cm. monthly.
Began publication in 1949. Cf. N. W. Ayer & Son's directory, 1955.
Official publication of the Photographers' Association of America.

1. Photography — Period.   I. Photographers' Association of
America.
TR1.P712   770.5   56–17726

NN   0059691   DLC CLSU

National photographic annual. 1st–
1950–
Sydney.
v. illus. 27 cm.
Editor : 1950–   N. A. Wilson.

1. Photography—Yearbooks.   I. Wilson, Neville A., ed.

770.58   51–34042

NN   0059692   DLC

National photographic dealer
see   Photo dealer.

National Photographic Dealers Association.

TR1
.N3

Photo dealer.

₍New York, NPD Corp., etc.₎

National Photographic Dealers Association
see also Master Photo Dealers and Finishers' Association.

National Photographic Library, Washington, D. C.
National Photographic Library bulletin.

Washington, D. C., 1906–   25½ – 36cm.
nos. illus. (incl. maps.)
Monthly.

no. 1
Jan., 1906   called v. 1   ; Jan., 1908   called
Title varies: Jan., 1906   , Photographic Library bulletin₍; published by the₎
Institute of Historical Research₍;   National Photographic Library
bulletin.

NN   0059697   NN NIC

34
3018

National photographic series.   Philadelphia,
Quaker City Co., 1894.

NN   0059698   DLC

National Photographic Society.
Finder
see under title

National physical achievement standards committee.
National physical achievement standards. A physically fit
America. Instruction book ... National physical achievement
standards committee. New York ₍National recreation associa-
tion₎ ·1931₎

cover-title, 13 p. diagrs. 21½ᵐ.

1. Physical education and training—U. S.   I. National recreation
association.   II. Title : A physically fit America.

A 40–883

Ohio state univ. Library
for Library of Congress   ₍2₎

NN   0059700   OU

National physical laboratory, *Teddington, Eng.*
see
Teddington, Eng. National physical laboratory.

National Physical Laboratory of India, *Delhi*
see
Delhi. National Physical Laboratory of India.

National Physical Recreation Society.
The Gymnasium magazine; a journal devoted to
the interest of physical education
see under title

₍**National Physicians' Committee for the Extension of Medical Service**₎
The American people: what they think—about doctors, medical care and prepayment plans. A challenge to private enterprise ... ₍Chicago?ᵗ ·1944₎

30 p. 23 cm.

Based on data compiled by the Opinion Research Corporation, Princeton, N. J.

1. Medicine, State—U. S. ₍1. State medicine—U. S.₎ 2. Insurance,
Health—U. S. ₍2. Health insurance—U. S.₎   I. Opinion Research
Corporation, Princeton, N. J.   II. Title.

Med 47–2563

U. S. Army Medical Library   [W6P3]
for Library of Congress   ₍2₎

NN   0059704   DNLM NN NNC

**National Physicians' Committee for the Extension
of Medical Service.**
₍Clippings on socialized medicine; selected
from newspapers and periodicals and containing
items both pro and con. Chicago, 1940–49₎
6 boxes.

NN   0059705   ICJ

W
275
AA1
qN2

NATIONAL Physicians Committee for the
Extension of Medical Service
₍Collection of publications₎

The library has a collection of miscellaneous publications of this organization
kept as received. These publications are
not listed nor bound separately.
1. Health insurance - U. S. 2. State
medicine - U. S.

NN   0059706   DNLM

**National physicians' committee for the extension of medical
service.**
Compulsion, the key to collectivism; a treatise on and evidence of attempts to foist on the American people compulsory
health insurance, and explanation of the implications involved.
Chicago, Ill., The National physicians committee ₍1946₎

192 p. illus. (ports., facsim.) 28 x 22ᵐ.

"Presents a comprehensive factual summary of hearings before the
Committee on education and labor of the United States Senate on the
fourth revision of the Wagner-Murray-Dingell bills (S. 1606–HR. 4730),
as introduced on November 19, 1945."—Pref.

1. Insurance, Health—U. S. 2. Medical economics.   I. Title.

HD7102.U4N3   °31.25442   46–7989

NN   0059707   DLC MBCo Mi WHi CU WaS Wa MB ICJ ViU

R723
.5
.S5

**National physicians' committee for the
extension of medical service.**

Simpson, Herbert Downs, 1879–
Health protection, a study of pre-payment medical service
plans, by Herbert D. Simpson ... Chicago, The National physicians' committee for the extension of medical service ₍1946₎

VOLUME 407

⌐National physicians' committee for the extension of medical service┐
Opportunity for private enterprise or benefits for business
through cooperative group insurance. A report on employer-
employe group insurance programs, and conclusions based on
nation-wide surveys of worker and management opinions as
to need and value in terms of employer benefits and employe
security and satisfaction. ⌐Chicago, 1944┐
46, ⌐2┐ p. 23ᵐ.
1. Insurance, Group—U. S. 2. Labor and laboring classes—Medical
care. 3. Insurance, Health—U. S. I. Title.
45–13297
Library of Congress   HG8830.N37
⌐3┐   368.4

NN   0059709   DLC NIC DNAL ICJ

**IIH
.MA**   **National physicians' committee for the
extension of medical service**

Political medicine and freedom of enterprise; the continuing threat of collecti-
vist control. A factual statement on the
compulsory health insurance provisions of
the Social Security Amendments of 1945
(Wagner–Murray–Dingell S. 1050 HR. 3293)

and an explanation of some of their
meanings and implications. [Chicago,
Ill.? 1946?]
26 p.   19cm.
Cover title.

NN   0059711   WHi

National physicians committee for the extension of medical service.
A symposium — comment and opinion on political medicine in
the United States...   Chicago, Nat. physicians committee
⌐1943┐   11 p.   illus.   28cm.
Newspaper editorials relative to U. S. Senate bill 1161.

1. Medicine, State—U. S.
N. Y. P. L.   October 29, 1946

NN   0059712   NN

**B1a16
A64**   National physicians' committee for the extension of medical service.
World conflict, American medicine and the
N.P.C. An explanation of American medicine's
improved position and of the National physicians' committee in terms of current needs
and war-time responsibility. [Chicago,1941]

NN   0059713   CtY

National piano manufacturers association.
Consumer investigation for National piano manufacturers asso-
ciation, 1938. Conducted by Lawrence H. Selz ...   ⌐New York:
National piano manufacturers assoc., c1938┐   60 p. incl. diagrs.
21½cm.
Form questionnaire inserted.

I. Piano—Trade and stat.—U. S.
N. Y. P. L.   ⌐z, Lawrence H.   April 15, 1942

NN   0059714   NN

National piano manufacturers' association of
America, inc.
... Mail investigation on piano instruction
among public school systems, winter and spring
1948.   Chicago, Foote, Cone & Belding, 1948.
53 numb. leaves.   tables.   29 cm.
At head of title: Research department.
1. Piano. Instruction & study. 2. Piano.
Methods. Juvenile. I. Title.

NN   0059715   MiEM

National piano travelers association.·
The piano travelers association book; a reference book
... comp. by the Educational committee; for the benefit of
the members of the National piano travelers association
...   ⌐New York, Rand, McNally & co., ʹ1915┐
1 p. l., 194 p. 21½ x 12ᵐ.
p. 188–194, blank for "Memorandum."

1. Music trade—U. S. 2. Commercial law—U. S.   I. Title.

Library of Congress   HD9999.M8U6   15–11482

NN   0059716   DLC NN

National piano travelers association.
The piano travelers association book; a reference book
... comp. by the Educational committee for the benefit of
the members of the National piano travelers association
...   ⌐New York, Rand, McNally & co.┐ 1916.
2 p. l., 258, ⌐2┐ p. 1 illus. (facsim.) 21½ x 12ᵐ.
2d edition.

1. Music trade—U. S. 2. Commercial law—U. S.

Library of Congress   HD9999.M8U6 1916   16–16271

NN   0059717   DLC ICRL ICJ NN

**389.9
N2196C**   National Pickle Packers Association.
Consolidated report.

[n.p.]

1. Pickles.   Statistics.

NN   0059718   DNAL

**SB337
.B3**   **National Pickle Packers Association.**

Banadyga, Albert Alexander.
Cucumbers for pickles, a 1948 survey of literature dealing
with their production. Oak Park, Ill., National Pickle
Packers Association, 1949.

**389.9
N2196M**   National Pickle Packers Association.
Mid-West crop intake report.

Oak Park, Ill.

1. Pickles.   Statistics.

NN   0059720   DNAL

**389.9
N2196N**   National Pickle Packers Association.
Northern crop intake report.

Oak Park, Ill.

1. Pickles.   Statistics.

NN   0059721   DNAL

**91.51
N21W**   National Pickle Packers Association.
Warning against use of cucumbers grown on
land treated with benzene hexachloride.
Oak Park, Ill., 1950.
sheet.

1. Cucumbers.   2. Benzene hexachloride.
Effect on flavor.

NN   0059722   DNAL

**389.9
N2196W**   National Pickle Packers Association.
Washington letter.

[n.p.]

NN   0059723   DNAL

**389.9
N2196?**   National Pickle Packers Association.
Statistical Committee.
Report.
[n.p.]

1. Pickles.   Statistics.

NN   0059724   DNAL

**389.9
N2196S**   National Pickle Packers Association. Statistical Committee.
Special bulletin.
[n.p.]

NN   0059725   DNAL

National pictorial brain power monthly
see   National brain power monthly.

National pictorial monthly
see   National brain power monthly.

The **National** pictorial primer, designed for the use of schools
and families. Embellished with more than 150 fine engravings. New York, G. F. Cooledge ⌐185–?┐
48 p.   illus.   20 cm.

1. Primers—1800–1870.

PE1119.A1N3   66–59848

NN   0059728   DLC InU CtY NjP

The **National** picture gallery in the rotunda of the Capitol, a
collection of paintings illustrating the discovery of America
and the early history of the United States. Executed expressly by order of Congress, by the most celebrated American artists. Washington, ʹ1860.
1 p. l., 12 pl., port. 23 x 29ᵐ.
Illustrated and engraved t.-p.
Copyright date on cover, 1859.
Part of the plates signed: R. Metzeroth sc.

1. Washington, D. C.—Capitol. 2. Paintings—Washington, D. C.
3. Mural painting and decoration. I. Metzeroth, Robert.
42–51577
Library of Congress   N853.N3

NN   0059729   DLC

**W.C.L.
760.942
N277P**   National Picture Print Society.
Proceedings. v. 1–6, 1935/36–1940/41.
London.
6 v. in   plates. 25 cm.   annual.

Called also National Picture Print Society
for the Study of Nineteenth Century Engraving
and Colour Picture Printing.
1. Prints. Gt. Brit. Societies, etc. 2.
Engraving. Gt. Brit. Societies, etc.

NN   0059730   NcD

National Picture Print Society for the Study of
Nineteenth Century Engraving and Colour
Picture Printing
see   National Picture Print Society.

VOLUME 407

636.4 National Pig Breeders' Association, London.
N215h   Herd book. v.
         London,
             v. illus. 24cm.

         Some vols. issued in parts. Some parts of
         vols. lack the vol. numbering of the series.

         1. Swine—Herd-books.

NN   0059732   IU CU-A OU

National Pig Breeders' Association.
    N.P.B.A. leaflet
        see under title

National pig breeders' association.
Greenwood, Major, *jr.*
    Report to the council of the National pig breeders' as-
sociation on the present state of knowledge of swine fever,
with special reference to the available statistics. By Major Greenwood, jr. ... Borrowash, Derby, The National
pig breeders' association, 1914.

47.2   National Pigeon Association, inc.
N21   Project on genetics. [n.p.] 1950.
            [36] p. (Its NPA information booklet
                no. 1)

         1. Pigeons. Genetics. I. Hollander,
W F II. National Pigeon Association,
inc. N.P.A. information booklet no.1.

NN   0059735   DNAL

National pillars association, Manila.
AP7
.P5
    Pillars; magazine of the youth. v. 1, no. 1-12; Dec. 1943-
Dec. 1944. [Manila, 1943-44]

The National Pilot.
    The Pilot. v. 1-3 (no. 1-156); Sept. 6, 1821-Sept. 11, 1824.
    New-Haven, S. M. Dutton.

(The) National pilot.   Petersburgh, Va.
    Established 1887

NN   0059738   NRAB

NATIONAL PILOTS ASSOCIATION.
    NPA   [New York, 1955] [15] p. 23cm.

    Cover title.

1. Aeronautics—Assoc. and org.—U.S. t. 1955.

NN   0059739   NN

National pink sheet ...   Chicago, National
    theatre supply company, 19 -
        Monthly.

NN   0059740   WaSp

The National pink sheet; supply and equipment
    section ...   Chicago, National theatre supply
    co., 19 -
        Issued bi-monthly.

NN   0059741   WaSp

National pipe and supplies association.
    Proceedings of the   annual convention
        see its   Report of the proceedings of the
    annual convention.

HD9999 National pipe and supplies association.
.P65N3   Report of the proceedings of the ...
        annual convention of the National pipe and sup-
        plies association ... [Pittsburg, Warde press,
        19
            v.   23cm.

        Title varies: Proceedings of the
    annual convention.

NN   0059743   DLC NN

National Pipe Bending Co.
    The national feed-water heater. New Haven,
    Conn., the Co., 1905.
        24p. illus.

NN   0059744   ICRL

NA7130 [National plan service, inc.]
.N36   [Distribution plan book "Style A".   Chicago,
fol.   1932]
            53 p. illus. (incl. plans) 37 cm.
            "Copyrighted by National plan service, inc."
        p. 2.
        Title from copyright application.

NN   0059745   DLC

NA7130 [National plan service, inc.]
.N37   A home of your own ...   [Chicago, 1931]
fol.   86 p., 1 l.   illus. (part col., incl. plans)
        30.5 cm.
            (Title from page [3])
            "Prepared, published and copyrighted by
        National plan service, inc." p. [2]

NN   0059746   DLC

728.6   National plan service, inc.
N213h   Homes for better living. [n.p. Author? c1941]
          cover-title, 63 [1] p. illus., diagrs.

             1. Architecture, Domestic - Designs and plans
        I. Title.

NN   0059747   WaPS

728.6   National plan service, inc.
N213hm   Homes of moderate cost. [n.p. Author? c1941]
          cover-title, 39 [1] p. illus. (part col.)
        diagrs.

             1. Architecture, Domestic - Designs and plans
        I. Title.

NN   0059748   WaPS

728.6   National plan service, inc.
N213hs   Homes of the southland. [n.p. Author? c1941.]
          cover-title, 31 [1] p. illus., diagrs.

             1. Architecture, Domestic - Designs and plans
        I. Title.

NN   0059749   WaPS

NA7130 [National plan service, inc.]
.N38   Homes that grow. [Chicago, 1933]
fol.   cover-title, [8] p. illus.(incl. plans)
        33cm.

         Copyrighted by National plan service.

         1. Architecture, Domestic—Designs and
    plans. I. Title.

NN   0059750   DLC

728.6   National plan service, inc.
N213n   New model homes. [n.p. Author? 1941?]
        31 [1] p. illus., diagrs.

         "Copyrighted by National plan service, inc."

             1. Architecture, Domestic - Designs and plans
        I. Title.

NN   0059751   WaPS

NA7127 [National plan service, inc.]
.N445   Our book of attractive small homes ...
        [Chicago, 1930]
            63. illus. (incl. plans) 28 cm.
            "Prepared, published and copyrighted by
        National plan service, inc." p. [2]

NN   0059752   DLC

728.6   National plan service, inc.
N213p   Petite homes of budget appeal. [n.p. Author?
        1941?]
            40 p. illus. (part col.) diagrs.

         "Copyrighted by National plan service, inc."

             1. Architecture Domestic - Designs and plans.
        I. Title.

NN   0059753   WaPS

NA8201 [National plan service, inc.]
.N3   Practical farm buildings.   [Chicago, 1934]
            cover-title, 64 p. illus. (incl. plans)
        28 cm.
            "Copyrighted by National plan service."
        p. [1]

NN   0059754   DLC

728.6   National plan service, inc.
N213s   Select homes. [n.p. Author? 1941?]
          cover-title, 49 p. illus. (part col.) diagrs.

         "Copyrighted by National plan service, inc."

             1. Architecture, Domestic - Designs and plans.
        I. Title.

NN   0059755   WaSp

National plan service, inc.
    Small home service.
    [Chicago, National plan service, inc., c1941-1944]
        9 pts. in 1 v.

NN   0059756   OC1

NA7127 [National plan service, inc.]
.N446   Small homes. [Chicago, 1933]
            cover-title, 48 p. illus. (incl. plans)
        26.5 x 35 cm.
            "Copyrighted by National plan service."
        p. 48.

NN   0059757   DLC

VOLUME 407

NA7127
.N446 [National plan service, inc.]
1935   Small homes. [Chicago, 1935]
cover-title, 48 p. illus.(incl. plans)
26½x35cm.

"Copyrighted by National plan service."—
p. 48.

1. Architecture, Domestic—Designs and plans.
I. Title.

NN 0059758 DLC

[National plan service, inc.]
Style trends. [Chicago, 1944]
cover-title, 32 p. Illus. (part col., incl. plans) 28 x 21½ᵐ.

1. Architecture, Domestic—Designs and plans.   I. Title.
44-53263
Library of Congress   NA7127.N447
[2]   728.6084

NN 0059759 DLC

631.22 National plan service, inc.
N213s   Successful farm buildings. [n. p. Author?
1941?]
cover-title, 64 p. illus., diagrs.

"Copyrighted by National plan service, inc."
Illustrated cover-title.

1. Farm buildings. 2. Architecture, Domestic -
Designs and plans.

NN 0059760 WaPS

PNC
728.6 National plan service, inc.
N213w   Western living homes. [n.p. Author? 1941?]
cover-title, 24 [1] p. illus., diagrs.

"Copyrighted by the National plan service,
inc."

1. Architecture, Domestic - Designs and
plans. 2. Archite   cture, Northwest Pacific.

NN 0059761 WaPS

National planning ...
see under   [Contreras, Carlos]

National Planning & Research, Inc.
The center for the North Shore. Boston?,
[1955]
12 p. illus., maps, charts, graphs, tabs.

Market survey and analysis for a regional
shopping center for the North Shore at
Peabody, Mass. prepared for Jordan Marsh
Company.

NN 0059763 MH-BA

National Planning Association.
Agricultural policy; a joint statement adopted by members
of the Board of Trustees and of agriculture, business, labor, and
international committees. [Washington, 1949]
7 p. 28 cm. (*Its* Special report no. 23)
Caption title.

1. Agriculture and state—U. S.   I. Title.   (Series)

HC101.N3522 no. 2?   338.1   49-5207*

NN 0059764 DLC MB

National Planning Association.
The Agricultural research and marketing act of 1946; a
consideration of basic objectives and procedures. [Wash-
ington, 1948]
iv, 16 p. 28 cm. (National Planning Association. A special report, no. 19)

1. Agricultural research. 2. Farm produce—Marketing. 3. Science
and state—U. S.   (Series)

HC101.N3522 no. 19   630.72   49-5430*

NN 0059765 DLC MB Or OrCS DNAL NNC ViU

SF401
.R4W4   **National planning association.**

Weiss, Francis Joseph, 1898–
The Alaskan reindeer industry, by Francis Joseph Weiss ...
[Washington, National planning association, 1941]

D
808   National Planning Association.
N3   America must help feed Europe this winter;
a report. Washington [1945?]
15 p. map. 23 cm. 0.10 (pbk.)
Caption title.
"A special report."
1. Reconstruction (1939-1951)—Europe. 2.
United Nations Relief and Rehabilitation
Administration. I. Title.

NN 0059767 IEdS OrU Or

National Planning Association.
The American economy in 1960

see under

Colm, Gerhard, 1897–

National Planning Association.

Galloway, George Barnes, 1898–
American pamphlet literature of public affairs (a descriptive
list of current pamphlet series) by George B. Galloway ...
Washington, D. C., National economic and social planning association, 1937.

National Planning Association.
American policy in the new phase of the cold war; a joint
statement by members of the Board of Trustees and the
Agriculture, Business, Labor, and International Committees
of the National Planning Association, adopted at the twentieth anniversary joint meeting, Washington, D. C., December 14, 1954. [Washington, 1955]
25 p. 20 cm. (*Its* Special report no. 35)

1. U. S.—For. rel.—1945–   2. World politics—1955–
I. Title.

HC101.N3522 no. 35   327.73   56-1461 ‡

NN 0059770 DLC MB DNAL ViU NcD

National Planning Association.
**American policy in the new phase of the
cold war**

see also under

**National Planning Association. Committee on
International Policy.**

National Planning Association.
America's economic preparedness; a statement of the
Board of Trustees of the National Planning Association,
prepared by its chairman, H. Christian Sonne. [Washing-
ton] 1949.
14 p. 20 cm. (*Its* Special report no. 26)
Caption title.

1. U. S.—Economic policy.   I. Sonne, Hans Christian, 1891–
II. Title.   (Series)

HC106.5.N28   330.973   50-11569

NN 0059772 DLC DAU MB Or ViU

National planning association.
America's new opportunities in world trade. [Washington]
National planning association [1944]
cover-title, iv, 79 p. 19½ᵐ. (Planning pamphlets, nos. 37–38)

1. U. S.—Commercial policy.   I. Title.
45-147
Library of Congress   HC101.N352 no. 37/38
[8]   (330.973) 392

OrCS ViU-L TxU ViU
NN 0059773 DLC FTaSU OEac DAU ViU-L LU MiU MB WU

National Planning Association.
America's world food responsibilities; a
statement unanimously approved by NPA members
at the joint meetings of the National planning
association ... December 10, 1946. [Washing-
ton, 1947]
[4] p. 22.5 x 10 cm.

NN 0059774 DNAL Or OrU

HG3881 National Planning Association
N32   [Analysis of Keynes-White plans for international monetary stabilization] Wash.
[1943?]
71 l. 29 cm

1. CURRENCY QUESTION 2. INTERNATIONAL
FINANCE I. T

NN 0059775 NjP NNC

280.9
N2153A   **National Planning Association.
Annual meeting.
[Washington,**

1. U.S. Economic policy.

NN 0059776 DNAL LU

HC188   National Planning Association.
.S28Z3

Zarur, Jorge, 1916–
A bacia do médio São Francisco; uma análise regional.
Rio de Janeiro, Serviço Gráfico do I. B. G. E., 1947.

HC101   National Planning Association.
.N352
no. 88   **Buck, Robert K**
Beginning farmers; a vulnerable group in American agriculture. Prepared for the NPA Agriculture Committee on
National Policy. [Washington, National Planning Associa-
tion] 1954.

National Planning Association.
Beyond the Marshall Plan
see under Galbraith, John Kenneth, 1908–

National planning association.
The big 4 in Germany
see under Glickman, David Lloyd, 1914–

National planning association.
Britain's trade in the post-war world ... [Washington] National planning association [1941]
cover-title, 35, [1] p. 19½ᵐ. (Planning pamphlets, no. 9)

1. Gt. Brit.—Econ. condit. 2. Gt. Brit.—Comm.   I. Title.
42-16252
Library of Congress   HC101.N352 no. 9
[4]   330.942

NN 0059781 DLC LU NjR ViU-L ViU OU OCU PU-PSW

VOLUME 407

[National planning association]
... Britain's trade in the post-war world. London [etc.] Oxford university press, 1942.

32 p. 18½ᶜᵐ. (America faces the war. No. 15)

"First issued as no. 9 of the Planning pamphlet series by the National planning association, Washington, D. C. ... now reprinted in an abridged form."—p. [2]

1. Gt. Brit.—Econ. condit. 2. Gt. Brit.—Comm. I. Title.

43–4149

Library of Congress   HC256.4.N28 1942
                    [3]   330.942

NN   0059782   DLC DAU ViU-L FTaSU MB PSt MiU MsU NIC

National Planning Association.
Business performance abroad
see its   Case study in an NPA series on
business performance abroad.

National Planning Association.
Can farmers afford to live better?
see under   Nelson, Lowry, 1893–

National Planning Association. Case studies on causes of
industrial peace under collective bargaining
see Causes of industrial peace under collective bargaining.

National Planning Association.
Case study in an NPA series on United States business
performance abroad. 1st–
[Washington, 1953–

no. in   v. illus., maps (part col.) 24 cm.

Title varies: 11th–12th, Case study in an NPA series on business performance abroad.
Cover title, 1st–   : United States business performance abroad (11th–12th : Business performance abroad)

1. Corporations, American—Case studies. I. Title. II. Title: United States business performance abroad. III. Title: Business performance abroad.

HD2709.N322   53–2647 rev 3

MeB OrU WaBeN
NN   0059786   DLC NN NBuC P DCU KU FTaSU NcRS OC1

HD8072
.C314

National Planning Association.

Causes of industrial peace under collective bargaining; case
studies. [no.] 1–   Sept. 1948–
[Washington] National Planning Assn.

HD8072
.G7

National Planning Association.

Golden, Clinton Strong, 1888–   ed.
Causes of industrial peace under collective bargaining.
Edited by Clinton S. Golden and Virginia D. Parker for
the CIP Committee of the National Planning Association.
New York, Harper [1955]

National planning association.
Causes of industrial peace under collective
bargaining. Hickey-Freeman and Amalgamate
clothing workers of America
see Straus, Donald B.
Hickey-Freeman ...

National Planning Association.

Weiss, Francis Joseph.
... Chemical utilization of fish products in Alaska, by
Francis Joseph Weiss ... [Washington, D. C., 1941]

National Planning Association.
China's relief needs. [Washington, 1945]

cover-title, 52 p. 19 cm. (Planning pamphlets, no. 40)

American Council data paper, no. 4.
"Submitted by the American Council as a document of the ninth conference of the Institute of Pacific Relations, to be held ... January 6 to 18, 1945."

1. World War, 1939–1945—Civilian relief—China. I. Title. II. Series. III. Series: Institute of Pacific Relations. American Council. Papers, no. 4.

HC101.N352 no. 4   940.5314451   48–1055*

NN   0059791   DLC OrP LU MB OrCS

National planning association.
China's relief needs. [Washington] National planning association [1945]

cover-title, 2 p. 1., 52 p. 19½ᶜᵐ. (Planning pamphlets, no. 40)

1. World war, 1939–   —Civilian relief—China. I. Title.

45–3786

Library of Congress °   D809.C5N3
                    [10]   940.5314451

TxU OU ICJ ViU OC1W
NN   0059792   DLC FTaSU PSt ViU-L MiU NcGU WU MB ICJ

National planning association.
Clothing and shelter for European relief ... [Washington] National planning association [1944]

cover-title, iv, 47, [1] p. diagrs. 19½ᶜᵐ. (Planning pamphlets, no. 34)
Bibliographical foot-notes.
"By the Special project on relief and rehabilitation of the National planning association."

1. World war, 1939–   —Civilian relief—Europe. I. Title.

44–6355

Library of Congress   HC101.N352 no. 34
                    [7]   (330.973) 940.53144

ViU-L MH-BA MB OU
NN   0059793   DLC FTaSU NcGU MH-L LU MiU PSt WU ViU

National planning association.
Collective bargaining between Libbey-Owens-
Ford glass company and Federation of glass ...
see   Harbison, Frederick Harris
Libbey-Owens-Ford glass company ...

National planning association.
The crisis in transportation ... [Washington, D. C.] National planning association [1941]

cover-title, 26 p. diagr. 19½ cm. (Planning pamphlets, no. 7)

1. Transportation—U. S. 2. Railroads—U. S. I. Title.

HC101.N352 no. 7   41—22803
                    (330.973)   385.0973

NN   0059795   DLC ViU OU MiU OCU LU MB FTaSU

National Planning Association.
The current crisis; a statement of the Committee on International Policy of the National Planning Association prepared by Frank Altschul, chairman, NPA International Committee. [Washington] 1950.

11 p. 20 cm. (Its Special report no. 27)
Cover title.

1. U. S.—For. rel.—1945–   2. U. S.—Defenses. I. Altschul, Frank, 1887–   II. Title. (Series)

E744.N95   397.73   50–11642

NN   0059796   DLC Or MB MH

National Planning Association.
Current tax policy; a statement of the Steering Committee of the National Planning Association. [Washington] 1949.

[4] p. 20 cm. (Its Special report no. 24)

1. Taxation—U. S. I. Title. (Series)

HJ2377.N35   336.2   49–48528*

NN   0059797   DLC MB IEdS Or ViU

National planning association.
Defense planning and labor policy ... [Washington, D. C.] National planning association [1941]

cover-title, 24 p. 19½ᶜᵐ. (Planning pamphlets, no. 5)

1. U. S.—Economic policy. 2. World war, 1939–   —Economic aspects—U. S. I. Title.

42–13855

Library of Congress   HC101.N352 no. 5
— — Copy 2.   HC106.4.N39
                    [3]   (330.973) 330.973

NN   0059798   DLC LU MsU MiU MB ViU-L ViU OO OU OCU

National planning association.
The development of a policy for industrial
peace in atomic energy
see under   Straus, Donald B.

National planning association.
Discussion and study outline on social security
see under [Burns, Eveline Mabel
(Richardson)] 1900–

HC101
.N353
no.36
1955

National Planning Association.

Economic expansion; opportunities and
challenge, a joint statement by the Board,
Agriculture, Business, Labor, and International Committee Members of the National
Planning Association present at the twentieth
anniversary joint meeting, December 13 and
14, 1954, Washington, D. C. [Washington] 1955.
7 p. 23 x 10cm. (Its Special report, no. 36)

1. U. S.—Econ. condit.—1945–   I. Title.
II. Ser.

NN   0059801   ViU IEdS NcD

National Planning Association.
Economic preparedness for peace; a report of the meeting
of the NPA Board of Trustees, December 8 and 9, 1952.
Washington [1953]

20 p. 20 cm. (Its Special report no. 32)

1. U. S.—Economic policy. 2. Economic policy. I. Title.

HC106.5.N2845   54–3081 ‡

NN   0059802   DLC Or NcD OOxM ViU NNC

HC
101
N3522
no.21

National Planning Association.
Efficiency in defense expenditure; a joint
statement adopted by members of NPA's Board of
Trustees and its Agriculture, Business, Labor
and International Committees present at the
NPA joint meeting, January 31, 1949. [Washington, D. C., 1949]

[4] p. 22 cm. (Its Special report no. 21)
Caption title.

1. U. S.—Dept. of Defense—Appropriations
and expenditures. I. Title.

NN   0059803   IEdS MB MH-BA

HD9698
.A2M31

National Planning Association.

Mason, Edward Sagendorph, 1899–
Energy requirements and economic growth, by Edward S.
Mason and the staff of the NPA project on the economic
aspects of the productive uses of nuclear energy. Washington, National Planning Association [1955]

National planning association.
European order and world order
see under Political and economic planning.

VOLUME 407

National planning association.

Europe's uprooted people; the relocation of displaced population ... ₍Washington₎ National planning association ₍1944₎

cover-title, ii, ₍2₎, 50 p., 1 l. fold. maps. 19½ᵐ. (Planning pamphlets. No. 36)

"Mr. Bertram Pickard wrote the report for the sponsoring committee."—Foreword.
Bibliographical foot-notes.

1. Migration, Internal—Europe. 2. Reconstruction (1939-   )—Europe. 3. World war, 1939-   —Occupied territories.   ɪ. Pickard, Bertram, 1892-   ɪɪ. Title.

Library of Congress   HC101.N352 no. 36   44-47875
                             ₍15₎   (330.973) 940.53144

NN 0059806   DLC WU MH-L MiU CaBViP OrCS MH PSt OCH
LU MB FTaSU NNZI ViU-L ViU MH-BA OO OU OC1W

National Planning Association.
Federal-State-Local relations in agriculture
see under   Black, John Donald, 1883-

National planning association.

Fertilizers in the postwar national economy ... ₍Washington₎ National planning association ₍1945₎

cover-title, iv, 48 p. illus. (maps) diagrs. 19½ᵐ. (Planning pamphlets, no. 42)

"Reference and reading list": p. iv.

1. Fertilizers and manures. 2. Agriculture—U.S.   ɪ. Title.

Library of Congress °   HC101.N352 no. 42   45-5987
———— Copy 2.   HD9483.N37
                      ₍8₎   (330.973) 338.1718

NN 0059808   DLC PSt NcGU MB FTaSU LU PU ViU-L ViU
MH-BA TxU OU OO OC1W MiU MH-L OrCS

National planning association.

The Food and agriculture organization, a joint statement by the Agriculture, Business, and Labor committees on national policy and the Committee on international policy of the National planning association. ₍Washington, 1945₎

8 p. 28ᵐ.

1. Food and agriculture organization of the United nations (Proposed)
                                              45-6605

Library of Congress   HD9000.1.N3
                             ₍4₎   338.10611

NN 0059809   DLC OrU Or NN

National Planning Association.

Benedict, Murray Reed, 1892-
Food and feed reserves. Prepared for the NPA Agriculture Committee on National Policy. ₍Washington, National Planning Association₎ 1951.

HC101
.N352
no. 76

National planning association.

A food and nutrition program for the nation ... ₍Washington₎ National planning association ₍1945₎

cover-title, iv, 35 p. 19½ cm. (Planning pamphlets, no. 46)

"A report by a sub-committee of the agriculture, business, and labor committees on national policy."

1. Nutrition. 2. Food supply—U.S.   ɪ. Title.

HC101.N352 no. 46   (330.973) 613.2   45—6528
———— Copy 2.   TX360.U6N27

NN 0059811   DLC LU MH-L MB FTaSU MiU MH-BA NBuG ViU
TxU OU OO OC1W NcGU OrCS

National planning association.
Food as a weapon. Washington, D.C. ₍1942?₎
6 l.

1. Starvation.   ɪ. Title.

NN 0059812   NNC

89
2132
ttʰ

National planning association.
Food for Europe after victory.   Washington
₍194-?₎
51 p.

1. Food supply. Europe. 2. Reconstruction
(1939-   ) Europe. Food relief.   ɪ. Title.

NN 0059813   DNAL CtY

National planning association.

Food for Europe after victory ... ₍Washington₎ National planning association ₍1944₎

cover-title, 1 p. l., 42 p. 19½ᵐ. (Planning pamphlets. No. 29)

1. Food supply—Europe. 2. World war, 1939-   —Civilian relief—Europe.   ɪ. Title.

Library of Congress   HC101.N352 no. 29   44-2494
———— Copy 2.   HD9015.A3N3
                      ₍8₎   (330.973) 338.1

NN 0059814   DLC ViU-L LU PSt MH-L FTaSU NIC ViU OU

National planning association.

For a better post-war agriculture ... ₍Washington₎ National planning association ₍1942₎

cover-title, 47 p. 19½ᵐ. (Planning pamphlets, no. 11)

1. Agriculture—Economic aspects—U.S.   ɪ. Title.

                                              43-11149
Library of Congress   HC101.N352 no. 11
———— Copy 2.   HD1765.1942.N3
                      ₍4₎   (330.973) 630.973

NN 0059815   DLC GAT PSt LU FTaSU MB WU OrCS ViU-L
LU ViU OU OCU Or CaBViP MH-BA

National Planning Association.

Lorimer, Frank, 1894-
Foundations of American population policy, by Frank Lorimer, Ellen Winston ₍and₎ Louise K. Kiser for the Committee on population studies and social planning of the National economic and social planning association. New York and London, Harper & brothers. 1940.

National planning association.

4 for 4; questions for national action, proposed by the National planning association. ₍Washington, 1945₎

34, ₍1₎ p. illus. (incl. facsims.) 25½ᵐ.

1. U.S.—Economic policy.   ɪ. Title.

                                              46-12336
Library of Congress   HC106.5.N3
                                              338.91

NN 0059817   DLC Or MB N ICU NN

National Planning Association.
A framework for long-range agricultural policy ...
see under   National planning association.
Agriculture committee on national policy.

National Planning Association.
Fundamentals of labor peace

see under

National planning association. Committee on the causes of industrial peace under collective bargaining.

TX353
.B62

National Planning Association. A food and nutrition program for the nation.
Black, John Donald, 1883-
Future food and agriculture policy, a program for the next ten years, by John Donald Black and Maxine Enlow Kiefer. 1st ed. New York, McGraw-Hill Book Co., 1948.

DD119
.W5
1944

National planning association.
                    FOR OTHER EDITIONS
                    SEE MAIN ENTRY
Whittlesey, Derwent Stainthorpe, 1890-
German strategy of world conquest, by Derwent Whittlesey, with 29 maps and diagrams. ₍London₎ F. E. Robinson & co.
₍1944₎

National planning association.

Germany's challenge to America's defense ... ₍Washington, D.C.₎ National economic and social planning association ₍1941₎

cover-title, 40 p. 19½ᵐ. (Planning pamphlets, no. 4)

1. Germany—Economic policy. 2. U.S.—Defenses. 3. World war, 1939-   —Germany.   ɪ. Title.

                                              41-10545 Revised
Library of Congress   HC101.N352 no. 4
———— Copy 2.   D742.G4N3
                      ₍r42d3₎   (330.973) 330.943

NN 0059822   DLC MsU DAU WU MB ViU OCU

NATIONAL PLANNING ASSOCIATION
Goals of cooperation, a declaration of interdependence. Joint statement by the agriculture, and labor members of the National planning association; unanimously adopted December 1946.
Author ₍1946₎
14 p. illus. ₋

NN 0059823   Or

National Planning Association.

Good health is good business; a joint subcommittee report. ₍Washington, 1948₎

iv, 44 p. 20 cm. (Planning pamphlets, no. 62)
Cover title.

1. Hygiene, Public. 2. Medical economics.   ɪ. Title.   (Series)
HC101.N352 no. 62   614   48-10946*

NN 0059824   DLC MU MB MH-L PPFRB LU MiU OU OO TxU
MH-BA ViU DNLM PU OCU OrPR OrCS MtU

National planning association.

Guides for post-war planning ... ₍Washington₎ National planning association ₍1941₎

cover-title, 31 p. 19½ᵐ. (Planning pamphlets, no. 8)

1. U.S.—Economic policy. 2. Reconstruction (1939-   )—U.S.
ɪ. Title.
                                              43-11133
Library of Congress   HC101.N352 no. 8
———— Copy 2.   HC106.4.N394
                      ₍5₎   (330.973) 338.91

NN 0059825   DLC LU FTaSU NIC MB Or OrCS ViU-L
ViU OU OCU MH-BA

TP149
.W38

National planning association.

Weiss, Francis Joseph, 1898-
... Industrial utilization of agricultural products (cellulose, lignin, and allied raw materials) by Francis Joseph Weiss ... ₍Washington, 1943₎

NATIONAL PLANNING ASSOCIATION.
Information for the press. Jan.11, 1943-date (incomplete)
Washington.   v.   28cm.

Irregular.
Title varies: Sept. 22, 1950-date, Information for the press and radio (1955-date, most issues lack title).

1. Economic policy--U.S.--Per. and soc. publ. I. National planning association. Information for the press and radio.

NN 0059828   NN IU

VOLUME 407

National planning association.
International development loans ... ₍Washington₎ National planning association ₍1942₎
cover-title, 38 p. 19½ᵐ. (Planning pamphlets, no. 15)

1. Investments, Foreign. 2. Commercial policy. I. Title.

Library of Congress	HC101.N352 no. 15	42–50708
——— Copy 2.	HG4538.N3	
	₍45f1₎	(330.973) 338.91

OCU
NN   0059829   DLC LU PSt FTaSU MB OrU ViU-L ViU OU

National planning association.
International economic collaboration; role of the Economic and social council in the United nations organization, a report by the NPA Committee on international policy ... ₍Washington, 1946₎
v, 26 p. 19½ᵐ. (On cover: Planning pamphlets, no. 50)

United nations. Economic and social council. 2. Economic policy. I. Title.

Library of Congress	HC101.N352 no. 50	46–5041
——— Copy 2.	HC59.N3	
	₍7₎	(330.973) 338.91

TxU MtU
NN   0059830   DLC MH OC1W OrPS LU KU MiU NcGU MB ViU

HC106.5   National Planning Association.
N34   Joint planning by Americans in agriculture, business, labor and the professions at NPA's annual meeting. [Washington]
v.   illus.   28 cm.
1. U.S. Econ. condit. I. Title.

NN   0059831   DI

National Planning Association.
Joint planning by Americans in agriculture, business, labor and the professions, at NPA's 1951 annual meeting. ₍Washington, D.C., 1952₎
36 p.   illus.(incl.ports.)   27½cm.

1. U.S. - Economic conditions - 1945-
I. Title.

NN   0059832   OrCS LU PU

National planning association.
Joint statement on social security by agriculture, business and labor ... ₍Washington₎ National planning association ₍1944₎
cover-title, 1 p. l., ix, 36 p. 19½ᵐ. (Planning pamphlets. No. 33)

1. Insurance, State and compulsory—U. S. 2. Public welfare—U. S.
44–5599

| Library of Congress | HC101.N352 no. 33 | |
| | ₍5₎ | (330.973) 331.2544 |

MH-BA OU
NN   0059833   DLC LU PSt MiU WU MH-IR MB ViU-L NNZI

National planning association.
... A joint statement on the Food and agriculture organization by the Agriculture, Business, and Labor committees on national policy and the Committee on international policy ...
see *its*
The Food and agriculture organization.

National Planning Association.
Joint statement on the reconversion of industry to peace; agriculture, business and labor committees on National policy of the National planning association. [Washington, D.C., 1943?]
cover-title, folder.   23 x 10.5 cm.

NN   0059835   DPU

National Planning Association.
Latin America and the freedom from want. ₍Washington, 1942₎
2 v. (328 l.) diagrs., tables. 28 cm.
Cover title.
HN253.N3
——— Abstract of report. ₍Washington, 1942₎
14 l. 28 cm.
Cover title.
1. Spanish America — Soc. condit. 2. Spanish America — Econ. condit.—1918–
HN253.N32   338.98   48–36965*‡

NN   0059836   DLC ICU DPU CU

HC165   National planning association.
.S6
Soule, George Henry, 1887–
Latin America in the future world, by George Soule, David Efron and Norman T. Ness (under the supervision of Alvin H. Hansen) for the National planning association. New York, Toronto, Farrar & Rinehart, inc. ₍1945₎

HC101   National Planning Association.
.L6
Looking ahead. v. 1–   Feb. 1953–
₍Washington₎ National Planning Association.

*HC101   National Planning Association.
.N3522   Management-labor cooperation in cutting
no. 15   costs; a statement by the Labor Committee on National Policy of the National Planning Association. [Washington, 1947]
[4] p. 28 cm. (Its SR-15)
"Second printing."

1. Costs, Industrial--U. S.   I. Title.
II. Series: National Planning Association. Special report,   no. 15.

NN   0059839   MB OrU Or

National Planning Association.
Manpower: the Nation's first resource; report of the NPA Special Committee on Manpower Policy. ₍Washington₎ 1953.
55 p. 20 cm. (Planning pamphlets, no. 83)

1. Manpower—U. S.   I. Title.

| HC101.N352 no. 83 | 331.112 | 53—11711 ‡ |
| ——— Copy 2. | HA17.5.U5N3 | |

PSt TxU PSC ODW MH-L LU WU FTaSU CaBVaU MtU OrCS
NN   0059840   DLC ViU MH-BA DI NN NcD MiU OO OCU PHC

National Planning Association.
The manual of corporate giving; edited by Beardsley Ruml in collaboration with Theodore Geiger. Chapters by Will W. Alexander ₍and others.₎ Washington, 1952₎
415 p. 24 cm.

1. Corporations—Charitable contributions—U. S.   I. Ruml,
Beardsley, 1804–   ed. II. Title: Corporate giving.

HV95.N38   361.7   52—10976 ‡

PWpM
WaWW WaSpG PU-W WaT OrP IdU Wa OrCS WaS PPFRB
PRosC ViU TU TxU KEmT MtBC KyBgW OrU NBuU
WaTC PPF-B FU-L PV PCM NcRS PP PLF PSt CU
NN   0059841   DLC NIC IdPI PU-W MtBuM Or OrPR

National Planning Association.
Monetary policy to combat inflation, a statement by the conference of university economists called by the National Planning Association at Princeton, New Jersey, October 12–14, 1951. ₍Washington₎ 1952.
15 p. 20 cm. (Its Special report no. 31)

1. Currency question—U. S.   I. Title.
HC101.N3522 no. 31   332.4973   58–29429 ‡

NN   0059842   DLC OC1W ViU NNC NcD MB NN NIC

National Planning Association.
Must we have food surpluses?
see under title

National Planning Association.
NPA gold medal award for outstanding contribution through planning to the betterment of human life. Presentation and acceptance speeches : 1952 award, William S. Paley; 1953 award, Jean Monnet. Washington ₍1955†₎
21 p. 20 cm. (Its Special report no. 37)

1. Economic policy. 2. Paley, William Samuel, 1901–   3. Monnet, Jean, 1888–   I. Title: Outstanding contribution through planning to the betterment of human life.

HC101.N3522 no. 37   57–4181 ‡

NN   0059844   DLC CLU NcD OOxM MB OrCS

NATIONAL PLANNING ASSOCIATION
NPA's joint meeting, December 9–10, 1946;
report to members. ₍Author, 1947₎
₍15₎ p. illus. (incl. ports.)

NN   0059845   Or

National planning association.
NPA's ninth anniversary, 1934–1943. Report to members ... Washington, D. C., National planning association ₍1943₎
₍11₎ p. illus. (ports.)   28 x 22ᵐ.

1. U. S.—Economic policy.
44–51250

| Library of Congress | HC106.4.N395 | |
| | ₍3₎ | 338.91 |

NN   0059846   Or NNC

NATIONAL PLANNING ASSOCIATION
NPA's principles and objectives; a statement by the board of trustees. 800 Twenty-first St., N. W., Washington, D. C., Author ₍1947₎
₍8₎ p.

NN   0059847   Or

National Planning Association.
NPA's principles and objectives; a statement by the Board of Trustees.   Washington [1948]
[6] p.   23 cm.   (pbk.)
Cover title.
1. National Planning Association. I. Title.

NN   0059848   IEdS

National planning association.
National budgets for full employment ... ₍Washington₎ National planning association ₍1945₎
cover-title, viii, 96 p. diagrs. 19½ᵐ. (Its Planning pamphlets, nos. 43 and 44)

1. U. S.—Economic policy. 2. Unemployed—U. S.   I. Title.
45–5740

| Library of Congress | HC101.N352 no. 43/44 | |
| | ₍10₎ | (330.973) 338.91 |

FTaSU MH-BA TxU ODW OU OO OC1W OrCS CaBVaU
NN   0059849   DLC DAU LU NSyU NcGU MiU PSt OrPS ViU

National planning association.
National planning association, origin, objective, organization. Washington, D. C., National planning association ₍1943₎
₍15₎ p. diagr. 25½ᵐ.

45–15406

| Library of Congress | H11.N53 | |
| | ₍2₎ | 338.91 |

NN   0059850   DLC NN DPU

VOLUME 407

National planning association.
National policy for aviation; aircraft production, air forces, air commerce, a statement by the NPA Board of trustees and a report by the NPA Advisory committee on the aircraft industry ... ₍Washington, 1946₎
xi, 68 p. 19½ᵐ. (*On cover:* Planning pamphlets, nos. 51–52)
"Suggested reading and reference": p. 66–68.

1. Aeronautics—U. S. 2. Aeroplane industry and trade—U. S. ɪ. Title.
Library of Congress ――― Copy 2. | HC101.N352 no. 51/52 TL521.N29 | 46–5075
₍8₎ | (330.973) 629.130973

MH–BA OEac OC1W
NN 0059851 DLC PPFRB MtU PSt LU MiU MH–L MB NcGU

National Planning Association.
Rose, Cornelia Bruère, 1907–
National policy for radio broadcasting, by C. B. Rose, jr. Report of a committee of the National economic and social planning association. New York and London, Harper & brothers, 1940.

National Planning Association.
The need for further budget reform, a joint statement by the Board, Agriculture, Business, Labor, and International Committee members of the National Planning Association present at the twentieth anniversary joint meeting, December 13 and 14, 1954, Washington, D. C., and The Federal budget and the national economy; how to make the Federal budget a better tool of fiscal policy, a staff report by Gerhard Colm with the assistance of Marilyn Young. ₍Washington₎ 1955.
vi, 101 p. 20 cm. (Planning pamphlets, no. 90)
1. Budget—U. S. ɪ. Colm, Gerhard, 1897– ɪɪ. Title. (Series)
HC101.N352 no. 90 | 336.73 | 55–2626
Library of Congress

NN MiU PSt
OrCS N CaBVaU OCU OOxM PHC NcD OO PSC TxU MH–BA ViU
NN 0059853 DLC LU MU MtU MH–L OrLgE FTaSU DAU

National Planning Association.
Needed : a civilian reserve. Recommendations of the NPA Special Committee on Manpower Policy and a report by Helen Hill Miller. ₍Washington₎ 1954.
49 p. 20 cm. (Planning pamphlets, no. 86)

1. Manpower—U. S. ɪ. Title.
HC101.N352 no. 86 | 331.112 | 54–12076 ‡

PPT TxU PHC PSt OO NN OOxM OCU LU OrCS MiU OrU
NN 0059854 DLC PSt MH–L FTaSU WU MtU ViU PSC PPD

National planning association.
A new American policy in China
see under Gulick, Luther Halsey, 1892–

National Planning Association.
National planning conference, *Detroit,* 1937.
New horizons in planning; proceedings of the National planning conference, held at Detroit, Michigan, June 1–3, 1937. American city planning institute, American planning and civic association, American society of planning officials, National economic and social planning association. Chicago, Ill., American society of planning officials ₍1937₎

National Planning Association.
The next step of American foreign economic policy; a joint statement by NPA members from agriculture, business, labor, and the professions attending the annual joint meeting of the National Planning Association, December 4, 1951. Washington, 1951.
12 ℓ. 28cm. (Its Information for press and radio)

NN 0059857 IU

National planning association.
A note on defense policy and organization. 1940. [Washington, D.C.? 1940]
6 numb. ℓ. chart.
Manifold copy.

NN 0059858 MH–PA

National planning association.
HC101 .N352 no. 59
Condliffe, John Bell, 1891–
... Obstacles to multilateral trade, by J. B. Condliffe. ₍Washington, National planning association, 1947₎

National Planning Association.
Old-age security for farm people ...
see under National planning association. Agriculture committee on national policy.

National planning association.
On the future of international investment. Washington ₍1943₎
44 ℓ.

1. Investments, Foreign. 2. Investments, Foreign – U. S. ɪ. Title: International Investment.

NN 0059861 NNC

National Planning Association.
"Operation bootstrap" in Puerto Rico
see under Chase, Stuart, 1888–

National Planning Association.
Opportunities for economic expansion. A report of the NPA Steering Committee. ₍Washington₎ 1954.
25 p. 20 cm. (*Its* Planning pamphlets, no. 87)

1. U. S.—Economic policy. ɪ. Title.
HC101.N352 no. 87 | 54–14612 ‡

PPT OOxM PHC OO PSC NN OCU MB MtU MiU OrCS
NN 0059863 DLC WU FTaSU MH–L LU PSt ViU TxU NcD

National Planning Association.
Organization of the United States Government for technical cooperation; a statement by the NPA Special Policy Committee on Technical Cooperation. ₍Washington, 1955₎
25 p. 23 cm. (*Its* Technical cooperation in Latin America)

1. Technical assistance, American—Spanish America. ɪ. Title.
HC165.N33 | 338.973 | 55–2651 rev ‡

CaBVa IdPI OrPR
PPD IU ViU TxU OOxM OU MsU ScCleU OrCS MiD MtBC OrU
NN 0059864 DLC CU MB NcGU Or NcD OOxM OC1W ODW

National Planning Association.
Organizing the U.S. government for foreign economic operations; a statement of the NPA Steering Committee, June 18, 1951. Washington 1951.
10 ℓ. 28cm.
Caption title.

1. U.S. Economic policy. 2. Economic assistance, American. I. Title.

NN 0059865 OrU

National planning association.
... Origin, objective, organization
see its National planning association, origin, objective, organization.

National Planning Association.
The outlook after the two Geneva conferences, a note of warning; a policy statement by the members of the Committee on International Policy. ₍Washington₎ 1955.
15 p. 23 x 10 cm. (*Its* Special report 38)

1. U. S.—Foreign economic relations. ɪ. Title. (Series)
A 57–6659
Virginia. Univ. Libr.
for Library of Congress ₍2₎

NN 0059867 ViU MB NcD IEdS CLU

National Planning Association.
HD7106 .U5B28
Ball, Robert M
Pensions in the United States; a study prepared for the Joint Committee on the Economic Report by the National Planning Association. Washington, U. S. Govt. Print. Off., 1952.

National planning association.
Plan. Washington, D. C.: National planning assoc. ₍1941?₎
4 ℓ. 20½cm.

1. Economic planning—Assoc. and org.—U. S.—D. C.—Washington.
N.Y.P.L. June 8, 1942

NN 0059869 NN

National Planning Association.
Plan age
see under title

National planning association.
A plan for Britain ... ₍Washington, D. C.₎ National economic and social planing association ₍1941₎
cover-title, 56 p. 19½ cm. (Planning pamphlets, no. 3)
Articles reprinted from weekly magazine, Picture post, London, January 4, 1941. *cf.* p. ₍1₎

1. Gt. Brit.—Economic policy. 2. Gt. Brit.—Soc. condit. ɪ. Title.
HC101.N352 no. 3 ――― Copy 2. | 330.942 HC256.4.N8 | 41–5276

NN 0059871 DLC ViU OCU OO PSt MB MiU Or

[National Planning Association]
... Planning activities in the Pacific Northwest and in California. Washington, D. C., The Association, 1936.
32 p. O.

NN 0059872 CaBViP

National Planning Association.
Planning by Americans in agriculture, business labor, the professions; 1949 report to members ..

NN 0059873 PU–PSW

National Planning Association.
Planning courses in American colleges.
193
[Washington, D.C., 193 19½cm.
no.

1. Economic planning—Study and teaching—U.S.

NN 0059874 NN MH LU IU NRU

VOLUME 407

National planning association.

Planning pamphlets ... ₍Washington, D. C.₎ National economic and social planning association ₍19

National Planning Association.

Woodrow Wilson Foundation.
The political economy of American foreign policy; its concepts, strategy, and limits; report of a study group sponsored by the Woodrow Wilson Foundation and the **National** Planning Association. ₍William Y. Elliott, chairman₎ New York, Holt ₍1955₎

HF1455
.W6

National Planning Association.
The position of business on fiscal and wage policy in depression
    see under   Fortune.

NATIONAL PLANNING ASSOCIATION.

Post-war reconstruction group; restatement of war aims. 1940. n.p., [1940].

Manifold copy. ff.6.

NN 0059878   MH-PA

National Planning Association.
Private investment in underdeveloped countries; a statement of principles by the Steering Committee of the National Planning Association. ₍Washington₎ 1951.
    9 p. 20 cm. (Its Special report no. 30)
    Caption title.

    1. Investments, American. 2. Investments, Foreign. I. Title.
(Series)
    HG4538.N33   332.6   52-15

NN 0059879   DLC MB ViU

National Planning Association.
Private pension plans ...
    see under   National Planning Association.
Business Committee on National Policy.

National planning association.

NA9010
.N45

National conference on planning.
Proceedings of the conference. 1935-42. Chicago, Ill., American society of planning officials ₍1935?-42₎

National Planning Association.
A program for the nonmilitary defense of the United States; a statement on national policy by the NPA Special Committee on Nonmilitary Defense Planning, and The tasks of nonmilitary defense and the present status of planning, by William H. Stead. ₍Washington₎ 1955.
    xxxiii, 97 p. 20 cm. (Planning pamphlets, no. 92)
    Bibliography: p. 91-96.

    1. U. S. — Civilian defense. I. Stead, William Henry, 1890-
The tasks of nonmilitary defense and the present status of planning.
    II. Title: Nonmilitary defense of the United States.   (Series)

    HC101.N352 no. 92   355.23   55-2688

        OYesA
    PSt NN TxU DI MH-L MiU PPD LU FTaSU DAU MtU OrCS
NN 0059882   DLC NBuU OCU OOxM NcD OO PHC PSC ViU

HC101
.P8

Public policy digest of the National planning association
    no. 1-   Jan. 15, 1940-
    Washington, D. C., 1940-

National planning association.
Recommendations on national aviation policy submitted to the Board of trustees, National planning association, by William A. M. Burden, chairman, NPA Advisory committee on the aircraft industry. Washington, Nat. planning assoc. , 1945.
    10 p.   23 cm.
    1. Aeronautics - U. S. I. Burden, William Armistead Moale, 1906-

NN 0059884   NN NcD IU Or OU

National planning association.
Reconversion of industry to peace; report by officers of the agriculture, business and labor committees on national policy of the National planning association. ₍Washington, 1943₎
    iv, 24 p. 19½ cm. (On cover: Planning pamphlets, no. 24)

    1. U. S.—Indus. 2. Defense contracts— U. S. 3. Reconstruction
(1939-1951)—U. S.   I. Title.
    HC101.N352 no. 24   330.973   43—22875
    ——— Copy 2.   HC106.4.N397

        FTaSU WU OrPR
NN 0059885   DLC DPU ViU-L OU OCU MB NIC LU PSt

National Planning Association.
Recovery in Europe
    see under   Galbraith, John Kenneth, 1908-

National planning association.
Relief and rehabilitation study guide, prepared for the National planning association by Spencer Coxe. Washington, D. C., National planning association ₍1944₎
    12 p. 19½ cm.
    Title from p. ₍2₎ of cover.
    "Reading list": p. ₍8₎ of cover.

    1. World war, 1939-   —Civilian relief—U. S. 2. United nations
relief and rehabilitation administration. I. Coxe, Spencer. II. Title.
                                        45-2668
    Library of Congress   D809.U5N27
                    ₍4₎   940.53144

NN 0059887   DLC DNAL DPU

National planning association.
Relief for Europe, the first phase of reconstruction; an NPA group study. ₍Washington, 1942₎
    2 p. l., 59 p. 19½ cm. (On cover: Planning pamphlets, no. 17)
    Bibliographical foot-notes.

    1. Reconstruction (1939-   ) 2. World war, 1939-   —Hospitals,
charities, etc. I. Title.
    Library of Congress   HC101.N352 no. 17   43-5441
    ——— Copy 2.   D808.N3
                    ₍8₎   (330.973) 940.53144

        OrCS ViU OCU OU
NN 0059888   DLC FTaSU MB LU PSt NIC NcGU MH-L ViU-L

HC101   National Planning Association.
N352   Report. no. 1-   1939-
    Washington, D. C.
        v. illus. 23 cm.

    Title varies: no. 1-131 1939-72 its
    Planning pamphlets.
    Name of association varies: 1939-Jan 1941
    National Economic and Social Planning
    Association.

    1. United States   - Econ. condit. -
    Collections   I. A, T, S anals

NN 0059889   NcRS NBuC FTaSU

National Planning Association.
Report
    see also   Planning pamphlets.

National planning association.
Report of the Committee on the textile industry in the United States of America. Washington, D. C., National economic and social planning association, 1937.
    cover-title, iii, 41 p. 28½ᵐ.

    1. Textile industry and fabrics— U. S.   37-12376 Revised
    Library of Congress   HD9855.N3
                    ₍r42f2₎   338.4

NN 0059891   DLC NN NNC

National Planning Association.
Report on activities.
Washington.
    v. 23-26 cm.

    1. U. S.—Economic policy—Societies, etc.

    HC101.N35215   62-19713 rev

        TxU MiU UU NN
NN 0059892   DLC FTaSU IU NcGU OrPS NBuT N NSyU DPU

National Planning Association.
Report to members.
    ₍Washington?₎
        v. illus., ports. 28 cm. annual.

    HB1.N3   338.973   49-52834*‡

NN 0059893   DLC MH-BA OrU NNC DNAL CU TxU C PPT

National Planning Association.
Reports on the productive uses of nuclear energy. [no. 1]- Washington, D. C. [1955]-
    nos. tables, diagrs. 23 cm.
    1. Atomic energy. 2. Nuclear engineering.
    I. Title: Productive uses of nuclear energy.
    Contents.

NN 0059894   OrCS OCl MiD NjP CU IEN INLP

National planning association.
A retirement system for farmers
    see under   Benedict, Murray Reed, 1892-

National Planning Association.
The role of business in orderly price adjustments ...
    see under   National planning association.
Business committee on national policy.

National Planning Association.
The role of universities in technical cooperation; a statement by the NPA Special Policy Committee on Technical Cooperation. ₍Washington, 1955₎
    xiv, 28 p. 23 cm. (Its Technical cooperation in Latin America)

    1. Technical assistance in Spanish America. 2. Universities and
colleges—U. S. I. Title.   (Series)

    HC165.N335   338.98   55-3275

        NN IdU OrPR OrU CaBVa
    PPD PBL PSt OOxM OClW MiU OU IU TxU MiD NcGU MsSM
NN 0059897   DLC CoU Or OrCS DNAL CaBVaU MtBC CU NcD

VOLUME 407

National planning association.
A selected bibliography of books on economic and social planning, 1935–1936 ... Washington, D. C., National economic and social planning association ₁1936?₁

11. ₁1₁ p. 19½ᶜᵐ.

"Prepared by George B. Galloway."

1. Economic policy—Bibl. 2. Industry—Organization, control, etc.— Bibl. I. Galloway, George Barnes, 1808–

Library of Congress Z7164.E2N33

44–12269

NN 0059898 DLC Or DL NN IU

National Planning Association.
Sharon Steel Corporation and United Steel-
workers of America
see under Miller, J Wade, Jr.

National Planning Association.
Special report.

Washington ₁19

v. illus. 20–28 cm.

1. U. S.—Economic policy—Collections.

HC101.N3522

55–57860 ‡

NN 0059900 TxLT NN P IdU OU WvU DAU MiU CtY TxU OCl Vi MiD DLC NcRS AAP GEU MBU KU CtNIC NhD MdBJ

National planning association.
The stakes of Bretton Woods, a statement by the Committee on international policy of the National planning association. ₁Washington, 1945₁

24 p. 28 x 21½ᶜᵐ.

1. International monetary fund (Proposed) 2. International bank for reconstruction and development (Proposed) I. Title.

45–6739

Library of Congress HG255.N3

₁12₁ 332.15

NN 0059901 DLC MB CoU Or NNC NNUN DPU ICU NN

National planning association.

JK1061
.H4
1945 a Heller, Robert, 1899– FOR OTHER EDITIONS SEE MAIN ENTRY

Strengthening the Congress, by Robert Heller. Washington, D. C., The National planning association ₁1945₁

National Planning Association.
Studies in development progress
see under title

National Planning Association.
Summarized minutes of NPA meeting on industrial relations, a special report to members. Washington ₁1946₁

30 p. 28 cm.

The meeting was held at Princeton, Aug. 9–10, 1946.

1. Industrial relations—U. S.

HD8057.N46 338.91 48–18260*

NN 0059904 DLC OrU Or

National Planning Association.
Summary report of Meetings on the Impact of Mobilization on American Communities
see under Meeting on the Impact of Mobilization on American Communities, Washington, 1951.

National planning association.
... Survey of post-war activities in federal agencies. Washington, D. C., 1943.

1 v. 28ᶜᵐ.

Loose-leaf; reproduced from type-written copy.

1. U. S.—Executive departments. I. Title: Post-war activities in federal agencies.

Library of Congress JK691.N35 45–14908

₁2₁ 353

NN 0059906 DLC

National Planning Association.
The tasks of nonmilitary defense and the present status of planning. Appendix to a study issued by the National Planning Association on the present status of nonmilitary defense planning in certain Federal agencies. Washington, U. S. Govt. Print. Off., 1955.

v, 57 p. 24 cm. (84th Cong., 1st sess. Senate. Document no. 60)

An appendix to the association's report, A program for the non-military defense of the United States.

1. U. S.—Civilian defense. I. Title. (Series: U. S. 84th Cong., 1st sess., 1955. Senate. Document no. 60)

UA927.N33 355.23 55–61803

NN 0059907 DLC

National Planning Association.
Technical cooperation—sowing the seeds of progress, a statement by the NPA Special Policy Committee on Technical Cooperation. ₁Washington, 1955₁

6 p. 23 cm. (*Its* Technical cooperation in Latin America)

1. Technical assistance, American—Spanish America. I. Title.

HC165.N34 338.98 55–3035 rev ‡

NN 0059908 MiD NN TU OOxM PPD DNAL MtBC OrPR OrCS CaBVa DLC CoU DAU WaU CU TxU OrU MiU OU FMU

National planning association.
Toward building a better America
see under Altschul, Frank, 1887–

National planning association.
UNRRA: gateway to recovery ... ₁Washington₁ National planning association ₁1944₁

cover-title, 2 p. l., 84 p. 19½ᶜᵐ. (Planning pamphlets, no. 30–31)

Bibliographical references included in "Notes" (p. 73–84)

1. United nations relief and rehabilitation administration.

44–5644

Library of Congress HC101.N352 no. 30/31

₁5₁ (330.973) 940.53144

NN 0059910 ViU MH–BA OU OCU OO OrCS DLC WU MiU NcGU LU PSt MB MH–L ViU–L

National Planning Association.
The United States and the lesser developed countries of the world; a statement of principles by the Steering Committee of the National Planning Association. ₁Washing-
ton₁ 1951.

12 p. 20 cm. (*Its* Special report no. 29)

Caption title.

1. Technical assistance, American. I. Title. (Series)

HC60.N33 338.91 51–3998

NN 0059911 DLC ViU MB DPU

National planning association.
United States' cooperation with British nations ... ₁Washington₁ National planning association ₁1941₁

cover-title, 51 p. 19½ᶜᵐ. (Planning pamphlets, no. 6)

1. World war, 1939– —Economic aspects. 2. Reconstruction (1939–) 3. U. S.—For. rel.—Gt. Brit. 4. Gt. Brit.—For. rel.— U. S. I. Title.

43–2323

Library of Congress HC101.N352 no. 6

₁8₁ (330.973) 940.53144

NN 0059912 DLC PPCuP PSt MiU TxU WaTC ViU OU OCU

National planning association.
Urban redevelopment and housing
see under ₁Greer, Guy₁

National planning association.
...The V-day problem of military aircraft procurement; a joint resolution by the Agriculture, Business, and Labor committees on national policy and the Committee on international policy of the National planning association, and the Interim report of the NPA Advisory committee on the aircraft industry... Washington, 1945. 9, iv f. 28cm.

1. Aeroplanes—Trade and stat.— U. S.
N. Y. P. L. November 24, 1947

NN 0059914 NN Or

National planning association.
Veblen's prophetic vision. ₁Washington, D.C.?₁ 1940.

5 numb. l.
Manifold copy.

NN 0059915 MH

National planning association.
War and our Latin American trade policy. ₁Washington₁ National economic and social planning association ₁1939₁

cover-title, 36 p. incl. tables. 19½ᶜᵐ. (Planning pamphlets, no. 2)

1. U. S.—Comm.—Spanish America. 2. Spanish America—Comm.— U. S. 3. U. S.—Commercial policy. 4. Germany—Commercial policy. I. Title.

A 43—2355

Illinois. Univ. Library for Library of Congress HC101.N352 no. 2
————— Copy 2. HE3090.N47
₁a47e1₁† 382

NN 0059916 IU DLC ViU–L MB OU

National planning association.
When demobilization day comes ... ₁Washington₁ National planning association ₁1942₁

cover-title, 35, ₁1₁ p. 19½ᶜᵐ. (Planning pamphlets, no. 14)

1. World war, 1939– —Economic aspects—U. S. 2. Reconstruction (1939–)—U. S. I. Title.

42–22946

Library of Congress HC101.N352 no. 14
₁3₁ (330.973) 940.5314473

NN 0059917 DAU MiU MB Or WaS OrCS DLC FTaSU LU ViU–L OU OCU OClFRB ViU

National planning association.
Why I am in the labor movement
see under title

National Planning Association
see also
Canadian-American Committee.

National Planning Association. Agriculture Committee on National Policy.
The agricultural research and marketing act of 1946 ...
see under National Planning Association.

VOLUME 407

National Planning Association. *Agriculture Committee on National Policy.*
Dare farmers risk abundance? What do you think? [An Agriculture Committee report. Washington, National Planning Association, 1947]

v, 53 p. 20 cm. (Planning pamphlets, no. 56)

1. Agriculture—Economic aspects—U. S.   ɪ. Title.   (Series)
HC101.N352 no. 56   338.1   48–1405 rev*
——— Copy 2.   HD1765 1947.N3

ViU FTaSU MiEM MtU OrCS
NN   0059921   DLC WU MH–L MiU OYesA TxU LU MB MH–BA

National Planning Association. Agriculture Committee on National Policy.
Federal-state-local relations in agriculture
see under   Black, John Donald, 1883–

National planning association. Agriculture committee on National policy.
A framework for long-range agricultural policy
see under   Heline, Oscar.

HC101 .N352 no. 79
National Planning Association. Agriculture Committee on National Policy.
Soth, Lauren K
How farm people learn new methods. Prepared for the NPA Agriculture Committee on National Policy. [Washington, National Planning Association] 1952.

HC101 .N352 no. 66
National Planning Association. Agriculture Committee on National Policy.
Must we have food surpluses? As food surpluses come back should we: 1. Eat them up at home? 2. Send them overseas? 3. Refuse to produce them? Washington, National Planning Association, Agriculture Committee on National Policy, 1949.

National Planning Association. *Agriculture Committee on National Policy.*
Old-age security for farm people; a statement by the NPA Agriculture Committee. Washington, National Planning Association [1949]

18 p. 23 x 10 cm. ([National Planning Association] Special report no. 22)

1. Old age pensions—U. S. 2. Farmers—Pensions—U. S.   ɪ. Title. (Series)
HC101.N3522 no. 22   331.25443   50–806 rev

NN   0059926   DLC ViU MH–BA MB Or DNAL

National Planning Association. Agriculture Committee on National Policy.
Underemployment in American agriculture
see under
Moore, Arthur L

National Planning Association. *Agriculture Committee on National Policy.*
Using American agricultural surpluses abroad; a statement by the NPA Agriculture Committee on National Policy, and a report by Howard R. Tolley. [Washington, National Planning Association] 1955.

30 p. 20 cm. (Planning pamphlets, no. 91)

1. Produce trade—U. S. 2. Surplus agricultural commodities—U. S.   ɪ. Tolley, Howard Ross, 1889–1958.   ɪɪ. Title.
HC101.N352 no. 91   338.14   55–3010 rev ‡
——— Copy 2.   HD9006.N33

OCU NN FTaSU LU PPD MiU PSt DS WU MtU
NN   0059928   DLC TxU LU PSC NcD OO PHC OOxM MiU ViU

National Planning Association. *Business Committee on National Policy.*
Corporate income taxes during the transition from war to peace, a report of the Business Committee on National Policy. Washington [1944]

4 p. 28 cm.
Caption title.

1. Corporations—U. S.—Taxation. 2. Income tax—U. S.   ɪ. Title.
HD2753.U6N37   336.243   45–6487 rev*

NN   0059929   DLC NN DPU MB

HC101 .N352 no. 75
National Planning Association. Business Committee on National Policy.
Chase, Stuart, 1888–
"Operation Bootstrap" in Puerto Rico. Report on progress, 1951; prepared for the NPA Business Committee on National Policy. [Washington, National Planning Association] 1951.

Pam. Coll. S130 no. 44
National Planning Association. *Business Committee on National Policy.*
Private pension plans; a statement by the NPA Business Committee on National Policy ... [Washington] 1946.
29 p. 19½ cm. (National Planning Association. Special report, no. 44)

Caption title.
"Report ... prepared by Theodore Geiger and Rosanne McLaughlin of the NPA staff."
Bibliographical references included in footnotes.
1. Pensions.   U. S. ɪ. Geiger, Theodore   ɪɪ. Title

NN   0059931   NcD

National Planning Association. *Business Committee on National Policy.*
Renegotiation of defense contracts; a statement of the Business Committee on National Policy of the National Planning Association. [Washington] 1950.
19 p. 20 cm. (National Planning Association. Special report no. 28)
Caption title.

1. Renegotiation of government contracts—U. S.   ɪ. Title. (Series)
HC101.N3522 no. 28   A 51–6120 rev 2
Indiana. Univ. Libr.
for Library of Congress   [r65d½]†

NN   0059932   InU MH–BA ViU MB Or DLC

284.3 N216
National Planning Association. Business Committee on National Policy.
The role of business in orderly price adjustments. [Washington, D.C.] 1947.
4 p.

NN   0059933   DNAL OrU NN

National planning association. Canadian-American committee
See
Canadian-American committee.

National Planning Association. *Committee of New England.*
The economic state of New England; report. Directors of research and editors: Arthur A. Bright, Jr. [and] George H. Ellis. Staff economists: William H. Miernyk, Ray S. Kelley, Jr. [and] Edward K. Smith. Contributing economists: John H. Bragg [and] Robert A. Nelson. New Haven, Yale University Press, 1954.
xii, 738 p. maps, diagrs., tables. 25 cm.
Includes bibliographies.

1. New England—Econ. condit.   ɪ. Title.
HC107.A11N25   330.974   53—7768

KEmT DAU MH–BA DI PPT NNC NBuU OrU OrPS WaS WaTC DNAL MB TU NN MiU NcD TxU OOxM NcRS OU OrP KEmT DAU
NN   0059935   DLC PSt PU PSC OCl PPD PBL MShM NBuG

National Planning Association. Committee of New England.
The economic state of New England; report
I–II.   Boston, New England Council, 1954.
2 v.   charts.   24 cm.
No. I entitled: Transition in the New England economy, serves as an introduction to the series of reports (S330.974)
No. II entitled: Goals for New England is concluding report in series. Published also in one vol. S330.974 N58*

NN   0059936   N MB MH–BA DI PPT NNC

330.974 N21f
National Planning Association. Committee of New England.
...The financial resources of New England and their use... Boston, The New England Council, 1953.
49 p. 23 cm.   (National Planning Association. Committee of New England. Report, no. 11)

At head of title: The economic state of New England.

NN   0059937   LU DNAL

99.13 N21
National Planning Association. Committee of New England.
The forests of New England. Report. Boston, New England Council, 1953.
34 p.   (Its The economic state of New England. no. 1)

1. New England. Forestry. I. Kelley, Ray S   ɪɪ. National Planning Association. Committee of New England. The economic state of New England. no. 1.

NN   0059938   DNAL

HC107 A11N3 no. 4
National Planning Association. Committee of New England.
Minerals and New England. Boston, New England Council, 1954.
viii [1, 137]–169 p. diagrs., tables. 23 cm. (Its The economic state of New England. Report no. 4)
Bibliography, p. 169.

1. Mines and mineral resources - New England. I. Title.   (Series)

NN   0059939   DI

HC107 A11N3 no. 15
National Planning Association. Committee of New England.
Technical research in New England. Boston, New England Council, 1954.
viii [1, 557]–592 p. diagr., tables. 23 cm. (Its The economic state of New England. Report no. 15)
Bibliography, p. 592.

1. Research. I. Title. (Series)

NN   0059940   DI

HC107 A11N3 no. 6
National Planning Association. Committee of New England.
The vacation business of New England. Boston, New England Council, 1954.
viii [1, 225]–251 p. diagrs., tables. 23 cm. (Its The economic state of New England. Report no. 6)
Bibliography p. 251.

1. Tourist trade - New England. I. Title. (Series)

NN   0059941   DI

VOLUME 407

HC107
A11N3 National Planning Association.   Committee of
no.5   New England.
        Water, fuel and energy in New England.
    Boston, New England Council, 1954.
        viii [1, 171]-224 p. diagrs., tables.
    23 cm. (Its The economic state of New
    England. Report no. 5)
        Bibliography, p. 224.

            1. Water-supply - New England. 2. Fuel -
        New England. 3. Power resources - New
        England. I.   Title. (Series)

    NN 0059942   DI

331.11   National Planning Association.. Committee of
qN277B   the South.
            Bi-racial employment practices in three
        plants of the International Harvester Company,
        by John Hope, II. [Washington] 1952.
            iii, 224 ℓ. illus. 28 cm.

            "Preliminary draft - not for publication
        nor for circulation outside of the Committee
        of the South."
            Bibliographical footnotes.
            1. Negroes.   Employment. 2. Inter-
        national Harvest-   er Co. I. Hope, John, 1909-
        II. Title.

    NN 0059943   NcD

HC107   National Planning Association. Committee of the
.A13H65   South.
        Hoover, Calvin Bryce, 1897-
            Economy of the South; report of the Joint Committee on
        the Economic Report on the impact of Federal policies on
        the economy of the South [prepared on behalf of the Na-
        tional Planning Association's Committee of the South by
        Calvin B. Hoover and B. U. Ratchford] Washington, U. S.
        Govt. Print. Off., 1949.

331.11   National Planning Association. Committee of
qN277EM   the South.
            The employment of Negroes: a case study
        of the Birmingham metropolitan area, by Langston
        T. Hawley. [Washington] 1952.
            168 ℓ. 27 cm.

            "Preliminary draft - not for publication
        nor for circulation outside of the Committee
        of the South."
            Includes bib-   liographical references.

            1. Negroes. Employment. 2. Negroes.
        Birmingham, Ala. I. Hawley, Langston Thacker.
        II. Title.

    NN 0059945   NcD

Pam.   National Planning Association. Committee
Coll.   of the South.
            Initial meeting, Birmingham, November
15908   21, 1946. [Washington, D.C.] 1946.
            7 p. illus. 27½cm.

            1. Southern States. Economic conditions. 2.
        Regional planning. Southern States.

    NN 0059946   NcD Or NcU

National planning association.   Committee of the *South*.
    Meeting. [no. 1

Washington, D. C. [1946   no. illus.   28cm.
    [No. 1   consists of comments, press reports, list of members, etc.

    1. Economic planning—U. S.—   Southern states. 2. Regional planning
    —U. S.—Southern states.
    N. Y. P. L.   March 17, 1950

    NN 0059947   NN

National Planning Association. *Committee of the South.*
    New industry comes to the South; a summary of the report
    on location of industry. Washington, National **Planning**
    Association, 1949.
        xv, 32 p. 23 cm. (*Its* Reports, no. 1)

            1. Southern States—Indus. 2. Industries, Location of.   I. Title.
            (Series)
            HN79.A2N35 no. 1   338   49-4207*
            ——— Copy 2.   HC107.A13N29

        NcD PU-W PPF CaBVaU OrPR OrU
    NN 0059948   DLC N OOxM OC1W OU PU-PSW TxU NIC

National Planning Association. *Committee of the South.*
    Reports. no. 1-   May 1949-
    [Washington]
        nos. 23 cm.

        1. Southern States—Soc. condit.

        HN79.A2N35   338.975   49-4208*

        NcU CtNIC
    TxbT OrPR NcGU NcRS KMK NN OrCS DAU GEU Or CaBVaU
    NN 0059949   DLC PPT PSt NcD Vi TU TxU ICU InU MsU

National Planning Association. *Committee of the South.*
    Selected studies of Negro employment in the South, pre-
    pared for the NPA Committee of the South. Washington,
    National Planning Association [1953-54]
        5 v. (x, 483, a-l p.) Illus. 23 cm. (*Its* Reports, no. 6)
        Bibliographical footnotes.
        CONTENTS.—1. Negro employment in 3 southern plants of Interna-
    tional Harvester Company, by J. Hope, II.—2. 4 studies of Negro em-
    ployment in the Upper South, by D. Dewey.—3. Negro employment
    in the Birmingham metropolitan area, by L. T. Hawley.—4. 2 plants:
    Little Rock, by E. W. Eckard and B. U. Ratchford. 3 companies:
    New Orleans area, by H. W. Wissner.—5. Negro employment prac-
    tices in the Chattanooga area, by W. H. Wesson, jr.
        ——— Copy 2.   E185.8.N29

        ——— Another issue. [1955]
        x, 483, a-l p. Illus. 24 cm. (*Its* Report no. 6)
                                    HN79.A2N35 no. 6 1955

        1. Negroes—Employment. 2. Negroes—Southern States.   I. Title.
        II. Title: Negro employment in the South.   (Series)
        HN79.A2N35 no. 6 1953   53-12662 rev
                                    *331.63 331.98

        PSC OU ViHaI NcU Vi NN NcD MiU PSt CU MB N WaU WHi
    NN 0059951   DLC MU GAT OOxM MsSM NcRR TxU PBL PP

338.975
N277s   National planning association. Committee of
            the South.
            A sharp look ahead. [Atlanta, Ga., 1953]
            8p. 23cm.

    NN 0059952   TxDaM

E183.7
.N3   National planning association. Committee
            on international policy.
            American policy in the new phase of the
        cold war; a statement ... Washington, 1954.
            17 p.

            1. World politics. 2. U.S. - Foreign policy.
        3. Foreign policy - U.S. I. Title.

    NN 0059953   DS

National Planning Association. Committee on
    International Policy.
        American policy in the new phase of the
        cold war

        see also under

        National Planning Association.

National planning association. Committee on
    international policy.
        America's new opportunities in world trade
        see under   National planning association.

National planning association. Committee on
    international policy.
        America's vital interest in European recovery.
    Washington, D. C., 1947.
        8 p.

        I. Title: European recovery.

    NN 0059956   NNC NN Or

National Planning Association. Committee on
    International Policy.
        The current crisis ...
        see under   National planning association.

National planning association. Committee on
    international policy.
        International economic collaboration ...
        see under   National planning association.

National Planning Association. Committee on
    International Policy.
        The stakes of Bretton Woods ...
        see under   National planning association.

National planning association. Committee on
    post-war employment problems
        Report on Huntsville, Alabama. Washington,
    D. C., 1943.
        19 l.

        At head of title: Confidential.

        1. Huntsville, Ala. - Economic conditions.

    NN 0059960   NNC

National Planning Association. Committee on the
    Causes of Industrial Peace under Collective
    Bargaining.
        American velvet company
        see under   Paul, George S

National Planning Association. Committee on the
    Causes of Industrial Peace under Collective
    Bargaining.
        Case studies
        see   Causes of industrial peace under
    collective bargaining; case studies.

National planning association. Committee on the
    causes of industrial peace under collective
    bargaining.
        The Dewey and Almy chemical company ...'
        see under   MacGregor, Douglas Murray,
    1906-

HD8072
.C314   National Planning Association. Committee
no.14   on the Causes of Industrial Peace under
1953   Collective Bargaining.

            Fundamentals of labor peace, a final
        report. Washington, National Planning
        Association [1953]
            119 p. 23cm. (Causes of industrial peace
        under collective bargaining. Case study no.14)

            1. Collective bargaining—U. S. 2. Collective
        labor agreements—   U. S. I. Title.
        II. Ser.

    NN 0059964   ViU CaBViP NNC MH-BA InU MiU

VOLUME 407

National planning association. Committee on the causes of industrial peace under collective bargaining.
Lockheed aircraft corporation and International association of machinists; a case study
see under   Kerr, Clark, 1911-

National planning association. Committee on the causes of industrial peace under collective bargaining.
Minnequa plant of Colorado Fuel and Iron Corporation ...
see under   Zinke, George W.

National planning association. Committee on the causes of industrial peace under collective bargaining.
Nashua gummed and coated paper company and seven A F L unions
see under   Myers, Charles Andrew, 1913-

National Planning Association. Project on the Economic Aspects of the Productive Uses of Nuclear Energy.
Energy requirements and economic growth

see under

Mason, Edward Sagendorph, 1899-

National Planning Association. Special Committee on Manpower Policy
see
National Planning Association.

National Planning Association. Special Committee on Nonmilitary Defense Planning
see
National Planning Association.

National Planning Association. Special Committee on Technical Cooperation
see
National Planning Association.

National Planning Committee (*India*)
Animal husbandry and dairying. Chairman, Sir Chunilal V. Mehta; secretary, M. R. Ramaswamy Sivan. Fisheries. Chairman, B. Sundara Raj; secretary, S. B. Setna. Horticulture. Chairman, G. S. Cheema; secretary, Jabir Ali. Reports of sub-committees, ed. by K.T. Shaw. ₁1st ed.₎ Bombay, Vora ₁1948₎
227 p. 22 cm. (National Planning Committee series)

1. Animal industry—India. 2. Dairying—India. 3. Horticulture—India. I. Shah, Khushal Talaksi, ed. II. Title. (Series)
SF55.I 4N3   338.1   49-27364*

NN   0060001   DLC WaU CU-A MiU TxU WU

National Planning Committee (*India*)
Chemical industries, report of the sub-committee. Chairman, J. C. Ghosh; secretary, R. C. Shah; ed. by K. T. Shah. ₁1st ed.₎ Bombay, Vora ₁1947₎
148 p. 22 cm. (National Planning Committee series ₍2₎)

1. Chemical industries—India. I. Shah, Khushal Talaksi, ed. II. Title. (Series)
HD9657.I 42N3   338.4766   49-17206*

NN   0060002   DLC MiU MoU

National Planning Committee (*India*)
Chemical industries, report of the sub-committee. Chairman, J. C. Ghosh; secretary, R. C. Shah; ed. by K. T. Shah. Bombay, Vora ₁1948₎
150 p. 23 cm. (National Planning Committee series)

1. Chemical industries—India. I. Shah, Khushal Talaksi, ed. (Series)
HD9657.I 42N3   1948   338.4766   49-27320*

NN   0060003   DLC PU DNAL MoU CaBVaU CU NcD CtY

National Planning Committee (*India*)
Communications, report of sub-committee. Chairman, Sir Rahimtulla Chinoy; secretary, S. K. Mitra; ed. by K. T. Shah. Bombay, Vora ₁1948₎
140 p. maps. 22 cm. (National Planning Committee series)

1. Postal service—India. 2. Telecommunication—India. 3. Tourist trade—India. I. Shah, Khushal Talaksi, ed. II. Title. (Series)
HE7215.N3   383   49-27315*

NN   0060004   DLC PU MiU MoU NcD CU CtY

National Planning Committee (*India*)
Crops—planning and production, report of the sub-committee. Chairman, Sir T. Vijayaraghavacharya; secretary, Bholanath Singh; ed. by K. T. Shah. ₁1st ed.₎ Bombay, Vora ₁1948₎
204 p. tables. 23 cm. (National Planning Committee series)

1. Field crops—India. I. Shah, Khushal Talaksi, ed. II. Title. (Series)
SB187.I 6N35   633   49-27367*

NN   0060005   DLC DNAL CU-A PU WU O NcD CtY

National Planning Committee (*India*)
Currency and banking, report of the sub-committee. Chairman, Manu Subedar; secretary, C. N. Vakil; edited by K. T. Shah. ₁1st ed.₎ Bombay, Vora ₁1948₎
181 p. 23 cm. (National Planning Committee series)

1. Banks and banking—India. 2. Currency question—India. I. Shah, Khushal Talaksi, ed. II. Title. (Series)
HG3284.N3   332.1   50-27851

NN   0060006   DLC NN FU CU CtY MoU

National Planning Committee (*India*)
Engineering industries and scientific instruments industries. Reports of the sub-committee₍s₎: Engineering industries; chairman, P. N. Mathur; secretary, M. N. Dalal. Industries connected with scientific instruments; chairman, P. N. Ghosh; secretary, G. P. Paranjpe. Ed. by K. T. Shah. Bombay, Vora ₁1948₎
249 p. fold. maps, fold. diagr. 22 cm. (National Planning Committee series)

1. Machinery—Trade and manufacture—India. 2. India—Indus. 3. Scientific apparatus and instruments. I. Shah, Khushal Talaksi, ed. II. Title. (Series)
HD9705.I 42N3   338.4   49-27321*

NN   0060007   DLC PU CU WU NcD MoU

LA
1151
.N29   National Planning Committee (India)
General education and technical education & developmental research. General education chairman, Sir Radhakrishnan; secretary E.V. Aryanayakam. Technical education chairman, M.N.Saha; secretary,H.L.Roy. Edited by K.T. Shah. ₁1st ed.₎ Bombay, Vora ₁1948₎
209 p. illus. (National Planning Committee series)

1.Education--India. I.Shah, Khushal Talaksi,ed. II.Title. 2.Technical education--India.

NN   0060008   MiU MoU CU CtY

National planning committee (*India*)
Handbook of National planning committee, compiled by K. T. Shah. Bombay, Vora & co., ltd. ₁1946₎
3 p. l., ₍5₎-166 p. 25ᶜᵐ.

"The following pages contain the substance of the material published in Handbooks, nos. I, II, III, IV, published by the National planning committee in 1939-40."--Pref.
"First edition, January, 1946."

1. India—Economic policy. I. Shah, Khushal Talaksi, comp.
HC435.N36   338.954   47-21329

NN   0060009   DLC WaU

HC435
.S477   **Shah, Khushal Talaksi.**
India's national plan, its nature, scope, and administration. ₁1st ed.₎ Bombay, Vora ₁1947₎

National Planning Committee (*India*)
Industrial finance, report of the sub-committee. Chairman, A. D. Shroff; secretary, J. K. Mehta; ed. by K. T. Shah. ₁1st ed.₎ Bombay, Vora ₁1948₎
206 p. 22 cm. (National Planning Committee series)

1. Credit—India. 2. Capital—India. I. Shah, Khushal Talaksi, ed. II. Title. (Series)
HG3729.I 4N3   332.742   49-27317*

NN   0060011   DLC MoU NN PU CtY

National Planning Committee (*India*)
Insurance, report of the sub-committee. Chairman, Sir Chunilal V. Mehta; secretary, K. S. Ramachandra Iyer; ed. by K. T. Shah. ₁1st ed.₎ Bombay, Vora ₁1948₎
160 p. 22 cm. (National Planning Committee series)

1. Insurance—India. I. Shah, Khushal Talaksi, ed. II. Title. (Series)
HG8703.N3   368.954   49-27318*

NN   0060012   DLC PU CtY NcD

National Planning Committee (India)
Labour; report of sub-committee. Chairman: N. M. Joshi. Secretary: V. R. Kalappa. Edited by K. T. Shah. ₁1st ed.₎ Bombay, Vora ₁1947₎
195 p. 21 cm. (National Planning Committee series)
Includes bibliographical references.

1. Labor policy—India. I. Joshi, Narayan Malhar, 1879-1955. II. Shah, Khushal Talaksi, ed. III. Title. IV. Series.
HD8686.5.N3   78-288510
                                       MARC
NN   0060013   DLC NcD WaU MoU DLC-P4 ICU

National Planning Committee (*India*)
Land policy, agricultural labour & insurance, report of the sub-committee. Chairman, K. T. Shah; secretary, Radha Kamal Mukerjee; ed. by K. T. Shah. ₁1st ed.₎ Bombay, Vora ₁1948₎
176 p. 23 cm. (National Planning Committee series)

1. Land tenure—India. 2. Agricultural laborers—India. 3. Agriculture—Economic aspects—India. I. Shah, Khushal Talaksi, ed. II. Title. (Series)
HD875.N3   333   49-27253*

NN   0060014   DLC PU CLU CtY NcD CU MoU

282.182
In25   National Planning Committee. (*India*)
Land policy, agricultural labour & insurance (report of the sub-committee)
Bombay, Vora [1949]
176 p. (National Planning Committee series)

NN   0060015   DNAL

National Planning Committee (*India*)
Manufacturing industries, report of the sub-committee. Chairman, Ambalal Sarabhai; secretary, Nazir Ahmed; ed. by K. T. Shah. ₁1st ed.₎ Bombay, Vora ₁1947₎
185 p. 23 cm. (National Planning Committee series ₍1₎)

1. India—Manuf. I. Shah, Khushal Talaksi, ed. II. Title. (Series)
HD9736.I 5N3   .338.4   49-17208*

NN   0060016   DLC ICU ViU CU PU MiU WU MH MoU NcD

VOLUME 407

National Planning Committee (*India*)
Mining and metallurgy, report of the sub-committee.
Chairman, D. N. Wadia; secretary, V. S. Dubey; **ed. by K.
T. Shah.** ₁1st ed.₎ Bombay, Vora ₁1948₎
130 p. 22 cm. (National Planning Committee series)

1. Mineral industries—India.   ɪ. Shah, Khushal Talaksi, ed.
ɪɪ. Title.   (Series)

HD9506.I 42N3   338.2   49–27313*

NN 0060017   DLC PU MoU CtY

National Planning Committee (*India*)
National health. Chairman, S. S. Sokhey; secretary, J. S.
Nerurkar; edited by K. T. Shah. ₁1st ed.₎ Bombay, Vora
₁1948₎
256 p. 22 cm. (National Planning Committee series)

1. India—Sanit. affairs.   ɪ. Shah, Khushal Talaksi, ed. ɪɪ. Title.
(Series)

RA529.N3   614.0954   50–20404

NN 0060018   DLC NcD DNLM CtY IU NN FU MoU CaBVaU

National Planning Committee (*India*)
National housing, report of sub-committee. Chairman,
S. D. Prabhavalkar; secretary, V. G. Shete; ed. by K. T.
Shah. ₁1st ed.₎ Bombay, Vora ₁1948₎
141 p. 22 cm. (National Planning Committee series)

1. Housing—India. 2. Cities and towns—Planning—India.
ɪ. Shah, Khushal Talaksi, ed. ɪɪ. Title.   (Series)

HD7361.A3N3   331.833   49–27314*

NN 0060019   DLC CtY PU NcD WaU

National planning committee (*India*)
National planning committee. no. ₁1₎–
Being an abstract of the proceedings and other particulars
relating to the National planning committee. Bombay, K. T.
Shah, honorary secretary, National planning committee
₁1939?–
no. 25*.

This publication is called "Handbook" in notes on verso of t.-p. of
no. 2 and of no. 3.

1. India—Economic policy.   2. National planning committee (India)

Library of Congress   HC431.N32   42–7998
                             ₁2₎   330.954

NN 0060020   DLC

HC435   NATIONAL PLANNING COMMITTEE (India)
.N27   National Planning Committee series. Bombay,
         Vora ₁1949₎
         v.

1. India—Economic policy.

NN 0060021   ICU

            National Planning Committee (India)
HC435
.S478
        Shah, Khushal Talaksi.
            National planning, principles & administration. ₁1st ed.₎
        Bombay, Vora ₁1948₎

National Planning Committee (*India*)
Population, report of the sub-committee. Chairman,
Radhakamal Mukherjee; secretary, B. C. Guha; **ed. by K. T.
Shah.** ₁1st ed.₎ Bombay, Vora ₁1947₎
xv, 145 p. 22 cm. (National Planning Committee series ₁6₎)

1. India—Population.   ɪ. Shah, Khushal Talaksi, ed. ɪɪ. Title.
(Series)

HB3639.N33   312   49–17207*

NN 0060023   DLC MiU MoU MtU

312.54 National Planning Committee (India)
N21p   Population. Chairman, Radhakamal Mukherjee;
1949   secretary, B. C. Guha; ed. by K. T. Shah. ₁2d
        ed.₎   Bombay, Vora ₁1949₎
          174p. 22cm. (National Planning Committee se-
        ries)

1. India--Population. I. Shah, Khushal Talaksi,
ed. II. Title. (Series)

NN 0060024   IU CU MH NN NIC

HD   National Planning Committee (India)
9556   Power and fuel. Chairman, Megh Nad Saha;
.I42   secretary, A. K. Shaha; edited by K. T. Shah.
N32   ₁1st ed.₎ Bombay, Vora ₁1947₎
          157p. 22cm. (National Planning Committee
        series)

1. Power resources--India. 2. Fuel.
I. Shah, Khushal Talaksi, ed. II. Title.
(Series)

NN 0060025   IU MiU MoU

National Planning Committee (*India*)
Power and fuel, report of the sub-committee. Chairman,
K. T. Shah; secretary, Gyan Chand; edited by K. T. Shah.
Bombay, Vora ₁1949₎
152 p. 22 cm. (National Planning Committee series)

1. Electric utilities—India.   ɪ. Shah, Khushal Talaksi, ed.
ɪɪ. Title.   (Series)

HD9685.I 42N3   621.3   52–21993

NN 0060026   DLC IEN MH ICU CtY NN NIC CSt

National planning committee (*India*)
... Priorities in planning (food, education, housing) ₁by₎
K. T. Shah. Bombay, Vora & co., ltd. ₁1946₎
1 p. l., ii, 43, ₁1₎ p. 24½*.
At head of title: National planning committee.
"First edition, October, 1946."

1. Food supply—India.   2. Education—India.   3. Housing—India.
ɪ. Shah, Khushal Talaksi.   ɪɪ. Title.

HD9016.I 42N3   338.954   47–19047

NN 0060027   DLC DNAL NcD CtY

National Planning Committee (*India*)
Public finance, report of the sub-committee. Chairman,
K. T. Shah; secretary, Gyan Chand; edited by K. T. Shah.
₁1st ed.₎ Bombay, Vora ₁1949₎
130 p. 23 cm. (National Planning Committee series)

1. Finance, Public—India.   ɪ. Shah, Khushal Talaksi, ed.
ɪɪ. Title.   (Series)

HJ1312.N3   336.54   50–28517

NN 0060028   DLC CU IU FU NN CtY MoU TNJ IU

National Planning Committee (*India*)
Report, edited by K. T. Shah. ₁1st ed.₎ Bombay, Vora
₁1949₎
257 p. 23 cm.

1. India—Economic policy.   ɪ. Shah, Khushal Talaksi, ed.

HC435.N37   338.954   50–21596

CaBVaU
NN 0060029   DLC MoU KMK ICU ViU CtY TxU CU WaTC

National Planning Committee (*India*)
River training and irrigation, report of sub-committee.
Chairman, Nawab Ali Nawaz Jung Bahadur; secretary,
U. N. Mahida; ed. by K. T. Shah. ₁1st ed.₎ Bombay, Vora
₁1947₎
148 p. 22 cm. (National Planning Committee series)

1. Hydraulic engineering—India.   ɪ. Shah, Khushal Talaksi, ed.
ɪɪ. Title.   (Series)

TC103.N3   627.1   49–27359*

NN 0060030   DLC PU DNAL WaU TxU ICU

National Planning Committee (*India*)
Rural and cottage industries, report of the sub-committee.
Chairman, S. C. Das Gupta; secretary, C. A. Mehta; ed. by
K. T. Shah. ₁1st ed.₎ Bombay, Vora ₁1948₎
275 p. 23 cm. (National Planning Committee series)

1. Artisans—India. 2. India—Indus.   ɪ. Shah, Khushal Talaksi,
ed. ɪɪ. Title.   (Series)

HD2346.I 5N3   338.63   49–27252*

NN 0060031   DLC DNAL PU NN NcD CtY MoU

National Planning Committee (*India*)
Rural marketing and finance. Chairman, Ramdas Pan-
tulu; secretary, Sudhir Sen; ed. by K. T. Shah. ₁1st ed.₎
Bombay, Vora ₁1947₎
166 p. 22 cm. (National Planning Committee series)

1. Produce trade—India. 2. Farm produce—Marketing.   ɪ. Shah,
Khushal Talaksi, ed. ɪɪ. Title.   (Series)

HD9016.I 42N33   338.14   49–27251*

NN 0060032   DLC MiU CU PU MoU CtY NcD

National Planning Committee (*India*)
Soil conservation and afforestation, report of the subcommittee. Chairman, J. N. Mukherjee; secretary, S. P.
Agharkar; ed. by K. T. Shah. ₁1st ed.₎ Bombay, Vora
₁1948₎
195 p. 22 cm. (National Planning Committee series)

1. Soil conservation—India. 2. Afforestation—India.   ɪ. Shah,
Khushal Talaksi, ed. ɪɪ. Title.   (Series)

S623.N35   631.45   49–27686*

NN 0060033   DLC NcD CtY PU CU–A

National Planning Committee (*India*)
Trade, report of the sub-committee. Chairman, Kasturb-
hai Lalbhai; secretary, J. J. Anjaria; ed. by K. T. Shah.
₁1st ed.₎ Bombay, Vora ₁1947₎
282 p. tables. 22 cm. (National Planning Committee series)

1. India—Comm.   ɪ. Shah, Khushal Talaksi, ed. ɪɪ. Title.
(Series)

HF3786.N3   380.954   49–27316*

NN 0060034   DLC CU ICU MiU MoU MH OrU

National Planning Committee (*India*)
Transport services, report of the sub-committee. Chairman, D. R. Gadgil; secretary, F. P. Antia; edited by K. T.
Shah. ₁1st ed.₎ Bombay, Vora ₁1949₎
264 p. 22 cm. (National Planning Committee series)

1. Transportation—India.   ɪ. Shah, Khushal Talaksi, ed.
ɪɪ. Title.   (Series)

HE271.N3   385   50–27850

NN 0060035   DLC MiU MoU WU CtY NN

National Planning Committee (*India*)
Woman's role in planned economy, report of the sub-com-
mittee. Chairwoman, Lakshmibai Rajwade; secretaries,
Mridula Sarabhai, Mrs. Purvis N. Dubash; ed. by K. T.
Shah. ₁1st ed.₎ Bombay, Vora ₁1947₎
265 p. 22 cm. (National Planning Committee series)

1. Women in India. 2. Woman—Employment—India.   ɪ. Shah,
Khushal Talaksi, ed. ɪɪ. Title.   (Series)

HQ1381.N3   396   49–27319*

NN 0060036   DLC MiU CU MH ICU PU CaBVaU

National planning conference
see
National conference on planning.

VOLUME 407

National Planning Conference (*Ireland*)
National planning and reconstruction; the official handbook of the National Planning Conference. Dublin, Parkside Press, 1944.
xx, 183 p. illus. 25 cm.

1. Ireland—Soc. condit. 2. Regional planning—Ireland. 3. Cities and towns—Planning—Ireland. I. Title.

HN398.I 7N3   711.3   48–35093*

NN 0060038   DLC DNAL CSt-H NNC

National planning for town and country in Great Britain.
(*In* International labour review. February, 1943. v. 47, p. ₁197–206₎
"An analysis of ... the Uthwatt and the Scott reports ... followed by a brief account of government action."

1. Cities and towns—Planning—₍Gt. Brit.₎ 2. Regional planning—Gt. Brit. 3. Gt. Brit. Expert committee on compensation and betterment. Final report. 4. Gt. Brit. Committee on land utilization in rural areas. Report.   L 43–155

U. S. Dept. of labor. Libr
for Library of Congress   [HD4811.I 65 vol. 47]
₍3₎   (331.05)

NN 0060039   DL

... National planning for town and country in Great Britain ... Montreal, I₍nternational₎ l₍abour₎ o₍ffice₎ 1943.
cover-title, ₍2₎–11 p. 23½cm.
At head of title: International labour office.
"Reprinted from International labour review, vol. XLVII. no. 2, February 1943."
"An analysis of ... the Uthwatt and the Scott reports ... followed by a brief account of government action."
Bibliographical foot-notes.

1. Cities and towns—Planning. 2. Regional planning—Gt. Brit. 3. Gt. Brit. Expert committee on compensation and betterment. Final report. 4. Gt. Brit. Committee on land utilization in rural areas. Report.

NN 0060040   ViU

National Planning Institute, *Cairo*
see
Cairo. Maʻhad al-Takhṭīṭ al-Qawmī.

National plans, inc., *Detroit.*
A book of homes, especially designed to meet the demand for homes ranging in price from $2,000 to $20,000. Detroit, Mich., National plans, inc., ₍1925.
5 l. ₍1₎ p. illus. (incl. plans) 31cm.
Advertising matter: p. 46–51.

1. Architecture, Domestic—Designs and plans. I. Title.
                                                     25–17130
Library of Congress   NA7130.N4

NN 0060042   DLC

National Plans Committee on Standardization of Antigens and Procedures in Testing for Pullorum Disease, Ithaca, N. Y., 1949.
Report of meeting.   [Washington, 1949]
7 p.
1. Pullorum disease. Congresses. I. U.S. Bureau of Animal Industry. Animal Husbandry Division.

NN 0060043   DNAL

SF   National Plans Conference.
481   Regional conferences on the National
N28R   Poultry Improvement Plan. ₍Washington₎
U. S. Dept. of Agriculture, Bureau of Animal Industry, Animal Husbandry Division, 1940.
103 p. tables, diagr. 27 cm.

1. Poultry - Congresses. 2. Poultry - U. S. I. National Poultry Improvement Plan. II. U. S. Bureau of Animal Industry. Animal Husbandry Division.

NN 0060044   NIC

Z6455   National plant board.
.A45D7
Drake, Carl John, 1885–
Bibliography of the state plant pest laws, quarantines, regulations and administrative rulings of the United States of America, by Carl J. Drake ... ₍Ames, Ia., 1942₎

National plant board.
Minutes of the ... annual meeting.
₍n. p., 19
v. maps. 28cm.
No meeting held in 1943.
Reproduced from type-written copy.

1. Plant quarantine — U. S. 2. Botany — Pathology. 3. Agricultural pests.
                                                     46–35411
Library of Congress   SB987.N3

NN 0060046   DLC OU DNAL

SB   National Plant Board. National Weed
612   Committee.
N26Ou   Outline of a proposed national program of weed research and control. Ames, Iowa State College of Agriculture and Mechanic Arts, Extension Service, 1937.
16 p. 28 cm.

1. Weeds - U. S. 2. Weed control. I. Title.

NN 0060047   NIC

SB   National Plant Board. National Weed
612   Committee.
N26   Report of results of national noxious weed questionnaire. ₍Powell, Wyoming, National Weed Committee, 1937₎
5 l. 28 cm.

Caption title.

1. Weeds - U. S. 2. Weed control. I. Title.

NN 0060048   NIC

National Plant, Flower and Fruit Guild.
The Altruist. A quarterly magazine
see under *title*

National plant, flower and fruit guild.
Annual report.
₍Bristol, Conn.,
v. 22½cm.
Report year ends in April.

                                CA 10–638 Unrev'd
Library of Congress   HV696.F4N32

NN 0060050   DLC

National plant, flower and fruit guild. *New York city branch.*
... Annual report.
₍New York?₎
v. 21½cm.
Title of 12th report: National plant, flower and fruit guild ... New York city branch ... Annual report.

                                CA 9–4208 Unrev'd
Library of Congress   HV696.F4N34

NN 0060051   DLC

National plant, flower and fruit guild. *Washington, D. C. branch.*
Annual report.
Washington, D. C.,
v. 20½cm.
Report year ends December 31.

                                                5–31598†

NN 0060052   DLC

---

57   National Plant Food Institute.
Am30   Our land and its care. [Washington, D.C., 1947]
64 p.
1. Fertilizers. 2. Plant nutrition. 3. Soil conservation. U.S. I. U.S. Office of education. Agricultural education service. II. Title.

NN 0060053   DNAL

---

57   National Plant Food Institute.
Am30   Our land and its care. [2d ed. Washington,
Ed. 2   1948]
64 p.

NN 0060054   DNAL

---

57   National Plant Food Institute.
Am30   Our land and its care. [2d ed.
Ed.2   Washington, 1949]
1949   64 p.

1. Fertilizers. 2. Plant nutrition. 3. Soil conservation. U.S. I. U.S. Office of Education. Agricultural Education Service. II. Title.

NN 0060055   DNAL

---

57   National Plant Food Institute.
Am30   Our land and its care. ₍3d ed. Washington,
Ed.3   1955₎
72 p.

Previous ed. by American Plant Food Council, inc.

1. Fertilizers. 2. Plant nutrition. 3. Soil conservation. U.S. I. U.S. Office of Education. Agricultural Education Service. II. American Plant Food Council. III. Title.

NN 0060056   DNAL NIC NN CU

National Plant Food Institute
see also
American Plant Food Council.
National Fertilizer Association (*1925–1955*)

A56.9   National Plant Materials Workshop.
N212   ₍Report₎
₍Washington₎

1. Soil-binding plants. 2. Soil conservation. Congresses. 3. Water. Conservation. Congresses. I. U.S. Soil Conservation Service. Plant Technology Division.

NN 0060058   DNAL

National Plant Nematode Conference. 3d, Birmingham, Ala., 1940.
Proceedings. [Washington, Bureau of Plant Industry, U.S. Dept. of Agriculture, 1940]
[135]-150 p. 27 cm. (Plant disease reporter. Supplement 124)
1. Nematode diseases of plants. Congresses. 2. Nematoda. Congresses. I. Title: Proceedings of the third National Plant Nematode Conference.

NN 0060059   NNBG

VOLUME 407

National Plastering Industry Joint Apprenticeship Committtee
see
National Plastering Industry's Joint Apprenticeship and Training Committee.

National Plastering Industry's Joint Apprenticeship and Training Committee.
National standards of apprenticeship for the crafts of the plastering industry. 1945–
[Washington, U. S. Dept. of Labor, Manpower Administration, Bureau of Apprenticeship and Training.
v. illus. 21–27 cm.
Vols. for 1945– issued by the committee under a variant name: National Plastering Industry Joint Apprenticeship Committee.
Vols. for 1945– published by Bureau of Apprenticeship and Training (called 1945– Apprentice Training Service)
1. Apprentices—U. S. [1960–] 2. Plasterers—U. S. r. U. S. Bureau of Apprenticeship and Training. II. Title.

HD4885.U5N35 L 65–39 rev
U. S. Dept. of Labor. Library
for Library of Congress [2]†

NN 0060061 DL DLC

National plastic relief company, *Cincinnati.*
Architectural & decorative ornaments. [Catalogue] Cincinnati, O.
1 v. illus. 30½ᶜᵐ.
Only latest issue in Library is kept on shelf.

1. Decoration and ornament, Architectural.

Library of Congress NA3686.N3 CA 17–2065 Unrev'd

NN 0060062 DLC

Avery
AA
3680
N21
National Plastic Relief Company, Cincinnati.
Architectural & decorative ornaments.
2d ed. Cincinnati, O., 1921.
78 p. (chiefly illus.) 28cm. (Its Catalogue. 2)

1. Decoration and ornament, Architectural.

NN 0060063 NNC

The national platforms of the republican and democratic parties from 1856 to 1880 inclusive. Washington, 1880.
JK2357 31 p.
[Union republican congressional committee, presidential campaign. 1880. Document no. 27]

NN 0060064 DLC OO Nh IHi IaU ICN OClWHi ViU NIC

National platforms of the Republican, Democratic, Fusion populist or Peoples ...
see under Union Pacific railway company.

National platforms of the republican, democratic, prohibition, national peoples ...
see under Union Pacific railway company.

National platforms of the three big political parties... Brooklyn–New York, 1912. (In Eagle library, no. 166, 1912, p. 104–115)

NN 0060067 DL

National play bureau
Jewish non-royalty plays and pageants, holiday, historical, general.
New York, National play bureau, 1937.
[6], 34 numb. l. (It's Publication no. 8)

NN 0060068 OC1

National play bureau.
Patriotic holiday plays, non-royalty, part 2; Memorial Day, Flag Day, Fourth of July.
New York, National play bureau, Amateur play dep't., 1937.

Play bureau publication no.18.

NN 0060069 IaDuC

822.95
N28 National play bureau, New York.
Play bureau publication ... no.1–
1936–

NN 0060070 MiU

NATIONAL PLAYING FIELDS ASSOCIATION, London.
Journal. v. 1–23; July, 1930–1963. London.
23 v. illus. 22–25cm.

Quarterly.
Publication suspended Aug. 1939–Sept. 1945.
Title varies: 1934–Sept. 1946, 1949–63, Playing fields; 1947–48, Recreation review.
Absorbed: Central council of physical recreation. Bulletin, Jan. 1947 (not in the library).

No more published?

1. Athletics--Per. and soc. publ. I. Title: Playing fields. II. Title: Recreation review. III. Central council of physical recreation. Bulletin.

NN 0060072 NN

National Playing Fields Association, *London.*
Memorandum on the selection of land for the purpose of a playing field, by P. Maud. London [1946]
12 p. 22 cm.

1. Playgrounds. I. Maud, Philip, 1870–1947. II. Title: Selection of land for the purpose of a playing field.

A 49–5137*
Harvard Univ. Library
for Library of Congress [1]

NN 0060073 MH

309.136 National Playing Fields Association, London.
N216p Playgrounds for blocks of flats. A report
1954 prepared for the Ministry of Housing and Local Government. London, 1954.
31p. illus. 22cm.

1. Playgrounds. I. Title.

NN 0060074 IU NcRS

NATIONAL PLAYING FIELDS ASSOCIATION, London.
Report...and accounts...
19
London[, 19 22cm.
no.
19 cover-title reads: Annual report.

1. Playgrounds—Gt. Br.

NN 0060075 NN

National Playing Fields Association, *London.*
Spotlight on British sport. Louis Palgrave, editor. Croydon, Home Pub. Co. [1953?]
216 p. illus. 22 cm.

1. Sports—Gt. Brit. I. Palgrave, Louis, ed. II. Title.

GV605.N3 55–22184 ‡

NN 0060076 DLC

National plumbago company.
Prospectus of the National plumbago company organizing at Jersey City, New Jersey. Capital stock — $100,000 divided into 1000 shares of $100 each... Jersey City, Davison & co. [1878]
12 p. illus. 21cm.

NN 0060077 NN

National plumbeotype gallery
see under Plumbe, John.

M
National plumbing and heating contractor.
Toronto, National Association of Master Plumbers and Heating Contractors of Canada, 1955–
illus. monthly.

1. Plumbing—Period. 2. Heating—Period. 3. Periodicals—Canada. I. National Association of Master Plumbers and Heating Contractors of Canada.

NN 0060079 CaOTP

The National plumbing and heating news. v. 1–
Mar. 15, 1924–
[New York, The National plumbing and heating news publishing co., 1924–
v. illus., diagrs. 30½ᶜᵐ. semimonthly.

1. Plumbing—Period. 2. Heating—Period.
37–34137
Library of Congress TH6101.N33
[3] 696.05

NN 0060080 DLC NN

National Plumbing Code Coordinating Committee
see Coordinating Committee for a National Plumbing Code.

National plumbing code illustrated. 1952–
Washington, Manas Publications.
v. illus., diagrs. 22 cm.
Vols. for 1952– by V. T. Manas.
"Illustrating: American Standards Association A. S. A. A 40.8—1955 National plumbing code and Report of the Coordinating Committee." (varies)

1. Plumbing—Laws and regulations—U. S. I. Manas, Vincent Thomas, 1895– II. American Standards Association. American standard national plumbing code. III. Coordinating Committee for a National Plumbing Code. Report.

TH6164.N3 696.973 58–20251 rev

WaT OrU IdU LN MiU WaSp
NN 0060082 DLC NbU MB TxU NN NcRS OrCS OrP WaS

National Pneumatic Company.
Door and step control. New York [1920]
186 p. illus.

NN 0060083 ICJ •

National poetry (a collection of poems)
From- Supplement to Niles (Weekly) Register v. 9. 1816. 25 cm. p. 83–96.

NN 0060084 RPB

VOLUME 407

National poetry anthology. 1949–
　　Los Angeles, National Poetry Association.
　　　　v.　24 cm.
　　"Written by teachers in schools and colleges."

　　1. College verse.　I. National Poetry Association.

　　PN6110.C7N333　　　811.5082　　　　50–12

　　MtBuM NNC
NN　0060085　　DLC OC1JC TU PPT PP IaAS NcU OC1 OrU

National poetry association.
　　America sings; annual anthology of college poetry.　[1st–
　　Los Angeles, Calif. [1944–
　　　　v.　24ᶜᵐ.

　　1. College verse.　I. Title.

　　Library of Congress　　　PN6110.C7N333　　　46–19722
　　　　　　　　　　　　　　　[3]　　　　　　811.5082

　　KyLoU OC1W IdPI CoAIC PJB PPULC NRU IdU–SB
　　TNJ OOxM PU OCU WaE1C PSt NBuU NcGU OC1ND MoU WaS
NN　0060086　　DLC TxU OO MdBJ NBuT CtN1C LU TxLT

National poetry Association.
PN6110
.C7N333
National poetry anthology. 1949–
　　Los Angeles, National Poetry Association.

National Poetry Association.
　　The new alphabetical thesaurus and wordfinder
　　　　see under　Hartman, Dennis, 1894–

PN6110
.H4H26
National Poetry Association.

Hartman, Dennis, 1894–　　ed.
　　Poetry for holidays. Los Angeles, National Poetry As-
　　sociation [1953]

National Poetry Association.
　　Poetry reader for all grades, based on information sup-
　　plied by more than 2,000 high school teachers.　Los Angeles
　　[1954]
　　　　276 p.　23 cm.

　　1. English poetry (Collections)　2. American poetry (Collections)
　　I. Title.

　　[PR1175]　　　820.82　　　A 63–5206 ‡
　　　　　　　　　　　　　　　　　　　　Cancel
　　Printed for Card Div.
　　Library of Congress　　　[1]

NN　0060090　　MiDW WaSp

National Poetry Association.
　　Rhyming dictionary, a dictionary of rhymes
　　　　see under　National High School Poetry
　　Association.

PN
6110
.C7N37
National Poetry Association.
　　Voice of young America. 1937–1951. [Dennis
　　Hartman, ed.]　Los Angeles, Calif. [1951]
　　　　272 p.　23cm.

　　Poems.
　　A collection of works of contributors to the
　　annual anthologies of the National High School
　　Poetry Association and the National Poetry
　　Association.

　　1. College verse.　2. School verse.　3. American
　　poetry (Collections)　I. National High School
　　Poetry Association.　II. Hartman, Dennis, 1894–
　　ed.　　　　III. Title.

NN　0060093　　KyLoU

PS3503
.U64B8
no.24
National Poetry Clubs, Santa Barbara, Calif.
　　Vincent G. Burns, noted poet and author.
　　[Santa Barbara, Calif., 1946?]
　　　　Broadside.　([2] p.)　port.　38 cm.
　　[Burns pamphlets, no. 24]

　　1. Burns, Vincent Godfrey, 1893–
　　I. Title.

NN　0060094　　ViU

National poetry council.
　　[Invitation to attend the Congress of American poets to be held
　　in New York City, June 14–Oct. 12, 1936.　New York? 1936?]
　　2 l.　28cm.

　　Signed: Edwin Markham, Chairman [of the National poetry council]
　　Includes "Agenda of the Congress of American poets" for June 14–Sept. 25, 1936,
　　and "Program for…July 24–25–26, 1936."
　　Accompanied by an undated press release, 1 leaf.

　　1. Poets, American—Assoc. and org.　I. Markham, Edwin, 1852–1940.
　　II. Congress of American poets.

NN　0060095　　NN

National Poetry Exhibition, 1st, New York, 1928.
　　[Souvenirs, advertisements and other printed matter in con-
　　nection with the National Poetry Exhibition.　New York, 1927–
　　1928.]　7 pieces in 1 v.　4°.

　　1. Poetry, American.
　　N. Y. P. L.　　　　　　　　October 27, 1928

NN　0060096　　NN

National Poetry Exhibition. 1st, New York, 1928.
　　Whispering walls
　　　　see under title

PS301
.S63
National Poetry Society of America.

Stanza.　v. 1–2, no. 7; spring 1947–summer/fall 1949.　Wash-
　　ington, National Poetry Society of America.

National poets memorial of the United States of America.
　　The National poets memorial of the United States of America
　　(a non-profit society of the citizenry)…　Providence: National
　　poets memorial of the United States of America [1941]　14 p.
　　27½cm.

　　1. Poets, American.
　　N. Y. P. L.　　　　　　　　March 29, 1943

NN　0060099　　NN

National Poland-China journal
　　see　The Hog breeder.

National Poland-China record association.
　　The National Poland-China record …　v. 28–
　　1906–　　　　　Dayton, O., United brethren publishing
　　house; [etc., etc.] 1906–
　　　　v.　23½ᶜᵐ.
　　Vol. 43–　　have imprint Winchester, Ind., The Winchester pub-
　　lishing company, 1921–
　　Name of association varies: 1906–16, National Poland-China record
　　company.—1917–　　, National Poland-China record association.
　　Preceded by the Ohio Poland-China record (v. 1–　　published by the
　　Ohio Poland-China record association; v. 7–27, by the Ohio Poland-
　　China record company) and the Central Poland-China record (v. 1–26)

　　first published by the Central swine record association, of Indiana, later
　　by the Central Poland-China record association. In January, 1906, the
　　Ohio Poland-China record company and the Central Poland-China rec-
　　ord association united to form the National Poland-China record com-
　　pany, and the "National Poland-China record" superseded the publica-
　　tions of the earlier associations, its first issue being numbered "v. 28",
　　in continuation of the numbering of the earlier series.

　　1. Swine—Herd-books.　2. Poland-China swine.

　　Library of Congress　　　SF393.P7O　　　7–6649 Revised

NN　0060102　　DLC InLP NcRS GU ICJ OU

National Poland-China record company
　　see
National Poland-China record association.

National police agency.
　　History…of the passage of Lincoln from
　　Harrisburgh to Washington.　Chicago, 1868.

NN　0060104　　NjP

National police agency.
　　Tests on passenger conductors, made by the National police
　　agency.　Allan Pinkerton, principal …　January 1st, 1867.
　　Chicago, G. H. Fergus, printer [1867]
　　32, [3] p. incl. tables.　22½ᶜᵐ.

　　1. Railroad conductors.　I. Pinkerton, Allan, 1819–1884.

　　New York.　State library　　　　　　　A 21—699
　　for Library of Congress　　　[a41b1]

NN　0060105　　N MH–BA

National police automobile directory and yearbook. 1st–
　　1949–
　　Costa Mesa, Calif., W. O'Brien.
　　　　v.　illus.　28 cm.

　　1. Automobiles—Yearbooks.

　　TL5.N3　　　629.2058　　　49–23720*‡

NN　0060106　　DLC MsU OrP NN MB OC1 MiD

National police convention. *St. Louis*, 1871.
　　Official proceedings of the National police convention, held
　　at the city of Saint Louis, Missouri, on the 20th, 21st and
　　23d days of October, 1871.　With an appendix.　Printed by
　　resolution of the convention. St. Louis, R. & T. A. Ennis,
　　printers [1871]
　　　　104, xxxv p.　23½ᶜᵐ.

　　In original (cloth) binding, lettered: National police convention, St.
　　Louis, Mo., 1871.

　　1. Police—Congresses.　2. Police—U. S.
　　Library of Congress　　　HV8132 1871　　　10–22237
　　————　Copy 2.　　In paper cover lettered like the cloth
　　binding.　　　　　　[a35b1]

NN　0060107　　DLC

NATIONAL POLICE CONVENTION, Saint Louis, 1871.
　　Official proceedings, 1871.　St. Louis [1871]
8°.

Microfilm (master negative)

NN　0060108　　NN

The National police gazette … v. 1–
　　Oct. 16, 1845–
　　New York [Camp & Wilkes, etc.] 1845–19
　　　　v.　illus., plates, ports.　39–41½ᶜᵐ.　weekly.

　　Editors: Oct. 1845–　　　　　　E. E. Camp, George Wilkes,
　　　　　　　　　R. K. Fox.

　　1. Crime and criminals—Period.　2. Sports—Period.　I. Camp,
　　Enoch E., ed.　II. Wilkes, George, ed.　III. Fox, Richard Kyle, 1846, ed.

　　　　　　　　　　　　　　　　　　ca 8—2606 Unrev'd
　　Library of Congress　　　HV6201.N2

NN　0060109　　DLC NN MdBE CoD OU

VOLUME 407

Micro
Film
D108   National police gazette. v.1-
reels   Sept. 1845-
3318   reels. 35mm. (American periodical
etc.   series: 1800-1850. APS A1038)

For history of periodical, see the reel
guide. American Periodicals, 7.6951 .A44 36th.
Microfilm (positive). Ann Arbor, University
Microfilms, 1793.

NN 0060110   PSt

National police gazette.
    The Forrest divorce case. Catharine N. Forrest
against Edwin Forrest
    see under   Forrest, Mrs. Catharine
Norton (Sinclair) 1818-1891, plaintiff.

National Police Gazette.
    FULL account of the burning of the Brooklyn
theatre, Dec.5,1876. New York published at the
office of the "National police gazette",[1876]

    1.8°. pp.16. Ports.and other illustr.
    Cover-title.

NN 0060112   MH NBHi

National Police Gazette.
    ...Hanging of Guiteau! Pictorial history of his crime and
execution... [New York, 1882.] 4 l. illus. (incl. ports.)
f°.

    Caption-title.
    At head of title: Police gazette extra.

1. Garfield, James Abram, 20th pres.   U. S.—Assassination. 2. Guiteau,
Charles Julius, 1841-1882. 3. Murder   —Trials—U. S.—D. C.—
Washington.
N. Y. P. L.   May 27, 1932

NN 0060113   NN

Case
Broadside
21   [NATIONAL POLICE GAZETTE]
        [Illustration, with caption:] Buried in
        a barrel. How millionaire Newberry of Chi-
        cago, who died at sea, was interred in Grace-
        land cemetery.
            23 x 9cm.
        From the issue of December 26, 1868 (?)
        For identification of journal, see verso,
        top of 3rd column.
            In frame,   27 x 21cm.

NN 0060114   ICN

The national police gazette.
    The life and adventures of John A. Murrell, the great
western land pirate, with twenty-one spirited illustrative engravings. Philadelphia, T. B. Peterson and
brothers [184-?]

The National police gazette.

    The lives of the felons, or American criminal calendar.
Compiled in part from the New-York "National police gazette", and corrected, enlarged and revised on careful comparison with the criminal records of the various states ... New-
York, G. F. Nesbitt, printer, 1846.

                        FOR OTHER EDITIONS
    National police gazette.   SEE MAIN ENTRY
Lohman, *Mrs.* Anna (Trow) 1812-1878, *defendant.*
    ... Wonderful trial of Caroline Lohman, alias Restell, with
speeches of counsel, charge of court and verdict of jury. ⟨Re-
ported in full for the National police gazette.⟩ ... [3d ed.]
New York city, Burgess, Stringer, & co.; Boston, Redding &
co.; [etc., etc., °1847]

The National Police Journal. (New York, 1917-   )
    see The Police Journal.

HV7551
.N3   National police magazine.
            [Chicago, 1913]
              v.   25 1/2 cm.

NN 0060119   DLC

A national policy; an account of the emergency programme
    advanced by Sir Oswald Mosley, M. P. London, Macmillan
    and co., limited, 1931.

    iv, 62, [1] p. 20cm.

    "This exposition of the emergency policy put forward by Sir Oswald
Mosley and sixteen other labour members of Parliament was drafted by
Allan Young, John Strachey, M. P., W. J. Brown, M. P., Aneurin Bevan,
M. P."

    1. Gt. Brit.—Economic conditions—1918–   2. Gt. Brit.—Economic
policy. I. *Mosley, Sir Oswald, bart., 1896–   II. Title.
                                                 A 36–119
    Title from Univ. of Cin-   cinnati HC256.3.O8 Printed by L. C.

NN 0060120   OCU MH NN

The national policy as set forth by Mr. Asquith, Sir Edward Grey,
Mr. Churchill, Mr. Lloyd George, Mr. Austen Chamberlain, Mr.
Balfour, Mr. Bonar Law, Mr. Arthur Henderson, and others...
London: Union of Democratic Control [1915]. 13(1) p., 1 l. 8°.
(Union of Democratic Control. Pamphlets. no. 6.)

    Cover-title.

1. European war, 1914– .—Peace   terms. 2. Series.
N. Y. P. L.   April 13, 1916.

NN 0060121   NN DCU-IA

[National policy committee]
    Economic prospects in Arkansas. Report of a session in
Little Rock, May 11, 1946 ... [Washington, 1946]

    1 p. l., 28 p., 1 l. 21½ x 11½cm. (National policy report. No. 40)

    1. Arkansas—Econ. condit.   I. Title.

    HC107.A8N3   330.9767   47–208

NN 0060122   DLC ViU

National policy committee.
    Financial policy: the British loan, the public debt. Report
of sessions in Philadelphia and Cleveland, February 20 and
January 26, 1946 ... [Washington, 1946]

    1 p. l., 41 p. 21½ x 11½cm. (National policy report. No. 37)
    Reproduced from type-written copy.

    1. Debts, Public—Gt. Brit. 2. Finance—U. S.   I. Title.

    Library of Congress   HJ8027.N25   46–4970

                                                [3]   336.343

NN 0060123   DLC ViU

National policy committee
    ... Hemispheric policy ...
        see under title

[National policy committee]
    Is housing on the way? Report of a session in Portland,
May 2, 1946 ... [Washington, 1946]

    1 p. l., 15, [2] p. diagrs. 21½ x 11½cm. (National policy report. No.
41]

    1. Housing—U. S.   I. Title.

    HD7293.N38   331.833   47–242

NN 0060125   DLC ViU

[National policy committee]
    Long term farm policy. Soil management. World com-
modity agreements. Report of sessions in Minneapolis, Des
Moines, Cleveland, February 14, 15 and March 23, 1946 ...
[Washington, 1946]

    1 p. l., 33 p. 21½ x 11½cm. (National policy report. No. 39)

    1. Agriculture and state—U. S. 2. Soil conservation—U. S. 3. Farm
produce. I. Title. II. Title: Soil management. III. Title: World commodity agreements.
    HD1765 1946.N3   338.1   46–8153

NN 0060126   DLC ViU

370.973   National policy committee
N2772m   ...Memorandum of the special com-
              mittee on education as a means of
              transmitting the democratic heritage.
              Washington, D.C., The Committee, 1941.
Educ.   cover-title, 23p. O. (Its Special
              committee memoranda, no.13)

NN 0060127   IaU MoU

National policy committee.
    ... Memorandum of the special committee on
implications to the United States of a German
victory. Washington, D.C., The National policy
committee, 1940.
    cover-title, 45 p. 21½ x 11½cm. (Its Special
committee memoranda no.11)

    1. World war, 1939–   —Influence and results. 2.
World war, 1939–   —U.S. 3. World war, 1939–   —
Germany. I. Title: Implications to the United States
of a German victory. II. Ser.

NN 0060128   ViU OO MH

NATIONAL POLICY COMMITTEE.
    Memorandum of the Special Committee on the
Dynamics of Civil Mobilization. Washington, D.C.
1941.

    22 x 11 cm. pp.26.
    Paper cover serves as title-page.
    "Special Committee memoranda,12."

NN 0060129   MH

NATIONAL POLICY COMMITTEE.
    Memorandum of the Special Committee on the
Purpose of the Armed Forces. Washington, D.C.,
1939.

    22 x 11 cm. pp.22.
    Paper cover serves as title-page.
    "Special Committee memoranda,7."

NN 0060130   MH DNAL

National policy committee.
    Memorandum of the Washington dinner on
labor's part in the administration of the war.
Washington, D.C., 1943.

    28 p. 21.5 x 11.5 cm.
    "National policy memoranda, 19."

NN 0060131   MH

NATIONAL POLICY COMMITTEE.
    Memorandum on housing. Washington, D.C.,1939.

    22 x 11 cm. pp.20.
    Paper cover serves as title-page.
    "Special memoranda,5."

NN 0060132   MH-SD

VOLUME 407

National policy committee.
... Mid-westerners look at South America, by Howard Hill, Harlow L. Walster, S. D. Myres ₍and others₎ ... Washington D. C., The National policy committee, 1942.

cover-title, 64 p. 21½ᵐ. (National policy papers. No. 4)

CONTENTS.—Excerpts from a South American diary, 1941, by Howard Hill.—Agricultural trends in Argentina and Brazil, by H. L. Walster.—A Texian views South America, by S. D. Myres, Jr.—Impressions below the equator, by H. E. Terrell.—Is South America hedging on the war? By William Hessler.—What are the Nazis up to in South America? By Earl Hall.—Findings in South America, by J. G. Patton.

1. South America—Descr. & trav. 2. South America—Econ. condit.—1918–   3. Agriculture—South America.   I. Title.

42–15165

Library of Congress   E740.N35 no. 4
                           ₍2₎   (973.91) 918

NN   0060133   DLC TxU

HC106.4   **National policy committee.**
N279   Mobilization in the middle country; regional conference of the National policy committee, Des Moines, Iowa, March 28–29, 1941. ₍Washington, D.C., National policy committee, 1941₎

1 p.l., 28 p. 21½x11½ᶜᵐ.

1. European war, 1939– - Econ. aspects - U.S. 2. U. S. -   Defenses. I. Regional conference of the   National policy committee. II.   Title.

NN   0060134   CSt

National Policy Committee.
The National Policy Committee, its story, its technique, cross country comment on labor-management relations. Washington, 1947.

152 p. 21 cm.

1. Industrial relations—U. S.

HD8055.I 5N3   331   48–12951*

NNC IdU MtU CaBViP
NN   0060135   DLC PU-L WaS OO CU NN TU ICU MiU ViU

National policy committee.
National policy memoranda. no. 1–
Washington, D. C., 1937–

nos. 21½ x 11½ᵐ.

Title varies: no. 1–17, Special committee memoranda (no. 5–6, Special memoranda)
no. 18–   National policy memoranda.

1. U. S.—Economic policy. 2. U. S.—Pol. & govt.

41–7338 Revised

Library of Congress   HC101.N45
                           ₍r44g3₎   330.973

N
NN   0060136   DLC TxU MH-BA CSt OCl OCU ViU MNS OrU

National policy committee.
National policy papers. no. 1–
Washington, D. C., 1940–

nos. 21½ᵐ.

Reproduced from type-written copy.

I. Title.

43–18329

Library of Congress   E740.N35
                           ₍2₎   973.91

NN   0060137   DLC DNAL GEU IU CSt NN OCl OO

National Policy Committee.
National policy reports. no. 1–
Washington, 19–

NN   0060138   GEU NN CtY IaAS OU ICU NcD CU NhD

₍**National policy committee**₎
New alignments in political parties. Report of a session in Philadelphia, May 27, 1946 ... ₍Washington, 1946₎

1 p. l., 15, ₍2₎ p. illus. (maps) 21½ x 11½ᵐ. (National policy report. No. 42)

1. Political parties—U. S.   I. Title.

JK2263 1946.N3   329   47–275

NN   0060139   DLC ViU

National policy committee.
Occasional news letter. no.

Washington, D. C., 1941–   nos. 28cm.
Ceased publication, 194

1. United States—Politics—Per.   and soc. publ.
N. Y. P. L.   August 8, 1945

NN   0060140   NN OrU

National policy committee.
Price control wage policy inflation. Report of sessions in Seattle, Portland, Philadelphia, February 19, 20 and March 18, 1946 ... ₍Washington, 1946₎

1 p. l., 47 p. 21½ x 11½ᵐ. (National policy report. No. 38)
Reproduced from type-written copy.

1. Price regulation—U. S. 2. Wages—U. S.   I. Title.

46–4851

Library of Congress   HB236.U5N3
                           ₍3₎   338.526

NN   0060141   DLC ViU

National Policy Committee.
Report of a session in Billings, Montana: Upper Missouri River development. Billings, Mont., Dec. 1 & 2, 1944. ₍Washington, 1945₎

21 p. 22 cm. (*Its* National policy reports, no. 28)

1. Regional planning—Missouri Valley.   (Series: National Policy Committee. National policy report no. 28)

HN79.A172N3   55–57193

NN   0060142   DLC ViU

₍**National policy committee**₎
... Report of a session in Chicago: International civil aviation. Chicago, Illinois, March 15, 1945. ₍Washington, 1945₎

1 p. l., 29 p. 21½ x 11½ᵐ. (National policy reports. No. 29)
"Meeting ... jointly sponsored by the Chicago council on foreign relations and the National policy committee."—p. 1.
Bibliography: p. 29.

1. International civil aviation conference, Chicago, 1944.   I. Title.
II. Title: International civil aviation.

JX5771.I 47 1944j   387.70631   47–18962

NN   0060143   DLC ViU

National policy committee.
... Report of a session in Des Moines, Iowa: Food problems in war and peace. Des Moines, Iowa, July 18, 1944. ₍Washington, 1944₎

1 p. l., 20, ₍2₎ p. 21½ x 11½ᵐ. (National policy reports. No. 25)
Reproduced from type-written copy.

1. Food supply. 2. World war, 1939–   —Food question.   I. Title: Food problems in war and peace.

45–21

Library of Congress °   HD9000.6.N3
                           ₍4₎   338.1063777

NN   0060144   DLC ViU

National policy committee.
... Report of a session in Philadelphia: The formulation of a bipartisan foreign policy. Philadelphia, Pennsylvania, May 26, 1943. ₍Washington, 1943₎

1 p. l., 24 p. 21½ x 11½ᵐ. (National policy reports. No. 15)
Reproduced from type-written copy.
Bibliography: p. 21–22.

1. U. S.—For. rel.—1933– 2. Political parties—U. S.   I. Title: The formulation of a bipartisan foreign policy.

44–484

Library of Congress   E744.N27
                           ₍3₎   327.73

NN   0060145   DLC ViU

National policy committee.
... Report of a session of the Philadelphia group: American economic interests in the Far East. Philadelphia, Pennsylvania, May 23, 1944. ₍Washington, 1944₎

1 p. l., 20, ₍2₎ p. 21½ x 11½ᵐ. (National policy reports. No. 24)
Reproduced from type-written copy.
Bibliography: p. 19–20.

1. U. S.—Comm.—East (Far East) 2. East (Far East)—Comm.—U. S.   I. Title: American economic interests in the Far East.

44–13308

Library of Congress   HF3119.N3
                           ₍3₎   382

NN   0060146   DLC ViU

National policy committee.
... Report of a session of the Philadelphia group: Legislation for fair employment practice. Philadelphia, Pennsylvania, April 18, 1945. ₍Washington, 1945₎

1 p. l., 20, 1 l. 21½ x 11½ᵐ. (National policy reports. No. 32)
Reproduced from type-written copy.

1. Discrimination in employment—U. S.   I. Title: Legislation for fair employment practice.

45–8010

Library of Congress °   HD4903.N3
                           ₍3₎   331.11

NN   0060147   DLC ViU

National policy committee.
... Report of a session of the Philadelphia group: What effect will the end of the war with Germany have on Philadelphia. Philadelphia, Pennsylvania, January 5, 1944. ₍Washington, 1944₎

1 p. l., 20, ₍2₎ p. diagrs. 21½ x 11½ᵐ. (National policy reports. No. 21)
Reproduced from type-written copy.
Bibliography: p. 19–20.

1. Labor supply—Philadelphia. 2. Philadelphia—Econ. condit.

44–3835

Library of Congress   HD5726.P5N27

NN   0060148   DLC PPCPC ViU

National policy committee.
Report of the Mid-South citizenship conference ..
see under   National policy committee.
Mid-South citizenship conference.

National policy committee.
... Report of the New England meeting, Andover, Massachusetts, June 13–14, 1942: How can the 1942 elections help win the war? Washington, D. C., The National policy committee, 1942.

1 p. l., 24 p. 21½ x 11½ᵐ. (National policy reports. No. 8)
Reproduced from type-written copy.

1. World war, 1939–   —U. S. 2. U. S.—Pol. & govt.—1933–
I. Title: How can the 1942 elections help win the war?

43–3293

Library of Congress   D769.1.N3

NN   0060150   DLC

National policy committee.
... Report of two sessions in Philadelphia: Manpower in the Philadelphia area. The Beveridge report and postwar social security. Philadelphia, Pennsylvania, March 3 and April 21, 1943. ₍Washington, 1943₎

1 p. l., 24 p. 21½ x 11½ᵐ. (National policy reports. No. 12)
Reproduced from type-written copy.

1. Labor supply—Philadelphia. 2. Gt. Brit. Inter-departmental committee on social insurance and allied services. Social insurance.

43–18410

Library of Congress   HD5726.P5N28
                           ₍2₎   331.2544

NN   0060151   DLC ViU

VOLUME 407

National policy committee.
... Report of two sessions of the Philadelphia group: Postwar problems in education. Philadelphia, Pennsylvania, February 14, and March 13, 1944. ₍Washington, 1944₎

1 p. l., 26, ₍2₎ p. 21½ x 11½ᶜᵐ. (National policy reports. No. 22)
Reproduced from type-written copy.

1. Education—U. S. I. Title: Postwar problems in education.

44-6483

Library of Congress LA210.N37
₍3₎ 370.973

NN 0060152 DLC ViU

National policy committee.
... Report of two sessions of the Philadelphia group: Resolution of industrial conflict. Philadelphia, Pennsylvania, October 10, 1945 and November 28, 1945. ₍Washington, 1945₎

1 p. l., 19 p. 21½ x 11½ᶜᵐ. (National policy reports. No. 33)
Reproduced from type-written copy.

1. Industrial relations—U. S. I. Title: Resolution of industrial conflict.

46-3088

Library of Congress HD8072.N2837
₍3₎ 331

NN 0060153 DLC ViU

National policy committee.
... Reports of sessions in Cleveland and Chicago: U. S. policy for world trade. Cleveland, Ohio, October 20, 1945, Chicago, Illinois, January 8, 1946. ₍Washington, 1946₎

1 p. l., 40 p. diagrs. 21½ x 11½ᶜᵐ. (National policy reports. No. 35)
Reproduced from type-written copy.

1. U. S.—Commercial policy.

46-3090

Library of Congress HF1456 1945.N35
₍3₎ 382

NN 0060154 DLC ViU

National policy committee.
... Reports of sessions in Cleveland, Philadelphia, and Arkansas. World organization as proposed at Dumbarton Oaks. Cleveland, Ohio, Oct. 14, 1944, Philadelphia, Penna., Nov. 10, 1944, Little Rock, Ark., Dec. 2, 1944. ₍Washington, 1945₎

1 p. l., 49, ₍1₎ p. 21½ x 11½ᶜᵐ. (National policy reports. No. 26)
Reproduced from type-written copy.

1. Washington, D. C. Conversations on international organization, 1944. 2. International organization.

45-5631

Library of Congress JX1976.3.N3
₍4₎ 341.1

NN 0060155 DLC ViU

National Policy Committee.
Reports of sessions in Philadelphia and Cleveland: The citizen and city hall; Strengthening the Congress. Philadelphia, Penna., Mar. 13, 1945; Cleveland, Ohio, Feb. 17, 1945. ₍Washington, 1945₎

33 p. 22 cm. (*Its* National policy reports, no. 30)

1. Philadelphia—Pol. & govt. 2. U. S. Congress. (Series: National Policy Committee. National policy report no. 30)

JS1270 1945.N3 56-237

NN 0060156 DLC ViU

National policy committee.
... Reports of sessions in Philadelphia and Cleveland: What war-time patterns of government should continue into the peace? Unions, management and government after the war. Philadelphia, Penna, April 13, 1944. Cleveland, Ohio, May 20, 1944. ₍Washington, 1944₎

1 p. l., 26 p., 2 l. 21½ x 11½ᶜᵐ. (National policy reports. No. 23)
Reproduced from type-written copy.

1. U. S.—Economic policy. 2. Industrial relations—U. S. 3. Reconstruction (1939—   )—U. S. I. Title: What war-time patterns of government should continue into the peace? II. Title: Unions, management and government after the war.

44-7202

Library of Congress HC106.4.N43
₍5₎ 330.973

NN 0060157 DLC ViU

National policy committee.
Special committee memoranda
see its
National policy memoranda.

National policy committee.
Special memoranda
see its
National policy memoranda.

NATIONAL POLICY COMMITTEE.
Suggestions for policy committees considering relief. Washington,[1938].

Manifold copy. ff.10.

NN 0060160 MH-PA

₍National policy committee₎
U. S. relations with Russia; bibliography and report of a session in Cleveland, October 8, 1946 ... ₍Washington, 1946₎

1 p. l., 20 p. 21½ x 11½ᶜᵐ. (National policy report, no. 43)

1. U. S.—For. rel.—Russia. 2. Russia—For. rel.—U. S. I. Title.

E183.8.R9N33 327.730947 47-3811

NN 0060161 DLC Mi

National Policy Committee.
Universal military training; report of a session in Minneapolis, December 2, 1946. ₍Washington, 1946₎

21 p. 22 cm. (*Its* National policy report no. 44)

1. Military service, Compulsory—U. S. 2. Military education—U. S. I. Title. II. Series.

UB353.N34 355.22 47-7224*

NN 0060162 DLC ViU

National Policy Committee.
Working principles for labor-management relations. Washington, 1947—

pts. 28 cm.

At head of title: Preliminary draft. Not for publication ...

1. Industrial relations—U. S. I. Title: Labor-management relations.

HD6971.N27 331 47-5304*

NN 0060163 DLC NcU MH-IR

National policy committee
see also
Arkansas policy committee.

National policy committee
see also
Minnesota policy committee.

National policy committee. *Cleveland policy committee*
see
Cleveland policy committee.

National policy committee. Mid-South citizenship conference, *Memphis, 1940.*
Report of the Mid-South citizenship conference of the National policy committee, Memphis, Tennessee, September 13-14, 1940. [Washington D.C., National policy committee, 1940]

1 p. l., 31 p. 21.5 x 11.5 cm.
1. U. S. Econ. policy. 2. Southern states. Econ. condit. 1918–   I. Mid-South citizenship conference.

NN 0060167 CSt

National policy committee. *Mid-South citizenship conference.* 2d, Vicksburg, Miss., 1942.
... Report of the second Mid South citizenship conference. War and postwar changes in mid South industry and agriculture. Washington, D. C., The National policy committee, 1942.

1 p. l., 19 p. 21½ x 11½ᶜᵐ. (National policy reports. No. 6)
Reproduced from type-written copy.

1. Southern states—Indus. 2. Agriculture—Southern states. 3. Agriculture—Economic aspects. I. Title: War and postwar changes in mid South industry and agriculture.

42-18055

Library of Congress HC107.A13N3 1942

NN 0060168 DLC ViU OO

National policy committee. *Mid-South citizenship conference.* 3d, Memphis, 1943.
... Report of the third Mid South citizenship conference: Our foreign affairs. Memphis, Tennessee, June 7, 1943. ₍Washington, 1943₎

1 p. l., 21 p. 21½ x 11½ᶜᵐ. (National policy reports. No. 14)
Reproduced from type-written copy.

1. U. S.—For. rel.—1933–   I. Title: Our foreign affairs.

43-22894

Library of Congress E744.N3 1943
₍3₎ 327.73

NN 0060169 DLC ViU

National policy committee. Special committee on implications to the United States of a German victory.
... Memorandum of the Special committee on implications to the United States of a German victory.
see under National policy committee,

National policy committee. Special committee on investment.
...Memorandum of the Special committee on investment, public and private. Washington,D.C., The National policy committee, 1940.

332.6
N277

cover-title, 22 p. 21½ᶜᵐx11ᶜᵐ. (Special committee memoranda, no.8)

1.Investments.

NN 0060171 CSt

HC
101
N45
no.16

National Policy Committee. Special Committee on the Domestic Requirements for Victory. Memorandum. Washington,National Policy Committee,1942.
27p. 22cm. (National Policy Committee. Special Committee memoranda, no. 16)

1. World War, 1939-1945 - Economic aspects - U. S. (Series: National Policy Committee. National policy memoranda, no. 16)

NN 0060172 MU

National Policy Conference of State Extension Economists. 2d, Monticello, Ill., 1951.
Increasing understanding of public problems and policies
see under Conference on increasing understanding of public problems and policies.

VOLUME 407

National policy for aviation ...
    see under   National planning association.

A national policy for historic sites and monuments
    see under   [Chatelain, Verne Elmo] 1895–

A national policy for industry
    see under   McLintock (Thomson) and company, London.

... A national policy in development of water resources ...
    see under   [Hoover, Herbert Clark, Pres. U.S.] 1874–1964.

National policy memoranda
    see under   National policy committee.

National policy players' guide and dream book. Containing all the Lucky number for policy playing ... Chicago, F. J. Drake & Co. [cop. 1902]
  209 p.   16°.

NN   0060179   NN

National policy reports
    see under   National policy committee.

HF1755
.N27
1865
Toner
Coll.
    The national policy. Tracts for the times. Number one. Conducted by John Williams, editor of "The Iron age." Subject—Who needs protection? By a western farmer. New York, The office of "The Iron age"; Chicago, J.A. Norton, 1865.
  [14] p.   24cm.

    1. Free trade and protection—Protection. I. Williams, John, editor of the Iron age.

NN   0060181   DLC

E
464
C585
v.44
no.3
    The National policy. Who needs protection? By a Western farmer. New York, Office of "The Iron Age", 1865.
  [6] p. 25cm. (Tracts for the times. No. 1)

    Running title: Who needs protection?

    1. Free trade and protection—Protection. I. A Western farmer. II. Title: Who needs protection?

NN   0060182   NIC

    The national policy. Tracts for the times. Number one. Conducted by John Williams, editor of "The Iron age." Subject—Who needs protection? By a western farmer. New York, Office of "The Iron age"; Chicago, J. A. Norton, 1866.
  cover-title, [12] p. 22ᶜᵐ.

    I. Williams, John, editor of the Iron age.

    5-6608†

NN   0060183   DLC

    The National policy. Tracts for the times—Number 2. Subject: British free trade. How it affects the agriculture and the foreign commerce of the union. Conducted by John Williams, editor of "The Iron Age," 80 Beekman Street. Chicago, John A. Norton, bookseller and publisher, and agent for the writings of Henry C. Carey, 126 1/2 Dearborn Street, 1866.

NN   0060184   PHi

National Polish committee of America.

[Konopczyński, Władysław] 1880–
    ... A brief outline of Polish history. 2d ed. Genève, Imprimerie Atar, 1920.

National Polish Committee of America.
  Economic life of Poland
    see under   Comité des publications encyclopédiques sur la Pologne, Fribourg.

National Polish committee of America.
    The Jews in Poland: official reports of the American and British investigating missions ... Chicago, Ill., The National Polish committee of America [1920]
  64 p. 28ᶜᵐ.

    CONTENTS. — Preface.—Letters of transmittal, American report.—The Morgenthau report.—The Jadwin and Johnson report.—An excerpt from the Jadwin-Johnson report.—Letter of transmittal, British report (Sir H. Rumbold).—The Samuel report.—The Captain Wright report.—Typical hymns of hate.—The truth?—The situation.—The Polish treaty.

    1. Jews in Poland. I. Paris. Peace conference, 1919. U. S. II. Gt. Brit. Mission to Poland.

Library of Congress   DS135.P6N3   27–4982

    OCH MiU   MnU ICJ
NN   0060187   DLC CU OrU PU PPAmP IU MB ICU OCl OO

National Polish Committee of America.
  Polish encyclopaedia
    see under title

National Polish committee of America.
  Polish encyclopaedic publications
    see under title

NATIONAL POLISH COMMITTEE OF AMERICA.
    The pre-war economic position of Poland. Chicago, National Polish Department of America, [1918.]

    1. 8°. Pamphlet.
    Cover serves as title-page.

NN   0060190   MH PU

National Polish Committee of America.
  ... Vie économique de la Pologne
    see under   Comité des publications encyclopédiques sur la Pologne, Fribourg.

NATIONAL POLISH DEPARTMENT OF AMERICA
  See NATIONAL POLISH COMMITTEE OF AMERICA

National political campaign of 1944 ... [Washington, D. C., The United States news, 1944]
  2 v. front. (port., v. 2) 28ᶜᵐ.

    Illustration and portraits (part col.) on covers.

    CONTENTS.—pt. I. Proceedings of Republican national convention held at Chicago, June 26–28, including full texts of addresses and platform.—pt. II. Proceedings of Democratic national convention held at Chicago, July 19–21, including full texts of addresses and platform.

    1. Campaign literature, 1944. I. Republican party. National convention. 23rd, Chicago, 1944. II. Democratic party. National convention, Chicago, 1944. III. The United States news.

    A 44–4333

Illinois. Univ. Library
  for Library of Congress   [7]

NN   0060193   IU ICJ OCl OClW OO OU MB

JQ620
B45N27
    National political economy of Bharatiya Samajik Republic. [Edited by: J.K. Banerjee. Calcutta, N. Gangooli Service and Goodwill Mission c195–?]
  358 p. ports.

    1. Bharat, India (State) – Pol. & govt. 2. Bharat, India (State) – Econ. condit. 3. India – Constitutional law. I. Banerjee, J.K., ed.

NN   0060194   CU

.QS
N277p
1832
    NATIONAL Political Union
    Anatomy; proceedings respecting legislative interference in the study of anatomy, and the supply of bodies for anatomical research. Newington Causeway [Eng.] Barnes, 1832.
  24 p.

NN   0060195   DNLM MnU DNAL

National Political Union.
  British taxes dissected
    see under title

National Political Union.
    Proceedings at the second annual meeting of the National Political Union, held at the Crown and Anchor Tavern, Strand, on Monday, February 4, 1833. Joseph Hume, Esq., M. P., in the chair. London, Office of the National Political Union [etc., 1833]
  24 p. 21cm. (Pamphlet no. 19)

NN   0060197   NNC

National Political Union.
    Taxes on knowledge. Debate in the House of Commons, on the 15th June, 1832, on Mr. Edward Lytton Bulwer's motion "for a select committee to consider the propriety of establishing a cheap postage on newspapers and other publications." With a comment in the form of notes; and the article from the "Examiner" newspaper, of Sunday, 17th June, 1832. Southwark, Printed by W. Barnes, 1832.
  48 p. 21cm. (Pamphlet no. 13)

NN   0060198   NNC

National polity and finance
    see under   [Jerdan, William] 1782–1869.

National polo pony society
    The National polo pony stud book. v. 1– New York, National polo pony society, c1925–

NN   0060200   OCl

National Pony Society.
  National pony stud book
    see   The Polo and riding pony stud book.

VOLUME 407

The national pony stud book

see

The Polo and riding pony stud book

National Popular Government League.
.... Addresses delivered at the reconstruction conference of the
131056 National Popular Government League. Washington, D. C., January 9, 10 and 11, 1919. In seven sections. .... [Washington], 1919.

7 nos. in 1 vol. 23½ᶜᵐ.

Contents.— 1. Buffer employment, land, housing. 16 p.— 2. New marketing systems, the farmer and reconstruction. 16 p.— 3. The railroad question. 20 p.— 4. Labor and reconstruction. Women and reconstruction. 16 p.— 5. Education. 16 p.— 6. Popular government. 13 p.—7. International. 15, [1] p.

NN 0060203 ICJ OO OrU Or DL OU

National Popular Government League.
American principles and the Wadsworth Amendment
see under King, Judson, 1872-

280.12
N2143 National popular government league.
American utilities and American democracy.
Washington, D.C. 1934.
8 numb. l. (Its Bulletin no. 168)

1. Public utilities. U.S. 2. Industry and state. U.S. 3. Electric power-plants. U.S.
I. King, Judson. II. Title.

NN 0060205 DNAL

JK2274
.N343 National popular government league.
...Bulletin, no.
Washington, [19
v. 8°

NN 0060206 DLC MiU NN ICJ Or OrU

JV83
7N277 National Popular Government League.
B Bulletin. no. 1- 1913-
Washington.

Microfilm copy (negative) made by the State Historical Society of Wisconsin.

1. U.S. - Pol. & govt. - 20th cent.

NN 0060207 WHi

National Popular Government League.
Canada's Teapot Dome and its American parallels
see under King, Judson, 1872-

National Popular Government League.
The first year and a look ahead
see under King, Judson, 1872-

335
N2193F National popular government league.
Fundamental democracy in America. Washington, D.C., 1943.
6 p. (Its Bulletin no. 206)

NN 0060210 DNAL

National Popular Government League.
The initiative and referendum elections of 1924
see under King, Judson, 1872-
(supplement)

National Popular Government League.
The initiative and referendum elections of 1926
see under King, Judson, 1872-

National Popular Government League.
Labor and reconstruction, Women and reconstruction ... Addresses delivered ...
see under title

National popular government league, Washington, D.C.
Pamphlets.
Washington, 1910-1920.
21 v.

NN 0060214 OU

[National Popular Government League, Washington, D. C.]
[Pamphlets.] Washington, 1912-24. 17 nos. 8°.

Contents: KING, J. New dangers to majority rule. Initiative, referendum and recall. OWEN, R. L. People's rule versus boss rule. KENT, W. Democracy and efficiency. VROOMAN, C. S. Initiative and referendum in Switzerland. MONTAGUE, R. W. The Oregon system at work. KING, J. The first year and a look ahead. Circulars: Privilege vs. democracy. The confusion of property with privilege. KING, J. The state-wide initiative and referendum. HAYNES, J. R. Direct government in California. Addresses delivered at the Reconstruction Conference of the League — in 7 sections. BETTMAN, A., and H. SWINBURNE. Do we need more sedition laws? Report upon the illegal practices of the United States Department of Justice. The seizure of Haiti by the United States. NORRIS, G. W. Against the seizure of Haiti. How reclamation is being wrecked and why.

1. Legislation, Direct—U. S.
N.Y.P.L. September 26, 1927

NN 0060215 NN

National Popular Government League.
Power records of Hoover and Roosevelt
see under King, Judson, 1872-

National popular government league, Washington, D.C.
... Report ... Washington, D.C., National popular government league, 1915-
v. 23 cm.
Vol. 1 has title: The first year and a look ahead ...

NN 0060217 ICU

National popular government league.
... Report upon the illegal practices of the United States Department of justice ...
see its To the American people; report ...

E183
.8
.H2F7 National popular government league.

Foreign policy association.
The seizure of Haiti by the United States; a report on the military occupation of the Republic of Haiti and the history of the treaty forced upon her, by Frederick Bausman ... Alfred Bettman ... [and others] Issued by the Foreign policy association, April, 1922, New York ... Endorsed and distributed by the National popular government league ... Washington, D. C. [Washington, 1922]

National popular government league.
The TVA labor relations policy at work
see under King, Judson, 1872-

National popular government league.
To the American people; report upon the illegal practices of the United States Department of justice. R. G. Brown ... Zechariah Chafee, jr. [and others] ... Washington, D. C., National popular government league, 1920.

67 p. illus. (ports., facsims.) 23½ᶜᵐ.

Prepared by a committee of twelve lawyers, May 1920, under the auspices of the National popular government league.

1. U. S. Dept. of justice. 1. Brown, Rome Green, 1862- 11. Title. 111. Title: Illegal practices of the United States Department of justice.

Library of Congress 23-10545

NN 0060221 DLC MH-L NPV DL NcD MiU OU OOxM

NATIONAL POPULAR GOVERNMENT LEAGUE.
Value of Muscle shoals in the South. By Judson King, director. [Washington, 1926.]
4°. pp. 4.
Without title-page. Caption title.
"Bulletin No.104, April 10, 1926."
At head of title: Congressional Record, 69th Congress, 1st session.

NN 0060222 MH

National Popular Government League.
...The value of Muscle Shoals to the south. (National popular government league, Bulletin, no. 104. April. 10, 1926) 1926.
13 p.
Mimeographed sheets.

NN 0060223 OC1

National popular government league.
Who will get the $100,000,000 for farm electrification? Washington, D.C., 1935.
10 numb. l. (Its Bulletin no. 171)

NN 0060224 DNAL

National popular government league.
Why the power joker in the New England flood-control compacts?
see under King, Judson, 1872-

The National popular review. An illustrated journal of preventive medicine, applied sociology and current medical sciences. Chicago, Ill., [1892-1895].

Library has vol. 1-4, no. 5, July 1892-May 1894; vol. 6, no. 3, 5, March, May, 1895. illus., ports. 26ᶜᵐ.

Editor: P. C. Remondino.
Subtitle varies slightly.
Monthly.
Vol. 6, incorrectly numbered vol. 7 on cover-title.
Vol. 1, no. 2-5, Aug.-Nov. 1892; vol. 2, no. 1, 2, 6. Ian.. Feb., June, 1893. vol. 3, no. 1, 3, July, Sept. 1893, wanting.

NN 0060226 ICJ Nh ICHi DNLM ICRL

National portrait gallery, Ireland

see

Dublin. National gallery of Ireland.

National portrait gallery, *London*

see

London. National portrait gallery.

The National portrait gallery of distinguished Americans
see under [Herring, James] 1794-1867, ed.

VOLUME 407

The national portrait gallery of eminent personages, now living or recently deceased, after photographs from Her Majesty's private collection, and from the studios of the most eminent photographers in the kingdom. Engraved on steel by D.J.Pound. With memoirs by the most able authors. London, J.Tallis [1859]

Cover-title: The drawing room portrait gallery.

NN   0060230   MH

National portrait gallery of illustrious and eminent personages, chiefly of the nineteenth century
      see under   Taylor, William Cooke, 1800-1849.

National portrait gallery of illustrious and eminent personages of the nineteenth century
      see under   [Jerdan, William] 1782-1869.

National Portrait Society, London.
     Catalogue of the annual exhibition...
[no.]
[London, 191   16°.

1. Portraits (British).—Exhibi-   tions, Gt. Br.: Eng.; London.
N. Y. P. L.   January 26, 1916.

NN   0060233   NN

920.042
N213   National portraits.   n.p.[18--]
     [140]p. plates.

     Binder's title.

NN   0060234   IU

National portraits of England. [Published by Harding and Lepard, circa 1824-1830]

NN   0060235   PPPM

The **National** post. v. 1, no. 1-5; May 6–July 1, 1911.
New York, The National post company, 1911
[226] p. illus. 31ᶜᵐ. biweekly.
Merged into the Success magazine, which continued as Success magazine and the National post.

1. Success.

                             12–36222
Library of Congress   HF5386.A2N3

NN   0060236   DLC

National Post Office Clerks' Association.
     Bill 5664. Introduced by S.S. Cox. For the relief of post-office clerks
         see under   Cox, Samuel Sullivan, 1824-1889
(supplement)

National Postal Transport Association.

[Strickland, Henry W   ]
     Adjustment of postal salaries; digest of editorial comment from leading newspapers. Washington [1924]

HFBP75   National Postal Transport Association.
.N225   Charter, constitution, by-laws and ritual.
C   [n.p.] 18   -19
           v.   13½-18cm.

     Title varies: Constitution and by-laws.

NN   0060239   WHi

National Postal Transport Association.
    Charter,constitution,by-laws and ritual.
1937-1939. [Portland,Me.,Printwell Printing Co.,1938.]

    nar.16°.   pp.40.
    Cover serves as title-page.

NN   0060240   MH

National postal transport association.
    Charter, constitution, by-laws and ritual,
1951-1953. [Portsmouth, n.d.]   v, 58 p.   16cm.

    1. Postal service—Assoc. and org.—U.S.

NN   0060241   NN

HFBP75   **National Postal Transport Association.**
N225
MIS   [Miscellaneous ephemeral materials not fully catalogued]

     NB. – Such materials are shelved in pamphlet-boxes marked with a period (.), a plus (+) or a quotation-mark (") ahead of the second line of the call-number. Search should be made in all three locations, although material may not be found in any one or two of them.

NN   0060242   WHi

National postal transport association.
    The most mail

     see under

    Association of American Railroads.

HD6350   National Postal Transport Association.
.P73R3
      The Postal transport journal.

      Washington [etc.]

HFBP75   National Postal Transport Association.
"N225   Proceedings. v. – , 18   -19 .
P   v.   30cm.

    v. 34 as published in The Railway Post Office (v. 41, no. 4; Nov. 1939; Sections 2-3)
     Earlier Proceedings contained in the bound file of the Railway Post Office held by the library.

NN   0060245   WHi MiD

HFBP75   National Postal Transport Association.
.N225   The railway postal clerk and the Railway
MIS   Mail Association. [Boston, E.L. Grimes, 1923?]
      8 p.   18cm.

     Cover title.

NN   0060246   WHi

National Postal Transport Association.
    Report of the national president.

     [n. p.]
       v. 23 cm.
      Reports for 19   published by the association under an earlier name: Railway Mail Association.

     1. Railway mail service—U. S.   2. Postal service—U. S.—Employees.
HE6175.N3   49–37416 rev*‡

NN   0060247   DLC

National postal transport association. *Woman's auxiliary.*
    Cook book, with complete instructions in household management ... Compiled by the Woman's auxiliary of the Railway mail association. [n. p.] 1916.
    99 p. 25½ cm.

     1. Cookery, American.

TX715.N335   44–25934 rev

NN   0060248   DLC

R396   National postal transport association - Women's
N213h   auxiliary - Spokane branch
      [Historian's book;manuscript in ledger, covering various years].   n.p.,n.d.

     Before 1950 called: Railway mail association - Women's auxiliary - Spokane branch.
    The society existed from 1909 to 1963.

NN   0060249   WaSp

R396   National postal transport association - Women's
N213   auxiliary - Spokane branch
      [Scrapbooks,1909-1963].   n.p.,n.d.   3v., illus.

     Before 1950 called: Railway mail association - Women's auxiliary - Spokane branch.

NN   0060250   WaSp

R396   National postal transport association - Women's
N213s   auxiliary - Spokane branch
      [Secretary's book;manuscript in loose-leaf note book,1956-1963].   n.p.,n.d.

     Before 1950 called: Railway mail association Women's auxiliary - Spokane branch.
    The society existed from 1909 to 1963.

NN   0060251   WaSp

National Potato Association, Chicago.
    [Publications of the National Potato Institute, 1929-1932]   [Chicago, 1929-32]
    1 v. (various pagings)
    1. Potatoes. Societies, etc.

NN   0060252   CU

National Potato Chip Institute.
    The chipper hostess
     see under title

75.9
N214   National Potato Chip Institute, inc.
    Fats & oils. Article.

    Cleveland,

     1. Potato chips. Research. 2. Fats and oils.

NN   0060254   DNAL

TX803   National Potato Chip Institute.
.P8P6
     Potato chipper.

     [Cleveland, National Potato Chip Institute]

VOLUME 407

National Potato Chip Institute, inc.
Potatoes. Article. [1]–46. Cleveland,
1949–56.
Ceased. cf. Note from the issuing office on
claim slip, Oct. 6, 1958.
1. Potato chips. Research.

NN   0060256   DNAL

Mann
SB   National Potato Conference, Chicago,
211   1928.
P8   Proceedings of the National Potato
N21   Conference held by the Agricultural
Council of the Central Western Shippers
Advisory Board, in the Palmer House,
Chicago, Illinois, Dec. 4 and 5, 1928.
Omaha, Nebr., American Railway
Association, 1928.
64 p. tables. 28 cm.

1. Potato   es - Congresses.

NN   0060257   NIC OrCS

281.375
N21   National Potato Council.
The National Potato Council answers the
potato problem.   Washington [1954]
[8] p.

1. Potatoe industry and trade. U.S.
I. Case, W   M

NN   0060258   DNAL

75.9
N215   National Potato Council.
Potatoes [Release]
Washington.

1. Potatoes.

NN   0060259   DNAL

National Potato Institute.
[Bulletin.]
no. A1–

Chicago, 1929   4°.
v.
Irregular.
Jan.   multigraphed.
Title supplied, called "Our no."

1. Potato—Per. and soc. publ.
N. Y. P. L.   June 5, 1931

NN   0060260   NN

National Potato Institute.
General report.
no. 1–

Chicago, 1929   4°.
v.
Weekly (irregular, Jan. 28 – May 4, 1929; irregular, July 3–
Title varies: Jan. 28 – March 16, Weekly report; March 28, 1929 –
General report.
Multigraphed.
1929   includes miscellaneous material.

1. Potato—Per. and soc. publ.
N. Y. P. L.   December 16, 1931

NN   0060261   NN

National Potato Institute.
Minutes of the meeting of the directors...
19

Chicago, 19   4°.
no.
Multigraphed.

1. Potato—Assoc. and org.—U. S.
N. Y. P. L.

NN   0060262   NN

National Potato Utilization Conference.
Proceedings.
[n. p.]
v.   27 cm.
First conference held in 1948.
Title varies: Program and papers. –   *Report*
Vols. for   issued by the conference under a variant name:
Potato Utilization Conference.

1. Potatoes—Congresses.

SB211.P8N38   61–45082 rev

NN   0060263   DLC OrPS GU IU N OU DNAL

National Potato Utilization Conference.
Program and papers
see its
Proceedings.

National potteries company, *Minneapolis.*
Manual of instructions for operating National pottery machine for the manufacture of turned concrete pottery products,
prepared by National potteries company. Minneapolis, Minn.,
°1934.
cover-title, 18 numb. l.   VII pl. 22 x 35½cm.
Mimeographed; text runs parallel with back of cover.

1. Pottery. 2. Concrete construction.   I. Title: Turned concrete pottery products.

                                               CA 35–90 Unrev'd
Library of Congress   TP817.N3
Copyright AA 139768   666.6

NN   0060265   DLC

47.9
N2124   National poultry advisory council.
Bulletin.   [Chicago]
1. Poultry. U.S. 2. Poultry. Societies.

NN   0060266   DNAL

47
N213   National poultry advisory council.
Chicken brooding & rearing program.
[Chicago, 1943]
[8] p.
1. Incubators and brooders. 2. Poultry.
I. U.S. Bureau of animal industry. II. Title:
Poultry conservation for victory.

NN   0060267   DNAL

47
N213L   National poultry advisory council.
Laying house program of poultry conservation
for victory.   [Chicago, 1943]
[14] p.
1. Poultry. 2. Poultry houses and equipment.
I. U.S. Bureau of animal industry. II. Title.
III. Title: Poultry conservation for victory.

NN   0060268   DNAL

National poultry advisory council.
Minutes.   [Chicago?]
1. Poultry. U.S. 2. Poultry. Societies.

NN   0060269   DNAL

National poultry advisory council.
Report of executive secretary.
[Chicago]
1. Poultry. U.S. 2. Poultry. Societies.

NN   0060270   DNAL

National poultry advisory council.
Turkey rearing program of poultry conservation
for victory.   [Chicago, 1943]
[8] p.
1. Turkeys. I. U.S. Bureau of animal industry.
II. Title: Poultry conservation for victory.

NN   0060271   DNAL

National poultry and game association
see
National poultry, butter and egg association.

SF481   National Poultry Breeders' Roundtable.
P54   Proceedings.
1952–   (1st–
[Kansas City, Mo., etc., Poultry Breeders
of America, 1952–
v. illus. 29cm.

Issued by body under former names: 1952–60
(1st–9th) Poultry Breeders' Roundtable.–
1961–69 (10th–18th) National Poultry Breeders'
Roundtable.– 1970– (19th–   National
Breeders' Roundtable.

1. Genetics - Cong.   2. Poultry - Cong. I.
Poultry Breeder   s' Roundtable. II.
National Poult   ry Breeders' Round-
table.

NN   0060273   OrCS MoU

National Poultry, Butter and Egg Association.
Bulletin
see   National poultry, butter and egg bulletin

National poultry, butter and egg association.
Hand book.
[Chicago,
v. illus., ports. 23cm.
Advertising matter interspersed.

                                               CA 16–547 Unrev'd
Library of Congress   HD9001.N42

NN   0060275   DLC

National poultry, butter and egg association.
Proceedings of the ... annual convention.
[New York,
v. 23½cm.
1913 erroneously numbered 6th on t-p.

1. Produce trade—U. S. 2. Poultry. 3. Eggs. 4. Butter.
                                               CA 16–548 Unrev'd
Library of Congress   HD9001.N4

NN   0060276   DLC

National poultry, butter & egg association.

The request of the National poultry, butter
& egg association for an appropriation from
the Congress of the United States of America
... Chicago [1925]
16 p.

NN   0060277   DNAL

The National poultry, butter & egg bulletin.
v.

Chicago, 191   f°.
v. illus.
Monthly.
Published by the National Poultry, Butter and Egg Association.

1. Poultry.—Per. and soc. publ.   2. Dairy products.—Per. and soc.
publ.
N. Y. P. L.   April 16, 1923.

NN   0060278   NN NIC

VOLUME 407

Mann
SF   National Poultry Conference. 2d, Reading,
481   Eng., 1907.
N26P   Proceedings.
1907   1 v. (various paging) 25 cm.

       Typewritten title page and index supplied.

       1. Poultry.   I. Title.

NN   0060279   NIC

National Poultry Conference. *2d, Reading*, 1907. L636.06261 Q700
**744   Second National Poultry Conference held at University College,
Reading, July 8, 9, 10 & 11, 1907. Official report. **Edited by**
Edward Brown, ... London, The National Poultry **Conference**,
1907.
    xxx, 382 p. front. 25½ᶜᵐ.
    "List of members," p. [xxiii]-xxx.

NN   0060280   ICJ IU NN OU

       National Poultry Conference, *Ottawa*, 1944.
         Proceedings, National Poultry Conference. **Organized by**
the Poultry Production Services, Dominion Dept. of Agriculture. Ottawa, Minister of Agriculture, 1944.
         72 p. 25 cm.

         1. Poultry—Congresses. 2. Poultry—Canada.

         SF481.N23 1944   636.506371   48–15482*

NN   0060281   DLC MiEM IU DNAL NN CaBVaU CU

National Poultry Council.
    Constitution of the National Poultry Council... [Notting-
ham? 1924.] 2 l. 4°.
    Caption-title.

1. Poultry—Breeding and raising—   Assoc. and org.—Gt. Br.
N. Y. P. L.   June 7, 1926

NN   0060282   NN

National Poultry Council.
    Minutes...
192
[London, 192   4°.
   no.

1. Poultry—Breeding and raising—   Assoc. and org.—Gt. Br.
N. Y. P. L.   April 8, 1929

NN   0060283   NN

National Poultry Council.
    The poultry industry in 19
[London,] 19   f°.
   nos.

1. Poultry—Trade and stat.—Gt. Br.
N. Y. P. L.   July 25, 1930

NN   0060284   NN

National Poultry Council.
    ...Powers of local authorities in respect to the keeping of
fowls and other poultry and in connection with council houses
... [London: The National Poultry Council, 1922.] 2 l. 4°.
(National Poultry Council. Leaflet no. 1.)
    Caption-title.

1. Poultry—Breeding and raising—   Assoc. and org.—Gt. Br.
N. Y. P. L.   June 7, 1926

NN   0060285   NN

NATIONAL POULTRY COUNCIL.
   ...A record of construction, extension, organisation and
protection. London [1931] 28 p. plates. 21½cm.

   Cover-title.

786814A. 1. Poultry—Breeding and raising—Assoc. and org.
—Gt.Br.

NN   0060286   NN

National Poultry Council.
   Register of records in laying trials.
v. 1–
[Nuneaton], Eng.], 1927–   obl. 8°.
   nos.   tables.

1. Poultry—Per. and soc. publ.
N. Y. P. L.   August 26, 1929

NN   0060287   NN DNAL TU

NATIONAL POULTRY COUNCIL.
   ...Report.
19
London[, 19   4°.
   no.

1. Poultry—Per. and soc.   publ.

NN   0060288   NN

       National Poultry Council
         see also   Joint Committee of the National
       Poultry Council and the National Farmers'
       Union on Marketing.

       National poultry digest
         see   Poultry digest.

       National Poultry Improvement Plan.
         Regional conferences on the National Poultry
       Improvement Plan
         see under   National Plans Conference.

National Poultry Institute, Topeka, Kan.
    Lesson with questions...
no. 1–
Topeka, Kan., 1914–   8°.
   v. in   illus.

    Contents: no. 1. How to start in the business.
    no. 2. Why standard-breds?
    no. 3. Location.
    no. 4. Poultry houses.

     no. 5. Fixtures and appliances.
     no. 6. Mating and breeding.
     no. 7. Hatching with hens.
     no. 8. Hatching eggs with incubators.
     no. 9. Raising chicks with hens.
     no. 10. Raising chicks with brooders.
     no. 11. Poultry feeding.
     no. 12. How and what to feed.
     no. 13. Management of the flock.
     no. 14. Market eggs and poultry.
     no. 15. Handling and selling standard-bred stock.

     no. 16. Preparations for exhibition.
     no. 17. The poultry shows.
     no. 18. Diseases of poultry.
     no. 19. Parasites, insects and destroyers — bad habits.
     no. 20. Turkeys, ducks and geese.

NN   0060294   NN

National poultry institute, incorporated, *Washington, D. C.*
   ... Commercial poultry farming course. Adams Center,
N. Y., The National poultry institute, inc. [°1943–
     v. illus. 19½ᶜᵐ.
     Cover-title.
     Vol. 1, rev. ed.; v. 2, 12th ed., rev.
     Title varies slightly.
     CONTENTS.—[v. 1] Lesson 1. Opportunities in poultry keeping. Les-
son 2. Opportunities in the poultry industry. Lesson 3. Locating the
poultry plant. Lesson 4. Planning a poultry farm.—[v. 2] Lesson 5. Poultry houses and equipment. Lesson 6. Interior arrangements and other
buildings.

     1. Poultry. 2. [Poultry—U. S.   I. Title.
     U. S. Dept. of agr. Library   47N21 1943   Agr 44–192
     for Library of Congress   SF487.N34
                       [3]†   636.5

NN   0060295   DNAL DLC

National poultry institute, incorporated, *Washington, D. C.*
   How to raise poultry for profit. Washington, D. C.,
The National poultry institute, incorporated [°1920]
    cover-title, 48 p. illus. (incl. ports.) diagrs. 19ᶜᵐ.

    1. Poultry.   I. Title.

    Library of Congress   SF487.N35   20–22051

NN   0060296   DLC

National poultry institute, incorporated, *Washington, D. C.*
   How to raise poultry for profit. Washington, D. C.,
The National poultry institute [°1921]
    56 p. illus. (incl. ports.) diagrs. 23ᶜᵐ.

    1. Poultry.   I. Title.

    Library of Congress   SF487.N35 1921   21–17752

NN   0060297   DLC DNAL

SF   **National Poultry Institute, inc., Washington,**
487   D. C.
N27H   How to raise poultry for profit. Washing-
1922   ton [c1922]
       56 p. illus. 23 cm.

       1. Poultry. I.   Title.

NN   0060298   NIC

SF   **National Poultry Institute, inc., Washington,**
487   D. C.
N27H   How to raise poultry for profit. Washing-
1924   ton [c1924]
       60 p. illus. 23 cm.

       1. Poultry. I.   Title.

NN   0060299   NIC

     National Poultry Institute, Inc., Washington, D. C.
       National poultry journal, a practical...
       see under title

     National Poultry Institute, inc., Washington, DC
Lamon, Harry Miles, 1872–
    Poultry breeding and selection, by Harry M. Lamon ...
Washington, D. C., H. M. Lamon [°1932]

SF   **National Poultry Institute, inc., Washington,**
487   D. C.
N27   Poultry farming course. Lesson no. 1–
       [Washington] c1920–
       v. illus. 20 cm.

       1. Poultry   - Study and teaching.
       I. Title.

NN   0060302   NIC DNAL

     National poultry institute, incorporated,
       Washington, D. C.
       ... Poultry judging and breeding course ...
    Lessons. [Washington, D. C.] 1920-21. no. 37-57.
    unb. not acc.
       Lessons no. 37–41 are questions to be used in
connection with American standard of perfection,
issued by the American poultry association. 47, 9
       Lessons no. 44-57 are questions to be used in
connection with "The mating and breeding of poultry"
[by H. M. Lamon] 47.

NN   0060303   DNAL

VOLUME 407

The National poultry journal. v. 1–
[London] 1920–
v. illus. 28 cm.
Organ of the National utility poultry society,
and affiliated societies.

NN 0060304   CaBVaU

National poultry journal... [London.]
v. 1

London: W. J. Todd, 1930–   30½ cm.
v. illus.

Monthly.
Supersedes the National laying test journal.

1. Poultry—Per. and soc. publ.
N. Y. P. L.   October 9, 1933

NN 0060305   NN DNAL

The National poultry journal; a practical poultry paper published
by practical poultrymen.
v.

Washington, D. C., 19   4°.
v. illus. (incl. ports.)

Monthly.
"Published by the National poultry journal, a branch of the National Poultry
Institute, Inc., Washington, D. C."
Editor : H. M. Lamon.

1. Poultry—Per. and soc. publ.
N. Y. P. L.   August 3, 1925

NN 0060306   NN

National poultry monitor.
v. 1–

Ashland, O.: W. A. Jeffrey & Co. [etc., etc.], 1880–   4°.
v. in illus., plates.

Monthly.
Editors: Oct., 1880–Feb. 1885, W. A. Jeffrey; Mar., 1885–June, 1886, J.
Wallace; July, 1886–Dec., 1887, W. D. Page.
July, 1886–Dec., 1887 running title : National monitor of poultry and pets.
Jan., 1887 incorrectly called Jan. 1886.
July, 1886 absorbed Poultry and pets, The Poultry nation, The Elyria weekly
poultry news.

1. Per. and soc. publ.
N. Y. P. L.   May 23, 1919.

NN 0060307   NN NIC

SF   National Poultry Organization Society, Lon-
481   don.
N27   Journal. v. 1–7; 1907–Oct. 1913. London, Simpkin, Marshall, Hamilton, Kent.
7 v. illus. 26 cm. quarterly.

Society merged into Agricultural Organization Society, 1913.

1. Poultry - So   cieties.

NN 0060308   NIC OU NN DLC

SF   National Poultry Organization Society, Lon-
481   don.
N27L   Leaflet. no. 1–
19 -   London.
nos. illus. 23 cm.

Ceased publication 1913?
Society merged into Agricultural Organization Society, 1913.

1. Poultry - So   cieties.

NN 0060309   NIC

National poultry organization society, London.

Brown, Edward, 1851–
... Report on the poultry industry in America. By
Edward Brown ... London, National poultry organisa-
tion society, 1906.

National poultry organization society.

Brown, Edward, 1851–
... Report on the poultry industry in Belgium. By Edward Brown ... London, National poultry organization
society limited, 1910.

National poultry organization society
... Report on the poultry industry in Denmark & Sweden.
By Edward Brown ... London, National poultry organisa-
tion society, limited, 1908.

ix, 112 p. illus., plates. 24½ᵐ.

1. Poultry—Denmark. 2. Poultry—Sweden.   I. Brown, Sir Edward, 1851–

Library of Congress   SF488.D4N3   8—28294

NN 0060312   DLC OrCS DNAL ICJ

National poultry organization society.

Brown, Edward, 1851–
Report on the poultry industry in Germany, by Edward Brown ... London, National poultry organization
society, limited, 1912.

National Power Corporation.
Report.
Manila.

v. 24 cm. annual.
Report year ends June 30.

1. Electric utilities—Philippine Islands.

HD9685.P54N34   621.312   53–16148 ‡

NN 0060314   DLC CU

National power corporation.
Report on Marikina river multi-purpose project
of June, 1954. Manila, 1954.
1 v.
--- ---- Manila, 1958.
121 p. illus., maps.
LR has:
1. Power supply. Luzon. 2. Luzon. Power
supply. 3. Philippines. Power. Luzon. I. Title.:
Marikina river multi-purpose project.

NN 0060315   DS

HD9685   National Power Corporation.
P6N33   Review of activities and accomplishments, Jan.11,
Docu-   1937 to Dec.31, 1947. Manila, 1948.
ments   68 p. illus.,maps(part fold.)
Dept.

1. Electric utilities - Philippine Islands.

NN 0060316   CU

National power glider ...
see
National glider and airplane news.

National Power Show, New York
see
New York (City) National Exposition of Power
and Mechanical Engineering.

National Power Use Workshop, St. Louis, 1955.
Profits from electrified farms

see under

U.S. Rural Electrification Administration.

The National preacher
see The National preacher and village
pulpit.

The National preacher and village pulpit. Original—
monthly. From living ministers of the United States. v. 1–
31, June 1826–Dec. 1857; new ser., v. 1–
Jan. 1858–
New York, W. H. Bidwell [etc.]
v. in ports. 23 cm.

Title varies: June 1826–May 1828, The National preacher.—June
1828–Dec. 1857, The American national preacher (caption title, June
1828–Aug. 1831 : The National preacher)—
The National preacher and the prayer-meeting.
Editors: 1826–38, A. Dickinson. — 1839–40, D. Mead. — 1841–47,
W. H. Bidwell.—1848–49, J. M. Sherwood.—1850, F. C. Woodworth.—
1851–52, J. M. Sherwood.—1853–56, E. Carpenter.—1857–
W. H. Bidwell.

Ceased publication in 1866. Superseded by Western pulpit. Cf.
Union list of serials.
INDEXES:
Subject index.
Vols. 1–38, 1826–64. 1 v.

1. Sermons—Period.   I. Bidwell, Walter Hilliard, 1798–1881, ed.
II. Carpenter, Eber, ed.   III. Dickinson, Austin, 1791–1849, ed.   IV.
Mead, Darius, ed.   V. Sherwood, James Manning, 1814–1890, ed.   VI.
Woodworth, Francis Channing, 1812–1859, ed.   VII. Title: The Amer-
ican national preacher.

BV4200.N3   2–641 rev 2*

AAP MMeT
TxU CtY OU WaPS   NbU MNS NjP PMA NcD PPEB MiA1bC
NN 0060322   DLC NjNbS IEG CU MiU OU OO OC1WHi N P

Film   The National preacher and village pulpit.
810.5   v.1–31, June 1826–1857; n.s. v.1–9,
AP   Jan.1858–Dec.1866. New York.
1800–50   4reels. monthly. (American periodicals
Reels   series: 1800–50, 1039)
1087–90

Title varies: June 1826–May 1828, The
National preacher.– June 1828–Dec.1857,
The American national preacher (caption
title, June 1828–Aug.1831: The National
preacher).–   The National
preacher and the prayer-meeting.
Superseded by Western pulpit.

INDEXES:
Vols.1–38, 1826–64.

Microfilmed by University Microfilms,
Ann Arbor, Mich.

NN 0060324   NcU PSt MoU

The National preacher and village pulpit.
[New York, 1865]

p. [105]–165, [1] 23cm. 3|4 green morocco.
A reprint of sermons 13–18 on Lincoln, from
volume 39, nos. 5–6, May–June 1865, with continuous pagination and signatures.
Separately issued as a prospectus to sell the
complete set of 38 volumes. cf. p. [166]
Contents.--Sermon 13. Gurley, P. D. In memoriam of President Lincoln.--14. Beecher, Robert R.
Personal forgiveness and public justice.--16.
Spear, Samuel T. Our national sorrow.--17. Williams, William R.   God vailing himself even
when bringing sal-   vation.--18. Tyng, Ste-
phon H. Victory   and reunion.

NN 0060325   CSmH

National preaching mission series
see under Federal Council of the Churches
of Christ in America. National Preaching Mission
Committee.

VOLUME 407

JK2352
1946
.E3
National precinct workers.

East, John Leonard.
Republican precinct worker's handbook, by John Leonard East. Washington, Chicago, National precinct workers, inc. ₁1946₎

National prejudice, opposed to the national interest, candidly considered in the detention or yielding up Gibraltar and Cape-Briton by the ensuing treaty of peace: with some observations on the natural jealousy of the Spanish nation, and how far it may operate to the prejudice of the British commerce if not removed at this crisis. In a letter to Sir John Barnard, knight. London, Printed for W. Owen ₁etc.₎ 1748.

2 p. l., 9–50 p. 20¼ᶜᵐ.

1. Gibraltar. 2. Cape Breton — Hist. 3. Aix-la-Chapelle, Peace of, 1748.

3–4706

Library of Congress   DP302.G41N3 1748

MiU-C
NN   0060328   DLC MnU MH CtY IaU N MB ViU RPJCB

National premium advertising association, Inc.
The use of premiums in business. The promotion of thrift.
N.Y., Nat'l. premium adv. ass., n.d.
113 p.

NN   0060329   OO

National premium advertising association.
Use of premiums in business. The value of thrift.
New York, The Association ₁1916₎
113 p. 16½ᶜᵐ

1. Advertising. 2. Rewards (Prizes, etc.)

NN   0060330   DFT

National Premium advertising association.
The use of Premuims in business. The value of Thrift. New York, 1917. 12° 113 p.

NN   0060331   PBL

National preparatory school committee
see   National council of student Christian associations.   National preparatory school committee.

... National preparedness and school efficiency
see under   ₁Mendelsohn, Sigmund₎

National Presbyterian church in Mexico
see
Iglesia nacional presbiteriana en México.

National preservers association.

The **Glass** packer; a magazine of food packing. v. 1–
Oct. 1928–
₁New York, Ogden-Watney publishers, inc.₎ 1928–

389.3
N214
₁National preserving company of Baltimore₎
The "Baltimore process" of progressive pneumatic evaporation. ₁Baltimore, Innes, 1872₎
36 p.

NN   0060336   DNAL

National Press, Inc.
... Illustrated cuts; a cut for every business. We offer them to our thousands of satisfied customers as further evidence of our desire to be of the greatest possible service to them. Chicago, Milwaukee ₁etc.₎ ₁19--?₎
cover-title, ₁256₎ p. illus. 23ᶜᵐ.
At head of title: A picture is worth a thousand words.

1. Advertising. I. Title.

NN   0060337   ViU

The National Press and Telegraphy. Elizabethtown, N.M. 1869–
Elizabethtown, N. M., Dawson & Osborne, 1869–
nos. Lg. folio. In manila folder.

NN   0060338   CSmH

National press club of Washington, *Washington, D. C.*
Constitution and by-laws of National press club of Washington ... ₁Washington? 1911?₎
18 p. 14ᶜᵐ.

CA 16–136 Unrev'd

Library of Congress   PR4899.W28N2

NN   0060339   DLC

National Press Club of Washington, *Washington, D. C.*
Dateline: Washington; the story of national affairs journalism in the life and times of the National Press Club. Edited by Cabell Phillips ₁and others₎ Garden City, N. Y., Doubleday, 1949.
vii, 307 p. illus., ports. 22 cm.
Written to commemorate the fortieth anniversary of the National Press Club.
CONTENTS.—An introductory note, by A. Krock.—Prehistory, by D. Aikman.—From such a bond, by S. Hart.—This is how it used to be, by B. N. Timmons.—The placid twenties, by F. Knebel.—"We interrupt this program," by T. F. Koop.—Moisture, a trace, by H. J. Dodge.—"And here we sit today!" By H. Morrow.—Tradesmen's entrance, by H. J. Dodge.—"Just one more, please," by H. L. Kany and

W. C. Bourne.—Handouts, by B. Catton.—Autocrats of the breakfast table, by C. Phillips.—World War II, by L. C. Wilson.—Passed by censor, by G. Creel, B. Price, E. Davis, and W. A. Kinney.—The diplomatic correspondent, by W. R. Deuel.—Every day is election day, by F. C. Othman.—Coverage today, by T. L. Stokes.—Journalist and journalese, by C. B. Jones.

1. Journalism—Washington, D. C.   I. Phillips, Cabell B. H., ed.   II. Title.
PN4899.W29N3 1949   071.53   49–11680*

PPSOPR OrCS
NN   ViU ICU MB NcD NNC NNUN OCl PPT OClW OU PP WaWW
0060341   DLC WaE IdU OrU Or OrP IdPI Wa CoU

National Press Club of Washington, *Washington, D. C.*
Dateline: Washington; the story of national affairs journalism in the life and times of the National Press Club. Edited by Cabell Phillips ₁and others₎ 1st ed.₎ Garden City, N. Y., Doubleday, 1949.
ix, 431 p. illus., ports. 22 cm.
"Commemorating the fortieth anniversary of the National Press Club."
CONTENTS.—An introductory note, by A. Krock.—Prehistory, by D. Aikman.—From such a bond, by S. Hart.—This is how it used to be, by B. N. Timmons.—The placid twenties, by F. Knebel.—"We interrupt this program," by T. F. Koop.—Moisture, a trace, by H. J. Dodge.—"And here we sit today!" By H. Morrow.—Tradesmen's

entrance, by H. J. Dodge.—"Just one more, please," by H. L. Kany and W. C. Bourne.—Handouts, by B. Catton.—Autocrats of the breakfast table, by C. Phillips.—World War II, by L. C. Wilson.—Passed by censor, by G. Creel, B. Price, E. Davis, and W. A. Kinney.—The diplomatic correspondent, by W. R. Deuel.—Every day is election day, by F. C. Othman.—Coverage today, by T. L. Stokes.—Journalist and journalese, by C. B. Jones.—Roster of the National Press Club (p. ₁300₎–431)
1. Journalism—Washington, D. C.   I. Phillips, Cabell B. H., ed.   II. Title.
PN4899.W29N3 1949a   071.53   49–48964*

CoU OU ViU
NN   0060343   DLC MoU PPSOPR PP CoU OCl PPT OClW

National press club of Washington, *Washington, D. C.*
Year book, National press club of Washington.
₁Washington, 19
v. illus. 15½ᶜᵐ.

1. Press—Washington, D. C.—Societies.

13–26954

Library of Congress   PN4899.W28N3

NN   0060344   DLC MiU

National press photographer.
New York.
v. illus., ports. 29 cm. monthly.
Began publication with Apr. 1946 issue. Cf. Union list of serials.
Official publication of National Press Photographers Association.

1. Photography, Journalistic—Period.   I. National Press Photographers Association.
TR820.N272   778   55–31601

NN   0060345   DLC TxU MiEM FU GU OkS DSI NN

National Press Photographers Association.
Complete book of press photography. ₁Joseph Costa, editor₎ New York, ₁1950.
206 p. illus., ports. 31 cm.
"An annotated bibliography for the photo-journalist, by Clifton C. Edom": p. 127–137.

1. Photography, Journalistic.   I. Title.
TR820.N3   778   50–10702

MsSM OrCS MtU CaBVa OrU Or WaS CU ScU
NN   0060346   DLC DNAL PSt PP TxU IaU IU WU MB MnU

TR820
.N272
National Press Photographers Association.
National press photographer.
New York.

DS
421.5
.N3
National Press Syndicate.
Random selections. Bombay, National Information & Publications ltd. ₁1947₎
138 p.
"Articles published at various times during the last three years in the Indian press."

1. India - Addresses, essays, lectures.   I. Title.

Contents.—Where are you going to, my pretty maid, by Kamaladevi Chattopadhyaya.—Independence day, by J. B. Kripalani.—Jayaprakash, by Asoka Mehta.—The future of western civilization, by C.E.M. Joad.—What is democracy, by Khan Abdul Ghani Khan.—In memory of H. G. Wells, by Mulk Raj Anand.—The boundaries of art, by J. H. Cousins.—My master in slippers, by Anil K. Chanda.   —Mahatma Gandhi and

the modern world, by Amiya Chakravarty.—The agricultural economics conference, by M. L. Cantwala.—Pussyfoor, by C. Rajagopalachari.

NN   0060350   NNC

National Pressed Steel Company.
Handbook of national steel lumber manufactured by the National Pressed Steel Co. Massillon, Ohio, prepared by H. M. Naugle, R. W. Van Horn ₁and₎ Stanley Macomber. Massillon, O. ₁1920?₎ 72 p. incl. diagrs., tables. 16°.

52685A. 1. Steel.—Dealers' catalogues. 2. Building (Iron and steel).—Tables, calculations, etc.   logues.
N. Y. P. L.   August 25, 1922.

NN   0060351   NN

VOLUME 407

National pressed steel co.
Handbook of National steel lumber, produced by the National pressed steel co. ... prepared by the Steel lumber division, under the direction of H. M. Naugle, Stanley Macomber ... [Massillon, O.] [1921.

3 p. l., 5–183 p. diagrs. 17ᵐᵐ.

Second edition.
Cover-title: National steel lumber sections.

1. Steel, Structural. 2. Steel, Structural—Tables, calculations, etc. I. Naugle, H. M. II. Macomber, Stanley. III. Title. IV. Title: National steel lumber.

Library of Congress   TA685.N3   22–5705

NN   0060352   DLC OCl

National Pressure Cooker Company
see
National Presto Industries, inc.

National presto industries, inc.
Book of instructions and canning formulæ. Eau Claire, Wis., Northwestern steel & iron works [n. d.]
20 p., 1 l. 19½ cm.

1. Canning and preserving.

U. S. Dept. of Agr. Libr.   389.3N82
for Library of Congress   [r59c¾]   Agr 17–1207 rev 2

NN   0060354   DNAL

389.25   **National presto industries, inc.**
N217   The national de luxe pressure cooker. Pressure cooking & canning. Instructions and recipes. [Eau Claire, Wis., 1935]
76 p.   illus.   23 cm.

NN   0060355   DNAL

389.25   **National presto industries, inc.**
N217N   The national handbook of pressure cooking and canning. A complete manual on the science of cooking and canning under steam pressure. Recipes, minus, time-tables.   Eau Claire, Wis. [1935]
76 p.   illus.   23 cm.

NN   0060356   DNAL

National Presto Industries, inc.
National Presto cooker (model '40') recipe book ...   Eau Claire, Wis. [1947]
127 p.   illus. (part col.)   17 cm.
Cover title.
Published by the company under its earlier name: National Pressure Cooker Company.

1. Pressure cookery.   I. Title: Presto cooker (model '40') recipe book.

TX840.P7N38   641.58   53–23210 rev

NN   0060357   DLC

National presto industries, inc.
National recipes and menus for "National" pressure cooker; also simultaneous cooking ...   Eau Claire, Wis., Northwestern steel & iron works [1923]
cover-title, 52 p.   illus.   23 cm.

1. Pressure cookery.   2. Menus.   I. Title.

TX840.P7N4   24–99 rev 2

NN   0060358   DLC

National Prestressed Concrete Conference.
Proceedings.
Wellington, N. Z., Technical Publications.

v.   illus., ports., diagrs.   22 cm.

Conferences for   sponsored by the New Zealand Ministry of Works and the New Zealand Portland Cement Association.

1. Prestressed concrete—Congresses.

TA680.N3   624.183   61–27254

NN   0060359   DLC NN

284.8   **National price digest.**
N21   New York, Biddle purchasing co.,

1. Food. Prices. 2. Prices. U.S. 3. Prices. Periodicals. I. Biddle purchasing co. II. Title: Price index.

NN   0060360   DNAL

National Primary Election League.
National conference   on practical reform of primary elections, held ... Jan. 20 and 21, 1898
see under   National conference on practical reform of primary elections, New York, 1898.

National primer, adapted to the capacities of young beginners ... Baltimore, M. B. Roberts, 1823.
36 p.   illus.   14ᵐᵐ.

1. Primers—1800–1870.

Library of Congress   PE1119.A1N35   12–6784

NN   0060362   DLC

The NATIONAL primer, or Primary spelling book, upon a new plan; by which Young children may more easily learn words of two syllables, than they have generally learned words of one syllable. Boston, Published by William Peirce, 1835. 36 p. illus., music. 15cm.

In original printed green paper covers.

Songs with music: p. 33–36.

1. Primers, American.   I. Title: Primary spelling book, upon a new plan...

NN   0060364   NN MH

The NATIONAL principia. v. 1–5, no. 27 [no. 1–235]: Nov. 19, 1858–June 14, 1866.   New York.   5 v. 37–63cm.

Irregular.
Vol. 5, no. 1[–27, Apr. 21, 1864–June, 1866) reprint edition published in 1969 by the Negro universities press, New York in the series the Black experience in America; Negro periodicals in the United States, 1840–1960. America; Negro periodicals in the United States, 1840–1960.

Title varies: Nov. 19, 1858–Aug. 25, 1864, Principia; June 29–July 6, 1865, Principia and national era; Jan. 11–Mar. 8, 1866, New York principia.
Edited by W. Goodell, Nov. 19, 1859–Aug. 25, 1864 (with G. B. Cheever, Oct. 23, 1862–Aug. 25, 1864).
Absorbed the National era, Washington, D.C., June 29, 1965.-- cf. v. 5, no. 19, p. 4.

1. Slavery--Per. and soc. publ.   --U. S. I. Goodell, William, 1792–1878, ed. II. Cheever, George Barrell, 1807–1890, ed. III. Principia. IV. Principia and national era. V. New York principia.

DAU
NN   0060366   NN NB NIC PrU MB OO ViU GU InU TxU

The National principia for lovers of science, universities, colleges, schools, teachers, and pupils of every grade
see under   [Loomis, William Isaacs]

NATIONAL PRINT CUTTERS ASSOCIATION OF AMERICA. [MISCELLANEA: CONSTITUTIONS, PROCEEDINGS ETC]
N.P., 1898 –
v.   34 cm.

NN   0060368   MdBJ

National printer-journalist [a journal for printing and allied trades]
Chicago [National printer-journalist company] 18
v. illus., plates (part col.) ports. 30½ᵐᵐ. monthly.

Editor: B. B. Herbert.
Official paper of the National editorial association.

1. Printing—Period. 2. Journalism—Period.   I. Herbert, Benjamin Briggs, 1843–1917, ed. II. National editorial association of the United States.

Library of Congress   Z119.N27   CA 7—5245 Unrev'd

ICJ OrU ICJ
NN   0060369   DLC N OU   KyU ICHi NN WaU NNC

NATIONAL PRINTER-JOURNALIST
Portland convention number. v.16, no.5. May, 1899.   Chicago, National Editorial Association, 1899.
p.341–[420] (i.e., 79 p.)   illus.

NN   0060370   Or

National printer – journalist
see also   Mail order journal, 1883–

Wing   **NATIONAL PRINTERS' MATERIALS CO.,** New York.
fZ   Specimens of enameled wood type manufactured
40583   by the National Printers' Materials Co.   New
.615   York [1887]
        cover-title, 71p.   illus.   34cm.

NN   0060372   ICN

Z   **National Printers' Protective Fraternity.**
120   Constitution of the National Printers' Pro-
.N214   tective Fraternity. Wilmington, Del., James
        & Webb Print. Co., 1887.
16, 4 p.

"Constitution amended, revised and adopted by the National Fraternity, at the second annual convention, Kansas City, Mo., March 1, 2, 3, and 4, 1887."

With this is bound the General laws of the National Printers' Protective Fraternity.

NN   0060374   NNC

National printing company, *New York.*
National cipher code, no. 1, for dealers in leather belting, hose ... New York, National printing co., 1880.
2 p. l., 14 p.   15ᵐᵐ.

Library of Congress   HE7677.1.N3   CA 7–4230 Unrev'd

NN   0060375   DLC

VOLUME 407

National printing company, *New York.*
National cipher code, no. 2, for dealers in vulcanized rubber goods adapted to mechanical purposes: hose couplings, reels, pipes, &c., &c. New York, National printing co., 1880.
2 p. l., 37 p. 15ᶜᵐ.

1. Cipher and telegraph codes—Rubber goods.

ᴄᴀ 7—3401 Unrev'd

Library of Congress   HE7677.R85N2

NN   0060376   DLC

National printing education journal. v. 1–
Sept. 1941–
Menominee, Mich., National association for printing education.

NN   0060377   OC1

HD9999   NATIONAL PRINTING EQUIPMENT ASSOCIATION.
.P853U5   ...Annual report... 1st–   1933/34–
N3   ｟New York, 1934–
v. 22½ cm.
Report year ends Aug.31.

NN   0060378   ICU

NATIONAL PRINTING EQUIPMENT ASSOCIATION, INC., New
York.
The problem of surplus used machinery...a discussion embodying a remedy. New York, N.Y.: National Prtg. Equipment Assoc., Inc., 1934 13 p. 28cm.

783150A. 1. Printing—Machinery and supplies—Trade and stat.—U.S., 1934.

NN   0060379   NN NNC

National Printing Ink Research Institute
see Lehigh University, Bethlehem, Pa.
National Printing Ink Research Institute.

National Printing Workers Union
see
National Union of Printing Workers.

National prison association
see   American Correctional association.

National Prison Association of the United States of America
see
American Correctional Association.

National prison congress
see
American correctional association.
Proceedings of the ... annual congress of correction.

National Prison Emergency Committee
see   National Committee on Prisons.
National Prison Emergency Committee

National prison reform congress
see   American correctional association.
Proceedings of the ... annual congress of correction.

National Prisoners' Aid Association.
HV7231
.D4
The Delinquent. v. 1–8, no. 5; Jan. 1911–May 1918. New York.

National Pro Football League
see **National Football League.**

National Probation and Parole Association
see
National Council on Crime and Delinquency.

National Probation Association
see
National Council on Crime and Delinquency.

National Probation Officers' Association
see
National Council on Crime and Delinquency.

National process company, inc., New York.
The National way to market. ｟New York, National process company, c1945｠ 16 l. illus. 36cm.

NN   0060392   NN

National process company, inc., *New York.*
Reproduction problems; an analysis and description of reproduction processes. New York city, National process company, inc., ｟*1927｠
14 p. illus. 18½ᶜᵐ.
Reproduced from type-written copy.

1. Photolithography. 2. Copying processes.   ɪ. Title.
43–36189
Library of Congress   TR940.N3

NN   0060393   DLC FMU

National process company, inc., *New York.*
Repro-prints ... New York city, National process company, inc. ｟1928｠
24 p. illus. 18½ᶜᵐ.
Reproduced from type-written copy.

1. Photolithography. 2. Offset printing.   ɪ. Title.
43–21703
Library of Congress   TR940.N32

NN   0060394   DLC

National process company, inc., *New York.*
Type it and repro-print it ... New York city, National process company, inc. ｟*1927｠
38 p., 1 l. illus. 18½ᶜᵐ.
"Photo-offset lithographed."

1. Photolithography. 2. Offset printing.   ɪ. Title.
43–21704
Library of Congress   TR940.N33

NN   0060395   DLC

W 1   NATIONAL Proctologic Association
NA566   Journal. v. 13, no. 2–v.22, no. 3/4;
Oct. 1940–Nov./Dec. 1949. Biloxi, Miss. ｟etc.｠
10 v. in   illus., ports.
W1 NA566
Continues the Journal of the American College of Proctology.
No more published?
1. Proctology - period.   Title: Journal of the National Proctologic Association

NN   0060396   DNLM OU NcU-H PPHa

National produce exchange (*Philippines*)
Annual report. 1937–

Manila, Bureau of printing, 1939–
v. tables. 23ᶜᵐ.
1937–   issued by the National produce exchange.

1. Farm produce—Marketing.
39–28405
Library of Congress   HD9016.P54N27
——— 2d set.   ｟2｠   332.64

NN   0060397   DLC CtY

National producing company, *Kansas City, Mo.*
... "Swing out," a three-act comedy drama with musical specialties. Kansas City, Mo., National producing company, *1939.
cover-title, 56 p. plates. 18ᶜᵐ.
At head of title: The show of shows.

ɪ. Title.
45–47146
Library of Congress   PN6120.A5N34

NN   0060398   DLC

National Production Authority
see U. S. *National Production Authority.*

4HB   National Productivity Council (India)
734   Speaking of productivity. [2d ed.   ｠
India [19   ｠
28 p.

NN   0060400   DLC-P4

Natural products marketing act commission (*British Columbia*)
see
British Columbia. *Natural products marketing act commission.*

qR620.6   NATIONAL professional association of engineers,
N213D   architects & scientists.
Dispatch.
Seattle. Seattle professional engineering employees' association.

Quarterly.

NN   0060402   WaS

National profit sharers association.
The National profit sharers association ... ｟Worcester, Davis press, *1915｠
32 p. illus. 20½ᶜᵐ.

16–2918
Library of Congress   HF5436.N3

NN   0060403   DLC

A national program for financing the public schools in the United States
see under ｟Morse, Herbert North｠ 1872–

VOLUME 407

National Program letter
see under National Education Program.

The national program of the Hungarian
Gömbös government.

See under

Gömbös, Gyula. 1886-1936

National program service.
Chairman's handbook. [Chicago, National
program service, 1948]
1 v. (loose-leaf) illus. 26 cm.

NN 0060407 Mi

National Programming Committee
see National Spiritual Assembly of the Bahá'is of the
United States and Canada. *National Programming Committee.*

National progress.
v. 1

Philadelphia, W. H. MacFarland, jr., 1945–
28cm.
v.

Semimonthly.
[Vol. 1, no. 47] (Aug. 15, 1947) lacks numbering.
Editor : 1945– , W. H. MacFarland, jr.

1. Nationalism and nationality—
Farland, W. Henry, ed.
N. Y. P. L.
Per. and soc. publ.—U.S. I. Mac-
November 23, 1949

NN 0060409 NN

National Progressive club.
Lincoln day banquet...February 12, 1913.
[New York, The Schilling press, 1912]
cover-title, [26] p. 33.5 cm.
Portrait laid on cover-title.
"Declaration of principles of the Progres-
sive party" p. [7]-[18]; "Platform of the
National Progressive party of the State of
New York", p. [19]-[25].

NN 0060410 MiU-C

National Progressive Committee
see
Progressive Party (*Founded 1912*) *National Committee.*

National progressive conference. Committee on
unemployment and industrial stabilization.
Long-range planning for the regularization of
industry. The report of a subcommittee of the
Committee on unemployment and industrial stabilization of the National progressive conference.
J. M. Clark, chairman, J. Russell Smith, Edwin S.
Smith, George Soule. 1932.
23 p. 23 1/2cm.

Reprinted from the New republic, January 13,
1932, Vol. LXIX, no. 893–part two.
Pamphlet not regularly catalogued
Pamphlets on un- employment in the United
States, no. 45.

NN 0060412 DLC PSt GEU InU NNCE

National Progressive Party
see Progressive Party (Founded 1912)

JK 238.7 The National Progressive Party, causes that
N3 created it, who compose it. [New York,
Mail and Express job print, 1912]
15 p. 24 cm.

1. Progressive Party (Founded 1912)

NN 0060414 OU

. National Progressive Union.

The National Federation of Miners and Mine Laborers (organized
in 1885) and the National Progressive Union (organized in 1889)
merged in 1890 to form the United Mine Workers of America.
Works by these bodies are found under the name used at the time
of publication.

National Progressive Union.

Proceedings [of the Miners' Convention]
see under Miners' Convention, Indianapolis, 1889.

National prohibition...
v. 1
Franklin, Pa., 1916-17.
v.
f°.

Monthly.
Editor : W. P. F. Ferguson.

1. Prohibition.—Per. and soc. publ.
1861-
N. Y. P. L.
2. Ferguson, William Porter Frisbee,
1861- , editor.
April 23, 1919.

NN 0060417 NN WaS

National prohibition; a brief on the law
see under [Anderson, Oliver Perry]
1869-

The NATIONAL prohibition amendment. n.p.,
[1918?].

23 cm. pp.45.
Paper cover serves as title-page.

NN 0060419 MH

National prohibition and the church.

Cut from The Unpopular review, New York,
Oct.-Dec., 1915, v.IV, no.3, p.308-324.

NN 0060420 MH

HV5089 National prohibition board of strategy.
.Z9 A declaration of principles, by the National
no. 297 prohibition board of strategy (adopted at
Washington, D.C., June 1, 1932) [Washington,
D.C., National prohibition board of strategy, 1932]
7 p. 23 x 9.5 cm.
Pamphlets on prohibition ... in the U.S.
no. 297.

NN 0060421 DLC

178.5 National Prohibition Bureau.
N2127 Temperance recitations on the various phases
of prohibition of the liquor traffic. New
York, Prohibition Bureau [189-?]
1v. (unpaged) 25cm.

1. Prohibition. 2. Temperance. Exercises,
recitations, etc. I. Title. xProhibition
Bureau.

NN 0060422 OrU

National prohibition camp-ground association
The place to spend the summer. The place
to live all winter. The national prohibition
park, Staten Island...
n.p., n.d.
44 p.

NN 0060423 OClWHi

National prohibition committee
General John Bidwell.
New York, National prohibition committee, n.d.
4 p.

NN 0060424 OU

National Prohibition Park Company.
The place to spend the summer.
see under National prohibition camp-
ground association.

National Prohibition Park Company.
[Program for the seventh season of summer meetings in the university temple, National prohibition
park, Staten Island, New York, 1897. 1 p.l., 44 pp.,
1l. Staten Island : [The Company, 1897]. ob. 24°.

NN 0060426 NN

National prohibition park co.,
...Prohibition Pakk, (Westerleigh) New York city.
Port Richmond, [n/y.]

F127
.S7N27

NN 0060427 DLC

National prohibition party.
[Campaign literature. 3 numbers of the New voice
leaflets; The National prohibition platform for 1900; and
"The full dinner pail," reprint from the New voice, Sept.
13, 1900] Chicago, Dickie & Woolley, 1900.
5 pieces. 16° and 8°.

1–5864

NN 0060428 DLC

---

*BROAD-
SIDE National Prohibition Party.
1888 National Prohibition ticket. For President,
.N375 Clinton B. Fisk. For Vice-President, John
A. Brooks. Election, Tuesday, November 6th,
1888. [n. p., 1888]
broadside. illus. 17 x 7½cm.

1. Fisk, Clinton Bowen, 1828-1890. 2. Presidents—
U. S.—Election—1888. 3. U. S.—Pol. & govt.—
1885-1889. I. Title.

NN 0060429 ViU

National prohibition party.

Wilson, Alonzo E.

Prohibition hand book and voter's manual, 1900. Chicago, A. E. Wilson [1900]

NATIONAL PROHIBITION PARTY.
The Prohibition Party in Maine; its platform,
its candidates, its convention, its address to the
temperance people. Auburn, Me., W.S.Morse, 1880.

21 cm. pp.16.
At head of title: 1880.

NN 0060431 MH

VOLUME 407

The **National** prohibitionist.
v.

Chicago, 19   v.   illus.   35cm.

Semimonthly (slightly irregular).
"Published...by the Prohibition national committee."
March, 1933, v. 2, no. 5, was first issue (assumed the volume numbering of the Prohibition defender and no-tobacco journal, new series; the latter continued publication under its first title, the No-tobacco journal, for two numbers only).
Title varies: v.1-29, The National prohibitionist; v.30-   The National statesman.
In Jan. 1962 absorbed The Christian statesman.

1. Temperance—Per. and soc.   publ. I. Prohibition party. National committee.
N. Y. P. L.   September 22, 1944

NN   0060432   NN MH OU ICJ

National prohibitionist, Chicago.

Babson, Roger Ward, 1875–
Our campaign for the presidency in 1940; America and the churches, by Roger W. Babson ... Chicago, National prohibitionist, 1941.

The **National** prohibitionist, a journal of good citizenship.
        -17;   -Aug. 24, 1911.
New York, W. P. F. Ferguson; ₍etc., etc.₎   -1911.
v.   illus. 35-37ᶜᵐ.   weekly.

Title varies: -Nov. 14, 1907, The Defender; a national journal devoted to the discussion of the prohibition issue.
Nov. 28, 1907-Aug. 1911, The National prohibitionist.
Editor: -Aug. 1911, W. P. F. Ferguson.
Published in Chicago, Nov. 1907-Aug. 1911.
In Nov. 1907 absorbed the Home defender and took over the subscription list of the New voice (previously discontinued)
Merged into the Vindicator.

1. Prohibition—Period.   I. Ferguson, William Porter Frisbee, 1861– ed. II. The Defender; a national journal.

Library of Congress   HV5285.N2

        CA 9-589 Unrev'd

NN   0060434   DLC OrU

The **National** prohibitionist and practical reformer.
v. 1
New York, 1882.   f°.

1. Prohibition. 2. Temperance.—   BLACK TEMPERANCE COLL.
N. Y. P. L.   Per. and soc. publ.
        March 11, 1920.

NN   0060435   NN

HV5089   National prohibitory amendment guide.   n.d.
.Z9   [1 l.]   [Pamphlets on prohibition in the
no. 172   U.S. no. 172]

NN   0060436   DLC

National Project in Agricultural Communications.
Agricultural communications

see under

National Agricultural Communications Conference, Michigan State College, 1954.

National Project in Agricultural Communications.
There's a career ahead
see under   Association of State Universities and Land-Grant Colleges. Division of Agriculture.

D070   National Project in Agricultural Communica-
N213   tions.
        You can write and edit effective agricultural publications; a report on the Agricultural economics writing short course, Oregon State College, Corvallis. ₍East Lansing, Mich.?, 1954₎
        cover-title, 32 p.   illus.

NN   0060439   NNC DNAL IU IdU

National projects in educational measurement
        see under   Invitational Conference on Testing Problems.

National prophecy and prayer conference, *Chicago,* 1940.
Prophecy and prayer; from the National prophecy and prayer conference, at Chicago, October 13 to 20, 1940. Wichita, Kan., Defender publishers ₍1940₎

62 p.   illus. (incl. ports.)   26½ᶜᵐ.

1. End of the world.   I. Title.   41-7684

Library of Congress   BT875.A343 1940
        ₍2₎   236

NN   0060441   DLC

National prosperity, the reward of national equity
        see under   Tract Association of Friends.

National protection for Oklahoma Indians
        see under   Indian Rights Association.

Ga   **National Protective Association,** Columbus,
H09341   Ga.
N27A4   Instructions to agents.   Columbus, Ga.,
        Thos. Gilbert, 1897.
        48 p.   14cm.

        Cover title.

        1. Insurance, Health - Rates and tables.
        2. Insurance, Accident - Rates and tables.

NN   0060444   GU NcD TxU

334.7   **National Protective Association,** *Columbus, Ga.*
N213n   The National Protective Association, a friend in adversity.   Protects you when, from sickness or accident, you are unable to protect yourself ...   Columbus, Ga., T. Gilbert, printer [n.d.]
        [4]p.   15cm.

NN   0060445   TxU

National protective association, *Minneapolis.*
By-laws of the National protective ass'n ...   ₍Minneapolis, Furbush & co., ᶜ1890₎

20 p.   14½ᶜᵐ.

        CA 9-1875 Unrev'd
Library of Congress   HG8963.N73A2

NN   0060446   DLC

National Protective Association, Minneapolis.
Report of the National Protective Association, on the working of Prohibition in Iowa and Kansas.   Supplement to Bonfort's wine and spirit circular, July 25, 1887.   New York: Bonfort & Leoser, 1887.   40 p.   16°.

In: VTZ p. v. 189, no. 7.

1. Prohibition, U.S.: Iowa. 2. Prohibition, U.S.: Kansas.
N. Y. P. L.   BLACK TEMPERANCE COLL.
        April 12, 1919.

NN   0060447   NN

HV5078   The National protective association of the wine
T6   beer and spirit trade.

        Proceedings of the second annual convention of the National protective association of the wine beer and spirit trade, held at Cincinnati, Ohio, September 13, 1887.   Constitution and by-laws and list of members.   Louisville, Ken., Office of the Association [1887?]

        16p.   21cm.   (Bound with: Thomann, Gallus. Colonial liquor laws.   1887)

NN   0060448   NBuG

National protective fraternal order of buffaloes of the world.
Ritual ... National protective fraternal order of buffaloes of the world, for Texas and jurisdiction. ₍Tyler? Tex., ᶜ1909₎

40 p.   diagr.   21½ cm.

        HS2259.B92 1909   10-2285

NN   0060449   DLC

335.4   **National Protest March,** Gt. Brit.
M578   Why we march; programme of the National Protest March. ₍London, Marston, 193-?₎
v.2   15 p.   cover illus.   23 cm.
no.2
        ₍No. 2₎ in a volume with binder's title:
        Miscellaneous pamphlets, v. 2.
        1. Unemployed. Gt. Brit. 2. Insurance, Unemployment. Gt. Brit. I. Title.

NN   0060450   NcD

National Protestant Alliance of the United States.
Constitution and by-laws of subordinate lodges of the National Protestant Alliance of the United States.   Philadelphia, 1874.   14 p.   24°.

"Principles of the National Protestant Alliance," 5 p. at end.

NN   0060451   NN

National Protestant Alliance of the United States.
Constitution and by-laws of supreme excellent national grand lodge and subordinate lodges of the National Protestant Alliance of the United States.   Philadelphia: J. G. Bates, 1874.   14, 5 p.   24°.

NN   0060452   NN

National Protestant Committee on Scouting.
The scout program in Protestant churches. A manual of practical procedures related to the program of the church.   N. Y., Protestant committee on scouting, n.d.
xii, 82 p.   illus.   20.5 cm.

NN   0060453   MiDW

National Protestant Committee on Scouting.
The scouting program in Protestant churches; a manual showing how the Protestant churches and the Boy Scouts of America can work together in the interest of the boy membership of the church. ₍New York, Boy Scouts of America, ᶜ1951.

50 p.   illus. 21 cm.

1. Boy Scouts. 2. Church work with children.   I. Title.

HS3313.B5N3   369.43   52-19507 ‡

NN   0060454   DLC

VOLUME 407

National Protestant Council on Higher Education.

Annual report...
[no.]

[New York, 191   22½cm.
nos.

1. Education, Moral and religious—Per. and soc. publ.—
U.S.

NN 0060455   NN PPLT PPPrHi NcD OO DHEW

National Protestant Council on Higher Education.
Christian education
see   The Christian scholar.

BV1460 National Protestant Council on Higher Education.
.C58
Christian higher education. A handbook. 1928–
Washington [etc.]

BV1460 National Protestant Council on Higher Education.
.C6
The Christian scholar.
[Somerville, N. J., etc.]

National Protestant Council on Higher Education.

Does education pay? Chicago, Illinois.
The Council of church boards of education
and the Association of American colleges,
1919.
(12) p. illus. (incl.) diagrs.) 20½ cm
(Philomath college bulletin, vol. 14, no.7,
May, 1919)

NN 0060459   DHEW

National Protestant Council on Higher Education.
Association of American colleges.
The efficient college. Read before the Association of
American colleges, at Chicago, Ill., January 21st, 1916.
[Chicago? 1916]

National Protestant Council on Higher Education.
Handbook
see
Christian higher education. A handbook.

FOR OTHER EDITIONS
SEE MAIN ENTRY
National Protestant Council on Higher Education.
Wickey, Gould, 1891–
A national survey of courses in Bible and religion in Amer-
ican universities and colleges, under the auspices of the Coun-
cil of church boards of education [by] Gould Wickey and Ruth
A. Eckhart ... [Bloomington, Ind., Printed for the Indiana
council on religion in higher education] 1936.

National Protestant Council on Higher Education.
... Proceedings of the ... annual meeting ...
Lancaster, Pa., 19-

NN 0060463   WaPS

National Protestant Council on Higher Education.
A statistical survey of Illinois colleges, by B. Warren
Brown, survey secretary, under the direction of Richard
Watson Cooper, executive secretary. [Chicago, 1917]

78 p. diagrs. 23 cm.

Published by the council under its earlier name: Council of Church
Boards of Education.

1. Universities and colleges—Illinois—Stat.   I. Brown, Benjamin
Warren, 1885–

LA267.N35   E 17–408 rev*
U. S. Office of Education.   Library
for Library of Congress   [r55c½]]

NN 0060464   DHEW NN OU ICJ OO DLC

National Protestant Council on Higher Education.
Kelly, Robert Lincoln, 1865–
Theological education in America; a study of one hundred
sixty-one theological schools in the United States and Canada,
by Robert L. Kelly ... with a foreword by Rt. Rev. Charles
Henry Brent ... New York, George H. Doran company [1924]

National Protestant Council on Higher Education.
Yearbook, 1919. Chicago, 1919.

NN 0060466   ODW

National Protestant Council on Higher Education
see also National Council of the Churches of Christ in
the United States of America.

National Protestant magazine. v.1–3;
1844–46. New York, 1844–46.
3v.

NN 0060468   KyU

National Protestant Society.
Appeal of the protestants of Ireland, to their brethren,
the protestants of England and Wales. *London:
Roake & Varty, printers,* [1832]. 1l. f°.

NN 0060469   NN

National Protestant Union.
Last words to electors; Mr. Gladstone's con-
fessions and Romish tendencies reviewed
see under title

National proverbs: Arabia. London, F. Palmer [1913]
3 p. l., 9–76 p. 17°ᵐ.
Title in red and black, within black ornamental woodcut borders.
Text in black, within red ruled borders.

1. Proverbs, Arabian.

NN 0060471   MiU ICN NN OCH

National proverbs: Belgium, comp. by Jan Tratsaert ..
London, F. & C. Palmer [1915]
79, [1] p. 17°ᵐ.
Text in Flemish and French, with English translation on opposite page.
Title in yellow and black within ornamental woodcut borders.
Text within yellow ruled borders.

1. Proverbs, Belgian.   I. Tratsaert, Jan.

NN 0060472   MiU

National proverbs: China. London, F. Palmer [1913]
3 p. l., 9–81 p. 17°ᵐ.
Title in yellow and blue, within blue ornamental woodcut borders.
Text in blue, within yellow ruled borders.

1. Proverbs, Chinese.

NN 0060473   MiU MH NN UU IU

National proverbs: England.   London: F. & C. Palmer, Ltd.
[1915.]   3 p.l., 5–78 p.   16°.

1. Proverbs (English).
N. Y. P. L.   May 28, 1920.

NN 0060474   NN

NATIONAL Proverbs. France. London, F. Palmer,
[1913].
pp. 91.
Text in English and French.   Prov.150.17

NN 0060475   MH

National proverbs: France.   Philadelphia: D. McKay [1913].
91 p.   16°.
Printed in England.
Text in French and English.

1. Proverbs (French).
N. Y. P. L.   June 10, 1929.

NN 0060476   NN

National proverbs: Holland. London, **F. & C. Palmer**
[1915]
3 p. l., 9–78 p. 17°ᵐ.
Title in red and brown, within brown ornamental woodcut borders.
Text in brown, within red ruled borders.

1. Proverbs, Dutch.

NN 0060477   MiU NN

National proverbs: India. London, C. Palmer & Hay-
ward [1916]
63, [1] p. 17°ᵐ.
"The present volume of Indian proverbs has been selected by ... Mr. Abdul
Hamid Minhas."
Title in yellow and black, within ornamental woodcut borders.
Text within yellow ruled borders.

1. Proverbs, Indian.   I. Abdul Hamid Minhas.

NN 0060478   MiU OCl

National proverbs: Ireland.   Philadelphia: D. McKay [191–].
86 p.   16°.
Printed in England.

1. Proverbs (Irish).
N. Y. P. L.   June 10, 1920.

NN 0060479   NN

National proverbs: Ireland. London, F. Palmer,
[1913]
86 p. 17 cm.

NN 0060480   MH CaBVaU

398.9 National proverbs: Italy.   Philadelphia,
N277   David McKay [n.d.]
91p. 17cm.
"Printed at the Arden Press, Letchworth,
England".
Text in Italian and English in green print
within red line borders.

1. Proverbs, Italian.

NN 0060481   NcU NNC MH

VOLUME 407

Y
0571
.61
    National proverbs: Italy.   London[1913]
        Italian and English on opposite pages.

NN 0060482   ICN

    National proverbs: Japan. Philadelphia,
D. McKay [191-?]
    cover-title, 76 p.

    1. Proverbs, Japanese.

NN 0060483   NNC MH CU

398.9
N2771
    National proverbs: Japan.   London, F. Palmer
[1913]
    76p.   17cm.

    1. Proverbs, Japanese.

NN 0060484   UU

PG3130
N4
    National proverbs: Russia.   London,
F.Palmer [1913]
    79 p. 17cm.

    1.Folk literature. Russian - Translations into English.

NN 0060485   CSt MoU CU MH NNC MiU ICN

    National proverbs: Serbia. London, C. **Palmer and Hayward** [1915]
    91 p.   17ᶜᵐ.
    "The present volume of Serbian proverbs has been selected by **Miss K. Amy** Turner ... valuable assistance in the compilation was ... given by ... **M. W. M. Petrovitch** ..."
    Title in red and blue, within blue ornamental woodcut border.
    Text in blue, within red ruled border.

    1. Proverbs, Serbian.   ɪ. Turner, K. Amy, comp.

NN 0060486   MiU MH CU InU

    National proverbs: Spain.   Philadelphia: D. McKay [1913]
    95 p. 16cm.
    Printed in England.
    Spanish and English on opposite pages.

948126A. 1. Proverbs, Spanish.
N. Y. P. L.   October 25, 1938

NN 0060487   NN MH ViU

    National proverbs: Wales. [1st ed.] **London,**
C. Palmer [1920]
    53 p.

    Welsh and English.

    1. Proverbs, Welsh.

NN 0060488   NNC MH MiU

    National Provident Institution, London.
        A record of the first hundred years of the National Provident Institution
        see under   Hazell, Stanley.

HG8853
.N3
1836
    National Provident institution , London.
      [Tables] London, Bradbury and Evans, printers, 1836.
      15 p. tables. 22 cm.

      1. Insurance, Life--Gt. Brit.--Rates and tables.

NN 0060490   MB

    National Provident Institution for Assurance of Lives, Endowments, and Annuities
      see   National Provident Institution, London.

    National Provincial and Union Bank
    see **National Provincial Bank, ltd.**

    National Provincial Bank, Ltd.
      Annual general meeting...
19

[London, 19   8°.
  no.
    Report year ends Jan. 30.

1. Banks and banking—Gt. Br.—   Eng.—London.
N. Y. P. L.   October 27, 1930

NN 0060493   NN ICJ

    National Provincial Bank Limited.
      ...Annual report and balance sheet...

London   4°.
  no.   tables.
    Fitting-title.

1. Banks and banking—Gt. Br.
N. Y. P. L.   September 3, 1926

NN 0060494   NN ICJ

    National provincial bank, ltd.
      Bold adventure

      see under

      Ellis, Aytoun.

    National Provincial Bank, Limited.
      National Provincial Bank, Limited. [London, 1927.] 28 p.
  illus. 8°.
    Repr.: Bankers' magazine. Jan., 1927.

1. Banks and banking—Gt. Br.—Eng.   —London.
N. Y. P. L.   November 29, 1927

NN 0060496   NN

332.10942
N213r
    National Provincial Bank, Ltd.
      Review. no.1-   Feb. 1948-
    London.
      no. in v. illus. 25cm.

      1. Banks and banking - Gt. Brit. 2. Gt. Brit. - Econ. condit. - Period.

NN 0060497   TxU IU NN OrU CLSU CtY IU CLU

    National Provincial Bank of England
    see **National Provincial Bank, ltd.**

    The National provisioner.
      New York [The National provisioner publishing co.; etc., etc.] 18
        v. illus. (incl. ports.) 32½ cm. weekly.
      Editors: J. H. Senner (with J. F. Hobbs, Aug. 1898–July 1902; and others)
      Official organ of the American meat packers' association, Oct. 1906-

      1. Meat industry and trade—Period.   ɪ. Senner, Joseph Henry, 1846–1908, ed. ɪɪ. Hobbs, John F., ed. ɪɪɪ. American meat institute.

TS1950.N3   CA 8—3205 Unrev'd

    GU CaBVaU IU ViBlbV
NN 0060499   DLC OU MiU DFT MB ICRL ICJ ScCleU

    National Provisioner.
      Consolidated catalogs and engineering bluebook
      see under title

    National provisioner.
      Meat packers guide, 1939-
      see under title

50
N214
    National provisioner.
      ...The meat packing industry... [Chicago?]
    1940.
      22 p.   illus.,map. 30cm.
      At head of title: An active, receptive, year-around market for your products.

      1. Meat industry and trade. U.S.

NN 0060502   DNAL

q664.9
N213m
    National provisioner.
      Meat plant refrigeration and air conditioning ...
    The first thirty-seven lessons on the National provisioner's course.   [Chicago, Ill., The National provisioner, 19
      v. illus., tables, diagrs.

      1. Meat industry and trade--U.S. 2. Refrigeration and refrigerating machinery. I. Title.

NN 0060503   DNAL MiD OCl IU

    National provisioner.

    The Packers' encyclopedia; blue book of the American meat packing and allied industries; a hand-book of modern packing house practice, a statistical manual of the meat and allied industries, and a directory of the meat packing, provision, sausage manufacturing, rendering and affiliated trades. Paul I. Aldrich, editor. Chicago, The National provisioner [1922]

    National provisioner.

    The Packers' encyclopedia.
      Pork packing; volume ɪɪ—revised edition, the Packers' encyclopedia; a test book for the pork packer and sausage maker, compiled by A. W. Goedert and S. K. Maddux. Chicago, Ill., The National provisioner [1932]

HD9413
.A5
    The National provisioner.

    Purchasing guide for the meat industry. v. 1-
    1939–
    Chicago, National provisioner [etc.]

    National provisioner.

    The Packers' encyclopedia.
      Sausage and meat specialties; part 3. The Packer's encyclopedia; a practical operating handbook for the sausage and meat specialty manufacturer, compiled by the National provisioner. Chicago, Ill., The National provisioner [1938]

VOLUME 407

HD9410.5
.N3

The National provisioner.
The "significant sixty"; a historical
report on the progress and development
of the meat packing industry, 1891-1951.
375 p. illus., ports. 29 cm. (The
National provisioner. sec.2. Jan. 26, 1952)

1. Meat industry and trade—U.S.

NN 0060508   TU MB NIC InU PPT CU MiD

Z
338.176213
N213n   National provisioner.
Why the price of meat is high.   [New York,
1902?]
17ℓ.   20cm.

"Extracts from the National provisioner of
dates April 5th and 12th."

1. Beef - Prices.   I. Title.

NN 0060509   TxU

National provisioner publishing co.
Directory and hand-book of the meat and provision
trades and their allied industries for the United States
and Canada ... New York, Chicago [etc.] The National
provisioner publishing co. [1895]
441 p. illus., fold. tab. 19½ᶜᵐ.
Advertising matter interspersed.
CONTENTS.—pt. I. Directory and trade lists.—pt. II. (a) Pork and beef
packing. (b) Cotton-seed oil manufacture. (c) Condensed survey of the
trade.
1. Meat industry and trade—U. S.—Direct. 2. Meat industry and trade—
Canada—Direct. 3. Cotton-seed oil.   I. Title.

Library of Congress   HD9413.N3   11—5560

NN 0060510   DLC ViU IdU

National provisioner publishing co.
The manufacture of cotton seed oil and allied products,
including cake, meal, foots, soap-stock, &c. The application and uses of machinery. Complete list of mills, re-
fineries in the United States and abroad. New York,
Chicago [etc.] The National provisioner publishing co.
[1897]
3 p. l., 88 p. 19½ᶜᵐ.

1. Cotton-seed oil.

Library of Congress   [TP681.N27   9—2353†

NN 0060511   DLC MU

National provisioner publishing company.
The manufacture of glue and gelatine, the application and uses
of machinery, etc. Complete list of manufacturers and dealers in
the United States and Canada ... New York [etc.] The National provisioner pub. co. [1898]   223 p.   illus.   20cm.

Based upon a series of articles published in the National provisioner, with much
additional material.
Many pages left blank for "Memoranda."

872585A. 1. Pastes, glues, etc.—   Manufacture. 2. Pastes, glues,
etc.—Manufacture—Direct.
N. Y. P. L.   January 10, 1938

NN 0060512   NN ICJ

The national psalmist, 1859,
see under   Hackett, Charles Danvers,
compiler.

The national psalmist; a collection of the most
popular and useful psalm and hymn tunes;
together with a great variety of new tunes,
anthems, sentences, and chants; the whole
forming a most complete manual of church
music for choirs, congregations ... and
musical associations... 1848, [c. 1848]
see under   Mason, Lowell, 1792-1872, comp.

National psalmody... A collection of tunes,.
set to a course of Psalms selected from the new
version by the Rev. J. T. Barrett... London,
1819
see under   Jacob, Benjamin,
1778-1829.

The national psalmist. Consisting of original
and standard psalm and hymn tunes, chants,
responses, and anthems. ...
see under   Hackett, Charles Danvers,
comp.

BF173
A2N3   National Psychological Association for
Psychoanalysis.
Bulletin.
New York.
v.   22cm.

1. Psychology - Societies, etc.
2. Psychoanalysis - Societies, etc.

NN 0060517   NcRS

HV1598
.B38   National Psychological Research Council for the
Blind.
Bauman, Mary Kinsey, 1910–
A manual for the psychological examination of the adult
blind; prepared by Mary K. Bauman and Samuel P. Hayes.
New York, Psychological Corp., ᶜ1951.

National Psychological Research Council for the Blind.
Research suggestions on psychological problems associated
with blindness. [Washington] Federal Security Agency,
Office of Vocational Rehabilitation [1951]
III, 20 p. 24 cm.
Bibliography: p. 17-20.

1. Blind.   I. Title.

HV1598.N3   362.4   51–61325

DNLM
NN 0060519   DLC IU NNU-W CU PP OrU OrCS Or WaTC

The National public accountant. v. 1-6, no. 8; Oct. 1949–
Aug. 1956. Washington [etc.] National Society of Public
Accountants.
6 v. in 4. illus., ports. 24-29 cm. monthly (irregular)
Ceased publication with Aug.? 1956 issue.
Absorbed the society's Flash in May 1951.
Superseded in Oct. 1956 by the National public accountant and the
PA (later, the National public accountant)
L. C. set incomplete; scattered numbers wanting.

1. Accounting—Period.   I. National Society of Public Accountants.
HF5601.N334   60–40521

NN 0060520   DLC

National public and labor relations service
bureau, inc., New York.
Mariano, John Horace.
The employer and his labor relations, by John H. Mariano ..
New York city, National public & labor relations service bureau,
inc. [ᶜ1941]

National public and labor relations service
bureau, inc., New York.
Mariano, John Horace.
Outlines for post-war planning (a syllabus of suggestions,
plans, ideas) by John H. Mariano ... New York city, National public and labor relations service bureau, inc. [1943]

National public and labor relations service
bureau, inc., New York.
Mariano, John Horace.
Smaller business and post war industrial relations, by John
H. Mariano ... New York city, National public and labor rela-
tions service bureau, inc. [1943]

HD6961
.M3   National public and labor relations service
bureau, inc., New York.
Mariano, John Horace.
Wartime labor relations, by John H. Mariano ... New York
city, National public & labor relations service bureau, inc. [1944]

F1418
.N3   National public discussions committee.
The National extempore-discussion contest on inter-American
affairs for colleges and universities. Sponsored by Office of
coordinator of inter-American affairs. 1942. New York
city, National public discussions committee, inc. [1942]

National public domain league.
Bulletin [s]

HD189
.N3

NN 0060526   DLC DNW

National public domain league.
Why you should join the National public domain
league.
[Denver, 1909]

HD189
.N35

NN 0060527   DLC

National Public Health Engineering Conference, *University
of Florida*
see
Florida Municipal and Sanitary Engineering Conference,
University of Florida.

... National public health; papers, opinions, letters,
etc., relative to the national public health, in the consideration of Senate bill (S. 6049) "A bill establishing a
Department of public health, and for other purposes ..."
Washington, Govt. print. off., 1910.
240 p. diagrs. 23ᶜᵐ. ([U.S.] 61st Cong., 2d sess. Senate. Doc. 637)
Presented by Mr. Owen. Referred to the Committee on public health
and national quarantine and ordered printed, June 18, 1910.
"S. 6049 ... A bill establishing a Department of public health, and for
other purposes": verso of t.-p.
1. U. S.—Sanit. affairs. 2. Hygiene, Public.   I. Owen, Robert Latham, 1856–   II. U. S. Congress. Senate. Committee on public
health and national quarantine. III. U. S. 61st Cong., 2d sess., 1909-1910.
Senate.

Library of Congress   RA11.A3 1910 d   10–35983

NN 0060529   DLC DNLM DL ICJ MiU OO

National Public Housing Conference
see
National Housing Conference.

National public school and free press defense
league.
The Protestant standard; the new voice of the old menace.
v. 1–   May 24, 1920–
East Orange, N. J., 1920–

VOLUME 407

National public school association.

Richson, Charles, 1806–1874.
A comparison of two educational bills of 1852. A letter to Salis Schwabe, esq., to show the points of agreement and difference in the educational measures proposed by the National public school association and the Manchester and Salford committee on education. By Rev. Charles Richson, M. A. London, Rivingtons; [etc., etc., 1852]

National public school association.

Explanations on the objects of education, as proposed by the National public school association ... London, Groombridge and sons, 1851.

21 p. 19¼ᶜᵐ.
Reprinted from the 'Westminster and foreign quarterly review,' for July, 1851.

1. Education—Gt. Brit. 2. Religious education—Gt. Brit.
E 10–182
Library, U. S. Bur. of   Education LA633.N2

NN   0060533   DHEW

National public school association.

Historical sketch of educational movements, preceding the formation of the National public school association ... London, Groombridge and sons [1851]

30 p. 20ᶜᵐ.
Reprinted from the "Westminster and foreign quarterly review," for January, 1851.

1. Church and education [in] Gt. Brit. 2. National public school association.
E 14–2269
Library, U. S. Bur. of   Education LC116.G7N35

NN   0060534   DHEW

National public school association.

National education not necessarily governmental, sectarian or irreligious, shown in a series of papers, read at the meetings of the Lancashire public school association. London, C. Gilpin; [etc., etc.] 1850.

xviii, 212 p. 17½ᶜᵐ.
Introduction signed: Samuel Lucas.

1. Education—Gt. Brit. 2. Religious education—Gt. Brit. I. Lucas, Samuel, 1811–1865, ed.
E 10–1015
Library, U. S Bur. of   Education LA632.N25

NN   0060535   DHEW CtY

National Public School Association.
Report of the proceedings at a meeting of the general council of the Association, including a paper by the Rev. S. Davidson, ... held at Manchester, Dec. 1st, 1851.   Manchester, A. Ireland and Co., 1851.
28 p. 8°.
1. Education. Associations, U.S. 2. Davidson, Rev. S., D.D.

NN   0060536   NN

NATIONAL PUBLIC SCHOOLS' ASSOCIATION.

See NATIONAL PUBLIC SCHOOL ASSOCIATION.

National public utilities committee.
... Report. no. 2- July, 1918-
Washington, 1918-
v.

NN 0060538   MH-BA

National public welfare league, Kansas City.
   (Miscellaneous pamphlets)
Kansas City (n.d.)
3 v.

NN   0060539   DL

NATIONAL PUBLIC WORKS DEPARTMENT ASSOCIATION.
This tells why the government should have a department of public works. Presented by the National public works department association.   [Washington, D.C., 1921?] 32 p. incl. tables. 23cm.

Cover-title.

900983A. 1. United States—Executive departments, etc., Proposed—Public works.

NN 0060540   NN

National publications society series.
no. 1

Bombay: Vora & co., publishers, ltd. [1937   18½cm.
v.

1. No subject. I. National   publications society.
N. Y. P. L.   June 2, 1938

NN   0060541   NN

National publicity bill organization.
Belmont, Perry, 1851–
   ... The abolition of the secrecy of party funds: the origin of the movement, its purpose and effect, by Perry Belmont ... Washington [Govt. print. off.] 1912.

National publicity bill organization.
   ... Annual report.
[Washington, Gov't print. off., 1907–
   v. 23ᶜᵐ.
   Report dated Jan. 7, 1907, is pub. as Senate doc. 195, 59th Cong., 2d sess., with title: ... Report of National publicity bill organization ... First annual report ...
   President: 1905, Perry Belmont.

1. Belmont, Perry, 1851–
6–35070

NN   0060543   DLC NjP

National publicity bill organization.
   ... Minutes of first meeting in Washington, D. C., and an address to the public. Washington, D. C., Globe printing company [1906]
   cover-title, 28 p. 23ᶜᵐ.

1. Elections—U. S.—Campaign funds.
45–50667
Library of Congress   JK1997.N3

NN   0060544   DLC

National publicity bill organization.
   ... Publicity of election contributions and expenditures ... Abstract of laws relating to the publicity of election contributions and expenditures. Prepared by the National publicity bill organization. To accompany S. 5777 ... [Washington, Gov't print. off., 1908]
   18 p. 23ᶜᵐ. [U. S.] 60th Cong., 1st sess. Senate. Doc. 337)
   Presented by Mr. Tillman, referred to the Committee on privileges and elections and ordered printed, Feb. 27, 1908.
   Laws of various states.
   1. Election law—U. S.   I. U. S. 60th Cong., 1st sess., 1907–1908. Senate.
8–35183
Library of Congress   JK1997.A4 1908a

NN 0060545   DLC MiU OO ICJ

National publicity bill organization.
Belmont, Perry, 1851–
   Return to secret party funds; value of Reed committee, by Perry Belmont ... New York, London, G. P. Putnam's sons, 1927.

National Publicity Bill Organization.
   Speeches of Hon. Perry Belmont, president, and Hon. William Jennings Bryan, Hon. Samuel Gompers, Hon. William E. Chandler, Hon. Edwin Warfield, Hon Herman A. Metz, Hon. Alexander Troup, at a meeting of the National Publicity Bill organization, held at the Victoria Hotel, N.Y., Tuesday, April 16, 1907. [n.p. 1907]
   22p.

YA
8125

NN   0060547   DLC NjP

National publicity council for health and welfare services.
Annual reports and how to improve them, edited by Mary Swain Routzahn ... New York, Social work publicity council, 1941.

1 p. l., 20 numb. l. 28ᶜᵐ.
Reproduced from type-written copy.

1. Charity organization. 2. Reports—Preparation.   I. Routzahn, Mary Brayton (Swain) 1880–   ed. II. Title.
41–20583 Revised
Library of Congress   HV29.N3
[r44e2]   361.8

NN   0060548   DLC CaBVaU NN NNC OU CU

National publicity council for health and welfare services, inc.
   Appraising your interpretation program.
N.Y., Social work publicity council, 1938.
8 p. 28 cm.

NN   0060549   PPT

National publicity council for health and welfare services, inc.
   Board education handbook
   see under title

National Publicity Council for Health and Welfare Services.
   The board member's manual
   see under Demorest, Charlotte K.

National publicity council for wealth and welfare services.
The case story. New York, N.Y.: Social Work Publicity Council, 1935. 18 f. 28cm.

Cover-title.
Reproduced from typewritten copy; cover printed.

820951A. 1. Social service—Methodology. I. Title.

NN   0060552   NN IaU IU

National publicity council for health and welfare services.

The case worker interprets. Chapters from experience in writing, broadcasting, movie making, organizing meetings, editing news. New York, N. Y., Social work publicity council, 1937.
   cover-title, 16 p. 28 cm.

Mimeographed; cover printed.
"Made up in part of excerpts from papers presented at a joint meeting of the Social work publicity council and the Family welfare association of America,   held ... in connection with the 1937   session of the National conference of social work. and in part of brief

Continued in next column

VOLUME 407

Continued from preceding column

descriptions of projects ... reported by correspondence." p. 2.
"For ready reference": p. 16.

1. Advertising – Social service. 2. Publicity.
3. Social service.   I. Title.

NN   0060554   Vi

**National publicity council for health
and welfare services.
Channels.**
New York, Social work publicity council [19

National publicity council for health
and welfare services.
Editorial opinion and social work; a selection of representative
newspaper editorials.   New York, N. Y.: Social work publicity
council, 1934.   17 p.   27 x 21½cm.

1. Social work.
N.Y.P.L.   February 4, 1938

NN   0060556   NN IaU

National publicity council for health and welfare services.
Exhibits, how to plan and make them ...   New York, National publicity council for health and welfare services (formerly Social work publicity council) 1943.
1 p. l., 29 p. illus. 27½ᵐ. ["How-to-do-it" series]
Reproduced from type-written copy.
"Books for exhibit makers": p. 29.

1. Exhibitions. 2. Publicity.   I. Title.

Teachers college library,   Columbia univ.
for Library of Congress   [3]

                                         A 45–3754

NN   0060557   NNC-T Mi CU OrU-M WaS NNC OU

606
N213e
1946   NATIONAL PUBLICITY COUNCIL FOR HEALTH AND WELFARE SERVICES.
Exhibits, how to plan and make them ...   New York, National publicity council for health and welfare services, 1946.
1 p. l., 29 p. illus. 27½cm. ["How-to-do-it" series]
Reproduced from type-written copy.
"Books for exhibit makers": p. 29.
"[First printing] March 1943. Second printing, 1946."
1. Exhibitions.   2. Publicity. I. Title.

NN   0060558   TxU NN

National publicity council for health
and welfare services.
Filming social facts; a symposium on the making and use of
motion pictures, by B. N. Skellie...Arch A. Mercey...[and] Elsa
Volckmann...   New York, Social work publicity council, 1939.
19 f.   28cm.

1. Moving pictures—Social and
N.Y.P.L.   economic aspects. I. Skellie, B. N.
                                              April 21, 1948

NN   0060559   NN

National publicity council for health and welfare services.
Good press relations; based on interviews with 22 newspaper
editors and reporters in 13 cities. New York, N. Y., Social
work publicity council, 1939.
cover-title, 3 p. l., 3–21 numb. l. 28½ᵐ.
Compiled by Florence M. Seder.

1. Social service. 2. Press.   I. Seder, Florence M., comp. II. Title.
                                                       A 44–1607 rev
Kentucky. Univ. Library
for Library of Congress   [r47c2]

NN   0060560   KyU

PN4130   National publicity council for health and
.P3   welfare services.
Partridge, Helen, 1902–
How to make a speech and enjoy it, by Helen Partridge,
illustrated by Mary Stevens. New York, National publicity
council, 1944.

National publicity council for health and
welfare services.
Routzahn, *Mrs.* Mary Brayton (Swain) 1880–
How to plan a public relations program, by Mary Swain
Routzahn ... New York, N. Y., Social work publicity council,
1939.

National Publicity Council for Health and Welfare
Services.
Interpretation of public social work, compiled from the News
bulletins, December, 1934 – May, 1935...   New York, N. Y.:
Social Work Publicity Council, 1935. 15 f. 28cm.

Reproduced from typewritten copy.
CONTENTS.—Dust storms of criticism hit relief.—How the public agencies tell
their story: The defensive attitude. Taking the offensive.—Specific approaches to their
public.—Some sources for facts and philosophies.

820951A. 1. Charities, Public—U. S.,   1934–1935. 2. Labor, Unemployed—
N.Y.P.L.   U. S., 1934–1935.
                                                       May 12, 1936

NN   0060563   NN IaU

National Publicity Council for Health and Welfare Services.
Meeting criticisms of public welfare.   New York: Social work
publicity council, 1935. 6 f. 27½cm.
Cover-title.
Reproduced from typewritten copy.

1. Charities, Public—U. S.
N.Y.P.L.   I. Title.
                                              January 4, 1938

NN   0060564   NN IaU

National publicity council for health and welfare services, inc.
...Memo to members.

New York, 1946.   no.   28cm.
Irregular.

1. Publicity, Social service—Per.   and soc. publ.—U. S.
N.Y.P.L.   December 6, 1951

NN   0060565   NN

National Publicity Council for Health and Welfare Services.
News bulletin.
no.

New York, 192   4°.
nos.
Monthly (irregular).
Multigraphed.

1. Social work—Per. and soc. publ.—   U. S.
N.Y.P.L.   October 14, 1931

NN   0060566   NN DL NNF

LC6519   National publicity council for health and
.H3   welfare services.
Haller, Ruth.
Planning your meeting, by Ruth Haller ... New York, N. Y.,
National publicity council, 1944.

National publicity council for health and welfare services.
Public relations in public welfare; a digest for interpreters.
Current public attitudes toward relief and people on relief—
how these attitudes came about—facts and figures which answer misinterpreters. New York, N. Y., Social work publicity
council, 1938.
cover-title. 2 p. l., 2–17 numb. l. 28ᵐ.
Compiled by Hilary Campbell and Mary Swain Routzahn.
"This is one of the 'how-to-do-it' pamphlets which are published from
time to time by the Council."—p. [2] of cover.

1. Social service. 2. Unemployed—U. S. 3. U. S.—Econ. condit.—
1918–1945.   I. Campbell, Miss Hilary, comp. II. Routzahn, Mary
Brayton (Swain) 1880– joint comp. III. Title.
                                                       A 40–1377 rev
Grosvenor library   HV41.S7
for Library of Congress   [r47c2]

NN   0060568   NBuG NN CU PBm LU

National Publicity Council for Health and Welfare
Services.
Public relations program
see under   Bright, Sallie Everson, 1905–

National Publicity Council for Health and Welfare
Services.
[Publications]
Library has: [no. 1–20]   1935–[1942]

NN   0060570   MiD

National Publicity Council for Health and Welfare Services.
Publicity awards.
192

New York, 192   4°.
nos.
1929, also called Special bulletin.
Title of institution varies: 19   Committee on Publicity Methods in Social
Work, New York; 1930–   Social Work Publicity Council, New York.
Multigraphed.

1. Social work—Per. and soc. publ.
N.Y.P.L.   November 5, 1931

NN   0060571   NN

301.154
N21p   [National publicity council for health and welfare
        services]
        [Publicity directory...   New York, the Council
1943]
        caption-title, pp. 16-32. 25½cm.
Excerpt from Channels, v.20, no.4, 20th
anniversary issue, Feb. 1943.

1. Publicity. 2. Hygiene, Public. 3. Social
service. I. Title.

NN   0060572   LU

National Publicity Council for Health and Welfare
Services.
Reading references on interpretation and
publicity, 1940 ...   New York, 1940.
12 l.
1. Social service.— Bibl.

NN   0060573   ICU

361.8   National Publicity Council for Health and Welfare
Sol3r   Services.
        [Rural routes to community understanding of pub-
lic welfare programs.   New York, Social work
publicity council, 1940]
caption-title, 19p. illus. 28½cm.
Mimeographed.

1. Sociology, Rural. 2. Social service.

NN   0060574   LU NN CU

National Publicity Council for Health and Welfare Services
Short plays about social problems; a descriptive list.
Revised, June, 1935...   New York city: Social Work Pub-
licity Council [1935] 8 f. 27½cm.
Cover-title.
Reproduced from typewritten copy.

874624A. 1. Drama, American—Bibl. 2. Drama, American—
Political and social relations—Bibl.

NN   0060575   NN

VOLUME 407

National Publicity Council for Health & Welfare Service.
Slides, how to make and use them. New possibilities of the lantern slide. Getting slides made--and making them. Filmslides. Sound slidefilms. Apparatus--types and makers. Sources of materials for slide-making.   New York, National publicity council, 1941.
cover-title, 10p. 28cm.

1. Lantern slides.   I. Title.

NN   0060576   LU

National Publicity Council for Health and Welfare Services.
Speaking up for character-building and recreation. Issued by the Social Work Publicity Council and the united educational program of the National Social Work Council, 1932.   [New York] 1932.   31 p.   23cm.

816848A. 1. Character. 2. Recreation. I National Social Work Council, New York.

NN   0060577   NN DL

National Publicity Council for Health and Welfare Services.
Social work at the microphone.   New York, N. Y.: Social Work Publicity Council [1935]   17 f.   28cm.

Cover-title.
Reproduced from typewritten copy; cover printed.
Bibliography, f. 14-16.

820951A. 1. Social service.   2. Radio—Broadcasting. I. Title.
N. Y. P. L.   May 12, 1936

NN   0060578   NN IaU KyU

National Publicity Council for Health and Welfare Services.
The volunteer as an interpreter of social work.   New York: Social work publicity council, 1936.   7 f.   27½cm.

Cover-title.
Reproduced from typewritten copy.

1. Social service—Methodology.
N. Y. P. L.

NN   0060579   NN IaU

National Publicity Council for Health and Welfare Services.
The volunteer as an interpreter of social work.   New York, Social work publicity council [1936]
7 numb. l.   29 cm.
cover-title.
Mimeographed.
"Second printing, June, 1936".
1. Social service. I. Title.

NN   0060580   CU

National Publicity Council for Health and Welfare Services.
Writing the annual report.   New York, N.Y.: Social Work Publicity Council, 1935.   11 f.   27½cm.

Cover-title.
Reproduced from typewritten copy.

820951A. 1. Social service—Papers, reports, etc. 2. Reports—Preparation.

NN   0060581   NN IaU

National publicity council for health and welfare services.
Writing the annual report ... 5th ed., rev. and enl., June 1938. New York, N. Y., Social work publicity council, 1938.
cover-title, 1 p. l., 12 numb. l.   28ᶜᵐ.
Mimeographed.

1. Social service. 2. Reports—Preparation.   I. Title.
A 40–3138 rev

No. Carolina. Univ. Libr.
for Library of Congress   [r47c2]

NN   0060582   NcU PPT

National Publicity Council for health & welfare services. Chicago Chapter.

"I see by the papers..."   (Chicago, 1937)
cover-title, 60 p. incl. illus., tables, diagrs.   27½cm.

NN   0060583   DL

The National publisher.
[Chicago] National Editorial Assn.
v. illus., ports. 30 cm. monthly.
Began publication in 1919. Cf. Union list of serials.

1. Journalism—Period.   I. National Editorial Association.

PN4700.N38   58–21025

NN   0060584   DLC NN TxU UU NNC

National Publishers Association
see
Magazine Publishers Association.

DKMEE   National Publishing Association for the
1N27   Promotion of Holiness.
P   Proceedings of holiness conferences held at Cincinnati, Nov. 26, 1877, and at New York, Dec. 17, 1877. Philadelphia, [n.d.]
225 p.

Microfilm copy (positive) made by M.I.T. Libraries, 1964.

1. Methodist Chur   ch - Congresses. I. National Holiness   Association.

NN   0060586   WHi

National Publishing Co.
Commerce, Manufacturers and resources of Providence, R. I. A historical, statistical and descriptive review, 1882. Prov., 1882.
148p. 8°

NN   0060587   MWA

NATIONAL publishing company.
᪲ Commerce, manufactures, and resources of the city of Newark.
[N. Y.] 1881. 132 pp. Illus. 8°.

NN   0060588   MB

National publishing co.
[Babcock, Louis M   ]
The Fifty-second Congress. A souvenir album. Containing photographic presentments of the members and officers of both houses, together with the contemporaneous officials of the other branches of the government at Washington and the principal government buildings. Copyright, 1893, by Louis M. Babcock. Washington, D. C., New York, National publishing co., ᶜ1893.

National publishing company,
Lima city and Allen County directory... 1897–98...
Lima, O., National publishing co., 1897
2 p. l., 13–688 p.

NN   0060590   OClWHi

National Publishing Company, Akron, O.
Illustrated industrial souvenir magazine
Akron and vicinity
see under title

National Publishing Company, Boston.
Complete map of Vermont showing highways and natural features with an index of all cities, villages, post-offices and railroad stations, compiled from the latest government surveys and original sources.   Boston, c1902.
1 sheet 36 x 56 in folded in covers.
Scale: 3 miles to an inch.

NN   0060592   MH–BA

National Publishing Company, Boston.
"Good roads." The standard road-book. Connecticut. Complete road-maps, showing quality of the roads...   Boston, 1897.
28 l.   double maps.   8°.   (New England series. Book 9.)

1. Cycling—Guides, maps, etc.,   U. S.: Connecticut.
N. Y. P. L.   December 21, 1920

NN   0060593   NN CtY ICJ

National Publishing Company, Boston.
"Good roads". The standard road-book. Hudson river section
see under   National Publishing Co., New Haven.

National Publishing Company, Boston.
"Good roads." The standard road-book of New York State
see its   The standard road-book of New York State.

GZ901   National Publishing Company, Boston.
"G77   Imperial atlas of Gratiot county, Michigan
N2   ... Boston, 1901.
65, xxxii p. col. maps. 49 cm.

1. Gratiot county, Mich. - Maps.

NN   0060596   WHi DLC

National Publishing Company, Boston.
New railroad, post-office and county map of Kansas. Boston, ᶜ1902.
col. map 88 x 95 cm.
Scale 1 : 1,330,560; 21 miles to 1 inch.
"No. 56."
"With complete index of all post-offices and railroad stations, giving populations and locations."
On verso: The United States and its new possessions. [ca.] 1 : 6,840,000, "No. 50."

1. Kansas—Maps. 2. Railroads—Kansas—Maps. 3. U. S.—Maps.

G4200 1900 .N3   Map 65–554

NN   0060597   DLC

National Publishing Company, Boston.
New railroad, post-office and county map of Kansas. Boston, ᶜ1902.
col. map 88 x 95 cm.
Scale 1 : 1,330,560; 21 miles to 1 inch.
"With complete index of all post-offices and railroad stations, giving populations and locations."
"No. 249."
On verso: The United States and its new possessions. [ca.] 1 : 6,840,000, "No. 231."

1. Kansas—Maps. 2. Railroads—Kansas—Maps. 3. U. S.—Maps.

G4200 1902 .N3   Map 65–555

NN   0060598   DLC

F2   National Publishing Co., Boston.
N28   The National Publishing Company's railroad, post office, township and county map of Massachusetts, Rhode Island and Connecticut. Boston, Mass., c1900.
map.   90x95cm. fold. to 24½x12cm.

1. Massachusetts.-Description.-Maps.
2. Connecticut.-Description.-Maps.
3. Rhode Island.-   Description.-Maps.

NN   0060599   NBuG

VOLUME 407

National Publishing Co., *Boston,*   No. 31 in Map 118.2
The National Publishing Company's New railroad, post-office, township, and county map of New England, compiled from the latest government surveys and other official sources.
Boston. 1900. Size, 36 × 28¾ inches. Scale, 12 miles to 1 inch.
Submap. — Map of the business portion of Boston.

M4698 — New England. Geog. Maps.

NN 0060600   MB Nh

Map
G
3800
1901
N3

National Publishing Co., Boston, Mass.
New railroad, post office, township and county map of New York, with distances between stations.   Boston, ᶜ1901.
col. map 99 x 115 cm. folded to 25 cm.

Scale 7½ miles to 1 inch.

1.   New   York (State)--Maps.

NN 0060601   NIC

National publishing company, *Boston.*
Specials' manual; how to contract & train salesmen. Boston, Mass., National publishing company, 1901.
44 p. 17ᶜᵐ.

1. Commercial travelers.

1-18481

Library of Congress   HF5451.N3

NN 0060602   DLC

NATIONAL PUBLISHING COMPANY, Boston.
The standard road-book of New York State. Complete road-maps, showing quality of the roads.   Boston, c1897.   144 p.   36 double col. maps. 24cm. (New York series of "Standard road books." Book 1.)

At head of title: "Good roads."

1. New York(State)--Maps, 1897.   2. Roads--U.S.--New York.
I. New York series of "Standard   road books."   t. 1897.

NN 0060603   NN

National Publishing Co., *Boston.*   M912.742 Q200
The National Publishing Company's Topographic map of the White Mountains and central New Hampshire. Boston, Mass., The National Publishing Co., ᶜ1902.
1 map. 91¼x97ᶜᵐ.
Scale, 10.3ᶜᵐ.=8 miles.
"This map is based upon the latest U. S. gov't, state and private surveys and original field work."
Index to post offices and railroad stations, principal lakes, streams and mountains.

NN 0060604   ICJ

National publishing company, Boston, Mass.
Tourists' standard road book and directory of New York State...
Boston, 1897.

GV1045
.N3

NN 0060605   DLC

National Publishing Company, *Boston.*
The United States and its new possessions; Puerto Rico, Cuba, Hawaii, the Philippines and Alaska, with general maps of the continents of Europe, Asia, Africa and Pan-America. Boston, 1900, ᶜ1899.
col. map 88 x 96 cm.
Scale ca. 1:6,840,000.
"XXXIX."
Includes table of "Travel distances," and 10 inset maps.

1. U. S.—Maps.

G3700 1900 .N3   Map 65-560

NN 0060606   DLC

National Publishing Company, *Boston.*
The United States and its possessions: Puerto Rico, Hawaii, the Philippines and Alaska; with generalized maps of the continents of Europe, Asia, Africa and Pan-America. Boston, 1900, ᶜ1899.
col. map 88 x 96 cm.
Scale ca. 1:6,840,000.
"No. 50."
Includes 10 insets and distance table.

1. U. S.—Maps.

G3700 1900 .N3   Map 65-552

NN 0060607   DLC

National Publishing Company, *Boston.*
The United States and its new possessions; Puerto Rico, Cuba, Hawaii, Philippine Islands and Alaska; with general maps of Europe, Asia, Africa, and Pan-America. Boston, ᶜ1902.
col. map 88 x 95 cm.
Scale ca. 1:6,840,000.
"No. 233."
Includes "Travel distances," 10 insets, and index, "Cities in the United States."

1. U. S.—Maps.

G3700 1902 .N3   Map 65-553

NN 0060608   DLC

National Publishing Company, Chicago.
History of Harrison County, Iowa
see under title

National publishing company, *Indianapolis.*
Instructions applying to plates and copies. Modern writing. Indianapolis, Ind., National publishing company [1895]
26 p. 30 pl. 9 x 23ᶜᵐ.

1. Penmanship.

11-26560

Library of Congress   Z43.N27

NN 0060610   DLC

National publishing company, Louisville, Ky.
Illustrated industrial souvenir and magazine of Greater Peoria, "Pearl of the prairies"... Louisville, Ky., 1904.
64p. illus., ports. 35cm.

NN 0060611   IHi

National Publishing Co., New Haven.
Commerce, manufacturers & resources of New Haven, Conn.
see under title

National Publishing Co., *New Haven.*   974.7 P700
"Good roads." The standard road-book. Hudson river section. Complete road-maps, showing quality of the roads. .... Boston, Mass., National Publishing Co., ᶜ1897.
[23] p. 11 fold. maps. 23 x 11ᶜᵐ.   (New York series, book 2.)

NN 0060613   ICJ

National publishing company, inc., New Haven.
Illustrated memoir of the world war ... [New Haven, National publishing co., inc., ᶜ1930]

National publishing company, New Orleans.
Complete sketch of the Second District and the famous French market of the city of N.O.   N.O.,n.p.,1912

NN 0060615   LNHT

National publishing company, Philadelphia.
Illustrated biographical album of northeastern Nebraska ... Philadelphia, Omaha, National publishing company, 1893.

National Publishing Company, Philadelphia.
The National Plumbeotype Gallery
see under   Plumbe, John.

Atlas
coll'n

National Publishing Company, Philadelphia
Plat book of Nobles County, Minnesota. Compiled and published by the National Publishing Co. Philadelphia, Printed by F. Bourquin, 1888.
68 p. incl. 31 col. maps.   45x39cm.

NN 0060618   MnHi

Atlas
coll.

National publishing co, Philadelphia comp.
Plat book of Pocahontas County, Iowa, compiled and published by the National publishing co... [Philadelphia, 1887.
62 p. incl. 26 maps.   46cm.

NN 0060619   MnHi

National publishing co., Philadelphia.
Superb photographs of famous scenes, 1892
see under   Adams, Charles H.

D769
.85
K4Y6

National publishing company, Richmond.
... Young American patriots; the youth of Kentucky in world war II ... Richmond, Va., National publishing company [1947]

D769
.85
.O3Y6

National Publishing Company, Richmond.
Young American patriots; the youth of Ohio in World War II. Richmond, National Pub. Co. [1947]

D769
.85
.V8Y6

National publishing company, Richmond.
Young American patriots; the youth of Virginia in world war II ... Richmond, Va., National publishing company [ᶜ1945]

National Publishing Company, Seattle.
Greater Seattle illustrated; most progressive metropolis of the twentieth century. A glance at her history. A review of her commerce. A description of her business enterprises... Compiled and published by National Publishing Company... Seattle, Wash. [1907.]   38-239 p. front., illus. (incl. ports.) ob. 12°.

1. Seattle, Wash.
N. Y. P. L.   January 16, 1924.

NN 0060624   NN CSmH WaU

F899
S4N3

National Publishing Company, Seattle, comp.
Greater Seattle illustrated; the most progressive metropolis of the twentieth century. [Seattle] Lowman & Hanford [1909?]
239 p. illus. 20x28cm.

1. Seattle - Description. I. Title.

NN 0060625   CU-B

VOLUME 407

National Publishing Company, Seattle.
Seattle of to-day, illustrated; the metropolis of the Pacific coast, the gateway to Alaska and the Orient, the most progressive city of the twentieth century, compiled... by National Publishing Company... Seattle: National Pub. Co. ₍1907?₎ p. ₍37–₎231. front., illus. (incl. ports.) ob. 12°.

1. Seattle. Wash.
N. Y. P. L.   November 16, 1923.

NN 0060626   NN CaBViP WaU WaS Wa

National publishing house for the blind
see under   Sherrod, Dempsey B.

₍National pure art committee₎ *Boston, Mass.*
Masculine nudity in art. Boston, 1898.
18 p. illus. 18½ᵐ.
Signed: National pure art committee, Boston, Mass.

1. Nude in art.   I. Title.
                                              99–3088
Library of Congress   N72.N3

NN 0060628   DLC

National pure food and drug congress. *1st, Washington, D. C.,* 1898.
Journal of proceedings of the National pure food and drug congress held in Columbian university hall, Washington, D. C., March 2, 3, 4, and 5, 1898. Washington, D. C., 1898.
54 p. 23½ᵐ.

1. Food adulteration and inspection — Congresses. 2. Drugs — Adulteration and analysis.
                                              34–40739
Library of Congress   HD9000.9.U5A65 1898

NN 0060629   DLC ICJ DNLM OClW-H

National pure food and drug congress. *2d, Washington, D. C.,* 1899.
Report of proceedings of the second annual convention of the National pure food and drug congress held in Columbia university hall, Washington, D. C., January 18, 19, 20 and 21, 1899. Hightstown, N. J., The Barr press ₍1899₎
103 p. 23½ᵐ.

1. Drugs—Adulteration and analysis. ₍1. Drugs—Adulteration and inspection₎ 2. Food adulteration and inspection—Congresses. ₍2. Food—Adulteration and inspection₎ 3. Materia medica. 4. ₍Drugs—Congresses₎ 5. ₍Food—Congresses₎
                                              Agr 9–1350 Revised
Library, U. S. Dept. of   Agriculture 389.9.N213
Library of Congress   HD9000.9.U5A65 1899
———— Copy 2.   ₍r35b2₎   614.306373

NN 0060630   DNAL

National Pure Food Convention. Proceedings of the ..., held at Washington, Wednesday, January 19, 1887. 11 pp. 4°. *New York,* 1887.

NN 0060631   DNLM

NATIONAL PURITY ASSOCIATION.
[Circulars, cuttings from The Christian life, etc.]
=   Chicago, 1890–97. 9 pphs. 8°.

NN 0060632   MB

National purity association.

The **Christian** life, a journal of progress, devoted to race improvement.

Morton Park, Ill., National purity association, 18

National purity congress. *1st, Baltimore,* 1895.
The National purity congress, its papers, addresses, portraits. An illustrated record of the papers and addresses of the first National purity congress, held under the auspices of the American purity alliance ... Baltimore, October 14, 15 and 16, 1895. Ed. by Aaron M. Powell ... New York, The American purity alliance, 1896.
xvi, 453 p. illus. (ports.) 24ᵐ.

1. Prostitution.   I. American purity alliance.   II. Powell, Aaron Macy, 1832–   ed.
                                              6–2879
Library of Congress   HQ103.N27 1895

NN 0060634   DLC NNC NIC CU MtU ViU NjP ODW

GV1491
.E55   **National Puzzlers' League.**

           The **Enigma.**

           Scranton.

National Puzzlers' League.
A key to puzzledom; or, Complete handbook of the enigmatic art, comp. and pub. under the auspices of the Eastern Puzzlers' League. New York, W. W. Delaney, 1906.
145 p. 23 cm.
"Authorities of puzzledom": p. ₍38₎

1. Puzzles.   I. Title.
                                              34–12630 rev*
GV1493.N3   793.73

NN 0060636   DLC MB MdBP TxU

National puzzlers' league.
Boyer, John Q.
Real puzzles; a handbook of the enigmatic art ... published under the auspices and by the authority of the National puzzlers' league, organized July 4, 1883; by John Q. Boyer, Rufus T. Strohm, George H. Pryor, decorations, cover and jacket designs by John Q. Boyer ... Baltimore, Md., The Norman, Remington co., 1925.

National qualified teachers league of music.
The **American** music journal, an artistic independent publication for progressive musicians.

Cleveland, The American music journal co. ₍19

National quarantine and sanitary association

see

National quarantine and sanitary convention.

WA
N275q   NATIONAL Quarantine and Sanitary
1860   Convention
              Quarantine regulations as approved
         by the National Quarantine and Sanitary
         Association of the United States, 1860.
         Boston, Rand & Avery, 1860.
              39 p. illus.

NN 0060640   DNLM DLC

National quarantine and sanitary convention. *1st, Philadelphia,* 1857.
Minutes of the proceedings of the Quarantine convention, held at Philadelphia by invitation of the Philadelphia board of health, May 13–15, 1857. Philadelphia, Crissy & Markley, printers, 1857.
60 p. 23ᵐ.

1. Hygiene, Public—Congresses. 2. Quarantine—U. S.
                                              7–39617
Library of Congress   RA422.N4 1857

NN 0060641   DLC DNLM MB CtY ICJ

National quarantine and sanitary convention. *2d, Baltimore,* 1858.
Draft of a metropolitan sanitary code. (Reported to the Committee on internal hygiene,) by Henry G. Clark ... ₍Boston, G. C. Rand & Avery, printers, 1859₎
23, ₍1₎ p. 30ᵐ.
cover-title, 1 p. L, 19, ₍1₎ p. 30ᵐ.

1. Hygiene, Public.   I. Clark, Henry Grafton.
                                              8–21734–5†
Library of Congress   RA416.N22

NN 0060642   DLC DNLM MiU

National quarantine and sanitary convention. *2d, Baltimore,* 1858.
Minutes of the proceedings of the second annual meeting of the Quarantine and sanitary convention, convened in the city of Baltimore, April 29, 1858. Baltimore, Printed by J. D. Toy, 1858.
28 p. 23ᵐ.

1. Hygiene, Public—Congresses. 2. Quarantine—U. S.
                                              7—39618
Library of Congress   RA422.N4 1858

NN 0060643   DLC

RA 422
N3   National Quarantine and Sanitary Convention, 3d,₎
1859 a   New York, 1859.
          Minutes of the Third National Quarantine and Sanitary Convention, held in the city of New York, April 27th, 28th, 29th and 30th, 1859. New York, Baker, 1859.
          52 p. 23 cm.

1. Hygiene, Public - Congresses.   2. Quarantine - United States - Congresses.

NN 0060644   OU DLC MH

National quarantine and sanitary convention. *3d, New York,* 1859.
Proceedings and debates of the third National quarantine and sanitary convention, held in the city of New York, April 27th, 28th, 29th, and 30th, 1859. Reported by Chas. Collar and Wm. Anderson ... Board of councilmen, September 19, 1859. Document no. 9. New York, E. Jones & co., printers to Board of councilmen, 1859.
728 p. 23 cm.

1. Hygiene, Public—Congresses. 2. Quarantine—U. S.   I. New York (City) Board of assistant alderman.
RA422.N4 1859   8—3908 †

DNLM ICRL MnU–B
NN 0060645   DLC OCl MWA ViU PU NjR NN Nh MiU ICJ

National quarantine and sanitary convention. *4th, Boston,* 1860.
Proceedings and debates of the fourth National quarantine and sanitary convention, held in the city of Boston, June 14, 15, and 16, 1860. Reported for the City council of Boston. Boston, G. C. Rand & Avery, city printers, 1860.
288 p. incl. 3 pl. 24ᵐ.

1. Hygiene, Public—Congresses. 2. Quarantine—U. S.   I. Boston. City council.
                                              8—3907
Library of Congress   RA422.N4 1860

ICJ OO
NN 0060646   DLC DNLM MnU–B ICRL NcD Nh OCl NjP

National quarantine and sanitary convention.
4th, Boston, 1860.
... Report of Committee on external hygiene
see under   National quarantine and sanitary convention. Committee on external hygiene.

National Quarantine and Sanitary Convention. 4th, Boston, 1860.
Report on Civic cleanliness
see under   Committee on Civil Cleanliness and the Economical Disposition of the Refuse of Cities.

VOLUME 407

NATIONAL QUARANTINE AND SANITARY CONVENTION.
4th, Boston, 1860.
Report on registration, presented to the Quarantine
and sanitary convention, at its fourth annual meeting,
held in the city of Boston, June 14, 1860, by Edwin M.
Snow... [Boston, 1860] 24 p. incl. forms. 24cm.

1. United States—Stat., Vital—Registration. I. Snow,
Edwin Miller., 1820–1888.

NN 0060649 NN Nh DNLM

RA665
.N3 National quarantine and sanitary convention.
Committee on external hygiene.
Quarantine regulations as approved by the
National quarantine and sanitary association
of the United States. 1860. Boston, G. C.
Rand & Avery, printers, 1860.
39 p. 23 1/2cm.

1. Quarantine—U. S. I. Title.

NN 0060650 MB MH DNLM

National quarantine and sanitary convention. *Committee on external hygiene.*
Quarantine regulations. National quarantine and sanitary
association. Report of committee on external hygiene, 1860.
New York, E. Jones & co., printers [1860]
46 p. 27cm.

1. Quarantine—U. S. I. Title.
8—20476

Library of Congress RA665.N3

NN 0060651 DLC DNLM

RA665
.N3 National quarantine and sanitary convention.
1860b Committee on external hygiene.
Toner ... Report of Committee on external hygiene.
Coll. 1860. New York, E. Jones & co., printers [1860]
46 p. 23cm.

At head of title: Quarantine regulations.
National quarantine and sanitary association.
Also published, with some additions, under
title: Quarantine regulations as approved by the
National quarantine and sanitary association of
the U. S.

NN 0060652 DLC

National quarantine and sanitary convention. *Committee on quarantine.*
Report of the Committee on quarantine. [Philadelphia,
1859]
84 p. 23cm.
Caption title.

1. Quarantine.
8—8785†

Library of Congress RA655.N2

NN 0060653 DLC DNLM

WA NATIONAL Quarantine and Sanitary
N279r Convention. Committee on the Internal
1860 Hygiene of Cities
Report. [Washington? 1860?]
190 p.
Caption title.

NN 0060654 DNLM

National quarantine and sanitary convention. *Committee on the utility of wet docks.*
Report of the Committee on the utility of wet docks in
connection with quarantines, and the propriety of placing the
entire establishment under the jurisdiction of the United States
government ... New York, June 1, 1860. Boston, G. C. Rand &
Avery, 1860.
28 p. 23½cm.

——— 1. Quarantine—U. S. 2. Docks.
Copy 4. [Drake's Boston pamphlets, v. 66,
no. 5]

RA665.N2 6—38306 rev

NN 0060655 DLC DNLM Nh

National Quarantine Committee of the New York
Academy of Medicine
see New York Academy of Medicine.
National Quarantine Committee.

National Quarter Horse Breeders Association.
Permanent stud book. no. 1–
[Knox City, Tex., 1947–
v. illus. 24 cm.

1. Quarter horse. 2. Horses—Stud-books. [2. Stud-book (Horse)]
SF293.A1N3 636.168 Agr 48–196*
U. S. Dept. of Agr. Libr. 42.9N214
for Library of Congress [3]†

NN 0060657 DNAL InLP DLC

SF293 **National Quarter Horse Breeders Association.**
.Q3Q28
The Quarter horse. v. 1–4, no. 7; Apr. 1946–Oct. 1949.
[Houston, Tex., etc.]

The **National** quarterly review ... v. 1–34, June 1860–Mar.
1877; v. 35–41 (2d. ser., v. 1–7), July 1877–Oct. 1880. New
York, Pudney & Russell [etc.] 1860–80.
41 v. port. 23½cm.

Editors: June 1860–Sept. 1876, E. I. Sears.—Dec. 1876–Apr. 1880, D. A.
Gorton (with C. H. Woodman, 1879–80.)—July–Oct. 1880, C. H. Wood-
man.
Published by Pudney & Russell, 1860; E. I. Sears, 1861–76; D. A. Gor-
ton, etc., 1877–80.
No more published.

I. Sears, Edward Isidore, 1819–1876, ed. II. Gorton, David Allyn,
1832–1916, ed. III. Woodman, Charles H., ed.
1–3016 Revised

Library of Congress AP2.N35

NcRS MB OO
NN 0060659 DLC TxDW NcD WaS NjP KyU KU TxU N

361.8 National Quota Committee.
N195b ... Basic community percentages. 19
New York, 19
v. 28cm.

Composed of sheets, each for a different
state: Alabama basic community percentages, etc.

1.Social service—Statistics. I.Title.

NN 0060660 LU

National quotation bureau, incorporated, New
York.
... Corporation bond offering book ... v. 1–
New York, The National quotation bureau, incorporated,
°1906–

National quotation bureau, incorporated, New
York.
The **National** monthly corporation bond summary (with for-
eign government edition ...
New York [etc.] The National quotation bureau incorporated,
°19

National quotation bureau, incorporated,
New York.
The National monthly municipal bond summary ...
New York, The National quotation bureau, incorporated,
°19

National quotation bureau, incorporated, New
York.
The **National** monthly stock summary ... Jan. 19
New York [etc.] The National quotation bureau incorporated,
°19

National quotation bureau, incorporated, *New York.*
The over-the-counter securities market.
New York, c1939.
31 p.

NN 0060665 OC1FRB

National quotation bureau, incorporated, New York.
... Yearly stock book.
New York, The National quotation bureau, incorpo-
rated,

40.29 **National Rabbit Council of Great Britain and
N21 the Dominions.**
Year book. *1932–*
[London]

1. Rabbits. Societies.

NN 0060667 DNAL

National rabbit federation.
The American rabbit magazine ... v. 1–3; Dec. 1925–Aug.
1928. Pomona, Calif. [W. A. Bixler; etc., etc., 1925–28]

National radiator company.
National heating guide. Blue book of the
industry. Johnstown, Pa., National radiator
corporation [°1930]
1 p.l., 396 p., 1 l., illus.(part col.) map, tables,
diagrs. 18½cm.
"National engineering data, compiled by Samuel E.
Dibble": p.291–396.

1. Heating—Catalogs. I. Dibble, Samuel Edward,
1882– II. Title.

NN 0060669 ViU NjP OC1U ICRL

National radiator company
Through half a century; a story of progress
in the American way, 1894–1944.
Johnstown, Pa., The National radiator co., 1944.
32 p.

NN 0060670 OC1

National Radical Union.
A unionist policy for Ireland ... with a preface
by the Rt. Hon. J. Chamberlain ... London,
1888.
12,124 p.
"Reprinted from the Birmingham daily post".
No. 17 of a volume of pamphlets.
I. Chamberlain, Joseph, 1836–1914.

NN 0060671 NjP

VOLUME 407

... The **National** radio artists directory ...

₍Hollywood, Calif., New York, etc.₎ L. Lauria₍ ʿ19

v. illus. (incl. ports.) 28 x 21½ᵉᵐ.

Quarterly, 19   3 v. a year, 19
Cover-title.
Title varies : no.   -3, Radio artists directory of Hollywood ; no. 4-
The National radio artists directory.

1. Radio—Biog. 2. Actors, American—Direct. 3. Actresses, American—Direct.   ɪ. Title: Radio artists directory of Hollywood.

                           41–15977 (rev. ʿ42)
Library of Congress   TK6545.A1N3
                                  792

   NN   0060672   DLC NN

HE8670 National radio conference.
.U6A1N3   Proceedings...
      Washington, Govt. print. off.,
      v.   23ᵉᵐ.

      1. Radio.

   NN   0060673   ICU OCl

National radio conference. *3d, Washington, D. C., 1924.*
    ... Recommendations f ⸳ regulation of radio adopted by the
third National radio conference called by Herbert Hoover, secretary of commerce. October 6–10, 1924 ... Washington, Govt.
print. off., 1924.

1 p. L, 35 p. incl. form.   25ᵉᵐ.

At head of title: United States Department of commerce.

1. Radio—Laws and regulations. 2. Telegraph, Wireless.   ɪ. U. S.
Dept. of commerce. ɪɪ. Title.
                              24—27302
Library of Congress   HE8670.U6A4 1924 d

  MH-L OCl 00
  NN   0060674   DLC NN N IU WaWW OrCS OrU Or ICU ICJ

National radio conference. *4th, Washington, D. C., 1925.*
    Proceedings of the fourth National radio conference and
recommendations for regulation of radio. Conference called
by Herbert Hoover, secretary of commerce. Washington,
D. C., November 9–11, 1925 ... Washington, Govt. print. off.,
1926.

iv, 38 p. incl. tab.   25ᵉᵐ.

1. Radio.   ɪ. U. S. Dept. of commerce. ɪɪ. Title.
                            26—26087 rev.
Library of Congress   HE8670.U6A4 1925 d

  ICJ
  NN   0060675   DLC WaWW OrCS OrU MH-L MiU 00 OClFRB

National Radio Exhibition.
    Official catalogue.
₍no. 1
₍London, 1926   4°.
    v.   illus. (incl. ports.), plans.

1. Radio—Exhibitions—Gt. Br.—   Eng.—London.
N. Y. P. L.   August 20, 1928

   NN   0060676   NN

National Radio Exposition. *4th, ₍New York, 1925.*   )
    Personnel of the Fourth Annual National Radio Exposition,
September 12–19th (inclusive) 1925, Grand Central Palace. ₍New
York, 1925.₎   68 p. incl. tables.   illus. (incl. ports.)   8°.

Advertising matter included.

1. Radio—Exhibitions—U. S.—   N. Y.—New York.
N. Y. P. L.   February 9, 1927

   NN   0060677   NN

TK6370   National radio institute, Washington, D. C.
.A5N3   Advanced course in aircraft radio.
    Washington, D. C., National radio institute
    ₍c1932₎
    6 pam. in 1 cover.   illus., diagrs.
22cm.

    Title from slip pasted on cover.
    Contents.—IVA. The application of radio
to air craft.—no. 2VA. Airplane radio equipment.—no. 3VA. Aircraft radio power supplied.
—no. 4VA. Fundamental aircraft radio trans-

mitter circuits.—no. 5VA. Aircraft radio-
telephone transmitters.—no. 6VA. Aircraft
radio-telephone and radiotelegraph transmitters.

   NN   0060679   DLC

TK6570   National radio institute, Washington, D. C.
.B7N37   Advanced course in broadcasting, commer-
    cial and ship radio stations. Washington,
    D. C., National radio institute [c1932]
    6 pam. in 1 cover   illus., diagrs.
22cm.

    Title from slip pasted on cover.
    Contents.—no. 1CA. Technical development
of commercial radio.—no. 2CA. The arc trans-
mitter.—no. 3CA. Spark transmitters.—no. 4CA.

Pickup devices; speech input analysis.—
no. 5CA. Impedance matching networks, pads
and volume controls.—no. 6CA. Transmission
lines; volume indicators; monitors.

   NN   0060681   DLC

TK6553   National radio institute, Washington, D. C.
.N35   Advanced course in radio servicing and
    merchandising. Washington, D. C., National
    radio institute [c1932]
    6 pam. in 1 cover.   illus., diagrs.
22 cm.

    Title from slip pasted on cover.
    Contents.—No.1RA. Installation service.
—no. 2RA. Radio servicing in the home.—no.
3RA. Testing with meters at the work bench.—
no. 4RA. Testing vacuum tubes.—no. 5RA.

Testing sound reproducing devices.—6RA Bench
servicing of power packs and other sources of
power.

   NN   0060683   DLC

National radio institute, Washington, D. C.
    Advanced course in sound pictures and
public address systems. Washington, D. C.,
National radio institute [c1932]
    6 pam. in 1 cover.   illus., diagrs.
22cm.

    Title from slip pasted on cover.
    Contents.—No. 1PA. Power supplies of
power audio amplifiers.—no. 2PA. Acoustics
of buildings.—no. 3PA. Design of outdoor
public address systems.—no. 4PA. Indoor

public address systems.—no. 5PA. Studio
sound shooting, part 1.—no. 6PA. Studio
sound shooting, part 2.

   NN   0060685   DLC

TK6630   National radio institute, Washington, D. C.
.N3   Advanced course in television (theory
    and practice) Washington, D. C., National
    radio institute [c1932]
    6 pam. in 1 cover.   illus., diagrs.
22cm.
    Title from slip pasted on cover.
    Contents.—no. 1TA. Essentials of tele-
vision.—part. I.—no. 2TA. Essentials of
television, part. II.—no. 3TA. Optics.—

no. 4TA. Geometric optics.—no. 5TA. Applied
optics.—no. 6TA. Television quality requirements.

   NN   0060687   DLC

National radio institute, *Washington, D. C.*
    Common radio terms, symbols, abbreviations. ɪx–ʟ. Wash-
ington, D. C., National radio institute ₍ʿ1937₎
    cover-title, 64 p. illus.   22ᵉᵐ.

1. Radio—Dictionaries.   ɪ. Title.
                                38–1942
Library of Congress   TK6544.N3
———— Copy 2.
Copyright AA 253350   ₍3₎   621.38403

   NN   0060688   DLC

National radio institute, *Washington, D. C.*
    ... Complete course in practical radio ... Washington, D. C.
₍ʿ1929₎
    56 pt. in 1 v. illus., diagrs.   23½ᵉᵐ.

1. Radio.   ɪ. Title.
                                29–22023
Library of Congress   TK6550.N25

   NN   0060689   DLC

National radio institute, *Washington, D. C.*
    Complete course in practical radio ... Washington, D. C.,
National radio institute ₍ʿ1931₎
    45 pt. in 1 v. illus., diagrs.   23½ᵉᵐ.
    Title from cover.

1. Radio.   ɪ. Title.
                                31–35426
Library of Congress   TK6550.N25 1931
Copyright A 46456   ₍2₎   621.3845

   NN   0060690   DLC

National radio institute, Washington, D.C.
    Frequency-modulated signals. The F.M. receiver.
Washington, D.C. [c.1941]
    36 p. diagrs., illus.   22 cm.
    Cover-title.

   NN   0060691   MH

National radio institute, Washington, D. C.
    How to eliminate man-made interference. Wash-
ington, National radio institute ₍1937₎
    cover-title, 29 p. illus., diagrs.
(₍6RH-1)

    1. Radio - Interference.

   NN   0060692   NNC

National radio institute, *Washington, D. C.*
    How tuned circuits function. Coupling radio circuits.
9FR–3. Washington ₍1945₎
    29 p. illus. 22ᵉᵐ.

1. Electric resonators.   ɪ. Title.
                              45–5388
                          Brief cataloging
Library of Congress   TK6565.R43N3

   NN   0060693   DLC MH

National Radio Institute, Washington, D.C.
    Journal
      see   NRI journal.

National radio institute, *Washington, D. C.*
    Mathematics for radiotricians ... Washington, D. C., Na-
tional radio institute, 1942.
    1 p. L, 140, ₍2₎ p. diagrs. 22ᵉᵐ.
    On cover : Special edition for members of the National radio institute
Alumni association, Washington, D. C.

1. Mathematics. 2. Radio—Tables, calculations, etc.   ɪ. National
radio institute, Washington, D. C. Alumni association. ɪɪ. Title.
                              42–50369
Library of Congress   TK6552.N33
                     ₍5₎   510

   NN   0060695   DLC ICJ ICU NN OClJC

VOLUME 407

National Radio Institute, Washington, D.C.
  NRI journal
    see under title

National Radio Institute, Washington, D.C.
  NRI news
    see   NRI journal.

National radio institute, *Washington, D. C.*
  N. R. I. service manual ... National radio institute, Washington, D. C. New York, N. Y., Prepared and produced exclusively for the National radio institute, Washington, D. C., by J. F. Rider, inc., °1946–

    v. illus., diagrs. 29½ x 24ᶜᵐ.

    On spine : NRI manual service.
    Loose-leaf.

    1. Radio.   ɪ. Title.

Library of Congress   TK6553.A1N36   46–4110

    621.38402

NN   0060698   DLC CU

National radio institute, Washington, D.C.
  Peak and band-pass R.F. tuning circuits. Washington, D.C. [1940]

    29 p. diagrs., illus. 22 cm.
    Cover-title.
    "1940 ed."

NN   0060699   MH

National radio institute, *Washington, D. C.*
  Radio and electronic dictionary. ɪx–2. Washington, D. C., National radio institute ₁1943₎

    cover-title, 96 p. illus. 22ᶜᵐ.

    Earlier edition, 1937, published under title: Common radio terms, symbols, abbreviations. ɪx–1.

    1. Radio—Dictionaries. ɪ. Title: Electronic dictionary.

    43–10050

Library of Congress   TK6544.N3 1943

NN   0060700   DLC

National radio institute, *Washington, D. C.*
  Radio mathematics; the use of trigonometry in radio. No. 12SB. Reference book. Washington, D. C., National radio institute ₁°1932₎

    cover-title, 28 p. diagrs. 22ᶜᵐ.

    1. Trigonometry. 2. Radio—Tables, calculations, etc. ɪ. Title.

    43–27648

Library of Congress   TK6552.N34

NN   0060701   DLC

National Radio Institute, Washington, D.C.
  Radio quiz book
    see under   Smith, James Ernest.

National radio institute, *Washington, D.C.*
  Radio receiver troubles; their cause and remedy. ₁1939 ed.₎ Wash., D. C., National radio institute, °1937.
    36 p.

NN   0060703   MiD

National Radio Institute, *Washington, D. C.*
  Radio-television-electronics dictionary. ɪx–3. Washington ₁1951₎

    96 p. illus. 22 cm.

    Published in 1937 under title : Common radio terms, symbols, abbreviations. ɪx–1.

    1. Radio — Dictionaries. 2. Television — Dictionaries. 3. Electronics—Dictionaries. ɪ. Title.

    TK6544.N3   1951   621.38403   51–6195 †

NN   0060704   DLC

National radio institute, *Washington, D. C.*
  Telecine projectors; picture and R. F. circuits in television transmitters. 67CH–1. Washington, D. C., National radio institute ₁1942₎

    cover-title, 29 p. illus., diagrs. 22ᵐ.

    "A lesson text of the N. R. I. course which trains you to become a radiotrician & teletrician."

    1. Television. 2. Cinematography. ɪ. Title.   42–17122

Library of Congress   TK6630.N35

NN   0060705   DLC

National radio institute, Washington, D.C.
  Transmitting antennas and couplers. Washington, D.C. [1940]

    29 p. diagrs., illus. 22 cm.
    Cover-title.
    "1940 ed."

NN   0060706   MH

National radio institute
  Trouble shooting in D. C., A. C. and battery operated sets; reference book. ₁Rev. ed.₎ Wash. ₁The Author, 1935₎
    28 p. diagrs.

NN   0060707   MiD

National radio institute. Washington, D.C.
  28 tested methods for making extra money; reference book. Wash., D. C. ₁The Author₎ °1933.
    56 p. illus.

NN   0060708   MiD

National radio institute, Washington, D. C.
  Alumni association.

National radio institute, *Washington, D. C.*
  Mathematics for radiotricians ... Washington, D. C., National radio institute, 1942.

National Radio news
    see   NRI journal.

National Radio Pulpit (Radio program)
  National Radio Pulpit, a presentation of the National Broadcasting Company; produced by Broadcasting and Film Commission, National Council of the Churches of Christ in the United States of America. New York ₁The Commission₎ 1923–
    v.

    Publication date varies.
    Preachers include Ralph W. Sockman, Robert J. McCracken, David C. Read, Ernest T. Campbell.

  BV4301
  .N213

NN   0060711   CtHC

National radio-TV news
    see   NRI journal.

National radio-television news directory
    see   Mike and screen press directory.

National radium institute (inc).
Parsons, Charles Lathrop, 1867–
  ... Extraction and recovery of radium, uranium and vanadium from carnotite, by Charles L. Parsons, R. B. Moore, S. C. Lind and O. C. Schaefer. National radium institute cooperative agreement ... Washington, Govt. print. off., 1915.

National radium institute (inc.)
Kithil, Karl L.
  ... Mining and concentration of carnotite ores, by Karl L. Kithil and John A. Davis. ⟨Prepared under a cooperative agreement with the National radium institute⟩ Washington, Govt. print. off., 1917.

NATIONAL Radium Products Company
  ₁Collection of publications₎

    The library has a collection of miscellaneous publications of this organization kept as received. These publications are not listed nor bound separately.
    1. Radium

  WN
  300
  qN277

NN   0060716   DNLM

₁National radium products company₎
  An outline of radium and its emanations; a complete handbook for the medical profession. ₁New York, National radium products company, °1924₎

    cover-title, 33 p. 23ᶜᵐ.

    "This copy is ... of a limited edition and is loaned, remaining the sole property of the publishers."

    1. Radium—Therapeutic use. ɪ. Title.

    24–1150

Library of Congress   RM859.N3

NN   0060717   DLC DNLM

National radium trust (*Gt. Brit.*)
  Annual reports of the National radium trust and Radium commission ...

  London, H. M. Stationery off., 1930–

    v. illus., tables, forms. 25ᶜᵐ. (₁Gt. Brit. Parliament. Papers by command₎ Cmd. 3678

    1. Radium—Therapeutic use. ɪ. Radium commission (Gt. Brit.)

    30–32688

Library of Congress   RM859.N35

    ₍2₎   615.84

NN   0060718   DLC CaBVaU MiU DL NN

National railroad agents' association.
  Proceedings of the ... annual session. Chicago,
    v.

NN   0060719   MH-BA

National Railroad Association.

The Railfan.

  Toledo, National Railroad Association₎

  HE2714
  .N33

National Railroad Company of Mexico.
Sutton, Eli Ransome, 1869–1934.
  Mexico, stories of the highlands of the tropics, telling of the best things in Mexico and how to see them, by Eli R. Sutton. Issued by the passenger department of the National Railroad Company of Mexico. ₁Chicago, Rogers & Smith Co., 1904₎

VOLUME 407

National Railroad Company of Mexico.
  Organization of National railroad company
  of Mexico ... ₍New York? 1902₎
  2 v. 27½ᶜᵐ.

  In English and Spanish.

  1. Railroads - Mexico.

NN 0060722 NNC

National railroad company of Mexico.
  Report.
  ₍New York 19
  v. maps. 30ᶜᵐ.
  Report year ends Dec. 31, 19 05; June 30, 1906–
  Title varies: 190 –05, Annual report of National railroad company of
  Mexico.
  1906– Report of National railroad company of Mexico.

                                              20–2869
  Library of Congress   HE2820.N3A4

NN 0060723 DLC ICJ CU

National railroad company of Mexico
  see also
  Ferrocarriles nacionales de Mexico.
  Mexican National Railroad.
  Mexican National Railroad Company.

National Railroad Convention, *Memphis*, 1849.   656.0973
  Minutes and proceedings of the Memphis Convention, assem-   K900
  bled October 23, 1849. [Memphis, Tenn.?, 1849?]
  68 p. 22½ᶜᵐ.
  Caption title.
  A convention called to consider the establishment of a railroad which should
  connect the valley of the Mississippi with the Pacific Ocean. *cf.* p. 6.

NN 0060725 ICJ CtY MiU

National railroad convention, *St. Louis*, 1849.
  Proceedings of the National railroad convention, which
  assembled in the city of St. Louis, on the fifteenth of October, 1849. To which is prefixed the proceedings of the
  primary meetings of the citizens of St. Louis, held previous to the meeting of said convention. St. Louis, Printed by Chambers & Knapp, 1850.
  98 p. 21ᶜᵐ.

  1. Pacific railroads—Early projects. 2. Railroads—Congresses.

                                              A 18–84
  Title from Bureau of   Railway Economics. Printed by L. C.

NN 0060726 DBRE NcU CtY MiU MoS

National railroad convention, *Philadelphia*, 1850.
  Proceedings of the convention in favor of a national
  rail road to the Pacific Ocean through the territories of
  the United States. Held in Philadelphia April 1st, 2nd
  & 3rd, 1850. Philadelphia, Crissy & Markley, printers,
  1850.
  79 p. 21ᶜᵐ.
  An adjourned meeting of the National railroad convention, St. Louis,
  1849.

  1. Pacific railroads—Early projects. 2. ₍Railroads—Conventions₎
  ₁. Title.

                                              A 20–1241
  Title from Bureau of   Railway Economics. Printed by L. C.

NN 0060727 DBRE MiU

National railroad convention, *St. Louis*, 1875.
  Proceedings of the National railroad convention at St.
  Louis, Mo., November 23 and 24, 1875, in regard to the construction of the Texas & Pacific railway as a southern transcontinental line from the Mississippi valley to the Pacific
  ocean on the thirty-second parallel of latitude. Published by
  order of the convention, John H. Harrell, of Arkansas, secretary. St. Louis, Woodward, Tiernan & Hale, printers, 1875.
  x, ₍11₎–208 p. front. (fold. map) 23½ᶜᵐ.
  1. Texas and Pacific railway. 2. Railroads—Congresses. ɪ. Harrell,
  John M.
                                              A 10–2026
  Bureau of Railway   Economics. Printed by L. C.

MiU OOxM OClWHi
NN 0060728 DBRE CtY NcU ICU KyU IU OFH ICJ NN

National Railroad Master Blacksmiths' Association.
  see International Railroad Master Blacksmiths' Association.

National railroad of Nicaragua
  see
  Ferrocarril nacional de Nicaragua.

National railway appliances association.
  Year book ... annual exhibition ...
  ₍Chicago₎ National railway appliances association, Publication committee
  v. front., illus. 31ᶜᵐ.

  1. Railroads—Equipment and supplies.

  Library of Congress   TF6.N6   13–4771

NN 0060731 DLC OCl ICJ

₍National Railway Company of New Jersey.₎
  ... Charter and organization of the National Company constructing the National Railway from Philadelphia to New York,
  with statement in relation thereto. Charter perpetual. Philadelphia: Moss & Co., 1873. 119 p. incl. tables. 4°.

  "Reprinted November 1895."

  1. Railways, U. S. (Indiv.): National   Railway. 2. Title.
  N. Y. P. L.   January 13, 1922.

NN 0060732 NN

National Railway Company of Tehuantepec
  see Ferrocarril Nacional de Tehuantepec.

National railway convention, *Philadelphia*, 1866.
  Proceedings of the National railway convention, at the
  Musical fund hall, Philadelphia, Pa. July 4th & 5th, 1866.
  Philadelphia, E. C. Markley & son, printers, 1866.
  16 p. 23ᶜᵐ.

  1. Iron industry and trade—U. S. 2. Railroads—U. S.
                                              A 15–1770
  Title from Bureau of   Railway Economics. Printed by L. C.

NN 0060734 DBRE MiU NcU

National railway convention, *New York*, 1867.
  Proceedings of the National railway convention, at the St.
  Nicholas hotel, New York, May 8th and 9th, 1867. New York,
  C. F. Ketcham, printer, 1867.
  36 p. 22ᶜᵐ.

  1. Railroads—U. S.—Congresses. ₍1. Railroads—Conventions₎
  ₁. Title.
  Bur. of railway econ. Libr.   A 20—1239
  for Library of Congress   HE2717.N33 1867

NN 0060735 DBRE DLC MiU

National Railway Historical Society.
  Bulletin.
  ₍Westmont, N.J., etc.₎
  v. in illus. 23cm.

  Frequency varies.

  1. Railroads - U.S. - Societies. etc.

MnHi
NN 0060736 MtU PHi NcD AzU PPF NN MdBE NSyU

  Membership list.
  ₍Baltimore₎   no.   23cm.

NN 0060737 NN

National Railway Historical Society. Connecticut   HE4201
  Valley Chapter.   .T7

  Transportation. v. 1–
  Jan. 1946–
  ₍Warehouse Point, Conn.₎ National Railway Historical So-
  ciety, Connecticut Valley Chapter.

National Railway Historical Society, North Jersey
  Chapter.
  The Marker
  see under title

National Railway Historical Society--Philadelphia   388
  Chapter.   N216r
  Rail transit in Philadelphia. Joseph M.
  Mannix, editor. ₍Philadelphia₎ 1954.
  31p. illus. 28cm.

  1. Street railroads--Philadelphia. 2. Phila-
  delphia--Rapid transit. I. Mannix, Joseph M.,
  ed. II. Title.

NN 0060740 IU

The National railway instruction bureau, *St. Louis.*
  Instruction book no. one on general rules for railroad
  brakemen and firemen. St. Louis, Mo., The National railway instruction bureau ₍1905₎
  140 p. illus. 15½ᶜᵐ.

  1. Railroads—Trainmen's manuals.

  Library of Congress   TF557.N2 Copyright   5–41804

NN 0060741 DLC

The National railway instruction bureau, *St. Louis.*
  Instruction book no. two on rules and duties of conductors, trainmen and baggagemen. St. Louis, Mo., The
  National railway instruction bureau ₍1905₎
  54 p. 15½ᶜᵐ.

  1. Railroads—Trainmen's manuals.

  Library of Congress   TF557.N23 Copyright   6–8859

NN 0060742 DLC

The National railway instruction bureau, *St. Louis.*
  Instruction book no. two on rules and duties of engineers and firemen. The firing of locomotives. St. Louis,
  The National railway instruction bureau ₍1905₎
  89 p. illus. 15½ᶜᵐ.

  1. Locomotives—Handbooks, manuals, etc.   6–12167

  Library of Congress   TJ607.N6 Copyright

NN 0060743 DLC

National railway labor panel emergency board
  see U.S. National railway labor panel.

VOLUME 407

National Railway Publication Co., *New York.*   **A912.73 Q900**
General railway map engraved expressly for the official guide of the railways and steam navigation lines, of the United States, Porto Rico, Canada, Mexico, and Cuba. Comprising maps of the United States, Cuba, Porto Rico, the Philippines etc. New York, National Railway Publication Co., °1909.
1 map. 97¼ x 138¼ᶜᵐ.

NN   0060745   ICJ

National Railway Publication Company.   No. 92 in *Map 118.3
General railway map engraved expressly for the Official guide of the railways and steam navigation lines of the United States, Porto Rico, Canada, Mexico, and Cuba.
= New York. 1915. Size, 37¾ × 52 inches. Scale (computed), 60 miles to 1 inch.   Folded.
Submaps. — Alaska. — Philippine Islands. — Guam. — Howland I. and Baker I. — Hawaii. — Samoa. — Tutuila I. — Map of Central America showing the Panama Canal. — Porto Rico.

K6343 — United States. Geog. Maps. _ _anada. Geog. Maps. — Mexico. Geog. Maps. — United States. R.Rs. — Canada. R.Rs. — Mexico. R.Rs.

NN   0060746   MB

Map
G
3701   **National Railway Publication Co.**
P3   General railway map engraved expressly
1918   for the official guide of the railways and
N3   steam navigation lines of the United States
          ...   New York, 1918.
          col. map 100 x 132 cm.

          Scale 1 inch to approx. 60 miles.

          1. U. S.--Maps.   2. Railroads--U.S.--Maps.

NN   0060747   NIC IU

NATIONAL RAILWAY PUBLICATION COMPANY.
Map of the Northern Pacific railroad and tributary country. Philadelphia,[1872].

1 sheet.   21 1/2 x 28 in.
Scale: 105 miles to the inch.
Inset: Northern hemisphere.

NN   0060748   MH-BA

National Railway Publication Company
917.5
N277M   A memento of the General Ticket Agents'
excursion from Philadelphia to Florida, and up the St. John's River. 1871. Philadelphia, The Leisenring Steam Printing House [1871?]
44 p. front. (map)   24 cm.

1. Southern states. Description and travel.

NN   0060749   NcD CSmH

National railway publication company.

... The Official guide of the railways and steam navigation lines of the United States, Porto Rico, Canada, Mexico and Cuba ... Issued under the auspices of the American association of passenger traffic officers ... New York, The National railway publication company, 18

National Railway Publication Company.
HE1971
.O4

The Official list of inter-line ticket agents and passenger traffic officers of the United States, Canada, and Mexico.

New York, National Railway Publication Co.

385.097   [National railway publication company]
N213r
1866   Railway map of the United States and Canada, showing all the railroads completed and in progress. Carefully compiled from official sources for Travelers' official railway guide.   [Philadelphia 1866?]
map 60x90cm. fold. to 17x24cm.
Scale ca.1:1,900,800.
Includes 2 insets.
On verso: Map   of the Pennsylvania Central R.R, the   Panhandle route, and the Pittsburg, Ft. Wayne and Chicago R.R.

NN   0060752   KU

National railway service corporation.

Ballantine, Noten D   1872–
Address by N. D. Ballantine ... before the Traffic club of New York. New York, September 25th, 1923 ... Baltimore, National association of owners of railroad securities [1923]

National railway service corporation.
... National railway service corporation. Alternative bases for rehabilitation of unserviceable interchange freight cars. [Baltimore? 192-]
9 p.   24ᶜᵐ.
Caption title.
At head of title: From National association of owners of railroad securities, headquarters, Baltimore, Md.

1. Railroads—Freight-cars. [1. Cars, Freight—Repairs]   I. National association of owners of railroad securities.

A 22–1835
Title from Bureau of   Railway Economics. Printed by L. C.

NN   0060754   DBRE

National Railway of Tehuantepec
see   Ferro-carril nacional de Tehuantepec.

National railway training association.
Book of instructions for electric railway motor-men and conductors.
TF965   Kansas City, Mo., c1909–
.N3

NN   0060756   DLC

National Railways of Mexico
see   Ferrocarriles Nacionales de Mexico.

A60.19
N21   **National Range Workshop.**
Report.
[Washington]

1. Range conservation program. Congresses.
I. U.S.   Soil Conservation Service.

NN   0060758   DNAL

HF5573
.N35   National rating bureau, Chicago.
Rating guide. 19   ed.   Chicago, Ill., National rating bureau, Division of nations credit syndicate [c1935–
v.   23½cm.

Title from cover.

1. Credit guides--U.S.   I. Title.

NN   0060759   DLC

National Raw Silk Exchange, New York.
By-laws and rules.   [New York, 1928–1929.]   12°.
Cover-title.
Various paging.
Loose leaf portfolio, with tab index.
Includes: List of officers, governors, committees and members; and Certificate of incorporation.

436416A.   1. Silk exchange—U. S.
N. Y. P. L.   October 7, 1929

NN   0060760   NN

National raw silk exchange, inc., New York.
By-laws and rules.   [New York, N.Y., 1933?]
1 v.   various pagings.

Loose leaf.
Cover title.
Includes list of officers, governors, committees and members, 1932-1933; also by-laws, rules and list of members of the National raw silk exchange clearing association, inc.

NN   0060761   MH-BA

National Raw Silk Exchange, New York.
National Raw Silk Exchange, Inc., 1928.   New York City, cop. 1928].   191.   front., illus.   8°.
Written by Julius B. Baer.

547443A.   1. Silk exchange—U. S.   I. Baer, Julius Bernard, 1881–
N. Y. P. L.

NN   0060762   NN MH-BA PPULC ICJ

677.46   **National Rayon Corporation**
N213m   Manufacturing process of rayon yarn.
Bombay, Satguru Printers [19]
7 p.

Cover title.

1. Rayon industry and trade - India.
I. Title.

NN   0060763   WaU

National Rayon Corporation.
The National Rayon Corporation Ltd., manufacturers of rayon or artificial silk yarn, an introduction. Bombay [1950?]
9 p.   fold. map.

1. Rayon industry and trade - India.

NN   0060764   WaU

The National readership survey
see
Institute of Practitioners in Advertising.
A national survey of readership of newspapers and magazines on a continuing basis.

National Reading Conference
Evaluating college reading programs
see its
Yearbook.

National Reading Conference
Exploring the goals of college reading programs
see its
Yearbook.

National Reading Conference.
Improving reading programs for college students and adults
see its
Yearbook.

VOLUME 407

LB2365
.R4N3

National Reading Conference. Proceedings.

National Reading Conference.
Yearbook. ₁1st₁–
Apr. 1952–
Milwaukee, etc., National Reading Conference, etc.

National Reading Conference
Techniques and procedures in college and adult reading programs
see its
Yearbook.

National Reading Conference
What colleges are doing with reading programs
see its
Yearbook.

National Reading Conference.
Yearbook. ₁1st₁–
Apr. 1952–
Milwaukee, etc., National Reading Conference, etc.
v. 23–28 cm.

Title varies: Apr. 1952, Proceedings.
Some vols. have also distinctive titles : Dec. 1952, Improving reading programs for college students and adults.—1953, What the colleges are doing in reading improvement programs.—1954, Evaluating college reading programs.—1955, Exploring the goals of college reading programs.—1956, Techniques and procedures in college and adult reading programs.—

1958, Starting and improving college reading programs.—

1960, Phases of college and other adult reading programs.—

1962, New developments in programs and procedures for college-adult reading.
Vols. for Apr. 1952–   issued by the conference under an earlier name: Southwest Reading Conference for Colleges and Universities.
Selections from the 1st–3d yearbooks were reprinted in 1955 by the conference under the title : What the colleges are doing in planning and improving college reading programs.

1. Reading (Higher education)—Yearbooks. 2. Reading—Remedial teaching—Yearbooks.   I. National Reading Conference. Proceedings.   II. Title: Improving reading programs for college students and adults.   III. Title: What the colleges are doing in reading improvement programs.   IV. Title: Evaluating college reading programs.   V. Title: Exploring the goals of college reading programs.   VI. Title: Techniques and procedures in college and adult reading programs.   VII. Title: Starting and improving college reading programs.   VIII. Title: Phases of college and other adult reading programs.   IX. Title: New developments in programs and procedures for college-adult reading.

LB2365.R4N3   54–34620 rev 2

IdU NSyU TNJ-P DAU NcRS KMK IU MiU DCU NBuC NBuT
NN   0060774   DLC TxU CLSU MtBC KU WaU WaChenE WaWW

National Reading Conference for Colleges and Adults
see
National Reading Conference.

National ready mixed concrete association.
Admixtures for concrete
see under   American Concrete Institute. Committee 212.

National ready mixed concrete association
Bibliography from current periodicals on ready-mixed concrete, prepared by Engineering division, National ready mixed concrete association. ₁The Author₁ 1931.
26 *l.*

NN   0060777   MiD

National ready mixed concrete association
Bibliography from current periodicals on ready-mixed concrete, prepared by Engineering division, National ready mixed concrete association. Wash. ₁The Author₁ 1933.
32 *l.*

Includes Supplement, 1935. 3 *l.*

NN   0060778   MiD

National Ready Mixed Concrete Association.
Cold weather concreting . . .
see under   Clemmer, Harold Francis, 1889–

National ready mixed concrete association.
Control of quality of ready-mixed concrete.   Washington, National ready mixed concrete assoc. ₁1944₁ 71 p.   23cm.

1. Cement and concrete—Manufacture.
N. Y. P. L.   March 27, 1945

NN   0060780   NN

691.3   **National Ready Mixed Concrete Association.**
N215c   Control of quality of ready-mixed concrete.
1945   ₂2d ed.₂   Washington ₂1945₂
75p. 23cm.

"List of references": p. 73–75.

1. Concrete. I. Title: Ready mixed concrete. II. Title.

NN   0060781   IU

TA439   **National Ready Mixed Concrete Association.**
.N3   Control of quality of ready-mixed concrete.
no.44   3d ed. ₁Washington₁ 1953.
1953   76 p.   23cm.   (Its Publication, no. 44)

Bibliography: p. 73–76.

1. Concrete—Testing. I. Title. II. Ser.

NN   0060782   ViU IU OrP

National Ready Mixed Concrete Association.
List of laboratory investigations
see under   National Sand and Gravel Association.

National ready mixed concrete association.
Manual.   National ready mixed concrete association.   Washington, D. C. ₁1941₁ 84 p.   23cm.
"Selected list of references on proportioning concrete mixtures," p. 14–16.

1. Cement and concrete.
N. Y. P. L.   January 11, 1943

NN   0060784   NN WaS

National Ready Mixed Concrete Association.
₁Minor publications₁
Includes some of its numbered series.

NN   0060785   ICJ

National ready mixed concrete association.
Proposed recommended practice for winter concreting
see under   American Concrete Institute. Committee 604.

NATIONAL READY MIXED CONCRETE ASSOCIATION.
Publication.
Washington.   no.   illus.   23–28cm.

Irregular.
Various numbers issued in revised eiditions; some are reprints. Various numbers also form issues of National sand and gravel association. Circular.

Published by its Engineering division.

1. Cement and concrete—Per. and soc. publ.   I. National ready mixed concrete association. Miscellaneous publication.

NN   0060788   NN MiD

National ready mixed concrete association.
Recommended practice for selecting proportions for concrete
see under   American Concrete Institute. Committee 613.

National ready mixed concrete association.
Recommended practices for sampling and testing ready-mixed concrete.   Washington ₁1949₁ 20 p. 23cm.

1. Cement and concrete—Testing. 2. Cement and concrete—Testing, 1949.

NN   0060790   NN ViU

R666.8   **National Ready Mixed Concrete Association**
N208s   Specifications and test methods for ready-mixed concrete. 1st ed. ₁Washington, D. C.₁ 1953.
58 p. illus.   (It's Publication no. 47)

Cover title.

1. Concrete – Specifications   I. T.
2. Concrete – Testing

NN   0060791   MiD ViU

National Ready Mixed Concrete Association.
Selected list of references to literature on ready mixed concrete
see under   McKim, Pearl O

National ready mixed concrete association.
Standards for operation of truck mixers and agitators . . .   Washington ₁1941?₁ 4 *l.*   23cm.

1. Cement and concrete—Manufacture. 2. Cement and concrete—Manufacture, 1941.

NN   0060793   NN

NATIONAL READY MIXED CONCRETE ASSOCIATION.
[Year book]
Washington.   v.   23cm.

1. Cement and concrete—Assoc. and org.

NN   0060794   NN

National Ready Mixed Concrete Association. Committee on Cost Accounting
Outline manual of cost accounting for the ready mixed concrete industry. Washington, Author, c1948.
28 p.

NN   0060795   WaT

TA441   National Ready Mixed Concrete Association.
.N33   Engineering Division.

National Sand and Gravel Association. Engineering Division.
Annual report.
₁Washington₁

National Ready Mixed Concrete Association. Engineering Division.
Bibliography . . .
see under   National Ready Mixed Concrete Association.

VOLUME 407

National ready mixed concrete association. Engineering division.
Cold weather ready mixed concrete. Washington, D. C., 1951.
14 p. 23cm. (Its: Publication)

1. Cement and concrete—Effect of temperature. t. 1951.

NN 0060798 NN

The national ready reckoner: a series of commercial
tables containing calculations suited for all trade purposes : with profit and discount tables, and wages calculator. London and Glasgow, W. Collins, sons, &
company, 1878.
768 p. 17½ᵐ.

1. Ready-reckoners.

15-25771

Library of Congress HF5699.N3

NN 0060799 DLC

National real estate and building journal. v. —59, no. 6;
—June 1958. ₍Cedar
Rapids, Iowa, etc.₎ Stamats Pub. Co., etc.₎
v. in illus., ports., diagrs., plans. 25–31 cm.
Frequency varies.
Began publication with Mar. 1910 issue.
Official publication of the National Association of
Real Estate Boards (called in —Apr. 1916, National Asso-
ciation of Real Estate Exchanges) and other similar organizations.
Title varies: —May 1943, Aug.-Sept. 1944, National real
estate journal.—June 1943–July 1944, The New national real estate
journal.
Vols. for 1917, 1920–58 include an annual roster of realtors.

Issues for Aug. 19, 1929–Mar. 1943 include section: The Nareb
news.
Merged into Buildings.
L. C. set incomplete: v. 6–8, 19, 24–31 and scattered issues wanting.

1. Real estate business—U. S.—Period. ɪ. National Association
of Real Estate Boards. ɪɪ. Title: National real estate journal. ɪɪɪ.
Title: The New national real estate journal.

HD251.N35 46-36719 rev*

WaS MiU
NN 0060801 DLC CU CtU KyU MB OU LNL CoD TxU NN N

National real estate and building journal. 22
L333.073
... Directory issue, containing the official roster of realtors ...
₍Chicago, 1938– ₎
Library has 1938 *to date.* illus., plans, diagrs. 31ᵐ. annual.
Issued as an extra April number of National real estate journal.
Cover-title.
Title varies: 1938, Official directory of realtors; building reference guide.

NN 0060802 ICJ

National real estate and building journal.
How to advertise real estate effectively, how
to get leads by mail, how to make the right
sales appeal, ads that produce results. n.p.,
Compiled and copyrighted by National real estate
journal, 1942.

cover-title,130p. illus.(incl.ports.,facsims.,
tables) 28½cm.

NN 0060803 MoU

National real estate and building journal.
Practical appraising methods. 2d rev. ed.
A helpful guide for preparing appraisal reports on all common types of properties - residences, apartment buildings, office buildings,
stores, farms & farm land, industrial property.
Compiled ... by National real estate journal.
Chicago ₍1939?₎
cover-title,128 p. illus., plans, facsims.,
tables, forms, diagrs. 28ᵐ.

1. Real property - Valuation.

NN 0060804 NNC

National real estate and building journal.
KF567
.8
.R6
Rosenberger, Jesse Leonard, 1860–
Real estate decisions of the supreme courts of the vari-
ous states, from March, 1910, to April, 1912, digested
especially for the National real estate journal, by J. L.
Rosenberger ... Chicago, R. L. Polk & co., ₍1912.

NATIONAL real estate directory;
successor to Jackson's real estate directory...names and addresses of leading real estate dealers, abstractors,
loan companies and real estate attorney
of the United States, showing cities an
villages, and counties in which located
Kansas City, Mo. Directory pr.

Compilers: 1930– G.F.Schroeder
& Schroeder Branstetter.

NN 0060806 WaS OCl MB MiD

HD253
.N35
National real estate handbook and directory,
19-- ₍New York, Dornost, Publishing Co.₎
v. annual.

1. Real estate business - U. S. - Direct.

NN 0060807 NBuU

National real estate journal
see
National real estate and building journal.

HJ2360
.N43
1940
National real estate tax conference, Washington,
D.C.,1940.
... Resolutions adopted, addresses in full,
excerpts from addresses...
Chicago.Ill.₍1940₎ ₍(12) pieces₎ 28cm.

NN 0060809 DLC Or

The national realist movement of America ...
see under [Smith, Fred] 1888–

National realty journal. v. 1, no. 1–2; Mar.–Apr. 1911.
₍Chicago, National journal realty company, 1911₎
₍74₎ p. illus. 31ᵐ. monthly.
Continued as American bond and realty journal.

1. Real estate business—Period.

12-4996

Library of Congress HD251.A4

NN 0060811 DLC

The national recipe book, containing nearly one thousand recipes on all subjects, including many never before made public ... Battle Creek, Michigan publishing
company, 1872.
148 p. 18ᵐ.

1. Receipts.

7-23925†

Library of Congress TX153.N27

NN 0060812 DLC

National recipes and menus for "National"
pressure cooker
see under National presto industries, inc.

National reciprocity. A magazine devoted to reciprocity
and its value to our trade with other nations. v. 1,
no. 1–10; Sept. 1902–June 1903. Chicago, National
reciprocity league ₍1902–03₎
1 v. in 2. 23ᵐ. monthly
Official organ of the National reciprocity league.

1. Reciprocity--Period.

4—775

Library of Congress HF1731.N3

NN 0060814 DLC OrU MiU OU OO NIC MH

337.9
N21p
National Reciprocity Conference, Chicago, 1905.
Proceedings of the National Reciprocity
Conference held in the Illinois Theatre at Chi-
cago, Illinois, August 16–17, 1905. Published
by authority of the National Committee of the
American Reciprocal Tariff League. Chicago
₍1905₎
124p. 23cm.

1. Reciprocity. 2. Tariff--U.S.

NN 0060815 IU IEN ICJ NjP OU

National reciprocity convention. *1st, Washington, D. C.,*
1901.
Proceedings of the National reciprocity convention held
under the auspices of the National association of manufacturers of the United States of America. Washington,
D. C., November 19 and 20, 1901. ₍Washington? 1901₎
1 p. l., 186 p. 23ᵐ.

1. Reciprocity. 2. Tariff—U. S. ɪ. National association of manufacturers.

7-18376

Library of Congress HF1731.N4

NN 0060816 DLC MH-L Nh OU

137
227.2
National reciprocity convention. 1st,
Washington, D. C., 1901.
Second notice. Philadelphia, 1901.
₍4₎ p. 23cm.

NN 0060817 MH-L Nh

National reciprocity league, Chicago.

National reciprocity. A magazine devoted to reciprocity
and its value to our trade with other nations. v. 1,
no. 1–10; Sept. 1902–June 1903. Chicago, National
reciprocity league ₍1902–03₎

National reciprocity league. **Minnesota branch.**

Hay, Eugene Gano, 1853–
Reciprocity with Canada ; report of Eugene G. Hay,
to the advisory board of the Minnesota branch of the
National reciprocity league, upon the present attitude of
the United States and Canada and the prospects for reciprocity between the two countries. Minneapolis, Minn.,
The Minnesota branch of the National reciprocity league
₍1903₎

The National reclamation act, progress of the
government surveys in the Payette and Boise
valleys ...
see under Payette-Boise Water Users'
Association.

333.7
N213b
National Reclamation Association.
The beginning of the National Reclamation
Association. Documents, correspondence,
and newspaper reports from the first Western
States Reclamation Conference, Western
Governors' Conference, General Governors'
Conference. ₍Salt Lake City? 1930₎
1v.(various pagings) 26cm.

1. Reclamation of land. U.S. I. Western
Governors' Conference. II. Governors'
Conference. xWestern Reclamation Conference.

NN 0060821 OrU

VOLUME 407

National Reclamation Association.
  Board bulletins. v.

Washington
  v. 28cm.

NN   0060822   OrU

National Reclamation Association.
  Bulletins. v.

Washington,
  v. 28cm.

NN   0060823   OrU

National Reclamation Association.
  Desirable principles of state water legislation. Final report of Committee appointed
  pursuant to resolution no. 13, 11th annual
  convention, 1942. Presented at the 15th
  annual convention, Omaha, Nebraska, October 9,
  1946. ⟨Washington, 1946?⟩
  82 l.

NN   0060824   NNC-L DI

HD1694
A5N4   National Reclamation Association.
             National water policy statement, presented to the Task Force on Water Resources
           and Power of the Commission on Organization of the Executive Branch of the Government. Denver, Colorado, May 17, 1954.
           Washington, 1954.
           43 l.   28 cm.
           Cover title.

             1. Water resources development - U.S.
           I. U.S. Commission on Organization of the
           Executive Branch of the Government (1953-
           1955). Task Force on Water Resources and
           Power. II. Title.

NN   0060826   DI

National Reclamation Association.
  Preliminary report of the program adopted at
  the 5th-   annual meeting of the National reclamation association. n.p., The association, 1936-
  1 v. nar. O.

NN   0060827   CaBViP

National Reclamation Association.
  Principles suggested for adoption in the
  preparation of a uniform water act. Presented
  in the form of a progress report by the committee
  appointed pursuant to Resolution no.13, adopted
  by the National Reclamation Association at the
  11th Annual Meeting, October 14-16, 1942, Denver,
  Colorado. ⟨Berkeley, Calif.?⟩ 1943.
  92 l. 29cm.

  Signed Wells A. Hutchins, Chairman, for the
  committee.

NN   0060828   OrU MtBC

TC823
.N3   National reclamation association.
         Proceedings of ... annual meeting, National
       reclamation association and Association of
       western state engineers ... v.1-37; 1932-69.

       [Salt Lake City?
         v. map. 23cm.
         Issued by the Association after 1969 under its
       later name, National Water Resources Association.
       1. Reclamation of land--U.S. I. Association
       of western state engineers.

       CaBVaU DI MH-BA IdU MiU NN DNAL ICRL CU
NN   0060829   DLC MtU CoU IdPI Or OrCS Wa WaS OrU

NATIONAL RECLAMATION ASSOCIATION, COMP.
  ⟨A program to stabilize the western half of
  the United States with a reimbursable expenditure of from 55 to 65 million dollars a year.⟩
  Washington, D.C., Author ⟨1940⟩
  Sheet folded to ⟨6⟩ p.

NN   0060830   Or

TC809
N3   National Reclamation Association.
         Reclamation, a national investment. Long
       range planning, assured returns. [Washington? 1948].
       15 [17] p.   col. illus., diagrs., tables.
       28 cm.
       Cover title.

         1. Reclamation of land - U.S. 2. Natural
       resources - U.S.

NN   0060831   DI Or IdPI

389
N2136   National Reclamation Association.
           Reclamation, today's opportunity. Food
         for the world, energy for the peace.
         ⟨Washington, D.C., 1947⟩
         14 p.

NN   0060832   DNAL Or

National reclamation association.
  ...A report on what to do to prevent devastating
  floods in the Ohio and Mississippi rivers and in the
  lower Mississippi Valley ...
  [Washington, 1927]
TC425
.M6N25

NN   0060833   DLC

55.9
N212R   National Reclamation Association.
           Resolutions.

         Washington.

           1. Irrigation. Societies.

NN   0060834   DNAL OrU DI Or

National reclamation association.
  Resolutions adopted by the 7th annual meeting of the National reclamation association, held in Reno, Nevada, October
  11-12-13, 1938. ⟨Washington, D. C., National reclamation association, 1938?⟩
  11 p. 23 x 10ᵐ.

    1. Reclamation of land—U. S. 2. Soils—Societies.
                                                      42-30426
    Library of Congress   TC823.N32 1938 c

NN   0060835   DLC

National Reclamation Association.
  Special letters. v.

Washington,
  v. 28cm.

NN   0060836   OrU

National reclamation association.
  Thanks to irrigation

    see under

    Miller, A   L   1892-

SB
112
.N32   National Reclamation Association. Agricultural Research Committee.
          Report on soil and water problems and
        research needs of the West ⟨by ... Harry
        Bashore, Chairman. n.p., 1951⟩
        35,25 l. illus., tables. 28cm.

          Cover title: Soil and water research.
          1. Irrigation farming. 2. Agricultural
        research. 3. Agriculture. The West.
        I. Bashore, Harry William, 1880-   II. Title:
        Soil and water pro   blems and research needs of
        the West.

NN   0060838   OrU IdU OrCS AzU

National Reclamation Association. *Agricultural Research
  Committee.*
    Soil and water problems and research needs of the West;
  report. Washington, U. S. Govt. Print. Off., 1952.
    v, 24 p. 24 cm. (82d Cong. 2d sess. Senate. Document no. 98)

    1. Irrigation farming. 2. Agricultural research. 3. Agriculture—
  The West. I. Title.   (Series: U. S. 82d Cong. 2d sess., 1952.
  Senate. Document no. 98)

    SB112.N3   631.6072   52-60523

NN   0060839   DLC NIC

National reclamation association. *Committee to confer with
  western governors to provide the machinery to study and
  preserve integrity of state water laws.*
    Preservation of integrity of state water laws; report and
  recommendations, October, 1943, of committee of the National
  reclamation association, appointed pursuant to Resolution no. 9,
  adopted at annual convention of association, October, 1942.
  Members of committee: Clifford H. Stone, chairman ... Gus T.
  Backman ... Jean S. Breitenstein ... ⟨and others⟩ ⟨Denver,
  The Peerless printing co., 1943⟩
    xii, 176 p. 23ᶜᵐ.
    Includes bibliographies.
    1. Water-Laws and   legislation—U. S.   I. Stone, Clifford H., 1888-   ford H. II. Title.
                                                          44-1837
    Library of Congress   HD1694.A5N4
                                     ⟨4⟩   333.91

       Or IdPI OrU Wa NN
NN   0060840   DLC DI MtU CU DNAL WaU-L MtBC MtU OrP

HD
1694   National Reclamation Association. Committee
A55   to Prepare Uniform Water Code for Consider
1946   ation of the West.
             Desirable principles of state water legislation; final report of committee appointed
           pursuant to Resolution no.13, Annual Convention, 1942. Presented at the 15th Annual
           Convention, Omaha, Nebraska, October 9, 1946.
           ⟨Washington, D. C., National Reclamation
           Association, 1946⟩
           128 l. 29cm.

NN   0060841   C CU NN DNAL

L333.7   National Reclamation Association. Legis
N213m   lative Committee.
             Meeting. Denver, Colo., 1949.
             1v. (various pagings) 29cm.

             1. Water. Laws and legislation.

NN   0060842   OrU

L333.7   National Reclamation Association. Legisla
N213r   tive Committee.
             Report to the Board of Directors.
           ⟨Washington? 1950⟩
             1v. (various pagings) 29cm.

             1. Water. Laws and legislation.

NN   0060843   OrU

National Reclamation Association. *Water Policy Committee.*
    A national water policy; report. Approved in principle
  as the general water policy of the National Reclamation Association at the annual meeting of the association in Long
  Beach, California on November 14, 1952. Washington
  ⟨1952?⟩
    14 p. 23 cm.

    1. Water resources development—U. S. I. Title.

    HD1694.A4N44   55-20043 ‡

NN   0060844   DLC NN TxU CU DI DNAL CaBViP OrU

VOLUME 407

National reclamation magazine.
Reclamation and farm engineering ... v. 1–4, 7–10; Dec.1921–
Sept. 1926. ₁Chicago, etc., National reclamation publishing
company, 1921–26₁

National reconstruction. v. 1–
Aug. 1942–
New York, Committee on Wartime Planning for Chinese
Students in the United States.
v. in   illus., diagrs. 23 cm.
Semiannual, 1942; annual, 1943–
Title also in Chinese; some articles in Chinese, some in English.

1. China — Econ. condit. — Period. 2. Reconstruction (1989–   )—
China.   ɪ. Committee on Wartime Planning for Chinese Students in
the United States.
HC426.A1N3   330.951   47–41084*

NN   0060846   DLC NN OrU ViU ICRL OCl NNC

34.1   National reconstruction.
N21   Agriculture issue.   New York, Committee on
Wartime Planning for Chinese students in the
United States, 1944.
164 p.
Vol. 5, July 1944.
1. China. Agriculture. 2. Agriculture.
Economic aspects. China. I. National reconstruc-
tion. v.3. July 1944.

NN   0060847   DNAL

National reconstruction and the duty of the
profession ...
see under   [Washburn, Emory] 1800–1877.

National reconstruction journal
see   National reconstruction.

The National record. v. 1–   March, ʾ
1943–   Washington, D.C., 1943
v. illus. 42.5 cm. monthly.
Editor: R.R. Reynolds.
Supersedes the American vindicator.

NN   0060850   NcD

The National record of education; containing
current news and statistics of colleges and
schools in the United States. v.1, no.1–
May 1866–
New York, School apparatus company (1866)
1 v. illus. 23 cm.

NN   0060851   DHEW CU

National Record Office, *Copenhagen*
see
Denmark. *Rigsarkivet.*

The National recorder. Containing essays upon
subjects connected with political economy,
science, literature, &c.; papers read before
the Agricultural Society of Philadelphia; a
record of passing events; selections from
foreign magazines, &c. &c. v.2–5; July 3,
1819–June 30, 1821. Philadelphia: Published
by Littell & Henry. Clark & Raser, printers.
₁1819–21₁
4v. weekly.
9–13394
Library has vol. 4 only.

NN   0060853   PMA DCU TxH

National recorder. v.2–5; July 1819–June ᴹᶠ1821.
Philadelphia, Littell & Henry.
4v. illus. weekly. (American periodical
series: 1800–1850)
Microfilm ed., positive copy.
Continues Philadelphia register, and national
recorder.
Superseded by Saturday magazine.

NN   0060854   ICRL TxH DCU

The **National** recorder of religious and literary intelligence. v. 1, no. 1–7; 1859. Washington, 1859.
80 p. 35ᶜᵐ. monthly.
L. D. Johnson, editor.

ɪ. Johnson, Lorenzo D., ed.

9–4275

NN   0060855   DLC

National Records Management Council
Controlled record making and record
keeping, Department of Public Welfare,
City of Detroit. [Detroit?] 1952.
17 ℓ. diagrs.

On cover: A National Records Management Council Installation.

NN   0060856   MiD PU-PSW Or

---

352   National Records Management Council.
.164   Manual of procedures and operations
qN276   VALVE-controlled record keeping, City
73–1839 of New York. Prepared for the Mayor's
Committee on Management Survey of the
City of New York. [New York, 1951?]
11, [12] ℓ. 28 cm.

1. Public records.--New York (City)
I. New York (City) Mayor's Committee on
Management Survey. II. Title

NN   0060857   N NN NBC NIC

National Records Management Council
Operating manual for controlled record keeping; prepared for the Dept.
of Public Welfare, City of Detroit.
[Detroit, 1952?]
16 ℓ. diagrs.

NN   0060858   MiD

National Records Management Council.
Proceedings
see under   Conference on Records
Management.

National Records Management Council.
A records management program for the State of Israel;
report to the Government of Israel. Tel-Aviv, 1955.
2, iii, 57 ℓ. illus. 27 cm. (USOM public administration report)
Cover title.
Prepared under the auspices of the U. S. Operations Mission to
Israel.

1. Records.   I. Israel. United States. II. Operations Mission
to Israel. III. Title. IV. Series.
HF5736.N34   73–150007

NN   0060860   DLC

TR   National Records Management Council.
825   Streamlining and safeguarding property
N27+   recording: a report to the Mayor's Committee on Management Survey, April 30,
1951. ₁New York₁ 1951.
49 ℓ. illus. 28cm.

1. Photography of documents. I. New
York ₁City₁ Mayor's Committee on
Management   Survey. II. Title:
Property rec   ording.

NN   0060861   NIC NN

NATIONAL RECORDS MANAGEMENT COUNCIL.
Summary report on record keeping control for
the Mayor's committee on management survey in the
city of New York. [New York, 1952] 13 p. illus.,
fold. tables. 28cm.

1. Inventories--U.S.--N.Y.--New York. I. New York (City). Management
survey, Mayor's committee on   t. 1952

NN   0060862   NN

---

025. 171   National Records Management Council.
N532yNaV   Valve-controlled record keeping; a report of the
installation of record keeping control for the Mayor's
Committee on Management Survey in the City of New
York. [New York] 1951.
20p. illus. 28cm.

1. Records 2. Archives - New York (City) L New York (City)
Mayor's Committee on Management Survey. IL Title.

NN   0060863   NBC NN NIC

National Records Management Council. *Technical Information Service.*
Guide to selected readings in records management.   1954–
New York.
v. 28 cm.

1. Business records—Bibl.   ɪ. Title.
Z7164.C81N313   016.6515   54–43000

NN   0060864   DLC OrCS CaBVaU

National Records Management Council. *Technical Information Service.*
Index to Federal record keeping requirements. New
York ₁1955₁
32 p. 28 cm.

1. Business records—U. S.   ɪ. Title.

55—56445 ‡

InU NcG OCl FTaSU Or Wa
NN   0060865   DLC CaBVaU OrCS OrP ICN ViU MiD NIC

National Records Management Council. *Technical Informa-
tion Service.*
Quality controlled paperwork and record keeping. New
York, National Records Management Council ₁1954₁
32 p. 28 cm. (Technical Information Service bulletin)
Bibliography: p. 32.

1. Business records.   ɪ. Title.
HF5547.N183   651.5   54–14594

IU
NN   0060866   DLC CaBVaU TU NN FTaSU DI OCl MH-BA

National Recovery Administration
see
U. S. *National Recovery Administration.*

The National Recovery Administration, an
analysis
see under   Lyon, Leverett Samuel, 1885–

National recovery of the American way
see under   General welfare federation of
America, inc.

National Recovery Review Board
see   U.S. National Recovery Review Board.

VOLUME 407

National Recreation and Park Association.

In 1965 the National Recreation and Park Association was formed by the merger of the American Institute of Park Executives, the National Recreation Association, the National Conference on State Parks, the American Recreation Society, and the American Association of Zoological Parks and Aquariums. In 1971 the American Association of Zoological Parks and Aquariums again became an independent organization.

Works by these bodies are found under the name used at the time of publication.

National recreation association.
The ABC's of public relations for recreation; a primer for the recreation worker ...   New York, N. Y., National recreation association, °1946.
64 p. illus. (part col.) 21¼ᵐ.
Includes bibliographies.

1. Recreation—U. S. 2. Publicity.   I. Title.
                                          46–2475
Library of Congress   GV53.N27
                             ₍₃₎   790

NN   0060872   DLC PSt MsU OrP OCl

₍NATIONAL RECREATION ASSOCIATION₎
Abraham Lincoln ₍playlets, lists of songs, recitations & plays₎ ₍Author₎ ₍1948₎
17 p. (MP 4)

Mimeographed.
Bibliography: p. 11-17.

NN   0060873   Or

E457.7   **National Recreation Association**
-N28   Abraham Lincoln ₍suggestions for Lincoln's
Lincoln   birthday programs₎ ₍New York, Playground and
Collection Recreation Association of America, 1928?₎
            12 ℓ.   28 cm. (its M. P. no.4)

Mimeographed

1. Lincoln Day

NN   0060874   RPB

784.624 **National Recreation Association.**
N21a   Action songs.   New York ₍n.d.₎
           10 p.   illus.

NN   0060875   MtBC OrCS MiDP

---

796   **National Recreation Association.**
N213a   Active games for the live wires, prepared
           for the National Recreation Association by
           Muriel E. McGann. New York ₍°1952₎
           32 p. illus. 22 cm. (The games series,
           no. 1)

1. Athletics. 2. Games. I. McGann, Muriel
E., comp. II.   Title.

NN   0060876   CLobS Or

National recreation association.

Pangburn, Weaver Weddell.
    Adventures in recreation, by Weaver Weddell Pangburn. Prepared for National recreation association. New York, A. S. Barnes and company, incorporated, 1936.

National recreation association.

Price, Betty.
    Adventuring in nature, by Betty Price ... New York city, National recreation association ₍°1939₎

---

790   **NATIONAL RECREATION ASSOCIATION.**
N21a   Agencies of the federal government
           concerned with recreation: trends, inad-
           equacies, needs. New York, The associa-
           tion, 1954.
           47 p. (National recreation association.
           State and federal recreation service.
           Publication, no.3)

"Issued January 1954."
"Contains the results of an inquiry conducted by the Association with the

cooperation of the Federal Inter-Agency Committee on Recreation and the thirteen Federal agencies most concerned with recreation".- Introduction, p.5.

1. Recreation - U. S. I. U. S. Federal
inter-agency committee on recreation.

NN   0060880   WaU IaU DI

National recreation association.

Erskine, John, 1879–
    Amateur music and recreation leadership, by John Erskine, LL. D. Richer uses of music in recreation, by Augustus D. Zanzig. New York city, Playground and recreation association of America ₍1929?₎

National Recreation Association.
    An American recreation guide, a special defense project. Armed forces ed. ₍New York, 1952–
    v. 28 cm.
    Supplement to its Off-post recreation for the armed forces.
    CONTENTS.—

8. The Pacific Northwest.

1. U. S.—Descr. & trav.—Guide-books. 2. Recreation—U. S. I.
National Recreation Association. Off-post recreation for the armed
forces. II. Title.
    E169.N294   917.95   52–4873

NN   0060882   DLC CaBViPA

National Recreation Association.
    An American recreation guide; National and State parks, recreation areas, and historic sites. ₍New York, 1954–
    v. 28 cm.
    CONTENTS.—

3. The South.

1. U. S.—Descr. & trav.—Guide-books. 2. Recreation—U. S.
I. Title.
    E169.N2942   917.3   54–3078 ‡

NN   0060883   DLC DI

National recreation association.
    Annotated bibliography for music leader in camp, playground, recreation center... ₍New York city: National recreation assoc., 1941₎ 4 l. 28cm.

Reproduced from typewritten copy.

1. Camping—Bibl. 2. Children   —Music for—Bibl.
N. Y. P. L.   August 14, 1942

NN   0060884   NN

C
016.78   **National recreation association.**
N277   Annotated bibliography for music leaders
           in camp, playground, and recreation center.
           N.Y. ₍1946₎
           8p. 23cm.

1.Music. Bibliography. 2. Music.
Incidental. I. Title.

NN   0060885   N

National recreation association.
    Annual report ...
New York city, National recreation association
    v. illus. 25½ᵐ.

1. Play. 2. Amusements.
                                         A 36–743
Title from Teachers Col-   lege Libr. Printed by L. C.

NN   0060886   NNC-T IU TU OrCS

₍National recreation association₎
    ... Annual report of Dr. Henry S. Curtis, Secretary of the Playground association of America. New York city, Reprinted for the Playground association of America and the Playground extension committee of the Russell Sage foundation ₍1909?₎
    15 p. 23ᶜᵐ. ₍Russell Sage foundation. Dept. of child hygiene. Pamphlet no. 20₎
    At head of title: No 41.
    "Reprinted from Proceedings of the second annual Playground congress ..."
    1. Playgrounds. I.   Curtis, Henry Stoddard,
1870–   II. Ser.

NN   0060887   ViU

797.25 **National Recreation Association.**
N21a   Aquafun; water games, water carnival. **New**
           York ₍1953₎
           30p. 23cm.

1. Aquatic sports. I. Title. II. Title:
Water games. III. Title: Water carnival.

NN   0060888   IU Wa

National recreation association.
    Arts and crafts for the recreation leader, prepared for the National recreation association by Frank A. Staples, director, arts and crafts. New York, N. Y., National recreation association, °1943.
    48 p. illus. 28 x 22ᶜᵐ.
    "Sources of information": p. ₍2₎ of cover.

1. Handicraft. I. Staples, Frank A., 1900–   II. Title.
                                              44–1917
Library of Congress   TT157.N3

OEac PSt
NN   0060889   DLC OrPR Wa CaBVaU WaSp Or OLak OCl

National recreation association.
    Arts and crafts for the recreation leader, prepared for the National recreation association by Frank A. Staples, director, arts and crafts. New York, N. Y., National recreation association, 1944.
    48 p. illus. 28 x 22ᶜᵐ.
    "Sources of information": p. ₍2₎ of cover.

NN   0060890   ViU TxU

---

680   **National Recreation Association.**
N21ar   Arts and crafts program manual, a planning
           guide for all ages. Prepared by Frank A.
           Staples. New York, 1954.
           71p. illus. 28cm.

1. Handicraft. I. Title.

NN   0060891   IU CaBVa

National recreation association.
    Athletic badge test for boys ... New York city, Playground and recreation association of America, [1916]
    8 p. illus. 23 cm. (No. 105)
    Reprinted from The Playground, April, 1913. Rev. 1916.
    1. Playgrounds. 2. Physical education and training.

NN   0060892   CU

VOLUME 407

National Recreation Association.
  Athletic badge test for boys.   New York,
Playground and Recreation Association of
America [1922]
  8 p.   illus.   23 cm.   (Its [Reprint] no. 105)
  1. Athletics.   I. Title.   II. Ser.

NN   0060893   ViU

National recreation association.
  Athletic badge tests for boys and girls, prepared for the
Bureau of education by the Playground and recreation asso-
ciation of America ...   Washington Govt. print. off., 1923.
  III, 17, [1] p. illus. 23 cm.   ([U. S.] Bureau of education. [Physi-
cal education series, no. 2])

  1. Athletics.   I. Title.   E 23—246
  U. S. Office of Education.   Library   GV341.U6A3
  for Library of Congress   GV201.U5 no. 2
  ———— Copy 2.   GV436.N3 1923

NN   0060894   DHEW WaWW WaS DLC MiU OC1 OO

National recreation association.
  Athletic badge tests for boys and girls. Prepared for the
Office of education by the National recreation association, for-
merly named Playground and recreation association of America
...   Washington, U. S. Govt. print. off., 1931.
  III, 19, [1] p. illus. 23ᶜᵐ. ([U. S. Office of education. Physical educa-
tion series no. 2]
  On cover: Revised.

  1. Physical education and training. 2. Athletics.   I. Title.
  U. S. Off. of educ. Library   E 31—342
  for Library of Congress   GV201.U5 no. 2a
  ———— Copy 2.   GV436.N3 1931

NN   0060895   DHEW PPT WaWW DLC MiU OU

National Recreation Association.
  Athletic badge test for girls ...   New York
city, Playground and recreation association of
America. [1916]
  15 p.   illus.   23 cm.   (No. 121)
  Reprinted from The Playground, August, 1916.
  Revision largely the work of Lee F. Hanmer.
  1. Playgrounds. 2. Physical education and
training. I. Hanmer, Lee Franklin, 1871-

NN   0060896   CU

---

fGV1763
.N386 National Recreation Association.
         The barn dance returns!   New York
       [1939?]
       6, [1] p. illus., music. 27cm.

       Cover title.
       Reprinted from Recreation, Nov. 1937.

       √1. Folk dancing, American. √I. Title.

NN   0060897   AAP RPB

GV1763
.N3   National recreation association.
         The barn dance returns! [New York,
       National recreation association, 1946]
       cover-title,7p. illus. 26cm.
       Contains music.
       "Reprinted 1946."
       "A brief bibliography on square
       dancing": p.7.

         1.Dancing. 2.Dancing - Folk and
       national dances. I.Title.

NN   0060898   NNU-W

National recreation association.
  A bibliography for the recreation library.
[New York, 1946]
  13 l.
    1. Amusements - Bibliography. 2. Recreation -
  Bibliography.

NN   0060899   NNC

A371.3   National recreation association.
N21b   Bibliography of school assemblies.   [New York,
         National recreation association, 1940]
         8 numb.l.

         Caption title.
         Mimeographed.

           1. Schools--Exercises and recreations--Bibl.   I.
         Title: School assemblies.

NN   0060900   IU

National recreation association.
  Bibliography on dancing ...   [New York city: National rec-
reation assoc., 1939]   7 l.   28cm.
  Reproduced from typewritten copy.
  CONTENTS.—Folk dancing.—Clog, tap and character dances.—Social dancing.—
Miscellaneous.

  1. Dancing—Bibl.
  N. Y. P. L.   August 14, 1942

NN   0060901   NN

[National recreation association]
  Bibliography on dancing ... [New York,
National recreation association, 1944?]
  11 l.

    1. Dancing - Bibliography. I. Title.

NN   0060902   NNC

Drama   National recreation association.
*Z5784.C5   Bibliography on school assemblies ... includ-
N28   ing information on how to organize assemblies,
         suggestions as to plays, pageants, and other
         program material suitable for holidays and
         special days or for various school departments
         ... [1940?]

           8 numb. l.   28cm.

           Caption title.

NN   0060903   NBuG

A790   National Recreation Association.
N21b   Bibliography on the design and equipment of
         recreation areas and structures. [New York,
         National Recreation Association, 1949]
         8l. 28cm.

           Caption title.

           1. Recreation--Bibl.

NN   0060904   IU PPCPC

309.136 National Recreation Association.
N21br   A brief study of recreation for Claremont,
         N.H. Prepared for the Recreation Development
         Committee. New York, 1948.
         44p. illus. 28cm.

           Cover title.

           1. Claremont, N.H.--Recreational Activities.
         2. Claremont, N.H.--Playgrounds. 3. Recreation
         --Claremont, N.H.

NN   0060905   IU

---

309 136 National Recreation Association.
N21b   A brief study of recreation for the city of
         Albany, Georgia, prepared for the Board of
         City Commissioners   New York, 1950
         45l. 28cm.

           1. Albany, Ga.--Recreational activities.
         2. Albany, Ga.--Parks I Title II Title:
         Recreation for the city of Albany, Georgia.

NN   0060906   IU

National recreation association.

  Garber, Paul Edward.
    Building and flying model aircraft; a guide for youthful be-
  ginners in aeronautics, prepared for Playground and recreation association of America, by Paul Edward Garber ... New
  York, The Ronald press company [c1928]

       National Recreation Association.
SK601
.H18   Hammett, Catherine Tilley.
         The camp program book, prepared for the National Rec-
       reation Association by Catherine T. Hammett and Virginia
       Musselman. Illustrated by André. New York, Association
       Press, 1951.

National recreation association.
  Camping out; a manual on an organized camping [by] the
Playground and recreation association of America, New York.
New York, The Macmillan company, 1924.
  xx p., 1 l., 636 p. incl. illus., forms, diagrs. front., plates. 16½ᶜᵐ.
  Preface signed: L. H. Weir, editor.
  Contains bibliographies.

  1. Camping.   I. Weir, Lebert Howard, ed. II. Title.

  Library of Congress   SK601.N45
                                                    24–10010 rev.

NN   0060909   DLC CU OU OO OC1 OU Or WaS MtU

National Recreation Association.
  Camping out; a manual on organized camping
[by] the Playground and recreation association of
America, New York. New York, Macmillan Co.,
1925.
  xx, 636 p.   illus., forms, diagrs., plates.
17 cm.
  Prefaced signed: L.H. Weir, editor.
  Includes bibliographies.

NN   0060910   PU-Penn

National recreation association.
  Camping out; a manual on organized camping by
the Playground and recreation association of
America, New York, New York, The Macmillan co.,
1927.
  1 l., 633 p.

NN   0060911   MiU OU

---

790   National recreation association.
N27c   A challenge to America, a report
        for 1930.   New York city, National
        recreation association [1931?]
        [3]p. illus. O.

NN   0060912   IaU

National recreation association.
  Charges and fees for community recreation facilities and
activities of public park, recreation and school systems. Re-
port of a study made by the National recreation association.
New York city, National recreation association, 1932.
  4 p. l., 158 p. 23ᶜᵐ.
  "Study ... made by Charles E. Reed of the Field department of the
National recreation association."—Foreword.

  1. Recreation—U. S. 2. Recreation—Canada. 3. Community centers.
4. Parks. 5. Playgrounds.   I. Reed, Charles E. II. Title.
                                                    32–33377
  Library of Congress   GV53.N28
                                   [a44h1]   796.007

NN   0060913   DLC OrU PSt MoU MiU OU

National recreation association.

  U. S. Children's bureau.
    ... Children's year leaflet no. 1 [–13] Washington, Govt.
  print. off., 1918–19.

VOLUME 407

National recreation association.
The Christmas book.
N.Y., Playground and recreation association of
America, c1926.
94 p.

NN 0060915 OC1 OLak

NATIONAL RECREATION ASSOCIATION.
The Christmas book. New York City, Playground
and Recreation Association of America, [1929,
cop.1926].

pp.93.
"Revised,1929."

NN 0060916 MH

National recreation association.
The Christmas book. New York city, National recreation
association (ᵣ1932₎
96 p. 11 x 15ᶜᵐ.
Bibliography : p. 79–88.
"List of Christmas music" : p. 88–94.

1. Christmas plays. I. Title.
E 38–145
U. S. Off. of educ. Library   PN6120.C5N3
for Library of Congress   ₍2₎

NN 0060917 DHEW WaSp WaT ODW OO OC1

National recreation association.
The Christmas book ... New York National
recreation association, c1941
see under Ickis, Marguerite, 1897–

ₑNATIONAL RECREATION ASSOCIATION₎
A Christmas carnival in carols and pantomimes.
Author ₑ1949₎
5 ℓ.

Mimeographed.

NN 0060919 Or OrP

National Recreation Association.
Christmas crafts and decorations. New York ₍1953₎
59 p. illus. 22 cm.

1. Christmas decorations. 2. Christmas cards. 3. Handicraft.
I. Title.
TT870.N35   745   54–3403 ‡

NN 0060920 DLC IdPI Or WaS WaT AU WaSp PPPL

ₑNational recreation association₎
Church music and the new leisure. ₍New York, National
recreation association,193–?₎
15 p. 23ᶜᵐ.
Caption title.

1. Church music. I. Title.
42–45288
Library of Congress   MT88.N17C4

NN 0060921 DLC CCSC

National recreation association.
A city and country life movement; a million and a half
people achieve recreation systems in twelve months, 1913–
1914. ₍New York city, Playground and recreation association
of America, 1914₎
23, ₍1₎ p. illus. (incl. ports.) 22½ᶜᵐ. (₍Its Publications₎ no. 132)
Caption title.

Continued in next column

Continued from preceding column

1. Playgrounds. 2. Play. ₍2. Recreation₎   I. Title.
E 14–1213 Revised
Library, U. S. Office of   Education LB3518.N2P6 1914

NN 0060922 DHEW OC1

National recreation association.
Clubs in the recreation program. New York ₍1947₎
₍24₎ p. illus. 16ᶜᵐ.

1. Clubs.
HS2519.N3   367   47–20247
Brief cataloging

NN 0060923 DLC

QT   NATIONAL Recreation Association
250   ₍Collection of publications₎
q N276
The library has a collection of miscellaneous publications of this organization
kept as received. These publications are
not listed nor bound separately.
1. Invalids - Recreation & entertainment
2. Recreation

NN 0060924 DNLM

GV421   ₍National Recreation Association₎
.N3
no.181   Community drama and expert leadership.
1920   New York ₍1920?₎
5 p. 23cm. (Its ₍Reprints₎ no. 181)
"Reprinted from the Playground, November, 1920."

1. Community plays, etc. I. Ser.

NN 0060925 ViU

National Recreation Association.
Community drama; suggestions for a community-wide
program of dramatic activities, prepared by the Playground
and recreation association of America. New York, London,
The Century co. ₍1926₎
xi, 240 p. front., illus. plates. 21½ cm.
Contains bibliographies.

1. Community plays, etc. I. Title.
PN3203.N3   26—15012

ViU NcD NIC WaSp WaS MtU WaTC CaBVa CaBVaU WaWW
NN 0060926 DLC NIC GU TxU ODW OC1 OU OO OCU MiU

National recreation association.
Community music; a practical guide for the conduct of community music activities, prepared by the Playground and recreation association of America. Boston, C. C. Birchard and company, 1926.
4 p. l., ₍3₎–193 p. 21ᶜᵐ. (Lettered on cover: The Laurel library)
"The first edition of the Community music handbook ₍was₎ published
in 1920."—Introd.
"Sources of information" at end of each chapter.

1. Community music.
27–19027 rev.
Library of Congress   MT87.N2C7
Copyright A 891284   ₍r32e2₎   780.79

CaBVaU MtU OU OC1 MiU OOxM
NN 0060927 DLC OKentU NSyU IdU MtBC WaS Or OrP

National recreation association.
Community recreation buildings as war memorials; planning, financing, construction and operation of community recreation buildings ... New York, N. Y., National recreation
association ₍1944₎
55 p. illus. (incl. plans) 27½ x 21½ᶜᵐ.

1. Community centers. I. Title.
44–34351
Library of Congress   NA4510.C7N3

NN 0060928 DLC OC1 OC1W Or WaS KEmT PSt TU NcD

National Recreation Association.
Community recreation for defense workers; a special defense publication. ₍New York, 1952₎
31 p. illus. 23 cm.

1. Recreation—U. S. I. Title.
GV171.N2C   790   52–3645 ‡

NN 0060929 DLC OrU

HV1423 ₑNational recreation association₎
N28   A community recreation program for men in
uniform in defense time ... ₍New York city,
National recreation association, 1941?₎
cover-title,32 numb. ℓ. 22cm.

1. Soldiers.-Recreation. I. Title.

NN 0060930 NBuG MiD NN OU

₍National recreation association₎
A community recreation program for men in uniform in
defense time. He will go to town. ₍New York, 1943?₎
cover-title, 32 numb. l. 22ᶜᵐ.
Compiled by National recreation association. cf. Pref.
Reproduced from type-written copy.

1. Soldiers—U. S. 2. Soldiers—Recreation. I. Title. II. Title: He
will go to town.
A 44–2198
Illinois. Univ. Library
for Library of Congress   ₍2₎

NN 0060931 IU Or OrU

309.136 National Recreation Association.
N21cr   Community recreation salaries: 1955. A
National Recreation Association report prepared
by Recreation Personnel Service. New York,
1955.
20p. 28cm.

1. Recreational leadership. I. Title.

NN 0060932 IU

National recreation association.
Community recreation: suggestions for recreation boards,
superintendents of recreation and community recreation workers. New York city, The Playground and recreation association of America and Community service (incorporated) 1919.
122 p. 17ᶜᵐ.
"General bibliography on play and recreation" : p. 100–102.

1. Community centers. I. Community service, inc. II. Title.
22–25425 rev.
Library of Congress   GV53.N3

NN 0060933 DLC Or OrPR OU

#GV54   National Recreation Association.
.A11N3 Community resources directory. ₑCompiled by
C. E. Brewster₎ Bedford, Mass., L. G. Hanscom
Field ₑ1955₎
355 p. 26cm.
"Massachusetts in detail and also gives some
information on Maine, New Hampshire, Vermont and
nearby Canada."
On cover: New England community resources
directory.
1. Recreation—Massachusetts—Direct. 2. Recreation—New Eng   and—Direct. I.Brewster,
C. E., comp.   II. Title.

NN 0060934 MB

National Recreation Association.
Community service project, Olympia, Puyallup
& Tacoma Area, Washington, for McChord Air Force
Base. Directory of community activities, organizations, resource persons, recreational areas and
facilities. Compiled jointly by National Recreation Association & Washington State Parks & Recreation Committee in collaboration with Office of
Community Services, Hamilton A. F. B., California.
₍Seattle? 1954₎
72 p.

NN 0060935 Wa

VOLUME 407

National Recreation Association.
Community sports and athletics; organization, administration, program. New York, A. S. Barnes, 1949.
ix, 500 p. diagrs. 22 cm.
Bibliography: p. 486–496.

1. Sports—Organization and administration.   I. Title.

GV713.N3   796   49–11312*

IdU CaBVa Or OrCS OrU CaBVaU
NN   0060936   DLC TxU PSt PJB WaT NcD OOxM O Wa

PN3155   National Recreation Association.
N3   The community theater in the recreation
pam   program. New York [°1952]
            20 p. 22cm. (p 63)

1. Amateur theatricals. 2. Community plays,
etc. I. Title.

NN   0060937   OrCS

309.136 National Recreation Association.
N21com   A comprehensive recreation plan for the
            town of Tonawanda, Erie County, New York.
            Prepared for the town board. New York,
            1952.
            79ℓ. maps(part fold.) tables. 29cm.

1. Tonawanda, N.Y.—Recreational activities
2. Tonawanda, N.Y.—Parks. I. Title.

NN   0060938   IU

National Recreation Association.
Comrades in play, leisure time activities
which the young men and young women of America
can enjoy together.   New York, Community
service (incorporated), 1920.
84 p.   19 cm.
Suggested bibliography: p. 72–73.
1. Amusements. I. Title.

NN   0060939   CU

National recreation association.
The conduct of community centers; a practical guide for
community center workers ... New York city, National recreation association [°1936]
48 p. illus. 21½ᶜᵐ.
"A few sources of information": p. 47–48.

1. Community centers.   I. Title.
                                          36–36983
Library of Congress   LC231.N367
——— Copy 2.
Copyright AA 219666   [3]   374.28

NN   0060940   DLC Or MB OU

National recreation association.
The conduct of playgrounds.
New York city, Playground and recreation
association of America, 19–
17 numb. l.

NN   0060941   OU

National recreation association.
The conduct of playgrounds; a practical guide for playground workers ... New York city, National recreation association, °1936.
48 p. 21½ᶜᵐ.
"A brief bibliography for the playground worker": p. 48; "Sources
of information" at end of some of the sections.

1. Playgrounds.
                                          36–13023
Library of Congress   GV423.N32
——— Copy 2.
Copyright AA 203345   [3]   796

NN   0060942   DLC CaBVaU IdPI AU OCl OU AAP MsU

National recreation association.
The conduct of playgrounds; a practical guide for playground workers. New York, N. Y., National recreation association, °1945.
56 p. 21½ᶜᵐ.
"Revised, 1945."
Includes bibliographies.

1. Playgrounds.
                                          46–16688
Library of Congress   GV423.N32 1945
                                [2]   796

NN   0060943   DLC OCl

309.136 National Recreation Association.
N21co   Conduct of school community centers, a practi-
            cal guide.   New York [c1946]
            44p. 22cm.

1. Community centers.

NN   0060944   IU CaBViP ICU Or

National recreation association.
Cooperative study and evaluation of the leisure-time problem
in Tulsa and of the agencies related thereto, made under the aus-
pices of a group representing public and private civic, social and
recreational agencies. By Eugene T. Lies, special representative,
National recreation association, assisted by Mrs. Eswald Pottot.
[Tulsa, Okla.] 1936.   76 f. incl. tables.   28cm.
Reproduced from typewritten copy.
"Bibliography," f. 73–76.

1. Leisure. 2. Recreation—U. S.   —Okla.—Tulsa. 3. Education,
Adult—Okla.—Tulsa. I. Lies,   Eugene Theodore, 1876–
II. Pottot, Mrs. Eswald.
N. Y. P. L.   November 23, 1937

NN   0060945   NN

National recreation association.
County parks; a report of a study of county parks in the
United States ... New York, Playground and recreation asso-
ciation of America, 1930.
xi, 150 p. incl. front., illus., maps. 25ᶜᵐ.
"The editorial work was done by George D. Butler."—Foreword.
"Summary of legislation relating to county parks": p. 111–133.
"A brief bibliography of interest to park executives": p. 107–109.

1. Parks—U. S. 2. Playgrounds.   I. Butler, George D., ed. II. Title.
                                          30–23416 rev.
Library of Congress   SB482.A468
——— Copy 2.
Copyright A 27168   [r32j2]   711

                                                WaS OU MiU OCl Or WaTC OrU
NN   0060946   DLC IdPI ViU DeU LU NIC INS CU TU

National Recreation Association.
County recreation. New York, 19
10, 4l. 29cm.
Caption title.
Reproduced from typewritten material.
"Scoring sheet for community recreation
appraisal schedule." 4l. at end.

NN   0060947   NcU

NATIONAL RECREATION ASSOCIATION
Craft projects for camp and playground.
Author c1953.
31 p. illus.

NN   0060948   Or IdPI

National recreation association.

Ickis, Marguerite, 1897–
Crafts in wartime, prepared for the National recreation association by Marguerite Ickis ... New York city, National recreation association [1942]

National Recreation Association.
Dances and games. Omaha, Neb., 1943.
13 p. music. 22 cm. (Congress dance series. 4
in 1)

NN   0060950   NcU

793.3   National recreation association.
N21d   Dances and their management.   [New York,
            National recreation association, 1936]
            caption-title. 7 numb. l. 28cm.
            Mimeographed.
            Bibliography: p.7.

1. Dancing. 2. Dancers. 3. Games. I. Title.

NN   0060951   LU

GV1751 National Recreation Association.
.N29   Dances and their management. [New York,
Q   1941]
            7numb.l., 8l. 31cm.
            Caption title.
            Reproduced from type-written copy.

1. Dancing. I. Title. S

NN   0060952   PSt

GV1746 National Recreation Association.
qN3   Dances and their management. New York
pam   [1952?]
            5 l. 28cm. (P81-5-52)

1. Balls (Parties). 2. Dancing. I.Title.

NN   0060953   OrCS

National recreation association
Dancing 'neath the stars. 4p. Author
[1941]

NN   0060954   OrP

National recreation association.

Dryden, Mrs. Maude L.
Day camping, by Maude L. Dryden; some practical suggestions for a new field in camping ... New York city, National
recreation association [°1939]

309.13605 National Recreation Association.
NAT   Defense recreation bulletin. Defense
            industrial bulletin no.
            New York.
            no. 28cm.

NN   0060956   IU

GV1493 National Recreation Association.
N3   Dinner table fun. New York [°1951]
pam   19 p. 22cm. (MP185)

1. Literary recreations. 2. Indoor games.

NN   0060957   OrCS

GV53   National Recreation Association.
N18   Directory.
R
            New York.
            v. 23cm.
            "Advisory groups, service affiliates, ser-
            vice associates, professional societies and
            associations."

1.Recreation - U.S. - Direct.

NN   0060958   OrCS

VOLUME 407

NATIONAL RECREATION ASSOCIATION.
Donated parks and play areas in the United States; prepared by the Playground and Recreation Association of America. New York [, 1930?]. 15 p. plates. 8°.

Plates printed on both sides.

588180A. 1. Parks—U.S. 2. Playgrounds—U.S.

NN 0060959 NN

---

j602 National Recreation Association
N21e Easter crafts and games. New York [°1952]
15 p. illus.

1. Easter 2. Handicraft I. Title

NN 0060960 MiD Or IdPI OrCS

---

793 [National recreation association]
N21ea Easy stunts, a collection of ten entertaining stunts ... [New York, National recreation association, 1938?]
10 numb.l.

Caption-title.
Mimeographed.

1. Amateur theatricals. I. Title.

NN 0060961 IU OrP

GV1471 National Recreation Association.
N18 Easy stunts and skits. New York [n.d.]
pam 32 p. 22cm.

Processed.

1. Amusements. I. Title.

NN 0060962 OrCS

National recreation association.

Jacks, Lawrence Pearsall, 1860–
Education through recreation, by Lawrence Pearsall Jacks ... New York and London, Harper & brothers, 1932.

National recreation association.
88 successful play activities, suggestions for conducting special play activities in which the competitive element may be introduced. New York city, Playground and recreation association of America [°1927]
4 p. l., 120 p. diagrs. 17cm.

1. Playgrounds. 2. Games. 3. Athletics. I. Title.

Library of Congress   GV423.N33

27—5591 rev.

NN 0060964 DLC OU OLak OC1

National recreation association.
88 successful play activities. Here are the old time games—with some new ones—which children can play among themselves. Here, too, are handcraft, drama, music, and nature play activities ... New York, National recreation association [°1933]
2 p. l., 119 p. diagrs. 16cm.
Earlier editions, 1927, 1929, published by the Playground and recreation association of America. Name of the association changed in 1932.
"A few publications of the N.R.A. for playground workers": p. 117–118.

1. Playgrounds. 2. Games. 3. Athletics. I. Title. II. Title: Play activities.

Kansas City, Mo. Pub. libr.   A 34–1392
for Library of Congress   [GV423.N]
[n38f2,]   796

NN 0060965 MoK CU WaT OrLqE ODW

National recreation association.
88 successful play activities. Here are entered the old time games -- with some new ones - which children can play among themselves. Here, too, are handicraft, drama, music and nature activities. ..
New York city, The Author, [c1936]
95 p.

NN 0060966 OU CaBVaU IdU OC1

National Recreation Association.
88 successful play activities. [8th ed.]
New York [1948, c1929]
93 p. illus.

NN 0060967 Wa

GV
171 National Recreation Association.
.N27 88 successful play activities. Here are the
1951 old-time games, with some new ones, which children can play among themselves. Here, too, are handcraft, drama, music and nature activities ... [9th ed.]
New York [1951]
96 p. illus.
Includes bibliography.

1. Games. 2. Athletics. I. Title. II. Title: Play activities.

NN 0060968 MiU PSt OC1

[National recreation association]
11 % plus ... [New York, 1947]
[32] p. illus. 16cm.

1. Recreation. 2. Old age. I. Title.
GV184.N3   790   47–22480
Brief cataloging

NN 0060969 DLC

National Recreation Association.
Emergency recreation services in civil defense; a special defense project of the National Recreation Association. [New York, 1951]
31 p. illus. 23 cm.

1. Recreation—U.S. 2. Civilian defense. I. Title.
GV53.N314   790   51–8251 ‡

NN 0060970 DLC Wa

---

507 National Recreation Association.
N215e Enjoying nature; nature centers, nature trails, trailside museums. [Prepared by Reynold E. Carlson. New York, National Recreation Association, 1946.
40p. illus. 22cm.

Bibliography: p. 39–40.

1. Nature study. 2. Natural history museums. I. Carlson, Reynold Erland. II. Title.

NN 0060971 IU OrCS Or

---

q793 National recreation association, comp.
N21e Entertainment stunts. [New York, 1932?]
10 numb.l.

Caption title.
Autographed from typewritten copy.

NN 0060972 IU

---

793 [National recreation association]
N21e Entertainment stunts. [New York city, National recreation association, 1942]
1942 5p.

Caption title.
Mimeographed.

1. Games. I. Title.

NN 0060973 IU

National recreation association.
Essential national service. The National recreation association submits a report of 1934 service given on request to localities in every state in the United States. [New York city, 1935]
cover-title, 12 p. 25½ cm.

NN 0060974 DL

+
GV1229 National recreation association.
.N27 Fact and fiction party; an evening of fun with books. [New York, National recreation association, 1940.
6 numb. l. illus. 31cm.
Caption title.
Mimeographed.

1. Games. I. Title.

NN 0060975 NNU-W

---

790 National Recreation Association.
N21f Fees and charges in community recreation. New York [1948?]
30l. 28cm.

Cover title.

1. Recreation. 2. Community centers. I. Title.

NN 0060976 IU

National recreation association.
A few of the many things all America does for the men in uniform through War camp community service. [New York, Nat. recreation assoc., 1941] 48 p. 23cm.

1. Soldiers—Welfare work—U.S.   2. Seamen—Welfare work—U.S.
N.Y.P.L.   November 24, 1947

NN 0060977 NN

National Recreation Association.

A few of the playgrounds secured last year in cities in which the Playground and Recreation Association of America worked. [New York, 1914]
15 p. illus. 24cm. (Its [Reprints] no. 132)

1. Playgrounds. I. Ser.

NN 0060978 ViU OO

ML128 National Recreation Association.
.S2 A few references on singing games. New
qN3 York [1950?]
pam 3 l. 28cm.

1. Singing games - Bibl. I. Title.

NN 0060979 OrCS

National Recreation Association.
Fiesta
see under Kron, Marion G
[Supplement]

---

j372.23 National Recreation Association
N21f Finger plays for the very young. New York, °1952.
16 p. illus.

1. Kindergarten - Games and Songs

NN 0060981 MiD OC1W PSt Wa OrCS

VOLUME 407

National recreation association.

GV4
.I6
1932
International recreation congress. *1st, Los Angeles, 1932.*
First International recreation congress. Proceedings, July 23–29, 1932, Los Angeles, California. Under the auspices of the National recreation association. ₁Los Angeles, National recreation association, 1933₎

796
N2132f
National recreation association.
Fitness ... for victory. ₁New York city, National recreation association, 1942?₎
cover-title, ₁24₎p. illus.

1. Recreation. 2. Sports. I. Title.

NN 0060983 IU OCl

National Recreation Association.
Flag raising ceremonies suggested for six days in camp. New York, National recreation association [1944]
2 l. 28 cm.
Mimeographed.
1. Flags. I. Title.

NN 0060984 MiEM

J796
N277f
National Recreation Association
Flying high; kites and kite tournaments
New York₁c1952₎
16p. illus. 22cm. (National Recreation Association. Publication ₁no. P 65₎)

1.Kites. I.Title. II.Series.

NN 0060985 CLSU MiD WaS

National recreation association.

Breen, Mary J.
For the storyteller, prepared by Mary J. Breen. New York city, National recreation association, ˚1938.

National recreation association.

Frieswyk, Siebolt Henry.
Forty approaches to informal singing, by Siebolt H. Frieswyk ... Varied approaches to the art of conducting informal singing, with suggested music material ... New York city, National recreation association ₁˚1939₎

₁National recreation association₎

Fun at the "meetin' place". 4p.
Author₁1940₎

Amusements for a "pioneer party".

NN 0060988 OrP

National recreation association.
Fun for everyone; a pocket encyclopedia of good times, suggestive social and recreational programs for community groups.
New York, Community service, 1922.
112 p.

NN 0060989 OU

National recreation association.
Fun for everyone; a pocket encyclopedia of good times. Suggestive social and recreational programs for community groups. New York city, Playground and recreation association of America, 1926.
118 p.

NN 0060990 OU

National Recreation Association.
Fun for Mother's day: a banquet and party, a play and lists of plays, songs and poems for Mother's day. New York, National Recreation Association, c.1932.
30 p.

NN 0060991 CaBVa

National recreation association.

Bowers, Ethel, *ed.*
... Fun for threesomes for wartime recreation, edited for the National recreation association by Ethel Bowers ... New York city, National recreation association ₁1943₎

National Recreation Association.
Games and plays for school morale; a course of graded games for school recreation. New York, National Recreation Association, 1929.
Rev ed.

NN 0060993 OrLgE

National recreation association.
Games for boys and men ... New York city, National recreation association, ˚1938.
110, ₁2₎ p. illus. (incl. music) diagrs. 21½ cm.
Includes bibliographies.

1. Games.

GV171.N27 793 38—16453

OrLgE
NN 0060994 DLC OCl OU OOxM Or OrCS WaS CaBVaU

National Recreation Association.
Games for boys and men ... New York city, Association press, 1940.
110, ₁2₎ p. illus. (incl. music) diagrs. 22cm.
Includes bibliographies.
"Second edition, 1940."

NN 0060995 PSt

National recreation association.
Games for boys and men. Third ed.
New York, Association press, 1941.
112 p.

NN 0060996 OCl Mi

GV171
N325
1946
National recreation association.
Games for boys and men. 6th ed. New York, 1946,c1938.
112p. illus.(incl. music) 22cm.

Includes bibliographies.

1. Games.

NN 0060997 IaU

National recreation association.
Games for children ... New York city, National recreation association ₁1943₎
62 p. illus. 21½ cm.
"Singing games" (with music): p. 5–11.

Continued in next column

Continued from preceding column

1. Games. I. Title.

43–6391

Library of Congress GV1203.N28

₁3₎ 796.1

NN 0060998 DLC NcGU TU CaBViP DPU

National recreation association.
Games for quiet hours and small spaces ... New York city, National recreation association, ˚1938.
59 p. illus., diagrs. 21½ cm.

1. Games. I. Title.
Library of Congress GV1201.N3 39–3450
——— Copy 2.
Copyright AA 255894 ₁2-2₎ 793

OCl OOxM
NN 0060999 DLC NcGU TU MtBC OrU CaBVaU Or OU

National recreation association.
Games for quiet hours and small spaces. New York city, National recreation association, 1940.
59 p. illus., diagrs. 21½ cm.
"Second edition."

1. Games. I. Title.
41–20299
Library of Congress GV1201.N3 1940
₁3₎ 793

NN 0061000 DLC OrPR

National recreation association.
Games for quiet hours and small spaces ...
3d edition. New York city, National recreation association, 1941.
59 p. illus., diagrs. 21.5 cm.

NN 0061001 NcD-W OO

793
N21ga
National recreation association.
Games for quiet hours and small spaces, prepared by the National recreation association ... 5th ed. ... New York city, Association press, 1942.
59p. illus., diagrs.

1. Games. I. Title.

NN 0061002 IU

National Recreation Association.
Games for quiet hours and small spaces.
New York city, National recreation association, 1945.
59 p. 21.5 cm.
"Sixth edition".

NN 0061003 MiEM

National Recreation Association.
Games for the Christmas season. New York ₁1953₎
48 p. 22 cm.

1. Christmas. 2. Games. I. Title.

GV1229.N27 793 53–3957 ‡

NN 0061004 DLC Or WaS IdPI OrCS OrP TxU PPPL

VOLUME 407

National recreation association.
  Games for the playground; some typical active and quiet games for children from six to fourteen years of age ... New York city, National recreation association, °1936.
  35 p. diagrs. 21½ᶜᵐ.

  1. Games. 2. Playgrounds. ɪ. Title.   36–20200

  Library of Congress   GV1203.N3
  ———— Copy 2.
  Copyright AA 214025   ₃₎   796

NN   0061005   DLC CaBVaU Or IdU MB OU OOxM NN

634
N21g   **National Recreation Association.**
  Gardening; school, community, home.   New York ₍1940₎
  60p. illus. 23cm.

  "Printed aids": p.57–59.

  1. Gardening.

NN   0061006   IU Or WaS MiU MiD DLC OLak MBH

National recreation association.
  Gay nineties.   N.Y.,Author,₍1951₎.
  illus.

  Mimeographed.
  Description of the amusements in vogue during the gay nineties,for those who wish to revive them for modern parties.
  Includes music.
  "Collections of old favorite songs": p.20.

NN   0061007   Wa WaSp OrP Or

National recreation association.
  Gifts and gadgets made of paper.
  New York city, National recreation association ₍1942₎
  6 numb. l.

NN   0061008   OO

National recreation association.
  Girls' clubs.
  New York city, Playground and recreation association of America, 1925.
  8 numb. l. (Its Bulletin no. 1291)

NN   0061009   OU

National Recreation Association.
  Golf courses; data secured from questionnaires sent by the Bureau of Municipal Research of Schenectady, N.Y. to 100 municipal golf courses in the United States in 1942. New York [1946]

  8 p.

NN   0061010   MH

309.136 **National recreation association.**
N21g   "Gotta date tonight?" ...   New York, National recreation association ₍1943₎
  11p. illus.

  "Reprinted from Recreation, January, April and May, 1943."

  1. Adolescence. 2. Community centers. I. Title.

NN   0061011   IU PSt OrP

National Recreation Association.
  A guide to free and inexpensive publications on recreation and leisure. New York ₍195-₎
  28 p. 29 cm.

  1. Recreation – Bibl. 2. Leisure – Bibl.

NN   0061012   DI

National recreation association
  Handcraft and hobby bibliography.
  New ᴸork city, ₍1936₎
  2 p. l., 2–118 numb.

NN   0061013   OU

National Recreation Association.
  Handcraft for home, school, playground and summer camp.   New York City, Playground and Recreation Association of America [cop. 1925]
  32 p. folded plates. f°.
  Manifold copy.

NN   0061014   MH

National recreation association.
  Handcraft for home, school, playground and summer camp.
  New York city, Playground and recreation association of America ₍1927₎
  32 p.

NN   0061015   OU ODW

National recreation association.
  Handicraft for home, school, playground and summer camp ... Revised and reprinted 1930. New York city, Playground and recreation association of America ₍1930₎
  1 p. l., 79 p. incl. fold. diagrs. 35 x 30ᶜᵐ.

  Autographed from type-written copy.
  Contains references.

  1. Handicraft. 2. Toys. ɪ. Title.   E 32–106

  Library, U. S. Office of   Education   TT157.P5
  Library of Congress   [TT168.N3 1930]
  ———— Copy 2.   ₍a34d1₎

NN   0061016   DHEW OC1 OLak OrU

National recreation association.
  Handicraft for home, school, playground and summer camp. Revised and reprinted 1930. New York city, Playground and recreation association of America ₍1933₎
  1 p. l., 79 p. incl. fold. diagrs. 35x30 cm.

NN   0061017   TU

National recreation association.

Ickis, Marguerite, 1897–
  Hands up, prepared for the National recreation assocition ₍1₎ by Marguerite Ickes ₍1₎ Drawings by Helen Lauck ... New York city, National recreation association ₍1942₎

National recreation association.

Zanzig, Augustus Delafield.
  Heigh-ho for a merry spring! By Augustus D. Zanzig ... New York city, National recreation association ₍1935₎

National recreation association.
  Hints for hostesses in service clubs.
  ₍New York, c1944₎
  31, ₍1₎p. illus. 18cm.

NN   0061020   PSt

National recreation association.

M1977
.C5S7   **Surette, Thomas Whitney,** 1861–1941, *comp.*
  ... The home and community song book, by Thomas W. Surette and Archibald T. Davison; sponsored by Better homes in America, inc., & National recreation ass'n. Complete ed.: words, melodies & pianoforte accompaniment ... Boston, Mass., E. C. Schirmer music co. ₍1931₎

NN   0061012   DI

796
N2132h **National recreation association.**
  Home made play apparatus.   New York city, National recreation association ₍c1940₎
  cover-title, ₍11₎p. diagrs.

  Mimeographed.
  "M.P. #277-5-40."

  1. Playgrounds--Apparatus and equipment. I. Title.

NN   0061022   IU

National recreation association.
  Home play ... New York, N. Y., National recreation association, °1945.
  95 p. illus. 21½ᶜᵐ.
  Includes bibliographies.

  1. Recreation. 2. Amusements. 3. Games. ɪ. Title.   45–19434

  Library of Congress   GV1201.N33
            ₃₎   790

NN   0061023   OrLgE
            DLC NIC PSt NcGU CaBVaU WaS WaTC MtBC

GV1201
.M9   **National recreation association.**

  ₍Musselman, Virginia W ₎
  Home play in wartime; stay at home recreation on a war bond budget. ₍New York, National recreation association, incorporated, °1942₎

National recreation association.
  Home play. Suggestions for recreation activities of various kinds within the home, and for backyard equipment, game courts and activities. New York, Playground and recreation assoc. of America, n.d.
  48 p. illus. 22cm.

  1. Play. 2. Games. I. Title.

NN   0061025   NcD OU

National recreation association.
  Home playground and indoor playroom.
  NewYork, Playground and recreation assoc. of America, 1926.
  10 l.

NN   0061026   OO

790
N21h   **National recreation association.**
  Home playground and indoor playroom.   ₍New York city, National recreation association, 1941₎
  9 numb.l.

  Caption title.
  Mimeographed.
  "M.P. #73-4-41."
  "A brief bibliography": leaves 8-9.

  1. Play. 2. Playgrounds. I. Title.

NN   0061027   IU NcGU

VOLUME 407

GV
426
.N3
National Recreation Association
Homemade play apparatus.   New York ₍1952₎
13 p.   illus.   23cm.

1. Playgrounds - Apparatus and equipment

NN   0061028   WU

GV54
.N8A3
subser.
National Recreation Association.

North Carolina. *Recreation Commission.*
Hospital recreation; a report of the southern regional
institute on hospital recreation. 1st–
1953–
Raleigh.

National recreation association.
How a city can celebrate Independence day without loss of
life or fire damage.   (Plan approved by Municipal conference
of Playground congress, Pittsburgh, May 10-14, 1909) New
York, Dept. of child hygiene of the Russell Sage foundation
₍1909?₎
   31 p. illus. 23ᶜᵐ. ₍Russell Sage foundation. Dept. of child hygiene.
Pamphlets, no. 31₎
   On cover: A safer, saner fourth of July with more patriotism and
less noise.
   "Independence day: a civic opportunity" ₍by₎ William Orr: p. 8–18.

   1. Fourth of July celebrations.   I. Orr, William, 1860–
                                                    E 10–1748 Revised 2
Library, U. S. Office of   Education E286.N2
Library of Congress   E286.A1427

NN   0061030   DHEW CU OO DLC

National recreation association.
How people "play" in forty American cities;
based on facts gathered in recreation surveys.
Comp. by the Playground and recreation
association of America...
New York city, The Association, 1916.
   56 numb. l.

NN   0061031   OU

National recreation association.
How to celebrate Hallowe'en.
N.Y., n.d.
18 p.

NN   0061032   OC1

₍NATIONAL RECREATION ASSOCIATION₎
How to celebrate Washington's birthday.
₍Author₎ ₍1948₎
   17 *l.* (MP 3)

   Mimeographed.
   Bibliography: p. 11–17.

NN   0061033   Or OrP

J
680
N213h
National Recreation Association.
How to do it: arts and crafts projects
for the recreation program, prepared for
the National Recreation Association by Frank
A. Staples. ₍New York, °1953₎
   30 *l.* illus. 28cm.

   1. Handicraft.   I. Staples, Frank A.,
1900–   II. T.

NN   0061034   MiDW PSt

National recreation association.
                              FOR OTHER EDITIONS
                              SEE MAIN ENTRY
Zanzig, Augustus Delafield.
   How to make and play a shepherd pipe, by Augustus D.
Zanzig ... New York city, National recreation association
₍1942₎

B
B8245n
National Recreation Association.
   Howard Braucher: July 19, 1881–May 22, 1949.
₍Tribute in loving memory of its late President,
Howard Braucher, by the National Recreation
Association.   New York, 1949₎
   56p. illus., ports., facsim. 28cm.

   Caption title.

   1. Braucher, Howard S., 1881–1949.

NN   0061036   IU MiD NIC MB DNAL

GV421
.N35
1937d
National recreation association.
   The importance of recreation in modern
life. Topics for group discussion, twenty-
second National recreation congress ...
Atlantic city, N.J., May 17–21, 1937.
Sponsored by National recreation association
... New York city ₍1937?₎
   24 p.   21½cm.
   I. Title.

NN   0061037   DLC

National Recreation Association.

Dyer, Donald B
   In-service education for community center leadership.
Prepared for the National Recreation Association by Donald
B. Dyer and staff. New York, National Recreation Associa-
tion ₍1955₎

National recreation association.
   Indianapolis recreation survey, prepared for the General
civic improvements committee of the Indianapolis chamber of
commerce, January–March, 1914. Compiled under the direction of the Playground and recreation association of America,
Francis R. North, field secretary. ₍Indianapolis, 1914₎
   60 p. fold. plan, fold. diagr. 23ᶜᵐ.

   1. Indianapolis—Playgrounds.   I. North, Francis Reid, 1876–
II. Indianapolis. Chamber of commerce. III. Title.

Library of Congress   GV431.I 5N3
                                            15–9352 rev.

NN   0061039   DLC OU

National Recreation Association.
   Inexpensive costumes

   see under

   Lamkin, Nina B

₍National recreation association₎
   Inexpensive puppets. ₍New York, National recreation asso-
ciation, 1938₎
   5 numb. l. illus. 28ᶜᵐ.
   Caption title.
   "A few books on hand puppets": numb. leaf 5.

   1. Puppet-plays.   I. Title.
                                            A 40–864
Ohio state univ. Library
   for Library of Congress

NN   0061041   OU

National Recreation Association.
   Informal dramatics

   see under

   Musselman, Virginia W

GV171
.B85
1949
National Recreation Association.
                              FOR OTHER EDITIONS
                              SEE MAIN ENTRY
Butler, George Daniel, 1893–
   Introduction to community recreation, prepared for the
National Recreation Assn. 2d ed. New York, McGraw-Hill
Book Co., 1949.

E161
qN3
pam
National Recreation Association.
   Joseph Lee memorial pageant. New York,
National Recreation Association ₍1952?₎
   7 numb. *l.* 28cm.

   "Adapted from a script written by Patricia Koltonski ... and presented in Rutland,
Vt., July 28–29, 1941."

NN   0061044   OrCS

National Recreation Association
   Katchina dolls

   see under

   Ickis, Marguerite, 1897–

National recreation association.
   Know your community; suggestions for making a study of
community recreation needs ... New York, N. Y., National
recreation association, °1943.
   24 p. 21½ᶜᵐ.
   "A brief bibliography": p. 24.

   1. Recreation. 2. Social surveys.   I. Title.
                                            44–20330
Library of Congress   GV14.5.N27
                                   ₍2₎   790

NN   0061046   DLC

National recreation association.
   Know your community; suggestions for making a study
of community recreation needs ... New York, N. Y., National recreation association, 1946, c1943.
   24 p. 21½ cm.
   "A brief bibliography": p. 24.

   "Second edition, 1946."

NN   0061047   OU

309.136
N21k
1955
National Recreation Association.
   Know your community; suggestions for making
a study of recreation resources and needs.
₍Rev. ed.₎   New York ₍1955₎
   v, 22p. illus. 23cm.

   "P218."

   1. Recreation. 2. Social surveys. I. Title.

NN   0061048   IU Wa Or

National recreation association.
   Layout and equipment of playgrounds. ₍New York city₎
The Playground and recreation association of America, 1921.
   60 p. fold. plans. 17ᶜᵐ.

   1. Playgrounds.   I. Title.
                                            22–25423 rev.
Library of Congress   GV423.N36
                                   ₍r32e2₎

NN   0061049   DLC OrPR WaS

VOLUME 407

National recreation association.
Layout and equipment of playgrounds.
New York city The Playground and recreation
association of America, 1922.
69 p.

NN 0061050 OEac MtBC

National recreation association.
The leisure hours of 5,000 people; a report of a study of
leisure time activities and desires ... New York city, National recreation association [1934]
cover-title, 3 p. l., 2-3, 3a, 4-83 numb. l. incl. form. 28ᶜᵐ.
Mimeographed.

1. Leisure.   I. Title.

Library of Congress   HD4904.7.N3
                                        34-19904
                              [7]   331.015

        IU ICJ ViU OU ODW OC1 OC1W
NN 0061051   DLC NcD CU NIC Or OrCS OrU OC1h NN DL

National Recreation Association.
The leisure hours of 5,000 people; Summary of a study of
leisure time activities and desires ... [New York city, National
recreation association [1939]
4 numb. l. 30cm.
Mimeographed.

NN 0061052 PSt OU

National recreation association.

[Zanzig, Augustus Delafield]
Let freedom sing, a wartime guide for music leaders. [New
York, National recreation association, incorporated, 1943]

National recreation association.

Bowers, Ethel, ed.
... Let's plan a party. For all occasions. Edited by
Ethel Bowers ... New York city, National recreation associa-
tion [1941]

National recreation association.

Let's sing the same songs. Prepared by National recreation
association ... New York city [National recreation association,
1942?]
1 p. l., 13, [1] p. 21½ᶜᵐ.
"Courtesy of the Voice of Firestone."
Some songs with piano accompaniment, others unaccompanied.

1. Songs (Collections)   I. Title.

Library of Congress   M1629.N33L3
                                        42-16011
                              [2]   784.8

NN 0061055 DLC NcD

National recreation association.
List of song books and of songs with descants
for boys.
New York city, 1934.
3 l.

NN 0061056 OU

National Recreation Association.
Living memorials.   New York, The Association, 1944?
n.p.

NN 0061057 PPCPC

National recreation association.
Long range recreation plan, city of Baltimore, Maryland,
prepared for the Commission on city plan, 1941, by Weaver W.
Pangburn ... [and] F. Ellwood Allen ... of the National recreation association.   Baltimore, Md., Dept. of public recreation,
1943.
x, 100 p. front., illus. (incl. plans) maps (part fold.) diagrs. 28 x 22ᶜᵐ.
"Correction" slip mounted on frontispiece.

1. Baltimore—Recreational activities.   I. Baltimore. Commission
on city plan.   II. Pangburn, Weaver Weddell.   III. Allen, F. Ellwood.
IV. Baltimore. Dept. of public recreation.   V. Title.

                                                            44-1381
Library of Congress   GV54.M3B36
                              [3]   796.09752

NN 0061058 DLC PSt

q309.136 National Recreation Association.
N21d   Long range recreation plan, city of Dan-
ville, Virginia, prepared for the Recreation
Commission by National Recreation Association,
F. Elwood Allen [and] Arthur H. Jones.
Danville, Va., J. T. Townes Ptg. Co. [1943?]
44p. illus., maps. 31cm.

Cover title.
Bibliography: p.49.

NN 0061059 IU

309.136 National Recreation Association.
N21f   Long range recreation plan, city of Fort
Wayne, Indiana. Prepared for the city of
Fort Wayne. [New York] 1944.
67p. illus., maps. 29cm.

Bibliography: p.67.

1. Fort Wayne, Ind.—Recreational activities
I. Title.

NN 0061060 IU OC1

National recreation association.
Long range recreation plan, city of Portland, Maine; prepared for Park commission and City planning board by National recreation association ... New York city, 1943.
2 p. l., 90 p. incl. illus. (maps) plans (1 fold.) 28 x 21½ᶜᵐ.
Reproduced from type-written copy.
Bibliography: p. 89-90.

——— Recommendations as to adminstration, program, and leadership personnel, supplemental to the Long range recreation
plan for the city of Portland ... [New York, 1943]
2 p. l., 13 numb. l. 28 x 21½ᶜᵐ.
Reproduced from type-written copy.

1. Portland, Me.—Recreational activities.   I. Portland, Me. Park
commission.   II. Portland, Me. City planning board.   III. Title.
                                                    44-534 Revised
Library of Congress   GV54.M2P67 Suppl.
                              [2]   790.941

NN 0061062 DLC NN OC1

309.136 National Recreation Association.
N21b   Long range recreation plan, town of Belleville, New Jersey, prepared for town of
Belleville.   New York, 1944.
85l. illus., maps. 28cm.

1. Belleville, N.J.—Recreational activities. I. Title.

NN 0061063 IU

309 136 National Recreation Association.
N21e   Long range recreation plan, town of East
Hartford, Connecticut, prepared for the Park
Board. [New York] 1942
65l. maps 28cm.

1. East Hartford, Conn.—Recreational activities. 2. East Hartford, Conn.—Parks
I. Title.

NN 0061064 IU

National recreation association.
Long range recreation plan, town of Kearny, New Jersey. Prepared for the Board of recreation commissioners by National
recreation association ...   [New York? 1942] v, 56 f. illus.
28cm.

244025B. 1. Recreation—U.S.—N.J.   —Kearny. I. Kearny, N.J.
Recreation commissioners board.
N.Y.P.L.   September 20, 1943

NN 0061065   NN OC1 NNC

GT3980 National Recreation Association.
N3   Look – a parade! Suggestions for formal
pam   and informal parades and floats. New
York [n.d.]
21 p. illus. 22cm.

1. Processions. I. Title.

NN 0061066 OrCS

National recreation association.
Making a book for community songs accompaniment;
New York City, National recreation association,
1932.
1 l. 28cm. (M.B. no.120)
Caption title.

NN 0061067 OrCS

National recreation association.
Manual of recreational activities for young men's work
camps; what to do. Prepared by the National recreation association ... [New York? 1934]
76 p. diagrs. 23ᶜᵐ.
Includes bibliographies.

1. Recreation. 2. Games. 3. Amateur theatricals.
                                                    36-1684
Library of Congress   GV171.N3
                              [a44e1]   790

NN 0061068   DLC Wa Or OrP OC1

j602   National Recreation Association
N21m   Masks, fun to make and wear. New York
[1952?]
8 p. illus.

Reproduced from type-written copy.

1. Masks (for the face)

NN 0061069 MiD

GV1229 National Recreation Association.
N295   Mental games. New York [*1951]
pam   16 p. illus. 22cm.

Cover title.
Processed.

1. Games. I. Title.

NN 0061070 OrCS

GV53   NATIONAL RECREATION ASSOCIATION.
.N23   [Miscellaneous publications]

1. Recreation—U.S.

NN 0061071 ICU

VOLUME 407

National Recreation Association.
   Mixers to music for parties and dances
      see under   Musselman, Virginia W., comp.

ZM
793
N213m
National Recreation Association.
   More fun enroute [for our armed forces]
   New York, c1944.
      [3]-34p. illus. 14cm.

NN   0061073   TxU

National recreation association.
   ...Municipal and county parks in the United
   States. Under the direction of George D. Butler
   member of staff, National recreation association.
   Washington, U. S. Govt. print. off., 1935-40.

      I. Butler, George D.   II. U. S. National
   park service.

NN   0061074   MiD

National recreation association.
   ... Municipal and county parks in the United States, 1935.
Under the direction of George D. Butler, member of staff,
National recreation association. Washington, U. S. Govt.
print. off., 1937.
   ix, 147 p. incl. tables, diagrs. xiii pl. (incl. front., map, plan) on 8 l.
23cm.
   At head of title: United States Department of the interior, Harold L.
Ickes, secretary. National park service, Arno B. Cammerer, director.
Washington, in cooperation with the National recreation association,
Howard S. Braucher, secretary, New York.
   "The National park service assumed a large share of the responsibility
for gathering the information used in this report. The study was directed and the report prepared by George D. Butler of the National
recreation association."—Foreword.
   1. Parks—U.S.   I. Butler, George D.   II. U. S. Na-
tional park service.   III. Title.
   Library of Congress   SB482.A4686   37-28808
   ———— Copy 2.   [10-5]   352.7

           OCU OU OO
NN   0061075   DLC WaTC MtBC WaWW OrCS OrU TU NIC Or

SB482
.A4N36
R.R.
NATIONAL RECREATION ASSOCIATION.
   Municipal and county parks in the United States,
   1940. A report of a study conducted by the Nation-
   al park service with the cooperation of the Ameri-
   can institute of park executives and the National
   recreation association, under the direction of
   George D. Butler. New York [1940]
      viii, 173 p. diagrs.

      1. Parks—U.S.

NN   0061076   ICU NNU-W MiD IaU

National recreation association.
   Municipal and county parks in the United States, 1940; a
report of a study conducted by the National park service with
the cooperation of the American institute of park executives
and the National recreation association, under the direction of
George D. Butler. New York, National recreation association
[1942]
   viii, 173 p. incl. illus. (map) tables, diagrs. 23½cm.
   "The National park service assumed the major responsibility for
gathering the data used in this report. The study was directed and the
report prepared by George D. Butler of the National recreation association."—Foreword.
   1. Parks—U. S.   I. Butler, George D.   II. U. S. National park
service.   III. American insti-   tute of park executives.   IV. Title.
   Harvard univ. Library   A 44-2970
   for Library of Congress   [SB482.A]
                                [7]   352.7

           WaU WaS
NN   0061077   MH CU MU Or NcD MB NIC IU TU RPB ViU

National recreation association.
   ... Municipal golf; construction and administration. New York city, Playground and recreation association of America [1927?]
      47 p. incl. illus., tables, forms. 23 cm.

      At head of title: No. 216.
      "A brief bibliography of municipal golf": p. 47.

Continued in next column

Continued from preceding column

   1. Golf-links.   I. Title.

NN   0061078   Vi

National recreation association.

Zanzig, Augustus Delafield.
   Music and men, prepared by Augustus D. Zanzig; a manual
for planning and developing musical activities in communities
near training or manufacturing centers—of army, navy or
industry ...   New York city, National recreation association
[*1941]

National recreation association.

Zanzig, Augustus Delafield.
   Music in American life, present & future, prepared for the
National recreation association by Augustus Delafield Zanzig;
with a foreword by Daniel Gregory Mason. London, New
York [etc.] Oxford university press [*1932]

National Recreation Association.
   National Joseph Lee day; a tribute to a builder of
   the national recreation movement, July 28th ...
      see under   National Joseph Lee day
   committee.

National recreation association.

Howland, Amy Richmond.
   National physical achievement standards for girls; instruction book and scoring tables ... prepared by Amy R. Howland,
PH. D., for the National recreation association.   New York city,
[1936.

National recreation association
   Nature music.
   New York city, 1937.
      1 p. l., 8 l.

NN   0061083   OU

Z
259
N3
National Recreation Association.
   Nature prints.   New York [1953]
      16 p.   illus.   22 cm.

   1. Nature-printing and nature-prints.

NN   0061084   IEdS

National Recreation Association.
   Negro spirituals and music composed by
   Negroes.   New York, 1937.
      15 l.   27.5 cm.

NN   0061085   NcD

National recreation association.
   The new leisure challenges the schools. Shall recreation enrich or impoverish life? Based on a study made for the National recreation association by Eugene T. Lies; with a foreword by John H. Finley.   New York,   National
Recreation Association [*1933]
   326 p., 2 l. plates. 23½cm.
   Bibliography: p. [304]-314.

NN   0061086   NcU

National recreation association.
   The new leisure challenges the schools. Shall recreation
enrich or impoverish life? Based on a study made for the
National recreation association by Eugene T. Lies; with a foreword by John H. Finley, LL. D. Washington, D. C., National
education association of the United States [*1933]
   326 p., 1 l. plates. 23½cm.
   Bibliography: p. [304]-314.
   1. Leisure.   2. Education—Aims and objectives.   3. Education—Curricula.   4. Student activities.   5. Education of adults.   6. Amusements.
7. Community centers.   I. Lies, Eugene Theodore, 1876-   II. Title.
   Library of Congress   BJ1498.N35
   ———— Copy 2.   33-29516
   Copyright A 65366   [5]   370.1

           OC1 MiU OU ODW
           NcRS DL NN OrMonO WaS DHEW OrLgE MB ViU CaBVa WaU
NN   0061087   DLC MtU IdPI OrCS Or WaTC CaBViP NcD

National recreation association.
   The new play areas; their design and equipment, edited for
the National recreation association by George D. Butler. New
York, A. S. Barnes and company, 1938.
   xiii, 242 p. incl. front., illus. 27¾cm.
   "The National recreation association prepared 'Play areas—their de-
sign and equipment', which was first published in 1928 ... a thorough
revision of 'Play areas' has been made."—Introd.
   Bibliography: p. 228-237.
   1. Playgrounds.   2. Playgrounds—Apparatus and equipment.
I. Butler, George D., ed.   II. Title.   III. Title: Play areas.
   Library of Congress   GV423.N38 1938   38-22473
   ———— Copy 2.
   Copyright A 121008   [5]   796

           OCU OrLgE OrMonO OrCS Or OC1 OO OU ODW
NN   0061088   DLC IdU OrU NcGU NN NIC CoU MU MiU WaS

National recreation association.
   The normal course in play; practical material for use in the
training of playground and recreation workers, prepared by
the Playground and recreation association of America, under
the direction of Joseph Lee, president. New York, A. S.
Barnes and company, 1925.
   x, 261 p. 23½ p.
   "Sources of information" at end of each chapter.

   1. Play.   2. Community centers.   I. Title.
   Library of Congress   LC231.N37
                                                25-18386 rev.

           WaSp CaBVaU MiU OCU   OOxM DHEW
NN   0061089   DLC WaU OU OO NSyU WaTC IdPI MtU MtBC

National recreation association.
   The normal course in play; practical material
for use in the training of playground and recreation workers, prepared by the Playground and recreation association of America, under the direction
of Joseph Lee, president.   New York, A.S.
Barnes and company, 1929.
   x, 268 p.   24 cm.
   "Sources of information" at end of each chapter".
   1. Play.   2. Community centers.   I. Title.

NN   0061090   CU

National recreation association.
   The normal course in play; practical
material for use in the training of playground
and recreation workers, prepared by the
Playground and recreation association of
America under the direction of Joseph Lee,
president; rev. and enl.
N.Y., 1929.

NN   0061091   ODW IdU WaS OC1W

309.136
N21du
National Recreation Association.
   Notes and comments on public recreation in
   Duluth, Minnesota, with special reference
   to population, material areas and facilities,
   program, government and executive organiza-
   tion, finances, together with notes on al-
   lied public agencies. By L. H. Weir.
   [New York, 1946.
      113l. 28cm.

      1. Duluth, Minn.—Recreational activities.
   2. Duluth, Minn.—Parks.   I. Weir, Lebert
   Howard.

NN   0061092   IU

VOLUME 407

National Recreation Association.
Off-post recreation for the armed forces, a special defense project. ₍New York, 1952₎
31 p. illus. 23 cm.

1. Soldiers—Recreation. I. Title.

U766.N3   355.12   52-27554 ‡

NN   0061093   DLC

E169
.N294

National Recreation Association. Off-post recreation for the armed forces.

National Recreation Association.
An American recreation guide, a special defense project. Armed forces ed. ₍New York, 1952-

---

National recreation association
FOR OTHER EDITIONS
SEE MAIN ENTRY
... **Official** rules of playground baseball, approved as official by the National rules committee of the National recreation association, Ernest W. Johnson, chairman ... Rev. Jan. 1932. New York, Pub. for the committee by American sports publishing co., °1932.

National recreation association.

Fisher, *Mrs.* Dorothea Frances (Canfield) 1879–
On a rainy day, prepared for the National recreation association by Dorothy Canfield Fisher and Sarah Fisher Scott; illustrated by Jessie Gillespie. New York, A. S. Barnes and company ₍°1938₎

NATIONAL RECREATION ASSOCIATION.
The organization of municipal recreation programs. [New York, 1938].

Manifold copy. ff.11. Tables.
"M.P. no. 224."

NN   0061097   MH-PA OU PPCPC

[National Recreation Association, New York]
Our **neighbors to the South**! A bibliography listing references including dances, music, plays, pageants, festivals, customs, games, party plans, and sources of program material from Central and South America. [New York, 1941]
8 p. 28 cm.
Mimeographed; printed on one side of the leaf.
1. South America. Social life and customs.
Bibl. 2. Central America. Social life and customs. Bibl. 3. Amusements. South America. Bibl. 4. Amusements Central America. Bibl.

NN   0061098   MB

National recreation association
Our neighbors to the South: a bibliography listing references including dances, music, plays, pageants, festivals, customs, games, party plans, and other sources of program material from Central and South America.
New York, National recreation association, 1942.
11 numb. 1.

NN   0061099   OU

₍National recreation association₎
Our neighbors to the south! A bibliography listing references including dances, music, plays, pageants, festivals, customs, games, party plans, and other sources of program material from Central and South America ... ₍New York, 1944?₎

11 numb. l. 28 x 21½ᵐ.

Caption title.
Reproduced from type-written copy.
Classified and annotated ; priced.

1. Spanish America—Bibl. I. Title.

                                              44-8395

Library of Congress   Z1601.N33
                          ₍4₎   016.918

NN   0061100   DLC TxU IU ICU

National recreation association.
Outdoors, indoors, prepared for the National recreation association by Reynold E. Carlson, director, Nature recreation service. Drawings by E. H. Peterson ... New York, N. Y., National recreation association, °1945.

52 p. illus. 21½ᵐ.
Includes bibliographies.

1. Nature study. I. Carlson, Reynold Erland. II. Title.

                                              45-14127

Library of Congress   QH53.N27
                          ₍3₎   574

NN   0061101   DLC Or GU PSt OC1

National Recreation Association.
The Pacific Northwest: Idaho - Montana - Oregon Washington; all national, state and local parks and recreation areas. ₍New York, c1952₎
95 p. (An America recreation guide. Armed Forces edition)

NN   0061102   Wa

793
N21pa

National Recreation Association.
Pageants and programs for school, church and playground. New York ₍1954?₎
iii, 42p. illus. 21cm.

Contains song with music.
Contents.- We build together.- America sings.- Music unites the nations.- I hear America singing.- Children of the Americas.- Americans all.- Who are we of the United States?

1. Pageants. 2. Entertaining.

NN   0061103   IU OrCS

GV421
.N33

National recreation association.
[Pamphlets.]
N.Y.,
                          8*

NN   0061104   DLC

791.6
N21p

₍National recreation association₎
A Pan-American carnival. [New York city, National recreation association, 1941]
cover-title, 19 numb. l. illus.

Mimeographed.
Dedication signed: Joy Montgomery Higgins.
"Source material": leaves 18-19.

1. Festivals. 2. Musical festivals. I. Higgins, Joy Montgomery. II. Title.

NN   0061105   IU NBuG

National recreation association.
... Park recreation areas in the United States. May, 1928. Washington, U. S. Govt. print. off., 1928.
v, 95 p. incl. illus., tables, maps (1 fold.) 23ᵐ. (Bulletin of the United States Bureau of labor statistics, no. 462. Miscellaneous series)
At head of title: U. S. Department of labor. James J. Davis, secretary. Bureau of labor statistics. Ethelbert Stewart, commissioner.
Issued also as House doc. 158, 70th Cong. 1st sess.
A study undertaken in conjunction with the American institute of park executives at the request of the National conference on outdoor recreation. Lebert H. Weir directed the work. *cf.* Pref.
1. Parks—U. S. 2. Playgrounds—₍U. S.₎ I. Weir, Lebert Howard. II. National conference on outdoor recreation. III. American institute of park executives. IV. Title.
                                              L 28—152
U. S. Dept. of labor. Libr   HD8051.A5 no. 462
for Library of Congress   HD8051.A62 no. 462
———— Copy 2.   SB482.A469

NN   0061106   DL NNC WaWW DLC MiU

National recreation association.
... Park recreation areas in the United States, 1930 ... May, 1932. Washington, U. S. Govt. print. off., 1932.
v, 116 p. incl. tables. 23ᵐ. (Bulletin of the United States Bureau of labor statistics, no. 565. Miscellaneous series)
At head of title: United States Department of labor. W. N. Doak, secretary. Bureau of labor statistics. Ethelbert Stewart, commissioner.
"The Bureau of labor statistics was largely responsible for gathering the material ... The study was conducted and the report prepared by George D. Butler, of the National recreation association (formerly the Playground and recreation association of America)"—Pref.
An earlier study was issued in 1928 as Bulletin no. 462 of the U. S. Bureau of labor statistics.
Issued also as House doc. 122, 72d Cong. 1st sess.
1. Parks—U. S. 2. Playgrounds—₍U. S.₎ I. Butler, George D. II. U. S. Bureau of labor statistics. III. Title.
                                              L 32—62
U. S. Dept. of labor. Libr   HD8051.A5 no. 565
for Library of Congress   [HD8051.A62 no. 565]

NN   0061107   DL OrPS WaWW DLC

National recreation association.

Weir, Lebert Howard, *ed.*
Parks, a manual of municipal and county parks compiled as a result of a nation-wide study of municipal and county parks conducted by the Playground and recreation association of America, in co-operation with the American institute of park executives at the request of the National conference on outdoor recreation. This study was made possible through funds granted by the Laura Spelman Rockefeller memorial. Edited by L. H. Weir, director of the study ... New York, A. S. Barnes and company, 1928.

National recreation association.
Parties, A to Z; novel ideas for twenty-six parties ... New York, N. Y., National recreation association ₍1944₎
96 p. 21½ᵐ.

1. Amusements. I. Title.

                                              44-9571

Library of Congress   GV1471.N3
                          ₍5₎   793

                   00xM
NN   0061109   DLC TU NcC NcGU WaS OrCS WaT Or OC1

National recreation association.

Bowers, Ethel, *ed.*
Parties for special days of the year, edited by Ethel Bowers ... New York city, National recreation association ₍°1936₎

M1985
.B72P3

National recreation association.

Bowers, Ethel.

Parties, musical mixers and simple square dances, prepared by Ethel Bowers ... New York city, National recreation association ₍°1937₎

National recreation association.

Bowers, Ethel, *ed.*
Parties, plans and programs; a guide for the social recreation leader and organization executive, edited by Ethel Bowers ... New York city, National recreation association, °1936.

₍NATIONAL recreation association.

Parties plus; fun for threesomes, ed by Katherine F. Barker   N Y Author, c1943   60p illus

NN   0061113   WaT

National Recreation Association.
Parties plus; let's plan a party for all occasions see under Bowers, Ethel.

National recreation association.

Bowers, Ethel.
Parties plus; stunts and entertainments for wartime recreation, edited for the National recreation association by Ethel Bowers ... New York city, National recreation association ₍1942₎

VOLUME 407

National recreation association.
Breen, Mary J.
FOR OTHER EDITIONS
SEE MAIN ENTRY
Partners in play; recreation for young men and women together, prepared for the National recreation association and National board, Young women's Christian associations, by Mary J. Breen. New York, A. S. Barnes and company, incorporated, 1936.

National recreation association.

Breen, Mary J.
The party book, prepared for the National recreation association by Mary J. Breen; illustrated by Hamilton Greene. New York, A. S. Barnes and company ₍ᶜ1939₎

NATIONAL RECREATION ASSOCIATION
Party favors₍ by Reba Esh₎ Author c1941.
₍5₎ ℓ. illus.

Processed.

.NN 0061118   Wa

National recreation association.

U. S. *Children's bureau.*
... Patriotic play week: suggestions to local child-welfare committees ... Prepared in collaboration with the Child welfare department of the Woman's committee, Council of national defense, and the Playground and recreation association of America. Washington, Govt. print. off., 1919.

National recreation association.

Fredrikson, Clark L.
The picnic book, prepared for the National recreation association by Clark L. Fredrikson. New York, A. S. Barnes and company ₍1942₎

₍National recreation association₎
Picnic programs. ₍New York, National recreation association, 1938₎
cover-title, 21 p., 2 ℓ. 15¼ᵐ.
No. 195.
"For the compilation of picnic material which appears in this booklet, the National recreation association is indebted to the Dept. of public playgrounds and recreation of Reading, Pa., and to Charles K. Brightbill ... to the Extension service of the Iowa State college of agriculture."—Foreword.

1. Games. I. Title.   A 40-865

Ohio state univ. Library
for Library of Congress   ₍2₎

NN 0061121   OU

796.1 National recreation association.
N21p   Picnic programs … ₍New York, N.Y., 1941₎
7 numb. l.
Mimeographed.
"M.P.#251-6-39."

1. Games. I. Title.

NN 0061122   IU NcGU PSt

GV1201 National Recreation Association.
.N38   Picnic programs. ₍New York, National
Q   Recreation Association, 1944?₎
7 numb. l. 31 cm.
Caption title.
Reproduced from type-written copy.

Continued in next column

Continued from preceding column

1. Games. 2. Picnicking. I. Title. S

NN 0061123   PSt

Buffalo
*GV431.B9
N2   National Recreation Association.
Plan of recreation areas and facilities,
Buffalo, N. Y. New York, 1946.
112 numb. ℓ. plans. 28cm.

NN 0061124   NBuG IU

725.8 National Recreation Association.
N21p   Planning a community recreation building;
important principles and features involved
in planning a community recreation building.
New York ₍1945₎
12p. illus. 28cm.
Bibliography: p.12.

1. Recreation centers. I. Title.

NN 0061125   IU PSt IaU

725.8 National Recreation Association.
N21pℓ Planning a community recreation building.
New York ₍1955₎
29p. illus. 22cm.

1. Recreation centers. I. Title.

NN 0061126   IU ICarbS

725.8 National recreation association
N27p   Planning an industrial recreation
building; important principles and
features involved in planning an
industrial recreation building.
New York, N.Y. The Assn. ₍1941₎
cover-title, 12p. plans. ₵
Bibliography: p.12.

NN 0061127   IaU

PN3203 National Recreation Association.
N32   Planning and producing a local pageant.
pam   New York ₍ᶜ1952₎
20 p. 22cm.

1. Pageants. I. Title.

NN 0061128   OrCS

GV183 National Recreation Association.
.D3
Dauncey, Helen M
Planning for girls in the community recreation program. Prepared for the National Recreation Association by Helen M. Dauncey. New York, National Recreation Association ₍1953₎

GT4965 National Recreation Association.
.M3
McGann, Muriel E
Planning for Halloween; large and small groups and community-wide celebrations. Prepared for the National Recreation Association. New York, National Recreation Association ₍1954₎

National Recreation Association.
Planning for patriotic holidays

see under

McGann, Muriel E

Pam.   National Recreation Association.
Coll.   Plant-centered recreation for defense
workers--organization and administration.
48081 ₍New York, 1952₎
39 p. 23 cm.
Bibliography: p. 35-36.

1. Industrial recreation. I. Title.

NN 0061132   NcD PPD

National recreation association.
Play and home planning; extracts from the Tentative reports of the President's conference on home building and home ownership. New York, National recreation association ₍1932?₎
(8) p. illus. 23 cm.

NN 0061133   DL

---

790   ₍National recreation association₎
N21p   Play and recreation in the church. ₍New York,
National recreation association, 1942₎
9p.
Caption title.
Mimeographed.

1. Church entertainments. I. Title.

NN 0061134   IU

National recreation association.
Play areas, their design and equipment, prepared by Playground and recreation association of America. New York, A. S. Barnes and company, 1928.
xvi, 206 p. incl. front., illus., plans, diagrs. 27½ᵐ.
"The editorial work was done ... by George D. Butler."—Foreword.
Bibliography: p. 191-201.

1. Playgrounds. 2. Playgrounds—Apparatus and equipment.
I. Butler, George D., ed. II. Title.
28-19701 Revised
Library of Congress   GV423.N38

MtU WaS OrU ViU ODW OU OO OCl
NN 0061135   DLC CaBVa DHEW MU PSt KEmT NIC KMK NcU

---

796   National recreation association.
P69p   Play areas, their design and equipment, pre-
1935   pared by National recreation association, formerly named Playground and recreation association
of America. New York, A. S. Barnes and company, 1935.
206p. incl. front., illus., plans, diagrs.
"The editorial work was done ... by George D. Butler."--Foreword.
Bibliography: p.191-201.

NN 0061136   IU DI

National recreation association.

Hobbs, Mabel Foote.
Play production made easy; prepared for the National recreation association, by Mabel Foote Hobbs. Pantomimes and very short plays, by Marion Holbrook. New York city, National recreation association ₍ᶜ1933₎

VOLUME 407

National recreation association.
Play space in new neighborhoods; a committee report on standards of outdoor recreation areas in housing developments ... New York city, National recreation association ₍*1939₎

23 p. 22ᶜᵐ.

Title on two leaves.
Plan on p. ₍3₎ of cover.
"A few references to the design and equipment of recreation areas": p. 23.

1. Playgrounds.   I. Title.

Library of Congress   GV425.N3
———— Copy 2.
Copyright AA 290857   ₍3₎   796

39–33284

NN   0061138   DLC PSt Or OOxM MH

National Recreation Association.
The playground leader – his place in the program

see under

Musselman, Virginia. ✓

National recreation association.
Playground layout and equipment.
New York city, National recreation association 1939.
4 numb. l.

NN   0061140   OU

National Recreation Association.
Playground leaders
see under   Forsberg, Raymond T

796.068 National Recreation Association.
N21p   Playground series. no.1–

New York, 1952–
no.   illus.   22cm.

NN   0061142   IU

NA6800 National recreation association.
.N39   Playground shelter buildings. ₍New York,
Q   N.Y., National recreation association, 1944₎
           3 numb.l.   plans.   31cm.

Caption title.
Mimeographed.

1. Playgrounds.   I. Title.

NN   0061143   PSt

National Recreation Association.
Playground shelter buildings. [New York, 1949]

3 p.   3 plans.

NN   0061144   MH

National Recreation and Park Association.
Playground summer notebook. 1st–   ed.;
1944?–
Washington.
                    annual?

l. Playgrounds – Period.

NN   0061145   GU IU

National recreation association.
Playground surfacing.
New York city, Playground and recreation
association of America, 1924.
5 numb. l.

NN   0061146   OU

GV423   National Recreation Association.
.B8   FOR OTHER EDITIONS
1950   SEE MAIN ENTRY –
        Butler, George Daniel, 1893–
        Playgrounds, their administration and operation. Pre-
        pared for National Recreation Association. Rev. ed. New
        York, Barnes, 1950.

                    Recreation
394.268 National   Association.
C55n   Plays, pageants and ceremonials for the
        Christmas season. New York ₍1953?₎
        76 p.   21 cm.

1. Christmas. 2. Christmas plays.

NN   0061148   N OC1

National recreation association

Portland recreation survey, Portland,
Maine, October and November, 1913.
Prepared for the Portland Board of trade
under the direction of the Playground and
recreation association of America.
₍Portland₎ 1913.

82p.   front., plan, tab.   23cm.

1. Portland, Me.––Playgrounds. 2. Portland, Mo. Board   of trade.

NN   0061149   RPB OU OC1

National recreation association.
Power in play; a report for 1926. New York city,
Playground and recreation association of America (1926)
16 p. illus. 23½ cm

NN   0061150   DHEW

National Recreation Association.
Preliminary report on the nation-wide survey
of teen centers, a project in adult education at
Teachers College, Columbia University, by
Louis D. Yuill. New York [1945?]
6 l.   31 cm.
Caption title.
1. Recreation centers. I. Columbia University.
Teachers College. II. Yuill, Louis D.

NN   0061151   N

National Recreation Association.

International Recreation Congress.
Proceedings. 1932–
₍New York, etc.₎ National Recreation Association.
GV4
.I 57

                National Recreation Association.
D810
.E8D43
1941   Defense Recreation Conference, Baltimore, 1941.
        Proceedings of the ... conference, September 29, 1941, held
        in connection with the 26th National Recreation Congress ...
        New York, National Recreation Assn. ₍1941?₎

RA973   National Recreation Association.
.N4
        New York University. School of Education.
        Proceedings of the hospital recreation institute.

        New York, National Recreation Association.

National recreation association.
Program suggestions for the enrichment of adult life, prepared by National recreation association. Washington, D. C.,
The National commission on the enrichment of adult life, National education association ₍1932?₎

19 p. 23ᶜᵐ.

"Some national organizations enriching adult life": p. 19.

1. Education of adults. ₍1. Adult education₎ I. Title.

Library, U. S. Office of   Education LC5219.N2

E 32–535

NN   0061155   DHEW Or NN

National recreation association.
Program suggestions for the enrichment of adult life. Prepared by National recreation association. Washington, D. C.,
The National commission on the enrichment of adult life, National education association ₍1932₎

19 p. 23ᶜᵐ. ₍National commission on the enrichment of adult life.
Publication no. 2₎

1. Education of adults. ₍1. Adult education₎ 2. Leisure. I. Title.

U. S. Off. of educ.   Library   LC5251.N12 no.2
for Library of Congress   ₍2₎

E 41–213

NN   0061156   DHEW OrPR

A371.89 ₍National recreation association₎
N21p   Program suggestions for Washington's birthday;
        a bibliography listing plays, pageants, music,
        stories, poems and other program material
        ₍New York, 1943₎
        9 numb.l.

        Mimeographed.

        1. Amateur theatricals––Bibl. 2. Schools––
        Exercises and recreation. 3. Washington, George,
        pres. U.S., 1732-1799––Anniversaries, etc.

NN   0061157   IU

+
GV1229 National recreation association.
.N33   Progressive parties. ₍New York,
        National recreation association, 1942₎
        13 numb. l. diagrs. 31cm.
        Caption title.
        Mimeographed.
        "A few publications on social recrea-
        tion": p.12-13.

        1.Games. I.Title.

NN   0061158   NNU–W PSt

309.136 National Recreation Association.
N21pr   Proposals for the improvement of public
        recreation, Concord, New Hampshire.   New
        York, 1947.
        ii, 51l. 29cm

        1. Concord, N.H.––Recreational activities.
        2. Concord, N.H.––Parks. I. Title.

NN   0061159   IU

National recreation association.
Prospectus: Playground association of America ... ₍Wash-
ington? D. C., 1906?₎

cover-title, 20 p. front., illus., plates. 23ᶜᵐ.

Continued in next column

VOLUME 407

Continued from preceding column

1. Playgrounds—Societies.

Library of Congress   GV421.N36   CA 12-649 rev.

NN   0061160   DLC OO

National recreation association.
    Publications.
New York, The association, 19–

NN   0061161   OC1ND

National recreation association.
    Publications of the Playground and recreation association of America. New York ₁1913₎
    15 p. 15ᶜᵐ. (*Its* ₁Pamphlets₎ no. 63)
    Caption title.

1. Playgrounds—Bibl.

Library of Congress   GV421.N33 no. 63   CA 15-1559 rev.

NN   0061162   DLC Or

National recreation association.
    Publications.
New York, Playground and recreation association of America, 1923.
    20 p.

NN   0061163   MiU

E158
.R3

    National Recreation Association.

    Rand McNally vacation guide: United States, Canada, Mexico.
    Chicago.

National recreation association.

Recreation. v. 1–   Apr. 1907–

New York, etc., 1907–

₁National recreation association₎
    Recreation, a major community problem; the why, the what and the how of public recreation.
₁New York, National recreation association, c1936₎
    cover-title, 36 p. 23ᶜᵐ.

    Introduction signed: Weaver W. Pangburn.
    "Bibliography": p. 33-34.

    1. Recreation – U. S. 2. Playgrounds – U. S.

NN   0061166   NNC OrU OrP WaPS OC1CC

309.136   ₁National recreation association₎
N21re   Recreation, a major community problem. The
1944   why, the what and the how of public recreation.
    ₁New York city, National recreation association, 1944₎
    36p.

    Bibliography: p.33-34.

    1. Recreation.

NN   0061167   IU DI

National Recreation Association.
    Recreation; a problem of grass roots; the why, the what and the how of public recreation.
New York [c1948]
    29 p.   23 cm.
    Bibliography: p. 26-27.
    1. Recreation.   I. Title.

NN   0061168   PSt

National Recreation Association.
    Recreation activities for adults; a guide to the planning and conducting of recreation activities for adult groups.
New York, Association Press, 1950.
    vii, 178 p. illus. 23 cm.
    The material was brought together by George D. Butler, much of it having appeared in Recreation for men, published in 1944. Cf. p. ₁vi₎-vii.
    Includes bibliographies.

    1. Recreation.   I. Butler, George Daniel, 1893–   II. Title.

    GV171.N323   790   50-9350

OrP WaS
KyLxCB KyLx MBH DI TU OC1W TxU KyWaT OCU OrU OrCS
NN   0061169   DLC NcGU Or WaT CaBVa PGladM PPT NcD

    National Recreation Association.

GV185
.R4

    Recreation and park yearbook.   1908–
    New York, National Recreation Association.

National recreation association.
    Recreation and the church ... New York, N. Y., National recreation association ₁1944₎
    40 p.   diagrs.   21½ᵐ.
    On cover: A manual for leaders.
    "Selected bibliography": p. 34-39.

    1. Recreation.   2. Church entertainments.

    Library of Congress   BV1620.N3   44-25640 Revised
    ₁r44d2₎   259

NN   0061171   DLC TU

National recreation association.
    Recreation and the church... New York, N. Y., National recreation association ₁1946₎
    79 p. diagrs.

    On cover: A manual for leaders.
    "Selected bibliography": p. 34-39, 71-76.

NN   0061172   MiD Or CaBVaU WaS

259R
N277r   National recreation association.
1947   Recreation and the church ... New York, N.Y., National recreation association ₁1947, °1946₎
Theol.   79p. illus.,diagrs. 22cm.
    On cover: A manual for leaders.
    "Selected bibliography": p. 71-77.
    "Third edition, 1947."

    1. Recreation. 2. Church entertainments. I. Title.

NN   0061173   TxDaM OU

259   National recreation association.
N277r   Recreation and the church. 4th ed.   New York, National Recreation Association, 1951.
    40p.

    On cover: A manual for leaders.

    1. Recreation.   2. Church entertainments.

NN   0061174   ICarbS

National Recreation Association.
    Recreation and the church.   New York, National Recreation Association ₁1951, °1946₎
    80p. illus., plans. 22cm.

    Bibliography: p.71-77.

NN   0061175   NcU

National recreation association.
    Recreation and unemployment; suggestions for community groups who are trying to meet the need of the unemployed for activities which will fill their leisure hours happily and constructively, and will help in maintaining courage and mental and physical well-being ... New York city, National recreation association ₁°1933₎
    2 p. l., 58 p. 16ᶜᵐ.
    "Select bibliography": p. 54-58.

    1. Amusements. 2. Leisure. 3. Unemployed—U. S.   I. Title.
    A 33—3265

    Illinois. Univ. Library
    for Library of Congress   ₁a41d1₎

NN   0061176   IU NN OrU Or

National recreation association.
    Recreation areas in real estate subdivisions.
New York city, Playground and recreation association of America, 1930.
    ₁15₎ p. incl. illus., tables. 28 cm.

    In publicizing the work of those real estate subdividers who have created play spaces in their real estate developments, the Playground and recreation association has been joined by the Harmon foundation. cf. Foreword.
    1. Playgrounds. I. Harmon foundation, inc.
    II. Title. III.   Title: Real estate
    subdivisions,   Recreation areas in.

NN   0061177   Vi Or IdU-SB OCU

National Recreation Association.
    Recreation areas, their design and equipment, prepared for National Recreation Assn. by George D. Butler. New York, A. S. Barnes ₁1947₎
    xvi, 174 p. illus., plans, diagrs. 31ᶜᵐ.
    "Successor to two earlier volumes, 'Play areas—their design and equipment' and 'New play areas—their design and equipment,' issued in 1928 and 1938, respectively. The material used in the preceding volumes has been completely revised and new sections have been added."

    Bibliography: p. 165-169.

    1. Playgrounds. 2. Playgrounds—Apparatus and equipment.
    I. Butler, George D. II. Title.
    GV423.N386   796   47-4770*

    NcRS PWcS WaTC IdU OrCS OrP MtU WaS OrU WaT
NN   0061179   DLC ViU Or NcU CoU MtBC MB TxU PSt

₁National Recreation Association₎
    ... **Recreation** as a function of the church ...
New York city, Playground and recreation association of America ₁1920₎
    1 p.l., 8 p.   23ᶜᵐ. ₁National recreation association.
    Reprints₎ no. 178₎
    "Suggestions by H. A. Atkinson": p. 7-8.
    "Reprinted from the Playground, August, 1920."

    1. Amusements. 2. Church entertainments. I. Atkinson, Henry Avery, 1877–

NN   0061180   ViU OU.

National Recreation Association.
    Recreation as a profession in the southern region; report of a joint study by the National Recreation Association and the Southern Regional Education Board, 1952-1954. New York ₁°1955₎
    xiv, 210 p. illus., maps. 24 cm.

    1. Recreation leadership. 2. Recreation—Southern States.
    I. Southern Regional Education Board. II. Title.
    GV54.A13N3   790   55-62142

    NcC PP NIC OU MsSM AU OrPS MiU MtU OrU
NN   0061181   DLC Wa IdU Or IU TU NN TxU ODW OOxM

VOLUME 407

National recreation association.

Bowers, Ethel.
Recreation for girls and women; prepared for the National recreation association by Ethel Bowers ... New York, A. S. Barnes and company, incorporated, 1934.

National recreation association.
Recreation for industrial workers; a guide for workers in charge of recreation in industrial plants ... Rev. ed. New York, N. Y., National recreation association, 1945.

48 p. diagrs. 22^{cm}.

Includes bibliographies.

1. Recreation. 2. Welfare work in industry.

46–3998

Library of Congress   HD7395.R4N35 1945

⟨3⟩   331.845

NN 0061183 DLC TxU

National recreation association.
Recreation for men; a guide to the planning and conducting of recreation activities for men's groups. Prepared ... by the National recreation association. New York, N. Y., National recreation association ⟨1944⟩

196 p. illus., diagrs. 21^{cm}.

"The material in this book has been brought together by George D. Butler."—p. 196.
Includes bibliographies.

1. Recreation. I. Butler, George D. II. Title.

45–10772

Library of Congress   GV171.N325

⟨2⟩   790

NN 0061184 DLC PSt OCl TU NcC NRU OOxM IU

National recreation association.
Recreation for men; a guide to the planning and conducting of recreation activities for men's groups. Prepared and published by the National recreation association ... New York, Association press ⟨1945⟩

196 p. illus., diagrs. 21^{cm}.

Includes bibliographies.

NN 0061185 Or CaBVa

GV184
.W5

National Recreation Association.

Williams, Arthur Milton, 1894–
Recreation for the aging. Prepared for the National Recreation Association. New York, Association Press ⟨1953⟩

National recreation association.
Recreation for war workers, a guide for workers in charge of recreation in war plants ... New York, N. Y., National recreation association, 1943.

72 p. illus. 21½^{cm}.

1. Recreation. 2. Welfare work in industry.

43–12911

Library of Congress   HD6971.N3

⟨3⟩   331.845

NN 0061187 DLC OCl

National recreation association.
Recreation for workers, a guide for workers in charge of recreation in war plants ... 2d ed., 1944 ... New York, N. Y., National recreation association ⟨1944⟩

72 p. illus., diagrs. 21½^{cm}.

First edition, 1943, has title: Recreation for war workers.
Includes bibliographies.

Continued in next column

Continued from preceding column

1. Recreation. 2. Welfare work in industry. I. Title.

44–37397

Library of Congress   HD6971.N3 1944

⟨2⟩   331.845

NN 0061188 DLC OCl

National Recreation Association.
Recreation in Richmond
see under   Pangburn, Weaver Wedell.

National recreation association.
Recreation leadership standards; standards of training, experience, and compensation for positions in community recreation ... New York, N. Y., National recreation association, °1944.

30 p., 1 l. 21½^{cm}.

1. Recreation.

45–1029

Library of Congress °   GV14.5.N29

⟨2⟩   790.69

NN 0061190 DLC

National recreation association.
Recreation needs, today – tomorrow.
New York, 1944.
21 p.

NN 0061191 OU

190
N21r6i

National Recreation Association.
A recreation plan for the city of Lincoln, Nebraska, prepared for the city council under a grant of funds by the Cooper Foundation. New York, 1948.
85l. illus., fold.maps. 28cm.

1. Lincoln, Neb.--Parks. 2. Lincoln, Neb.--Playgrounds. I. Title.

NN 0061192 IU PSt

309.136
N21rem

National Recreation Association.
Recreation plan for the city of Marion, Ohio, prepared for the Recreation Board under a grant of funds by the Marion Rotary Club. New York, 1949.
89p. fold.map, plans. 28cm.

1. Marion, Ohio--Recreational activities. 2. Marion, Ohio--Parks. I. Title.

NN 0061193 IU

309.136
N21rs

National Recreation Association.
A recreation plan for the city of Shaker Heights, Ohio. New York, 1948.
viii, 67p. fold.maps. 28cm.

Cover title.

1. Shaker Heights, Ohio--Parks. 2. Shaker Heights, Ohio--Playgrounds. I. Title.

NN 0061194 IU PSt

711.558
N21r

National Recreation Association.
Recreation plan for the city of Tucson and Pima County. New York, 1952.
2v. in 1. 28cm.

Continued in next column

Continued from preceding column

Contents.– pt.1. Recreation plan for the city of Tucson, Arizona, prepared for the mayor and City Council.– pt.2. Recreation plan for Pima County, Arizona, prepared for the County Park and Recreation Committee.

NN 0061195 IU

National Recreation Association.
Recreation plan for the city of Whittier and environs
see under   Whittier Regional Recreation Planning Committee.

---

q309.136
N21rf

National Recreational Association.
Recreation plan for the town of Franklin, Southampton County, Virginia, prepared for the Town Council. New York, 1951.
35l. 29cm.

1. Franklin, Va.--Recreational activities. 2. Franklin, Va.--Parks. I. Title.

NN 0061197 IU

National recreation association.
Recreation plan for Toledo, Ohio. The Toledo council of social agencies, The city of Toledo, The Toledo public schools, The Toledo Catholic parochial schools, The Metropolitan park board. Toledo, Ohio, The Toledo council of social agencies, 1945.

[6],11,93 leaves. maps(part fold.) tables. 27cm.

"Prepared by National recreation association."

NN 0061198 CLSU PSt MiD IU OCl

309.136
N21rw

National Recreation Association.
A recreation plan for Williamsport, Penna ⟨sponsored by the Lycoming County. Social Planning Council⟩ New York, 1947
51l. fold.maps. 28cm.

1. Williamsport, Pa.--Recreational activities. 2. Williamsport, Pa.--Parks

NN 0061199 IU

National Recreation Association.
Recreation survey, Detroit
see under   Haynes, Rowland.

National Recreation Association.
Recreation survey, Minneapolis
see under   Weir, Lebert Howard.

National Recreation Association.
A recreation survey of the city of Providence
see under   North, Francis Reid, 1876–

VOLUME 407

National recreation association.
Recreation while on the mend in hospitals and at home ...
New York, N. Y., National recreation association, ᶜ1944.

100 p. illus., diagrs. 21½ᵐ.

Bibliography: p. 96–100.

1. Amusements. 2. Recreation. 3. Games. 4. Convalescence.
I. Title.

Library of Congress   GV1229.N3   44–47264
                             ₍5₎   790

NcGU
NN 0061203   DLC OC1 OO OU OOxM WaT Or OrCS TU NcC

National Recreation Association.
Recreational games and programs
see under   Martin, John A., writer on
recreation.

q309.136 National Recreation Association.
N21rc   Recreational survey, Claremont, N.H.
         ₍New York₎ 1948.
         44ℓ. fold.map. 29cm.

Cover title.

1. Claremont, N.H.--Recreational activities
2. Claremont, N.H.--Parks. I. Title.

NN 0061205   IU

GV
701   National recreation association.
.N3   Recreative athletics; suggestions for
1922   practical conduct of recreative athletics,
         games and sports, and for the promotion
         of physical efficiency. New York, Commun-
         ity Service, 1922.
         148 p. illus.

NN 0061206   MoU

National recreation association.
Recreative athletics; suggestions for programs of recreative
athletics, games and sports, and for the promotion of physical
fitness. Rev. ed. Prepared by the Playground and recreation
association of America ... New York, A. S. Barnes and company, 1925.

127 p. illus., diagrs. 23½ x 10½ᵐ.
"A brief bibliography": p. 125–126.

1. Athletics. I. Title.
                                            CA 27–117 rev.
Library of Congress   GV701.N3 1925

NN 0061207   DLC DHEW MiU OU

National recreation association.
Recreative athletics; suggestions for programs of recreative
athletics, games and sports, and for the promotion of physical fitness. Rev. ed. Prepared by the Playground and recreation association of America ... New York, A. S. Barnes and
company, 1926.

127 p. illus., diagrs. 23½ x 10ᵐ.
"A brief bibliography": p. 125–126.

1. Athletics. I. Title.
                                            27–988 rev.
Library of Congress   GV701.N3 1926

NN 0061208   DLC OO OOxM

National recreation association.
Recreative athletics; suggestions for programs of recreative athletics, games and sports, and for conducting the program. Rev. and enl. ed. Prepared by the Playground and
recreation association of America. New York, A. S. Barnes
and company, 1929.

3 p. l., 200 p.   24 x 11½ cm.
"A brief bibliography": p. 198–200.

Continued in next column

Continued from preceding column

1. Athletics.   I. Title.

GV701.N3 1929   29—26575

NN 0061209   DLC OCU OC1 OC1h IU

National recreation association.
Recreative athletics, suggestions for programs of recreative
athletics, games and sports and for conducting the program.
Rev. and enl. edition, prepared by the Playground and recreation association of America. New York, A. S. Barnes and company, 1930.

3 p. l., 202 p.   diagrs. 24 x 11½ᵐ.
"A brief bibliography": p. 198–200.

1. Athletics.   I. Title.

Library of Congress   \GV701.N3 1930   31–12935 rev.
.   ₍r32d2₎   796

NN 0061210   DLC MiHM OC1UI WaS WaWW OrLgE IdU OC1W

309.136 National Recreation Association.
N21ra   A report of a study on recreation of
         Absecon Island, 1945.   Atlantic City, Citi-
         zens' Recreation Committee of Absecon Island
         ₍1945₎
         48p. fold.maps, diagr. 23cm.

Bibliography: p.43-44.

1 Absecon Island--Recreational activities.
I. Title: Recreation of Absecon Island.

NN 0061211   IU OU PSt

280.6
N213R   National recreation association.
         Report of ten years of service by the National
         recreation association to the United States De-
         partment of agriculture and to the state col-
         leges of agriculture in the field of rural re-
         creation leadership training, May 1, 1927 to
         April 30, 1937.   New York city ₍1937₎
         27 numb.l. 28cm.

Mimeographed.

NN 0061212   DNAL

National recreation association.
A report of the committee of the National recreation association on training, experience and compensation in community recreation work ... New York city, National recreation association, ᶜ1938.

24 p. 21½ᵐ.
On cover: Standards of training, experience and compensation in community recreation work.

1. Community centers.   I. Title. II. Title: Training, experience and
compensation in community recreation work.

Library of Congress   GV53.N32   38–19733
Copyright AA 260701   ₍3₎   790.69

NN 0061213   DLC NBuG OrU OrCS OU

National recreation association.
Report on public recreation in Washington, D. C. and en-
virons, submitted by National recreation association to the
National capital park and planning commission. Washington,
D. C., 1934.

cover-title, 175 l. incl. forms. 26½ᵐ.
Various pagings.
Mimeographed.

1. Washington, D. C.—Parks.   I. U. S. National capital park and
planning commission. II. Title. III. Title: Public recreation in Washington. Report on.

                                                35–14190
Library of Congress   GV54.D5N3
                        ₍2₎   796.09753

NN 0061214   DLC DI

National Recreation Association.
Research in recreation completed.
see under National Recreation Association.
National Advisory Committee on Recreation
Research.

National recreation association.

Zanzig, Augustus Delafield.
Roads to music appreciation, by Augustus D. Zanzig ...   A
guide to listener and to teacher or leader ...   New York city,
National recreation association ₍ᶜ1939₎

National recreation association.
Rural and small community recreation; practical suggestions
for recreation activities in rural districts and small towns.
Revised and enlarged ...   New York city, Playground and
recreation association of America, 1929.

3 p. l., 186 p. 24ᵐ.
"Sources of information" at end of some chapters.

1. Amusements. 2. Playgrounds. 3. Community centers.   I. Title.
                                                A 41–381
Minnesota. Univ. Libr.
  for Library of Congress   ₍2₎

NN 0061217   MnU NcD NcGU OrU Or ODW OU

National recreation association.
Rural recreation ...   New York, N. Y., National recreation
association ₍1946₎

111 p. illus. 21½ᵐ.
Includes music.
Bibliography at end of most of the chapters. "Camp bibliography":
p. 111.

1. Recreation. 2. Amusements.   I. Title.

GV1201.N35   790   46–8453

NN 0061218   DLC KyWaT NcRS CaBVaU Or WaTC Wa WaT

J394.2 National Recreation Association.
V23N   St. Valentine's day. New York ₍1952?₎
        18 p.

Reproduced from type-written copy.

1. Valentine's Day

NN 0061219   MiD

790
N213s   ₍National recreation association₎
         Schedule for the appraisal of community
         recreation. ₍New York, National recreation
         association, n.d.₎
         30 numb. ℓ. (M.P. no. 167)

Mimeographed.

1. Community centers. 2. Playgrounds – Apparatus
and equipment. I. Title: The appraisal of
community recreation, Schedule for.

NN 0061220   WaPS

790
N27s   ₍National recreation association₎
         Schedule for the appraisal of com-
         munity recreation.   ₍N.Y.?, The
         Assn.? 1933?₎
         30ℓ. tables. Q.

Caption title.
Autographic reproduction of typewritten
copy.

NN 0061221   IaU

VOLUME 407

National recreation association.
Schedule for the appraisal of community
recreation
NewYork, National recreation association, 1939?
30 numb. 1.

NN 0061222   OC1

790
N21sc   National recreation association.
Schedule for the appraisal of community recreation.   New York, N.Y., National recreation
association [1944]
cover-title, 27 numb. 1. 28cm.

"M.P. 291-10-44."
Reproduced from type-written copy.
"Scoring sheet for community recreation ap-
praisal schedule": 4 1. at end.

1. Recreation.   I. Title.

NN 0061223   LU MiD IU

GV171   National Recreation Association.
.N38   Schedule for the appraisal of community
Q   recreation.   New York,N.Y.,National Recreation
Association[1947-48]
27, 4p. 31cm.

1. Recreation.

NN 0061224   PSt

790
N213s
National Recreation Association.
Schedule for the appraisal of community
recreation.   New York [c1951]
45p. 21cm.

I. Recreation. I. Title.

NN 0061225   TxU MiU CaBVaU MsU WaS Wa OrP

National Recreation Association.
Schedule for the appraisal of community
recreation.   New York [1954, c1951]
45p. 22cm.

NN 0061226   NcU

National Recreation Association.
School-community recreation relationships;
and analysis of a study in eleven Ohio cities.
N.Y., The Association, 1940.
16 p.

NN 0061227   PPCPC OU

TH4763   National Recreation Association.
A12N3   Selected bibliography on the construction,
administration and operation of swimming
pools. [New York, 1949]
5 1.

Caption title.

NN 0061228   CU

National recreation association.
Silver bells and cockle shells, and seven other plays; eight
plays and pageants for children. New York city, National
recreation association [1936]
60 p. illus. 21½ᵐ.

1. Children's plays.   I. Title.
PN6120.A4S55   A 40-2239

Grosvenor library   PN6120.A4N3
for Library of Congress   [2]

NN 0061229   NBuG IU Or DLC OC1 OU

National Recreation Association.
Simple puppetry

see under

Musselman, Virginia W

M1977   National recreation association.
.C5Z3
Zanzig, Augustus Delafield, ed.

Singing America, song and chorus book, compiled, ar-
ranged and edited for the National recreation association by
Augustus D. Zanzig. Ed. with accompaniments ... Boston,
C. C. Birchard & company [1941]

793   National recreation association.
N21si   Six more dramatic stunts.   New York city,
National recreation association [1942]
23 numb.1.

Mimeographed.
"Bibliography of short play and stunt collections": p.21-22.

1. Amateur theatricals. I. Title.

NN 0061232   IU

National Recreation Association
Six more dramatic stunts. Rev. Author, 1948.
22 p.
Bibliography of short play and stunt
collections: p. 21-22.

NN 0061233   OrCS Or

R793   National recreation association.
N213   Six new dramatic stunts.   N.Y.,Author,n.d.
(Its P122)

For clubs: short plays which can be rehearsed
and produced the same evening.

NN 0061234   WaSp OLak Or

q793   National recreation association.
N21s   Six new dramatic stunts, prepared by
Community drama service.   New York
city, National recreation association
[1934?]
20 numb.1.

Mimeographed.

NN 0061235   IU

National recreation association.
Six new dramatic stunts, prepared by
Community drama service.
New York, National recreation association [1938]
20 numb. 1., [2] 1.

NN 0061236   OC1

NATIONAL RECREATION ASSOCIATION.
Six new dramatic stunts.   Author [1948?]
37 p.   (M.P. 168)

Bibliography: p. 35.

NN 0061237   Or OrCS

790.19   National Recreation Association.
N276   Six new dramatic stunts. New York, National
Recreation Association [c1952?]
32 p. 22 cm.

NN 0061238   N

[National recreation association]
Song books for children and for youth...   [New York city,
1941?] 8 f. 28cm.

Reproduced from typewritten copy.
Caption-title.

1. Children's songs—Bibl.
N.Y.P.L.   August 14, 1942

NN 0061239   NN

National recreation association
Songs for informal singing. Set I-III
Selected by the National recreation association
New York City [1938-
3 v.

NN 0061240   OU

F215
N3   National Recreation Association.
The South. Alabama, Florida, Georgia, Ken-
tucky, Mississippi, North Carolina, South
Carolina, Tennessee, Virginia, West Virginia.
[New York, c1954]
126 p. 28 cm.
At head of title: An American recreation
guide. National and state parks, recreation
areas and historic sites.
Map on cover.

1.Southern   States – Descr. & trav.2.
Recreation – South-   ern States.3.National
parks and reserves   Southern States.I.Title.
II.Title: American ...creation guide.

NN 0061241   DI DLC

F396
N3   National Recreation Association.
The Southwest. Arkansas, Louisiana, New Mexico, Oklahoma, Texas. National and state parks,
recreation areas and historic sites. A special
defense project of the National Recreation Association. [New York, c1953]
67 p. 28 cm.
At head of title: An American recreation
guide. Armed forces edition.
Map on cover.
1.Southwest, New – Descr. & trav.2.Recreation
– Southwest, New.   3.National parks and reserves — Southwe   New. I.Title. II. Title:
American recrea-   tion guide.

NN 0061242   DI

National Recreation Association.
The Southwest: Arkansas, Louisiana, New Mexico,
Oklahoma, Texas. Rev. ed. New York, 1954.
67 p.
At head of title: An American recreation guide...

NN 0061243   IU

VOLUME 407

309.136 National recreation association.
N21s   Space requirements for the children's play-
        ground; a suggested standard based upon the space
        required for the facilities, apparatus and game
        areas which are considered essential to the well
        balanced playground program.   New York city,
        National recreation association ₍1934₎
        24p. illus.

        "Reprinted from Recreation, August and Septem-
        ber, 1934."

NN   0061244   IU WaPS OC1

National recreation association.
    Stadiums. New York city, Playground and recreation asso-
ciation of America ₍1926₎
    11, ₍1₎ p. 27½ᶜᵐ. (*On cover:* Reprint, no. 219)
    Reprinted from "The Playground", July, 1926.

    1. Stadia.   I. Title.
                                                    E 32-637
    Library, U. S. Office of   Education NA6860.N2

NN   0061245   DHEW IdU-SB Or

National recreation association.
    Standards for neighborhood recreation areas and facilities.
New York, N. Y., National recreation association, 1943.
    16 p. 21½ᶜᵐ.

    1. Recreation.   I. Title.
                                                    44-20829
    Library of Congress   GV171.N34
                               ₍2₎   796

NN   0061246   DLC OrU Or PPCPC OU OC1 NN

National recreation association.
    Standards: playgrounds, playfields, recreation buildings, in-
door recreation facilities. New York, N. Y., National recreation association ₍1944?₎
    13, ₍1₎ p. 21½ᶜᵐ.

    1. Recreation. 2. Playgrounds.   I. Title.
                                                    44-8382
    Library of Congress   GV171.N33
                               ₍3₎   796

NN   0061247   DLC WaS Or OrCS NN ICRL ICJ NNC

National Recreation Association.
    Starting a recreation program

    see under

    Hill, Beatrice H

National recreation association.

Zanzig, Augustus Delafield.
    Starting and developing a rhythm band, by Augustus D.
Zanzig. New York city, National recreation association ₍1937₎

National recreation association.

Zanzig, Augustus Delafield.
    Starting and maintaining a community orchestra, by Augus-
tus D. Zanzig; foreword by Ernest La Prade ... New York
city, National recreation association ₍1940₎

National recreation assiciation.
    A Stephen C. Foster program. ₍New York,
National recreation assiciation, n.d.₎

    Reproduced from typewritten copy.

NN   0061251   InU

[National recreation association]
    Stories of the Christmas carols.   [New York,
194-?]
    7 p.   28 cm.
    Mimeographed; printed on one side of the leaf.
    1. Carols. I. Title.

NN   0061252   MB

J783.86 National Recreation Association
N21s   Stories of the Christmas carols. New
        York ₍1952?₎
        8 l.

        Reproduced from type-written copy.

        1. Carols 2. Christmas   I. Title

NN   0061253   MiD MB

National Recreation Association.
    Storytelling; why, where, when, how

    see under

    Musselman, Virginia W

National Recreation Association.
    A study of recreation and parks in Topeka,
Kansas. Prepared for the Board of Com-
missioners of the City of Topeka, Kansas.
New York, 1955.
    iv, 86 l. map, tables. 28cm.

    Cover-title: A long range recreation plan,
Topeka, Kansas.

NN   0061255   NNC-A

309.136 National Recreation Association.
N21rmo   A study of recreation resources and needs
        in Monroe Township, Gloucester County, New
        Jersey, prepared for the Board of Park and
        Playground Commissioners.   New York, 1950.
        28p. 28cm.

        1. Monroe Township, N.J.--Recreational ac-
        tivities. 2. Monroe Township, N.J.--Parks.
        I. Title: Recre-   ation.

NN   0061256   IU

309.136 National Recreation Association.
N21rm   A study of recreation services in Maplewood,
        New Jersey, prepared for the Township Plan-
        ning Board.   New York, 1950.
        34l. 29cm.

        1. Maplewood, N.J.--Recreational activities.
        2. Maplewood, N.J.--Parks. I. Title: Recre-
        ation services in Maplewood, New Jersey.

NN   0061257   IU PSt

National Recreation Association.
    A study of the public recreation properties,
programs and inter-agency relationships in
Philadelphia.   Philadelphia, 1952.
    42 p.
    "Conducted for the Dept. of Recreation of Phila."

NN   0061258   PPBMR PU-PSW PPCPC

National recreation association.
GV1471
.B673
    Bowers, Ethel, *ed.*
        ... Stunts and entertainments for wartime recreation, edited
    for the National recreation association by Ethel Bowers ...
    New York city, National recreation association ₍1942₎

793   ₍National recreation association₎
N21st   Stunts, contests, relays.   ₍New York, Nation-
        al recreation association, 1942?₎
        9 numb.l.

        Caption-title.
        Mimeographed.

        1. Games. I. Title.

NN   0061260   IU LU

GV1471
.N32   National Recreation Association.
        Stunts, contests, relays.   New York,
    National Recreation Association ₍1952₎

        17 p. illus. 24 cm.

        1. Indoor games.   I. Title.

NN   0061261   AAP OrCS CLobS

National recreation association
    Suggestions for a recreation survey.
New York city, Playground and recreation
association of America, 1923.
    7 numb. l.

NN   0061262   OU

J394.2 National Recreation Association
S17N   Suggestions for a St. Patrick's day
        program. New York ₍°1952₎
        23 p. illus.

        1. St. Patrick's day

NN   0061263   MiD

₍National recreation association₎
    Suggestions for an amateur circus. ₍New York, National
recreation association, 1938₎
    15, ₍3₎ numb. l. illus. 28ᶜᵐ.
    Caption title.
    "A few references on amateur circuses" : 3 leaves at end.

    1. Circus.   I. Title: Amateur circus.
                                                    A 40-866
    Ohio state univ. Library
        for Library of Congress   ₍2₎

NN   0061264   OU OrP Or OrCS Wa

VOLUME 407

791.3
N21s
1939₃

National recreation association.
Suggestions for an amateur circus.   ₍New York,
1939₃
cover-title, 18 numb.l. illus.

Mimeographed.
Bibliography: leaves 16-17.

1. Circus. 2. Amateur theatricals.

NN   0061265   IU

791.3
N21s
1949

National Recreation Association.
Suggestions for an amateur circus.   ₍New
York, 1949₃
16ℓ. illus. 28cm.

Cover title.
Bibliography: leaves 15-16.

1. Circus. 2. Amateur theatricals.

NN   0061266   IU

J793.1
N21s9

National Recreation Association.
Suggestions for an amateur circus.
New York ₍°1951₃
27 p. illus.

1. Circus, Amateur   I. Title

NN   0061267   MiD

National recreation association.
Suggestions for fall activities. rev. ed.
New York city, Playground and recreation
association of America, 1927.
7 numb. l.

NN   0061268   OU

₍National recreation association₃
Suggestions for making a community recreation survey.
₍New York, 1932₃
13 numb. l. 28ᶜᵐ.

Caption title.
M. P. 156.
Reproduced from type-written copy.
"A brief bibliography": leaves 2-3.

1. Recreation.   I. Title. II. Title: A community recreation survey.

A 42-4171

Ohio state univ. Library   GV427.N27
for Library of Congress   ₍2₃

NN   0061269   OU OrU IaU

National recreation association
Suggestions for making a community recreation
survey.
New York, National recreation association ₍1938₃
13 numb. l.

NN   0061270   OC1

GV1201
.N3

National Recreation Association.
Suggestions for recreation activities
in homes for the aged.   ₍New York,
n.d.₃
4ℓ. 29cm.
Mimeographed.

NN   0061271   NNU-W

National recreation association.
Suggestions for recreation institutes.
New York city, Playground and recreation
association of America, 19-
14 numb. 1.

NN   0061272   OU

National recreation association.
Suggestions in community drama for the enrichment of
adult life, prepared by National recreation association. Washington, D. C., The National commission on the enrichment of
adult life, National education association ₍1935₎₎
18 p. 23ᶜᵐ.
Bibliography: p. 17-18.

1. Community plays, etc. 2. Drama. 3. Education of adults. ₍3.
Adult education₎   I. National commission on the enrichment of adult
life. II. Title.
E 35-79
Library, U. S. Office of   Education PN3203.N3

NN   0061273   DHEW WaTC

796.1
N27s

National recreation association.
Summer playground note book ₍no.1-
12, June 4-August 20, 1943₃
New York, The Assn. ₍1944₃
cover-title, unp. illus. Q.

Reproduced from typewritten copy.

NN   0061274   IaU

917.3
N214s

National Recreation Association.
Summer vacations, U.S.A.   ₍Chicago₃
Rand, McNally ₍1952₃
80p. illus., ports., maps. 28cm.

1. Vacations. 2. Travel. 3. U.S.--Descr.
& trav. I. Title.

NN   0061275   IU OC1

797.2
N2136s

₍National recreation association₎
Swimming badge tests for boys and girls.   ₍New
York city, National recreation association, 1941₎
7 numb.l.

Caption title.
Mimeographed.
"Literature on swimming and water sports": p.7.

1. Swimming. I. Title.

NN   0061276   IU

National recreation association.
Teen age centers; bird's-eye view.   ₍New York₎ National recreation association ₍1944₎
23 p. col. illus. 21½ᶜᵐ.

1. Recreation--U. S. 2. Youth--U. S.   I. Title.
44-29581
Library of Congress   HQ796.N37
₍2₎   790

NN   0061277   DLC CaBVaU Or GU TU OU

HQ85
.M85

National recreation association.

₍Musselman, Virginia W   ₎
Teen trouble; what recreation can do about it. ₍New
York, 1943₎

Drama
PN4305.T5
N28

National recreation association.
The Thanksgiving book; harvest-time
traditions, ceremonies, and entertainment
ideas. New York city, National recreation
association ₍°1942₃

47p. illus. 21½cm.

1. Thanksgiving day.

NN   0061279   NBuG OLak OO PSt

National recreation association.
They are not alone. New York city [1941?]

[47] p. 21 cm.
Caption-title.

NN   0061280   MH

Bial6
Z9
1941n

National recreation association.
To the mothers and fathers of America.
[New York, National recreation association,
1941]

NN   0061281   CtY

National recreation association.
Training for community leadership citizenship
education for young people between the ages of
16 and 21 years, what is being done by different
types of organizations for the 'teen age...
New York city, Playground and recreation
association of America, 1922.

NN   0061282   OU

GV53
.B8

National Recreation Association.

Butler, George Daniel, 1893-
Training volunteers for recreation service, prepared for
the National Recreation Assn. ₍New York, °1942₎

National recreation association.
Training volunteers for recreation service ... Revised December, 1946. ₍New York, 1946₎
28 p. 22ᶜᵐ.

1. Recreation--Study and teaching.   I. Title.
GV14.5.N297   790.7   47-20610
                                    Brief cataloging

NN   0061284   DLC Wa

National recreation association.
Training your playground leaders, an institute syllabus ...
New York city, National recreation association ₍1943₎
1 p. l.,iv (i. e. v), 65 p. 22ᶜᵐ.

Reproduced from type-written copy.
Includes "References."

1. Recreation.   I. Title.
43-10867
Library of Congress   GV14.5.N3
                             ₍3₎   796.07

NN   0061285   DLC TU CaBVaU Wa Or MiD OC1

VOLUME 407

796
N21tr

National recreation association.
Treasure hunts.   New York City, National
recreation association [1942]
cover-title, 9 numb. 1. 28cm.

"M.P. 212-4-42."
Reproduced from type-written copy.

1. Games.   I. Title.

NN   0061286   LU Or

National Recreation Association.
Tribute in loving memory of Howard Braucher
see its   Howard Braucher.

National recreation association.
Twentieth century neighborliness how it is
finding expression through neighborhood
organization...
New York city, Playground and recreation
association of America, 1922.
15 numb. 1.   (Its Bulletin, no. 672)

NN   0061288   OU

National recreation association.
Types of municipal recreation areas; a discussion of types of recreation areas recognized as
essential, with suggestions for their function,
size, location and layout, and for the necessary
leadership. N.Y.,National recreation associatior
[1937]
[1],3-7p.   illus.   27cm.

Reprinted from Recreation, March 1937.

NN   0061289   OrU

National Recreation Association.
Undergraduate recreation curricula in 35 colleges and universities; a summary. New York [1948]
25 l.   28 cm.
Caption title.

1. Universities and colleges—U. S.—Curricula. 2. Recreation.
I. Title.
A 50–6800
Catholic Univ. of   America. Library
for Library of Congress   [3]

NN   0061290   DCU MiU IU N NNC

309.136   National Recreation Association.
N21un   Unusual ideas in playground equipment.   New
York [195-]
13p.   illus.   22cm.

Cover title.

1. Playgrounds.   Title.

NN   0061291   IU

National recreation association.

Ickis, Marguerite, 1897–
Victory gardens; harvesting and drying, prepared for the
National recreation association by Marguerite Ickis ... [New
York, 1943]

54
N21

National Reclamation Association.
"The voice of the West"; resolutions ...
adopted by the 18th annual convention, Salt Lake
City, 1949.   Washington [1949?]
23 p.
1. Reclamation of land.   Western States.

NN   0061293   DNAL

National recreation association.
Volunteer service in the recreation movement.
New York, National recreation association, n.d.
9 p.

NN   0061294   OU

ND2133
.S8
1948

National Recreation Association.

Staples, Frank A   1900–
Water-color painting is fun, prepared for the National
Recreation Assn. by Frank A. Staples. New York, Whit-
tlesey House [1948]

797.25   National recreation association.
N21w   Water games and stunts ...   [New York, N.Y.,
1941]
7 numb.1.

Mimeographed.
"M.P.#158-6-41."
"A brief bibliography on recreational swim-
ming": leaf 7.

1. Aquatic sports.   I. Title.

NN   0061296   IU

National recreation association.

Zanzig, Augustus Delafield.
Ways to musical good fortune, by Augustus D. Zanzig. Suggestions on how to meet the problem of providing more wide-
spread participation in music on the part of individuals and
community groups. New York city, National recreation association [1936]

NATIONAL RECREATION ASSOCIATION.
What recreation executives do.   New York,
[19 -?].

Manifold copy.   pp.3.

NN   0061298   MH

National Recreation Association.
What small communities are doing.   New York,
Playground and Recreation Association of America
[1916]
[8] p.   23 cm.   (Its [Reprint] no. 138)
"Reprinted from the Playground February,
1916".
1. Playgrounds. Stat. I. Ser.

NN   0061299   ViU

National recreation association.
When Bob came home; a report.   New York city, Playground and recreation association of America, incorporated
[1927?]
15 p. incl. illus., forms. 23½cm.
Caption title: ... The story of an American city in 1927.

1. Community centers. 2. Community life.   I. Title.
E 32–378
Library, U. S. Office of   Education HT155.N23

NN   0061300   DHEW

National Recreation Association.   Yearbook
see   Recreation and park yearbook.

National recreation association.
... A year's growth in the play movement, 1911–1912, by
H. S. Braucher, secretary, Playground and recreation association of America.   New York city, Playground and recreation
association of America [1912]
16 p.   23ᶜᵐ.   ([Its Publications] no. 107)

1. Playgrounds—[U. S.] 2. Play. [2 Recreation]   I. Braucher,
Howard S., 1881–   II. Title.
E 15–1977 Revised
Library, U. S. Office of   Education LB3518.N2P6 1912

NN   0061302   DHEW NN

E169
.R24

National Recreation Association.

Rand, McNally and Company.
Your Rand McNally vacation guide.   [Chicago, Rand Mc-
Nally [and] National Recreation Association [New York,
1953]

---

f790.6   National recreation association. Board
N27o   of Directors.
...Official proceedings. Twenty-
fifth anniversary meeting...held in
the Cabinet room, White House, Washington, D.C., April 13, 1931.
[Washington, D.C., United States daily
pub. corp., 1931]
10p. ports. F.
At head of title: Supplement to The United
States daily, section II, vol.VI, no.47.

NN   0061304   IaU DL

National Recreation Association.   Bureau of
Educational Dramatics.
Hobbs, Mabel Foote.
Six Bible plays, by Mabel Hobbs and Helen Miles; issued
under the auspices of the Bureau of educational dramatics,
Playground and recreation association of America.   New
York and London, The Century co. [°1924]

National recreation association.   *Committee on a normal
course in play.*
... A course in play for grade teachers from the tentative
report of the Committee on a normal course in play of the
Playground association of America.   New York city, Playground association of America [1910]
cover-title, 105 p.   23ᶜᵐ.   ([National recreation association. Publica-
tions] no. 74)

1. Play.
E 11–259 Revised
Library, U. S. Office of   Education LB1137.N2

NN   0061306   DHEW OrP

National recreation association.   *Committee on a normal
course in play.*
... An institute course in play from the tentative report of
the Committee on a normal course in play of the Playground
association of America.   New York city, Playground association of America [1910]
cover-title, 55 p.   23ᶜᵐ.   ([National recreation association. Publica-
tions] no. 73)
Contains bibliographies.

1. Play.
E 11–260 Revised
Library, U. S. Office of   Education LB1137.N21

NN   0061307   DHEW OrP OO OCl OClW

VOLUME 407

National recreation association. *Committee on a normal course in play.*
... A normal course in play for professional directors from the tentative report of the Committee on a normal course in play of the Playground association of America. New York city, Playground association of America ₁1910₁
cover-title, 169 p. 23ᵐ. (₁National recreation association. Publications₁ no. 72)

1. Play.

E 11-261 Revised 2

Library, U. S. Office of   Education LB1137.N22

NN   0061308   DHEW OrP OO OC1 OC1W

National recreation association. *Committee on athletics for boys.*
... Athletics for boys ... New York city ₁1909?₁
25 p. 23ᵐ. ₁Russell Sage foundation. Dept. of child hygiene. Pamphlets, no. 36₁
At head of title: no. 78.
A. K. Aidinger, chairman.
"Reprinted from Proceedings of the third annual Playground congress, Pittsburgh, Pa., May 10-14, 1909, for the Playground association of America."
Bibliography: p. 6-9.

1. Athletics.   i. Aidinger, Albert Kurwin.

E 10-1676 Revised 2

Library, U. S. Office of   Education GV701.N3
Library of Congress   GV343.N3₁₁

NN   0061309   DHEW DLC OO OC1

National Recreation Association. *Committee on Folk Dancing.*
Report. New York City ₁1909?₁
23 p. 23 cm. ₁Russell Sage Foundation. Dept. of Child Hygiene. Pamphlets, no. 35₁
At head of title: No. 77.
Reprinted from Proceedings of the third annual Playground Congress, Pittsburgh, Pa., May 10-14, 1909, for the Playground Association of America.
"Books on folk dancing": p. 15-21.

1. Folk dancing.

GV1743.N3   E 10-1677 rev 2*

U. S. Office of Education.   Library
for Library of Congress   ₁r61j₁₁†

NN   0061310   DHEW DLC

National recreation association. *Committee on games.*
... Education through play and games. Report suggesting games to be used by schools as part of our educational system ... New York city, Playground and recreation association of America ₁1917₁
12 p. 23ᵐ. (₁National recreation association. Publications₁ no. 153)
Reprinted from the Playground, February, 1917.
Bibliography: p. 10-12.

1. Play.   i. Title.

E 17-382 Revised

Library, U. S. Office of   Education LB1137.N2

NN   0061311   DHEW

National Recreation Association. Committee on In-Service Training.
Playground leaders, their selection and training

see under

Forsberg, Raymond T

790
N21s
    National Recreation Association. Committee on Standards of Training.
Securing and maintaining standards in community recreation personnel, a report of the Committee on standards of training, experience and compensation in community recreation work. New York city, National recreation association ₁c1940₁
15p.

1. Community centers. I. Title.

NN   0061313   IU NNC DNAL MiD OrU NN

National recreation association. *Committee on surfacing.*
Surfacing playground areas, a committee report on the surfacing of areas devoted primarily to children's play and to specially surfaced courts used for tennis, handball and other similar games. New York city, National recreation association ₁1932?₁
1 p. l., 24 p. illus. 28ᵐ.
L. R. Barrett, chairman.

1. Playgrounds.   i. Barrett, L. R.   ii. Title.

E 33-53

Library, U. S. Office of   Education GV424.N2

NN   0061314   DHEW CaBVaU PSt OC1 OU

National recreation association. Community drama service.
Fun for Hallowe'en, prepared by Community drama service.
New York city, National recreation association ₁193-?₁
1 p. l., 13 numb. l.

NN   0061315   OO PSt

National Recreation Association. Community Drama Service.
List of pageants, masques and festivals; arranged by Community drama service. New York city, Playground and recreation association of America, 19-
7 numb. l.

NN   0061316   OU

National recreation association. Community drama service.
A Mothers' day program.
New York, ₁1931?₁
17 numb. l.

NN   0061317   OC1

National Recreation Association. Community Drama Service.
Six new dramatic stunts
see under   National Recreation Association.

National Recreation Association. In-Service Training Committee
see
National Recreation Association. Committee on In-Service Training.

National recreation association. Joint rules committee

see

National recreation association. National rules committee.

R790.16
N277r
    National Recreation Association. National Advisory Committee on Recreation Research. Editorial Board.
Research in recreation completed in 1953 and 1954. New York ₁introd. 1955₁
25p.

Cover title.

1. Recreation--U.S.--Bibliography.

NN   0061321   ICarbS AU OrU IU PSt NcU

National Recreation Association. National Advisory Committee on Recruitment, Training and Placement of Recreation Personnel. Committee on In-Service Training
see
National Recreation Association. Committee on In-Service Training.

National recreation association. National physical education service.
... News letter ...
[New York,
v. tables. 28 cm.
Issued monthly, except July and August.
Mimeographed.
1. Physical education and training. U.S.

NN   0061323   OrCS Or

National recreation association. *National physical education service.*
What state departments of education are doing in physical and health education ... National physical education service of the Playground and recreation association of America. New York city ₁1930?₁
2 p. l., 55 ₁i. e. 58₁ numb. l. 28¼ᵐ. (Study and report. 4)
Leaves numbered 21a, 21c, and 21b follow leaf numbered 21. Mimeographed.

1. Hygiene—₁Study and, teaching—U. S.₁ 2. Physical education and training—U. S. 3. Education and state—U. S.   i. Title.

E 33-1230

Library, U. S. Office of   Education GV223.N26
     ₁3₁

NN   0061324   DHEW

National Recreation Association. National Rules Committee on Playground Baseball
Official rules of playground baseball
see under title

GV881
.A1 O 43
    National Recreation Association. National Rules Committee on Playground Baseball.
Official softball guide.

St. Petersburg, Fla., Amateur Softball Association; ₁etc., etc.₁

National recreation association. Pacific Northwest district recreation conference.
[Report of proceedings]   Tacoma-Seattle. Author.
Typewritten.
Library has:
1st - 2d,   1930-1931
No more conferences held.

NN   0061327   WaS

National recreation association. Play in institutions service.
Barnes, Jeanne H
Young folks in homes, prepared for the Play in institutions service of the National recreation association by Jeanne H. Barnes ... New York city, National recreation association ₁1942₁

PN
1657
N3
    [**National Recreation Association.** Program Dept.]
Drama is recreation. [New York, n.d.]
[12]p. illus. (The Performing arts as recreation, 2)

Cover title.

1. Drama. 2. Amateur theatricals.

NN   0061329   UU

VOLUME 407

National Recreation Association. *Recreation Leadership Standards Committee.*
Personnel standards in recreation leadership, what they are, how to apply them; a committee report. New York, National Recreation Association ₁1949₎
47 p. 22 cm.

1. Recreation leadership.   ɪ. Title.

GV14.5.N35   796.069   49–49268*

NN   0061330   DLC PSt OrPS OrU NN TU TxU OOxM

National Recreation Association. *Research Dept.*
Outdoor swimming pools; considerations in planning, basic design features, pool construction factors. By George D. Butler, director. ₁New York, National Recreation Association ₁1955₎
19 p. illus. 29 cm.
Includes bibliography.

1. Swimming pools.   ɪ. Butler, George Daniel, 1893–
ɪɪ. Title.

TH4763.N3   63–3330 ‡

        MtU
NN   0061331   DLC NcRS NcU CU PSt OU FU TxU IU WaT

National Recreation Association. State and
   Federal Recreation Service.
   Publication. No.1–   1953–
New York, 1953–
   v.   28 cm.
   Each publication has distinctive title: No.1.
The recreational resources of the United States.
–No.2. The role of the federal government in
the field of public recreation.–No.3. Agencies of
the federal government concerned with recreation₎

NN   0061332   MtU Wa

GV53
N3   **National Recreation Association. State and**
        Federal Recreation Service.
        The role of the federal government in the
field of public recreation. [New York, 1953?]
53 p.   28 cm.   (Its Publication no. 2)

        1. Recreation – U.S. ɪ. Title. ɪɪ. Title:
Federal government in the field of public
recreation. (Series)

NN   0061333   DI

National Recreation Association. Western Division
   Institute Conference.
   Summary report.
Pasadena, Calif.,

NN   0061334   DNAL

309.136 National Recreation Congress.
N211p   A collection of selected papers. 1st–

1907–
New York, National Recreation Association.
      v. illus., plates, ports., plans, diagrs.
23–28cm.

      Title varies: 1907–56, 1958–59, Proceedings.–
1957, General session speeches and section
meeting summaries.– 1960, Selected papers.

      Issue for 1907 lacks series title.
      Issued 1907–09 by the congress under an ear-
lier name, Playground Congress of America.
      Issued 1910–36 in Playground (and its succes-
sors, Playground and recreation; Recreation)
Independent publication of the proceedings was
resumed with the 22d congress, 1937.

Continued in next column

Continued from preceding column

      Issue for 1907 reprinted from Charities and
the commons, v.18, Aug.3, 1907, p.471–565.
      Issues for 1908–09 include the congress's
Year book.
      Congress in 1941 held in conjunction with
Defense Recreation Conference; 1942, with War
Recreation Congress; 1956, with International

Recreation Congress.
      Some issues have also a distinctive title.
None published 1943–1945.

NN   0061338   IU

National Recreation Congress.
A collection of selected papers
see also its   Proceedings.

National recreation congress.
      … Proceedings … ₁1st₎–3d,
₁1907₎–09, 193
New York, N. Y., National recreation association ₁1907–
   v. illus., plates, ports., map, plans, diagr. 23ᶜᵐ.
Title varies: 1st, 1907 (without title)
   2d–3d, 1908–09, Proceedings of the … annual Playground congress …
     and Year book. (At head of title: Playground association of Amer-
     ica)
   193   Proceedings, National recreation congress (with slight
     variation)
   Proceedings for 1907, published also in Charities and the commons,
     v. 18, no. 18, Aug. 3, 1907, p. 471–565.

Continued after the 3d congress, 1909, in Playground (and its succes-
sors, Playground and recreation; Recreation) v. 4–29, 1910–36. Separate
publication of the proceedings was resumed, however, with the 22d congress, 1937.

1. Playgrounds—Congresses.   ɪ. National recreation association.

                                             9–10018 (rev. '41)
Library of Congress   GV421.N3
                        ₍2₎   796.00273

                MsU ICarbS ICU WaU KyU ScU FTaSU DI PPCPC
                MtU OrP KyU WaTC CaBViP ICRL Or OrPR OrU Wa WaS
NN   0061341   DLC CtNIC IU NcD MtBC DAU IdU ODW PBL

4HV   **National Recreation Congress. 24,**
743   **Pittsburgh, 1909.**
         How a city can celebrate Independence
Day without loss of life or fire damage.
New York, Dept. of Child Hygiene of the
Russell Sage Foundation.
         31 p.

         (Department of Child Hygiene of the
Russell Sage Foundation [Publication]
no.31)

NN   0061342   DLC-P4

National recreation congress. 22d, Atlantic City, 1937.
      The importance of recreation in modern life. Twenty-second
National recreation congress…   Atlantic City, N. J., May 17–
21, 1937. Sponsored by National recreation association.   New
York city, 1937.   24 p.   22cm.

"Topics for group discussion."

1. Recreation—Congresses—U. S.   —N. J.—Atlantic City, 1937.
ɪ. National recreation association.
N. Y. P. L.   June 4, 1940

NN   0061343   NN

National recreation congress. 23d, Pittsburgh, Pa., 1938.
      Search for the good life; topics for group discussion, twenty-
third National recreation congress, Pittsburgh, Pa., October 3–7,
1938…   ₁New York: National recreation assoc., 1938₎   23 p.
21½cm.

1. Recreation—U. S.   ɪ. National   recreation association.
N. Y. P. L.   March 21, 1941

NN   0061344   NN

National recreation congress. 24th, Boston, Mass., 1939.
      Recreation — and the American way of life. Topics for group
discussion. Twenty-fourth National recreation congress, Boston,
Mass., October 9–13, 1939.   ₁New York: National recreation
assoc., 1939₎   35 p.   21½cm.

1. Recreation—U. S. ɪ. National   recreation association.
N. Y. P. L.   March 21, 1941

NN   0061345   NN

D790
N21
1941   National recreation congress. 26th, Baltimore,
        1941.
            Topics for group discussion. 26th National
        recreation congress, Baltimore, Maryland,
        Sept. 29 to Oct. 3, 1941. General theme: The
        America we defend. Sponsored by National re-
        creation association. ₁New York, 1941₎
            40 p. 20ᶜᵐ.
            1. Recreation - Congresses.
            ɪ. National recreation association.

NN   0061346   NNC

GV4   National recreation congress. 27th, Cincinnati,
N35   1942.
1942   Proceedings of the War recreation congress,
        27th National recreation congress, Cincinnati,
        Ohio, September 28 to October 2, 1942. New York
        city, National recreation association, c1942.

            230p. 23cm.

            1. Amusements.–Congresses.
            2. World war, 1939-   .–Recreation.

NN   0061347   NBuG

National recreation congress. *27th, Cincinnati,* 1942.
      … Questions for group discussion. Sponsored by National
recreation association. New York city ₁1942₎
      39, ₁1₎ p. 20½ x 11½ᶜᵐ.
      At head of title: War recreation congress, Cincinnati, Ohio, Septem-
ber 28–October 2, 1942.

1. Recreation—Congresses. 2. Athletics—Congresses.
                                          48–6392 Revised
Library of Congress   GV4.N35 1942 d
                        ₁r43c2₎   790.76

NN   0061348   DLC

National Recreation School, New York
   see
   New York (City) National Recreation School.

National Recreation Workshop
   see
   National Workshop on Recreation.

National Red Cross Society of China
   see
   Red Cross. China. Red Cross Society of China.

        National re-dedication, New York.
Ok10   [Minor publications]
N2125m   26cm.
        "A nation-wide, non-partisan movement inau-
gurated by a group of national organizations
in behalf of American liberty and democracy."

NN   0061352   CtY

VOLUME 407

National Reference Library, *Cleveland*
    see Cleveland. National Reference Library.

National refining company.
    Annual report.
    [Cleveland, Ohio]   25cm.

Ndy36
U2
N216b

NN 0061354   CtY

National Refining Company.
    En-ar-co- national news; oil trade journal
    see under title

Natural reflexions on the present conduct
of his Prussian Majesty: the concern which
England has, and part she ought to take in
the present broils of the Empire; the balance of power, and politics of English-
E——ns; arising from the perusal of the
King of Prussia's Rescript and Manifesto,
lately published by Monsieur Andrie, Minister from Prussia at this Court. In a
letter to a gentleman in the country ...
London, Printed for M. Cooper, 1744.
    [1] l.,   56 p. 20cm.

NN 0061356   NIC

National reflections upon the present debates about
    peace and war. In two letters to a member of
    parliament from his steward in the country.
    [anon] London, J. Morphew, 1712.
        1 p.l., 76 p. 12°. [Miscellaneous
    pamphlets. v. 592:7]

NN 0061357   DLC

Microfilm
*E185
.5
.N295

    The National reflector. Dec. 8,
    1895–Dec. 25, 1897. Wichita, Kan.,
    1895–97.
        1 reel.
        Microfilm copy (positive) made by
    the Library of Congress photoduplica-
    tion service.
        Weekly.
        Scattered issues missing.
        1. Negro newspapers (American)
        2. Newspaper   s, English.

NN 0061358   MB KU–RH KMK

    NATIONAL reform almanac for 1849. N.Y.,
    [1848].
        Wdcts.   US 10070.54

NN 0061359   MH

National Reform Association (Founded 1844)

HD4801
.Y8
Rare Bk
Coll

The People's rights and organ of the National Reform Asso-
    ciation.

    New York, J. Windt & G. H. Evans.

National Reform Association (Founded 1844)

HD4801
.Y8
Rare Bk
Coll

Young America. v. 1–
    Oct. 31, 1829–   ; new ser., v. 1–
    Mar. 16, 1844–
    New York.

National Reform Association (*Founded 1849*)
    see
    National Parliamentary and Financial Reform Associa-
    tion.

National Reform Association (Founded 1863)
    Bibliography prepared by a committee of the National Reform
    Association. A list of works treating of the origin, nature, sphere
    and end of civil government. n. t.-p. [Pittsburgh, Pa.: the
    association, 1912?] 36 p. 8°.

    Government.—Bibliography.
N. Y. P. L.   July 24, 1912.

NN 0061363   NN IU

National Reform Association (Founded 1863)
    The Christian statesman.
    Pittsburgh, Pa., National reform association,

National reform association (Founded 1863)
    A declaration of principles for Christian
    civic world reconstruction. A remarkable
    document, worth its weight in gold for
    leaders of thought throughout the world.
    Phila., National reform association, 1918.
    16 p.

NN 0061365   00

National reform association (Founded 1863)

LC111
.F5
1947

                                FOR OTHER EDITIONS
                                SEE MAIN ENTRY

    Fleming, William Sherman, 1865–
    God in our public schools, by W. S. Fleming, D. D. With
    introduction by Luther A. Weigle ... Pittsburgh, Pa., The
    National reform association [1947]

National Reform Association (Founded 1863)
    National reform documents
    see under title

National reform association (Founded 1863)
    National reform manual; suggestions and data
    for district secretaries and others. Philadel-
    phia, Christian statesman office, 1877.

NN 0061368   MH

National Reform Association (Founded 1863)
    The national reform movement
    see under McAllister, David, 1835–1907.

National Reform Association (Founded 1863)
    Our educational system – is it Christian or
    secular?
        see under [Wylie, Richard Cameron]
    1846–

National Reform Association (Founded 1863)
    A plea for religion in the nation.   Pittsburgh: [the assoc.,]
    1907.   28 p., 2 l.   24°.

    1. Religion, U. S.
N. Y. P. L.   January 3, 1913.

NN 0061371   NN

National reform association (*Founded 1863*)
    Proceedings of the national convention to secure the reli-
    gious amendment of the Constitution of the United States.
    Held in Pittsburg, February 4, 5, 1874. With an account of
    the origin and progress of the movement. Philadelphia,
    Printed by the Christian statesman association, 1874.
        1 p. l., 108 p. 24 cm.
        Cover-title: Proceedings of the fifth National reform convention, to
    aid in maintaining the Christian features of the American govern-
    ment ...
        1. Church and state in the U. S.   I. Title.

    JK361.N25   12–10560 rev

NN 0061372   DLC 00

National Reform Association (Founded 1863)
    Prohibition series.
    [no.]

    [Pittsburgh, 1930   nar. 8°.
    nos.

    1. Prohibition—U. S. I. Title.
N. Y. P. L.   March 10, 1931

NN 0061373   NN

National reform association (Founded 1863)
    World's Christian citizenship conference. *1st, Philadel-*
    phia, 1910.
        Report of the World's Christian citizenship conference
    held in Philadelphia, Pa., U. S. A., November 16–20, 1910.
    Pittsburgh, Pa., National reform association [1910?]

National reform association (Founded 1863)
    World's Christian citizenship conference. *2d, Portland,*
    Or., 1913.
        Second World's Christian citizenship conference, Port-
    land, Oregon, June 29–July 6, 1913. Official report.
    Pittsburgh, Pa., The National reform association [1913]

National Reform Association (Founded 1863)
    A world-wide survey of present day mormonism
        see under Davis, Oscar Franklyn, 1861–

National reform association (Founded 1863)

HN8
.W4
1919a

    World's Christian citizenship conference. *3d, Pittsburgh,*
    1919.
        The world's moral problems; addresses at the third
    World's Christian citizenship conference held in Pittsburgh,
    Pa., U. S. A. November 9–16, 1919. Pittsburgh, Pa., The
    National reform association, [1920.

VOLUME 407

National Reform Conference, Manchester, 1965.
  Parliamentary reform. Report of proceedings
    see under   National Reform Union.

National reform documents.
v. 1
Philadelphia: National Reform Assoc.,   16°.
  v.

Monthly.
Editor: , T. P. Stevenson.

NN   0061379   NN

338.942 National Reform League.
N21p   Propositions of the National Reform League,
       for the peaceful regeneration of society.
       ₍London, 1850₎
         4p. 20cm.

       Caption title.

       1. Gt. Brit.--Economic policy. I. Title.

NN   0061380   IU MH NN IEN

National reform tracts. [London]
       see under   National Parliamentary and
Financial Reform Association.

National Reform Union.   320.942
                                                       4
  National Reform Union leaflets. ... ₍Manchester, 1887?-
1902₎
  Library has no. 4-210. 22½ᶜᵐ.

  Incomplete.
  With these are bound 13 unnumbered National Reform Union pamphlets.

NN   0061382   ICJ

National Reform Union.   324.42 M501
ᴹ⁵⁰¹ᵖ Parliamentary reform. Report of proceedings at the National
Reform Conference, held in the Free Trade Hall, Manchester,
May 15th and 16th, 1865. ... . Manchester, The National Reform Union, [1865].
   137 p. 17ᶜᵐ.

NN   0061383   ICJ

DT930   National reform union.
.A2 O 35
       Ogden, H   J
       ... The war against the Dutch republics in South Africa, its
origin, progress, and results, by H. J. Ogden. Annotated with
extracts from books, newspapers, pamphlets, and speeches by
members of Parliament and other leaders of public opinion ...
Manchester ₍Eng.₎ The National reform union ₍1901₎

National reform union.
       ... Year book.
Manchester ₍Eng.₎ National reform union
       v. 18½ᶜᵐ.
At head of title: National reform union.
Contains statistics of the public expenditures of Great Britain.

  1. Gt. Brit.--Appropriations and expenditures. I. Title.

                                         CA 34-700 Unrev'd
Library of Congress   HJ1023.N3   336.42

NN   0061385   DLC NN DL

Film   National Reformatory Union.
15248   The authorized report of the first provincial
       meeting of the National Reformatory Union, held
       at Bristol, on the 20th, 21st, and 22nd of
       August, 1856.   London, Cash ₍1856?₎
         viii,172p.

       Microfilm (negative). London, British
       Museum, 1972. 1 reel.
         On reel with Osborn, William Cook. The plea
       of "not guilty". London, 1847; and Murray,
       Amelia. Remarks on education in 1847. London,
       1847.

       1. Reformatories. - Gt. Brit.

NN   0061386   IaU CtY

National Reformed Church of Holland
       see Gereformeerde Kerken in Nederland.

A national reformer.
       The money and currency juggle ...
         see under title

*BJ1
.N3   National reformer ... v. 1, no. 6, Feb., 1839.
       [Philadelphia] Board of managers of the A. M
       R. society, 1839.
         1 v. 21cm.
         Editor: W. Whipper.

       1. Ethics--Period. 2. Slavery in the U. S.
       --Cases. I. American moral reform society.
       II. Whipper, William, ed.

NN   0061389   MB

FILM   The National reformer. no.1-12;
21026   Sept.1838-1839.
HN   Philadelphia.
         12 no. on 1 reel. On film (negative)

       Microfilm.
       No.1-12 also called v.1.
       Pub. by the Board of Managers of the American
       Moral Reform Society.
       No more published.

NN   0061390   GU

DA   National reformer. New series, no. 1-35,
815   1846-1847.   New York, Greenwood Reprint
N35   Corp., 1969.
         1 v. 26 cm. weekly

       Reprint of a periodical published in
       Douglas.

       1. Gt. Brit. - Hist. - 19th cent.

NN   0061391   PPT

The National reformer; radical advocate and freethought
journal. v. 1-62; Apr. 14, 1860-Oct. 1, 1893. London,
Holyoake & co. ₍etc.₎, 1860-93.
       62 v. in 58. port. 33-47½ cm. weekly.
       No. 1-2 of v. 1 issued monthly.
       Vol. 5-62 called new series.
       Title varies: Apr. 1860-Aug. 1861, The National reformer.
       Sept. 1861-Feb. 18, 1877, The National reformer; secular advocate
       and freethought journal.
       Feb. 25, 1877-Oct. 1893, The National reformer; radical advocate
       and freethought journal.

Editors: Apr. 1860-Aug. 1861, J. Barker and "Iconoclast" (i. e. C.
Bradlaugh)--Sept. 1861-Feb. 1863, C. Bradlaugh.--Mar. 1863-
Apr. 22, 1866, J. Watts.--Apr. 29, 1866-Feb. 1891, C. Bradlaugh
(assisted from May 1881-Oct. 1887, by Annie Besant)--Mar. 1891-
Oct. 1893, J. M. Robertson.
No more published.
"Out of the ashes of the little Investigator rose the National re-
former ... the National reformer in dying gives birth to the Free
review." *cf.* National reformer, v. 62, p. 212.

                                         2-25218

NN   0061393   DLC ICJ

FILM   The National reformer; radical advocate and
X190   freethought journal. v.1-62; Apr.14,1860-
       Oct.1,1893. London, Holyoake & co. ₍etc.₎,
       1860-93.
         62 v. in 58. port. 33-47½ cm. weekly.
         No.1-2 of v.1 issued monthly.
         Vol.5-62 called new series.
         Title varies: Apr.1860-Aug.1861, The National
       reformer--Sept.1861-Feb.18,1877, The National
       reformer; secular advocate, and freethought
       journal.--Feb.25,1877-Oct.1893, The National
       reformer; radical advocate and freethought
       journal.
         Editors: Apr.1860-Aug.1861, J.Barker and
       "Iconoclast" (i.e. C.Bradlaugh)--Sept.1861-

         Feb.1863, C.Bradlaugh.--Mar.1863-Apr.22,1866,
       J.Watts.--Apr.29,1866-Feb.1891, C.Bradlaugh
       (assisted from May 1881-Oct.1887, by Annie
       Besant).--Mar.1891-Oct.1893, J.M.Robertson.
         No more published.
         "Out of the ashes of the little Investigator
       rose the National reformer ... the National
       reformer in dying gives birth to the Free re-
       view." Cf.National reformer, v.62,p.212.
         Microfilm (positive). Washington, Library
       of Congress Photoduplication Service, 1964.
       21 reels.

NN   0061395   MiU PSt MH

The National reformer, and Manx weekly review
of home and foreign affairs.
no. 1-110.
Nov. 16, 1844-May 29, 1847.
₍Douglas, Isle of Man, Printed and Published
by J. B. O'Brien, 1844-47₎
       v. 24ᶜᵐ.

NN   0061396   NNC CoU NSyU TxU GU IaAS MB

National reformer, in government, law,
property, religion, and morals. 1837
       see Bronterre's national reformer,
in government, law, property, religion,
and morals.

National Refrigerator Market Report, inc.
       National refrigerator market report; the blue book of
trade-in values for used refrigerators. Illustrated retail
edition.
Los Angeles.
       v. illus., tables. 12 x 19 cm.
       Published in Philadelphia, 19

       1. Refrigerators.   I. Title: Blue book of trade-in values for used
refrigerators.
       TP496.N3   621.56   42-19592 rev*

NN   0061398   DLC

National Refugee Service. Annual report.
see its Refugees. Annual report.

296.06 National refuges service.
N   Budget. N. ₍.₎, National refugee service, 1941.

       Library has:
1941
1942

NN   0061400   NNZI

National refugee service.
       Dividends from new Americans; a report prepared by the Na-
tional refugee service describing business enterprises established
in the United States by refugees. ₍New York: Nat. refugee
service, inc., Dept. of information and statistics, 1941₎ 12 p.
illus. 23cm.

       1. Refugees--U. S.
       N. Y. P. L.   August 6, 1942

NN   0061401   NN

VOLUME 407

National refugee service.
Emigre service release. ₍no. 1–₎23 (July 25, 1940 – Dec. 5, 1941).
New York, 1940–41.   23 nos.   28cm.

Irregular.
Nos. 1–18 (July 25, 1940 – July 17, 1941) have title: Community service release.
Each issue is devoted to one of three topics: Employment and retraining, Migration, or Activities of special committees.
No more published.

1. Refugees—U.S. 2. Refugees,   German—U. S. I. Title.
II. Title: Community service release.
N. Y. P. L.   April 23, 1943

NN   0061402   NN

National refugee service.
NRS community bulletin
see under title

D809   National refugee service.
U5N2   NRS needs in 1945. A program of aid
and adjustment for America's newcomers
... New York ₍1945₎
cover-title, 20 p.   23cm.

NN   0061404   MnHi

National refugee service
...Quarterly report of the executive director. Jan./March, 1940 – July/Sept., 1941. ₍New York₎ 1940–41.   5 nos.   28 – 30cm.

July – Dec., 1940 not published; for that period see its: Refugees... The annual report of the National refugee service, inc.
No more published.

1. Refugees—U.S. 2. World   war, 1939–   —Refugees. 3. World
war, 1939–   —Jews.
N. Y. P. L.   June 18, 1943

NN   0061405   NN Ctʏ

National Refugee Service.
Refugees.   Annual report.

New York.
     v. illus.   28 cm.

1. World War, 1939–1945—Refugees.

D809.U5N283   940.53159   49–36741*‡

NN   0061406   DLC NN OCH ICU OCl NNZI

National refugee service.
... Report of the executive director, September–October, 1939. ₍New York, 1939?₎
cover-title, 12 numb. l.   27½ x 21½ᵐ.
Reproduced from type-written copy.

1. Refugees, Political. 2. U. S.—Emig. & Immig.

                       46–36561
Library of Congress   HV640.N3
                   ₍2₎   361.3

NN   0061407   DLC

National refugee service.
They can aid America; survey of alien specialized personnel. New York, Nat. refugee service ₍1942₎   13 p.   22cm.

1. Refugees—U.S. 2. Occupa-   tions—Choice. 3. World war, 1939–
—Labor—U. S.
N. Y. P. L.   March 29, 1944

NN   0061408   NN OrU MH

D 809 U5 N3   National Refugee Service.
     You who feel secure. ₍New York, 1940?₎
     ₍12₎ p. illus.

     Cover title.

     1. Refugees, Jewish. 2. World War,
1939–1945--Refugees. I. Title.

NN   0061409   UU

National Refuges for Homeless and Destitute
Children
see   Shaftesbury Homes, London.

The National register, Bedford, Mass., 1908-
see under   John Bean Association.

The **National** register. v. 1–   (no. 1–   );
Jan. 4, 1808–
London ₍J. B. Bell and J. De Camp, etc.₎ 1808–
     v.   illus. (incl. plan) plates, ports., maps.   25ᵐ.   weekly.
Caption title.
Vol. 1 consists of either Sunday or Monday edition; v. 2–   of Monday edition.
Vols. 1, 7–   have no title-pages; title-pages of v. 2–6 read as follows: v. 2–3, The Sunday edition of the weekly newspaper, entitled the National register; v. 4, The Monday edition of the weekly newspaper, entitled the National register; v. 5–6, The National register, Sunday and Monday newspaper.

     Published by J. B. Bell and J. De Camp, 1808–10; by G. Fisher (E. Roche, printer) 1810–12; by H. Hay, 1812–
     Numbering irregular: no. 94, 315–316, 325–326, 332 repeated; no. 361–365 omitted.
     With v. 1 is bound: Bell and De Camp's edition of the trial of Gen. Whitelocke, commander of the forces appointed to attack Buenos Ayres (36 p.)

                          39–1862
Library of Congress   AP4.N24
                 ₍2₎   052

NN   0061413   DLC NN TxU ICRL DN AU ICU

The **National** register, a weekly paper, containing a series of the important public documents, and the proceedings of Congress; statistical tables, reports and essays, original and selected, upon agriculture, manufactures, commerce, and finance; science, literature and the arts: and biographical sketches: with summary statements of the current news and political events: making two volumes yearly. v. 1–8, v. 9, no. 1–6; Mar. 2, 1816–Feb. 5, 1820. Washington city ₍J. K. Mead, etc.₎ 1816–20.
9 v. in 7.   24½–26ᵐᵐ.
No more published?
1. Political science—Period. 2. U. S.—Pol. & govt.—Period. 3. U. S.—Pol. & govt.—1816–1820.
                          10–28838†
Library of Congress   JK1.N3

NN   0061414   DLC NcD OClWHi MHi

AP2 Am358 Reels 800-801   The National register; a weekly paper containing a series of the important public documents and the proceedings of Congress; statistical tables, reports and essays, original and selected, upon agriculture, manufactures, commerce, and finance, science, literature and the arts and biographical sketches with summary statements of the current news and political events ... . v. 1–10;

     Mar. 2, 1816–Oct. 7, 1820//
Washington City, J.K. Mead ₍etc.₎
1816–20.
     2 reels. (American periodical series: 1800–1850, reels 800–801, APS 1040)
IaAS
     Microfilm copy made by University Microfilms, Ann Arbor, Mich. Positive.

NN   0061416   IaAS LU DNAL MoU

The National register; pertinent facts about colored Americans. 1st-   ed.
Louisville, Ky., Register Publications, 1952–
     v.   27 cm.
Editor: v. 1-   T. J. Johnson.

1. Negroes—Direct. 2. Negroes—Biog. 3. Negroes—Education.
I. Johnson, T. J., ed.

E185.96.N37   325.260973   53–32943

NN   0061417   DLC

The National register, Sunday and Monday newspaper
see   The National register. London.

National Register of Archives, London
see under   Gt. Brit. National Register of Archives.

National register of accommodation
see under   Scottish Tourist Board.

National register of Belgian draft horses
see under   Belgian Draft Horse Corporation of America.

The national register of French draft horses
see under   National French Draft Horse Association.

National register of German, Hanoverian and Oldenburg Coach Horse Association of America
see under   German, Hanoverian and Oldenburg Coach Horse Association of America.

The NATIONAL register of interior designers. 1951-
New York, National register pub. co.   v.   24cm.

1. Interior decoration--Direct. --   U. S.

NN   0061424   NN

WE 22 FA1 N2   The NATIONAL register of medical auxiliary services ... Chiropodists.
     London, Board of Registration of Medical Auxiliaries, 193-? -
        v.
     1. Chiropodists - Gt. Brit. - Direct.
I. Board of Registration of Medical Auxiliaries.

NN   0061425   DNLM CaBVaU

VOLUME 407

WB
22
FA1
N2d

The NATIONAL register of medical auxiliary
services ... Dietitians.

London, Board of Registration of
Medical Auxiliaries, 194-? -
v.
1. Dietitians - Direct. - Gt. Brit.
I. Board of Registration of Medical
Auxiliaries.

NN   0061426   DNLM

WW
22
FA1
N13

The NATIONAL register of medical
auxiliary services ... Dispensing
opticians.
London, Board of Registration of
Medical Auxiliaries ₍193-?₎-
v.
1. Opticians - Gt. Brit. - Direct.
I. Board of Registration of Medical
Auxiliaries.

NN   0061427   DNLM CaBVaU

The NATIONAL register of medical auxiliary services: operating theatre technicians. 1st-
ed.,   19 -
London, Board of Registration of Medical Auxiliaries.

v. 25 cm.

1. Medicinae - Direct. I. Board of Registration of Medical Auxiliaries. II. Title: Operating theatre technicians.

NN   0061428   CaBVaU

WW
22
FA1
N2

NATIONAL register of medical auxiliary
services ... Orthoptists.

London, Board of Registration of Medical
Auxiliaries, 193-? -
v.
1. Orthoptists - Gt. Brit. - Direct.
I. Board of Registration of Medical
Auxiliaries.

NN   0061429   DNLM CaBVaU

WN
22
FA1
N2

NATIONAL register of medical auxiliary
services ... Radiographers. /

London, Board of Registration of Medical
Auxiliaries, 19
v.
Consists of those members of the
Society of Radiographers who have
voluntarily registered with the board.
1. Radiological technicians - Gt. Brit. -
Direct. I. Board of Registration of Medical
Auxiliaries. II. Society of Radiographers

NN   0061430   DNLM

WV
22
FA1
N2

The NATIONAL register of medical auxiliary
services ... Speech therapists.

London, Board of Registration of Medical
Auxiliaries ₍1942?₎-55.
12 v.
Superseded by the Register of the
College of Speech Therapists.
1. Speech therapists - Gt. Brit. -
Direct. I. Board of Registration of
Medical Auxiliaries.

NN   0061431   DNLM CaBVaU

National register of Norman horses
see   National French Draft Horse Association.
The national register of French draft horses.

National register of scholarships and fellowships.

New York, World Trade Academy Press ₍19

v. 28 cm.

Compiler: J. L. Angel.
Issued in   vols.: v. 1, Scholarships and loans.

1. Scholarships—U. S.   i. Angel, Juvenal Londoño, 1907–
comp.

LB2848.N3   378.33   58—900

NN   0061433   DLC TxU AAP MBH NbU MiU NN PU LU

National register publishing company.
The agency list of the Standard advertising
register
see   Standard directory of advertising
agencies.

HF6146
.T42A25

National Register Publishing Company.

Advertiser commercial code guide.
Skokie, Ill., National Register Pub. Co.

National register publishing company.
List of oil burner manufacturers.
New York, National register publishing co.,
1933.
8 numb. l.

NN   0061436   OC1

National Register Publishing Company.
The standard advertising register
see   Standard directory of advertisers.

National register publishing company.
Wines and liquors.
New York, National register publishing co., 1934.
18, 10 p.

NN   0061438   OC1

National Registration League.
Proceedings of the Design Registration Convention of Manufacturers, Merchants, Importers,
Designers
see under   Design Registration Convention
of Manufacturers, Merchants, Importers, Designers
and Trade Associations, New York, 1913.

National Regulator Company, Chicago.
A regulator which does not require regulating.
The National Temperature Regulator patented for
automatically controlling hot air, steam or hot
water heating apparatus in residences ...
Chicago, 1904.
32 p.   illus.   12°.

NN   0061440   NN

National Rehabilitation Association.

HD7255
.A2N35

Journal of rehabilitation. v. 1–
Jan. 1935–
₍Washington, etc., National Rehabilitation Association₎

National rehabilitation association, inc.

National rehabilitation news ... dedicated to the vocational rehabilitation of physically handicapped persons. v. 1–
Jan. 1935–
₍Des Moines, Ia., National rehabilitation association, inc.,
1935–

National Rehabilitation Association.
Newsletter
see   NRA newsletter.

National Rehabilitation Association.
Proceedings
see under   National Conference on
Employment of the Disabled, Washington, D. C.,
1941.

National rehabilitation association.
... Yearbook 1st–   1933–

₍n. p.₎ 1933–

v. illus. 22½ᶜᵐ.

President: 1933–   Oscar M. Sullivan.

1. Disabled—Rehabilitation, etc.—U. S.   i. Sullivan, Oscar
Matthias, 1881–

E 34–368

Library, U. S. Office of   Education UB363.N2

NN   0061445   DHEW

T371.9
N213e

National Rehabilitation Association. Region
8.
Exhibits shown at the Conference of the
National Rehabilitation Association, Region
8, Texarkana, U.S.A., May 19-21, 1952.
[Austin? 1952?]
v1, 51p. 24cm.

1. Disabled - Rehabilitation. 2. Defec-
tive and delinquent classes - Education.

NN   0061446   TxU

National rehabilitation committee
see
American legion. *National rehabilitation committee.*

National rehabilitation conference of the
American legion.

See

American legion. National rehabilitation conference.

National rehabilitation news
see Journal of rehabilitation.

VOLUME 407

National Relay Conference, *Oklahoma State University.*
Papers. 1st-   1953-
₍Phoenix? Ariz. etc.₎ National Association of Relay Manufacturers ₍etc.₎
v. illus. 29 cm. annual.

Vols. for 1953–57 issued without title.
Cover title. Proceedings.
Vols. for 1953–   issued under earlier names of the conference:
1953–56, Symposium on Electro-Magnetic Relays.—1957-   National Conference on Electromagnetic Relays.
Conferences for 1953-   sponsored by the School Electrical Engineering, Oklahoma State University (1956-   with the National Association of Relay Manufacturers)

Papers of the 13th (1965) conference include papers presented at the 2d International Conference on Electromagnetic Relays which was held simultaneously.

1. Electric relays—Congresses.   I. National Association of Relay Manufacturers.   II. Oklahoma.   State University of Agriculture and Applied Science, Stillwater.   School of Electrical Engineering.   III. National Relay Conference, Oklahoma State University.   Proceedings.

TK2851.N33   621.3173   A 55–8003 rev
Columbia Univ.   Libraries
for Library of Congress   ₍r66f2₎†

          IdU MtBC CoU
NbU NBuU ViU TxU MiU LU CoU KMK NcRS IU WaSpG WaU
NN 0061451   NNC DLC ICJ OC1 UU WaS MsSM NSyU OCU

National Relay Conference, Oklahoma State
    University.
    Papers. 1st-
June 1953-
Stillwater, Okla. [etc.]
    v. illus. 29 cm. annual.
    Microfilm (negative) Phoenix, Arizona,
National Association of Relay Manufacturers.
2 reels. 16 cm.

NN 0061452   WU

National relief commission.
Report of the executive committee of the National relief commission, organized "for the care of sick and wounded soldiers, sailors and marines, and for the relief of the families of combatants" during the war between the republic of the United States and the kingdom of Spain ... ₍Philadelphia, Press of Times printing house, 1900?₎
251, iii p. 2 col. pl. (incl. front.) 26½ᶜᵐ.
Cover-title: Report ... 1898–99.
1. U. S.—Hist.—War of 1898—Hospitals, charities, etc.
Library of Congress   E731.N27
                                                      4—1362

NN 0061453   DLC MB OC1 OO

National relief commission.
    A song book for soldiers and sailors ...
Philadelphia [1898?]
    cover-title, 32 p. 15 x 12 cm.

NN 0061454   CtY

National relief commission.
    Spanish phrase book for American soldiers and
sailors.   Philadelphia, Pa. [c1898]
    32 p. 15.5 cm.

NN 0061455   CtY

National relief fund, *London.*
Final statement of the accounts of the National relief fund up to the 16th April, 1923. (In continuation of Cmd. 1272, 1921) ... London, H. M. Stationery off. ₍printed by Harrison & sons, ltd.₎ 1923.
7 p. incl. tables. 24½ᶜᵐ. ₍Gt. Brit. Parliament. Papers by command₎ Cmd. 1955₎
G. H. Murray, chairman.
1. Pensions, Military—Gt. Brit. 2. Charities—Gt. Brit.   I. Murray, Sir George Herbert, 1849-   II. Title.
Library of Congress   D638.G7A42
                                                      23–17101

NN 0061456   DLC DL MiU

National relief fund, *London.*
Report ₍and Final report₎ on the administration of the National relief fund ... ₍1914/15 up to the 1st March, 1921₎
London, H. M. Stationery off., 1915–21.
10 v. 33½ᶜᵐ. ₍Gt. Brit. Parliament. Papers by command₎ Cd. 7756, 8169, 8286, 8449, 8621, 8920, 9111; Cmd. 16, 356, 1272₎
Amalgamation of the National relief fund and the Soldiers' and sailors' families association.
G. H. Murray, chairman.
Issued every six months, March 31, 1915, to September 30, 1918. The report "up to 30th June, 1919" covers "the nine months ending June 30, 1919." The Final report covers the period from June 30, 1919, to March 1, 1921.
1. Pensions, Military—Gt. Brit. 2. Charities—Gt. Brit.   I. Murray, Sir George Herbert, 1849-   II. Soldiers' and sailors' families association.
                                                      21–13208
Library of Congress   D638.G7A4

NN 0061457   DLC DL MiU

331   National Religion and Labor Foundation.
N218s   Social vision for the church and labor. ₍A
              partial report of the fifteenth anniversary con-
              ference of the National Religion and Labor Founda-
              tion in Pittsburgh, Pennsylvania, January 12–14,
              1948₎ New Haven, Conn. ₍1948₎
              34p. 23cm.

              1. Church and labor. I. Title.

NN 0061458   IU N NN MH–IR

331.88   ₍National religion and labor foundation₎
N2131w   Walking together, religion & labor.   ₍New
              Haven, Conn., 1946₎
              30p. illus.

              Bibliography: p.28–30.

              1. Labor and laboring classes--U.S.--1914-
              2. Trade-unions--U.S. 3. Sociology, Christian.

NN 0061459   IU NcD NN WHi NjP

National religion and labor foundation.
    Walking together: religion and labor.   ₍Columbus, 1955?₎
folder (₍6₎ p.)   22cm.

        1. Labor--U. S., 1926-   2. Religion-₍Influence, Political and
social.

NN 0061460   NN

National religious liberty association
                                see
Religious liberty association, *Washington, D. C.*

National Religious Training School, Durham, N.C.
    Bulletin. Durham, Institution, 1910.
    v. O.

NN 0061462   NcD

J   NATIONAL remonstrance. To the Commons house of
54572   Parliament in their collective capacity assem-
.158   bled.   [London, Hetherington, 1838?]
              4p. (National association tracts. no.2)

              Caption title.
              Remonstrance in reference to the People's char-
              ter, etc.
              Binder's title: Chartism.

NN 0061463   ICN

363.05   National renaissance bulletin.
NAT   v. 1-
              1949-
              New York, National Renaissance Party.
              v. illus. 28cm.

NN 0061464   IU MiU NN

NATIONAL RENAISSANCE PARTY.
    Anti-Semitic pamphlets, press releases, etc.
distributed by the National renaissance party.
v. p., 1955?₎   9 pieces

    Film reproduction. Negative.
    Target title: Pamphlets, press releases, etc. distributed by the National renaissance party.
    Most of the material published by Le Blanc publishers.
1. Jews--Anti-Semitic writings.   2. Anti-Semitic writings.
I. Le Blanc publishers. New   York.

NN 0061465   NN

National Renaissance Party.
    National renaissance bulletin
        see under title

National Renaissance Party.
    This is Israel's Record ...
    4 p.   1 inserted leaf.   28 cm.
    1. Israel-Attacks on.

NN 0061467   NNJ

TS1980   National Renderers Association.
.R4   The Renderers' yearbook.
              Chicago, National Renderers Association.

National Reorganization Army of Mexico
        see Mexico. National Reorganization
        Army of Mexico.

National Reorganization Conference, *Washington, D. C.,*
1949.
    ₍Speeches delivered at the National Reorganization Conference, Washington, D. C., December 12–13, 1949. Press releases₎ Washington, 1949.
    23 pamphlets. 29 cm.
    Sponsored by the Citizens Committee for the Hoover Report.
    1. U. S.—Executive departments. 2. U. S. Commission on Organization of the Executive Branch of the Government.
    JK677 1949   353   50–5735

NN 0061470   DLC

National Reorganization Conference, *Washington, D. C.,*
1949.
    Text of speeches delivered at the National Reorganization Conference, Washington, D. C., December 12–13, 1949. New York, Citizens Committee for the Hoover Report ₍1949?₎
    3 v. 28 cm.
    CONTENTS.—1. The average citizen views his government and reorganization.—2. Reorganization problems.—3. Reorganization as viewed by the members of the Administration, the Congress, and the chairman of the Hoover Commission. The role of the citizen, education and the press in achieving "better government at a better price."
    1. U. S.—Executive departments. 2. U. S. Commission on Organization of the Executive Branch of the Government.
                                                      A 51–7419
    Brown Univ. Library   JK643.C47N32
    for Library of Congress   ₍8₎

NN 0061471   RPB NcU OrU IEN NcRS

VOLUME 407

National reorganization of business, by a business man... London: Power-Book Co., 1910. vi, 373 p. 12°.

275049A. 1. Economics—Essays and misc. 2. Great Britain—Social conditions. 3. A business man.
N. Y. P. L. April 29, 1927

NN 0061472 NN

National Repeal Convention of the Friends of Ireland in the United States of America, Philadelphia, 1842.
Report of the proceedings of the National Repeal Convention of the Friends of Ireland, in the United States of America, held in the city of Philadelphia, February 22d and 23d, 1842... Philadelphia: M. Fithian, 1842. 39 p. 8°.

1. Ireland.—History, 1842.
N. Y. P. L. May 18, 1922.

NN 0061473 NN NNC DLC OClWHi

National reporter system.

Arkansas decisions reported in the Southwestern reporter, vols. 1 to ₍300₎ ... inclusive. August, 1886, to ₍February, 1928₎ ... St. Paul, West publishing co., 1915–28.

National reporter system. FOR OTHER EDITIONS SEE MAIN ENTRY

West Virginia. *Laws, statutes, etc.*
The code of West Virginia, 1906; containing the Declaration of independence; the Constitution of the United States and laws thereof concerning naturalization and the election of United States senators; the constitution of the state; the code, as amended by legislation to and including the year 1905 and notes to all prior laws and applicable decisions. Comp. by members of the editorial staff of the National reporter system. St. Paul, Minn., West publishing co., 1906.

National reporter system.

South eastern reporter.
... Digest of decisions of the Supreme courts of appeals of Virginia and West Virginia, and Supreme courts of North Carolina, South Carolina, Georgia. Reported in the Southeastern reporter, volumes 1–₍125₎ ... ₍1887–1925₎ with a table of cases digested. Edited by the editorial staff of the National reporter system. St. Paul, West publishing co., 1895–1925.

National reporter system.

Pacific reporter.
Digest of the Pacific reporter, volumes 1–120 ₍1883–1912₎ and ... state and territorial reports ... Edited by members of the editorial staff of the American digest system ... St. Paul, West publishing co., 1913.

National reporter system.

Minnesota. *Laws, statutes, etc.*
The general statutes of the state of Minnesota as amended by subsequent legislation, with which are incorporated all general laws of the state in force December 31, 1894, compiled and edited by Henry B. Wenzell, assisted by Eugene F. Lane, with annotations by Francis B. Tiffany and others, and a general index by the editorial staff of the National reporter system ... St. Paul, Minn., West publishing co., 1894.

Law

National reporter system.

Bowie, Robert Richardson, 1909– *ed.*
Government regulation of business; cases from the National reporter system. 1955 ed. Brooklyn, Foundation Press, 1955.

National Reporter System.
Judicial and statutory definitions of words and phrases
see under title

National reporter system. FOR OTHER EDITIONS SEE MAIN ENTRY

Law

West Publishing Company, St. Paul.
Key number classification, comprising the complete scope and arrangement of topics, subdivisions and key numbers as used in the decennials and other key number digests of the American digest system as well as all units of the National reporter system. St. Paul, 1950.

National reporter system.

Louisiana. *Supreme court.*
... Louisiana reports, v. ₍49–52₎, 104–108; cases argued and determined in the Supreme court of Louisiana reported in the Louisiana reports, vol. 49–52, 104–108, and the Southern reporter, vol. 21–32 ... 1897–1902/1903. With cross-reference tables, tables of cases cited, tables of code sections, legislative acts and articles of the constitution cited and construed. Reported by the editorial staff of the National reporter system. St. Paul, West publishing co., 1898–1903.

National reporter system.

West publishing co., St. Paul.
Manual of National reporter system and all key-number digests, including the American digest system, reporter digests, state digests. How to find the case in point. St. Paul, West publishing co., 1941.

National reporter system.
National reporter blue book; complete tables showing volume and page of the Reporter for every case found in the corresponding state reports. St. Paul, West publishing co., 1928.
1900 p. 26ᶜᵐ.
Tables mounted on inside of cover.
——— 1936 Permanent supplement; complete tables showing volume and page of the Reporter for every case found in the corresponding state reports. St. Paul, Minn., West publishing co. ₍ᶜ1936₎
500 p. 26ᶜᵐ.
——— Copy 2.
Copyright A 111631

——— ... Cumulative supplement ₍1938– ₎ Complete tables showing volume and page of the Reporter for every case found in the corresponding state reports ... St. Paul, Minn., West publishing co. ₍ᶜ1938–
v. 25½ᶜᵐ.
At head of title: National reporter blue book. "Supplementing 1936 Permanent digest."
1. Annotations and citations (Law)—U. S. I. West publishing co., St. Paul. II. Title. III. Title: Blue book, National reporter.

29–392 Revised

MH-L MH DN IU CoD NNC-L ICarbS CLL NBuU-L MB CoDU
NN 0061485 DLC WaU-L OrU CaBVaU DI NcU-L IU ViU-L

National reporter system.

Prentice-Hall inc., New York.
New York state tax cases; a convenient collection of unabridged cases from New York and federal courts relating to the corporation franchise and personal income taxes of New York state; decisions date from 1890 up to May, 1926. New York, Prentice-Hall, inc., 1926.

National reporter system.
New York supplement; cases argued and determined in the Court of appeals, Supreme and lower courts of record of New York state, with key number annotations. v. 1– May/Aug. 1888–
St. Paul, West publishing co., 1888–19

National reporter system.

North eastern reporter; cases argued and determined in the courts of Illinois, Indiana, Massachusetts, New York, Ohio, with key number annotations ... July/Sept. 1885–Mar./Apr. 1936. St. Paul, Minn., West publishing co., 1885–1936.

National reporter system.

Law

North western reporter ... cases argued and determined in the courts of Iowa, Michigan, Minnesota, Nebraska, North Dakota, South Dakota, Wisconsin. v. 1–300, Apr./Aug. 1879–1942; 2d ser., v. 1– St. Paul, Minn., West publishing co., 1879–19

National reporter system.

Law

Mississippi. *Courts.*
Reports of cases argued and determined in the Supreme court, High court of errors and appeals, and the Superior court of chancery of Mississippi. ₍Dec. 1839–
Annotated ed., unabridged, with notes and references by the editorial corps of the National reporter system ... St. Paul, West publishing co., 1907–

National Reporter System.

Law

Alabama. *Supreme Court.*
Reports of cases argued and determined in the Supreme Court of Alabama. 2d ed., unabridged, with notes and references by the Editorial Corps of the National Reporter System. Book 1–49; ₍1820–86₎ St. Paul, West Pub. Co., 1904–11.

National Reporter system

Louisiana. *Supreme court.*
Reports of cases argued and determined in the Supreme court of Louisiana and in the Superior court of the territory of Louisiana. ₍1809–1896₎ Annotated ed., unabridged, with notes and references by the editorial corps of the National reporter system ... St. Paul, West publishing co., 1907–13.

National reporter system.

South eastern reporter; cases argued and determined in the courts of Georgia, North Carolina, South Carolina, Virginia, West Virginia, with key number annotations. v. 1– Feb./May, 1887–
St. Paul, Minn., West publishing co., 1887–19

National reporter system.
... The **South western** reporter ... Comprising all the current decisions of the Supreme courts of Arkansas, Missouri, Tennessee and Texas, Courts of appeals of Kentucky and Missouri, courts of civil and criminal appeals and Commission of appeals of Texas, with key-number annotations ... Aug./Dec. 1886–Jan./Feb. 1928. St. Paul, West publishing co., 1887–1928.

National reporter system.

Southern reporter; cases argued and determined in the courts of Alabama, Florida, Louisiana, Mississippi ... 1887–19

VOLUME 407

National repository, devoted to general and religious literature, criticism, and art. Daniel Curry, D. D., editor. v. 1–8; Jan. 1877–Dec. 1880. Cincinnati, Hitchcock and Walden ₍etc.₎; New York, Nelson and Phillips ₍etc.₎ 1877–80.

8 v. in 5. illus., ports. 24½–25ᶜᵐ. monthly.

Preceded by the Ladies' repository.
No more published.

ₜ. Curry, Daniel, 1809–1887, ed

Library of Congress   AP2.N354   4–29545

MiU PCarlD
NN   0061496   DLC OrU IEG PPiD KU OClJC MnU OU OCl

National republic; a monthly magazine of fundamental Americanism. v.1–
Mar. 4, 1905–
Washington.
v. illus. 31cm.

Sub-title varies.
Title varies: v.1–11, 1905–Mar. 1925, National Republican.

I. National Republican.

DNW OCl FTaSU
MiKW InNd NBuG NN MeWC In OrP MB MnNC NbHi CU DLC
NN   0061497   NIC OrU WaS ICJ CtY WHi CSmH MdBJ IaU

National republic.
Americans, avoid the chains of the vicious dictatorships: Communism, Socialism, Fascism, Nazism.   Washington, National republic ₍1936?₎ 16 p. 23cm.

Caption-title.

1. Bolshevism. English.   2. Fascism. 3. Socialism. 1933–
N.Y.P.L.   March 10, 1944

NN   0061498   NN

National republic.
Leninism ... Lewisism ...
see under title

National Republic.
Light turned on. A demand by the people for self government
see under title

National republic.
The National republic. [Special Lincoln issue] vol. XVIII, no. 10, February, 1931.

NN   0061501   MiKW

*
E
457.7   National republic.
N27   The National republic's "Hour of tribute to Lincoln". Addresses broadcast during the National republic's "Hour of tribute to Lincoln," Lincoln's birthday, 1926. ₍Washington, D.C., The National republic, 1926₎
cover-title, ₍8₎ p. incl. illus.

Portrait on cover.
Addresses by C.D. Wilbur, Hubert Work, W.M. Jardine, Herbert Hoover, J.E. Watson, C.M. Ramseyer, J.B. Payne, Mrs. John D. Sherman, and Mrs. Anthony W. Cook. Prayer by James E. Freeman.
1. Lincoln, Abraham, Pres. U.S.--Tributes. I. Title: Hour of   tribute to Lincoln.

NN   0061502   CStbS

National republic lettergram.
no.

Washington ₍National republic, 19   nos.   35 – 36cm.
Irregular.

1. Bolshevism—Per. and soc. publ.   —U.S. 2. Fascism—Per. and soc.
publ.—U.S. 3. Americanism—Per.   and soc. publ.
N.Y.P.L.   May 11, 1945

NN   0061503   NN

National Republic of Vietnam
see
Vietnam.

National republican ₍Daily₎
Washington, 1861–73.
Title varies: from 1861 to 1870, Daily National republican.

NN   0061505   MB

A national Republican ₍Daily₎
The case of Georgia ...
see under title

44   The National ₍ Republican₎[Daily]
The combined foreign and consular and senatorial edition of the National Republican.   [Washington, The National Republican Co., 1887]
9 l.   unp.   fol.

NN   0061507   DLC

National Republican. ₍Daily₎
Minds out of tune
see under title

National Republican ₍Daily₎
National geology
see under title

National Republican [Daily]
see also   Daily National Republican.
Washington, D.C.

National Republican [Monthly]
see   National Republic.

National Republican association, Washington, D.C.
see   Republican association, Washington, D.C.

Pam.   National Republican Camp of Veterans and their
Coll.   Sons of the United States of America.

39886   Declaration of principles and articles of association. Incorporated, Feb. 16, 1897. Indianapolis, Miller Sons ₍1897?₎
23 p. 15 cm.

Cover title.

1. National Republican Camp of Veterans and their Sons of   the United States of America.

NN   0061513   NcD

The National Republican campaign songster. 1880. Garfield & Arthur ... ₍Syracuse, N. Y., W. O. Moffitt, 1880₎
29 p. 14¾ᶜᵐ.
Without music.

1. Campaign songs, 1880—Republican.   ₜ. Moffitt, William O., Syracuse, N. Y., pub.

Library of Congress   E685.N275   18–434

NN   0061514   DLC

NATIONAL republican campaign songster.
Cincinnati, O., 1888.

pp.47.   US 6468.5(3).

NN   0061515   MH OClWHi

National Republican Central Committee of Baltimore
see
National Republican party. Maryland. Baltimore.

                                        FOR OTHER EDITIONS
National Republican club.   SEE MAIN ENTRY

Black, Frank Swett, 1853–1913.
Abraham Lincoln; an address by Frank S. Black before the Republican club of New York city, February 12, 1908. ₍New York? 1908₎

National Republican Club
Lincoln, Abraham, pres. U. S., 1809–1865.
Abraham Lincoln's lost speech, May 29, 1856. A souvenir of the eleventh annual Lincoln dinner of the Republican club of the city of New York, at the Waldorf, February 12, 1897. New York, Printed for the committee. 1897.

National Republican club
Addresses delivered at the Lincoln dinners of the National Republican club in response to the toast Abraham Lincoln, 1910–1927. ₍New York₎ Priv. print. for the National Republican club, 1927.

478 p. front. (port.) 24¾ᶜᵐ.

"This edition is limited to five hundred copies of which this copy is number 97."

1. Lincoln, Abraham, pres. U. S.—Addresses, sermons, etc.

Library of Congress   E457.8.N284   28–8554

NN   0061519   DLC WaTC WaT TxU NIC

VOLUME 407

National Republican club.
Addresses delivered at the Lincoln dinners of the Republican club of the city of New York in response to the toast Abraham Lincoln, 1887–1909. ₁New York₎ Priv. print. for the Republican club of the city of New York, 1909.

4 p. l., ₁7₎–358 p. front. (port.) 24½ᶜᵐ. $5.00
"This edition is limited to five hundred copies." This copy not numbered.

1. Lincoln, Abraham, pres. U. S.—Addresses, sermons, etc.
9–21977 Revised
Library of Congress   E457.8.N28

NN   0061520   DLC InU NNC MiU-C MB OClW

National Republican club.
Addresses delivered at the Lincoln dinners of the Republican club of the city of New York in response to the toast Abraham Lincoln, 1887–1909. ₁New York₎ Priv. print. for the Republican club of the city of New York, 1909. ₁New York₎ Reprinted, ₁Tenny press₎ 1927.

4 p. l., ₁7₎–376 p. front. (port.) 24½ cm.
On cover : Lincoln addresses 1887–1909. The National Republican club.
"Second edition."
"This edition is limited to five hundred copies, of which this copy is number 82."
The "… Addresses ₁of Emil G. Hirsch and Henry E. Tremain₎ did not appear in the first   edition."—2d prelim. leaf.
1. Lincoln, Abraham,   pres. U. S.—Addresses, sermons, etc.
E457.8.N282   28—8553

MiU OClWHi InU NNC
NN   0061521   DLC CaBVaU NcD TxU MiU-C DI NIC NN CSmH

National Republican Club.
Addresses delivered by Herbert Hoover, Harold G. Hoffman ₁and₎ Glenn Frank, at the forty-ninth annual Lincoln dinner of the National Republican Club, February 12, 1935. Toastmaster: Theodore Roosevelt. New York ₁1935?₎

28 p. 22 cm.

1. Lincoln, Abraham, Pres. U. S. 2. Lincoln Day addresses. I. Hoover, Herbert Clark, Pres. U. S., 1874–   II. Hoffman, Harold Giles, 1896–

E457.7.N29   923.173   58–52710

NN   0061522   DLC NN

National Republican club,

American ideals; a symposium. ₁Addresses delivered at Saturday discussions of the Republican Club, March 27th, 1915, by Hon. John Bassett Moore…Right Rev. David H. Greer…Thomas Mott Osborne…Hamilton Wright Mabie…Oswald G. Villard …Rear Admiral Robert E. Peary…Rev. Frederick Lynch… Dr. James J. Walsh… Letters received from…Charles W.

Eliot…Elmer Ellsworth Brown…   New York: Saturday Discussions Committee, Republican Club ₁1915₎. 40 p. 8°.

1. Americans, The. 2. Character (National), U. S. 3. Moore, John Bassett, 1860–   4. Greer, David Hummell, bishop, 1844– . 5. Osborne, Thomas Mott, 1859– . 6. Mabie, Hamilton Wright, 1846– . 7. Villard, Oswald Garrison, 1872– . 8. Peary, Robert Edwin, 1856– . 9. Lynch, Frederick Henry, 1867– . 10. Walsh, James Joseph, 1865– . 11. Title. 12. Title: Ideals, American.
N. Y. P. L.   February 1, 1916.

NN   0061524   NN MH

National Republican club,

American ideals from the standpoint of the statesman; addresses delivered at the non-partisan Saturday discussions of the Republican Club, March 24, 1917. New York: Saturday Discussions Committee, Republican Club ₁1917₎. 31 p. 8°.

Cover-title.
Addresses by Dr. M. W. Stryker, Hon. Chas. A. Towne, Gen'l Leonard Wood, Mr. Chas. E. Russell, and Hon. Everett Colby.

1. European war, 1914– .—Address-   es, sermons, etc. 2. Ideals, U. S. 3. Title.
N. Y. P. L.   August 14, 1917.

NN   0061525   NN

E457.7
N262   **National Republican club**
L   Annual dinner, the Republican club of the city of New York, to commemorate the anniversary of the birth of Abraham Lincoln … New York,
v. plate 20½cm.
Menu and program.
1. Lincoln, Abraham, Pres. U. S. - Anniversaries, etc.
E457.7.N262 L

NN   0061526   DI NNC

National Republican club,

Appeal to delegates to the Republican National Convention. ₁Chicago, 1912.₎ 4 l. 8°.

1. United States.—Politics, 1912.
N. Y. P. L.   April 21, 1913.

NN   0061527   NN

329.6   The National republican club,
N213b   The bulletin board … New York, 1934–

NN   0061528   WaPS

National republican club
Complimentary dinner tendered to Fred H. Wilson, Esq., at the Republican club of the city of New York, Saturday, April 1st, 1905.
n.p. [19-]

unpaged. illus., ports. 26 cm.
Hand lettered and decorated title-page with portrait inset.
33 p. of proceedings (typewritten)
Original letters from invited guests bound in.

NN   0061529   MH

973.7L63   **National Republican Club.**
FN21f   First annual dinner of the Republican Club of the City of New York at Delmonico's. The seventy-eighth anniversary … of Lincoln's birthday, Feb'y 12th, 1887. New York, Mercantile Printing and Stationery Co.₁1887₎
folder. 25cm.

Includes menu, names of members and guests, and speakers.
Signed by speakers.

NN   0061530   IU

National Republican Club.
Is religious faith declining in the United States?
see under title

National Republican club,
Memorial service in honor of the memory of the late James Schoolcraft Sherman, vice-president of the United States, held at the Republican club of the city of New York … on Sunday afternoon, the twenty-fourth of November, nineteen hundred and twelve. ₁New York₎ Republican club of the city of New York, 1913.

47 p. front. (port.) 23½ᶜᵐ.

1. Sherman, James Schoolcraft, 1855–1912.

13–12043 Revised
Library of Congress   E664.S55N2

NN   0061532   DLC NN

National Republican Club,
National republican club bulletin
see under title

National Republican club,
National Republican club, inc., organized September 25th, 1879, incorporated May 18th, 1886 as the Republican club of the city of New York; name changed to National Republican club, inc., June, 1919 …
₁New York₎

v. fronts, plates. 20½ᶜᵐ.
Includes by-laws, list of officers, committees, members, etc.
Title varies :   The Republican club of the city of New York …
National Republican club, inc. …

5–33041 Revised
Library of Congress   JK2359.N536
₁r41b2₎   329.6

NN   0061534   DLC NN NjP OkU

National Republican Club,
National Republican Club review
see under title

National Republican club,

Squiers, Arnon Lyon, ₁1869–   ed.
One hundred per cent American; addresses delivered by famous patriots of all shades of political belief at the Saturday luncheon meetings of the Republican club, New York, during the year 1918, ed. by Arnon L. Squiers, with a foreword by Theodore Roosevelt. New York, George H. Doran company ₁ᶜ1918₎

National Republican club,

The problem of international trade… [n.p., 19-   ]
16p.   (Document no. 58)   YA 13886

NN   0061537   DLC

National Republican club.
Proceedings at the … annual Lincoln dinner of the National Republican club, in commemoration of the birth of Abraham Lincoln … 1st–
1887–   New York ₁1887–19
v. plates, ports., diagrs. (part fold.) 23–26 cm.
Title varies: 1887–   Proceedings at the … annual dinner of the Republican club of the city of New York … on the … anniversary of the birthday of Abraham Lincoln …
1900–   Proceedings at the … annual Lincoln dinner of the Republican club of the city of New York …
19   Proceedings at the … annual Lincoln dinner of the National Republican club …
Sub-title varies.
1. Lincoln, Abraham,   pres. U. S.—Anniversaries, etc.
2. Lincoln, Abraham,   pres. U. S.—Addresses, sermons, etc.
Library of Congress   E457.7.N28   24—20924

NIC DNW CaBVaU
NN   0061538   DLC RPB CtNIC OFH OCl NjP Nh MB IU

308
Z
Box 698 **National republican club,**
Seating arrangement, fifty-first annual Lincoln dinner, National republican club, Waldorf-Astoria, February 12, 1937. ₁New York? 1937₎
₁6₎ p.

NN   0061539   NNC

National Republican Club.

Lincoln, Abraham, *pres. U. S.,* 1809–1865.
Selections from the works of Abraham Lincoln. A souvenir of the seventh annual Lincoln dinner of the Republican club of the city of New-York, at Delmonico's, February 11, 1893. New-York, Comp. by the committee, 1893.

VOLUME 407

National republican club
　　The spread of socialistic doctrine in New York city, report of special committee appointed by Hon. Charles D. Hilles, president National Republican club. Committee: Joseph Levenson, chairman, Elmer E. Cooley, Charles Park. Prepared by Mr. Levenson and submitted at regular meeting, September 16, 1919. ₍New York₎ 1919₎

20 p. 22¼ᵐ.

1. Socialism in New York (City) I. Levenson, Joseph, 1875– II. Title.

Library of Congress　　　　HX92.N5N3

20–1321

NN　0061541　　DLC NN

National Republican club,
　　To prevent pernicious discrimination. Report adopted by the Republican Club of the City of New York, December 18th, 1905. ₍New York, 1905.₎　4 p.　8°.

Caption-title.
Signed: James W. Hawes, chairman of Committee on National Affairs...

1. Freight.—Rates. U. S., 1905.
N. Y. P. L.　　　　　　　　October 26, 1916.

NN　0061542　　NN

National Republican club
　　What can be done to bring art closer to the people and increase their love for it. Addresses delivered at non-partisan Saturday discussions of the Republican club, March 4th, 1916, by Mr. Edward Robinson ... Mr. John E. D. Trask ... Mr. Grosvenor Atterbury ... ₍and others, ₎New York, Saturday discussions committee, Republican club, 1916₎

48 p. 23ᵐ.

1. Art—Addresses, essays, lectures.　I. Title.

Library of Congress　　　N7443.N3
　　　　　　　　　　　₍r34b2₎

17–2730 Revised

NN　0061543　　DLC DHEW NN MiD DSI

National Republican Club.　Committee on City Affairs.
　　Condemnation. Report of the Committee on city affairs ₍regarding the abuse of the commission system of condemning land for public uses₎.　New York: ₍Freytag Press,₎ 1910. 15(1) p.　12°.

1. Land.—Condemnation. 2. New　York city.—Government.
N. Y. P. L.　　　　N. Y. PUBLIC LIBRARY　January 20, 1911.

NN　0061544　　NN

National Republican club, Committee on National Affairs.
　　The American merchant marine shipping bill U. S. Senate ₍529₎. Report ... Regular meeting, March 18, 1907. ₍New York. 1907.₎ 14, (1) pp. Plates. [Document no. 70, 1907.] 12°.

G8567 — Shipping. American. — T.r. Marine, Mercantile. — Subsidies. Government.

NN　0061545　　MB MH

National Republican club, *Committee on national affairs.*
　　Government aid to American shipping. Document no. 57. The Republican club of the city of New York ... ₍New York, 1900₎

16 p. 21ᵐ.
A report written by A. L. M. Bullowa.

1. Shipping bounties and subsidies—U. S.　I. Bullowa, Alfred L. M.

Library of Congress　　HE743.U6N85

6–32617 Revised

NN　0061546　　DLC NN MB

National Republican Club. Committee on National Affairs.
　　The military needs of the United States
　　　see under　Stimson, Henry Lewis, 1867–

National Republican club. *Committee on national affairs.*
　　The Panama canal. Document no. 71, 1907. The Republican club of the city of New York ... Report of the Committee on national affairs ... regular meeting, May 20, 1907 ... ₍New York, 1907₎

20 p. illus. ₍maps₎ 20ᵐ.
Colored illustration on t.-p.

1. Panama canal.

Library of Congress　　TC774.N85

7–29746 Revised

NN　0061548　　DLC ICJ MB NjP MiU

Pam.　**National Republican Club,　Committee on**
Coll.　**National Affairs.**

37396　　Race discrimination. Doc. no. 72, 1908;
　　　　report. New York ₍1908₎
　　　　11 p. illus. 20 cm.

1. Race discrimination.　I. Title.

NN　0061549　　NcD

National republican club. Committee on national affairs
　　Report on Panama tolls and international relations, May 15, 1913. n.p. [1913]

15 p.　20.5 cm.

NN　0061550　　MH

National Republican Club.　₍Convention, Indianapolis, 1880.
　　Proceedings of the National Republican Club Convention, held at Indianapolis, Indiana, September 15th, 1880. With circular letter to the chairmen of Republican county committees, and the officers of Republican clubs.　Chicago, Ill. ₍The J. B. Jeffery "Old Reliable" Political Prtg. House₎ 1880.　19 p.　19½cm.

Cover-title.
Portraits on cover.

812519A.　1. United States—Politics,　　　1880.
N. Y. P. L.　　　　　　　　April 15, 1936.

NN　0061551　　NN IEN Nh OCIWHi

Pam　**National Republican Club,　Hughes Committee**
71-　**of Twenty-five.**
1495　[MISCELLANEOUS PUBLICATIONS]　New York.
　　　Partial Contents:　Report and Extracts (1908)

NN　0061552　　WHi

National republican club bulletin.
　　v. 1

New York, 1935　　　　　　　　28cm.
　　v.

Monthly (except July – Aug.).
Vol. 1, no. 1 (Feb., 1935) lacks numbering.
This publication and the News published by the National republican club supersede the club's Bulletin board.

1. United States—Politics—　　Per. and soc. publ. I. National
republican club, inc.　　　　　September 20, 1938
N. Y. P. L.

NN　0061553　　NN

National Republican Club, Inc.
　　　see　National Republican Club.

NATIONAL Republican Club review.
　　no.

New York, 1934　　　　　　28–33cm.
　　nos.

Biweekly (irregular).

1. United States—Politics—Per. and soc. publ. I. National Republican Club, Inc.

NN　0061555　　NN

National Republican Congressional Committee
　see
　Republican Congressional Committee.

National Republican convention of young men, *Washington, D. C.*
　see
　Washington, D. C.　National Republican convention of young men, 1832.

National republican editorial association. pam.

NN　0061558　　MNBedf

...　National Republican Grant and Wilson campaign songbook ... Washington, Union Republican congressional committee, 1872.

cover-title, 96 p. 15ᵐ.

1. Campaign songs, 1872—Republican.　I. Republican Congressional committee, 1871–1873.

Library of Congress　　E675.N27

17–2419

NN　0061559　　DLC NcD NN

329.6　**National Republican League of the United**
N213　　**States.**
　　　　Constitution of the National Republican League and the State Republican League of Oregon. ₍Portland, Ore., Multnomah Printing Co., 1908₎
　　　　15p.　17cm.

Cover title.

I. Republican League of Oregon.

NN　0061560　　OU

National Republican league of the United States.
　　Constitution of the National Republican league of the United States. Washington, D. C., Press of Judd & Detweiler, inc., 1910.

11 p.　15¼ᵐ.

12–19618

Library of Congress　　IK2354.N4

NN　0061561　　DLC

VOLUME 407

National Republican league of the United States.

Burk, Addison B   *d.* 1912.
Golden jubilee of the Republican party; the celebration in Philadelphia, June 17, 18 and 19, 1906, by Addison B. Burk, comp. under the direction of the Publication committee, Howard A. Chase, J. Lee Patton, J. Hampton Moore. Philadelphia ₁Town printing company₎ 1906.

Pam
71-1348   National Republican League of the United States. |
THE NATIONAL REPUBLICAN SOUVENIR. Cleveland, Ohio, Convention City Publishing Co., 1895.
   96 p.   illus.

NN   0061563   WHi OClWHi

Pam   National Republican league of the United States.
71-1435   POCKET MANUAL OF THE NATIONAL REPUBLICAN LEAGUE ... CHICAGO, 1898. Compiled by M.J. Dowling. [n.p., 1898]
   32 p.
   Cover title.

PARTIES: POLITICAL: REPUBLICAN: NATIONAL LEAGUE
Dowling, M. J   , comp.

NN   0061564   WHi

Pam   National Republican league of the United States.
71-1436   THE PRINCIPLES AND POLICIES OF THE REPUBLICAN PARTY. [New York, 1891]
   63 p.
   Cover title.

NN   0061565   WHi CtY

National Republican league of the United States.
Prospectus of the national convention, League of Republican clubs, Cleveland, June 19, 20, 21, 1895.
Cleveland, O., Cleveland printing & publishing co. 1895.
   64 p.

NN   0061566   OCl

National Republican league of the United States.
Report of proceedings ...   biennial convention ... ₁Washington, D. C.. 1910₎
   v. 23½ᵐ.

CA 12-538 Unrev'd

Library of Congress   JK2354.N3

NN   0061567   DLC

National Republican League of the United States.
Republican club book, 1904
see under title

Pam
JK2354
.N53   National Republican League of the United States.
Republican League handbook for permanent Republican club organization under the Republican League of the United States ... New York, 1888.
   cover-title, 1 p. ℓ., 45 ₁1₎ p., 2 ℓ.
   18 cm.

1. Republican Party. I. Title.

NN   0061569   T

National Republican League of the United States.
Welcome to the delegates to the National Republican League convention, Milwaukee, Aug. 25, 26, 27, 1896. Milwaukee, 1896
   32 p.   illus.

NN   0061570   WHi

National Republican Meeting, New York, Dec. 13, 1830
   see
New York (City) National Republican meeting, Dec. 13, 1830.

VCB
J13n   ₁National Republican Party₎
Our country and its laws. The execution of the unfortunate militiamen, fairly stated, and supported by official documents. ₁n.p., 1828₎
   40 p.   23cm.
   "Mr. Sloane's view," p.3-12.

1. Tennessee militiamen, Execution of, 1815.
2. Jackson, Andrew, Pres. U.S., 1767-1845.
3. Campaign literature, 1828. I. Sloane, John, 1779-1856. II. Tit?

NN   0061572   NcU CSmH

National Republican Party.   Connecticut. Convention of Young Men, 1832.
Proceedings of the state Convention of National Republican Young Men, holden at Hartford, on Wednesday, October 17, 1832. Hartford: Hanmer & Comstock₁, 1832?₎.   16 p.   8°.

1. United States—Politics, 1832.
N. Y. P. L.   April 11, 1927

NN   0061573   NN NNC ICN CtY IU

National Republican party.   *Connecticut. Middletown.*
Address to the electors of Middlesex County. ₁Middletown? Conn., 1828₎
   6 p.   24ᵐ.
   Caption title.
   Signed: Augustus Cook, Wm. L. Storrs ₁and 11 others₎ Committee on behalf of the National Republicans of the town of Middletown.

1. Campaign literature, 1828 — National Republican — Connecticut. I. Title.
                       17–22198
Library of Congress   E383.N264

NN   0061574   DLC

National Republican party.   *Delaware.*
Address to the people of Delaware, on the approaching presidential election: prepared in obedience to a resolution of the convention of the friends of the national administration, assembled at Dover, on the fifteenth day of July, 1828. Dover, Del., J. Robertson, printer, 1828.
   22 p.   21ᵐ.

Continued in next column

Continued from preceding column

1. Campaign literature, 1828—National Republican.   I. Title.
                       16–13269
Library of Congress   E380.N24

NN   0061575   DLC

₁**National Republican party.** *Indiana*₎
Address of the administration standing committee to their fellow-citizens of Indiana. ₁n. p., 1828₎
   22 p.   23ᵐ.
   Caption title.

1. Campaign literature, 1828—National Republican.
                       10–7993
Library of Congress   E380.N26

NN   0061576   DLC

₁**National Republican party.** *Indiana*₎
Proceedings of the administration convention held at Indianapolis, January 12, 1828. ₁Indianapolis, Printed at the office of the Indiana journal, 1828₎
   16 p.   24½ᵐ.   [*With* A dialogue between a colonel of the militia and a militiaman ... ₁n. p., 1828?₎]
   Caption title.

1. Campaign literature, 1828—National Republican.
                       6–43999
Library of Congress   E83.813.D53

NN   0061577   DLC CU In OCHP

₁**National Republican party.** *Kentucky*₎
An address to the freemen of Kentucky, from a convention of delegates friendly to the re-eleciton ₁1₎ of John Quincy Adams, as president of the United States, and held in the town of Frankfort, on the 17th, 18th, and 19th days of December, 1827. ₁Frankfort? 1828?₎
   16 p.   22ᵐ.
   Caption title.

1. U. S.—Pol. & govt.—1825-1829. 2. Campaign literature, 1827—National Republican—Kentucky.
                       11–28595
Library of Congress   E380.N265

NN   0061578   DLC

₁**National Republican party.** *Kentucky*₎
Address to the freemen of Kentucky, from a convention of delegates friendly to the re-election of John Quincy Adams, as president of the United States, held in the town of Frankfort, on the 17th, 18th and 19th days of December, 1827. Maysville, Ky., Printed at the office of the Eagle ₁1827?₎
   15, ₁1₎ p.   23ᵐ.

1. U. S.—Pol. & govt.—1825-1829. 2. Campaign literature, 1828—National Republican.   I. Title.
                       24–1261
Library of Congress   E380.N263

NN   0061579   DLC ICU

₁**National Republican party.** *Kentucky*₎
Proceedings of the administration convention held at Frankfort, Kentucky, on Monday, December 17, 1827. ₁Frankfort? Printed by J. H. Holeman, 1827?₎
   23 p.   23ᵐ.   ₁*With* National Republican party. Maryland. Proceedings of the Maryland administration convention. Baltimore, 1827₎
   Caption title.

1. U. S.—Pol. & govt.—1825-1829. 2. Campaign literature, 1827—National Republican—Kentucky.
                       8–19348
Library of Congress   E376.N26
———— Copy 2.   ₁Miscellaneous pamphlets, v. 916, no. 15₎
Library of Congress   AC901.M5 vol. 916

NN   0061580   DLC OCHP ViU

VOLUME 407

₁National Republican party. *Kentucky*₁

Proceedings of the National Republican convention, held at Frankfort, Kentucky, on Thursday, December 9, 1830. ₁Frankfort? 1831?₁

19 p. 23ᵐᵐ.

Caption title.
Criticizing the administration of Andrew Jackson and recommending the election of Henry Clay as president in 1832.

1. U. S.—Pol. & govt.—1829–1837. 2. Campaign literature, 1832—National Republican.   ɪ. Title. ɪɪ. Title: National Republican convention.

Library of Congress   E381.N27
                                                    24–22329

NN   0061581   DLC

E380
.N3   ₁National Republican Party. Kentucky. Clark County₁

Report of the committee to the people of Clarke County. ₁Winchester? Ky.₁ 1828.

cover-title, 32 p. 24 cm.

"At a meeting of the friends of the present administration" in Winchester, March 29th, 1828, a committee was appointed "to prepare an address on the subject of the next Presidential election, to be reported at the meeting of the people ...

on the 11th of April ₁1828₁"–p.₁1₁.
Committee composed of: Chilton Allan, Richard Hawes and James Simpson.

1. Campaign literature, 1828—National Republican—Ky. 2. Jackson, Andrew, Pres. U.S., 1767–1845. 3. Adams, John Quincy, Pres., U.S., 1767–1848.

NN   0061583   T

National Republican Party. Kentucky. Fayette County.

Address of the Fayette County Corresponding Committee, on the proceedings in the state of Kentucky, against the president, secretary of state and members of Congress; and on other subjects connected with the approaching presidential election.   Lexington: T. Smith ₁1828₁.   48 p.   8°.

At head of title: Supplement to the Kentucky reporter.

1. U. S.—Politics, 1828. 2. Adams,   John Quincy, 6. pres. of the U. S.
3. Jackson, Andrew, 7th. pres. of the   U. S. 4. Clay, Henry, 1777–1852.
N. Y. P. L.   March 29, 1917.

NN   0061584   NN

National Republican party. Kentucky. Jefferson county.

Administration convention. Proceedings had at a meeting of the friends of the administration at Louisville, Ky. [Louisville, Ky., W. W. Worsley, printer, 1827]

8 p. 21 cm.
Caption-title.
Abraham Hite, chairman.

1. Campaign literature, 1828—National Republican—Kentucky.   ₃ɪ. Hite, Abraham.

NN   0061585   CSmH

₁National Republican party. *Louisiana*₁

Proceedings of the delegates of the friends of the administration of John Quincy Adams, assembled in convention at Baton Rouge. New-Orleans, Printed by B. Levy, 1827.

28 p. 23ᵐᵐ. ₁With National Republican party. Maryland. Proceedings of the Maryland administration convention. Baltimore, 1827₁

1. U. S.—Pol. & govt.—1825–1829. 2. Campaign literature, 1827—National Republican—Louisiana.
                                                    8–19344

Library of Congress   JK2315.N28
———— Copy 2. ₁Miscellaneous pamphlets, v. 916, no. 14₁ AC901.M5 vol. 916

       MiD-B NN
NN   0061586   DLC NIC PHi PPL RP NcD ICU MBAt MdBP

₁National Republican party. *Maine*₁

Proceedings of a convention of the people of Maine, friendly to the present administration of the general government, and open and decided advocates for the re-election of John Quincy Adams to the office of President of the United States, holden in the Hall of representatives in Portland ... on the 23d of January, 1828. ₁n. p., 1828₁

12 p. 18ᵐᵐ. ₁With National Republican party. Maryland. Proceedings of the Maryland administration convention. Baltimore, 1827. 23ᵐᵐ₁

Caption title.

1. U. S.—Pol. & govt.—1825–1829. 2. Campaign literature, 1828—National Republican—Maine.

Library of Congress   E376.N26
                                                    8–19364

NN   0061587   DLC

National Republican party. Maryland.

Address of the young men of the National Republican party, of the Fifth congressional district, to the young men of the state of Maryland. ₁Baltimore, Printed by Sands & Neilson, 1832₁

National Republican party. Maryland.

An **address**, to the people of Maryland, from their delegates in the late National republican convention: made in obedience to a resolution of that body. Baltimore, Printed by Sands & Neilson, 1832.

₁National Republican party. *Maryland*₁

Proceedings of the Maryland administration convention, delegated by the people, and held in Baltimore, on Monday and Tuesday, July 23d. and 24th. 1827. ₁Baltimore₁ Printed at the office of the Baltimore patriot, 1827.

24 p. 23ᵐᵐ.

1. U. S.—Pol. & govt.—1825–1829. 2. Campaign literature, 1827—National Republican—Maryland.
                                                    8–19337

Library of Congress   E376.N26

NN   0061590   DLC MdBP MiU-C MB CSmH

National Republican party. Maryland. Baltimore.

An **address** to the people of Maryland, by the National Republican central committee of Baltimore, shewing the necessity of a vigorous and united action, to preserve the Constitution and laws, rights and liberties of the people of the United States. Baltimore, Printed by Sands & Neilson, 1832.

27 p. 23ᵐᵐ.

Signed: Luke Tiernan, chairman; Sam'l Sands, sec'y.

1. Campaign literature, 1832—National Republican. 2. U. S.—Pol. & govt.—1829–1837.   ɪ. Tiernan, Luke, 1757–1839.
                                                    22–16674

Library of Congress   E383.N268

NN   0061591   DLC MWA NN MB

National Republican party. Maryland. Baltimore.

The Central committee of National Republicans of the city of Baltimore, to the people of Maryland. ₁Baltimore, Printed by Sands & Neilson, at the office of the Freeman's banner, 1832₁

18 p. 22ᵐᵐ.

Caption title.

1. Campaign literature, 1832—National Republican. 2. U. S.—Pol. & govt.—1829–1837.   ɪ. Title.
                                                    10–8653

Library of Congress   E383.N27

NN   0061592   DLC MdU MB MiU-C

₁National Republican party. *Maryland. Baltimore co.*₁

Proceedings of the administration meeting, in Baltimore county, June, 1827. ₁Baltimore₁ Printed at the Baltimore patriot office, 1827.

12 p. 23ᵐᵐ. ₁With National Republican party. Maryland. Proceedings of the Maryland administration convention. Baltimore, 1827₁

1. U. S.—Pol. & govt.—1825–1829. 2. Campaign literature, 1827—National Republican—Maryland.   ɪ. Title.
                                                    8–19341
PHi
Library of Congress   JK2315.N26
———— Copy 2. ₁Miscellaneous pamphlets, v. 916, no. 9₁ AC901.M5 vol. 916

NN   0061593   DLC PHi

₁National Republican party. *Maryland. Harford Co.*₁

... Meeting of the friends of the administration in Harford County, Md. ₁n. p., 1828₁

12 p. 21½ᵐᵐ. ₁With National Republican party. Maryland. Proceedings of the Maryland administration convention. Baltimore, 1827₁

Caption title.

1. U. S.—Pol. & govt.—1825–1829. 2. Campaign literature, 1828—National Republican—Maryland.
                                                    8–19457

Library of Congress   E376.N26

NN   0061594   DLC

₁National Republican party. *Massachusetts*₁

Address of the central committee appointed by a convention of both branches of the legislature friendly to the election of John Q. Adams as president and Richard Rush as vice-president of the U. States, held at the state-house in Boston, June 10, 1828, to their fellow-citizens. ₁Boston? 1828₁

24 p. 8°.
Caption title.

1. U. S.—Pol. & govt.—1825–1829. 2. Campaign literature, 1828—National Republican—Massachusetts.
                                                    8–19460

Library of Congress
———— Copy 2.   ₁With National Republican party.
Maryland. Proceedings con-   of the Maryland administration con-
vention. Baltimore, 1827₁
Library of Congress   E376.N26

NN   0061595   DLC

₁National Republican party. *Massachusetts*₁

Address of the central committee appointed by a convention of both branches of the legislature friendly to the election of John Q. Adams as president and Richard Rush as vice-president of the U. States, held at the State house in Boston, June 10, 1828, to their fellow-citizens. ₁Boston(?)1828₁

24 p. 24½ᵐᵐ.

Signed by Sherman Leland and thirteen others.

1. Campaign literature, 1828—National Republican. Massachusetts. 2. U. S. Pol. & govt. 1825–1829. ɪ. Title.
                                                    10–7994

Library of Congress   E380.N27

NN   0061596   DLC N

National Republican Party, Massachusetts.   *4226.163
National Republican ticket. For Governor, Levi Lincoln. For Lieut. Governor, Samuel T. Armstrong ...
[Boston? 1833.] Broadside. Size, 11¼ × 6¼ inches.

NN   0061597   MB

                National Republican Party. Massachusetts.
*XbH   National Republicans. At a numerous meeting
.829   of citizens ... The following resolutions were
.N21M   unanimously adopted ... Charles Wells, Chairman
             ... Monday, May 11, 1829.
             [Boston, 1829]

             broadside. 28 x 22cm.

NN   0061598   MB

VOLUME 407

National Republican party. *Massachusetts. Convention,* 1832.

Journal of the proceedings of the National Republican convention, held at Worcester, October 11, 1832 ... Boston, Stimpson & Clapp, 1832.

75 p. 22½ᶜᵐ.

9-32739†

Library of Congress   JK2318.M42 1832

ViU IEN NBuHi

NN   0061599   DLC NN ICN MiD-B MiU MoKu PU MH MB

National Republican Party. Missouri.

Proceedings and address of the Anti-Jackson convention of Missouri, to their fellow-citizens. Fayette. Patten. 1828? 47 pp. 8°.

G906 — Presidential elections. 1828. — Missouri. Conventions. — Jackson, Andrew, 7th President of the United States. 1767-1845.

NN   0061600   MB MoSM

National Republican Party. National Convention, Baltimore, 1831.

An address, to the people of Maryland, from their delegates in the late National Republican convention...

see under title

National Republican party. *National convention, Baltimore,* 1831.

Journal of the National Republican convention, which assembled in ... Baltimore, Dec. 12, 1831, for the nominations of candidates to fill the offices of president and vice-president ... Washington, Printed at the office of the National journal ₍1831₎

32 p. 22½ᶜᵐ.

1. Campaign literature, 1831—National Republican.

9-32459†

Library of Congress   JK2313 1831

NN   0061602   DLC PPL MWA MB NN MnU Nh MiU-C

ˣXH
.828
.N19R

National Republican Party. New Hampshire.

Address of the great state convention of Friends of the Administration, assembled at the capitol in Concord, June 12, 1828, with the Speech of Mr. Bartlett, in reply to the charges which have been made against Mr. Adams. Concord₍N.H.₎: Published by order of the Convention. 1828.

24p.   18.5cm.

Shaw/Shoemaker 34381.

NN   0061603   MB PHi DLC

₍National Republican party.₎ *New York (State)₎*

Address of the state convention of delegates from the several counties of the state of New-York to the people, on the subject of the approaching presidential election. Albany, Printed by Beach, Denio & Richards, 1828.

16 p. 23ᶜᵐ. ₍With National Republican party. Maryland. Proceedings of the Maryland administration convention. Baltimore, 1827₎

1. U. S.—Pol. & govt.—1825-1829. 2. Campaign literature, 1828—National Republican—New York.

8-19452

Library of Congress   E376.N26

NN   0061604   DLC ViW NIC N PU

National Republican Party. New York (State)

A brief account of General Jackson's dealings in Negroes

see under title

National Republican party. *New York (State)*

New-York National Republican state convention ... Address to the electors of the state of New York ... ₍Albany, Office of the Daily freeman's advocate, 1831₎

4 p. 24ᶜᵐ.

Caption title.

1. Campaign literature, 1832—National Republican.

10-9988

Library of Congress   E385.N29

NN   0061606   DLC

National Republican Party. New York (State)

To the people of the State of New York [Dec. 12, 1827]

see under   National Republican Party. Virginia.

National Republican party. New York, Albany. (State)

The political character of John Quincy Adams delineated. Being a reply to certain observations in the address of Gen. Peter B. Porter and others. Albany, Printed for the Albany Argus, by D. M'Glashan, 1828.

National Republican party. *New York (State) Convention,* 1828.

New-York state convention. ₍Albany? 1828₎

33 p. 18ᶜᵐ.

Caption title.

1. Campaign literature, 1828—National Republican—New York (State)

10-7995 Revised

Library of Congress   JK2320.A8N7 1828

CSmH

NN   0061609   DLC MH PHi MB MiU-C TxU MiU-C NN WaS

National Republican Party. New York (State) Convention, 1828.

Report of the state convention held at the capitol in the city of Albany, to select suitable candidates for president and vice-president of the United States of America.   New York, Sickels, Printer to the General Republican committee, 1828.

42 p.   21 cm.

1. Campaign literature, 1828.– National Republican.

NN   0061610   NN PHi

National Republican party. New York (State) Cortland county.

[Text begins] ... Young men of Cortland county. Resolutions and address, adopted by the Convention of Republican young men of the county of Cortland ...   [Cortland, N.Y.] 1828.

4 p.   21 cm.

NN   0061611   CSmH

National Republican Party. New York (State)   New York.

Great National Republican meeting in the City of New York

see under   New York (City) National Republican Meeting, Dec. 13, 1830.

National Republican party. *North Carolina.*

Address of the administration convention, held at Raleigh, Dec. 20, 1827. To the freemen of North Carolina. ₍Raleigh, 1828₎

8 p.   22ᶜᵐ.

Caption title.
Signed 30 January, 1828, by W. Gaston and four others.

1. U. S.—Pol. & govt.—1825-1829. 2. Campaign literature, 1828—National Republican—North Carolina.

14-6430

Library of Congress   JK2320.A8N8 1827
———— Copy 2.   ₍Miscellaneous pamphlets, v. 1016, no. 10₎
                            AC901.M5 vol. 1016
———— Another issue.   ₍Miscellaneous pamphlets, v. 916, no. 26₎
                            AC901.M5 vol. 916

NN   0061613   DLC MiU-C ICN TxU MBAt NN

₍**National Republican party.** *North Carolina₎*

Address of the administration convention, held in the capitol at Raleigh, Dec. 20th, 1827.₎ To the freemen of North Carolina. Raleigh, Printed by J₎ Gales & son, 1827.

15 p. 23ᶜᵐ. ₍With National Republican party. Maryland. Proceedings of the Maryland administration convention. Baltimore, 1827₎

Address dated January 30, 1828, and signed by a committee of five.

1. U. S.—Pol. & govt.—1825-1829. 2. Campaign literature, 1828—National Republican—North Carolina. ₁. Title.

8-19852

Library of Congress   JK2315.N26

NN   0061614   DLC MWA CtY ICJ NcU

₍**National Republican party.** *Ohio₎*

Proceedings and address of the convention of delegates, that met at Columbus, Ohio, Dec. 28, 1827, to nominate a ticket of electors favorable to the reelection of John Quincy Adams, President of the United States, to be supported at the electoral election of 1828. ₍Columbus₎ Printed by P. H. Olmsted, 1827.

17 p. 23ᶜᵐ. ₍With National Republican party. Maryland. Proceedings of the Maryland administration convention. Baltimore, 1827₎

1. U. S.—Pol. & govt.—1825-1829. 2. Campaign literature, 1827—National Republican—Ohio.

8-19355

Library of Congress   E376.N26

NN   0061615   DLC NN OKentU T IU O PPL OU OClWHi PHi

National Republican Party. Ohio.

Verhandlungen und Addresse von der Convention der Delegaten, welche sich den 28sten December, 1827, in Columbus, Ohio versammelten, um ein Electoral Ticket zu gunsten der Wieder-Erwählung von John Quincy Adams, President der VereinigtenStaaten, zu formiren, welches bey der Electoral Wahl in 1828 unterstützt werden soll. Germantown, Ohio: Gedruckt in der Druckerey der National Zeitung der Deutschen von Eduard Schaffer, 1828.

24 p.   18.5 cm.

NN   0061616   MBAt

National Republican Party. Ohio. Warren Co.

Warren county administration meeting. [Lebanon, Office of the Western star, Nov. 19, 1827]

8 p.   20 1/2 cm.

Caption-title.
Printed in double columns.
Signed at end: Jeremiah Morrow, chairman.

1. Campaign literature--1828--Republican. I. The Western star, Lebanon, O.

NN   0061617   CSmH OClWHi

VOLUME 407

[National Republican party. *Pennsylvania*]
    Democratic convention. [Harrisburg, Printed at the office of the Harrisburg argus, 1828]
    iv, 20 p. 23ᶜᵐ. [*With* National Republican party. Maryland. Proceedings of the Maryland administration convention. Baltimore, 1827]
    Caption title.
    Proceedings and address of the convention of delegates opposed to the election of Andrew Jackson to the presidency; meeting at Harrisburg, Jan. 4-5, 1828.

    1. U. S.—Pol. & govt.—1825-1829. 2. Campaign literature, 1828—National Republican—Pennsylvania.
                                            8-19358
    Library of Congress   E376.N26

NN 0061618   DLC

National Republican party. *Pennsylvania*.
    Proceedings of the National Republican convention of Pennsylvania, which assembled at Harrisburg, on the twenty-ninth day of May, one thousand eight hundred and thirty-two, for the nomination of an electorial ticket. Published by order of the convention. Harrisburg, Printed at the Intelligencer office [1832]
    32 p. 21ᶜᵐ.

    1. Campaign literature, 1832—National Republican.
                                            10-32012
    Library of Congress   E383.N292

NN 0061619   DLC

[National Republican party. *Pennsylvania. Philadelphia*]
    Report of the proceedings of the town meeting in the city of Philadelphia. July 7th, 1828. [Philadelphia? 1828]
    1 p. l., 22 p. 23ᶜᵐ. [*With* National Republican party. Maryland. Proceedings of the Maryland administration convention. Baltimore, 1827]
    Meeting of friends of the national administration.

    1. U. S.—Pol. & govt.—1825-1829. 2. Campaign literature, 1828—National Republican—Pennsylvania.
                                            8-19454
    Library of Congress   E376.N26

NN 0061620   DLC NN PPRF

National Republican party. *Rhode Island*.
    Examination of certain charges against Lemuel H. Arnold, esq., the National Republican candidate for governor, being a report of the committee, appointed April 12, 1831. Providence, 1831.
    28 p. 24ᶜᵐ.
    Report signed by William Pabodie and 12 other members of the committee.

    1. Arnold, Lemuel Hastings, 1792-1852. 2. Campaign literature, 1831—National Republican—Rhode Island. 3. Rhode Island—Pol. & govt.—1775-1865. i. Title.
                                            17-15478
    Library of Congress   F83.N27

NN 0061621   DLC MiD-B

National Republican Party. Virginia.
    The American system. Internal improvements and domestic manufactures. For President, John Quincy Adams. Vice-President, Richard Rush. Virginia Electoral Ticket ... cn.p. Wheeling? 1828;
    Broadside. 19 x 8 cm.

NN 0061622   WvWO

AC901   National Republican Party. Virginia.
.M5   At the meeting of the friends of the present administration, held at the... town of Winchester, on the 29th of March 1828. n.p.,n.d.
            32 p.

        (Miscellaneous pamphlets, 916:27)

NN 0061623   DLC

National Republican party. Virginia.
    To the people of the state of New York. [Virginia anti-Jackson convention, Saturday, Dec. 12, 1827. 1827]
    16 p. 21ᶜᵐ.

    1. Jackson, Andrew, pres. U. S., 1767-1845.
    2. Campaign literature, 1827 - National Republican - Virginia.

NN 0061624   NNC MBAt PPPrHi T

National Republican Party. *Virginia. Convention, 1828*.
    Proceedings of the Anti-Jackson Convention held at the capitol in the city of Richmond, with their address to the people of Virginia, accompanied by documents. Richmond, Franklin Press, 1828.
    38 p. 21 cm.

    1. Campaign literature, 1828—National Republican. 2. U. S.—Pol. & govt.—1825-1829. 3. Jackson, Andrew, Pres. U. S., 1767-1845.

    E380.N33   49-39044*

NN 0061625   DLC Vi ViU ICU IU CSmH

National Republican Party. *Virginia. Convention, 1828*.
    Proceedings of the Anti-Jackson Convention held at the capitol in the city of Richmond, with their address To the people of Virginia, accompanied by documents. Richmond, Printed by S. Shepherd, 1828.
    Microfilm copy, made in 1942 by the Library of Congress, of a copy in Duke University Library. Negative.
    Collation of the original, as determined from the film: 38 p.
    "To the people of Virginia" also published separately under title: The Virginia address.

    1. Campaign literature, 1828—National Republican. 2. U. S.—Pol. & govt.—1825-1829. 3. Jackson, Andrew, Pres. U. S., 1767-1845.

    Microfilm F-8   Mic 50-191

NN 0061626   DLC

National republican party. Virginia. Convention, 1828.

    Verhandlungen der Anti-Jackson convention. Hagerstown, 1828.
    35 p.

NN 0061627   NN

National Republican party. *Virginia. Convention, 1828*.
    The Virginia address. [Richmond? 1828]
    8 p. 22¼ᶜᵐ.
    Caption title.
    Issued by a convention of delegates opposed to the election of Andrew Jackson to the presidency, meeting in Richmond Jan. 8-12, 1828.

    1. U. S.—Pol. & govt.—1825-1829. 2. Campaign literature, 1828—National Republican—Virginia. i. Title.
                                            8-19361 Revised
    Library of Congress   JK2320.A5V85 1828
    ———— Copy 2.
    ———— Copy 3.   [*With* National Republican party, of the Maryland administration convention. Baltimore, 1827]
    Maryland. Proceedings of the con-   JK2315.N26
    vention. Baltimore, 1827]
    ———— Copy 4. [Mis-   cellaneous pamphlets, v. 916, no. 23]
    Library of Congress   AC901.M5 vol. 916

    MdBP ViU ICN
NN 0061628   DLC ViW MB MnHi NNHi MH NN CtY MiU-C

AC901   National republican party. Virginia. Convention
.M7   1828.
            A voice from Virginia! Address ... to the people of Virginia.
            8 p. (Moore pamphlets, 91:9)

NN 0061629   DLC MH

National Republican party. Virginia. Convention, 1832.
    Proceedings of the National Republican convention of Virginia, which convened at Staunton on the 16th of July, 1832. Published by order of the convention. Lynchburg, Fletcher & Toler, 1832.
    24 p. 22 cm.
    Bound with others.

NN 0061630   NcD

National Republican Party. Washington, D. C.
    The National journal—extra. July 20, 1831. Washington, 1831.

JK2357   The national Republican platform, St. Louis,
1896 b   Mo., 1896. Topeka, Kan. [1896]

NN 0061632   DLC

National republican souvenir
        see under   National Republican League of the United States.

National Republican young men.
    Meeting of young men ... [1832]
        see   Address of the young men of the National Republican Party, of the Fifth Congressional District, to the young men of the state of Maryland.

National Republican young men.

Washington, D. C. National Republican convention of young men, 1832.
    Proceedings of the National Republican convention of young men, which assembled in the city of Washington May 7, 1832. Washington, Printed by Gales & Seaton, 1832.

National Republican Young Men.
    Proceedings of the state Convention of National Republican Young Men, holden at Hartford, on Wednesday, October 17, 1832
        see under   National Republican Party. Connecticut. Convention of Young Men, 1832.

National Republicans. At a numerous meeting of citizens ... Monday, May 11, 1829
        see under   National Republican Party. Massachusetts.

WE   National Research and Manufacturing Company,
168.8   San Diego, Calif.
qN277f   Subcontractor's final report on an investi-
1947   gation of low pressure laminates for pros-
no.8   thetic devices; design and fabrication of
           above-knee and below-knee artificial legs;
           preparation of a production survey for manu-
           facture of artificial plastic legs. Covering
           the period from February, 1946 through April,
           1947. [Washington?, 1947]

Continued in next column

VOLUME 407

Continued from preceding column

55, 156 ℓ. illus. (National Research Council. Committee on Artificial Limbs. ₍Final report, no. 8₎)

Contract no.: VAm-21223; project no.: 14.

Photocopy (positive)

Film 6 —— —— Film copy.

1. Leg, Prosthetic   Series.

NN   0061640   DNLM

AGRICULTURE
S22
N3
National Research and Teaching Conference in Agricultural Cooperation.
₍Proceedings₎ 1st-
1954-
₍n.p.₎
v. 26 cm.

Issued 1954-61 by the Conference under its earlier name: National Conference on Research and Teaching in Agricultural Cooperation.
Sponsored by the American Institute of Cooperation, the University of Nebraska and Farmer Cooperative Service.

NN   0061641   OU DNAL MtBC

National research bureau, Inc.
Aviation digest-index of trade and technical publications. Dec.1944-
Chicago, 1944-
v.

Continues Aviation associates, Chicago. A.I.R. digest.

NN   0061642   MH-BA

658
N22b
National Research Bureau, inc.
Better supervision, practical ideas of men in many fields. ₍Chicago? 1945?₎
52 pamphlets in 1v. illus. 22cm.

NN   0061643   IU OC1

National Research Board
see   National Research Council.

HF
5801
N276+
National Research Bureau, inc.
Advertising executive's idea library.
Chicago.
v. illus. 28cm.

1. Advertising--Period.   2. Sales and salesmanship--Period.   I. Title.

NN   0061645   NIC OC1

HF5805
D49
National Research Bureau, inc.
Directory of cooperative advertising plans.
Chicago, National Research Bureau.

National research bureau, inc.
Directory of discount houses and self-service department stores
see under title

HC110
.D5D55
National Research Bureau, inc.
Directory of industrial parks and districts.
Chicago, National Research Bureau.

National research bureau, inc.
Encyclopedia of business information sources ... Compiled by the research staff, the National research bureau, inc.; W. C. Hanson, consulting editor ... ₍Chicago₎ The National research bureau, inc. ₍1946?₎
2 v. illus. 29¼ x 28¼ᵐ.
Title-page in v. 1 only.
Loose-leaf; to be kept up to date by supplements.

1. Information service—U. S.   I. Hanson, W. C., ed.   II. Title: Business information sources.
46-6077
Library of Congress   HF5001.N27
₍5₎   650.3

NN   0061649   DLC OrCS NN LU NNC OC1 OC1U

National research bureau, inc.
Farm digest
see under title

---

q659.1
N217f
National Research Bureau, inc.
42 ways to cut your direct mail costs. Chicago, 1952.
45p. illus. 28cm.

Cover title.

1. Advertising, Direct-mail.   2. Office equipment and supplies.   3. Mail-order business. I. Title

NN   0061651   IU

National Research Bureau, inc.
How to write great letters
see under   Bury, Charles.

National research bureau, Inc.
Management methods, a clearing house of management information.
Chicago,
v. semimonthly.

NN   0061653   MH-BA

National research bureau, Inc.
Merchandising digest. Chic., Ill. ₍The Author₎ 1934-
v.
Partial contents:
Advertising and marketing
Automotive; shop practices, super service stations, tires and batteries.
Finance and commerce

NN   0061654   MiD

---

q659.1
N217d
National Research Bureau, inc.
NRB direct mail manual ₍by₎ Homer J. Buckley ₍and others₎   Chicago, 1948.
1v.(loose-leaf) illus., ports. 30cm.

1. Advertising.   2. Mail-order business.   I. Buckley, Homer J.   II. Title: Direct mail manual.

NN   0061655   IU

HF5466
qN2
National Research Bureau, inc.
NRB direct mail manual. Chicago, Ill., 1949-
1 v. illus. 29cm.

Loose-leaf.

1. Mail-order business.   2. Advertising.   I. Title.   II.   Title: Direct mail manual. x: R B

NN   0061656   OrCS ICarbS

National Research Bureau, inc.
NRB public speaking manual
see its
Public speaking manual.

658
N22s
National Research Bureau, inc.
NRB sales training manual. ₍Case histories of sales training methods₎   Chicago ₍1953?₎
97p. illus. 28cm.

Cover title.
Bibliography: p.93.

1. Salesmen and salesmanship.   I. Title: Sales training manual.   II. Title: Case histories of sales training methods.

NN   0061658   IU

R551.75
N27
National Research Bureau

N R B 250 successful sales and promotion letters. Author ₍n.d.₎
1 v. (unpaged)

1. Commercial correspondence.   2. Letter-writing.   I. Title.   II. Title: 250 successful sales and promotion letters.

NN   0061659   OrP

National Research Bureau, inc.
Operating briefs: new products, new processes, new materials.
Chicago,
v. semi-monthly.

Manifold copy.

NN   0061660   MH-BA IU

HM263
.P18
Spec.
Format
National Research Bureau, inc.

PR. Public relations idea library.
Chicago, National Research Bureau.

VOLUME 407

808.5   National Research Bureau, inc.
N21p   Public speaking manual. Compiled by
         the editorial staff of the National
         Research Bureau, inc. Editor-in-chief:
         Maxwell C. Ross. [Chicago] °1953.
            1 v. (loose-leaf) illus. 30 cm.

            1. Oratory. I. Title.

NN   0061662   LU MiU PPSKF

NATIONAL RESEARCH BUREAU, *INC.*
  [Publications.]
v.

Chicago, 19   4°.
  v.

Reproduced from typewritten copy.

NN   0061663   NN

National Research Bureau, Inc.
  The Salvation army; social service for men:
     standards and procedures
        see under   Salvation Army.

Law   National Research Bureau, inc.

         Laurin, Elmer F   1901-
            Standard income tax guide. 1953 ed. for 1952 income.
         [Chicago, National Research Bureau, 1952]

658.872 National Research Bureau, Inc.
N21t   Tested direct mail strategy; the handbook of
         direct mail planning [by] George J. Delaney [and
         others] Chicago, Ill. [n.d.]
            60 p.   illus. (ports.)

NN   0061666   MtBC

National Research Bureau, Inc.
  Tested public relations and publicity procedure
     see under   Baus, Herbert M., 1914-

NATIONAL RESEARCH BUREAU, INC.
  12 blue ribbon speeches, by 12 direct mail experts. [Chicago,
n.d.] 1 v. (various pagings) illus. (part col.), ports.   28cm.

    CONTENTS. — Mailing lists; danger spot of direct mail, by L. G.
Chait. —Selecting the right list for the right market, by S. Gale. —
Mail order, by J. E. Tillotson. —How to write direct mail copy that
sells, by M. C. Ross. —How to write to people, by O. E. Reed. —Seven
cardinal rules for direct mail success, by E. N. Mayer. —How to counter-
attack rising direct mail costs, by L. Kleid. —Advertising and merchandising, by H. P. Roberts. —   Color in advertising, by

H. K. Vahle. —How to "shake hands" through the mail, by C. B. Mills.
—Direct mail without guesswork, by G. W. Head. —Direct mail in
retail merchandising, by H. S. Mark.

1. Mail order business.

NN   0061669   NN

658.82   National Research Bureau, Inc.
N21t   200 best sales and promotion letters, written
         by a group of America's most outstanding direct
         mail writers. [n.p.] National Research Bureau,
         Inc. [1955?]
            1 v. illus.

            Editor: Robert Geary.

NN   0061670   MtBC OrCS CoU AU

National research bureau, inc.
  What makes people successful ... World's
interesting people. [194-?]
     51 pts. in 2 v. ports.

     Some of the parts are numbered.

NN   0061671   NNC OC1 MnU

National Research Bureau, Inc. Division of
         Research and Education.
         Digest-index metals
            see under title

National Research Centre, *Cairo*
     see
Egypt. *al-Markaz al-Qawmī lil-Buḥūth.*

SF   National Research Conference on Anaplasmosis
967   in Cattle, 2d, Stillwater, Oklahoma, 1953.
A6   Proceedings of the second national research
N38   conference on anaplasmosis in cattle.
1953   Oklahoma A. & M. College, Stillwater, February
         18 and 19, 1953. – [Stillwater: Oklahoma
         A. & M. College, 1953?].
            23 p.

            1. Anaplasmosis—Congresses. 2. Cattle
         diseases and pests. I. Title.

NN   0061674   KMK IU

National Research Conference on Creativity.

    This series of meetings was held 1955-64 under the following
names: 1st-3rd (1955-59): Research Conference on the Identification of Creative Scientific Talent; 4th-6th (1961-64): Utah Creativity Research Conference. Publications of these six meetings are
found under

     Utah Creativity Research Conference.

                                             L629.1529
                                             V201
National Research Corporation
  Air conditioning as a means of eliminating fog and frost
formation on glass surfaces in optical instruments (OEMsr
436) Boston [1942]
     4 p. [U.S. Office of Scientific Research and Development/
OSRD report no. 932]
  Issued as confidential; later declassified.

     629.1529   I. Series.

NN   0061676   ICJ

M08.95   National Research Corporation
N277b   Balloon-borne air-sampling device. [Re-
         port no.1-4] By Vincent C. Ball, Jr... [and]
         Glenn L. Mellen... [Cambridge, Mass.]
         1949-1950.
            4 v. illus., diagrs. 28cm.

            Research sponsored by Geophysical Research
         Directorate of the Cambridge Field Station,
         AMC, U.S. Air Force, under Contract No. AF 19
         (122)-90.

                    Continued in next column

                    Continued from preceding column

     "Bibliography": Report no.1, following text
[Report no.4], Final report.

NN   0061678   DAS

National Research Corporation
  Report of lithium research, March 15, 1943-Dec. 31, 1943. Boston, National Research Corporation [1944]
     11 p. flow sheets, diagrs., tables. 30cm. (U.S. Office of Sci-
entific Research and Development. OSRD report no. 3758)
  At head of letter of transmittal: Division 11, National Defense
Research Committee of the Office of Scientific Research and Development. "New processes for lithium production."

     I. U. S. National Defense Research Committee. Division 11.
II. Series. 669.751

NN   0061679   ICJ

535.1   National Research Corporation
N277s   Sorption of gases on pyrex glass. Final
         report.   Cambridge, Mass., 1950.
            22 [. illus., diagrs. 28cm.

            Research...made possible...by the Geophy-
         sical Research Directorate of the Cambridge
         Field Station, AMC, U.S. Air Force, under con-
         tract No. AF 19(122)-90.
            Processed.

NN   0061680   DAS

National research council.
  "Established in 1916 at the request of the President of the
United States under the charter of the National academy of
sciences. Acting as the division of science and research of the
Council of national defense."—Annual report. 2d, 1918, t.-p.
  Headquarters, Washington, D. C.

National Research Council.

    Publications of this body are included in the Microprint edition,
U. S. Government publications (non-depository) New York, Readex
Microprint Corporation, which contains all non-depository publications
cataloged in the Monthly catalog of United States Government publications, issued by the U. S. Superintendent of Documents, from Jan.
1953 (no. 696) to date.
    The items are arranged according to their numbers in the Monthly
catalog.

     TxF WHi WaPS WaU
     NRU NcRS NcU NjP NjR OC OU OrU PPi PPiU RPB RU Tx
NN   0061682   DLC CoU CtY GU ICRL   MH MdBE NIC NNC

WA   NATIONAL Research Council
240   Abstract of report of aerial spray
N277a   operations in the continental United States
1947   in 1946. Prepared for the Army Com-
         mittee for Insect and Rodent Control and
         published with the cooperation of the
         Chemical- Biological Coordination Center.
         [Washington] 1947.
            43 p. illus.
            Cover title.
            1. Aircraft in pest control

         I. U. S. Dept. of the Army. Army
         Committee for Insect and Rodent Control

NN   0061684   DNLM

National Research Council.
  Aircraft brakes. Progress report. 19 -
Washington.

NN   0061685   ICJ

VOLUME 407

National research council.

Bliss, Gilbert Ames, 1876–
... Algebraic functions, by Gilbert Ames Bliss ... New York, American mathematical society, 1933.

National research council.

Annotated bibliography of economic geology, prepared under the auspices of the National research council ... v. 1–
July 1929–
[Lancaster, Pa.] Economic geology publishing co., 1929–

R737   National research council.
.N26   Announcement of fellowships in the medical sciences, by the National research council. [Washington, D. C., 1936]
[4] p. 23cm.

"The administration of the fellowships is in charge of the Medical fellowship board of the National research council" ... p.[2]

I. National research council. Medical fellow-ship board. II.   Title. III. Title: Fellowships in the   medical sciences.

NN   0061688   DLC

National research council.
Annual report
see its
Report.

QC770   National Research Council.
.A5
Annual review of nuclear science. v. 1–
1952–
Stanford, Calif., Annual Reviews.

National Research Council.
Annual survey of American chemistry
see under   National Research Council. Division of Chemistry and Chemical Technology.

National Research Council.
Applied research in the United States

see under

Scott, Eugene W   ed.

National research council.
An appraisal of endocrinology; a report made to the directors of the John and Mary R. Markle foundation by a special com-mittee of the National research council consisting of Walter B. Cannon, chairman, Earl Engle, Curt Richter, Oscar Riddle, R. G. Hoskins ... with the assistance of Milton O. Lee. [Wash-ington?] 1936]
2 p. l., 7–83 p. 23ᶜᵐ.

1. Endocrinology.   I. John and Mary R. Markle foundation.
II. Title.
A 41–122

Wisconsin. Univ. Libr.
for Library of Congress   [2]

NN   0061693   WU OrU-M CaBVaU ICU OU IaU ICJ

National Research Council.
Army mental tests
see under   United States. Surgeon-General's Office.

National research council,
Available research facilities for war use.

See under

[Committee on war use of research facilities]

National research council.

Keith, Mary Helen.
A bibliography of investigations bearing on the compo-sition and nutritive value of corn and corn products, by M. Helen Keith ... Issued in mimeographed form by the National research council. Washington, D. C., 1920.

National research council.
... A bibliography of the analysis and measurement of human personality up to 1926. [By] Grace E. Manson. Washington, D. C., National research council, 1926.
cover-title, 59, [6] p. 24½ᶜᵐ. (Reprint and circular series of the Na-tional research council. no. 72)

1. Personality—Bibl. 2. Mental tests—Bibl.   I. Manson, Grace Evelyn, 1893–   II. Title: Analysis and measurement of human per-sonality.
27—4144
Library of Congress   Q11.N293 no. 72

NN   0061697   DLC OrPR MeB ViU OCl OU OClW MiU ICU

National Research Council.
Bibliography on rheumatoid arthritis and osteoarthritis and structural components
see under   National Research Council. Committee for Survey of Research on Rheumatic Diseases.

National Research Council.
Bulletin. no. 1–123; Oct. 1919–Apr. 1951. Washington.
123 no. in 45 v. illus. 26 cm. irregular.
No. 1–57 are called also v. 1–11.
No. 122 is dated Apr. 1951.
Superseded by the council's Publication. Cf. Union list of serials.

1. Research—Societies, etc.
Q11.N292   21–248 rev*

Or WaS
CtY-KS DHEW CtNIC NN MH-L IU MtU OClWHi
ODW TU OU OCU OOxM OCl DNLM NjP ICJ NjP
DPR KyU CSfM P MNS MB NNCC CCC NhD NIC MiU
NN   0061699   DLC PU-Sc ViU OClW GEU NBuU LNL

National Research Council.
By-laws (ed. of Mar. 15, 1938) article II-Membership. (Washington, 1929)
9 p. 28 cm.

NN   0061700   DNLM

National Research Council.
Catalog of publications
see its   Publications catalog.

National research council.
... Clean coal; the effect of high ash upon thermal efficiency, amount of boiler plant, amount of transporta-tion equipment ... [New York, 1918]
cover-title, 2 p. l., 2–8 numb. l. incl. tab. diagrs. 29 x 22ᶜᵐ.
Text autographed from type-written copy.
At head of title: The National research council, Washington, D. C. Prepared for the Engineering committee of the National research coun-cil by the J. G. White engineering corporation.
"Reprinted by the J. G. White engineering corporation, New York."
1. Coal.   I. White, J. G., engineering corporation, New York.
II. Title.
20–8132
Library of Congress   TP325.N3

NN   0061702   DLC CU MiD OU MH

Q   **NATIONAL** Research Council
11   [Collection of publications]
qN277
The library has a collection of miscel-laneous publications of this organization kept as received. These publications are not listed nor bound separately.

NN   0061703   DNLM

National Research Council.
Committee on work in industry. Report of the meeting of March 9, 1938.
see under   National Research Council. Committee on Work in Industry.
Report...

National Research Council.
The composition of milks
see under   Macy, Icie Gertrude, 1892–

National Research Council.
Conference on abstracting and documentation of scientific literature ... Abstract of discussion
see   Conference on Abstracting and Documentation of Scientific Literature, Washington, D.C., 1935.
Abstract of discussion.

National Research Council.
Conference on the importance and needs of systematics in biology

see under

National Research Council. Division of Biology and Agriculture.

National Research Council.
Conference on the mechanisms of hormone action

see under

National Academy of Sciences, Washington, D.C.

National research council.
Consolidated report upon the activities of the National re-search council, 1919 to 1932. Prepared in the office of the permanent secretary with the assistance of the chairmen of divisions of the council. Washington, D. C., 1932.
3 p. l., 269 p. 27 x 21ᶜᵐ.
Mimeographed text, with printed t.-p. and cover-title.
"Publications of the National research council" [10] p. inserted at end of volume. 23 x 17½ᶜᵐ.

1. National research council—Hist. 2. Research—Societies, etc.
32–30162
Library of Congress   Q11.N29422
[3]   507.2

NN   0061709   DLC OClW ICJ NN MBCo

VOLUME 407

National Research Council.
Contributions to the theory of partial
differential equations

see under

Bers, Lipman, 1914- ed.

National Research Council.
The coroner and the medical examiner
see under   National Research Council.
Committee on Medicolegal Problems.

Q180
.U5A5
1947b

National Research Council.

U. S. *Office of Scientific Research and Development.*
Cost analysis of research and development work and related
fiscal information, June 1940–November 1946. Prepared by
OSRD Budget and Finance Office. Washington, National Research Council, 1947.

National research council.
Council of national defense. National research council.
Basis of organization and means of co-operation with
state councils of defense. Washington, May 1, 1917.
[Washington, D. C., 1917]
cover-title, 15, [1] p. 15ᶜᵐ.

19–16537

Library of Congress   D570.8.N3A5 1917

NN   0061713   DLC

Z5055
.U49D6

National research council.

Doctoral dissertations accepted by American universities.
no. 1–   1933/34–
New York, The H. W. Wilson company, 1934–

National research council.
An exhibit prepared under the auspices of the National research council with the cooperation of the Chemical war service of the United States army. Now permanently installed at
the Smithsonian institute, Washington, D. C. [New York,
The Chemical foundation, 1921]
cover-title, 16 p. illus. 20½ᶜᵐ.

Signed: H. E. Howe.
Third edition. *cf.* National research council. List of publications ...
November 1926.

First edition (1921) issued under title: An exhibit under the auspices
of National research council, prepared by the Chemical warfare service
to show the American people what the chemist has done and may do
for them in war and peace; 2d ed. (1921) under title: A popular chemical exhibit under the auspices of the National research council.

1. Chemistry, Technical—Exhibitions. 2. Chemical warfare. 3. Coal-
tar products.   I. Smithsonian Institution.   II. U. S. Chemical warfare
service.   III. Howe, Harrison Estell, 1881–   IV. Title.

41–10282

Library of Congress   TP6.N35 1921 b

[3]   660.74

NN   0061716   DLC Or OO MiU   NN DNW

National research council.
An exhibit under the auspices of National research council.
Prepared by the Chemical warfare service to show the American people what the chemist has done and may do for them
in war and peace. [Washington, D. C., 1927?]
cover-title, 15 p. illus. 21½ᶜᵐ.

Signed: Edwin E. Slosson.

1. [Chemical warfare] 2. Coal-tar products.   I. U. S. Chemical
warfare service.   II. Slosson, Edwin Emery, 1865–   III. Title.

War 27–6

Library, U. S. Army   War College   TP953.N271

NN   0061717   DNW WaWW Or

National Research Council. Fellowships in medicine
see National Research Council. *Medical Fellowship
Board.* List of fellows.

National Research Council. Fellowships in the medical
sciences
see National Research Council. *Medical Fellowship
Board.* List of fellows.

National research council.
Final report on the Flint-Beecher tornado
[1953]
see under   Michigan. State University,
East Lansing. Social Research Service.

National research council.

Zon, Raphael, 1874–
Forest resources of the world, by Raphael Zon and William
N. Sparhawk ... with a foreword by Gifford Pinchot; prepared under the authority of the secretary of agriculture of
the United States and in coöperation with the National research council ... 1st ed. New York [etc.] McGraw-Hill book
company, inc., 1923.

National Research Council.
The function of safety belts in crash
protection
see under title

National research council.

U. S. *Civil aeronautics administration.*
Fundamentals of basic flight maneuvers for civilian pilot
training (supplementary student material) (1st ed.) ... Department of commerce, Civil aeronautics administration, Division of research. [Washington] National research council,
°1942.

National research council.

Michigan. University. *San Carlos mountains expedition,*
1930.
The geology and biology of the San Carlos mountains,
Tamaulipas, Mexico; reports of the University of Michigan
expedition to the San Carlos mountains in 1930, directed by
Lewis Burnett Kellum; members of the expedition: Harley H.
Bartlett ... Edson S. Bastin ... Lee R. Dice ... Ralph W. Imlay ... Lewis B. Kellum ... George W. Rust ... [and] Edward H.
Watson ... Ann Arbor, University of Michigan press, 1937.

... Handbook of physical constants, edited by Francis Birch,
chairman, J. F. Schairer [and] H. Cecil Spicer. [New York]
The Society, 1942.
ix, 325 p. diagrs. 25 cm. (Geological society of America. Special
papers, no. 36)
Compiled under the direction of an editorial committee of the National research council. *cf.* Pref.
Includes "References."

1. Geology—Tables, etc. 2. Chemistry. Physical and theoretical—
Tables, etc. 3. Physics—Tables, etc.   I. Birch, Francis, ed.   II.
Schairer, John Frank, 1904–   joint ed.   III. Spicer, Herbert Cecil,
1898–   joint ed.   IV. Title.   V. Title: Physical constants.

42–10732

Library of Congress   Q199.N25

[44u3]   508

DSI NcD OCl OO OU OCU ViU MoU GU CaBVaU
NN   0061725   DLC OYesA IdPI WaTC MtBuM WaU NNC DAU

National Research Council.
Handbook of scientific and technical societies
and institutions of the United States and Canada
see   Scientific and technical societies of
the United States and Canada.

National research council.
... A history of the National research council, 1919–1933.
Washington, D. C. [National research council] 1933.
61 p. 25ᶜᵐ. (Reprint and circular series of the National research
council. no. 106)
First published as series of articles in Science magazine. *cf.* Foreword.

1. National research council—History.

C D 34—84

Library of Congress.   Card div.   Q11.N293 no. 106

OrU OCU OCl OOxM MiU OC1W ODW OU KMK CaBVaU WaS
NN   0061727   DLC WaT OrPR MB DNLM DAS DAU CoU ViU

T176
.I 65

National Research Council.

Industrial research laboratories of the United States. [1st]
ed.; 1920–
Washington, Bowker Associates.

National Research Council.
Insect control committee. Coordination center.
Abstracts of current information on insect and
rodent control.
see under   National Research Council.
Insect Control Committee.
Abstract bulletin.

National research council.
International critical tables of numerical data of physics, chemistry and technology prepared under the auspices of the International research council. Fundamental constants and conversion factors. Washington, D. C.,
National research council [1923?]
15 p. 23ᶜᵐ.

Table of "The viscosity of water" (folded leaf, laid in)

1. Science—Tables, etc.   I. Title.

24–16018

Library of Congress   Q199.N3

NN   0061730   DLC

National research council.
International critical tables of numerical data, physics,
chemistry and technology, prepared under the auspices of the
International research council and the National academy of
sciences by the National research council of the United States
of America; editor-in-chief: Edward W. Washburn ... associate editors: Clarence J. West ... N. Ernest Dorsey ... 1st ed.
New York [etc.] Pub. for the National research council by the
McGraw-Hill book company, inc., 1926–30.
7 v. diagrs. 28½ᶜᵐ.

Continued in next column

VOLUME 407

Continued from preceding column

"Errata" leaves inserted.
Contains bibliographies.

Q199.N32

———— Index, index des matières, sachverzeichnis, indice, volumes I to VII. New York and London, Pub. for the National research council by the McGraw-Hill book company, inc., 1930.

1 p. l., 43 p. 28 cm.

Q199.N32 Index 1930, vol. 1–7

———— Index. Volumes I–VII. Compiled by Clarence J. West ... with the collaboration of Callie Hull ... New York and London, Pub. for the National research council by the McGraw-Hill book company, inc., 1933.

vii, 321 p. 28½ cm.

1. Science—Tables, etc. I. Washburn, Edward Wight, 1881– ed. II. International council of scientific unions. III. National academy of sciences, Washington, D. C. IV. West, Clarence Jay, 1886– comp. V. Hull, Callie, joint comp. VI. Title.

26—10495

Library of Congress   Q199.N32 Index 1933, vol. 1–7

₍a50r33b⁵3₎   508

OrSaW OrU-M WaWW WaSp OrPS OrCS CaBVa
WaTC Wa ViU ICJ TU NcRS NcD WaT MtU OrU
KEmT MH UU MB NNBG OKentU WaChenE CaBVaU
MiHM PPT MBCo MiU OCl OClW OCU OO ODW DLC
IdU MtBuM MU AAP FU-HC DN-Ob OClW WaS CU
NN 0061731   OKentU IdU-SB OrPR OClW MtBC

National research council. International critical tables.
Bichowsky, Francis Russell, 1889–
The thermochemistry of the chemical substances. The assembly of a self consistent table of "best" values for the heats of formation of the chemical substances (except carbon compounds containing more than two carbon atoms), including heats of transition, fusion, and vaporization. By F. Russell Bichowsky ... and Frederick D. Rossini ... New York, Reinhold publishing corporation, 1936.

National research council. International critical tables.

National research council. *American committee on annual tables.*
Annual tables of physical constants and numerical data ... 1941– ... Princeton, N. J., American committee on annual tables, National research council ₍1942–

v. 23ᶜᵐ.

Loose-leaf; reproduced from type-written copy.
"To constitute a permanent continuation of International critical tables and a current tabulation of critically edited numerical data."
Includes "Literature references."

1. Science—Tables, etc. 2. Physics—Tables, etc. I. National research council. International critical tables. II. Title.

42–15971

Library of Congress   Q199.N33

₍3₎   508

NN 0061735   DLC

National research council. FOR OTHER EDITIONS SEE MAIN ENTRY

... **International** directory of anthropologists ... ₍2d ed.₎ Washington, D. C., 1940.

GC10
.I5
National Research Council.

International directory of oceanographers.

Washington, National Academy of Sciences–National Research Council.

National Research Council.
International scientific congresses held since 1930...
      see under   Washington, D.C. Library of the National Academy of Sciences and the National Research Council.

National Research Council. List of fellows in the medical sciences
see **National Research Council.** *Medical Fellowship Board.* List of fellows.

National Research Council.
List of manuscript bibliographies in geology and geography
      see under   Little, Homer Payson, 1884–   comp.

National Research Council.
List of members and officers (American Geophysical Union)
      see under   American Geophysical Union.

National research council.
... List of publications of the National research council and its fellows and partial list of papers having their origin in the activities of its committees to January 1, 1926. Washington, D. C., 1926.

cover-title, 70 p. 25ᶜᵐ. (Reprint and circular series of the National research council. no. 73)

"A revision and extension of the list which appeared as Reprint and circular series number 25 (February, 1922)"

1. National research council—Bibl.

27–4145

Library of Congress   Q11.N293 no. 73

MiU
NN 0061742   DLC OrU OrPR ViU CoU OCl OClW OU OOxM

National research council.

List of the serial publications of foreign governments, 1815–1931, edited by Winifred Gregory for the American council of learned societies, American library association, National research council ... New York, N. Y., The H. W. Wilson company, 1932.

National Research Council.
Manual of clinical mycology
      see under title

National research council.

San Francisco bay marine piling committee.
Marine borers and their relation to marine construction on the Pacific coast, being the final report of the San Francisco bay marine piling committee, prepared under the direction of the San Francisco bay marine piling committee, cooperating with the National research council and the American wood-preservers' association; C. L. Hill and C. A. Kofoid, editors-in-chief. San Francisco, Calif., The Committee. 1927.

National Research Council.
Meeting of Penicillin Investigators, 7 and 8 February, 1946
      see under   Meeting of Penicillin Investigators, Washington, D. C., 1946.

National Research Council.
₍Minor publications and forms.₎

NN 0061747   ICJ

National research council.
Mobilizing scientific facts for industrial uses. Washington, D. C., National research council ₍1924?₎

8 p. l., 23, ₍1₎ p. 16½ᶜᵐ.

"The following pages give but a brief outline of the purpose and magnitude of the work that is to be published as 'International critical tables of numerical data of physics, chemistry and technology'."—Foreword.

1. National research council. International critical tables of numerical data of physics, chemistry and technology. I. Title.

C D 37–16

Library of Congress   Card div. Q199.N28

NN 0061748   DLC NN DL IU

Q11
.N293
no.130
1948   **National Research Council.**
The National Academy of Sciences and the National Research Council. Washington, 1948.

5 p. illus. 25cm. (Its Reprint and circular series, no. 130)
Cover title.
"Reprinted from Science, September 3, 1948, vol. 108, no. 2801, pages 234–238."

1. National Academy of Sciences, Washington, D. C. 2. National Research Council. I. Ser.

NN 0061749   ViU

National Research Council.
The national importance of scientific and industrial research
      see under title

National research council.
National intelligence tests; manual of directions for use with Scale A, form 1–   and Scale B, form 1–   prepared under the auspices of the National research council, by M. E. Haggerty, L. M. Terman, E. L. Thorndike, G. M. Whipple, and R. M. Yerkes, chairman. Yonkers-on-Hudson, N. Y., World book company, 1920–

v. diagr. 20½ᶜᵐ.
Accompanied by Scale A—form 1–   ; Scale B—form 1– with key. 28ᶜᵐ.

1. Mental tests. 2. Grading and marking (Students) I. Haggerty, Melvin Everett, 1875–

21–8850

Library of Congress   LB1131.N25

NN 0061751   DLC Or ICJ MH NN DHEW

National research council.
National research council: divisions and committees; war organization. Established in April, 1916, at the request of the President of the United States, under the charter of the National academy of sciences. Acting as the department of science and research of the Council of national defense. Washington, 1918.

22 p. 24ᶜᵐ.

19–16536

Library of Congress   D570.8.N3A5 1918

NN 0061752   DLC DHEW

National Research Council.
The National Research Council: organization and members
      see its   Organization and members.

VOLUME 407

National Research Council.
    National Research Council–U. S. Public Health
Service meeting of penicillin investigators...
    see   Meeting of Penicillin Investigators,
Washington, D. C., 1946.

National research council.
    National research council fellowships in
medicine
        see   National Research Council. Medical
Fellowship Board.
    List of Fellows.

National research council.
    National research fellowships, 1919–1938. Physical sciences,
geology and geography, medical sciences, biological sciences.
Administered by the National research council. Washington,
D. C., 1938.
    iii, 95 p. 24½ᶜᵐ.

    1. Scientists, American—Direct.   i. Title.   ii. Title: Research fel-
lowships.

    Library of Congress   Q145.N25   38–25870
    ———— Copy 2.   ₃₃   507.2

NN   0061756   DLC CtY-M DSI

925   National Research Council.
N215na   National research fellowships, 1919–1944.
    Physical sciences, geology and geography,
    medical sciences, biological sciences. ₍Com-
    piled by Neva E. Reynolds₎ Washington,
    1944.
        iii, 142p.   25cm.

    1. Scientists, American—Direct.   I. Rey-
nolds, Neva E.   II. Title.   III. Title: Research fellowships.

NN   0061757   IU NNC-M NNC

National research council.
    National research fellowships in physics, chemistry and
mathematics
        see its
    Research fellowships in physics, chemistry and mathe-
matics.

National research council.
    National research fellowships in the biological sciences; ad-
ministered by the National research council, Washington, D. C.
October 1, 1935. ₍Washington? 1935₎
    61 p.   22½ x 10ᶜᵐ.

    1. Scholarships—U. S.
                                              42–44856
    Library of Congress   QH315.N33 1935

NN   0061759   DLC

National research council.
    National research fellowships in the natural sciences.
    ₍Washington₎ 19
        v.   23 x 10ᶜᵐ.

    1. Scholarships—U. S.   2. Endowment of research.
                                              43–26787
    Library of Congress   Q11.N2926

NN   0061760   DLC NN ICJ

National Research Council.
    News report.   v. 1–
    Jan./Feb. 1951–
    ₍Washington₎ National Academy of Sciences.
        v. in   illus.   26 cm.   bimonthly.
        Editor: 1951–   W. W. Atwood, Jr.

    1. Science—Period.   i. National Academy of Sciences, Washing-
ton, D. C.   ii. Atwood, Wallace Walter, 1906–   ed.

    Q11.N2928   505   A 52–1800 rev
    U. S. Dept. of Defense.   R & D Library
    for Library of Congress   ₍r55c2₎†

NN   0061761   DAL CU-S KU ICJ DLC OrU OrCS MtU

National Research Council.
    ... North American forest research
        see under   Society of American Foresters.
    Committee on American Forest Research.

National research council.
    ₍Officers, committees₎ ₍Washington, D. C., 1917₎
        32 p.   18ᶜᵐ.

                                              19–16538
    Library of Congress   D570.8.N3A4 1917

NN   0061763   DLC

Q180   National Research Council.
U5N297   Opportunities for postdoctoral research in the physical
    and mathematical sciences at the National Bureau of Stand-
    ards, Washington, D. C.–Boulder, Colorado; postdoctoral
    resident research associateships recommended by the Na-
    tional Academy of Sciences–National Research Council.
    Washington.
        v.   23 cm.   annual.

    Cover title.   Resident research associateships,
postdoctoral, tenable at National Bureau of Standards, Washington,
D. C., and Boulder, Colorado, in association with the National Academy of Sciences–National Research Council.

    1. Research—U. S.   i. U. S. National Bureau of Standards.   ii.
Title.   iii. Title: Postdoctoral resident research associateships.   iv.
Title: Resident research associateships.
    Q180.U5N297   62–64976

NN   0061765   DLC NBuU

National research council.
    ... Organization and members.   1919/20–
    Washington, D. C., 1919–
        v.   22½ᶜᵐ.
    At head of title: National research council.
    Additional matter (4, ₍2₎ p.) inserted between p. 8 and 9 of issue for
1919/20.

    Library of Congress   Q11.N294   CA 24–317 Unrev'd
                                 ₍2₎

     OOxM ODW OClW OO   NcRS NcD ICJ UU
     MB DNW P RP MsSM MiU ViU KMK NN NNuN MH-GM TU ICN
NN   0061766   DLC NIC DHEW GEU KyLoU NNBG TxFTC DPU

National Research Council.
    Parking meters
        see under   Levin, David Richard, 1913–

National Research Council.
    A partial list of the publications of the National Research
Council to June 1920.   ₍n. p., 1920.₎   14 f.   4°.
    Typewritten.

    1. Research.—Bibliography.
    N. Y. P. L.   December 5, 1922.

NN   0061768   NN

NATIONAL RESEARCH COUNCIL.
    . A partial list of the publications of the National
research council to June 1920.   [n. p., 1920]
14 l.   27cm.
    Film reproduction. Negative.

    1. Research--Bibl.   2. National research council--Bibl.

NN   0061769   NN

National research council.
    ... A partial list of the publications of the National re-
search council to January 1, 1922.   Washington, D. C.
1922.
    cover-title, 15 p.   16ᶜᵐ.   (Reprint and circular series of the National re-
search council.   no. 25)
    "Revised and reprinted from the Proceedings of the National academy
of sciences ₍vol.₎ 7, 1921, pages 351–362."

    1. National research council—Bibl.
    Library of Congress   Q11.N293   no. 25   23–10833
    ———— Copy 3.   Z5055.U4N2

NN   0061770   DLC OrU ViU NN CoU

National research council.
    U. S.   *Civil aeronautics administration.*
    Patter; basic flight maneuvers for civilian pilot training.
(1st ed.)   Department of commerce, Civil aeronautics administration, Division of research.   Philadelphia, Pa., Printed by
Stephenson-brothers, ᵒ1942.

National Research Council.
    Periodical bibliographies and abstracts for
the scientific and technological journals of the
world
        see under   National Research Council.
    Research Information Service.

₍National Research Council.₎
    Periodical bibliographies and abstracts for the scientific jour-
nals of the world...   ₍Washington, D. C., 1919.₎   28 l.   4°.
    Caption-title.
    Mimeographed.

    1. Science.—Bibliography.   2. Science.   —Per. and soc. publ.: Bibliography.
    N. Y. P. L.   September 5, 1922.

NN   0061773   NN

National Research Council.
    Physical and chemical aspects of basic
mechanisms in radiobiology
        see under
    National Academy of Sciences.

National research council.
    White, Henry Seely, 1861–
    Plane curves of the third order, by Henry Seely White
... published with the cooperation of the National research
council.   Cambridge, Mass., The Harvard university
press, 1925.

VOLUME 407

National research council.

Battelle memorial institute, *Columbus, O.*
Prevention of the failure of metals under repeated stress, a handbook prepared for the Bureau of aeronautics, Navy department, by the staff of Battelle memorial institute, under the auspices of the National research council of the National academy of sciences. New York, J. Wiley & sons, inc.; London, Chapman & Hall, limited, 1941.

QE513
.N3
National Research Council.
Conference on Nuclear Processes in Geologic Settings.
Proceedings. ₁1st₁–   1953–
Washington.

National Research Council.
Proceedings of the Alaskan Science Conference
see under   Alaskan Science Conference.

National research council.

Weiss, Albert Paul, 1879–1931.
Psychological principles in automotive driving, by Albert P. Weiss, PH. D. ₁and₁ Alvhh R. Lauer, PH. D.; under the auspices of the National research council, 1927–1929. Columbus, The Ohio state university, 1930.

National research council.
Psychology for the fighting man, prepared for the fighting man himself by a committee of the National research council, with the collaboration of Science service ... Washington, The Infantry journal ₁ᶜ1943₁
456 p. incl. illus., diagrs. 16 cm.
On cover: A fighting forces-Penguin special, S212.

1. Psychology.   I. Science service, inc.   II. Infantry journal.   III. Title.
A 44—1208
Enoch Pratt Free Libr.
for Library of Congress   ₁a51x1₁

IU-M NcC NcD WaT OYesA IdU OrPR OrU-M WaS OrU
NN 0061780   MdBE AU DSI LU MH NNC OCl OCU OO OU

National Research Council.
Psychology for the fighting man, prepared for the fighting man himself by a committee of the National Research Council, with the collaboration of Science Service ... 2d ed. Washington, The Infantry journal, Penguin books ₁c1944₁
379 p. illus., diagrs. 17cm.
On cover: A fighting forces-Penguin special, S212.

I. Science Service, Washington D. C.   II. Infantry journal.
355.015

NN 0061781   ICJ NcC ViU NNU-W IaU

National research council.
Psychology for the returning serviceman, prepared by a committee of the National research council, edited by Irvin L. Child ... and Marjorie Van de Water ... Washington, Infantry journal; New York, Penguin books ₁1945₁
6 p. l., 243 p. illus. 16¼ᵐ.
On spine: Fighting forces Penguin special. S229.
"First edition, first published February, 1945."

1. Veterans. 2. Psychology, Applied. 3. Disabled — Rehabilitation, etc.   I. Child, Irvin Long, 1915–   ed.   II. Van de Water, Marjorie, 1900–   joint ed.   III. Title.
45–35044
Library of Congress   BF636.N3
₁30₁   150.13

OCl OO TxU
NN 0061782   DLC OrU-M OrU OrCS MH DNLM LU NcC ODW

Z
7405
.N25
National Research Council.
Publications catalog.
Washington.

Title varies: –1957, Catalog of publications.

NN 0061783   MiU CaBVaU

National research council
Publications of National research fellows in the biological sciences

see its

Reprints of papers by National research fellows in the biological sciences

National research council.

National academy of sciences, *Washington, D. C.*
Publications of the National academy of sciences of the United States of America (1915–1926) ... Washington, D. C., The Academy; Easton, Pa., Mack printing company, 1926.

National research council.
Publications of the National research council. Bulletin series, Reprint and circular series, supplementary list, index to titles. Washington, D. C., 1942.
₁15₁ p. 23ᵐ.

1. Science—Bibl.—Catalogs.
43–4098
Library of Congress   Z5055.U4N27 1942
₁3₁   016.5

NN 0061786   DLC OrU DI-GS NhD

National research council.

American institute of mining and metallurgical engineers.
Pyrometry; the papers and discussion of a symposium on pyrometry held by the American institute of mining and metallurgical engineers at its Chicago meeting, September, 1919, in coöperation with the National research council and the National bureau of standards. New York city, The Institute, 1920.

National Research Council.
Recommended dietary allowances

see under

National Research Council. Food and Nutrition Board.

National research council.
Report ... 2d–   ₁1916/18₁–
Washington, Govt. print. off., 1918–
v. 23ᵐ.
Title varies: ₁1916/18₁–1921 (2d–6th) Annual report of the National research council.
1921/22–   (₁7th–   Report of the National research council.
The first report was not issued separately, but is included in the Report of the National academy of sciences for 1916; subsequent reports are continued in the Report of the academy and are also published in separate form. The preliminary report of the organizing committee of the council and minutes of the meetings of the executive board are issued regularly in the Proceedings of the academy beginning with v. 2.

The 2d report includes a financial summary for Sept. 1, 1916 to Mar. 1, 1918 (18 months); the 3d-5th reports. 1918-20, are for the calendar year; the 6th–   1921–   are each for the year ending June 30 (thus the 6th covers only the period from Jan.–June 1921)

1. Research. 2. Research, Industrial.
18–15333 (rev. '29)
Library of Congress   Q11.N29

MMeT MB NcD OU MiU IdU Or ICJ DNLM
NN 0061790   DLC KEmT DNAL TxLT NcD DAU MtU WvU PBL

National Research Council.
Report of a Conference on Bibliography
see under   National Research Council.
Research Information Service.

330.9
N21A
National Research Council.
Report of the chairman of the Council to the Administrative Committee concerning the activities of the Council.
₁Washington?₁

1. U.S. Research.   I. National Research Council.   Report of the activities of the Council

NN 0061792   DNAL DLC

330.9
N21L
National Research Council.
Report of the National Livestock and Meat Board fellowships.
₁Washington?₁

1. Fellowships.   I. National Livestock and Meat Board.

NN 0061793   DNAL

National research council.
Report of the permanent secretary to the executive board.
(Washington, D.C.) 19
v. 28 cm.
Mimeographed.

NN 0061794   DNLM

Q11
.N2812
National Research Council.

National Academy of Sciences, *Washington, D. C.*
Report of the treasurer.
₁Washington₁

National research council.
Reprint and circular series of the National research council. no. 1–
₁Washington, D. C., National research council, 1920–
v. 25ᵐ.
Reprinted from Chemical and metallurgical engineering, Psychological review, Journal of the American ceramic society, and other periodicals.

1. Research—Societies, etc.
20—11214
Library of Congress   Q11.N293

TxLT ICarbS ICJ ViU TU MH NIC DHEW Or CaBVaU
NN 0061796   DLC DNLM OC1MN NcD MsU AAP ICJ NN CoU

W 5
N277r
1940
NATIONAL Research Council
Reprints of articles by fellows in medicine of the National Research Council.
₁Washington₁ 1922-40.
13 v. illus.
Title varies slightly.
1. Medicine

NN 0061797   DNLM

VOLUME 407

National research council.
Reprints of papers by National research fellows in the biological sciences. v. 1–   ; 1923/25–
₁Washington, D. C., National research council, 1923?–
v. illus., plates, maps, diagrs. 25ᶜᵐ.

Binder's lettering: Publications of National research fellows in the biological sciences.
These separately issued papers, chiefly pamphlets, have been collected and bound in volumes with type-written t.-p. and table of contents for each volume. Vol. 4, 1928, to which 72 nos. have been assigned, is in 4 parts, each separately bound; pts. 3 and 4 comprise volumes which

had been previously published as independent works, entitled respectively: (pt. 3) Coming of age in Samoa; a psychological study of primitive youth for western civilisation, by Margaret Mead, 1928; (pt. 4) A catalogue of the Mesozoic *Mammalia* in the Geological department of the British museum, by George Gaylord Simpson, 1928.

1. Biology—Collected works.   I. Title.   II. Title: Publications of National research fellows in the biological sciences.

Library of Congress   QH1.N115   CA 30–702 Unrev'd

NN   0061799   DLC NN DNLM

Q180
.U5A45

National Research Council.

U. S. *National resources committee. Science committee.*
Research—a national resource ... Washington, U. S. Govt. print. off., 1938–41.

National Research Council.
Research and development personnel in industrial laboratories, 1950; report of the National Academy of Sciences-National Research Council to the National Scientific Register under contract SAE-1219. ₁Washington₁ Federal Security Agency, Office of Education ₁1952₁
iii, 13 p. illus., maps. 23 cm. (₁U. S. National Scientific Register₁ Scientific manpower series, no. 1)
Earlier ed., issued in May 1951, has different format and lacks imprint. Series designation appears only on cover.

1. Research, Industrial.   I. Title.   (Series)   E 52–45

U. S. Office of Education   Library Q180.U5A43 no. 1 1952
for Library of Congress   ₁5₁

NN   0061801   DHEW PPD DI

National research council.
Research fellowships in physics, chemistry and mathematics. Administered by the National research council ... Jan. 1, 1935–
₁Washington, D. C., 1935–
v. 23 x 10ᶜᵐ.

1. Scholarships—U. S.   2. Endowment of research.   I. Title.   II. Title: Fellowships in physics, chemistry and mathematics.
37–11595

Library of Congress   Q11.N2935
₁2₁   507.94

NN   0061802   DLC

National Research Council.
Research laboratories in industrial establishments of the U.S.
see   Industrial research laboratories of the United States.

National Research Council.
Sanitary milk and ice cream legislation in the United States.
see under   Dahlberg, Arthur Chester, 1896–

Q127
.U6B4

National Research Council.

Berkner, Lloyd Viel, 1905–
Science and foreign relations; international flow of scientific and technological information. ₁Washington₁ International Science Policy Survey Group ₁1950₁

T176
.A5
1941

National research council.

U. S. *National resources committee. Science committee.*
Science at your service ... condensed summary ... prepared by Research advisory service, Liberty bank of Buffalo. ₁Buffalo, 1941₁

AS15
.H3

National Research Council.

Scientific and technical societies of the United States and Canada. ₁1st₁–   ed. Washington, National Academy of Sciences, National Research Council, 1927–

National Research Council.
Scientific discovery and the wireless telephone
see under   American Telephone and Telegraph Company.

National research council.

Brockett, Paul, 1872–
... Scientific publications from Germany, by Paul Brockett ... ₁Washington, D. C., 1917?₁

National Research Council.
Sodium-restricted diets

see under

National Research Council. Food and Nutrition Board.

LA838
.D4

National Research Council.

De Witt, Nicholas.
Soviet professional manpower, its education, training, and supply. Washington, National Science Foundation, 1955.

National Research Council.
Structure and properties of solid surfaces; a conference arranged by the National Research Council, Lake Geneva, Wisconsin, September 1952. Edited by Robert Gomer and Cyril Stanley Smith. ₁Chicago₁ University of Chicago Press ₁1953₁
xvi, 491 p. illus. 22 cm.
Bibliographical footnotes.

1. Solids.   2. Surface chemistry.   I. Gomer, Robert, ed.   II. Smith, Cyril Stanley, 1903–   ed.   III. Title.

QC282.N3 1952   *541.8 541.31   53–13496

PPSOPR
NIC CU NbU NjR MCM IU WU OrPR OC1U PPiU OCU
KU PPT MtBuM OrCS IdPI IdU CaBVaU MoSW IaAS
PSt TxU OrU MU NBC CaOTU OCoB CtY IaU InNd
TU OC1L PP PPD PPF MBCo NcRS PBL PU-Sc OU
NN   0061812   DLC ScCleA MB OC1 ViU NN ICJ NcD

National Research Council.
Summary proceedings ₁and papers of the Joint Conference ...₁
see under   Joint Conference on Problems of Area Research in Contemporary Africa, Princeton University, 1953.

National research council.

Day, Herbert Ernest.
A survey of American schools for the deaf, 1924–1925, conducted under the auspices of the National research council; report prepared by Herbert E. Day ... Irving S. Fusfeld ... ₁and₁ Rudolf Pintner ... Washington, D. C., The National research council, 1928.

National Research Council.
Survey of university patent policies, preliminary report, by Archie M. Palmer, director of survey. Washington, 1948.
iv, 168 p. 28 cm.
Includes "References."

1. Patents—U. S.   2. Universities and colleges—U. S.   I. Palmer, Archie MacInnes, 1896–   II. Title.

T223.Z1N35   608   48–3061*

ICU PPD IdPI TU TxU ViU MtBC
NN   0061815   DLC DI WaU–L CU OU MiEM MiU NcRS PPHa

National Research Council.
Symposium on microseisms

see under

U.S. Office of Naval Research.

TX158
.U62

National research council.

U. S. *Bureau of human nutrition and home economics.*
Tables of food composition in terms of eleven nutrients. Prepared by Bureau of human nutrition and home economics, U. S. Department of agriculture, in cooperation with National research council ... ₁Washington, U. S. Govt. print. off., 1945₁

National research council.

Lauer, Alvhh Ray, 1896–
Tentative manual of tests for automotive operators, with instructions, directions and cautions on administration and interpretation of psychological and clinical tests ... by Alvhh R. Lauer ... Issued June 25, 1934. ₁Washington, D. C., 1934₁

National research council.
... Tour of industrial exploration, South America, 1941. ₁Washington?₁ 1941?₁
cover-title, 102 p. 23ᶜᵐ.
Condensation of reports prepared by each member of the tour. cf. Pref.

1. Spanish America—Econ. condit.—1918–   2. Natural resources.   I. Title.
43–3815

Library of Congress   HC165.N35
₁3₁   330.98

NN   0061819   DLC ICJ TxU

National research council.

American geophysical union.
... Transactions of the American geophysical union. 2d– annual meeting; ₁1921₁–
Washington, D. C., Published by the National research council of the National academy of sciences, 1922–

VOLUME 407

National research council.

Eisenhart, Luther Pfahler, 1876–
Transformations of surfaces, by Luther Pfahler Eisenhart ... Princeton, Princeton university press; ₍etc., etc.₎ 1923.

National Research Council.
University research and patent problems; composite report of five regional conferences ... by Archie M. Palmer. Washington, 1949.
83 p. 28 cm.
"Conferences were held in Denver, Berkeley, Chicago, New York and Atlanta during April and May 1949."

1. Research. 2. Patents. 3. Universities and colleges—U. S. ɪ. Palmer, Archie MacInnes, 1898– ɪɪ. Title.

Q180.A1N28   507.2   50–60177

NcRS ICU MH PPT PPHa ViU
MtU CLSU GAT WaU PSt CU DNAL NIC NjR MiHM TU OU
NN   0061822   DLC IdPI IdU OrU WaTC WaU-L OrPR MtBC

National research council.
The War metallurgy committee, a report of its purposes, aims and work. ₍Washington₎ National academy of sciences, National research council ₍1943₎
15, ₍1₎ p. diagr. 23ᶜᵐ.
"Information release, IR2."

1. National research council. War metallurgy committee.
                                                            43–16326
Library of Congress   TN623.N3
                                ₍3₎   669.072

NN   0061823   DLC

QE35
.P4

National research council.

Penrose, Richard Alexander Fullerton, 1863–1931.
What a geologist can do in war, prepared by R. A. F. Penrose, Jr., for the Geological committee of the National research council. Philadelphia, J. B. Lippincott company, 1917.

National Research Council
see also **Conference Board of the Associated Research Councils.**

National research council
see also
Industrial research institute, *New York.*

National research council
see also **Joint committee on forestry of the National research council and the Society of American foresters.**

National research council
see also
Joint committee on indexing and abstracting in the major fields of research.

National research council
see also
Joint committee on Latin American studies.

National research council
see also **Pacific science conference,** *Washington, D. C.,* 1946.

National research council
see also
Tropical plant research foundation, *Washington, D. C.*

National Research Council. *Ad Hoc Committee on Fluoridation of Water Supplies.*
Report. November 29, 1951. Washington, National Academy of Sciences, National Research Council, 1952.
ɪᵥ, 8 p. 25 cm. (National Research Council. Publication 214)
Bibliography: p. 7–8.

1. Water—Fluoridation.   (Series)

RA591.5.N3   617.6   55–2335

PSt CU NN NNC ViU DNLM OrCS CaBViP OrU
NN   0061832   DLC CaBVaU IdPI ICJ CU-M RPB MiD PBL

National Research Council. *Advisory Board of Quartermaster Research and Development*
see
National Research Council. *Advisory Board on Military Personnel Supplies.*

National Research Council. Advisory Board on Military Personnel Supplies.
Methods for evaluation nutritional adequacy and status

see under

U.S. Quartermaster Food and Container Institute for the Armed Forces, Chicago.

National Research Council. Advisory Board on Military Personnel Supplies.
Proceedings ₍of the₎ Joint army-navy-air force conference on elastomer research and development
              see under
Joint Army-Navy-Air Force Conference on Elastomer Research and Development.

National Research Council. *Advisory Board on Military Personnel Supplies*
see also
National Research Council. *Committee on Quartermaster Problems.*

National Research Council. *Advisory Committee on Artificial Limbs.*
Artificial limb program, five years of progress; a report by the executive director. ₍n. p.₎ 1951.
1 v. 28 cm.

1. Artificial limbs.   ɪ. Title.

RD756.N24   54–44873 ‡

NN   0061837   DLC ICJ DNLM

WE
172
qN277a
1949

NATIONAL Research Council. Advisory Committee on Artificial Limbs
Artificial limb program; report of results of conference, standing committees on lower and upper extremity prosthesis, under general supervision of Advisory Committee on Artificial Limbs, National Research Council. Washington, 1949.
₍62₎ p.
1. Artificial limbs

NN   0061838   DNLM

RD756
.N29

NATIONAL RESEARCH COUNCIL. Advisory Committee on Artificial Limbs.
Artificial limb program; report of results of conference, standing committees on lower and upper extremity prosthesis, under general supervision of Advisory Committee on Artificial Limbs, National Research Council, New York, May 1–4, 1950.
New York, 1950
1v. (various pagings) illus.

1. Artificial limbs.

NN   0061839   ICU DNLM NN

RD756
.A1A7

National Research Council. Advisory Committee on Artificial Limbs.
Artificial limbs. v. 1–
Jan. 1954–
₍Washington₎

WE
172
qN277f
1953

NATIONAL Research Council. Advisory Committee on Artificial Limbs
Final report... A program for the improvement of the below knee prosthesis with emphasis on problems of the joint, submitted by Denver Research Institute, University of Denver. Denver, 1953.
76 ℓ. illus.
Contract V-100-LM-4089.
Sponsored by the Veterans Administration.
1. Artificial limbs

NN   0061841   DNLM

RD756
.N65

National Research Council. Advisory Committee on Artificial Limbs.
Northrop Corporation.
Final report on artificial arm and leg research and development. ₍Compiled and written by Gilbert M. Motis, supervisor, Prosthesis Dept., Hawthorne, Calif., 1951₎

National Research Council. Advisory Committee on Artificial Limbs.
Fundamental studies of human locomotion...
see California. University. Prosthetic Devices Research Project.
Subcontractor's report on fundamental studies of human locomotion...

National Research Council. *Advisory Committee on Artificial Limbs.*
Human limbs and their substitutes; presenting results of engineering and medical studies of the human extremities and application of the data to the design and fitting of artificial limbs and to the care and training of amputees. In summary and correlation of a research program for the Dept. of Medicine and Surgery, U. S. Veterans Administration, and for the Office of the Surgeon General, Dept. of the Army. ₍By₎ Paul E. Klopsteg, Philip D. Wilson, et al. New York, McGraw-Hill, 1954.
844 p. illus. 24 cm.
1. Artificial limbs.   ɪ. Klopsteg, Paul Ernest, 1889– ed.
ɪɪ. Wilson, Philip Dun-   can, 1886–   ed. ɪɪɪ. Title.
RD756.N27   617.57   53—8999 ‡

OCIU TxU FU-HC
MB NBuG OCIW-H Wa WaSp IU DNLM CaBVaU OrU OrU-M
NN   0061844   DLC WaU PSt PU NcD PPT PPC CU TU ICJ

VOLUME 407

WE
172
qN277i
1954

NATIONAL Research Council. Advisory
Committee on Artificial Limbs
Improved artificial limbs for lower
extremity amputations. Final report
covering the period July 1947 through
December 1950 of Catranis, inc.,
Syracuse, N. Y. ₍Washington, 1954₎
1 v. (various pagings) illus.
Contract no. VAm-22995.
Continues Subcontractors' final
report on artificial limb development for

above-knee amputees, by C. C. Bradley &
Sons, inc. and Catranis, inc.
1. Artificial limbs I. Catranis,
inc., Syracuse, N. Y.

NN   0061846   DNLM

National Research Council. *Advisory Committee on Artificial Limbs.*
Progress report.
₍Berkeley, Calif.₎
v. illus. 28 cm.

1. Artificial limbs.

RD756.A1N313   55-25507 ‡

NN   0061847   DLC

W 2
A
N28pr

NATIONAL Research Council. Advisory
Committee on Artificial Limbs
Progress report ₍on₎ activities ...
conducted by the Prosthetic Devices
Study.

₍New York, 195?₎-
1. Artificial limbs   I. New York
University. Prosthetic Devices Study

NN   0061848   DNLM

National Research Council. Advisory Committee
on Artificial Limbs.
Progress report [of the] International
Business Machines Corporation, Electrical Arm
Project
see under Electrical Arm Project.

W 2
A
qN28p

NATIONAL Research Council. Advisory
Committee on Artificial Limbs
Progress report ₍by the₎ University of
Denver, Institute of Industrial Research,
Mechanics Division.

Denver ₍195-?₎-
v.
I. Denver, University. Institute of
Industrial Research. Mechanics
Division

NN   0061850   DNLM

W 1
NA616

NATIONAL Research Council. Advisory
Committee on Artificial Limbs
Relazione sugli studi ed esperimenti
americani sulle protesi e sull'ortopedia
moderna.
Treviso, Sindacato nazionale produttori
apparecchi ortopedici e di protesi, 1949.
4 no.
Translation of the Committee's Progress
report.
Called also Bollettino, n. 1-4 of the
Sindacato nazionale produttori apparecchi

ortopedici e di protesi, in which publication
later reports of the Committee are continued as a section.
1. Artificial limbs - Period.
2. Orthopedic apparatus - Period.
I. Sindacato nazionale produttori apparecchi
ortopedici e di protesi, Treviso. Bollettino, n. 1-4   Title

NN   0061852   DNLM

W 2
A
qN28r

NATIONAL Research Council. Advisory
Committee on Artificial Limbs
Report ₍on₎ Project no. 115.
no. 115/1-
New York, Prosthetic Devices Study,
Research Division, College of Engineering,
New York Univ., 1949?-
v. illus.
Contract V1001 M184.
1. Artificial limbs
I. New York University. Prosthetic
Devices Study

NN   0061853   DNLM

National Research Council. Advisory Committee
on Artificial Limbs.
Report to the Committee on Artificial Limbs
see under Army Prosthetics Research
Laboratory.

W 2
A
qN28re

NATIONAL Research Council. Advisory
Committee on Artificial Limbs
₍Reports on the₎ Prosthetic Devices
Research Project, Institute of Engi-
neering Research, University of Cali-
fornia. Berkeley, ₍194-₎-
v. illus.
1. Artificial limbs - Collected works
I. California. University. Prosthetic
Devices Research Project

NN   0061855   DNLM NcU

WE 172
N 28   c·vu

National Research Council. Advisory Committee
on Artificial Limbs.

A survey of 23 upper extremity child
amputees at the Mary Free Bed Hospital, Grand
Rapids, Michigan. New York, Prosthetic
Devices Study, Research Division, College of
Engineering, New York University, 1955.

84 1.   tables.   28 cm.

Research Division, project no. 115, report
no. 115.17.   Contract V1001 M184.

NN   0061856   CaBVaU

National Research Council. *Advisory Committee on Artificial Limbs*
see also
√National Research Council. *Committee on Artificial
Limbs.*
√National Research Council. *Prosthetics Research Board.*

TP
290
.A5
N27

National Research Council. **Advisory Committee
on Hazards of Ammonium Nitrate Transportation.**
A compendium on the hazards of water transportation and the manufacture, handling, storage,
and stowage of ammonium nitrate and ammonium
nitrate fertilizers. Report to the United States
Coast Guard. Washington, D. C., 1953.
53 leaves   diagrs., tables   35 x 47 cm.
Photostat of typescript original.
Collation of original: ix, 252 num. leaves
28 cm.
1. Ammonium   nitrate.

NN   0061858   DCU

National Research Council. *Advisory Committee on International Technologic Assistance.*
Report on the utilization of waste gases in Saudi Arabia,
by a special panel of the Advisory Committee on International Technologic Assistance, under Contract SCC-21718,
Task order no. 1, Foreign Operations Administration.
Washington, Division of Engineering and Industrial Research, National Academy of Sciences-National Research
Council, 1954.
11 l., 165 p.   map, diagrs., tables.   28 cm.

Continued in next column

Continued from preceding column

CONTENTS.—Letter of transmittal.—Final recommendations of special panel.—The utilization of waste gases in Saudi Arabia; staff report to the special panel. Bibliography (p. 157-165)

1. Gas, natural—Saudi Arabia. 2. Petroleum industry and trade—
By-products.   I. Title: The utilization of waste gases in Saudi
Arabia.   II. Title: Waste gases in Saudi Arabia.

TN882.S35N3   54-60032

NN   0061860   DLC DNAL DI DS

National Research Council. Advisory committee
on metals and minerals.
Brief statement concerning the current
copper situation, prepared by Walter C. Smith.
American society for metals, Cleveland Ohio,
June 20, 1941.
1, 4 p.

NN   0061861   DAL

TN500
.N3

National *Research Council.*
Advisory Committee on Metals and Minerals.
Report on the beneficiation of low grade
Arkansas bauxite ores by a Sub-Committee of the
Advisory Committee on Metals and Minerals,
National Academy of Sciences and National Research
Council, November 10, 1941. [Washington? 1941?]
36 l.   diagrs.   28 cm.
Photostat copy (negative)
1. Beneficiation. 2. Ore dressing.
3. Bauxite ores. I. National Research Council.

NN   0061862   DI

National research council. Advisory committee
on metals & minerals.
Report on the substitution of low-alloy high-
strength steels for the ordinary structural steels
in freight car and analogous construction, by
W.H. Eisenman, American society for metals,
Cleveland, Ohio., July 14, 1941.
1, 5p.

NN   0061863   DAL

TN799
C6N2

**National Research Council. Advisory
Committee on Metals and Minerals.
Uses and possible substitutes for cobalt.**
[Cleveland, 1942]
26 l.   tables.   27 cm.
Photostat (negative)
Bibliography, 1.26.

1. Cobalt. I. Title.

NN   0061864   DI

225
N21612

National Research Council. **Agricultural
Board.**
Directory.
₍Washington?₎

NN   0061865   DNAL

5
N213

National Research Council. **Agricultural
Board.**
Proceedings.
₍Washington₎

1. Agriculture. Research. U.S. Congresses.

NN   0061866   DNAL DLC

VOLUME 407

National Research Council. *Agricultural Board. Committee on Animal Health*
see
National Research Council. *Committee on Animal Health.*

National Research Council. *Agricultural Board. Committee on Animal Nutrition*
see
National Research Council. *Committee on Animal Nutrition.*

National Research Council. *Agricultural Board. Committee on Feed Composition.*
see
National Research Council. *Committee on Feed Composition.*

National Research Council. *Agricultural Board. Committee on Preservation of Indigenous Strains of Maize*
see
National Research Council. *Committee on Preservation of Indigenous Strains of Maize.*

National Research Council. *Agricultural Board. Committee on Training of Research Workers in Agriculture*
see **National Research Council.** *Committee on Training of Research Workers in Agriculture.*

National Research Council. *Agricultural Research Institute.*
Proceedings, annual meeting.
Washington.
v. illus. 26 cm.

1. Agricultural research.

S1.N415   55–61372 ‡

    OU IdPI CaBVaU MtBC
NN 0061872   DLC WaTC OrCS ICJ IdU MtU OrP OrU IEN

National Research Council. *Agricultural Research Institute*
see also

International Conference on the Use of Antibiotics in Agriculture.

National research council. *Aircraft pilots, Committee on selection and training of*
see
National research council. *Committee on selection and training of aircraft pilots.*

National Research Council. Alaskan Science
Conference
see Alaskan Science Conference.

National research council. *American committee on annual tables.*
Annual tables of physical constants and numerical data ... 1941– ... Princeton, N. J., American committee on annual tables, National research council ₁1942–
v. 23ᶜᵐ.
Loose-leaf; reproduced from type-written copy.
"To constitute a permanent continuation of International critical tables and a current tabulation of critically edited numerical data."
Includes "Literature references."

1. Science—Tables, etc.   2. Physics—Tables, etc.   I. National research council. International critical tables.   II. Title.

Library of Congress   Q199.N33   42–15971
                             ₍3₎   508

        PU-Math NcD TU ViU
NN 0061876   DLC OrP MtU ICRL CoDU DNAL OCIW ICJ

National research council. American
geophysical union.

See

American geophysical union.

National research council. American institute
of biological sciences.

See

American institute of biological sciences.

National Research Council . Animal Breeding
Committee
see National Research Council. Committee
on Animal Breeding.

National Research Council. *Animal Health Committee*
see
National Research Council. *Committee on Animal Health.*

National Research Council. Animal nutrition,
Committee on
see National Research Council. Committee
on Animal Nutrition.

National Research Council. Anthropology
Committee
see National Research Council. Division
of Behavioral Sciences. Anthropology Committee.

National research council. Anthropology and
psychology, Division of
see National research council. Division
of Behavioral Sciences.

National Research Council. *Aviation Psychology, Committee on*
see **National Research Council.** *Committee on Aviation Psychology.*

National Research Council. *Atomic Bomb Casualty Commission*
see **Atomic Bomb Casualty Commission.**

National research council. Bibliography on
orthogonial polynomials committee
see National Research Council. Committee
on a Bibliography on Orthogonal Polynomials.

National Research Council. Biology and
Agriculture, Division of
see National Research Council. Division
of Biology and Agriculture.

RA644   NATIONAL RESEARCH COUNCIL. Board for the Coordi-
.M2N27   nation of Malarial Studies.
         Bulletin on malaria research; comprising minutes
         of meetings of the Board and its Panels and of
         the various malaria committees which preceded the
         Board. 1943–46.   Washington.
         2 v. (viii, 1477 p.)

            1. Malarial fever—Societies. 2. Malarial
         fever—Prevention.

NN 0061888   ICU IU

Z6664   National research council. Board for the
.M3R8   coordination of malarial studies.
         Ruch, Theodore Cedric, 1906–
            Malaria in simian primates: a classified bibliography with
         annotations, prepared at the request of the Board for the co-
         ordination of malaria ₍sic₎ studies, National research council,
         Washington, D. C., by T. C. Ruch ... ₁New Haven, 1944₎

W 2   NATIONAL Research Council. Board for
AA1   the Coordination of Malarial Studies
qN14m   Malaria report. no. 1–
         Mar. 20, 1943–
         Washington.
             v.   illus.
             Early reports, issued by various
         agencies, collected and arbitrarily
         numbered by the National Research
         Council.
             Some reports are typewritten copies
         or photocopies (positive or negative)

             Abstracts only for some reports.
             1. Malaria - Period.   Title

NN 0061891   DNLM

National Research Council. *Building Research Advisory Board.*
    BRAB building science directory; a directory of reference works, abstracts and technical periodicals. ₁n. p., 1953?₎
    11 p. 28 cm.

    1. Building—Bibl. I. Title. II. Title: Building science directory.

Z5853.M4N26   56–29804

NN 0061892   DLC

TH23   National Research Council. Building
qN33   Research Advisory Board.
         BRAB notes, no.1–33; May 15, 1950–Apr.23,
         1954. Washington, 1950–54.
         33 nos. in 1 v. 28cm.

             Processed.
         Ceased publication with no.33, Apr. 1954,
         and was superseded by Building science
         reporter.

             1. Building tra₵   I. Title.

NN 0061893   OrCS

VOLUME 407

National Research Council. Building Research Advisory Board.
Building better from modular drawings. The modular method in building construction. ₍Washington, Housing and Home Finance Agency, Office of the Administrator, Division of Housing Research, 1954₎
22 p. illus. 27cm.

NN   0061894   NcD

National Research Council. *Building Research Advisory Board.*
Condensation control in buildings, as related to paints, papers, and insulating materials. ₍Conference₎ February 26 and 27, 1952, conducted by the Building Research Advisory Board, Division of Engineering and Industrial Research, National Research Council ₍and₎ National Academy of Sciences. Washington, 1952.
118 p. illus. 28 cm. (*Its* Research conference report no. 4)
Bibliography: p. 111–113.
1. Dampness in buildings.   I. National Academy of Sciences, Washington, D. C.   II. Title.   (Series)

TH9031.N3 1952   54–4958

       DCU OCU NNC
NN   0061895   DLC OrCS OrP IdU DAS MB NN OU PSt NIC

National Research Council. *Building Research Advisory Board.*
Fire resistance of non-load-bearing exterior walls. National Academy of Sciences, November 21, 1950. Washington, 1951.
60 p. illus., diagrs. 28 cm. (*Its* Research conference report, no. 2)
On cover: Proceedings.
Bibliography: p. 58–60.

1. Building, Fireproof. 2. Walls.   I. Title.   (Series)

TH1069.N3   693.82   59–42030

NN   0061896   DLC CSt OrCS PSt NN

National Research Council. *Building Research Advisory Board.*
Housing and building in hot-humid and hot-dry climates. ₍Conference₎ Nov. 18 and 19, 1952, conducted by the Building Research Advisory Board. Washington, 1953.
iv, 177 p. illus., maps, diagrs. 28 cm. (*Its* Research conference report no. 5)
Includes bibliographies.

1. Architecture and climate. 2. Architecture, Domestic.   I. Title. (Series)

NA2540.N3 1952   55–61079

      PU-FA MiD NIC NNC
NN   0061897   DLC DAS OrCS IdU OrU MU LU DI NN OU OCU

National Research Council. *Building Research Advisory Board.*
Laboratory design for handling radioactive materials. Washington, 1952.
140 p. illus., tables. 28 cm. (*Its* Research conference report, no. 3)
On cover: Proceedings.
"Sponsored by the American Institute of Architects and the Atomic Energy Commission, November 27 and 28, 1951."
Bibliography: p. 129–135.

1. Laboratories.   I. Title.   (Series)

TH4652.N3   727.562148   59–41622

      OrCS CoU FMU
NN   0061898   DLC DCU NN NcD PU-FA NIC NNC MiU MnU

National Research Council. *Building Research Advisory Board.*
Porcelain enamel in the building industry ₍conference proceedings₎ November 12 and 13, 1953. Sponsored by the Building Research Advisory Board and the Porcelain Enamel Institute. Conducted by the Building Research Institute ... Washington, 1954.
vi, 146 p. illus., diagrs., tables. 28 cm. (*Its* Research conference report no. 6)
National Research Council. Publication 303.
1. Enamel and enameling. 2. Architecture.   I. Porcelain Enamel Institute.   II. Title.   (Series. Series: National Research Council. Publication 303)

TA455.E5N3   1953   666.2   54–3808

      PSt NN DCU ViU NNC AAP OrU OrCS
NN   0061899   DLC WaTC OrP CaBVaU IdPI OU MB PU-Sc

National Research Council. *Building Research Advisory Board.*
Preliminary bibliography of housing and building in hot-humid and hot-dry climates. ₍Washington₎ 1953.
32 p. 28 cm.
Caption title.

———— Supplement. 1953–
Austin.
v. 28 cm. annual. (Texas. University. Bureau of Engineering Research. Special publication. No. 27

Published under the joint sponsorship of the Bureau of Engineering Research, the University of Texas and the Committee on Tropical Housing and Building, Building Research Advisory Board, National Research Council.   Z5943.D7N272

1. Architecture and climate—Bibl.   I. Texas. University. Bureau of Engineering Research.   II. Title: Housing and building in hot-humid and hot-dry climates.   (Series)

Z5943.D7N27   55–62317

NN   0061901   DLC FTaSU NN IU NNC CU ICJ CLSU WaU DAS

TH23
.N33
National Research Council. *Building Research Advisory Board.*
Report.
Washington.
v. 28 cm.

1. Building—U. S. 2. Building research.

TH23.N33   51–26478 ‡

NN   0061902   DLC DNAL

TH
23
N333
National Research Council. Building Research Advisory Board.
Report to the Federal Housing Administration. no.1-   1955-
Washington, National Academy of Sciences, 1955-
v. illus., maps. 23-28 cm.

Some are Publications of the National Research Council.
I. U.S. Federal Housing Administration.
II. National Research Council. Publication.

NN   0061903   LU DLC OrCS IdPI P DCU KMK

NATIONAL research council. Building research advisory board.
Research conference report.
Wash., D.C. illus. diagrs.

No.1-3 also called Research correlation conference. Proceedings.

NN   0061904   WaS DLC CU MtBC

National Research Council. *Building Research Advisory Board.*
School building costs. ₍Washington, 1953₎
83 p. 28 cm.

"Working conference sponsored by the American Institute of Architects, the Chamber of Commerce of the United States, and the U. S. Office of Education. Conducted by the Building Research Advisory Board at the National Academy of Sciences. December 2 and 3, 1952."
Errata slip inserted.

1. School-houses—U. S.   I. Title.

LB3218.A1N33   371.62   55–60262

NN   0061905   DLC OrU CU DI

National Research Council. *Building Research Advisory Board.*
Study of conservation in building construction, performed by the Building Research Advisory Board under contract DPA-3 ₍and DPA-5₎ between the Defense Production Administration and the National Academy of Sciences. Final report. Washington, 1952–53.
2 v. tables. 29 cm.

1. Building research.   I. Title.

TH153.N3   52–61447 rev

NN   0061906   DLC OrCS MiU IU IEN DCU AAP DAS

National Research Council. *Building Research Advisory Board.*
A study of slab-on-ground construction for residences. Conducted by the Building Research Advisory Board for the Federal Housing Administration under contract no. HA—fh-646, June 30, 1955. Washington, National Academy of Sciences, National Research Council, Division of Engineering and Industrial Research, 1955.
50 p. diagrs. 28 cm. (National Research Council. Publication 385)
On cover: A report of a study performed for the Federal Housing Administration by a special advisory committee of the Building Research Advisory Board.
1. Dwellings.   I. U. S. Federal Housing Administration.   II. Title: Slab-on-ground construction for residences. (Series)

TH4811.N3   690   55–60060

      NN IU NcD ViU DI PBL ICJ PSt FU
NN   0061907   DLC WaTC CaBVaU IdPI OrCS OrP Wa MiHM

National Research Council. *Building Research Advisory Board.*
A survey of housing research in the United States. Washington, Housing and Home Finance Agency, Office of the Administrator, Division of Housing Research, 1952.
x, 723 p. 26 cm.

1. Housing research. 2. Housing—U. S.   I. U. S. Housing and Home Finance Agency.

HD7287.N25   331.833072   52—60079

    NN NcD OOxM OU ViU OC1JC DAU TU OC1 OrP WaS OrCS Or
NN   0061908   DLC OC1U CU CoU OCU MB PLF PPD PSt TxU

National Research Council. *Building Research Advisory Board.*
Weather and the building industry. A research correlation conference on climatological research and its impact on building design, construction, materials and equipment, National Academy of Sciences, January 11 and 12, 1950. Washington, 1950.
vi, 158 p. illus., maps, charts, tables. 28 cm. (*Its* Research conference report, no. 1)
On cover: Proceedings.
Bibliography: p. 154–158.
1. Architecture and climate.   I. Title.   (Series)

NA2540.N35   720.15515   50–58188 rev 2

NN   0061909   DLC NN PSt OrPS DAS MH NNC

National Research Council, *Building Research Council.*
Register of members.
Washington.
v. 28 cm.

1. Building research—U. S.—Direct.

TH12.N3   58–60242 ‡

NN   0061910   DLC

HD
9715
U5N27+
National Research Council. Building Research Institute.
Associations and societies of the building industry in the United States. 1st ed. ₍Washington, 1955₎
₍46₎p. 28cm.

Cover title.

1.Construction industry—U.S.—Direct.
I.Title.

NN   0061911   NIC MiD DAIA

VOLUME 407

National Research Council. *Building Research Institute.*
Metal curtain walls. The edited papers and discussions of a research correlation conference conducted by the Building Research Institute in the Chamber of Commerce of the United States in Washington, D. C., on September 28 and 29, 1955. Washington, Building Research Institute, Division of Engineering and Industrial Research, National Academy of Sciences, National Research Council, 1955.
ii, 190 p. illus., diagrs., tables. 28 cm. (National Research Council. Publication 378)
On cover: Proceedings.
1. Walls. 2. Metal-work. 3. Metals.   I. Title.   (Series)

TH2231.N3 1955   691.7   55–60063

IU ViU NN PSt Wa CaBVa WaTC OrP Or WaS CaBVaU
NN 0061912   DLC KMK MiHM ViBldV NcRS CU MiU NcD

National Research Council. *Building Research Institute.*
Modular measure; the edited papers and discussions of a research correlation conference entitled Modular coordination: its value in contemporary building, conducted by the Building Research Institute at the National Academy of Sciences, Washington, D. C., December 9, 1954. ₍Editor: Charles R. Koehler₎ Washington, 1955.
66 p. 28 cm.

1. Building—Societies, etc.   I. Title.

TH1.N45   56–61527

NN 0061913   DLC IU MiU

National Research Council. *Building Research Institute.*
Plastics in building; the uses, past and present, and the potentialities of plastics in building as reported at a conference conducted by the Building Research Institute, October 27 and 28, 1954, at the Chamber of Commerce of the United States in Washington, D. C. ₍Editor: Charles R. Koehler₎ Washington, 1955.
x, 149 p. illus., ports. 29 cm. (National Research Council. Publication 337)

1. Plastics.   I. Title.   (Series)

TA455.P5N3 1954   691.9   55–60009

CaBVaU MtBC IdPI WaT OrU DAU
CaBVa PBL ODW NcD ViU TxU PSt PU-Sc PMarhSO OU MiU
NN 0061914   DLC OrCS ICJ IdU NcRS WaTC OrP WaS PP

National Research Council. Building Research Institute.
Porcelain enamel in the building industry

see under

National Research Council. Building Research Advisory Board.

National Research Council. *Building Research Institute.*
Plastics Study Group.
Plastics in building illumination
see its
Report on the meeting.

qR690.6 **NATIONAL Research Council. Building Research**
N2131P **Institute.**
₍Publication₎
Washington. National Academy of Sciences-National Research Council. illus.
(National Research Council. Publication)

Conference papers.
This set is arbitrarily numbered in the order of the non-consecutive numbering of the National Research Council Publication.

Continued as: Building Research Institute. Publication.

NN 0061918   WaS

TA 455 **National Research Council.** *Building Research Institute.*
P5 N36 *Plastics Study Group.*
Report on the meeting.
Washington.
v. illus. 28 cm.
Began publication with report of Nov. 1955 meeting.
Report of Mar. 1958 meeting has also a distinctive title: Plastics in building illumination.
Title varies slightly.

1. Plastics.

TA455.P5N36   691.92   59–752 rev

NN 0061919   DLC OU KU MiU MB

TH **National Research Council--Building Research**
1 **Institute.**
.N565 Technical reprint. no.1-

Washington, 1955-
no. illus. 28cm.

Each no. has also a distinctive title.

1. Building.

NN 0061920   IU MiU

National research Council. Central Petroleum Committee
see also   American Petroleum Institute. Research Project.

National Research Council. *Channelization Committee*
see
National Research Council. *Highway Research Board. Committee on Channelization.*

National Research Council. Chemical-Biological Coordination Center.
The bactériostatic activity of 3500 organic compounds for Mycobacterium tuberculosis var. hominis

see under

Youmans, Guy P

National Research Council. Chemical-Biological Coordination Center.
CBCC positive data series
see under title

Q **National Research Council. Chemical-**
11 **Biological Coordination Center.**
.N29495 The Chemical-Biological Coordination Center of the National Research Council. Washington.
v. illus. 25cm.
Science
Includes 2 issues dated Sept. 1954, with slightly different titles: The Chemical-Biological Coordination Center of the National Academy of Sciences. National Research Council.

NN 0061925   KU GAT

QU **NATIONAL Research Council. Chemical-**
24 **Biological Coordination Center**
N277c The Chemical-Biological Coordination
1950 Center of the National Research Council. Washington, 1950.
20 p.
Cover title.

NN 0061926   DNLM

National Research Council. *Chemical-Biological Coordination Center.*
The Chemical-Biological Coordination Center of the National Research Council. Washington ₍1954₎
33 p. 25 cm.

QD51.5.N3A42   574.19072   55–60574 ‡

NN 0061927   DLC WaTC ICJ OrCS OrP OrU CaBVaU IdPI

QU **NATIONAL Research Council. Chemical-**
15 **Biological Coordination Center**
qN277c ₍Classification of₎ enzymes; an
1953 alphabetical listing. Rev., Oct. 1953.
₍Washington, 1953₎
21 ℓ.
1. Enzymes

NN 0061928   DNLM

QU **NATIONAL Research Council. Chemical-**
24 **Biological Coordination Center**
qN277 ₍Collection of publications₎

The Library has a collection of miscellaneous publications of this organization kept as received. These publications are not listed or bound separately.

NN 0061929   DNLM

SB951 **National Research Council. Chemical-**
.N28 **Biological Coordination Center.**
1954
Compounds active as fungicidal agents (data from preliminary screening tests) Washington, D. C., 1954.
a-b, 22 p. 28cm.
At head of title: Chemical-Biological Coordination Center screening program.
1. Pesticides—Testing. 2. Fungicides.
I. Title.

NN 0061930   ViU DNAL OrCS DNLM PPSKF PBL IU

National Research Council. Chemical-Biological Coordination Center
Detailed biology code. 5th ed., no date.
63p. processed.

A code for punched cards.

NN 0061931   OClW

National Research Council. *Chemical-Biological Coordination Center.*
Detailed biological code. 6th ed. ₍Washington₎ ©1952.
54 l. 30 cm.
——— Key. 2d ed. ₍Washington₎ 1953-
1 v. (loose-leaf) 30 cm.

QH324.N33 1952 Key

1. Punched card systems—Biological chemistry.   I. Title.

QH324.N33 1952   574.19   53–1073 rev ‡

NN 0061932   DLC

VOLUME 407

National Research Council. *Chemical-Biological Coordination Center.*
First symposium on chemical-biological correlation, May 26–27, 1950. Washington, National Academy of Sciences, National Research Council, 1951.
415 p. illus. 25 cm. (National Research Council. Publication 206)
Includes bibliographies.

1. Chemotherapy — Collected works. 2. Chemicals — Physiological effect. i. Title: Chemical-biological correlation. (Series)

RM260.N3 1950   615.1082   52–3359

NN   0061933   DLC ViU NNC IdPI IdU OrU-M OrU

QU
15
qN277g
1949

NATIONAL Research Council. Chemical-Biological Coordination Center
General biological code ᵣbyᵢ Biological Codification Panel, Chemical-Biological Coordination Center. ᵣWashingtonᵢ 1949.
23 p.
Cover title.
1. Biochemistry 2. Biology
3. Punched card systems

Title: Chemical-biological correlation
Series: National Research Council. Publication 206 ᵣetc.ᵢ

NN   0061935   DNLM

National Research Council. *Chemical-Biological Coordination Center.*
A method of coding chemicals for correlation and classification. Washington, 1950.
98 p. 28 cm.
"Codification chart": 3 leaves inserted.
Bibliography: p. 5.

1. Chemistry—Classification. 2. Punched card systems.

QD7.N3   540.12   51–3182

PPSKF
NN   0061936   DLC OrU OrCS ICU ICJ MB DNAL DNLM ICRL

QK
731
.N3

National Research Council. Chemical-Biological Coordination Center.
Plant regulators; data from preliminary screening tests. [Washington] 1955.
4 v. in 1. (National Academy of Sciences–National Research Council. Publication 384)

CBCC Positive data series, no. 2–5.

(s)

#Growth inhibiting substances.
Plant regulators.
National Academy of Sciences–National Research Council. Publication 384)

NN   0061938   MoU CaBVaU

QP501
.N3

NATIONAL RESEARCH COUNCIL. Chemical-Biological Coordination Center.
Review no.1–
Washington, D.C., 1946–
nos. in   diagrs.

1. Biological chemistry—Collected works.

CU OrCS IdU OrU DLC
NN   0061939   ICU MiEM NdU NcRS OU NN ICJ NIC DNLM

National Research Council. Chemical-Biological Coordination Center.
Statistical information on component parts of chemical compounds

see under

Dale, Estaleta.

National Research Council. *Chemical-Biological Coordination Center.*
Summary tables of biological tests. v. 1–
Oct. 1949–
Washington.
v. 28 cm. bimonthly.

1. Pesticides—Testing.

SB951.N3   632.9505   52–2709

DNLM NN NNCC N
NN   0061941   DLC CU MtBC ICJ DNAL LNL   NIC NNC-M

386
N2127t

National Research Council. Chemical-Biological Coordination Center.
Types of questions answered by the CBCC with specific examples. Washington, 1955.
9 l.

1. National Research Council. Chemical-Biological Coordination Center. 2. Information services. I. Wood, G   Congdon.

NN   0061942   DNAL OrCS

National Research Council. *Chemical Subcommittee*
see
National Research Council. *Chemistry Subcommittee.*

National Research Council. Chemical utilization of coal, Committee on
see National Research Council. Committee on Chemical Utilization of Coal.

National Research Council. *Chemistry of Coal, Committee on the*
see
National Research Council. *Committee on the Chemistry of Coal.*

National Research Council. *Chemistry Subcommittee.*
Annotated bibliography of analytical methods for pesticides. Prepared for the Food Protection Committee, Food and Nutrition Board, National Research Council. Washington, 1952–54.
2 v. 28 cm. (National Research Council. Publication 241)
Supplements to be issued from time to time.
CONTENTS. — section 1. Aldrin-dieldrin. Benzene hexachloride. Chlordane-heptachlor. DDT. — section 2. Insecticides: botanicals, fumigants, inorganic, organic. Fungicides. Herbicides. Rodenticides.

1. Pesticides—Abstracts. 2. Pesticides—Bibl. (Series)

SB951.N33   632.95   A 55–962
Michigan. Univ. Libr.
for Library of Congress   ᵣ1ᵢ†

ViU DI DCU CLSU LU DLC OrU
NN DNLM WaTC IdPI DNAL MsU PSt TxU OU PBL PPJ NcD
NN   0061946   MiU CaBVaU GAT MoU ICJ NNC N OrCS OrP

389
M2198

National Research Council. Civil Defense Foods Advisory Committee.
The vulnerability of the food industries to chemical, biological, and radiological warfare agents. Washington ᵣU.S. Govt. Print. Off.ᵢ 1955.
167 p.

NN   0061947   DNAL

National Research Council. *Clay Minerals Committee*
see
National Research Council. *Committee on Clay Minerals.*

National Research Council. *Committee for Investigation of Waste Disposal.*
A study of the disposal of chemical waste at sea; report of the Committee for Investigation of Waste Disposal, by Alfred C. Redfield and Lionel A. Walford. Washington, National Academy of Sciences, National Research Council, 1951.
vii, 49 p. illus., maps. 26 cm. (National Research Council. Publication 201)
Bibliography: p. 49.
1. Factory and trade waste. 2. Water—Pollution. 3. National Lead Company. i. Redfield, Alfred Clarence, 1890– ii. Walford, Lionel Albert, 1905– iii. Title: Disposal of chemical waste at sea. (Series)

TD899.N3   628.541   54–845

WaTC
ViU MH NNC CU MiD CU-M TxU NNC-M DPAHO MiHM MoU
NN   0061949   DLC Wa OrCS MtBC CaBVaU OrP ICJ NN

HQ
5
N277r

NATIONAL Research Council. Committee for Research in Problems of Sex
Reprints of reports on investigations supported wholly or in part by the Committee on Research in Problems of Sex, Division of Medical Sciences, National Research Council. Washington, 1922–
v. illus.
Special vol. 1, 1927-1929-1931, issued in addition to a regular v. 1 for 1922-25.
1. Research 2. Sex

NN   0061950   DNLM

National research council. Committee for research in problems of sex.

Allen, Edgar, 1892–   ed.
Sex and internal secretions; a survey of recent research ... editor, Edgar Allen ... associate editors, Charles H. Danforth ... Edward A. Doisy ... with forewords by Robert M. Yerkes ... Baltimore, The Williams & Wilkins company, 1939.

ZWE
344
qN277b
1948

NATIONAL Research Council. Committee for Survey of Research on Rheumatic Diseases
Bibliography on rheumatoid arthritis and osteoarthritis and structural components. Washington, 1948.
74 p.
1. Arthritis - Bibl.

NN   0061952   DNLM OrU-M

616.991
N277f

National Research Council—Committee for Survey of Research on Rheumatic Diseases.
Final report. Washington, 1949.
80p. 28cm.

Bibliography: p.79–80.

1. Arthritis. 2. Rheumatic fever. 3. Rheumatism.

NN   0061953   IU ICU

VOLUME 407

RC927
N21
1948

National Research Council. Committee for
Survey of Research on Rheumatic Diseases.
Preliminary report. Washington, D.C., 1948.
115 p.

1. Rheumatism. 2. Medical research.

NN   0061954   NNC-M OC1

National research council. *Committee on a bibliography on
orthogonal polynomials.*
... A bibliography on orthogonal polynomials. Report of the
Committee on a bibliography on orthogonal polynomials, Divi-
sion of physical sciences, National research council: J. A.
Shohat, chairman ... Einar Hille ... Joseph L. Walsh ...
Washington, D. C., Published by the National research council
of the National academy of sciences, 1940.
    ix, 204 p. 25½ᶜᵐ. (Bulletin of the National research council. no. 103,
Aug. 1940)
    1. Functions, Orthogonal—Bibl.   I. Shohat, James Alexander, 1886–
II. *Hille, Einar, 1894–   III. Walsh, Joseph Leonard, 1895–   IV.
Title.
                                                                   41–5948
    Library of Congress   Q11.N292 no. 103
    ——— Copy 2.   ₁8₎   (506) 517.35

NN   0061955   DLC WaTC MiD MiEM CU OC1W OO ViU

525.98   National Research Council—Committee on a
N21m   National Atlas of the United States.
            Map standardization for a loose-leaf national
          atlas. Recommendations of the Committee on a
          National Atlas of the United States. Washing-
          ton, National Academy of Sciences, National
          Research Council, 1955.
            5p. 2 fold. maps. 28cm.

            Scale of the two sample base maps:
          1:10,000,000.

NN   0061956   IU ScU DAS CLSU N NN ICarbS

National research council. *Committee on a textbook of military psychology.*
    Psychology for the armed services, prepared by a committee
of the National research council, with the collaboration of
many specialists, edited by Edwin G. Boring ... Washington,
The Infantry journal ₁1945₎
    xvii, 533 p. illus., diagrs. 21½ᶜᵐ.
    "Prepared under the direction of the Committee of the National research council's
Committee on a textbook of military psychology."—Acknowledgments.
    "First edition July 1945."
    "References" at end of each chapter except chapter 24.
    1. War—Psychological aspects. 2. Psychology. 3. Psychological war-
fare.   I. Boring, Edwin Garrigues, 1886–   ed. II. Title.
                                                                   45–6821
    Library of Congress °   BF121.N3
                                       ₁20₎   355.43

NN   0061957   DNLM ViU NcGU OC1 OC1W OOxM O MiHM
                 DLC IdU MtU NBuU CU NIC DAU KEmT CtY-M

BF121   National Research Council. Committee on a
.N3   Textbook of Military Psychology.
1948   Psychology for the armed services, prepared by
          a committee of the National Research Council,
          with the collaboration of many specialists.
          Edited by Edwin G. Boring. ₁3d ed.₎ Washington,
          Infantry Journal Press ₁1948₎
            xvii, 533 p. illus. 22cm.
            Includes bibliographies.
            1. War—Psychological aspects. 2. Psychologi-
          cal warfare.   I. Boring, Edwin Garrigues,
          1886–   ed.   II. Title.

NN   0061958   MB IU

QH
91
.N3   **National Research Council.** *Committee on a Treatise on
           Marine Ecology and Palaeoecology.*
           Report. no. ₁1₎–11; 1940/41–1950/51. Washington.
           11 no. 27 cm. annual.
           At head of title: National Research Council, Division of Geology
         and Geography.
           Reports for 1940/41–1945/46 issued under earlier names of the
         committee: 1940/41, Subcommittee on the Ecology of Marine Organ-
         isms: 1941/42–1945/46, Committee on Marine Ecology as Related to
         Paleontology.
           Issued as an appendix to the division's Report.
           L. C. set incomplete: no. 4, 1943/44 wanting.
           1. Marine fauna. 2. Marine flora.- 3. Paleontology.   I. National
         Research Council. Division of Earth Sciences. Report. Appendix.

    QH91.N3   574.92   43–5332*

NN   0061959   DAU TNJ TxLT CStbS RPB PSt NNC OCU IaU MH ICU MoU
                 DLC LU ICJ OU NN DNAL OC1 LNT CoD TxU

National research council. *Committee on acoustics.*
    ... Certain problems in acoustics. Compiled by the Na-
tional research council Committee on acoustics. Washington,
D. C., Published by the National research council of the National academy of sciences, 1922.
    cover-title, 31 p. 25ᶜᵐ. (Bulletin of the National research council.
no. 23 (v. 4, pt. 5) Nov. 1922)
    Bibliography at end of the articles.

    1. Sound.   I. Title: Acoustics, Certain problems in.
                                                     23–13637 Revised
    Library of Congress   Q11.N292 no. 23

NN   0061960   OC1W NcRS MiU OO OCX OCU OU ViU
                 DLC WaTC OrPR CaBVaU OrU NN KEmT OU

National research council. *Committee on acoustics of buildings.*
    ... Bibliography of acoustics of buildings, prepared under
the auspices of the Comittee ₁!₎ on acoustics of buildings, National research council, by F. R. Watson ... ₁Washington,
D. C., 1931₎
    ₁1₎, 14–43 p. 24¼ᶜᵐ. (Reprint and circular series of the National re-
search council. no. 99)
    "Reprinted from Journal of the Acoustical society of America, July,
1931, vol. II, no. 5, pp. 14–43."
    CONTENTS.—pt. I. General.—pt. II. Acoustics of rooms.—pt. III. Sound-
insulation.
    1. Architectural acoustics—Bibl.   I. Watson, Floyd Rowe, 1872–
                                                          31–31088
    Library of Congress   Q11.N293 no. 99
                                       ₁3₎   (508) 016.53484

NN   0061961   MiU OC1 OC1W
                 DLC CoU PPFr OrU NcD ViU OCU O OOxM

National research council. Committee on
aerobiology.

American association for the advancement of science. *Section on medical sciences.*
    Aerobiology ... Publication committee: Elvin C. Stakman,
chairman, Edmund B. Lambert, Stuart Mudd, Malcolm H.
Soule; edited by Forest Ray Moulton. Washington, D. C.,
American association for the advancement of science, 1942.

National research council. *Committee on African anthropology*
    see
National research council. *Committee on the anthropology
of Africa.*

National Research Council. Committee on Air-
  Entraining Concrete
  see   National Research Council. Highway
Research Board. Dept. of Materials and Construction. Committee on Air-Entraining Concrete.

National research council. *Committee on algebraic numbers.*
    ... Algebraic numbers. Report of the Committee on alge-
braic numbers, National research council, by L. E. Dickson,
H. H. Mitchell, H. S. Vandiver, G. E. Wahlin. Washington,
D. C., Published by the National research council of the National academy of sciences, 1923.
    cover-title, 96 p. 25ᶜᵐ. (Bulletin of the National research council.
no. 28 (v. 5, pt. 3) Feb. 1923)

    1. Numbers, Theory of.   I. Dickson, Leonard Eugene, 1874–
II. Mitchell, Howard Hawks, 1885–   III. Vandiver, Harry Shultz,
1882–   IV. Title.
                                                     23–18695 Revised
    Library of Congress   Q11.N292 no. 28

NN   0061965   MoU AAP MB NN MiU OO OOxM OC1 OU NcRS ViU IU
                 DLC PU-Math OrU CaBVaU WaTC OrPR CLU

National research council. *Committee on algebraic numbers.*
    ... Algebraic numbers—II. Report of the Committee on
algebraic numbers. H. S. Vandiver, chairman; G. E. Wahlin.
Washington, D. C., Published by the National research council
of the National academy of sciences, 1928.
    cover-title, 1 p. l., 111 p. 25ᶜᵐ. (Bulletin of the National research
council. no. 62, Feb. 1928)
    "The ... Committee on algebraic numbers published in February,
1923 as Bulletin no. 28, a report on algebraic numbers which aimed
to cover all the literature on the theory of algebraic numbers after
1895."—Pref.
    1. Numbers, Theory of.   I. Vandiver, Harry Shultz, 1882–
II. Wahlin, Gustaf Eric, 1880–   III. Title.
                                                          28–13369
    Library of Congress   Q11.N292 no. 62

NN   0061966   MB NN MiU OO OCU OOxM ViU
                 DLC WaWW CaBVaU OrU WaTC KEmT MoU NcD

Z7401   National Research Council. Committee on American
.H35   Scientific and Technical Bibliography.

          Hawkins, Reginald Robert, 1902–   *ed.*
            Scientific, medical, and technical books published in the
          United States of America, 1930–1944; a selected list of titles
          in print, with annotations. Prepared under the direction of
          the National Research Council's Committee on Bibliography
          of American Scientific and Technical Books. Washington,
          1946.

VM989   National Research Council. Committee on
.H3   Amphibious Operations.

          Hahn, Walter A 1921–
            On using self contained underwater breathing apparatus,
          by Walter A. Hahn and Christian J. Lambertsen. Wash-
          ington, 1952 ₁i. e. 1953₎

VM 989   National Research Council. Committee on
N 38   Amphibious Operations. Panel on Underwater
          Swimmers.

            Report of the Cooperative Underwater
          Swimmer Project, prepared for the Office of
          Naval Research, with the cooperation of
          Amphibious Forces, U.S. Pacific Fleet and
          Scripps Institute of Oceanography. San
          Diego, Calif., 1952.
            95 p. diagrs.   26cm.
            Bibliography   p. 57

NN   0061969   CaBVaU

BF105   National Research Council. Committee on
.N3   Animal Breeding.
            A survey of animal breeding. Washington,
          D.C., 1931.
            35 p. 27 cm.

            1. Stock and stock breeding—U.S.

NN   0061970   TU OrCS DNAL MsSM KMK

VOLUME 407

National Research Council. *Committee on Animal Health.*
Report. 1st-6th. Washington ₁1943-46₎
     6 v. 25 cm. (National Research Council. Reprint and circular series)
     Each report has also distinctive title.
     L. C. set incomplete: v. 3 wanting.

     1. Veterinary medicine—Collected works.   (Series)

     Q11.N293   44-8075 rev*

NN   0061971   DLC

.41
N216R   National research council. Committee on
      animal health.
      ... Report on the intramammary therapy of
      bovine mastitis. 1st-   Jan.1946-
      Washington, D.C., 1946-
         v.   28cm.   irregular.

      Processed.

NN   0061972   DNAL

389.79
N21A   National research council. Committee on
      animal nutrition.
      Annual report of activities.
      ₁n.p.₎

      1. Animal nutrition. 2. Feeding stuffs.

NN   0062001   DNAL

National research council. *Committee on animal nutrition.*
     ... Cooperative experiments upon the protein requirements for the growth of cattle—II. Report of the Subcommittee on animal nutrition, presented for the subcommittee by E. B. Forbes, chairman, with the collaboration of S. I. Bechdel, C. D. Jeffries and Max Kriss. Washington, D. C., Published by the National research council of the National academy of sciences, 1924.
     cover-title, 44 p. 25ᶜᵐ. (Bulletin of the National research council. no. 42 (v. 7, pt. 6) Feb. 1924)
     1. Proteids. 2. Cattle. 3. Metabolism.   I. Forbes, Ernest Browning, 1876–   II. Bechdel, Samuel Irvin, 1886–   III. Jeffries, C. D.   IV. Title.   V. Title: Protein requirements for the growth of cattle.

                     25-15042 Revised
     Library of Congress   Q11.N292   no. 42

      NcRS ViU
NN   0062002   DLC OrSaW OrPR WaTC CaBVaU OrU WaWW

National research council. *Committee on animal nutrition.*
     ... The determination of the protein requirements of animals and of the protein values of farm feeds and rations. Report of the Subcommittee on animal nutrition, by H. H. Mitchell. Washington, D. C., Published by the National research council of the National academy of sciences, 1926.
     cover-title, 44 p. 25 cm. (Bulletin of the National research council. no. 55 (v. 11, pt. 1) Mar. 1926)

     1. Feeding. 2. Proteids.   I. Mitchell, Harold Hanson, 1886–   II. Title.   III. Title: Protein requirements of animals.   IV. Title: Protein values of farm feeds and rations.

     Q11.N292   no. 55   27—4209
     ——— Copy 4.   QP551.N3

NN   0062003   DLC MB TxU NcRS WaTC OrPR CaBVaU

National Research Council. **Committee on Animal Nutrition.**
     The effect of storage of grains on their nutritive value. Prepared by a subcommittee consisting of D. B. Jones, Chairman, G.S. Fraps ₁and others₎ Washington, D.C. ₁1943₎
     14 p.   25cm. (Its 7th Report)
     National Research Council. Reprint and circular series. no. 116, March, 1943.
     "References": p. 13-14.
     1. Nutrition. 2. Feeding and feeding stuffs. 3. Grain. I. Title. II. Ser. III. Ser.

NN   0062004   ViU IU MiEM

National research council. **Committee on animal nutrition.**
     The fluorine problem in livestock feeding, by. H. H. Mitchell. Fourth report of the Committee on animal nutrition of the National research council ... Washington, D. C. ₁1942₎
     2 p.l., 10 p. incl. tab.   25ᶜᵐ. (On cover: National research council. Reprint and circular series, no. 113, June, 1942)
     Bibliography: p. 9-10.
     1. Fluorine. 2. Feeding and feeding stuffs. I. Mitchell, Harold Hanson, 1886–   II. Title. III. Ser.

NN   0062005   ViU

National Research Council. Committee on Animal Nutrition.
     The fluorosis problem in livestock production
     see under   National Research Council. Committee on Animal Nutrition. Subcommittee on Fluorosis Problems.

National Research Council. *Committee on Animal Nutrition.*
     Hormonal relationships and applications in the production of meats, milk, and eggs; a report of the Committee on Animal Nutrition prepared by the Subcommittee on Hormones. ₁Washington₎ Agricultural Board, National Research Council, 1953.
     iv, 54 p.   25 cm. (National Research Council. Publication 266)
     "Literature published prior to July 1952 forms the basis for the report."
     Includes bibliographies.

     ——— Supplement. Washington, National Academy of Sciences–National Research Council, 1959.
     iv, 53 p.   25 cm. (National Research Council. Publication 714)
     "Covers the literature published from July 1952 through May 1957."
     Includes bibliographies.
                     SF768.N3 Suppl.

     ——— Supplement 1966. Washington, National Academy of Sciences–National Research Council, 1966.
     87 p.   25 cm. (National Research Council. Publication 1415)
     Includes bibliographies.
                     SF768.N3 Suppl. 2

     1. Hormones. 2. Feeding.   I. Title.   (Series: National Research Council. Publication 266, ₁etc.₎)

     SF768.N3   636.087   54-1683

     OU PBL PSt NN CU CtY CLSU CaBVaU DNAL
     Wa MiU AAP OrU MtU IdU WaTC CSt NNC OC1 TxU ViU
NN   0062009   DLC NIC ICJ IdPI GAT OrCS NNC OrP MB

National research council. *Committee on animal nutrition.*
     Iodine, its necessity and stabilization, prepared by a subcommittee consisting of W. B. Griem, chairman, E. B. Hart, J. W. Kalkus ₁and₎ Howard Welch. Second report of the Committee on animal nutrition of the National research council ... Washington, D. C. ₁1942₎
     2 p. l., 7 p. 24½ᶜᵐ. (On cover: National research council. Reprint and circular series, no. 111, May, 1942)

     1. Iodine.   I. Griem, Walter B., 1900–
                       43-51858
     Library of Congress   Q11.N293   no. 111
           ₁5₎   (506)   636.0877

NN   0062011   DLC ViU

National Research Council. Committee on Animal Nutrition.
     Is animal protein an essential constituent of swine and poultry rations?
     see under   Mitchell, Harold Hanson, 1886–

National research council. *committee on animal nutrition.*
     ... Mineral nutrient requirements of farm animals, report of the Subcommittee on animal nutrition presented for the Committee by E. B. Forbes, chairman. Washington, D. C., 1924.
     cover-title, 12 p.   24ᶜᵐ. (Reprint and circular series of the National research council. no. 60)

     1. Nutrition.   I. Title.   C D 34-45

     Library of Congress   Q11.N293   no. 60

NN   0062013   DLC OrU MiU OC1W ViU NN

National research council. *Committee on animal nutrition.*
     ... Mineral nutrition of farm animals, by H. H. Mitchell ... and F. J. McClure ... Prepared under the auspices of the Committee on animal nutrition, Division of biology and agriculture, National research council. Washington, D. C. ₁Published by the National research council of the National academy of sciences₎ 1937.
     135 p. 25ᶜᵐ. (Bulletin of the National research council. no. 99. April, 1937)
     "Literature cited": p. 89-118.
     1. Feeding and feeding stuffs.   I. Mitchell, Harold Hanson, 1886–   II. McClure, Frank James, 1896–   III. Title.   IV. Title: Nutrition of farm animals, Mineral.
                         37–10954
     Library of Congress   Q11.N292   no. 99
     ——— Copy 2.   Q11.N292   no. 99, 2d set
           ₁5₎   (506)   636.0877

NN   0062014   DLC CaBVaU WaS MU NcRS NcD ViU

National research council. *Committee on animal nutrition.*
     ... The minimum protein requirements of cattle. Report of Committee on animal nutrition ₁by₎ H. H. Mitchell ... ₁Washington, D. C., Published by the National research council of the National academy of sciences, 1929₎
     84 p. 24½ᵐ. (Bulletin of the National research council. no. 67, Feb. 1929)
     Bibliography: p. 79-84.

     1. Feeding and feeding stuffs. 2. Proteids.   I. Mitchell, Harold Hanson, 1886–   II. Title.
                         29—0872
     Library of Congress   Q11.N292   no. 67

     ICJ ViU
NN   0062015   DLC WaWW WaTC OrPR CaBVaU NcD TxU MB

National Research Council. Committee on Animal Nutrition.
     Nutrient requirements for domestic animals
     see its   Recommended nutrient allowances for domestic animals.

636.085
N272n   National Research Council. Committee on
no.7   Animal Nutrition.
      Nutrient requirements for foxes and minks; a report of the Committee on Animal Nutrition, prepared by the Subcommittee on Fur Bearer Nutrition, Lorin E. Harris, chairman ₁and others₎ Washington, Division of Biology and Agriculture, National Research Council, 1953.
      30 p. illus. tables. 25 cm. (Its Nutrient requirements for domestic animals, no. 7. Publi-   cation 296)
      1. Feeding   and feeding stuffs. 2. Foxes. 3. Minks. I. Title. Series.

NN   0062017   N OU OCU CLSU

National Research Council. Committee on Animal Nutrition.
     Nutrient requirements for poultry; a report of the Committee on Animal Nutrition, prepared by the Subcommittee on Poultry Nutrition. Rev. Jan. 1954. Washington, D. C., Agricultural Board, Division of Biology and Agriculture, National Research Council, 1954.
     27 p. illus. 25 cm. (Its Nutrient requirements for domestic animals, no. 1)
     National Research Council. Publication 301.
     Includes bibliography.

     1. Poultry. Feeding and feeding stuffs. I. Title. Series.

NN   0062019   N CU OU DCU CLSU

VOLUME 407

National research council. *Committee on animal nutrition.*
Nutrition and reproduction of farm animals, by Paul H. Phillips. Third report of the Committee on animal nutrition of the National research council ... ·Washington, D. C. ₁1942₎

2 p. l., 8 p. 24½ᵐ. (*On cover:* National research council. Reprint and circular series, no. 112, May, 1942)

Bibliography: p. 7-8.

1. Nutrition. 2. Reproduction. 3. Cattle. ɪ. Phillips, Paul Horrell, 1898- ɪɪ. Title.

Library of Congress   Q11.N293 no. 112   43-51837

₍5₎   (506)   636.08451

NN   0062020   DLC OU ViU

National research council. *Committee on animal nutrition.*
... On the formulation of methods of experimentation in animal production. Report of the Subcommittee on animal nutrition. Presented for the committee by E. B. Forbes and H. S. Grindley. Washington, D. C., Published by the National research council of the National academy of sciences, 1923.

cover-title, 54 p. 25 cm. (Bulletin of the National research council, no. 33 (v. 6, pt. 2) June 1923)
"References to literature on methods and equipment": p. 49-54.
1. Stock and stock-breeding—Research. ɪ. Forbes, Ernest Browning, 1876- ɪɪ. Grindley, Harry Sands, 1864- ɪɪɪ. Title. ɪᴠ. Title: Experimentation in animal production. ᴠ. Title: Animal production. Experimentation in. ᴠɪ. Title: Methods of experimentation in animal production.

Q11.N292 no.32   23—13641

TxU ViU NcRS OrU
NN   0062021   DLC WaTC OrPR CaBVaU OO OOxM MiU

National research council. *Committee on animal nutrition.*
... Problems in the field of animal nutrition, by Subcommittee on animal nutrition ... ₍Washington, D. C., National research council, 1923₎

cover-title, 8, ₍1₎ p. 24½ᵐ. (Reprint and circular series of the National research council. no. 46)
"Reprinted from Science, vol. LVII, no. 1481, pages 567-571, May 18, 1923."

1. Nutrition. ɪ. Title.

Library of Congress   Card Div.   Q11.N293 no. 46
CD 34-34

NN   0062022   DLC MiU OCl OClW TxU ViU NN

National Research Council. Committee on Animal Nutrition.
Recommended nutrient allowances for domestic animals. Washington, National Research Council, 1944-73. Publication)

no. illus. 24-28 cm. (National Research Council. Publication)
Vols. issued 1953-54 have title: Nutrient requirements for domestic animals. Beginning 1958: Nutrient requirements of domestic animals.
No. 11 by Subcommittee on Fish Nutrition, National Research Council.
Includes earlier editions of some volumes.
Later editions are issued as National Academy of Sciences publications.
Includes bibliographies.

CONTENTS: no. 1. Nutrient requirements of poultry.
no. 2. Nutrient requirements of swine.
no. 3. Nutrient requirements of dairy cattle.
no. 4. Nutrient requirements of beef cattle.
no. 5. Nutrient requirements of sheep.
no. 6. Nutrient requirements of horses.
no. 7. Nutrient requirements of minks and foxes.
no. 8. Nutrient requirements of dogs.
no. 9. Nutrient requirements of rabbits.
no. 10. Nutrient requirements of laboratory animals: cat, guinea pig, hamster, monkey, mouse, rat.
no. 11. Nutrient requirements of trout, salmon, and catfish.

1. Feeding. 2. Feeds. ɪ. National research council. Subcommittee on Fish Nutrition. ɪɪ. Title. ɪɪɪ. Title: Nutrient requirements for domestic animals. ɪᴠ. Title: Nutrient requirements of domestic animals. ᴠ. Series. ᴠɪ. Series: National Academy of Sciences, Washington, D. C. Publication.

SF95.N32   54-60841
MARC
rev 4
Library of Congress   ₍r74g⁵⁾

OrCS OrP MsSM WU IEN INS WU NbU-M MBCo
CLSU Wa WaS CaBVa WU-M IdU CaBVaU NjR MtBC Or
TU MiEM PU CtY DNAL PSt MoU NcRS GAT NBuC OU
WaTC MtU IdPI OrU-M CLSU PU-V NBuG MiU TxU AAP
NN   0062025   DLC UU IU NIC NcD OCl FMU ViU DCU

National research council. *Committee on animal nutrition.*
Report.

Washington, D. C. ₍19
nos. 25-27½ᵐ.

Nos.   issued as the council's Reprint and circular series, no.
Nos. 1, 5-6, 8,   reproduced from type-written copy.
Nos.   published by the council's Division of biology and agriculture. Each report has also distinctive title.

1. Nutrition. 2. Feeding and feeding stuffs.

43-51858 Revised 2
Library of Congress   SF95.N27
₍r45e2₎   636.085

NN   0062027   DLC OrCS IU PSt CU WvU TU DNAL

National research council. Committee on animal nutrition.
... Suggestions for meeting the poultry feed situation during 1943; prepared by: G.F. Heuser, chairman, sub-committee, H. J. Almquist, R. M. Bethke, H. S. Wilgus, H. W. Titus ... Washington, D.C., Division of biology and agriculture ₍1943₎

10p. (₍National research council₎ Committee on animal nutrition. Report no.8

NN   0062028   MiEM

National research council. Committee on animal nutrition.
... The use of phosphorus-containing substitutes for bone meal in livestock feeding with particular reference to the fluorine hazard, prepared by H. H. Mitchell ... Washington, D.C., Division of biology and agriculture, 1943.

5 p. (₍National research council₎ Committee on animal nutrition. Report no.10)

NN   0062029   MiEM

National Research Council. Committee on Animal Nutrition.
see also   Conference on Energy Metabolism, State College, Pa., 1935.

National Research Council. Committee on Animal Nutrition. Subcommittee on Fluorosis Problems.
The fluorosis problem in livestock production, a report of the Committee on Animal Nutrition. Prepared by the Subcommittee on Fluorosis Problems. P. H. Phillips, chairman ₍and others₎. Washington₎ Agricultural Board, National Academy of Sciences, National Research Council, 1955.

17 p. illus. 25 cm. (National Research Council. Publication 381)
Includes bibliography.
1. Fluorine—Toxicology. 2. Veterinary toxicology. ɪ. Title. ɪɪ. Series.

SF757.5.N27 1955   636.089'59   55-60040 ‡

MiU NN ICJ GU IdPI MtBuM OrCS OrP Or Wa
NN   0062031   DLC CaBVaU WaTC DNAL NcD CU PBL ViU

Q11
.N247   NATIONAL RESEARCH COUNCIL. Committee on Applied
no.128   Mathematical Statistics.
Personnel and training problems created by the recent growth of applied statistics in the United States; a report by the Committee on Applied Mathematical Statistics of the National Research Council. Washington, D. C. ₍1947₎

17 p. (National Research Council. Reprint and circular series, no.128)

1. Mathematical statistics—Study and teaching.

NN   0062032   ICU ViU

QA276
.B38   National Research Council. Committee on Applied Mathematical Statistics.

Bennett, Carl Allen, 1921-
Statistical analysis in chemistry and the chemical industry ₍by₎ Carl A. Bennett ₍and₎ Norman L. Franklin. Sponsored by the Committee on Applied Mathematical Statistics, the National Research Council. New York, Wiley ₍1954₎

National Research Council. *Committee on Artificial Limbs.*
Annual report. 1st-   1945/46-
Evanston, Ill.

₍v. illus. 28 cm.
Reports for 1945/46-   issued by the committee under an earlier name: Committee on Prosthetic Devices.

1. Artificial limbs.

RD756.A1N3   617.57   48-18655*

NN   0062034   DLC MiU

National Research Council. Committee on Artificial Limbs.
Calif. Univ. Prosthetic Devices Research Subcommittee's report on fundamental studies of human locomotion...
see   California. University. Prosthetic Devices Research Project.
Subcontractor's report on fundamental studies of human locomotion...

WE
168.8   National Research Council. Committee on
qN277a   Artificial Limbs
1948   Artificial limb program; working conference and symposium, 10-14 May, 1948, program. Washington ₍1948?₎
2, 71.

1. Extremities, Prosthetic

NN   0062036   DNLM

WE
168.8   National Research Council. Committee on
qN277f   Artificial Limbs
1947   ₍Final report, nos. 1-15. Washington?, 1947₎
v. in illus.

1. Extremities, Prosthetic

NN   0062037   DNLM

National Research Council. Committee on Artificial Limbs.
Progress report ₍to the₎ Committee on Artificial Limbs, National Research Council
see under   International Business Machines Corporation. Electrical Arm Project.

National Research Council. Committee on Artificial Limbs.
Report
see its   Annual report.

National Research Council. Committee on Artificial Limbs.
Subcontractor's final report on an investigation of low pressure laminates for prosthetic devices
see under   National Research and Manufacturing Company, San Diego, Calif.

National Research Council. Committee on Artificial Limbs.
Subcontractor's final report on research and development of arms and hands operated by electrical...
see under   International Business Machines Corporation. Prosthetic Devices Research Project.

VOLUME 407

National Research Council. *Committee on Artificial Limbs.*
Terminal research reports on artificial limbs ... covering the period, 1 April 1945 through 30 June 1947. Washington, 1947.

95 p. illus., ports. 28 cm.

1. Artificial limbs. ₁1. Extremities, Prosthetic₎

Med 48–620

U. S. Army Medical Libr.   [WE168.8qN277t 1947]
for Library of Congress   ₁1₎

NN   0062042   DNLM WaS ICJ ICU MiU NNC

National Research Council. *Committee on Artificial Limbs*
see also **National Research Council.** *Advisory Committee on Artificial Limbs.*

National research council. *Committee on atomic structure.*
... A general survey of the present status of the atomic structure problem. Report of the Committee on atomic structure of the National research council, by David L. Webster ... and Leigh Page ... Washington, D. C., Published by the National research council of the National academy of sciences, 1921.

cover-title, p. ₁335₎-395. diagrs. 25ᶜᵐ. (Bulletin of the National research council. no. 14 (v. 2, pt. 6) July 1921)

1. Atomic theory.   I. Webster, David Locke, 1888–   II. Page, Leigh, 1884–   III. Title.   IV. Title: Atomic structure problem.

22–3009 Revised

Library of Congress   Q11.N292 no.14

NN   0062044   DLC CaBVaU OrPR NcRS ViU NNC

WD   **NATIONAL Research Council. Committee**
700   **on Aviation Medicine**
qN278a   Appraisal of projects in aviation
1942   medicine. ₁Report submitted by Walter
    R. Miles₎ ₁New Haven, 1942₎
    51 ℓ.
    Caption title.
    1. Aviation medicine
    I. Miles, Walter Richard, 1885–

NN   0062045   DNLM

Z5064   **National research council. Committee on**
.M5H6   **aviation medicine.**
   Hoff, Ebbe Curtis, 1906–
    A bibliography of aviation medicine, by Ebbe Curtis Hoff and John Farquhar Fulton, prepared for the Committee on aviation medicine, Division of medical sciences, National research council, acting for the Committee on medical research, Office of scientific research and development, Washington, D. C. Springfield, Ill., Baltimore. Md., C. C. Thomas, 1942.

Z6669   **National research council. Committee on**
.F8   **aviation medicine.**
   Fulton, John Farquhar, 1899–
    A bibliography of visual literature, 1939–1944, compiled by John F. Fulton, Phebe M. Hoff and Henrietta T. Perkins. Prepared by the Committee on aviation medicine, Division of medical sciences, National research council, acting for the Committee on medical research, Office of scientific research and development. Washington, D. C., 1945.

ZWD   **NATIONAL Research Council. Committee**
700   **on Aviation Medicine**
N277b   Bibliography on aviation medicine.
1946   ₁Washington?₎ 1946.
    2 v.
    A list of reports on aviation medicine which are on file in the Division of Medical Sciences, National Research Council.
    1. Aviation medicine - Bibl.

NN   0062048   DNLM MBCo

National Research Council. Committee on Aviation Medicine.
Conference on acclimatization, 17 June 1949, Washington, D. C.
    see under   Conference on Acclimatization, Washington, D. C., 1949.

TL555   **NATIONAL RESEARCH COUNCIL. Committee on Aviation**
.N3   **Medicine.**
(B)   Conference on ultrasonics and explosive decompression. Washington, D. C., 1947.
    ₁37₎ p.
    Bibliography: Appendix B.

    1. Aeronautics--Medical aspects.   2. Supersonic waves.

NN   0062050   ICU DNLM IU-M

TL555   **National Research Council. Committee on Avia-**
.Y3   **tion Medicine.**
   Yale University. *School of Medicine. Aeromedical Research Unit.*
    Studies in aviation medicine, carried out under the direction of the Committee on Aviation Medicine, Division of Medical Sciences, N. R. C., acting for the Committee on Medical Research, O. S. R. D. Responsible investigator, John F. Fulton. New Haven, Yale Univ. School of Medicine, Laboratory of Physiology ₁1946₎

National Research Council. Committee on Aviation Medicine. Subcommittee on Clothing
    see   **National Research Council. Subcommittee on Clothing.**

National Research Council. *Committee on Aviation Medicine. Subcommittee on Decompression Sickness.*
    Decompression sickness; caisson sickness, diver's and flier's bends, and related syndromes. Compiled under the auspices of the Subcommittee on Decompression Sickness, Committee on Aviation Medicine, Division of Medical Sciences, National Research Council, Washington, D. C. Philadelphia, Saunders, 1951.

xii, 437 p. illus. 25 cm.
Edited by John F. Fulton, chairman.
Bibliography: p. 398–424.

1. Caisson-disease.   I. Fulton, John Farquhar, 1899–   ed.
II. Title.

RC965.C7N3   612.274   51–6141

OrU-M MBCo DNLM
NN   0062053   DLC CaBVaU WaS CaBVa ViU ICJ MiU

National Research Council. *Committee on Aviation Medicine. Subcommittee on Oxygen and Anoxia.*
    Handbook of respiratory data in aviation. Prepared under the direction of the Subcommittee on Oxygen and Anoxia of the Committee on Aviation Medicine, Division of Medical Sciences, National Research Council acting for the Committee on Medical Research, Office of Scientific Research and Development. Washington, 1944–

1 v. (loose-leaf) diagrs., tables. 29 cm.

1. Flight—Physiological aspects. 2. Respiration.   I. U. S. Office of Scientific Research and Development. Committee on Medical Research.   II. Title: Respiratory data in aviation.

RC1075.N36   *616.98   629.13256   56–695

NN   0062054   DLC IU-M MBCo DNLM CtY-M

National Research Council. Committee on Aviation Medicine. Yale Aeromedical Research Unit
    see   **Yale University. School of Medicine. Aeromedical Research Unit.**

TL555   **National Research Council. Committee on**
N28   **Aviation Psychology.**
    An investigation of the relationship between visual ability and flight performance. Washington, U.S. Civil Aeronautics Administration, 1948.
    xii, 123 p. illus., tables, diagrs. (part col.) 27½cm. (U.S. Civil Aeronautics Administration. Division of Research Report no. 78)

    Processed.
    Bibliography: p. 89.
    1. Sight.   2. Aeronautics -

NN   0062056   OrCS

W 2   **NATIONAL Research Council. Committee**
AA1   **on Aviation Psychology**
qN19r   Report. no. 1-
    Mar. 1949-
    Washington, Division of Aviation
    Medicine, Bureau of Medicine and Surgery,
    U. S. Navy.
    v.
    Anals

NN   0062057   DNLM DLC NNC NNC-M

National Research Council. Committee on Aviation Psychology.
    A standardized form for the ATR flight-check
    see under   American Institutes for Research in the Behavioral Sciences.

National Research Council. Committee on Aviation Research.
    The development of a research program on advanced synthetic electronic type flight simulators...
       see under   Fitzpatrick, Robert.

National research council. *Committee on batholith problems.*
    Annotations of selected papers on the mechanics of igneous invasion with special reference to batholiths, April 27, 1935. Prepared by S. W. Sundeen with the assistance of the Committee on batholith problems, Division of geology and geography, National research council, Washington, D. C. ... ₁Washington, D. C., National research council, 1935₎
2 p. l., 54 ℓ. 27 cm.
Frank F. Grout, chairman.
Exhibit B of Appendix A: Annual report of the division for 1934-35.
Mimeographed.
1. Rocks, Igneous. 2. Batholiths.   I. Sundeen, Stanley Wilford, 1909–   II. Title.

[QE461.N   ]   G S 36—35
U. S. Geol. Survey. Libr.
for Library of Congress   ₁a66d₎

NN   0062060   DI-GS MtU IdU MsU DAU IaU OU

National research council. *Committee on batholith problems.*
    Comments on magmatic stoping, April 27, 1935. Compiled by the Committee on batholith problems, Division of geology and geography, National research council, Washington, D. C. Washington, D. C., National research council, 1935.

cover-title, 1 p. l., ll, 47 p. plate. 27 cm.

Frank F. Grout, chairman.
Exhibit C of Appendix A, Annual report of the Division for 1934-35.
Mimeographed.

1. Batholiths.   I. Title.

[QE461.N   ]   G S 35—298
U. S. Geol. Survey. Libr.
for Library of Congress   ₁a63d₎

NN   0062061   DI-GS MtU IdU DAU IaU OU TU MsU

552.1   **National Research Council--Committee on Batholith**
N212c   **Problems.**
1938   Comments on magmatic stoping, April 27, 1935. Compiled by the Committee on Batholith Problems, Division of Geology and Geography, National Research Council, Washington, D.C. Washington, D.C., National Research Council, 1938.
    ii, 47p. illus. 27cm.

    Cover title.
    First published 1935. Reprinted 1938.
    "Exhibit C of Appendix A, annual report of the Division for 1934-   35."

NN   0062062   IU

VOLUME 407

National research council. Committee on batholith problems.
Partial miscibility of magmas, by Clarence N. Fenner. ₍Washington, National research council, 1933₎
6 p. 28cm.

Exhibit C of Appendix A, Annual report of division for 1932/33.

NN 0062063 IdU

QE461 National Research Council. Committee on
.N37 Batholith Problems.
Problems of the batholiths, April 22, 1933. Washington, D.C., National Research Council ₍1933₎
59 p. illus., diagrs. 27 cm.
At head of title: National Research Council. Division of Geology and Geography. Frank F. Grout, chairman.
Exhibit B of Appendix A, Annual report of the division for 1932-33.

1. Batholiths. I. Title.

NN 0062064 TU OU IU FU IaU DI-GS IaU

National Research Council. Committee on Batholith Problems.
Problems of the batholiths. Washington, 1938.
59 p. diagr.
"Exhibit B of Appendix A, Annual Report of Division [1933]"
Reprinted with added addenda 1938.

NN 0062065 NNC MtU IEN CtY DI-GS CaBVaU

National research council. *Committee on bibliography of American scientific and technical books*
see
National research council. *Committee on American scientific and technical bibliography.*

W 2 NATIONAL Research Council. Committee on
A Blood and Blood Derivatives
qN31b Bulletin₂ blood and blood derivatives.
Mar. 1948-Apr. 1951. Washington.
2 v. illus.
Superseded by the Bulletin on blood and related problems of the Council's Committee on Blood and Related Problems.
Comprises the minutes of the Committee's 1st-9th meeting, of its conferences, panels and Ad Hoc Committee on Blood Refrigeration.

1. Blood - Period. 2. Blood substitutes Title

NN 0062068 DNLM

W National Research Council. Committee
1 on Blood and Blood Derivatives
NA6198 Minutes of meeting. 1st- ;
Mar. 8, 1948-
Chicago ₍etc.₎

NN 0062069 DNLM

National Research Council. Committee on Blood and Blood Derivatives.
The preservation of the formed elements and of the proteins of the blood
see under Conference upon the Preservation of the Erythrocytes, Leucocytes, Platelets and Plasma Proteins, Harvard University, 1949.

National Research Council. *Committee on Blood and Related Problems*
see
National Research Council. *Committee on Blood and Transfusion Problems.*

National Research Council. Committee on Blood
and Transfusion Problems.
W2 **Bulletin, blood and related problems.**
A Mar. 1952-
N36427b Washington.

National Research Council. Committee on Blood and Transfusion Problems
Conference on Differential Agglutination of Erythrocytes.
see under

Conference on Differential Agglutination of Erythrocytes, Washington, D.C., 1952.

National Research Council. Committee on Blood and Transfusion Problems.
Progress report. Contract no. DA-49-007-MD-150.
see under

Iowa. University. College of Medicine.

National Research Council. *Committee on Bridges*
see
National Research Council. *Highway Research Board. Committee on Bridges.*

G74 NATIONAL RESEARCH COUNCIL. Committee on
.N3 Careers in Geography.
(Ge) A career in geography. ₍Washington₎ 1954.
19 p.
"Prepared by a Joint Committee on Careers in Geography, of the Association of American Geographers and the National Research Council.

1. Geography as a profession. I. Title.

NN 0062076 ICU NNC OCIW

National Research Council. *Committee on Careers in Geography.*
A selected bibliography on careers in geography. ₍Washington₎ 1951.
9 l. 28 cm.

1. Geography as a profession—Bibl. I. Title: Careers in geography.
Z6004.P5N38 016.91069 53-17575

NN 0062077 DLC

National Research Council. *Committee on Careers in Geography.*
Some basic facts about geographers and geography in the United States. ₍Washington₎ 1951.
11 l. 28 cm.
Bibliographical footnotes.

1. Geography as a profession.
G74.N3 910.69 51-8807

NN 0062078 DLC

National Research Council. Committee on
Catalysis
see also National Research Council. Committee on Contact Catalysis.

National Research Council. Committee on
Causes and Prevention of Highway Accidents
see National Research Council. Highway Research Board. Committee on Causes and Prevention of Highway Accidents.

National research council. *Committee on celestial mechanics.*
... Celestial mechanics. A survey of the status of the determination of the general perturbations of the minor planets, by A. O. Leuschner. Washington, D. C., Published by the National research council of the National academy of sciences, 1922.
cover-title, 73 p. 25ᶜᵐ. (Bulletin of the National research council. no. 25 (v. 4, pt. 7) Dec. 1922)
Appendix to the Report of the Committee on celestial mechanics, published as Bulletin no. 19 (v. 4, pt. 1) Sept. 1922.

1. Mechanics, Celestial. I. Leuschner, Armin Otto, 1868-
II. Title.
23-18693 Revised
Library of Congress Q11.N292 no. 25

NN 0062081 DLC OrSaW CaBVaU OrPR CU OrU ViU NN

National research council. *Committee on celestial mechanics.*
... Celestial mechanics. Report of the Committee on celestial mechanics of the National research council, by E. W. Brown ... chairman; G. D. Birkhoff ... A. O. Leuschner ... H. N. Russell ... Washington, D. C., Published by the National research council of the National academy of sciences, 1922.
cover-title, 22 p. 25 cm. (Bulletin of the National research council. no. 19 (v. 4, pt. 1) Sept. 1922)
An appendix to this report, by A. O. Leuschner, was published as Bulletin no. 25 (v. 4, pt. 7) of the National research council. Dec. 1922.
1. Mechanics, Celestial. I. Brown, Ernest William, 1866-1938. II. Birkhoff, George David, 1884-1944. III. Leuschner, Armin Otto, 1868-IV. Title.
Q11.N292 no. 19 23—13634

ViU NcD NcRS NN
NN 0062082 DLC OrSaW CaBVaU OrU OrPR WaTC NNC

National Research Council. Committee on
Cellulose and Allied Substances.
see National Research Council. Division of Chemistry and Chemical Technology. Committee on Cellulose and Allied Substances.

National Research Council. Committee on
Cereals.
The facts about enrichment of flour and bread
see under National Research Council. Food and Nutrition Board.

TX560 National Research Council. Committee on
.B8 Cereals.
N22 Flour and bread enrichment, 1949-50.
pam Washington, 1950.
16 p. tables, map. 25cm.

1. Flour. 2. Bread. 3. Food, Enriched.
I. Title. x₎ National Research Council. Food and Nutrition Board. Committee on Cereals

NN 0062085 OrCS NIC

Q11 National research council. Committee on
.N292 cereals.
no. 112 **Kik, Marinus Cornelis,** 1896-
... The nutritional improvement of white rice, by M. C. Kik and R. R. Williams, for the Committee on cereals, Food and nutrition board. Washington, D. C., National research council, National academy of sciences ₍1945₎

VOLUME 407

National Research Council. *Committee on Channelization*
see
National Research Council. *Highway Research Board.
Committee on Channelization.*

National research council. *Committee on chemical data for
ceramists.*
... Data on chemicals for ceramic use; formulas, molecular
weights, colors, crystal forms, densities, refractive indices,
melting points, boiling points, transition points, decomposition
temperatures. Based on report of the Committee on chemical
data for ceramists, Division of chemistry and chemical technology, National research council. Alexander Silverman,
chairman ... George W. Morey, Frederick D. Rossini. Wash-

ington, D. C., The National research council, National acad-
emy of sciences ₁1943₎
94 p. 24½ᵐ. (Bulletin of the National research council, no. 107.
June 1943)
"Published originally in mimeographed form."—Pref.
Bibliography: p. 74–94.

1. Chemicals. 2. Pottery.   I. Silverman, Alexander, 1881–

Library of Congress   Q11.N292 no. 107   43–50019
                           ₍20₎   (506) 666.3

PSt Nc–SC NcD ViU
NN 0062089   DLC CaBVaU OrPR WaTC WaS FMU CU TxU

National Research Council. *Committee on Chemical Data
for Ceramists.*
Data on chemicals for ceramic use; formulas, molecular
weights, colors, crystal forms, densities, refractive indices,
melting points, boiling points, transition points, decomposition temperatures, based on Report of the Committee on
Chemical Data for Ceramists, Division of Chemistry and
Chemical Technology, National Research Council. ₁Rev.
ed.₎ Washington, Published by University of Pittsburgh
for National Research Council, National Academy of
Sciences, 1949.

Bibliography: p. 151–198.

1. Chemicals. 2. Pottery.   (Series: National Research Council.
Bulletin, no. 118)
        Q11.N292 no. 118   666.3   51–60341

ViU DI ICU
NN 0062091   DLC WaTC WaS WaU MiU PSt NcRS MB TxU

CHEMISTRY
D666.3
AN213

National research council. *Committee on
chemical data for ceramists.*
Final report of the Committee on chemical
data for ceramists to the Division of chemistry and chemical technology of the National
research council. ₁Pittsburgh, 1942₎
182 l.

1. Pottery – Bibliography. 2. Chemicals –
Bibliography.

NN 0062092   NNC

National Research Council. Committee on
Chemistry
    see   Conference on Electrical Insulation.
Committee on Chemistry.

National Research Council. *Committee on Chemical Utilization of Coal.*
Chemistry of coal utilization. H. H. Lowry, chairman
₁and editor₎ New York, Wiley ₁1945₎
2 v. (xiii, 1864, xv–cv p.) illus., diagrs., tables. 23 cm.
Bibliographical footnotes.
——— Supplementary volume. H. H. Lowry, editor. Prepared by the Committee on Chemistry of Coal, Division of
Chemistry and Chemical Technology, National Academy of
Science–National Research Council. New York, Wiley
₁1963₎
viii, 1142 p. illus., diagrs., tables. 27 cm.
Bibliographical footnotes.
                                        TP953.N3 Suppl.

1. Coal. 2. Coal-tar products.   I. Lowry, Homer Hiram, 1896–
ed.   II. National Research Council. Committee on the Chemistry
of Coal.   III. Title.   IV. Title: Coal utilization.

TP953.N3   662.6   45–5498 rev*

TxU OU OCl NcD NcRS OOxM TU MB CU ICJ WU ViU DI–GS
WaS WaT NN WaWW OKentU CU–I CaBVaU CaBViP CtY MiHM
NN 0062095   DLC IdU MeB MtU AAP MtBuM OrCS OrU OCU

HQ750
.A1C47

National research council. Committee on child
development.
Child development abstracts and bibliography. v. 1–
June/Sept./Dec. 1927–
Washington, D. C., National research council ₁etc.₎, 1927–

National Research Council. Committee on Child
Development.
Directory of research in child development.
[Washington, 1927]
        see under   Marston, Leslie Ray, 1894–

Q11
.N293
no. 102

National research council. Committee on child
development.
Hicks, James Allan, 1897–   comp.
... Directory of research in child development. 2d ed.
Compiled for National research council Committee on child
development, by J. Allan Hicks. Washington, D. C., National research council, 1931.

National research council. Committee on child
development.
Conference on research in child development. 2d, Wash-
ington, 1927.
... Second Conference on research in child development,
Washington, D. C., May 5–7, 1927 ... ₁Washington, D. C.,
Committee on child development, National research council,
1927?₎

National research council. Committee on
child development.
Conference on research in child development. 3d, Toronto,
1929.
... Third Conference on research in child development, University of Toronto, Toronto, Canada, May 2–4, 1929 ...
₁Washington, D. C., Committee on child development, National
research council, 1929?₎

National Research Council. Committee on Child
Development.
Conference on research in child development. 4th, Chicago,
1933.
... Fourth Conference on research in child development, the
University of Chicago, Chicago, Illinois, June 22–24, 1933 ...
₁Washington, D. C., Committee on child development, Na-
tional research council, 1933₎

National Research Council. *Committee on Child Development*
see also **Conference on Emergency Problems of Children
and Youth,** Washington, D. C., 1941.

National Research Council. *Committee on Child Development*
see also **Conference on War and Postwar Child Services
and Research,** Chicago and Washington, D. C., 1943.

TN941
C557

National Research Council. Committee on Clay
Minerals.
Clay Minerals Society.
Clays and clay minerals; proceedings of the conference.
1st–   1952–
Oxford, New York ₁etc.₎ Pergamon Press, Symposium Pub-
lications Division ₁etc.₎

National Research Council. *Committee on Clay Minerals*
see also
National Conference on Clays and Clay Minerals.

National Research Council. Committee on
Colloids.
Proposed National Institute for Research
in Colloid Chemistry
    see under   **Wisconsin. University.**

QH366
J43

National Research Council. *Committee on Common
Problems of Genetics, Paleontology, and
Systematics.*
Jepsen, Glenn Lowell, 1904–   ed.
Genetics, paleontology, and evolution, ed. by Glenn L.
Jepsen, Ernst Mayr ₁and₎ George Gaylord Simpson, for the
Committee on Common Problems of Genetics, Paleontology,
and Systematics, of the National Research Council. Prince-
ton, Princeton Univ. Press, 1949.

National Research Council. Committee on
Compaction of Subgrades and Embankments
    see   **National Research Council.** Highway
Research Board. Committee on Compaction of
Subgrades and Embankments.

National Research Council. *Committee on Conservation*
see
National Research Council. *Committee on Use and Care
of Natural Resources.*

National research council. *Committee on contact catalysis.*
... Report of the Committee on contact catalysis. ₁1st–
₁1922–
₁Washington, D. C., National research council, 1922–
        v. 24½ᵐ.
Cover-title.
The 1st report was published in the Journal of industrial engineering
chemistry, 1922; subsequent reports (to 1932) were published each year
in the Journal of physical chemistry. 1st–9th (1922–32) were reissued
as Reprint and circular series of the National research council, no. 30,
50, 59, 66, 78, 83, 90, 94, 103. 10th/11th (1935) issued separately in
mimeographed form.
Seventh report, 1929, has title: Enzyme catalysts, seventh report of
the Committee on contact catalysis, National research council.

The 12th report has title: Twelfth report of the Committee on catalysis, National research council. New York, John Wiley & sons, inc.; London, Chapman & Hall, limited, 1940.
Bibliographies included.

1. Catalysis.
                                        C D 34—65

Library of Congress.   Card div. QD501.N3
                           ₁40r38h1₎   541.39

WaWW ICJ CoU IU PPF CaBVaU MtBC
NN 0062111   DLC WaTC OrPR IdU OrU–M OrU OrCS WaT

VOLUME 407

National research council. *Committee on density currents.*
... Lake Mead density currents investigations, 1937-1940 ... Submitted by the subcommittee on lake Mead, Interdivisional committee on density currents, National research council. Denver, Col., 1941.

2 v. front., plates, maps, tables (part fold.) diagrs. (part fold.) 28ᵐ.

At head of title: United States Dept. of the interior, Bureau of reclamation.
Title from label mounted on cover.

1. Mead, Lake. I. U. S. Bureau of reclamation.

43-12945

Library of Congress   GC293.M4N3

₍2₎   551.48

NN   0062112   DLC

National Research Council. *Committee on Density Currents.*
Lake Mead density currents investigations, submitted by the Subcommittee on Lake Mead, Interdivisional Committee on Density Currents, National Research Council. ₍Washington₎ U. S. Dept. of the Interior, Bureau of Reclamation ₍1948₎

3 v. illus., maps. 23 cm.

CONTENTS.—v. 1-2. 1937-1940. 2 v.—v. 3. 1940-1946.

1. Mead, Lake. I. U. S. Bureau of Reclamation.

GC293.M4N3 1948   551.48   51-4390

NN   0062113   DLC DNAL IaU IU

Mann
R
111
Z991
no. 20

National Research Council. *Committee on Dental Health.*
Control of tooth decay. Washington, 1953.
18 p.

1. Teeth – Care and hygiene. 2. Teeth – Diseases. I. Blakeslee, Alton L II. Title.

NN   0062114   NIC IaU CU DNLM MiU PU-D DNAL OrCS

National Research Council. *Committee on Dental Health.*
The problem of providing optimum fluoride intake for prevention of dental caries; a report of the Committee on Dental Health of the Food and Nutrition Board, prepared by the Subcommittee on Optimum Fluoride Levels. ₍Washington₎ Division of Biology and Agriculture, National Research Council, 1953.

15 p. tables. 25 cm. (National Research Council. Publication 294)

Bibliography: p. 13-15.

1. Teeth—Diseases. 2. Water—Fluoridation. I. Title: Providing optimum fluoride intake for prevention of dental caries. (Series)

RK331.N29   617.6   54-61612

CaBVaU IdPI CU-M OrCS Or OrU OrPS
PBL NcD TU CU ViU ICJ PU-D OrPS OkU-M OrU ICJ IU
NN   0062115   DLC DNAL WaTC OkU-M MsU NN DNLM PSt

National Research Council. *Committee on Dental Health.*
A survey of the literature of dental caries, prepared for the Food and Nutrition Board, National Research Council, under the supervision of the Committee on Dental Health, P. C. Jeans, chairman. By Guttorm Toverud ₍and others₎ Washington, National Academy of Sciences, National Research Council, 1952.

ix, 567 p. illus. 26 cm. (₍National Research Council₎ Publication 225)

Bibliography: p. 509-567.

1. Teeth—Diseases. 2. Teeth—Diseases—Bibl. I. Toverud, Guttorm, 1896- II. Title. (Series)

RK331.N3   617.6   53—60466

OC1W-H N IdPI IdU CU NIC MtBC ICJ UU MBCo OrU-M
CaBViP OrCS WaS PWpM LU PPJ PU-D DCU DPAHO KMK
NcU NNC ViU NN DNAL WaTC CU ICU InU CaBVaU OrCS
NN   0062116   DLC DNLM PSt FU-HC PPT-D PBL OU OC1

W
1
NA62364

National Research Council. *Committee on Follow-up Studies*
Minutes of meeting. 1st-May 10, 1948-
Colorado Springs, Colo.
v.

NN   0062117   DNLM

National Research Council. *Committee on Design, Construction and Equipment of Laboratories.*
Laboratory design; National Research Council report on design, construction, and equipment of laboratories. Edited by H. S. Coleman with an introd. by Roland Wank. New York, Reinhold Pub. Corp. ₍1951₎

ix, 398 p. illus. 31 cm.

Bibliography: p. 388-389.

1. Laboratories. I. Coleman, Harry Shipp, 1886- ed. II. Title.

Q183.N3   507.2   51-1665

MiHM CU MtU DNLM NN KEmT MB MtBuM CaBVaU WaSpG
MtBC IdPI CaBVa OrP GAT CLU TU NcU ViU TxU ICJ IdU
NN   0062118   DLC OrAshS WaT WaS OrU-M OrPR OrCS DI

---

q727.5
N21l
1955

National Research Council--Committee on Design, Construction and Equipment of Laboratories.
Laboratory design; National Research Council report on design, construction, and equipment of laboratories. Edited by H. S. Coleman with an introd. by Roland Wank. New York, Reinhold Pub. Corp. c1955.
viii, 392p. illus. 31cm.

Bibliography: p.388-389.

NN   0062119   IU OU ViU MH

National Research Council. *Committee on Design, Construction and Equipment of Laboratories*
see also **National Research Council.** *Committee on the Construction and Equipment of Chemical Laboratories.*

QH511
.S6
1952a

National Research Council. *Committee on Developmental Biology.*

Society for the Study of Development and Growth.
Dynamics of growth processes ₍by₎ L. M. Kozloff ₍and others₎ Edited by Edgar J. Boell. Princeton, Princeton University Press, 1954.

National research council. *Committee on diagnosis and pathology of nutritional deficiencies.*
... Inadequate diets and nutritional deficiencies in the United States, their prevalence and significance. Report of the Committee on diagnosis and pathology of nutritional deficiencies, Food and nutrition board, H. D. Kruse, M. D., chairman ... Washington, D. C., The National research council, National academy of sciences ₍1943₎

viii, 56 p. incl. tables. 24½ᵐ. (Bulletin of the National research council, no. 109. Nov. 1943)
"References": p. 48-56.

1. Nutrition. 2. Diet. 3. Deficiency diseases. I. Title.

44-7378

Library of Congress   Q11.N292 no. 109

₍18₎   (506) 613.2

OCU ViU

NN   0062122   DLC WaTC CaBVaU Or NcRS OOxM OC1 OU

389.1
N2184

National Research Council. *Committee on Diagnosis and Pathology of Nutritional Deficiencies.*
The prevalence of inadequate diets and deficiency states in the United States together with a consideration of their significance. Draft report. Washington ₍1943?₎
47 l.

NN   0062123   DNAL

HV610
1953
.N43

National Research Council. *Committee on Disaster Studies.*

Instituut voor Sociaal Onderzoek van het Nederlandse Volk.
Studies in Holland flood disaster 1953 ₍by the₎ Instituut voor Sociaal Onderzoek van het Nederlandse Volk, Amsterdam ₍and the₎ Committee on Disaster Studies of the National Academy of Sciences, National Research Council, Washington, D. C. ₍The Hague?₎ 1955

HV
593
qN277w
1955

NATIONAL Research Council. Committee on Disaster Studies
The Worcester County tornado; a medical study of the disaster. Final report submitted Sept. 1, 1954. By Henry J. Bakst ₍and others₎ ₍Washington₎ 1955.
ix, 92 p. illus.
Study organized by the Massachusetts General Hospital.
1. Disasters 2. Hospitals - Massachusetts I. Bakst, Henry Jacob,
1906- II. Massachusetts General Hospital. ₍Ind.₎ Title

NN   0062126   DNLM

National Research Council. *Committee on Disaster Studies*
see also
National Research Council. *Disaster Research Group.*

ZWM 100
N 2l
1954

National Research Council. *Committee on Disaster Studies. Subcommittee on Clearinghouse.*
Bibliography on psychological reaction to disaster. [Washington, D.C.] 1954.

16 p. 28 cm.

Caption title.

1. Disasters - Bibl. I. Title.

NN   0062128   CaBVaU

W 2
A
N318r
no. 1
1954

NATIONAL Research Council. Committee on Disaster Studies. Subcommittee on Clearinghouse
Roster of disaster personnel, Jan. 1954, comp. by C. D. Nearman. Washington, 1954.
51 p. (Its Report, no. 1)
Earlier ed. has title: A preliminary roster of disaster personnel, July 1, 1953.
1. Disasters I. Nearman, C
D comp. Title Series

NN   0062129   DNLM OrU

N 25
1955

National Research Council. *Committee on Disaster Studies. Subcommittee on Clearinghouse.*
Selected bibliography on children's reactions to stress and to crises. [Washington, D.C.] 1955.

8 p. 28 cm.

Caption title.

1. Disasters - Bibl. 2. Stress (Physiology) - Bibl. I. Title

NN   0062130   CaBVaU

VOLUME 407

National Research Council. Committee on
Disaster Studies. Subcommittee on Clearinghouse.

Selected bibliography on problems of
families in disaster. [Washington, D.C.] 1954.

3 p. 28 cm.

Caption title.

1. Disasters - Bibl. I. Title.

NN   0062131   CaBVaU

National Research Council. Committee on Drug
Addiction.
The indispensable use of narcotics, by
various authors
see under title

National research council. Committee on drug
addiction.

Krueger, Hugo Martin, 1902–
The pharmacology of the opium alkaloids ... By Hugo
Krueger ... Nathan B. Eddy ... and Margaret Sumwalt ...
[Washington, U. S. Govt. print. off., 1941–43]

National research council. *Committee on drug addiction.*
... Report of Committee on drug addiction, 1929–1941 and
Collected reprints, 1930–1941. [Washington, 1941]
xxx, 1581 p. incl. illus., tables (1 fold.) diagrs. (2 fold.) 27½ᵐ.

At head of title: National research council.
Includes bibliographies.

1. Narcotic habit.

Library of Congress   RC369.N28   42–16745

[3]   615.783

DI NNC ICJ NN ViU PWpM
NN   0062134   DLC OO WaU IU DAU DNLM NNUN OC1 OCU

National research council. *Committee on drug addiction.*
... Studies on drug addiction, with special reference to chemical structure of opium derivatives and allied synthetic substances and their physiological action ... Prepared by direction of the surgeon general ... Washington, U. S. Govt. print.
off., 1938.
viii, 143 p. incl. illus., tables, diagrs. 23½ᵐ. (U. S. Public health
service. Supplement no. 138 to the Public health reports)

At head of title: U. S. Treasury department. Henry Morgenthau, jr.,
secretary. Public health service. Thomas Parran, surgeon general.
"By Lyndon F. Small, consultant in alkaloid chemistry, U. S. Public
health service, University of Virginia, Nathan B. Eddy, consultant
biologist in alkaloids, U. S. Public health service, University of Michigan,
Erich Mosettig, research associate in organic chemistry, University of
Virginia, and C. K. Himmelsbach, passed assistant surgeon, U. S. Public
health service."
"References": p. 35–36, 112–113, 128–129.
"List of publications of the Committee on drug addiction, National
research council, 1930–1937": p. 131–138.

1. Narcotic habit. 2. Narcotics.   I. Small, Lyndon Frederick, 1897–
II. Eddy, Nathan Browne, 1890–   III. Mosettig, Erich, 1808–
IV. Himmelsbach, Clifford Keck, 1907–   V. Title. VI. Title: Drug
addiction, Studies on.
38–28876
Library of Congress   RA11.B177 no. 138
———— Copy 2.   RC369.N3
[18]   (614.06173)   615.783

NN   0062136   DLC WaWW OrCS OrU DNLM

National Research Council. Committee on Drug
Addiction and Narcotics.
Bulletin, drug addiction and narcotics. 2 Oct. 1947–17 Feb.
1965. Washington.
27 v. in   illus.
Issued by the Committee on Drug Addiction and
Narcotics, National Research Council.
Called also Minutes of meeting.
Continued by Bulletin, Problems of drug
dependence.
1. Drug Abuse - period. I. National Research
Council. Committee on Drug Addiction and Narcotics.
II. National Research Council. Committee on Drug
Addiction and Narcotics. Minutes of meeting.
III. Title: Bulletin on drug addiction and narcotics.

W2
A
N319b

NN   0062137   DNLM MBU NNC-M

National Research Council. Committee on
Durability of Concrete, Physical Aspects
see   National Research Council. Highway
Research Board. Committee on Durability of
Concrete, Physical Aspects.

National Research Council. Committee
on Economics of Motor Vehicle Size and
Weight
see   National Research Council. Highway
Research Board. Committee on Economics of
Motor Vehicle Size and Weight.

National Research Council. Committee on
Educational Policy in Agriculture.
Mimeo series publication. no.1–
Washington, D. C.
v. 28cm.

S531
N35

1. Agriculture - Study and teaching

NN   0062140   NcRS

National Research Council. Committee on Effect
of Controlled Access Expressways on Urban
Areas
see   National Research Council. Highway
Research Board. Committee on Effect of Controlled
Access Expressways on Urban Areas.

National research council. Committee on
effects of radiation upon living
organisms

see

National research council. Committee on the
effects of radiation on living organisms.

National Research Council. Committee on
Electrical Core Losses
see   National Research Council. Division
of Engineering and Industrial Research.

National Research Council. *Committee on Electrical Insula-*
tion
see **Conference on Electrical Insulation.**

National research council. *Committee on electrodynamics of*
moving media.
... Electrodynamics of moving media. Report of the National research council Committee on electrodynamics of moving media, by W. F. G. Swann, John T. Tate, H. Bateman,
E. H. Kennard. Washington, D. C., Published by the National research council of the National academy of sciences,
1922.
cover-title, 172 p. diagrs. 25ᵐ. (Bulletin of the National research
council. no. 24 (v. 4, pt. 6) Dec. 1922)
Bibliography accompanies the article by Bateman.
1. Electrodynamics. 2. Relativity (Physics)   I. Swann, William
Francis Gray, 1884–   II. Tate, John T. III. Bateman, Harry, 1882–
IV. Title. V. Title: Mov-   ing media, Electrodynamics of.
23–18692 Revised
Library of Congress   Q11.N292 no. 24

OO OCU OOxM TxU NN ViU
NN   0062145   DLC OrU OrPR CaBVaU WaTC NcRS NcD OU

National research council. Committee on fats.
A report on margarine
see under   National Research Council.
Food and Nutrition Board.

National Research Council. *Committee on Feed*
Composition.
Composition of corn in the United States, 1946–
1947. Prepared by a subcommittee consisting of
B.H. Schneider, chairman, K.C. Beeson [and] H.L.
Lucas. Washington, Agricultural Board, Division
of Biology and Agriculture, National Research
Council [1953]

iii, 26 p. map. (National Research Council.
Publication [Combined series] no. 258)
Its Report, no. 2.
I. Series. II. National Research Council.
Committee on Feed Composition. /Report, no. 2.
543.819   633.219   633.3

NN   0062148   ICJ CaBVaU OrCS PBL CLSU NcD

National Research Council. *Committee on Feed Composi-*
tion.
Report.
Washington [19
v. illus. 25 cm. (National Research Council. Publication.
258
Each report has also a distinctive title.

1. Feeding and feeding stuffs—Analysis.

SF97.N3   636.0851   53–63733 ‡

NN   0062149   DLC CaBVaU CtY NN

National Research Council. *Committee on Flexible Pave-*
ment Design
see
National Research Council. *Highway Research Board.*
Committee on Flexible Pavement Design.

National Research Council. Committee on Food
and Nutrition
see   National Research Council. Food
and Nutrition Board.

National Research Council. *Committee on Food Compo-*
sition.
Tables of food composition, giving proximate, mineral, and
vitamin components of foods. Washington [1943]
[19] l. 22 x 28 cm.

1. Food—Tables, calculations, etc. 2. Food—Analysis.   I. Title.

TX537.N28   50–49109

NN   0062152   DLC DNAL NIC

National research council. Committee on Food
Composition.
Tables of food composition giving proximate,
mineral and vitamin components of foods. Rev. ed.
Washington [1943]
23 numb. l.
"Committee on food composition."

389.1
N2183
1943
rev.

NN   0062153   DNAL

National research council. Committee on Food
Composition.
Tables of vitamin losses in cooking of foods...
[by]... Committee on food composition ...
Washington, D.C., 1943.
4 numb l.   22 x 28 cm.
Processed.
1. Vitamins. I. Title: Vitamin losses in
cooking of foods.

389.1
N2183T

NN   0062154   DNAL

VOLUME 407

389.1
N2183
1944
National research council. Committee on Food
Composition.
Tables of food composition giving proximate
mineral and vitamin components of foods.
Washington, D.C. [1944]
22 p.

NN 0062155   DNAL

QU
145
qN277
NATIONAL Research Council. Committee
on Food Economics
[Collection of publications]

The library has a collection of miscellaneous publications of this organization kept as received. These publications
are not listed nor bound separately.
1. Nutrition

NN 0062156   DNLM

389
N2192
National research council. Committee on food
habits.
Acute food problems under war conditions.
Liaison session, February 12, 1944.   Washington
[1944]
30 p.
1. United nations relief and rehabilitation
administration. 2. Reconstruction (1939-   )
Food relief. 3. World war, 1939-   Food
questions. I. Title: Food problems under war
conditions.

NN 0062157   DNAL

389
N2194Ad
National research council. Committee on
food habits.
Attitudes toward dividing the American food
supply with our allies.   [Washington? D.C.,
1943?]
10 p.

1. Attitude (Psychology) 2. Food supply. U.S.
3. World war, 1939-1945. Food question. I.
Woodward, Patricia. II. Shippee, Eva.

NN 0062158   DNAL

389
N2194A
National research council. Committee on
food habits.
Attitudes toward sending food abroad after
the war. [Washington? 1944?]
25 p.

NN 0062159   DNAL

389
N2194Ar
National research council. Committee on
food habits.
Attitudes toward the effect of point
rationing on the choice of food.   [Washington?
1943]
16 p.

NN 0062160   DNAL

389
N2194
National research council. Committee on
food habits.
Attitudes toward the use of soybeans as
food.   [Washington? 1943?]
11 p.

NN 0062161   DNAL

389
N2194At
[National research council] Committee on food
habits.
Attitudes towards increased consumption of
bread.   [Washington? D.C., 1943]
15 p.

1. Attitude (Psychology) 2. Bread. I. Shippee,
Eva.

NN 0062162   DNAL

389.9
N2134C
1941
National Research Council. Committee on
Food Habits.
Conference with the Committee on Food
Habits held under the auspices of Division
of Anthropology and Psychology, May 23 and
24.   Washington, 1941.
p. 93-190.

1. Food consumption. U.S. 2. Food habits.
Congresses. 3. Nutrition. Congresses.
I. Title.

NN 0062163   DNAL MH

389.9
N2134C
National research council. Committee on food
habits.
... Conference with the Committee on food
habits, held under the auspices of Division
of anthropology and psychology, June 27 and
28. . Washington, D.C., 1941.
.cover-title, p.[191]-350   28cm.

Processed, cover printed.
Not for publication.

NN 0062164   DNAL

50
N215
National research council. Committee on food
habits.
Current attitudes toward the meat rationing
program. [Washington? D.C., 1943?]
9 p.

NN 0062165   DNAL

389
N2194C
[National research council] Committee on food
habits.
Current attitudes toward the point rationing
program. [Washington? D.C., 1943?
12 p.
1. Attitude (Psychology) 2. Rationing,
Consumers U.S. I. Woodward, Patricia.
II. Shippee, Eva.

NN 0062166   DNAL

389.1
N218
National research council. Committee on food
habits.
A group test for determining the anchorage
points of food habits; a preliminary report on
a study directed by Kurt Lewin... [Washington,
1942]
21 p.   28cm.
Processed.
"This study has been conducted by Alex Bavelas,
Leon Festinger, Patricia Woodward, and Alvin
Zander..."- Acknow   ledgements.

NN 0062167   DNAL MH

FILM
641.1
N213g
National Research Council--Committee on Food
Habits.
A group test for determining the anchorage
points of food habits; a preliminary report on
a study directed by Kurt Lewin. [Iowa City,
Child Welfare Research Station, State Universi-
ty of Iowa [1942]
Microfilm copy of report in the U.S. Dept. of
Agriculture Library made in 1956. Negative.
Collation of the original: 21p. forms.
Bibliographical   footnotes.

NN 0062168   IU

389
N219LH
[National research council] Committee on food
habits.
Housewives' awareness of current food
problems.   [Washington? D.C., 1942?]
6 p.

NN 0062169   DNAL

389.9
N2134L
National research council. Committee on
food habits.
Liaison session.
Washington, D.C.

1. Food habits. 2. Food supply. 3.
World war, 1939-   Food question.

NN 0062170   DNAL

National research council. *Committee on food habits.*
... Manual for the study of food habits; report of the Committee on food habits ... Washington, D. C., The National
research council, National academy of sciences [1945]
142 p. 24½ᵐ. (Bulletin of the National research council. No. 111,
January 1945)
"The main outlines of the problem and some account of the pilot
studies were published in 1943 as [a report of the committee entitled]
The problem of changing food habits (National research council-Bulle-
tin 108)."—Pref.
"How to find references in the field of food habits" (bibliography):
p. 97. Bibliography: p. [99]-135.
1. Man—Food habits.

Library of Congress °   Q11.N292 no. 111   45-7494
[20]   (506) 613.2

NN 0062171   O OOxM OC1 OCU NcRS NcD DNLM
DLC MiU NIC OC1W-H CLU MoU GAT ViU

GT2860
.N3
NATIONAL RESEARCH COUNCIL. Committee on food
habits.
[Miscellaneous publications]

1. Food-Hist.

NN 0062172   ICU

National research council. *Committee on food habits.*
... The problem of changing food habits; report of the Committee on food habits, 1941-1943 ... Washington, D. C., The
National research council, National academy of sciences [1943]
177 p. diagrs. 25ᵐ. (Bulletin of the National research council. No.
108, October 1943)
Bibliography at end of some of the chapters.

1. Food. 2. Diet. 3. Nutrition.   I. Title: Food habits.
44-2196
Library of Congress   Q11.N292 no. 108
[12]   (506) 613.2

NN 0062173   WU-M NIC NcD NcRS OU OC1 OCU ViU NNC Wa
DLC CaBVaU WaTC CaBVa WaT DNLM MoU

VOLUME 407

National research council. Committee on Food Habits.
    The relationship between food habits and problems of wartime
emergency feeding.   Washington: Committee on food habits,
Division of anthropology and psychology, National research
council ₁1942₎   5, 4 f.   28cm.

1. Food in war time—U. S.
N. Y. P. L.   June 3, 1943

NN   0062174   NN DNAL

389
N2194R   National research council. Committee on
        food habits.
        A report on the morale building value of
    specific foods in the American diet.
    Washington ₁1942₎
        15 numb. l.

NN   0062175   DNAL

389.1
N218Ra   National research council. Committee on
        food habits.
        Research on appetite levels. Special
    session, February 13, 1944.   Washington
    ₁1944₎
        53 p.

        1. Food. Research. 2. Food habits.
    3. Diet. New England. 4. Nutrition. 5
    Rats. Food habits.

NN   0062176   DNAL

389.1
N218Ro   National research council. Committee on food
        habits.
        The role of milk in American culture.
    [Washington? 194?]
        41 p.
        1. Milk. 2. Milk as food. 3. Food habits.
    I. Joffe, Natalie F. II. Janis, Marjorie.
    III. Shippee, Eva. IV. Woodward, Patricia.

NN   0062177   DNAL

389
N2194S   National research council. Committee on food
        habits.
        Small conference on problems of food supply,
    food habits, and nutrition in China.   Washington,
    D. C., 1943.
        26 p.
        1. Food supply. China. 2. China. Food
    habits. 3. Nutrition.

NN   0062178   DNAL

389.1
N218S   National research council. Committee on food
        habits.
        Some aspects of the work of the Committee on
    food habits, Division of anthropology and
    psychology, National research council...
    Washington ₁1942₎
        6 p.   28cm.
        Processed.
        "A summary of this report was presented by
    Miss Mary Sweeny at the meetings of the Food and
    nutrition division of the American home econo-

mics association at the 35th annual meeting
held at Boston, Massachusetts, on June 23rd,
1942."

        1. Food habits.

NN   0062180   DNAL

641.0943 National Research Council.   Committee on
N213   Food Habits.
        Some central European food patterns and
    their relationship to wartime programs of
    food and nutrition.   Washington ₁1943-
        pts. in   v.   28cm.

        Includes bibliographies.
        Contents.- ₁pt.1₎ Czech and Slovak food
    patterns, by Svatava Pirkova-Jakobson and
    Natalie Joffe.- ₁pt.2₎ Hungarian food pat-
    terns, by Natalie Joffe.- ₁pt.3₎ Polish food
    patterns, by Su   la M. Benet and Natalie
    Joffe.

NN   0062181   OrU

140
N21   National research council. Committee on food
        habits.
        A study of some personality factors in block
    leaders in low income groups...   Washington,
    D. C. [1943?]
        20 p₎   28 cm.
        Not for publication.

NN   0062182   DNAL

Mann
TX   National Research Council. Committee on
357   Food Habits.
Z99   Summary of conference with the Committee
no. 47 on Food Habits. Washington, 1941.
        8 p.

        1. Food habits

NN   0062183   NIC DNAL NN

National Research Council. *Committee on Food Habits.*
    Translating science into living habits. Liaison session of
the committee, May 19, 1945. Washington ₁1945₎
    65 p. 28 cm.
    Cover title.

    1. Man—Food habits.   ₁. Title.

    TX511.N34   339.42   51–23983

NN   0062184   DLC

National Research Council. Committee on Food
    Protection
    see
National Research Council. Food Protection
    Committee.

National Research Council. Committee on Forestry
    Forest research in the United States: report of
the Committee on Forestry, Division of Biology
and Agriculture. Nov.1, 1938. ₁Washington, D.
C.₎
    iii, 138 ℓ. 27cm.

NN   0062186   IdU NcRS OCl

National Research Council. Committee on Frost
    Heave and Frost Action in Soil
        see   National Research Council. Highway
Research Board. Committee on Frost Heave and
Frost Action in Soil.

National Research Council. Committee on
    Geologic Research.
    ... Report of the Subcommittee on the
    Ecology of Marine Organisms
        see under   National Research Council.
Committee on a Treatise on Marine Ecology and
Pleoecology.

National Research Council. Committee on
    Geometric Highway Design
        see   National Research Council. Highway
Research Board. Committee on Geometric Highway Design.

National Research Council. Committee on Growth.
    Collected reprints. Grants in aid by the
American Cancer Society
        see under   American Cancer Society.

RC262   National Research Council. Committee on Growth.
.N3
    National Research Council. *Committee on Veterans Medical*
    Problems.
        Expected incidence of certain neoplastic diseases in vet-
    erans. Washington ₁1947₎

National research council. Committee on
    glacial map of North America.
    Glacial map of North America
        see under   National Research Council.
Division of Earth Sciences.

QP88   National research council. Committee on
N37   growth
        Report of the Conference on tissue
Med.   culture, Hershey, Pa., November 10-13,
    1946. Sponsored by the Committee on growth
    of the National research council, acting
    as advisor for research to the American
    cancer society. ₁Hershey, Pa., 1947₎
        14p. 28cm.

        Cover title.

NN   0062193   IaU DNLM AAP CSf

National Research Council. *Committee on Growth.*
    Report to American Cancer Society, inc.

    ₁Washington₎
        v. 23 cm. annual.
    Report year ends June 30.

        1. Cancer research—Yearbooks.
    RC262.N254   616.994072   51–6267 ‡
    [U. S. Army Med. Libr.: 1. Cancer research. W1 NA624]

ICRL CaBVaU MtBC
NN   0062194   DLC ICJ IdU MtU Or OrCS OrU OrU-M Wa

QV   NATIONAL Research Council. Committee
282   on Growth
qN277r   Reprint of articles on the nitrogen
1947   mustards; laboratory and clinical studies
    from the American Association for the
    Advancement of Science monograph:
    Approaches to tumor chemotherapy.
    ₁New York₎ 1947.
        96 p. illus.
        1. Nitrogen mustards

NN   0062195   DNLM NNU

VOLUME 407

National Research Council. *Committee on Growth.*
The research attack on cancer, 1946; a report on the American Cancer Society research program. ₍Washington, 1946₎
20 p. 23 cm.

1. American Cancer Society, New York. 2. Cancer—U. S.   I. Title.

RC261.N3 1946a   616.994   Med 47–3014*

NN 0062196   DLC DNLM

National research council. *Committee on growth.*
The research attack on cancer, 1946; a report on the American cancer society research program (revised August 31, 1946) by the Committee on growth of the National research council. ₍Washington, 1946₎
32 p. 28 x 21½ cm.

A preliminary report has been issued covering the initial nine-month period of the committee's research. The present report covers its initial 14 months of operation. *cf.* Introd.

RC261.N3

———— Supplement ... (Covering approved grants and fellowships through February 25, 1947) ... ₍Washington, 1947₎
20 p. 28 x 21½ cm.

1. American cancer society, New York. 2. Cancer—U. S.   I. Title.

RC261.N3 Suppl.   616.994072   Med 47–1870

NN 0062198   DLC OrSaW NNC ViU

National Research Council. *Committee on Growth*
see also **Conference on Nutrition in Relation to Cancer,** New York, 1946.

National Research Council. *Committee on Growth*
see also **Symposium on the Use of Isotopes in Biological Research,** *University of Chicago,* 1947.

W
1   National Research Council. Committee
NA6242   on Hearing
Minutes of meeting.

₍Washington, 194
v.

NN 0062201   DNLM

National research council – Committee on heat transmission
A directory of research on heat transmission in the educational institutions in the U.S. and Canada. N.Y., Committee on heat transmission.

Autographed from typewritten copy.

NN 0062202   OC1

National research council. Committee on heat transmission.
                                                     FOR OTHER EDITIONS
McAdams, William Henry, 1892–   SEE MAIN ENTRY
Heat transmission, by William H. McAdams ... Sponsored by the Committee on heat transmission, National research council. 2d ed., rev. and enl. New York and London, McGraw-Hill book company, inc., 1942.

National research council. *Committee on heat transmission.*
Minutes of conference on heat transfer by radiation and a brief synopsis of present knowledge on radiation of heat. Report of the Committee on heat transmission, Division of engineering and industrial research, National research council. New York city, Committee on heat transmission, 1929.
cover-title, 1 p. l., 21 numb. l. 27½ x 21½ᶜᵐ.
Reproduced from type-written copy.
"Preliminary report ... prepared after the first meeting of Sub-committee 'D'."—Foreword.
"Bibliography on radiant heat transfer ₍by₎ H. C. Hottel and C. Gilmore ₍¹₎": leaves 9–21.
1. Heat—Radiation and absorption.   I. Hottel, Hoyt Clarke, 1903–   II. Gilmore, Charles Hoffmann, 1902–   III. Title : Heat transfer by radiation.
                                                                    45–45989

Library of Congress   QC331.N3

NN 0062204   DLC

NATIONAL RESEARCH COUNCIL. Committee on Heat Transmission.
Report of the committee on Heat Transmission, National Research Council; definitions, nomenclature, symbols and units for heat transmission. New York City, 1928. 12 p. incl. tables. 8°.

599295A. 1. Heat--Transmis-   sion.

NN 0062205   NN

National Research Council. *Committee on Highway Capacity*
see
National Research Council. *Highway Research Board. Committee on Highway Capacity.*

National Research Council. Committee on Highway Costs
see **National Research Council. Highway Research Board. Committee on Highway Costs.**

National Research Council. Committee on Highway Organization and Administration
see **National Research Council. Highway Research Board. Committee on Highway Organization and Administration.**

Psychology
D158
N2133
National research council. Committee on highway safety research.
The field of highway safety research; a brief outline. Revised August 1952. Washington, D. C., 1952.
42 p.

"References": p. 40-42.

NN 0062210   NNC

National Research Council. *Committee on Highway Safety Research.*
Health, medical and drug factors in highway safety; proceedings of the second highway safety research correlation conference, April 5–6, 1954, Washington, D. C. Washington, National Academy of Sciences, National Research Council ₍1954₎
1 v. (various pagings) 28 cm. (National Research Council. Publication 328)

1. Automobile drivers. 2. Traffic accidents.   I. Title. II. Title: Highway safety.   (Series)

TL152.N287 1954   614.862   54–4713

ICJ DI DNLM OC1W-H
PSt TxU NcD PBL ViU NNC-M FTaSU PPC CaBVaU IdPI
NN 0062211   DLC OrP Wa WaTC FU-HC OrCS MBCo IU

National Research Council. Committee on Highway Safety Research.
Proceedings of the highway safety research correlation conference
see under **Highway Safety Research Correlation Conference.**

National Research Council. Committee on Highway Taxation and Finance
see **National Research Council. Highway Research Board. Committee on Highway Taxation and Finance.**

National Research Council. *Committee on Human Migrations*
see
National Research Council. *Committee on Scientific Problems of Human Migration.*

National Research Council. *Committee on Human Reproduction.*
Pregnancy wastage; proceedings of a conference sponsored by the Committee on Human Reproduction, National Research Council, in behalf of the National Committee on Maternal Health, inc. Edited by Earl T. Engle. Springfield, Ill., Thomas ₍1953₎
254 p. illus. 24 cm.

1. Pregnancy.   I. Engle, Earl Theron, 1896–   ed. II. Title.

RG556.N3 1953   618.3   53–8641 ‡

TU NNC-M ICJ CtY-M
NN 0062215   DLC CaBVaU OrU-M OrU PPC OOxM OU DNLM

National Research Council. *Committee on Human Reproduction.*
Studies on testis and ovary, eggs and sperm; proceedings of a conference sponsored by the Committee on Human Reproduction, National Research Council, in behalf of the National Committee on Maternal Health, inc. Edited by Earl T. Engle. Springfield, Ill., Thomas ₍1952₎
237 p. illus. 24 cm.

1. Reproduction.   I. Engle, Earl Theron, 1896–   ed. II. Title.

QP251.A1N3 1952   612.6   52–9909 ‡

NIC ICJ ViU NNC-M DNLM
NN 0062216   DLC CaBVaU OrU-M OrU LU PPHa OCU NcD

National Research Council. *Committee on Human Reproduction*
see also **Conference on the Normal and Pathological Physiology of Pregnancy,** *New York,* 1948.

National research council. *Committee on hydrodynamics.*
... Report of the Committee on hydrodynamics, Division of physical sciences, National research council. Hugh L. Dryden, Francis D. Murnaghan, H. Bateman ... Washington, D. C., Published by the National research council of the National academy of sciences, 1932.
3 p. l., 3–634 p. diagrs. 25 cm. (Bulletin of the National research council. no. 84, Feb. 1932)
The members of this committee of the National research council, Division of physical sciences, are: Francis D. Murnaghan, chairman; H. Bateman, H. L. Dryden, Rear Admiral D. W. Taylor, S. M. Woodward.
"References" accompany the articles, supplemented by "Additional references," p. 583–601.
1. Hydrodynamics.   I. Dryden, Hugh Latimer, 1898–   II. Murnaghan, Francis   Dominic, 1893–   III. Bateman,   Harry, 1882–1946.   32—9264
Library of Congress   Q11.N292 no. 84 2d set
                                        ₍a48t1₎   (506)   532.5

NIC ViU MH-GM CU
NN 0062218   DLC OrPR CaBVaU OrU TxU MU DAU NcD

VOLUME 407

National Research Council. *Committee on Improvement of Methods in Gravity Measurements*
   see also
National Research Council. *Committee on Isostasy.*

National Research Council. *Committee on Industrial Chemistry.*
   Report.
   Washington.
     v.   28 cm.   annual.
     Report year ends June 30.

     1. Chemistry, Technical.

   TP1.N37   660.6173   59–60548 ‡

  NN   0062220   DLC

RC963
.U53

National research council. Committee on industrial medicine.
  U. S. *National institutes of health. Division of industrial hygiene.*
    Manual of industrial hygiene and medical service in war industries, issued under the auspices of the Committee on industrial medicine of the Division of medical sciences of the National research council, prepared by the Division of industrial hygiene, National institute of health, United States Public health service; William M. Gafafer, D. SC., editor. Philadelphia and London, W. B. Saunders company, 1943.

National research council. *Committee on information, Division of medical sciences*
   see
National research council. *Division of medical sciences. Committee on information.*

W
1
NA6247

National Research Council. Committee on Insect and Rodent Control
  Minutes of meeting. 1st–
  Oct. 20, 1948–
  Washington.
    v.

  NN   0062223   DNLM

QU
145
N2765

National Research Council. Committee on International Nutrition Programs.

  [Collection of publications]

    The Library has a collection of miscellaneous publications of this organization kept as received. These publications are not listed or bound separately.
    1. International Cooperation   2. Nutrition

  NN   0062224   DNLM

National Research Council. Committee on International Scientific Publication.
  Chemistry newsletter
    see under title

National Research Council. Committee on International Scientific Publication.
  Guia de instituciones y sociedades científicas latinoamericanas
    see under   Pan American Union. Science and Technology Section.

National Research Council. Committee on International Scientific Publication
  List of scientific and technical journals of Latin America. Boston[1952]
    1v.(various pagings)
    Reproduction of typewritten copy.

    1. Science. Periodicals. Bibliography. 2. Technology. Periodicals. Bibliography. 3. Spanish American periodicals. Bibliography. I. Title

  NN   0062227   MBdAF

National Research Council. *Committee on International Scientific Publication.*
  Report.
  [Washington]
    v.   30 cm.   annual.
    Report year ends Mar. 31.

  Q11.N29496   506.273   58–60985 ‡

  NN   0062228   DLC

National Research Council. *Committee on International Technologic Assistance*
  see
National Research Council. *Advisory Committee on International Technologic Assistance.*

QE
696
N3

National Research Council. Committee on Interrelations of Pleistocene Research.
  Pleistocene research. New York, Geological Society of America, 1949.
    p.1305–1525. illus., maps, plate. 25 cm. (Bulletin of the Geological Society of America, v.60, no.9)
    Includes bibliographies.
    1. Geology, Stratigraphic - Pleistocene. 2. Paleontology - Pleistocene. 3. Geographical distribution of animals and plants.   4. Paleoclimatology. I. Title. (Series: Geological Society of America. Bulletin. v.60,   no.9)

  NN   0062230   MH-GS MiU

National research council. *Committee on ionization potentials and related subjects.*
  ... Critical potentials, by K. T. Compton and F. L. Mohler. Washington, D. C., Published by the National research council of the National academy of sciences, 1924.
    cover-title, 135 p. diagrs. 25ᶜᵐ. (Bulletin of the National research council. no. 48 (v. 9, pt. 1) Sept. 1924)
    "This monograph is the first of a series which, when complete, will form the report of the National research council Committee on ionization potentials and related subjects. The committee consists of the following members: Paul D. Foote ... chairman, K. T. Compton ... Saul Dushman ... F. L. Mohler ... H. N. Russell ... S. E. Sheppard ... J. H. Van Vleck."—p. [1]
    Bibliography : p. 128–135.
    1. Electrostatics.   I. Compton, Karl Taylor, 1887–
    II. Mohler, Fred Loomis.   1893–   III. Title.   IV. Title: Potentials, Critical.   [r31g2)   25–5122 Revised
    Library of Congress   Q11.N292   no. 48

    NcRS ViU MB
  NN   0062231   DLC WaTC OrPR CaBVaU OrU NIC LU AU

National research council. *Committee on ionization potentials and related subjects.*
  ... Quantum principles and line spectra [by] J. H. Van Vleck. Washington, D. C., Published by the National research council of the National academy of sciences, 1926.
    cover-title, 316 p. diagrs. 25ᶜᵐ. (Bulletin of the National research council. no. 54 (v. 10, pt. 4) Mar. 1926)
    "This monograph is part of the report of the National research council Committee on ionization potentials and related subjects. The committee consists of the following members: Paul D. Foote ... chairman; K. T. Compton ... Saul Dushman ... F. L. Mohler ... H. N. Russell ... S. E. Sheppard ... J. H. Van Vleck."—p. [1]
    1. Spectrum analysis. 2. Ionization of gases.   I. Van Vleck, John Hasbrouck, 1899–   II. Title.
                                27–4208 Revised
    Library of Congress   Q11.N292   no. 54

    PU-Sc PHC MB ViU
  NN   0062232   DLC CaBVaU WaTC OrPR MH CU NcRS

National research council. Committee on isostasy.
  Bowie, William, 1872–
    Comments on isostasy, made by authors of geological and geophysical books and papers. Compiled by William Bowie, chairman, Committee on isostasy, Division of geology and geography, National research council. Washington, D. C., National research council, 1932.

National Research Council. Committee on Joint Material in Concrete Pavements
    see   **National Research Council. Highway Research Board. Committee on Joint Material in Concrete Pavements.**

National Research Council. Committee on Land Acquisition and Control of Highway Access and Adjacent Areas
    see   **National Research Council. Highway Research Board. Committee on Land Acquisition and Control of Highway Access and Adjacent Areas.**

National Research Council. Committee on Landslide Investigations
    see   **National Research Council. Highway Research Board. Committee on Landslide Investigations.**

National research council. *Committee on Latin American anthropology.*
  Survey of research on Latin America by United States scientists and institutions. [By] Alexander Lesser for the Committee on Latin American anthropology, Division of anthropology and psychology, National research council. Washington, D. C., 1946.
    2 p. l., 133 p.   27 x 21ᶜᵐ.
    "This project of the Committee on Latin American anthropology ... was sponsored jointly by the National research council, the American council of learned societies, and the Social science research council."

    "The purpose of this survey ... is to make available to the United States delegation to the fourth general assembly of the Pan American institute of geography and history of Caracas, Venezuela, information on the work of United States institutions and agencies which is relevant to the work of the institute."—Introd.

    1. Spanish America. 2. Research.   I. Lesser, Alexander, 1902– II. Pan American institute of geography and history. 4th congress, Caracas, 1946.

   F1408.N3   980.07   47–2915

  NN   0062238   DLC NcD NN ICU DNAL NIC

G918.06
N214g

National research council. Committee on Latin American geography.
  Geographic work in Latin America by Latin American geographers, government agencies and geographic societies. Preliminary edition issued at Northwestern university, by the Committee on Latin American geography, Division of geology and geography, National research council. Clarence F. Jones, chairman of the Committee. Washington, D.C., National research council, 1951.
    1p.l., vi, 176p. 28cm.

  NN   0062239   TxU DPU

National Research Council. Committee on Load Carrying Capacity of Roads as Affected by Frost Action
    see   **National Research Council. Highway Research Board. Committee on Load Carrying Capacity of Roads as Affected by Frost Action.**

VOLUME 407

National research council. *Committee on luminescence.*

... Selected topics in the field of luminescence. Report of the National research council, Committee on luminescence, by Ernest Merritt, Edward L. Nichols and C. D. Child. Washington, D. C., Published by the National research council of the National academy of sciences, 1923.

cover-title, 126 p. 25ᶜᵐ. (Bulletin of the National research council. no. 30 (v. 5, pt. 5) Mar. 1923)

Bibliography, 1906–1922: p. 79–126.

1. Radiation. 2. Fluorescence. I. Merritt, Ernest George, 1865– II. Nichols, Edward Leamington, 1854–1937. III. Child, Clement Dexter, 1868– IV. Title: Luminescence.

23—18696

Library of Congress   Q11.N292 no. 30

PU NcRS ViU
NN   0062241   DLC OrSaW WaWW CaBVaU OrU OrPR WaTC

National Research Council. Committee on Maintenance of Joints in Concrete Pavements as Related to the Pumping Action of the Slabs see **National Research Council. Highway Research Board. Committee on Maintenance of Joints in Concrete Pavements as Related to the Pumping Action of the Slabs.**

National Research Council. *Committee on Marine Ecology and Paleoecology* see **National Research Council.** *Committee on a Treatise on Marine Ecology and Paleoecology.*

National Research Council. *Committee on Marine Ecology as Related to Paleontology* see **National Research Council.** *Committee on a Treatise on Marine Ecology and Paleoecology.*

National Research Council. Committee on maternal and Child Feeding.
... The composition of milks
see under   Macy, Icie Gertrude, 1892–

Q11
.N292
no. 123

National Research Council. Committee on Maternal and Child Feeding.
Toverud, Kirsten (Utheim) 1890–
Maternal nutrition and child health; an interpretative review, by Kirsten Utheim Toverud, Genevieve Stearns and Icie G. Macy. Prepared for the Committee on Maternal and Child Feeding of the Food and Nutrition Board, National Research Council. Washington, National Research Council, National Academy of Sciences, 1950.

QA47
.M29

National research council. Committee on mathematical tables and other aids to computation
Mathematical tables and other aids to computation. v. 1– (no. 1–); Jan. 1943– ₍Washington₎ The National research council ₍1943–

National research council. *Committee on mathematical tables and other aids to computation.*
... Report 1–
Washington, D. C., The National research council, National academy of sciences, 1941–

v. tables. 25½ cm. (Bulletin of the National research council, no. 105. Feb., 1941)

1. Mathematics—Tables, etc.

Q11.N292 no. 105   510.835   41–25183 rev

NN   0062248   DLC CaBVaU MB

RC66
.U5
1944 a

National research council. Committee on medical records.

U. S. *National archives.*
... Report of a survey of medical records created by the federal government, prepared by the National archives in collaboration with the Committee on medical records of the National research council ... Washington, 1945.

National Research Council. Committee on Medicine.
A manual of tropical medicine.
see under   Mackie, Thomas Turlay, 1895–

National Research Council. Committee on Medicine and Surgery.
Progress report
see under
Iowa. University. College of Medicine.

National Research Council. Committee on Medicine and Surgery.
Second conference on platelets
see   Conference on Platelets, Washington, D.C.
Proceedings.

National Research Council. *Committee on Medicine and Surgery. Subcommittee on Blood and Related Problems* see **National Research Council.** *Committee on Blood and Transfusion Problems.*

National research council. *Committee on medicolegal problems.*
... A compendium of the statute law of coroners and medical examiners in the United States, by George H. Weinmann; issued under the auspices of the Committee on medicolegal problems, National research council. Washington, D. C., Published by the National research council of the National academy of sciences, 1931.

cover-title, 240 p. 24½ᵐ. (Bulletin of the National research council. no. 83 (Aug. 1931))

1. Coroners—U. S. 2. Medical jurisprudence—U. S. I. Weinmann, George H.

31—34263

Library of Congress   Q11.N292 no. 83
———— Copy 2.   ₍a37f1₎   347.96

NcD MB ViU
NN   0062254   DLC WaTC CaBVaU OrU OrPR MU MH-L

National research council. *Committee on medicolegal problems.*
... The coroner and the medical examiner, issued under the auspices of the Committee on medicolegal problems by Oscar T. Schultz and E. M. Morgan, with a supplement on medical testimony, by E. M. Morgan. ₍Washington, D. C., Published by the National research council of the National academy of sciences, 1928₎

cover-title, 101 p. 24½ᵐ. (Bulletin of the National research council. no. 64, July 1928)

Bibliographical foot-notes.
"Supplementary note" (₍2₎ p.) inserted at end of volume.

1. Coroners—U. S. 2. Medical jurisprudence—U. S. 3. Autopsy. I. Schultz, Oscar John Theodore, 1877– II. Morgan, Edmund Morris, 1878– III. Title. IV. Title: Medical examiner.

Library of Congress   Q11.N292 no. 64   28–28831
———— Copy 2. "Supplementary note" (₍2₎ p.) inserted at end of volume.   ₍a36e1₎

NcRS NcD ICJ ViU
NN   0062255   DLC WaTC OrPR OrU OrU-M CaBVaU DNLM

National research council. *Committee on medicolegal problems.*
... Possibilities and need for development of legal medicine in the United States, with a supplement on university departments in the field of criminology. Prepared for the National research council Committee on medicolegal problems by Oscar T. Schultz ... Washington, D. C., Published by the National research council of the National academy of sciences, 1932.

ix, 135 p. 25½ᵐ. (Bulletin of the National research council. no. 87, Oct. 1932)

"References": p. 182–185.

1. Medical jurisprudence—U. S. I. Schultz, Oscar John Theodore, 1877– II. Title. III. Title: Legal medicine in the United States, Possibilities and needs for development of. IV. Title: University departments in the field   of criminology.

33—2747

Library of Congress   Q11.N292 no. 87
———— Copy 2.   ₍a40k1₎   (506) 340.6

NcD ViU
NN   0062256   DLC WaTC CaBVaU WaS OrPR OrU ICU

National research council. *Committee on medicolegal problems.*
... A survey of the law concerning dead human bodies, by George H. Weinmann; issued under the auspices of the Committee on medicolegal problems, National research council. Washington, D. C., Published by the National research council of the National academy of sciences, 1929.

cover-title, 199 p. 25ᵐ. (Bulletin of the National research council. no. 73, Dec. 1929)

1. Dead, The. 2. Medical jurisprudence—U. S. 3. Autopsy. 4. Coroners—U. S. I. Weinmann, George H. II. Title. III. Title: Law concerning dead human bodies.

30—6058

Library of Congress   Q11.N292 no. 73

NcD MB ViU
NN   0062257   DLC CaBVaU OrPR OrU WaTC DNLM NcRS

National research council. Committee on methods of measurement of radiation.
Forsythe, William Elmer, 1881–   ed.
Measurement of radiant energy, edited by W. E. Forsythe ... Contributors: Charles G. Abbot, Elliot Q. Adams, Loyal B. Aldrich ₍and others₎ ... Prepared under the direction of A. C. Hardy, Herbert E. Ives and W. E. Forsythe constituting a Committee on methods of measurement of radiation of the Division of physical sciences, National research council. 1st ed. New York and London. McGraw-Hill book company, inc., 1937.

National Research Council. Committee on Milk see **National Research Council. Food and Nutrition Board.**

National research council. *Committee on milk, meat and legumes.*
The nation's protein supply; prepared by the Committee on milk, meat and legumes, W. C. Rose, chairman, D. B. Jones, W. J. Morse ₍and₎ R. C. Pollock, August, 1942. Report of the Food and nutrition board of the National research council. Washington, D. C. ₍1942₎

1 p. l., 10 p. incl. tables. 24½ᵐ. (On cover: National research council. Reprint and circular series, no. 114, August, 1942)

"References and notes": p. 10.

1. Food supply—U. S. 2. Proteins. I. Rose, William Cumming, 1887– II. Title.

44–2641

Library of Congress   TX360.U6N3
₍5₎   338.1

NN   0062260   DLC NNC-M ViU

44
N2173

National Research Council. Committee on Milk Production, Distribution, and Quality.
Milk quality and milk regulations; information concerning a study to be made by the National Research Council. ₍Washington? 1949?₎
folder (₍5₎ p.)

1. Milk. Care and handling. I. Title.

NN   0062261   DNAL

National Research Council. Committee on Milk Production, Distribution, and Quality.
Sanitary milk control
see under
Dahlberg, Arthur Chester, 1896–

VOLUME 407

National Research Council. *Committee on Neurobiology.*
Survey of neurobiology. Washington, 1952.
40 p. 25 cm. (National Research Council. Publication 237)
—— Survey on neurobiology. Bibliography of genetic neurology, compiled and annotated by Agnes S. Burt. Washington, 1952.
131 p. 28 cm. (National Research Council. Publication 237. Suppl.)
QP352.N3 Suppl.
1. Nervous system—Collected works. 2. Nervous system—Bibl. I. Burt, Agnes Sanxay, 1917–   (Series)

QP352.N3   612.8072   53–4031 rev

LU PBL OU DNLM TxU MiU PSt
WaTC CU-M IdPI ICJ CaBVaU OrCS FTaSU ViU OrP CU
NN   0062263   DLC DCU NN OC1W C OkU-M CLSU NcD PPHa

National Research Council. Committee on Nuclear Science.
Conference on absolute B counting
see under Conference on Absolute B Counting.

National Research Council. *Committee on Nuclear Science.*
Mass differences; a compilation of experimental atomic mass differences found from beta decay, reaction energies, microwave data, alpha decay, and mass doublets. [Washington, 1954]–59.
2 v. illus., tables. 27 cm. (*Its* Nuclear science series, report no. 16, 25)
National Research Council. Publication 336, 649.
Cover title.
Vol. 2 has imprint: Washington, National Academy of Sciences, National Research Council.
"Prepared at the suggestion of the Subcommittee on Nuclear Constants of the Committee on Nuclear Science."

Vol. 1, reprinted from Reviews of modern physics, v. 26, no. 4; v. 2, reproduced photographically from v. 29, no. 4 and v. 30, no. 2, pt. 1.
Includes bibliographies.

1. Atomic mass.   i. Title.   (Series: National Research Council. Committee on Nuclear Science. Nuclear science series, report no. 16 [etc.]   Series: National Research Council. Publication 336 [etc.])

QC771.N33 no. 16,25   539.74   55–291 rev

CLU NN IdPI WaTC LU
NN   0062266   DLC TxU NN ViU MB MiU NcD CU FU-HC

National research council. Committee on Nuclear Science.
Nuclear science series. Preliminary report.

Washington.
(National research council. Publication. [no.] 205, 207

NN   0062267   NN ICJ CtY

National Research Council. *Committee on Nuclear Science.*
Nuclear science series; report. no. 1–
Washington, 1948–
no. in v. illus. 25–28 cm.
Reports no. 11–   issued as National Research Council publication.
No. 15 lacks numbering.
Subtitle varies slightly.

1. Atomic energy—Collected works. 2. Nuclear physics—Collected works.   i. Title.   (Series: National Research Council. Publication)

QC771.N33   *539.7082   55—58929

WaS WaU LU P INS InLP PPF CtNlC NBuU
NN   0062268   DLC DP CaBVaU AAP WaTC IdPI OrCS OrU

National Research Council. Committee on Nuclear Science.
Nuclear processes in geologic settings
see Conference on Nuclear Processes in Geologic Settings. Proceedings.

National Research Council. Committee on Nuclear Science.
Physical, biological, and administrative problems associated with the transportation of radioactive substances
see under Evans, Robley Dunglison, 1907–

National Research Council. Committee on Nuclear Science.
QE513 .N3
Conference on Nuclear Processes in Geologic Settings.
Proceedings. [1st]–   1953–
Washington.

National Research Council. Committee on Nuclear Science.
Techniques of particle energy control with Van de Graaff accelerators
see under Bailey, Carl L.

National Research Council. *Committee on Nuclear Science.*
Subcommittee on Radiobiology
see **National Research Council.** *Subcommittee on Radiobiology.*

National research council. *Committee on numerical integration.*
... Numerical integration of differential equations. Report of Committee on numerical integration, Division of physical sciences, National research council, Albert A. Bennett, William E. Milne, Harry Bateman ... Washington, D. C., Published by the National research council of the National academy of sciences, 1933.
108 p. 24½ cm. (Bulletin of the National research council. no. 92, Nov. 1933)
The members of this committee of the Division of physical sciences, National research council are: Albert A. Bennett, chairman; William E. Milne, Harry Bateman, and Lester E. Ford.

Includes bibliographies.

1. Differential equations.   i. Bennett, Albert Arnold, 1888–   ii. Milne, William Edmund, 1890–   iii. Bateman, Harry, 1882–1946.   iv. Title.   v. Title: Report.

Q11.N292 no. 92   (506) 517.38   34—1417

CU KEmT CaBVaU
NN   0062275   DLC WaWW OrPR WaS OrU OC1W ViU NcRS

National Research Council. Committee on Nutrition
see **National Research Council. Committee on Animal Nutrition.**

National research council. *Committee on nutrition in industry.*
The food and nutrition of industrial workers in wartime. Report of the Committee on nutrition in industry of the National research council. Washington, D. C. [1942]
3 p. l., 17 p. 24½ᵐ. (On cover: National research council. Reprint and circular series, no. 110, April, 1942)
"References and suggested sources of information on nutrition": p. 17.
Its First report.

NN   0062277   ViU

National research council. *Committee on nutrition in industry.*
The food and nutrition of industrial workers in wartime. 2d printing. Report of the Committee on nutrition in industry of the National research council. Washington, D. C. [1942]
3 p. l., 17 p. 24½ᵐ. (On cover: National research council. Reprint and circular series, no. 110, April, 1942)
"References and suggested sources of information on nutrition": p. 17.

1. Nutrition. 2. Labor and laboring classes.   i. Title.
43–5008
Library of Congress   Q11.N298 no. 110
[4]   (506) 613.2

NN   0062278   DLC Or

National Research Council. Committee on Nutrition of Industrial Workers
see **National Research Council. Committee on the Nutrition of Industrial Workers.**

National Research Council. *Committee on Nutrition Surveys.*
Nutrition surveys: their techniques and value, by Committee on Nutrition Surveys, Food and Nutrition Board, Division of Biology and Agriculture. Washington, National Research Council, National Academy of Sciences, 1949.
v, 144 p. 26 cm. (Bulletin of the National Research Council, no. 117)
Includes bibliographies.
1. Nutrition—Research.   i. Title.   (Series: National Research Council. Bulletin no. 117)
[Q11.N292 no. 117]   A 52–9035

Vassar College. Library
for Library of Congress   [10]

DNLM NjR PSt PPWM CU NcU-H OC1W-H
NN   0062280   NPV PSC WaTC IdPI WaT Wa CU TxU MnU

National Research Council. Committee on Nutritional Aspects of Ageing.
Investigations of human requirements for B-complex vitamins
see under title

National Research Council. Committee on Oceanography.
GC10 .I5
International directory of oceanographers.

Washington, National Academy of Sciences–National Research Council.

National Research Council. *Committee on Oceanography.*
Oceanography, 1951; a report on the present status of the science of the sea. Washington, National Academy of Sciences–National Research Council, 1952.
vii, 36 p. illus. 25 cm. (National Research Council. Publication 208)

1. Oceanographic research.   i. Title.   (Series)

GC57.N3   551.46   52–61341 rev

OrP WaTC MsU ViU PHC PBm NNC MiU NN ICJ TxU
NN   0062283   DLC DAS DI PBL NcD CaBVaU IdPI OrCS

National Research Council. Committee on Oceanography.
551.46
N277r
1929
Report [submitted Nov. 18, 1929. Washington, 1929]
164 ℓ.

Imperfect: p. 164 (Recommendations) wanting.
Chairman, F.R. Lillie; secretary, H.B. Bigelow, who prepared the report.

1. Oceanographic research.   I. Lillie, Frank Rattray, 1870–1947.   II. Bigelow, Henry Bryant, 1879–

NN   0062284   TxCM DI ICU OC1W NjP

VOLUME 407

National Research Council. *Committee on Operations Research.*
Operations research, with special reference to non-military applications. Washington, National Research Council, 1951.
12 p. 23 cm.

1. Operations research.　I. Title.

Q175.N25　　　658.072　　　53–3611 ‡

NN　0062285　　DLC OrP OrU CU NN

W 2　　NATIONAL Research Council. Committee
A　　on Ophthalmology
N336b　　Bulletin ₍of₎ ophthalmology.
6–7 Dec. 1947–
Washington.
no.
Continues the same title issued by the
Subcommittee on Ophthalmology of the
National Research Council.
Called also Minutes of meeting,
6th–

1. Ophthalmology – period.　Title

NN　0062287　　DNLM

National Research Council. *Committee on Paleobotany.*
Report.
Washington.
v. 28 cm.
At head of title,　　　： National Research Council,
Division of Geology and Geography.
Issued as an appendix to the division's Report. Reports prior to not issued separately.

1. Paleobotany.—Bibl.　I. National Research Council. Division of Earth Sciences. Report. Appendix.

Z6033.P2N3　　　55–29418

DI–GS PBm WaTC MtBuM
NN　0062288　　DLC KMK KyU NcU ScU MtU PLF OCU DI

National Research Council. Committee on
Parking
see　National Research Council. Highway
Research Board. Committee on Parking.

National Research Council. Committee on
Patent Policy.

Agenda: Conference on patent policies.
Washington, D. C., 1935.
76 p.　28cm.
Reproduced from typewritten copy.

1. Patents—U. S.　I. Conference on Patent
Policy, Washington, D. C., 1935.

NN　0062290　　ViU

National Research Council. Committee on
Patent Policy.

Transcript of discussion at a conference
on patent policy held under the auspices
of the Committee on Patent Policy, March
29, 1935. Washington, D. C. ₍1935₎
ii, 114 p.　28cm.
Reproduced from typewritten copy.

1. Patents—U. S.　I. Conference on Patent
Policy, Washington, D. C., 1935.

NN　0062291　　ViU

National Research Council. *Committee on Pathology.*
Atlas of tumor pathology, prepared at the Armed Forces
Institute of Pathology under the auspices of the Subcommittee on Oncology of the Committee on Pathology of the
National Research Council. ₍Washington, 1950?₎–
1 v. (loose-leaf)　illus.　27 cm.
Include bibliographies.

1. Tumors.　I. U. S. Armed Forces Institute of Pathology.

RD651.N37　　　616.992　　　50–61290

NN　0062292　　DLC CaBVaU OrCS ICU DNLM MoU KMK ICJ

National Research Council. *Committee on Pathology.*
... Future development of the Army Institute of Pathology.
Submitted to the Surgeon General of the United States Army
... ₍Washington? 1945₎
vi, 49 numb. l.　28 cm.　(*Its* Pathology report, no. 2)

1. U. S. Army Institute of Pathology.

　　　　　　　　　　　　　　　　　　Med 47–2405
U. S. Army Medical Library　　　[W1NA6273　no. 2]
for Library of Congress　　　　₍2₎

NN　0062293　　DNLM

W　　National Research Council. Committee on
1　　Pathology
NA6271　　Minutes of meeting.

Washington ₍194

v.

NN　0062294　　DNLM

National Research Council. *Committee on Pathology.*
Pathology report.
₍Washington? 194
v. 28 cm.
At head of title: National Research Council, Division of Medical
Sciences acting for the Committee on Medical Research of the Office
of Scientific Research and Development.

1. U. S. Office of Scientific Research and Development. Committee
on Medical Research.

　　　　　　　　　　　　　　　　　　Med 48–891
U. S. Army Medical Libr.　　　[W1NA6273]
for Library of Congress　　　　₍2₎

NN　0062295　　DNLM

QV　　National Research Council. Committee on Pharmacognosy
766　　and Pharmaceutical Botany.
N277s　　A survey of the wild medicinal plants of the United
1937　　States; their distribution and abundance. [Washington,
1937?]
133 p.　illus.
Assembled for the Committee in the Division of
Drug and Related Plants, Bureau of Plant Industry, U.
S. Dept. of Agriculture from the reports of several
authors.
I. Title

NN　0062296　　DNLM MiD CU

National Research Council. Committee on Pharmacognosy and Pharmaceutical Botany.
A survey of the wild medicinal plants of the
United States, their distribution and abundance,
comp. by the Committee on pharmacognosy and
pharmaceutical botany, Division of biology and
agriculture, National research council.　₍Washington, D. C., 1940₎
₍4?₎ p. incl. maps　27cm.
Processed.

NN　0062297　　DNAL OrCS

National Research Council. *Committee on Photobiology.*
The luminescence of biological systems; proceedings of the
conference on luminescence, March 28–April 2, 1954, sponsored by the Committee on Photobiology of the National
Academy of Sciences-National Research Council and supported by the National Science Foundation. Edited by
Frank H. Johnson. Washington, American Association for
the Advance of Science, 1955.
xiv, 452 p.　illus.　24 cm.
Includes bibliographies.
1. Phosphorescence.　I. Johnson, Frank Harris, 1908–　　ed.
II. Title.　III. Title: Conference on luminescence.

QH641.N3　1954　　　574.144　　　54–12547

WaT OrU–M OrMonO
CU–M TxHM O MoU FU–HC IdU MtBC NNBG OrPS MtU OrU
PPAN NcD ICJ FMU MB DNAL OC1 PU–BZ PPC KEmT DI
NN　0062298　　DLC DNLM DI PRaW OU OC1W TxU TU ViU

National research council. *Committee on photochemistry.*
... Report of the Committee on photochemistry. ₍1st₎–
₍1928₎–
₍Washington, D. C., National research council, 1928–
v. incl. illus., diagrs.　24 cm.　(Reprint and circular
series of the National research council. no. 81, 96,
The Committee on photochemistry is a committee of the Division
of chemistry and chemistry technology of the National research council.　Chairman: 1928–　　H. S. Taylor.
Reprinted from the Journal of physical chemistry, April, 1928,
p. 481–575; Sept. 1930, p. 2049–2091.
Bibliographies accompany many of the articles.
1. Photochemistry.　I. Taylor, H. S.

Q11.N293　no. 81, 96　　　　　　C D 34—67

NN　0062299　　DLC ViU NIC MiU CaBVaU OrPR

National Research Council. Committee on
Physico-Chemical Phenomena in Soils
see　National Research Council. Highway
Research Board. Committee on Physico-Chemical
Phenomena in Soils.

National Research Council. Committee on Physics
of the Earth.
Physics of the earth
see under title

550　　NATIONAL RESEARCH COUNCIL. Committee on physics
P569　　of the earth. Subsidiary committee on seismology.
v.6　　... Seismology, by the Subsidiary committee on
Physics　　seismology, Division of physical sciences, with
Lib'y　　the cooperation of Division of geology and geography and American geophysical union, National research council ...　Washington, D.C., Published
by the National research council of the National
academy of sciences, 1933.
viii, 223p.　illus. maps, diagrs.　25cm.
(Physics of the earth - VI)

Bulletin of the National research council.
no.90, Oct. 1933.

1. Earthquakes. I. Title. II. National research council. Bulletin, no.90. III. Series
(contents)

NN　0062303　　TxU IU OCX

National research council. Committee on
physiological optics.
Troland, Leonard Thompson, 1889–
... The present status of visual science, by Leonard Thompson Troland. Washington, D. C., Published by the National
research council of the National academy of sciences, 1922.

National Research Council. *Committee on Plant and Crop
Ecology. Committee on Conservation*
see
National Research Council. *Committee on Use and Care
of Natural Resources.*

VOLUME 407

National Research Council. Committee on Plant
Pathology.
    ... Phytopathological projects. List no. 1-
    see under   American Phytopathological
    Society. Advisory Board of American Plant
    Pathologists.

507.2   National Research Council—Committee on Polar
N215re   Research.
        Report on United States Antarctic research
        activities planned. Report to SCAR.   -1963.
        Washington, National Research Council.
          v. 22x28cm.

        Absorbed in 1962 by its Report on United
        States Antarctic research activities and United
        States research activities, planned. Report to
        SCAR.

        NN 0062307   IU CaBVaU

National Research Council. *Committee on Preservation of*
Indigenous Strains of Maize.
    Collections of original strains of corn, I: report. Washington, National Academy of Sciences, National Research Council ₁1955?₁
        300 p. 28 cm.
        Cover title.

        1. Maize.

    SB191.M2N19   633.15   56–60272

        NN 0062308   DLC DNAL

National research council. *Committee on problems of*
deafness. Subcommittee on the value of individual
hearing aids for hard of hearing children in school
        see
National research council. *Subcommittee on the value of*
individual hearing aids for hard of hearing children in
school.

National Research Council. Committee on Problems
of Drug Dependence.
    Bulletin, drug addiction and narcotics
    see under   National Research Council.
Committee on Drug Addiction and Narcotics.

National Research Council. Committee on
    Problems of Drug Dependence.
    Bulletin, problems of drug dependence
    see also   National Research Council.
Committee on Drug Addiction and Narcotics.
    Bulletin, drug addiction and narcotics.

National research council. Committee on
    problems of neurotic behavior.
Anderson, Oscar Daniel, 1903–
    ... A long-term study of the experimental neurosis in the
sheep and dog, with nine case histories, by O. D. Anderson
and Richard Parmenter ... Washington, D. C., Published with
the sponsorship of the Committee on problems of neurotic behavior, Division of anthropology and psychology, National research council, 1941.

National research council. *Committee on problems of neu-*
rotic behavior.
    Problems of neurotic behavior; the experimental production
and treatment of behavior derangement, appraisal of field and
statement of proposals. Prepared by the Committee on problems of neurotic behavior, Division of anthropology and psychology, National research council. Washington, D. C., 1938.
        cover-title, 28 numb. l. 27½ x 21½ᵐ.
        Reproduced from type-written copy.

        1. Neuroses. 2. Psychology, Pathological.   I. Title.   II. Title: Neu-
rotic behavior.

        Library of Congress   RC343.N34   42–46616

        NN 0062313   DLC NIC RPB

National research council. Committee on
    problems of neurotic behavior.
French, Thomas Morton, 1892–
    ... Psychogenic factors in bronchial asthma ... by Thomas
M. French, M. D., and Franz Alexander, M. D., with the collabo-
ration of Catherine L. Bacon, M. D., Siegfried Bernfeld, M. D.,
Edwin Eisler, M. D. ₁and others₁ ... ₁Menasha, Wis., Printed
by the George Banta publishing company₁ 1941–

RC49   National Research Council. Committee on Problems
.P8   of Neurotic Behavior.

Psychosomatic medicine; experimental and clinical studies.
v. 1–   Jan. 1939–
₁New York₁ Paul B. Hoeber.

National research council. Committee on
    problems of neurotic behavior.
Benedek, Therese (Friedmann) 1892–
    ... The sexual cycle in women; the relation between ovarian
function and psychodynamic processes, by Therese Benedek ...
and Boris B. Rubenstein ... Washington, D. C., Pub. with the
sponsorship of the Committee on problems of neurotic behavior, Division of anthropology and psychology, National research council, 1942.

National research council. Committee on
    problems of neurotic behavior.
Kardiner, Abram, 1891–   FOR OTHER EDITIONS
                                    SEE MAIN ENTRY
    The traumatic neuroses of war, by Abram Kardiner ...
sponsored by the Committee on problems of neurotic behavior,
Division of anthropology and psychology, National research
council. New York, London, P. B. Hoeber, inc. ₁ᶜ1941₁

National research council. *Committee on processes of ore*
deposition.
    Ore deposits as related to structural features, prepared un-
der the direction of the Committee on processes of ore deposition of the Division of geology and geography of the National
research council, Washington, D. C. Edited by W. H. New-
house. Princeton, N. J., Princeton university press; London,
H. Milford, Oxford university press, 1942.
        3 p. l., ₁ix₁-xi, 280 p. incl. illus. (incl. maps) diagrs., profiles. 31½ᵐ.
        Bibliographical foot-notes.

        1. Ore-deposits.   I. Newhouse, Walter Harry, 1897–   ed.

                                                        42–25535
        Library of Congress   TN263.Nᵤ
                                    ₁25₁   553.1

    WaS WaTC OrCS TU ICJ OrU MtBC
    ICF MH CU MeB MtBuM MtU IdU CaBVaU Or OrP WaSp
    NN 0062318   DLC OCU OO OCl ViU MiHM TxU NcRS NcD

National Research Council. *Committee on Prosthetic De-*
vices
    see **National Research Council.** *Committee on Artificial*
    Limbs.

Q11   National Research Council. Committee on
.N293   Protein Foods.
no.131
1950   The problem of heat injury to dietary
        protein. Washington ₁1950₁
        19 p. 25cm. (National Research Council.
        Reprint and circular series, no. 131)

        Bibliography: p. 16–19.

        1. Food research. 2. Proteins. 3. Protein
        metabolism. 4. Nutrition. I. Title. II. Ser.

        NN 0062320   ViU

National research council. *Committee on psychiatric investi-*
gations.
    The problem of mental disorder; a study undertaken by the
Committee on psychiatric investigations, National research
council; members of the committee, Madison Bentley, chairman ... ₁and₁ E. V. Cowdry ... 1st ed. New York and London, McGraw-Hill book company, inc., 1934.
        x, 388 p. 23½ᵐ.
        "This study was supported by a grant from the Carnegie corpora-
tion."

        1. Insanity.   I. Bentley, Isaac Madison, 1870–   II. Cowdry, Ed-
mund Vincent, 1888–   III. Title. IV. Title: Mental disorder, The
problem of.

        Library of Congress   RC602.N3   34–38574
        ——— Copy 2.
        Copyright A 77019   ₁a41t2₁

    NNC-M MB WaU ViU WaSpG
    MnU-B NcRS NcD DNLM OO OOxM OC1W ODW OCU NN
    NN OrLgE OrMonO OrSaW WaTC FMU NIC NcU-H WU KEmT
    NN 0062321   DLC OrCS OrU-M MsSM OrU OCX CaBVaU

National Research Council. *Committee on Quartermaster*
Problems.
    Final report on QMC project no. 31, coatings, organic.
₁Washington? 1944?₁
        115 l. 28 cm.

        1. Corrosion and anti-corrosives. 2. Drying oils. 3. Tin plate.

    TA491.N3   620.1122   49–38653*‡

        NN 0062322   DLC ICJ

National research council. Committee
    on radiation
        see
National research council. Committee on
    the effects of radiation on living
    organisms.

QH652   National Research Council. Committee on
.H6   Radiation Biology.

Hollaender, Alexander, 1898–   *ed.*
    Radiation biology, edited by Alexander Hollaender with
the cooperation of Austin M. Brues ₁and others₁ New York,
McGraw-Hill, 1954–56.

National research council. *Committee on radiation in gases.*
    ... Molecular spectra in gases. Report of the Committee on
radiation in gases. Edwin C. Kemble, Raymond T. Birge,
Walter F. Colby, F. Wheeler Loomis, Leigh Page. Washing-
ton, D. C., Published by the National research council of the
National academy of sciences, 1926.
        cover-title, 358 p. plates, diagrs. 25ᵐ. (Bulletin of the National
research council. no. 57 (v. 11, pt. 3) Dec. 1926)
        Bibliographies included.
        1. Spectrum analysis.   I. Kemble, Edwin Crawford, 1889–
II. Birge, Raymond Thayer, 1887–   III. Colby, Walter Francis, 1880–
IV. Title.
                                                27–10056 Revised
        Library of Congress   Q11.N292 no. 57
        ——— ——— Copy 2.
        ——— ——— Copy 3.
        ——— ——— Copy 4.   QC451.N3

        NN 0062325   DLC WaTC OrPR CaBVaU NcRS ViU NN

VOLUME 407

535.84 National research council--Committee on
N21m radiation in gases.
Molecular spectra in gases. Washington, D.C., 1930.
366p. plate, tables, diagrs.
(Bulletin of the National research council, no.57, December, 1926)

Contains bibliographies.

NN 0062326 IU MiU OCU OO ViU OOxM

National research council. *Committee on rational transformations.*
... Selected topics in algebraic geometry; report of the Committee on rational transformations: Virgil Snyder, Arthur B. Coble, Arnold Emch, Solomon Lefschetz, F. R. Sharpe, Charles H. Sisam. Washington, D. C., Published by the National research council of the National academy of sciences, 1928.
cover-title, 395 p. 25cm. (Bulletin of the National research council. No. 63, Apr. 1928)
Bibliography at end of each chapter.

CONTENTS.—Quadratic Cremona transformations ₁by₁ Arnold Emch.—Analysis of singularities of plane algebraic curves ₁by₁ Arnold Emch.—Linear systems of plane curves ₁by₁ F. R. Sharpe.—Planar Cremona transformations ₁by₁ Arthur B. Coble.—Multiple correspondences between two planes ₁by₁ Virgil Snyder.—Involutions on rational curves ₁by₁ Virgil Snyder.—Correspondences on non-rational curves ₁by₁ Virgil Snyder.—Cremona transformations in space and hyperspace ₁by₁ Arthur B. Coble.—(1, 2) correspondences between S'₁ and 8r, r₁ 2 ₁by₁ Virgil Snyder.—Reduction of singularities of space curves and surfaces ₁by₁ Arnold Emch.—Multiple correspondence in space and hyperspace ₁by₁ Virgil Snyder.—The mapping of a rational surface on a plane ₁by₁ F. R.

Sharpe.—The mapping of a rational congruence on a plane ₁by₁ F. R. Sharpe.—Involutions on irrational surfaces ₁by₁ Charles H. Sisam.—Transcendental theory ₁by₁ S. Lefschetz.—Singular correspondences between algebraic curves ₁by₁ S. Lefschetz.—Hyperelliptic surfaces and abelian varieties ₁by₁ S. Lefschetz.

1. Geometry, Algebraic. 2. Geometry, Algebraic—Bibl. I. Snyder, Virgil, 1869– II. Coble, Arthur Byron, 1878– III. Emch, Arnold, 1871– IV. Lefschetz, Solomon, 1884– V. Sharpe, Francis Robert, 1870– VI. Sisam, Charles Herschel, 1879– VII. Title. VIII. Title: Algebraic geometry, Selected topics in.
28—10005
Library of Congress Q11.N292 no. 63
₁a41h²2₁ (506) 516

MH MiU OC1W OU OC1 OO OOxM ICJ MB ViU NcRS
NN 0062329 DLC WaTC WaWW CaBVaU OrPR KEmT MoU NcD

National research council. *Committee on rational transformations.*
... Selected topics in algebraic geometry—II. Supplemental report of the Committee on rational transformations ₁by₁ Virgil Snyder, Amos H. Black and Leaman A. Dye. Washington, D. C., Published by the National research council of the National academy of sciences, 1934.
cover-title, xii, 84 p. 24½cm. (Bulletin of the National research council. no. 96, Nov. 1934)
Bibliography at end of each chapter.

CONTENTS.—Curved and ruled surfaces, by Virgil Snyder.—The mapping of systems of curves, by L. A. Dye.—Systems of lines in 8₄; irregular surfaces, by Virgil Snyder.—Cremona transformations, by Virgil Snyder.—Multiple correspondences, by Virgil Snyder.—Surfaces and varieties, by A. H. Black.

1. Geometry, Algebraic. 2. Geometry, Algebraic—Bibl. I. Snyder, Virgil, 1869– II. Black, Amos Hale, 1902– III. Dye, Leaman Andrew. IV. Title. V. Title: Algebraic geometry, Selected topics in.
35–21074
Library of Congress Q11.N292 no. 96

ViU OCU OC1W MiU
NN 0062331 DLC WaTC OrPR OrU CaBVaU NcRS OO OU

National research council. *Committee on research chemicals.*
... American research chemicals; comp. for the Committee on research chemicals and the Research information service by Clarence J. West, National research council. Washington, D. C., 1921.
cover-title, 28 p. 25¼cm. (Reprint and circular series of the National research council. no. 23)
1. Chemicals—Manufacture and industry—U. S. I. National research council. Research information service. II. West, Clarence Jay, 1886– comp. III. Title. IV. Title: Research chemicals.
CA 22–229 Unrev'd
Library of Congress Q11.N293

NN 0062332 DLC OrU ViU CoU OU OC1W MiU OC1

National research council. *Committee on research chemicals.*
... American research chemicals. First revision. Compiled for the Committee on research chemicals and the Research information service by Clarence J. West, National research council. Washington, D. C., 1922.
cover-title, 37 p. 1 illus. 24½cm. (Reprint and circular series of the National research council. no. 35)
1. Chemicals—Manufacture and industry—U. S. I. National research council. Research information service. II. West, Clarence Jay, 1886– comp. III. Title. IV. Title: Research chemicals.
CD 34–27
Library of Congress Card Div. Q11.N293 no. 35

NN 0062333 DLC ViU OrU MiU OCU OC1

National research council. *Committee on research chemicals.*
... Fine and research chemicals. Second revision. Compiled for the Committee on research chemicals, Division of chemistry and chemical technology, by Clarence J. West, secretary of the Committee. Washington, D. C., 1923.
cover-title, 45 p. 24½cm. (Reprint and circular series of the National research council. no. 44)
1. Chemicals—Manufacture and industry—U. S. I. West, Clarence Jay, 1886– comp. II. Title. III. Title: Research chemicals.
CD 34–33
Library of Congress Card Div. Q11.N293 no. 44

NN 0062334 DLC ViU CoU MiU OCU OC1 OC1W NN

WK NATIONAL Research Council. Committee on
5 Research in Endocrinology
N277r Reprints of reports of investigations
₁1948 supported wholly or in part by the Committee on Research in Endocrinology, Division of Medical Sciences, National Research Council. Washington, 1938-48.
9 v. illus.
1. Endocrinology

NN 0062335 DNLM

National Research Council. Committee on
Research in Problems of Sex
see National Research Council. Committee for Research in Problems of Sex.

National Research Council. Committee on
Resistance of Bituminous Materials to
Deterioration Caused by Physical and Chemical
Changes
see National Research Council. Highway Research Board. Committee on Resistance of Bituminous Materials to Deterioration Caused by Physical and Chemical Changes.

National Research Council. Committee on
Roadside Development
see National Research Council. Highway Research Board. Committee on Roadside Development.

National Research Council. Committee on
Rural Traffic and Safety Problems
see National Research Council. Highway Research Board. Committee on Rural Traffic and Safety Problems.

National Research Council. Committee on
Sanitary Engineering. Subcommittee on
Sewage Treatment
see National Research Council. Subcommittee on Sewage Treatment.

W National Research Council. Committee on
1 Sanitary Engineering and Environment
NA6355 Minutes of meeting.
Washington ₁194
v.

NN 0062341 DNLM

National Research Council. Committee on Sanitary Engineering and Environment.
Report on investigation of sewage treatment in low-temperature areas, by Harold Allen Thomas, Jr. [Washington] 1950.
43 p. illus.

I. Thomas, Harold Allen.

NN 0062342 ICJ

National Research Council. Committee on
Sanitary Engineering and Environment. Subcommittee on Shelter and Clothing
see National Research Council. Subcommittee on Shelter and Clothing.

National research council. Committee on
scientific aids to learning.

Hogan, John Vincent Lawless, 1890–
Auditory aids in the class room: a report on the cost of providing auditory aids by broadcasting, by wire lines and by records, prepared for the Committee by John V. L. Hogan and R. M. Wilmotte ... New York, Committee on scientific aids to learning, 1938.

National research council. *Committee on scientific aids to learning.*
Broadcast receivers and phonographs for classroom use. New York, Committee on scientific aids to learning, 1939.
94, ₁1₁ p. 1 illus., plates, diagrs. 23½cm.
1. Radio—Apparatus and supplies. 2. Phonograph. 3. Radio in education. 4. Phonograph in education. I. Title.
39–23027
Library of Congress LB1044.5.N4
———— Copy 2.
Copyright A 133054 ₁8₁ 371.333

MH PU
NN 0062345 DLC OrMonO OrU KEmT OCU OC1W OU ICJ

National research council. *Committee on scientific aids to learning.*
Central sound systems for schools. New York, Committee on scientific aids to learning, 1940.
69 p. illus., diagrs. 23cm.
"All of the report, with the exception of the first chapter, was written by Professor W. M. Hall of Massachusetts institute of technology. The first chapter was written by Mr. Paul C. Reed."—Foreword.
1. Sound—Recording and reproducing. 2. Radio in education. 3. Phonograph in education. 4. Schools—Furniture, equipment, etc. I. Hall, William Mott. II. Reed, Paul C. III. Title. IV. Title: Sound systems for schools.
40–12517
Library of Congress TK6401.N3
———— Copy 2.
Copyright ₁5₁ 621.381

NN 0062346 DLC KEmT OU OrU OrMonO

National Research Council. *Committee on Scientific Aids to Learning.*
Eye fatigue in the reading of microfilm; report of the Advisory Committee to the Committee on Scientific Aids to Learning. Members of the Advisory Committee: Adelbert Ames, Jr., chairman, Wallace O. Fenn ₁and₁ Walter F. Dearborn. ₁n. p.₁ 1938.
26 l. 28 cm.
Bibliography: p. 22–26.
1. Eyestrain. 2. Microfilms. I. Title.
RE48.N3 55–53644

NN 0062347 DLC NN

VOLUME 407

National Research Council. Committee on
Scientific Aids to Learning.
Local broadcasts to schools
see under   Stewart, Irvin, 1899-   ed.

National research council. Committee on Scientific Aids
to Learning.
Microphotography for scholarly purposes; report of an inquiry
by the Committee on scientific aids to learning, July, 1940.
₁New York, 1940₁   40 f.   27½cm.

Reproduced from typewritten copy.

1. Photography—Reproductions of   books, manuscripts, etc.
N. Y. P. L.   August 26, 1941

NN   0062349   NN NNC DNAL

371.33523
N277m National Research Council. Committee on
Scientific Aids to Learning.
Motion picture projectors for classroom
use. Prepared for the committee by Herbert
R. Jensen.   New York, 1940.
117 f.

Includes bibliography.

1. Moving-picture projectors. 2. Moving-pictures
in education.   I. Jensen, Herbert R
II. Title.

NN   0062350   ICarbS

Z265
.J86   National research council. Committee on
vol. 1,   scientific aids to learning.
no. 3,   Tate, Vernon Dale, 1909-
pt. 2   ... The present status of equipment and supplies for microphotography, a report prepared for the Committee on scientific
aids to learning, by Vernon D. Tate ... ₁Chicago, American
library association, 1938₁

National research council. Committee on
Scientific aids to learning.
Report of the advisory committee to the
Committee on scientific aids to learning,
November 1, 1938
see its   Eye fatigue in the reading of
microfilm.

National research council. *Committee on scientific aids to
learning.*
School recording technique. New York, Committee on
scientific aids to learning, 1941.

51 p. illus., plates, diagrs. 23ᶜᵐ.

"Intended as a companion volume to the report by the same author
on Sound recording equipment for schools, published by the Committee
on scientific aids to learning in 1940 ... The author ... is Professor
Karl S. Van Dyke."—Foreword.

1. Sound—Recording and reproducing. 2. Schools—Furniture, equipment, etc.   I. Van Dyke, Karl Skillman, 1892-   II. Title.

Library of Congress   TK6565.R4N28
                                      41–17774
                            ₁15₁   681.84322

NN   0062353   DLC InU KEmT OC1

National Research Council. Committee on
Scientific Aids to Learning
Sheet microfilm; advantages, techniques,
costs.
see under   Bennett, Ralph Decker, 1900-

National research council. *Committee on scientific aids to
learning.*
Sound recording equipment for schools. New York, Committee on scientific aids to learning, 1940.

52 p. 1 illus., plates, diagrs. 23ᶜᵐ.

"The present report was prepared by Professor Karl S. Van Dyke ...
who was assisted by Mr. R. L. Brown."—Foreword.

1. Sound—Recording and reproducing. 2. Schools—Furniture, equipment, etc.   I. Van Dyke, Karl Skillman, 1892-   II. Brown, Richard
Leland, 1912-   III. Title.

Library of Congress   TK6565.R4N3
                                      40–11861
————— Copy 2.
Copyright   ₁5₁   681.843

OC1 OU
NN   0062355   DLC OrMonO OrLgE OrU ICJ KEmT PU InU

National research council. Committee on Scientific Aids to
Learning.
Specification for broadcast receiver for school use... Second
draft, September 21, 1939. Prepared for the Committee on
scientific aids to learning...by John V. L. Hogan and Raymond
M. Wilmotte.   ₁New York, 1939₁   15, 16, 4 f.   28cm.

1. Radio—Receiving apparatus.   I. Hogan, John Vincent Lawless,
1890-   II. Wilmotte, Raymond   Maurice, 1901-
N. Y. P. L.   August 13, 1947

NN   0062356   NN

National research council. Committee on Scientific Aids to
Learning.
...A study of broadcast receivers and phonographs for use in
the classroom. Prepared for the committee by John V. L. Hogan
and R. M. Wilmotte, January 27, 1939... ₁New York, 1939₁
59 f.   28cm.

1. Radio—Receiving apparatus.   2. Phonograph. I. Hogan, John
Vincent Lawless, 1890- . II. Wil-   motte, Raymond Maurice, 1901-
N. Y. P. L.   August 25, 1947

NN   0062357   NN

Q183
.M75   National research council. Committee on
scientific aids to learning.
Mueller, Ronald.
A study of the radio and phonograph as instructional aids
in the teaching of science in the Rochester schools, by Roland
Mueller, with a foreword by Harry A. Carpenter. July,
1940. New York, N. Y., Committee on scientific aids to learning ₁1940₁

D371.335
N213   National research council. Committee on
scientific aids to learning.
Survey of school experience with motion
picture projection equipment (edited for the
assistance of individual manufacturers) February, 1940. New York, Committee on scientific aids to learning ₁1940₁
108 l. tables.

1. Moving-picture projection. 2. Moving-
pictures in education.

NN   0062359   NNC

D371.335
N2143   National research council. Committee on scientific aids to learning.
Use of phonograph records as an aid to the
teaching of science. Preliminary print. New
York, Committee on scientific aids to learning,
c1939.
1 p. l., ii, 53 numb. l.   27⅜ᶜᵐ.

Extracts, edited by Irwin Stewart, from the
report made by Harry A. Carpenter on the use of
forty phonograph records in general science at
the seventh grade level. cf. Pref.
Reproduced from   type-written copy.

NN   0062360   NNC PU-Penn PU NNU

National research council. *Committee on scientific
aids to learning*
see also
Georgia committee on sound recordings for schools.

National research council. *Committee on scientific problems
of human migration.*
... Final report of the Committee on scientific problems of
human migration. Clark Wissler ... ₁Washington, D. C.,
1929₁

1 p. l., 21 p.   24ᶜᵐ. (Reprint and circular series of the National research council. no. 87)

"Publications resulting from the work of the Committee on scientific
problems of human migration": p. ₁17₁-21.

1. Man—Migrations. 2. Research.   I. Wissler, Clark, 1870-
                                                        C D 34–59
Library of Congress   Card Div. Q11.N293 no. 87

NN
NN   0062362   DLC PPF OrPR ViU OCU OU OC1 OOxM MiU

National research council. Committee on
scientific problems of human migration.
Minnesota. University. *Dept. of psychology.*
Minnesota mechanical ability tests; the report of a research
investigation subsidized by the Committee on human migrations of the National research council and conducted in the
Department of psychology of the University of Minnesota,
by Donald G. Paterson and Richard M. Elliott, directors of
the investigation, L. Dewey Anderson, chief investigator,
Herbert A. Toops, statistical consultant, Edna Heidbreder,
editor of the report. Minneapolis, The University of Minnesota press ₁*1930₁

National research council. *Committee on scientific problems
of human migration.*
... The work of the Committee on scientific problems of
human migration, National research council, submitted for the
Committee by Robert M. Yerkes, chairman ... ₁Washington,
D. C., National research council, 1924₁

cover-title, p. 189–196. 24½ᶜᵐ. (Reprint and circular series of the National research council. no. 58)

"Reprinted from Journal of personnel research, volume III, October,
1924, pp. 189–196."

1. Man—Migrations. 2. Research.   C D 34–44

Library of Congress   Card Div. Q11.N293 no. 58

NN   0062364   DLC ViU OrPR OCU OC1W OU MiU

QE581
.T82   National Research Council. Committee on
1955   Sedimentation.   FOR OTHER EDITION:
                                    SEE MAIN ENTRY
Trask, Parker Davies, 1899-   ed.
Recent marine sediments, a symposium. Reprinted by
permission of the American Association of Petroleum Geologists, with the addition of a review of advances in the field
of study of recent marine sediments since 1939 ... Tulsa,
Okla., 1955.

National research council. *Committee on sedimentation.*
... Report of the Committee on sedimentation. ₁1st₁-
₁1919/20₁-
Washington, D. C., National research council of the National
academy of sciences ₁1920₁-

v. illus., pl., diagrs. 24½ cm.

Report year ends in April.
The Committee on sedimentation is a committee of the Division of
geology and geography of the National research council.
The 6th-8th reports, published 1925-27, have title: Researches in
sedimentation in 1924₁-1926/27₁; report of the Committee on sedi-
mentation.
Chairman: 1919/20-1922/23, T. W. Vaughan.—1923/24-1930/32, W.
H. Twenhofel.—1932/34-   A. C. Trowbridge.

The first 8 reports, published 1920-27, were "issued in mimeographed form by the National research council," and are of slightly
varying size; beginning with the 9th report, 1927/28, the reports are
issued in printed form in the Reprint and circular series of the council,
as no. 85, 92, 98, and in the Bulletin series, no. 89, 98.
Bibliographies accompany many of the articles.
A mimeographed copy of a preliminary report of the committee for
1927/28 (2 p.) issued as Appendix H of the Annual report of the
Division of geology and geography of the National research council
for 1927/28, is inserted in report of the committee for 1926/27, following p. 78; the same matter is repeated in the printed report for
1927/28.
1. Sedimentation and deposition.   I. Vaughan, Thomas Wayland,
1870-1952. II. Twen-   hofel, William Henry, 1875-   III.
Trowbridge, Arthur   Carleton, 1885-   IV. Title. v. Title.
Researches in   sedimentation.
QE581.N3   29—4564

OU
NhD TxLT KEmT DAU NN IU MtU KyU PBL OCX NbU OC1
NN   0062367   DLC IdU-SB OOxM MB IU ICJ DI NcRS

VOLUME 407

National Research Council. Committee on Sedimentation.
Tables for the determination of detrital minerals.
Washington 1942. (In: National Research Council
Committee on Sedimentation. Reports 1940-1941)
(QE581.N3)

NN 0062368 DLC

National research council. Committee on
sedimentation. FOR OTHER EDITIONS
SEE MAIN ENTRY
Twenhofel, William Henry, 1875–
Treatise on sedimentation; prepared under the auspices of
the Committee on sedimentation, Division of geology and
geography, National research council of the National academy
of sciences, by William H. Twenhofel ... and collaborators.
2d ed., completely rev. Baltimore, The Williams & Wilkins
company, 1932.

National research council. Committee on
sedimentation. Subcommittee on nomenclature
and classification of sediments.
Tarr, William Arthur, 1881–
... Terminology of the chemical siliceous sediments, by W. A.
Tarr. Washington, D. C., National research council, Division
of geology and geography, 1936.

National research council. Committee on
sedimentation. Subcommittee on nomenclature and classification of sediments.
Twenhofel, William Henry, 1875–
... Terminology of the fine-grained mechanical sediments,
by W. H. Twenhofel. Washington, D. C., National research
council, Division of geology and geography, 1936.

National research council. *Committee on selection and training of aircraft pilots.*
... The aircraft pilot; 5 years of research, a summary of out-
comes, by Morris S. Viteles, chairman, Committee on selection
and training of aircraft pilots, June 15, 1945, a report to the
Division of research, Civil aeronautics administration. ₁Washington, 1945₎
3 p. l., 46 p. illus., diagrs. 28½ x 22ᶜᵐ.
At head of title: National research council, Division of anthropology
and psychology.
Bibliography: p. 37–42.
1. Air pilots—U. S. 2. Aeronautics—Study and teaching.   I. Viteles,
Morris Simon, 1898–   II. U. S. Civil aeronautics administration.   III.
Title.
45–8374
Library of Congress *   TL712.N3
₁5₎   629.1325207

NN 0062372 DLC

National research council. Committee on
selection and training of aircraft pilots.
Viteles, Morris Simon, 1898–
An analysis of photographic records of aircraft pilot performance. Section A: A study of criteria of pilot proficiency
derived from motion photographs of flight performance, by
Morris S. Viteles and Albert S. Thompson. Section B: Supplemental report, an analysis of scores on aspects of flight performance, by Albert S. Thompson ... Washington, D. C. ₁1944₎

National Research Council. *Committee on Selection and
Training of Aircraft Pilots.*
. Annual meeting.

Washington.
v. 28 cm.

1. Air pilots—U. S. 2. Flight training.

TL712.N32   629.1325207
49–3991*‡

NN 0062374 DLC

150.13 NATIONAL RESEARCH COUNCIL. Committee on select-
F216 ion and training of aircraft pilots.

The contribution of psychology to aviation;
addresses at the annual meeting of the Committee
on selection and training of aircraft pilots,
National research council, by Major General D.N.
W.Grant... Commodore J.C.Adams... W.A.H.Burden
...₁and others₎ Washington,D.C.,Civil
aeronautics administration,Division of research,1945.
iii p.,1₽.,25,₁1₎p. 20cm.

NN 0062375 PU

National research council. *Committee on selection and training of aircraft pilots.*
... An historical introduction to aviation psychology. Prepared by National research council Committee on selection and
training of aircraft pilots, October, 1942. Washington, D. C.,
Civil aeronautics administration, Division of research ₁1942₎
cover-title, 2 p. l., iii, 71 (i. e. 72) p. illus., diagrs. 26ᶜᵐ. (₁Civil
aeronautics administration₎ Report no. 4)

At head of title: Restricted. Not for publication.
Page 58a inserted.
Reproduced from type-written copy.

"Prepared with the editorial assistance of N. L. Munn."
"Written primarily to become Chapter I of the text on aviation psychology, which is under preparation by the Committee on selection and
training of aircraft pilots."—Letter of transmittal.
Bibliography: p. 63–71.

1. Aeronautics—Medical aspects.   I. Munn, Norman Leslie, 1902–
II. Title. III. Title: Aviation psychology.
A 44–2255
Wesleyan univ.   Library
for Library of Congress   ₁TL555.U5   no. 4₎
₁3₎   (629.1306173)

NN 0062377 CtW CtY-M OrU-M

National Research Council. *Committee on Selection and
Training of Aircraft Pilots.*
History and development of the Ohio State flight inven-
tory. Pt. II: Recent versions and current applications.
Washington, Civil Aeronautics Administration, Division of
Research, 1945.
(U. S. Civil Aeronautics Administration. Report no. 51)
Microfilm copy made in 1951 by the Library of Congress. Negative.
Collation of the original: x, 34 p.

1. Aeronautics—Ohio. 2. Aeronautics—Flights.   (Series)

Microfilm TL–7   Mic 52–271

NN 0062378 DLC

National Research Council. *Committee on Selection and
Training of Aircraft Pilots.*
Manual for the administration of the Ohio State flight
inventory. 2d ed. Washington, Dept. of Commerce, Civil
Aeronautics Administration, Division of Research, 1943.
Microfilm copy made in 1951 by the Library of Congress.
Collation of the original: v, 47 p.

1. Aeronautics—Ohio. 2. Aeronautics—Flights.   I. U. S. Civil
Aeronautics Administration.

Microfilm TL–7   Mic 52–327

NN 0062379 DLC ICJ

National Research Council. *Committee on Selection and
Training of Aircraft Pilots.*
The medical requirements of the Civil Aeronautics Administration and the recommended medical requirements of
the Personnel Licensing Division of the Provisional International Civil Aviation Organization. Washington, Civil
Aeronautics Administration, Division of Research, 1947.
vii, 75 p. 28 cm.

1. Aeronautics—Medical aspects. 2. U. S. Civil Aeronautics Administration. 3. Provisional International Civil Aviation Organization.
TL555.N3   629.132562   47–46320*

NN 0062380 DLC OU ICJ OrCS

National research council. Committee on
TL555 selection and training of aircraft pilots.
.W4
Wendt, George Richard, 1906–
... Motion sickness in aviation, by G. R. Wendt. May 1944 ...
Washington, D. C. ₁1944₎

National research council. Committee on
selection and training of aircraft pilots.
Report on the Boston-Midwest project ...
November 1945. Washington, D.C., Civil
aeronautics administration, Division of research
₁1945₎
xiii, 103 p. incl. illus., tables. (Report no.
52)

Manifold copy.
"The work at Boston was under the direction of
Rose A.McFarland" - cf. p.vi.

NN 0062382 MH-BA

629.1325 NATIONAL RESEARCH COUNCIL. Committee on selec-
Un35 tion and training of aircraft pilots.
no.61
The role of fatigue in pilot performance,
prepared by National research council, Committee on selection and training of aircraft pilots for the Civil aeronautics board at the request of the Division of research, Civil aeronautics administration. Washington,D.C.,
1946.
2₽.,iii-xi,120p. incl.diagrs. 28cm.
(₁U.S.₎ Civil aeronautics administration. Division of re-   search. Report no.61)
"Bibliogra-   phy" p.113-116.

NN 0062383 PU

629.1325 NATIONAL RESEARCH COUNCIL. Committee on selec-
Un35 tion and training of aircraft pilots.
no.62
Study of visual and cardiovascular standards
in relation to success in flight training, prepared by National research council, Committee on
selection and training of pilots. Washington,
D.C.,1946.
ix,267p. incl.tables,form. 27½cm. (₁U.
S.₎ Civil aeronautics administration. Division
of research. Report no.62)
"Errata" leaf   inserted.

NN 0062384 PU

National Research Council. *Committee on Selection and
Training of Aircraft Pilots.*
The tricks of the trade, a handbook for flight instructors.
Prepared ₁for the Civil Aeronautics Administration, Divi-
sion of Research. Washington₎ 1947.
iv, 41 p. illus. 22 cm.

1. Flight training.
TL712.N38   629.13252   48–45667*

NN 0062385 DLC CU

National Research Council. *Committee on Selection and
Training of Aircraft Pilots.*
The tricks of the trade, a handbook for flight instructors.
Prepared ₁for the Civil Aeronautics Administration, Divi-
sion of Research. Washington₎ 1947.
50 p. illus. 22 cm.

1. Flight training.   I. Title.
TL712.N38 1947a   52–61847 ‡
*629.126 629.13252

NN 0062386 DLC CU

VOLUME 407

HV
1626
N277f
1948

NATIONAL Research Council. Committee on
Sensory Devices
Final report. ₁Washington? 1948₁
34 *l.*
"Contract VAm 21223."
Imperfect: p. 16-21 and all after
p. 34 wanting.

1. Blind - Aids

NN 0062387   DNLM

HV
1626
⁊ N277p
1947

NATIONAL Research Council Committee
on Sensory Devices
Progress report and summary of projects under contract VAm-21223.
₁Washington?₁ 1947.
53 *l.*
CSD 47-3.
Cover title.
1. Blind - Aids

NN 0062388   DNLM

National Research Council. Committee on Sensory
Devices.
A supersonic blind aid ...
see under   Brush Development Company.
Cleveland.

**National Research Council. Committee on Ship Construc-
tion.**

The Committee on Ship Construction of the National Research
Council was appointed in 1946. In 1948 it was reconstituted as the
Committee on Ship Steel, and in 1952 the parallel Committee on
Ship Structural Design was appointed. In 1963 these two commit-
tees were replaced by the Ship Hull Research Committee, which
was reorganized in 1968 under the name Ship Research Committee.
Works by these bodies are found under the following headings
according to the name used at the time of publication:

**National Research Council. Committee on Ship Construction.
National Research Council. Committee on Ship Steel.**

TA492
.P7D3

National Research Council. Committee on Ship
Construction.
Davis, Harmer Elmer, 1905–
Progress report on causes of cleavage fracture in ship plate:
flat plate tests, by H. E. Davis, G. E. Troxell, A. Boodberg ...
₁and others₁ University of California under Navy contract
Nobs–31222. Committee on ship construction, Division of
engineering & industrial research, National research council,
advisory to Bureau of ships, Navy department under Contract
Nobs–34231 ... ₁Washington₁ 1946.

National Research Council. Committee on Ship Steel.

The Committee on Ship Construction of the National Research
Council was appointed in 1946. In 1948 it was reconstituted as the
Committee on Ship Steel, and in 1952 the parallel Committee on
Ship Structural Design was appointed. In 1963 these two committees were replaced by the Ship Hull Research Committee, which
was reorganized in 1968 under the following headings
according to the name used at the time of publication:

**National Research Council. Committee on Ship Construction.
National Research Council. Committee on Ship Steel.**

National Research Council. Committee on
Ship Steel.
Investigation of the influence of deoxidation
see under   Battelle Memorial Institute,
Columbus, Ohio.

W 2
A
N3647b

NATIONAL Research Council. Committee on
Shock
Minutes of the meeting.

Washington, 195
v. illus.

Continues Bulletin [on] shock issued by
Subcommittee on Shock, National Research
Council.
38th meeting, 29 Jan. 1959, joint meeting with the Subcommittee on Plasma.

43d meeting, 17 Dec. 1960, joint meeting with the Committee on Trauma.
1. Shock - period. I. National Research
Council. Committee on Trauma II. National Research Council. Subcommittee on
Plasma

NN 0062395   DNLM

National research council. *Committee on shoreline investigations.*
... Studies of mean sea-level; report of the Committee on
shoreline investigations, National research council ₁by₁ Douglas Johnson. Washington, D. C., Published by the National
research council of the National academy of sciences, 1929.
50 p. illus. (maps) diagrs. 24½ᶜᵐ. (Bulletin of the National research
council. no. 70, July 1929)

1. Tides—New York. 2. Shore-lines.   I. Johnson, Douglas Wilson,
1878–   II. Title. III. Title: Sea-level. Studies of mean.

Library of Congress   Q11.N292 no. 70   29–16997

NcD OU OCU OU ViU MB ICJ
NN 0062396   DLC WaTC OrPR CaBVaU OrU DAU NcRS

National Research Council. Committee on Snow
and Ice Removal
see   National Research Council. Highway
Research Board. Dept. of Maintenance. Committee on Snow and Ice Removal.

National Research Council. Committee on Soil –
Bituminous Roads
see   National Research Council. Highway
Research Board. Committee on Soil-Bituminous
Roads.

National Research Council. Committee on
Soil-Cement Roads
see   National Research Council. Highway
Research Board. Committee on Soil-Cement
Roads.

National Research Council. *Committee on Solids.*
Imperfections in nearly perfect crystals; symposium held
at Pocono Manor, October 12-14, 1950. Editorial committee: W. Shockley, chairman ₁and others₁ New York, Wiley
₁1952₁
xii, 490 p. illus. 22 cm.
Includes bibliographies.

1. Crystallography.   I. Shockley, William, 1910–   ed.
II. Title.
QD905.N3   548   52—5957

MtBC OrPR OrP OrPS OrU MtU OrCS CaBVaU
PPT PPS OC1W PU MiHM ICJ MB NN TxU IdU IdPI MtBuM
NN 0062400   DLC OC1U KMK KEmT CU ViU ScC1eU TU

National Research Council. *Committee on Solids.*
Phase transformations in solids; symposium held at Cor-
nell University, August 23-26, 1948. Editorial committee:
R. Smoluchowski, chairman, J. E. Mayer ₁and₁ W. A. Weyl.
New York, Wiley, 1951.
x, 660 p. illus. 22 cm.
Includes bibliographies.

1. Phase rule and equilibrium. 2. Solids.   I. Smoluchowski, Roman, ed. II. Title.
QD501.N32 1948   541.39   51–13368

CU CaBVaU MtBuM OrCS OrPR OrU IdU MtU WaS
NN 0062401   DLC ViU MiHM ICJ TU TxU MoU NcU MH

National Research Council. Committee on Solids
Structure and properties of solid surfaces
see under   National Research Council.

614.78
N213p

National Research Council. Committee on Sound
Control.
Progress report of Project II, December 1,
1941. Part I: the effects of noise on
psychomotor efficiency. Part II: Noise reduction in aircraft as related to communication annoyance and aural injury. S. S.
Stevens, Director of Research. Cambridge,
Mass., Psychological Laboratory, Harvard
University, 1941.
125 *l.* illus.
1. Noise - Physiological effect. 2. Noise
control. I. Stevens, S. S. II. Title. III
Title: The effects of noise on psychomotor
efficiency. IV. Title: Noise reduction in
aircraft as related to communication,
annoyance and aural injury.

NN 0062404   MsSM NNC IU DNLM

National Research Council. *Committee on Sound Sounding
and Oceanographic Thermographs*
see
National Research Council. *Committee on Submarine Configuration and Oceanic Circulation.*

National Research Council. Committee on
Specialized Personnel.
Practices in collection and maintenance of
information on highly trained and specialized
personnel in the United States
see under   Conference Board of the
Associated Research Councils. Committee on
Specialized Personnel.

National Research Council. Committee on
Stabilized Turf Shoulders
see   National Research Council. Highway
Research Board. Committee on Stabilizaed Turf
Shoulders.

National research council. Committee on state
archaeological surveys.
Archaeological field work in North America
see under title

VOLUME 407

National Research Council. Committee on state
archaeological surveys.
Circular series,
Ann Arbor, Michigan , The Committee,
v. illus., plates, facsims.   28cm.

Mimeographed.
Editor:.   Carl E. Guthe.

1. Archaeology---Societies. I. Guthe, Carl
Eugen, 1893- , ed.

NN 0062409   LNHT MH-P

National research council. *Committee on state archaeological
surveys.*
Conference on southern pre-history, held under the auspices
of the Division of anthropology and psychology, Committee
on state archaeological surveys, National research council,
Hotel Tutwiler, Birmingham, Alabama, December 18, 19 and
20, 1932. Washington, D. C., National research council ₍1932?₎
iv numb. l., 97 p., 1 l. front., maps. 27 x 21ᶜᵐ.
Mimeographed.
Bibliography: p. 59.
1. Southern states—Antiq. 2. Indians of North America—Southern
states. 3. Mounds—U. S.

| Library of Congress | F211.N28 | 33–17570 |
| ——— Copy 2. | ₍2₎ | [970.4] 913.75 |

NN 0062410   DLC OrU MsSM FMU CU ICU NcD OU IU

National research council. *Committee on state archaeological
surveys.*
... Guide leaflet for amateur archaeologists ... Washington,
D. C., National research council, 1930.
11 p. illus., diagrs. 24ᶜᵐ. (Reprint and circular series of the National research council. no. 93)
"Issued under the auspices of the Committee on state archaeological
surveys, Division of Anthropology and psychology, National research
council."
1. Archaeology. I. Title.
                                     C D 34—62
Library of Congress.   Card div. Q11.N293 no. 93

NN 0062411   DLC OrPR OrU Or MiU ViU OU PPiHi

National research council. Committee on state
archaeological surveys.
913.73   The Indianapolis archaeological conference; a
N277   symposium upon the archaeological problems of
the north central United States area. Held under the auspices of the Division of anthropology and psychology,Committee on state archaeological surveys,National research council...
Indianapolis, Indiana,December 6,7 and 8,1935.
Washington, D. C., ₍1937₎
vii, 82 p. fold. tab. 27ᵐ.
Deals with the upper Mississippi valley and
the Great Lakes   region.
Reproduced from   type-written copy.
1.U.S. - Antiquities. I. Title.

NN 0062412   CSt WHi InU

National Research Council. Committee on State
Archaeological Surveys.
Policies of the Committee - abstracted from
a paper prepared by Carl E. Guthe for the
American anthropological association, December,
1929. [Washington, D. C., 1929]
[1] p.   38 cm.

NN 0062413   MH-P

National research council. *Committee on state archaeological surveys.*
... Report of the conference on midwestern archaeology, held
in St. Louis, Missouri, May 18, 1929; including a report of an
open meeting of the committee, held May 17, 1929. Issued
under the auspices of the Committee on state archaeological
surveys of the Division of anthropology and psychology of the
National research council. Washington, D. C., Published by
the National research council of the National academy of
sciences, 1929.
120 p. incl. plates. front. 25ᵐ. (Bulletin of the National research
council. no. 74, Dec. 1929)

Continued in next column

Continued from preceding column

Preface signed: Knight Dunlap, chairman, Division of anthropology
and psychology, National research council.
1. U. S.—Antiq. 2. Indians of North America—Antiq. 3. Mounds—
U. S.   I. Dunlap, Knight, 1875–   II. Title. III. Title: Conference
on midwestern archaeology. IV. Title: Midwestern archaeology, Conference on.
                                          30–6174 Revised
Library of Congress   Q11.N292 no. 74

CU NcD OClW ViU OU OOxM OCU PU
NN 0062415   DLC OrSaW OrPR WaTC CaBVaU KEmT DSI

E
77.94   National Research Council. Committee on State
N375x   Archaeological Surveys.
State archaeological surveys; suggestions
in method and technique, prepared by the Committee
on State Archaeological Surveys, Division of
Anthropology and Psychology, National Research
Council, Clark Wissler, Chairman, Amos W.
Butler, Roland B. Dixon, F.W. Hodge, Berthold
Laufer. Washington, D.C., 1923.
24 l. 27cm.

Mimeographed.

NN 0062416   WyU OrCS   InU IaU

Mu
571   ₍NATIONAL RESEARCH COUNCIL. Committee on state
N215.2   archeological surveys₎

A suggested classification of cultures.
₍University of Michigan,Museum of anthropology,
1932₎
3₍1₎ℓ. 31cm.

Mimeographed.
Caption-title.
Imprint supplied from letter.

With this is bound a mimeographed letter
dated April 4, 1933, issued by the Committee on
State archeological surveys.

NN 0062418   PU

National research council. *Committee on state geological
surveys.*
... Summary information on the state geological surveys
and the United States geological survey. Compiled under the
direction of the National research council Committee on state
geological surveys ... Washington, D. C., Published by the
National research council of the National academy of sciences,
1932.
3 p. l., 136 p. 24½ᵐ. (Bulletin of the National research council.
no. 88, Nov. 1932)
"Committee members: M. M. Leighton, chairman; E. F. Bean, H. A.
Buehler, Arthur Keith, Henry B. Kummel, Waldemar Lindgren."
1. Geological surveys. 2. U. S. Geological survey.   I. Leighton,
Morris Morgan, 1887–   II. Title. III. Title: State geological surveys.
                                          33–4085
| Library of Congress | Q11.N292 no. 88 | |
| ——— Copy 2. | ₍5₎ | (506) 557.3 |

OClW OU OCU ViU OO MB
NN 0062419   DLC WaTC CaBVaU OrU WaS OrPR NcD

G551.7
N213   National Research Council. Committee on
Stratigraphy.
Correlation charts ₍of the post-Prote-
rozoic sedimentary formations of North Amer-
ica₎ by Carl O. Dunbar, chairman ₍and others₎
with the collaboration of about 70 additional
stratigraphers. New York, Geological
Society of America, 1942-60.
2 v. illus., maps. 25cm.
A set made up of offprints from the Bulletin of the Geological Society of America
v.53-55, 59, 63-65, 71.

Title from Introduction (pub. 1942; plan
later slightly modified) Contents as in
Geological Society of America. Books in
print, 1963; no.10c not published.
Includes bibliographies.

Continued in next column

Continued from preceding column

Contents.
₍v.1₎ Introduction. 1. Cambrian. 2. Ordovician.
3. Silurian. 4. Devonian. 5. Mississippian. 6.
Pennsylvanian. 7. Permian.
₍v.2₎ 8a. Triassic (excl. Canada) 8b. Triassic
of Canada. 8c. Jurassic (excl. Canada) 8d. Jurassic of Canada. 9. Cretaceous of Atlantic and Gulf
coastal plain. 10a. Cretaceous of Greater Antilles

Central America, Mexico. 10b. Cretaceous of
Western interior of United States. 10d. Cretaceous
of Greenland, Alaska. 10e. Cretaceous of Pacific
Coast. 11. Cenozoic of western North America.
12. Cenozoic of Atlantic and Gulf coastal plain
& Caribbean region.
1. Geology, Stratigraphic. 2. Geology of
North America. 3.   Rocks, Sedimentary. I.
Geological Socie-   ty of America. II. Dunbar,
Carl Owen, 1891-   III. Title.

NN 0062423   MnU CaBViP OU NNC

National research council. *Committee on structural petrol-
ogy.*
... Final report of the Committee on structural petrology,
1937 ... T. S. Lovering, chairman ... ₍Washington, D. C.,
National research council, 1938₎
4 p. l., 103 (i. e. 115) p. illus., diagrs. 27 cm.
At head of title: National research council. Division of geology
and geography ...
Paging irregular.
Contains reviews of 20 papers by various members of the Com-
mittee.
"Selected papers on structural petrology": p. 2–5.
1. Petrology—Societies, etc.   I. Lovering, Thomas Seward, 1896–
QE420.N3   G S 39–162
U. S. Geol. Survey. Libr.
for Library of Congress   ₍a56c½₎†

TxU DLC
NN 0062424   DI-GS OrU ICJ MU DAU MU ODW OO TU

National research council. Committee on submarine configuration and oceanic circulation.
Report ...
₍Washington, D. C.,
v. 27.5cm.
Issued in mimeographed form as Appendix V
of Annual report Division of geology and
geography.

NN 0062425   MtU CaBVaU DLC DI-GS IaU CtY CU DAS

National Research Council. Committee on Surface
Drainage of Highways
see   National Research Council. Highway
Research Board. Committee on Surface Drainage
of Highways.

National Recreation Association. Committee on
Surfacing.
Surfacing playground areas (supplement) New
York ₍1952₎
27 p.

NN 0062427   Wa

National research council. *Committee on surgery.*
Abdominal and genito-urinary injuries, prepared under the
auspices of the Committee on surgery of the Division of medical sciences of the National research council ... Philadelphia
& London, W. B. Saunders company, 1942.
xv, 131 p., 2 l., xxi-xxii p., 1 l., 135-243 p. illus., diagrs. 24ᵐ. (Its
Military surgical manuals. ₍III₎)
"References" at end of most of the chapters.
1. Abdomen—Surgery. 2. Genito-urinary organs—Surgery. 3. Gunshot wounds. 4. Surgery, Military.   I. Title.

| Library of Congress | RD156.N3 | 42-22284 |
| | ₍10₎ | 617.46 |

NN 0062428   DLC OrU-M IdPI ICRL NcD DNLM ViU OU

VOLUME 407

National Research Council. Committee on Surgery.
Abstract of minutes of meeting
see its Minutes of meeting.

National research council. *Committee on surgery.*
Burns, shock, wound healing and vascular injuries, prepared under the auspices of the Committee on surgery of the Division of medical sciences of the National research council ... Philadelphia & London, W. B. Saunders company, 1943.

[308] p. illus., diagrs. 24 cm. [Its Military surgical manuals, v]
Various pagings.
Bibliography at end of each chapter of the section, Burns.

1. Surgery, Military. 2. Burns and scalds. 3. Shock. 4. Wounds—Treatment. 5. Blood vessels—Wounds and injuries.

RD151.N3　　　　617.99　　　　43—2699

ICRL TU WaU RPB TxU O ViU NcD IdPI CaBVaU
NN　0062430　　DLC OrU OrU-M OrCS IParkA NcD-N IEdS

WO
100
qN277
NATIONAL Research Council. Committee on Surgery
[Collection of publications]
The library has a collection of miscellaneous publications of this organization kept as received. These publications are not listed nor bound separately.

NN　0062431　　DNLM

National research council. *Committee on surgery.*
Manual of standard practice of plastic and maxillofacial surgery, prepared and edited by the Subcommittee on plastic and maxillofacial surgery of the Committee on surgery of the Division of medical sciences of the National research council, and representatives of the Medical department, U. S. army ... Philadelphia & London, W. B. Saunders company, 1942.

xiii p., 1 l., 432 p. illus., diagr. 24cm. (Its Military surgical manuals. [1])

1. Surgery, Plastic. 2. Face—Surgery. I. U. S. Surgeon-general's office. II. Title.

Library of Congress　　RD118.N3　　　　42-17393
　　　　　　　　　　　　　　[12]　　　　　　　　　617.95

NcD DNLM ICJ ViU OU
NN　0062432　　DLC CaBVaU IdPI OrU OrU-M OrU-D WaU

National research council. *Committee on surgery.*
A manual of surgical anatomy, prepared under the auspices of the Committee on surgery of the Division of medical sciences of the National research council, by Tom Jones and W. C. Shepard. Philadelphia and London, W. B. Saunders company, 1945.

xvi, 195 p. illus. (part col.) 28cm. (Its Military surgical manuals. [VII])

1. Anatomy, Surgical and topographical. I. Jones, Thomas Smith, 1885- II. Shepard, Willard Cameron, 1886-

　　　　　　　　　　　　　　　　　　　　45-35154
Library of Congress *　　QM531.N3
　　　　　　　　　　　　[5]　　　　　　　　　611.9

OOxM OU
NN　0062433　　DLC OrU-M MtU CaBVaU PU ViU CLSU

National research council. *Committee on surgery.*
Military surgical manuals. Philadelphia and London, W. B. Saunders company, 1942–45.

7 v. illus. (part col.) diagrs. 24cm.

"Prepared under the auspices of the various subcommittees of the Committee on surgery of the Division of medical sciences of the National research council and ... edited by the Committee on Information."—Introd. v. 1.
Includes bibliographies.

I. Title.

　　　　　　　　　　　　　　　　42-17394 Revised

NN　0062434　　DLC ICJ CtNlC AAP

W 2
A
N354b
NATIONAL Research Council. Committee on Surgery
Minutes of meeting. [1st]-15th; 15 June 1940-23 Oct. 1943.
[Washington]
15 no. in
Title varies: 26 July 1940-12 Oct. 1940, 21 May 1941-17 Jan. 1942, Abstract of minutes of meeting.
Includes Minutes of meeting of Special Ad Hoc Committee on Courses in

Surgery, 20 Feb. 1942.
Continued by the committee's Bulletin of surgery.
1. Surgery - Period. I. National Research Council. Special Ad Hoc Committee on Courses in Surgery

NN　0062436　　DNLM

National research council. *Committee on surgery.*
Neurosurgery and Thoracic surgery. Prepared and edited by the subcommittees on neurosurgery and thoracic surgery of the Committee on surgery of the Division of medical sciences of the National research council ... Philadelphia & London, W. B. Saunders company, 1943.

xvi, 218 p., 2 l., xxi-xxiv p., 1 l., 221-310 p. illus. 24cm. [Its Military surgical manuals, vi]

1. Nervous system—Surgery. 2. Chest—Surgery. 3. Gunshot wounds.
　　　　　　　　　　　　　　　　　　43-4820
Library of Congress　　RD593.N3　1943
　　　　　　　　　　　　[20]　　　　　　　617.48

ViU
NN　0062437　　DLC OrU-M CaBVaU OrU DNLM ICRL NcD

National research council. *Committee on surgery.*
Ophthalmology and otolaryngology, prepared and edited by the subcommittees on ophthalmology and otolaryngology of the Committee on surgery of the Division of medical sciences of the National research council ... Philadelphia & London, W. B. Saunders company, 1942.

xviii, 157 p., 2 l., xxiii-xxviii p., 1 l., 161-331 p. incl. illus., tables, diagrs. 24cm. (Its Military surgical manuals, II)

1. Ophthalmology. 2. Ear—Diseases. 3. Throat—Diseases. 4. Surgery, Military. I. Title.

Library of Congress　　RE45.N3　　42-22233
　　　　　　　　　　　　[10]　　　　　　　617.7

NN　0062438　　DLC TU ICRL NcD DNLM ViU OrU OrU-M

RE 45
.N277
NATIONAL RESEARCH COUNCIL—Committee on surgery
Ophthalmology and otolaryngology, prepared and edited by the subcommittees on ophthalmology and otolaryngology of the Committee on surgery of the Division of medical sciences of the National research council. Philadelphia and London, W. B. Saunders, 1943.
157 p., 161-331 p. illus. (Its Military surgical manuals, II)

1. Ophthalmology. 2. Ear—Diseases. 3. Throat—Diseases. 4. Surgery—Military.
I. Title.　　　　　　Optom.cds.

NN　0062439　　InU

National research council. *Committee on surgery.*
Orthopedic subjects, prepared and edited by the Subcommittee on orthopedic surgery of the Committee on surgery of the Division of medical sciences of the National research council ... Philadelphia & London, W. B. Saunders company, 1942.

xii, 306 p. illus. 24cm. [Its Military surgical manuals. IV]
Includes bibliographical references.

CONTENTS.—sect. I. Ununited fractures, by P. B. Magnuson.—sect. II. Injuries of the spinal column, by A. G. Davis.—sect. III. Compound fractures, by J. A. Key.—sect. IV. Osteomyelitis, by J. A. Key.

1. Orthopedia. I. Magnuson, Paul Budd, 1884- II. Davis, Arthur George, 1887- III. Key, John Albert, 1890-

　　　　　　　　　　　　　　　　　43-3378
Library of Congress　　RD721.N3
　　　　　　　　　　　　[10]　　　　　　　617.3

ViU OU ICRL
NN　0062440　　DLC OrU-M CaBVaU OrU IdPI NcD WaU DNLM

RC91
.N3
1950
National Research Council. *Committee on Surgery.*
Symposium on burns; held at the request of the Committee on Medical Sciences of the Research and Development Board, National Military Establishment, by the Subcommittee on Burns of the Committee on Surgery of the National Research Council, November 2-4, 1950. Washington, National Academy of Sciences, National Research Council, 1951.

207 p. graphs, tables. 25 cm.
"Appendix A, Participants": p. 194-207.
1. Burns and scalds. 2. Medicine, Military. I. Title.

　　　　　　　　　　　　　　　　　A 51–8749
U. S. Research and　　Development Board. Library
for Library of Congress　　[5]

MiU
NN　0062441　　DAL DLC DNLM MsU InU IU ICJ NcU ViU

National Research Council. *Committee on Survey of Food and Nutrition Research.*
Survey of food and nutrition research in the United States. 1947-
[Washington]
v. 26 cm.

1. Nutrition—Research. 2. Food—Analysis. I. Title.

TX537.N3　　　　641.072　　　　A 49–203 rev*
John Crerar Library
for Library of Congress　　[r51u5]†

WaS CLobS DNAL ICRL NIC IdPI OrP WaWW MtBC MiU
AAP N CaBVaU CU IU NN TU ICU MB PBL PPSKF OrCS ICJ
NN　0062442　　DLC NNC-M NcU-H MU IdU WaT TNJ-P Or

WU
269
qN277f
1945
National Research Council. Committee on Survey of Literature on Dental Caries
Flourine and dental caries, draft report by ... Food and Nutrition Board ... [Washington, D. C.] 1945.
v. 161 [26] p.

Bibliography: [26] p. at end.

1. Fluorine 2. Teeth - Caries

NN　0062443　　DNLM

TA710
.T7
National Research Council. Committee on Symposium on Sedimentation.
Trask, Parker Davies, 1899- *ed.*
Applied sedimentation. New York, Wiley, 1950.

National Research Council. Committee on Symposium on Sedimentation.
Bibliography on dolomite
see under Clee, Virginia Edith.

QC100
.U555
no. 510
National Research Council. Committee on Tables of Constants.
U. S. *National Bureau of Standards.*
Tables of chemical kinetics, homogeneous reactions [by] National Bureau of Standards [and] National Research Council, Committee on Tables of Constants. Editorial office Frick Chemical Laboratory, Princeton University. [Washington, U. S. Govt. Print. Off.] 1951-

---

National research council. *Committee on tables of positive ternary quadratic forms.*
... A table of Eisenstein-reduced positive ternary quadratic forms of determinant ≤ 200. Report of the Committee on tables of positive ternary quadratic forms. Burton W. Jones [chairman] ... [Washington, D. C., Published by the National research council of the National academy of sciences, 1935]
51 p. 24½cm. (Bulletin of the National research council. no. 97, June 1935)
Running title: Eisenstein-reduced quadratic forms.

1. Forms, Ternary. 2. Forms, Quadratic. I. Jones, Burton Wadsworth, 1902- II. Title. III. Title: Eisenstein-reduced quadratic forms.

Library of Congress　　Q11.N292　no. 97　　35-19858
——— Copy 2.　　　　[5]　　　　(506) 512.81

CaBVaU
NN　0062447　　DLC MiU OO OCl OCU NcRS ViU MB WaTC

VOLUME 407

National research council. Committee on
tables of positive ternary quadratic
forms.
A table of Eisenstein-reduced positive
ternary quadratic forms of determinant$\leqq$
200. Report of the Committee on tables
of positive ternary quadratic forms.
Burton W. Jones [chairman] ... [Washington,
D. C., Published by the National research
council by the National academy of
sciences, 1935]
(Bulletin of the National research
council. no.   97. June, 1935)

Microfilm copy of the original, made in
1960. Negative.
Collation of the original: 51 p.
Running title: Eisenstein-reduced
quadratic forms.

1. Forms, Ternary. 2. Forms, Quadratic.
I. Jones, Burton Wadsworth, 1902–
II. Title.   III. Title:
Eisenstein-   reduced quadratic
forms.

NN   0062449   MoSU

National research council. *Committee on tectonics.*
Catalogue of small-scale geologic maps useful for broader
regional studies (with chief emphasis on modern maps) (Pre-
lim. ed.) (Exhibit A of appendix L, Annual report of divi-
sion) April 22, 1933. Prepared under the auspices of the
Committee on tectonics, Division of geology and geography,
National research council of the United States of America, by
Walter H. Bucher and a staff of contributors. Washington,
D. C., National research council [1933]
1 p. l., vi, 132 p. 27 x 21ᶜᵐ.
Includes only part I. North America.
Verso of p. v, 20, 105 and 118 blank.
Mimeographed.
1. Geology—North Amer-   ica—Maps—Bibl. 2. Maps—Bibl.—
Catalogs. I. Bucher,   Walter Herman, 1888–

Library of Congress   Z6026.G3N3   33-20411
———— Copy 2.   [5]   016.557

OCl O OCU DN
NN   0062450   DLC CaBVaU IdU MtU NN ViU MsSM WU

GDA-caq National research council--Committee on tecton-
1944   ics.
N3   Tectonic map of the United States ... Prepared
under the direction of the Committee on tectonics, Division of geology and geography, National
research council. [Tulsa, Okla.] The American
association of petroleum geologists, 1944.
col. map on 2 sheets. 121x195½cm.

"Scale 1:2,500,000."
Lists sources and contributors.
Insets: Index map showing areas covered by

structure contours on different horizons.- Index
map showing areas for which committee members
were responsible in compiling tectonic map.

1. U.S.--1944. 2. Geology, Structural--U.S.--
1944. I. American association of petroleum
geologists. II. Title.

NN   0062452   IU MH

National Research Council. *Committee on Testing Isostasy
in the Basin Ranges*
see
National Research Council. *Committee on Isostasy.*

National Research Council. *Committee on the Anthropology of Africa.*
Personnel list of Africa; a compilation of persons familiar
with the colonies, territories and countries of Africa and
adjacent islands, with their addresses and data on their experience. Washington, Ethnogeographic Board, 1942–
v. 28 cm.
Subtitle of v. 3– varies.
——— Index to lists of African personnel. Washington, Ethnogeographic Board, 1944.
54 l. 28 cm.
1. Africa—Biog. I. Title.

DT18.N3 Index

DT18.N3   916   44–10105 rev*

NN   0062454   DLC

National Research Council. *Committee on the Anthropology of Oceania.*
Personnel list of Asia, June 12, 1942; a compilation of
persons familiar with the countries of Asia, with their addresses and data on their experience. Washington, National
Research Council, 1942.
12 l. 28 cm.

1. Asia—Biog.   I. Title.

DS32.N3   915   51–47908

NN   0062455   DLC CtY

National Research Council. *Committee on the Anthropology of Oceania.*
Personnel list of Oceania; a compilation of persons familiar with the islands of the Pacific with their addresses and
data on their experience. Washington, National Research
Council, 1942.
v. 28 cm.

1. Oceanica—Biog.   I. Title.

DU4.N3   919   51–33054

NN   0062456   DLC IEN

Z
675.M4   National Research Council. Committee on the Army
N2785r   Medical Library.
1951   Report ... concerning the status of the Army Medical
Library. [Washington, 1951]
6 leaves.
Committee chairman: George W. Corner.
1. Libraries, Medical - District of Columbia 2. Army
Medical Library. I. Title II. Title: Corner report

NN   0062457   DNLM

National research council. *Committee on the atmosphere and
man.*
... Causes of geographical variations in the influenza epidemic of 1918 in the cities of the United States. Report of
the Committee on the atmosphere and man. Prepared for the
Division of biology and agriculture and the Division of medical
sciences, National research council. Presented by Ellsworth
Huntington, chairman. Washington, D. C., Published by the
National research council of the National academy of sciences,
1923.
cover-title, 36 p. incl. tables. 25ᶜᵐ. (Bulletin of the National research council. no. 34 (v. 6, pt. 3) July 1923)

1. Influenza—U. S. 2. Climatology, Medical.   I. National research
council. Division of biology and agriculture. II. National research
council. Division of medical sciences. III. Huntington, Ellsworth, 1876–
IV. Title. V. Title: Geographical variations in the influenza epidemic of
1918. VI. Title: Influenza epidemic of 1918.

Library of Congress   Q11.N292 no.34   23–13642 Revised

NcD ViU MiU OO OCU OU OOxM
NN   0062459   DLC WaWW WaTC OrPR CaBVaU OrU DAS

National research council. *Committee on the atmosphere
and man.*
... Weather and health; a study of daily mortality in New
York city. Prepared under the direction and with the advice
of the Committee on the atmosphere and man, Division of
biology and agriculture, National research council, by Ellsworth Huntington ... Washington, D. C., Published by the
National research council of the National academy of sciences,
1930.
161 p. diagrs. 24½ᶜᵐ. (Bulletin of the National research council.
no. 75, April 1930)

Bibliography: p. 125–137.

1. Weather—Mental and physiological effects. 2. Mortality. 3. New
York (City)—Statistics, Vital. 4. Climatology, Medical.   I. Huntington,
Ellsworth, 1876–   II. Title. III. Title: Mortality in New York city.

Library of Congress   Q11.N292 no. 75   30–16236
———— Copy 2.   [10]   (506) [613.11] 613.13

OCU OClW NcRS OOxM
NN   0062461   DLC WaTC CaBVaU OrPR OrU ViU OCl OO

National Research Council. Committee on the
Chemistry of Coal.
TP953
.N3   National Research Council. *Committee on Chemical Utili-
zation of Coal.*
Chemistry of coal utilization. H. H. Lowry, chairman
[and editor] New York, Wiley [1945]

National Research Council. Committee on the
Chemistry of Colloids
see National Research Council. Division
of Chemistry and Chemical Technology. Committee on the Chemistry of Colloids.

National research council. *Committee on the construction
and equipment of chemical laboratories.*
A report of the National research council committee on the
construction and equipment of chemical laboratories. New
York, N. Y., The Chemical foundation, incorporated, 1930.
2 p. l., vii–xiii, 340 p. incl. front., illus. 24ᶜᵐ.
"Index of dealers in laboratory equipment and apparatus" (1 p. l.,
8 p.) laid in.
"First edition—3000. February, 1930."
Bibliography at end of chap. xix.
1. Chemical laboratories.

Library of Congress   QD51.N3   30–10069
Copyright A 21574   [6]   [727.5] 542.1

OCU OU MiU OCl IdU ICJ MiHM
NIC OrSaW DAU CU MB CtY-M NIC NcD NN MiD MB DNLM
NN   0062464   DLC WaS CaBVaU OrPR CoU MtBC OKentU

National Research Council. *Committee on the Construction
and Equipment of Chemical Laboratories
see also* National Research Council. *Committee on Design, Construction and Equipment of Laboratories.*

National Research Council. Committee on the
Deterioration of Bituminous Pavements by the
Effect of Water
see National Research Council. Highway
Research Board. Committee on the Deterioration
of Bituminous Pavements by the Effect of Water.

National research council. Committee on the
effects of radiation on living organisms.

Duggar, Benjamin Minge, 1872–   *ed.*
Biological effects of radiation; mechanism and measurement
of radiation, applications in biology, photochemical reactions,
effects of radiant energy on organisms and organic products
... Edited by Benjamin M. Duggar ... with the cooperation
of Janet Howell Clark, Kenneth S. Cole, Farrington Daniels
... [and others] 1st ed. ... New York and London, McGraw-
Hill book company, inc., 1936.

National research council. *Committee on the effects of radiation on living organisms.*
Cumulative report, 1928–1934, Committee on effects of radiation upon living organisms. Division of biology and agriculture, National research council. [Washington, D. C., 1935]
3 p. l., 2–54 numb. l. 27½ᶜᵐ.
Multigraphed.

1. Radiation. 2. Light — Physiological effect. 3. Plants, Effect of
light on.

36–2920
Library of Congress   QH651.N3
[2]   574.52223

NN   0062468   DLC NcD PU OCU NNC MnU

National research council. Committee on the
effects of radiation on living organisms.
Hollaender, Alexander.
... An experimental study of the problem of mitogenetic
radiation, by Alexander Hollaender and Walter D. Claus: a
report on work conducted in the Laboratory of plant physiology, Department of botany, University of Wisconsin, September, 1934 to June 30, 1936. [Washington, D. C., Published by
the National research council of the National academy of
sciences, 1937]

VOLUME 407

VET
KF
3835
.N3

National Research Council. Committee
on the Laws, Rules, and Regulations
Governing Animal Health in the
United States.
Laws, rules and regulations governing animal health in the United
States; a survey of measures in
effect in 1946. Prepared for the
Agricultural Board, National Research Council. Washington, 1952.
123 p.
Cover title.
#Veterinary hygiene--Law and legis-
lation--United States.
(A)Laws, rules and regulations governing animal health in the

United States.

NN 0062471 MoU IU

QE508
.N3

National research council. *Committee on the measurement
of geologic time.*
... Report of the Committee on the measurement of geologic time ...
[Washington, D. C., National research council, 19

v. 27½ cm. (Appendix ... of the Annual report of the Division
[of geology and geography])
At head of title, 1931/32-   : National research council, Division of geology and geography, Washington, D. C.
Title varies: 19   -1930/31, Report of the Committee on the measurement of geological time by atomic disintegration.
1931/32-   ... Report of the Committee on the measurement of
geologic time.

The reports form appendixes to the annual reports of corresponding
date of the Division of geology and geography of the National research
council : 1927/28, Appendix F; 1928/29-19   Appendix II (1931/32-
issued separately)
Alfred C. Lane, chairman.
Mimeographed.

1. Geological times.   I. Lane, Alfred Church, 1863-

QE508.N3   550.1   33—31619

MoU MiU CU MtU GEU CSt LU MBdAF
NN 0062473 DLC MH-GM PLF IdU NjR MsU LNT TxLT

National Research Council. Committee on the
Measurement of Geologic Time.
Select bibliography of the literature dealing
with the relation of radioactivity to geologic
problems
see under Wells, Roger Clark, 1877-

National Research Council. *Committee on the Measurement
of Geological Time by Atomic Disintegration*
see
National Research Council. *Committee on the Measurement of Geologic Time.*

[National research council. *Committee on the nutrition of
industrial workers]*
Industrial feeding management. Washington, U. S. Dept.
of agriculture, War food administration, 1945.
cover-title, ii, 46 p. illus. (diagrs.) 23½ᶜᵐ. (U. S. War food administration. [Office of distribution]; NFC-14)
"Prepared by the Committee on the nutrition of industrial workers of
the National research council in collaboration with the War food administration."—Verso of t.-p.
Supersedes Manual of industrial nutrition issued by U. S. Food distribution administration as its NFC-1.
"Sources of industrial feeding and nutrition educational materials":
p. 41-45. "Literature cited": p. 45-46.
1. Nutrition. 2. [Nutrition in industry]   I. U. S. War food administration. II. Title.
Agr 45-197
U. S. Dept. of agr. Library   1F733N no. 14
for Library of Congress   [TX551.U52 no. 14]
[4]   (331.834)

NN 0062476 DNAL ICJ

National research council. Committee on
the Nutrition of Industrial Workers.
Institutional feeding in industry.
Washington [1944?]
53 p.

Prepared by the Committee on the nutrition
of industrial workers.

NN 0062477 DNAL

R613.2
N213n

National Research Council. Committee on the
Nutrition of Industrial Workers
The nutrition of industrial workers;
second report of the Committee on Nutrition
of Industrial Workers, Food and Nutrition
Board, National Research Council. Washington [1945]
34 p. (National Research Council. Reprint and circular series, no. 123)

Bibliography: p. 33-34.

NN 0062478 MiD ICU FU

National research council. *Committee on the physical causes
of deafness.*
... The physical causes of deafness, report of the Committee
on the physical causes of deafness ... [Washington, D. C., National research council, 1928]
1 p. l., 100 p. incl. tables. 24ᶜᵐ. (Reprint and circular series of the
National research council. no. 82)
Cover imprint: Chicago, American medical association, 1928.
On cover: Reprinted from the Archives of otolaryngology, May, 1928,
v. 7, p. 415-513.
CONTENTS.—pt. I. Method of study. [By] Charles W. Richardson, M. D.—
pt. II. Statistical studies of the children in the public schools for the deaf.
[By] George E. Schambaugh, M. D., assisted by E. W. Hagens, M. D., J. W.
Halderman, M. C., R. W. Watkins, M. D.
1. Deafness.   I. Title.
CD 34-57
Library of Congress.   Card div. Q11.N293 no. 82
[a39c1]   (506)

NN 0062479 DLC MU ViU MiU OCU OC1W OC1

National research council. *Committee on theories of
magnetism.*
Theorien des magnetismus; bericht des Komitees über
theorien des magnetismus des National research council
in Washington, von S. J. Barnett, L. R. Ingersoll, J. Kunz,
S. L. Quimby, E. M. Terry, S. R. Williams, A. P. Wills.
Nach der im Bulletin of the National research council
erschienenen veröffentlichung übersetzt von Joseph Würschmidt. Mit 67 abbildungen. Braunschweig, F. Vieweg
& sohn akt.-ges., 1925.
x, 309 p. diagrs. 22½ᶜᵐ. (*Added t.-p.:* Die wissenschaft ... bd. 74)

Translated from Bulletin of the National research council, no. 18 (v. 3,
pt. 3)
Bibliographical foot-notes.

1. Magnetism.   I. Wills, Albert Potter, 1873-   II. Würschmidt,
Joseph, 1886-   tr.
26-702
Library of Congress   QC753.N3

NN 0062481 DLC OC1W ICJ MiU

National research council. *Committee on theories of magnetism.*
... Theories of magnetism. Report of the Committee on
theories of magnetism of the National research council, by
A. P. Wills, S. J. Barnett, L. R. Ingersoll, J. Kunz, S. L.
Quimby, E. M. Terry, S. R. Williams ... Washington, D. C.,
Published by the National research council of the National
academy of sciences, 1922.
cover-title, 261 p. diagrs. 25ᶜᵐ. (Bulletin of the National research
council. no. 18 (v. 3, pt. 3) Aug. 1922])
1. Magnetism.   I. Wills, Albert Potter, 1873-   II. Barnett,
Samuel Jackson, 1873-   III. Ingersoll, Leonard Rose, 1880-   IV.
Title.
22-21985 Revised
Library of Congress   Q11.N292 no. 18
———— Copy 2.
———— Copy 3.   [r31d2]
———— Copy 4.   QC753.N28

WaTC OrPR CaBVaU
NN 0062482 DLC IEN NcRS MiU OCU OU OO ViU OOxM

National Research Council. Committee on
Therapeutic Nutrition.
Therapeutic nutrition
see under Pollack, Herbert, 1905-

National Research Council. Committee on
Therapeutic Nutrition. Subcommittee on
Undernutrition and Starvation
see National Research Council. Subcommittee on Undernutrition and Starvation.

National Research Council. *Committee on Toxicology.*
Armed Forces index of occupational health methods and
equipment. Project no. OX 6404001. [Washington] 1955.
65 p. illus. 28 cm.

1. U. S.—Armed Forces—Sanit. affairs. 2. Industrial hygiene—
U. S. 3. Military hygiene—U. S.   I. Title.
UH603.N3   331.82   58-60668 ‡

NN 0062485 DLC OkU ViU MiU DNLM MnU NNU DPAHO

QA 11
N35
1954a

National Research Council. Committee on Training
and Research in Applied Mathematics.
Final report on a survey of training and
research in applied mathematics in the United
States, conducted by the National Research Council
under Contract NSF-C7 with the National Science
Foundation. [Washington, 1954]
[6], 60 l.

1. Mathematics - Study and teaching. I. Title:
Training and research in applied mathematics in
the United States.

NN 0062486 TxHU

National Research Council. *Committee on Training of Research Workers in Agriculture.*
The shortage of professional workers in agriculture and
forestry; report. Washington, National Research Council
[1947]
20 p. 25 cm. (National Research Council. Reprint and circular
series, no. 127)

1. Agriculture as a profession. 2. Forestry as a profession.
I. Title.   (Series)
S494.5.N3   630.69   53-60760

NN 0062487 DLC ViU

W
1
NA6395

National Research Council. Committee on
Transfusions
Minutes of the meeting.
[Washington, 19
v.

Title varies slightly.

NN 0062488 DNLM

UG
447
qN277f
1945

NATIONAL Research Council. Committee
on Treatment of Gas Casualties
Fasciculus on chemical warfare
medicine, prepared for the Committee on
Medical Research of the Office of Scientific
Research and Development by the Committee on Treatment of Gas Casualties,
Division of Medical Sciences of the
National Research Council. Washington,
1945.
3 v. illus.

Contents.—v. 1. Eye.—v. 2. Respiratory tract. — v. 3. Skin and systemic
poisons.
1. Chemical warfare 2. Gas poisoning
I. U. S. Office of Scientific Research and
Development. Committee on Medical
Research Title Title: Chemical
warfare medicine

NN 0062490 DNLM

VOLUME 407

QX
353
qN277t
1943

NATIONAL Research Council. Committee on
Trematode Diseases and their Molluscan
Intermediate Hosts in the Islands of the
Southwest Pacific
Trematode diseases and their molluscan
intermediate hosts in the islands of the
Southwest Pacific. ₁Washington 1943?₁
10, 3, 9 ℓ.
Report prepared by the committee for
the Ethnogeographic Board

1. Mollusks   2. Parasitic diseases -
East (Far East)   3. Trematoda

NN   0062492   DNLM

National Research Council. *Committee on Undersea Warfare.*
An annotated bibliography of submarine technical literature, 1557 to 1953. Washington, 1954.
xiii, 261 p. 25 cm. (National Research Council. Publication 307)
"Prepared for the Office of Naval Research."

1. Submarine boats—Bibl.   I. U. S. Office of Naval Research.
II. Title : Submarine technical literature.   (Series)

Z6834.S9N3   016.623825   54–60800

WaS CaBVaU
TxU NcD MB DCU PPT PBL PSt PP NN IdPI OrCS OrP
NN 0062493   DLC WaTC MiHM GAT NcD NNC ViU ICJ

National Research Council. Committee on
Undersea Warfare.
Physics of sound in the sea
see under   Research Analysis Group.

National Research Council. Committee on
Undersea Warfare.
Proceedings of the underwater physiology
symposium
see   Symposium on Underwater
Physiology.
Underwater physiology; proceedings.

National Research Council. *Committee on Undersea War-
fare.*
A survey report on basic problems of underwater acoustics
research, prepared by the Panel on Underwater Acoustics.
Washington, 1950.
v, 187 p. diagrs. 25 cm.
"One of a series of survey reports prepared for the Office of Naval
Research by technical advisory panels of the ... committee."
Bibliographical footnotes.

1. Underwater acoustics.   I. U. S. Office of Naval Research.

QC225.N3   534   50–61452

OrPR
IdU ICJ NBuU NIC TU TxU ICU MB MiHM NNC PBL OrCS
NN 0062496   DLC MtU WaT OrU-M WaS OrU OrCS MtBC

National Research Council. *Committee on Undersea War-
fare.*
A survey report on human factors in undersea warfare,
prepared by the Panel on Psychology and Physiology.
Washington, 1949.
x, 541 p. illus. 26 cm.
"One of a series of survey reports prepared for the Office of Naval
Research by technical advisory panels of the ... Committee on Under-
sea Warfare."
Includes bibliographies.

——— Supplement. Washington, National Academy
of Sciences–National Research Council, 1954.
92 p. illus. 25 cm.
Includes bibliographies.
V210.N3 Suppl.

1. Submarine warfare. 2. Psychology, Military. 3. Naval hygiene.
4. Physiology.   I. U. S. Office of Naval Research.

V210.N3   623.9   51–60845 rev

FU–HC
DNLM NcU ICJ CU MU KEmT OrPS CtY-M PPL PPF FMU
NN 0062498   DLC MtBC MsU WaS ViU AAP TU WaTC MH

RC1015
.S9
National Research Council. Committee on Undersea
Warfare.
Symposium on Underwater Physiology.
Underwater physiology; proceedings. ₁1st-   1955–
Baltimore ₁etc.₁ Williams & Wilkins Co. ₁etc.₁

National Research Council. Committee on
Uniform Highway Accounting
see   National Research Council. Highway
Research Board. Committee on Uniform Highway
Accounting.

National Research Council. *Committee on Use and Care of
Natural Resources.*
Present needs for research on the use and care of natural
resources. Prepared for the Ford Foundation. Washington, National Academy of Sciences, National Research Council, 1953.
35 p. 25 cm. (National Research Council. Publication 288)

1. Natural resources—U. S.   2. Natural resources—Research.
I. Ford Foundation.   II. Title.

HC103.7.N25   333.72   54–61045 ‡

DI CU ICJ LU ViU TxU NNC DNAL FTaSU C OrP OrCS
NN 0062501   DLC WaTC CaBVaU IdPI NN OU PBL PSt

National Research Council. *Committee on Veterans Medical
Problems.*
Expected incidence of certain neoplastic diseases in veterans. Washington ₁1947₁
16, ₁5₁ p. 28 cm.

1. Tumors₁—Epidemiology and statistics₁
Med 48–307
U. S. Army Medical Libr.   RC262.N3
for Library of Congress   ₁2₁

NN 0062502   DNLM PPC CU ICJ ICU

National Research Council. *Committee on Veterans Medical Problems.*
Report on the value and feasibility of a long-term program of follow-up study and clinical research. Washington, 1946.
86 p. 25 cm.

1. Medical research.

R850.N3   610.72   51–28769

NN 0062503   DLC MiU DNLM

National research council. *Committee on war metallurgy*
see
National research council. *War metallurgy committee.*

National Research Council. Committee on War
Service of Anthropologists
see   National Research Council. Division
of Behavioral Sciences. Committee on War Service on Anthropologists.

412–9
N215
National Research Council. Committee on Wild
life Studies.
Report.
[Washington?]

1. Wild life. Research.

NN   0062506   DNAL

National research council. *Committee on work in industry.*
Fatigue of workers, its relation to industrial production, by
Committee on work in industry of the National research council. New York, Reinhold publishing corporation, 1941.
165 p. 23½ᵐ.

1. Fatigue. 2. Employment management.   I. Title.
41–23488
Library of Congress   HD4904.5.N3
₁6₁   331.822

OrP WaS CaBVa CaBVaU OrU-M OrCS DNAL
OO OU OOxM OCl ICJ ViU OClW NcRS NcD NcC Or OrU
NN 0062507   DLC AU ICRL UU FTaSU DNLM GU CU TU

National research council. Committee on work
in industry. Fatigue of workers.
Carskadon, Thomas Reynolds, 1900–
... Workers and bosses are human; collective bargaining at
work, by T. R. Carskadon ... ₁New York, Public affairs committee, incorporated, 1943₁

National Research Council. Committee on Work
in Industry.
Report of
the meeting of March 9, 1938.   New York, 1938.
58 p.
Report is on the experiments and counseling
program of the Western Electric Hawthorne
division.

NN 0062509   MH–BA

National research council. *Committee on work in industry. Subcommittee on rehabilitation*
see
National research council. *Subcommittee on rehabilitation.*

National research council. *Committee on x-ray spectra.*
... Data relating to x-ray spectra, with a brief statement of
their bearing on theories of the structure of atoms and the
mechanism of radiation, by William Duane ... Washington,
D. C., Published by the National research council of the National academy of sciences, 1920.
cover-title, p. ₁383₁–408. 25ᵐ. (Bulletin of the National research
council. no. 6 (v. 1, pt. 6) Nov. 1920)
"This monograph is the first of a series which, when complete, will
form the report of a committee of the Division of physical sciences of
the National research council. This Committee on x-ray spectra consists of the following members: William Duane ... chairman, Bergen
Davis ... A. W. Hull ... D. L. Webster."—p. ₁388₁ foot-note.
The other reports were issued as Bulletins no. 7 and 20 of the National
research council.

1. X-rays.   I. Duane, William, 1872–   II. Title.
21–8492 Revised
Library of Congress   Q11.N292 no. 6
——— Copy 2.
——— Copy 3.
——— Copy 4.   QC481.N3

NcRS OOxM OU OO OCU MiU ViU
NN 0062512   DLC WaTC OrPR OrU CaBVaU WaWW KEmT

VOLUME 407

National research council. *Committee on X-ray spectra.*

... Intensity of emission of X-rays and their reflection from crystals, by Bergen Davis ... and Problems of X-ray emission, by David L. Webster ... Washington, D. C., Published by the National research council of the National academy of sciences, 1920.

cover-title, p. [409]-455. diagrs. 25ᵐ. (Bulletin of the National research council. no. 7 (v. 1, pt. 7) Dec. 1920)

"This monograph is the second of a series which, when complete, will form the report of a committee of the Division of physical sciences of the National research council. This committee on X-ray spectra

consists of the following members: William Duane ... chairman, Bergen Davis ... A. W. Hull ... D. L. Webster."—p. [409] foot-note.
The other reports were issued as Bulletins no. 6 and 20 of the National research council.
Bibliography at end of each article.

1. X-rays.   I. Davis, Bergen, 1869–   II. Webster, David Locke, 1888–   III. Title.   IV. Title: Problems of X-ray emission.
21—8493
Library of Congress   Q11.N292 no. 7
———— Copy 2.   QC481.N32

OCU MiU ViU
NN 0062514   DLC CaBVaU OrPR WaTC NcRS OOxM OU OO

National research council. *Committee on x-ray spectra.*

... Secondary radiations produced by x-rays, by Arthur H. Compton ... Washington, D. C., Published by the National research council of the National academy of sciences, 1922.

cover-title, 56 p. pl., diagrs. 25ᵐ. (Bulletin of the National research council. no. 20 (v. 4, pt. 2) Oct. 1922)

"This monograph is the third and last of a series which forms the report of the Committee on x-ray spectra, of the Division of physical sciences, of the National research council. This committee consists of the following members: William Duane ... chairman; Bergen Davis ... A. W. Hull ... D. L. Webster ... Arthur H. Compton."—p. 1, foot-note.
The other reports were issued as Bulletins no. 6 and 7 of the National research council.

1. X-rays.   I. Compton, Arthur Holly, 1892–   II. Title.
23–13635 Revised
Library of Congress   Q11.N292 no. 20

MiU OU OOxM OCU OO ViU NN
NN 0062515   DLC WaTC OrPR OrU CaBVaU KEmT NcRS

National research council. *Committee on x-rays and radioactivity.*

... Radioactivity. Report of Committee on x-rays and radioactivity, National research council, by A. F. Kovarik and L. W. McKeehan. Washington, D. C., Published by the National research council of the National academy of sciences, 1925.

cover-title, 203 p. 25ᵐ. (Bulletin of the National research council. no. 51 (v. 10, pt. 1) Mar. 1925)

"This monograph is part of the report of the National research council Committee on x-rays and radioactivity. The committee consists of the following members: A. H. Compton ... chairman; W. P. Davey ... A. F. Kovarik ... L. W. McKeehan."—p. 1.

Author index to bibliographical references throughout the work: p. 173–203.

1. Radioactivity.   I. Kovarik, Alois Francis, 1880–   II. McKeehan, Louis Williams.
25–15046 Revised
Library of Congress   Q11.N292 no. 51

MiU OU OOxM OO OCU NNC MB
NN 0062517   DLC WaTC OrSaW CaBVaU OrPR OClW NcD

National Research Council. Committee on X-Rays and Radioactivity.

Radioactivity; report of Committee on x-rays and radioactivity, National Research Council. A.F.Kovarik and L.W.McKeehan. [2d printing, with additions and corrections. Washington, D.C., National Research Council of the National Academy of Sciences, 1929.]

"Bulletin of the National Research Council, March, 1929, No.51."

NN 0062518   MH WaWW KEmT ViU OU

National Research Council. Conference on Abstracting and Documentation of Scientific Literature, Washington, 1935
    see   Conference on Abstracting and Documentation of Scientific Literature, Washington D.D., 1935.

National Research Council. *Conference on Electrical Insulation*
see   Conference on Electrical Insulation.

National Research Council. *Conference on Glossary of Terms in Nuclear Science and Technology*
see   National Research Council Conference on Glossary of Terms in Nuclear Science and Technology.

National Research Council. Conference on Insecticide Resistance and Insect Physiology
    see   Conference on Insecticide Resistance and Insect Physiology, University of Cincinnati, 1951.

National research council. Construction and equipment of chemical laboratories, Committee on the
    see   National Research Council. Committee on the Construction and Equipment of Chemical Laboratories.

National Research Council. Core Loss Committee
    see   National Research Council. Division of Engineering.

National research council. *Density currents, Committee on*
see
National research council. *Committee on density currents.*

National Research Council. *Dept. of Design*
see
National Research Council. *Highway Research Board. Dept. of Design.*

National Research Council. Design, Construction and Equipment of Laboratories, Committee on
    see   National Research Council. Committee on Design, Construction and Equipment of Laboratories.

National Research Council. *Disaster Research Group*
see also
National Research Council. *Committee on Disaster Studies.*

National Research Council. Division of Anthropology and Psychology
    see   National Research Council. Division of Behavioral Sciences.

572.06   National Research Council. Division of
N213a   Behavioral Sciences.
Anthropology and psychology, the borderland division of the National Research Council. Prepared by Dorothy McLean, Division secretary. [Washington, D. C.] [1954]
35 [3] iii, L.

Bibliography: p. [35–36]

I. McLean, Dorothy.   II. Title.

NN 0062530   WaU

National research council. Division of Behavioral Sciences.
Conference on experimental psychology, *Carlisle, Pa.,* 1928.
Conference on experimental psychology, held under the auspices of the Division of anthropology and psychology, National research council, Carlisle, Pa., March 30 and 31, 1928. Washington, D. C., National research council [1928?]

National Research Council. Division of Behavioral Sciences.
Conference on individual differences in special and general abilities
    see under   Conferences on Individual Differences in Special and General Abilities, New Haven, 1931.

National Research Council. Division of Behavioral Sciences.
Conference on individual psychological differences ...
    see under   Conference on Individual Differences in the Character and Rate of Psychological Development, Iowa City, Iowa, 1930.

National Research Council. Division of Behavioral Sciences.
Conference on racial differences
    see under   Conference on Racial Differences, Washington, 1928.

National research council. Division of Behavioral Sciences.
Conference on regional phenomena, *Washington, D. C.,* 1930.
Conference on regional phenomena, held under the auspices of the Social science research council and the Division of anthropology and psychology, National research council, Washington, D. C., April 11 and 12, 1930. Washington, D. C., Division of anthropology and psychology, National research council [1930]

National Research Council. Division of Behavioral Sciences.
Conference on the problems of the deaf
    see under   Conference on problems of the deaf and hard of hearing.

150.6   National research council.   Division of
N2132c   Behavioral Sciences.
[Conferences.]
[Wash.] 1926–   28cm.

Contents.
1. Experimental study of human emotions, New York, 1926.
2. Problems of the deaf, Washington, 1928.
3. Racial differences, Washington, 1928.
4. Experimental psychology, Carlisle, Pa., 1928.
5. Editors and business managers of anthropologic and psychologic[ ] periodicals, Washington, 1928.

NN 0062537   OrU

VOLUME 407

National research council. Division of
Behavioral Sciences.

American anthropological association.
General index, American anthropologist, Current anthropological literature, and Memoirs of the American anthropological association, 1888–1928.
[Menasha, Wis.] 1930–

**National research council. Division of
Behavioral Sciences.**
Grants-in-aid made by the national research council within the fields of anthropology and psychology, 1929–1936; a brief history of the grants since their beginning, with resulting publications, for the Division of anthropology and psychology.   [Washington, D. C.? 1937]
20 p.   28 cm.
Caption title.
Mimeographed.

NN   0062539   DSI

National Research Council. *Division of Behavioral Sciences.*
In quest of glacial man, a plan of cooperation between excavators and the representatives of the sciences of man and of the earth, prepared for National Research Council, Division of Anthropology and Psychology, by Madison Bentley. Washington, D. C., National Research Council, 1931.
20 p.   illus., map.   24 cm.   (Reprint and circular series of the National Research Council, no. 100)
1. Glacial epoch.   2. Excavations (Archaeology)   3. Man, Prehistoric.   I. Bentley, Isaac Madison, 1870–1955.   II. Title.   (Series: National Research Council. Reprint and circular series, no. 100)

Q11.N293   no. 100   CD 34–64 rev

NN   0062540   DLC OrU ViU KEmT OrPR OU PPF TxU

**National Research Council. Division of Behavioral
Sciences.**
International directory of anthropologists
see under title

National research council. Division of
Behavioral Sciences.
List of 43,200 dissyllable words and paralogs systematically compiled and arranged for further selection to provide adequate lists for experimental work on learning. Division of anthropology and psychology, National research council [1933?]
1 p. l., 79 l.   28ᶜᵐ.

I. Title: Dissyllable words.   II. Title: Paralogs.

NN   0062542   NNC OrU

HM291
.C63
1940b

National Research Council. Division of Behavioral Sciences.
Conference Concerning Psychological Factors in Morale,
Washington, D. C., 1940.
Psychological factors in morale; a report. Washington, National Research Council, 1940.

NN   0062544   CaBVaU

National Research Council. Division of Behavioral
Sciences.
Report. 19–
v.

National Research Council. *Division of* Behavioral
_Sciences.
Conference on problems of the deaf and hard of hearing.
2d, Washington. 1929.
... Research recommendations of the second conference on problems of the deaf and hard of hearing, Washington, D. C., February 1 and 2, 1929 ... Washington, D. C., 1929.

National Research Council. *Division of* Behavioral
Sciences.
see also
Conference Concerning Psychological Factors in Morale, *Washington, D. C.,* 1940.
Symposium on Air Force Human Engineering, Personnel and Training Research.

National Research Council. Division of Behaviora
Sciences. Anthropology Committee.
Suggestions relating to the new national army by the Anthropology committee of the National research council.   [By Aleš Hrdlička]
n.p., 1917.
3 p.   26 cm.
"Reprinted from the Proceedings of the National academy of sciences, vol. 3, p. 526–528 August, 1917."

NN   0062547   MH-P

National Research Council. *Division of Behavioral Sciences.
Committee on Child Development*
see
National Research Council. *Committee on Child Development.*

National Research Council. *Division of Behavioral Sciences.
Committee on Disaster Studies*
see
National Research Council. *Committee on Disaster Studies.*

National Research Council. *Division of Behavioral Sciences.
Committee on Food Habits*
see
National Research Council. *Committee on Food Habits.*

National Research Council. *Division of Behavioral Sciences.
Committee on Latin American Anthropology*
see
National Research Council. *Committee on Latin American Anthropology.*

National Research Council. *Division of Behavioral Sciences.
Committee on Problems on Neurotic Behavior*
see
National Research Council. *Committee on Problems of Neurotic Behavior.*

National Research Council. *Division of Behavioral Sciences.
Committee on Scientific Problems of Human Migration*
see
National Research Council. *Committee on Scientific Problems of Human Migration.*

National Research Council. *Division of Behavioral
Sciences. Committee on Selection and Training of Aircraft Pilots*
see
National Research Council. *Committee on Selection and Training of Aircraft Pilots*

National Research Council. *Division of Behavioral Sciences.
Committee on State Archaeological Surveys*
see
National Research Council. *Committee on State Archaeological Surveys.*

National Research Council.   Division of
Behavioral Sciences. Committee on War Service of Anthropologists.
Anthropology during the war and after.
[Washington, D.C.]1943
19p.   28cm.
Report compiled by Ralph L. Beals (Committee Chairman), F.L.W. Richardson, Julian H. Steward,Jr. &   Joseph E. Weckler.
Processed.
Cover title.

NN   0062556   MH-P

National research council. Division of
Behavioral Sciences. Conference of Editors and Business Managers of Anthropological and Psychology Periodicals.
see

Conference of editors and business managers of anthropological and psychological periodicals, Washington, D.C., 1928

National Research Council. *Division of Behavioral Sciences.
Disaster Research Group*
see
National Research Council. *Disaster Research Group.*

330.9
N215A

National Research Council. Division of Biology and Agriculture.
Agenda, annual meeting.   Washington.
1925 and 1934 issues include minutes, reports and papers of various committees for these years.

NN   0062559   DNAL

QH301
.N3

NATIONAL RESEARCH COUNCIL.   Division of biology and agriculture.
... Bimonthly report.   v.1–   Apr.1942–

[Washington, D.C., 1942–
v.

1. Biology--Societies.   2. Agriculture--Societies.

NN   0062560   ICU DNAL

**National research council.   Division of biology
and agriculture.**

National research council. *Committee on the atmosphere and man.*
... Causes of geographical variations in the influenza epidemic of 1918 in the cities of the United States. Report of the Committee on the atmosphere and man. Prepared for the Division of biology and agriculture and the Division of medical sciences, National research council. Presented by Ellsworth Huntington, chairman. Washington, D. C., Published by the National research council of the National academy of sciences, 1923.

VOLUME 407

National research council. *Division of biology and agriculture.*
Check list of native and introduced drug plants in the United States (not including insular possessions in the West Indies and the distant Pacific) Prepared under the auspices of the Committee on pharmaceutical botany and pharmacognosy of the Division of biology and agriculture of the National research council, by E. N. Gathercoal, with the collaboration of H. W. Youngken ... Chicago, 1942.
32 l. 28 x 22ᶜᵐ.
Reproduced from type-written copy.
1. Botany, Medical. 2. Botany—U. S. ɪ. Gathercoal, Edmund Norris, 1874– ɪɪ. Youngken, Heber Wilkinson, 1885– ɪɪɪ. Title: Drug plants in the United States.
43–17406
Library of Congress   RS164.N35
[8]   615.32

NN   0062562   DLC NcU NcRS NN NNBG NcU OU PSt

Botany
D570
N21
National Research Council. Division of Biology and Agriculture.
Conference on the importance and needs of systematics in biology, April 22, 1953. Sponsored by the Division of Biology and Agriculture and organized by the Society of Systematic Zoology. [Washington, 1953?]
iii, 53, 9, 5 p. tables.

At head of title: National Academy of Sciences, National Research Council.

NN   0062563   NNC OU DI

National Research Council. Division of Biology and Agriculture.
Cooperative experiments upon the protein requirements for the growth of cattle. First report of the Subcommittee on protein metabolism in animal feeding
see under   National Research Council. Subcommittee on Protein Metabolism in Animal Feeding.

National Research Council. Division of Biology and Agriculture.
Cooperative experiments upon the protein requirements for the growth of cattle. II: report of the subcommittee on animal nutrition ...
see under   National Research Council. Committee on Animal Nutrition.

National Research Council. *Division of Biology and Agriculture.*
Directory.
Washington.
v. 28 cm.

QH301.N335   61–65644

NN   0062566   DLC DNAL OU

330
N2143
[**National Research Council. Division of Biology and Agriculture**]
Memorandum concerning the scientific research bills now before the United States Senate. [Washington? D.C.] 1945.
9 p.
1. Research. 2. Government aid. I. Title: Scientific research bills now before the United States Senate.

NN   0062567   DNAL

National Research Council. *Division of Biology and Agriculture.*
Minutes of the annual meeting.
Washington.
v. 28 cm.

1. Biology—Societies, etc. 2. Agriculture—Societies, etc.

QH301.N33   56–30820 ‡

NN   0062568   DLC DNAL

National research council. Division of biology and agriculture.
National nutrition; some projects of research in the underlying sciences looking to more economical use of our food resources.... Washington, D. C., Division of biology and agriculture.
National research council (1921?)
15 p. 23 x 10 cm.

NN   0062569   DL

225
N2164   **National research council. Division of biology and agriculture.**
Personnel.
[Washington? D.C.]

I. author Officers and members including divisional committees.

NN   0062570   DNAL

National Research Council. Division of Biology and Agriculture.
A plan for cooperative research on the salt requirements of representative agricultural plants, prepared for a special committee of the Division of biology and agriculture of the National research council. Edited by Burton E. Livingston. Second edition. Baltimore, 1919.   54 p. incl. tables.   23cm.

Bibliography, p. 7–8.

1. Plants—Nutrition. 2. Agriculture—Experiments. I. Livingston, Burton Edward, 1875– , ed.
N. Y. P. L.   May 9, 1938

NN   0062571   NN IU CU WaU NjR

National Research Council. *Division of Biology and Agriculture.*
Report of the chairman
Washington.
v. 28 cm. annual.
Report year ends June 30.

1. Biology—Societies, etc. 2. Agriculture—Societies, etc.

QH1.N116   58–38270

NN   0062572   DLC

National Research Council. Division of Biology and Agriculture.
Sodium-restricted diets ...
see under   National Research Council. Food and Nutrition Board.

National Research Council. *Division of Biology and Agriculture. Agricultural Board*
see National Research Council. Agricultural Board.

National Research Council. *Division of Biology and Agriculture. Agricultural Research Institute*
see
National Research Council. *Agricultural Research Institute.*

National Research Council. *Division of Biology and Agriculture. Committee for Investigation of Waste Disposal*
see **National Research Council.** *Committee for Investigation of Waste Disposal.*

National Research Council. Division of Biology and Agriculture. Committee on Animal Breeding
see National Research Council. Committee on Animal Breeding.

National Research Council. *Division of Biology and Agriculture. Committee on Animal Health*
see
National Research Council. *Committee on Animal Health.*

National Research Council. *Division of Biology and Agriculture. Committee on Animal Nutrition*
see
National Research Council. *Committee on Animal Nutrition.*

National Research Council. *Division of Biology and Agriculture. Committee on Conservation*
see
National Research Council. *Committee on Use and Care of Natural Resources.*

National Research Council. Division of Biology and Agriculture. Committee on Forestry.
see National Research Council. Committee on Forestry.

National Research Council. Division of Biology and Agriculture. Committee on Pharmacognosy and Pharmaceutical Botany
see National Research Council. Committee on Pharmacognosy and Pharmaceutical Botany.

National Research Council. *Division of Biology and Agriculture. Committee on Photobiology*
see
National Research Council. *Committee on Photobiology.*

National Research Council. *Division of Biology and Agriculture. Committee on Plant and Crop Ecology*
see
National Research Council. *Committee on Plant and Crop Ecology.*

VOLUME 407

National Research Council. *Division of Biology and Agriculture. Committee on Preservation of Indigenous Strains of Maize*
see
National Research Council. *Committee on Preservation of Indigenous Strains of Maize.*

National research council. Division of biology and agriculture. Committee on radiation

see

National research council. Committee on the effects of radiation on living organisms.

National Research Council. *Division of Biology and Agriculture. Committee on Radiation Biology*
see
National Research Council. *Committee on Radiation Biology.*

National research council. Division of biology and agriculture. Committee on the atmosphere and man

see

National research council. Committee on the atmosphere and man

---

National Research Council. Division of Biology and Agriculture. Committee on the Effects of Radiation and Living Organisms
see **National Research Council.** Committee on the Effects of Radiation on Living Organisms

---

National Research Council. *Division of Biology and Agriculture. Committee on Training of Research Workers in Agriculture*
see **National Research Council.** *Committee on Training of Research Workers in Agriculture.*

National Research Council. *Division of Biology and Agriculture. Committee on Use and Care of Natural Resources*
see
National Research Council. *Committee on Use and Care of Natural Resources.*

National Research Council. *Division of Biology and Agriculture. Institute of Laboratory Animal Resources*
see
National Research Council. *Institute of Laboratory Animal Resources.*

National Research Council. Division of Biology and Agriculture. Special Committee on Salt Requirements of Representative Agricultural Plants
see **National Research Council.** Division of Biology and Agriculture.

National Research Council. Division of Biology and Agriculture. Subcommittee on Protein Metabolism in Animal Feeding
see National Research Council. Subcommittee on Protein Metabolism in Animal Feeding.

National research council. *Division of chemistry and chemical technology.*
Annual survey of American chemistry ... v. 1–10. 1925/26–35. New York, Published for National research council by the Chemical catalog company, inc. [1927–36]
10 v. tables, diagrs. 21½ cm.
Editors: 1925/26, W. J. Hale and C. J. West.—1926/27–35, C. J. West.
Vol. ɪ has title: A survey of American chemistry.
Vol. ɪᴠ covers an eighteen months period, July 1, 1928 to Dec. 31, 1929.
Includes bibliographies.
1. Chemistry—Yearbooks.   ɪ. Hale, William Jay, 1876–   ed.   ɪɪ. West, Clarence Jay, 1886–   joint ed.   ɪɪɪ. Title.

QD1.N3   27—4512

ICJ MiHM UU WvU NcD DNAL LNL
NcD TU OC1 OC1W OU OOxM MiU NNC-M ViU NcRS OCU
NN   0062595   DLC NIC OAkU KMK CtN1C PPiD TxLT MsU

National research council. *Division of chemistry and chemical technology.*
Chemical progress in the South; compiled and edited by Division of chemistry and chemical technology, National research council ... New York, N. Y., The Chemical foundation, incorporated, 1930.
xi p., 1 l., 282 p. illus., fold. maps. 24 cm.
"Check list of chemical periodicals in the libraries of the South": p. 285–281.
"Standard reference books": p. 281–282.
1. Chemicals—Manufacture & industry—Southern states. 2. Chemistry, Technical. 3. Southern states—Indus. 4. Industrial statistics. ɪ. Title.

Library of Congress   TP23.5.N3   31—947

                                      [51g½]   660.975

NN   0062596   DLC WaTC TU NcD OU NcRS

National research council. *Division of chemistry and chemical technology.*
List of heads of departments of chemistry and chemical engineering in American universities and colleges. Issued by the Division of chemistry and chemical technology, National research council. Washington, D. C., 1940.
cover-title, 1 p. l., 32 numb. l. 27½ x 21ᶜᵐ.

1. Chemists.   ɪ. Title.

Library of Congress   QD40.N33   41—10589

                                      [2]   540.71173

NN   0062597   DLC ICJ RPB OC1

National research council. *Division of chemistry and chemical technology.*
List of heads of departments of chemistry, chemical engineering and biochemistry in American universities and colleges. Issued by the Division of chemistry and chemical technology, National research council. Washington, D. C., 1944.
cover-title, 51 p. 27½ x 21½ᶜᵐ.
Reproduced from type-written copy; corrections in manuscript.

1. Chemists.   ɪ. Title.

Library of Congress   QD40.N33 1944   44—47098

                                      [3]   540.71173

NN   0062598   DLC NNC

301
N2122   National research council. Division of chemistry and chemical technology.
         ... Minutes of meeting,

4°

1. Chemistry. Societies.   2. Chemistry. Technology. Societies.

NN   0062599   DNAL

National Research Council. *Division of Chemistry and Chemical Technology.*
Report.
Washington [etc.]
v. 24–28 cm. annual.
Title varies: Report of the chairman at the annual meeting.

1. Chemistry—Societies, etc.

QD1.N25   43–42613 rev*

NN   0062600   DLC DNAL

National Research Council. *Division of Chemistry and Chemical Technology.*
Report of the chairman at the annual meeting
see its
Report.

National Research Council. Division of Chemistry and Chemical Technology.
A survey of American chemistry ...
see its   Annual survey of American chemistry.

National Research Council. Division of Chemistry and Chemical Technology. Committee on Cellulose and Allied Substances.
A survey of the American literature in the field of cellulose and related subjects, 1933 through 1937
see under   Lewis, Harry Fletcher, 1891–

National research council. *Division of chemistry and chemical technology. Committee on chemical data for ceramists*
see
National research council. *Committee on chemical data for ceramists.*

National research council. *Division of chemistry and chemical technology. Committee on chemical utilization of coal*
see
National research council. *Committee on chemical utilization of coal.*

National Research Council. Division of Chemistry and Chemical Technology. Committee on Contact Catalysis
see   **National Research Council.** Committee on Contact Catalysis.

National Research Council. *Division of Chemistry and Chemical Technology. Committee on Design Construction and Equipment of Laboratories*
see
National Research Council. *Committee on Design, Construction and Equipment of Laboratories.*

National Research Council. *Division of Chemistry and Chemical Technology. Committee on Industrial Chemistry*
see
National Research Council. *Committee on Industrial Chemistry.*

VOLUME 407

National Research Council. Division of Chemistry and
Chemical Technology. *Committee on the Chemistry of Coal*
　　see
　　National Research Council. *Committee on the Chemistry
　　of Coal.*

NN 0062609

National Research Council. *Division of Chemistry and
Chemical Technology. Committee on Toxicology.*
　　see
　　National Research Council. *Committee on Toxicology.*

National research council. Division of chemistry
and chemical technology. Committee on the chemistry of colloids.
Holmes, Harry Nicholls, 1879–
　　... Bibliography of colloid chemistry, by Harry N.
Holmes, chairman, Committee on the chemistry of colloids, Division of chemistry & chemical technology. Preliminary ed. Washington, D. C., National research council, 1923.

National Research Council. *Division of Chemistry and
Chemical Technology. Prevention of Deterioration Center*
　　see
　　National Research Council. *Prevention of Deterioration
　　Center.*

National research council. *Division of chemistry and chemical technology. Survey of antimalarial drugs*
see National research council. *Survey of antimalarial
drugs.*

National Research Council. Division of Earth
　　Sciences.
　　Annual report
　　　　see its　Report.

National research council. Division of Earth
　　Sciences.
　　Bibliography of isostasy
　　　　see under　Knopf, Adolph, 1882–
comp.

National research council. *Division of earth sciences.*
　　... Bibliography of military geology and geography, pre-
pared under the direction of W. H. Bucher, chairman, Divi-
sion of geology and geography, National research council.
₍New York₎ The Society, 1941.
　　18 p.　23 cm.
　　At head of title: The Geological society of America.
　　"Compiled by the Division of geology and geography of the Na-
tional research council and is being issued jointly by it and the
Geological society of America."—Foreword.

　　1. Geology—Bibl.　2. Military geography—Bibl.　ɪ. Bucher, Walter Herman, 1888–

Z6031.N3　　　　016.35547　　　　42–14320 rev

　　ICJ CSt NNC
　　NcRS OCl OOxM TxU MiU CoU NIC OU NN OCU CtY IU
NN 0062616　　DLC OrU OrCS IdU MtBuM NjR MH NcD

National Research Council. Division of Earth
　　Sciences.
　　Bibliography on dolomite
　　　　see under　Clee, Virginia Edith.

National research council. Division of Earth
　　Sciences.
　　Careers in geology.　New York, McGraw-Hill, c1948
　　₍4₎p.　illus.　28cm.

　　"Reprinted from Engineering and Mining Journal,
October 1948."

NN 0062618　　NcU

National research council. Division of Earth
　　Sciences.
Mathews, Edward Bennett, 1869–
　　... Catalogue of published bibliographies in geology, 1896–
1920. Compiled by Edward B. Mathews for Research information service and Division of geology and geography, National research council.　Washington, D. C., Published by the
National research council of the National academy of sciences,
1923.

National research council. Division of Earth
　　Sciences.
　　Color chart for field description of sedimentary rocks ...
　　　　see under　Goldman, Marcus Isaac, 1881·

National Research Council. Division of Earth Sciences.
　　Fellowships and other awards to promote research in geology
and geography, 1928; compiled by the Division of Geology and
Geography, Waldemar Lindgren, chairman, and arranged for
publication by Research Information Service.　Washington,
D. C.: National Research Council, 1928.　35 p.　28cm.

　　Reproduced from typewritten copy.

799363A.　1. Geology—Research.　　　2. Geography—Research. ɪ. Lind-
gren, Waldemar, 1860–　.　　　　gren, Waldemar, 1860–　. ɪɪ. National Research Council.
Research Information Service.
N. Y. P. L.　　　　　　　　　　　　　　　　　　　March 12, 1936

NN 0062621　　NN

National research council. *Division of earth sciences.*
　　The geography of Europe; a presentation of some aspects
of European geography for the use of members of the Students' army training corps.　Edited by Ellsworth Huntington and Herbert E. Gregory; prepared and issued under the
auspices of the Division of geology and geography, National
research council.　New Haven, Yale university press, 1918.
　　95, ₍1₎ p.　23½ cm.
　　"Essential books" : p. 9; "Reference books" : p. ₍96₎
　　1. Geography—Text-books—1870–1945.　2. Europe—Descr. & trav.—
1800–1918.　ɪ. Huntington, Ellsworth, 1876–1947, ed.　ɪɪ. Gregory,
Herbert Ernest, 1869–　ed.

D910.N3　　　　　　　　　　　　　　　　19–1881 rev

　　NcD NcC MA OClW OU MiU
　　MtBuM IdU OrCS OrPR OrU Or WaTC ICRL OKentU
NN 0062622　　DLC DNW ICJ NjP MB NN OO OCl OCU·

National research council. *Division of earth sciences.*
　　... Glacial map of North America ... 1st ed. New York,
The Geological society of America, 1945.
　　col. map.　133 x 201 cm. on 2 sheets each 140 x 105 cm.　(₍Geological
society of America₎ Special papers, no. 60, pt. 1)
　　Scale 1 : 4,555,000; approximately 1 inch to 72 miles.
　　"Lambert conformal conic projection."
　　"Form lines on the land ... ₍and₎ on the sea floor."
　　"Compiled and edited by a committee on the Division of geology
and geography, National research council ... Richard F. Flint (chair-
man)"
　　Insets: Index map showing compilers of glacial data.—Glacial
map of the north polar hemisphere.

　　———　... Bibliography and explanatory notes, by
Richard Foster Flint ...　₍New York₎ 1945.
　　viii, 37 p.　24½ cm.　(Geological society of America. Special papers,
no. 60, pt. 2)

　　1. Geology—North America—Maps.　2. Glacial epoch.　3. Geology—
North America—Bibl.　ɪ. Flint, Richard Foster, 1902–　ɪɪ. Title.

G3301.C3 1945.N33　　　　　　　　Map 46–359 rev

　　NIC NcD TxU DAU Or OrU CaBVaU MtBC OrPS NcD TxU
NN 0062624　　DLC InU DNAL DI Wa CaBViP WaS MoU

National Research Council. Division of Earth
　　Sciences.
　　Glacial map of North America, compiled and
edited by a committee of the Division of Geology
and Geography, National Research Council, Washington, D.C. ... Richard F. Flint (chairman) ... 1st
ed., 1945, 2d printing rev., 1949.　New York,
Geological Society of America, 1949.
　　2 maps each 133 x 101 cm.　(Geological Society
of America. Special papers, no. 60, pt. 1)
　　Scale 1:4,555,000; ca. 1"₌72 mi.
　　Contents.—Eastern half.—Western half.

　　1. Glaciers – N.　　Amer. 2. Maps. I. Flint,
Richard Foster. II.　　Title.　(Series)

NN 0062625　　DI IU NIC

National research council. *Division of earth sciences.*
　　Introductory meteorology, prepared and issued under the
auspices of the Division of geology and geography, National
research council.　New Haven, Yale university press, 1918.
　　xii, 149, ₍1₎ p.　illus. (incl. charts) 12 pl., diagrs.　23½ cm.
　　Most of the plates are printed on both sides.
　　"The manuscript has been prepared by the staff of the United
States Weather bureau ...　Considerable portions of the book are
taken verbatim from ... the Journal of the Franklin institute."—Pref.
　　"List of works on meteorology" : p. ₍147₎–149.

　　1. Meteorology.　ɪ. U. S. Weather bureau.

QC863.N3　　　　　　　　　　　　18–20866 rev

　　TU CU OKentU DAL DAS
　　NcD NcC OCl ODW MiU ViU OO OOxM ICJ　MH-GM NN MB
NN 0062626　　DLC OrAshS WaTC Or OrU OrU-M NBuU

National research council. *Division of Earth Sciences.*
　　... List of manuscript bibliographies in geology and geography, comp. by Homer P. Little, executive secretary, division of geology and geography, National research council
Washington, D. C., 1922.
　　cover-title, 17 p.　26 cm.　(Reprint and circular series of the National research council. no. 27)

　　1. Bibliography—Bibl.—Geography.　2. Bibliography—Bibl.—Geology.　3. Geography—Bibl.　4. Geology—Bibl.　ɪ. Little, Home
Payson, 1884–

Q11.N293　no. 27　　　　　　　　　23—1083

NN 0062627　　DLC CSt MiU OClW OOxM OCU OU NN CoU

National research council. *Division of earth sciences.*
　　Military geology and topography, a presentation of certain phases of geology, geography and topography for military purposes.　Herbert E. Gregory, editor; prepared and
issued under the auspices of the Division of geology and
geography, National research council.　New Haven, Yale
university press, 1918.
　　2 p. l., ₍iii₎–xv, 281 p.　illus. (incl. charts) 9 pl., diagrs.　23½ cm.
　　Most of the plates are printed on both sides.
　　List of collaborators : p. iii–iv.
　　"References" at end of many of the chapters.
　　1. Military topography.　2. Military geography.　3. Maps, Military.
4. Mines and mineral resources—U. S.　ɪ. Gregory, Herbert Ernest,
1869–　ed.　ɪɪ. Title.

QE33.N3　　　　　　　　　　　　18–20624 rev

　　OrPR MtU OrU WaTC CaBVaU
　　MB MH-Z NN OCl OClW ODW OU NcD CU OrCS MtBuM GU
NN 0062628　　DLC DAL MoU DSI CIJ ViU OO TxU MiU

National research council. Division of Earth
　　Sciences.
　　Minutes of the annual meeting –　Aug 25, 192₎–
(Washington) 1925–
　　v. 28 cm.

NN 0062629　　DI-GS

NATIONAL RESEARCH COUNCIL. Division of Earth
　　Sciences.
　　Minutes of the meeting. [1st]–2nd, May 1–June 5/6,
1919.　Washington.　2 no.　28cm.

　　No more published?

NN 0062630　　NN

VOLUME 407

National Research Council. *Division of Earth Sciences.*
Pleistocene eolian deposits of the United States, Alaska, and parts of Canada. Compiled by National Research Council, Committee for the Study of Eolian Deposits, Division of Geology and Geography, James Thorp and H. T. U. Smith, co-chairmen. With cooperation of ... State and Provincial soil and geological surveys of the United States and Canada ... ₁New York₁ Geological Society of America, 1952.
col. map 123 x 198 cm. on 2 sheets 133 x 105 cm.
Scale 1 : 2,500,000 ; approximately 1 inch to 40 miles.
Insets: Southwestern Canada. — Alaska. — Loveland (Illinois) loess.—Schematic soil map ₁of Anglo-America₁—Land-use map ₁of Anglo-America₁
1. Geology—U. S.—   Maps.   ɪ. Geological Society of
America. ɪɪ. Title.
G3701.C5 1952.N3   Map 53–1536 rev

NN 0062631   DLC FU NIC MtU

National Research Council. Division of Earth
Sciences.
Problems of the batholiths
see under   National Research Council.
Committee on Batholith Problems.

National Research Council. *Division of Earth Sciences.*
Report.
Washington.
v. 28 cm. annual.
Issued for   accompanied by appendices, consisting of reports of the division's committees. In a few cases the committee report is preliminary and the complete report is issued separately. Beginning with   committee reports are issued separately.
Reports for   issued by the division under its earlier name: Division of Geology and Geography.
1. Geology—Societies, etc. 2. Geology—U. S.

QE1.N2   550.6273   55–60788

NN 0062633   DLC MH-GS MiU CLU NN

QH91
.N3

National Research Council. Division of Earth
Sciences. Report. Appendix.

National Research Council. *Committee on a Treatise on Marine Ecology and Paleoecology.*
Report. no. ₁1₁–11; 1940/41–1950/51. Washington.

Z6033
.P2N3

National Research Council. Division of Earth
Sciences. Report. Appendix.

National Research Council. *Committee on Paleobotany.*
Report.
Washington.

National Research Council. *Division of Earth Sciences.*
Suggestions concerning desirable lines of research in the fields of geology and geography ₁by₁ National Research Council, Division of Geology and Geography. Edited by Edson S. Bastin for physical geology, Carl O. Dunbar for paleontology and stratigraphy and Robert S. Platt for geography. ₁Washington, National Research Council₁ 1936.
83 p. 28 cm.
1. Geological research. 2. Geographical research.   ɪ. Bastin, Edson Sunderland, 1878–   ed. ɪɪ. Title.
QE40.N37   550.72   G S 37–96 rev*
U. S. Geol. Survey. Libr.
for Library of Congress   ₁r55gⁱ⁄₂₁†

DLC TxU
NN 0062636   DI-GS OrU OCU OCl OO OU IU ViU DAU

National Research Council. Division of Earth
Sciences. Committee on a National Atlas of
the United States
see
National Research Council. Committee on a
National Atlas of the United States.

National Research Council. *Division of Earth Sciences.*
Committee on Batholith Problems
see
National Research Council. *Committee on Batholith Problems.*

National Research Council. *Division of Earth Sciences.*
Committee on Careers in Geography
see
National Research Council. *Committee on Careers in Geography.*

National Research Council. *Division of Earth Sciences.*
Committee on Clay Minerals
see
National Research Council. *Committee on Clay Minerals.*

National Research Council. Division of Earth
Sciences. Committee on Geologic Research.
see   National Research Council.
Committee on Geologic Research.

National Research Council. Division of Earth
Sciences. Committee on Glacial Map of North
America
see   National Research Council.
Committee on Glacial Map of North America.

National Research Council. *Division of Earth Sciences.*
Committee on Isostasy
see
National Research Council. *Committee on Isostasy.*

National Research Council. *Division of Earth Sciences.*
Committee on Marine Ecology as Related to Paleontology
see
National Research Council. *Committee on a Treatise on Marine Ecology and Paleoecology.*

National Research Council. *Division of Earth Sciences.*
Committee on Oceanography
see
National Research Council. *Committee on Oceanography.*

National Research Council. *Division of Earth Sciences.*
Committee on Paleobotany
see
National Research Council. *Committee on Paleobotany.*

National Research Council. *Division of Earth Sciences.*
Committee on Processes of Ore Deposition
see
National Research Council. *Committee on Processes of Ore Deposition.*

National Research Council. *Division of Earth Sciences.*
Committee on Sedimentation
see
National Research Council. *Committee on Sedimentation.*

National Research Council. *Division of Earth Sciences.*
Committee on Shoreline Investigations
see
National Research Council. *Committee on Shoreline Investigations.*

National Research Council. *Division of Earth Sciences.*
Committee on State Geological Surveys
see
National Research Council. *Committee on State Geological Surveys.*

National Research Council. *Division of Earth Sciences.*
Committee on Structural Petrology
see
National Research Council. *Committee on Structural Petrology.*

National Research Council. *Division of Earth Sciences.*
Committee on Submarine Configuration and Oceanic Circulation
see
National Research Council. *Committee on Submarine Configuration and Oceanic Circulation.*

National Research Council. *Division of Earth Sciences.*
Committee on Symposium on Sedimentation
see
National Research Council. *Committee on Symposium on Sedimentation.*

National Research Council. *Division of Earth Sciences.*
Committee on Tectonics
see
National Research Council. *Committee on Tectonics.*

National Research Council. *Division of Earth Sciences.*
Committee on the Measurement of Geologic Time
see
National Research Council. *Committee on the Measurement of Geologic Time.*

National Research Council. *Division of Earth Sciences.*
Minerals and Metals Advisory Board
see
National Research Council. *Materials Advisory Board.*

National Research Council. Division of Earth
Sciences. Rock-color chart committee
see   National Research Council.
Rock-Color Chart Committee.

National Research Council. *Division of Earth Sciences.*
Subcommittee on the Ecology of Marine Organisms
see
National Research Council. *Committee on a Treatise on Marine Ecology and Paleoecology.*

National research council. Division of
educational relations.   FOR OTHER EDITIONS
                            SEE MAIN ENTRY
Aydelotte, Frank, 1880–
... Honors courses in American colleges and universities, by Frank Aydelotte ... Washington, D. C., Published by the National research council of the National academy of sciences, 1924.

VOLUME 407

National research council. Division of educational relations.
   The National research council announcement of tne Division of educational relations. Washington, D.C., 1919
     7, (1) p. 23½ cm

NN   0062660   DHEW

National research council. *Division of educational relations.*
   Opportunities for a career in scientific research, issued by the Division of educational relations of the National research council. Washington, D. C., 1927.
   3 p. l., (139) p. diagr. 22½ᶜᵐ.
   Each article has special t.-p. and separate pagination. They have been previously issued separately.
   CONTENTS.—Open letter to college seniors, by C. E. Seashore.—Agricultural research as a career, by E. D. Ball.—Anthropology as a career, by C. Wissler.—A research career in astronomy, by P. W. Merrill.—Botanical research as a career, by J. M. Coulter.—The field for chemists, by W. D. Bancroft.—Engineering research as a career, by A. A. Potter.—Forestry as a career, by H. S. Graves.—Geology as a career, by J. F. Kemp.—Industrial research and its opportunities, by J. Mills.—Mathematics as a career, by C. J. Keyser.—Research in the medical sciences, by F. P. Gay.—Physics as a career, by G. W. Stewart.—Psychology as a career, by C. E. Seashore, R. Dodge, E. L. Thorndike, S. I. Franz, and W. V. Bingham.—The research career in public health, by D. L. Edsall.—Zoological research as a career, by C. E. McClung.

   1. Research. 2. Profession, Choice of.   I. Title.

   Library of Congress   Q181.N35
                          27–22624

    DHEW
    PU-BZ MiU ODW OO OU OCU ViU OC1 MB ICJ NN ICRL
NN   0062662   DLC MtBC OrCS OrU Or TU NIC CU NcD

National Research Council. Division of Educational Relations. Medical Fellowship Board
       see   National Research Council. Medical Fellowship Board.

National Research Council. Division of Engineering.
   Annual report
       see under   National Research Council. Division of Engineering and Industrial Research.

National research council. *Division of engineering.*
   Bibliography on core losses in electrical machinery and related subjects 1885–1924, prepared by the Core loss committee of the Engineering division National research council. (New York), 1925.
   1 p. l., v, 139 (i. e. 140), 19 numb. l. 28 x 22½ᶜᵐ.
   Autographed from type-written copy.
   Preface signed: The Core loss committee, A. E. Kennelly, chairman.
   Revision and enlargement of a bibliography covering the period 1885–1922 originally prepared by the Engineering societies library, New York city.
   Classified with author index.
   1. Electric machinery—Bibl.   I. Kennelly, Arthur Edwin, 1861–   I. Title: Core losses in electrical machinery.
                          25–6178
   Library of Congress   Z5834.M2N2

NN   0062665   DLC MtBC OrCS WaS WaTC NN OC1 ICJ

National Research Council. Division of Engineering.
   The Division of Engineering of the National Research Council in coöperation with Engineering Foundation. New York City: Engineering Societies Building, 1921. 16 p. 4°.

   1. Engineering.—Assoc. and organi-   zations, U. S.
   N. Y. P. L.   September 20, 1924

NN   0062666   NN

National Research Council. Division of Engineering.
   The Division of Engineering of the National Research Council in coöperation with Engineering Foundation. Purposes: to encourage, initiate, organize, and co-ordinate fundamental and engineering research and to serve as a clearing-house for research information in the field of engineering. New York City, 1922. 36 p. 4°.

   1. Engineering.—Assoc. and organiz-   tions, U. S. 2. United Engineering Society, New York. Engineering   Foundation.
   N. Y. L.   May 22, 1923.

NN   0062667   NN DLC MiD OU OCU OO WaPS IU MB OCU

National research council. *Division of engineering*
       see also
National research council. *Division of engineering and industrial research.*

National Research Council. Division of Engineering. Advisory Board on Highway Research
       see
National Research Council. Highway Research Board.

National Research Council. Division of Engineering. Building Research Advisory Board
       see
National Research Council. Building Research Advisory Board.

National Research Council. Division of Engineering. Core Loss Committee
       see   National Research Council. Division of Engineering.

National Research Council. *Division of Engineering and Industrial Research.*
   Annual report.
   Washington.
     v. 28 cm.
   Report year ends June 30.
   Cover title   : Engineering and industrial research.
   Vols. for   include Minutes of annual meeting
   1. Engineering research—U. S.—Societies, etc. 2. Research, Industrial—U. S.—Societies, etc.   I. Title: Engineering and industrial research.

   TA23.N35   68–6165

NN   0062672   DLC IU PSt OU

National research council. *Division of engineering and industrial research.*
   ... Bibliography on core losses in electrical machinery and related subjects 1885–1924, prepared by the Committee on electrical core losses, Division of engineering and industrial research, National research council. Issued in mimeographed form by the National research council. Washington, D. O., 1925.
   2 p. l., iv, (1), 138, 18, 5 p. 27½ x 21ᶜᵐ.
   Preface signed: The Core loss committee, A. E. Kennelly, chairman.
   Revision and enlargement of a bibliography covering the period 1885–1922 originally prepared by the Engineering societies library, New York city.
   Classified, with author index.
   "List of periodicals and   their abbreviations": 5 p. at end.
   1. Electric machinery—   Bibl.   I. Kennelly, Arthur Edwin,
   1861–   II. Title: Core   losses in electrical machinery.
   Library of Congress   Z5834.M2N2 1925 a   26–13083

NN   0062673   DLC

Nationai research council. *Division of engineering and industrial research.*
   A bibliography on research; selected articles from the technical press, 1923—1924—1925 (by) National research council, Division of engineering and industrial research. New York city (1925)
   46 p. 23 cm.
   Introduction signed: Maurice Holland, director, Division of engineering and industrial research.
   "No attempt has been made to include references on specific researches in the industries, as this bibliography is intended to cover only general articles on research."—p. 6.

   —— Five years of research in industry, 1926–1930; a reading list of selected articles from the technical press, compiled by Clarence J. West ... for the Division of engineering and industrial research, National research council ... New York, N. Y., National research council, Division of engineering and industrial research, 1930.
   91 p. 23 cm.

   Foreword signed: Maurice Holland, director, Division of engineering and industrial research, National research council.

   Z7914.R5N2   Suppl.

   1. Research, Industrial—Bibl. 2. Technology—Bibl.   I. West, Clarence Jay, 1886–1953, comp.   II. Title: Five years of research in industry.

   Z7914.R5N2   016.607   26—26716

    OU OCU OO MiU OC1W ICJ NcD WaU NIC GAT
NN   0062676   DLC ICRL NN KEmT MA ICU DL CU MB NcRS

620.7   National research council--Division of
N213d   engineering and industrial research.
1925   Division of engineering and industrial research of the National research council in cooperation with Engineering foundation. Purposes: to encourage, initiate, organize, and co-ordinate fundamental and engineering research in the field of industry ... New York, 1925.
     21p.

NN   0062677   IU

National Research Council. Division of Engineering and Industrial Research.
   Five years of research in industry 1926–1930
       see its   A bibliography on research.

National research council. *Division of engineering and industrial research.*
   Marine structures, their deterioration and preservation; report of the Committee on marine piling investigations of the Division of engineering and industrial research of the National research council. By William G. Atwood and A. A. Johnson, with the collaboration of William F. Clapp, of Robert C. Miller ... of H. W. Walker, H. S. McQuaid and Marjorie S. Allen ... Washington, D. C., National research council (1924)
   4 p. l., 534 p. illus., xiv pl. on 7 l., maps (part fold.) diagrs. 23ᶜᵐ.
   Bibliography: p. 462–522.
   1. Marine borers. 2.   Wood—Preservation. 3. Hydraulic engineering.   I. Atwood,   William Greene, 1872–   II. Johnson, Arthur Albert,   1875–   III. Title.
   Library of Congress   TC200.N3   24—18305

    CaBVaU IdU WaU Or WaT WaE CoDBR
    OC1 MiU NcRS WU IdPI KEmT MsSM CU WaTC WaS OrCS
NN   0062679   DLC ICJ MB NIC TU PPAN OU OCU OOxM

National Research Council. Division of Engineering and Industrial Research.
   Organization, aims and activities of the Highway Research Board
       see under   National Research Council. Highway Research Board.

VOLUME 407

National research council. Division of
engineering and industrial research.
Ross, Malcolm Harrison, 1895–   *ed.*
Profitable practice in industrial research; tested principles
of research, laboratory organization, administration, and operation, edited by Malcolm Ross, with the collaboration of Maurice Holland and William Spraragen; prepared under the
auspices of the National research council, Division of engineering and industrial research.   New York and London, Harper
& brothers, 1932.

TA492   National research council. Division of engi-
.P7D3   neering and industrial research.
Davis, Harmer Elmer, 1905–
Progress report on causes of cleavage fracture in ship plate:
flat plate tests, by H. E. Davis, G. E. Troxell, A. Boodberg ...
₍and others₎ University of California under Navy contract
Nobs–31222. Committee on ship construction, Division of
engineering & industrial research, National research council,
advisory to Bureau of ships, Navy department under Contract
Nobs–34231 ... ₍Washington₎ 1946.

National Research Council. Division of Engineering and Industrial Research.
Report
see its   Annual report.

National Research Council. Division of Engineering and Industrial Research.
Report of investigation of low cost improved
roads
see under   Conner, Carlton Nudd, 1882–

607.2   National research council--Division of
N21r   engineering and industrial research.
Research a paying investment; an analysis of 800 replies received to a questionnaire sent out by the Division of
engineering and industrial research of
the National research council to million-
aire manufacturing companies of the
United States.   Statistical analysis
made by the McGraw-Hill publishing company, inc. New York city.   New York

[1928?]
cover-title, 15p.

NN   0062686   IU

National Research Council. Division of Engineering and Industrial Research.
Research in hard times
see under   Holland, Maurice, 1891–

HD6068   National research council. Division of
.B23   engineering and industrial research.₎
Baetjer, Anna Medora, 1899–
Women in industry, their health and efficiency ... Prepared
in the Army industrial hygiene laboratory by Anna M. Baetjer
... Philadelphia and London, W. B. Saunders company, 1946.

National Research Council. Division of Engineering and Industrial Research. Advisory Board
on Quartermaster Research and Development
see   National Research Council.
Advisory Board on Military Personnel Supplies.

National Research Council. *Division of Engineering and
Industrial Research. Advisory Committee on Artificial
Limbs*
see
National Research Council. *Advisory Committee on Arti-
ficial Limbs.*

National Research Council. *Division of Engineering and
Industrial Research. Advisory Committee on International
Technologic Assistance*
see
National Research Council. *Advisory Committee on Inter-
national Technologic Assistance.*

National Research Council. *Division of Engineering and
Industrial Research. Building Research Advisory Board*
see **National Research Council.** *Building Research Advisory Board.*

National Research Council. *Division of Engineering and
Industrial Research. Building Research Institute*
see
National Research Council. *Building Research Institute.*

National Research Council. Division of Engineering and Industrial Research. Committee on
Electrical Core Losses
see   National Research Council. Division of
Engineering and Industrial Research.

National Research Council. *Division of Engineering and
Industrial Research. Committee on Electrical Insulation*
see **Conference on Electrical Insulation.**

National research council. *Division of engineering and
industrial research. Committee on heat transmission*
see
National research council. *Committee on heat transmission.*

National Research Council. *Division of Engineering and
Industrial Research. Committee on Quartermaster
Problems*
see
National Research Council. *Committee on Quartermaster
Problems.*

National Research Council. *Division of Engineering and
Industrial Research. Conference on Electrical Insulation*
see **Conference on Electrical Insulation.**

National Research Council. Division of Engineering and Industrial Research. Core Loss
Committee
see   National Research Council. Division
of Engineering and Industrial Research.

National research council. *Division of engineering and
industrial research. Highway research board*
see
National research council. *Highway research board.*

National Research Council. *Division of Engineering and
Industrial Research. Maritime Cargo Transportation Conference*
see
National Research Council. *Maritime Cargo Transportation Conference.*

National Research Council. *Division of Engineering and
Industrial Research. Materials Advisory Board*
see
National Research Council. *Materials Advisory Board.*

National Research Council. Division of Engineering and Industrial Research. Minerals and
Metals Advisory Board
see   National Research Council.
Materials Advisory Board.

National Research Council. *Division of Engineering and
Industrial Research. Prosthetics Research Board*
see
National Research Council. *Prosthetics Research Board.*

National research council. *Division of engineering and
industrial research. War metallurgy committee*
see
National research council. *War metallurgy committee.*

National research council. Division of
federal relations.
Allen, Edwin West, 1864–1929.
... Co-operation with the federal government in scientific
work. Prepared for the divisions of federal and of states relations, National research council, by E. W. Allen ... Washington, D. C., Published by the National research council of
the National academy of sciences, 1922.

U.S.   National Research Council. Division of Foreign
Q   Relations.
11   ... Minutes and reports, annual meeting,
.N293   1937.   Washington, D.C. [1937–
date   v.   28 cm.
Multigraphed.

NN   0062707   DPU

National Research Council. *Division of Geology and Geography*
see
National Research Council. *Division of Earth Sciences.*

National research council. Division of
Mathematical and Physical Sciences.
Rietz, Henry Lewis, 1875–   *ed.*
Handbook of mathematical statistics, by H. L. Rietz, editor-
in-chief, H. C. Carver, A. R. Crathorne, W. L. Crum, James W.
Glover, E. V. Huntington, Truman L. Kelley, Warren M.
Persons, Allyn A. Young, members of the Committee on the
mathematical analysis of statistics of the Division of physical
sciences of the National research council. Boston, New York
₍etc.₎ Houghton Mifflin company ₍ᶜ1924₎

VOLUME 407

QA47
.M29

National Research Council. Division of Mathematical and Physical Sciences.

Mathematics of computation. v. 1–   (no. 1–   );
Jan. 1943–
Washington, National Research Council.

National research council. *Division of mathematical and physical sciences.*
... Systems of electrical and magnetic units; papers presented before the American section, International union of pure and applied physics, Chicago, June 24, 1933. Richard T. Glazebrook, Henri Abraham, Leigh Page, George A. Campbell, Harvey L. Curtis and Arthur E. Kennelly. Washington, D. C., Published by the National research council of the National academy of sciences, 1933.

vi, 112 p. diagrs. 24½ cm. (Bulletin of the National research council, no. 93, Dec. 1933)

1. Electric units. 2. Magnetism. I. Glazebrook, Sir Richard Tetley, 1854–1935. II. Title.

Q11.N292 no. 93   537.7   **34–1419 rev**

OC1 OC1W OU ViU OrU WaTC
NN   0062711   DLC MiU WaS OrPR CaBVaU LU NcRS OCU

National Research Council. *Division of Mathematical and Physical Sciences*
    see also
National Research Council. *Division of Mathematics.*

National Research Council. *Division of Mathematical and Physical Sciences*
    see also
National Research Council. *Division of Physical Sciences*
(1951–)

National Research Council. *Division of Mathematical and Physical Sciences. Committee on a Bibliography on Orthogonal Polynomials*
    see
National Research Council. *Committee on a Bibliography on Orthogonal Polynomials.*

National Research Council. *Division of Mathematical and Physical Sciences. Committee on Acoustics*
    see
National Research Council. *Committee on Acoustics.*

National Research Council. *Division of Mathematical and Physical Sciences. Committee on Acoustics of Buildings*
    see
National Research Council. *Committee on Acoustics of Buildings.*

National Research Council. *Division of Mathematical and Physical Sciences. Committee on Algebraic Numbers*
    see
National Research Council. *Committee on Algebraic Numbers.*

National Research Council. *Division of Mathematical and Physical Sciences. Committee on Atomic Structure*
    see
National Research Council. *Committee on Atomic Structure.*

National Research Council. *Division of Mathematical and Physical Sciences. Committee on Celestial Mechanics*
    see
National Research Council. *Committee on Celestial Mechanics.*

National Research Council. *Division of Mathematical and Physical Sciences. Committee on Electrodynamics of Moving Media*
    see
National Research Council. *Committee on Electrodynamics of Moving Media.*

National Research Council. *Division of Mathematical and Physical Sciences. Committee on Hydrodynamics*
    see
National Research Council. *Committee on Hydrodynamics.*

National Research Council. *Division of Mathematical and Physical Sciences. Committee on Ionization Potentials and Related Subjects*
    see
National Research Council. *Committee on Ionization Potentials and Related Subjects.*

National Research Council. *Division of Mathematical and Physical Sciences. Committee on Luminescence*
    see
National Research Council. *Committee on Luminescence.*

National Research Council. *Division of Mathematical and Physical Sciences. Committee on Mathematical Tables and Other Aids to Computation*
    see
National Research Council. *Committee on Mathematical Tables and Other Aids to Computation.*

National Research Council. *Division of Mathematical and Physical Sciences. Committee on Methods of Measurement of Radiation*
    see
National Research Council. *Committee on Methods of Measurement of Radiation.*

National Research Council. *Division of Mathematical and Physical Sciences. Committee on Nuclear Science*
    see
National Research Council. *Committee on Nuclear Science.*

National Research Council. *Division of Mathematical and Physical Sciences. Committee on Numerical Integration*
    see
National Research Council. *Committee on Numerical Integration.*

National Research Council. *Division of Mathematical and Physical Sciences. Committee on Physics of the Earth*
    see
National Research Council. *Committee on Physics of the Earth.*

National Research Council. *Division of Mathematical and Physical Sciences. Committee on Physiological Optics*
    see
National Research Council. *Committee on Physiological Optics.*

National Research Council. *Division of Mathematical and Physical Sciences. Committee on Radiation in Gases*
    see
National Research Council. *Committee on Radiation in Gases.*

National Research Council. *Division of Mathematical and Physical Sciences. Committee on Rational Transformations*
    see
National Research Council. *Committee on Rational Transformations.*

National Research Council. *Division of Mathematical and Physical Sciences. Committee on Solids*
    see
National Research Council. *Committee on Solids.*

National Research Council. *Division of Mathematical and Physical Sciences. Committee on Tables of Positive Ternary Quadratic Forms*
    see
National Research Council. *Committee on Tables of Positive Ternary Quadratic Forms.*

National Research Council. *Division of Mathematical and Physical Sciences. Committee on Theories of Magnetism*
    see
National Research Council. *Committee on Theories of Magnetism.*

National Research Council. *Division of Mathematical and Physical Sciences. Committee on X-ray Spectra*
    see
National Research Council. *Committee on X-ray Spectra.*

National Research Council. *Division of Mathematical and Physical Sciences. Committee on X-rays and Radioactivity*
    see
National Research Council. *Committee on X-rays and Radioactivity.*

National Research Council. *Division of Mathematical and Physical Sciences. Photo-electric Committee*
    see
National Research Council. *Photo-electric Committee.*

National Research Council. *Division of Mathematical and Physical Sciences. Subcommittee on Molecular Physics*
    see
National Research Council. *Subcommittee on Molecular Physics.*

VOLUME 407

National Research Council. Division of
Mathematical and Physical Sciences.
Sub-Committee on Volcanology.
Volcanology
see   Physics of the earth. vol. I:
Volcanology.

National Research Council. Division of Mathematical and Physical Sciences. Subsidiary
Committee on Seismology
see   National Research Council. Committee on Physics of the Earth. Subsidiary
Committee on Seismology.

QA47
.M29

National Research Council. Division of
Mathematics.

Mathematics of computation. v. 1–   (no. 1–   );
Jan. 1943–
Washington, National Research Council.

National Research Council. Division of Mathematics
Proceedings of the Symposium on special
topics in applied mathematics.
see under

Symposium on Special Topics in Applied
Mathematics, Evanston, 1953.

National Research Council. *Division of Mathematics.*
Report.
Washington.
v. 27 cm. annual.
Report year ends June 30.

QA1.N38   55–61311 ‡

NN   0062743   DLC

National Research Council. *Division of Mathematics*
see also
National Research Council. *Division of Mathematical and*
Physical Sciences.

W 2
A
N36ag

NATIONAL Research Council. Division of
Medical Sciences
Agenda ₍of the₎ annual meeting.

Washington, 19
v. illus.
1. Research - Medical - Period.

NN   0062745   DNLM

National Research Council. Division of Medical
Sciences.
Annual report
see its   Report.

National research council. Division of medical
sciences.
National research council. *Committee on the atmosphere and
man.*
... Causes of geographical variations in the influenza epi-
lemic of 1918 in the cities of the United States. Report of
the Committee on the atmosphere and man. Prepared for the
Division of biology and agriculture and the Division of medical sciences, National research council. Presented by Ellsworth Huntington, chairman. Washington, D. C., Published
by the National research council of the National academy of
sciences, 1923.

W 2
A
N36c

NATIONAL Research Council. Division of
Medical Sciences
Circular letter.
Washington ₍1929?₎–
v.

NN   0062748   DNLM

WB
1
AA1
qN5

NATIONAL Research Council. Division of
Medical Sciences
₍Collection of publications₎

The Library has a collection of
miscellaneous publications of this
organization kept as received. These
publications are not listed or bound
separately.

NN   0062749   DNLM

W 2
AA1
qN23c

NATIONAL Research Council. Division of
Medical Sciences
₍Collection of reports, bulletins, etc.₎

A miscellaneous collection of proceedings of conferences, reports, and minutes
of meetings, etc., of various boards,
committees and subcommittees of the
Division may be found in the Document
Section.

NN   0062750   DNLM

Q
11
qN2771c
1944

NATIONAL Research Council. Division of
Medical Sciences
Committees on military medicine.
₍Washington?₎ 1944.
21 p.

NN   0062751   DNLM

W
22
A
N3d

NATIONAL Research Council. Division of
Medical Sciences
Directory.
Washington, D. C.

1. Societies, Medical - U. S. -
directories

NN   0062752   MBCo

National Research Council. Division of Medical
Sciences.
A follow-up study of World War II prisoners
of war

see under

Cohen, Bernard Milton, 1904–

National research council. Division of
medical sciences.
McKinley, Earl Baldwin, 1894–
A geography of disease; a preliminary survey of the incidence and distribution of tropical and certain other diseases
... by Earl Baldwin McKinley ... Washington, D. C., The
George Washington university press, 1935.

WA
240
N278i
1951

NATIONAL Research Council. Division of
Medical Sciences
Insecticides, rodenticides, and fumigants employed in public health activities.
₍Washington, 1951₎
6 p.
Caption title.
1. Fumigation 2. Insecticides
3. Rats - Extermination

NN   0062755   DNLM

NATIONAL RESEARCH COUNCIL – Division of
Medical Sciences.
An investigation of conditions in the depart-
ments of the preclinical sciences; a report of
a committee of the division, Joseph Erlanger,
C.M.Jackson ₍and others₎. Chicago, American
Medical Association, 1920.

pp.28. Cover serves as title-page.
"Reprinted from The Journal of the American
Medical Association   Apr.17.1920.vol.74, pp.
1117-1122"

NN   0062756   MBCo

National Research Council. *Division of Medical Sciences.*
List of fellows in the medical sciences
see National Research Council. *Medical Fellowship
Board. List of fellows.*

National Research Council. Division of Medical
Sciences.
Manual of clinical mycology
see under title

UH
215
AA1
qN2m
1944

NATIONAL Research Council. Division of
Medical Sciences
₍ Medical history of the Second World
War. Proposed publication ₎
Washington, 1944-45.
3 no. in 1 v.
Contents: Prospectus. — Guide for
authors. — Letter to the authors of vol. 1
announcing the withdrawal of the National
Research Council from the project.

NN   0062759   DNLM ICU

National Research Council. Division of Medical
Sciences.
Minutes, annual meeting.

Washington, 19 –
v.

Issues for 1951-53 included in the Annual
reports of the division for 1950/51-1952/53.

NN   0062760   NcU-H

VOLUME 407

W 2
A
N36m

NATIONAL Research Council. Division of
Medical Sciences
Minutes of meeting of Executive Com-
mittee.

Washington, 19
v.
Issues for 19   include Annual
report of the Chairman and others.
I. National Research Council. Division
of Medical Sciences. Annual report.

NN 0062761   DNLM NcU-H

QP82
.N4

National Research Council. Division of
Medical Sciences.

Newburgh, Louis Harry, 1883–   ed.
Physiology of heat regulation and the science of clothing;
prepared at the request of the Division of Medical Sciences,
National Research Council. Philadelphia, Saunders, 1949.

RC156
.R89

National research council. Division of
medical sciences.

Russell, Paul Farr, 1894–
Practical malariology, prepared under the auspices of the Division of medical sciences of the National research council ₍by₎
Paul F. Russell ... Luther S. West ... ₍and₎ Reginald D. Man-
well ... Foreword by Raymond B. Fosdick ... 238 illustrations, 8 in color. Philadelphia, London, W. B. Saunders company, 1946.

National Research Council. Division of Medical
Sciences.
Primate malaria
see under   Aberle, Sophie Bledsoe de,
1899–

National Research Council. *Division of Medical Sciences.*
Report.
Washington.
ˈv. 27 cm. annual.
Report year ends June 30.

R15.N35   610.72   55–31028 ‡

NN 0062765   DLC WU CtY-M DNLM NcU-H PPiU-H MnU

National Research Council. Division of Medical
Sciences.
A summary of current literature on anthio-
maline
see under   National Research Council.
Division of Medical Sciences. Office of Medical
Information.

National Research Council. *Division of Medical Sciences.*
Symposium on atherosclerosis,⁄held under the auspices of
the Division of Medical Sciences, National Academy of
Sciences—National Research Council, at the request of the
Human Factors Division, Air Force Directorate of Research
and Development, 22–23 March, 1954. Washington, 1954
₍i. e. 1955₎
249 p. illus. 26 cm. (National Research Council. Publication
338)
Includes bibliographies.
1. Arteriosclerosis. ɪ.⁄Title.   (Series)

RC692.N3 1954   616.13   55—60010

OrP WaTC CaBVaU OrCS IdPI WaS MBCo
PBL PPT ViU TxU NcD PSt OU ICJ DNLM OC1W GU AAP
NN 0062767   DLC PPC IU NN PU-Med MiU Wa MtBC PPJ

National Research Council. *Division of Medical Sciences.*
Symposium on stress, ʼsponsored jointly by Division of
Medical Sciences, National Research Council and the Army
Medical Service Graduate School, Walter Reed Army Medi-
cal Center, 16–18 March 1953. Washington, Army Medical
Service Graduate School ₍1953₎
ɪx, 332 p. illus. 24 cm.
Includes bibliographies.

1. Stress (Physiology)   ɪ. U. S. Army Medical Service. Graduate School. ɪɪ. Title.

QP356.N3 1953   54–61219

ICU PPT-M PPJ NNC PU-Med-TS NcU PPJ
PPWM OU OO PPC PU-M OrU PU-V MiU NcD ICJ ViU DNLM
NN 0062768   DLC CaBVaU Wa OrU-M OC1W IU CSt TU

National Research Council. *Division of Medical Sciences.*
Symposium on treatment of trauma in the Armed Forces,
sponsored jointly by the Division of Medical Sciences of the
National Research Council and the Army Medical Service
Graduate School, Walter Reed Army Medical Center, 10–12
March 1952. Washington, Army Medical Service Graduate
School ₍1952₎
1 v. (various pagings) illus., diagrs., tables. 27 cm.
Includes bibliographies.

1. Wounds.   ɪ. U. S. Army Medical Service. Graduate School.
ɪɪ. Title.

RD156.N32 1952   *614.88 617.14   53–61227

PPJ ViU CtY-M ICU NcD IU CaBVaU OrU-M
NN 0062769   DLC DNLM PPWM PPHa OU CU-M MiU PPT-M

National Research Council. Division of Medical
Sciences.
Tuberculosis in the Army of the United States
in World War II

see under

Long, Esmond Ray, 1890–

HD6068
.B23

National research council. Division of
medical sciences.

Baetjer, Anna Medora, 1899–
Women in industry, their health and efficiency ... Prepared
in the Army industrial hygiene laboratory by Anna M. Baetjer
... Philadelphia and London, W. B. Saunders company, 1946.

National Research Council. *Division of Medical Sciences*
see also

onferences sponsored by the
division, e. g., Conference on Insecticide Resistance and
Insect Physiology, University of Cincinnati, 1951.

National Research Council. Division of Medical
Sciences. Ad Hoc Committee on Fluoridation
of Water Supplies
see   National Research Council. Ad Hoc
Committee on Fluoridation of Water Supplies.

National Research Council. *Division of Medical Sciences.*
Committee for Research in Problems of Sex
see **National Research Council.** *Committee for Research*
in Problems of Sex.

National research council. *Division of medical sciences.*
Committee on aviation medicine

see

National research council. *Committee on aviation medicine.*

National Research Council. Division of Medical
Sciences. Committee on Drug Addiction
see   National Research Council.
Committee on Drug Addiction.

National research council. *Division of medical sciences.*
Committee on growth
see **National research council.** *Committee on growth.*

National research council. *Division of medical sciences.*
Committee on industrial medicine

see

National research council. *Committee on industrial medi-*
cine.

RM735
.A6

National research council. Division of medical
sciences. Committee on information.

American medical association. *Council on physical medi-*
cine.
Manual of occupational therapy, prepared by the Council
on physical therapy of the American medical association, the
Committee of the American occupational therapy association,
and the Subcommittee on physical therapy and Committee on
information of the Division of medical sciences of the National
research council. ₍Chicago, 1943₎

RM700
.A73

National research council. Division of
medical sciences. Committee on information.

American medical association. *Council on physical medi-*
cine.
Manual of physical therapy, prepared by the Council on
physical therapy of the American medical association, the
Subcommittee on physical therapy and the Committee on information of the Division of medical sciences of the National
research council. ₍Chicago, 1942₎

RC970
.W3

National research council. Division of medical
sciences. Committee on information.

War medicine, a periodical containing original contributions,
news and abstracts of articles of military, naval and similar
interest related to preparedness and war service. v. 1–
Jan. 1941–
Chicago, American medical association ₍1941

National research council. Division of
medical sciences. Committee on medicolegal problems

see

National research council. Committee on
medicolegal problems.

National Research Council. *Division of Medical Sciences.*
Committee on Pathology
see **National Research Council.** *Committee on Pathol-*
ogy.

National Research Council. Division of Medical
Sciences. Committee on Research in Endocrinology
see   National Research Council. Committee on Research in Endocrinology.

VOLUME 407

National Research Council. *Division of Medical Sciences. Committee on Sanitary Engineering*
see National Research Council. *Committee on Sanitary Engineering.*

National Research Council. *Division of Medical Sciences. Committee on Shock*
see
National Research Council. *Committee on Shock.*

National research council. *Division of medical sciences. Committee on surgery*
see
National research council. *Committee on surgery.*

National Research Council. Division of Medical Sciences. Committee on Treatment of Gas Casualties
see National Research Council. Committee on Treatment of Gas Casualties.

National Research Council. *Division of Medical Sciences. Committee on Veterans Medical Problems*
see National Research Council. *Committee on Veterans Medical Problems.*

National Research Council. Division of Medical Sciences. Executive Committee
see National Research Council. Division of Medical Sciences.

National Research Council. *Division of Medical Sciences. Medical Fellowship Board*
see National Research Council. *Medical Fellowship Board.*

RC156
.T27

National research council. Division of medical sciences. Office of medical information.
Temkin, Owsei, 1902–
... Antimalarial drugs, general outline ₍by₎ Owsei Temkin, M. D. ₍and₎ Elizabeth M. Ramsey, M. D. Issued by the Office of medical information ... Washington, 1944.

RM171
.P5

National research council. Division of medical sciences. Office of medical information.
Phalen, James Matthew, 1872–
... The blood plasma program ₍by₎ James A. ₍!₎ Phalen, M. D., colonel, U. S. army. Issued by the Office of medical information ... Washington, 1944.

QL536
.K54

National research council. Division of medical sciences. Office of medical information.
Knight, Kenneth Lee, 1915–
... Keys to the mosquitoes of the Australasian region, including a synopsis of their distribution and breeding habits, by Kenneth L. Knight ... Richard M. Bohart ... and George E. Bohart ... Issued by the Office of medical information ... Washington, 1944.

ZW
1
qN276m

NATIONAL Research Council. Division of Medical Sciences. Office of Medical Information. Medical news. v. 1–7; Dec. 21, 1942–Aug. 20, 1946.
₍Washington₎
7 v. in 3.
Typewritten copy.
No more published?
1. Medicine – World War II – indexes

NN 0062795 DNLM

RC156
.A3

National research council. Division of medical sciences. Office of medical information.
Aberle, Sophie Bledsoe de, 1896–
... Primate malaria ₍by₎ S. D. Aberle, M. D. Issued by the Office of medical information (under grant of the Johnson & Johnson research foundation) March 1945. ₍Washington, 1945₎

National Research Council. *Division of Medical Sciences. Office of Medical Information.*
... Report on blast injuries ... ₍n. p.₎ 1943.
44 p. 28 cm.

1. Explosions₍—Injurious effects₎

Med 48–795

U. S. Army Medical Libr. for Library of Congress | [WO700qN277r 1943] ₍1₎

NN 0062797 DNLM

RC234
.T4

National research council. Division of medical sciences. Office of medical information.
Temkin, Owsei, 1902–
... A report on the medicinal treatment of filariasis bancrofti ₍by₎ Owsei Temkin, M. D. Issued by the Office of medical information ... Washington, 1945.

National research council. Division of medical sciences. Office of medical information.
... Report on the treatment of thermal burns general outline. Prepared by the Office of medical information ... ₍Washington, D.C.₎ 1943.
2 p. ℓ., 23 p. 28 cm.
At head of title: National research council. Division of medical sciences.
Reproduced from type-written copy.
"References": p. ₍19₎–23.

NN 0062799 MtU IU-M

RC751
.W37

National research council. Division of medical sciences. Office of medical information.
Waring, James Johnston, 1883–
... Spontaneous pneumothorax ₍by₎ James J. Waring, M. D Issued by the Office of medical information ... Washington 1944.

National research council. *Division of medical sciences. Office of medical information.*
... A summary of current literature on anthiomaline, prepared by the Office of medical information. Washington ₍1944₎
3 p. l., 36 p. diagr. 28 x 21½ᵐ.
At head of title: National research council. Division of medical sciences.
Reproduced from type-written copy.
"Issued August 18, 1943 ... Republished July, 1944."
Bibliography: p. ₍82₎–36.

1. Anthiomaline.
44–41657

Library of Congress * RS167.A6N6 ₍3₎ 615.286

NN 0062801 DLC DNAL ViU

National Research Council. *Division of Medical Sciences. Panel on the Sterilization of Blood and Plasma*
see
National Research Council. *Panel on the Sterilization of Blood and Plasma.*

National Research Council. *Division of Medical Sciences. Prosthetics Research Board*
see
National Research Council. *Prosthetics Research Board.*

National research council. *Division of medical sciences. Subcommittee on anesthesia*
see
National research council. *Subcommittee on anesthesia.*

W
1
NA673

National Research Council. Division of Medical Sciences. Subcommittee on Materials and Equipment.
Minutes of meeting. 1st–
Feb. 22, 1948– Washington,
v.

NN 0062805 DNLM

National research council. *Division of medical sciences. Subcommittee on physical therapy*
see
National research council. *Subcommittee on physical therapy.*

W
1
NA6735

National Research Council. Division of Medical Sciences. Subcommittee on Publicity
Minutes of meeting. Dec. 11, 1940–
₍Washington₎
v.

NN 0062807 DNLM

National Research Council. *Division of Medical Sciences. Subcommittee on Waste Disposal*
see
National Research Council. *Subcommittee on Waste Disposal.*

National Research Council. *Division of Medicine and Related Sciences*
see also
National Research Council. *Division of Medical Sciences.*

National Research Council. *Division of Physical Sciences (1919–1947)*
see
National Research Council. *Division of Mathematical and Physical Sciences.*

National Research Council. Division of Physical Sciences (1951–)
Report. 195 –
Washington.

NN 0062811 MiU

VOLUME 407

GC41
.S93
1952

National Research Council. Division of Physical Sciences (1951–)

Symposium on Oceanographic Instrumentation, *Rancho Sante Fe, Calif., 1952.*
Symposium on oceanographic instrumentation, Rancho Santa Fe, California, June 21-23, 1952. Sponsored by the Office of Naval Research [and] Division of Physical Sciences, National Research Council. [Washington, Division of Physical Sciences, National Academy of Sciences-National Research Council. 1954]

National Research Council. *Division of Physical Sciences (1951–)*
  see also
National Research Council. *Division of Mathematical and Physical Sciences.*

National Research Council. *Division of Physical Sciences (1951–) Committee on Nuclear Science*
  see
National Research Council. *Committee on Nuclear Science.*

National Research Council. *Division of Physical Sciences (1951–) Mine Advisory Committee*
  see
National Research Council. *Mine Advisory Committee.*

National research council. *Division of research extension*
  see also
National research council. *Division of engineering and industrial research.*

D620.72
N215

National research council. Division of states relations.
Conditions determining the nature of the research work undertaken by state governmental agencies; papers presented at the annual meeting of the Division of states relations, National research council, May 27, 1926. Washington, D. C. [1926]
2 p. l., 55 (i. e. 56) p. 27½ᵐ.

Reproduced from type-written copy.
Contents.--Introductory remarks, by A. F. Woods.--The responsibility of the state for research, by J. C. Merriam.--Conditions determining the nature of research work in agriculture, by R. W. Thatcher.--Conditions determining the nature of research work in public health, by E. G. Williams.--Some conditions controlling state geological surveys, by H. B. Kimmel.--The function of the state government in the promotion of research, by T. W. Page.--State archaeological research, by A. V. Kidder.--Work of the Illinois state natural history survey, by S. A. Forbes.
1. Research. 2. State encouragement of science, literature, and ar   t.

NN   0062819   NNC DI-GS   ICU IU OrCS

National research council. Division of states relations.
Allen, Edwin West, 1864-1929.
... Co-operation with the federal government in scientific work. Prepared for the divisions of federal and of states relations, National research council, by E. W. Allen ... Washington, D. C., Published by the National research council of the National academy of sciences, 1922.

Q11
.N292
no. 49

National research council. Division of states relations.

White, Leonard Dupee, 1891–
... An evaluation of the system of central financial control of research in state governments. Prepared for the Division of state relations, National research council, by Leonard D. White ... Washington, D. C., Published by the National research council of the National academy of sciences. 1924.

National research council. Division of states relations.
Goodspeed, Thomas Harper, 1887–
... The organization and activities of the Committee on scientific research of the State council of defense of California. Prepared from the final report of the committee, by T. H. Goodspeed ... Washington, D. C., Published by the National research council of the National academy of sciences, 1923.

National research council. Division of states relations.
Douglas, James Roy, 1890–
...The research activities of departments of the state government of California in relation to the movement for reorganization; prepared for the Division of states relations of the National research council, by James R. Douglas ... Washington, D. C., Published by the National research council of the National academy of sciences, 1921.

National research council. Division of states relations.   FOR OTHER EDITIONS SEE MAIN ENTRY
White, Leonard Dupee, 1891–
... The status of scientific research in Illinois by state agencies other than the University of Illinois. Prepared for the Division of states relations, National research council, by Leonard D. White ... Washington, D. C., Published by the National research council of the National academy of sciences, 1923.   OTHER EDITIONS UNDER AUTHOR

National Research Council. *Earth Science Division*
  see
National Research Council. *Division of Earth Sciences*

National Research Council. Ecology of Marine Organisms, Subcommittee on the
  see   National Research Council.
Committee on a Treatise on Marine Ecology and Paleoecology.

National Research Council. Electrical Insulation, Committee on
  see   Conference on Electrical Insulation.

National Research Council. Emergency Committee on Psychology.
... Handbook and agenda
  see under   Intersociety constitutional convention of psychologists, New York, 1943.

National research council. *Emergency committee on psychology. Subcommittee on a textbook of military psychology*
  see
National research council. *Committee on a textbook of military psychology.*

[National research council. Emergency committee in psychology. Subcommittee on survey and planning]
First report ... by Edwin G. Boring, Alice I. Bryan, Edgar A. Doll [and others] [1942]
619-630 p.

"Offprint from the Psychological bulletin, vol. 39, no. 8, October, 1942."
1. Boring, Edwin Garrigues, 1886– II. Bryan, Alice Isabel, 1902–

NN   0062830   NNC

[National research council. Emergency committee in psychology. Subcommittee on survey and planning]
Psychology as science and profession, by Edwin G. Boring, Alice I. Bryan, Edgar A Doll [and others] [1942]
761-772 p.

A supplement to its First report.
"Off-printed from the Psychological bulletin, vol. 39, no. 9, November, 1942."

NN   0062831   NNC

National Research Council. Engineering and Industrial Research Division
  see   National Research Council. **Division of Engineering and Industrial Research.**

National Research Council. Engineering Committee.
Clean coal ...
  see under   National Research Council.

National Research Council. Engineering Division
  see   National Research Council. **Division of Engineering.**

Q11
.N2913

National research council. Executive board.
...Minutes of the meeting...
[Washington, D.C. 1933–
  v.   28 cm.

NN   0062835   DLC DI-GS

389.9
N2135B

National Research Council. Food and Nutrition Board.
Bread and flour enrichment.

Washington.

NN   0062836   DNAL

389.1
N2183C

National research council. Food and nutrition board.
Civilian requirements in the United States for concentrated vitamins. [Washington, 1943]
6 p.

1. Vitamins, Synthetic. I. Title.

NN   0062837   DNAL

VOLUME 407

RC298
.J6

National Research Council. Food and Nutrition Board.

Jolliffe, Norman, *ed.*
Clinical nutrition, edited by Norman Jolliffe, F. F. Tisdall and Paul R. Cannon for the Food and Nutrition Board of the National Research Council. [New York] Hoeber [1950]

SF253
.M2
1953

National Research Council. Food and nutrition Board.   FOR OTHER EDITIONS
                                            SEE MAIN ENTRY

Macy, Icie Gertrude, 1892–
The composition of milks; a compilation of the comparative composition and properties of human, cow, and goat milk, colostrum, and transitional milk, prepared by Icie G. Macy, Harriet J. Kelly, and Ralph E. Sloan for the Food and Nutrition Board, with the consultation of the Committee on Maternal and Child Feeding. Washington, National Academy of Sciences, National Research Council, 1953.

QU
22
AA1
qN2d

NATIONAL Research Council. Food and
     Nutrition Board
          Directory.
     Washington, 19
          v.
     1. Nutrition - U. S. - direct.

NN 0062840   DNLM

389.1
N2183F

National research council. Food and nutrition board.
The facts about enrichment of flour and bread. Washington [1943?]
15 p.

"Committee on cereals."

NN 0062841   DNAL

389.1
N2183F
suppl.

National Research Council. Food and Nutrition Board.
The facts about enrichment of flour and bread; supplement. Washington, 1945.
8 p.

NN 0062842   DNAL

National Research Council. Food and Nutrition Board.
     Food charts
          see under   American Medical Association.
     Council on Foods and Nutrition.

389
N2193

National research council. Food and nutrition board.
How we can share our food and maintain good nutrition at home. Washington [1944]
4 p.

1. Food supply, U.S. 2. War and agriculture (1939-   ) U.S. 3. World war, 1939-
Food question. U.S.

NN 0062844   DNAL

National Research Council. Food and Nutrition Board.
     Institutional feeding in industry
          see under   National Research Council.
     Committee on the Nutrition of Industrial Workers.

National Research Council. Food and Nutrition Board.
     Medical survey of nutrition in Newfoundland ... 1945
          see under title

National Research Council. *Food and Nutrition Board.*
Memorandum on questions submitted by the Cabinet Committee on World Food Programs, December 13, 1946. Washington [1946?]
14 p. 28 cm.
"Prepared for the board by its Special Committee on the Emergency Food Situation."

1. Nutrition. 2. Deficiency diseases.

TX551.N377   613.2   48–13213*

NN 0062847   DLC

National Research Council. Food and Nutrition Board.
The nutrition of industrial workers ...
     see under   National Research Council.
Committee on the Nutrition of Industrial Workers.

389.3
N218P

National Research Council. Food and Nutrition Board.
Principles and procedures for evaluating the safety of intentional chemical additives in foods. Washington, 1954.
8 p.

1. Chemicals in food processing.

NN 0062849   DNAL

W
1
NA674

National Research Council. Food and Nutrition Board
     Proceedings.

Washington [1940-
     v. illus.

Indexes:
     Vols. 1-4, 1940-44, with v. 4.
     1. Nutrition - Periodicals

NN 0062850   DNLM DNAL

44
N2172P

National research council. Food and nutrition board.
Progress report of the Committee on milk. [Washington?] 1943.
6 p.

NN 0062851   DNAL

TX
551
.38
1941

National Research Council. Food and Nutrition Board.
Recommended daily dietary allowances [Washington] 1941.
6p.

NUTRITION
DIET
Recommended daily dietary allowances

NN 0062852   KMK

1.902
A2R244

National Research Council. Food and Nutrition Board.
Recommended daily dietary allowances. Rev. 1948. Washington, 1949.
[3] p.

Issued Dec. 12, 1949.

1. Dietaries. 2. Nutrition. I. U.S. Bureau of Human Nutrition and Home Economics.

NN 0062853   DNAL KMK

National Research Council. *Food and Nutrition Board.*
Recommended dietary allowances. [1st-] ed.; 1943-
Washington.
     v. 25 cm.
Vol. for 1943-   issued as National Research Council. Reprint and circular series (Q11.N298) ; 19   -64 as the council's Publication; 1968-   as National Academy of Sciences. Publication.
1. Diet.   I. Title.   (Series: National Research Council. Reprint and circular series. Series: National Research Council. Publication. Series: National Academy of Sciences, Washington, D. C. Publication)

TX551.N39   63–65472

OrU ICJ DNLM PSt NIC DNAL
WaChenE ViU LU AAP CU MnU OU CtU MnU NNC-M NNC
PU-D OClW OrCS WvFS NBuC NB NjR NcD MoU TxU MB
NN 0062854   DLC OrP IdPI CaBVaU KMK PBL OC1 PU

TX551
.N38
1943

National Research Council. Food and Nutrition Board.
Recommended dietary allowances; [a report of the Food and Nutrition Board, National Academy of Sciences-National Research Council] Washington, D. C., National Academy of Sciences-National Research Council, 1943.
51. tables. 25 cm.

Photocopy of original.
Cover title.
1. Diet.   I. Title. II. Title:
Dietary   allowances]
allowances]

Photocopy of original.
Cover title.
Bibliography: 1. 30-36.

1. Diet. I. Title. II. Title: Dietary allowances.

NN 0062856   AAP

389.9
N2135R

National research council. Food and nutrition board.
Report of the activities,

[Washington? D.C.,

1. Food. 2. Nutrition.

NN 0062857   DNAL

National Research Council. *Food and Nutrition Board.*
A report on margarine. Prepared by the Committee on Fats, L. A. Maynard, chairman. Report of the Food and Nutrition Board of the National Research Council. Washington [1943]
20 p. illus. 25 cm. (National Research Council. Reprint and circular series, no. 118)
Bibliography : p. 19-20.

1. Oleomargarine.   I. Maynard, Leonard Amby, 1887-
I. Title.   (Series)

Q11.N293 no. 118   614.326   43–50920 rev

NN 0062858   DLC O ViU

VOLUME 407

389.1
N2183Ri
[National Research Council. Food and
Nutrition Board]
Resolution concerning rice improvement
adopted by Food and Nutrition Board, May 7,
1949. [Washington, 1949]
sheet.

1. Rice as food.

NN 0062859   DNAL

National Research Council. *Food and Nutrition Board.*
Sodium-restricted diets; the rationale, complications, and
practical aspects of their use. Prepared by a committee of
the Food and Nutrition Board: C. S. Davidson, chairman
[and others] Washington, Division of Biology and Agriculture, National Research Council, 1954.
vi, 71 p. tables. 25 cm. (National Research Council. Publication
325)
Includes bibliographies.

1. Salt-free diet. I. Title. (Series)

RM237.9.N3   *615.85 613.23   54–60765

   NcU ScCleU
   TxU DNAL ICJ PBL PPD PSt DNLM AAP MsU Wa OClW GU
NN 0062860   DLC OrCS CaBVaU IdPI OrP WaTC ViU NN

389
N2193S   National Research Council. Food and
Nutrition Board.
Statement of stockpiling of foods for
relief purposes. Washington, 1944.
sheet.

1. Food policies and programs. U.S.
I. Title: Stockpiling of foods for relief
purposes.

NN 0062861   DNAL

National Research Council. Food and Nutrition
Board.
Survey of food and nutrition research in the
United States ...
see under   National Research Council.
Committee on Survey of Food and Nutrition
Research.

Home Economics
he   National Research Council. *Food and*
TX   Nutrition Board.
551   Symposium on nutrition surveys: Papers
N27S   read before the Food and Nutrition Board...
Dec. 2, 1944. Washington, D.C., 1944.
69 p. illus. tables. 28 cm.

Mimeographed.

Contents: the development of nutrition
surveys in the U. S. Public Health Service,
by W. H. Sebrell and W. Wilkins.— Regional
dietary surveys, by E. Phipard.— Techniques

used, and some findings in the New York area,
by H. D. Kruse.— Micro methods, their use in
surveys and education, by O. A. Bessey.— The
cooperative project at Vanderbilt University,
by J. B. Youmans.— Findings on examinations
of newborn infants and infants during the
neo-natal period which appear to have a
relationship to the diets of their mothers

during pregnancy, by H. C. Stuart.— Studies
under way in the North Dakota area, by D. F.
Milam.— Nutrition surveys in the New Orleans
area, by G. Goldsmith.— Feeding operations
in naval stations, by C. M. McCay.

1. Nutrition. 2. Diets. I. Title:
Nutrition surveys, symposium on. II. Title.

NN 0062865   NIC DNAL

National Research Council. Food and Nutrition
Board.
Tables of food composition ...
see under   National Research Council.
Committee on Foood Composition.

National Research Council. Food and Nutrition
Board.
Tables of vitamin losses in cooking of foods
see under   National Research Council.
Committee on Food Composition.

National Research Council. Food and Nutrition
Board.
Therapeutic nutrition

see under

Pollack, Herbert, 1905–

National Research Council. Food and Nutrition
Board.
Use of chemical additives in foods ...
see under   National Research Council.
Food Protection Committee.

National research council. *Food and nutrition board.*
Committee on cereals
     see
National research council. *Committee on cereals.*

National Research Council. *Food and Nutrition Board.*
Committee on Dental Health
see **National Research Council.** *Committee on Dental*
Health.

National research council. *Food and nutrition board.*
Committee on diagnosis and pathology of nutritional
deficiencies
     see
National research council. *Committee on diagnosis and path-*
ology of nutritional deficiencies.

National research council. *Food and nutrition board.*
Committee on fats
     see
National research council. *Committee on fats.*

National Research Council. *Food and Nutrition Board.*
Committee on Food Composition
see **National Research Council.** *Committee on Food*
Composition.

National Research Council. Food and Nutrition
Board. Committee on Milk
     see   National Research Council. Food
and Nutrition Board.

National research council. *Food and nutrition board.*
Committee on milk, meat and legumes
     see
National research council. *Committee on milk, meat and le-*
gumes.

National Research Council. Food and Nutrition
Board. Committee on Milk Production,
Distribution, and Quality
     see   National Research Council. Commit-
tee on Milk Production, Distribution, and Quality.

National Research Council. *Food and Nutrition Board.*
Committee on Nutrition Surveys
see **National Research Council.** *Committee on Nutrition*
Surveys.

National Research Council. *Food and Nutrition Board.*
Committee on Survey of Food and Nutrition Research
see **National Research Council.** *Committee on Survey*
of Food and Nutrition Research.

National Research Council. Food and Nutrition
Board. Committee on Survey of Literature on
Dental Caries
     see   National Research Council.
Committee on Survey of Literature on Dental
Caries.

National Research Council. Food and Nutrition
Board. Committee on the Nutrition of
Industrial Workers
     see   National Research Council. Commit-
tee on the Nutrition of Industrial Workers.

National Research Council. Food and Nutrition
Board. Committee on Therapeutic Nutrition
     see   National Research Council.
Committee on Therapeutic Nutrition.

National Research Council. *Food and Nutrition Board.*
Food Protection Committee
see **National Research Council.** *Food Protection Com-*
mittee.

National Research Council. Food Habits, Committee on
     see   National Research Council.
Committee on Food Habits.

National Research Council. Food Protection
Committee.
Annotated bibliography of analytical methods
for pesticides

see under

National Research Council. Chemistry Subcommittee.

VOLUME 407

National research council. Food protection committee.
Safe use of chemical additives in foods, basic principles involved in evaluating safety in the use of chemical additives in foods; basic considerations involved in evaluating hazards encountered in the use of pesticides on foods; basic considerations in the development of a new agricultural pesticide intended for use in connection with food production. Statements prepared by the Food protection committee, Food and nutrition board, National research council, National academy of sciences. Washington, D. C., 1952. 26 p. 20cm.

·Cover title.

1. Food—Analysis. 2. Pesticides. I. Title. t. 1952.

NN 0062886 NN DNAL DNLM NIC

National Research Council. *Food Protection Committee.*
The safety of artificial sweeteners for use in foods, a report. ₍Washington₎ 1955.
10 p. 25 cm. (National Research Council. Publication 386)
Includes bibliography.

1. Saccharin. 2. Cyclamates. ɪ. Title.

QP981.S2N3   614.3   56-60271 ‡

WaTC DNLM DNAL
CU MiD ViU ScCleU CaBVaU IdPI OrCS OrP
NN 0062887   DLC CtY-M NN CU-M LU NcD ICJ PBL MiU

National Research Council. *Food Protection Committee.*
The safety of mono- and diglycerides for use as intentional additives in foods; a report. ₍Washington₎ 1952.
14 p. tables. 25 cm. (National Academy of Sciences, National Research Council. Publication 251)
Cover title.
Bibliography: p. 12–14.

1. Glycerides. 2. Food—Analysis. ɪ. Title: Additives in foods. (Series: National Research Council. Publication 251)

TX553.G5N3   614.3   54–123

NN WaTC
PSt ICJ OCl TxU PBL MiU MiD CU LU ViU OrP CLSU
NN 0062888   DLC OrU DNAL DNLM CaBVaU IdPI OrCS

National Research Council. *Food Protection Committee.*
The safety of polyoxyethylene stearates for use as intentional additives in foods; a report. ₍Washington₎ 1953.
19 p. 25 cm. (National Research Council. Publication 280)
Cover title.
Bibliography: p. 18–19.

1. Polyoxyethylene stearates. ɪ. Title. (Series)

QP981.P8N23   614.31   53–63698

WaTC DNAL
PSt PBL TxU ICJ NNC ViU NNC-M CU-M OrCS OrP
NN 0062889   DLC CaBVaU IdPI OC1W DNLM NN OCl

TX
535   National Research Council. Food Protection Com-
.N28   mittee.
         Use of chemical additives in foods. Washington, Food and Nutrition Board, National Research Council, National Academy of Sciences, 1951.
         24 p. 20 cm.

1.Food. I.Title: Chemical additives in foods.

NN 0062890   MiU DNAL DNLM NIC

National Research Council. *Food Protection Committee.*
Chemistry Subcommittee
see
National Research Council. *Chemistry Subcommittee.*

National Research Council. Geology and Geography, Division of
see National Research Council. Division of Earth Sciences.

National Research Council. Heat Transmission, Committee on
see National Research Council. Committee on Heat Transmission.

National Research Council. Highway Research Board.
The Advisory Board on Highway Research of the National Research Council was organized in 1920. In 1924, the name was changed to Highway Research Board and in 1974 to Transportation Research Board.
Works by this body published before the change of name in 1974 are found under
National Research Council. Highway Research Board.

TL154   National Research Council. Highway Research
N3   Board.
Land-   Abatement of highway noise and fumes; presented at the
scape   thirty-fourth annual meeting, January 11-14, 1955. Washington,
Arch.   1955.
Library   iv, 47 p. illus. (Its Bulletin 110)

           Includes bibliographies.

           Contents. - Abatement of highway noise with special reference to roadside design; first report of Special Task Committee on Roadside Design to Reduce Traffic Noise, Dust, and Fumes (1953 study) by W. H. Simonson. - Motor vehicle noise studies, by D. M. Finch. - Second report of Special   Task Committee ... by W. H. Simonson.

NN 0062895   CU DNAL MU NBuU ViU

TE   National Research Council. Highway Research
7   Board.
N28   Air-entrained concrete; properties of air
no.70   voids and service record of pavements. Pre-
Engi-   sented at the thirty-second annual meeting,
neering January 13-16, 1953. Washington, 1953.
         23p. illus. 25cm. (Its Bulletin, 70)

         National Research Council. Publication, 261.

           1. Pavements,   Concrete. I. Title. (Series)

NN 0062896   MU NBuU ViU

TE1   National Research Council. Highway Research
B85   Board.
no.2   An analysis of general state enabling
         legislation dealing with automobile parking
         facilities. Reported by David R. Levin.
         Washington, 1947.
         89 p. (Its Bulletin 2)

         National Research Council. Publication.

           1. Automobile parking. I. T. Series.

NN 0062897   NBuU OrP Or NIC MH ViU NcD NNC TxDaM

National Research Council. Highway Research Board.
Analysis of landslides
see under National Research Council. Highway Research Board. Committee on Landslide Investigations.

VF
NAC   National Research Council. Highway
2063   Research Board.
N21   An analysis of state enabling legisla-
no.7   tion of special and local character deal-
         ing with automobile parking facilities.
         Reported by David R. Levin... Washington,
         Highway Research Board, Division of
         Engineering and Industrial Research,
         National Research Council, 1947.
         (Bulletin no. 7)

NN 0062899   NIC FTaSU NBuU

National Research Council. Highway Research Board.
Annual report
see its Report.

National research council. *Highway research board.*
... Apparatus used in highway research projects in the United States. Results of census by Advisory board on highway research, Division of engineering, National research council, in cooperation with the Bureau of public roads, United States Department of agriculture, by C. A. Hogentogler ... Washington, D. C., Published by the National research council of the National academy of sciences, 1923.
cover-title, 91 p. illus., diagrs. 25ᶜᵐ. (Bulletin of the National research council. no. 35 (v. 6, pt. 4) Aug. 1923)
1. Roads. ɪ. U. S. Bureau of public roads. ɪɪ. Hogentogler, Chester Allen, 1887– ɪɪɪ. Title. ɪᴠ. Title: Highway research projects in the United States.
Library of Congress   Q11.N292 no.35
——— Copy 2.   23–13643 Revised
——— Copy 3.
——— Copy 4.   TE23.N58

NIC ViU
NN 0062901   DLC WaTC OrPR OrU CaBVaU OCl MiU OU

TE   National Research Council. Highway Research
7   Board.
N28   The appraisal of terrain conditions for
no.13   highway purposes. Presented at the 27th annual
Engi-   meeting, 1947. Washington, 1948.
neering 91p. 25cm. (Its Bulletin, 13)

           1. Soils - Classification. 2. Soils - Maps. I. Title. (Series)

NN 0062902   MU NIC ViU

Pamphlet
Z   National Research Council. Highway
7+   Research Board.
         Automobile parking in the United
         States, selected references, 1946-1952.
         Washington, D. C., 1953.
         x, 119 p. 28cm. (Its Bibliography 14)

           1. Automobile parking--Bibl.

NN 0062903   NIC TxU CLSU

National Research Council. Highway Research Board.
Better laws for better highways
see under National Research Council. Highway Research Board. Committee on Highway Laws.

Z7295
.N3   National Research Council. Highway Research
         Board.
         Bibliography. no.1–
         Washington, Highway Research Board, 1947–
         v. illus. 25-28cm.

         No.13– issued as a number of the National Research Council. Publication.

           1. Highway research—Collected works. I. Series: National Academy of Sciences, Washington//Publication.

MsU DLC
CU TxU TU CtY ICJ NN NjR WvU PBL FTaSU OrP ScU
NN 0062905   ViU WaU CaBVaU MB WaS Wa OrCS Or GU

VOLUME 407

National Research Council. Highway Research
Board.
Bibliography on durability of concrete
see under   National Research Council.
Highway Research Board. Committee on Durabili-
ty of Concrete, Physical Aspects.

National Research Council. *Highway Research Board.*
Bibliography on frost action in soils; annotated. ₍Wash-
ington₎ 1948.
11 l., 57 p. *illus. (Its Bibliography no. 3)*
Annotated by Alfred Walton Johnson.

1. Soils—Bibl. 2. Frost—Bibl. 3. Roads—Frost damage—Bibl.
(Series)

Z5074.S7N3   016.6257   49–735*

TxU
NN   0062907   DLC PPD NIC ViU MtBC DNAL Or CoU

625.70
N213b1   National Research Council. Highway Research
Board.
Bibliography on methods and apparatus for
determining soil moisture content. ₍Washing-
ton₎ 1950 ₍caption, 1951₎
11 p. 28cm.

1. Soil moisture - Bibl. I.T.

NN   0062908   MiDW MtBC

National Research Council. Highway Research
Board.
Bibliography on resistance of bituminous
materials to deterioration caused by physical and
chemical changes
see under   National Research Council.
Highway Research Board. Committee on Resistance of Bituminous Materials to Deterioration
Caused by Physical and Chemical Changes.

National Research Council. Highway Research
Board.
Bibliography on uses of highway planning
survey data
see under   United States. Federal
Works Agency. Library.

TE1
.N43   National Research Council. Highway Research
no.105   Board.
1955
Bituminous paving mixtures; fundamentals
for design. Washington, 1955.
45 p. illus. 25cm. (Its Bulletin, 105)
National Research Council. Publication, 355.
Includes bibliographies.

1. Bituminous materials. I. Ser. II. Ser.

NN   0062911   ViU NBuU

National Research Council. *Highway Research Board.*
Bulletin. no. 1–362. Washington, 1946–62.
362 no. in   v. illus. 25 cm.

Bulletins no. 47–362 issued as the council's Publication.
Merged with National Research Council. Highway Research
Board. Meeting. Proceedings, to form Highway research record.
L. C. set incomplete: scattered issues wanting.

1. Road construction—Collected works.   (Series: National Research Council. Publication)

TE7.N28   49–4946 rev 2*

MB TU LU ICJ CtY TxU MiU IU CSt TxU MsU OAkU CU
NN   0062912   DLC UU DCU MiD NcD WvU MnU OU NN PSC

016.62013   National Research Council. **Highway**
N277c   Research Board.
Calcium chloride in concrete, annotated. Washington, D.C., 1952.
vi, 57p. 28cm. (Its Bibliography,
13)

National Research Council. Publication, 217.

1. Concrete - Bibl. I. Title. II.
Series. III. Series: National Research
Council. Publication

NN   0062913   CLSU

National Research Council. Highway Research
Board.
Central city property

see under

Wendt, Paul Francis, 1908–

National Research Council. Highway Research
Board.
Circular
see under   National Research Council.
Highway Research Correlation Service.

National Research Council. *Highway Research Board.*
Classified subject and author index on the Proceedings of
Second International Conference on Soil Mechanics and
Foundation Engineering. ₍Washington₎ 1949.
vii, 32 p. 28 cm. *(Its Bibliography no. 5)*
Includes an English translation of the titles of the papers in
Abhandlungen ueber Bodenmechanik und Grundbau, 1939–1948, a pub-
lication of the German Highway Research Society (p. 28–30)

1. International Conference on Soil Mechanics and Foundation
Engineering. 2d, Rotterdam, 1948. Proceedings. 2. Soil mechanics—
Bibl. 3. Foundations—Bibl.   (Series)

TA710.I 5 1948a   620.19   50—1113

NN   0062916   DLC MB DNAL ViU CoU FTaSU TxU UU

National Research Council. Highway Research
Board.
Committee report and manual of recom-
mended testing procedures on load carrying
capacity of roads as affected by frost action
see under   National Research Council.
Highway Research Board. Committee on Load
Carrying Capacity of Roads as affected by Frost
Action.

TE1
B85   National Research Council. Highway
no.58   Research Board.
Compaction of embankments, subgrades,
and bases. Washington, 1952
84 p.   (Its Bulletin 58)

National Research Council. Publication 240.

1. Embankments. I. T. Series.
Series: National Research Council.
Publication   240.

NN   0062918   NBuU DI ViU

National Research Council. Highway Research
Board.

Compaction of soil. Two papers presented
at the twenty-eighth annual meeting, 1948.
Washington, 1949.
iii, 17 p. diagrs. 25cm. (Its Bulletin,
no. 23)

1 Soil moisture. I. Ser.

NN   0062919   ViU NBuU DNAL

National research council. **Highway research**
board.

... Compaction of subgrades and embankments.
Washington, D. C., Highway research board, 1945.
25 p. incl. tables, diagrs. (Its Wartime road problems no. 11)
Dated August 1945.
At head of title: Highway research board. Division of
engineering and industrial research. National research
council.
"References": p. 23–25.

1. Roads—U. S. 2. Embankments. I. Title. II. Ser.

NN   0062920   ViU

NATIONAL RESEARCH COUNCIL. Highway Research Board.
Concrete resurfacing of concrete pavement in
various stages of deterioration; presented at the
thirty-third annual meeting, January 12–15, 1954.
Washington, 1954.
39 p. diagrs., tables. (Its Bulletin 87)

National Research Council. Publication 313.

1. Pavements, Concrete. I. Title.

NN   0062921   GAT ViU

National Research Council. Highway Research
Board.
Controlled access expressways in urban
areas ...
see under   National Research Council.
Highway Research Board. Committee on Effect
of Controlled Access Expressways on Urban Areas.

National research council. **Highway research**
board.

... Curing concrete pavements under wartime
restrictions on critical materials. Washington,
D.C., Highway research board, 1942.
16 p. 23cm. (Its Wartime road problems no. 1)
At head of title: Highway research board. Division of
engineering and industrial research, National research
council.
Dated July 1942.
A supplementary page numbered in duplicate page 11 and
containing information omitted by error in original issue:
laid in.

1. Pavements, Concrete. 2. Roads—U.S. I. Title.
II. Ser.

NN   0062923   ViU

TE7
.N3   National Research Council. Highway Research
no.1–R   Board.
1952
Curing of concrete pavements. Rev. ed.
₍Washington₎ 1952.
19 p. 23cm. (Its Current road problems, no.
1–R)
Bibliography: p. 18–19.

1. Pavements. I. Title: Concrete pavements.
II. Ser.

NN   0062924   ViU IdPI

National Research Council. *Highway Research Board.*
Current road problems. no. 1–
Washington, 1942–

v. 23 cm.

Title varies: 1942–   Wartime road problems.
Some issues also in revised editions.

1. Roads—U. S. I. Title.

TE7.N3   625.8   42–38734 rev*‡

OrU LU OrP DPR
NN   0062925   DLC CaBVaU MtBC KMK CSt C ICJ OrCS

VOLUME 407

NATIONAL RESEARCH COUNCIL. Highway Research Board.
Deleterious constituents of Indiana gravels;
presented at the thirty-third annual meeting,
January 12-15, 1954. Washington, 1954.
10 p. diagrs., tables. (Its Bulletin 94)

National Research Council. Publication 342.
Bibliography: p.8.

1. Gravel. 2. Concrete. I. Title.

NN 0062926   GAT ViU NBuU MU

National research council. Highway research
board.
... Design of concrete pavements requiring
a minimum of steel. Washington, D.C., Highway
research board, 1942.
13 p. incl. diagrs. 23cm. (Its Wartime road problems
no.3)
At head of title: Highway research board, Division of
engineering and industrial research, national research
council.
Dated September 1942.
1. Pavements, Concrete 2. Steel. I.Title. II.Ser.

NN 0062927   ViU

TE1   National Research Council. Highway Research
B85   Board.
no.8   Design of flexible pavement using the tri-
axial compression test. Washington, 1947.
63 p. (Its Bulletin 8)

National Research Council. Publication.

1. Pavements - Kansas. I. T. Series.

NN 0062928   NBuU IU NNC MiD

National Research Council. Highway Research
Board.
Design of flexible pavements ...
see under National Research Council.
Highway Research Board. Committee on Flexible
Pavement Design.

National research council. Highway research
board.
... Design of highway guards. Washington, D. C
Highway research board, 1942.
14 p. illus. (incl. diagrs.) 23cm. (Its
Wartime road problems. no. 2)

Dated August 1942.
1. Roads—U.S. 2. Accidents—Prevention. I. Title.
II. Title: Highway guards. I. Ser.

NN 0062930   ViU

TE1
.N43   National Research Council. Highway Research
no.72   Board.
1953
Directional channelization and determination of pavement widths. Presented at the
thirty-second annual meeting, January 13-16,
1953. Washington, 1953.
49 p. diagrs., map. 25cm. (Its Bulletin, 72)
National Research Council. Publication, 263.
1. Pavements—Testing. I. Title. II. Ser.
III. Ser.

NN 0062931   ViU NBuU PPCPC

HF5429   National Research Council. Highway Research
.J563   Board.
Jonassen, Christen Tonnes, 1912-
Downtown versus suburban shopping. Columbus, Bureau
of Business Research. Ohio State University [1953]-54.

TL152   National Research Council. Highway Research
N25   Board.
Driver characteristics and accidents, presented at the 32nd annual meeting, January 13-1
1953. Washington, D. C., 1953.
vii, 54p. illus. 25cm. (Its Bulletin 73)

National Academy of Sciences, National
Research Council. Publication 264.

NN 0062933   NBuG ViU PU-W

TE1   National Research Council. Highway
B85   Research Board.
no.75   Effect in concrete of pellet and
flake forms of calcium chloride.
Presented at the 32nd annual meeting,
January 13-16, 1953. Washington,
1953.
18 p. (Its Bulletin 75)

National Research Council. Publication 268.

NN 0062934   NBuU ViU

National Research Council. *Highway Research Board.*
The effect of limited access expressways on existing street
systems. [Compiled by Dorothy Bright, librarian] Washington, Highway Research Board, Division of Engineering
and Industrial Research, National Research Council, 1947.
13 p. 28 cm. (*Its* Bibliography, no. 1)

1. Express highways—Bibl.   I. Bright, Dorothy H.   II. Title.
(Series)
Z7295.N3   016.3881   50-14197

NN 0062935   DLC TxU FMU CoU FTaSU NIC ViU

RE 923   NATIONAL RESEARCH COUNCIL--Highway Research
.N27   Board
Effect of tinted windshields and vehicle
headlighting on night visibility. Presented
at the 32d annual meeting, Jan. 13-16, 1953.
Washington, 1953.
61 p. illus. (Its Bulletin 68)
National Research Council. Publication 259.
1. Night vision. 2. Automobiles--Lighting.
3. Automobiles--Windows and windshields. 4.
Automobile driving at night. I. Title. Ser.
Ser.: National Research Council. Publication
259.

NN 0062936   InU NNC-M NBuU

TE   National Research Council. Highway Research
7   Board.
N28   Engineering applications of soil surveying and
no.83   mapping. Presented at the thirty-second
Engi-   annual meeting, January 13-16, 1953. Washing-
neering   ton, D. C.,1953.
73p. illus. 25cm. (Its Bulletin 83)

National Research Council. Publication 293.

1. Roads – Sur-   veying. 2. Roads – Design.
I. Title. (Serie   s)

NN 0062937   MU NBuU DNAL GAT ViU IU

S   National Research Council. Highway Resear
591   Board.
N27E   Engineering soil survey mapping. Presented at the thirtieth annual meeting, 1951.
Washington, 1951.
iii, 95 cm. illus., maps (part. fold. in
pocket) tables. 26 cm. (Its Bulletin no. 46)

1. Soil-surveys - U. S. 2. Soil mechanics
3. Agriculture   - Maps - U. S. 4. Photography, Aeria   1. I. Title. II. Series.

NN 0062938   NIC IEN ViU DNAL

NATIONAL RESEARCH COUNCIL. Highway Research Board.
Experiment in extension programs [for county
highway engineers] Presented at the thirty-second
annual meeting, January 13-16, 1953. Washington,
1953.
15 p. illus. (Its Bulletin 85)

National Research Council. Publication 299.

1. Road construction. I. Title.

NN 0062939   GAT ViU NBuU IEdS

National Research Council. Highway Research
Board.
Expressways. Committee report and three
papers presented at the twenty-seventh
annual meeting, 1947. Washington, 1948.
iii, 21 p. illus. maps. fold. diagrs. 25cm.
(Its Bulletin no. 16)
1. Express highways—U. S. 2. Traffic engineering—
U. S. I. Ser.

NN 0062940   ViU PPT OU NIC NBuU Or

National Research Council. Highway Research
Board.
Factors related to frost action in soils ...
see under Highway Research Council.
Highway Research Board. Committee on Frost
Heave and Frost Action in Soil.

TE1
.N43   National Research Council. Highway Research
no.78   Board.
1953
Filling and sealing of joints and cracks
in concrete pavements. Presented at the
thirty-second annual meeting, January 13-
16, 1953. Washington, 1953.
38 p. diagrs. 25cm. (Its Bulletin, 78)
National Research Council. Publication, 276.
1. Pavements, Concrete. I. Ser. II. Ser.

NN 0062942   ViU

National Research Council. *Highway Research Board.*
Final report on Road Test One-MD; effect of controlled
truck axle loadings on concrete pavement. Washington,
1952.
vii, 142 p. illus., maps. 28 cm. (*Its* Special report 4)
National Academy of Sciences, National Research Council. Pub-
lication 227.
"Tests were conducted ... approximately 9 mi. south of La Plata."
Includes bibliographies.
1. Road Test One-MD.   (Series. Series: National Research
Council. Publication 227)
TE24.M3N3   *625.7 625.84   53—1540

OrP CaBViP OClW
NN 0062943   DLC UU N DI ViU PSt PU-FA FTaSU MtBC

VOLUME 407

TE1
B85
no.80
National Research Council. Highway Research
Board
Flexible-pavement design. Washington,
D. C., 1953.
15 p. (Its Bulletin, 80)

National Research Council. Publication
282.

1. Pavements - U. S. I. T. Series.
Series: National Research Council. Publication 282.

NN 0062944 NBuU PPD ViU

National Research Council. *Highway Research Board.*
Frost action in roads and airfields; a review of the litera-
ture, by A. W. Johnson, engineer of soils and foundations,
Highway Research Board. Washington, 1952.
xii, 287 p. illus., map. 28 cm. (*Its* Special report no. 1)
National Academy of Sciences, National Research Council. Publi-
cation 211.
Bibliography: p. [253]–281.

1. Roads—Frost damage. 2. Frozen ground. 3. Frost—Bibl. I.
Johnson, Alfred Walton, 1902– II. Title. (Series. Series:
National Research Council. Publication 211.)

TE153.N357   625.7   52—10072

OC1U CoU IdU OC1W
NN 0062945   DLC DNAL DAS KMK IaU NcU DI PSt ViU

National Research Council. *Highway Research Board.*
Frost action in soils, a symposium. Presented at the
thirtieth annual meeting, January 9–12, 1951. Washington,
1952.
ix, 385 p. illus. 25 cm. (*Its* Special report, no. 2)
National Research Council. Publication 213.
Includes bibliographies.

1. Roads—Frost damage. 2. Soil physics. I. Title. (Series.
Series: National Research Council. Publication no. 213.)

TE153.N35722 1951   624.151   52–61159 rev 2

UU IdU MtBC OrCS OrP OC1W PCM PSt PV DAS
NN 0062946   DLC DI DNAL ViU OC1U NcU KMK CaBVaU

National research council. Highway research
board.
... Granular stabilized roads. Washington,
D. C., Highway research board, 1943.
27 p. illus., tables, diagrs. 23cm. (Its
Wartime road problems. no. 5)

Dated February 1943.

1. Roads—U. S. I. Title. II. Ser.

NN 0062947 ViU

NATIONAL RESEARCH COUNCIL. Highway Research Board.
Highway accidents and related factors; presented
at the thirty-third annual meeting, January 12-15,
1954. Washington, 1954.
54 p. illus., diagrs., tables. (Its Bulletin
91)

National Research Council. Publication 334.
Includes bibliographies.

1. Traffic accidents. I. Title.

NN 0062948 GAT NBuU ViU

VF
NAC
2170
N21
National Research Council. Highway
Research Board.
Highway and thorofare planning and
programming in relation to urban planning
and development, by I. S. Shattuck... and
K. B. Rykken ... [Wash., D.C., 1950]
(Bulletin, no. 31)

"Presented at the 29th annual meeting..
December 1949"

NN 0062949 NIC ViU

National Research Council. Highway Research
Board.
Highway capacity manual
see under National Research Council.
Highway Research Board. Committee on Highway
Capacity.

TE1
B85
no.12
National Research Council. Highway
Research Board.
Highway finance. Five papers presented at the 27th annual meeting,
1947. Washington, 1948.
64 p. (Its Bulletin 12)

National Research Council. Publication.

1. Roads - Finance. I. T. Series.

NN 0062951 NBuU MtBC PPT

TE1
.N43
no.62
1952
National Research Council. Highway Research
Board.

Highway-materials surveys. Presented at
the thirty-first annual meeting, January,
1952. Washington, 1952.
113 p. illus. 25cm. (Its Bulletin, 62)
National Research Council. Publication, 247.
Bibliography: p. 113.

1. Road materials. I. Title. II. Ser.
III. Ser.

NN 0062952 ViU PPD NBuU MU

288
N21H
National Research Council. Highway Research
Board.
Highway planning. Washington, 1948.
42 p. (Its Bulletin no.17)

1. Roads. Planning. I. National Research
Council. Highway Research Board. Bulletin
no.17.

NN 0062953 DNAL PPT PSt NIC ViU NBuU

National Research Council. Highway Research
Board.
Highway planning and urban development, presented at the thirty-first annual meeting, January 1952. Washington, D.C., 1952.
12p. (Bull.64)

NN 0062954 PPCPC

351.811
qN27
National Research Council. Highway Research
Board.
Highway relationships in Maryland. Washington, D.C., 1952.
vii, 51 p. maps., diagr. 28 cm. (Its
Special report no. 6)
National Academy of Sciences, National Research Council. Publication 229.
1. Roads. Maryland. 2. Highway law. Maryland. I. Title. Series: National Research
Council. Highway Research Board. Special report no. 6.

NN 0062955 N

National research council. Highway research
board.
Highway research abstracts. Issued by the Highway research
board of the National research council. Highway research
information service. no. 1– May 1931–
Washington, D. C. [1931–

TE151
N38
National Research Council. Highway Research
Board.
Highway Research Census. Prepared by [the]
Committee on Research Activities, American
Association of State Highway Officials and
[the Highway Research Board] Washington,
D. C. [1939]
1 v. 28cm.

Cover title: Highway research projects.

1.Highway research - Census. I.Title.
II.Title: Highway research projects.
III.American Association of State High-
way Officials. Committee on Research Activit-

NN 0062957 NcRS ViU

National Research Council. Highway Research
Board.
Highway research news
see under title

National research council. *Highway research board.*
Highway research, 1920–1940, prepared by Committee on
research activities, American association of state highway officials, F. V. Reagel, chairman, and Highway research board,
R. W. Crum, director; edited by A. R. Rankin. [Washington]
Highway research board, Division of engineering and industrial research, National research council and American association of state highway officials [1940]
vi, 133 p. 24ᵐ.

Z7295.N32

———— Supplement. 1942–   [Washington,
1942–
v. 24ᵐ.

Editor: 1942–   Fred Burggraf.

1. Roads—U. S.—Bibl. I. American association of state highway
officials. Committee on research activities. II. Rankin, Ardery Robert,
1910–   ed. III. Burggraf, Fred, ed. IV. Title.

40-31898 Revised

Library of Congress   Z7295.N32 Suppl.
[3]   016.6257

NN 0062960   DLC Or ICJ OC1 OU CU PSt FMU MH-GM

National Research Council. Highway Research
Board.
Highway research organizations

see under

Campbell, Moses Earl.

National research council. *Highway research board.*
... Highway research projects in the United States; results
of census by Advisory board on highway research, Division
of engineering, National research council, in cooperation with
the Bureau of public roads, United States Department of
agriculture, by William Kendrick Hatt ... Washington,
D. C., Published by the National research council of the
National academy of sciences, 1922.
cover-title, ii, 168 p. diagr. 25 cm. (Bulletin of the National research council. no. 21 (v. 4, pt. 3) Oct. 1922)
1. Highway research. I. U. S. Bureau of public roads. II. Hatt,
William Kendrick, 1868–

Q11.N292 no. 21   23—18691
———— Copy 4.   TE23.N6 1922

NN
0062962   DLC WaTC OrPT CaBVaU OrU MiU OO OU

National Research Council. Highway Research
Board.
Highway research review
see under title

TE1
.N43
no.53
1952
National Research Council. Highway Research
Board.

Highway sufficiency ratings. Presented at
the thirty-first annual meeting, January
1952.
69 p. diagrs. 25cm. (Its Bulletin, no. 53)

National Research Council. Publications, no. 228.

1. Roads—Testing. I. Title. II. Ser. III.
Ser.

NN 0062964 ViU OC1W DI NIC

VOLUME 407

TE
.7
N28
no.92
Engi-
neering
National research council. Highway research
board.
Highway-user taxation, presented at the
thirty-third annual meeting, January
12-15, 1954. Washington, 1954.
48p. illus. 25cm. (Its Bulletin 92)

National research Council. Publication 340.

1. Automobiles - Taxation. 2. Motor
fuels - Taxation. I. Title. (Series)

PU-W
NN 0062965   MU NBuU MtU CaBViP MH-L ViU GAT

NA9325
.G6
National research council. Highway research
board.
Gordon, George B
... Highway war memorials, by George B. Gordon ... Washington, D. C., Highway research board, 1945.

TE1
.N43
no.35
1951
National Research Council. Highway Research
Board.
Highways with a narrow median. Washington,
1951.
95 p. illus. 25cm. (Its Bulletin, no. 35)

1. Roads—U. S. 2. Roads—Construction. I. Ser.

NN 0062967   ViU NBuU

National Research Council. Highway Research
Board.
Implications of sociological research for
urban passenger transportation policy
see under Meyerson, Margy Ellin.

National Research Council. Highway Research
Board.
Index to Proceedings
see under National Research Council.
Highway Research Board. Meeting.
Proceedings.

National Research Council. *Highway Research Board.*
Index to publications
see its
Publication index.

National Research Council. *Highway Research Board.*
Intergovernmental cooperation in highway affairs; a
recommended action program for effective relationships.
Washington, 1953.
iv, 7 p. 25 cm. (*Its* Special report 9)
National Research Council. Publication 267.
Bibliography: p. 7.

1. Roads—U.S. I. Title. (Series. Series: National Research
Council. Publication 267)

HE355.N3   388.1   54–809

ViU LU MiU IaU
NN 0062971   DLC FTaSU UU MtBC PSt PPT PU-W N NcD

TE
7
N28
no.66
Engi-
neering
National Research Council. Highway Research
Board.
Intergovernmental relationships in highway affairs. Presented at the thirty-second
annual meeting, January 13-16, 1953.
Washington,1953.
15p. 25cm. (Its Bulletin, 66)

National Research Council. Publication
255.
Includes bibliography.

NN 0062972   MU NBuU

National Research Council. Highway Research
Board.
Investigation of wind forces on highway
bridges ...
see under National Research Council.
Highway Research Board. Committee on Bridges.

National Research Council. *Highway Research Board.*
Investigational concrete pavements; progress reports of
cooperative research projects on joint spacing, State Highway Departments of California, Kentucky, Michigan, Minnesota, Missouri, Oregon and the Public Roads Administration. Washington, Highway Research Board, Division of
Engineering and Industrial Research, National Research
Council, 1945.
108 p. illus., diagrs. 24 cm. (*Its* Research reports, no. 3B)
"Structural efficiency of transverse weakened-plane joints, by Earl
C. Sutherland ... and Harry D. Cashell": p. 80–108.
1. Pavements, Concrete. 2. Roads, Experimental.   I. Sutherland,
Earl Chalmers. II. Cashell, Harry D. III. Series.

TE278.N34   625.84   48–2189*

NN 0062974   DLC MoU UU ViU

National Research Council. Highway Research
Board.
Joint, crack, and undersealing materials
see under Lovell, Charles William.

National Research Council. Highway Research
Board.
Laboratory analysis of soils ...
see under National Research Council.
Highway Research Board. Dept. of Soils.

TE7
.N28
subser.
National Research Council. Highway Research
Board.
Land acquisition.
Washington.

S
711
N275
National Research Council. Highway Research
Board.
Land acquisition and control of adjacent
area. Presented at the thirty-first annual
meeting, January 1952. Washington, D.C.,
1952.
iv, 56 p. illus 25 cm. (Its Bulletin
55)

1. Eminent domain. U.S. 2. Roads. U.S.
3. Roadside improvement. I. Title.

NN 0062978   N ViU NBuU

TE1
.N43
no.10
1948
National Research Council. Highway
Research Board.
... Land acquisition and control of
highway access and adjacent areas, including special papers. Washington, 1948.
42 p. illus. 25cm. (Its Bulletin, no. 10)

1. Right of way—U.S. 2. Highway law—U. S.
I. Title. II. Ser.

NN 0062979   ViU

National Research Council. Highway Research
Board.
Land acquisition and control of highway
access and adjacent areas. Report of committee and four papers presented at the
twenty-eighth annual meeting, 1948. Washington, 1949.
iv, 40 p. illus. 25cm. (Its Bulletin no. 18)

1. Right of way—U. S. 2. Highway law—U. S.
I. Title. II. Ser.

NN 0062980   ViU NBuU NIC Or

National Research Council. Highway Research
Board.
Landslides; a selected annotated bibliography.
see under Tompkin, Jessie M.

TE1
.N43
no.54
1952
National Research Council. Highway Research
Board.
Load capacity of roads affected by frost.
Presented at the thirty-first annual meeting,
January, 1952. Washington, 1952.
17 p. illus. 25cm. (Its Bulletin, no. 54)
National Research Council. Publication, no. 232.

1. Roads—Frost damage. I. Title. II. Ser.
III. Ser.

NN 0062982   ViU NBuU MU

NATIONAL RESEARCH COUNCIL. Highway Research Board
Load-carrying capacity of frost-affected roads;
presented at the thirty-third annual meeting,
January 12-15, 1954. Washington, 1955.
23 p. illus., diagrs., tables. (Its Bulletin
96)

National Research Council. Publication 344.

1. Roads - Frost damage. I. Title.

NN 0062983   GAT ViU

TE1
.N43
no.40
1951
National Research Council. Highway Research
Board.
Load carrying capacity of roads as affected
by frost action. Washington, National
Research Council, 1951.
38 p. diagrs. 25cm. (National research
Council. Highway Research Board. Bulletin, no. 40)
"Presented at the thirtieth annual meeting, 1951."
Bibliography: p. 38.
1. Roads—Frost damage. I. Title. II. Ser.

NN 0062984   ViU NBuU

National Research Council. Highway Research
Board.
Maintenance costs. Presented at the
twenty-ninth annual meeting, 1949. Washington, D. C., 1950.
20 p. diagrs. 25cm. (Its Bulletin, no. 29)

1. Roads—Maintenance and repair. I. Ser.

NN 0062985   ViU

VOLUME 407

National Research Council. Highway Research
Board.

Maintenance costs. Report of Committee
and two papers presented at the twenty-
eighth annual meeting. Washington, 1949.
14 p. diagrs. 25cm. (Its Bulletin no. 21)

1. Roads—Maintenance and repair. I. Ser.

NN   0062986   ViU

National Research Council. Highway Research Board.

Maintenance methods for preventing and correct-
ing the pumping action of concrete pavement slabs.
Washington, D. C., 1947.
30 p. illus. 23cm. (Its current road problems.
No. 4-R. Rev. ed.)
At head of title: Highway Research Board, Division
of Engineering and Industrial Research, National Research
Council.

1. Roads—Maintenance and repair. 2. Pavements,
Concrete. I. Title. II. Ser.

NN   0062987   ViU

TE   National Research Council. Highway Research
7   Board.
N28   Manpower needs in highway engineering.
no.106   Presented at the thirty-fourth annual meeting,
Engi-   January 11-14, 1955. Washington,1955.
neering   30p. 25cm. (Its Bulletin, 106)

National Research Council. Publication, 357)

1. Road construction. 2. Manpower - U. S.
I. Title. (Series)

NN   0062988   MU ViU NBuU

National Research Council. *Highway Research Board.*
   Mapping and subsurface exploration for engineering purposes. Washington, 1952.
   iii, 54 p. illus., maps. 25 cm. (*Its* Bulletin 65)
   National Academy of Sciences-National Research Council publication 252.

   1. Soil-surveys—Addresses, essays, lectures. 2. Geology—Maps—
Addresses, essays, lectures. 3. Road materials—Addresses, essays,
lectures.   i. Title   (Series. Series: National Research Council.
Publication 252)

TE7.N28 no. 65   67-7232

NN   0062989   DLC NBuU PPD DI ViU

UG330   National Research Council. Highway Research
.N4   Board.

Nelson, Harold Easton.
   Military road construction in foreign theaters. Presented
at the twenty-eighth annual meeting, 1948. Washington,
Highway Research Board, Division of Engineering and Industrial Research, National Research Council, 1949.

Egleston
D625.7
N2132
National research council. Highway research
   board.
   [Miscellaneous publications.

   Unbound pamphlets.

   1. Roads - U. S.

NN   0062991   NNC

TE1   National Research Council. Highway Research
.N43   Board.
no.56
1952   Night visibility. Presented at the
thirty-first annual meeting, January, 1952.
Washington, 1952.
   77 p. illus. 25cm. (Its Bulletin, no. 56)
   National Research Council. Publication, no. 236.
   Includes bibliographies.

   1. Automobiles—Lighting. I. Title. II.
Title: Visibility. III. Ser. IV. Ser.

NN   0062992   ViU NBuU PPD NNC

TE1   National Research Council. Highway Research
.N43   Board.
no.89
1954   Night visibility. Presented at the thirty-
third annual meeting, January 12-15, 1954.
Washington, 1954
   75 p. illus. 25cm. (Its Bulletin, 89)
   National Research Council. Publication, 323.
   Includes bibliographies.

   1. Night vision. I. Ser. II. Ser.

NN   0062993   ViU NBuU IEdS

National Research Council. Highway Research
   Board.
   Off-street parking
      see under   National Research Council.
Highway Research Board. Committee on Parking.

National Research Council. Highway Research
   Board.
   One-way streets. Panel discussion held
at the twenty-ninth annual meeting, 1949.
Washington, 1950.
   33 p. 28cm. (Its Bulletin, no. 32)

   1. Streets. 2. Traffic engineering. I. Title.
II. Ser.

NN   0062995   ViU NBuU

National research council. *Highway research board.*
   Organization, aims and activities of the Highway research
board. [Washington, D. C.] Division of engineering and industrial research, National research council [1935]
   1 p. l., 16 p., 1 l. 25½ᵐ.

Library of Congress   TE1.N468   37-15084
                                    [3]   625.706273

NcRS
NN   0062996   DLC OrCS Wa Or ICJ OC1 UU NIC NcD NN

Avery
AC
N2145
no.76
National Research Council. Highway Research
   Board.
   Origin and destination surveys; methods
and costs. Presented at the thirty-second
annual meeting, January 13-16, 1953.
Washington, D. C., 1953.
   v, 65 p. illus. 25cm. (Its Bulletin 76)

National Research Council. Publication
269.

NN   0062997   NNC PU-W N ViU

National Research Council. Highway Research
   Board.
   Parking. Eight papers presented at the
28th annual meeting, 1948
      see under   National Research Council.
Highway Research Board. Committee on Parking.

TEL   National Research Council. Highway
B85   Research Board.
no.15   Parking. Report of committee and
three papers presented at the 27th
annual meeting, 1947. Washington,
1948.
   31 p.   (Its Bulletin 15)
   National Research Council. Publication.

   1. Automobile parking. I. T.
Series.

NN   0062999   NBuU PPCPC ViU NIC PPT

National Research Council. Highway Research
   Board.
   Parking and buying habits of a store's
customer
      see its   Parking as a factor in business.

National Research Council. Highway Research
   Board.
   Parking and its relationship to business
      see its   Parking as a factor in business.

National Research Council. *Highway Research Board.*
   Parking as a factor in business: containing five papers
presented at the thirty-second annual meeting, January 13-
16, 1953. Washington, 1953 [i. e. 1954]
   xxv, 321 p. illus., maps (3 fold.) 28 cm. (*Its* Special report 11)
   National Research Council. Publication 273.
   Bibliography: p. 309-321.
——— Shopper attitudes, a supplement. Washington,
1955.
   iv, 71 p. maps, diagrs., tables. 28 cm. (*Its* Special report 11-A)
   National Research Council. Publication 273a.
                                             HE371.A2N32 Suppl. a

——— Shopping habits and travel patterns, a supplement. Presented at the thirty-fourth annual meeting, January 11-14, 1955. Washington, 1955.
   v, 21 p. map, diagrs., tables. 28 cm. (*Its* Special report 11-B)
   National Research Council. Publication 273b.
   Bibliography: p. 20-21.
                                             HE371.A2N32 Suppl. b

——— Parking and buying habits of a store's customers, a supplement. Presented at the thirty-fifth annual
meeting, January 17-20, 1956. Washington, 1956.
   v, 18 p. map, diagrs., forms, tables. 28 cm. (*Its* Special report
11-C)
   National Research Council. Publication 273c.
                                             HE371.A2N32 Suppl. c

——— Parking and its relationships to business; summary report of project. Washington, 1956.
   iv, 16 p. diagrs., table. 28 cm. (*Its* Special report 11-D)
   National Research Council. Publication 273d.
                                             HE371.A2N32 Suppl. d
   1. Automobile parking—U. S. 2. Retail trade—U. S. 3. Real property—Valuation—U. S.   i. Title. ii. Title: Shopper attitudes. iii.
Title: Shopping habits and travel patterns. iv. Title: Parking and
buying habits of a store's customers. v. Title: Parking and its relationships to business.   (Series. Series: National Research Council.
Publication 273, 273a—

HE371.A2N32   388.3   54-61500 rev

PPBMR MtBC WaTC WaT N IEN IaU
OC1 PPD LU NIC GEU-B PPCPC GU MsU FTaSU OC1U OC1W
NN   0063005   DLC LU NcD PP PSt PU-W PU-FA PPT ViU

National Research Council. Highway Research
   Board.
   Parking meters

   see under

   Levin, David Richard, 1913-

National Research Council. Highway Research Board.
   Parking requirements in zoning ordinances

   see under

   Levin, David Richard, 1913-

VOLUME 407

National research council. Highway research board.

... Patching concrete pavements with concrete. Washington, D.C., Highway research board, 1943.
16 p. tab. diagrs. 23cm. (Its Wartime road problems no.6)
Dated July 1943.

1. Roads—Maintenance and repair. 2. Pavements, Concrete. I. Title. II. Ser.

NN 0063008 ViU CaBViP

TE1
B85
no.36
National Research Council. Highway Research Board.
Pavement marking. Presented at the 30th annual meeting, 1951. Washington, 1951.
24 p. (Its Bulletin 36)

National Research Council. Publication.

1. Road marking. I. T. Series.

NN 0063009 NBuU ViU

TE1
.N43
no.57
1952
National Research Council. Highway Research Board.

Pavement-marking materials. Presented at the thirty-first annual meeting, January, 1952. Washington, 1952.
128 p. illus. 25cm. (Its Bulletin, no. 57)
National Research Council. Publication, no. 239.
Includes bibliographies.

1. Pavements. I. Title. II. Ser. III. Ser.

NN 0063010 ViU NBuU

TE1
B85
no.20
National Research Council. Highway Research Board.
Pavement performance. Two papers presented at the 28th annual meeting, 1948. Washington, 1949.
70 p. (Its Bulletin 20)

National Research Council. Publication.

1. Pavements. I. T. Series.

NN 0063011 NBuU ViU

TE1
.N43
no.52
1952
National Research Council. Highway Research Board.

Performance of concrete pavement on granular subbase. Presented at the thirty-first annual meeting, January 1952. Washington, 1952.
36 p. illus. 25cm. (Its Bulletin, no. 52)
National Research Council. Publication, no. 226.
Bibliography: p. 23.
1. Pavements, Concrete. I. Title: Granular subbase. II. Ser. III. Ser.

NN 0063012 ViU NBuU

535.5
N213p
National Research Council—Highway Research Board.
The polarized headlight system. By Edwin H. Land, J. H. Hunt and Val J. Roper. Presented at the twenty-seventh annual meeting, 1947. Washington, D.C., Highway Research Board, Division of Engineering and Industrial Research, National Research Council, 1948.
iv, 36p. illus. 25cm. (Its Bulletin no.11)

NN 0063013 IU

TE1
.N43
no.39
1951
National Research Council. Highway Research Board.

Precasting highway bridges and structures. Washington, 1951.
19 p. illus. 25cm. (Its Bulletin, no. 39)
Bibliography: p. 18–19.

1. Bridges—Construction. I. Title. II. Ser.

NN 0063014 ViU NBuU

National Research Council. Highway Research Board.
Prevention of moisture loss in soil-cement with bituminous materials
see under National Research Council. Highway Research Board. Committee on Soil-Cement Roads.

National research council. Highway research board.

Conference on highway economics, *Agricultural and mechanical college of Texas,* 1941.
... Proceedings of the Conference on highway economics conducted by the School of engineering of the Agricultural and mechanical college of Texas in cooperation with the Highway research board of the National research council, College Station, Texas, February 24–28, 1941 ... College Station, Tex. ₁1941₎

National Research Council. Highway Research Board.
Proceedings of the annual meeting
see under National Research Council. Highway Research Board. Meeting.

NATIONAL RESEARCH COUNCIL. Highway research board.
Publication. 1–362 (incomplete)
Washington, 1946–62. no. 25–28cm.

Beginning with no. 47 issued in the series of Publications of the National research council.
Superseded by Highway research record.

1. Roads—Per. and soc. publ.

NN 0063018 NN

National Research Council. *Highway Research Board.*
Publication index. 1921–49—
Washington.

v. 25 cm.

Title varies: 1921–49, Index of publications.
Issue for 1950–55 called supplement to 1921–49 issue.

1. Roads—Bibl.—Catalogs. 2. Transportation, Automotive—Bibl.—Catalogs. 3. Airports—Bibl.—Catalogs.

Z7295.N325 50–11761 rev

WaS Or ICU N
NCU NjR NN IU ViU MB PSC DNAL IEN NNC MtBC WaT OrP
NN 0063019 DLC MiU OU ICJ AAP KU TxU OrPS CLSU

625.706
N277c
no.9-2R
National Research Council. Highway Research Board.
Recommended practice for snow removal and treatment of icy pavements. Washington, D.C., 1948.
17 p. illus. 23cm. (Its Current road problems, no.9-2R, 2d rev.)
By the Dept. of Maintenance, Committee on Snow and Ice Removal.

1. Snow - Removal.

NN 0063020 CSt

TE1
.N43
no.34
1951
National Research Council. Highway Research Board.

Reflectors and night visibility. Presented at the twenty-ninth annual meeting, 1949. Washington, 1951.
54 p. illus. 26cm. (Its Bulletin, no. 34)

1. Automobiles—Lighting. I. Title. II. Ser.

NN 0063021 ViU NBuU

National Research Council. *Highway Research Board.*
Relocation of public utilities due to highway improvement: an analysis of legal aspects. Washington, 1955.

vii, 204 illus., profiles, tables. 29 cm. (*Its* Special report 21)
National Research Council. Publication 353.
Bibliography: p. 201.
Appendices (p. ₁85₎–199) : A. Table of State statutory and constitutional provisions concerning occupancy of State highways by public utilities.—B. Digest of selected cases affecting public utility relocation.

1. Highway law—U. S. 2. Public utilities—U. S. I. Title.
(Series. Series: National Research Council. Publication 353)

388.1 55—14571

MtBC NcU IaU
NN 0063022 DLC UU FTaSU FU ViU NcD PSt MiU DI

TE
1
N36
National Research Council. Highway Research Board.
Report. 1946–
Washington.
v. illus. 28 cm.

1. Highway research.

NN 0063023 LU NcRS MiU

National Research Council—Highway Research Board
Report of a study of the highway laws. ...
Wash., D.C., 1948–

pt. 1–

NN 0063024 OCl

National research council. Highway research board.
U. S. *Bureau of public roads.*
... Report to Congress on study and research of traffic conditions and measures for their improvement, June 30, 1937. Letter from the acting secretary of agriculture transmitting a report on the investigation of traffic conditions, with recommendations ... Washington, U. S. Govt. print. off., 1937.

National research council. *Highway research board.*
... Reports and special papers presented at the ... annual meeting.

Washington, D. C., 19
v. illus., diagrs. 27½cm.
At head of title, 19 : Highway research board, Division of engineering and industrial research, National research council. Committee on roadside development.
Cover-title, 19 : Roadside development.
Reproduced from type-written copy.
Editor: 19 Fred Burggraf.
1. Roadside improvement. I. Burggraf, Fred, ed.

44–28685 Revised

Library of Congress TE153.N35
₁r45c2₎ 625.77

NN 0063026 DLC DI NcD OU TxU

National Research Council. Highway Research Board.
Requirements for off-street automobile parking facilities in zoning and other local ordinances
see under Levin, David Richard, 1913–

VOLUME 407

TE1
.N43
no.63
1952

National Research Council. Highway Research
Board.
Resealing joints and cracks in concrete
pavements (Minnesota). Presented at the
thirty-first annual meeting, January 1952.
Washington, 1952.
19 p. illus. 25cm. (Its Bulletin, 63)
National Research Council. Publication, 248.

1. Pavements, Concrete. I. Title. II. Ser.
III. Ser.

NN   0063028   ViU NBuU

National Research Council. Highway Research
Board.
Research abstracts. Highway research
information service

see

Highway research abstracts.

National Research Council. Highway Research
Board.
Research reports, no.1-
1945-   Washington, D.C., 1945-
v. incl.illus.

1. Highway engineering - Collected works.
2. Roads - U. S.   I. Title.

CaBVaU OrP Or OrCS Wa
NN   0063030   ScU DLC LU KyU AAP MiD MB OrCS IdU ICJ

National Research Council. Highway Research
Board.
Right-of-way problems
see under   National Research Council.
Highway Research Board. Committee on Land
Acquisition and Control of Highway Access and
Adjacent Areas.

TE
7
N28
no.27
Engi-
neering

National Research Council. Highway Research
Board.
Road surface properties; report of Committee
and paper on rubber in bituminous pavement.
Presented at the 29th annual meeting, 1949.
Washington,1950.
24p. illus. 25cm. (Its Bulletin, 27)

Includes bibliography.

1. Pavements. 2. Pavements, Bituminous.
I. Title. (Series)

NN   0063032   MU ViU NBuU

S
625.84
qN277pr

National Research Council. Highway Research
Board.
Road test One-MD, a progress report;
papers presented at the annual meeting of the
Highway Research Board, January 9-12, 1951.
(Washington, 1951)
49 p. illus. 28 cm.

1. Pavements. Concrete. I. Title.

NN   0063033   N

625.84
qN277

National Research Council. Highway Research
Board.
Road test one-MD; brief description and
summary of major findings. (n.p.)1952.
17l. 28 cm.

1. Pavements. Concrete. I. Title.

NN   0063034   N

TE1
.N43
no.60
1952

National Research Council. Highway Research
Board.
Road-user characteristics. Presented at
the thirty-first annual meeting, January, 1952.
66 p. illus. 25cm. (Its Bulletin, 60)

National Research Council. Publication, 244.

Bibliography: p. 66.

1. Automobile drivers. 2. Accidents—Prevention.
I. Title. II. Ser.

NN   0063035   ViU IEdS

National research council. *Highway research board.*
Roadside development

see its

Reports and special papers presented at the ... annual
meeting.

National Research Council. *Highway Research Board.*
Roadsides: their use and protection. Presented at the
thirty-second annual meeting, January 13–16, 1953. Washington, 1954.
iii, 48 p. illus. 28 cm. (*Its* Special report 17)
National Research Council. Publication 290.

1. Roadside improvement. I. Title.   (Series. Series: National Research Council. Publication 290)

TE153.N3574   625.77   54–61889

FTaSU MU MtBC IaU UU
NN   0063037   DLC NcD PPCPC PPT PSt DNAL ViU MiD

TE1
B85
no.37

National Research Council. Highway
Research Board.
Roughness and skid resistance. Presented at the 30th annual meeting,
1951. Washington, 1951.
55 p.   (Its Bulletin 37)

National Research Council Publication.

1. Roads. I. T. Series.

NN   0063038   NBuU ViU

HE
371
.A2
N3

National research council. Highway research
board.
... Route selection and traffic assignment.
A compendium of correspondence relating to a
suggested technique. (Washington,D.C.?) Highway research board correlation service, 1950.
ii,79 (i.e.89) numb.l. illus. 28 cm.
Leaves 7-16 duplicated in foliation.

1. Traffic engineering—U.S. I. Title.

NN   0063039   MiU

National research council. *Highway research board.*
Rural traffic problems; papers at the eighteenth annual meet-
ing, by the Committee on rural traffic and safety problems,
Department of traffic, Highway research board. Washington,
D. C., Highway research board, Division of engineering and
industrial research, National research council, 1939.
cover-title, 51 l. diagrs. 27cm.
Leaves variously numbered.

1. Traffic regulations—U. S. 2. Roads—U. S.   I. Title.   42–43341

Library of Congress   HE371.A2N33
(2)   388.30973

NN   0063040   DLC UU IU

National research council. Highway research board.
... Salvaging old high type flexible pavements.
Washington, D.C., Highway research board, 1945.
25 p. incl. illus., tables. 23cm. (Its Wartime road
problems no.10)
Dated April 1945.

1. Pavements. 2. Roads—U.S. I. Title. II. Ser.

NN   0063041   ViU

TE1
B85
no.47

National Research Council. Highway
Research Board.
Salvaging old pavements by resurfacing. Presented at the 30th
annual meeting, January 9, 1951.
Washington, 1952.
35 p.   (Its Bulletin 47)

National Research Council. Publication 245.

NN   0063042   NBuU

National Research Council. *Highway Research Board.*
A selected bibliography on highway safety (annotated)
(Washington) 1947.
v, 45 p. 23 cm. (*Its* Bibliography, no. 2)
Cover title.
———— Supplement. (Washington) 1949–
v. 23 cm. (*Its* Bibliography, no. 2)
Z7164.T81N32 Suppl.

1. Traffic accidents—Bibl.   (Series)

Z7164.T81N32   016.614862   48–24219 rev*

IaU UU CoU MsU Or OrCS OrP WaS MB NIC ICarbS
NN   0063043   DLC FTaSU PPD PPCPC NNC TxU IU ViU

R016.526982
N277s

National Research Council. Highway Research
Board.
A selected list of references on aerial
surveying and mapping, 1929-1949. Compiled
by the staff of the Highway Research Board.
Washington, D. C. (1949?)
9 p. 28cm.

1. Aerial photogrammetry. I. Title:
Aerial surveying   and mapping, 1929-
1949.

NN   0063044   FU MtBC

National Research Council. Highway Research
Board.
Shopper attitudes
see its   Parking as a factor in business.

National Research Council. Highway Research
Board.
Shopping habits and travel patterns
see its   Parking as a factor in business.

National Research Council. Highway Research
Board.
Silicate of soda as a soil stabilizing agent
see under   Laws, W. Derby.

National Research Council. Highway Research
Board.
Soil and soil-aggregate stabilization

see under

Symposium on the Science of Soil Stabilization.
Washington, 1955.

ST
9138
.671
.35

National Research Council. Highway Research
Board.
Soil-bituminous roads. Washington, 1946.
52 p. illus. 23 cm. (Its Current road
problems,12)

Hans F.Winterkorn, chairman of the
Committee on Soil-Bituminous Roads.
Bibliography: p.43-44.

1.Roads - U.S. 2.Pavements, Bituminous.
I.Winterkorn,   Hans Friedrich, 1905-

NN   0063049   NjP NIC ViU

VOLUME 407

TE1
.N43
no.42
1951

National Research Council. Highway Research
Board.

Soil compaction. Washington, National
Research Council, 1951.
20 p. illus. 25cm. (National Research
Council. Highway Research Board. Bulletin, no. 42)
"Presented at the thirtieth annual meeting, 1951."
Bibliography: p. 20.

1. Soil mechanics. I. Title. II. Ser.

NN   0063050   ViU NBuU DNAL

NATIONAL RESEARCH COUNCIL. Highway Research Board.
Soil density and stability; presented at the
thirty-third annual meeting, January 12-15, 1954.
Washington, 1954.
64 p. illus., diagrs., tables. (Its Bulletin
93)

National Research Council. Publication 341.
Includes bibliographies.

1. Soil stabilization. I. Title.

NN   0063051   GAT ViU MtU

4021A.54
National Research Council. Highway Research
Board.
Soil exploration and mapping. Presented at
thr 29th annual meeting, 1949. Washington,
1950.
iii, 121 p. illus., maps (1 fold. in pocket)
25cm. (Its Bulletin, no. 28)
Includes bibliographies.

1. Soils (Engineering) 2. Geophysics.
I. Title.

NN   0063052   MB CaBVa IEN ViU NBuU NIC

TE1
B85
no.100

National Research Council. Highway
Research Board.
Soil freezing. Presented at the
33rd annual meeting, January 12-15,
1954. Washington, 1955.
35 p. (Its Bulletin 100)

National Research Council. Publication 348.

1. Soil freezing. I. T. Series.
Series: National Research Council.
Publication   348.

NN   0063053   NBuU GAT ViU PSt CSt DNAL DAS OClW

4021A.70
National Research Council. Highway Research
Board.
Soil mechanics and soil stabilization, ed.
by Roy W. Crum. Washington [c1939]
433 p. illus. 25cm.
Pt. II of the Proceedings of its eighteenth
annual meeting held at Washington, D. C., Nov.
28-Dec. 2, 1938.

1. Soils (Engineering) I. Crum, Roy Winchester, 1885-   ed. II. Title.

NN   0063054   MB

Q11
N2934
no.260

National Research Council. Highway Research
Board.
Soil stabilization; presented at the thirty-
second annual meeting, January 13-16, 1953.
Washington, D. C., 1953.
v, 57 p. illus., diagrs., tables. 25 cm.
(National Research Council. Publication 260)
At head of title: Highway Research Board.
Bulletin 69.
Bibliographies included.

1.Soil mechanics. I.Title. (Series. Series:
National Research   Council. Highway Research Board.   Bulletin 69)

NN   0063055   DI NBuU PSt ViU DNAL

290
N215St

National Research Council. Highway Research
Board.
Soil temperature and ground freezing.
Washington, 1953.
124 p. (Its Bulletin no. 71)

National Research Council. Publication,
262.

NN   0063056   DNAL NBuU PSt CSt

285
N21

National Research Council. Highway Research
Board.
Soils committee reports and special papers
presented at the twenty-seventh annual meeting,
1947. Washington, 1948.
40 p. (Its Bulletin, n° 14)

1. Roads. Research. 2. Soil (Engineering)
I. National Research Council. Highway Research
Board. Bulletin.no.14. II. Title: Frost heave
and frost action in soil.

NN   0063057   DNAL ViU NBuU

National Research Council. Highway Research
Board.
Some economic effects of highway improve-
ment
see under National Research Council.
Highway Research Board. Dept. of Economics,
Finance and Administration.

National Research Council. Highway Research
Board.
Special report
see HRB Special report.

National research council. *Highway research board.*
... Speed regulation and control on rural highways; report of a special investigation by Raymond G. Paustian ...
[Washington, D. C.] Highway research board, 1940.
87 p. incl. tables, diagrs. 24½ cm.
At head of title: Highway research board, Division of engineering
and industrial research, National research council.
"The Highway research board arranged the project under the sponsorship of the Public roads administration and with the cooperation of
the National safety council."—Foreword.
"References": p. 87.

1. Speed limits—U. S.   1. U. S.   Bureau of public roads.   II. National safety council.   III. Paustian, Raymond George.   IV. Title.

HE371.A2N34   388.30973   41-13823

NN   0063060   DLC CU OU NNC ICJ NN

TE1
B85
no.51

National Research Council. Highway
Research Board.
Squeal of tires rounding curves.
Presented at the 31st annual meeting,
January, 1952. Washington, 1952.
16 p. (Its Bulletin 51)

National Research Council. Publication 223.

NN   0063061   NBuU ViU

NATIONAL RESEARCH COUNCIL. Highway Research Board.
Stabilization of soils; presented at the thirty-
third annual meeting, January 12-15, 1954. Washington, 1955.
52 p. illus., diagrs., tables. (Its Bulletin
98)

National Research Council. Publication 346.
Includes bibliographies.

1. Soil stabilization. I. Title.

NN   0063062   GAT IdU ViU OClW

National Research Council. Highway Research
Board.
State highway administrative bodies, a
study.
see under National Research Council.
Highway Research Board. Committee on Highway
Organization and Administration.

National Research Council. Highway Research
Board.
State highway department practices in
filling, sealing, and maintaining joints in
concrete pavements
see under National Research Council.
Highway Research Board. Committee on Joint
Material in Concrete Pavements.

TE153
.N36
no.12-F
1951

National Research Council. Highway
Research Board.

Stress distribution in a homogeneous soil.
Presented at the twenty-ninth annual meeting,
1949. Washington, 1951.
36 p. diagrs. 25cm. (Its Research report
no. 12-F)
Bibliography: p. 34.

1. Soil mechanics. 2. Strains and stresses.
I. Ser.

NN   0063065   ViU FU NNC MoU N

National Research Council. *Highway Research Board.*
Structural effects of heavy-duty trailer on concrete pave-
ment; a supplemental investigation to Road test one-MD.
Presented at the 32d annual meeting, Jan. 13-16, 1953.
Washington, 1953.
iii, 32 p. illus. 25 cm. (*Its* Special report 14)
National Research Council. Publication 283.

1. Pavements, Concrete. 2. Pavements — Testing.   I. Title.
(Series. Series: National Research Council. Publication 283)

TE278.N35   *625.7   625.84   54-61076

MiU ViU
NN   0063066   DLC MtBC IaU OClU FTaSU GU PSt NcD

RE 923
.N273

NATIONAL RESEARCH COUNCIL--Highway Research
Board
Studies in night visibility. Presented at
the 30th annual meeting, 1951. Washington,
1951.
51 p. illus. (Its Bulletin 43)

1. Night vision. 2. Automobiles--Lighting.
3. Automobile driving at night. I. Title.
Ser. Optom.cds.

NN   0063067   InU ViU NBuU IU NNC-M

TE1
.N43
no.45
1951

National Research Council. Highway Research
Board.

Subsurface drainage. Washington, 1951.
20 p. diagrs. 25cm. (Its Bulletins, no. 45)

1. Drainage. I. Title. II. Ser.

NN   0063068   ViU NBuU DNAL

National Research Council. Highway Research Board.
Summary bulletin of the proceedings of the annual meetings
...
[no.

Washington, D. C., 192   8°.
no.
1923-24 in 1 no., published in 1925.
1923-24; cover-title.
[1923-24] full title reads: Summary bulletin of the proceedings of the annual
meetings of the Highway Research Board. Division of Engineering and Industrial Research, National Research Council.

1. Roads—Assoc. and org.—U. S.
N. Y. P. L.   June 5, 1926

NN   0063069   NN ICU DLC CU

VOLUME 407

National Research Council. Highway Research
Board.
Surface drainage
see under   National Research Council.
Highway Research Board. Committee on Surface
Drainage of Highways.

National Research Council. *Highway Research Board.*
Survey and treatment of marsh deposits, annotated ¡by
A. W. Johnson, engineer of soils and foundations¡ Wash-
ington, 1954.
xi, 95 p. 28 cm. (*Its* Bibliography 15)
National Research Council. Publication 314.

1. Pavements—Abstracts. 2. Marshes—Abstracts.   I. Title.
(Series. Series : National Research Council. Publication 314)

TE250.N34   625.73082   54–60169

NIC CU UU
NN   0063071   DLC DNAL ViU MB TxU PSt IaU FTaSU CoU

256.1(200)
qN363sf National Research Council. Highway
Research Board.
¡Symposium: Frost heave and frost action
in soil; papers, January 1951. Washington?
n.d.¡
1 v. (various pagings) illus.,maps.
30 cm.
Incomplete; has 11 papers.
Reproduced from typewritten copy.
"Not released for publication."
S(200)   Also issued in the Board's Special
N363hs report no.2, 1   952, with title:
no.2   Frost action i   n soils; a

symposium presented at the 30th annual
meeting, January 9–12, 1951.

1.Frost. 2.Roads-Frost damage.
3.Soil physics. I.Title. II.Title: Frost
heave and frost action in soil.

NN   0063073   DI-GS

National Research Council. Highway Research
Board.
Symposium; investigations of the design
and control of asphalt paving mixtures ...
see under   United States. Army.
Corps of Engineers.

625.8   National Research Council--Highway Research
N215s   Board.
A symposium on soil-cement mixtures for
roads. Edited by Roy W. Crum.   Washington,
1937.
105p. illus., diagrs., tables. 25cm. (Its
Proceedings, 17th annual meeting, pt. 2, 1937)
At head of title: Division of Engineering
and Industrial Research, National Research
Council.

NN   0063075   IU

TE200   National research council. Highway research
.U6   board.
1936   U. S. *Bureau of mines.*
... Tabular summary of state specifications for liquid
asphaltic road materials in effect January 1, 1936. Published
by the United States Bureau of mines with the assistance of
the United States Bureau of public roads of the Department of
agriculture and the Highway research board of the National
research council ... ¡Washington¡ U. S. Govt. print. off., 1936.

TE1   National Research Council. Highway Research
.N43   Board.
no.102
1955   Tests on large culvert pipe. Presented
at the thirty-third annual meeting, January
12–15, 1954. Washington, 1955.
18 p. illus.   25cm. (Its Bulletin, 102)
National Research Council. Publication, 350.
Bibliography: p. 18.

1. Pipe—Testing. I. Ser. II. Ser.

NN   0063077   ViU NBuU

National Research Council. Highway Research
Board.
Thickness of flexible pavements. rev. ed.
Washington, 1949.
49 p. illus.   23cm. (Its Current road problems,
no. 8)
Bibliography: p. 47–49.

1. Pavements. 2. Road materials. I. Ser.

NN   0063078   ViU N OrP

National Research Council. *Highway Research Board.*
Time-saving methods in highway engineering. Washington, 1955–1956.
14 pts. (iv, 388 p.) 28 cm.

1. Road construction.   I. Title.

TE153.N35742   625.7   57—45322

NcU IU NIC MiU OU IaAS
NN   0063079   DLC CaBVa WaS Wa NN DP FU WaU PPCPC

TE1   National Research Council. Highway Research
.N43   Board.
no.74
1953   Traffic-accident studies. Presented at
the thirty-second annual meeting, January
13–16, 1953. Washington, 1953.
53 p. illus. 25cm. (Its Bulletin, 74)
National Research Council. Publication, 265.

1. Traffic accidents—U. S. I. Ser. II. Ser.

NN   0063080   ViU NBuU PU-W

TE1   National Research Council. Highway Research
.N43   Board.
no.61
1952   Traffic assignment. Presented at the
thirty-first annual meeting, January, 1952.
Washington, 1952.
70 p. illus. 25cm. (Its Bulletin, 61)
National Research Council. Publication, 246.

1. Traffic engineering. I. Title. II. Ser.
III. Ser.

NN   0063081   ViU NBuU PPCPC

National Research Council. *Highway Research Board.*
Traffic research problem statements, presented at the 31st
annual meeting, January 14–18, 1952. Washington, 1952.
33 p. 25 cm. (*Its* Special report, no. 3)

1. Traffic regulations—Congresses.   I. Title.

HE369.N33 1952i   325.702   53–1426 ‡

NN   0063082   DLC MtBC MiU LU NcD ViU UU

HE369   National Research Council. Highway Research
N33   Board.
1952a   Traffic research problem statements,
presented at the 31 st annual meeting, January
14–18, 1952. Washington, 1952.
33p. 25cm. (Its Special report, no.3)

Photocopy.   Ann Arbor, Mich., University
Microfilsm, 1970. 21cm.

1. Traffic regulations - Congresses. I.
Title.

NN   0063083   IaU FTaSU

TE1   National Research Council. Highway Research
.N43   Board.
no.41
1951   Traffic surveys by post cards. Washington,
National Research Council, 1951.
30 p. diagrs. 25cm. (National Research
Council. Highway Research Board. Bulletin no. 41)
"Presented at the thirtieth annual meeting, 1951."

1. Traffic surveys. I. Ser.

NN   0063084   ViU NBuU

TE   National Research Council. Highway Research
7   Board.
N28   Training highway-department personnel. Wash-
no.103 ington, D. C., 1955.
16 p. illus.   25 cm. (Its bulletin 103)
National Research Council. publication 351.
Presented at the thirty-third annual meeting,
Jan. 12–15, 1954.

1. Highway Departments—Employees. 2. Employees, Training of—   U. S. I. Title. sf

NN   0063085   IEdS NBuU ViU

388.2   National Research Council--Highway Research
N215t   Board.
Travel to commercial centers. Presented at
the 32d annual meeting, Jan. 13–16, 1953.
Washington, 1953.
v, 38p. illus. 25cm. (Its Bulletin 79)

National Academy of Sciences, National
Research Council. Publication 281.

NN   0063086   IU NIC ViU NBuU

National Research Council. Highway Research
Board.
Trends in land acquisition ...
see under   National Research Council.
Highway Research Board. Committee on Land
Acquisition and Control of Highway Access and
Adjacent Areas.

National Research Council. Highway Research
Board.
Trends in legislation for off-street parking
facilities

see under

U.S. Bureau of Public Roads.

NATIONAL RESEACH COUNCIL -HIGHWAY RESEACH
BOARD
The truck weight problem in highway transportation.   Author, 1949–1950?
112 p. in 5 v.

NN   0063089   Or

VOLUME 407

National Research Council. **Highway Research**
Board.

The truck weight problem in highway transportation. ₍Washington₎ 1950.
127 p. illus. 28cm. (Its Bulletin, no. 26)
Cover title.

Bibliography: p. 123-125.

1. Motor-trucks. 2. Transportation, Automotive.
I. Title. II. Ser.

NN 0063090 ViU

TE1
B85
no.109
National Research Council. Highway Research
Board.
Ungraded aggregates in bituminous mixes.
Presented at the 34th annual meeting, Jan-
uary 11-14, 1955. Washington, 1955.
49 p. (Its Bulletin, 109)

National Research Council. Publication, 361.

1. Pavements, Bituminous. I. T. Series.
Series: National Research Council. Publication. 361.

NN 0063091 NBuU ViU

388.2
N215u
National Research Council—Highway Research
Board.
Urban traffic congestion. Presented at the
33d annual meeting, Jan. 12-15, 1954. Wash-
ington, 1954.
iv, 39p. illus. 25cm. (Its Bulletin 86)

National Academy of Sciences, National
Research Council Publication 312.
Bibliography: p. 23-25.

NN 0063092 IU PU-W ViU PPCPC GAT MiD NBuU

Mann
Ref.
S
591
N27
National Research Council. Highway Re-
search Board.
The use of agricultural soil maps and the
status of agricultural soil mapping in the
United States. Presented at the Twenty-
Eighth annual meeting, 1948. Washington,
Highway Research Board, Division of Engi-
neering and Industrial Research, National
Research Council, 1949.
iii, 128 p. maps (part. fold.) tables.
26 cm. (Its Bulletin no. 22)

Cover title: Engineering use of agricultural soil maps.

NN 0063093 NIC ViU ICarbS DNAL FTaSU

625.706
N277c
no.13-R
National Research Council. Highway Research
Board.
Use of air-entrained concrete in pavements
and bridges. ₍Washington,D.C.₎ 1950.
74 p. illus. (Its Current road problems,
no. 13-R, rev. ed.)
By the Dept. of Materials and Construction,
Committee on Air-Entraining Concrete.
"References to the literature on air entrain-
ment": p. 63-74.

1. Concrete. 2.   Concrete - Testing. I.
Title: Air-ent   rained concrete.

NN 0063094 CSt OrP

National Research Council. Highway Research
Board.
Use of calcium chloride in granular
stabilization of roads
see under Cuthbert, Frederick Leicester,
1913-

TE1
.N45
no.33
1951
National Research Council. Highway Research
Board.
Use of parking motor revenues. Presented
at the twenty-ninth annual meeting, 1949.
Washington, 1951.
28 p. 25cm. (Its Bulletin, no. 33)

1. Parking meters. I. Ser.

NN 0063096 ViU NBuU

National research council. Highway research
board.
... Use of soil-cement mixtures for base
courses. Washington, D.C., Highway research
board, 1943.
30 p. illus. (incl. diagrs.) 23cm. (Its Wartime
road problems. no.7)
Dated October 1943.

1. Road materials. I. Title. II. Title: Soil-cement
mixtures for base courses. III. Ser.

NN 0063097 ViU

TE1
.N43
no.104
1955
National Research Council. Highway Research
Board.
Vehicle climbing lanes. Presented at the
thirty-fourth annual meeting, January 11-14,
1955. Washington, 1955.
33 p. illus. 25cm. (Its Bulletin, 104)
National Research Council. Publication, 354.
Bibliography: p. 11.

1. Highway research—U. S. I. Title. II. Ser.
III. Ser.

NN 0063098 ViU IEdS

TE1
B85
no.107
National Research Council. Highway Research
Board.
Vehicle operation as affected by traffic
control and highway type. Presented at the
34th annual meeting, January 11-14, 1955.
Washington, 1955.
62 p. (Its Bulletin 107)

National Research Council. Publication 358.

1. Traffic regulations. I. T. Series.
Series: National Research Council. Publication 358.

NN 0063099 NBuU PPCPC ViU

TE1
.N43
no.115
1955
National Research Council. Highway Research
Board.
Vertical sand drains for stabilization of
embankments. Presented at the thirty-fourth
annual meeting, January 11-14, 1955. Washington, 1955.
52 p. illus. 25cm. (Its Bulletin, 115)
National Research Council. Publication, 402.
Includes bibliographies.

1. Drainage. I. Ser.

NN 0063100 ViU NBuU

NATIONAL RESEARCH COUNCIL. Highway Research Board.
Vertical sand drains; presented at the thirty-
third annual meeting, January 12-15, 1954. Washington, 1954.
37 p. illus., diagrs., tables. (Its Bulletin,
90)

National Research Council. Publication 326.
Includes bibliography.

1. Road drainage. I. Title.

NN 0063101 GAT PU-Sc ViU

TE1
.N43
no.44
1951
National Research Council. Highway Research
Board.
Volcanic ash and laterite soils in high-
way construction. Washington, National
Research Council, 1951.
29 p. illus. 25cm. (Its Bulletin, no. 44)
Bibliography: p. 28-29.

1. Volcanic ash, tuff, etc. 2. Laterite. 3.
Roads—Construction. I. Ser.

NN 0063102 ViU NBuU

National Research Council. *Highway Research Board.*
The WASHO road test. Washington, 1954-55.
2 pts. illus., tables. 28 cm. (*Its* Special report 18, 22)
National Research Council. Publication 310, 360.
"Sponsored by the Western Association of State Highway Officials."
Contents.—pt. 1. Design, construction, and testing procedures.—
pt. 2. Test data, analyses, findings.

1. Road construction—Collected works. I. Title. (Series.
Series: National Research Council. Publication 310, etc.)

TE7.N32   625.7072   54-61901 rev

FU CaBViP IdU MtBC
NN 0063103   DLC FTaSU IaU PSt MiU ViU NcD DI UU

National Research Council. *Highway Research Board.*
Wartime road problems
see its
Current road problems.

TE
7
N28
no.50
Engi-
neering
National Research Council. Highway Research
Board.
Weighing vehicles in motion. Presented
at the thirty-first annual meeting, Jan., 1952.
Washington, 1952.
27 p. illus. 25cm. (Its Bulletin, 50)

1. Motor vehicles. 2. Weights and
measures. I. Title. (Series)

NN 0063105 MU NBuU CaBViP

National Research Council. Highway Research
Board.
What parking means to business...
see under Automotive Safety Foundation.

NATIONAL RESEARCH COUNCIL. Highway research
board.
Yearbook.
[Washington]   v.   25cm.

Members and committees.

1. Roads--Assoc. and org.--U.S.

NN 0063107 NN MiD

National Research Council. *Highway Research Board.*
Yearbook, December 1949. ₍Washington? 1950?₎
v, 51 p. diagr. 25 cm.

TE1.N467 1949   625.706273   51-29502

NN 0063108   DLC IU ICJ OrCS IdU OrP NN

VOLUME 407

710.1   National Research Council--Highway Research
N215z   Board.
         Zoning for truck-loading facilities, require-
         ments for off-street truck-loading-and-unload-
         ing facilities in zoning and other local
         ordinances ₍by₎ David R. Levin.   Washington,
         1952.
           x, 101p. illus. 25cm. (Its Bulletin 59)

           National Academy of Sciences - National
         Research Council. Publication 243.

NN   0063109   IU NcU CaBViP MoSW PPCPC NBuU

National Research Council. *Highway Research Board*
see also **Joint Committee on Roadside Development.**

National Research Council. Highway Research
  Board. Advisory Committee on Study of
  Parking and its Relationships to Business.
  What parking means to business
        see under   Automotive Safety Foundation

National Research Council. *Highway Research Board.* *An-*
nual Meeting
       see
National Research Council. *Highway Research Board.*
Meeting.

National Research Council. *Highway Research Board.*
Channelization Committee
       see
National Research Council. *Highway Research Board.*
Committee on Channelization.

National Research Council. *Highway Research Board.*
Bridges, Committee on
       see
National Research Council. *Highway Research Board.*
Committee on Bridges.

National Research Council. *Highway Research Board.*
Committee on Bridges.
   Distribution of load stresses in highway bridges; pre-
sented at the thirty-first annual meeting, January 1952.
Washington, 1952.
   v, 85 p. illus., tables. 25 cm. (₍National Research Council₎
Highway Research Board. Research report 14-B)
   National Academy of Sciences. National Research Council. Publi-
cation 253.
   Includes bibliographies.
   1. Strains and stresses. 2. Bridges.   (Series. Series: National
Research Council. Publication 253)

   TG265.N3   624.2   54-706

NN   0063115   DLC TxU PPD N ViU MsU MoU OrU

388.1   **National Research Council.   Highway Research**
qN27853   **Board.   Committee on Bridges.**
         Investigation of wind forces on highway
         bridges, presented at the thirty-second
         annual meeting, January 13-16, 1953. Washing-
         ton, 1953.
           ii, 30 p. illus., diagrs. 28 cm.
         (Highway Research Board. Special report 10)

           1. Bridges. 2. Wind-pressure. I. Title.
         Series: National Research Council. Highway
         Research Board.   Special Report 10)

NN   0063116   N IClU DAS

National research council. *Highway research board. Com-*
mittee on causes and prevention of highway accidents.
   Bibliography, street and highway safety, prepared **for the**
Committee on causes and prevention of highway accidents,
Highway research board, by the staff of the library of the
Bureau of public roads. Washington, D. C., Distributed by
Highway education board ₍1928?₎
   cover-title, 17 p. l., 388 numb. l. 27 x 20½ᵐ.

   Autographed from type-written copy.
   Introductory note signed : A. B. Fletcher, chairman.
   Caption title: Annotated index to articles on highway safety and
allied subjects.

   "Includes 2389 items from ... 177 American and foreign periodicals."
(List on p. l. 7-17)

   Classified with author index.

   1. Traffic regulations—Bibl. 2. Accidents—Prevention—Bibl. 3. Automobiles—Accidents—Bibl. 4. Highway law — Bibl. 5. Cities and
towns—Planning—Bibl.   I. U. S. Public roads administration. Library. II. Fletcher, Austin Bradstreet, 1872-1928. III. Title: Street and
highway safety, Bibliography.

   Library of Congress   Z7164.T81N3

                                              29—2906

NN   0063118   DLC WaS MtU OrP CoU ICRL CU TU ViU OCU

TE175
.N29   **National Research Council.** *Highway Research Board.*
          Committee on Channelization.
            Channelization; the design of highway intersections at
          grade. Washington, 1952.
            247 p. illus., plans. 28 x 44 cm. (Highway Research Board. Spe-
          cial report 5)
            Half title : Channelization ; a cooperative project. Committee on
          Channelization, Highway Research Board ₍and₎ Texas Engineering
          Experiment Station, Texas A. & M. College.
            1. Traffic engineering. 2. Roads—Design. I. Texas. Agricultural
          and Mechanical College, College Station. Engineering Experiment Sta-
          tion. II. Title.   (Series: National Research Council Highway Re-
          search Board. Special report 5)

                                              A 54—2851

          Michigan. Univ. Libr.
          for Library of Congress   ₍56e1₎

NN   0063119   MiU MtBC CaBVaU OrP CoU N ViU PSt DLC

625.7
N277b   **National research council. Highway research**
no.5   **board. Committee on compaction of subgrades**
           and embankments.
Science   Report of Committee on compaction of sub-
           grades and embankments; presented at the twenty-
           sixth annual meeting 1946. Washington, D.C.,
           Highway research board Division of engineering
           and industrial research, National research
           council, 1947.
             iv, 23p. 24cm. (National research council.
           Highway research board. Bulletin no. 5)
             1. Embankments.   2. Road construction. I.
           Title. II. Seri   es (contents)

NN   0063120   TxDaM PPT ViU Or NNC NBuU

National Research Council. *Highway Research Board.*
Committee on Durability of Concrete, Physical Aspects.
   Bibliography on durability of concrete, physical reactions;
annotated. ₍By the Committee on Durability of Concrete—
Physical Reactions. Washington₎ 1951.
   vii, 35 p. 28 cm. (National Research Council. Highway Research
Board. Bibliography no. 8)

   1. Concrete—Bibl.   (Series)

   Z5853.M4N3   016.62013   51-5135 rev

NN   0063121   DLC MB FTaSU TxU UU CoU ViU DI-GS

National Research Council. *Highway Research Board.*
Committee on Economics of Motor Vehicle Size and
Weight.
   Time and gasoline consumption in motor truck operation
as affected by the weight and power of vehicles and the rise
and fall in highways; report prepared by Carl Saal. Washington, Highway Research Board, Division of Engineering
and Industrial Research, National Research Council, 1950.
   v, 73 p. illus., diagrs., tables. 25 cm. (National Research Council.
Highway Research Board. Research report no. 9-A)
   1. Motor-trucks. 2. Automobiles—Fuel consumption. I. Saal,
Carl C. II. Title.   (Series)

   TL230.N27   629.2538   56-1

NN   0063122   DLC TxU FU N MoU ViU

366.2   National Research Council--Highway Research
N218c   Board--Committee on Effect of Controlled
            Access Expressways on Urban Areas.
            Controlled access expressways in urban a-
          reas, a symposium; report of Committee on
          Controlled Access Expressways in Urban Areas.
          Washington, Highway Research Board, Division
          of Engineering and Industrial Research, Na-
          tional Research Council, 1950.
            41p. (National Research Council. Highway
          Research Board. Bulletin no. 25)

NN   0063123   IU CaBVa NIC PPCPC NBuU

National Research Council. *Highway Research Board.*
Committee on Flexible Pavement Design.
   Design of flexible pavements: presented at the thirty-third
annual meeting, January 12-15, 1954. Washington, 1954.
   v, 77 ⁚ illus. 25 cm. (Highway Research Board. Research re-
port 16-B)
   National Research Council. Publication 321.
   Includes bibliographies.

   1. Pavements—Testing. I. Title. II. Title: Flexible pavements.
(Series: National Research Council. Highway Research Board. Research reports, 16-B. Series: National Research Council. Publication 321)

   TE250.N345   *625.7 625.8   54-60632

NN   0063124   DLC MoU MsU OClW NcRS ViU

290
N215   **National Research Council.   Highway Research**
         Board. Committee on Frost Heave and Frost
         Action in Soil.
           Factors related to frost action in soils,
         presented at the thirty-fourth annual meeting,
         January 11-14, 1955.   Washington, 1955.
           110 p.   (National Research Council. High-
         way Research Board. Bulletin 111)

           National Research Council. Publication 364.

NN   0063125   DNAL ViU OU CSt DAS

National Research Council. Highway Research
  Board. Committee on Frost Heave and Frost
  Action in Soil.
    Frost action in soils ...
        see under   National Research Council.
Highway Research Board.

National Research Council. Highway Research
  Board. Committee on Frost Heave and Frost
  Action in Soil.
    Soil freezing ...
        see under   National Research Council.
Highway Research Board.

National Research Council. Highway Research
  Board. Committee on Frost Heave and Frost
  Action in Soil.
    Soil temperature and ground freezing ...
        see under   National Research Council.
Highway Research Board.

National Research Council. *Highway Research Board.*
Committee on Geometric Highway Design.
   Research needed in geometric highway design ... pre-
sented at the thirty-second annual meeting, January 13-16,
1953. Washington, 1953.
   49 p. 25 cm. (Highway Research Board. Special report 12)
   National Research Council. Publication 277.
   "Selected references" under each research problem statement.

   1. Roads—Design. 2. Highway research. I. Title.   (Series:
National Research Council. Highway Research Board. Special report 12. Series: National Research Council. Publication 277)

   TE175.N3   625.7   54-61232

                  ViU MiU
NN   0063129   DLC MtBC OClW OCIU UU LU PSt PPD

VOLUME 407

TE175
N3
1953a
National Research Council. *Highway Research Board.*
Committee on Geometric Highway Design.
Research needed in geometric highway design ... presented at the thirty-second annual meeting, January 13–16, 1953. Washington, 1953.
49 p. 25 cm. (Highway Research Board. Special report 12)
National Research Council. Publication 277.
"Selected references" under each research problem statement.
Photocopy. Ann Arbor, Mich., University Microfilms, 1968. 21cm.

NN   0063130   IaU

HE
370
.N32
National Research Council. Highway Research Board. Committee on Highway Capacity.
Highway capacity manual. [Washington] 1948.
1 v. (various pagings)   28 cm.

NN   0063131   MiU

National Research Council. *Highway Research Board.*
Committee on Highway Capacity.
Highway capacity manual; practical applications of research, by the Committee on Highway Capacity, Dept. of Traffic and Operations. Washington, U. S. Dept. of Commerce, Bureau of Public Roads, 1950.
x, 147 p. illus., tables. 24 cm.
"Published in Public roads, vol. 25, no. 10, October 1949, and no. 11, December 1949."

1. Roads. 2. Traffic surveys.   I. Title.

HE370.N34   388.1   50—60367

       NIC TxU ICJ ICU OrCS OrP CaBVaU IdU WaT WaWW
NN   0063132   DLC PPCPC FU MsSM CU PPT MB OU MiU

FILM
13767
HE
Environ.
Design
Library
National Research Council. *Highway Research Board.*
Committee on Highway Capacity.
Highway capacity manual; practical applications of research, by the Committee on Highway Capacity, Dept. of Traffic and Operations. Washington, U. S. Dept. of Commerce, Bureau of Public Roads, 1950.
x, 147 p. illus., tables.   On film (negative)
"Published in Public roads, vol. 25, no. 10, October 1949, and no. 11, December 1949."
Microfilm. Original in Library of Congress.

NN   0063133   CU

National Research Council. *Highway Research Board.*
Committee on Highway Costs.
Know your highway costs; highway control sections, a basic procedure for keeping adequate cost and operating records of the highway plant. Washington, 1953.
iii, 30 p. illus., maps. 25 cm. [National Research Council] Highway Research Board. Special report 13)
National Research Council. Publication 278.
Bibliographical footnotes.
1. Road construction—Accounting. 2. Roads—Maintenance and repair—Accounting.   I. Title.   (Series. Series: National Research Council. Publication 278)

HF5686.R6N3   625.7   54–951

NN   0063134   DLC MtBC PSt PPT ViU MiU NjP

HF5686
R6N3
1953a
National Research Council. *Highway Research Board.*
Committee on Highway Costs.
Know your highway costs; highway control sections, a basic procedure for keeping adequate cost and operating records of the highway plant. Washington, 1953.
iii, 30 p. illus., maps. 25 cm. [National Research Council] Highway Research Board. Special report 13)
National Research Council. Publication 278.
Bibliographical footnotes.
Photocopy. Ann Arbor, Mich., University Microfilm, 1968. 21cm.

NN   0063135   IaU FTaSU

National Research Council. Highway Research Board.
Committee on Highway Costs.
Sufficiency rating formula procedures.
[Washington, 1951]
43 p.

NN   0063136   Wa

S
388.1
N27855
National Research Council. Highway Research Board. Committee on Highway Laws.
Better laws for better highways. Presented at the thirty-third annual meeting, January 12-15, 1954. Washington, D. C. 1954.
22 p. illus., maps. 25 cm. (Highway Research Board. Bulletin 88)
National Research Council. Publication no. 316.

1. Highway law. U.S.   I. Title.

NN   0063137   N ViU GAT IU MiD NBuU

National Research Council. *Highway Research Board.*
Committee on Highway Organization and Administration.
Merit system provisions in State highway employment, a study. [Washington] 1952.
82 p. 27 cm.

1. Roads—U. S. 2. Civil service—U. S.—States.   I. Title.

HE355.N32   53–60948 ‡

NN   0063138   DLC MtBC MiU

TE
324
.C6
N28
National Research Council. Highway Research Board. Committee on Highway Organization and Administration.
Report of a study of the highway laws, organization, and procedures of Colorado. [Washington] 1948-49.
2 v.   maps, diagrs.   28 cm.

1. Colorado. State Highway Dept. 2. Highway law--Colorado.

NN   0063139   MiU

TE1
B85
no.3
National Research Council. Highway Research Board. Committee on Highway Organization and Administration.
Report of committee on highway organization and administration, including summary of aims and activities and special papers, presented at the 26th annual meeting, 1946. Washington, 1947.
23 p.   (Its Bulletin 3)

National Research Council. Publication.

1. Highways.   I. T. Series.

NN   0063140   NBuU NNC PPT OrP

National Research Council. *Highway Research Board.*
Committee on Highway Organization and Administration.
Retirement provisions in State highway employment, a study. [Washington] 1952.
iii, 54 p. tables. 28 cm.
Bibliography: p. 53.

1. Civil service pensions—U. S.—States. 2. Roads—U. S.   I. Title.

HE355.N322   53–61576

NN   0063141   DLC MtBC MiU FU

National Research Council. Highway Research Board. Committee on Highway Organization and Administration.
Salary and wage practices of state highway departments; a study by the Committee on Highway organization and administration. Washington, Highway research board, Division of engineering and industrial research, National research council, 1947.
v, 46 p. tables. 25 cm. (Highway research board. Bulletin, no. 9)

"Presented at the   27th annual meeting."

NN   0063142   NNC MtBC Or ViU NBuU

National Research Council. *Highway Research Board.*
Committee on Highway Organization and Administration.
State highway administrative bodies, a study. [Washington] 1952.
vi, 153 p. tables. 28 cm.
Bibliography: p. 149–153.

1. Roads—U. S.   I. Title.

HE355.N324   53–61575

NN   0063143   DLC MiU PU-Sc IU PPT Or

National Research Council. *Highway Research Board.*
Committee on Highway Organization and Administration.
State highway organization charts. Washington, 1954.
viii, 51 p. diagrs. 28 cm. [National Research Council] Highway Research Board. Special report 20)
National Research Council. Publication 352.

1. Highway departments—U. S.   I. Title.   (Series. Series: National Research Council. Publication 352)

HE355.N326   55–60219

NN   0063144   DLC CaBViP MtBC OClW ViU PSt OCl PPT

HE355
N326
1954a
National Research Council. *Highway Research Board.*
Committee on Highway Organization and Administration.
State highway organization charts. Washington, 1954.
viii, 51 p. diagrs. 28 cm. [National Research Council] Highway Research Board. Special report 20)
National Research Council. Publication 352.
Photocopy. Ann Arbor, Mich., University Microfilms, 1968. 21cm.

NN   0063145   IaU FTaSU

National Research Council. Highway Research Board. Committee on Highway Taxation and Finance.
Highway finance ; selected references, 1950-1953.
see under

Hamlin, Ina Marie, 1896-

625.7
N21s
National Research Council--Highway Research Board--Committee on Highway Taxation and Finance.
Selected references on trends and forecasts for estimating highway requirements. Committee on Highway Taxation and Finance, Department of Economics, Finance and Administration. Washington, 1955.
21p. 28cm. (Its Memorandum no.3)

Caption title.
Highway Research Correlation Service. Circular   265.

NN   0063147   IU

National Research Council. *Highway Research Board.*
Committee on Joint Material in Concrete Pavements.
State highway department practices in filling, sealing, and maintaining joints in concrete pavements; summary of replies to two questionnaires. Washington, 1950.
16 p. 28 cm.

1. Roads, Concrete.   I. Title.

TE278.N36   *625.7 625.84   53–25738 ‡

       CSt NN MtBC
NN   0063148   DLC OrCS MB IU ViU FU TxU ICJ MiD

TE1
.N43
no.30
1951
National Research Council. Highway Research Board. Committee on Land Acquisition and Control of Highway Access and Adjacent Areas.
Progress in roadside protection. Report and special papers. Presented at the twenty-ninth annual meeting, 1949. Washington, 1951.
50 p. diagrs. 25cm. (National Research Council. Highway Research Board. Bulletin, no.30)
1. Roadside improvement. 2. Traffic accidents—U. S.   I. Ser.

NN   0063149   ViU NIC NBuU

VOLUME 407

Egleston
D625.7
N2138   National Research Council. Highway Research
no.4,   Board. Committee on Land Acquisition and Con-
10   trol of Highway Access and Adjacent Areas.
         Report of Committee on land acquisition and
control of highway access and adjacent areas,
and special papers.
1946-
Washington, Highway research board, Division
of engineering and industrial research, National research council, 1947-
    v.   illus., maps, tables. 25cm.
(Highway research board. Bulletin, no. 4,

    Presented at the 26th-   annual meeting.
1946-
    Title varies slightly.

    1. Highway engineering. 2. Right of way.

NN 0063151   NNC ViU NBuU

TE
7   National Research Council. Highway Research
N28   Board. Committee on Land Acquisition and Control
no.77   of Highway Access and Adjacent Areas
Engi-   Right-of-way problems; presented at the
neering thirty-second annual meeting, January 13-16,
         1953. Washington, D. C., 1953.
         72p. illus. 25cm. (Its Bulletin, no.77)

    National Research Council. Publication, 275.

    1. Right of way   (Traffic regulations)
    I. Title. (Serie   s)

NN 0063152   MU NBuU MiD ViU PPCPC

Fine Arts
NAC   National Research Council. Highway Research
722   Board. Committee on Land Acquisition and
N266   Control of Highway Access and Adjacent Areas.
         Trends in land acquisition. Presented at
the 33d annual meeting, January 12-15, 1954.
Washington, D. C., 1955.
         82 p. 25cm. (National Research Council.
Highway Research Board. Bulletin no. 101)
(National Research Council. Highway Research
Board. Publication 349)
         Issued as its   Annual report for 1953.
         1. Eminent do   main--U. S. 2. Highway law
--U. S. I. Its   Annual report, 1953. II.
Title.

NN 0063153   NIC IU ViU PPCPC PPBMR NBuU DI

National Research Council. Highway Re-
    search Board. Committee on Landslide
    Investigations.
    Analysis of landslides, presented at the
thirty-first annual meeting, January, 1952.
Washington, D. C., 1952.
    iii, 39 p. illus. 25 cm. (Highway
Research Board Bulletin 49)

    1. Landslides.

NN 0063154   DNAL NBuU ViU OU

National Research Council. *Highway Research Board.
Committee on Load Carrying Capacity of Roads as Affected by Frost Action.*
    Committee report and manual of recommended testing
procedures on load carrying capacity of roads as affected by
frost action. Committee report presented at the 29th annual
meeting, 1949. Washington, Highway Research Board, Division of Engineering and Industrial Research, National
Research Council, 1950.
    iv, 18 p. illus. 25 cm. (Highway Research Board. Research re-
port no. 10-D)
    1. Roads—Frost damage. 2. Highway research.   I. Title: Load
carrying capacity of roads as affected by frost action.   (Series: National Research Council.   Highway Research Board.   Research
report no. 10-D)
    TE153.N3575   625.761   59-34880

NN 0063155   DLC TxU FU NNC N MoU ViU DNAL

National Research Council. *Highway Research Board.
Committee on Maintenance of Concrete Pavement as Re-
lated to the Pumping Action of Slabs*
    see
National Research Council. *Highway Research Board.
Committee on Maintenance of Joints in Concrete Pave-
ments as Related to the Pumping Action of the Slabs.*

**National Research Council. Highway Research
Board. Committee on Maintenance of
Joints in Concrete Pavements as Related
to the Pumping Action of the Slabs.**
    Special papers on the pumping action of
concrete pavements. [Ed. by Fred Burggraf.
Washington, 1946]
    67 p. illus. Fold. maps. 27cm. ([National
Research Council] Highway Research Board. Research
reports no. 1 D.) 1946 Suppl.)
    Cover title.
    "Presented for the   twenty-fifth annual
meeting."
    Mimeographed.
    1. Pavements, Concrete. I. Burggraf, Fred, ed.
II. Ser.

NN 0063157   ViU NcD MoU NNC

625.84
N213sp
Engin   National Research Council. Highway Research
Lib'y   Board. Committee on Maintenance of Joints
         in Concrete Pavements as Related to the
         Pumping Action of Slabs.
         Special papers presented for the twenty-
fourth annual meeting (unassembled) Edited
by Fred Burggraf. Washington, 1945.
         iii, 135p. illus.,diagrs.,tables. 27½cm.
([National Research Council] Highway Re-
search Board. Research reports, no.1D)
         1. Pavements, Concrete. I. Burggraf,
Fred, ed. II. Series.

NN 0063158   TxU MoU MiD NNC

National Research Council. Highway Research
    Board. Committee on Maintenance of Joints
    in Concrete Pavements as Related to the
    Pumping Action of the Slabs.
    A survey of pumping in Illinois
    see under Illinois. Division of High-
ways.

National Research Council. Highway Research
    Board. Committee on Parking.
    Off-street parking; legislative trends and
administrative agencies; summary report presented at the thirty-first annual meeting,
January 17, 1952. Washington, D. C., 1952.
    v, 41 p. (Highway Research Board. Bulle-
tin 48)

NN 0063160   NNC ViU IdPI OrP NBuU MU

NAC   National Research Council. Highway Research
2059   Board. Committee on Parking.
N25   Parking. Eight papers presented at the
         twenty-eighth annual meeting, 1948. Washing-
ton, Highway Research Board, Division of Engineering and Industrial Research, National
Research Council, 1949.
         73 p. illus. 25cm. (Highway Research
Board bulletin no. 19)

    1. Automobile parking--U.S. I. Title.

NN 0063161   NIC IU ViU MH PPCPC IEdS NBuU Or OrP

National Research Council. Highway Research
    Board. Committee on Physico-Chemical
    Phenomena in Soils.
    Soil and soil-aggregate stabilization
    see under Symposium on the Science
of Soil Stabilization, Washington, 1955.

National Research Council. *Highway Research Board.
Committee on Resistance of Bituminous Materials to Deterioration Caused by Physical and Chemical Changes.*
    Bibliography on resistance of bituminous materials to
deterioration caused by physical and chemical changes, annotated. [Washington] 1951.
    89 p. 28 cm. ([National Research Council] Highway Research
Board. Bibliography no. 9)

    1. Bituminous materials—Bibl.   I. Title.   (Series)

    Z5524.B58N38   *016.6257 016.62585   53-839

NN 0063163   DLC UU OClW FTaSU IaU CoU MB FMU NIC

National Research Council. *Highway Research Board.
Committee on Roadside Development.*
    Mechanization of roadside operations; a summary of the
reports on equipment for roadside operations by a special
project committee on the Committee on Roadside Development. Washington, 1953.
    ii, 37 p. illus. 28 cm. (Highway Research Board. Special
report 16)
    National Research Council. Publication 289.
    1. Road machinery.   I. Title.   (Series: National Research
Council. Highway Research Board. Special report 16. Series: National Research Council. Publication 289)

    TE223.N3   625.7   54-61351

NN 0063164   DLC FTaSU UU IaU MtBC DNAL PSt ViU

TE 220   National Research Council. Highway Research
N27   Board. Committee on Roadside Development.
         Reference material on stabilized turf shoulders
1947. [n. p.] Department of Design, Committee
on Roadside Development, Sub-committee on Shoulders [1947]
         1 v. (various pagings) tables. 28 cm.

    Cover title.
    1. Road construction. 2. Soil stabilization.
    I. Title: Stabilized turf shoulders.

NN 0063165   OU Wa

**National Research Council. *Highway Research Board.
Committee on Roadside Development.***
    Reports, including special papers.

    Washington.
    v. in   illus. 24-28 cm. annual.
    Reports for 19   called   from the numbering of the
annual meetings of the Highway Research Board.
    Title varies: 19   Report.—19   Roadside development; re-
ports.—19   Reports and special papers (cover title, 19
Roadside development)
    Reports for 19   -39 issued by the Joint Committee on Roadside
Development.
    Summarized reports included in the board's Proceedings.
    Report for 1939 in   2 pts.
    1. Roadside improve-   ment—Collected works.
    TE153.N35754   625.77   44—28685*

    PU MB OrP PBL NjR FU NcD ICJ DI CU OCl
    ScCleU DPR MiD NNC MdBJ N IdU OrU WaS CaBVaU OU
NN 0063166   DLC IU MiU DNAL NN Or PPF MsU KMK

National Research Council. *Highway Research Board.
Committee on Roadside Development.* Roadside development
    see its Reports, including special papers.

National Research Council. Highway Research
    Board. Committee on Roadside Development.
    Project Committee on Parking Turnouts and
    Rest Areas
    see
National Research Council. Highway Research
    Board. Project Committee on Parking Turnouts
    and Rest Areas.

National Research Council. Highway Research
    Board. Committee on Rural Traffic and
    Safety Problems.
    Rural traffic problems
    see under National Research Council.
Highway Research Board.

VOLUME 407

National Research Council. Highway Research
Board. Committee on Snow and Ice Removal
see National Research Council. Highway
Research Board. Dept. of Maintenance. Committee on Snow and Ice Removal.

National Research Council. Highway Research
Board. Committee on Soil-Bituminous Roads.
Soil-bituminous roads
see under National Research Council.
Highway Research Board.

625.84
N213p
Engin
Lib'y

National Research Council. Highway Research
Board. Committee on Soil-Cement Roads.
Prevention of moisture loss in soil-cement
with bituminous materials; [report] presented at the twenty-eighth annual meeting,
1948. Washington, 1949.
1v, 34p. illus. 25cm. ([National Research Council] Highway Research Board. Research report no.8-F)
"Results of four field experiments conducted in Illinois, Kansas, Nebraska and
Arkansas."

NN 0063172 TxU NNC FU DNAL ViU N MoU

National Research Council. *Highway Research Board.
Committee on Stabilized Turf Shoulders.*
Concluding report of Special Task Committee on Stabilized Turf Shoulders. Presented at the thirty-third annual meeting, January 12–15, 1954. Washington [National
Academy of Sciences, National Research Council] 1954.
13 p. illus. 28 cm. (Highway Research Board. Special report
19)
National Research Council. Publication 320.
Includes bibliography.
1. Grasses. 2. Roadside improvement.

SB433.N3　　　625.77　　　54–60861 ‡

MtBC DNAL
NN 0063173 DLC UU IaU PSt MiU NcD ViU FTaSU ICIU

National Research Council. *Highway Research Board.
Committee on Surface Drainage of Highways.*
Culvert hydraulics, presented at the thirty-second annual
meeting, January 13–16, 1953. Washington, 1953.
iv, 71 p. illus. 25 cm. (Highway Research Board. Research re-
port 15-B)
National Research Council. Publication 287.
Includes bibliographies.
1. Culverts. I. Title. (Series: National Research Council.
Highway Research Board. Research report 15-B. Series: National
Research Council. Publication 287)

TE213.N3　　　625.78　　　54–61311

NN 0063174 DLC OrU OClW DNAL MoU MsU N TxU NcD ViU

National Research Council. *Highway Research Board.
Committee on Surface Drainage of Highways.*
Scour around bridges. Presented at the thirtieth annual
meeting, 1951. Washington, Highway Research Board, Division of Engineering and Industrial Research, National
Research Council, 1951.
iv, 22 p. illus. 25 cm. (Highway Research Board. Research
report no. 13-B)
1. Bridges—Foundations and piers. 2. Hydraulic models. I. Title.
(Series: National Research Council. Highway Research Board. Research report no. 13-B)

TG390.N3　　　624.2　　　59–35926

NN 0063175 DLC MoU ViU DI N WaU NNC

625.74
N2746

National Research Council. Highway Research
Board. Committee on Surface Drainage
of Highways.
Surface drainage. Committee report and
three papers presented at the twenty-ninth
annual meeting, 1949. Washington, D.C.,
Highway Research Board, Division of Engineering and Industrial Research, National Research
Council, 1950.
iii, 54 p. illus. 25 cm. (National Research Council. Highway Research Board.
Research report　　no. 11-B)
Includes bib-　　liographies.
1. Road drainage. 2. Drainage.

NN 0063176 DLC NNC DGW MoU DAS DNAL ViU

National Research Council. *Highway Research Board.
Committee on Surface Drainage of Highways.*
Surface drainage of highways. Committee report and
three papers presented at the twenty-seventh annual meeting, 1947. Washington, 1948.
29 p. illus. 25 cm. (Highway Research Board. Research report
6-B)

1. Road drainage. I. Title.

TE215.N3 1947　　　625.74　　　56–27970 ‡

NN 0063177 DLC N TxU MoU Or

National Research Council. *Highway Research Board.
Committee on the Deterioration of Bituminous Pavements
by the Effect of Water.*
Effect of water on bitumen-aggregate mixtures. Wash-
ington, 1954.
v, 45 p. 28 cm. ([National Research Council] Highway Research
Board. Bibliography 17)
National Research Council. Publication 332.
1. Pavements, Bituminous—Abstracts. I. Title. (Series.
Series: National Research Council. Publication 332)

TE270.N33　　　　　　55–60218

FTaSU TxDaM
NN 0063178 DLC PSt TxU NIC CU ViU IaU CoU UU

NATIONAL RESEARCH COUNCIL - Highway Research
Board - Committee on Uniform Highway
Accounting.
Report. Progress report on development of a
system, by Anson Marston, Robley Winfrey.
Washington, 1937.

Manifold copy. pp.42.

NN 0063179 MH-PA

National Research Council. *Highway Research Board.
Committee on Uses of Highway Planning Survey Data
see* National Research Council. *Highway Research
Board. Joint Committee on Uses of Highway Planning
Survey Data.*

National Research Council. *Highway Research Board. Committee TO-4 on Highway Capacity
see*
National Research Council. *Highway Research Board.
Committee on Highway Capacity.*

National Research Council. *Highway Research Board.
Dept. of Design. Committee on Bridges
see*
National Research Council. *Highway Research Board.
Committee on Bridges.*

National Research Council. *Highway Research Board.
Dept. of Design. Committee on Flexible Pavement Design
see*
National Research Council. *Highway Research Board.
Committee on Flexible Pavement Design.*

National Research Council. *Highway Research Board.
Dept. of Design. Committee on Geometric Highway De-
sign
see*
National Research Council. *Highway Research Board.
Committee on Geometric Highway Design.*

National Research Council. *Highway Research Board.
Dept. of Design. Committee on Surface Drainage of
Highways
see*
National Research Council. *Highway Research Board.
Committee on Surface Drainage of Highways.*

288
N214

National Research Council. Highway Research
Board. Dept. of Economics, Finance and
Administration.
Some economic effects of highway improvement. Washington, 1953.
21 p. (National Research Council. Highway Research Board. Bulletin no. 67)

National Research Council. Publication 256.

NN 0063186 DNAL ViU PPCPC FTaSU NBuU

National Research Council. *Highway Research Board.
Dept. of Economics, Finance and Administration
see also* National Research Council. *Highway Research
Board. Joint Committee on Uses of Highway Planning
Survey Data.*

National Research Council. *Highway Research Board.
Dept. of Economics, Finance and Administration. Com-
mittee on Economics of Motor Vehicle Size and Weight
see*
National Research Council. *Highway Research Board.
Committee on Economics of Motor Vehicle Size and
Weight.*

National Research Council. *Highway Research Board.
Dept. of Economics, Finance and Administration. Com-
mittee on Highway Costs
see*
National Research Council. *Highway Research Board.
Committee on Highway Costs.*

National Research Council. *Highway Research Board.
Dept. of Economics, Finance and Administration. Com-
mittee on Highway Laws
see*
National Research Council. *Highway Research Board.
Committee on Highway Laws.*

National Research Council. *Highway Research Board.
Dept. of Economics, Finance and Administration. Committee on Highway Organization and Administration
see*
National Research Council. *Highway Research Board.
Committee on Highway Organization and Administration.*

National Research Council. Highway Research
Board. Dept. of Economics, Finance and
Administration. Committee on Highway
Taxation and Finance
see National Research Council. Highway
Research Board. Committee on Highway Taxa-
tion and Finance.

National Research Council. *Highway Research Board.
Dept. of Economics, Finance and Administration. Committee on Land Acquisition and Control of Highway Access and Adjacent Areas
see*
National Research Council. *Highway Research Board.
Committee on Land Acquisition and Control of Highway Access and Adjacent Areas.*

VOLUME 407

National Research Council. *Highway Research Board. Dept. of Economics, Finance and Administration. Division of Administration and Management Studies*
see
National Research Council. *Highway Research Board. Division of Administrative and Management Studies.*

National Research Council. *Highway Research Board. Dept. of Economics, Finance and Administration. Division of Finance, Taxation and Cost Studies. Committee on Highway Taxation and Finance*
see
National Research Council. *Highway Research Board. Committee on Highway Taxation and Finance.*

National Research Council. *Highway Research Board. Dept. of Highway Design*
see
National Research Council. *Highway Research Board. Dept. of Design.*

National Research Council. *Highway Research Board. Dept. of Maintenance. Committee on Load Carrying Capacity of Roads as Affected by Frost Action*
see
National Research Council. *Highway Research Board. Committee on Load Carrying Capacity of Roads as Affected by Frost Action.*

National Research Council. *Highway Research Board. Dept. of Maintenance. Committee on Maintenance of Joints in Concrete Pavements as Related to the Pumping Action of the Slabs*
see
National Research Council. *Highway Research Board. Committee on Maintenance of Joints in Concrete Pavements as Related to the Pumping Action of the Slabs.*

National Research Council. *Highway Research Board. Dept. of Materials and Construction. Bituminous Division. Committee on Resistance of Bituminous Materials to Deterioration Caused by Physical and Chemical Changes*
see National Research Council. *Highway Research Board. Committee on Resistance of Bituminous Materials to Deterioration Caused by Physical and Chemical Changes.*

National Research Council. Highway Research Board. Dept. of Materials and Construction. Committee on Air-Entraining Concrete.
Use of air-entrained concrete in pavements and bridges
see under National Research Council. Highway Research Board.

National Research Council. *Highway Research Board. Dept. of Materials and Construction. Committee on Durability of Concrete, Physical Aspects*
see
National Research Council. *Highway Research Board. Committee on Durability of Concrete, Physical Aspects.*

National Research Council. Highway Research Board. Dept. of Maintenance. Committee on Snow and Ice Removal.
Recommended practice for snow removal and treatment of icy pavements
see under National Research Council. Highway Research Board.

National Research Council. *Highway Research Board. Dept. of Materials and Construction. Committee on the Deterioration of Bituminous Pavements by the Effect of Water*
see
National Research Council. *Highway Research Board. Committee on the Deterioration of Bituminous Pavements by the Effect of Water.*

56.43
N212   National Research Council. Highway Research Board. Dept. of Soils.
Laboratory analysis of soils: grain size and liquid limit; presented at the thirty-third annual meeting, January 12-15, 1954. Washington, 1955.
37 p. (National Research Council. Highway Research Board. Bulletin 95)

1. Soil. Analysis. Methods. I. National Research Council. Highway Research Board. Bulletin 95. II. National Research Council. Publication 343.

NN 0063205   DNAL GAT ViU NBuU

National Research Council. *Highway Research Board. Dept. of Soils, Geology and Foundations. Committee on Frost Heave and Frost Action in Soil*
see
National Research Council. *Highway Research Board. Committee on Frost Heave and Frost Action in Soil.*

National Research Council. *Highway Research Board. Dept. of Soils, Geology, and Foundations. Committee on Landslide Investigations*
see
National Research Council. *Highway Research Board. Committee on Landslide Investigations.*

National Research Council. *Highway Research Board. Dept. of Soils, Geology, and Foundations. Project Committee on Stabilized Soil Road Surfaces*
see
National Research Council. *Highway Research Board. Project Committee on Stabilized Soil Road Surfaces.*

National Research Council. *Highway Research Board. Dept. of Soils Investigations*
see
National Research Council. *Highway Research Board. Dept. of Soils, Geology and Foundations.*

National Research Council. *Highway Research Board. Dept. of Traffic and Operations*
see also National Research Council. *Highway Research Board. Joint Committee on Uses of Highway Planning Survey Data.*

National Research Council. *Highway Research Board. Dept. of Traffic and Operations. Committee on Channelization*
see
National Research Council. *Highway Research Board. Committee on Channelization.*

National Research Council. *Highway Research Board. Dept. of Traffic and Operations. Committee on Highway Capacity*
see National Research Council. *Highway Research Board. Committee on Highway Capacity.*

National Research Council. *Highway Research Board. Design, Dept. of*
see
National Research Council. *Highway Research Board. Dept. of Design.*

National Research Council. *Highway Research Board. Division of Administrative and Management Studies. Committee on Land Acquisition and Control of Highway Access and Adjacent Areas*
see
National Research Council. *Highway Research Board. Committee on Land Acquisition and Control of Highway Access and Adjacent Areas.*

National Research Council. Highway Research Board. Division of Engineering and Industrial Research.
Curing of concrete pavements
see under National Research Council. Highway Research Board.

National Research Council. *Highway Research Board. Highway Design, Dept. of*
see
National Research Council. *Highway Research Board. Dept. of Design.*

National Research Council. *Highway Research Board. Highway Laws Committee*
see
National Research Council. *Highway Research Board. Committee on Highway Laws.*

National Research Council. Highway Research Board. Highway Research Correlation Service.
see National Research Council. Highway Research Correlation Service.

National Research Council. Highway Research Board. Joint Committee on Maintenance Personnel.
Progress report of Joint Committee on Maintenance Personnel, Highway Research Board, Washington, D. C., January 11-14, 1955; American Association of State Highway Officials, Seattle, Washington, November 8-11, 1954. [Washington, 1954]
5, [8] p. tables.

NN 0063219   Wa

Z7295
.U55   National Research Council. Highway Research Board. Joint Committee on Uses of Highway Planning Survey Data.
U. S. *Federal Works Agency. Library.*
Bibliography on uses of highway planning survey data, annotated. Compiled for the Committee on Uses of Highway Planning Survey Data by the staff of the Libraries of the Federal Works Agency, Public Roads Administration. [Washington] 1948.

Egleston
D625.7
N2138 National Research Council. Highway Research
no.6   Board. Joint Committee on Uses of Highway Planning Survey Data.
Report of Committee on uses of highway planning survey data, including special papers. Washington, Highway research board, Division of engineering and industrial research, National research council, 1947.
vi p., 1 l., 40 p. illus., maps, tables, diagrs. 25ᶜᵐ. (Highway research board. Bulletin, no. 6)

"Presented at the twenty-sixth annual meeting, 1946."
1. Roads. 2. Cities and towns - Planning.

NN 0063221   NNC ViU NBuU

VOLUME 407

National Research Council. *Highway Research Board.*
Meeting.
Proceedings. 2d–41st; 1922–62. Washington.
40 v. in 89. illus., maps, diagrs., tables. 25 cm. annual.
Proceedings for 1922–23 issued as the council's Bulletin no. 32 and 43 (Q11.N292) ; 1952–62 issued as the council's Publication.
Issued 1922–23 by the board under its earlier name: Advisory Board on Highway Research.
Merged with the board's Bulletin to form Highway research record.
Report for 1922 includes a summarised account of preliminary and organization meetings in 1919, 1920 and 1921.
L. C. set incomplete : 23d wanting.
Index for v. 1–12, 1921–32, with v. 12.
1. Highway research—Societies, etc.   (Series: National Research Council. Bulletin. Series: National Research Council. Publication)

TE1.N45   26–10982 rev 3*

OrU Or WaTC Wa OrCS OrP KyU KMK UU DI LU OAkU DPR
MtBuM OCU OU OO OCl MiU CU IdU CaBVaU MtBC OrPR
NN 0063222   DLC NBuU MB TU NcRS NcD NIC ViU ICJ NN

National Research Council. Highway Research
Board. Meeting. 31st, Washington, 1952.
Off-street parking ...
     see under National Research Council.
Highway Research Board. Committee on Parking.

National Research Council. Highway Research
Board. Project Committee on Fillers and
Cushion Courses for Brick and Block Pavements.
Report of project committee on fillers
     see under Crandell, John Stanley, 1884–

National Research Council. *Highway Research Board.*
Project Committee on Parking Turnouts and Rest Areas.
Parking turnouts and rest areas; summary and report by Project Committee, presented at the thirty-first annual meeting, Highway Research Board. George B. Gordon, chairman. Washington, 1952.
iii, 52 p. illus. 28 cm. (National Research Council. Highway Research Board. Special report 7)
National Academy of Sciences. National Research Council. Publication 230.
Bibliography: p. 52.
1. Automobile parking. 2. Road construction. I. Title.   (Series. Series : National Research Council. Publication 230)

TE153.N358   625.77   52–14426

NN 0063225   DLC PPT PSt ViU NcD

Sci
TE.   National Research Council. *Highway Research · Board.*
7   *Project Committee on Parking Turnouts and Rest Areas.*
N281   Parking turnouts and rest areas; summary and report by
no.7   Project Committee, presented at the thirty-first annual meeting, Highway Research Board. George B. Gordon, chairman. Washington, 1952. Ann Arbor, University
Microfilm, 1970.
iii, 52 p. illus. 28 cm. (National Research Council. Highway Research Board. Special report 7)
National Academy of Sciences. National Research Council. Publication 230.
Bibliography : p. 52.
1. Automobile parking. 2. Road construction. I. Title.
II. National Research Council. Publica-
tion 230.   ser.

NN 0063226   FTaSU

TE153   National Research Council. *Highway Research Board.*
N358   *Project Committee on Parking Turnouts and Rest Areas.*
1952a   Parking turnouts and rest areas; summary and report by
Project Committee, presented at the thirty-first annual meeting, Highway Research Board. George B. Gordon, chairman. Washington, 1952.
iii, 52 p. illus. 28 cm. (National Research Council. Highway Research Board. Special report 7)
National Academy of Sciences. National Research Council. Publication 230.
Bibliography : p. 52.
Xerox copy, Ann Arbor, Michigan, 1968.

NN 0063227   IaU

National Research Council. Highway Research
Board. Project Committee on Stabilized
Soil Road Surfaces.
     ... Patching concrete pavements with
concrete
     see under National Research Council.
Highway Research Board.

National research council. *Highway research board.* **Project**
committee on stabilized soil road surfaces.
... Progress report of Project committee on stabilized soil road surfaces ... [1st]– [Washington, D. C.] Division of engineering and industrial research, National research council, 1935–
     v. illus., diagrs. 25ᵐ.
At head of title: Highway research information service. Highway research board.
1. Road materials. 2. Soils (Engineering) I. Title: Highway research information service.
Library of Congress   TE1.N463   37–12777
                              (2)   625.74

NN 0063229   DLC U OrCS DNAL NN ICJ ViU OCl

National Research Council. *Highway Research Board.* *Re-*
search Correlation Service.
     see
National Research Council. *Highway Research Correla-*
tion Service.

National Research Council. *Highway Research Board.*
Special Committee on Highway Laws
     see also
National Research Council. *Highway Research Board.*
Committee on Highway Laws.

National Research Council. *Highway Research Board.*
Special Committee on Stabilized Turf Shoulders
     see
National Research Council. *Highway Research Board.*
Committee on Stabilized Turf Shoulders.

710.2   **National Research Council. Highway Research Board**
N218p   —Special Task Committee on Planning and Manage-
ment of Roadside Vegetation.
Planning and management of roadside vegetation.
[Washington, D.C.? 1954?]
iii, 71p. illus. 28cm.
"Not released for publication."
1. Roadside improvement. 2. Trees. I. Title.

NN 0063233   IU

National Research Council. *Highway Research Board.*
Special Task Committee on Stabilized Turf Shoulders
     see
National Research Council. *Highway Research Board.*
Committee on Stabilized Turf Shoulders.

National Research Council. Highway Research
Board. Stabilized Soil Road Surfaces,
Project Committee on
     see National Research Council. Highway
Research Board. Project Committee on Stabiliz-
ed Soil Road Surfaces.

National Research Council. *Highway Research Board.*
Stabilized Turf Shoulders, Committee on
     see
National Research Council. *Highway Research Board.*
Committee on Stabilized Turf Shoulders.

National Research Council. *Highway Research Board.*
Traffic and Operations Dept.
     see **National Research Council.** *Highway Research*
Board. Dept. of Traffic and Operations.

TL725   National Research Council. Highway Research
.3   Correlation Service.
.R8M3   **McLeod, Norman William,** 1904–
Airport runway evaluation in Canada. Washington, Highway Research Board, Division of Engineering and Industrial Research, National Research Council, 1947–48.

National Research Council. Highway Research
Correlation Service.
Annual report to the American Association of
State Highway Officials for the year ending June 30
19   [Washington, D.C., National
Research Council]
     v. illus.
Report year ends June 30.

NN 0063239   Wa

National Research Council. Highway Research
Correlation Service.
Annual report to the Research Correlation
Service Advisory Committee. Washington, D.C.,
National Research Council [19
     v. illus.
Report year ends December 31.

NN 0063240   Wa

625.7   National Research Council. Highway Research
qN2775   Correlation Service.
Circular. no. 1– ; Dec. 1945–
Washington, D.C.
     no.   illus. 29 cm.
1. Roads. Societies.

OCl MB IU OU NN OrCS CU Wa FMU MiD
NN 0063241   N ScCleU ICU ICJ WvU PBL PPF NIC TxU

TE1   National Research Council. Highway Research
.A3H5   Correlation Service.
Highway research review. no. 1–
June 1949–
[Washington] National Research Council, Highway Re-
search Correlation Service.

National Research Council. Highway Research
Correlation Service.
Route selection and traffic assignment
     see under National Research Council.
Highway Research Board.

National Research Council. Highway Safety
Research, Committee on
     see National Research Council. Committee
on Highway Safety Research.

National Research Council. Insect and Rodent
Control Committee.
     see National Research Council. Committee
on Insect and Rodent Control.

591.65   **National research council. Insect control**
N277A   **committee**
... Abstract bulletin, n.s. no. 1–
Abstracts of current information on insect and
rodent control. Washington, National research
council, 1945–
     v. tables. 27½cm.
Mimeographed.

CU NIC InU LU DI IdU MtU OrCS MH-C OrU Wa
NN 0063246   NcD N NNC IU ICU CtY TU InNd DNLM

VOLUME 407

423
N212

National Research Council. Insect Control
Committee.
DDT emulsions. ₍n.p.₎ 1946.
24 p. (Its Report no.185)

Coordination center review no.9.

NN 0063247   DNAL

423.9
N212M

National research council. Insect control
committee.
Minutes of the ... meeting of the Subcommittee on dispersal.

Washington, D.C...

NN 0063248   DNAL

W 2
A
N363r

NATIONAL Research Council. Insect Control
Committee
Report. no. 100-185; July 1, 1945-
Nov. 1, 1946. ₍Washington₎
85 no. in illus.
Continues the Report of the Insect
Control Committee of the U. S. Office of
Scientific Research and Development.
Report no. 132, 149, 163, 185 called
also Coordination Center review, no.
5-7, 9, respectively.
Report no. 114-116, 119-124, 148

called also O. S. R. D. reports no.
5487, 5510, 5710, 5566, 5729-5731, 5736,
6004, 6345, respectively.
1. Insecticides - Collected works
Series: Coordination Center review, no.
5-7, etc. Series: U. S. Office of
Scientific Research and Development.
Report, OSRD no. 5487, etc.

NN 0063250   DNLM DNAL NIC

386
N2122

National Research Council. Insect Control
Committee.
Studies on methylated naphthalene derivatives. ₍n.p.₎ 1946.
61 p. (Its Report. no.183)

NN 0063251   DNAL

National Research Council. Insect Control.
Committee for Micronesia
Economic insects of Micronesia
see under Bryan, Edwin Horace, 1898-

National Research Council. Insect Control
Committee for Micronesia
see also National Research Council.
Pacific Science Board.

National Research Council. *Institute of Animal Resources*
see
National Research Council. *Institute of Laboratory Animal Resources.*

QY
26
M276a

National Research Council. Institute of Laboratory
Animal Resources.

₍Animals for research: catalogs₎

A file of these publications will be found on the
shelves under the call number assigned.
1. Animals, Laboratory - catalogs

NN 0063255   DNLM

SF77
.N3

National Research Council. *Institute of Laboratory Animal
Resources.*
Animals for research; a directory of sources of laboratory
animals, equipment, and materials.
Washington, National Academy of Sciences, National Re-
search Council.
v. 25-31 cm.
Subtitle varies.
Vols. for 1961- issued as the Council's Publication and as
the Institute's Laboratory animals 2 (SF77.N33)
1. Laboratory animals—Direct. I. Title. (Series: National
Research Council. Publication. Series: National Research Council.
Institute of Laboratory Animal Resources. Laboratory animals, 2)

SF77.N3   65-62521

RPB
NN 0063256   DLC NjR MoU TxU NBuU ViU-M NbU-M KMK

National Research Council. *Institute of Laboratory Animal
Resources.*
Handbook of laboratory animals. Prepared by the Insti-
tute of Animal Resources, Committee on Handbook: H. G.
Herrlein, chairman ₍and others₎ Washington, National
Academy of Sciences–National Research Council, 1954.
v, 77 p. tables. 25 cm. (National Research Council. Publication
317)
Bibliography : p. 57–62.
1. Laboratory animals. 2. Laboratory animals—Diseases.
I. Title. (Series)

QL55.N3   636.9   54-60859 rev

PPHa PU-Z NN IdPI MiHM OrU OC1WHi
ICJ MB PPF-B PSt PPJ DNLM MiU CaBVaU OrP WaTC MtU
NN 0063257   DLC TxU N NcU-H ViU DNAL NcD PPSKF PBL

National research council. *Interdivisional committee on borderland fields between geology, physics and chemistry.*
Report of the Interdivisional committee of the National research council on borderland fields between geology, physics
and chemistry, 1937. T. S. Lovering, chairman. (Preliminary
mimeographed edition) Washington, D. C., Division of geology and geography, National research council, 1938.
1 p. l., ii numb. l., 73 p. 27ᶜᵐ.
Photoprinted.
1. Geophysics. 2. Geochemistry. I. Lovering, Thomas Seward,
1896-

U. S. Geol. survey. Library   G S 39–163
for Library of Congress   QE501.N3
₍a45c1₎†   550.72

NN 0063258   DI-GS MU NNC DNAL ICJ DLC OU

National research council. Interdivisional
committee on borderland problems of the life
sciences.
Conference on experimental neuroses and allied problems,
Washington, D. C., 1937.
... Conference on experimental neuroses and allied problems
under the auspices of the Inter-divisional committee on borderland problems of the life sciences, April 17 and 18, 1937.
Washington, D. C. ₍1937?₎

National research council. *Interdivisional committee on
density currents*
see
National research council. *Committee on density currents.*

National Research Council. *International Technologic Assistance, Advisory Committee on*
see
National Research Council. *Advisory Committee on International Technologic Assistance.*

National Research Council. Joint Advisory Committee on Scientific Publications
see Joint Advisory Committee on Scientific
Publications of the National Academy of Sciences
and the National Research Council.

National Research Council. Joint Committee
on Wildlife
see Joint Committee on Wildlife.

National Research Council. *Library*
see Washington, D. C. Library of the National Academy of Sciences and the National Research Council.

National Research Council. Marine Ecology and
Paleoecology, Committee on
see National Research Council. Committee
on a Treatise on Marine Ecology and Paleoecology.

National Research Council. Marine Ecology as
Related to Paleontology, Committee on
see National Research Council. Committee
on a Treatise on Marine Ecology and Paleoecology.

National Research Council. *Maritime Cargo Transportation
Conference.*
The S. S. Warrior; an analysis of an export transportation
system from shipper to consignee. By the Maritime Cargo
Transportation Conference, as part of a program undertaken
at the request of the Departments of Defense and Commerce.
Washington, National Academy of Sciences–National Re-
search Council, 1954.
vii, 53 p. illus., maps, tables. 28 cm. (National Research Council.
Publication 339)

—— A meteorologic and oceanographic analysis of the passage of the S. S. Warrior; a supplement to "The S. S. Warrior" study. Prepared for the Maritime Cargo Transportation Conference by Louis Allen ₍consultant to the staff₎
Washington, National Academy of Sciences–National Research Council, 1954.
21 l. maps, diagrs., tables. 28 cm.
Cover title.
Bibliography: leaves 20–21.
1. Warrior (Cargo ship) 2. Shipping—Case studies. I. Allen,
Louis, 1913–   HE736.N332 (Series)

HE736.N33   387.5   55-60014

ICJ PBL PU-W WaS CoU OrP WaTC
NN 0063268   DLC CaBVaU IdPI OrCS NN PSt CU ICU

TN7
N3
34-M

National Research Council. Materials
Advisory Board.
An appraisal of research and development of
permanent magnet materials. Report by Panel on
Permanent Magnet Materials. Washington, Divi-
sion of Engineering and Industrial Research,
Division of Geology and Geography, National
Academy of Sciences, National Research Council,
1953.
1 v. (various pagings) diagrs., tables.
27 cm. (Its Report no. 34-M)
Cover title.

1. Magnets. I. Title: Magnet materials.
(Series)

NN 0063269   DI

TN7
N3
4-M

National Research Council. Materials
Advisory Board.
Boron steels; first report of Panel on Sub-
stitution of Alloying Elements in Engineering
Steels of the Metallurgical Advisory Board.
Washington, 1951.
₍11₎ 25 p. diagrs., tables. 27 cm.
(Its Report no. MAB-4-M)
Cover title.

1. Boron. 2. Steel alloys I. Title. (Series:
National Research Council. Minerals and Metals
Advisory Board. Report no. MMAB-4-M)

NN 0063270   DI

TN7
N3
55-C

National Research Council. Materials Advisory
Board.
Conservation of industrial diamonds. Report
by Panel on Diamond Salvage and Reclamation.
Washington, Division of Engineering and Indus-
trial Research, Division of Earth Sciences,
National Academy of Sciences, National Research
Council, 1953.
vii ₍3₎ iii, 35 p. illus., diagrs. 27cm.
(Its Report no. MMAB-55-C)
Cover title.
Bibliography, p. 35.

1. Diamonds, Industrial. I. Title.
(Series)

NN 0063271   DI

VOLUME 407

TN7
N3
24-M
National Research Council.   Materials Advisory
    Board.
    Non-magnetic steels for naval use. Report of
the Panel on Non-magnetic Steels. Washington,
Division of Engineering and Industrial Research.
Division of Geology and Geography, National
Academy of Sciences, National Research Council,
1952.
    1 v. (various pagings) diagrs., tables (1
fold.) 27 cm. (Its Report no. MMAB-24-M)
    "Restricted, security information."
    Bibliography, 2 pages at end.

    1. Steel. I.   Title. (Series)

NN 0063272   DI

TN7
N3
30-C
National Research Council.   Materials Advisory
    Board.
    Production of cobalt supplies from low grade
ores. Report by Panel on Cobalt Supplies.
Washington, Division of Engineering and Indus-
trial Research, Division of Geology and Geogra-
phy, National Academy of Sciences, National
Research Council, 1952.
    vii [5] 22 p. diagr., table. 27 cm.
(Its Report no. MMAB-30-C)
    "Restricted, security information."

    1. Cobalt.   (Series)

NN 0063273   DI

TN7
N3
10-M
National Research Council.   Materials Advisory
    Board.
    Production of manganese from domestic sources;
report by Manganese Panel of the Metallurgical
Advisory Board. Washington, D.C., Division of
Engineering and Industrial Research, National
Academy of Sciences, National Research Council,
1951.
    iiiii [3] 47 p. diagrs., tables. 27 cm.
(Its Report no. MAB-10-M)
    Cover title.
    "Restricted."
    1. Manganese.   I.Title. (Series: Nat'l.
Res. Council. Min-   erals & Metals Advisory
Board. Report no.1   MMAB-10-M)

NN 0063274   DI

TN7
N3
71-C
National Research Council.   Materials Advisory
    Board.
    Production of manganese from domestic sources.
Supplement to MAB-10-M. Report by Manganese
Panel of the Materials Advisory Board. Wash-
ington, Division of Engineering and Industrial
Research, National Academy of Sciences, National
Research Council [1954]
    [5] vii, 31 p. 28 cm. (Its Report
no. MAB-71-C)

    1.Manganese.   (Series)

NN 0063275   DI

TN7
N3
101-M
National Research Council.   Materials Advisory
    Board.
    Report on columbium-tantalum by the Panel on
Columbium-Tantalum of the Materials Advisory
Board. Washington, Division of Engineering and
Industrial Research, National Academy of Sciences,
National Research Council, 1955.
    v, 16, 2 p. table. 28 cm. (Its Report
no. MAB-101-M)
    Cover title.
    Prepared and submitted to the Office of the
Assistant Secretary   of Defense (R & D) under

Contract DA-49-025-sc-83, between the Dept. of
Defense and the National Academy of Sciences.

    1. Columbium. 2. Tantalum. (Series)

NN 0063277   DI

TN7
N3
88-M
National Research Council.   Materials Advisory
    Board.
    Report on lithium by Panel on Lithium of the
Materials Advisory Board. Washington, Division
of Engineering and Industrial Research, National
Academy of Sciences, National Research Council
[1955]
    iv, 17 p. 28 cm. (Its Report no. MMAB-88-M)

    1. Lithium. (Series)

NN 0063278   DI

TN7
N3
99-C
National Research Council.   Materials Advisory
    Board.
    Report on natural muscovite block and film
mica, by Panel on Mica of the Materials Advisory
Board. Washington, Division of Engineering and
Industrial Research, National Academy of
Sciences, National Research Council, 1955.
    1 v. (various pagings) tables. 28 cm.
(Its Report no. MAB-99-C)
    Cover title.

    1. Mica. 2.   Muscovite. (Series)

NN 0063279   DI

TN7
N3
48-M
National Research Council.   Materials Advisory
    Board.
    Report on possibilities for nickel conserva-
tion in wartime. Abridged from MMAB-39-M, The
conservation of nickel for full mobilization, by
Nickel Conservation Panel. Washington, Division
of Engineering and Industrial Research, Division
of Earth Sciences, National Academy of Sciences,
National Research Council, 1953.
    1 v. (various pagings) diagrs., tables.
27 cm. (Its Report no. MMAB-48-M)
    Cover title.
    "Restricted,   security information."

    1. Nickel.   (Series)

NN 0063280   DI

TN7
N3
11-M
National Research Council.   Materials Advisory
    Board.
    Report on recommended research projects on
boron steels by the Panel on Substitution of
Alloying Elements in Engineering Steels. Wash-
ington, D.C., Minerals and Metals Advisory
Board, Division of Engineering and Industrial
Research, National Research Council, 1952.
    [11] 6 p. 27 cm. (Its Report no.
MMAB-11-M)

    1.Boron.2.Steel alloys.I.Title: Boron steels,
Recommended   research projects on.
(Series)

NN 0063281   DI

TN7
N3
95-M
National Research Council.   Materials Advisory
    Board.
    Report on reinforced plastics for airplane and
missile structures by Panel on Reinforced Plas-
tics for Aircraft Structures, Materials Advisory
Board. Washington, Division of Engineering and
Industrial Research, National Academy of Sciences,
National Research Council, [1955].
    1 v. (various pagings) 27 cm. (Its Report
no. MAB-95-M)

    1. Plastics.   I.Title: Reinforced plas-
tics for airplane a.   missile structures.
(Series)

NN 0063282   DI

National Research Council. *Materials Advisory Board.*
    Report on research and development of metals and alloys
for low temperature applications, by panel on metals for use
at low temperatures of the Materials Advisory Board.
Washington, Division of Engineering and Industrial Research, National Academy of Sciences, National Research
Council; distributed by the U. S. Dept. of Commerce, Office
of Technical Services, 1954.
    1 v. (various pagings) 27 cm.
    "PB 111453."
    Includes bibliographies.
    1. Metals at low temperatures.

TA459.N27   620.18   54-60711

NN 0063283   DLC WaS TxU NcD DI ICJ

TN7
N3
92-M
National Research Council.   Materials Advisory
    Board.
    Report on rubber by Panel on Rubber of the
Materials Advisory Board. Washington, Division of
Engineering and Industrial Research, National
Academy of Sciences, National Research Council,
1955.
    1 v. (various pagings) 28 cm. (Its
Report no. MAB-92-M)
    Cover title.

    1. Rubber. 2.   Rubber research. (Series)

NN 0063284   DI

TN7
N3
32-M
National Research Council.   Materials Advisory
    Board.
    Report on selection of alternate steels for
evaluation in naval armor by the AD Hoc Committee
on Naval Armor. Washington, Division of Engi-
neering and Industrial Research, Division of
Geology and Geography, National Academy of
Sciences, National Research Council [1952]
    vi [5] 33 p. diagrs., tables. 27 cm.
(Its Report no. MMAB-32-M)
    "Restricted, security information."
    Bibliography, p. 33.

    1. Steel. I.   Title: Naval armor.
(Series)

NN 0063285   DI

TN7
N3
87-M
National Research Council.   Materials
    Advisory Board.
    Report on stabilized austenitic stainless
steels by Panel on Stabilized Stainless Steels
of the Materials Advisory Board. Washington,
Division of Engineering and Industrial Research
Council [1954].
    v, 12 [3] p. 27 cm. (Its Report no.
MAB-87-M)

    1.Steel, Stainless.I.Title: Stabilized austen-
itic stainless   steels. (Series)

NN 0063286   DI

TN7
N3
50-C
National Research Council.   Materials Advisory
    Board.
    Report on the potential use of vanadium by
Panel on Vanadium. Washington, Division of
Engineering and Industrial Research, Division of
Earth Sciences, National Academy of Sciences,
National Research Council [1953]
    v, [5] 12 p. tables. 27 cm. (Its
Report no. MMAB-50-C)
    "Restricted, security information."

    1. Vanadium.   (Series)

NN 0063287   DI

TN7
N3
97-M
National Research Council.   Materials Advisory
    Board.
    Report on the processing and re-use of titan-
ium scrap by Titanium Process Review Committee
of the Materials Advisory Board. Washington,
Division of Engineering and Industrial Research,
National Academy of Sciences, National Research
Council, 1955.
    v, ii, 51 p. diagr. 28 cm. (Its Report
no. MAB-97-M)
    Cover title.
    Prepared under   contract DA-49-025-sc-83,
between the Dept.   of Defense and the National Academy of   Sciences.
    1.Titanium -   Metallurgy. (Series)

NN 0063288   DI

TN7
N3
59-M
National Research Council.   Materials Advisory
    Board.
    Report on the recovery of critical and stra-
tegic metals from high alloy scrap by Panel on
High Alloy Scrap Utilization. Washington,
Division of Engineering and Industrial Research,
Division of Earth Sciences, National Academy of
Sciences, National Research Council [1953]
    1 v. (various pagings) fold. diagr., tables
(2 fold.) 27 cm. (Its Report no. MMAB-59-M)

    1. Metals. I. Title: Critical and Strategic
metals.II.Title: High alloy scrap.
(Series)

NN 0063289   DI

VOLUME 407

TN7
N3
38-M

National Research Council. Materials Advisory
Board.
Research and development in magnesium alloys.
Report by Panel on Magnesium Alloys. Washing-
ton, Division of Engineering and Industrial Re-
search, Division of Geology and Geography, Na-
tional Research Council, 1953.
1 v. (various pagings) table. 27 cm.
(Its Report no. MMAB-38-M)
Cover title.
"Restricted, security information."

1.Magnesium al-   loys. I. Title. (Series)

NN 0063290   DI

TN7
N3
26-M

National Research Council. Materials Advisory
Board.
Substitutes for beryllium-copper alloys.
Washington, Division of Engineering and Indus-
trial Research, Division of Geology and Geogra-
phy, National Academy of Sciences, National
Research Council, 1952.
viii [1] 24 p. tables. 27 cm. (Its
Report no. MMAB-26-M)
Stamped: Business confidential.

1.Beryllium alloys. 2.Copper-beryllium alloys.
I. Title.   (Series)

NN 0063291   DI

TN7
N3
62-C

National Research Council. Materials Advisory
Board.
Supplementary report on production of cobalt
from low grade ores cobalt in the Ergani copper
mines by Panel on Cobalt Supplies. Washington,
Division of Engineering and Industrial Research,
Division of Earth Sciences, National Academy of
Sciences, National Research Council, 1953.
vi, [3] 4 p. 27 cm. (Its Report no.
MMAB-62-C)
Cover title.

1. Cobalt. I.   Title: Ergani copper
mines, [Turkey].   (Series)

NN 0063292   DI

National Research Council. Mathematics Division
see
National Research Council. Division of
Mathematics.

National Research Council. Measurement of
Geologic Time by Atomic Disintegration,
Committee on the
see National Research Council. Committee
on the Measurement of Geologic time.

National Research Council. Medical Fellowship
Board.
Annoucement of fellowships in the medical
sciences
see under National Research Council.

W 2
A
N3642a

NATIONAL Research Council. Medical
Fellowship Board
Annual report.
Washington, 19
v.
1. Research - Medical - U. S.
2. Scholarships & fellowships - U. S.

NN 0063296   DNLM NN KvU DLC CaBVaU NNC

National Research Council. *Medical Fellowship Board.*
List of fellows.
Washington.
v. 27 cm.
Title varies: 19   Fellowships in medicine; list of fellows
in medicine, past and active.—193   Fellowships in the medical
sciences; list of fellows in the medical sciences.—194 –48, List of
fellows in the medical sciences.
Issued 19   by the council; 194 –48 by the council's Division of Medical Sciences.
Issues cumulative from June 1922.

1. Physicians—U. S.—Direct. 2. Medicine—Study and teaching.

R712.A1N3   610.79   36–18313 rev 2*‡

NN 0063297   DLC ICU ICJ IU OrU-M DNLM

National Research Council. Medical Sciences,
Division of
see   National Research Council. Division
of Medical Sciences.

National Research Council. Metallurgical
Advisory Board.
see   National Research Council. Materials
Advisory Board.

RC1015
.S9

National Research Council. Mine Advisory
Committee.
Symposium on Underwater Physiology.
Underwater physiology; proceedings. [1st-   1955–
Baltimore [etc.] Williams & Wilkins Co. [etc.]

National Research Council. *Minerals and Metals Advisory
Board*
see
National Research Council. *Materials Advisory Board.*

National Research Council. National Materials
Advisory Board.

For works by this body issued under its
earlier name see

National Research Council. Materials
Advisory Board.

National Research Council. *Nuclear Science Committee*
see
National Research Council. *Committee on Nuclear Science.*

Q10
.I6N3
1955

National Research Council. Office of
International Relations.

A brief description of the International
Council of Scientific Unions (ICSU); information for delegates to international scientific meetings. Washington, National Academy
of Sciences-National Research Council, 1955.
33 p. 28cm.
Cover title.

1. International   Council of Scientific
Unions.

NN 0063304   ViU DNLM

National Research Council. *Office of International Relations.*
Information for delegates to international scientific meetings; United States participation in the International Council of Scientific Unions and its member unions. Washington,
1955.
15 p. 28 cm.

1. International Council of Scientific Unions.   I. Title.

Q10.N27   506.11   60–19560 ‡

NN 0063305   DLC ViU

National Research Council. Office of Medical
Information
see   National Research Council. Division
of Medical Sciences. Office of Medical Information.

National Research Council. *Office of Scientific Personnel.*
The baccalaureate origins of the science doctorates awarded
in the United States in the decade 1936 to 1945, inclusive.
Comp. under the direction of M. H. Trytten, director, Office
of Scientific Personnel. Washington, 1948.
93 p. 22 cm.

1. Science—Study and teaching. 2. Universities and colleges—
U. S.—Stat.   I. Title.

Q181.N38   507.1173   49–1646*

NN 0063307   DLC OrPR MtU OrU OOxM OU IU CU

National Research Council. *Office of Scientific Personnel.*
The baccalaureate origins of the science doctorates awarded
in the United States from 1936 to 1950 inclusive. Compiled
by the Office of Scientific Personnel, M. H. Trytten, director.
Washington, National Academy of Sciences, National Research Council, 1955.
v, 158 p. diagrs., tables. 28 cm. (National Research Council
Publication 382)
Bibliography: p. 156–158.

1. Science—Study and teaching. 2. Universities and colleges—
U. S.—Stat.   I. Title.   II. Title: Science doctorates awarded in the
U. S.   (Series)

Q181.N38 1955   507.1173   55–60043

OrCS TxU-M OrPR OrP AAP FU OU DNLM OOxM NN ScCleU
ICJ TxU ViU PBL PSt MiU OCU MiHM MBCo GU CaBVaU
NN 0063308   DLC MoSW GAT MH MB PWpM PPWM PPD NcD

SCHOOL OF LIBRARY SERVICE
D371.42
N213

National research council. Office of scientific personnel.
Human resources and the fields of higher
learning; a report of a preliminary survey
under the auspices of the Conference board of
associated research councils, Committee on
specialized personnel: M. H. Trytten, chairman [and others] 1948.
1 v. tables (1 fold.)

"The information was collected and evalu-
ated by this staff with the exception of the
material from the Social science research
center at the University of Minnesota ['High
level research talent: an analysis of supply
and demand factors,' prepared by C. Gilbert
Wrenn (45 l. in Section III)]" -p. v.
Bibliography on the supply and demand for
highly trained   personnel": 17 l. at
end.

NN 0063310   NNC

L378.2
N277d
R.R.

National Research Council. Office of Scientific Personnel.
Doctorate production in United States Universities. 1936/45-
Washington.

National Research Council. Publication
382, 460, 582, 1142.
"With baccalaureate origins of doctorates
..."

NN 0063311   IEN

LA831
.8
.G6

National Research Council. Office of Scientific
Personnel.

Gorokhoff, Boris Ivanovitch, 1917–
Materials for the study of Soviet specialized education.
Washington, 1952.

VOLUME 407

Q
181
qN277n
1945

NATIONAL Research Council. Office of Scientific Personnel
The national stake in the imperative resumption of training for the scientific professions. Special bulletin issued jointly by Office of Scientific Personnel, National Research Council and the American Council on Education. ₁Washington, 1945₎
32 p. illus. (OSP bulletin no. 22)
The American Council on Education. Higher education and national defense. Bulletin no. 84.

1. Science - Study & teaching
2. Scientists - U. S. I. American Council on Education. Series: National Research Council. Office of Scientific Personnel. Bulletin no. 22.

Series: American Council on Education. Higher education and national defense. Bulletin no. 84.

NN 0063315   DNLM

LA226
N375

National Research Council. Office of Scientific Personnel.
A report of a faculty personnel study in twenty-nine representative colleges and universities. Prepared by Lowell H.Hattery. Conducted for the President's Commission on Higher Education by the Committee on Specialized Personnel of Associated Research Councils. M.H. Trytten, Chairman ₁and others₎   Washington, 1948.
83p. tables. 27cm.

Four-council coöperative higher education survey.
Typescript copy.

1. Universities and colleges - U.S. I. Title: Faculty personnel study in 29 representative colleges and universities. II. Hattery, Lowell Harold,   1916-   III. U.S. President's Co-   mmission on Higher Education.

NN 0063317   IaU

National Research Council. Office of Scientific Personnel.
Soviet professional manpower

see under

De Witt, Nicholas.

National Research Council. *Office of Scientific Personnel.*
Technical report.
Washington.
no. 31 cm.

1. Science—Scholarships, fellowships, etc.

Q148.N3   507.9   60-32027 ‡

NN 0063319   DLC

National Research Council. Operations Research, Committee on
see   National Research Council. Committee on Operations Research.

National Research Council. Pacific Science Board.
Annual report
see its   Report.

QE565
.A8

National Research Council. Pacific Science Board.
Atoll research bulletin. no. 1/2-
Sept. 10, 1951-
Washington.

DU1
A8
no.1

National Research Council. Pacific Science Board.
Basic information papers on coral atoll ecology. Washington, 1951.
25 p.   28 cm.   (Atoll research bulletin. No. 1)

1. Coral reefs and islands. (Series)

NN 0063323   DI

Z5859
.M5B7

National Research Council. Pacific Science Board.
Bryan, Edwin Horace, 1898-
Bibliography of Micronesian entomology. Comp. for the Pacific Science Board of the National Research Council. ₁Honolulu?₎, 1948.

National Research Council. Pacific Science Board.
CIMA report
see under   Coordinated Investigation of Micronesian Anthropology.

National Research Council. *Pacific Science Board.*
Conservation in Micronesia; a report on two conferences held under the auspices of the Pacific Science Board in Honolulu, T. H., and Washington, D. C., in April and May 1948. Comp. by Harold J. Coolidge, executive secretary. Washington, National Research Council, 1948.
70 p. 28 cm.

1. Natural resources—Micronesia.   I. Coolidge, Harold Jefferson, 1904-
HC687.M5N3 1948   333.72   53-19656*

NN 0063326   DLC NN MU

National Research Council. Pacific Science Board.
Expedition to Raroia, Tuamotus

see under

Newell, Norman Dennis, 1909-

National Research Council. Pacific Science Board.
Handbook for atoll research

see under

Fosberg, Francis Raymond, 1908-   ed.

National Research Council. Pacific Science Board.
Health report on Kapingamarangi

see under   Miller, Ralph English, 1899-

National Research Council. Pacific Science Board.
The hydrology of Arno Atoll, Marshall Islands
see under   ₁Cox, Doak Carey₎ 1917-

Z5358
.O3S3

National Research Council. Pacific Science Board.
Sachet, Marie Hélène.
Island bibliographies: Micronesian botany, Land environment and ecology of coral atolls, Vegetation of tropical Pacific islands, by Marie-Hélène Sachet and F. Raymond Fosberg. Compiled under the auspices of the Pacific Science Board. ₁Washington₎ National Academy of Sciences, National Research Council, 1955.

GN671
.C3H3

National Research Council. Pacific Science Board.
Harvard University. *Peabody Museum of Archaeology and Ethnology. Expedition to Yap Island, Micronesia.*
The Micronesians of Yap and their depopulation; report of the Peaboby Museum Expedition to Yap Island, Micronesia, 1947-1948. Cambridge, Peabody Museum, Harvard University ₁1949?₎

Bℓ
1953P

National Research Council. Pacific Science Board.
Our heritage in the Pacific. The Pacific, the threat to its unique wild life. The Pacific world series. The Pacific War Memorial, the idea, its history, financial statement. [n.p., 1953?]
13p.

1. Pacific area. 2. Pacific War Memorial.

NN 0063333   CtY DI OrU

National Research Council. Pacific Science Board.
A partial list of the plants of the Midway Islands

see under

Neff, Johnson Andrew, 1900-

DU780
.V5

National Research Council. Pacific Science Board.
Vidich, Arthur J
Political factionalism in Palau, its rise and development. ₁Washington, Pacific Science Board, National Research Council₎ 1949.

DU1
A8
no.2

National Research Council. Pacific Science Board.
Preliminary papers for a symposium on coral atoll research. Washington, 1951.
14 p.   28 cm.   (Atoll research bulletin. No. 2)

1. Coral reefs and islands. (Series)

NN 0063336   DI

National Research Council. Pacific Science Board.
Reefs and sedimentary processes of Raroia

see under

Newell, Norman Dennis, 1909-

National Research Council. *Pacific Science Board.*
Report. 1st-   1947-
Washington.
v. 19 cm. annual.

Q180.A1N35   507.2   51-37304

NNC ICU
NN 0063338   DLC CaBVaU DNAL OrCS PU-Mu WU TxU NN

VOLUME 407

DU780 .U8

National Research Council. Pacific Science Board.

Useem, John.
Report on Palau. ₁Washington, Pacific Science Board, National Research Council, 1949₎

Q111 S4 no.20 R

National Research Council. Pacific Science Board.
Report on Raroia Atoll expedition. Scientific investigations in Micronesia. Washington, 1954.
1 v. (various pagings) illus., maps (part fold.), diagrs., tables. 29 cm. (Scientific investigations in Micronesia, 1949- SIM report no. 20)

Also DU1 no.31-36

Reports in this volume issued also as Atoll research bulletins 31-36. 1.Raroia Atoll Expedition.2.Natural resources – Raroia Atoll.3.Raroia Atoll. (Series)

NN 0063340   DI DS DNAL

Z3307 .R9K4

National Research Council. Pacific Science Board.

Kerr, George H   1911-
The Ryūkyū Islands; a preliminary checklist of reference materials arranged alphabetically ₁by₎ George H. Kerr with Higa Shuncho ₁and others₎ Prepared at Tokyo, Japan, for the Pacific Science Board, National Research Council, Washington, D. C., Apr.–July 1952. ₁n. p., 1952?₎

DU 500 N35

National Research Council. Pacific Science Board.
Scientific investigations in Micronesia. SIM report. no.1-   ₁Washington?₎ 1949-
v. illus. 29 cm.

"The SIM (Scientific Investigations in Micronesia) Program has developed as a successor to the former CIMA (Coordinated Investigation of Micronesian Anthropology) project with an enlarged scope that includes field research in the physical, biological, and life sciences."

1. Ethnology--Micronesia. 2. Micronesia. 3. Science--Micronesia. I. Title. II. Title: SIM report.

NN 0063343   LU NN

MIC-1 GN 669 N2 Govt. Doc. Rm.

National Research Council. Pacific Science Board.
Scientific investigations in Micronesia (SIM) reports; reports 1-27. Ann Arbor, University Microfilms, 1968?
Microfilm copy (positive): Washington ₁etc.₎ 1950-61.
Collation: 2 reels 35 mm.
Report no. 2-A issued also as Bernice P. Bishop Museum. Bulletin 209. 1952; no. 18 as Oregon State monographs. Studies in

zoology, no. 7, 1954; no. 26 as Bernice P. Bishop Museum. Bulletin 222. 1961. Report no. 27 also published by Yale University Press, 1962.
Includes bibliographies.

1. Ethnology - Micronesia. I. Title.

NN 0063345   NBuU

National Research Council. *Pacific Science Board.*
Scientific investigations in the Ryūkyū Islands (SIRI) ₁report₎ no. 1-
Washington, 1952.
v. illus. 29 cm.

1. Ethnology—Ryukyu Islands.   ɪ. Title.

DS895.R9N3   572.95281   53-36748 ‡

NN 0063346   DLC CaBVaU

GN669 .M8

National Research Council. Pacific Science Board.

Murdock, George Peter, 1897-
Social organization and government in Micronesia; final report. ₁Washington₎ Pacific Science Board, National Research Council ₁1949₎

DU500 .P3 pt.6

National research council. Pacific science board.
Vertebrate ecology of Arno, Marshall islands. Tucson, Univ. of Arizona press, 1950.
42 p. (N7-onr-291; T.O. IV. SIM report no.6)

1. Scientific investigations in Micronesia, 1949-1590. 2. P05.3(Arno atoll) - Marine biology. 3. Marine biology - Marshall islands(Arno atoll). 4. Series: SIM report no. 6. 5. Title.

NN 0063348   DS

---

437 N21

National Research Council. Pacific Science Board. Invertebrate Consultants Committee for Micronesia.
The problem of the giant African snail (Achatina fulica) in Micronesia.   ₁n. p., 1951?₎
30, 13 l.

Abridgement of original Final report of March 1950.

NN 0063349   DNAL

National Research Council. Pacific Science Board. Invertebrate Consultants Committee for the Pacific.
Report for 1847-1948
see   Bryan, Edwin Horace, 1898-
Economic insects of Micronesia.

422.9 N212

National Research Council. Pacific Science Board. Invertebrate Consultants Committee for the Pacific.
Report for 1949-1954.   Washington, 1954.
56 p.

1. Pacific Area. Entomology. I. Pemberton, Cyril Eugene, 1886-

NN 0063351   DNAL NIC

National Research Council. Pacific Science Board. Public Survey Unit.
Scientific investigations in the Ryukyu Islands; final report ...
see under   Ishino, Iwao, 1921-

National Research Council. Paleoecology and Marine Ecology, Committee on
see   National Research Council. Committee on a Treatise on Marine Ecology and Paleoecology.

National Research Council. Panel on Blood Coagulation.
Second conference on platelets

see under

National Research Council. Committee on Medicine and Surgery.

National Research Council. Panel on Metals for Use at Low Temperatures.
Report on research and development of metals and alloys for low temperature applications

see under

National Research Council. Materials Advisory Board.

National Research Council. *Panel on the Sterilization of Blood and Plasma.*
Symposium on the laboratory propagation and detection of the agent of hepatitis, held under the joint sponsorship of the Panel on the Sterilization of Blood and Plasma of the National Academy of Sciences, National Research Council, and the Commission on Virus and Rickettsial Diseases of the Armed Forces Epidemiological Board, Bellevue Hospital, New York City, 31 March, 1954. John R. Paul, chairman. Washington, National Academy of Sciences, National Research Council, 1954.

115 p. illus., tables. 25 cm. (National Research Council. Publication 322)

Includes bibliographies.

1. Hepatitis, Infectious.   ɪ. U. S. Armed Forces Epidemiological Board. Commission on Virus and Rickettsial Diseases. ɪɪ. Title. (Series)

RC848.I 6N3 1954   616.36   54-60812

OrP Wa OrU
PPT*M PPC PPJ PBL PPPCPh DNLM OCIW PPWM PSt IU MoU
NN 0063357   DLC CaBVaU WaTC IdPI PPSKF NN ViU NcD

National Research Council. Panel on Underwater Swimmers
see   National Research Council. Committee on Amphibious Operations. Panel on Underwater Swimmers.

National Research Council. Panel on Venereal Diseases.
Minutes of meeting
see under   National Research Council. Subcommittee on Venereal Diseases.

National research council. *Patent committee.*
... Report of the Patent committee of the National research council, presented for the Committee by L. H. Baekeland, acting chairman ... ₁Washington, D. C., National research council, 1919₎
cover-title, 24 p. 24ᶜᵐ. (Reprint and circular series of the National research council, no. 1)
"Published (without proposed bills) in Chemical and metallurgical engineering, February, 1919, vol. 20, no. 4, pages 150–151."

1. Patent laws and legislation—U. S.   ɪ. Baekeland, Leo Hendrik, 1863-
C D 34-2
Library of Congress   Card Div. Q11.N293 no. 1

OOxM MiU NN
NN 0063360   DLC OrPR OrU CoU ViU OCIW OU OCU OCl

National Research Council. Pharmacognosy and Pharmaceutical Botany Committee
see   National Research Council. Committee on Pharmacognosy and Pharmaceutical Botany.

National research council. *Photo-electric committee.*

Hughes, Arthur Llewelyn, 1883-
... Report on photo-electricity, including ionizing and radiating potentials and related effects, by Arthur Llewelyn Hughes ... Washington, D. C., Published by the National research council of the National academy of sciences, 1921.

National Research Council. Physical Sciences, Division of
see   National Research Council. Committee on Physical Sciences (1951-   )

VOLUME 407

National Research Council. *Prevention of Deterioration Center.*
Deterioration of materials: causes and preventive techniques; a collaboration under the joint auspices of the Services Technical Committee of the Dept. of Defense (contract no. N7onr–29127) and the Prevention of Deterioration Center, Division of Chemistry and Chemical Technology, National Academy of Sciences–National Research Council. Edited by Glenn A. Greathouse and Carl J. Wessel, director

and associate director, respectively, Prevention of Deterioration Center. New York, Reinhold Pub. Corp., 1954.

xvii, 835 p. illus., fold. col. map. 24 cm.

Includes bibliographies.

1. Materials—Deterioration. 2. Preservation of materials. I. Greathouse, Glenn Arthur, 1903– ed. II. Wessel, Carl John, 1911– ed. III. Title.

TA407.N3   620.1   54—7343

CaBVaU CaBVa MtBC OrCS OrP Wa WaS WaSp WaT IdPI
PU–Sc OCl PPJ PPD PBL NcD MiHM AU DSI ICN OC1W OC1U
NN 0063364   DLC MsSM OCU OOxM NN ICJ PPF NcRS MB

National Research Council. Prevention of Deterioration Center.
Fungicides: chemical, physical and biological data. [n. p., 1953–
v. (loose-leaf) 29 cm.
Caption title.
On spine: PDC handbook.
Includes bibliography.
1. Fungicides. I. Title.

NN 0063365   NcD

Z
7996
M7
N3

National Research Council. Prevention of Deterioration Center.
Informal bibliography on marine borers.
Washington, 1953.
9 l. 28 cm.

1. Marine borers—Bibl. I. Title.

NN 0063366   AkU

National Research Council. Prevention of Deterioration Center.
Minutes of the symposium on corrosion
see under Symposium on Corrosion, Washington, D.C., 1949.

TA407
.A1P7

National research council. Prevention of deterioration center.
Prevention of deterioration abstracts. v. 1–
Washington, D. C., Prevention of deterioration center, National research council, National academy of sciences [1946–

Z5853
.M4P75

National Research Council. Prevention of Deterioration Center.
Prevention of deterioration advance list.
Washington, Prevention of Deterioration Center, National Research Council.

National Research Council. *Prevention of Deterioration Center.*
Proceedings, Wrightsville Beach marine conference.
Washington, National Academy of Sciences, National Research Council.

v. illus. 25 cm. (National Research Council. Publication
Conference for   held under the joint auspices of the International Nickel Company and the Prevention of Deterioration Center.
1. Marine borers—Congresses. I. International Nickel Company. II. Title: Wrightsville Beach marine conference. (Series)

TC201.N35   691.1   52–61857 ‡

CSt DI LU NN CU NcD
NN 0063370   DLC OrU WaTC OrP MiHM NNC NcU TxU MiU

RD756
.A1A7

National Research Council. Prosthetics Research Board.
Artificial limbs. v. 1–
Jan. 1954–
[Washington]

National Research Council. *Prosthetics Research Board*
see also
National Research Council. *Advisory Committee on Artificial Limbs.*

National research council. *Psychology committee.*
... Report of the Psychology committee of the National research council, presented for the Committee by Robert M. Yerkes, chairman ... [Washington, D. C., National research council, 1919]
cover-title, 51 p. 24ᵐ. (Reprint and circular series of the National research council. no. 2)
"Published in the Psychological review, March, 1919, vol. 26, pages 83–149."

1. Mental tests. 2. Ability tests. 3. Psychology, Applied. I. Yerkes, Robert Mearns, 1876–
                                        C D 34–3
Library of Congress   Card Div. Q11.N293 no. 2

NNU–W   MiU MH
NN 0063373   MtU OrU DNW CoU NN ViU OCU OU OC1

National Research Council. Psychology Committee. Sub-committee on Methods of Examining Recruits
see National Research Council. Sub-committee on Methods of Examining Recruits.

National Research Council. Quartermaster Research and Development, Advisory Board on
see National Research Council. Advisory Board on Quartermaster Research and Development.

National Research Council. Radiation Biology, Committee on
see National Research Council. Committee on Radiation Biology.

National Research Council. *Research Analysis Group*
see
Research Analysis Group.

National research council. *Research information service.*   FOR OTHER EDITIONS SEE MAIN ENTRY
National research council. *Committee on research chemicals.*
... American research chemicals; comp. for the Committee on research chemicals and the Research information service by Clarence J. West, National research council. Washington, D. C., 1921.

National research council. *Research information service.*
... Bibliography of bibliographies on chemistry and chemical technology, 1900–1924; compiled by Clarence J. West and D. D. Berolzheimer for Research information service, National research council. Washington, D. C., Published by the National research council of the National academy of sciences, 1925.
cover-title, 308 p. 25ᵐ. (Bulletin of the National research council. no. 50 (v. 9, pt. 3) Mar. 1925)
                                        Q11.N292 no. 50
——— Copy 4.   Z5521.A1N3

Continued in next column

Continued from preceding column

——— ———First-   supplement, 1924– Compiled for Research information service by Clarence J. West and D. D. Berolzheimer. Washington, D. C., Published by the National research council of the National academy of sciences, 1929–
v. 24ᵐ. (Bulletin of the National research council. no. 71, 86; June 1929, Mar. 1932)
1. Bibliography—Chemistry. 2. Bibliography—Bibl.—Chemistry, Technical. 3. Chemistry — Bibl. 4. Chemistry, Technical — Bibl. I. West, Clarence Jay, 1886– II. Berolzheimer, Daniel Deronda, 1877–
                                        29—16995
Library of Congress   Q11.N292 no. 71, 86

OCl MiHM ICJ KEmT
NIC CSt NcRS NcD OO ODW ViU NN OU MiU MB OOxM OCU
NN 0063380   DLC KEmT WaWW CaBVaU OrU WaTC OrPR MeB

National research council. *Research information service.*
... Bibliography of bibliographies on psychology, 1900–1927; compiled by C. M. Louttit ... for Research information service, National research council. Washington, D. C., Published by the National research council of the National academy of sciences, 1928.
108 p. 24½ᵐ. (Bulletin of the National research council. no. 65, Nov. 1928)
CONTENTS.— Introduction.—pt. I. List of periodicals and general works searched.—pt. II. List of general bibliographies in psychology and allied subjects.—pt. III. List of bibliographies.—pt. IV. Subject index.
1. Psychology—Bibl. 2. Bibliography—Bibl.—Psychology. I. Louttit, Chauncey McKinley. II. Title.
                                        29–4566
Library of Congress   Q11.N292 no. 65

MiU OO OCU OCX ViU MB OC1W ICJ TxU
NN 0063381   DLC WaTC OrPR WaS OrU CaBVaU ICU NcD

National research council. Research information service.
Knobel, Max, 1898–
Bibliography of electro-organic chemistry, by Max Knobel, C. J. Brockman and Research information service, National research council. Washington, D. C., National research council, 1926.

National research council. Research information service.
Mathews, Edward Bennett, 1869–
... Catalogue of published bibliographies in geology, 1896–1920. Compiled by Edward B. Mathews for Research information service and Division of geology and geography, National research council. Washington, D. C., Published by the National research council of the National academy of sciences, 1923.

National research council. *Research information service.*
... Classified list of published bibliographies in physics, 1910–1922. Compiled for Research information service by Karl K. Darrow. Washington, D. C., Published by the National research council of the National academy of sciences, 1924.
cover-title, v, 102 p. 25ᵐ. (Bulletin of the National research council. no. 47 (v. 8, pt. 5) July 1924)
1. Bibliography—Bibl.—Physics. 2. Physics—Bibl. I. Darrow, Karl Kelchner, 1891– II. Title. III. Title: Bibliographies in physics.
                                        25–5123 Revised
Library of Congress   Q11.N292 no. 47
——— ——— Copy 2.
——— ——— Copy 3.
——— ——— Copy 4.   Z7141.A1N1

OrU ViU MeB
OCU OCl OCX OU TxU ViU WaS WaTC OrPR KEmT CaBVaU
NN 0063384   DLC WaWW OC1W MiU MB MiEM NcRS MiU OO

National research council. *Research information service.*
... Doctorates conferred in the sciences by American universities ... 1919/20–
Washington, D. C., National research council, 1920–
v. 25 cm. (Reprint and circular series of the National research council. no. 12, 26, 42, 75, 80, 86, 91.
Incomplete: 1919/20 (Repr. and circ. ser. no. 12) wanting.
Title varies: 1919/20–1920/21, Doctorates conferred in the sciences ... 1921/22, Doctorates conferred in the arts and sciences ... 1925/26– Doctorates conferred in the sciences ...
Compilers: 1919/20, Callie Hull.—1920/21– Callie Hull and Clarence J. West.

The first of this series, 1919/20, appeared in Science, v. 52, 1920, and as Repr. and circ. ser. no. 12 (out of print); 1920/21, in Science, v. 55, 1922, and as Repr. and circ. ser. no. 26; 1921/22, in School and society, v. 17, 1923, and as Repr. and circ. ser., no. 42. 1922–25 not published. Statistics for chemistry for these years were published in Journal of chemical education, v. 3, 1926 (p. 77–90), and for the medical sciences in Archives of pathology and laboratory medicine, v. 1, 1926 (p. 259–262.)
1. Dissertations, Academic—U. S.—Bibl. 2. Science—Bibl. I. Hull, Callie. II. West, Clarence Jay, 1886– III. Title.
Q11.N293   30—17654
——— ——— 3d set.   Z5055.U49N2

CaBVaU OrPR
NN 0063386   DLC CoU FTaSU OCU OU OOxM OC1W MiU NN

VOLUME 407

National research council. *Research information service.*
... Fellowships and scholarships for advanced work in science and technology. Compiled by Research information service. Washington, D. C., Published by the National research council of the National academy of sciences, 1923.
cover-title, 94 p. 25cm. (Bulletin of the National research council. no. 38 (v. 7, pt. 2) Nov. 1923)

1. Scholarships—U. S. I. Title.
24-11295 Revised
Library of Congress Q11.N292 no. 38

OCl MiU OU ViU MB
NN 0063387 DLC CaBVaU OrPR OrU NcD NcRS OOxM OO

National research council. *Research information service.*
... Fellowships and scholarships for advanced work in science and technology. 2d ed. Compiled by Callie Hull and Clarence J. West for Research information service, National research council. Washington, D. C., Published by the National research council of the National academy of sciences, 1929.
154 p. 24½cm. (Bulletin of the National research council. no. 72, Aug. 1929)
The 1st edition was published as Bulletin no. 38 (v. 7, pt. 2) of the National research council, November, 1923.
1. Scholarships—U. S. 2. Endowment of research. I. Hull, Callie. II. West, Clarence Jay, 1886– III. Title.
29—28504
Library of Congress Q11.N292 no. 72
——— Copy 2. LB2338.N3 1929

OO NcD MH MB ViU IU
NN 0063388 DLC CaBVaU OrPR WaTC OrU OCl OU OCU

National research council. *Research information service.*
... Fellowships and scholarships for advanced work in science and technology. 3d ed. Compiled by Callie Hull and Clarence J. West for Research information service, National research council. Washington, D. C., Published by the National research council of the National academy of sciences, 1934.
194 p. 24½ cm. (Bulletin of the National research council. no. 94, June 1934)
The 1st and 2d editions were published as Bulletin of the National research council, no. 38, Nov. 1923 and no. 72, Aug. 1929, respectively.
1. Scholarships—U. S. 2. Endowment of research. I. Hull, Callie. II. West, Clarence Jay, 1886-1953. III. Title.
Q11.N292 no. 94 507.2 34—29509

ViU NN CaBVaU OrPR
NN 0063389 DLC NcRS DNLM OCl OClW OO OCU PSt

National research council. *Research information service.*
... I. The fourth census of graduate research students in chemistry, 1927. II. Support of graduate research in chemistry in American universities, 1927–1928. Compiled for Research information service, National research council by Clarence J. West and Callie Hull ... [Washington, D. C., National research council, 1928]
13 p. tables (1 fold.) 24cm. (Reprint and circular series of the National research council. no. 84)
"Reprinted from Journal of chemical education, July, 1928, vol. 5, no. 7, pp. 882–884; and August, 1928, vol. 5, no. 8, pp. 1005–1014."
1. Research—Statistics. I. West, Clarence Jay, 1886– II. Hull, Callie.
C D 34-58
Library of Congress. Card div. Q11.N293 no. 84

NN 0063390 OOxM OCl OClW

National research council. *Research information service.*
... Funds available in 1920 in the United States of America for the encouragement of scientific research. Compiled by the Research information service, National research council; Callie Hull, technical assistant. Washington, D. C., Published by the National research council of the National academy of sciences, 1921.
cover-title, 81 p. 25cm. (Bulletin of the National research council. no. 9 (v. 2, pt. 1) Mar. 1921)
Second edition published as Bulletin no. 66 of the National research council, Nov. 1928.
1. Endowment of research. 2. U. S.—Learned institutions and societies. I. Hull, Callie. II. Title.
21-11379 Revised
Library of Congress Q11.N292 no. 9
——— Copy 2.
——— Copy 3. [r31f2]
——— Copy 4. Q181.N37 1920

OOxm
NN 0063391 DLC CaBVaU OrPR OrU OCU OU MiU OO ViU

National research council. *Research information service.*
... Funds available in the United States for the support and encouragement of research in science and its technologies. 2d ed. Compiled for Research information service by Callie Hull and Clarence J. West. Washington, D. C., Published by the National research council of the National academy of sciences, 1928.
90 p. 24½cm. (Bulletin of the National research council. no. 66, Nov. 1928)
The 1st edition was published as Bulletin of the National research council, no. 9 (v. 2, pt. 1) Mar., 1921.
1. Endowment of research. 2. U. S.—Learned institutions and societies. I. Hull, Callie. II. West, Clarence Jay, 1886– III. Title. IV. Title: Research in science.
29-4565 Revised
Library of Congress Q11.N292 no. 66

OOxM NcD ViU MB ICJ
NN 0063392 DLC CaBVaU OrPR OrU WaTC OCl OO OCU

National research council. *Research information service.*
... Funds available in the United States for the support and encouragement of research in science and its technologies. 3d ed. Compiled for Research information service by Callie Hull and Clarence J. West. Washington, D. C., Published by the National research council of the National academy of sciences, 1934.
162 p. 24½ cm. (Bulletin of the National research council. No. 95, June 1934)
The 1st and 2d editions were published as Bulletin of the National research council, no. 9, 1920 and no. 6. Nov. 1928, respectively.
1. Endowment of research. 2. U. S.—Learned institutions and societies. I. Hull, Callie. II. West, Clarence Jay, 1886– III. Title. IV. Title: Research in science.
Q11.N292 no. 95 507.2 34—29510

LU OrPS CaBVaU WaTC DHEW
NN 0063393 DLC NcRS OCl OO OCU OClW DNLM ViU NN

National research council. Research information service.
... Handbook of scientific and technical societies and instutitions of the United States and Canada
see Scientific and technical societies of the United States and Canada.

National Research Council. *Research Information Service.*
Industrial research laboratories of the United States
see **Industrial** research laboratories of the United States.

National research council. *Research information service.*
... Intellectual and educational status of the medical profession as represented in the United States Army, by Margaret V. Cobb and Robert M. Yerkes. Washington, D. C., Published by the National research council of the National academy of sciences, 1921.
cover-title, [457]-532 p. diagrs. 25 cm. (Bulletin of the National research council. no. 8 (v. 1, pt. 8) Feb. 1921)

1. U. S. Army—Surgeons. 2. Physicians—U. S. I. Cobb, Margaret Vara, 1884– II. Yerkes, Robert Mearns, 1876– III. Title.
Q11.N292 no. 8 22—19382

OrU WaTC OrPR CaBVaU DHEW
NN 0063396 DLC OClW MiU OCU OO OU NcRS ViU MeWC

Q11 .N293 no. 20
National research council. Research information service.
Swanton, Walter Irving, 1869–
... Libraries in the District of Columbia, comp. by W. I. Swanton in co-operation with the Research information service of the National research council and Special libraries ... [Washington, D. C., National research council, 1921]

National research council. *Research information service.*
... List of manuscript bibliographies in astronomy, mathematics and physics, comp. for Research information service, National research council, by Clarence J. West and Callie Hull. Washington, D. C., 1923.
cover-title, 14 p. 26 cm. (Reprint and circular series of the National research council. no. 41)

1. Bibliography—Bibl.—Astronomy. 2. Bibliography—Bibl.—Mathematics. 3. Bibliography—Bibl.—Physics. 4. Astronomy—Bibl. 5. Mathematics—Bibl. 6. Physics—Bibl. I. West, Clarence Jay, 1886-1953. II. Hull, Callie.
Q11.N293 no. 41 23—10831

OrU KEmT
NN 0063398 DLC MiU OOxM OCU OCX ViU NN CoU WaS

National research council. *Research information service.*
... List of manuscript bibliographies in chemistry and chemical technology, comp. for Research information service, National research council, by Clarence J. West and Callie Hull ... [Washington, 1922]
cover-title, 17 p. 25½cm. (Reprint and circular series of the National research council. no. 36)
"Reprinted from the Journal of industrial and engineering chemistry, vol. 14, no. 12, page 1075, December, 1922."
1. Bibliography—Bibl.—Chemistry. 2. Bibliography — Bibl. — Technical chemistry. 3. Chemistry—Bibl. 4. Chemistry, Technical—Bibl. I. West, Clarence Jay, 1886– II. Hull, Callie.
23—10830
Library of Congress Q11.N293 no. 36
——— Copy 3. Z5521.A1N2

CoU CU
NN 0063399 DLC WaS OrU OOxM OCl OClW MiU ViU NN

National research council. *Research information service.*
... List of manuscript bibliographies in the biological sciences, comp. for Research information service by Clarence J. West and Callie Hull. Washington, D. C., 1923.
cover-title, 51 p. 24½cm. (Reprint and circular series of the National research council no. 45)
Arranged under subjects.
Classification used in the list: p. 2–3.

1. Bibliography—Bibl.—Biology. 2. Biology—Bibl. I. West, Clarence Jay, 1886– II. Hull, Callie.
23-12134
Library of Congress Q11.N293 no. 45
——— Copy 3. Z5320.N27

OCU ICJ OrU
NN 0063400 DLC KEmT NIC ViU OClW OU NN OCl MiU

Z5523 .A52
National Research Council. Research Information Series.
American Chemical Society.
List of periodicals abstracted by Chemical abstracts, with key to library files and other information.
Columbus, O.

National research council. *Research information service.*
... A list of seismologic stations of the world. Compiled under the auspices of the Section of seismology of the American geophysical union with the cooperation and assistance of the Research information service, National research council, United States of America, by Harry O. Wood ... Washington, D. C., Published by the National research council of the National academy of sciences, 1921.
cover-title, p. 397–538. 25cm. (Bulletin of the National research council. no. 15 (v. 2, pt. 7) July 1921)

Second edition published as Bulletin no. 82 of the National research council, Apr. 1931.

1. Earthquakes—Observatories. I. American geophysical union. Section of seismology. II. Wood, Harry Oscar, 1879– III. Title. IV. Title: Seismologic stations of the world.
22-3007 Revised
Library of Congress Q11.N292 no. 15
——— Copy 2.
——— Copy 3.
——— Copy 4. QE540.A2N3 1921

NN 0063403 DLC CaBVaU OrPR MiU OU OO ViU

National research council. *Research information service.*
... List of seismological stations of the world. 2d ed. Compiled under the auspices of the Section of seismology of the American geophysical union with the cooperation of the Research information service, National research council, U. S. A., by H. E. McComb ... and Clarence J. West ... Washington, D. C., Published by the National research council of the National academy of sciences, 1931.
2 p. l., 119 p. 24½cm. (Bulletin of the National research council. no. 82, Apr. 1931)
First edition published as Bulletin no. 15 of the National research council. July 1921.
1. Earthquakes—Observatories. I. American geophysical union. Section of seismology. II. McComb, Harold Edgar, 1886– III. West, Clarence Jay, 1886– IV. Title: Seismological stations of the world.
Library of Congress Q11.N292 no. 82 31—21783

OCU OO OCl OClW MiU ViU MB
NN 0063404 DLC CaBVaU WaTC OrPR DAS MU OrU NcRS

National research council. *Research information service.*
... Mechanical aids for the classification of American investigators, with illustrations in the field of psychology, by Harold C. Bingham ... Washington, D. C., Published by the National research council of the National academy of sciences, 1922.
cover-title, 50 p. plates, diagrs. 25cm. (Bulletin of the National research council. no. 22 (v. 4, pt. 4) Nov. 1922)
A study of methods, especially of the Findex system, for handling personnel records.
I. Bingham, Harold Clyde. 1888– II. Title. III. Title: Classification of American investigators. IV. Title: American investigators, Classification of. V. Title: Personnel records. VI. Title: Findex system.
23-13636 Revised
Library of Congress Q11.N292 no. 22

OCl OO OOxM ViU NN OrU WaTC OrPR
NN 0063405 DLC OrSaW CaBVaU KEmT NcD MiU OCU OU

National research council. *Research information service.*
... Periodical bibliographies and abstracts for the scientific and technological journals of the world. Compiled by Ruth Cobb ... Washington, D. C., Published by the National research council of the National academy of sciences, 1920.
cover-title, p. [131]-154. 25cm. (Bulletin of the National research council. no. 3 (v. 1, pt. 3) June 1920)
1. Science—Period.—Bibl. 2. Technology—Period.—Bibl. 3. Medicine—Period.—Bibl. 4. Bibliography—Bibl.—Science. 5. Bibliography—Bibl.—Technology. 6. Bibliography—Bibl.—Medicine. 7. Periodicals—Bibl. I. Cobb, Ruth. II. Title. III. Title: Abstracts for the scientific and technological journals of the world.
21-26023 Revised
Library of Congress Q11.N292 no. 3
——— Copy 2.
——— Copy 3.
——— Copy 4. Z7403.N27

WaWW MiU OCU OO OU OOxM ICJ ViU CaBVaU
NN 0063406 DLC NBuG MH-A OClW WaTC OrPR OrU WaS

VOLUME 407

National Research Council. *Research* **L507.161 5**
Information Service.
140173 [Publications.]
Includes report of the annual meeting.

NN 0063407 ICJ

National Research Council. **L010.6119 8300**
Research Information Service.
187847 Report of a conference on bibliography held in the offices of the
National Research Council, ... Washington, D. C., Saturday,
March 31, 1923. [Washington, D. C., 1923.]
[4], 49 p. 29ᵐ.
Caption title.
Mimeographed.
"This conference is primarily for the purpose of discussing the matter of indexing and
abstracting scientific literature."—p. [1].

NN 0063408 ICJ

National Research Council. *Research Information Service.* **L507 8201**
Reconnaissance survey of the scientific and technological infor-
150567 mation agencies of the world. Prepared for Research Infor-
mation Service, National Research Council, by Mr. J. David
Thompson. [Washington?], 1922.
[1], 27 leaves. IX charts. 29½ᶜᵐ.
Caption title.
Mimeographed.

NN 0063409 ICJ

National research council. Research Information
Service.
Reports (mimeographed).
v. 28 1/x22 cm.

NN 0063410 DBS

NATIONAL RESEARCH COUNCIL - RESEARCH INFORMA-
TION SERVICE
The research information service of the
National research council; a clearing-house for
information about the mathematical, physical
and biological sciences and their applications
in industry, commerce and education. Author
[1921?]
8 p.

NN 0063411 Or

National Research Council. *Research Information Service.*
Research information surveys on corrosion of metals, com-
piled by Harold F. Whittaker. Washington, 1923–24.
6 no. in 1 v. 28 cm.
Each part has special t. p.
Includes bibliographies.

1. Corrosion and anti-corrosives.   I. Whittaker, Harold Franklin,
1891–   comp.   I. Title.

TA459.N3   24–11386 rev*

NN 0063412 DLC MiU OCU OC1 NcRS ICJ IU

National Research Council. *Research Information Service.*
Research laboratories in industrial establishments of the
United States
see **Industrial** research laboratories of the United States.

National research council. *Research information service.*
Union list of foreign serials cited in Psychological index 1922 currently received in 114 libraries ... Issued by
Research information service of the National research
council. Washington, D. C., 1925.
cover-title, 4 p. l., 21 numb. l. 28ᵐ.
Mimeographed.

1. Periodicals—Bibl.—Union lists. 2. Medicine—Period.—Bibl. 3. Psychology—Period.—Bibl.   I. Title.

26–2923
Library of Congress   Z6945.N29

NN 0063414 DLC CU OC1 ODW OO OU OCU MiU ICJ

National Research Council. *Rock-Color Chart Committee.*
Rock-color chart. Washington, 1948.
[16] p. illus., mounted samples. 19 cm.
Cover title.

1. Rocks. 2. Color.   I. Title.

G S 49–39*
U. S. Geol. Survey. Libr.
for Library of Congress   [3]

NN 0063415 DI-GS MtBuM WaT OCU PBm OU NNC

National Research Council. Rock-color Chart
Committee.
Rock-color chart. New York, Distributed by
the Geological Society of America, 1951.
[16 p.] col. samples.

I. Title. 552 535.63

NN 0063416 ICJ NcD

National research council. Science advisory board
see Science advisory board.

National research council. Science advisory committee.
... Abstracts of reports of sub-committees. [New York, 1930]
82 l. 28½cm.

At head of title: National research council, Science advisory committee to A
century of progress, Chicago world's fair centennial celebration, 1933.
Reproduced from typewritten copy; cover printed.

207495B. 1. Exhibitions—Chicago,   1933.
N. Y. P. L.   January 29, 1943

NN 0063418 NN ICRL

National Research Council. Scientific Aids to
Learning, Committee on
see National Research Council. Committee
on Scientific Aids to Learning.

National Research Council. Sedimentation,
Committee on Symposium on
see National Research council. Committee on Symposium on sedimentation.

National research council. *Selection and training of
aircraft pilots, Committee on*
see
National research council. *Committee on selection and training of aircraft pilots.*

National Research Council. Ship Hull Research Committee.
The Committee on Ship Construction of the National Research
Council was appointed in 1946. In 1948 it was reconstituted as the
Committee on Ship Steel, and in 1952 the parallel Committee on
Ship Structural Design was appointed. In 1963 these two commit-
tees were replaced by the Ship Hull Research Committee, which
was reorganized in 1968 under the name Ship Research Committee.
Works by these bodies are found under the following headings
according to the name used at the time of publication:

National Research Council. Committee on Ship Construction.
National Research Council. Committee on Ship Steel.

National Research Council. Ship Research Committee.
The Committee on Ship Construction of the National Research
Council was appointed in 1946. In 1948 it was reconstituted as the
Committee on Ship Steel, and in 1952 the parallel Committee on
Ship Structural Design was appointed. In 1963 these two commit-
tees were replaced by the Ship Hull Research Committee, which
was reorganized in 1968 under the name Ship Research Committee.
Works by these bodies are found under the following headings
according to the name used at the time of publication:

National Research Council. Committee on Ship Construction.
National Research Council. Committee on Ship Steel.

National Research Council. *Special Committee on Highway
Laws*
see
National Research Council. *Highway Research Board.
Special Committee on Highway Laws.*

National research council. Sterilization of blood
and plasma, Panel on the.
See
National research council. Panel on the sterilization
of blood and plasma.

RD81   National Research Council. Subcommittee on
.F8   Anesthesia.   FOR OTHER EDITIONS
1944   SEE MAIN ENTRY
         Fundamentals of anesthesia, an outline, by Subcommittee on
         Anesthesia of Division of Medical Sciences, National Re-
         search Council. 2d ed. Chicago, American Medical Asso-
         ciation Press, 1944.

National Research Council. Sub-committee on
Anesthesia.
Fundamentos de anestesia
see under title

National Research Council. Subcommittee on
Animal Nutrition
see National Research Council. Committee
on Animal Nutrition.

National Research Council. Subcommittee on
Blood and Related Problems
see National Research Council. Committee
on Blood and Transfusion Problems.

National Research Council. Subcommittee on
Blood Substitutes.
The operation of a hospital transfusion
service
see under United States. Office of
Civilian Defense. Medical Division.

National research council. *Subcommittee on blood substi-
tutes.*
A technical manual on citrated human blood plasma, detail-
ing its procurement, processing, and use. Washington, D. C.,
U. S. Office of civilian defense [1942]
cover-title, 1 p. l., 41 p. 26 x 20ᵐ.
"Prepared for the Medical division, U. S. Office of civilian defense,
under the direction of the Subcommittee on blood substitutes of the
National research council."
Reproduced from type-written copy.

1. Blood—Plasma. 2. Blood—Transfusion.   I. U. S. Office of
civilian defense. Medical division. II. Title: Citrated human blood
plasma.   42–38437
Library of Congress   QP91.N3
                             [2]   615.37

NN 0063431 DLC DNLM

National research council. *Subcommittee on blood substitutes.*
A technical manual on the preservation and transfusion of
whole human blood. Washington, D. C., U. S. Office of civilian defense [1942]
cover-title, 1 p. l., 31 p. 26¼ᵐ.
"Prepared for the Medical division, U. S. Office of civilian defense,
under the direction of the Subcommittee on blood substitutes of the National research council."
Page 31 is p. [3] of cover.
Reproduced from type-written copy.
"References": p. 28–31.

1. Blood—Transfusion.   I. U. S. Office of civilian defense. Medical division.   42–38438
Library of Congress   RM171.N38
                             [2]   615.65

NN 0063432 DLC

VOLUME 407

National research council. *Subcommittee on chemilumines-cence.*

... Chemiluminescence; report of the subcommittee on chemiluminescence: E. Newton Harvey, chairman; Eliot Q. Adams, Allen D. Garrison, A. H. Pfund, Hugh S. Taylor ... ₍Washington, D. C., Published by the National research council of the National academy of sciences, 1927₎

62 p. 24½ cm. (Bulletin of the National research council. No. 59, Sept. 1927)

Bibliographical foot-notes.

CONTENTS.—Types of chemiluminescence ₍by₎ Allen D. Garrison.—Experimental methods used in the study of luminescence ₍by₎ A. H. Pfund.—Energetics, spectra, intensity and efficiency of chemiluminescence ₍by₎ Eliot Q. Adams.—Photochemistry and chemiluminescence. Kinetics of chemiluminescence ₍by₎ Hugh S. Taylor.—Bioluminescence ₍by₎ E. Newton Harvey.

1. Radiation.   I. Harvey, Edmund Newton, 1887–   II. Adams, Elliot Quincy, 1888–   III. Garrison, Allen D.   IV. Title.

Library of Congress   Q11.N292 no. 59

28—6659

NN ViU NcRS ICJ IU NIC WaTC OrPR OrU CaBVaU
NN 0063434   DLC LU NIC OO OU OCU OClW OCl MiU

National Research Council. *Subcommittee on Chemistry*
see
National Research Council. *Chemistry Subcommittee.*

National Research Council. Subcommittee on Clearinghouse.
see National Research Council. **Committee on Disaster Studies. Subcommittee on Clearinghouse.**

W 2   NATIONAL Research Council. Subcommittee
A   on Clinical Investigation
N3645r   Report. no. 1-14; 1941-43. ₍Washington?₎
                14 no. in 1 v. illus.
                Continued by the subcommittee's
            Clinical investigation report.
                1. Physiology - Collected works

NN 0063437   DNLM

National research council. *Subcommittee on clothing.*

... Clothing test methods, edited by L. H. Newburgh (physiological tests) and Milton Harris (physical tests) of Subcommittee on clothing of the National research council (U. S. A.) Washington, D. C., 1945.

v, 98 p. diagrs. 27½ x 21½ᶜᵐ.

At head of title: CAM no. 390.
"Lithoprinted."
"References" at end of some of the articles.

1. Clothing and dress.   I. Newburgh, Louis Harry, 1883–   ed.   II. Harris, Milton, 1906–   ed.   III. Title.

45-5946

Library of Congress   RA779.N3

₍2₎   613.48

NN 0063438   DLC DNLM

W   National Research Council. Subcommittee on
1   Clothing.
NA   Minutes. [Washington, 19
61974   v.
                Title varies slightly.

NN 0063439   DNLM

National Research Council. Subcommittee on Decompression Sickness
see National Research Council. **Committee on Aviation Medicine. Subcommittee on Decompression Sickness.**

W   National Research Council. Subcommittee on
1   Diagnosis and Therapeutics
NA6811   Minutes of the meeting.
                ₍Washington, 19
                    v.

NN 0063441   DNLM

National Research Council. Subcommittee on Follow-up Studies.
see National Research Council. **Committee on Dentistry. Subcommittee on Follow-up Studies.**

W 2   NATIONAL Research Council. Subcommittee
A   on Food Supply
N36455b   Bulletin ₍on₎ food supply.
                24 jan. 1948-
            Washington.
                v. illus.
                Title varies slightly.
                Issues for 24 Jan. 1948-   called also
            Minutes of the meeting, 1st-
                Includes the 1949 Conference on Germicidal Rinses and the joint meeting with the

Subcommittee on Water Supply on 12 Feb. 1951.
                1. Disinfection & disinfectants - Period.
            2. Food - Period.   3. Military hygiene -
            Congresses I. Conference on Germicidal Rinses, Washington, D. C., 1949 II. National Research Council. Subcommittee on Water Supply   Title

NN 0063444   DNLM

WA   NATIONAL Research Council. Subcommittee
240   on Food Supply
qN277g   A germicidal rinse compound for field
1952   use of the Armed Forces. ₍Washington₎
                1952.
                21 ₍2₎ p. illus.
                Cover title.
                Appendix: A standardized method for
            the determination of bactericidal activity
            of germicidal compounds containing
            halogens, by W. C. Morse and June C.
            Feder: p. 11-₍23₎

                1. Disinfection & disinfectants
            I. Morse, W   C   A
            standardized method for the determination
            of bactericidal activity of germicidal
            compounds containing halogens

NN 0063446   DNLM

WA   NATIONAL Research Council. Sub-
710   committee on Food Supply
qN277r   Report on the laboratory examination
1952   of frozen food plates, Washington, 1952.
                11 p.
                1. Food - Frozen

NN 0063447   DNLM

632.951
N   National Research Council. Subcommittee on
         Mammalogy.
            Instructions for using sodium fluoroacetate
         (compound 1080) as a rodent poison. Rev. October,
         1948. ₍n.p., 1949?₎
            1 v. 28 cm.

            Includes Addendum, January, 1949.

            1. Rodenticides. 2. Rat baits and repellents.
         3. Sodium fluoroacetate (compound 1080).
         I. Title.

NN 0063448   Wa

National Research Council. Subcommittee on Material and Equipment
see National Research Council. **Division of Medical Sciences. Subcommittee on Material and Equipment.**

W   National Research Council. Subcommittee
1   on Metabolism and Diseases of the
NA6828   Endocrine Glands
                Minutes of meeting.

                ₍Washington, 19
                    v.

NN 0063450   DNLM

UB336
.N3
            National Research Council. Sub-committee on
         Methods of Examining Recruits.
            ...Examiner's guide for the psychological examination of recruits, prepared by the Sub-committee on methods of examining recruits appointed by the Psychology committee of the National research council and the American psychological association, for limited use in the testing and perfecting of methods. ₍Washington, D.C., 1917.
            75p. diagrs. 23cm.

NN 0063451   NNU-W

UB   NATIONAL Research Council. Sub-Com-
336   mittee on Methods of Examining Recruits
N277e   Examiner's guide for the psychological
1917   examination of recruits. Rev. by direction
         of the Surgeon General of the Army.
         ₍Washington₎ Medical Dept., 1917.
            88 p. illus.
            Contains signature of General Gorgas.
            I. U. S. Surgeon-General's Office

NN 0063452   DNLM

National Research Council. Subcommittee on Methods of Examining Recruits.
            Examiner's guide for psychological examining in the army, prepared especially for military use. Rev. by direction of the Surgeon General of the Army and printed by the Medical Department, U. S. A., September 1917. 2d revision. Washington, Govt. Print. Off., 1918.

UB336   108p. illus. 24cm.
918N   At head of title: Confidential ... Name of examiner who is responsible for copy no. 110, Lt. Commander R. Dodge.

            1. U.S. Army - Examinations. 2. Mental tests. I. U.S. Surgeon General's Office. II. Ti   III. Title: Psychological examining in the army.   Prov: Dodge.

NN 0063453   CtY-M

National research council. *Subcommittee on molecular physics.*

... Molecular physics in relation to biology; report of the Subcommittee on molecular physics, of the National research council: M. Ascoli, Robert Chambers ... P. Lecomte du Noüy ... Washington, D. C., Published by the National research council of the National academy of sciences, 1929.

cover-title, 293 p. illus., II pl. (on 1 l.) diagrs. 25ᶜᵐ. (Bulletin of the National research council. no. 69, May 1929)

Chairman of committee: P. Lecomte du Noüy.
Bibliographical references accompany the articles.
1. Biological physics.   I. Lecomte du Noüy, Pierre, 1883–   II. Ascoli, Maurizio, 1876–   III. Chambers, Robert, 1881–   IV. Title.

29-16096

Library of Congress   Q11.N292 no. 69

NcRS OU MiU OClW ViU NcD TxU ICJ MB
NN 0063454   DLC OrSaW WaTC CaBVaU WaWW KEmT OO

W 2   NATIONAL Research Council. Subcommittee
A   on Ophthalmology
N336b   Bulletin of ophthalmology. 4 Jan.
         1944-29 May 1944; ₍new ser.₎ 15 Jan.
         1947-27-28 Sept. 1947. Washington.
            7 no. in   W2A N336b
            Continues the Subcommittee's
         Minutes of meeting.
            Issues for Jan. 15-Sept. 27/28, 1947
         called also Minutes of meeting ₍1st₎-5th.

            Continued by the same title issued by
         the Committee on Ophthalmology of the
         National Research Council.
            1. Ophthalmology - period.   Title

NN 0063456   DNLM

VOLUME 407

W 2
A
N336b

NATIONAL Research Council. Subcommittee
on Ophthalmology
Minutes of meeting. ₁1st₁-6th;
4 Sept. 1942-29 Oct. 1943. Washington.
6 no. in   W2A N336b
Continued by the Subcommittee's
Bulletin of ophthalmology.
1. Ophthalmology - period.

NN 0063457   DNLM

National Research Council. Subcommittee on
Orthopedic Surgery.
Orthopedic subjects
see under National Research Council.
Committee on Surgery.

National Research Council. *Subcommittee on Oxygen and Anoxia*
see
National Research Council. *Committee on Aviation Medicine. Subcommittee on Oxygen and Anoxia.*

W
1
NA68513

National Research Council. Subcommittee
on Personal Relations in Industry
Abstract of minutes of meeting.

₆Washington, 19
v.

NN 0063460   DNLM

W
1
NA68516

National Research Council. Subcommittee
on Pharmacy
₆Minutes₃

₆Washington, 19
v.

NN 0063461   DNLM

RM735
.A6

National research council. Subcommittee on
physical therapy.   FOR OTHER EDITIONS
                         SEE MAIN ENTRY
American medical association. *Council on physical medicine.*
Manual of occupational therapy, prepared by the Council
on physical therapy of the American medical association, the
Committee of the American occupational therapy association,
and the Subcommittee on physical therapy and Committee on
information of the Division of medical sciences of the National
research council. ₆Chicago, 1943₃ OTHER EDITIONS UNDER TITLE

W
1
NA6857

National Research Council. Subcommittee
on Prostheses
Minutes of meeting. 1st₋
Feb. 22, 1948₋
Washington.
v.

NN 0063463   DNLM

National research council. *Subcommittee on protein metabolism in animal feeding.*
... Cooperative experiments upon the protein requirements
for the growth of cattle. First report of the Subcommittee on
protein metabolism in animal feeding, Division of biology and
agriculture, National research council. Presented for the subcommittee by Henry Prentiss Armsby, chairman. Washington, D. C., Published by the National research council of the
National academy of sciences, 1921.
cover-title, p. 219-288. diagrs. 25ᶜᵐ. (Bulletin of the National research council. no. 12 (v. 2, pt. 4) June 1921)
1. Proteids. 2. Cattle. 3. Metabolism. I. Armsby, Henry Prentiss,
1853- II. Title. III. Title: Protein requirements for the growth of
cattle.
                                        21-17039 Revised
Library of Congress   Q11.N292 no. 12

NN 0063464   DLC WaTC OrPR OrU IU MiU OCU OU MB ViU

National Research Council. *Subcommittee on Radiobiology.*
Basic mechanisms in radiobiology; proceedings of ... con-
ference₍s₎ Washington, 1953-
v. illus., diagrs. 25 cm. (Nuclear science series ; ₆report no.
15₁
National Research Council. Publication 305
Part 1 not published.
Includes bibliographies.
CONTENTS.—2. Physical and chemical aspects.—
4. Cellular aspects.
1. Radiation—Physiological effect. I. Title. (Series: National
Research Council. Committee on Nuclear Science. Nuclear science
series; report no. 15 ₆etc.₁ Series: National Research Council. Publication 305 ₆etc.₁)
QC771.N33 no. 15,   etc. *574.191   54-60815 rev 2

NN 0063465   DLC ICJ ViU DNLM NcD NcRS TxU MiU NIC
     ICU FTaSU DPU IU CLSU CtY-M OrCS DNAL GU KyU
     PPF-B NN PPSKF FMU IdPI WaSpG MiHM ICarbS OCU
     PBm PPHa MB NNC PBL N TOU MoU CSt OU OC1W-H PPC

QH652
.C6

National Research Council. Subcommittee on
Radiobiology.

Copp, Douglas Harold, 1915-
Research and training facilities for radiobiology and for
use of isotopes in biology and medicine in the United States
and Canada. Preparation sponsored by Subcommittee on
Radiobiology, National Research Council, Division of
Mathematical and Physical Sciences, Committee on Nuclear
Science. ₆Washington, Division of Mathematical and Phy-
sical Sciences, National Research Council₁ 1950.

National Research Council. *Subcommittee on Radiobiology
see also* Symposium on Radiobiology, Oberlin College,
1950.

National research council. *Subcommittee on rehabilitation.*
Rehabilitation: the man and the job; report of the Subcommittee on rehabilitation of the Committee on work in industry, National research council; Elton Mayo, chairman ...
₆Washington₁ 1945.
5 p. l., 73 p. incl. forms, diagrs. 25ᶜᵐ. (On cover: National research
council. Reprint and circular series, no. 121, March, 1945)

1. Veterans—Employment—U. S.   I. *Mayo, Elton, 1880-
                                              45-36645
Library of Congress *   Q11.N296 no. 121
                     ₆0₁   (506) 355.115

NN 0063469   DLC ViU

UC430
N3
1946
Engin.
Library

National Research Council. Subcommittee on
Sewage Treatment.
Sewage treatment at military installations. Report of the
Subcommittee on Sewage Treatment of the Committee on Sanitary
Engineering, National Research Council, Division of Medical
Science. May 1946. [Lancaster, Pa., 1946]
787-1030 p. illus., map, tables.

Photoprint (positive) of article in Sewage works journal, v.18,
no. 5, Sept. 1946.
F. W. Mohlman, chairman.
"A final summary chapter [is] to be presented in a future issue."
"The NRC report," an editorial: p. 1029-1030.
Includes bibliography.

NN 0063470   CU

QT
245
qN277f
1952

NATIONAL Research Council. Subcommittee
on Shelter and Clothing
Functional requirements for arctic and
tropical shelters and clothing. Washington,
1952.
37 p.
1. Armies - Equipment 2. Clothing

NN 0063471   DNLM

W
1
NA6356

National Research Council. Subcommittee on
Shelter and Clothing.
Minutes of meeting. 1st₋   ; June 1,
1948₋
Washington.
v.

NN 0063472   DNLM

National Research Council. Subcommittee on Shock.
Investigation of "dextraven"

see under

U.S. National Bureau of Standards.

National Research Council. Subcommittee on
Shock
Progress report. Contract no. DA-L9-007-
MD-150.
see under

Iowa. University. College of Medicine.

National Research Council. Subcommittee on
Steroid Nomenclature.
Steroid nomenclature. ₆Chicago?1952?₁
22 L. 30cm.

Caption title.
Chairman of the Subcommittee: Byron
Riegel.

1. Chemistry - Nomenclature.
2. Steroids. I. Rigegel, Ernest Byron,
1906- II. Title.

NN 0063475   PSt

National Research Council. Subcommittee on
Survey and Planning
see [National Research Council. Emergency Committee in Psychology. Subcommittee on
Survey and Planning]

W 2
A
N36426b

NATIONAL Research Council. Subcommittee
on the Chemistry of Blood Coagulation
Bulletin ₆on the₁ chemistry of blood
coagulation. 5. Feb. -13. Nov. 1951.
Washington.
4 no. in 1 v.
Called also Minutes of the meeting,
1st-4th.
Continued by the Bulletin on blood
coagulation issued by the Council's Subcommittee on Blood Coagulation.
1. Blood - Period.

NN 0063477   DNLM

National Research Council. *Subcommittee on the Ecology
of Marine Organisms*
see
National Research Council. *Committee on a Treatise on
Marine Ecology and Paleoecology.*

National research council. *Subcommittee on the value of individual hearing aids for hard of hearing children in
school.*
Learning to use hearing aids; a study of factors influencing the decision of children to wear hearing aids. Report of
the Subcommittee of the Committee on problems of deafness
of the National research council ₆by₁ Arthur I. Gates and
Rose E. Kushner. New York, Teachers college, Columbia
university, 1946.
77 p. 22½ cm.
1. Hearing aids, Mechanical. 2. Children, Deaf. 3. Child study.
I. Gates, Arthur Irving, 1890- II. Kushner, Rose (Estrin) 1907-
III. Title.
RF300.N29   617.8   Med 47-1232
U. S. National Library   of Medicine [W6P3]
for Library of Congress   ₆a60z2;†

ICU
     OrSaW MtU WaTC MH OC1W KEmT NcGU NcRS TxU AAP NIC
NN 0063479   DNLM ICJ DLC PU-Penn N Mi OrPR TU OrP

VOLUME 407

National research council. *Subcommittee on the value of individual hearing aids for hard of hearing children in school.*
    ... The value of individual hearing aids for hard of hearing children; report of the Subcommittee of the Committee on problems of deafness, under the direction of Rudolf Pintner, PH. D. and Arthur I. Gates, PH. D. Washington, D. C., National research council, 1944.
    iv, 40 p. incl. tables. 23ᶜᵐ.
    "The present report, with only minor changes, was written by Dr. Stanton."—p. iii;
    1. Deaf—Education and institutions. 2. Hearing aids, Mechanical. 3. Children, Abnormal and backward. I. Pintner, Rudolf, 1884–1942. II. Gates, Arthur Irving, 1890– III. Stanton, Mildred Bacon, 1890– IV. Title.
    Harvard univ. Library   A 45–2835
       for Library of Congress °   RF300.N3
                   ₍5₎†   617.8

   NN   0063480   MH DLC TxU

WD
105
qN277r
1950
   NATIONAL Research Council. Sub-Committee on Undernutrition and Starvation
      Report. Prepared for the Committee on Therapeutic Nutrition, Food and Nutrition Board, National Research Council. ₍Washington₎ 1950.
      33 ℓ.   WD105 qN277r
      1. Food supply 2. Nutrition - Disorders 3. Starvation

   NN   0063481   DNLM

W 2
A
N366m
   NATIONAL Research Council. Subcommittee on Venereal Diseases
      Minutes of meeting. ₍1st₎–13th; Nov. 7, 1946–Jan. 27, 1955. Washington.
      13 no. in 2 v.
      Also called Bulletin, venereal diseases.
      5th meeting, Jan. 14, 1949, joint meeting with the Syphilis Study Section of the National Institutes of Health.
      Issued Jan. 27, 1955, by the Council's Panel on Venereal Diseases.
      1. Venereal diseases I. National

Research Council. Panel on Veneral Diseases II. U. S. National Institutes of Health. Division of Research Grants and Fellowships. Syphilis Study Section

   NN   0063483   DNLM

National Research Council. Sub-Committee on Volcanology
    see   National Research Council. Division of Mathematical and Physical Sciences. Sub-Committee on Volcanology.

National Research Council. Subcommittee on Waste Disposal.
    Collection and disposal of human wastes

    see under

    Clark, Lloyd K

National Research Council. Subcommittee on Waste Disposal.
    Garbage disposal

    see under

    Alter, Amos J

W
1
NA6937
   National Research Council. Subcommittee on Waste Disposal
      Minutes of meeting.

      Washington ₍194
        v.

   NN   0063487   DNLM

W
1
NA6938
   National Research Council. Subcommittee on Water Supply
      Minutes of meeting.

      Washington ₍194
        v.

      Some meetings held jointly with the Subcommittee on Waste Disposal.

      I. National Research Council. Subcommittee on Waste Disposal

   NN   0063488   DNLM

National Research Council. Subsidiary Committee on Meteorology.
    Meteorology...
      see   National Research Council. Committee on Physics of the Earth. Physics of the earth.

RM666
.A54W57
   National research council. Survey of anti-malarial drugs.
    Wiselogle, Frederick Yager, 1912–   *ed.*
      A survey of antimalarial drugs, 1941–1945 ... Ann Arbor, Mich., Edwards, 1946.

T223
.Z1P18
   National Research Council. Survey of university patent policies.
    Palmer, Archie MacInnes, 1896–
      University patent policies and practices. Washington, National Research Council of the National Academy of Sciences, 1952.

National research council. Symposium on radiobiology, 1950.

    See

Symposium on radiobiology, Oberlin college, 1950.

National Research Council. Tectonics, Committee on
      see   National Research Council. Committee on Tectonics.

W
1
NA6946
   National Research Council. Temporary Subcommittee on Water Inter-Connections and Cross Connections
    ₍Minutes₎

    ₍Washington, 19
      v.

   NN   0063494   DNLM

National Research Council. Transportation Research Board.
    The Advisory Board on Highway Research of the National Research Council was organized in 1920. In 1924, the name was changed to Highway Research Board and in 1974 to Transportation Research Board.
    Works by this body published before the change of name in 1974 are found under

    National Research Council. Highway Research Board.

National Research Council. *United States National Committee on URSI.*
    Program₍ joint meeting ₍of the₎ International Scientific Radio Union, U. S. A. National Committee ₍and₎ Institute of Radio Engineers.
    Washington.
    v. 23 cm.
    Vols. for 19   issued by the committee under an earlier name: American Section, International Scientific Radio Union.
    Meetings for 19   held also in conjunction with the American Geophysical Union, Section of Terrestrial Magnetism and Electricity.
    1. Radio—Societies, etc.   I. Institute of Radio Engineers.
    TK6540.N367   55–43885 ‡

   NN   0063496   DLC NNC TxU

National Research Council. *United States National Committee on URSI.*
    Report on the general assembly of URSI.
    ₍Washington?₎
    v. 28 cm.

    1. International Scientific Radio Union.
    TK5700.I 834   621.3840621   55—31605 ‡

      P CtY OrCS WaTC OrP IdPI NN IU MH-PR MtU MtBC OrU UU
   NN   0063497   DLC OU LU NcU TxU DSI MiU NcD NSyU

TA459
.G5
   National research council. War metallurgy committee.
    Gillett, Horace Wadsworth, 1883–
      An engineering approach to the selection, evaluation and specification of metallic materials, by H. W. Gillett ... Prepared for the War metallurgy committee of National academy of sciences, and the National research council advisory to the National defense research committee of the Office of scientific research and development, and the War production board. ₍Cleveland, The Penton publishing company, 1944₎

National research council. *War metallurgy committee.*
    Information release₍s₎
    ₍Washington₎ War metallurgy committee of the National academy of sciences, National research council ₍19
    nos. 23–28ᶜᵐ.
    Nos.   reproduced from type-written copy.

    1. Metals. 2. Mines and mineral resources. 3. Alloys.
                                44–27559
    Library of Congress   TN1.N3
                  ₍3₎   669.072

   NN   0063499   DLC

TA473
.G5
   National research council. War metallurgy committee.
    Gillett, Horace Wadsworth, 1883–
      Report on behavior of ferritic steels at low temperatures ... by H. W. Gillett and Francis T. McGuire. War metallurgy committee of National academy of sciences, National research council, advisory to National defense research committee of Office of scientific research and development and Office of production research and development of War production board. Philadelphia, Pa., American society for testing materials, 1945.

QD133
.B88
   National research council. War metallurgy committee.
    Brode, Wallace Reed, 1900–
      Report on standard samples for spectrographic analysis, by Wallace R. Brode and Bourdon F. Scribner. Results of survey sponsored by War metallurgy committee of National academy of sciences, National research council, advisory to National defense research committee of Office of scientific research and development and Office of production research and development of War production board. Philadelphia, Pa., American society for testing materials ₍1944₎

National Research Council. War Metallurgy Committee.
    ... Safe substitute solder for food cans; a report to the War production board by the Advisory division of the War metallurgy committee ... [Washington, D.C., 1943]
    8 l. (Information release no. 6)
    1. Solder and soldering. I. National research council. War metallurgy committee. Information release.

   NN   0063502   NNC

National research council. War metallurgy committee.
    Scheme for indexing metallurgical literature. ₍1944?₎
    15 p. 36ᶜᵐ.
    1. Classification - Books - Metallurgy.

   NN   0063503   NNC OClW

VOLUME 407

National Research Council. Waste disposal,
Committee for Investigation of
see   National Research Council. Committee
for Investigation of Waste Disposal.

National Research Council. *Waste Disposal, Subcommittee
on*
see
National Research Council. *Subcommittee on Waste Disposal.*

589.2   National research council, Canada.
N21a   ... Abstracts on fungi and bacteria affecting
various materials, by Muriel E. Whalley ... Ottawa, 1944.
cover-title, 228p.

"N.R.C. no.1215."

1. Fungi. I. Whalley, Muriel E.

NN   0063506   IU ICJ DNAL

National research council, *Canada.*
... Abstracts on penicillin and other antibiotic substances, by
Muriel E. Whalley, Research plans and publications section.
Ottawa, 1943.
cover-title, 1 p. l., 71 p. 27ᶜᵐ.

At head of title: National research council of Canada.
N. R. C. no. 1160.
Reproduced from type-written copy.
"Taken from the American chemical abstracts (1917–September 10,
1943, inclusive) and other material found in the library of the National
research council."

1. Penicillin. 2. ₍Antibiotic substances₎   I. Whalley, Muriel E.

Penn. state college. Libr.   A 44–1520
for Library of Congress   ₍4₎

OU PPUSDA
NN   0063507   PSt OrCS WaS OClW MH NNC NcRS ICJ IU

National research council, *Canada.*
... Abstracts on penicillin and other antibiotic substances.
(2d ed., rev. and enl.) By Muriel E. Whalley ... Ottawa,
1945.
cover-title, 1 p. l., 166, 10 p. 27 x 21ᶜᵐ.

At head of title: National research council of Canada.
Reproduced from type-written copy.
On cover: N. R. C. no. 1284.

1. Penicillin. 2. Antibiotics.   I. Whalley, Muriel S.

                                            46–1558
Library of Congress   RS161.N3 1945
                ₍4₎   615.3292411

NN   0063508   DLC CaBVaU DNLM

National Research Council, *Canada.*
Abstracts on synthetic rubber. 1943–
Ottawa.
v. in   28 cm. (N. R. C. no. 1136–37, 1343–44

Issued in 2 pts.: Articles; Patents.
Issues for 1943–   prepared by M. E. Whalley.

1. Rubber, Artificial—Abstracts.   I. Whalley, Muriel E.

TS1925.A1N3   678   A 45–3123 rev*
Grosvenor Library
for Library of Congress   ₍r47e2₎†

OCl DLC DNAL PPUSDA PPF
NN   0063509   NBuG WaS OrCS ICJ MiD OAkU NcRS OO

National Research Council, Canada.
Abstracts on the production of linseed oil
see under   National Research Council,
Canada. Research Plans and Publications Section.

National Research Council, Canada.
... Abstracts on utilization of sawdust
see under   National Research Council,
Canada. Research Plans and Publications Section.

National Research Council, Canada.
Abstracts on the utilization of straw
see under   National Research Council,
Canada. Research Plans and Publications Section.

National Research Council, Canada.
Abstracts on tall oil
see under   Whalley, Muriel E., comp.

National Research Council, Canada.

Addresses delivered at the official opening
of the Prairie Regional Laboratory, Saskatoon,
Sask. [Ottawa] National Research Council of
Canada [1949?]

72 p.   23 cm.

NN   0063514   CaBVaU

National Research Council, Canada.
Aerial prospecting for radio active materials, by E.
A. Godby [and others]   Chalk River, Ontario [1951]
1 v. (various pagings) illus., charts. 28cm. (Report. AECL-13.)

"CRR-495."
"Mr-17."
A joint report of the Divisions of mechanical engineering and atomic

energy of the National research council laboratories of Canada.

1. Prospecting—Instruments and apparatus. 2. Uranium. I. Canada.
Atomic energy of Canada, limited. II. Canada. Atomic energy of Canada,
limited. Report AECL. t. 1951.

NN   0063516   NN

National Research Council, Canada. Aeronautical
note AN.
National Research Council, Canada. *National Aeronautical
Establishment.*
Note. 1–14. Ottawa, 1948–56.

TL507   National Research Council, Canada. Aeronautical
N32   report AR.
National Research Council, Canada. *National Aeronautical
Establishment.*
Report. 1–23. Ottawa, 1947–58.

TL507   National Research Council, Canada.
N28   Aeronautical report LR.
Ottawa, 195
no. in   v. illus., plates, diagrs. 28 cm.

Title varies: Laboratory report LR.
Issued 195   by the Council's National Aeronautical Establishment.

1. Aeronautics—Collected works.   I. Title.

TL507.N28   63–44805

NN   0063519   DLC NBuU CU IU ICJ NN

National Research Council, Canada.
The analysis of the structural behaviour of
guyed antenna
see under   Schott, G   J

National Research Council, Canada.
Analytical methods for bacterial fermentations

see under

Neish, Arthur Charles.

National Research Council, Canada.
Annotated bibliography on the electrocution of
animals
see under   Whalley, Muriel E.

National Research Council, Canada.
Annual report
see its   Report.

National Research Council, Canada.
Annual report on support of university research. Compte
rendu annuel sur l'aide apportée à la recherche scientifique
dans les universités.
Ottawa.
v. 25 cm.
Report year ends Mar. 31.
English and French.
1. Research—Canada—Yearbooks. 2. Engineering research—Canada—Yearbooks. 3. Universities and colleges—Canada—Finance—Yearbooks. 4. National Research Council, Canada.   I. National
Research Council, Canada. Compte rendu annuel sur l'aide apportée
à la recherche scientifique dans les universités. II. Title. III. Title:
Compte rendu annuel sur l'aide apportée à la recherche scientifique
dans les universités.
Q180.C2N34a   507'.2071   73–645561
                                                    MARC-S

NN   0063524   DLC

National Research Council, Canada.
Antifreeze solutions for use in automobile
radiators
see under   Whalley, Muriel E., comp.

National Research Council, Canada.
Bearing metals and bearings, a list of articles
published between 1942 and 1946
see under   Ruedy, Richard, 1896–

A636.3   National research council, Canada.
N21b   Bibliography on nutrition of sheep, compiled
at the request of the National sheep committee by
Muriel E. Whalley   Ottawa, 1942.
cover-title, 86 numb. l.
N.R.C. no.1059.
Reproduced from typewritten copy.
"Compiled from Nutrition abstracts and reviews
(British) vols.1–10, 1931–41, and Experiment
station record (United States) vols.62–83, 1930–
40."
1. Sheep—Bibl. 2. Nutrition—Bibl. I. Whalley, Muriel E.

NN   0063526   IU DNAL ICJ

National Research Council, Canada.
Bibliography on soil mechanics, 1940–1944
see under   Ruedy, Richard, 1896–

National research council, *Canada.*
... Bibliography on the influence of mineral deficiencies on
growth and reproduction of farm animals, by **Muriel E.**
Whalley, Division of research information. Ottawa, 1937.
2 p. l., 2–89 numb. l. 27ᶜᵐ.
At head of title: National research council of Canada.
Mimeographed.

1. Domestic animals—Bibl. 2. Feeding and feeding stuffs—Bibl.
I. Whalley, Muriel E.
                                            37–38338
Library of Congress   Z5074.L7N3
                ₍5₎   016.6360877

NN   0063528   DLC MtBC OrCS NcRS ICJ

VOLUME 407

National research council, *Canada.*
   ... Bibliography on wool. Ottawa, 1927.

2 p. L, 2-174 numb. l. 32ᶜᵐ.

At head of title: National research council.
Prepared by M. E. Whalley.
Mimeographed.
Text runs parallel with back of cover.
Contents.—Sheep breeding and raising.—The wool textile industry.

   1. Wool trade and industry—Bibl. 2. Sheep—Bibl. I. Whalley,
Muriel E.
                 28-9284 Revised

Library of Congress   Z7971.N28

NN   0063529   DLC OrCS CU NcRS ICJ

National Research Council, Canada.
   ... Bibliography, substitutes for gasoline
as motor fuel ...
      see under   Hopkins, C   Y.

517
N21
    National Research Council, Canada.
    A booklet describing the organization and
work of the National Research Council of
Canada. ₜOttawa?₎ 1954.
18 p.

   1. National Research Council. Canada.
2. Canada. Research.

NN   0063531   DNAL

National Research Council, *Canada.*
   A building code for smaller municipalities, based on the
National building code (NRC no. 1068) and the Model
zoning by-law (NRC no. 859) Ottawa, 1947.
89 l. 28 cm. (*Its* N. R. C. no. 1536)
Cover title.
At head of title: Tentative.

   1. Building laws—Canada. I. Title.

TH226.A1N3   692.971   49-23575*

NN   0063532   DLC MiD CaBViP

National research council, *Canada.*
   ... Bulletin. no. 1–

Ottawa, 1918–
    v.   illus. 25ᶜᵐ.
Issued by the Honorary advisory council for scientific and industrial
research, no. 1–11; by the National research council, Canada, no. 12–
Bulletins no. 3 and no. 4 published under one cover.

   1. Research. 2. Research, Industrial. I. Canada. Honorary advisory council for scientific and industrial research.

                      20-6466 Revised

Library of Congress

—————— 2d set.   T7.N3

NN   0063533   DLC CaBVaU CU TxLT OrCS TxU

R11
.C37
    National Research Council, Canada.

    Canadian journal of biochemistry and physiology. v. 29–

    Feb. 1951–
    Ottawa, National Research Council, Canada.

TP1
.C25
    National Research Council, Canada.

    The **Canadian** journal of chemical engineering. v. 29–
    Jan. 1951–
    Ottawa.

QD1
.C285
    National Research Council, Canada.

    Canadian journal of chemistry. v. 29–
    Jan. 1951–
    Ottawa, National Research Council, Canada.

R11
.C37
    National Research Council, Canada.

    Canadian journal of medical sciences. v. 29–
    Feb. 1951–
    Ottawa, National Research Council, Canada.

QR1
.C25
    National Research Council, Canada.

    Canadian journal of microbiology. v. 1–
    Aug. 1954–
    Ottawa, National Research Council.

QC1
.N332
    National Research Council, Canada.

    Canadian journal of physics. v. 29–
    Jan. 1951–
    Ottawa, National Research Council, Canada.

Q1
.C19
    National Research Council, Canada.

    Canadian journal of research. v. 1-28; May 1929–Dec. 1950.
    ₜOttawa₎ National Research Council of Canada.

T1
.C23
    National Research Council, Canada.

    Canadian journal of technology.

    Ottawa, National Research Council, Canada.

QL1
.N1532
    National Research Council, Canada.

    Canadian journal of zoology. v. 29–
    Feb. 1951–
    Ottawa, National Research Council, **Canada.**

National research council, Canada.

Nova Scotian institute of science, *Halifax.*
   A catalogue of scientific periodicals in libraries of the Mari-
time provinces; prepared by Ernest Hess ... Published by the
Nova Scotian institute of science, with the assistance of the
National research council of Canada. Halifax, N. S., The
Imperial publishing co., limited, 1936.

National research council, Canada.

Whalley, Muriel E.
   ... The chemical composition and nutritive value of potatoes,
by Muriel E. Whalley, Division of research information.
Ottawa, 1935.

National research council, Canada.

Gagnon, Paul Édouard, 1901–
   ... Contribution to the study of *cis-trans* isomers derived from
3,3-diphenyl-1-hydrindone. Synthesis of 3,3-diphenylhydrin-
dene and some of its derivatives. By Paul E. Gagnon and
Ls. Phil. Charette ... ₜOttawa, 1941₎

National Research Council, Canada.
   The distribution of thunderstorms and the
frequency of lighting flashes
      see under   National Research Council,
Canada. Research Plans and Publications Section.

78
N213
    National Research Council, Canada.
    Extraction of rubber from plants, by Muriel E.
Whalley ... Ottawa, 1942.
    cover-title. 19 numb. l. 27 cm. (NRC
no. 1071)
    Processed.
    "References": 1:13; "Abstracts": leaves 14-19.
    1. Rubber. I. Whalley, Muriel E.

NN   0063547   DNAL MiD

National research council, Canada.
   ... Fellowships, studentships and bursaries.
Who's who. 1932– ₜOttawa, 1934– ₎
    v.   27.5 cm.
    Mimeographed on one side of page only.

NN   0063548   CaBVaU

TA
492
C7N28
    National Research Council, Canada
    Final report in connection with an aided
Civil   research on the lateral support of steel
Engin.   columns and struts, by C.R. Young and W.B.
    Dunbar. ₜn. p.₎ 1941.
    1 v. (various pagings) illus., diagrs.

    Typescript (carbon copy)

   1. Columns, Iron and steel 2. Struts
(Engineering) I. Young, Clarence Richard,
1879– II. Dunbar, William Bowie
CaOTU

NN   0063549   CaOTU

Q 145
N 28
    National Research Council, Canada.

    Graduate students at Canadian
universities in science and engineering. Etudiants gradués en science
et en génie dans les universités
canadiennes. 19 –
Ottawa.
         v.   28 cm. (Its
Publication)

NN   0063550   CaBVaU CaOTU

National Research Council, Canada.
   Handbook of scientific and technical societies
and institutions of the United States and Canada
    see   Scientific and technical societies of
the United States and Canada.

WD
700
qN277h
1946
    NATIONAL Research Council, Canada
    History of the Associate Committee
on Aviation Medical Research, 1939-
1945. Ottawa, 1946.
    78, 212 p.
    Includes bibliography of reports and
memoranda submitted to the committee,
Sept., 1939-Aug., 1945.
    1. Aviation medicine - Bibl.
2. National Research Council, Canada.
Associate Committee on Aviation Medical
Research

NN   0063552   DNLM CaBVaU

National Research Council, Canada.
   Ice on aircraft; a bibliography of recent articles
      see under   Ruedy, Richard, 1896–

GC181
.R8
    National research council, Canada.

    Ruedy, Richard, 1896–
      ... Illumination and visual range under water, by R. Ruedy
... Ottawa, 1942.

VOLUME 407

National Research Council, *Canada.*
List of technical translations. Ottawa ₁1953?₁
29 l. 28 cm.

1. Technology—Bibl.—Translations into English.   ɪ. Title.

Z7911.N34   56-2233 ‡

NN   0063555   DLC

National Research Council, Canada.
List of technical translations. Ottawa ₁1954₁
54 l. 28 cm.
Cover title.

1. Science—Bibl. 2. Aeronautics—Bibl.   ɪ. Title.

B7401.N33   016.5   59-54189

NN   0063556   DLC

Z7911   National Research Council, Canada.
N34   List of technical translations.
1954   Ottawa ₁1954₁
            63ℓ. 28cm.

            Includes supplements 1-4, to February,
            1958.

            1. Technology—Bibl.—Translations into
            English. I. Title.

NN   0063557   IaU NNC

National Research Council, Canada.
Low back pain and sciatica
        see under   National Research Council,
Canada. Subcommittee on Surgery.

---

q664.1   NATIONAL research council, Canada.
N213M   Manufacture of dextrose from corn starch, by
            Muriel E. Whalley.
            Ottawa. Author. 1943. 38p.

            Reproduced from type-written copy.
            N.R.C. no.1138.
            "References": p.37-38.

NN   0063559   WaS DNAL

National Research Council, Canada.
Mastitis in cows
        see under   Whalley, Muriel E.

TJ1   National Research Council, Canada.
.M4197
        Mechanical engineering report. LR. [Supplement]
        Ottawa, National Research Council of Canada

TJ1   National Research Council, Canada.
.M437
        Mechanical engineering report. MET. [Supplement]
        Ottawa, National Research Council of Canada

National Research Council, Canada.
Mechanical engineering report. MS.
        see under title [supplement]

National Research Council, Canada.
Mechanical engineering report. MT.
        see under title [supplement]

National Research Council, Canada.
Mechanical handling of coal
        see under   Ruedy, Richard, 1896-   comp.

National Research Council (Canada)
    N.R.C. no.1-   Ottawa, 1918-

    Minor publications only are included in this
    set; important monographs and subseries are cata-
    loged and classified separately.

NN   0063566   ICJ OrCS

PHYSICS
QC1   National Research Council, Canada.
N29   NRC bulletin.
            no. 1-
            1951-
            Ottawa.
            v. 26 cm. irregular.

            Each no. has distinctive title.

            1. Physics - Period.   I. Title.

NN   0063567   OU

Q1   National Research Council, Canada.
.N14
        NRC research news; issued by the Public Relations Branch,
        National Research Council of Canada. v. 1-
        Jan. 1948-
        Ottawa.

M(06)   National Research Council, Canada.
N277n   National Research Council Associate Commit-
            tee on Soil and Snow Mechanics. ₁Ottawa,
            Ont., 1951₁
            ₁4₁ p. 20cm.

            "List of technical memoranda": p.₁4₁

NN   0063569   DAS

National research council, Canada.

Ruedy, Richard, 1896-
    ... New hydraulic laboratories and their work, by R. Ruedy
    ... Ottawa, 1938.

QC   National Research Council, Canada
173   Notes on diffusion of neutrons without change
N27n   in energy. Notes on a series of seminars by
        G.Placzek, recorded and extended by G.M.Volkoff.
        Chalk River,Ont., 1943.
        [3],32,10ℓ. 28cm. (Its Atomic energy project,
        MT-4)
        Cover title.
        In lower right hand corner of cover: N.R.C.
        No.1548.

NN   0063571   NRU MiEM

387.1   National Research Council, Canada.
N21   The official methods used for assessing quality
            in Canadian dried whole egg powders.   [n.p.]
            1944.
            10 numb. l.
            1. Eggs, Dried—Analysis and examination.
            I. Canada. Dept. of agriculture. Science service.
            II. Canada. Special products board.

NN   0063572   DNAL

387.1   National Research Council, Canada.
N21   The official methods used for assessing
1947   quality in Canadian sugar dried whole egg
            powders. ₁n.p.₁ 1947.
            14 l.

NN   0063573   DNAL

TR810   National Research Council, Canada.
.H67
        Howlett, Leslie Ernest, 1903-
            Photography for forestry purposes, by L. E. Howlett and
        P. D. Carman. Ottawa, 1949.

National Research Council, Canada.
    Postdoctorate fellowships for fundamental research, ten-
able in the laboratories of the Department ₁of Mines and
Technical Surveys₁, Dominion observatories, Geological Survey of Canada, Mines Branch.

    ₁Ottawa₁
        v. illus. 24 cm.
    Issued by the council in co-operation with the Dept. of Mines and
Technical Surveys.
        1. Science—Scholarships, fellowships, etc.   ɪ. Canada. Dept. of
Mines and Technical Surveys.

Q180.A1N38   507.2   58-15849 ‡

NN   0063575   DLC

National Research Council, *Canada.*
    Postdoctorate fellowships for fundamental research ten-
able in the National Research Council Laboratories, Ottawa,
Canada and Prairie Regional Laboratory, University of
Saskatchewan, Saskatoon, Canada.
    ₁n. p.₁
        v. illus. 24 cm.

    1. Science—Scholarships, fellowships, etc.

Q180.C32   507.2   56-4738 ‡

NN   0063576   DLC NN

National Research Council, Canada.
    Postdoctorate fellowships for research in the biological
sciences, tenable in the laboratories of the Canada Department of Agriculture.
    ₁Ottawa₁
        v. illus. 24 cm.
    Issued by the council in co-operation with the Dept. of Agriculture
of Canada.

    1. Biological research. 2. Science—Scholarships, fellowships, etc.
ɪ. Canada. Dept. of Agriculture.

QH315.N34   574.072   58-16795 ‡

NN   0063577   DLC DNAL

National Research Council, Canada.
    Proceedings of the Conference on forestry
research...
        see under   Conference on Forestry Research
Ottawa, 1935.

VOLUME 407

RC421
N21
1942/

National research council, Canada.
Proceedings of the conference on motion
sickness. [1]-
Aug. 1942-
[Ottawa, 1942-
v. illus.

1st, Aug. 1942, "held jointly under the
Associate committee on medical research and
Associate committee on aviation medical re-
search"; 2d (June, 1943), 3d (Dec. 1944),

arranged by the Co-ordinating committee for
medical research.

1. Seasickness. 2. Airsickness. I. Title:
Conference on motion sickness.

NN 0063580   NNC

National research council, Canada.
... Proceedings of the conference on the
organization of medical research in Canada.
Ottawa, 1938.
1 p.l., iii, v.p.   27 cm.
At head of title: National research council.
Copy no. 83.

NN 0063581   CaBVaU

National research council, Canada.

Pacific science congress. *5th, Victoria and Vancouver, B. C.,*
1933.
... Proceedings of the fifth Pacific science congress ... Edited by the general secretary. Victoria, B. C., June 1–4, Vancouver, B. C., June 5–14, post-congress tour June 5 [i. e. 15]–19,
Canada 1933. [Toronto, University of Toronto press, 1934]

National Research Council, Canada.
Propagation of thunderstorms; a review
see under   Ruedy, Richard, 1896–

National Research Council, *Canada.*
Publications. [1st]   ed.; 1918–38—

[Ottawa]

v. 26 cm. (N. R. C. no. 808 [etc.])
The 1st ed. comp. in the council's Research Plans and Publications
Section ; the 2d in the Public Relations Branch.
The 1st ed. contains N. R. C. nos. 1–773 ; 2d ed., nos. 1–1412.
Kept up to date by supplements.

1. National Research Council, Canada—Bibl. 2. Technology—
Bibl.—Catalogs. 3. Science—Bibl.—Catalogs.

Z5055.C2N3   016.5   39–25583 rev*

MiD MH NN CSt DNLM CtY N CU MiU CaOOS
NN 0063584   DLC DAU CaBVaU NcRS DNAL TxU PP ICJ

National research council, *Canada.*
... Regulations governing bursaries, studentships and fellowships ... [Ottawa, Printed by F. A. Acland, 1929]
[4] p. 25ᶜᵐ.
At head of title : National research council.

1. Endowment of research. I. Title.
                                        29–30477 Revised
Library of Congress   Q181.N343 1929   607
——— Copy 2.   [r35c2]

NN 0063585   DLC

Q180
.C2N33

National research council, *Canada.*
Report.

Ottawa, 1918–
v. 25ᶜᵐ.
Report year ends March 31.
Issued by the Honorary advisory council for scientific and industrial
research, 1917/18–1923/24 ; by the National research council, Canada,
1924/25–
Title varies slightly.
1. Research. 2. Research, Industrial. I. Canada. Honorary advisory council for scientific and industrial research.
                                        20—6468
Library of Congress   Q180.C2N33

NN 0063586   DLC

National research council, *Canada.*
... Report. no. 1–

Ottawa, 1918–
v. illus., tables, diagrs. 23ᶜᵐ.
At head of title, no. 1–15, Dominion of Canada. The Honorary advisory council for scientific and industrial research.—no. 16–22, National
research council.—no. 23–   Dominion of Canada. National research council.
1. Research. 2. Research, Industrial. I. Canada. Honorary advisory council for scientific and industrial research. II. Title.
Library of Congress   T177.C2A3*   20–6464 Revised

DPR NIC TxU MiU NcD NcRS NBuG N TxLT MiD KMK DAU CU
CLSU NIC NBuG MiU OCl OClW ICJ DL WvU PBL OU NcU
NN 0063587   DLC DNLM OrCS ScCleU CaBVaU FTaSU NN

National Research Council, *Canada.*
Report no. MA.

Ottawa, 19
no. in   v. illus. 28 cm.

1. Aeronautics—Collected works.
TL507.N3   53–16072
              *629.107   629.13072

NN 0063588   DLC ICJ

National Research Council, Canada.
Report no MD
see under   National Research Council,
Canada. Division of Mechanical Engineering.
Low Temperature Laboratory.

National Research Council, Canada.
Report no. ME
see under   National Research Council,
Canada. Division of Mechanical Engineering.
Engine Laboratory.

National Research Council, Canada.
Report no. MF
see under   National Research Council,
Canada. Fuels and Lubricants Laboratory.

National Research Council, Canada.
Report no. MH
see under   National Research Council,
Canada. Division of Mechanical Engineering.
Hydraulics Laboratory.

National Research Council, Canada.
Report No. MM
see under   National Research Council,
Canada. Structures Laboratory.

National Research Council (Canada)
Report no. MP-1–   Ottawa. 1951–

NN 0063594   ICJ

National Research Council, Canada.
Report No. MR
see under   National Research Council,
Canada. Division of Mechanical Engineering.
Flight Research Section.

National Research Council, Canada.
Report no.MT-1-39.
Ottawa, 19 –1958.
v.
Crerar has unclassified numbers only.
Superseded by the council's Mechanical engi-
neering report, MT series.
Prepared by the Division of Mechanical Engi-
neering, Gas Dynamics Section.
I. National Research Council, Canada. Divi-
sion of Mechanical Engineering. Gas Dynamics
Section.   621.0716J

NN 0063596   ICJ

99.9
N21

National Research Council, Canada.
Report on establishment of experimental
tracts on University of New Brunswick
woodlot.
[n.p.]
(Its N.R.C. no.

1. Experimental forests. 2. Wood-Lots.
New Brunswick. I. National Research Council.
Canada. Associ-   ate Committee on For-
estry. II. Na-   tional Research Council
Canada. N.R.C.   no.1949, etc.

NN 0063597   DNAL

National Research Council, Canada.
Report on fast neutron dosimetry, by J. Dainty.
Chalk River, Ontario, 1950. 39, [1] p. charts, diagrs. 28cm.
(ITS: Atomic energy project. CRM-482)

Bibliography, p. [40]

1. Ionization chambers. 2. Neutrons. 3. Radioactivity--Gamma rays.
I. Dainty, J.

NN 0063598   NN

National Research Council, Canada.
Report on university support.

Ottawa.
v. 25 cm. (Its N. R. C.)
Cover title   : Report on university support for science,
engineering and medicine.

1. Scholarships—Canada. 2. Universities and colleges—Canada.

Q21.N3   506.171   59–45700

NN 0063599   DLC

National Research Council, *Canada.*
Review. 1938/39–
[Ottawa]
v. illus., ports. 26 cm. (Its N. R. C.)
Report year for 1938/39–   ends Mar. 31; for
Dec. 31.
Publication suspended 1941/42–45?
Beginning in 194 –   date given in title is one year in advance
of period covered by report.
Title varies: 1938/39–   Review of activities.

Q180.C2N332   50–47393 rev

CLU-M DNLM DPR ViBlbV
NN 0063600   DLC ICJ TxU NN N NSyU MsU DAU MiU FTaSU

VOLUME 407

National Research Council, Canada.
 Review
  see also   NRC review.
        National Research Council,
        Canada. Laboratories.
        NRCL

National Research Council, Canada.
 Review of activities
  see its   Review.

75   National Research Council, Canada.
N212   Review of potato research.   Ottawa,
       1941-
         pt.   (Its N. R. C. no. 1012-
         1. Potato starch. 2. Potatoes. Research.
       3. Potatoes. Utilization. I. Whalley, Muriel E.

NN   0063603   DNAL

SB197   National research council, Canada.
.P38
       Pavlychenko, Thomas Karp, 1892–
         ... Root systems of certain forage crops in relation to the
       management of agricultural soils, by Thomas Pavlychenko ...
       Ottawa, 1942.

AS15   National Research Council, Canada.
.H3
       Scientific and technical societies of the United States and
       Canada. [1st]– ed. Washington, National Academy
       of Sciences, National Research Council, 1927–

National Research Council, Canada.
 Students registered in the graduate schools
of Canadian universities in physical and earch
sciences, engineering and life sciences. 1952/
53-   Ottawa.
       v.   28 cm.   annual.
       1. Scientists - Canada - Directories. 2. Univer-
       sities and colleges - Graduate work.

NN   0063606   CaBVaU

National Research Council, Canada.
 Survey of professional salaries, engineers,
scientists, educators
  see under   McKim, F. L. W.

National research council, Canada.

Canada. *Bureau of statistics.*
 .... Survey of scientific and industrial laboratories in Canada.
Ottawa, 1941.

QC
175   National Research Council, Canada.
.N28   Tables of functions for the vibrational con-
       tributions to thermodynamic quantities. [Com-
       putations carried out by Misses] E. Miller
       [and] K. West [under the supervision of] H. J.
       Bernstein. Ottawa, 1951.
         36 p.   26 cm.   (Its NRC Bulletin no. 1)
       Cover title.

         1. Physics--Tables, etc. 2. Statistical mechan-
       ics. 3. Thermodynamics. I. Miller, Miss E.

NN   0063609   MiU

National Research Council, Canada.
 A table of integrals involving the functions
En (x)
  see under   Le Caine, Jeanne Starrett, 1917–

National Research Council, Canada.
 Technical papers presented to the Wind Power
Working Party. Compiled by the London Liaison
Office of the National Research Council of Canada.
London, H. M. Stationery Off. [1954]
       1 v.   (various pagings) illus. 27 cm.
       At head of title: Organisation for European
       Economic Co-operation. Committee for Produc-
       tivity and Applied Research (P. R. A.) Working
       Party No. 2 (Wind power) Printed ... on behalf
       of the European Productivity Agency, Paris,
       France.
       Includes references.

NN   0063611   DAS

National Research Council, *Canada.*
 Technical translation. TT1–
Ottawa, 1947–
       no. in   v. illus. 28 cm.
       Title varies   Translation.
       TT1-TT100 issued by the Council's Division of Mechanical En-
       gineering; TT101–   by the Council's Division of Information
       Services.

       1. Engineering—Translations into English—Collected works. I.
       National Research Council, Canada. Division of Mechanical En-
       gineering. II. National Research Council, Canada. Division of In-
       formation Services. III. National Research Council, Canada. Trans-
       lation.
       TJ7.N198   51-24380 rev

NN   0063612   DLC LU ICJ KyLoU OU CaBVaU IU

TJ7   National Research Council, Canada. **Translation.**
.N198
       National Research Council, *Canada.*
       Technical translation. TT1–
       Ottawa, 1947–

National Research Council, Canada.
 Test report: MET
  see under   National Research Council,
Canada. Division of Mechanical Engineering.

Q180   National Research Council, Canada.
C2N2
       War history of the associate committees of
       the National Research Council.   Ottawa [n. d.]
         120 l.   28cm.
         Cover title.
         Includes bibliographies.

NN   0063615   CaBVaU

National Research Council, Canada.
 Wood and charcoal as fuel for vehicles
  see under   National Research Council,
Canada. Research Plans and Publications Section.

National Research Council, Canada
 see also
 Canada. *Honorary Advisory Council for Scientific and
 Industrial Research.*
 Canadian Committee on Food Preservation.

National Research Council, *Canada. Associate Committee
on Army Medical Research.*
 Medical research and development in the Canadian Army
during World War II, 1942–1946. [Ottawa, 1946?]
       cover-title, 88 p., [45] l. plates, ports. 28 cm.
       Bibliography : [8] l. at end.

       1. Medicine, Military. 2. Medical research. 3. Canada. Army—Sanit.
       affairs. I. Title.
       RC971.N18   610.72   Med 47–3109*

NN   0063618   DLC

W 2   NATIONAL Research Council, Canada.
DC2   Associate Committee on Army Medical
N212pr   Research
         Proceedings of the meeting.
         1st-   1943-
         Ottawa.
           v. in   illus.
           1. Military medicine - Canada
           2. Research - Canada

NN   0063619   DNLM

W 2   NATIONAL Research Council, Canada.
DC2   Associate Committee on Army Medical
N212p   Research
         Proceedings of the meeting of the
       Executive.
         Ottawa [1942?-47?]
           v.

NN   0063620   DNLM

K 47   National research council, Canada. Associate
1962   committee on aviation medical research.
         Chronological list of reports and memoranda
       submitted to Associate committee on aviation
       medical research, National research council
       of Canada, Sept. 1939- Aug. 1945. Ottawa,
       1946.
         95-187 p.   22 x 28 cm.
         Bound with Kerr, William Krogvig. Biblio-
       graphy of Canadian reports in aviation
       medicine, 1939-   1945. Ottawa, 1962.

NN   0063621   CaBVaU

National Research Council, Canada. Associate
Committee on Aviation Medical Research.
 Fundamentals of aviation medicine
  see under   Moscow. Institut aviatsionnoĭ
meditsiny imeni I. P. Pavlova.

National Research Council, Canada. Associate
Committee on Aviation Medical Research.
 History of the Associate Committee on
Aviation Medical Research, 1939-1945
  see under   National Research Council,
Canada.

W 2   NATIONAL Research Council, Canada.
DC2   Associate Committee on Aviation Medical
N22p   Research
         Proceedings of the meeting of the
       Executive.
         Ottawa [1940?]-45.
           v. illus.
           1. Aviation medicine - Period.

NN   0063624   DNLM

VOLUME 407

WD 700
N38
1942
National Research Council, Canada. Associate
Committee on Aviation Medical Research.
Sub-committee on Oxygen Equipment.
Manual of oxygen and intercommunication
equipment. 1st ed. [Ottawa?] 1942.
109 p. illus. 25 cm.
At head of title: Royal Canadian Air
Force. Air Member for Aeronautical Engin-
eering.
"C. A. P. 307."
(1. Aeroplanes - Oxygen equipment.)
(2. Aeroplanes - IFF equipment.)
[3. Oxygen.]   [4. Communication.]

NN   0063625   CaBVaU DNLM

WD 700
N38
1943
National Research Council, Canada. Associate
Committee on Aviation Medical Research.
Sub-committee on Oxygen Equipment.
Manual of oxygen and intercommunication
equipment. 2d ed. [Ottawa] 1943.
133 p. illus. 27 cm.
C.A.P. 307.
"Use of Canadian oxygen assembly no. 1"
and diagram (2 leaves) inserted.

(1. Aeroplanes - Oxygen equipment.) (2.
Aeroplanes - IFF equipment.) [3. Oxygen.]
[4. Communication.] I. Title: Oxygen
and intercommunication equipment.

NN   0063627   CaBVaU

National Research Council, Canada. Associate
Committee on Aviation Medical Research.
Sub-committee on Oxygen Equipment.

Manual of oxygen and intercommunication
equipment. 3d ed. [Ottawa? Queen's
Printer?] 1945.

1 v. (looseleaf) illus. 27 cm.
C.A.P. 307.
Prepared for the Royal Canadian Air Force.

NN   0063628   CaBVaU

WD
700
N386
1946
National Research Council, Canada. Associate Committee on Aviation Medical Research. Subcommittee on Protective Clothing./
Review of the work of the Subcommittee
on Protective Clothing of the Associate
Committee on Aviation Medical Research,
1942-1945. [Authors: J.A. Kitching and
E. Page] Ottawa, 1946.
vii, 145 p. illus. 27 cm.

Bibliography: p. 145.

1. Aviation medicine. (2. Clothing,
Protective) [3. Protective clothing]
I. Kitching, John Alwyne, 1908-   II.
Page, E.   III. Title. a.

NN   0063630   CaBVaU

National Research Council, *Canada. Associate Committee
on Coal Classification and Analysis.*
Proceedings of the meeting.

Edmonton.
v. 32 cm.

1. Coal—Congresses. 2. Coal—Analysis.

TP325.N335   662.6   49–31560*‡

NN   0063631   DLC DI

National research council, Canada. Associate
committee on forestry.
... Interim report
see under   Mayall, K   M

National research council, Canada. Associate
committee on forestry.
Richards, E   S.
Les lots boisés de ferme de l'est du Canada, par E. S. Richards. Bulletin préparé sous la direction de la Commission
associée de sylviculture, Conseil national de recherches. Ottawa, Can. [J. O. Patenaude, o. s. i., imprimeur du roi] 1939.

National Research Council. Canada. Associate
Committee on Forestry.
Report on establishment of experimental
tracts on University of New Brunswick woodlot
see under   National Research Council,
Canada.

QC801
.N323
National Research Council, Canada. Associate
Committee on Geodesy and Geophysics.
Canadian geophysical bulletin. v. 1–
Jan./Mar. 1947–
Ottawa, Associate Committee on Geodesy and Geophysics,
National Research Council of Canada.

National Research Council, Canada. Associate
Committee on Geodesy and Geophysics.
Gravity measurements in Canada, January 1,
1951 to December 31, 1952. Report for Internation-
al Union of Geodesy and Geophysics, International
Association of Geodesy, tenth general conference,
Rome, Italy, 1954, compiled by M. J. S. Innes.
Ottawa, 1954.
11 p. fold. col. map.
'Canadian articles on gravity": p. 11.
1. Gravity. I. Innes, M. J. S.

NN   0063636   CaOTU

Pamph
Ge
N
National Research Council, Canada. Associate
Committee on Geodesy and Geophysics
Seismology and physics of the earth's
interior, for International Union of Geodesy
and Geophysics, Association of Seismology
and Physics of the Earth's Interior, tenth
general conference, Rome, Italy, 1954, compiled by J.H. Hodgson. Ottawa, 1954.
22p.

At head of title: National report for Canada
"Bibliography 1952-1954": p.18-22.

1. Earth -   Internal structure
I. Hodgson,   John Humphrey, 1913-

NN   0063637   CaOTU

National Research Council, Canada. *Associate Committee
on Geodesy and Geophysics
see also*
National Research Council, Canada. *Associate Committee on Geophysics.*

National Research Council, Canada. *Associate Committee
on Geophysics.*
Report. 1st; 1946. Ottawa.
16 p. 28 cm. annual.
Covers the period Oct. 24, 1945-1946.

1. Geophysics—Societies, etc.

QC801.N34   56–46363 rev

NN   0063639   DLC

National Research Council, Canada. *Associate Committee
on Geophysics
see also*
National Research Council, Canada. *Associate Committee on Geodesy and Geophysics.*

Or CS
TA710
N27
National Research Council, Canada. Associ-
ate Committee on Geotechnical Research.
Technical memorandum.
no.
Ottawa, 19
nos. in   v. illus. 18-28cm.

No.22,26,32,40 also numbered as Soil
mechanics bulletin no.2,4-6.
No. -86 issued by the committee under its
earlier name: Associate Committee on Soil
and Snow Mechanics.

1.Soil mechanics   - Soc. 2.Snow. I.
National Resea   rch Council, Canada.
Associate Comm   ittee on Soil and Snow

CaQMAI OrCS
NN   0063641   CoD TxU MB DNAL NN DLC ICJ CaBVaU

National Research Council, Canada. *Associate Committee
on Geotechnical Research.*

For works by this body issued under its earlier name *see*

National Research Council, Canada. *Associate Committee on Soil and Snow Mechanics.*

National research council, *Canada. Associate committee on
grain research.*
... Collected papers of the Associate committee on grain re-
search ... v. 1–   1929-1931–
[Ottawa, 1931–
v. illus., plates (part fold.) tables, diagrs. 25ᶜᵐ.
At head of title, v. 1–   : National research council of Canada.
Vol. 1 includes Papers no. 1 to no. 20 and two unnumbered reports.

1. Grain.   i. Title.
                           33–25390 Revised
Library of Congress   TS2120.N33
                       [r35d2]   679

NN   0063643   DLC IdU PP ICJ

National research council, Canada. Associate
committee on grain research.
Crampton, Earle Wilcox, 1895–
... The comparative feeding values for livestock of barley,
oats, wheat, rye and corn. A review and analysis of published
data. Prepared for the Associate committee on grain research,
by Earle W. Crampton ... Ottawa, J. O. Patenaude, acting
King's printer, 1933.

National research council, *Canada. Associate committee on
grain research.*
... The drying of wheat, covering an investigation by the
Associate committee on grain research ... Ottawa, 1929.
Ottawa, F. A. Acland, printer, 1929.
122 p. incl. illus., tables, diagrs. fold. pl. 25 cm. (National re-
search council, Canada. Report, no. 24)
At head of title: Dominion of Canada. National research council ...
"Paper no. 1 of the Associate committee on grain research."—p. 5.
H. M. Tory, chairman.
———— Copy 2.   T177.C2A3   no. 24

———— (Second report) by E. Stansfield and W. H.
Cook, covering an investigation under the Associate committee on grain research ... Ottawa, 1932.
104 p. illus., plates, tables (part fold.) diagrs. 25 cm. (National
research council, Canada. Report, no. 25)
At head of title: Dominion of Canada. National research council ...
"Paper no. 28 of the Associate committee on grain research."—p. 7.
H. M. Tory, chairman.
                         SB191.W5N32   1932
1. Wheat—Canada.   i. Tory, Henry Marshall, 1864–   ii. Stansfield, Edgar, 1878–   iii. Cook, William Harrison.   v. Title.
        SB191.W5N32   1929 (607) 683.11   30—6594

NN   0063646   DLC CaBVaU PP CU

National research council, *Canada. Associate committee on
grain research.*
... Interim report on protein content as a factor in grading
wheat. Prepared on behalf of the National research council
of Canada and the Board of grain commissioners for Canada
by the Associate committee on grain research of the National
research council ... Ottawa, 1929.
60 p. incl. tables. 24½ᶜᵐ. (National research council, Canada. Bulletin, no. 13)
At head of title: National research council ...
H. M. Tory, chairman.
1. Proteids. 2. Wheat—Canada.   i. Tory, Henry Marshall, 1864–
ii. Title.
                               30–6606 Revised
Library of Congress   SB191.W5N32   1929 b
———— Copy 2.   T7.N3   no. 13

NN   0063647   DLC CaBVaU CU

VOLUME 407

National research council, Canada.
Associate committee on grain
research. [paper]

see

National research council, Canada. Associate committee on grain research.
... Collected papers of the Associate
committee on grain research ...

W
20.5
qN275h
1946

NATIONAL Research Council, Canada.
Associate Committee on Medical Research
History, 1938-1946, by G. H. Ettinger.
[Ottawa, 1946?]
46, 9 *l*.
1. Research - Medical - Canada
I. Ettinger, G   H

NN 0063649   DNLM

National Research Council, Canada. Associate
Committee on Medical Research.
Low back pain and sciatica
see under   National Research Council,
Canada. Subcommittee on Surgery.

National Research Council, Canada. Associate
Committee on Medical Research.
Memorandum on amputations
see under   Lemesurier, A. B.

National Research Council, *Canada. Associate Committee
on Medical Research. Subcommittee on Shock and Blood
Substitutes*
see **National Research Council, *Canada*. Subcommittee
on Shock and Blood Substitutes.**

National Research Council, *Canada. Associate Committee
on Medical Research. Subcommittee on Surgery.*
see **National Research Council, *Canada*. Subcommittee
on Surgery.**

352.3
N214m

National Research Council, Canada—Associate
Committee on National Fire Codes.
Municipal fire department code.

Ottawa.
v. 23cm.

NN 0063654   IU

W 2
DC2
N25pr

NATIONAL Research Council, Canada.
Associate Committee on Naval Medical
Research
Proceedings of the meeting of the
Executive.
Ottawa [1943?-46?]
v.

NN 0063655   DNLM

59.9
N218Re

National Research Council, Canada. Associate Committee on Plant Breeding.
Report on co-operative tests of durum
wheat varieties.

[Winnipeg?]

1. Wheat, Durum. Testing. 2. Wheat,
Durum. Statistics. 3. Wheat. Canada.
Statistics. I. Canada. Experimental Farms.
Cereal Division. Cereal Breeding Laboratory.
II. Canada.   Dept. of Agriculture.
III. Title: Cooperative tests of durum
wheat varieties.

NN 0063656   DNAL

59.9
N218R

National Research Council, Canada. Associate Committee on Plant Breeding.
Report on co-operative tests of oat
varieties.

[Winnipeg?]

1. Oats. Testing. 2. Oats. Statistics.
I. Canada. Experimental Farms. Cereal
Division. Cereal Breeding Laboratory.
II. Canada. Dept. of Agriculture.
III. Title: Cooperative tests of oat
varieties.

NN 0063657   DNAL

National Research Council, Canada. Associate
Committee on Soil and Snow Mechanics.
Canadian papers presented
see under   International Conference on
Soil Mechanics and Foundation Engineering.
3d, Zurich and Lausanne, 1953.

National Research Council, Canada. Associate
Committee on Soil and Snow Mechanics.
The international classification for snow
(with special reference to snow on the ground) ...
see under   International Association of
Scientific Hydrology. Commission of Snow and Ice.

National Research Council, *Canada. Associate Committee
on Soil and Snow Mechanics.*
Method of measuring the significant characteristics of a
snow-cover, by G. J. Klein, D. C. Pearce and L. W. Gold.
Ottawa, 1950.

1 v. (various pagings) plates. 27 cm. (*Its* Technical memorandum no.18)

[National Research Council, Canada; N. R. C. no. 2269.
"Supersedes T. M. no. 5 and Division of Mechanical Engineering
Reports MM-192 and MM-202."

1. Snow.   I. Klein, George J.   (Series)

QC929.S7N3   551.57   51-8170

NN 0063660   DLC

National Research Council, Canada. Associate
Committee on Soil and Snow Mechanics.
Soil mechanics papers presented at the
Building Research Congress 1951
see under   Building Research Congress.

National Research Council, Canada. Associate
Committee on Soil and Snow Mechanics.
Technical memorandum
see under   National Research Council,
Canada. Associate Committee on Geotechnical
Research.

National Research Council, Canada. Associate
Committee on Soil and Snow Mechanics.
National Research Council Associate
Committee on Soil and Snow Mechanics
see under   National Research Council,
Canada.

National Research Council, Canada. *Associate Committee
on Soil and Snow Mechanics*
see also
Canadian Soil Mechanics Conference.

National Research Council, Canada. *Associate Committee on
Soil and Snow Mechanics. Soil Mechanics Subcommittee*
see
**National Research Council, Canada. Soil Mechanics Sub-
committee.**

National research council, *Canada*. *Associate committee on
spray painting.*
... Review of literature dealing with health hazards in spray
painting, prepared under the auspices of the Associate committee on spray painting. Ottawa, 1930.

44 p. 24 *cm*. (Bulletin no. 15)

At head of title: ... National research council of Canada.
O. Klotz, chairman.
Bibliography: p. 37-41, 43.

1. Occupations—Diseases and hygiene—Bibl.   I. Klotz, Oskar,
1878-   II. Title: Health hazards in spray painting. III. Title:
Spray painting, Health hazards in.
30-22882 Revised

Library of Congress   HD7269.P2C35 1930
———— Copy 2.   T7.N3 no. 15
[r3542]   [331.8223] 613.62

NN 0063666   DLC MiU

National Research Council, Canada. Associate
Committee on Storage and Transport of Food.
Poultry Section.
Proceedings of the meeting of the Poultry
Section of the Associate Committee on Storage
and Transport of Food, by the National Research
Council of Canada and Dominion Department of
Agriculture. l—   1936- Ottawa .

NN 0063667   CaOOAg

National Research Council, Canada. Associate
Committee on Substitute fuels for mobile
internal combustion engines. Subcommittee
on Producer Gas
see   National Research Council, Canada.
Subcommittee on Producer Gas.

TH226
N3
1950

National Research Council, Canada. Associate
Committee on the National Building Code.
A code for dwelling construction for
buildings housing one or two families.
Minimum standards to regulate the erection
and provide for the safety of buildings.
Ottawa, 1950.
77 p. illus.

NRC no.2261.
"An abridged version of the National
building code, as published in 1941." - p.1.

NN 0063669   CU DNAL

National Research Council, *Canada. Associate Committee
on the National Building Code.*
National building code of Canada, 1953. Ottawa [1953?—

1 v. (loose-leaf) illus., tables. 30 cm.

Errata slips inserted.

1. Building laws—Canada.   I. Title.

692.971   59-42554

MiU IU TxU DPAHO DAS
NN 0063670   DLC CaBVaU NN ViBIbV NNC DAIA CaOTU

National research council, *Canada. Associate committee on
Trail smelter smoke.*
Effect of sulphur dioxide on vegetation, prepared for the
Associate committee on Trail smelter smoke of the National
research council of Canada. Published under the authority
of the Honorable W. D. Euler, chairman of the Committee of
the Privy council on scientific and industrial research. Ottawa, Can., 1939.
xl, 206 p., 1 l., 207-447 p. incl. front., illus., tables. plates (2 col.)
2 fold. plans, diagrs. (part fold.) 26 *cm*.
At foot of t.-p.: N. R. C. no. 815.
Papers by various authors.
"References" at end of each chapter except x and xvi.
1. Plants, Effect of sul-   phur dioxide on.   2. Consolidated
mining & smelting co. of   Canada, limited.   I. Title.
40-639
Library of Congress   QK753.S85N3
[3]   628.53969

NcD CtY TU OU MH NNC ICJ NN CaOTU
NN 0063671   DLC CU MtBC OrCS MBCo OC1W MH-GM NcRS

SB611
.C6

National research council, Canada. Associate
committee on weed control.

Cook, William Harrison, 1903-
... Chemical weed killers, a review prepared for the Associate committee on weed control by W. H. Cook and A. C. Hal-
ferdahl ... Ottawa, Can., 1937.

VOLUME 407

National research council, *Canada. Associate committee on weed control.*
... Collected papers of the Associate committee on weed control... ₁v. 1–   1932–1937–
₁Ottawa, 1932–
   v. illus., plates, maps, tables, diagrs. 25ᶜᵐ.
   At head of title, ₁v. 1–   : National research council of Canada.
Vol. 1 includes Papers no. 1 to no. 19.

   1. Weeds—Canada.   I. Title.

                                          A 40-3264

Ohio state univ. Library
  for Library of Congress   ₁2₁

NN   0063673   OU ICJ CU

SB613   National Research Council, Canada. Associate
.C2A15   committee on weed control.
             [Publication, no. 1–
          Ottawa, 1932–
             v.   plates, maps, tables, forms.
          25.5 cm.

NN   0063674   DLC

National Research Council (Canada) Atomic Energy
  Project.
     CRE–1–   Chalk River, Ont., 19 –

NN   0063675   ICJ

WN   NATIONAL Research Council, Canada.
415   Atomic Energy Project
qN278d   The detection of alpha contamination
1950   with scintillation counters, by George
          Cowper. Chalk River, Ont., 1950.
             10 ℓ. illus. (National Research Council
          of Canada. N. R. C. no. 2390)
             CREL – 453.
             1. Radioactivity – Safety measures
          I. Cowper, George

NN   0063676   DNLM

WN   NATIONAL Research Council, Canada.
415   Atomic Energy Project
q N278de   The detection of radioactivity with
1950   scintillation counters, by George Cowper.
          Chalk River, Ontario, 1950.
             7 ℓ. illus. (National Research Council
          of Canada. N. R. C. no. 2391)
             CREL – 454.
             1. Radioactivity – Safety measures
          I Cowper, George

NN   0063677   DNLM

WN   NATIONAL Research Council, Canada.
415   Atomic Energy Project
qN277e   The estimation of radioactive strontium
1951   and other fission products in urine and
          water, by C. A. Mawson and I. Fischer.
          ₁Chalk River, Ontario, 1951₁
             20 ℓ. illus. (National Research
          Council of Canada. N. R. C. no. 2392)
             CRM – 455.
             1. Strontium – Radioactive
             2. Urine – Examination
          I. Mawson, C   A

NN   0063678   DNLM

National Research Council, Canada. Atomic
  Energy Project.
     Isotopes branch bulletin.   Chalk River,
  Ont., 1948–

NN   0063679   CaOKR

QD   NATIONAL Research Council, Canada,
453   Atomic Energy Project
qN278i   Isotopic analysis of deuterium oxide by
1949   density determinations, by I. A. W.
          Morrison ₁and others₁ Chalk River,
          Ontario, 1949.
             10 ℓ. illus. (National Research Council
          of Canada. N. R. C. no. 2389)
             CRE–449.
             Cover title.
             1. Deuterium oxide   I. Morrison,
          I   A   W

NN   0063680   DNLM

National Research Council, Canada, Atomic Energy
  Project.
     LT–1–   Chalk River, Ont., 19 –

NN   0063681   ICJ

WN   NATIONAL Research Council, Canada.
440   Atomic Energy Project
N277m   The medical applications of fission
1947   products and activated materials, by G. C.
          Laurence ₁and others₁ Rev. Chalk River,
          Ont., 1947.
             15 ℓ.   (N. R. C. no. 1607)
             "C R M – 337."
             Photocopy (negative)
             1. Radioactivity   I. Laurence,
          George Craig, 1905–

NN   0063682   DNLM

National Research Council, Canada, Atomic energy
  Project.
     PD–1–   Oak Ridge, U.S. Atomic Energy
  Commission. Technical Information Service,
  1946–

     I. U.S. Atomic Energy Commission.

NN   0063683   ICJ IU

National Research Council, Canada. Atomic
  Energy Project.
     Published papers of atomic energy of the
National Research Council
        see   Atomic Energy of Canada, ltd.
     Published papers.

WN   NATIONAL Research Council, Canada.
150   Atomic Energy Project
qN277s   A simple absolute radiometer for the
1951   measurement of high intensities of soft
          X-rays, by H. G. Heal. Chalk River,
          Ontario, 1951.
             6 ℓ. illus. (National Research Council
          of Canada. N. R. C. no. 2434)
             "CRC – 468. "
             1. Radiography – Apparatus
             2. Roentgen rays   I. Heal H   G

NN   0063685   DNLM

WN   **NATIONAL Research Council, Canada.**
415   Atomic Energy Project
qN278t   Therapeutic gamma ray sources, by
1946   W. V. Mayneord. Chalk River, Ont.,
          1946.
             20 p. illus. (N. R. C., no. 1595)
             1. Cobalt – Radioactive 2. Radium –
          Therapeutic use I. Mayneord, **William**
          Valentine

NN   0063686   DNLM

National Research Council (Canada) Atomic Energy
  Project. Research Division.
     CRC–1–   Chalk River, Ont., 19 –

NN   0063687   ICJ

National Research Council (Canada) Atomic Energy
  Project. Research Division.
     CREL–1–   Chalk River, Ont., 19 –

NN   0063688   ICJ

National Research Council (Canada) Atomic Energy
  Project. Research Division.
     CRM–1–   Chalk River, Ont., 19 –

NN   0063689   ICJ

National Research Council (Canada) Atomic Energy
  Project. Research Division.
     CRT–1–   Chalk River, Ont., 19 –

NN   0063690   ICJ

541.2   National research council, Canada. Atomic
N21n   energy project. Research Division.
             N.R.C. ₁Publications concerned with
          atomic energy₁ no.   –
          Chalk river, Ontario, 19 –
             cover-title   v. diagrs. 28cm.

             The overall N.R.C. number has been
          arbitrarily used to number these atomic
          energy publications.

             1. Atomic energy--Collections.

NN   0063691   LU ICJ

QD181   National Research Council, Canada. Atomic
.H1   Energy Project. Research Division.
qN3   Ortho- and para- hydrogen, a lecture
pam   given to the Chemical Institute of Canada,
          by C.B. Amphlett, Chalk River, Ont., 20
          March 1947. ₁n.p., 1947₁
             18 p. illus. 28cm. (N.R.C., no. 1680.
          LC-12)

             Mimeographed.
             Includes bibliography.

             1. Hydrogen.   I. Amphlet, C.B.
          II. Title.

NN   0063692   OrCS

307.9   National Research Council, Canada.
N2142   Canadian Committee on Fats and Oils.
             Annual report. 1st–
          1952–
          ₁Ottawa, Ont.₁

             Not for publication.

             1. Fats and oils. Research.

NN   0063693   DNAL

N 25   National Research Council, Canada. Canadian
1951   Committee on Culture Collections of Micro-
          organisms.

             Directory and catalogue of collections of
          micro-organisms maintained in Canada. Ottawa
          ₁1951₁

             1 v. (looseleaf)   29 cm.

             N.R.C. no. 2359.
             1. Culture media.   I. Title

NN   0063694   CaBVaU CaOTU

National Research Council, Canada. Canadian
  Committee on Food Preservation
        see   Canadian Committee on Food Preser-
     vation.

VOLUME 407

National Research Council (Canada) Canadian Committee on Storage and Transport of Food *see* Canadian Committee on Food Preservation.

National Research Council, Canada. Codes and Specifications Section.
A model zoning by-law. Ottawa,1939.

Manifold copy. 28 cm. ff.(3),11-111,37.
The project for the preparation of a model building code for use by Canadian municipalities was undertaken by a group of committees organized under the joint sponsorship of the National Research Council and the Department of Finance of Canada. The present document was undertaken and com-   pleted by the Committee on Health and Sanita-   tion.- cf.Foreword.

NN 0063697   MH-SD CaBViP

National Research Council, Canada. Codes and Specifications Section.
National building code. Pt.3,5. Ottawa,1941, 40.

Manifold copy. 21 cm. Diagrs.
"N.R.C.no.971,923."
"The project for the preparation of a model building code for use by Canadian municipalities was undertaken...by a group of committees organized under the joint sponsorship of the National Research   Council and the

Department of Finance of Canada."- Foreword.
Contents:-111.Engineering requirements.--v.Requirements bearing on health and sanitation

NN 0063699   MH-SD CaBVa

National Research Council, Canada. Codes and Specifications Section.
A standard plumbing by-law. Ottawa,1940.

Manifold copy. 21 cm. pp.vii,51.
At head of title:National building code.
"N.R.C.no.924."
The project for the preparation of a model building code for use by Canadian municipalities was undertaken by a group of committees organized under the joint sponsorship of the National Research   Council and the

Department of Finance of Canada. The present document is a contribution of the Committee on Health and Sanitation.- cf.Foreword.

NN 0063701   MH-SD

National Research Council, Canada. *Division des recherches en bâtiment*
see
National Research Council, Canada. *Division of Building Research.*

LB 2371
N 32
1955   National Research Council, Canada. Division of Administration. Personnel Branch.

List of students registered in the graduate schools of Canadian universities in science, engineering and medical sciences, 1955-1956. Ottawa, 1955.

1 v. (unpaged) 27 cm.

NN 0063703   CaBVaU

QH323
C2N2   National Research Council, Canada. Division of Applied Biology.

History of the wartime activities. Ottawa [n.d.]

ii, 145 l. 28cm.

Includes bibliographies.

NN 0063704   CaBVaU

S 133
N38
I5   National Research Council, Canada. Division of Applied Biology.
Industrial utilization of wastes and surpluses. no. 1-   1942-   Ottawa.

v. illus. irregular.

1. Surplus agricultural products - Period. 2. Agricultural products - Period. I. Title.

NN 0063705   CaBVaU PPUSDA

National Research Council, Canada. Division of Applied Biology.
Quarterly report v. 1, no. 1-
Jan/Mar. 1949-   Ottawa, 1949-
nos.   27 cm.
Processed.

NN 0063706   PPUSDA

National Research Council, Canada. Division of Atomic Energy.
The functions $E_n(x) = \int_1^\infty e^{-xuu} u^{-n} dx$
see under   Placzek, George, 1905-

National Research Council,Canada. Division of Atomic Energy.
MT-1--   1946-
Chalk River, Ont.

NN 0063708   MiU

TH7
N29
Arch.   National Research Council, Canada. Division
Library   of Building Research.
Better building bulletin. no.1-

[Ottawa] 1949-
v. in   illus.

English and French.

NN 0063709   CU DLC DAS NN

National Research Council, Canada. Division of Building Research.
Bibliography. no. 1-
Ottawa, 1951-   v.   28cm.

CONTENTS.
no. 1. Pearce, D.C. A bibliography on snow and ice. 1951.
no. 2. Frigon, R.A. Bibliography on civil defence, with special reference to structural protection. 1951.
no. 3. Legget, R.F. Short bibliography on foundations for buildings and bridges. 1952.
no. 4. Brodie, R.J. A bibliography of Canadian papers of interest in building research, to   June 30, 1951, by R.J. Brodie and others. 1952.

no. 5. McCrea, J.B. A bibliography on the wind action on structures. 1952.
no. 6. Eden, W.J. Soil mechanics literature published during 1951-1952. 1953.
no. 7.Tibbetts, D.C. A bibliography on demolition of structures. 1953.
no. 8. White, B.G. Literature survey of papers dealing with the use of heat for keeping roads, sidewalks and parking areas free from snow and ice. 1954.
no. 9. Eden, W.J. A selected   annotated bibliography of soil

mechanics literature. 1954.
no. 10. Tibbetts, D.C. A bibliography on cold weather construction. 1955.

NN 0063713   NN CaBVaU CU DLC

TA775
N3
Arch.   National Research Council, Canada. Division
Library   of Building Research.
Building foundations on permafrost; Mackenzie Valley N.W.T., by John A. Pihlainen. Ottawa, 1951.
37 l. maps, diagrs. charts. (Its Technical report, no. 8)

Joint contribution from the Directorate of Engineer Development, Canadian Army, and the Division of Building Research. Bibliography: p. 37.

1. Foundations. 2. Frozen ground. 3. Building - Mackenzie Valley. I. Pihla.inen, John A.

NN 0063714   CU DAS

National Research Council, Canada. *Division of Building Research.*
Building research. 1947-57—
Ottawa.
v. illus. 23 cm. ([National Research Council, Canada] NRC)
Annual, 1960-
Supersedes in part the division's Building research in Canada; a progress report.
Title varies: 1947-57, Ten years of building research.
1. Building research—Canada—Yearbooks. I. National Research Council, Canada. Division of Building Research. Ten years of building research. II. Title. III. Title: Ten years of building research.
TH26.N272   59-19692 rev

NN 0063715   DLC OU CU MiU NcD

National Research Council, Canada. *Division of Building Research.*
Building research in Canada; a progress report. v. 1-2; June 1951-Dec. 1958. Ottawa.
2 v. in l. illus. 28 cm. semiannual.
Superseded in part by its Building research, and in 1962, by its Building research news.
LC set incomplete: v. 1, no. 4 wanting.
1. Building research—Canada—Period. I. Title.
TH26.N27   66-32048

NN 0063716   DLC CaBVa NcU NN

National Research Council, Canada. Division of Building Research.
Building research note
see under title

National Research Council, Canada. *Division of Building Research.*
Climatological atlas of Canada, prepared by Morley K. Thomas. A joint publication of the Division of Building Research, National Research Council, and the Meteorological Division, Dept. of Transport, Canada. Ottawa, National Research Council, Canada, 1953.
256 p. map, col. charts, diagrs., tables. 24 x 31 cm.
"N. R. C. no. 3151."
"D. B. R. no. 41."
1. Canada—Climate. I. Thomas, Morley K. II. Canada. Meteorological Service. III. Title. Branch.
QC985.N35   *551.591   55-1971

NN 0063718   NBuU OrU OrCS MtU OrPS MH-GM CtY OCl NBuC PPAtR OCl TxU DNAL DAS CU NN PPAN CaBVa CaBVaU MtBC NNC DLC ICU DCU OU PSt PU-W CaOTU IU NIC

TH
155
N38
1955   National Research Council, Canada. Division
      of Building Research
      Course on better building; proceedings
Physical &   of meeting, April 26 and 27, 1955. Ottawa,
Applied Sci.   1955.
      ii, 54, 2 leaves. diagrs. (Its Technical paper, no. 31)

NN 0063719   CaOTU

National Research Council, Canada. Division of Building Research.
D.B.R.
Ottawa.   (Canada. Scientific and industrial research, Honorary advisory council for. N.R.C.)

NN 0063720   NN

VOLUME 407

TH26
.N28
National Research Council, Canada. *Division of Building Research.*
The Division of Building Research; what it is, what it does. Ottawa ₍195₋₎
32 p. illus. 18 cm.

1. Building research—Canada.

TH26.N28   59–33431 ‡

NN   0063721   DLC

National Research Council, Canada. Division of Building Research.
The durability of concrete under frost action

see under

Swenson, E   G

National Research Council, Canada. Division of Building Research.
A method of computing maximum snow loads

see under

Thomas, Morley K

TH
5201
N3
National Research Council, Canada.
Division of Building Research.
Permafrost and buildings. Prepared by J.A. Pihlainen. ₍Ottawa, E. Cloutier, Queen's Printer, 1955₎
27 p. illus. (Its Better building bulletin, 5)

NN   0063724   CaOTU NcD

National Research Council, Canada. Division of Building Research.
Permafrost investigations at Aklavik: 1953
see under   Pihlainen, John A.

National Research Council, Canada. Division of Building Research.
Proceedings ...
see under   Meeting on Concrete and Cement Research in Canada.

National Research Council, Canada. Division of Building Research.
Proceedings of the conference on building research, Ottawa, October 21 tp 23, 1953
see under   Conference on Building Research, Ottawa, 1953.

016.69
N277p
National Research Council, Canada. Division of Building Research.
Publications ... issued up to Ottawa.
v. 26 cm.

Cover title.
1. Construction. Bibliography

NN   0063728   DNAL DAS

National Research Council, Canada. Division of Building Research.
Research paper. no. 1-
19 -
₍Ottawa₎
      no.   illus. 25 cm.

1. Building - Collected works.

NN   0063729   CaBVaU DLC CaQMAI

National Research Council, Canada. Division of Building Research.
A selected annotated bibliography of soil mechanics literature, compiled by W. J. Eden. Ottawa, Division of Building Research, National Research Council, 1954.
9 L. 28cm.

NN   0063730   PBL

690
N218t
National Research Council, Canada—Division of Building Research.
₍Series of translations₎ 1st-
Feb.25, 1948-
Ottawa.
no. illus., diagrs., tables. 28cm.

Issued as no. of the council's Translation TT series.

NN   0063731   IU

National Research Council, Canada. *Division of Building Research.*
Short bibliography on foundations for buildings and bridges, prepared by the library staff under the direction of Miss R. J. Brodie, librarian. Ottawa, 1952.
4 l. 28 cm. (*Its* Bibliography no. 3)

1. Foundations—Bibl. 2. Engineering geology—Bibl.

Z7914.B9N3   59–47633 ‡

NN   0063732   DLC

290
N216
National Research Council, Canada. Division of Building Research.
Soil mechanics in Canada. Ottawa, 1947.
11 l.

1. Soil mechanics. I. Legget, Robert Ferguson.

NN   0063733   DNAL

National Research Council, Canada. Division of Building Research
Wind loads on buildings

see under

Schoemaker, R   L   A

National Research Council, Canada. Division of Building Research.
Winter design temperature data

see under

Thomas, Morley K

National Research Council, Canada. Division of Chemistry.
The rotproofing of textiles and related materials; a survey of literature, by Muriel W.Weatherburn. Ottawa, 1947.
184 p. illus. (National Research Council, Canada. N.R.C.no.1601)

I. Weatherburn, Muriel W. II. Series.   677.0279

NN   0063736   ICJ DNAL PPPTe

National Research Council, Canada. Division of Chemistry.
War history ... [n.d.]
153 l.

NN   0063737   CaBVaU

304
N217
National Research Council, Canada. Division of Chemistry. Laundry and Textile Research Laboratory.
Details of the application of dust-laying oil to fabrics. Ottawa, 1946.
7 p.
1. Dust. Prevention. 2. Emulsions.

NN   0063738   DNAL

National Research Council, Canada. Division of Information Services.
Publications of the National Research Council of Canada
see under   National Research Council, Canada.

TJ7
.N198
National Research Council, Canada. Division of Information Services.
National Research Council, *Canada.*
Technical translation. TT1-
Ottawa. 1947-

National Research Council, Canada. *Division of Information Services. Technical Information Service*
see
National Research Council, Canada. *Technical Information Service.*

TL501
.N345
National Research Council, *Canada. Division of Mechanical Engineering.*
Bulletin.
Ottawa.
v. in   illus. 28 cm. quarterly. (National Research Council, Canada. Report no. ME)
Issued 19   by the division's Aeronautical Laboratories.

1. Aeronautics—Period.

TL501.N345   51–17608 rev ‡

NN   0063742   DLC TxU CaOTP

National Research Council, Canada. Division of Mechanical Engineering.
Calculation of the influence of internal circulation in a liquid drop on heat transfer
see under

Conkie, W   R

National Research Council, Canada. Division of Mechanical Engineering.
Circulation and distortion of liquid drops

see under

Savic, P

VOLUME 407

621.438 National Research Council, Canada--Division of
N213d   Mechanical Engineering.
             Development of a test rig and 1000-hour test
         on blades of various alloys to determine the
         fouling and corrosive effects of the ash from
         the combustion of a western Canadian residual
         fuel, by R. J. T. Bruce and J. C. Vrana.
         Ottawa, National Research Council of Canada,
         1955.
             iii, 15 , ₆₆₉p. 14 plates. 28cm. (₍National
         Research Council, Canada₎ Report no.MT-28)

             Cover title.
             "Copy no.48."
             Bibliography: p.15.

             1. Gas-turbines. 2. Fuel research. I. Bruce,
         R. J. T. II. Vrana. J. C. III. Title.
         (Series)

    NN 0063746   IU

National Research Council, *Canada. Division of Mechanical
      Engineering.*
        Guide to the laboratories of the Division of Mechanical
    Engineering, National Research Council and of the National
    Aeronautical Establishment, Ottawa, Canada. ₍Ottawa?₎
    1955.
        20 l. illus. 28 cm.

        1. Canada. National Aeronautical Establishment. 2. **Hydraulic**
    laboratories—Canada. 3. Naval research—Canada.

    TL568.C33N3   57-44632

    NN 0063747   DLC

National Research Council, *Canada. Division of Mechanical
      Engineering.*
        Investigation of scavenging in small two-stroke cycle
    engines, by H. U. Wisniowski and H. Winterbottom. Otta-
    wa, National Research Council of Canada, 1953.
        iii, 7 p. 16 plates. 28 cm. (₍National Research Council, Canada₎
    Report no. ME-207)
        Cover title.
        Bibliography: p. 7.

        1. Gas and oil engines.   I. Wisniowski, H. U.   II. **Winterbottom,**
    H. III. Title.   (Series)

    TJ759.N3   621.43   56-43928

    NN 0063748   DLC

National Research Council, Canada. Division of
      Mechanical Engineering.
    National Science Library. Aeronautical Library.
        List of subject headings.
        Ottawa, National Science Library.

National Research Council, Canada. Division of
      Mechanical Engineering.
        Mechanical engineering report. DME MISC.
            see under title. [Supplement]

National Research Council, Canada. Division of
      Mechanical Engineering.
        Mechanical engineering report. MB
            see under title   [Supplement]

National Research Council, Canada. Division of
      Mechanical Engineering.
        Mechanical engineering report. MD
            see under title. [Supplement]

National Research Council, Canada. Division of
      Mechanical Engineering.
        Mechanical engineering report. ME
            see under title, [Supplement]

National Research Council, Canada. Division of
      Mechanical Engineering.
        Mechanical engineering report. MH
            see under title, [Supplement]

National Research Council, Canada. Division of
      Mechanical Engineering.
        Mechanical engineering report. MP
            see under title . [Supplement]

National Research Council, Canada. Division of
      Mechanical Engineering.
        Mechanical engineering report. MS
            see under title [Supplement]

National Research Council, Canada. Division of
      Mechanical Engineering.
        Mechanical engineering report. MT
            see under title [Supplement]

National Research Council, Canada. Division of
      Mechanical Engineering.
        Quarterly bulletin
            see its Bulletin.

National Research Council (Canada) Division of
      Mechanical Engineering.
        Report no.MI-1--   19 -   Ottawa.

        Crerar set begins with no.MI-817, Oct.22, 1956.

    NN 0063759   ICJ NN

National Research Council, Canada. Division of
      Mechanical Engineering.
        Report no. MR
            see under   National Research Council,
    Canada. Division of Mechanical Engineering.
    Flight Research Section.

National Research Council, Canada. Division
      of Mechanical Engineering.
        A review of radiation

            see under

        Baxter, D   C

---

532   National Research Council, Canada--Division of
N21s   Mechanical Engineering.
          Some dimensional considerations in fluid me-
      chanics, by J. G. La Berge.   Ottawa, 1948.
          iii, 63p. diagrs.

          Cover title.
          "Report no.MT-5."
          Bibliography: p.55-63.

          1. Fluid mechanics. 2. Physical measurements.
      I. La Berge, J. G. I. Title.

    NN 0063762   IU

National Research Council, *Canada. Division of Mechanical
      Engineering.*
        Spray nozzles for the simulation of cloud conditions in
    icing tests of jet engines, by N. Golitzine, C. R. Sharp ₍and₎
    L. G. Badham. Ottawa, 1950.
        iv, 11 p. 27 plates. 28 cm. (₍National Research Council, Canada₎
    Report no. ME-186)
        Cover title.
        Bibliography: p. 11.

        1. Nozzles. 2. Clouds.   I. Golitzine, G. II. Title.   (Series)

    TL567.N6N3   629.13078   52-156

    NN 0063763   DLC

TJ7   National Research Council, Canada. Division of
.N198   Mechanical Engineering.
         National Research Council, *Canada.*
            Technical translation. TT1-
         Ottawa. 1947-

TA401   National Research Council, Canada. Division
N29   of Mechanical Engineering.
           Test report. MET. no.1-
         Ottawa.
           v. 28cm.

           1. Materials - Testing - Coll. works

    NN 0063765   NcRS ICJ MiU IU

National Research Council, Canada. *Division of Mechani-
      cal Engineering*
        see also
    National Research Council, *Canada. National Aeronauti-
      cal Establishment.*

National Research Councl, Canada. Division of
      Mechanical Engineering. Aerodynamics
      Laboratory.
        Report no. MA
            see under   National Research Council,
    Canada.

National Research Council (Canada) Div.of Mechani-
      cal Engineering. Engine Laboratory.
        Report ME-1--   194 -   Ottawa.

        Crerar set begins with ME-186, 28 Aug.1950.

    NN 0063768   ICJ DLC

National Research Council (Canada) Division of Me-
      chanical Engineering, Flight Research Section.
        Report no.MR-1--   19 -   Ottawa.

        Crerar set begins with no.MR-16, 11 July 1951.

    NN 0063769   ICJ

National Research Council, Canada. Division of
      Mechanical Engineering, Fuels and Lubricants
      Laboratory
        see National Research Council, Canada.
    Fuels and Lubricants Laboratory.

National Research Council, Canada. Division of
      Mechanical Engineering. Gas Dynamics Section
        see National Research Council, Canada.
    Gas Dynamics Section.

VOLUME 407

National Research Council (Canada) Division of
<u>Mechanical</u> Engineering. Hydraulics Laboratory.
Report no.MH-1--   19 -   Ottawa.

     Crerar set begins with no.MH-22, Aug.2, 1951.

NN   0063772   ICJ MnU MH DLC

National Research Council (Canada) Division of
<u>Mechanical</u> Engineering. Low Temperature Labora-
tory.
Report no.MD-1--   194 -   Ottawa.

     Crerar set begins with MD-32, 17 Aug.1949.

NN   0063773   ICJ DLC

National Research Council (Canada) Div.of <u>Mechanical</u>
Engineering. Model Testing Basin.
Report no.MB-1--   19 -   Ottawa.

     Crerar set begins with no.MB-131, 21 Mar.1951.

NN   0063774   ICJ

National Research Council, Canada. Division of
Mechanical Engineering. Structures Laboratory
   see   National Research Council, Canada.
Structures Laboratory.

ZWB
100
qN277p
1954

NATIONAL Research Council, Canada.
     Division of Medical Research
       Publications arising from grants-in-
aid and fellowships, 1950-1953.
     [Ottawa, 1954?]
       42 ℓ.
       1. Medicine - Bibl. 2. Research -
Medical - Bibl.

NN   0063776   DNLM CaBVaU

WN
150
qN279b
1951

NATIONAL Research Council, Canada.
     Division of Physics
       Background information on cobalt 60
teletherapy units [by] A. Morrison.
Ottawa [1951]
       13 ℓ.   (National Research Council
of Canada. N. R. C. 2496)
       PR - 113.
       1. Cobalt - Radioactive 2. Radiog-
raphy - Apparatus   I Morrison, A

NN   0063777   DNLM

National Research Council (Canada) Division of
Physics.
     Divisional report. no. PR-1-   Otta-
wa, 19 -

NN   0063778   ICJ

National Research Council, Canada. Division of
Physics.
     Measurements of the build-up of Cobalt-60 gamma radiation in
iron and lead, by C. Garrett and G. N. Whyte.   Ottawa, 1954.
14 l., illus.   28cm.   (ITS: Divisional report. no. Pr-218)

     "N.R.C. No. 3257."
     Bibliography, l. 13-14.

     1. Radioactivity—Measurements.   2. Radioactivity—Gamma rays.
3. Cobalt—Isotopes. I. Canada.   Scientific and industrial research,
Honorary advisory council for.   Physics, Division of Divisional report.
II. Garrett, C. III. Whyte, G. N.   t. 1954.

NN   0063779   NN

National Research Council, Canada. Division of
Physics
     Photography for forestry purposes
       see under   Howlett, Leslie Ernest,
1903-

National Research Council, *Canada. Division of Physics
and Electrical Engineering.*
     The insulation of houses, by J. D. Babbitt. Ottawa, 1946.
23 p. 21 cm. (National Research Council of Canada. N. R. C. no.
1386)

     1. Insulation (Heat)   I. Babbitt, John D., 1908-   II. Title.

TH1715.N34   693   48-26747*

NN   0063781   DLC CU

National Research Council, *Canada. Division of Radio and
Electrical Engineering*
     see
     National Research Council, *Canada. Radio and Electrical
Engineering Division.*

National Research Council, Canada. Division of
Research Information.
     Bibliography on the influence of mineral defi-
ciencies on growth and reproduction of farm animals
       see under   National Research Council,
Canada.

National Research Council, Canada. Division of
Research Information.
     The chemical composition and nutritive
value of potatoes
       see under   Whalley, Muriel E.

National Research Council, Canada. *Division of Research
Information.*
     Soil temperatures in Canada, by R. Ruedy, Division of
Research Information. Ottawa, National Research Council
of Canada, 1937.
11 l. illus. 27 cm.

     1. Soil temperature. 2. Soils—Canada.   I. Ruedy, Richard, 1896-
II. Title.
S594.5.N3   58-53914 ‡

NN   0063785   DLC CU

National Research Council, Canada. Electrical
Engineering and Radio Branch
     see   National Research Council, Canada.
Radio and Electrical Engineering Division.

TJ1075
.A2M4

National Research Council, Canada. Fuels and
Lubricants Laboratory.
   Mechanical engineering report. MP.
     Ottawa, National Research Council of Canada

National Research Council, Canada. Fuels and Lubricants Laboratory.
     Report no.MF-2000--   19 -   Ottawa.

     Crerar set begins with no.MF-2781, Apr.19, 1950.

NN   0063788   ICJ DLC

TJ1
.M45

National Research Council, Canada. Gas Dynamics
Section.
   Mechanical engineering report. MT. [Supplement]
     Ottawa. National Research Council of Canada

National Research Council, Canada. Gas Dynamics Section.
     Report no. MT-39
       see under   National Research Council,
Canada.

Q183
C23

National Research Council, Canada   Laboratories.
     NRCL.
     19
     [Ottawa] 19
       v. illus. 26cm.

       Subtitle: Review of the activities of the
laboratories (varies slightly)
       Title changes: 1939/39-1940/41, 1946/47-
1953/54. Review (varies slightly) 1954/65-
1967/68. NRC review.   1970   NRCL
       Publication suspended 1941/42-1945/46.

     1.Research - Ca   nada. 2.Laboratories -
Canada - Period   I.National Research

NN   0063791   OrCS DLC

National Research Council, Canada. Laboratories
NRCL
     see also
NRC review.
National Research Council, Canada. Laboratories
Review.

027.171 National Research Council, Canada--Library.
N213R   Report.

     Ottawa.
       v. 28cm.

     Report year ends March 31.

NN   0063793   IU

National research council, *Canada. Library.*
     ... Serial publications in the library, 1940. Ottawa, 1940.
2 p. l., 130 numb. l. 27 x 21".

     At head of title : National research council of Canada.
In lower right corner of t.-p.: N. R. C. no. 914.
Reproduced from type-written copy.

     1. Periodicals—Bibl.—Catalogs. 2. Learned institutions and socie-
ties—Bibl.—Catalogs.
     Library of Congress   Z6945.O9   42-11684
         [2]   016.05

NN   0063794   DLC CaOTU OrCS

National Research Council, Canada. London
Liaison Office.
     Technical papers presented to the Wind Power
Working Party
       see under   National Research Council,
Canada.

HE
5614.5
.C2
N27

National Research Council, Canada. Motor Vehicle
Accident Study Group.
     Technical note.
     Ottawa.

NN   0063796   MiU

VOLUME 407

National Research Council, Canada. National
 Aeronautical Establishment.
 Aeronautical report. LR–
 see under National Research Council,
Canada.

National Research Council, Canada. *National Aeronautical
 Establishment*. Laboratory report LR
 see
National Research Council, Canada.
 Aeronautical report LR.

National Research Council, Canada. *National Aeronautical
 Establishment.*
 Note. 1–14. Ottawa, 1948–56.
 14 no. in 2 v. illus., diagrs. 28 cm.
 Title varies: no. 1–5, Aeronautical note AN.
 No. 1–5 issued by the National Research Council of Canada.

  1. Aeronautics—Collected works. I. National Research Council,
Canada. Aeronautical note AN.

TL507.N316   53–29011 rev

NN 0063799   DLC CU ICJ OU MiU NN WaU MiU

National Research Council, Canada. *National Aeronautical
 Establishment.*
 Report. 1–23. Ottawa, 1947–58.
 23 no. in 3 v. illus., diagrs. 28 cm.
 Title varies: no. 1–11, Aeronautical report AR.
 No. 1–11 issued by the National Research Council of Canada.

  1. Aeronautics—Collected works. I. National Research Council,
Canada. Aeronautical report AR.

TL507.N32   53–29010 rev

NN 0063800   DLC MiU CU ICJ OU

National Research Council, Canada. National
 Aeronautical Establishment.
  Summary of proceedings
   see under Symposium on High Speed
Aerodynamics, Ottawa, 1953.

National Research Council, Canada. *National Aeronautical
 Establishment*
 see also
National Research Council, Canada. *Division of Mechanical Engineering.*

National Research Council, Canada. National
 Research Laboratories. Division of Applied
 Biology
  see National Research Council, Canada.
Division of Applied Biology.

National research council, *Canada. Nitrogen fixation committee.*
 ... Nitrogen in industry. Submitted by the Nitrogen fixation
committee of the National research council, Professor J. C.
McLennan, chairman. Pub. by the authority of the sub-committee of the Privy council for scientific and industrial research. Ottawa, 1926. Ottawa, F. A. Acland, printer, 1927.
 55 p. incl. tables. 25ᶜᵐ. (Bulletin no. 12)
 At head of title: Dominion of Canada. National research council ...
 References: p. 54–55.
 1. Nitrogen—Fixation. 2. Nitrogen compounds.
                                 27–6918 Revised
Library of Congress   TP245.N8N35 1926
———— Copy 2.   T7.N3 no. 12
                       ₍r41d2₎   (607) 661.117

NN 0063804   DLC CaBVaU

National Research Council, Canada. Radio and
 Electrical Engineering Division.
  The Algonquin Radio Observatory.
  ₍Ottawa?₎
      v. illus. (ERB–714, 827,

  1. Astrophysical observatories. I. Title.

NN 0063805   CoBBS

National Research Council, Canada. Radio
 and Electrical Engineering Division.
  An analysis of radar ice reports

  see under

  Hood, A   D

National Research Council, Canada. *Radio and Electrical
 Engineering Division.*
 Bulletin.
 ₍Ottawa₎
      v. in illus. 26 cm. quarterly.

  1. Electric engineering—Societies, etc. 2. Electronics—Societies,
etc.

TK1.N38A25   61–36525 ‡

NN 0063807   DLC CaOTU

National Research Council (Canada) Radio and Electrical Engineering Division.
  ERA–1–   Ottawa, 19 –

NN 0063808   ICJ DLC DP

National Research Council (Canada) Radio and Electrical Engineering Division.
  ERB–1–   Ottawa, 19 –

NN 0063809   ICJ DLC

National Research Council, Canada –Radio and
 Electrical Engineering Division.
  New electronic aids to marine navigation.
  ₍Ottawa₎ 1951.
  12p. illus. 26cm.

  Caption title: Advances in the short-range
presentation of marine radars developed by
the National Research Council.

  1. Radar. I. Title.

NN 0063810   IU

National Research Council, Canada. Radio and
 Electrical Engineering Division.

 Progress report. April/June 1947–1955.
Ottawa.
   no.   illus. 28 cm.
 Issued 1947 under the division's earlier
name: Electrical Engineering and Radio Branch.

  1. Electric engineering – Research
Societies, etc.

NN 0063811   CaBVaU

National Research Council, Canada—Radio and
 Electrical Engineering Division.
  A system for remote control of fog-alarm
 stations. ₍Ottawa₎ 1953.
 12p. illus., map. 26cm.

  Caption title.

  1. Telecommunication. 2. Remote control.
3. Fog-signals. I. Title: Remote control of
fog-alarm stations.

NN 0063812   IU

National Research Council, Canada—Radio and
 Electrical Engineering Division.
  An underwater television system. ₍Otta-
 wa₎ 1953.
 12p. illus. 26cm.

  Caption title.

  1. Television. I. Title.

NN 0063813   IU

National Research Council, Canada. Radio Branch.

  The war history of the Radio Branch. Ottawa,
1948.

  131 p. illus. 28cm. (Report no. ERA–141)

  Includes bibliographies.

NN 0063814   CaBVaU

National Research Council, Canada. Research
 Information, Division of
  see National Research Council, Canada.
Division of Research Information.

National Research Council, *Canada. Research Plans and
 Publications Section.*
 Abstracts of articles and patents on the production of glyc-
erol by fermentation, by Muriel E. Whalley, Research Plans
and Publications Section. Ottawa, 1942.
 66 l. 28 cm. (₍National Research Council, Canada₎ N. R. C. no.
1070)
 Cover title.
 "Compilation ... made from the British abstracts and the American
chemical abstracts."
 1. Glycerin. I. Whalley, Muriel E.

TP973.N37   668.2   48–41060*

NN 0063816   DLC MiD WaS

National Research Council, Canada. Research
 Plans and Publications Section.
  Abstracts on synthetic rubber
   see under National Research Council,
Canada.

National Research Council, *Canada. Research Plans and
 Publications Section.*
 Abstracts on the production of linseed oil, by Muriel E.
Whalley, Research Plans and Publications Section. Ottawa, 1943.
 4 p. 28 cm. (₍National Research Council, Canada₎ N. R. C. no.
1148)
 Cover title.
 "Collected from the American chemical abstracts, 1907–1942 ... and
other material."
 1. Linseed-oil. I. Whalley, Muriel E.

TP682.N37   016.6653   48–41059*

NN 0063818   DLC DNAL

VOLUME 407

National Research Council, *Canada. Research Plans and Publications Section.*
Abstracts on utilization of sawdust, by Muriel E. Whalley, Research Plans and Publications Section. Ottawa, 1945.

103 p. 28 cm. (¡National Research Council, Canada¡ N. R. C. no. 1285)

Cover title.

1. Wood waste.   ɪ. Whalley, Muriel E.

TP996.W6N3   674   51-32508

NN   0063819   DLC ICJ CaBVaU WaS MiU DNAL TxU

National Research Council, Canada.   Research Plans and Publications Section.
Abstracts on the utilization of straw. Ottawa, 1944.
442 p.   (N. R. C. no. 1242)
Issued by Research plans and publications section.

NN   0063820   DNAL ICJ

National Research Council, *Canada. Research Plans and Publications Section.*
Bearing metals, an introduction to articles published between 1936 and 1941, by R. Ruedy, Research Plans and Publications Section. Ottawa, 1942.

66 l. diagrs. 28 cm. (¡National Research Council, Canada¡ N. R. C. no. 1082)

Cover title.
"Books": leaf 66.

1. Bearings (Machinery) 2. Metals. 3. Alloys.   ɪ. Ruedy, Richard, 1896- ɪɪ. Title.

TJ1061.N35   621.822   48-41061*

NN   0063821   DLC NNC

National Research Council, Canada.   Research Plans and Publications Section.
Bibliography on soil mechanics, 1940-1944
see under   Ruedy, Richard, 1896-

National Research Council, *Canada. Research Plans and Publications Section.*
The distribution of thunderstorms and the frequency of lightning flashes, a review by R. Ruedy, Research Plans and Publications Section. 2d ed., rev. and enl. Ottawa, 1945.

70 p. illus., maps. 28 cm. (¡National Research Council, Canada¡ N. R. C. no. 1282)

Cover title.
"References": p. 64-67.

1. Thunder-storms. 2. Lightning.   ɪ. Ruedy, Richard, 1896-

QC968.N3 1945   551.55   51-32231*

NN   0063823   DLC DAS ICJ

National Research Council, Canada. Research Plans and Publications Section.
...Factice; abstracts of articles and patents, by Muriel E. Whalley, Research plans and publications section.   Ottawa, 1942. 50 f.   28cm.   (N. R. C. no. 1054.)

At head of title: National research council of Canada.

1. Rubber—Substitutes—Bibl.   2. Factice—Bibl. I. Whalley, Muriel E., comp.
N.Y.P.L.   September 16, 1943

NN   0063824   NN ICJ

National Research Council, *Canada. Research Plans and Publications Section.* Publications of the ... council
see **National Research Council,** *Canada.* **Publications.**

National Research Council (Canada) Research Plans and Publications Section.
Rubber substitutes for cable insulation; abstracts of articles and patents, by Muriel E. Whalley. Rev. ed. Ottawa, 1946.
52 p. (National Research Council (Canada) / N.R.C., no. 1391)
Abstracts of patents: p. 33-52.
I. Whalley, Muriel E.   II. Series.

NN   0063826   ICJ

National Research Council, Canada. Research Plans and Publications Section.
...Wood and charcoal as fuel for vehicles (2d ed., rev. and enl.) By R. Ruedy...
Ottawa National research council of Canada, 1942

2-106 numb. l.

"Bibliography" p. 48-106.

NN   0063827   OO CU

National Research Council, *Canada. Research Plans and Publications Section.*
Wood and charcoal as fuel for vehicles, by R. Ruedy, Research Plans and Publications Section. 3d ed. Ottawa, 1944.

65 p. illus., diagrs. 28 cm. (¡National Research Council, Canada¡ N. R. C. no. 1187)

Cover title.

1. Gas-producers. 3. Wood. 3. Charcoal.   ɪ. Ruedy, Richard, 1896- ɪɪ. Title.

TL229.G3N33   662.7   49-41034*

NN   0063828   DLC CaBVa WaS Wa ICJ NN MiD MiU Wa CU

National Research Council, Canada. *Soil Mechanics Subcommittee*
see also
Canadian Soil Mechanics Conference.

621.365 National Research Council, Canada--Special
N217r   Committee on Applied Mathematics.Radio
           reports, no.1-₍14₎ Ottawa, 1943-44.
           14v. in 1. illus., diagrs. 28cm.

           Includes references.

NN   0063830   IU

TJ1   National Research Council, Canada. Structures
.M44   Laboratory.
         Mechanical engineering report. MS. [Supplement]
         Ottawa, National Research Council of Canada

National Research Council (Canada) Structures
Laboratory.
      Report no.MM-1--   19 -   Ottawa.

Crerar set begins with no.MM-225, 15 Aug.1950.

NN   0063832   ICJ DLC MnU

National Research Council, Canada. Sub-committee on Oxygen Equipment
      see   National Research Council, Canada.
Associate Committee on Aviation Medical Research.
Sub-committee on Oxygen Equipment.

National Research Council, *Canada. Subcommittee on Producer Gas.*
Gas producers for motor vehicles; general report of the Subcommittee on Producer Gas of the Associate Committee on Substitute Fuels for Mobile Internal Combustion Engines. 1st-
Nov. 1943-
Ottawa, E. Cloutier, Printer to the King.

v. illus. 26 cm. (N. R. C. no. 1220.
Issues for 1943-   by E. A. Allcut and R. H. Patten.

1. Automobiles—Testing. 2. Gas-producers.   ɪ. Allcut, Edgar Alfred, 1888-   ɪɪ. Title.

TL229.G3N35   629.25144   49-30767*

MiD
NN   0063834   DLC WaS OrCS NNC DNAL CU MH PSt ICJ

National Research Council, *Canada. Subcommittee on Shock and Blood Substitutes.*
The early recognition and treatment of shock, prepared by the Subcommittee on Shock and Blood Substitutes of the Associate Committee on Medical Research, National Research Council of Canada, Ottawa, Canada, 1943. ¡Ottawa, 1943¡

26 p. 21 cm. (National Research Council of Canada. N. R. C. no. 1111)
"Reprinted from the Canadian Medical Association journal, vol. 48: 196-205, March, 1943."

1. Shock.   ɪ. Title.

RD59.N3   617.21   51-50677

NN   0063835   DLC CU

W 6   NATIONAL Research Council, Canada.
P3   Subcommittee on Surgery.
         Low back pain and sciatica, by the ...
         Sub-committee on Surgery of the Associate
         Committee on Medical Research. Ottawa,
         1945.
         64 p. illus. (N. R. C. no. 1303)
         1. Backache

NN   0063836   DNLM OrU-M

W 2   NATIONAL Research Council, Canada.
DC2   Subcommittee on Surgery
N39p   Proceedings of the meeting.

         Ottawa ¡1938?¡-46.
         16 v. in illus.
         Includes also proceedings of the
         meetings of various sections of the sub-
         committee and the International Conference
         on Amputations and Artificial Limbs,
         Ottawa and Toronto, 1944.
         1. Surgery,

NN   0063837   DNLM

National Research Council, *Canada. Subcommittee on Surgery.*
Treatment of thermal burns. Ottawa, 1942.

48 p. 22 cm. (National Research Council of Canada. N. R. C. no. 1084)

Cover title.

1. Burns and scalds.   ɪ. Title.

RD131.N3   617.11   51-50681

NN   0063838   DLC NNC CU

WO   NATIONAL Research Council, Canada.
704   Subcommittee on Surgery
N277t   Treatment of thermal burns. 2d ed.,
1944   rev. Ottawa, 1944.
         iii, 58 p. illus. (N. R. C. no. 1202)
                   WO704 N277t
         1. Burns - Treatment

NN   0063839   DNLM NNC

VOLUME 407

WL
500
N38
1945

National Research Council, Canada. Subcommittee on Surgery. Section on Traumatic Injuries of the Nervous System./
Selected reprinting of transactions
and appendices of the section on Traumatic Injuries of the Nervous System.
Ottawa, 1945.
1 v. (various pagings) 27 cm.
Includes bibliographies.

(1. Nervous system - Wounds and injuries. 2. Nerves, Peripheral - Wounds
and injuries) [3. Nervous system - Injuries. 4. Peripheral nerves - Injur-
ies] I. Title: Traumatic injuries of
the   nervous system.
II. Title.

NN   0063841   CaBVaU

National Research Council, Canada. Technical
Information Service.
Shaft sinking by the freezing methods
see under   Ruedy, Richard, 1896-
comp.

National Research Council, Canada. Technical
Information Service.
Survey of continuous fermentation processes
see under   Whalley, Muriel E.

National Research Council, Canada. *Technical Information
Service.*
T. I. S. report.
Ottawa.
no.   28 cm.

1. Technology—Collected works.   I. Title.

T7.N35   58–26335

NN   0063844   DLC KU

National research council, American council of
learned societies and Social science research
council, Joint committee on Latin American
studies of the
see   Joint committee on Latin American
studies.

National Research Council and Board [Johannes-
burg]
see   South Africa. National Research
Council.

**National Research Council Conference on Glossary of
Terms in Nuclear Science and Technology.**
Glossary of nuclear energy terms. [Prelim. ed.] New
York, American Society of Mechanical Engineers [1950–52]
9 v. in 8.   23 cm.
On cover: Proposed American standard.
CONTENTS.—section 1. Physics.—section 2. Reactor theory.—sec-
tion 3. Reactor engineering.—section 4. Chemistry.—section 5. Chem-
ical engineering.—section 6. Biophysics and radiobiology.—section 7.
Instrumentation.—section 8. Isotopes separation.—section 9. Metal-
lurgy.
1. Atomic energy—Dictionaries.   I. Title.

QC772.N3   541.2   50–58212 rev

NN   0063847   DLC NNC MB TxHR NcD OrP WaS IdU PU-Sc

541.2
N211g

National Research Council Conference on
Glossary of Terms in Nuclear Science
and Technology.
Glossary of nuclear energy terms.
New York, American Society of Mechanical
Engineers [1950-53]
9 v. in 1.   24 cm.

On cover: Proposed American standard.

NN   0063848   LU DNLM PU PU-Sc

National Research Council Conference on Glossary
of Terms in Nuclear Science and Technology.
Glossary of nuclear energy terms. [Prelim.
ed.]   New York, American Society of Mechanical
Engineers [1951-53]
v.   23 cm.
On cover: Proposed American standard.
Contents. - section 1. Physics. - section 2.
Reactor theory. section 3. Reactor engineering. -

section 5. Chemical engineering. - section 6. Biophysics and radio biology.

NN   0063849   OU

*8216.155R
National Research Council Conference on Glossary
of Terms in Nuclear Science and Technology.
Glossary of nuclear energy terms. New York,
American Society of Mechanical Engineers [1953]
1 v. (various pagings) 23cm.
On cover: Proposed American standard.
"The preparation of the several sections ...
has been assisted by the joint program of the
Office of Naval Research and the Atomic Energy
Commission."

CONTENTS.—section 1. Physics (formerly general
terms)—section 2. Reactor theory.—section 3.
Reactor engineering.—section 4. Chemistry.—
section 5. Chemical engineering.—section 6.
Biophysics and radiobiology.—section 7. Instrumentation.—section 8. Isotopes separation.—
section 9. Metallurgy.
1. Atomic ener-   gy—Dictionaries.
I. Title.

DNLM PU-E1 OC1W
NN   0063851   MB OrU TxHU NN PP IEN PBL NcD NNC

National Research Council Conference on Glossary of Terms
in Nuclear Science and Technology.
A glossary of terms in nuclear science and technology.
New York, American Society of Mechanical Engineers
[1955]
a–d, 189 p.   diagrs.   22 cm.
On cover: Proposed American standard.
Preliminary ed. published in 1950–52 under title: Glossary of nuclear energy terms.
1. Atomic energy—Dictionaries.   I. Title.

QC772.N33   *539.7603   55–3002

MiU IU ICJ PSt TxU PPD ViBlbV OrCS TOU AAP
NN   0063852   DLC CaBVaU MtBuM FMU ScCleU OU NcD

National Research Council Conference on Nuclear Glossary
see   National Research Council Conference on Glossary
of Terms in Nuclear Science and Technology.

National Research Council of Egypt
see
Egypt. *al-Markaz al-Qawmī lil-Buḥūth.*

National Research Council of Israel
see
Israel. *ha-Mo'atsah ha-le'umit le-meḥkar ule-fituaḥ.*

National Research Council of Italy
see
Italy. *Consiglio nazionale delle ricerche.*

National Research Council of Japan
see
Japan. *Gakujutsu Kenkyū Kaigi.*

National Research Council of Music Education
see   Music Educators' National Conference. *Music Education Research Council.*

National Research Council of the Philippine Islands.
Bulletin.   no. 1–
Feb. 1935–
Manila.
no. in   v.   illus.   24 cm.   irregular.
Publication suspended Nov. 1941–Nov. 1948.
No. 2–9 called "Separate from Report 1."
Includes the 1934/35–   (1st–   ) Report of the
council.

1. Research—Societies, etc.

Q75.N25   506.1   34–27938 rev*

NcU CU
NN   0063859   DLC KyU NcD DL ICJ KyLoU OU NNC N OU

National research council of the Philippine islands.
A memorial to the members of the Constitutional convention.
Manila, P. I., National research council of the Philippine
islands, 1934.
cover-title, 12 p.   24ᶜᵐ.

1. Philippine islands. Constitution. 2. Research.

Library of Congress   Q181.N38   35–28220
                             [2]   507.2

NN   0063860   DLC CtY

National Research Council of the Philippine Islands.
Report
see its
Bulletin.

The National Research Council review
see   National Research Council, Canada.
Review.

National Research Development Corporation.
Report and statement of accounts.   1949/50–
London, H. M. Stationery Off.
v.   25 cm.   annual.
Report year ends June 30.

1. Research—Gt. Brit. 2. Inventions.

T177.G7N354   607   53–15439

NN   0063863   DLC NSyU NN

National research institute, *Washington, D. C.*
17 states say, Repeal the income tax amendment; limit U. S.
taxes to 25%. Washington, D. C., National research institute
[1944]
58 p.   illus. (map) diagr.   19½ᶜᵐ.

1. Income tax—U. S. 2. U. S. Constitution—Amendments.   I. Title.
                                                          44–35762
Library of Congress   HJ4652.N296
                             [3]   336.24

NN   0063864   DLC

VOLUME 407

National Research Institute for Genetics, *Mishima, Japan*
see
Kokuritsu Idengaku Kenkyūjo, *Mishima, Japan.*

National Research Institute of Agricultural
Economics, Tokyo
see Nōgyō Sōgō Kenkyujō, *Tokyo.*

National Research Institute of Agriculture, *Tokyo*
see
Nōgyō Sōgō Kenkyūjo, *Tokyo.*

National Research Institute of Chemistry, *Shanghai*
see
Chung yang yen chiu yüan. *Hua hsüeh yen chiu so, Nan-kang, Formosa.*

National Research Institute of China
see
Chung yang yen chiu yüan.

National Research Institute of Education, *Tokyo*
see
Kokuritsu Kyōiku Kenkyūjo, *Tokyo.*

National Research Institute of History and Philology
see
Chung yang yen chiu yüan. *Li shih yü yen yen chiu so, Nan-kang, Formosa.*

National Research Institute of Meteorology, *Nanking*
see
Chung yang yen chiu yüan. *Ch'i hsiang yen chiu so, Nanking.*

National Research Institute of Social Sciences, *Nanking*
see
Chung yang yen chiu yüan. *Shê hui k'o hsüeh yen chiu so, Nanking.*

National Research Institute of Social Sciences, *Shanghai*
see
Chung yang yen chiu yüan. *Shê hui k'o hsüeh yen chiu so, Nanking.*

National Research Laboratory of Metrology, *Tokyo*
see
Keiryō Kenkyūjo, *Tokyo.*

National research league
Statement of principles. New York city, National
headquarters ₁1935
4 p. 23 cm.

NN   0063876   DL

**National research project on reemployment opportunities
and recent changes in industrial techniques.**
Changes in farm power and equipment: tractors, trucks,
automobiles, field implements, mechanical cotton picker. ₁Phil-
adelphia, 1937–39₁
3 v. in 1. illus. (incl. maps) plates, tables, diagrs. 25½ᶜᵐ.
Title from cover.
Reproduced from type-written copy.
"This volume contains WPA National research project reports nos.
A–9, A–11, and A–2."
1. Agricultural machinery. 2. Cotton growing and manufacture—U. S.
I. Title.
Library of Congress   S675.N3   41–20432
                                          ₂₁   631.3

NN   0063877   DLC

**National research project on reemployment opportunities
and recent changes in industrial techniques.**
Changes in technology and labor requirements in crop pro-
duction: corn, cotton, wheat and oats. ₁Philadelphia, 1938–39₁
3 v. in 1. illus. (incl. maps) tables, diagrs. 25½ᶜᵐ.
Title from cover.
Reproduced from type-written copy.
"This volume contains WPA National research project reports nos.
A–5, A–7, and A–10."
1. Agricultural laborers—U. S. 2. Agricultural machinery. 3. Maize—
U. S. 4. Wheat—U. S. 5. Oats. 6. Cotton growing and manufacture—
U. S. I. Title.
Library of Congress   SB189.N35   41–20433
                                          ₃₁   633.0973

NN   0063878   DLC DFT

**National research project on reemployment opportunities
and recent changes in industrial techniques.**
Changes in technology and labor requirements in crop pro-
duction: vegetables, potatoes, sugar beets. ₁Philadelphia,
1937–39₁
3 v. in 1. illus. (incl. maps) plates, tables, diagrs. 25½ᶜᵐ.
Title from cover.
Reproduced from type-written copy.
"This volume contains WPA National research project reports nos.
A–12, A–4, and A–1."
1. Agricultural laborers—U. S. 2. Agricultural machinery. 3. Vege-
table gardening—U. S. 4. Beets and beet sugar—U. S. 5. Potatoes.
I. Title.
Library of Congress   SB321.N25   41–20988
                                          ₂₁   633.40973

NN   0063879   DLC

National research project on reemployment opportunities and recent changes in industrial
techniques.
U.S. *Bureau of agricultural economics.*
... Changing technology and employment in agriculture, by
John A. Hopkins. Issued May 1941. (Work projects administration, National research project on reemployment opportunities and recent changes in industrial techniques) Washington, D. C., U. S. Govt. print. off. ₁1941₁

**National research project on reemployment opportunities
and recent changes in industrial techniques.**
Changing technology: industrial instruments, industrial re-
search, fuel efficiency, capital formation. ₁Philadelphia, 1938–
40₁
4 v. in 1. illus., tables, diagrs. 25½ᶜᵐ.
Title from cover.
Reproduced from type-written copy.
"This volume contains WPA National research project reports nos.
M–1, M–4, E–5 and G–4."
1. Machinery in industry. 2. Industrial arts—Hist. 3. Machinery,
Automatic. 4. Research, Industrial. 5. Fuel. 6. Cement industries. I.
Title.
Library of Congress   T19.N3   41–20638
                                          ₃₁   609

NN   0063881   DLC

231.366
N21   National research project on reemployment
         opportunities and recent changes in indus-
         trial techniques.
           Conditions under which beet and cane sugar
         compete in the United States. New York,
         1937.
           41 numb. l.

           Issued by Special research section.

NN   0063882   DNAL

National Research Project on Reemployment
Opportunities and Recent Changes in Industrial
Techniques.
Effects of current and prospective technologi-
cal developments upon capital formation
see under   Weintraub, David, 1904–

**National research project on reemployment opportunities
and recent changes in industrial techniques.**
... Farm-city migration, Lancaster labor, Brazil labor,
Paterson broad-silk. ₁Philadelphia, 1939–40₁
4 v. in 1. illus., tables, diagrs. 25½ᶜᵐ.
At head of title: Studies of the effects of industrial change on labor
markets.
Title from cover.
Reproduced from type-written copy.
"This volume contains WPA National research project reports no. L–7,
L–4, L–9, and L–8."
1. Labor and laboring classes—U. S. 2. Unemployment—U. S. 3. Cit-
ies and towns—Growth. 4. Agricultural laborers—U. S. 5. Paterson,
N. J.—Econ. condit. 6. Lancaster, Pa.—Econ. condit. 7. Brazil, Ind.—
Econ. condit. I. Title.
Library of Congress   HD8072.N284   41–20545
                                          ₃₁   331.137973

NN   0063884   DLC

National Research Project on Reemployment
Opportunities and Recent Changes in Industrial
Techniques.
Fuel economy on railroads of the United
States, 1918–1937
see under   Blakemore, Maurice Neville,
1876–

**National research project on reemployment opportunities
and recent changes in industrial techniques.**
Industrial change and employment opportunity—a selected
bibliography. Prepared under the supervision of Alexander
Gourvitch with the assistance of Carolyn Blanks, Marion
Hayes, Esther Skala, and Sophie Udin. Work projects administration, National research project ... Philadelphia, Pa., 1939.
xv, 254 p. 25½ᶜᵐ. (*Its* Report no. G–5)
Reproduced from type-written copy.
Issued by the National research project on reemployment opportunities
and recent changes in industrial techniques.

—— Author index ... Work projects administration. National research project. ₁Philadelphia, 1940₁
cover-title, 1 p. l., 255–269 p. 25½ᶜᵐ. ₁*Its* Report no. G–5, Author
index₁
Reproduced from type-written copy.

1. Industry—Bibl. 2. Labor supply—Bibl. I. Title.
                                          39–29858 Revised
Library of Congress   Z7911.N35 Index
                                          ₃₁   330.973

NN   0063887   DLC MB FU OEac OCU OU CU

**National research project on reemployment opportunities
and recent changes in industrial techniques.**
... Job requirements, trade-union policy, longshore work,
cigar makers. ₁Philadelphia, 1937–39₁
4 v. in 1. illus., tables, diagrs., forms. 25½ᶜᵐ.
At head of title: Studies of the effects of industrial change on labor
markets.
Title from cover.
Reproduced from type-written copy.
"This volume contains WPA National research project reports nos.
L–6, L–8, L–2, and L–1."
1. Trade-unions—U. S. 2. Longshoremen—San Francisco. 3. Cigar
makers—U. S. 4. Cigar manufacture and trade—U. S. 5. Machinery in
industry. 6. Hours of labor—San Francisco. 7. San Francisco—Econ.
condit. 8. Minnesota—Indus. I. Title.
                                          41–20646
Library of Congress   HD8072.N2842
                                          ₄₁   331.0973

NN   0063888   DLC

National Research Project on Reemployment
Opportunities and Recent Changes in Industrial
Techniques.
Labor supply and employment; preliminary
statement of estimates prepared and methods used,
by Daniel Carson, assisted by Henrietta Liebman.
Philadelphia, Penn., Work projects administration,
National research project, 1939.
2 p. l., xxi, 330 numb. l. tables. 29 cm.
(Half-title: ... National research project on
reemployment opportunities and recent changes in
industrial techniques ... Studies of the labor
supply, productivity, and production)

Continued in next column

VOLUME 407

Continued from preceding column

Mimeographed.
1. Labor and laboring classes - U. S. - Hist.
I. Carson, Daniel. II. Liebman, Henrietta.
III. National research project on reemployment
opportunities and recent changes in industrial techniques. Studies of the labor supply, productivity,
and production. IV. Title.

NN 0063890   CU

HD8051
.A62
no. 660

National research project on reemployment opportunities and recent changes in industrial
techniques.
Evans, Wilmoth Duane, 1909–
... Mechanization and productivity of labor in the cigar
manufacturing industry. Prepared by W. D. Evans ...
Washington, U. S. Govt. print. off., 1939.

National research project on reemployment opportunities
and recent changes in industrial techniques.
Mechanization, employment, and output per man: bituminous
coal, coal statistics, 1935. ₍Philadelphia, 1937–39₎

2 v. in 1. illus. (incl. maps) tables, diagrs. 25½ᵐ.

Title from cover.
Reproduced from type-written copy.
"This volume contains WPA National research project reports nos.
E–9 and E–4."

1. Coal mines and mining—U. S. 2. Bituminous coal. 3. Coal-miners—
U. S. 4. Coal-mining machinery. I. Title.

41–20642

Library of Congress   TN805.A5N3

₍3₎   622.330973

NN 0063892   DLC

National research project on reemployment opportunities
and recent changes in industrial techniques.
Mechanization in selected industries: brick, cement, lumber.
₍Philadelphia, 1939–40₎

3 v. in 1. illus. (incl. map) tables, diagrs. 25½ᵐ.

Title from cover.
Reproduced from type-written copy.
"This volume contains WPA National research project reports nos.
M–2, M–3, and M–5."

1. Machinery in industry. 2. Brickmaking. 3. Cement industries.
4. Lumbering—U. S. I. Title.

41–22236

Library of Congress   TJ145.N3

₍2₎   338.4

NN 0063893   DLC

National Research Project on Reemployment
Opportunities and Recent Changes in Industrial
Techniques.
Mechanization in the brick industry
see under Van Tassel, Alfred J.

National Research Project on Reemployment
Opportunities and Recent Changes in Industrial
Techniques.
Mechanization in the cement industry
see under Perazich, George.

National research project on reemployment opportunities
and recent changes in industrial techniques.
Mineral technology and output per man studies. ₍Report
no. E–1—
Philadelphia, 1937–

v. illus., maps, tables, diagrs., forms. 25½ᵐ.

Photoprinted.
Issued by the National research project on reemployment opportunities
and recent changes in industrial techniques in cooperation with the U. S.
Bureau of mines, Report no. E–1—

1. Mineral industries—U. S. 2. Mines and mineral resources—U. S.
I. U. S. Bureau of mines. II. Title.

37–26629

Library of Congress   TN23.N35

———— 2d set.   ₍10–10₎   622.0973

DFT CaBVaU OrCS OrU Or WaE
NN 0063896   DLC CU TU OC1WHi OU OCU OC1 MB DL ICJ

National research project on reemployment opportunities
and recent changes in industrial techniques.
Mineral technology: technology, grade of ore, rock drilling,
underground loading. ₍Philadelphia, 1937–40₎

4 v. in 1. illus. (incl. maps) tables, diagrs. 25½ᵐ.

Title from cover.
Reproduced from type-written copy.
"This volume contains WPA National research project reports nos.
E–1, E–6, E–11, and E–3."

1. Mineral industries—U. S. 2. Mining machinery. 3. Miners—U. S.
4. Ores—U. S. 5. Rock-drills. I. Title.

41–20640

Library of Congress   TN275.N3

₍3₎   622.0973

NN 0063897   DLC

National research project on reemployment opportunities
and recent changes in industrial techniques.
... Philadelphia labor market studies ... ₍Report no. P–1–
P–8₎ ₍Philadelphia, 1937–39₎

8 v. in 9. tables, diagrs. 25½ᵐ.

Reproduced from type-written copy.
Issued by the National research project on reemployment opportunities
and recent changes in industrial techniques in cooperation with the Industrial research department, Wharton school of finance and commerce,
University of Pennsylvania.

1. Unemployed—Philadelphia. 2. Labor supply—Philadelphia. I.
Pennsylvania. University. Wharton school of finance and commerce.
Industrial research dept. II. Title.

38–26029 Revised

Library of Congress   HD5726.P5N3

₍r44f2₎   331.137974811

OCU OO DFT ICJ
NN 0063898   DLC CaBVaU Or OrU PHC MiD CU MB OC1

National research project on reemployment opportunities
and recent changes in industrial techniques.
Progress report.

₍Philadelphia ? 1937–

v. tables. 26ᵐ.

Lithographed.
Issued by the National research project on reemployment opportunities and recent changes in industrial techniques.

1. U. S.—Indus. 2. Unemployed—U. S. 3. Research, Industrial.

37–26287

Library of Congress   HC106.3.N358

———— 2d set.   ₍5₎   330.973

NN 0063899   DLC NNC

National research project on reemployment opportunities
and recent changes in industrial techniques.
... Radio workers, weavers and loom fixers, machinists,
hosiery workers. ₍Philadelphia, 1938–39₎

3 v. in 1. illus., tables, diagrs. 25½ᵐ.
At head of title: Philadelphia labor market studies.
Title from cover.
Reproduced from type-written copy.
"This volume contains WPA National research project reports nos.
P–2, P–4, P–5, and P–6."

1. Radio industry and trade—U. S. 2. Weavers—Philadelphia. 3.
Machinists—Philadelphia. 4. Hosiery. 5. Unemployed—Philadelphia.
6. Philadelphia—Econ. condit. I. Title.

41–22007

Library of Congress   HD5726.P5N36

₍2₎   331.137974811

NN 0063900   DLC

National research project on reemployment opportunities
and recent changes in industrial techniques.
... Recent trends, employment and unemployment, search for
work, long-term unemployed. ₍Philadelphia, 1937–39₎

4 v. in 1. illus. (incl. map) tables, diagrs., form. 25½ᵐ.

At head of title: Philadelphia labor market studies.
Title from cover.
Reproduced from type-written copy.
"This volume contains WPA National research project reports nos.
P–1, P–3, P–7, and P–8."

1. Unemployed—Philadelphia. 2. Labor and laboring classes—Philadelphia. 3. Philadelphia—Econ. condit.

41–20543

Library of Congress   HD5726.P5N37

₍2₎   331.137974811

NN 0063901   DLC

National research project on reemployment opportunities
and recent changes in industrial techniques.
... Report no. G–₍1₎—
Philadelphia, Pa., 1937–

v. illus., tables, diagrs. 25–26½ᵐ.

Photoprinted.

1. U. S.—Indus. 2. U. S.—Econ. condit.—1918– 3. Unemployed—
U. S.

39–29110

NN 0063902   DLC WaS PHC ICJ MB CU TU

National research project on reemployment
opportunities and recent changes in
industrial techniques.
Kaplan, Irving.
Research program of the National research project, by
Irving Kaplan. Paper prepared for the meeting of the Washington statistical society chapter of the American statistical
association, Washington, D. C., June 10, 1937. Philadelphia,
Pa., 1937.

National research project on reemployment opportunities
and recent changes in industrial techniques.
... Shut-down of Amoskeag textile mills. ₍Philadelphia,
1937–39₎

2 v. in 1. illus., tables, diagrs., forms. 25½ᵐ.
At head of title: Studies of the effects of industrial change on labor
markets.
Title from cover.
Reproduced from type-written copy.
"This volume contains WPA National research project report no. L–5
and data prepared for a conference of the International labour organiza-
tion."

1. Unemployed—Manchester, N. H. 2. Amoskeag manufacturing company, Manchester, N. H. 3. Manchester, N. H.—Econ. condit. I. Title.

41–22100

Library of Congress   HD9859.A5N3

₍2₎   331.13797428

NN 0063904   DLC

National research project on reemployment opportunities
and recent changes in industrial techniques.
Size and production of the aggregate farm enterprise. Employment in agriculture, 1909–36. ₍Philadelphia, 1938₎

2 v. in 1. illus. (maps) tables, diagrs. 25½ᵐ.

Title from cover.
Reproduced from type-written copy.
"This volume contains WPA National research project reports nos.
A–6 and A–8."

1. Farm produce—U. S. 2. Agricultural laborers—U. S. I. Title.

41–22006

Library of Congress   HD1765.1936.N35

₍2₎   338.10973

NN 0063905   DLC

National Research Project on Reemployment
Opportunities and Recent Changes in Industrial
Techniques.
Statistical problems confronted in the analysis
of the relationship between production, productivity
and employment
see under   Weintraub, David, 1904–

National research project on reemployment opportunities
and recent changes in industrial techniques.
... Studies in changing labor productivity. ₍Report no. B–1—

₍Washington, U. S. Govt. print. off., 1937–

v. illus., tables. 25½ᵐ.

Issued by the National research project on reemployment opportunities
and recent changes in industrial techniques in cooperation with United
States Bureau of labor statistics. Report no. B–1—

1. Labor productivity—U. S. 2. Machinery in industry. I. Title.

37–29039

Library of Congress   HD6331.A1N3

₍a46d1₎   331.0973

OC1 OCU OU DFT DL ICJ
NN 0063907   DLC CaBVaU OrCS OrU Or PHC CU TU MB

National research project on reemployment opportunities
and recent changes in industrial techniques.
... Studies in equipment changes and industrial techniques ...
₍Report no. M–1—
₍Philadelphia, 1938–

v. illus., tables, diagrs. 25½ᵐ.

Photoprinted, Report no. M–1—
Issued by the National research project on reemployment opportunities
and recent changes in industrial techniques, Report no. M–1—

1. Machinery, Automatic. 2. Machinery in industry. I. Title.

38–28874

Library of Congress   TJ153.A1N3

———— 2d set.   ₍8₎   621

OCU OU OC1 DFT ICJ OrCS OrU Or CaBVaU
NN 0063908   DLC FTaSU MiU CU ICJ NcD MsSM PHC MB

National Research Project on Reemployment Opportunities
and Recent Changes in Industrial Techniques.
Studies of changing techniques and employment in agriculture. ₍Report no. A–1–A–13. Philadelphia, 1937–41₎

13 v. in 14. illus., diagrs. 26 cm.

1. Agriculture—U. S. 2. Agricultural laborers—U. S. 3. Farm
mechanization—U. S.

S441.N3   630.973   37–28925 rev 2*

NN 0063909   DLC OU OC1 DFT ICJ TU CaBVaU Or OrCS

VOLUME 407

S441
.N3
Index
National Research Project on Reemployment Opportunities and Recent Changes in Industrial Techniques. Studies of changing techniques and employment in agriculture.
Yarnall, Sarah Little, 1902–
Index to Studies of changing techniques and employment in agriculture. Washington, 1941.

National research project on reemployment opportunities and recent changes in industrial techniques.
... Studies of productivity and employment in selected industries. ₍Report no. N–1₎
₍Philadelphia, 1938–
    v. tables, diagrs. 25½ cm.
Photoprinted, no. N–1–
Issued by the National research project on reemployment opportunities and recent changes in industrial techniques in cooperation with the National bureau of economic research, inc., Report no. N–1–
1. U. S.—Indus. 2. Labor productivity—U. S. I. National bureau of economic research, inc. II. Title. III. Title: Productivity and employment in selected industries. Studies of. IV. Title: Employment in selected industries, Studies of productivity and.

Library of Congress   HC106.3.N3582   38—26958
    ₍a50m½₎   338.0973

NN   0063911   DLC OCU OC1 OU DFT ICJ MB PHC

National research project on reemployment opportunities and recent changes in industrial techniques.
... Studies of the effects of industrial change on labor markets. ₍Report no. L–1–L–9₎ ₍Philadelphia, 1937–40₎
   9 v. illus., diagrs., tables. 25½ cm.
Reproduced from type-written copy.
Issued by the National research project on reemployment opportunities and recent changes in industrial techniques.
1. U. S.—Indus. 2. Labor supply—U. S. 3. Unemployed—U. S.

                 38–26198 Revised
Library of Congress   HD6331.A1N32
    ₍r44k3₎   331.137973

      ICJ OCU OO OC1 OU
NN   0063912   DLC OrCS Or OrU CaBVaU CU MB PHC DFT

National research project on reemployment opportunities and recent changes in industrial techniques.
... Studies of the labor supply, productivity, and production. ₍Report no. S-1–S-2₎ ₍Philadelphia, 1939–40₎
   2 v. in 4. tables, diagrs. 25½ cm.
Reproduced from type-written copy.
Issued by the National research project on reemployment opportunities and recent changes in industrial techniques.
1. Labor supply—U. S. 2. U. S.—Indus. 3. U. S.—Econ. condit.—1918–

                 39–26713 Revised
Library of Congress   HD5723.A37
    ₍r44c3₎   331.80973

     OU ICJ OC1 OCU
NN   0063913   DLC CaBVaU OrCS Or OrU PHC CU MB DFT

National research project on reemployment opportunities and recent changes in industrial techniques.
Summary of findings to date, March 1938, by David Weintraub and Irving Kaplan. Philadelphia, Pa., 1938.
   xiii, 156 p. incl. illus., tables, diagrs. 25½ cm.
Photoprinted.
Issued by the National research project on reemployment opportunities and recent changes in industrial techniques.
1. U. S.—Indus. 2. Unemployed—U. S. 3. Research, Industrial. I. Weintraub, David, 1904– II. Kaplan, Irving. III. Title.

                 38–26340
Library of Congress   HC106.3.N3585 1938
——— Copy 2.   ₍10–2₎   331.137973

NN   0063914   DLC Or MB OC1 OCU OU NN DFT

National research projet on reemployment opportunities and recent changes in industrial techniques.
Survey of economic theory on technological change and employment
    see under Gourvitch, Alexander.

HD6331
.W4
National research project on reemployment opportunities and recent changes in industrial techniques.
Weintraub, David, 1904–
Technological change, by David Weintraub and Lewis W. Hine ... Philadelphia, Pa., 1937.

National research project on reemployment opportunities and recent changes in industrial techniques.
Technology, employment, and output per man: copper, iron, placer gold. ₍Philadelphia, 1937–40₎
   3 v. in 1. illus., pl., maps, tables, diagrs., forms. 23½ cm.
Title from cover.
Reproduced from type-written copy.
"This volume contains WPA National research project reports nos. E–12, E–13, and E–2."
1. Gold mines and mining—U. S. 2. Iron mines and mining—U. S. 3. Copper mines and mining—U. S. 4. Miners—U. S. 5. Mining machinery. 6. Hydraulic mining. I. Title.

                 41–20639
Library of Congress   TN23.N37
    ₍3₎   622.0973

NN   0063917   DLC WaSp WaS

National research project on reemployment opportunities and recent changes in industrial techniques.
Technology, employment, and output per man: phosphate rock, crushed stone. ₍Philadelphia, 1938–39₎
   2 v. in 1. illus. (incl. maps) tables, diagrs. 26½ cm.
Title from cover.
Reproduced from type-written copy.
"This volume contains WPA National research project reports nos. E–7 and E–8."
1. Phosphate industry—U. S. 2. Miners—U. S. 3. Mining machinery. 4. Stone, Crushed. 5. Quarries and quarrying—U. S. 6. Stone dealers and workers. I. Title.

                 41–20641
Library of Congress   TN277.N3
    ₍3₎   338.2

NN   0063918   DLC

National research project on reemployment opportunities and recent changes in industrial techniques.
Unemployment and increasing productivity, by David Weintraub, assisted by Harold L. Posner. Prepared for the National resources committee. Report on technological trends and their social implications. Philadelphia, Pa., 1937.
   vii, 54 p. incl. tables, diagrs. 25 cm.
Photoprinted.
Issued by the National research project on reemployment opportunities and recent changes in industrial techniques.
"The present (second) impression is issued July 1937."—Verso of t.-p.
1. Unemployed—U. S. 2. U. S.—Indus. 3. U. S.—Econ. condit.—1918– 4. U. S.—Soc. condit. I. Weintraub, David, 1904– II. Posner, Harold Leonard, 1911– III. Title.

                 38–26073
Library of Congress   HD5723.A53 1937 a
——— Copy 2.   ₍5₎   331.137973

NN   0063919   DLC OrU OC1 OC1WHi OO OCU ODW DFT

National research project on reemployment opportunities and recent changes in industrial techniques.
... Unemployment and increasing productivity, by David Weintraub, assisted by Harold L. Posner. Prepared for the National resources committee. Report on technological trends and their social implications. National research project on reemployment opportunities and recent changes in industrial techniques. David Weintraub, director. Irving Kaplan, associate director. ₍Philadelphia? 1937₎
   4 p. l., 75 numb. l. incl. tables. diagrs. 26½ cm.
At head of title: Works progress administration. Harry L. Hopkins, administrator. Corrington Gill, assistant administrator.
Lithographed.
1. Unemployed—U. S. 2. U. S.—Indus. 3. U. S.—Econ. condit.—1918– 4. U. S.—Soc. condit. I. Weintraub, David, 1904– II. Posner, Harold Leonard, 1911– III. Title.
Library of Congress   HD5724.N35   37–26531
——— Copy 2.   ₍5₎   331.137973

NN   0063920   DLC NN MB DFT

National Research Project on Reemployment Opportunities and Recent Changes in Industrial Techniques.
Unemployment and technological change
    see under Gill, Corrington, 1898–

National Research Project on Reemployment Opportunities and Recent Changes in Industrial Techniques.
Unemployment in Philadelphia
    see under Pennsylvania. University.
Wharton School of Finance and Commerce. Industrial Research Dept.

National research project on reemployment opportunities and recent changes in industrial techniques.
The work and publications of the WPA National research project on reemployment opportunities and recent changes in industrial techniques. Work projects administration. National research project. ₍Philadelphia, 1939₎
   2 p. l., 8 p. 25 cm.
1. National research project on reemployment opportunities and recent changes in industrial techniques. 2. National research project on reemployment opportunities and recent changes in industrial techniques—Bibl. I. Title.
Library of Congress   Z7164.U56N3   40–26135
——— Copy 2.   ₍3₎   016.331137973

NN   0063923   DLC CLSU

016.331
N21w
1941
National Research Project on Reemployment Opportunities and Recent Changes in Industrial Techniques.
The work and publications of the WPA National research project on reemployment opportunities and recent changes in industrial techniques. Work projects administration. National research project. ₍Philadelphia, 1941₎
9 p. 25 cm.

NN   0063924   IU CU

National research project on reemployment opportunities and recent changes in industrial techniques.
Work and wages at the Amoskeag manufacturing company mills, 1927–35. Prepared for the Tripartite technical conference of the International labour organization. Philadelphia, Pa., 1937.
   2 p. l., 13 p. incl. tables, diagrs. 25 cm.
On 1st prelim. leaf: National research project on reemployment opportunities and recent changes in industrial techniques ... in cooperation with Social board, Bureau of research and statistics.
1. Amoskeag manufacturing company, Manchester, N. H. I. U. S. Social security board. Bureau of research and statistics. II. Tripartite technical conference on the textile industry, Washington, D. C., 1937. III. Title.

Library of Congress   HD9879.A5N3   45–25731

NN   0063925   DLC CU

National reserve association, *Kansas City, Mo. Supreme lodge.*
Constitution and laws of the Supreme lodge, southern jurisdiction, National reserve association ... Kansas City, Mo., The Burd & Fletcher ptg. co., 1896.
   46 p., 1 l. 13½ cm.

Library of Congress   HS1510.N271A3 1896   9–3968†

NN   0063926   DLC

National reserve association of the United States.
National citizens' league for the promotion of a sound banking system.
The National reserve association: advantages it will give the smaller banks and their communities, distributed by the American bankers' association. ₍Chicago, 1912₎

National Reserve Corporation.
Practical suggestions for the appraisal of residential properties for real estate loans
    see under Kniskern, Philip Wheeler, 1889–

National Resettlement Conference for Displaced Persons, *Chicago, 1949.*
Proceedings. Washington, U. S. Govt. Print. Off., 1949.
   xii, 72 p. 23 cm. (₍U. S.₎ 81st Cong., 1st sess., 1949. House. Document no. 220)
Conference held under the auspices of the Displaced Persons Commission.
1. World War, 1939–1945—Displaced persons. 2. U. S.—Emig. & immig. (Series)

D808.N37 1949   325.73   49–46939*

NN   0063929   DLC

VOLUME 407

National resistance council (*France*)

   see

Conseil national de la résistance (*France*)

HC106   National resources and foreign aid. [Washington? 1947?]
.5   46 *l.*
N285
Documents
Dept.

    1. U. S. - Economic conditions - 1945-   2. Economic
assistance, American.

NN   0063931   CU

National Resources Committee
    see U. S. National Resources Com-
mittee.

National Resources Security Company.
   The Upper Fraser Valley Farms are the front
yard of the great Fort George country.   Vancouver,
B.C. [1911?]
   sheet (48 x 32 cm.)   illus., maps.

   Caption title.

NN   0063933   CaBViPA

National responsibility for education of the colored people: A. The status of negro education [by] Kelly Miller.—B. The nation's responsibility to the South for
negro education [by] W. T. B. Williams.—C. The nation's responsibility to itself for negro education and
its constitutional power to render aid thereto [by] Isaac
Fisher.
   (*In* National education association of the United States. Addresses and
proceedings, 1918. p. 555-567)

   1. Negroes—Education.   I. Miller, Kelly, 1863–   II. Williams,
William Taylor Burwell, 1866–   III. Fisher, Isaac, 1877–

   Library, U. S. Bur. of   Education   E 19–552

NN   0063934   DHEW

National restaurant association.
   Addresses and discussions [at the annual convention] 19
    see its   Proceedings of the annual convention
and exposition.

National Restaurant Association.
   Addresses and discussions of the wartime
conference
    see its Proceedings of the annual
convention and exposition.

NATIONAL RESTAURANT ASSOCIATION
   By-laws.   Chicago. [194-?].
   11p.
   Cover-title.

   1. Restaurant industry

NN   0063937   MH-IR

National Restaurant Association.
   Conference notes on key points of effective
operating control
    see under   Chicago. University.
Graduate School of Business.

National Restaurant Association.
   The eighth short course lectures on planning
    see under   Chicago. University. Graduate
School of Business.

       National restaurant association.

T7
.U62   Bryan, Mary (De Garmo) 1891–
no. 39   ... Establishing and operating a restaurant ... Prepared by
   Mary de Garmo Bryan, Alberta M. Macfarlane, and E. R.
   Hawkins under the direction of Walter F. Crowder, Bureau of
   foreign and domestic commerce, United States Department of
   commerce ... In cooperation with the National restaurant as-
   sociation. With the assistance of Neva H. Radell, Charles H.
   Sevin, Grace E. Smith ... [and others] Washington, U. S.
   Govt. print. off. [1946]

NATIONAL RESTAURANT ASSOCIATION.
   A guide to popular restaurants. Chicago, Ill.,
1940.

   22 cm.

NN   0063941   MH OC1 OC1h

647.95   National Restaurant Association.
N21h   How to plan a system of employee
   training for restaurants.   Chicago [°1954]
   v, 68 p. illus. 28 cm.

   Cover title.

   1. Restaurants, lunch rooms, etc.--
Employees. I. Title.

NN   0063942   LU FTaSU NBNC

TX901   National restaurant association.
.N28   National restaurant bulletin.

   [Chicago] 19

National Restaurant Association.
   News bulletin.

   [Chicago]
   v. in   illus. 29 cm. monthly.

   "Authoritative information on current problems affecting the restaurant industry, an exclusive service to members ..."
   Running title   : National restaurant news
bulletin.
   Supplements accompany some numbers.

   1. Restaurants, lunch rooms, etc.—United States—Periodicals.
I. Title : National restaurant news bulletin.

   TX901.N27a   647'.95'05   74–641535
                                     MARC-S

NN   0063944   DLC

TX945   National Restaurant Association.
N28   Official directory.

   Chicago, 19_

   __vols. 22cm.

NN   0063945   NBuG

HF6201
.R4P4   National Restaurant Association.
   Planning for profits in 1953; a series
   of lectures at the eighth conference offered by the School of Business, The University of Chicago in cooperation with the
   National Restaurant Association, September,
   1952.   Chicago, 1952.
   58 p. 28 cm.

   1. Food industry and trade. 2. Profit.

NN   0063946   TU

National Restaurant Association.
   Proceedings of the annual convention and exposition.

   Chicago.
      v.   28 cm.

   1. Restaurant management—Congresses.

   TX945.N34   56–40543 ‡

        NN OrP WaS NN MiD
NN   0063947   DLC FTaSU ICU CaBVa NcC OC1 MtBC MH-BA

National restaurant association.
   Public opinion and private profit. Chicago, National restaurant association, 1931.
   1 p. l., 5–37, [1] p. incl. plates. 26ᶜᵐ.
   "In this book ... the Association has attempted to present to its members the reasons favoring the policy of coöperative advertising as a desirable and constructive Association activity."—p. [38]

   1. Advertising—Restaurants, lunch rooms, etc.   I. Title.

   Library of Congress   HF6161.R4N3   31–20783
   ———— Copy 2.
   Copyright A 39857   [2]   659.1

NN   0063948   DLC

National Restaurant Association.
   Record keeping, simplified for the small
restaurant ...
    see under   Horwath and Horwath, New York.

National restaurant association.
   Report on nation-wide survey of restaurant
operating data
    see under   Horwath & Horwath, New York.

National Restaurant Association.
   The seventh short course lectures on new
management methods for maintaining profits in
1952
    see under   Chicago. University.
Graduate School of Business.

TX945   **National Restaurant Association.**
.C43

   Chicago. University. *Graduate School of Business.*
    Short course lectures on modernization of food service fa-
cilities and operations in the restaurant industry, the School
of Business, the University of Chicago, June 17, 18 and 19,
1946 ... Comp. by the Educational Dept. of the National
Restaurant Assn. Chicago, °1946.

National Restaurant Association.
   Short course lectures on modernizing
management methods in the restaurant industry
    see under   Chicago. University.
Graduate School of Business.

National Restaurant Association.
   The sixth short course lectures on
management techniques
    see under   Chicago. University.
Graduate School of Business.

389.253   National Restaurant Association.
N213   Suggestions and recipes for meat alternates and
   extenders.   Chicago [1943?]
   17 numb. l.   28 cm.
   Processed.

NN   0063955   DNAL

VOLUME 407

TX907
.N35

National Restaurant Association.
Who's who in food service in America.
Chicago, National Restaurant Association.

647.95   National Restaurant Association. Educational
N21a   Dept.
              Apprentice training program.   Chicago
              ₁¹1946₎
              32 p. illus., ports. 28 cm.

              Cover title.

              1. Restaurants, lunch rooms, etc.

NN 0063957   IU

641.631 National Restaurant Association. Food and
N277p   Equipment Research Department.
              Pies; how to make, bake, fill, freeze and serve,
           including expert comment on crust, fillers, thickeners
           and meringues, and special recipes from member restau-
           rants. Comp. by G.T. Carlin ₍and others₎ as presented
           at the National Restaurant Association Convention
           Food Show of 1953. ₍Chicago, n.d₎
              11p. (Its Technical bulletin, no. 121)

              1. Pastry. I. Carlin, G   T
           comp.

NN 0063958   FTaSU

National restaurant bulletin.

₍Chicago₎ 19

              v. in illus. 28½ᵐ. monthly.

Caption title.
Official organ of the National restaurant association.

              1. Restaurants, lunch rooms, etc.—Period.   ɪ. National restaurant
           association.   45–41877
              Library of Congress   TX901.N2S
                                         ₍2₎   647.9505

NN 0063959   DLC

National restaurant news and management
     see **Restaurant** management.

The **National** retail clothier
Chicago, The National association of retail clothiers,
19

              v.   illus. 30½ᵐ. semimonthly.

Title varies: The Bulletin. Pub. by the National association of
       retail clothiers.
            Sept. 15, 1920, The National clothier.
       Oct. 1, 1920—   The National retail clothier.

              1. Clothing trade—Period.   ɪ. National association of retail clothiers.
                                                         CA 22–527 Unrev'd
              Library of Congress   HD9940.A1N3

NN 0063961   DLC ICRL

National retail clothier. v.6, no.6–v.25, no.1;
   Nov. 15, 1920–Jan. 2, 1930. Chicago, National
   Association of Retail Clothiers.
      20v. in 33. illus. semimonthly.

      Continues National clothier and is continued
   by National retail clothier and furnisher.
      Vol. 6, no.6–8 bound with National clothier,
   v.6, no.2–5.
      Vol. 25, no.1 bound with National retail
   clothier and furnisher, v.25, no.2–12.

NN 0063962   ICRL

National retail clothier and furnisher. v.25,
   no.2–v.30, no.8; Jan. 16, 1930–Oct. 1932.
   Chicago, National Association of Retail
   Clothiers and Furnishers.
      6v. in 4. illus. semimonthly.

      Continues National retail clothier and is
   continued by National clothier.
      Vol. 25, no.2–12 bound with National retail
   clothier, v.25, no.1.
      Vols. 29–30, no.8 bound with National clothier,
   v.30. no.9–12.

NN 0063963   ICRL

National retail clothier and furnisher
     see also **National clothier.**

National retail coal merchants' association.

      Organized November 1917, being the outgrowth of the Atlantic
   states retail coal merchants' association organized in September of
   the same year.

National retail coal merchants' association.
      ...Addresses delivered at third annual meeting,
   Detroit, Mich., June 10, 11, 12, 1920...
   Philadelphia, [1920?]

HD9541
.A46

NN 0063966   DLC DL

National retail coal merchants' association.
      Annual meeting. 1st–
   1918–
   Washington, D. C. ₍etc.₎ Issued from Association headquarters ₍1918–
      v. diagr. 23ᵐ.

      1. Coal trade—Societies.

      Library of Congress   HD9541.A45   20–2178

NN 0063967   DLC ICJ

National Retail Coal Merchants' Association.
   ₍Bulletin.₎
   no.

   Washington, D. C. ₍etc.₎, 19   8°.
   nos.
      Irregular.

      1. Coal—Trade and statistics, U. S.
   N. Y. P. L.   March 17, 1927

NN 0063968   NN

National Retail Coal Merchants Association.
      A chronology of oil, for the information of retail coal dealers.
   ₍Philadelphia? 1925.₎ 15 p. nar. 8°.

      1. Furnaces, Oil burning.
   N. Y. P. L.   March 23, 1926

NN 0063969   NN

National retail coal merchants' association.
      The **Coal** merchant.
      Philadelphia, Pa. ₍etc.₎, National retail coal merchants'
   association, 1919–

National retail coal merchants' association.
      Complete uniform accounting system for retail coal
   merchants. Philadelphia, National retail coal merchants
   association, 1922.
      24 p. 23ᵐ.

      1. Coal trade—Accounting.   ɪ. Title.

      Library of Congress   HF5686.C48N4   22–7661

NN 0063971   DLC OU NN ICJ IU

National retail coal merchants' association.
      Meeting of the executive committee ... Nov. 1918–

   Washington, D. C., Issued from National headquarters
   ₍1918–
      v. 23ᵐ.

   Report of the executive committee for May 1919   included in
   report of the 2d   annual meeting.

      Library of Congress   HD9541.A453   20–2177

NN 0063972   DLC

National retail coal merchants' association.
      Simplified uniform accounting system for retail coal
   merchants. Philadelphia, National retail coal merchants
   association, 1922.
      7 p. 23ᵐ.

      1. Coal trade—Accounting.   ɪ. Title.

      Library of Congress   HF5686.C48N42   22–7660

NN 0063973   DLC OU IU NN

National Retail Coal Merchants' Association.
      ...Statement of conditions and recommendations to United
   States Coal Commission at conference held at Washington, D. C.,
   November 25, 1922. ₍Philadelphia, 1922.₎ 20 p. 8°.

      Cover-title.

      1. Coal—Trade and statistics, U. S.,   1922.
   N. Y. P. L.   May 29, 1923.

NN 0063974   NN DFT DL

National retail coal merchants' association.
      ...Transportation bulletin...
   [Philadelphia,

HE2321
.C6N3

NN 0063975   DLC

National retail code authority, inc.
      ...Organization and operation of
   local retail code authorities...Wash.
   National retail code auth. 1934.

      9 numb. l.

NN 0063976   OO

National retail credit association
      Combined report of the minutes of the
   Dept. and specialty stores, Furniture
   and musical instruments group, Hardware
   and building material group...eighteenth
   annual convention, Toronto, Ont. Canada
   June 17th to 20th, 1930.
      126 p.

NN 0063977   OC1

VOLUME 407

National retail credit association.
Convention addresses... Twenty-ninth annual conference and credit sales forum, New York city, June 16-19, 1941. ₍New York: National retail credit assoc., 1941₎ 63 p. illus. (ports.) 29cm..

Cover-title: Speaking of credit in an emergency period.

1. Credit—Congresses—U. S.— N. Y.—New York, 1941.
N. Y. P. L. November 19, 1942

NN 0063978 NN

National Retail Credit Association.
The Credit World
see under title

HF5566 **National retail credit association.**
.P475
Phelps, Clyde William, 1897–
Important steps in retail credit operation; official handbook of the National retail credit association, by Dr. Clyde William Phelps ... St. Louis, Mo., National retail credit association, 1947.

National retail credit association.

Dakins, John Gordon, 1903–
The layman's handbook of regulation W, by J. Gordon Dakins... St. Louis, Mo., National retail credit association ₍1942₎

HF
5556 **National retail credit association.**
.N28   The new 4 point collection system,ed.by
Daniel J.Hannefin ... Saint Louis, National retail credit association [ᶜ1927]
32 p.   28cm.
In box,together with the Better letters bulletin,v.1,nos.1-5,April-August 1927,and forms,collection letters,follow-up record sheets,mounted collection stickers,etc.

NN 0063982 MiU

National retail credit association.

Schmalz, Carl Nelson, 1898–
... Operating statistics for the credit and accounts receivable departments of retail stores 1927, by Carl N. Schmalz ... Ann Arbor, University of Michigan, School of business administration, Bureau of business research, 1928.

Pamphlet
HF   **National Retail Credit Association.**
83   Physicians and dentists credit and collection manuals.   St. Louis, 1953.
55 p. illus. 19cm.

1. Collecting of accounts. 2. Credit.

NN 0063984 NIC PU-BZ OrU-M

National Retail Credit Association.
Proceedings of the department store group conferences...
see National Retail Credit Association. Department Store Group Conference. Proceedings...

National retail credit association.
Proceedings; retail credit forum: wartime problems and post-war plans. Statler hotel, St. Louis...June 15-16, 1943. ₍St. Louis, Nat. retail credit association, 1943₎ 91, 18 f. 28cm.

315800B. 1. Credit—Congresses—
trade—Congresses—U. S.—Mo.—St.
N. Y. P. L.
U. S.—Mo.—St. Louis, 1943. 2. Retail Louis, 1943.
February 7, 1946

NN 0063986 NN MH-BA

National retail credit association.

Dakins, John Gordon, 1903–
Regulation W and interpretations simplified; the layman's manual, by J. Gordon Dakins ... St. Louis, Mo., National retail credit association ₍1942₎

658.882 **National Retail Credit Association.**
N277r   Retail collection procedure and effective
collection letters.   St. Louis, Missouri, 1954.
71p.

1. Collecting of accounts.

NN 0063988 ICarbS CLSU AU WaS OrP NIC MiD NNU-W

HF5566 **National Retail Credit Association.**
.P5   FOR OTHER EDITIONS
1952   SEE MAIN ENTRY
Phelps, Clyde William, 1897–
Retail credit fundamentals; official textbook of the National Retail Credit Association. 3d ed. St. Louis, National Retail Credit Association, 1952.

HF5721 **National Retail Credit Association.**
.M34   FOR OTHER EDITIONS
1955   SEE MAIN ENTRY
Marra, Waldo J
Streamlined letters; official textbook of the National Retail Credit Association. ₍Rev. ed.₎ St. Louis, National Retail Credit Association, 1955.

National retail credit association
Successful credit department letters. St. Louis, Mo., National retail credit association.
n.d.

32 p.

NN 0063991 OC1

National retail credit association. Credit women's breakfast clubs of North America
see   Credit women's breakfast clubs of North America.

National retail credit association. Department store group conference.
Proceedings...
19

₍St. Louis, Mo.₎ 19   27½cm.
v.

Department store group conferences of 19   held as part of the association's
annual convention.

1. Credit—Per. and soc. publ.   —U. S.
N. Y. P. L.
September 17, 1942

NN 0063993 NN OC1 CU

332.7 **National retail credit association--Research di-**
N212c   **vision.**
Credit reports: an analysis of the costs of credit reports and time required to complete them in credit bureaus located in cities of approximately 250,000 population ...   St. Louis, Mo., 1935.
cover-title, 13 numb.l.

Mimeographed.
Arthur H. Hert, research director.

NN 0063994 IU

... National retail credit survey ...
see under [Plummer, Wilbur Clayton] 1889–

National retail drug trade council.

U. S. *National recovery administration.*
... Retail code and Retail drug code with explanatory comments. Prepared by the National recovery administration in collaboration with the National retail trade council and the National retail drug trade council. Washington, U. S. Govt. print. off., 1933.

National Retail Dry Goods Association
see
National Retail Merchants Association.

National Retail Farm Equipment Association
see
National Farm and Power Equipment Dealers Association.

National retail furniture agency.
The buyer's guide.

Grand Rapids, Mich., National retail furniture agency.
v. 23 cm.

NN 0063999 DL OC1

National retail furniture association.
Compelling one minute radio creations for progressive furniture dealers. The voice sells. Original and interesting telephone chats; proven volume builders, sold exclusively by the National retail furniture association to members only. Columbus, O., Ruth H. Carlile, ᶜ1939.
5 p. l., 100 numb. l. 29ᶜᵐ.
Mimeographed.

1. Radio advertising. 2. Advertising—Furniture trade. I. Title.

Library of Congress   HF6161.F95N3   39-30207
Copyright AA 308334   ₍2₎   659.1

NN 0064001 DLC

National Retail Furniture Association.
Furniture store operating experiences.

Chicago.
v. 28 cm.

1. Furniture industry and trade—U. S.

HD9773.U5N28   658.984   54-16060 ‡

NN 0064002 DLC IU NIC OC1

National Retail Furniture Association.
Furniture store operating experiences
see also   National Home Furnishings Association.
Operating experiences.

VOLUME 407

HF5568
.H36

National retail furniture association.

Haring, Albert, 1901–
Instalment credit comes of age, discussing the merits of and future need for consumer instalment credit, by Dr. Albert Haring ... Chicago, Ill., National retail furniture association ₁1943₎

NA6220
.A1M6

National retail furniture association.

Modern stores ... The store modernizing manual of the National retail furniture association.

₁Chicago, 19

TS840
.N28

National Retail Furniture Association.

National furniture review.

₁Chicago, National Retail Furniture Association₎

National retail furniture association.
Rugs and carpets, and how to sell them, by Jack Hand ... ₁Chicago, 1946₎
126 p. illus. 22ᵐ.

1. Rugs. 2. Carpets. ɪ. Hand, Jack.
HF6201.R83N3   658.89677643   47–20248
                                            Brief cataloging

NN   0064007   DLC OClCC PPT

National Retail Furniture Association.
The store modernizing manual of the National Retail Furniture Association
see Modern stores...

National retail furniture association.
Twenty-five years of action ... ₁Chicago, 1945₎
38, ₁2₎ p.incl.illus., ports.

NN   0064009   MH-BA

National retail furniture association.
What is a furniture store? The inside story of how a furniture store operates and its place in our American economy. Chicago, Ill., The National retail furniture association ₁ᵃ1943₎
29 p. incl. tables. 24ᵐ.
Prepared by Walter Kleeman, jr.
"Limited edition."

1. Furniture industry and trade—U. S.   ɪ. Kleeman, Walter.
ɪɪ. Title.
Library of Congress   HD9773.U5N3   45–12373
                           ₁2₎   658.945

NN   0064010   DLC OrCS

National retail furniture association.
What is a furniture store? The inside story of how a furniture store operates and its place in our American economy. Edited by Walter Kleeman, jr. Chicago ₁1946₎
30 p. tables.

"Revised, January, 1946."

1. Furniture industry and trade - U. S.
ɪ. Kleeman, Walter, ed.

NN   0064011   NNC

National Retail Furniture Association.
Why people don't buy furniture
see under   Millis Advertising Company, Indianapolis.

National Retail Furniture Association. Control and Management Division.
Annual report, store operating experiences
see   National Retail Furniture Association.
Furniture store operating experiences.

National retail furniture institute.
Proceedings of National retail furniture institute ...

Grand Rapids ₁ᵃ19
v. illus. (incl. ports.) 23ᵐ.
Cover-title.

1. Furniture industry and trade—U. S.

Library of Congress   HD9773.U7N35   26–9244

NN   0064014   DLC ICRL ICJ

National retail grocer ... Chicago, Ill
v.   illus., ports. 30ᵐ. monthly.
No general t.-p. and index.
Title varies: v. 26-31, The Retailers' journal.
1925 numbered v. 27, no. 1; v. 28, no. 2-12.

NN   0064015   ICJ NN

National Retail Hardware Association.
The hardware business, where and how to start? How much capital? [Indianapolis, Ind., 1955?]
23 p.   illus.
Cover title.

NN   0064016   OC1

National retail hardware association.
Hardware retailer.

Indianapolis ₁etc.₎ National retail hardware association, 19

TS403
.H36

National Retail Hardware Association.

Hardware retailer buyer's guide. 1954–

Indianapolis, National Retail Hardware Association.

National retail hardware association.
ᶜHardware retailers' sales manual. 1935-'36 edition. Published by National retail hardware association in cooperation with Hardware retailer advertisers. ₁Indianapolis, 1935₎
288 p. illus. 29½ᶜᵐ.

ɪ. title. 1. Hardware - U. S.

NN   0064019   NNC

National Retail Hardware Association.
The ₁hardware store ...
see its   Hardware Store Survey.

658
N2127h

National retail hardware association.
Hardware store survey; a study of margin, expense, profit ... ₁1922-27₎ Argos, Ind. ₁etc.₎, 1923-28₎
6v. tables, diagrs.

1925 issued by the Hardware retailer.
1923-27 designated on covers as 1924-28 editions.
Title varies: The hardware store; an intimate study of margin, expense, profit, 1922-24.
Continued in the July issue of the Hardware retailer.

NN   0064021   IU MiU NN OU MiD ICJ

National Retail Hardware Association
How to keep books departmentally, a manual of instruction designed to assist in the installation, guide in the maintenance and help in the closing of the association's departmental accounting system.   Indianapolis, Indiana [author] 1955.   51p. illus.

Accounting-Hardware trade (retail)

NN   0064022   NjN CaBVa OC1 AU

657.6
H2N2

National Retail Hardware Association
How to keep books without being a book-keeper; a manual of instruction designed to assist in the installation, guide in the maintenance and help in the closing of the association's accounting system, the Better business record. Indianapolis, ᶜ1954.
1 v. (loose—leaf) illus.

1. Hardware – Accounting   I. Title

NN   0064023   MiD

National retail hardware association.
How to start in the hardware business; suggestions for service veterans and others. Indianapolis, Ind. ₁1945?₎
8 p.

Caption title.

NN   0064024   MH-BA OC1 Or

---

q658.3
N2133H

NATIONAL retail hardware association.
IRHA hardware budget plan; a manual of operating procedures; prepared by Marketing analysis section.
[Indianapolis, Ind.] c1955. 78p. illus. forms. tables.

With which is bound: its Confidential instructions for salespeople. 16p.

NN   0064025   WaS

National Retail Hardware Association.
Management report. Indianapolis, Annual.
Title varies: –1955 A manual for management of retail hardware stores.

NN   0064026   CaBVa OC1 NIC MH-BA IEN

National Retail Hardware Association.
A manual for management of retail hardware stores
see its Management report.

National Retail Hardware Association.
₁Report of the annual congress.₎
19

₁Argos, Ind., 19
no.   ports.
19   a reprint from Hardware retailer.

1. Hardware.—Trade and statistics,   U. S.
N. Y. P. L.   October 14, 1924

NN   0064028   NN

VOLUME 407

National retail institute.
The book of Arlington County, Virginia; a scientific study of industrial and commercial facilities, and conditions and advantages of living in Arlington County ... prepared by the National retail institute. Washington, D. C., °1928.
52 p. incl. illus., maps, tables. 31ᶜᵐ.
Contains advertising matter.

1. Arlington Co., Va.   ɪ. Title.
Library of Congress   F232.A7N3   29-4455
——— Copy 2.

NN 0064029   DLC

National Retail Liquor Dealers' Association of America.
... President's report. [n.p.,
v. 22 cm.

NN 0064030   DLC

National retail liquor dealers' association of America.
Proceedings of the ... annual conference ...   -23d;
18   -1916. ₁n. p.₎ 18   -1916₎
v. illus., plates, ports. 22ᶜᵐ.
Title varies: 18   -1904, Proceedings of the ... annual convention, National retail liquor dealers' association of the United States.
1905-10, Proceedings of the ... annual convention, National liquor league of the United States of America.
1911-13, Proceedings of the ... annual conference, National retail liquor league of the United States of America.
1914-16, Proceedings of the ... annual conference, National retail liquor dealers' association of America.
1916 is "Advance copy."
No more published after 1916?
1. Liquor traffic—Socie-   ties.
Library of Congress   HD9851.N3   42-40526

NN 0064031   DLC

National Retail Liquor Dealers' Association of America.
... Secretary's report. [n.p.,
v. 22 cm.

NN 0064032   DLC

National Retail Liquor League of the United States of America
see National Retail Liquor Dealers' Association of America.

NATIONAL retail lumber dealers association
Here's a better way to build; the industry-engineered homes program 1948 Wash Author c1947 128p illus diagrs plans

NN 0064034   WaT

National retail lumber dealers association.
... How to select high quality exterior house paints. ₁Washington, 1935₎
₁4₎ p. illus. 28ᶜᵐ. (Special circular. October, 1935. ₁Scientific section. National paint, varnish and lacquer association, inc., Washington, D. C.₎)
Caption title.
At head of title: ... National retail lumber dealers assn. in cooperation with the Scientific section ... National paint, varnish and lacquer association, inc., Washington, D. C.
Illustrative matter: p. ₁2₎-₁4₎
1. Paint—Testing.
Library of Congress   TP936.5.N3   43-36776

NN 0064035   DLC

National retail lumber dealers association.
Inside the retail lumber and building materials industry. Washington [195-?]
32 p. illus. 29cm.

1.Lumber—Trade and stat.—U.S., 195-
2.Building materials—Trade and stat.—U.S., 195-   3.Building—U.S., 195-

NN 0064036   NN MH-BA

National Retail Lumber Dealers Association.
HD975   Retail store merchandising; lumber and
.5   building materials. ₁n.p., n.d.₎
qN3   1 v (loose leaf) 30cm.

1.Lumber trade. 2.Building materials.

NN 0064037   OrCS AAP

National retail lumber dealers association.
Survey of retail lumber stocks and sales.
Washington, D.C. no 1-243, 1940-1960.
Continued in supplements to the association Fingertip facts and figures.

NN 0064038   CU DNAL

National retail markets. ₁Chicago, National editorial association, °1933–
v. illus. (maps) 43½ x 28½ᶜᵐ.
Title from cover; loose-leaf; lithographed.
The National editorial association, with the cooperation of state publishers' associations, has formulated a program which includes publication, by state units, of a national market survey. cf. ₁v. 1₎, p. ₁3₎
Prepared by General marketing counselors, inc. cf. ₁v. 1₎, p. 116.
"Sources": ₁v. 1₎, p. 116.

1. Market surveys—U. S. 2. American newspapers—Direct. 3. Advertising. ɪ. National editorial association of the United States. ɪɪ. General marketing counselors, inc. ɪɪɪ. Title: Retail markets.
Library of Congress   HF5905.N3   34-2400
——— Copy 2.
Copyright   ₁3₎   658.80973

NN 0064039   DLC ICJ

National Retail Merchants Association.
The A B C's of informative selling. [New York, 1937]
[61]-128 p. (Its Bulletin, September, 1937)
1. Salesmen and salesmanship.

NN 0064040   NNC OC1 InU

National Retail Merchants Association.
Annual convention ...
see its Convention.

National Retail Merchants Association.
Annual report of the managing director...
19

New York₁, 19   4°.
no.
19   report year ends in Feb.

1. Dry goods—U. S.
N. Y. P. L.   August 11, 1930

NN 0064042   NN

National Retail Merchants Association.
HF5468
.S7
Stanton, Edward M
Branch stores: planning, merchandising, operating, promoting; a complete branch store operating guide. ₁New York₎ National Retail Dry Goods Association ₁1955₎

National Retail Merchants Association.
Bulletin
see
Stores.

National Retail Merchants Association.
The classification and distribution of expense in retail stores; report of committee of the National retail dry goods association ... [n.p., c1917]
2 v. in 1. forms. 27 cm.
"Errata" slip inserted.
1. Cost.- Accounting. 2. Department stores. Accounting. I. Title.

NN 0064045   CU

National Retail Merchants Association.
Confidential bulletin
see
Stores.

National Retail Merchants Association.
658   Consolidated and cooperative delivery.
N2159c Issued by Store managers' division and the Retail delivery association of the National retail dry goods association.
New York [c1931]
24p.

NN 0064047   IU OC1

National Retail Merchants Association.
Consumer goods import market in the United States
see under National Retail Merchants Association. Committee Advisory to the Economic Cooperation Administration.

National Retail Merchants Association.
Convention. 1st–   1912–
₁New York₎
v. group port. 24 cm. annual.
Issued 1912– by the association under its earlier name: National Retail Dry Goods Association.

1. Dry-goods—U. S.—Societies, etc. 2. Retail trade—U. S.—Societies, etc.
HD9951.N3   13-33831 rev 2

NN 0064049   DLC MiU InU

National Retail Merchants Association.
Department store radio advertising ...
see under National Retail Merchants Association. Sales Promotion Division.

National Retail Merchants Association.
Departmental merchandising and operating results of department stores and specialty stores
see National Retail Merchants Association. Controllers' Congress.
Departmental merchandising and operating results.

National Retail Merchants Association.
Digest of proceedings: spring meeting.
19
St. Louis ₁19
v.
19   cover-title.

1. Dry goods, U. S.
N. Y. P. L.   October 1, 1920.

NN 0064051   NN

VOLUME 407

National Retail Merchants Association.
Dynamic retailing in the modern economy; the role of retailing in distributing the nation's productive capacity. A report of a committee of over one hundred leading merchants under the chairmanship of Malcolm P. McNair. ₍New York₎ National Retail Dry Goods Association ₍1954₎
233 p. 23 cm.

1. Retail trade.   I. McNair, Malcolm Perrine, 1894–   II. Title.

HF5429.N258   54–4269 rev ‡

```
        NN MiD ODW OCl PU-W PBL TxU OU OClW WaT OOxM TU PPT
NN  0064052     DLC MiU CaBVa WaS CoU LU FU MH-BA NNC
```

National Retail Merchants Association.
The effect of personnel procedure on the job attitude of salespeople ...
    see under   National Retail Merchants Association. Personnel Group.

National Retail Merchants Association.
Furniture sales manual
    see under   Calahan, Lawrence Fox.

NATIONAL RETAIL MERCHANTS ASSOCIATION.
Home furnishings conference; [proceedings]
New York.   v.   28cm.

Annual.
Issued by the association's Merchandising division.

1. House furnishings--Trade and stat.--U. S. I. Title: Home furnishings conference; [proceedings].

```
NN  0064055     NN
```

National Retail Merchants Association.
How radio advertising works for retailers; a panel discussion by members of the National Retail Dry Goods Association and the National Association of Broadcasters.
n.p. [1947]

```
NN  0064056     MH
```

National Retail Merchants Association.
How to evaluate display
    see under   National Retail Merchants Association. Sales Promotion Division.

National Retail Merchants Association.
How to start a small store
    see under   Hah, Lew.

National Retail Merchants **Association.**

HB235
.U6N33   **National Industrial Conference Board.** *Statistical Division.*
Indexes of change in retail prices of department stores.
Jan. 31, 1941/Jan. 31, 1942–

New York.

National retail Merchants **association.**

The **Industrial outlook; a business review, pub. by the** National retail dry goods association
v.   –3;   –Mar. 1916. ₍New York,   –16₎

National Retail Merchants Association.
Joint management proceedings ...
    see its   Management and personnel proceedings.

National Retail Merchants Association.
Making profits out of model hobbies
    see under   Williams, Rollin.

National Retail Merchants Association.
Management and personnel proceedings.
New York.
        v.   in   diagrs. 28 cm. annual.
Title varies: 'Joint management proceedings.--
19 –39, Management conference proceedings.
Issued   by the association under its earlier name:
National Retail Dry Goods Association.
Includes convention proceedings of the Store Management Group and various other groups of the National Retail Merchants Association.

1. Personnel management--Societies, etc. 2. Retail trade--U. S.--Societies, etc.

HF5429.N26   42–3870 rev*

```
NN  0064063     DLC MH-BA OCl InU
```

National Retail Merchants Association.
Management conference proceedings ...
    see its   Management and personnel proceedings.

National Retail Merchants Association.
Manual of top management reports
    see under   Williams, Alvin P

National Retail Merchants Association.
Manual on internal audit and control
    see under   National Retail Merchants Association. Controllers' Congress.

National retail merchants association.
Manual on receiving department operations. ₍New York₎ National retail dry goods association ₍1938₎
₍33₎–118 p., 1 l. illus. (incl. forms) 31 cm.
"Compiled and edited by Leonard F. Mongeon ... assisted by Florence Barasch."
Reprinted from the Bulletin of the National retail dry goods association, v. 20, June 1938.
Pages 104–108, advertising matter.

1. Retail trade.   I. Mongeon, Leonard F., 1900–   ed. II. Title: Receiving department operations.

HF5429.N27   658.77   40–37342 rev

```
NN  0064067     DLC CSt TxU
```

HF5429   **National Retail Merchants Association. Manual on**
.N27   receiving department operations.
1947   **National Retail Merchants Association.** *Traffic Group.*
Manual on receiving department operations. Rev. ed.
Edited by Leonard Mongeon, assisted by Marie A. Longo.
New York ₍1947₎

National Retail Merchants Association.
Merchandise Sale Manual - Selling Sleep
    see under   McCollister, Frier.

National retail Merchants **association.**

Hahn, Lew, *ed.*
The merchants' manual, published under the auspices of the National retail dry goods association, edited by Lew Hahn ... and Percival White ... 1st ed. New York ₍etc.₎ McGraw-Hill book company, inc., 1924.

National Retail Merchants Association.
Net unit cost tables; a guide to buying under ceiling price regulations. New York, National Retail Dry Goods Association ₍1951₎
unpaged. 22 cm.

1. Discount—Tables, etc.   I. Title.

HG1654.N3   332.84   51–33585 rev ‡

```
NN  0064071     DLC
```

L381.33   **National retail** Merchants **association.**
N277o   Operating problems of the smaller store; proceedings of the forum session on smaller store problems held during the 21st annual convention of the National retail dry goods association ... N.Y., National retail dry goods association, c1932.
1 p. l., 2, 5–24 p.   28cm.

1. Retail trade. 2. Salesmen and salesmanship. I. Title.

```
NN  0064072     IEN
```

HF1134   **National Retail** Merchants **Association.**
.H3
subser.   **Harvard University.** *Bureau of Business Research.*
Operating results of department and specialty stores. 1921–
Boston ₍etc.₎ Harvard University, Graduate School of Business Administration, Division of Research ₍etc.₎

HF5468   **National Retail** Merchants **Association.**
.J8
Judelle, Beatrice, 1908–   *ed.*
Organization and operation of branch stores. ₍New York₎ National Retail Dry Goods Association ₍1953, *1952₎

National Retail Merchants Association.
Parking; how it is financed

see under

Automotive Safety Foundation.

ar Y   **National Retail Merchants Association.**
935   Plastics; a handbook for retailers. ₍New York?₎ Published by the Bulletin of the National Retail Dry Goods Association in Cooperation with the Society of Plastics Industry ₍1944₎
24–55 p. illus. 31cm.

I. Society of the Plastics Industry.

```
NN  0064076     NIC MiD
```

National retail Merchants **association.**
Postwar employment and selling; proceedings, general sessions, January, 1945 wartime conference ... N₍ew₎ Y₍ork, c₍ity₎ Store management and Personnel groups, National retail dry goods association ₍1945₎

3p. l., 59p.   29x22½cm.

```
NN  0064077     MoU
```

National Retail Merchants Association.
Price marking manual
    see under   National Retail Merchants Association. Traffic Group.

VOLUME 407

National retail merchants association.

Mazur, Paul Myer.
Principles of organization applied to modern retailing, by Paul M. Mazur ... with the assistance of Myron S. Silbert; written for the National retail dry goods association. New York and London, Harper & brothers, 1927.

National Retail Merchants Association.
Proceedings of N. R. D. G. A. clinic for retail secretaries, New York, May 10 and 11, 1948. New York, 1948.
68 p. illus.
Cover title.

NN 0064080 MH-BA

National Retail Merchants Association.
Proceedings of the postwar conference ... Absecon, N. J., Aug. 8-9, 1944, sponsored by the National Retail Dry Goods Association.

NN 0064081 InU

National Retail Merchants Association.
Publicity analysis of expenses of department and specialty stores, 1938-44. 1945.

NN 0064082 InU

National Retail Merchants Association.
A report on executive training courses
see under National Retail Merchants Association. Personnel Group.

National Retail Merchants Association. L381.3 S802
Report on retail trade conditions, Bethlehem, Penna., June 1928. Survey and report [made for Bethlehem Chamber of Commerce] by National Retail Dry Goods Association, Lew Hahn, managing director. [New York? 1928]
4 leaves, 166 numb. leaves, 1 leaf. illus., charts (1 fold.) forms. 28ᶜᵐ.
Mimeographed.
"The work of Professor Paul Nystrom and ... associates."—leaf 1l.

NN 0064084 ICJ MiU

National Retail Merchants Association. HF5429 .P595

Plant, George Lauderdale, 1900–
Retail job analysis and evaluation, by George Plant and John B. Pope. New York, Store Management and Personnel Groups, National Retail Dry Goods Assn. [1946]

National Retail Merchants Association. HF5429 .D78

Dun and Bradstreet, inc. *Marketing Services Company.*
Retail sales trends 1935-1944; a survey for National retail dry goods association. Prepared by Marketing and Research Service, Dun & Bradstreet, inc. New York, 1946.

National retail Merchants association.
Retail selling suggestions - pianos. [New York] Published by the National retail dry goods association in cooperation with the National piano manufacturers' association [1940]
cover-title, p.32-46. illus.
Reprinted from the Bulletin of the National retail dry goods association, May 1940.

NN 0064087 MH-BA

National Retail Merchants Association.
Retailers' calendar and promotional guide
see National Retail Merchants Association. Sales Promotion Division.
Sales promotion calendar.

National Retail Merchants Association.
Retailers' economic security plan, unanimously adopted at the 24th annual convention of the National Retail Dry Goods Association, January 15, 1935. [New York? 1935]
7 p. 22½cm.

821176A. 1. Insurance, Workmen's—U. S.

NN 0064089 NN

National Retail Merchants Association.
Sales promotion and budget planning calendar
see National Retail Merchants Association. Sales Promotion Division.
Sales promotion calendar.

National Retail Merchants Association.
Sales promotion budgeting-planning calendar for retailers, manufacturers and advertising agencies
see National Retail Merchants Association. Sales Promotion Division.
Sales promotion calendar.

National Retail Merchants Association.
Sales promotion calendar
see National Retail Merchants Association. Sales Promotion Division.
Sales promotion calendar.

National Retail Merchants Association.
Sales promotion calendar for retailers and national advertisers ...
see National Retail Merchants Association. Sales Promotion Division.
Sales promotion calendar.

National Retail Merchants Association.
The scope of training for retail store service
see under National Retail Merchants Association. Personnel Group.

National Retail Merchants Association.
Self-selection, a vital selling tool for the retailer and manufacturer
see under
Conference on Pakaging and Fixturing, New York, 1953.

National Retail Merchants Association.
A short glossary of retail terms
see under Wingate, John Williams, 1899–

National Retail Merchants Association.
Specialized training for salespeople ...
see under National Retail Merchants Association. Personnel Group.

National Retail Merchants Association.
Standard expense accounting manual for department stores and specialty stores
see under National Retail Merchants Association. Controllers' Congress.

National Retail Merchants Association.
The stationery manual ...
see under King, Mary Ellen.

National Retail Merchants Association. HD9951 .N36

Stores.
[New York, National Retail Dry Goods Association]

National retail merchants association. HD2778 .F64

Fox, Irving C
A study of Supreme court decisions on the anti-trust laws and the Federal trade commission act, prepared for the National retail dry goods association, by Irving C. Fox, general counsel ... New York, N. Y., National retail dry goods association [1935]

National Retail Merchants Association.
Survey of trade practices in the millinery trade
see under National Retail Merchants Association. Bureau of Trade Relations.

National Retail Merchants Association.
The training job ahead ...
see under National Retail Merchants Association. Personnel Group.

National Retail Merchants Association.
Trend of sales of silk, rayon and cotton ...
see under National Retail Merchants Association. Bureau of Research and Information

National Retail Merchants Association.
Trend of women's underwear sales ...
see under National Retail Merchants Association. Bureau of Research and Information.

National retail merchants association.
Twenty-five years of retailing ... 1911-1936 ... [New York] National retail dry goods association [1936]
276 p. illus. (incl. ports., plan) diagr. 34½ cm.
Includes advertising matter.

1. Retail trade—U. S. 2. Dry-goods—U. S. 3. Department stores—U. S. I. Title.
HD9951.N365 658.870973 36-14437 rev
CU TxU
NN 0064106 DLC PLF OCI OU NcU CoU WaS WaE MtU

National retail merchants association.

Bezanson, Anne.
Wage methods and selling costs; compensation of sales clerks in four major departments in 31 stores, by Anne Bezanson and Miriam Hussey ... in coöperation with the National retail dry goods association. Philadelphia, University of Pennsylvania press, 1930.

VOLUME 407

National Retail Merchants Association.
  We do $100,000
    see under National Retail Merchants
  Association. Bureau of Smaller Stores.

Pamphlet
HF   National Retail Merchants Association.
70   What the National Retail Dry Goods
       Association can do for your store.
       ₍New York, 195-?₎
       18 p. illus.

       1. Retail   trade.

NN   0064109   NIC

National Retail Merchants Association.
  The world of fashion
    see under National Retail Merchants
  Association. Personnel Group.

336.27   National retail Merchants association.
N2134y   T. & T.; you and taxes ... New York,
      Author ₍c1931₎
      29 p. illus.

NN   0064111   WaPS

UB
357   National retail merchants association.
.N28   Your store and the returning veteran; NRDGA
      policy manual on veteran employment. ₍New
      York, National retail dry goods association,
      1945₎
       cover-title,55,₍1₎ p.incl.forms.   28ᶜᵐ.

       1.Veterans--Employment--U.S.   2.Department
      stores.

NN   0064112   MiU OC1

HF   National Retail Merchants Association. Baltimore
5461   Group of Controllers.
.N26   309 ways to reduce expenses; a new manual of
      profit-making ideas. Prepared for the Control-
      lers' Congress, National Retail Dry Goods As-
      sociation. New York ₍Controllers' Congress,
      National Retail Dry Goods Association, c1954₎
      64 p.   23 cm.

       1.Department stores. I.Title.

NN   0064113   MiU OU InU MH-BA

National Retail Merchants Association. Bureau of
  Costume Art.
     The costume art program for the merchan-
  dising and promotion of piece goods and accessori-
  es. N.Y., 1928.
     35 p.

NN   0064114   OC1

NATIONAL RETAIL Merchants ASSOCIATION - Bureau
  of research and information.
  Report on merchandise control. Use of forms
and plans restricted to members of National
retail dry goods association. New York,1921

Mimeographed.
  1.Merchandising 2.Stores and store managemen
3.Dry goods I.National retail dry goods
association II.Title: Merchandise control.

NN   0064115   MH-BA

National retail merchants association-
  Bureau of research and information
  Report on public restaurants, their status,
  functions....Sept. 1924. N.Y. 1924.

NN   0064116   OC1

National retail merchants association. Bureau of research and information.
  Special report on bonus plans for delivery department. February 3, 1921. Comp.
  by Bureau of research and information, National retail dry goods association. New
  York, N. Y. (1921?)
     1 p. l., 23 p. p.   28 cm.

NN   0064117   DL

National Retail MerchantsAssociation. Bureau of Research and
  Information.
     Survey of leased departments; terms and contracts, prepared
by Grace J. Averill....   New York City, 1928.   64 p. incl.
tables.   4°.

     Typewritten, with the exception of three printed leaves.

  1. Department stores.   I. Averill,   Grace J.
  N. Y. P. L.   June 23, 1011

NN   0064118   NN DFT

National Retail Merchants Association. Bureau of Research and
  Trend of sales of silk, rayon and cotton in the drapery-uphol-
stery departments.
March, 1929 –

New York, 1929–   4°.
  nos.   illus.
     Prepared by the Bureau of Research and Information of the National Retail Dry
  Goods Association in cooperation with the Du Pont Rayon Company.
     1929–   are ₍no. 1–

  1. Textile fabrics—Trade and stat.   I. Title.
  N. Y. P. L.   April 13, 1931

NN   0064119   NN

National Retail Merchants Association. Bureau of
  Research and Information.
     Trend of sales of silk, rayon and cotton
in the piece goods departments, based on information secured from retail stores. Prepared by
Alexis Sommaripa. New York city, National
retail dry goods association, Bureau of research
and information, Bureau of costume art [c1928]
     51 p.   incl. map, charts.
     ---June 22, 1928. Supplementary to report
on same subject issued June 1, 1928. New York

city, National retail dry goods association, Bureau
of research and information, Bureau of costume
art [1928]
     18 p.   incl. tables, charts.   [Bound with
above]
     Prepared by Alexis Sommaripa.

NN   0064121   MH-BA

National retail merchants association. Bureau of
  research and information.
     Trend of women's underwear sales, based on in-
formation secured from retail stores and consumers
prepared by Alexis Sommaripa. New York, National
retail dry goods association ₍c1927-
     41 p. diagrs. 30½ cm.

     1. Underwear.   Sommaripa, Alexis. II. Title.

NN   0064122   NNC OC1

National Retail Merchants Association. Bureau of
  Research and Information.
     Trend of women's underwear sales, based on information
secured from retail stores; prepared by Alexis Sommaripa, W.
Henry Hooper, jr...   New York City: National Retail Dry
Goods Assoc.₍, 1928.₎   15 p.   diagrs.   4°.
     "A second study...covering the fiscal period, February 1, 1927, to February 1,
1928."

  430456A.   1. Underwear—Trade and   stat.   2. Silk, Artificial—Trade
  and stat.   3. Sommaripa, Alexis.   4. Hooper, W. Henry.
  N. Y. L.   September 27, 1929

NN   0064123   NN

National Retail Merchants Association. Bureau of
  Research and Information.
  Trends of sales of silk, rayon and cotton
in the piece goods dept. based on information
secured from retail stores. N.Y.
National retail dry goods association. 1939

     23 p.

NN   0064124   OCU

National Retail Merchants Association. Bureau of
  Smaller Stores.
     Corset dept. operation in smaller volume
stores. N.Y., 1941.
     29 numb. l.

NN   0064125   OC1

---

658   National retail merchants association--Bureau
N21621   of smaller stores.
      ... Local retail associations and their activi-
      ties. New York, N.Y., National retail dry
      goods association ₍1938₎
      cover-title, 80 numb.l. incl.forms.   (Ser-
      vice letter from the Bureau of smaller stores.
      no.6. Nov.15,1938)
      Mimeographed.

      1. Retail trade--U.S. 2. Trade and profession-
      al associations--U.S. I. Title

NN   0064126   IU TxU OC1

---

658   National retail merchants association--Bureau of
N2162w   smaller stores.
      We do $100,000; a small store analysis. New
      York, N.Y., Bureau of smaller stores, National
      retail dry goods association ₍1939₎
      cover-title, 20p.

      1. Retail trade--U.S. 2. Department stores.
      I. Title.

NN   0064127   IU InU OC1W

National Retail Merchants Association. *Bureau of Smaller
Stores.*
     The retail personnel primer. ₍New York, °1940₎
     165 p. forms. 23 cm.
     Published by the bureau under the association's earlier name:
  National Retail Dry Goods Association.
     Bibliography : p. ₍161₎–165.

     1. Clerks (Retail trade)   I. Title.

   HD8039.M39N3   658.3   40–4494 rev*

NN   0064128   DLC ODW OC1 OU TU CU OrU

National Retail Merchants Association. Bureau of
  Smaller Stores
    see also National Retail Merchants
  Association. Smaller Stores Division.

National Retail Merchants Association.
     Bureau of Trade Relations.
     Survey of trade practices in the millinery trade; the results of
a detailed survey of existing trade practices experienced in the
millinery trade, conducted jointly by the Millinery Association
of America and the National Retail Dry Goods Association and
approved by the Associated Millinery Men, Inc. the Eastern
Millinery Association and the Retail Millinery Association of
America. ... May, 1929. New York City, Bureau of Trade
Relations, National Retail Dry Goods Association ₍°1929₎
     28 p. diagrs. 29½ᶜᵐ.

NN   0064130   ICJ DFT

VOLUME 407

National Retail Merchants Association. *Bureau of* Trade Relations.
Survey of trade practices in the silk trade... ₁New York₎ Issued by the Bureau of trade relations, National retail dry goods assoc. and the Silk assoc. of America ₁193–?₎ 25, 15 f. incl. tables. 28½cm.

Reproduced from typewritten copy.

1. Silk—Trade and stat.—U. S.   I. Silk association of America.
N. Y. P. L.   August 28, 1940

NN 0064131   NN OCl

National Retail Merchants Association. *Committee Advisory to the Economic Cooperation Administration.*
Consumer goods import market in the United States; a report prepared by the National Retail Dry Goods Association and the Association of Buying Offices. ₁New York, 1949?₎
viii, 47 p. map. 28 cm.
"Survey ... undertaken by the Committee Advisory to the Economic Cooperation Administration of the National Retail Dry Goods Association."
Issued also under title: The market for imported consumer goods in the United States.
1. U. S.—Comm.—Europe. 2. Europe—Comm.—U. S.   I. Association of Buying Offices.   II. Title.

HF3092.N3 1949   *382.5   51–29110 rev

NN 0064132   DLC NN MH-BA NNC DS

National Retail Merchants Association. *Committee Advisory to the Economic Cooperation Administration.*
The market for imported consumer goods in the United States. Prepared by the National Retail Dry Goods Association and the Association of Buying Offices. Washington, Reprinted by the Economic Cooperation Administration, Office of Information ₁1949?₎
vi, 25 p. map (on cover) 26 cm.
"Survey ... undertaken by the Committee Advisory to the Economic Cooperation Administration of the National Retail Dry Goods Association."
Issued also under title: Consumer goods import market in the United States.
1. U. S.—Comm.—   Europe. 2. Europe—Comm.—U. S.   I. Association of Buying Offices.   II. Title.

HF3092.N3 1950   *382.5   51–809 rev

NN 0064133   DLC OrU MB ViU

National Retail Merchants Association. Committee for Services to Members.
How to analyze a selling department's operation. Prepared by the Committee for services to members... New York, Controllers' congress, National retail dry goods association, c1947.
20 p. incl. forms. 28.5 cm.

NN 0064134   MdBJ IU CSt MB OClCC MBSi NNC

National retail merchants association. *Committee for the study of wage problems.*
Preliminary report on commission and bonus methods; the Committee for the study of wage problems, Felix Vorenberg, chairman ... Surveys and reports under direction of Dr. B. M. Rastall ... New York city, National retail dry goods association, *1920.
51 p. incl. tables. 23½ cm.

1. Wages—U. S. 2. Dry-goods—U. S. 3. Bonus system.   I. Rastall, Benjamin McKie.   II. Title: Commission and bonus methods.

HD4966.D72U65   20–12822 rev

NN 0064135   DLC MiU OCl DL ICJ NcD

HD
4926   National retail merchants association. Com-
.N278   mittee for the study of wage problems.
Review of bonus systems. Comp. by Committee for the study of wage problems.
New York, N.Y., National retail dry goods association, Bureau of research and information [1920?]
1 p.ℓ., 14 ℓ. incl. tables. 28 x 22cm.
Mimeographed.

NN 0064136   MiU

National Retail Merchants Association. Committee on Cash Registers, Tube Systems and Telephone Authorization.
Report ... [no imprint]
7 l. 28 cm.
Caption title.
Multigraphed.
1. Department stores. 2. Credit.

NN 0064137   MiU

National Retail Merchants Association.
Committee on causes of customer returns
Reducing customer returns.....NY. ₙational retail dry goods association. 1930.

19 p.

NN 0064138   OCl OU

National Retail Merchants Association.
Committee on Dynamic Retailing in the Modern Economy.
Dynamic retailing in the modern economy
see under National Retail Merchants Association.

National Retail Merchants Association. Committee on the Costs of Personnel Departments in Stores of Various Sizes.
Report of the Committee on the Costs of Personnel Departments ...
see under National Retail Merchants Association. Personnel Group.

National retail merchants association. *Committee on the induction of the new executive.*
Report of the Committee on the induction of the new executive. August, 1930. New York, Personnel group, National retail dry goods association ₁1930₎
1 p. l., iv, 19 numb. l. 28½ᶜᵐ.
Autographed from type-written copy on one side of leaf only.
Natalie Kneeland, chairman.

1. Employment management.   I. Kneeland, Natalie.

NN 0064141   MiU OCl

658.882
N213ac National Retail Merchants Association.
Controllers' Congress.
Accounts payable productivity survey; first national survey in department and specialty stores of units of output as a measure of productivity. Raymond F. Copes, director of research. New York, Controllers' Congress Research Committee, National Retail Dry Goods Association, 1950.
84 p. illus. 28cm.

1. Retail trade – Accounting. I. Copes, Raymond F 1915- II. T.

NN 0064142   MiDW CSt MiD ICU MiU IU CaBVa

National Retail Merchants Association. *Controllers' Congress.*
Accounts receivable productivity survey, with addressing machine data; first national survey in department and specialty stores of units of output as a measure of productivity. Raymond F. Copes, director of Research. ₁1st ed.₎ New York, Controllers' Congress Research Committee, National Retail Dry Goods Association, 1951.
82 p. illus. 28 cm.

1. Collecting of accounts.   I. Copes, Raymond F., 1915- II. Title.

HF5556.N35   658.88   51–1652 rev

NN 0064143   DLC CaBVa

₁657   National retail merchants association--
N2151a   Controllers' congress.
Analysis of publicity expense, 1929.
Comp. by Controllers' congress and Sales promotion division, National retail dry goods association. New York, c1930.
30 l.

Autographed copy.

NN 0064144   IU OCl

National Retail Merchants Association.
Analysis of publicity expenses of department stores 1937-1938. ₁New York₎ c1939.
12 ℓ. incl. tables.

NN 0064145   MH-BA

National Retail Merchants Association. Controllers' Congress.
Analysis of publicity expenses, 1949 ed. A guide to retail publicity budgeting for department stores and specialty stores. New York [1949]
[10] p. tables. 27 cm.
1. Advertising. Department stores.

NN 0064146   MiU

National Retail Merchants Association. Controllers' Congress.
Annual convention, Controllers' congress of the National retail dry goods association. Report and digest of the proceedings ...
see its Yearbook.

National Retail Merchants Association. Controllers' Congress.
The Balance sheet
see under title

National retail merchants association. *Controllers' congress.*
Balance sheet manual for retail stores. Part I.A–Fixed assets and depreciation reserves. B–Reserves for accounts receivable. Prepared ... for the 17th annual convention of the Controllers' congress at Chicago, June 8th to 11th, 1936 ... New York, c1936.
2 p.ℓ., 36 numb.ℓ. incl.tables.

Manifold copy.

NN 0064149   MH-BA

₁658   National retail merchants association--
N2161c   Controllers' congress.
... Consumer demand through the controller. Standard expense classification on expense control. The cost of consumer demand. New York, 1929.
cover-title, 11p. (Official publication, 1929)

NN 0064150   IU

National Retail Merchants Association. *Controllers' Congress.*
Controllers' Congress Research Committee seminar on organizing for effective management; discussion outline. ₁New York₎ Controllers' Congress Research Committee, National Retail Dry Goods Association, *1954.
1 v. (various pagings) ports., diagrs. 28 cm.

1. Industrial organization.   I. Title: Seminar on organizing for effective management.

HD31.N35 1954   658.87   54–23134 rev

NN 0064151   DLC

VOLUME 407

658   National retail merchants association--Control-
N216ld   lers' congress.
            Departmental average gross sale values, spring
        season-1936, spring season-1937 ... also The study
        of average gross sale values as an aid to more
        profitable merchandising (by) H. I. Kleinhaus ...
        New York, N. Y., Controllers' congress, National
        retail dry goods association, c1938
            1 p.l., 9 numb.l.

            1. Retail trade--U.S. 2. Department stores. I.
        Kleinhaus, H. I.

    NN   0064152   IU MH-BA NNC OC1

National Retail Merchants Association. *Controllers' Con-*
gress.
    Departmental merchandising and operating results.

    New York.
        v. tables. 28 cm. annual.
        Began publication in 1924?
        Title varies: 1952-   Merchandising and operating results of
        departmentized stores.
        Other slight variations in title.
        Issued   under the association's earlier name: National
    Retail Dry Goods Association.
        Supplements accompany some vols.
        1. Department stores--U. S.--Yearbooks.

        HF5465.U5N28   658.871058   45-33031 rev 2*

                    CU CSt MdBJ
                CtY OC1 MB NN OCU OU IEN PPCuP IEN MiD TxLT KU OC1h
    NN   0064153   DLC OC1FRB DFT MiU PSt TxU IU TU ICJ

National Retail Merchants Association. *Controllers' Con-*
gress.
    Executive compensation survey of departmentized stores.

    New York.
        v. 23 cm. annual.
        Surveys for 19   issued under the association's earlier
    name: National Retail Dry Goods Association.

        1. Executives — Salaries, pensions, etc.— U. S. 2. Department
    stores—U. S.
        HD4965.5.U6N32   658.871   54-15880 rev

    NN   0064154   DLC

National retail merchants association. *Controllers' con-*
gress.
    The expense accounting manual for retail stores ... New
    York city, Controllers' congress, National retail dry goods
    association, ©1942.
        1 v. tables (part fold.) forms. 28 cm.
        Loose-leaf.
        "First published in 1922 as the 'Standard method of accounting for
    retail stores.' Followed by the 'Expense manual' published in 1928 and
    reprinted in 1933. Thereafter revised to include the 'Expense distribu-
    tion manual' and the 'Workroom accounting manual' and published as
    'A manual of expense accounting for retail stores' in 1937."
        1. Retail trade—Accounting.

        HF5635.N26   658.87   42-21046 rev

    NN   0064155   DLC ICJ

National Retail Merchants Association. Control-
    lers' Congress.
    Expense distribution manual, including
    charts and work sheet. The work of the Metro-
    politan controllers' ass'n, New York ...
    [New York] c1932.
        12 p.   table.

    NN   0064156   MH-BA

National retail merchants association. Con-
    trollers' congress.
    ... The expense manual ... New York city,
    Controllers' congress, National retail dry goods
    association, ©1928.
        1 v. fold.tables,forms. 28 cm.
        "Official publication."
        "Expense distribution manual including charts and work
    sheet; the work of the Metropolitan controllers' ass'n,
    New York ... Adopted by Controllers' congress,National
    retail dry goods association,June 15,1932." ©1932" (12
    p.,fold.form) inserted.
        1.Retail trade—Accounting. I.Title.

                    HF5681.N96N28

    NN   0064157   MiU MB OC1

National retail merchants association. Con-
    trollers' congress.
    ... The expense manual ... New York city,
    Controllers' congress,National retail dry
    goods association, 1933.

        1 v. fold.tables,forms.   28 cm.
        "Official publication."
        Loose-leaf.
        Cover-title: A manual of expense accounting for retail
    stores.

        1.Retail trade--Accounting. I.Title.

                    HF5681.N96N28 1933

    NN   0064158   ODW

NATIONAL RETAIL MERCHANTS ASSOCIATION.
        Controllers' congress.
        Expense saving ideas.
    New York.   v.   28cm.

        Compiled by its Gold award committee.

        1. Retail trade--Costs--U.S.

    NN   0064159   NN

National Retail Merchants Association. Con-
    trollers' Congress.
    Expenses can be reduced ...
        see under Kleinhaus, H   I

National Retail Merchants Association.
        Controllers' Congress.
        Financial and record-keeping manual
    for smaller stores
        see under Copes, Raymond F
    1915-   ed.

National Retail Merchants Association. Control-
    lers' Congress.
    Home furnishings survey ... New York,
    c1931-32.
        v. tables, charts.
        Contents: sect. 1. Furniture dept. -
    sect. 2. Domestic floor coverings dept. -
    sect. 3. China & glassware dept.

    NN   0064162   MH-BA

L381.331   National retail merchants   association.
N2771h   Controllers' congress.
            Home furnishings survey. Section III
        China & glassware department ...
        N.Y., Controllers' congress, National
        retail dry goods association, c1932.
            2 p. l., 2-21 numb. l.   29cm.

            By H.I.Kleinhaus.
            Mimeographed.

            1. Retail trade - Accounting. 2.
        Department stores. I. Kleinhaus, H.I.
        I. Title.   II. Title: China &
        glassware

    NN   0064163   IEN OC1

National Retail Merchants Association.
        Controllers' Congress.
        How to analyze a selling department's
    operation
        see under National Retail Merchants
    Association. Committee for Services to
    Members.

National Retail Merchants Association. *Controllers' Con-*
gress.
    Insurance manual for departmentized stores; a reference
    manual and buyers' guide for use in the administration and
    purchase of insurance for businesses in the distributive
    trades. Presented by the Insurance Committee of the Con-
    trollers' Congress, N. R. D. G. A. Edited and published by
    Controllers' Congress, N. R. D. G. A. [New York] 1955.
        194 p. illus. 24 cm.

        1. Insurance, Business. 2. Retail trade.   I. Title.

        HG8054.R4N3   368   55-1437 rev ‡

    NN   0064165   DLC CaBVa TU OU InU NN CU

National Retail Merchants Association. Control-
    lers' Congress.
    Internal audit, a manual for department
    stores and specialty stores ...
        see under   National Retail Merchants
    Association. Detroit Controllers' Group.

National retail merchants association. Con-
    trollers' congress.

Chicago controllers' association.
    Inventory manual for department stores and departmentized
    specialty stores. New York, N. Y., Controllers' congress,
    National retail dry goods association [°1936]

National Retail Merchants Association. *Controllers' Con-*
gress.
    Inventory taking manual for department and specialty
    stores. [New York, 1951]
        v, 43 p. forms. 28 cm.
        Published by the congress under the association's earlier name:
    National Retail Dry Goods Association.
        A revision of "Taking of inventory and inventory problems ...
    presented at the Chicago Wartime Conference of the Controllers'
    Congress [1944]"

        1. Inventories.   I. Title.

        HF5463.N28   658.787   51-1582 rev

    NN   0064168   DLC CaBVa NN

HF5463   National Retail merchants Association.
.P456   Controllers' Congress.
1952
        Philadelphia Retail Controllers' Association.
        Leased department survey. Prepared for the Controllers'
    Congress, National Retail Dry Goods Association. [2d ed.]
    New York [1952]

National Retail Merchants Association. Control-
    lers' Congress.
    Leased department survey in department and
    specialty stores
        see its   Leased departments.

---

658   National Retail Merchants Association—Con-
N2125ℓ   trollers' Congress.
            Leased departments; rates, policies and
        expenses in department and specialty stores.

        New York.
            v. tables. 28cm.

            Title varies: , Leased department
        survey in department and specialty stores; an
        analysis.

            Issued   by the association under
        its earlier name: National Retail Dry Goods
        Association.

    NN   0064172   IU MdBJ OrPS NN NIC TU TxU

VOLUME 407

658　National Retail Merchants Association--Control-
N2161m　　lers Congress.
　　Manual for productivity measurement in depart-
ment and specialty stores. Raymond F. Copes,
director of research.　New York, Controllers
Congress Research Committee, National Retail Dry
Goods Association ₍1952₎
　　12p.　28cm.

　　1. Retail trade--U.S.　2. Productivity accounting.　I. Copes, Raymond F., 1915-　　II.
Title.

NN　0064173　　IU CU TU OC1W PU-W MH-BA MiD NN

HF　National Retail Merchants Association. Control-
5463　　lers' Congress.
N2788　　Manual of budgetary procedure and control for
1953　departmentalized stores; a complete guide to
budget preparation with supporting schedules.
₍Rev.ed.₎ New York ₍1953₎
　　83 p.　28 cm.

　　1.Department stores.　2.Department stores--
Accounting.　I.Title.

NN　0064174　　MiU

National Retail Merchants Association. Controllers'Congress.
　　Manual of departmental merchandise content
for departmentized stores.　₍New York, 1953₎
　　125 p.　illus.

　　Letter of transmittal ₍3 p.₎ inserted.
　　Supersedes the Manual for "Departmental
classifications of the department store"
published by the Federal Reserve System.
Letter.

NN　0064175　　MH-BA OU NNC MiU IEN MiD NN

National Retail Merchants Association.
　　Controllers' Congress.
　　Manual of top management reports
　　　see under Williams, Alvin P

HF　National Retail Merchants Association. Con-
5667　　trollers' Congress.
N285　　Manual on internal audit and control. New York
₍1946₎
　　18 p.　form.　28 cm.
　　A reprint of the internal audit material prepared by the Detroit Controllers Group in 1936,
together with three other articles. Cf.Foreword.

　　1.Auditing.　2.Department stores--Accounting.

NN　0064177　　MiU NIC WaS InU

National retail merchants association. Controllers' Congress.
　　Manual on internal audit and control. New
York ₍1950₎
　　18 p.

　　First pub. in 1946.

　　1. Auditing.　I. Title: Internal audit and
control.

NN　0064178　　NNC CU

National retail merchants association. Controllers' congress.
　　... Merchandise purchase control (open-to-buy) for
the store of moderate size ... New York ₍Controllers'
congress, National retail dry goods association, ⁱ1927₎
　　11 p. incl. tables, forms.　28ᶜᵐ.　(National retail dry goods association.
Controllers' congress. Publication. v. 6, no. 2)
　　Cover-title.

　　1. Buying.

NN　0064179　　MiU

National Retail Merchants Association. *Controllers' Congress.*
　　Merchandising and operating results of departmentized
stores
　　　see its
　　Departmental merchandising and operating results.

National Retail Merchants Association. *Controllers' Congress.*
　　Official publication.　v. 1-
　　New York, 1922-
　　　v.　23-28 cm.　diagrs., forms, tables.

　　1. Retail trade--U. S.--Societies, etc.　2. Department stores--
U. S.--Societies, etc.
　　HF5429.N3　　　　　　　　　　59-59311

NN　0064181　　DLC ICU NN MiU IU MiD

₍National retail merchants association. Controllers' congress₎
　　The problem of surplus cotton. ₍1939₎
　　1 v.　tables, diagrs.

　　Cover-title.
　　Contents.--Resume of cotton report, December
19th, 1938.--Resume of cotton report, January
6th, 1939.--Cycles in cotton consumption, by
M. R. Cooper.
　　1. Cotton growing and manufacture - U. S.

NN　0064182　　NNC

HF　National Retail Merchants Association.
5681　　Controllers' Congress.
B9N37　　A procedural study of accounts payable
methods.　1949 ed.　New York, Controllers'
Congress, National Retail Dry Goods Association, 1949.
　　24 p.　28cm.

　　1. Accounting.　2. Purchasing.　I. Title.
　　II. Title:　Accounts payable methods.

NN　0064183　　CoU MiD ICU

National Retail Merchants Association. Controllers Congress.
　　Proceedings of the convention
　　　see its　Yearbook.

National Retail Merchants Association. Controllers' Congress.
　　Report and digest of the proceedings
　　　see its　Yearbook.

National retail merchants association - Controllers'
congress
　　The report to the manager from the controller
of a retail store, presented by Kenneth E.
Armstrong... N. Y. 1938
　　5 p. l., ii 49, 6 numb l.

NN　0064186　　OC1 DLC-P4

National Retail Merchants Association.
　　Controllers' Congress.
　　Retail control.
　　₍New York₎

National Retail Merchants Association. *Controllers' Congress.*
　　Retail excise tax manual, compiled by Controllers' Congress, National Retail Dry Goods Association.　Rev. ed.
New York, 1946.
　　cover-title, 20 p.　28 cm.
　　Errata : 2 leaves inserted.

　　1. Sales tax--U. S.　I. Title.
　　HJ5715.U6N37 1946　　　　336.2713　　　47-27033 rev*

NN　0064188　　DLC CSt MiU

National Retail Merchants Association - Controllers'
　　Congress
　　Retail excise tax manual. ₍Compiled and
edited by John J. Roberts.　New York, 1952₎
　　58p.

NN　0064189　　PPT OC1

National retail merchants association. Controllers' congress.
　　The retail inventory method in practical operation ₍by₎ H.I.Kleinhaus, manager, Controllers'
congress, National retail dry goods association,
ⁱ1932.
　　1 p.l.,16 numb.l.,1 l.incl.fold.tab.　28½ᶜᵐ.
　　Autographed from type-written copy.
　　"Fourth printing".
　　"List of publications of the Controllers' congress
relative to retail method in theory and practice": leaf
at end.
　　1.Inventories. 2.Retail trade--Accounting. I.Kleinhaus,
H.I.
　　　　　　　　　HF5681.S8N28

NN　0064190　　MiU MH-BA OU NNC IU InU MB

HF
5681　National retail merchants association. Control-
.S8　　lers' congress.
N28　　The retail inventory method in practical
1941　operation,by H.I.Kleinhaus,general manager,
Controllers' congress ...　New York, National
retail dry goods association, 1941.
　　2 p.l.,29 numb.l.,incl.forms (1 fold.)　29ᶜᵐ.

　　Reproduced from type-written copy.
　　"Revised edition."

　　1.Inventories. 2.Retail trade--Accounting. I.Klein-
haus,H.I.

NN　0064191　　MiU OU

HF
5681　National retail merchants association. Con-
.S8　　trollers' congress.
N28　　The retail inventory method in practical
1944　operation,by H.I.Kleinhaus,general manager,
Controllers' congress ...　New York, Con-
trollers' congress,National retail dry goods
association, 1944.
　　2 p.l.,23 (i.e.25) numb.l.incl.forms.　27 x 22ᶜᵐ.
　　Extra leaves numbered 11a and 15a.
　　Reproduced from typewritten copy.
　　"Revised edition."

　　1.Inventories. 2.Retail trade--Accounting. I.
Kleinhaus,H.I.

NN　0064192　　MiU OC1

National Retail Merchants Association. *Controllers' Con-
gress.*
　　The retail inventory method in practical operation.　Rev.
ed. New York, ⁱ1946.
　　24 p.　forms.　28 cm.
　　Published by the congress under the association's earlier name:
National Retail Dry Goods Association.
　　Cover title.

　　1. Inventories.　I. Title.
　　HF5681.S8N4 1946　　　658.787　　　47-20116 rev*

NN　0064193　　DLC IU TxU TU MdBJ CoU CU TNJ LU

HF　National retail merchants association. Con-
5681　　trollers' congress.
S8N4　　The retail inventory method in practical
1951　operation.　Rev. ed.　New York,1951.
　　25p.　forms.　28cm.

　　1. Inventories.　I. Title.

NN　0064194　　MU WaSp FMU NSyU UU

VOLUME 407

National retail merchants association. *Controllers' congress.*
The retail inventory method in practical operation. Rev. ed.
New York [1953]
cover-title, 24 p. forms. 28ᵐ.

NN   0064195   ViU PU-W

National Retail Merchants Association.
Controllers Congress.
150954 Retail inventory shortages and damages. Revised edition. New
York, Controllers Congress of the National Retail Dry Goods
Association, °1923.
49, [5] p. 24ᵐ.
The original publication upon which this revision is based was prepared by the
Committee on Inventory and Stock Shortages of the Controllers' Group of the Retail
Trade Board of the Boston Chamber of Commerce, who were likewise acting as a
committee with similar assignment from the Controllers' Congress of the National Retail
Dry Goods Association.

NN   0064196   ICJ MiD

National Retail Merchants Association. *Controllers' Congress.*
Seasonal distribution of sales—plus (departmental) Departmental sales percent to total store, departmental dollar
sales per square foot of selling space, departmental trend of
yearly sales. H. I. Kleinhaus, general manager, Controllers'
Congress, National Retail Dry Goods Association, assisted
by Philip Pond [and others.] New York, °1940]
39 p. 28 cm.
Published by the congress under the association's earlier name:
National Retail Dry Goods Association.
On cover: Department stores and specialty stores, 1939.
1. Department stores. 2. Seasonal variations (Economics)
I. Kleinhaus, H. I.
HF5465.U5N3   658.871   42–46654 rev*

NN   0064197   DLC MH-BA DFT OC1 OU NNC

National retail merchants association. Controllers' congress.
Small store accounting manual ... New York,
c1937.
43 numb. l.
Reproduction of typewritten copy.
1. Accounting - Retail trade. 2. Retail trade -
Accounting.

NN   0064198   NNC

National retail merchants association. Controllers' congress.
Small store accounting manual ... 2d ed.
March, 1938. New York, N.Y., Controllers' congress, National retail dry goods association
[1938]
1 p. l., 2 numb. l., 43 numb. l.   27½ᶜᵐ.
Mimeographed.
"Based upon the material contained in the 1922 pamphlets [A standard method of accounting for retail
stores, 2 v.]"--Introd.
1. Retail trade--Accounting.   I. Title.
HF5686.R43N28

NN   0064199   MiU OU OC1 IU

National retail merchants association.
Controllers' congress.
Small store accounting manual... 3d ed. N.Y.
[The Author] 1943, °1942.
49 p.
On cover: comp. by H. I. Kleinhaus.
Typewritten copy duplicated.
I. Kleinhaus, H. I.

NN   0064200   MiD ViU MiEM PSt OrP

HF
5686
.R43
N28
1944
National retail merchants association. Controllers' congress.
Small store accounting manual ... New York,
Controller's congress, National retail dry
goods association, 1944.
2 p. l., 49 p. incl. tables.   27½ᶜᵐ.
On cover: Compiled by H. I. Kleinhaus.
"Third edition, October, 1943; reprinted November,
1944."
Based upon "A standard method of accounting for retail stores", published by the Controllers' Congress
in 1922, and the latest issue of its "Expense accounting manual", June, 1942. cf. Introd.
1. Retail trade   --Accounting.   I. Kleinhaus, H. I., comp   II. Title.

NN   0064201   MiU

National Retail Merchants Association. Controllers'
Congress.
Standard expense accounting manual for department
stores and specialty stores. 1917-
New York.

Title varies: 1917, A report on the classification
and distribution of expenses in retail stores;
1922, A standard method of accounting for retail
stores.

MiD NIC CaBVa NBuG InU
NN   0064202   MiU NNC TxU ICU MH-BA TU NRU CSt CU

National Retail Merchants Association. *Controllers' Con-
gress.*
Standard expense center accounting manual; a manual for
the use of the distributive trades for classifying and controlling expenses. This manual includes these concepts
known as "production unit accounting." Presented by the
Standards Revision Committee, a sub-committee of the
Controllers' Congress Standardization Committee of the
N. R. D. G. A. [New York] Controllers' Congress, National
Retail Dry Goods Association, 1954 [i. e. 1955]
235 p. illus. 25 cm.
"Replaces the Controllers' Congress 'Standard expense accounting
manual.'"
1. Retail trade--   Accounting.   I. Title.
HF5635.N27   °657.5   56–1493 rev ‡

MiD TU InU IU OC1W TxU MtU WaS OrU PCtvL
NN   0064203   DLC MH-BA NNC CU PU-W CLSU LU OC1 OU

Nfh50
+922n
National retail merchants association.
Controllers' congress.
... A standard method of accounting for
retail stores ... Amplifying and revising
"The classification and distribution of
expense in retail stores" issued ... in
1917. New York, Controllers' congress of
the National retail dry goods association,
c1922.
2v. forms (part fold.) 29½ᶜᵐ. (Its Official
publication)
Contents.—v. 1. Descriptive text. -
v. 2. Charts.

NN   0064204   CtY MiU

HF5681
.S8B7
1951
National Retail Merchants Association. Controllers' Congress.   FOR OTHER EDITIONS
                                     SEE MAIN ENTRY
New England Controllers' Association.
Stock shortage control manual; a study of methods and
procedures to reduce inventory losses. Prepared for the
Controllers' Congress, National Retail Dry Goods Association. [4th rev. ed.] New York [Controllers' Congress, National Retail Dry Goods Association, 1951]

National Retail Merchants Association. Con-
trollers' Congress.
A survey of sales audit productivity. New
York [c1952]
58 p. chart, tables, form.
Prepared by the Controllers' Congress Research
Committee. - Cf. Fore.

NN   0064206   MH-BA IEN

National Retail Merchants Association. Controllers
Congress.
309 ways to reduce expenses
see under
National Retail Merchants Association. Baltimore
Group Controllers.

HF
5686
.R43
N285
National retail merchants association. Controllers' congress.
Workroom accounting manual, prepared by a
committee of the Metropolitan controllers association, New York, composed of Leo Hart, chairman ... C. E. McCarthy ... L. Earl Wilson ... [et
al.] Presented to the 17th annual convention
of the Controllers' congress at Chicago, June
8 to 11, 1936 ... [New York] Controllers' congress [National retail dry goods association]
c1936.
2 p. l., 2-8 numb. l.   27 x 21ᶜᵐ.
On cover: For department stores and specialty stores.
Reproduced from   typewritten copy.
1. Retail trade--   Accounting.   I. Metropolitan
controllers asso-   ciation, New York. II. Title.

NN   0064208   MiU MiD OC1

HF
5429
.A2
N271
National Retail Merchants Association. *Controllers' Con-
gress.*
Yearbook.
[New York]
v. in   26-28 cm.
Began publication in 1920.
Title varies: 19   -35, Report of the proceedings [of the] annual
convention (varies).—1936-46, The year book of retailing (varies).—
1947-48, Proceedings of the convention.
Issued   under the association's earlier name: National
Retail Dry Goods Association.
1. Dry-goods--U. S.--Yearbooks. 2. Retail trade--U. S.--Year-
books.
HD9951.N33   44–20182 rev*

NNC OC1CC MiU MoU MdBJ CU
NN   0064209   DLC NN OO OCU OU TxU ODW OOxM OC1 OU

National Retail Merchants Association.
Controllers' Congress.
The yearbook of retailing
see its   Yearbook.

National Retail Merchants Association.
Controllers' Congress. Committee on
Insurance
see   National Retail Merchants Associ-
ation. Controllers' Congress. Insurance
Committee.

National Retail Merchants Association. Control-
lers' Congress. Insurance Committee.
Insurance, by Committee on Insurance,
A. N. Fraser, chairman, George E. Brown [and]
J. S. R. Crawford. [New York] 1923.
105 p. illus.   23 cm. (Controllers'
Congress of the National Retail Dry Goods
Association. Official publication, v. 5, no. 1)

NN   0064212   IU NN

National Retail Merchants Association. Controllers Congress. Insurance Committee.
Insurance manual for departmentized stores
see under   National Retail Merchants
Association. Controllers' Congress.

National Retail merchants Association.
Controllers' Congress. Insurance Committee.
Insurance manual for retail merchants, by
Insurance Committee. [New York, National
Retail Dry Goods Association] 1925.
142 p. illus. 24 cm. (Its Official
publication. v. 8, no. 6, June 1925)
1. Insurance. 2. Retail trade. I.

NN   0064214   CaBVaU IU OC1W OC1 CSt IEN

National Retail Merchants Association.
Credit Management Division.
Better credit letters
see under Fitzpatrick, F   J

VOLUME 407

National Retail Merchants Association. Credit
Management Division.
HF5565
.N4
Credit management year book.

New York, Credit Management Division, National **Retail**
Dry Goods Association.

658.88   National Retail Merchants Association.
N277o   Credit Management Division.
101 profitable time and money saving ideas
for credit and collection departments; comp.
by A.L. Trotta.   New York, c1950.
62p. illus.

1. Credit.   2. Collecting of accounts.
I. Trotta, A   Leonidas,
comp. II. Title.

NN   0064217   FTaSU InU MiU CaBVa

658.883 National Retail Merchants Association.
N279p   Credit Management Division.
Productivity measurement and training
techniques for credit departments.
Edited by A.L.Trotta.   New York, c1953.
48p. 28cm.

1.Credit managers. 2.Office management.

NN   0064218   CLSU MiD MiU

National retail merchants association. *Credit management
division.*
Retail credit manual, compiled and edited by J. Anton
Hagios. [New York] National retail dry goods association,
Credit management division [1937]
cover-title, 52 p. illus., forms. 30½ cm.
"The Bulletin of the National retail dry goods association, June,
1937."

1. Credit—U. S. 2. Department stores—U. S. 3. Retail trade—
U. S. i. Hagios, Joseph Anton, 1905– ii. Title.

A 41–352 rev 2

Johns Hopkins Univ.   Library
for Library of Congress   [r59d]

NN   0064219   MdBJ

National Retail Merchants Association. Credit
Management Division.
HF5566
.D28
Dakins, John Gordon, 1903–
Retail credit manual; a handbook of retail credit. New
York, Credit Management Division, National **Retail Dry**
Goods Association, 1950.

HF
5667   National retail merchants association.
.N28   °Detroit controllers' group.
Internal audit, a manual for department
stores and specialty stores,prepared by the
Detroit controllers' group for the Control-
lers' congress,National retail dry goods as-
sociation ... New York [Controllers' congress,
National retail dry goods association, c1936,
cover-title,10 numb.l. 2 forms (1 fold.) 29 x 22½
"First presented at the 17th annual convention of the
Controllers' congress ... June 8 to 11,1936."

1.Auditing. 2.Retail trade—Accounting. I.National
retail dry goods association. Controllers' congress.
II.Title.

NN   0064221   MiU OC1 MH-BA

National Retail Merchants Association. Detroit
Controllers' Group.
Manual on internal audit and control
see under   National Retail Merchants
Association. Controllers' Congress.

HF 5439 NATIONAL RETAIL Merchants ASSOCIATION—Home Fur-
.E2 N2   nishings and Appliances Group
How department stores can get a bigger and
more profitable appliance and television volume.
N. Y. [1949?]
61 p.

Report of proceedings at the Major appliances
and television meeting conducted by the Home Furnishings and Appliances Group in conjunction with
the Mid-year convention of the Merchandising
Division, June 20, 1949.
Imperfect:p.3?   33 blank.

NN   0064223   InU

National Retail Merchants Association. *Merchandise Managers' Division*
see
National Retail Merchants Association. *Merchandising
Division.*

HF 5415 NATIONAL RETAIL Merchants ASSOCIATION—Merchandis-
.N237   ing Division
Basic stock list: hosiery (preliminary
questionnaire). [N.Y., [1954]
2+6 p. forms.

Cover-title.

1. Hosiery.

NN   0064225   InU

National Retail Merchants Association.
HF5437   Merchandising Division.
.N45   The Buyer's manual; a merchandising handbook. 1930-
ed. New York.

National retail merchants association. Merchandising division.
Compensation of merchandising executives in
department stores ... October 1939 ... New
York city, 1939.
1 p.l., 11, viii numb.l. incl.forms, tables.

NN   0064227   MH-BA

National Retail Merchants Association.
Merchandising Division.
Departmental merchandising manual,
men's clothing
see under Pennsylvania. University. Wharton School of Finance and
Commerce.

National Retail Merchants Association. Merchandising Division.
Departmental operating manual: sports and
casual wear
see under Los Angeles. University of
Southern California.

HF
5429   National Retail Merchants Association. Merchandis-
.A2   ing Division.
N2845   Departmental operating manual[s] 1st-
[1950]-
New York.

NN   0064230   MiU

National Retail Merchants Association.
Merchandising Division.
Dollar and unit merchandise planning
and budgeting
see under Meyer, Jerold S

National retail merchants association. *Merchandising division.*
Fabric identification in dresses; a study of the attitudes of
retailers toward identification tags and labels; the extent to
which they are furnished by the manufacturer, left on or removed by the retailer and demanded by the consumer ...
New York, N. Y., Merchandising division, National **retail**
dry goods association, 1940.
1 p. l., 18 numb. l. incl. tables. 29½ x 22½ cm.
Cover-title: A survey of fabric identification in dresses.
Reproduced from type-written copy.
1. Dressmaking. 2. Labels. 3. Rayon. i. Title.

HD9942.U42N3   659   41–12233 rev

NN   0064232   DLC OC1 DFT

National Retail Merchants Association. Merchandising Division.
Home furnishings conference; [proceedings]
see under   National Retail Merchants
Association.

National Retail Merchants Association.
Merchandising Division.
Latin American handicraft
see under U. S. Bureau of Foreign
and Domestic Commerce.

National Retail Merchants Association.
Merchandising Division.
Manual on the children's shoe department
operation
see under   Lester, Marjorie W

National Retail Merchants Association. Merchandising Division.
Markdown manual.   New York [1928]
15 p.

NN   0064236   MH-BA

W
687.11 National Retail Merchants Association.
N213m   Merchandising Division.
Men's alteration workroom costs & practices. Tabulation and analysis of a
questionnaire survey among department and
clothing stores. New York, The Men's and
Boy's Wear Group of the Merchandising Division, National Retail Dry Goods Association
[1950]
53 p. illus.,charts,tables. 26cm.

1. Men's clothing   I. T.

NN   0064237   MiDW MiU MH-BA InU

HF
5463   National Retail Merchants Association.
.N279   Merchandising Division.
1949   Men's wear sales in department stores 1949,
prepared by T.L.Blanke,director of Merchandise
research. New York [1949]
19 l.   28 cm.

1.Department stores. 2.Men's furnishing
goods.

NN   0064238   MiU

National Retail Merchants Association. Merchandising Division.
Merchandise control for piece goods.
New York [cop. 1929]
36 p.   Tables. and forms.

NN   0064239   MH-BA OC1

VOLUME 407

National retail merchants association. *Merchandising division.*
Merchandise control manual, by Merchandise managers' division of the National retail dry goods association. New York, National retail dry goods association [*1931]
5 p. l., 321, [3] p. incl. forms. 23 cm.

1. Department stores.   I. Title.

HF5463.N3   658.871   31-8299 rev

00xM OC1 CU TxU CoU
NN   0064240   DLC MB WaTC OrU CaBVa MtU IdU OrCS MiU

S1449   National Retail Merchants Association. Merchandising Division.
N5   Merchandise labeling. Preliminary report, May, 1938. A survey conducted by the Merchandising division ... National retail dry goods association. New York, The Association, c1938.
cover-title, 16 p. diagrs. 28 cm.
Processed.
1. Textile industry and fabrics – Testing. 2. Labeling. I. Title.

NN   0064241   DFT

National retail merchants association – Merchandising division
Merchandising a high school shop, May 1941, N.Y. 1941.
13 p.

NN   0064242   OC1

National Retail merchants Association. Merchandising Division.
380.33   Merchant's outlook. 1950. Compiled and
N277me   edited by Nova Eisnor. New York [1950]
1 v. (various pagings)   24cm.

1. Retail trade - U.S.   I. Eisnor, Nova, ed.

NN   0064243   CSt OU MiU

National Retail Dry Goods Association.
Merchandising Division.
NRDGA Television report...
see under   Hahn, Dane F

National Retail Merchants Association. Merchandising Division.
Proceedings [of the] joint convention, Merchandise Managers' Division, Sales Promotion Division. New York.

NN   0064245   MiU

National Retail Merchants Association. *Merchandising Division.*
The retailer's reference book of Federal Trade Commission rulings; a digest of Federal Trade Commission rulings of importance to retailers. New York, *1939–
1 v. (loose-leaf)   29 cm.
Published by the division under the association's earlier name: National Retail Dry Goods Association.

1. Retail trade—U. S.   I. U. S. Federal Trade Commission.   II. Title.   III. Title: A digest of Federal Trade Commission rulings of importance to retailers.

659.12   40-11508 rev*

NN   0064246   DLC OrU MiD OC1 OU CU DFT MH-BA TxU

National retail merchants association. *Merchandising division.*
The retailer's reference book of Federal trade commission rulings; a digest of Federal trade commission rulings of importance to retailers. Prepared by the Merchandising division, National retail dry goods association ... New York, N. Y., National retail dry goods association, *1939.
190 l. 29 cm.
Mimeographed.
1. Retail trade—U. S.   I. U. S. Federal trade commission.   II. Title.   III. Title: A digest of Federal trade commission rulings.

658.870973   40-31439 rev

NN   0064247   DLC MH-BA DFT

---

658   National Retail Merchants Association–Merchandising Division.
N212fr   Retraining buyers in retail stores, a consensus of merchandising experience, by E. H. Scull [and others]. New York, 1947]
36p. 28cm.

1. Buying.   2. Retail trade.   I. Scull, E. H.   II. Title.

NN   0064248   IU NNC TxU ICU NIC MH-BA NjR

HF   National Retail Merchants Association.
5463   Merchandising Division.
.N2818   Successful operation of the hat bar in department and specialty stores. New York, [1953?]
32 p.   25 cm.

1. Millinery.   2. Department stores--U.S.

NN   0064249   MiU OU InU MH-BA

HF   National Retail Merchants *Association. Merchandising Division.*
5463   Successful operation of the lamp and lamp
.N281   shade department in department and specialty stores. Prepared and published by the Merchandising Division, William Burston, manager. New York, National Retail Dry Goods Association [1955]
78 p.   26 cm.

1. Department stores--U.S.   2. Lamps.   3. Lamp shades.

NN   0064250   MiU MiD NIC MH-BA InU CaBVa

National retail merchants association–Merchandising division
A survey of drapery dept. merchandising, July 1935. Report of a study made in cooperation with N. Y Univ. school of retailing. N. Y. 1935.
8 numb. l.

NN   0064251   OC1

National retail merchants association–Merchandising division
A survey of grocery dept. merchandising, April 1936. Report of a study made in cooperation with Marion Harner. N.Y. Univ. school of retailing. N.Y. 1936.
9 numb. l.

NN   0064252   OC1

National Retail merchants Association. Merchandising Division.
Survey of men's furnishings sales --- by classifications; issued August - 1949. New York, Men's and Boys' Wear Group, National Retail Dry Goods Association, 1949.
Cover-title, 13 l., charts.

NN   0064253   MH-BA

National retail merchants association. Merchandising division
Survey of price zones of women's and misses' business and street dresses, May 1935. Report of a study made in cooperation with N. Y. Univ. school of retailing. N. Y. 1935.
6 p.

NN   0064254   OC1

Division,
National Retail Merchants Association. Merchandising
A survey of salary and bonus payment plans for buyers and divisional merchandise managers. A survey of salary and bonus payment plans used by department and speciality stores in compensating buyers and divisional merchandise managers. New York City [c1947]   59 p.   28cm.

1. Wages—Premium plan—U.S.

NN   0064255   NN MiU MH-BA IU MiD MdBJ

National retail merchants association – Merchandising division
A survey of shirt dept. merchandising. August 1936.
6 p.

NN   0064256   OC1

National Retail Merchants Association. Merchandising Division.
A survey on aging china and glassware stocks. N.Y., Nat. Retail Dry Goods Ass'n. May 1941.

NN   0064257   InU

National retail merchants association. Merchandising division.
The trade agreement with the United Kingdom. Items of interest to dept. and specialty stores, signed Nov. 17, 1938. ..... N.Y. 1939.
9, 15 numb. l.

NN   0064258   OCU

658.2   National Retail Merchants Association.
N213w   Merchandising Division
Want slip policies and systems in department stores. New York [n. d.]
33 [4] p. illus.

1. Records, Merchandise   2. Purchasing   3. Retail stores   I. Title

NN   0064259   MiD NjR TU

National Retail Merchants Association. Merchandising Division.
Want Slip Policies and Systems in Department Stores. N.Y. Nat. Retail Dry Goods Ass'n. April 1936.

NN   0064260   InU

National retail merchants association. Merchandising division.
Want slip policies and systems in department stores. New York [194-?]
33 p.   forms.

1. Department stores.   I. Title.

NN   0064261   NNC

VOLUME 407

HF 5461
.N 35
1947 Q
National retail merchants association. Merchandising division.
Want slip policies and systems in department
stores ... New York, N.Y., The Merchandising
division, National retail dry goods association
[1947?]
2 p.l., 33 p., 5 l. incl. forms. 28cm.

"Revised edition."
Reproduced from typo-written copy.

NN 0064262 MdBJ

658
N2126w
National Retail merchants Association--Merchandis-
ing Division.
Want slip policies and systems in department
stores. New York [1948]
33p. forms. 28cm.

1. Retail trade. 2. Salesmen and salesmanship

NN 0064263 IU InU MH-BA

658
N2126w
National Retail merchants Association--Merchandis-
ing Division.
Want slip policies and systems in department
stores. New York [1948]
33p. forms. 28cm.

1. Retail trade. 2. Salesmen and salesmanship.

NN 0064263 IU InU MH-BA

National retail merchants association.
Personnel group.
[Ely, Grace Darling] 1900–
American fashion designers ... New York city, Personnel
group, National retail dry goods association [pref. 1935]

National retail merchants association. *Personnel group.*
Arithmetic for executive training groups in department
stores. New York, Published by the Personnel group of the
National retail dry goods association [1934]
64 p. tables. 23 cm.
"Revised edition."
Compiled by Miss Irene M. Chambers. *cf.* Foreword.

1. Department stores. 2. Price marks.   I. Chambers, Irene
McAllister, comp. II. Title.
                                                    A 36–525 rev
Pennsylvania. Univ.   Library HF5461
for Library of Congress   [r58d⅟]

NN 0064265 PU NNC MiD

National retail merchants association. *Personnel group.*
Arithmetic for retail training ... New York, N. Y., Personnel group, National retail dry goods association, °1940.
84 p. tables. 23 cm.
"Third revision of the manual first published by the Personnel
group in 1931. Prepared by Irene M. Chambers."—Foreword.

1. Business mathematics.   I. Chambers, Irene McAllister.
II. Title.
HF5695.N35 1940   511.8   41–5425 rev

NN 0064266 DLC TxU

016.658
N21b
National retail merchants association. Personnel
group.
Bibliography for retailers... New York,
National retail dry goods assoc., [1944]
18p. 28 cm.

Foreword signed by Ruth Shapiro, personnel
assistant.

1. Retail trade--Bibl. I. Title.

NN 0064267 LU

SV.1
N278
National Retail Merchants Association. Person-
nel Group.
Bibliography for retailers. 2nd revision.
New York, 1946.
17 p.

Issued by the Association under its former
name: National Retail Dry Goods Association.
---- Selected list of books on retailing. New
York, 1956?
4 p. [Bound with the above]

Serves as a supplement to its Bibliography
for retailers.

1. Retail trade - Bibliography. I. Title.
II. Title: Selected list of books on retailing.

NN 0064269 MH-BA MiD

658.8
N21c
National retail merchants association. Personnel
group.
The college senior's attitude towards retailing... New York, National retail dry goods
assoc., [1942]
23p. 28cm.

1. Retail trade--U.S. 2. Salesmen and salesmanship. I. Title.

NN 0064270 LU OCU

National Retail Merchants Association. Personnel
Group.
The coordination of sales promotion and
training; report of a committee of the Personnel group National retail dry goods association. [New York city, National retail dry
goods association] °1932.
2 p.l.,iv,47 numb.l. 28½ x 21½cm.
Multigraphed.

1.Salesmen and salesmanship. I.Title. II.Title:
Sales promotion and training,The coordination of.

NN 0064271 MiU OCU

HF
5463
.N282
National Retail Merchants Association.
Personnel Group.
Current manpower and training problems.
New York [1951]
80 p. illus. 28 cm.

1.Department stores. 2.Employees,Train-
ing of.

NN 0064272 MiU

658.807
N277d
National Retail Merchants Association.
Personnel Group.
D.E.'s challenge and opportunity.
New York [1953]
14f. illus. 29cm.

1.Distributive education 2.Sales-
men and salesmanship - Study and
teaching.

NN 0064273 CLSU

658
N2161de
National Retail merchants Association--Personnel
Group.
The development of personnel testing in re-
tailing. New York [1937]
62p. illus. 23cm.

Bibliography: p.62.

1. Employment management. 2. Mental tests. 3
Retail trade. I. Title.

NN 0064274 IU LU OC1 MBS MiU

HP5429
.N296
NATIONAL RETAIL Merchants ASSOCIATION. Personnel
group.
The development of personnel testing in retailing. New York [1938]
63 p. illus. 22cm.

Bibliography:p.62.

1.Ability--Testing. 2.Retail trade.

NN 0064275 ICU

National Retail Merchants Association.
Personnel Group.
Directory of training films
see its   Training film directory.

National Retail Merchants Association. Personnel Group.
The effect of personnel procedure on the job
attitude of salespeople; report of a committee
of the personnel group,National retail dry
goods association. [New York, National retail
dry goods association. °1934.
2 p.l.,3-17 numb.l.   28½ x 22cm.
Multigraphed.

1.Employment management. 2.Department stores. I.
Title. II.Title: Personnel procedure.
                                    HF5549.N284

NN 0064277 MiU

National retail merchants association. *Personnel group.*
Employee attitude as affected by initial personnel procedure ... New York, Personnel group, National retail dry
goods association [1938]
61 p. 23 cm.

1. Personnel management.   I. Title.
                                                A 41–3520 rev
Ohio State Univ. Libr.
for Library of Congress   [r58c⅟]

NN 0064278 OU MH-BA O OC1

BF 431
.N27
National Retail Merchants Association. Personnel
Group.
Employee testing for retail stores,prepared by
Patricia Lee Jackson. N.Y., 1951.
84 p.

1. Ability--Testing. I. Jackson,Patricia Lee,
1916-

NN 0064279 InU OrU MiU TxU MH

National retail merchants association. *Personnel group.*
Employment department, organization and procedure ...
New York city, Personnel group, National retail dry goods
association [1939]
39, [1] p. incl. forms. 27½ cm.
Prepared for publication by O. Preston Robinson. *cf.* Foreword.

1. Personnel management. 2. Retail trade--U. S. 3. Department
stores--U. S.   I. Robinson, O. Preston, 1903–   II. Title.
HF5549.N34   658.3   41–10507 rev

NN 0064280 DLC OC1 OO MH-BA

National Retail Merchants Association. *Personnel Group.*
Employment standards and techniques. New York, Personnel Group, National Retail Dry Goods Association [1954?]
33 l. 28 cm.

1. Clerks (Retail trade) 2. Personnel management. 3. Recruiting
of employees.   I. Title.
HF5429.N323   658.3   56–3655 rev ‡

NN 0064281 DLC NN InU PU-W

VOLUME 407

HF
5549
.N288

National Retail Merchants Association. Personnel
Group.
Handling personnel & training problems in the
smaller store. New York [foreword 1950]
31 p.   28 cm.
A report of a panel discussion held at the
Mid-Year Conference of the Store Management and
Personnel Groups in Detroit, May, 1950. cf. Foreword.

1. Personnel management.   2. Employees, Training of
3. Department stores   --Employees.

NN   0064282   MiU InU

National Retail Merchants Association. *Personnel Group.*
Improving personnel administration. New York [1954]
110 p.   27 cm.
Issued by the group under the association's earlier name: **National Retail Dry Goods Association.**

1. Personnel management.   I. Title.
                                A 56-3970 rev
New York Univ.   Libraries HF5549
for Library of Congress   [r60c¼]

CaBVa
NN   0064283   NNU NN PU-W OCl InU MiD MiU MH-BA OU

HF
5549
.N2883

National Retail Merchants Association. Personnel
Group.
Improving public relations and employee produc-
tivity. New York [Foreword 1952]
83 p.   28 cm.
This report presents the personnel highlights
of the 41st annual NRDGA convention in New York,
January 1952. cf. Foreword.

1. Personnel management.   2. Department stores--
Employees.

NN   0064284   MiU OU

658.807
N211

National Retail Merchants Association. Personnel
Group.
The initial training of salespeople,...   New
York, National dry goods assoc. [1936?]
cover-title, 4 v. in 1. 28cm.

1. Salesmen and salesmanship. 2. Department
stores. I. Title.

NN   0064285   LU OU

658
N21123i

National retail merchants association--Personnel
group.
An inventory of your salespeople _   New York
city, Personnel group, National retail dry goods
association [1936]
v.

NN   0064286   IU

National Retail Merchants Association. Personnel
Group.
Maintaining a personnel staff in a war
economy ... N.Y., N.Y., Personnel group,
National retail dry goods association [1943]
30 p.

NN   0064287   MiEM OCl

HD9951
.N35

National Retail Merchants Association.
Personnel Group.

National Retail Merchants Association. *Store Management Group.*
Management handbook presenting the proceedings of the
mid-year conference.
New York

National Retail Merchants Association. **Personne.**
Group.
Merchandising arithmetic for retail training.
[Prepared] by Irene M. Chambers. New York,
Personnel Group, National Retail Dry Goods
Association, c1947.
53 p. illus. 28cm.

1. Business mathematics. I. Chambers, Irene
McAllister. II. T.

NN   0064289   MiDW InU IU NBuG NNC LU MiD CU

National Retail Merchants Association. Personnel
Group.
New personnel developments in training
and supervision. [New York, 1950]
138 p.

NN   0064290   MH-BA InU MiU

National Retail Merchants Associaiton. **Personnel**
Group.
Non-selling training ... New York,
National retail dry goods association [1932]
cover-title, 125 l. incl. diagrs.
28.5 cm.
Multigraphed.
1. Department stores. I. Title.

NN   0064291   OCU WaS IEN OU OCl MBS

L381.33
N2771o

National retail merchants association.
Personnel group
Organization of training departments.
[N.Y.] Personnel group, National retail
dry goods association, c1931.
52 p.   28cm.

1. Retail trade. 2. Salesmen and
salesmanship. I. Title.

NN   0064292   IEN OCl

L381.33
N2771p

National retail merchants association.
Personnel group.
The part time employee; report of a
committee of the Personnel group,
National retail dry goods association
... [N.Y., National retail dry goods
association, c1932]
16 p.   28cm.

1. Retail trade - U.S. I. Title.

NN   0064293   IEN

National retail merchants association.
Personnel group
Personnel highlights; 1944 wartime conference.
N. Y. 1944.

iii, 126 p.

NN   0064294   OCl

HF
5463
.N2823

National Retail Merchants Association. **Personnel**
Group.
The personnel job ahead. New York [1953]
90 p.   28 cm.

1. Personnel management. 2. Department stores
--Employees.

NN   0064295   MiU OU InU MH-BA

HF5549
.N3975

NATIONAL RETAIL Merchants ASSOCIATION. Personnel
group.
...Personnel reviews and ratings. New York city,
Personnel group, National retail dry goods association [1936]
3 pt. in 1 v. 28cm.

1. Employment management.

NN   0064296   ICU OCl OU

National Retail Merchants Association. Personnel Group.
Personnel techniques for increased production.   New York
[pref. 1949] 145 p. 28cm.

1. Retail trade.

NN   0064297   NN InU OU MiU

National retail merchants association.
Personnel group
Report of the Committee on the costs of
personnel departments in stores of various
sizes. 20 numb. l. N.Y 1928

NN   0064298   OCl

National retail merchants association.
Personnel group
Report of the Committee on the induction
of the new executive
    see under National retail merchants
association. Committee on the induction of the
new executive.

NN   0064299   OCl

National Retail Merchants Association. Personnel **Group.**
A report on executive training courses, compiled for the personnel group, National dry
goods association. [New York, N.Y.] National
retail dry goods association, c1930.
2 p.l., iv, 62 numb. l. 27½ x 21¼cm.
Cover-title: Executive training.

1. Employment management. I. Title: Executive training.

NN   0064300   MiU MBSi OU

National Retail Merchants Association. Personnel
Group.
A report on junior training, compiled
for the Personnel group, National retail
dry goods association. New York, 1930.
89 l.

NN   0064301   OCU OU

HF
5429
.N288

National Retail Merchants Association. Personnel
Group.
Retail training film directory. [1st-]   ed.
1936-
New York.

Title varies: 1936-19   Training film directory.

NN   0064302   MiU

National Retail Merchants Association.
Personnel Group.
Retail training film directory
    see also its Training film directory.

VOLUME 407

National Retail Merchants Association.
Personnel Group.
Retailing has a career for you! [New
York, c1954]
[24] p. illus. 23cm.
Published by the group under the associa-
tion's earlier name: National Retail Dry
Goods Association.

HF
5429
N2586

1. Retail trade as a profession. I. Title.

NN   0064304   CoU NNC

National Retail Merchants Association. Personnel Group.
...The scope of training for retail store service; a report of
the committee representing the personnel group of the National
Retail Dry Goods Association on the scope of training for retail
store service with special reference to leadership training in situations involving problems of human relationships. Hotel Drake,
Chicago, May 20, 21, 22, 23, 1929. [Washington, D. C.: Trade
and Industrial Education Service, Federal Board for Vocational

Education, 1929.]   viii, 94 p. incl. tables.   illus. (charts.)
sq. 4°
At head of title: Misc. 1012.
Text mimeographed.

1. Salesmanship and salesmen—   Education. 2. Retail trade—U. S.
I. United States. Vocational Education,   Federal Board for.
N. Y. P. L.   March 25, 1932

NN   0064306   NN PPiU OCl

HF5439   National retail merchants   association.
.D4N5   Personnel group.
        Specialized training for salespeople,
    comp. for the Personnel group, National
    retail dry goods association. [New
    York, N.Y.] National retail dry goods
    association, c.1930.
        1 p.l., vii,119 numb.l.   28cm.
        Mimeographed.

        1. Salesmen   and salesmanship.

NN   0064307   OSW OrU OCl OCU

National retail merchants association. *Personnel group.*
Store vacation policies, a study of the summer and winter
vacation policies in a group of representative member stores
... New York, N. Y., Personnel group, National retail dry
goods association [1941]
2 p. l., 15 numb. l. 29 cm.
Reproduced from type-written copy.

1. Vacations, Employee—U. S. 2. Retail trade—U. S.   I. Title.
HD5261.N32   331.816   41–19563 rev

NN   0064308   DLC OCl

National retail merchants association. Personnel
group.
A store's letters to the public; a manual of
representative letters covering typical consumer
situations dealt with by the superintendent's
office, the employment office, bureau of adjustments and complaints [and others] ... Comp. by
the Personnel group, National retail dry goods
association. [New York] National retail dry
goods association, c1934.
vi, 18 p. 22½cm.

1. Department stores. I. Title.

NN   0064309   NNC LU OCl IU

National Retail Merchants Association. Personnel
Group.
A study of shopping reports as an evaluation
of training, January 1931. N.Y., c1931.
13 p. 31 cm.

NN   0064310   OrU

National Retail Merchants Association—
Personnel Group.
Supervising people. New York [1950]
34p. 28cm.

658
N2123s

1. Personnel management. I. Title.

NN   0064311   IU OU MH-BA MiU

National Retail Merchants Association. Personnel
Group.
Training and holding employees.   New York
[1951]
123 p.
The proceedings of the Mid-Year Conference
of the Store Management and Personal Groups
held in Washington in May 1951.

NN   0064312   MH-BA ICU LU

National retail merchants association—
Personnel group
Training contingents; report of a committee of
the personnel group... N.Y. 1933]
139 numb l.

NN   0064313   OCl

National Retail Merchants Association. *Personnel Group.*
Training film directory.
New York, 19
v. 27 cm.
Directories published 19   issued under the association's
earlier name: National Retail Dry Goods Association.

1. Retail trade—Film catalogs.

HF5429.N32   54–29620 rev ‡

NN   0064314   DLC InU MiU MiEM NBuG MdBJ OCU

National Retail Merchants Association.
Personnel Group.
Training film directory
see also its Retail training film
directory.

National Retail Merchants Association. *Personnel Group.*
The training job ahead: proceedings, training sessions,
January, 1945 wartime conference. New York [1945]
75 p. 28 cm.
Published by the group under the association's earlier name: Na-
tional Retail Dry Goods Association.

1. Retail trade. 2. Distributive education. 3. Employees, Training
of.   I. Title.
HF5429.N268   371.42685887   45–7277 rev*

NN   0064316   DLC

National Retail Merchants Association.
Personnel Group.
Training techniques for non-selling employees.
New York, N.Y. [1949]
[6] 39 p. illus.
Manifold copy.

NN   0064317   MH-BA OU IU

National retail merchants association.
Personnel group.
Trends in fashion training, a manual
for fashion trainers. New York,
National dry goods association[1930]
92p.

NN   0064318   PSt IU OCU RPD OCl

National Retail Merchants Association. Personnel
Group.
The world of fashion.   New York [1930]
cover-title, 53 p.

NN   0064319   IU OCl OCU RPD

National retail merchants association. Personnel group.
The world of fashion. New York [1931]
cover-title, 61 p.
"Revised May, 1931."

1. Fashion.

NN   0064320   NNC OrU

National Retail Merchants Association. Ready-to-
Wear Group.
Report. 19 –
New York.

NN   0064321   MiU

National Retail Merchants Association. Ready-to-
Wear Group.
Selling the right size in the children's wear
dept. July 1940. N.Y. Ready to
wear group, National retail dry goods association
1940.
9 p.

NN   0064322   OCl

National Retail Merchants Association. *Retail Delivery
Association*
see
Retail Delivery Association.

National retail merchants association. Retail fur
council.
Fur digest
see under title

National retail merchants association.
Retail research institute.
Electronic data processing for
retailers. N.Y.[n.d.]   1v.(looseleaf)

NN   0064325   CaBVa

National Retail Merchants Association
Retail Research Institute.
Operations research in retailing; case
studies. New York [n.d.]
32 p. illus.

RESEARCH, INDUSTRIAL
RETAIL TRADE

HF
5429
N3

NN   0064326   KMK

National Retail Merchants Association. Sales
Promotion Division.
A compilation of ideas on internal store
promotion, comp. by Thomas Robb. New York,
Sales promotion division, National retail
dry goods association, 1936.
52p., 35cm.

NN   0064327   TU

VOLUME 407

National retail merchants association - Sales
promotion division.
...Customer analysis and control...
N.Y. c1931.

16 p.

NN   0064328   OC1

National retail merchants association. *Sales promotion
division.*
The daily planning guide, compiled by Frank W. Spaeth,
manager, Sales promotion division ... New York, Sales promotion division, National retail dry goods association [1933]

160 p. illus. 28 cm.

1. Retail trade. 2. Department stores. 3. Advertising.   I. Spaeth,
Frank William, 1903-   comp. II. Title.

HF5429.N33   658.87   33-13495 rev

NN   0064329   DLC MB

HF
6146
.R13
N28   National Retail merchants Association.
Sales Promotion Division.
Department store radio advertising. A
joint publication by National Retail Dry
Goods Association, Sales Promotion Division,
and Broadcast Advertising Bureau. [New
York, 1951]
[74] p. 28 cm.
1. Radio advertising--U.S. 2. Department
stores--U.S. I. Broadcast Advertising Bureau.

NN   0064330   MiU TxU WaS OrU MiD

National Retail Merchants Association. *Sales Promotion
Division.*
How to evaluate display; results of the NRDGA School
of Retailing, New York University, interior display evaluation study. [New York, *1947]

24 p. illus. 28 cm.

Published by the division under the association's earlier name:
National Retail Dry Goods Association.

1. Display of merchandise. 2. Dry-goods. I. Title.

HF5849.D73N3   659.157   50-33516 rev

CaBVa
NN   0064331   DLC MdBJ TU MiD InU CSt PPT PSt WaS

658.3
N197h   National Retail Merchants Association. Sales
Promotion Division.
How to plan anniversary sales (and other
storewide sales) [Compiled by Howard P.
Abrahams, May Stern [and] Irving C.
Eldredge] New York [*1955]
48 p. illus.

1. Sales   2. Retail trade   I. Abrahams,
Howard P.   I. T.

NN   0064332   MiD OC1 InU NIC MH-BA

659.1
N2128h   National Retail Merchants Association--Sales
Promotion Division.
How to use direct mail successfully. [New
York, 1949]
32p. illus. 28cm.

1. Advertising. 2. Retail trade. I. Title.

MH-BA
NN   0064333   IU NN NBuG MiU MiD IEN CaBVa WaS

National retail merchants association - Sales
promotion division
Legal and public holidays, dates of interest,
and calendar of special weeks and days.
1935.

23 numb. l.

NN   0064334   OC1

National retail merchants association. *Sales promotion
division.*
A new concept of retail sales promotion, embodying a con-
sumer-attuned, sales-minded program that spells increased
sales and profits! By Thomas Robb, manager, Sales promotion division ... New York, N. Y., Sales promotion division, National retail dry goods association [*1937]

64 p. pl. 35 cm.

1. Retail trade. 2. Retail trade—U. S. 3. Advertising.   I. Robb,
Thomas. II. Title. III. Title: Retail sales promotion.

HF5429.N34   658.87   38-6638 rev

NN   0064335   DLC MiD InU OC1 PPCuP PPT NN NNC IU

National retail merchants association - Sales
promotion division
One hundred best ads; selected from the
National retail dry goods association advertising
awards exhibition..Jan 1941...N.Y. 1941.

2 p. l., 100 p.

NN   0064336   OC1

National Retail Merchants Association. *Sales Promotion
Division.*
One hundred best retail advertisements.

[New York]
v. illus. 24-28 cm. annual.
Issued under the association's earlier name: National
Retail Dry Goods Association.

1. Advertising—Yearbooks.

HF5802.N35   659.1058   47-11292 rev*

OU NNC MiU CaBVa OC1U
NN   0064337   DLC TxU OCU TU CU NN IU MiD PPT OC1CC

NA6220
N3
National Retail Merchants Association. Sales
Promotion Division.
National Retail Merchants Association. *Store Management
Group.*
Planning the store of to-morrow, compiled by Store Man-
agement and Sales Promotion Divisions of the National Re-
tail Dry Goods Association. New York [1945]

National Retail Merchants Association. Sales Promotion Division.
Proceedings. 1925-1934. New York.
v.

Issues for 1931 published in its Year book; 1932,
in its Data book; 1933 never published.

NN   0064339   MiU

Merchants
National retail Merchants association. Sales
promotion division.
Proceedings ... annual convention.

New York,
v. diagrs. 28cm.

1. Retail trade - Congresses.

NN   0064340   NNC

National Retail Merchants Association. Sales
Promotion Division.
Proceedings of the joint convention,
Merchandise Managers' Division, Sales Promotion
Division
see under   National Retail Merchants
Association. Merchandising Division.

National Retail Merchants Association. Sales Promotion
Division.
Radio and the retailer; what some of the country's leading re-
tail sales promotion people think about it.   New York, c1940.

35 p. 29cm.

"Transcript of the 'Information please' radio session held on January 17, 1940.
Hotel Pennsylvania, New York."

1. Advertising—Mediums—Radio.   2. Advertising, Dry goods.

NN   0064342   NN OU

National retail merchants association. *Sales promotion
division.*
Radio broadcasting manual; the radio as a publicity medium for retailers; an appraisal with a resume of experiences, compiled by Frank W. Spaeth, manager, Sales promotion division ... New York, Sales promotion division, National retail dry goods association [1935]

80 p. illus. 28½ cm.

"A bibliography of broadcasting": p. 79-80.

1. Retail trade. 2. Radio advertising.   I. Spaeth, Frank William,
1903-   comp.

HF6146.R3N35   659.1   35-9135 rev

NN   0064343   DLC MB TxU OU WaS

National Retail Merchants Association.
Sales Promotion Division.
Retail advertising course
see under Harries, Llewellyn.

National Retail Merchants Association. Sales
Promotion Division.
The retail calendar and promotion guide ...
see its   Sales promotion calendar.

National Retail Merchants Association. Sales
Promotion Division.
The retailer's calendar and promotional
guide
see its   Sales promotion calendar.

---

fZ658.87
N21   National Retail Merchants Association. Sales
Promotion Division.
Sales promotion calendar.

[New York
v. 37-46cm.

Title varies: 19 -   as Retailer's calendar
and promotional guide.

1. Dry goods - Period.

OC1W PSt IdPI OrU MiD
NN   0064347   TxU MB NN OC1 IU MH-BA NN MiU CU GU

---

q658.82
N213s   National Retail Merchants Association.
Sales Promotion Division.
Sales promotion encyclopedia. **New York**
[c1928-
1v. (loose-leaf)

Issued 1928-   under the association's
earlier name: National Retail Dry Goods
Association.

1. Retail trade--Period. 2. Salesmen and
salesmanship--Period. I. Title.

NN   0064348   TxFTC

VOLUME 407

National Retail Merchants Association. *Sales Promotion Division.*
 Sales promotion year book. 1928–
New York.
  v. illus., diagrs. 27 cm.
  Issued 1928–   under the association's earlier name: National Retail Dry Goods Association.

 1. Retail trade—Period. 2. Salesmen and salesmanship—Period. 3. Periodicals. I. Title.
                                              A 31–423 rev*
Chicago. Univ. Libr.   HF5429
 for Library of Congress   ₍r58c₎₎

NN 0064349   ICU OC1

659.1 National retail merchants association--Sales pro-
N216s   motion division.
         A survey on the use of radio as a retail adver-
       tising medium … New York, National retail dry
       goods association, c1946.
       ₍9₎p.

       1. Radio advertising. I. Title: Radio as a re-
       tail advertising medium.

NN 0064350   IU TxU MBSi

---

658   National Retail merchants Association--Sales Pro-
N2124u   motion Division.
         Using your promotion tools more successfully.
       ₍New York₎ Sales Promotion Division and Visual
       Merchandising Group, National Retail Dry Goods
       Association ₍1949₎
       103p. 28cm.

       1. Salesmen and salesmanship. I. National Re-
       tail Dry Goods Association--Visual Merchandising
       Group. I. Title.

NN 0064351   IU

National Retail Merchants Association. Smaller
 Stores Division.
   Fall and Christmas planning for smaller stores

   see under

   Mongeon, Leonard F   1900–   ed.

National Retail Merchants Association. Smaller
 stores division.
   Financial and record-keeping manual

   see under

   Copes, Raymond F   1915–   ed.

National Retail Merchants Association. Smaller
 Stores Division.
   Getting the most out of your merchandising
 advertising and expense dollar. New York
 [c1948]
   134 p. chart, tables.
   Cover title.
   [Report of its] meeting in cooperation with
 Chicago Retail Merchants Association [and]
 Illinois Federation of Retail Associations,

 Sept. 30–Oct. 1, 1940, Palmer House, Chicago.

NN 0064355   MH-BA

National Retail Merchant Association. Smaller
 Stores Division.
   Improving smaller store advertising and
 promotion. N.Y., 1947.
   2–36 p. illus.
   Cover title.
   Material presented at the Smaller stores
 clinic, Sept. 9, 1947, in New York.
   1. Advertising – Dry-goods.

NN 0064356   InU

National Retail Merchants Association. *Smaller Stores Division.*
 Manual. no. 1–
 ₍New York, 1949–
   v. 23 cm.
   Numbers 1– issued under the association's earlier name: Na-
 tional Retail Dry Goods Association.

   1. Dry-goods—Collections.

 HF6201.D7N3   51–5384 rev

 FTaSU MdBJ TxLT UU
NN 0064357   DLC ICU CaBVaU MiU IEN MiDW CoU MiU

National Retail Merchants Association.
 Smaller Stores Division.
   Merchandise control manual for smaller
 stores
        see under   Mongeon, Leonard F
 1900–   ed.

National Retail Merchants Association.
 Smaller Stores Division.
   Sales promotion manual for smaller
 stores
        see under   Mongeon, Leonard F
 1900–   ed.

National Retail Merchants Association. Smaller
 Stores Division.
   Sales training manual for smaller stores

   see under

   Mongeon, Leonard F   1900–   ed.

National Retail Merchants Association.
 Smaller Stores Division.
   Smaller stores convention proceedings …
 New York.
   v.   27 cm.
   Mimeographed.
   A report of the sessions held by the Smaller
 stores group and of the general sessions of the
 mid-year convention of the National retail dry
 goods association.
   1. Retail trade – Congresses. I. Title.

NN 0064361   CU

National Retail Merchants Association.
 Smaller Stores Division
   see also National Retail Merchants
 Association. Bureau of Smaller Stores.

National Retail Merchants Association.
 Store Management Division
   see National Retail Merchants Association. Store Management Group.

L381.33 National Retail Merchants Association. Store
N2772   Management Group.
           Analysis of current management
         problems; a summary and analysis of
         some of the major problems of retail
         store management as developed at the
         annual meeting of the Store managers'
         division, National retail dry goods
         association, Pittsburgh, Pa., June
         13 to 16, 1932 … ₍N.Y.₎ Store
         managers' division, National retail
         dry goods association ₍1932?₎

NN 0064364   IEN

National Retail Merchants Association. Store
 Management Group.
   Branch store operations. New York ₍1954₎
 ii, 37, v 1. forms.

NN 0064365   NNC OU MH-BA MiU InU CaBVa

National retail merchants association. Store
 management group.
   ₍Changes in store and employee hours; analysis and discussion of the five-day employee week
 and its application to varying store open schedules. ₍N.Y.₎ Store management and personnel
 groups, National retail dry goods association
 ₍1947₎
   ₍cover-title, 1 p.l., 46p. 28½cm.

   Mimeographed.

NN 0064366   MBSi MH-BA MiD

National Retail Merchants Association. *Store Management Group.*
 Complaint clinic.
 New York.
   v. diagrs. 29 cm.
   Issued   under the association's earlier name: National
 Retail Dry Goods Association.

   1. Complaints (Retail trade)

 HF5429.N344   58–41826

NN 0064367   DLC OC1 MBSi

National retail merchants association. *Store management group.*
   Conserving wrapping supplies under national defense; a
 practical program to follow, actual economies applied, restricting gift wrapping policies, specific gift wrapping savings … New York, Store management group, National retail
 dry goods association, *1941.
   3 p. l., 48 numb. l. 28 x 21½ cm.
   Reproduced from type-written copy.

   1. Packaging. 2. Gift wrapping. I. Title.

 HF5770.N26   658.78844   42–2347 rev

NN 0064368   DLC OC1 DNAL

National Retail Merchants Association. *Store Management Group.*
   Controlling personnel and operating expenses
   see its
   Management handbook presenting the proceedings of
 the mid-year conference.

HF   National Retail Merchants Association. Store
5463   Management Group.
.N2828   Controlling shortages and improving protection.
       ₍Report summarizing two recent forums₎ New York
       ₍foreword 1953₎
         62 ₰.,16 p. illus. 28 cm.
         "Watch out for that thief!" (cover title,16 p.
       at end) also issued separately.

         1.Shoplifting. I.Title.

NN 0064370   MiU InU MH-BA MiD PU-W OU

VOLUME 407

HF5429 NATIONAL RETAIL Merchants ASSOCIATION—Store
.N236 Management Group
    Cost-cutting ideas for 1952. N.Y., 1952.
    126 p. illus.

    1. Cost. 2. Retail trade. I. Title

NN 0064371   InU OU MiU CLSU

National Retail Merchants Association. *Store Management
    Group.*
    Cost-cutting ideas for 1954. New York, 1954.
    62, 51 p. 28 cm.
    Published by the group under the association's earlier name: Na-
tional Retail Dry Goods Association.

    1. Department stores—U. S. 2. Stores, Retail.   I. Title.
                              A 56–3008 rev
Pittsburgh. Univ. Libr.   HF5463
 for Library of Congress   [r59b1]

NN 0064372   PPiU InU OU NN

National Retail Merchants Association. *Store Management
    Group.*
    Current operating and personnel problems
    see its
    Management handbook.

VF   **National Retail** Merchants **Association.**
NAC   Store Management Group.
2059   Customer parking facilities of retail
N22   stores. New York, The Association [1939]

NN 0064374   NIC

658.87 National Retail Merchants Association.
N213cu   Store Management Group.
    Customer returns and complaints. New
York [1948?]
    168 p. 28 cm.

    1. Complaints (Retail trade) I. T.

NN 0064375   MiDW MH-BA

HF 5429 NATIONAL RETAIL Merchants ASSOCIATION—
.N297 Store Management Group
    Customer returns and complaints. New
York [1949?]
    168 p.

    1. Complaints (Retail trade). I. Title.

NN 0064376   InU IU OU

National retail merchants association.
    Store management group.
    Customer returns and complaints.
N.Y., [1950?] 160p. (Its Proceedings
of mid-year conference, 1950)

NN 0064377   CaBVa MiD

HD4928 NATIONAL RETAIL Merchants ASSOCIATION. Store
.D5N3   management group.
    Dismissal wages; analysis of store practices in
giving dismissal notices and paying compensation
to regular employees when discharged for other
than cause. New York, Store management group,
National retail dry goods association, 1937.
    12 numb. l. 28 cm.
    Mimeographed.

    1. Wages—Dismissal wage.

NN 0064378   ICU

658.4 National Retail Merchants Association. Store
N213e   Management Group.
    Expense reduction. New York [1950]
    106p. 29cm.

    1. Retail trade. U.S. 2. Commercial
statistics. I. Title.

NN 0064379   OrU MiU InU

National Retail Merchants Association. Store
    Management Group.
    Expenses can be reduced ...
    see under Kleinhaus, H   I

National Retail Merchants Association. Store
    Management Group.
    Fall management conference ... N.Y.
[The Author]
    v.

NN 0064381   MiD

HF   National Retail Merchants Association. Store
5463   Management Group.
.N285   Gearing operations for more sales and less
expense. New York [1949]
    93 p. illus. 28 cm.

    1. Department stores. I. Title.

NN 0064382   MiU CaBVa InU NN

National Retail Merchants Association. Store
    Management Group.
    Joint management proceedings ...
      see National Retail Merchants Associa-
tion.
    Management and personnel proceedings.

658.87 National Retail Merchants Association. Store
N213k   Management Group.
    Keeping the store clean. New York [1953]
    46 l. illus. 28cm.

    1. Stores, Retail. 2. Cleaning. I. T.

NN 0064384   MiDW PU-W MH-BA MiU InU OU

National Retail Merchants Association. *Store Management
    Group.*
    Management and personnel forum
    see its
    Management handbook.

National Retail Merchants Association. *Store Management
    Group.*
    Management handbook presenting the proceedings of the
mid-year conference.
    New York.
    v. 28 cm.
    Began publication in 1924; 1931–32 not pub. *Cf.* Union list of
serials.
    Title varies: 19   –47, Proceedings of mid-year confer-
ence (varies).—   Mid-year convention proceedings.
    Issues for   have also distinctive titles: 1946, *Current
operating and personnel problems.*—1947. Management and personnel
forum.—1948, Controlling personnel and operating expenses.

    Proceedings for
name: National Retail Dry Goods Association and   under the
group's earlier name: Store Managers' Division.
    Conferences for 1946–   held in conjunction with the association's
Personnel Group.

    1. Dry-goods—U. S.—Societies, etc. 2. Retail trade—U. S.—Socie-
ties, etc.   I. National Retail Merchants Association. **Personnel
Group.**
    HD9951.N35   27–23010 rev 2*

NN 0064387   DLC CSt MH-BA NIC OC1 InU OU

L381.331 National retail merchants association.
N2773   Store management group.
    Merchandising and workroom opera-
tions of men's clothing departments ...
[N.Y.] Store management group, National retail dry goods association, c1932.
    3 p. l., 2–15 numb. l. tables
(1 fold.) diagr. 29cm.

    Mimeographed.
    Blank leaf inserted between 2d
prelim. leaf and 2d leaf.

    1. Depart   ment stores. I. Title

NN 0064388   IEN

National Retail Merchants Association. *Store Management
    Group.*
    Mid-year convention proceedings
    see its
    Management handbook.

National Retail Merchants Association. Store
    Management Group.
    Modern methods of merchandise handling.
New York [1948]
    31 p. incl. illus. fold. plan.

    "Summary of a session ... held jointly by
the Store Management and Delivery Groups at the
January 1948 Convention." - Foreword.

NN 0064390   MH-BA TxU InU

National Retail Merchants Association. Store
    Management Group.
    News bulletin. N.Y.
    v.
    Quarterly.

NN 0064391   CaBVa

National Retail Merchants Association. Store
    Management Group.
    New techniques for wrapping economics.
New York [foreword 1952]
    46 l. illus. 28 cm.
    1. Packing for shipment. I. Title.

NN 0064392   MiU OU InU MH-BA

HF   National Retail Merchants Association. Store
5686   Management Group.
.D5   Operating and personnel aspects of production
N29   unit accounting. New York [1953]
    41 l. 28 cm.

    1. Department stores—Accounting. I. Title; Pro-
duction unit accounting.

NN 0064393   MiU OU InU PU-W

VOLUME 407

National Retail Merchants Association. Store
   Management Group.
   Operating costs of retail food service units.
[New York, 1953]
   37 l.   29 cm.
   Cover title.
   1. Restaurants, lunch rooms, etc.
   2. Department stores.

NN   0064394   MiU OU OC1 InU MH-BA

HF
5463
.N28⁷   National Retail Merchants Association. Store
   Management Group.
   Operating major workrooms. New York ₁1949₎
   92 p.   illus.   27 cm.

   1.Department stores. I.Title.

NN   0064395   MiU InU MH-BA OU

HF
5461   National Retail Merchants Association. Store
.N29   Management Group.
   Planning and fixturing for better selling.
New York ₁1953₎
   41 l.   illus.   28 cm.

   1.Department stores. 2.Salesmen and salesmanship. I.Title.

NN   0064396   MiU MH-BA PU-W MiD InU OU

National Retail Merchants Association. *Store Management
Group.*
   Planning the store of to-morrow, compiled by Store Management and Sales Promotion Divisions of the National Retail Dry Goods Association. New York ₁1945₎
   120 p. illus., plans. 27 cm.

   1. Stores, Retail.   I. National Retail Merchants Association.
Sales Promotion Division. II. Title.

   NA6220.N3   725.21   45–19742 rev*

NN   0064397   DLC WaS Or PSt OU ICU OC1 MB

National Retail Merchants Association. *Store Management
Group.*
   Proceedings of mid-year conference
see its
   Management handbook presenting the proceedings of
the mid-year conference.

L381.67
N2772r   National Retail Merchants Association. Store
   Management Group.
   Reducing store expenses.   [New York] 1953.
   111,34 l. illus. 28cm.

   Cover title.

   1. Retail trade. 2. Department stores.

NN   0064399   IEN

National Retail Merchants Association. Store Management Group.
   Regular and Christmas gift wrap policies of
retail stores. N.Y. 1939.

   32 numb. l.

NN   0064400   OC1

National Retail Merchants Association. *Store Management
Group.*
   Restaurant report.
New York.
   v. in   28 cm.   annual.
   Title varies: 19   –39, Restaurant session proceedings—1941–42,
Store restaurant report.
   Issued   under the association's earlier name: National
Retail Dry Goods Association.

   1. Restaurants, lunch rooms, etc.—Yearbooks.

   TX901.N33   56–49172 rev ‡

NN   0064401   DLC InU MiD MH-BA OC1 CSt WaS

National retail merchants association. *Store management
group.*
   Restricting customer services under national defense; an
analysis of services offered and a guide to probable restrictions indicated under the national emergency ... New York,
Store management group, National retail dry goods association, ℂ1942.
   4 p. l., 39, A–I numb l.   28 x 21½ cm.
   Reproduced from type-written copy.

   1. Retail trade—U. S.   I. Title.

   HF5429.N345   658.8710973   42–12305 rev

NN   0064402   DLC OC1

National Retail Merchants Association. Store Management
Group.
   Simplification of wrapping and packing supplies; a report by
the Operating Committee on the Simplification of Supplies presenting simplified sizes of paper bags, folding boxes, set-up boxes,
and corrugated boxes, and general findings and recommendations
on the use of supplies in wrapping and packing department store
merchandise...   New York, N. Y.: Store Managers' Division,
National Retail Dry Goods Assoc., cop. 1931.   77 p. incl. tables.
chart, illus.   4°.

   1. Packing.
N. Y. P. L.   December 16, 1931

NN   0064403   NN MiD MB IEN

National Retail Merchants Association. Store
   Management Group.
   Simplified selling.   New York [1952?]
   41 l.   illus., plans.   28 cm.
   1. Retail trade. U.S. 2. Department
stores. 3. Salesmen and salesmanship. I. Title.

NN   0064404   IEN MiU IU OU PU-W MH-BA

658.87   National Retail Merchants Association. Store
N21st   Management Group.
   Stimulating production and reducing expense...   New York ₁1951₎
   173 p.   diagrs. 28cm.

   1. Retail trade. I. Title.

NN   0064405   LU MH-BA CaBVaU

HF
5463   National Retail Merchants Association. Store
.N2877   Management Group.
   Store delivery policies and practices; an
analysis of delivery policies,practices,costs,
and restrictions as reported by 252 department
and specialty stores. New York, c1953.
   63 p.   27 cm.

   1.Delivery of goods. I.Title.

NN   0064406   MiU MiDW MH-BA MiD IEN OU IU

HF
5465   National Retail Merchants Association.
.U62   Store Management Group.
N27   Store hours and employee schedules; an
   analysis of schedules prevailing among department and specialty stores in 258 cities.
New York, c1952.
   61,8 p.   tables.   28 cm.

   1.Store hours. 2.Department stores--Em-
ployees. 3.Department stores--U.S.

NN   0064407   MiU MH-BA

HF5429   NATIONAL RETAIL Merchants ASSOCIATION--STORE
.N246   Management group.
   Store manager's operating guide.   N.Y.
   ℂ1950₎
   142 p. illus.

   Discussions at mid-year conference, in
Detroit, May, 1950.

   1. Business--Small business--Management.
   2. Retail trade. I. Title.   Bus.cds.

NN   0064408   InU MiU MH-BA

National Retail Merchants Association. *Store Management
Group.*
   Store restaurant report
see its
   Restaurant report.

National retail merchants association. Store
   management group
   Strained customer relations: a summary of
the convention session held Jan. 18 1939. N.Y.
1939.

   2 p. l., 2–28, ₃3₎ l.

NN   0064410   OU

HF
5770   National Retail merchants Association. Store
.N27   Management Group.
   Supply purchasing and wrapping problems --1951.
   ₁Report ... from a panel discussion by leading
store executives held in January 1951₎ New York
₁foreword 1951₎
   34 l.   28 cm.

   1.Packing for shipment. 2.Containers. I.Title

NN   0064411   MiU InU MH

National Retail Merchants Association. *Store Management
Group.*
   Transportation costs and store delivery services. New
York, Store Management Group, National Retail Dry Goods
Association ₁1954?₎
   43, 6 l.   28 cm.

   1. Shipment of goods. 2. Delivery of goods.   I. Title.

   HF5761.N3   658.7885   56–3654 rev ‡

NN   0064412   DLC OU PU-W InU MH-BA MiU IU

National retail merchants association. *Store management
group.*
   Trends in compensating salespeople ... New York, N. Y.,
Store management group, National retail dry goods association ₁ℂ1938₎
   76 p. incl. tables. 28 cm.

   1. Wages--U. S. 2. Salesmen and salesmanship. 3. Retail trade.
I. Title.
   HD4966.S35U6   331.285887   39–588 rev

NN   0064413   DLC WaS OC1 OU CSt

National Retail Merchants Association. Store
   Management Group.
   Warehousing and delivery practices and
procedures. New York, N.Y. ₁1949₎
   3 p.l., 44 p. illus.

   Manifold copy.

NN   0064414   MH-BA CaBVa

VOLUME 407

L381.33 National Retail Merchants Association. Store
N2772w   Management Group.
        Workroom manual; a handbook on the
      function, organization and operation of
      workrooms in department and specialty
      stores, prepared by the Committee on
      workrooms of the Store managers' divi-
      sion...   N.Y., Store managers' divi-
      sion, National retail dry goods associa-
      tion, c1931.
        2 p. l., 104 p. incl. forms, plans.
      26cm.

NN 0064415   IEN WaS OCl

National Retail Merchants Association.
    Store Management Group.
    Workshop analysis of supply purchasing,
  wrapping and delivery.   New York [1950]
    78 p. illus.

NN 0064416   MH-BA InU OU MiU

National retail merchants association. *Store management
  group.*
    Wrapping supply manual; presenting standard sizes and
  specifications for paper bags, set-up boxes, folding boxes and
  corrugated boxes, and standard specifications for corrugated
  rolls ... N[ew] Y[ork] Store management group, National
  retail dry goods association, °1940.
    4 p. l., 122, 7 p. incl. tables. 29 x 24 cm.
    "N. R. D. G. A. standard specifications" (7 p. at end) has special
  t.-p.
    "To Anne McNamara ... rightfully goes the major credit for the
  preparation of this manual."—Pref.
    1. Packing for shipment. 2. Containers. 3. Boxes. 4. Cartons.
  I. McNamara, Anne. II. Title.

    HF5770.N3   658.78844   41–12859 rev 2

NN 0064417   DLC OCl

National Retail Merchants Association. *Store Managers'
  Division*
    see
National Retail Merchants Association. *Store Manage-
  ment Group.*

National retail merchants association. *Traffic group.*
    Manual on merchandise transportation: methods, costs,
  savings. [New York] Traffic group, National retail dry
  goods association, °1940.
    4 p. l., 175 p. incl. forms. 23 cm.
    Pages 171–175, advertising matter.
    "Suggested ... books": p. 12–14.

    1. Retail trade. 2. Shipment of goods. I. Title.

    HE203.N3   658.7885   40–32653 rev

NN 0064419   DLC WaS OrU OCl OU ICJ TU TxU CU

National Retail Merchants Association. *Traffic Group.*
    Manual on receiving department operations. Rev. ed.
  Edited by Leonard Mongeon, assisted by Marie A. Longo.
  New York [1947]
    xii, 366 p. illus. 23 cm.
    Published in 1938 by the National Retail Dry Goods Association,
  and in 1947 by the group under the association's earlier name: National Retail Dry Goods Association.

    1. Retail trade. I. Mongeon, Leonard F., 1900– ed. II. Na-
  tional Retail Merchants Association. Manual on receiving department operations. III. Title: Receiving department operations.

    HF5429.N27 1947   658.77   47–7030 rev*

NN 0064420   DLC CaBVa OrU TU TxU OU TNJ MiD

National Retail Merchants Association. *Traffic Group.*
    Price marking manual. New York [1930]
    80 p. (p. 52–80 advertisements) 26 cm. [National Retail Dry
  Goods Association] Official publication]
    Published by the group under the association's earlier name: Na-
  tional Retail Dry Goods Association.

    1. Price marks. I. Title.

    HF5374.N3   30–4825 rev*

NN 0064421   DLC MB OCl

National Retail Association. Traffic Group.
    Proceedings, annual convention ...
  Chicago.
    v.
    Manifold copy.

NN 0064422   MH-BA NN

National Retail Merchants Association. *Traffic Receiving
  and Marking Group.*
    Transportation claims manual, compiled by L. F. Mon-
  geon, traffic manager. New York [1928]
    35 p. forms. 24 cm. ([National Retail Dry Goods Association]
  Official publication, v. 1, no. 5)
    Cover title.
    Published by the group under the association's earlier name: Na-
  tional Retail Dry Goods Association.

    1. Freight and freightage—Claims. I. Mongeon, Leonard F.,
  1900–   II. Title.

    HE1795.N3   59–55569

NN 0064423   DLC

National Retail Merchants Association. *Visual Merchandising Group.*
    Display manual, National Retail Dry Goods Association,
  Visual Merchandising Group. Howard P. Abrahams [and
  others, special committee. New York, 1951]
    1 v. (loose-leaf) illus. 29 cm.

    1. Display of merchandise. 2. Show-windows.

    HF5845.N29 1951   659.157   51–14265 rev ‡

        CU
NN 0064424   DLC TxU NN MB TU MnU Or OrP Wa CaBVa

National Retail Merchants Association. *Visual Merchandising Group.*
    Display manual, National Retail Dry Goods Association,
  Visual Merchandising Group. Edward F. Engle, manager
  [and] Irving C. Eldredge, assistant manager. [New rev. ed.
  New York, 1955]
    150 p. illus. 28 cm.

    1. Display of merchandise. 2. Show-windows.

    HF5845.N29 1955   359.157   56–272 rev ‡

        PU-W NN OCl IdU
NN 0064425   DLC CaBVa LU PP OU NcC InU IU NIC

National Retail Pet Supply Association.

SF411
.N37   Pet shop management.

        [Los Angeles, I. W. Hall]

National retail trade council.
    U. S. *National recovery administration.*
    ... Retail code and Retail drug code with explanatory com-
  ments. Prepared by the National recovery administration in
  collaboration with the National retail trade council and the
  National retail drug trade council. Washington, U. S. Govt.
  print. off., 1933.

National retailer-owned grocers, inc.
    The Co-operative merchandiser ...
    [Chicago, National retailer-owned grocers, inc., 19

NATIONAL RETAILER-OWNED WHOLESALE GROCERS.
    The NROWG cooperative; a non-profit retailer-
  owned food and grocery cooperative. Washington,
  [1936?].
    pp.10.

NN 0064429   MH-PA

National Retired Teachers Association.
    Journal
      see   NRTA journal.

National Retired Teachers Association.
    NRTA journal
      see under title

National revenue reform association.
    Administration of customs collection and national banking
  laws. Important letters addressed to President of United
  States; Hon. William A. Richardson, secretary of Treasury,
  and Hon. George H. Williams, attorney-general of the United
  States, under instructions, by John C. Hopper, secretary,
  "National revenue reform association" ... New-York [J. W.
  Amerman, printer] 1873.
    39 p. 23½ᶜᵐ.
    At head of title: Examine!!! All who are interested, and who is not?
    1. Custom[s] administration—U. S. I. Hopper, John C. II. Title.

    Library of Congress   HJ6695.N3   8–32903

NN 0064432   DLC CtY OFH NN

National revenue reform association.
    Annual report of the secretary ...
  New York, 1872.
    v. 19ᶜᵐ.

    Library of Congress   HF1751.N3   CA 6–1038 Unrev'd

NN 0064433   DLC OFH

The National revenue review
    see under Canada. Dept. of National
  Revenue.

National Revere bank, *Boston.*
    History of the Revere bank of Boston, incorporated
  March, 1859; for private circulation. Cambridge, Printed
  at the Riverside press, 1886.
    3 p. l., [5]–32 p. front. (port.) 22½ᶜᵐ.

    I. Title.
                                              15–8771
    Library of Congress   HG2613.B74N3

NN 0064435   DLC ICJ NN

The **National** review. v. 1–
  July 1855–
  London, R. Theobald [etc.] 1855–64.
    v. 22½ᶜᵐ. quarterly.
    R. H. Hutton, Walter Bagehot, editors.

    1. Hutton, Richard Holt, 1826–1897, ed. II. Bagehot, Walter, 1826–
  1877, ed.
                                              CA 9–1646 Unrev'd
    Library of Congress   AP4.N245

NN 0064436   DLC NN N NIC OOxM NjP

FILM   The National review. v. 1–19, July 1855–Nov.
052   1864. London, R. Theobald [etc.]
NATR   19v. 23cm. quarterly.
          Vol. 19 called also n.s. v. 1.
          Supersedes Prospective review.
          Edited by R. R. Hutton and Walter Bagehot.
          Microfilm. Washington, Library of Congress
          Photoduplication Service, 1967. 4 reels.
          35mm.

NN 0064437   IU OCU

VOLUME 407

The **National** review. London, Mar. 1883–May 1950
see The **National** and English review.

DS651
.N28   The National review ...

ᵣManila, The National review co., inc.,
193
v.   illus.   31½ᶜᵐ.   weekly.

Each no. in 2 sections, English and
Spanish.
Editors: Federico
Mañgahas (English section), Francisco
Varona (Spanish section)

NN   0064439   DLC

National review. v. 1–
Nov. 19, 1955–
ᵣOrange, Conn., National Weekly,
v. illus. 29 cm. weekly (irregular)
Editor: 1955–   W. F. Buckley.
Beginning Oct. 4, 1958, alternate issues have title: **National review
bulletin** and Oct. 4, 1958–Apr. 4, 1959 are called v. 1, no. 1–14.

ɪ. Buckley, William Frank, 1925–

AP2.N3545   ᴸ 051   57–3062 rev

          AzTeS NStBU
NN   0064440   DLC NcU ViU ICarbS MoU TxU MiU NcGU

National review. v. 1–
Nov. 19, 1955–
ᵣOrange, Conn., National Weekly,
v. illus. weekly (irregular)

Editor: 1955–   W.F. Buckley.
Beginning Oct. 4, 1958, alternate issues
have title: National review bulletin and
Also   Oct. 4, 1958–Apr. 4, 1959 are called v. 1,
Microfiche no. 1–14.
Serial   --Microfiche.
1–11   fiche.
1₋14   Microfiche by   Microcard Editions,
1955–57   National Cash   Register Co.
Repl. 1/
RMnr ᴵ

NN   0064441   NcU

National review. v. 1–
Nov. 19, 1955–   [Orange, Conn., etc.]
v. illus. weekly.
Microfilm. Ann Arbor, University Microfilms.

NN   0064442   MoU ViU

The **National** review ...
ᵣShanghai,
v. illus., pl., ports. 34ᶜᵐ. weekly.

Title varies: Saturday evening **review**;
Saturday review.

1. China. 2. China—Econ. condit.
                              ᴄᴀ 16—542 Unrev'd
Library of Congress   AP8.N3

NN   0064443   DLC DNW NIC MSaE ICRL

National review (Shanghai)
The International Institute of China, from
"The national review" of China
see under   International **Institute of China**.

The National Review (Shanghai)
The ᵒquintuple loan agreement...

NN   0064445   DNW

385.0951   The national review (Shanghai)
N213r   The railways of China. With map.
1910   Shanghai ᵣ1910?,
23p. col.map(fold.) 21cm.

Cover title.

1. Railroads. China. I. Title.

NN   0064446   KU CtY DNW

          (Shanghai)
NATIONAL REVIEWᴧ The railways of China.
2d ed. Shanghai [1913] 1 p. l., 23 p. Map.
8°.
"1st ed. 1911."

NN   0064447   MSaE

National review. Silver Spring, Md.
see The **Drycleaner**.

The **National** review; a weekly newspaper devoted to all move-
ments for the general uplift of humanity. v. 1–
Feb. 14, 1914–
Washington, D. C. ᵣNational review publishing co., 1914–
v. 1 illus. 39¼ᶜᵐ.
Editor: Feb. 1914–   Euna C. Atwood.

ɪ. Atwood, Mrs. Euna (Olum) 1856–   **ed.**

                              27–25216
Library of Congress   AP⁸ N355

NN   0064449   DLC

The **National** review, incorporating the
English review
see The **National** and English review.

The **National** review annual, 1910.
The provinces of China, together with a history of the
first year of H. I. M. Hsuan Tung, and an account of
the government of China ... With a preface by Colonel
C. D. Bruce ... Shanghai, "The National **review**"
office, 1910.

National review bulletin
see
National review. Orange, Conn.

369.942
N284   National revival; a re-statement of **Tory**
principles, with an introd. by Lord **Willough**
by de Broke. London, H. Jenkins, **1913**.
xxii p., 1 ℓ., 149 p.   19½ cm.

NN   0064453   MiU

The **national** revolution, 20 years of mighty
achievements
see under [Portugal. Secretariado
nacional de informação e cultura popular]

National revolutionary party, *Mexico*
see
Partido nacional revolucionario, *Mexico*.

National reweaving institute, Atlanta.

Hieber, William S.
The art of reweaving ᵣby, William S. Hieber ... Atlanta,
Ga., National reweaving institute, 1942.

National rhymes of the nursery; with
introduction by George Saintsbury & drawings
by Gordon Browne. Lond., ᵣWells, Gardner,
1895.

314 p.

NN   0064457   OCl CaBVaU

National rhymes of the nursery; with introduction by George
Saintsbury and drawings by Gordon Browne.   New York: F. A.
Stokes Company ᵣ190–?,   xxix(i), 334 p., 1 pl.   illus.   8°.

NN   0064458   NN OCl OEac OClh

National rhymes of the nursery; with introduction by George Saintsbury & drawings
by Gordon Browne. Lond., Wells, Gardner,
1902.

NN   0064459   OO OCl

National rhymes of the nursery; with introduction by
George Saintsbury & drawings by Gordon Browne. New
York, F. A. Stokes company ᵣ1902?,
xviii, ᵣ334, p. illus. 21ᶜᵐ.

1. Nursery rhymes. ɪ. Saintsbury, George Edward Bateman, 1845–
1933.
                              A 11–1807
Minneapolis. Public library
for Library of Congress   ᵣa37d1,

NN   0064460   MnM

National rhymes of the nursery. With introduction by **George**
Saintsbury, and drawings by Gordon Browne.
— New York. Frederick A. Stokes Co. [1905.] xxix, 334 pp. **Illus.**
Plates. 21 cm., in 8s.

NN   0064461   MB

National rice and corn corporation (*Philippines*)
... Annual report.
1936–
Manila, Bureau of printing, 1937–
v. fold. tab. 28½ᶜᵐ.
At head of title, 1936–   : The National rice and corn **corporation.
Manila.**
Report for 1936 covers the period from April 7 to Dec. 31, 1936.

1. Rice and rice culture—Philippine islands. 2. Grain trade—**Philip-**
pine islands.   37–27841
Library of Congress   HD9016.P54N3
———— 2d set.   ᵣ3,   **338.1**

NN   0064462   DLC NN CtY ICJ

National rice and corn corporation (*Philippines*)
... Annual report of the manager to the board of **directors** ...
1936–
Manila, Bureau of printing, 1937–
v. plates, ports., tables, diagrs. 23ᶜᵐ.
At head of title, 1936–   : The National rice and corn **corporation,**
Manila.

                              43–48276
Library of Congress   HD9016.P6N3
                              ᵣ2,

NN   0064463   DLC CU CSt

VOLUME 407

SB191
.R5A25
National rice and corn corporation
(Philippines)
The Naric. v. 1–   no. 1–
May/June 1941–
Manila, Philippines ₍1941–

National Rice and Corn Corporation (Philippines)
Publication.
v.

NN 0064465   OrCS

National Rice and Corn Corporation (Philippines)
Report
see its   Annual report.

4HD
1622
National Rice and Corn Corporation (Philippines)
Solving the rice problem, by V. Buencamino. Manila, Bureau of Print.
1937.
18 p.

NN 0064467   DLC-P4 CSt

National Rifle Association (Gt. Brit.)
Bisley Common. Approximate plan of ranges.
London, Waterlow & Sons, 1860.
folded.   24°.

NN 0064468   NN

National rifle association (Gt. Brit)
National rifle association, Bisley Common
1905. Programme. London, Waterlow & sons, ltd.
253p. plates. 15½cm.

NN 0064469   DNW

GV
1163
N3
A3
National Rifle Association (Gt. Brit.)
Official jubilee souvenir, 1860, Wimbledon-Bisley, 1909. Full and interesting history of
50 meetings of the National Rifle Association.
With a foreword by Lord Cheylesmore. London,
Gale & Polden ₍1909₎
104p. illus. 18cm.

1. Shooting – Societies, etc. – Hist.
I. Title

NN 0064470   WU

National rifle association (Gt. Brit.)
Proceedings.   Lond. Murray.

v.   plates, ports. plans, O.

NN 0064471   CaBViP DNW

National Rifle Association (Gt. Brit.)
Rules. [London, Wright & Co., 1860]
10 p. 8°.

NN 0064472   NN

National rifle association of America
The ABC of pistol shooting. Wash., D. C.
₍The Author₎ °1940.
30 p. illus. (Special bulletin no. 101)

"Reprinted from The American rifleman".

NN 0064473   MiD

National rifle association of America.
The ABC of practical pistol instruction for home guards,
industrial guards, auxiliary police, compiled by the National
rifle association of America.   Washington, D. C. ₍1942₎
cover-title, 27 p. incl. illus., diagrs., form. 23ᶜᵐ.
"Guard force regulations," section 81.44 of F. R. doc. 42–4454, laid in.

1. Pistols.

Library of Congress   UD410.N3   42–22261
                                            ₍2₎   623.443

NN 0064474   DLC OLak OC1

National rifle association of America.
The ABC of practical riot gun instruction. Washington,
D. C., The National rifle association, °1942.
71 p. illus. 23ᶜᵐ.
On cover: Compiled by T. Frank Baughman.

1. Rifle practice.   I. Baughman, T. Frank, comp.   II. Title.
III. Title: Riot gun instruction.
                                                43–11778
Library of Congress   UD390.N3
                                            ₍2₎   623.442

NN 0064475   DLC WaS OC1

SK1
.A52
National Rifle Association of America.

American rifleman.

₍Washington, etc., National Rifle Association, etc.₎

National rifle association of America.
Annual report.
New York, The Association,
v. illus., plates. 23–23½ᶜᵐ.
Report for 1909– included in National board for the promotion of
rifle practice. Report of rifle shooting in the United States. 1909.

1. Rifle practice.
                                        CA 5–1660 Unrev'd
Library of Congress   GV1163.N25A2

NN 0064477   DLC Nh OC1 NN DNW NjP

National rifle association of America.
... Basic small arms instruction. Washington, D. C., The
National rifle association, °1942.
63 p. illus. 23ᶜᵐ.
At head of title: The ABC of .22 caliber rifle instruction for civilian
small arms firing schools.

1. Rifle practice.   I. Title.
                                                42–50280
Library of Congress   GV1177.N345
                                            ₀   799.31

NN 0064478   DLC OrP

National rifle association of America.
By-laws and charter. n.p., n.d.

NN 0064479   Nh

National rifle association of America.
General information governing the organization of rifle clubs. National rifle association
of America, New York City. New York, ₍n. p. n. d.₎
cover-title, 22, ₍2₎p. illus. charts. 19cm.

NN 0064480   DNW

National Rifle Association of America.
The guidebook to rifle marksmanship, prepared by the National
rifle association exclusively for O. F. Mossberg and
son ₍!₎ inc., New Haven, Conn. ₍Washington₎ The National
rifle association, °1942.
47 p. illus. 23ᶜᵐ.

1. Rifle practice.   I. Mossberg (O. F.) and sons, inc., New Haven.
II. Title: Rifle marksmanship.
                                                43–9501
Library of Congress   GV1177.N347
                                            ₍3₎   799.31

NN 0064481   DLC CU-B OrP OC1

National Rifle Association of America.
Handloading, an NRA manual
see under   Hatcher, Julian Sommerville.

National rifle association of America.

₍Prescott, Charles Edwin₎
How to become an expert shot. Dedicated to the National
guard of the state of New York. To which have been added
the regulations of the National rifle association and blanks for
recording matches. New York, Mercantile publishing company, 1875.

National Rifle Association of America.
How to shoot a rifle. ₍Washington, 1948₎
62 p. illus. 22 x 28 cm.

1. Rifle practice.
GV1177.N3475   799.31   48–8982*

NN MB
0064484   DLC OrCS Or CaBVa WaT WaS PSt KU MiU

GV1163
.N25AG
[National Rifle Association of America]
The idea book for club secretaries. [Washington, D. C., c1929]
1 p.l., 57 p. illus. 23 cm.

NN 0064485   DLC

National Rifle Association of America
The instructor's manual for junior
rifle clubs. Washington, Author, c1946.
96 p. illus.

Suggested additional reading: p. [97]

NN 0064486   WaT

GV
1167
1913e
National rifle association of America.
International and national shooting
tournament rifle and pistol matches of
l'Union internationale des federations et
Associations nationales de tir (Union of
international rifle associations.) and
the Confederación Pan-americana de tiro
(Pan-American shooting union) at Camp
Perry, Ohio, U.S.A. September 1st to 9th,
inclusive and the National rifle
association and Ohio state rifle
association matches August 15th to 30th
inclusive, 1913...Washington, D.C.
National rifle association of America
(1913?)
119 p. fold.front., illus.   16½ cm.

NN 0064488   DPU

VOLUME 407

National rifle association of America.
Junior instructors' training course. ₍The
Author₎ ᵉ1936.
66 p. illus.

"Suggested books" at end of some of the chapters.

NN 0064489   MiD

National rifle association of America.

₍W   , J   E
Long-range rifle shooting. A complete history of the
international long-range matches. Complete Elcho
shield scores. Rules and regulations of the N. R. A. ...
By the rifle editor of the "Forest and stream" and "Rod
and gun." New York, Forest and stream publishing
company, 1877.

TS535 National rifle association of America.
.S52
Smith, Walter Harold Black, 1901–
... Mannlicher rifles and pistols; original drawings by von
Kromar from the Steyr armory. Famous sporting and mili-
tary weapons. ₍By₎ Walter H. B. Smith ... Harrisburg, Pa.,
Washington, D. C., The Military service publishing company
₍1947₎

TS535 National Rifle Association of America.
.S53   FOR OTHER EDITIONS
1947   SEE MAIN ENTRY
Smith, Walter Harold Black, 1901–
Mauser rifles and pistols. ₍2d rev. print.₎ Harrisburg,
Pa., Military Service Pub. Co., 1947.

TS535 National rifle association of America.
S54
Smith, Walter Harold Black, 1901–
... The N. R. A. book of small arms ₍by₎ Walter H. B.
Smith ... Washington, D. C., The National rifle association
of America; Washington, D. C., Harrisburg, Pa., The Mili-
tary service publishing company ₍1946–

National Rifle Association of America.
NRA high power rifle rules; official rules and regulations
to govern the conduct of all high-powered rifle competition,
effective July 1, 1955. Washington, ᵉ1955.
xiii, 49 p. illus. 23 x 11 cm.

1. Rifle practice.   I. Title.   II. Title: High power rifle rules.

GV1173.N3   799.31   55–39152

NN 0064494   DLC

SK274 National Rifle Association of America.
N27   NRA hunter safety handbook. Washington
₍c1953₎
14 p. illus. 22 cm.
Cover title.

1. Shot-guns. 2. Hunting – U.S.

NN 0064495   DI

National Rifle Association of America.
NRA hunting annual.

₍Washington₎
v. illus. (part col.) 28 cm.
At head of title: North American hunting directory.

1. Hunting—North America—Directories—Periodicals. 2. Hunting—North America—Periodicals.   I. Title. II. Title; North
American hunting directory.

SK12.N35   799.2'097   73–641889
ISSN 0000–5690   MARC-S

NN 0064496   DLC

National Rifle Association of America.
NRA pistol rules; official rules and regulations to govern
the conduct of all pistol and revolver competition, effective
July 1, 1955. Washington, ᵉ1955.
47 p. illus. 23 x 11 cm.

1. Pistol shooting.   I. Title.   II. Title: Pistol rules.

GV1173.N32   799.31   55–39154 ₍

NN 0064497   DLC

National Rifle Association of America.
NRA rifle instructor's manual. Revised 1954.
Wash. D. C., c1952.
102 p. illus.

NN 0064498   Wa

799.3 National Rifle Association of America.
N21n   NRA shooting range plans.   Washington ₍n.d.₎
8 plans. 29cm.

Cover title.

1. Rifle-ranges.

NN 0064499   IU

National Rifle Association of America.
NRA small bore rifle rules; official rules and regulations
to govern the conduct of all smallbore rifle competition, effective July 1, 1955. Washington, ᵉ1955.
52 p. illus. 23 x 11 cm.

1. Rifle practice.   I. Title.   II. Title: Smallbore rifle rules.

GV1173.N33   799.31   55–39153 ₍

NN 0064500   DLC

National rifle association of America.
National rifle association's presentation of facts upon holding the National rifle matches annually. ₍Washington? D. C.,
1928₎
ᵃ cover-title, 36 p. 23ᶜᵐ.

1. Rifle practice.   I. Title: National rifle matches.

                                    CA 28–446 Unrev'd
Library of Congress   GV1163.N25A5 1928

NN 0064501   DLC

National rifle association of America.
Officers, objects, charter, and by-laws of the National rifle association...   New York, E. F. Brainard ₍1871₎   vi, 23 p.   11cm.

1. Rifle clubs—U. S.
N. Y. P. L.   April 21, 1947

NN 0064502   NN

National Rifle Association of America.
Official program... ₍of the National Championship Small Bore Tournament₎
see under   National Championship Small
Bore Tournament.

National rifle association of America.
Official program of the national matches..
and international matches...and the annual matches
of the National rifle asso. of America...
₍Washington₎ 1922–
v. illus. 23cm.
Advertisements interspersed.
Title varies
acc. ᵗᵒ nos.

NN 0064504   DNW

799.3 National rifle association of America.
N21o   Organizing for the greater enjoyment of rifle
and pistol shooting – the typical American sport.
Washington, D.C., National rifle association of
America ₍193-?₎
30p. illus.

On cover: The typical American sport.

NN 0064505   IU

---

f799.3 National Rifle Association of America.
N21out   Outdoor high-power rifle range; 10 target unit.
Washington ₍195-₎
₍4₎ℓ. plans. 42x57cm. (Modern NRA ranges)

Cover title.

1. Rifle-ranges.   I. Title.

NN 0064506   IU

---

f799.3 National Rifle Association of America.
N21ou   Outdoor pistol range designs; 20 target unit.
Washington ₍195-₎
₍8₎ℓ. plans. 42x57cm. (Modern NRA ranges)

Cover title.

1. Pistols.   I. Title.

NN 0064507   IU

National rifle association of America.
Practical home guard organization for reserve militia or
"minute men," compiled by the National rifle association of
America. Washington, D. C. ₍1942₎
cover-title, 15 p. diagr. 23ᶜᵐ.   UA42.N33
—— Practical home guard organization; supplementary bulletin covering application of the "minutemen" plan to large
cities. Washington, D. C., National rifle association of
America ₍1942₎
1 p. l., 8 p. 22½ᶜᵐ.
1. U. S.—Militia.   I. Title: Home guard organization.   42–22499

Library of Congress   UA42.N33 Suppl.
                        ₍2₎   355.36

NN 0064508   DLC MH

National rifle association of America.

Kuch, George J.
Practical organization of industrial plant protection, compiled by George J. Kuch. Washington, D. C., National rifle
association of America ₍1942₎

National Rifle Association of America.
Program of the annual meeting.   [Passaic]
1904–

NN 0064510   NjP

National rifle association of America.
Program of the N R A annual gallery rifle
and pistol promotion of rifle practice, Washington, D. C. ᵂashington , Govt. print. off., 1923₎
cover-title, 29p. illus. 16 cm.
76016·

NN 0064511   DNW

GV1163 National Rifle Association of America.
.N25A25   Program of the NRA ... gallery home range
matches for the rifle and pistol.   Washington,
D. C., The National rifle association of America.
v. illus. 21.5 cm.

NN 0064512   DLC

VOLUME 407

National rifle association of America.
...Programa del concurso panamericano internacional de tiro al blanco con fusil y revolver que se celebrara en los Estados Unidos d e America, bajo los auspicios de la National rifle association of America, del 18 de agosto al 9 de septiembre de mil novecientos trece.
[Washington? 1913]

GV1167
.N3

NN   0064513   DLC

National Rifle Association of America.
Programme of matches at Creedmoor, commencing September 13, 1886. [New York, 1886.]   32 p.   16°.

Title from cover.

1. Shooting, etc.—Associations, U. S.   MILITARY SERVICE INST.
N. Y. P. L.   November 26, 1913.

NN   0064514   NN

National Rifle Association of America.
Reloading information
        see under   The American rifleman.

National rifle association of America.

TS537   Karr, Charles Lee, 1914–
.K3   ... Remington handguns [by] Charles Lee Karr, jr. ... and Caroll Robbins Karr. Harrisburg, Pa., The Military service publishing company, 1947.

National Rifle Association of America.
Report
        see its   Annual report.

National rifle association of America.

National board for the promotion of rifle practice.
Report of rifle shooting in the United States.

[n. p.,

National rifle association of America.
Rifle shooting instruction for boys: the boy problem, ranges, equipment, care and cleaning, instruction, competition, prepared by the National rifle association of America ... Washington, D. C. [*1929]

1 p. l., 43 p. illus. 22½ᶜᵐ.

1. Rifle practice. 2. Rifles. 3. Rifle-ranges.   I. Title.

Library of Congress   GV1177.N35   29–27920

NN   0064519   DLC

National rifle association of America.
Rifle shooting instruction. Junior division.
Wash., D. C. [The Author, *1935]
[49] p. illus.

NN   0064520   MiD

National rifle association of America.
Rifle shooting instruction. Junior division ... **Prepared by** the National rifle association of America. Washington, D. C. [*1940]

67 p. illus., diagrs. 23ᶜᵐ.

Published in 1929 under title: Rifle shooting instruction for boys.

1. Rifle practice. 2. Rifles. 3. Rifle-ranges.   I. Title.

Library of Congress   GV1177.N35 1940   40–11881
——— Copy 2.
Copyright AA 334786   [2]   799.31

NN   0064521   DLC OC1 OEac

National rifle association of America.

Brookhart, Smith W.
Rifle training for war, by Lt. Col. S. W. Brookhart ... Published by the National rifle association of America for the National board for the promotion of rifle practice. 2d ed., rev. and enl. Washington, Govt. print. off., 1919.

GV1163
.N25A26 National rifle association of America.
Spring program of the NRA ... outdoor home range matches for the rifle and pistol. 19
Washington, D. C., The National rifle association of America [19
v. illus. 21cm.

NN   0064523   DLC

National Rifle Association of America.
Uniform hunter casualty report.   1950–
Washington, National Rifle Association.

National rifles, Washington, D.C.
see
District of Columbia infantry. National rifles.

National Right to Work Committee.
Religion, morality and the right to work; a reprint of several penetrating articles, letters and comments on this vital subject. Washington [1955?]
[24] p. illus.

Cover title.

NN   0064526   NNC

AP2
N3555
The National rip-saw.

St. Louis, Mo. [etc.]
nos. in   v. illus. 34½–41ᶜᵐ. monthly.
Caption title.
Editor: Kate R. O'Hare.
Ceased publication with no. 46 (Sept. 1924)?
cf. Union list of serials.

I. O'Hare, Kate Richards, 1877–   ed.

NN   0064527   DLC NN ICJ

The National rip-saw. v. 7–15; Apr. 1910 Sept. 1924. (Incomplete) Saint Louis, Mo. [etc.]

Monthly (slightly irregular.) Title varies: Mar. 1917–Apr. 1918, Social revolution; May, 1918, Social builder; Nov. 1922–Sept. 1924, The American vanguard. Ceased publication with Sept. 1924? Microfilm?

1. Socialism – Periodicals.

NN   0064528   NN

National rivers and harbors congress.
... Bulletin, no.
Washington, D. C.,
v. illus. 23ᶜᵐ.
At head of title: National rivers and harbors congress.
Title varies; 1931–40, National rivers and harbors news.

1. Inland navigation—Congresses. 2. Inland navigation—U. S.

Library of Congress   HE393.A4N33   27–2097

NN   0064529   DLC MB NN DNW WaS C DNAL ICU NN OrP

National Rivers and Harbors Congress.   627.06161 3
190774 [Minor publications.]

NN   0064530   ICJ

National rivers and harbors congress.

National waterways; a magazine of transportation. v. 1, no. 1–6; Nov. 1912–Oct. 1913. Washington, D. C., The National rivers & harbors congress, 1912–13.

National Rivers and Harbors Congress.
Parties and waterways. The history of waterway improvement in conventions of the great parties in the United States from the first convention of 1832 to the conventions of 1908, inclusive. Cincinnati: the Congress, 1908.   10 l.   16°.

1. Waterways, U. S.
N. Y. P. L.   January 18, 1911.

NN   0064532   NN Or

National rivers and harbors congress.
Proceedings of the ... convention, National rivers and harbors congress. [1st]–9th, 11th, 17th–24th; 1901–12, 1914, 1922–28. Washington, D. C. [etc.] 1901–[29]

18 v. illus., ports., diagrs. 22½ x 23½cm.

Title varies: Oct. 1901–Jan. 1906 (1st–2d) Report of the proceedings of the National rivers and harbors congress.
Dec. 1906–Dec. 1928 (3d–24th) Proceedings of the National rivers and harbors congress.
Imprint varies: 1901–06 (1st–2d) Baltimore—1906–11 (3d–8th) Cincinnati.—1912–28 (9th–24th) Washington, D. C.

The conventions were held in Washington, D. C., with the exception of the 1st, which was held in Baltimore in 1901. The 4th convention is misnumbered the 3d, on t.-p. of Proceedings. No Proceedings were issued for the 10th, 12th–16th conventions, 1913, 1915–20 (no conventions were held in 1917, 1918, 1921)
No more published.

1. Inland water transportation—Congresses. 2. Rivers—U. S. 3. Harbors—U. S. 4. U. S.—Public works. 5. Inland water transportation—U. S.
HE393.A4N3   386.0973   10–8074

NN   0064534   DLC OC1WHi Wa KyU DNAL KEmT MsSM NcC
PBL ICJ CU

National rivers and harbors congress.
Proceedings of the special "Council of war" meeting of the National rivers and harbors congress, Washington, D. C., April 26, 1938. [Washington, 1938]

cover-title, 1v, 28 p. 21½ᶜᵐ.

1. Inland navigation—Congresses. 2. Inland navigation—U. S.
                                               40–20669
Library of Congress   HE393.A4N315 1938
                            [2]   386.206373

NN   0064535   DLC MB NN

National rivers and harbors congress.
Resolutions adopted by the annual convention...
[no.]

[Washington, D. C., 19   23 x 10½cm.
nos.

1. Waterways—U. S. 2. Harbors   —U. S.
N. Y. P. L.   February 25, 1941.

NN   0064536   NN

VOLUME 407

National rivers and harbors congress.

Black, William Murray, 1855–
Some observations on water transportation, an address by Brig. Gen. William M. Black ... delivered before the thirteenth annual convention of the National rivers and harbors congress, Washington, D. C., December 7. 1916. ₍Washington? D. C., 1916₎

HE629
.N3
[National Rivers and Harbors Congress]
Waterway wisdom, as enunciated by presidents of the United States, national statesmen, governor of states , foreign diplomats, railroad officials, and men prominent in the commercial and industrial life of the nation. Physical data of rivers and harbors of the United States and of Europe, appropriations, etc., etc. List of waterway associations. [Cincinnati, The Ebbert & Richardson co., printers, 1910 ?]
78 p. 20.5 cm.

NN 0064538 DLC

National rivers and harbors congress.
8th, Washington, D.C., Dec. 6-8, 1911.
Fries, Amos Alfred, 1873–
National rivers and harbors congress. By Capt. Amos A. Fries ...
(*In* Professional memoirs, Corps of engineers, U. S. army, and Engineer department-at-large. Washington, 1912. 23ᶜᵐ. v. 4, p. 112-113)

National Rivers and Harbors Congress. 18th, Washington, D. C., 1922.
The American transportation problem and its solution; a symposium. Railways: C. H. Markham... Waterways: Cleveland A. Newton... Highways: F. W. Fenn... The merchant marine: Winthrop L. Marvin... "Are we merely partisans?" Maj. Gen. William M. Black... before the eighteenth convention of the National Rivers and Harbors Congress, Washington, D. C. December 7, 1922. ₍Washington, 1922?₎ 32 p. 8°.

1. Transportation, U. S.
N. Y. P. L.   March 21, 1924.

NN 0064540 NN MB Or

National Rivers and Harbors Congress.
20th, Washington, D. C., 1924. **Board** of directors.
Publications.

NN 0064541 DN

HE393
.A4N4
National Rivers and Harbors Congress. Indiana Branch.
Proceedings of ... annual convention. Indiana branch of the National rivers and harbors congress. Indianapolis, Ind., 1908–
v. 22.5 cm.
Cover -title.

NN 0064542 DLC

National Rivers and Harbor News
see National Rivers and Harbors Congress. Bulletin.

National road conference, *Asbury Park, N. J.*, 1894.
... Proceedings of the National road conference held at the Westminister church, Asbury Park, N. J., July 5 and 6, 1894 ... Washington, Govt. print. off., 1894.
63 p. illus. 23ᶜᵐ. (U. S. Dept. of agriculture. Office of road inquiry. Bulletin no. 10)

1. Roads—Congresses.
Agr 9–2427 Revised
Library, U. S. Dept. of   Agriculture 1R53B no. 10

NN 0064544 DNAL CU OO MdBP MB

National road conference and exhibition, London, 1915.
...National road conference and exhibition. ₍London₎ 1915.
173 p. illus. 25cm.
At head of title: County councils association.

223489B. 1. Roads—Congresses—councils association.   Gt. Br.—Eng.—London. I. County
N. Y. P. L.
                                    March 18, 1943

NN 0064545 NN

TE5
.M6
National Road Oil and Asphalt Congress.

Montana. *State Highway Commission.*
Proceedings of the Montana national bituminous conference. ₍1st₎-5th; 1935-39. Helena.

National road parliament, *Atlanta, Ga.,* 1895.
... Progress of road construction in the United States Reports by delegates to National road parliament held at Atlanta, Ga., October 17–19, 1895. Washington. Govt. print. off., 1897.
47 p. 23ᶜᵐ. (U. S. Dept. of agriculture. Office of road inquiry. Bulletin no. 19)

1. Roads. 2. Roads—Conventions.
Agr 9–2438
Library, U. S. Dept. of   Agriculture 1R53B no. 19

NN 0064547 DNAL OC1 OO CU NN MB

National Road Stage Company.
"New and extraordinary travelling accommodations ... to Baltimore, Washington City and Philadelphia. The National Road Stage Co. Since the opening of the Baltimore and Ohio Rail Road to Hancock ... For seats apply at our office on Water Street ... Wheeling, Va. August 1st 1842. Wm. K. Newman Agent John M. McCreary, printer -- Wheeling, Va.
Broadside. c. 30" x 24".
B.& O.Museum, Baltimore. WVW (photo). Illus. in Wheeling News-Register, Jun 6 1943. 590

NN 0064548 WvU

National road to California. Public meeting in Victoria, [Dec. 18, 1847 to take into consideration the propriety of urging upon the general and state governments the expediency and necessity of opening a military and wagon road from some point on Matagorda Bay to Chihuahua, Passo del Norte, Santa Fe,etc.] n.p., [1847?]
pp.8.
Without title -page. Caption title. Contains a letter signed:H.G.Catlett on the same subject.

NN 0064549 MH

C978.81
N213so
National Roadmasters' Association of America
Souvenir book and program ₍for the sixteenth annual convention of the National Roadmasters' Association of America (Railway Maintenance of Way Association) Denver, September 13th to 17th, 1898₎ Denver ₍Pub. for the local committee by the Carson-Harper Co.₎ 1898.
47p. illus., tables. 21 x 25cm.
Cover title.

NN 0064550 CoD

SK602
.A8N328
National Roads and Motorists' Association.

Camping and caravanning in N. S. W.
Sydney.

National Roads and Motorists' Association.
Technical guide to motor vehicle maintenance. 2d ed. Sydney, N. R. M. A. Technical Dept. ₍195-₎
96 p. illus. 21 cm.
Cover title.

1. Automobiles—Handbooks, manuals, etc. I. Title.
A 59–941
Detroit. Public Library
for Library of Congress

NN 0064552 MiD

National Roads and Motorists' Association.
Touring grounds around Sydney, ₍8th ed.₎ Sydney, N. R. M. A. Touring Dept. ₍195-?₎
64 p. maps. 14 x 22 cm.
Cover title.

1. New South Wales—Road maps. 2. Sydney—Suburbs and environs—Maps. I. Title.
G2756.P2N3 195–   Map 56–522

NN 0064553 DLC

[National Roadside Council]
Billboards and highway safety. ₍Washington, D. C., Printed for the National council for protection of roadside beauty by the American nature association of Washington, D. C., 1930₎
4 p. illus. 23ᶜᵐ.
Caption title.

1. Posters. 2. Automobiles—Accidents. I. Title.
Library of Congress   HF5843.N3
₍2₎   [388.1] 659.1

NN 0064554 DLC OrU

OrU
713.1
N21bi
National Roadside Council.

Billboards and unemployment. New York. ₍1930₎
₍3₎p. 30cm.
Caption title.

1. Billboards. 2. Bill-posting. 3. Roadside improvement. I. Title.

NN 0064555 OrU

National Roadside Council   FOR OTHER EDITIONS SEE MAIN ENTRY
American civic association.
Highway entrances to Washington—the federal city; a survey. ₍Washington₎ Pub. by the American nature association for the American civic association and the National council for protection of roadside beauty ₍1930₎

National roadside council.

The Roadside bulletin. – v. 5, no. 2; –Jan. 1938. New York, 19 38₎

National Roadside Council.
The roadsides of California: a survey. [Washington, D. C.?] Published by the American Nature Association for the National Council for Protection of Roadside Beauty [1931?]
47 p. illus. 24cm.

1. Roads. 2. Bill-posting. I. American Nature Association. II. Title.

NN 0064558 C CtY CU-B WaS NN MWelC IU OrU MiU

VOLUME 407

TE153
.N362

National roadside council.
The roadsides of North Carolina; a survey. Washington, D. C., Published by the American nature association of Washington, D. C., for the National council for protection of roadside beauty ₁1930₎

2 p. l., 34, ₁2₎ p. illus. 23 cm.

Half-title: The roadsides of North Carolina; report of a study of the problem of roadside improvement along the highways of that state.

1. Roads—North Carolina. 2. Billboards—North Carolina. I. Title.

TE153.N362   388.109756   32–32689 rev

NN   0064559   DLC NcD-L WaPS MiU CtY NN

National roadside council.
The roadsides of Oregon; a survey. Washington, D. C., Published by the American nature association of Washington, D. C., for the National council for protection of roadside beauty ₁1930₎

2 p. l., 34 p., 1 l. illus. 23 cm.

Half-title: The roadsides of Oregon; report of a study of the problem of roadside improvement along the highways of that state.

1. Roads—Oregon. 2. Billboards—Oregon. I. Title.

TE153.N363   388.109795   32–32688 rev

NN   0064560   NcD-L MiU WaPS WaU
                 DLC WaTC CU-B WaS OrU OrPR OrCS WaS

713.1
N21w

National Roadside Council.
Why not tax the rural billboard? New York ₁1930₎
folder (4p.) illus. 25cm.

1. Bill-posting.   2. Signs and sign-boards.   I. Title.

NN   0064561   OrU

National Roadside Council.

HF5843
.5
.A65
1931a

American Nature Association.
The Washington conference with the outdoor advertising industry and why it failed. Statement of American Nature Association and National Council for Protection of Roadside Beauty. To which is now added an analysis and criticism of the "Nelson plan" favored by the billboard interests, and a note of the master's report in the Massachusetts billboard cases. ₁Washington? 1931₎

713.1
N211

National Roadside council.
What you can do to hasten billboard control as an individual, as a community, as a state. The organized protest to the advertisers, the auxiliary survey, Virginia, Pennsylvania, Vermont, New York and Westchester precedents the state law. New York ₁1938₎
7p. 24cm.

1. Bill-posting.   2. Roadside improvement.

NN   0064563   OrU

National roller skating directory
see   National roller skating guide.

National roller skating guide. 1952–
₁New York, National Sports Publications₎

v. illus. 19 cm. annual.

Title varies: 1952–   National roller skating directory.
Editor: 1952–   A. R. Goodfellow.

1. Roller-skating—Yearbooks.   I. Goodfellow, Arthur R., ed.

GV851.N3   796.21   52–35873 rev †

NN   0064565   DLC WM OCl N NN CaBVa Wa WaE

National roofer. v. 1–
1939–
Chicago, etc., Shelter Publications, etc.₎

v. in   illus., ports. 28–31 cm. monthly.

Title varies: 1939–Feb. 1949, United roofer.
Published   1939–Aug. 1951 by the National Roofing Contractors' Association (called   1939–Feb. 1949, United Roofing Contractors' Association)

1. Roofing—Period.   I. National Roofing Contractors' Association.

TH2430.U55   45–49895 rev*

NN   0064566   DLC NN ICJ

NATIONAL roofer & building improvement contractor.
v. 11, no. 3–v. 20; Mar. 1949–1959.   Chicago,
Shelter publications [etc.₎ 11 v. in 7. illus. 29cm.

Lacking: v. 19, no. 6, June, 1958; v. 20, no. 10, Oct. 1960.
Monthly.
Vol. 16 repeated in numbering (1954, 1955; no. 1, 3, Jan., Mar. 1955 called v. 17).

For earlier file, whose numbering it continues, see United roofer.
Organ of the National roofing contractors' association, Mar. 1949–Aug. 1951.
Title varies: Mar. 1949–Nov. 1958, National roofer, siding and insulation contractor.
United with American roofer & siding contractor to form American roofer & building improvement contractor.

I. Roofing—Per. and soc. publ.   I. National roofing contractors'
association.   II. Title: nation-   al roofer, siding and insulation
contractor.   contractor.

NN   0064568   NN

National roofer, siding and insulation contractor
see   National roofer.

TH2445
.M3

National Roofing Contractors' Association.
McCawley, James.
The art of slating, edited by James McCawley.   New York, N. Y., J. McCawley, executive secretary, United roofing contractors association ₁1944?₎

TH2251
.M3

National Roofing Contractors' Association.
McCawley, James.
Asphalt and asbestos-cement shingle residing, a complete guide to the application of asphalt and asbestos-cement shingles to exterior walls, the preparation of sidewalls and the estimating of sidewall areas. By James McCawley ... New York, N. Y., J. McCawley, executive secretary, United roofing contractors association ₁1944?₎

National Roofing Contractors' Association.
Mineral wool insulation, installation manual
see under   McCawley, James, ed.

₁**National roofing contractors' association**₎
National pattern for local apprenticeship standards in the roofing industry.   Washington, D. C., U. S. Dept. of labor, Apprentice training service ₁1946₎

cover-title, 24 p. illus. (incl. forms) 20 cm.

"Formulated and adopted ... by the Executive committees of the United roofing contractors association and the United slate, tile and composition roofers, damp and waterproof workers association."—Foreword.

1. Apprentices—U. S.   2. Roofing.   I. United slate, tile and composition roofers, damp and waterproof workers' association.   II. U. S. Bureau of apprenticeship.   III. Title.

HD4885.U5N36   331.86   L 46–112 rev

U. S. Dept. of Labor,   Library
for Library of Congress   ₁r56g1₎†

NN   0064573   DL OrU Or ICJ MoU NN DLC

National Roofing Contractors' Association.

TH2430
.U55

National roofer. v. 1–
1939–
Chicago, etc., Shelter Publications, etc.₎

National Roofing Contractors' Association
see also
National Joint Apprenticeship and Training Committee for the Roofing Industry.

National Roosevelt association of the sovereign people of the United States.
We the people. v. 1 (no. 1–5/6); Mar.–July/Aug. 1934.
Long Beach, Calif. ₁1934₎

National Roosevelt Library, Chungking, China
see Chungking, China. National Roosevelt Library.

National roque association of America.
Roque guide and official rules governing the game, as adopted by the National roque association of America. Authorized ed., rev. and cor. by the National association up to August, 1902.   New York, American sports publishing company, 1902.

73 p. incl. front., illus. (incl. port., diagr.) 17 cm.   (On cover: Spalding's athletic library, v. 13, no. 148)

I. Title.

GV935.N35   3—11963

NN   0064578   DLC NN

National roque association of America.
Roque guide and official rules governing the game as adopted by the National roque association of America. Only authorized ed., rev. and cor. by the National association up to August, 1904.   New York, American sports publishing company, 1904.

71 p. incl. front., illus., ports., diagrs. 17ᵐᵐ.   (On cover: Spalding's athletic library, vol. xvii, no. 195)   4–13297

NN   0064579   DLC

GV935
N37
1906

National Roque Association of America.
Roque guide and official rules governing the game, as adopted by the National roque association of America.   Only authorized ed., rev. and cor. by the National association up to August, 1906. Charles Jacobus, official editor.   New York, American Sports Pub. Co., c1906.
69 p.   illus.   (Spalding's athletic library. Vol. XXIII, no. 271)

1. Croquet.   I. Jacobus, Charles, ed.

NN   0064580   CU

National roque association of America.
... Roque guide and official rules governing the game, as adopted by the National roque association of America. Only authorized ed., rev. and cor. by the National association up to August, 1910. Charles Jacobus, official editor. Committee on rules; W. H. Wahly, J. H. MacDonald, Charles Jacobus. New York, American sports publishing company, c1910.

68, ₁1₎ p. front, illus. (incl. ports.) 17ᵐᵐ.   (Spalding's athletic library. Group xi, no. 271)

1. Croquet.   I. Jacobus, Charles, ed.

Library of Congress   GV935.N35
                                          10–15811

NN   0064581   DLC

SB411
.N26

National rose society.
... Arrangements for
in which is included list of members, schedules of prizes, by-laws & regulations ...
Croydon [Eng.]
v.   21½ cm.

Cover-title.
At head of title: The National rose society.
1. Roses—Societies.

NN   0064582   DLC DNAL WaS Or

VOLUME 407

National Rose Society.
  Book of arrangements
    see its   Arrangements ...

NATIONAL ROSE SOCIETY.
  Constitution and rules relating thereto of
the National rose society. ₍Croydon, Author,
1947?₎
  8 p.

NN 0064584   Or

National rose society. A descriptive catalogue of exhibition
and garden roses. 4th and revised ed. To which is appended choice selections of varieties for exhibitions, for
standards, for pillars, for arches, for walls, for bedding, and
for pot culture; prepared by a committee of the National
rose society. 4°. pp. 36. pl. 6. Croydon, 1899.

NN 0064585   MBH

National rose society.
  A descriptive catalogue of exhibition and garden roses.
5th and rev. ed. ... To which is appended choice selections of varieties for exhibition, for standards, for pillars, for arches, for walls, for bedding, and for pot culture, prepared by a committee of the National rose society ... Croydon, Printed by J. W. Ward, 1902.
  37 p. 6 pl. 25ᶜᵐ.

  1. Roses—₍Varieties₎

                                          Agr 26-544

  Library, U. S. Dept. of   Agriculture 97N212N

NN 0064586   DNAL

SB608   National rose society.
R8N3   The enemies of the rose, by George Massee and Fred V.
Land-   Theobald. Illustrated by Miss C. M. Beard. Ed. by the Hon.
scape   secretary, under the direction of the publications committee.
Arch.   [Croydon, Eng.] 1908.
Library   85 p. plates₍VIII col.₎

  At head of title: The National rose society's handbook on the
fungus and insect pests of the rose.

  1. Roses - Diseases and pests. I. Massee, George Edward,
1850-1917. II. Theobald, Frederick Vincent, 1868-1930

NN 0064587   CU MH-A

National rose society.
  ... The enemies of the rose. 1910 ed. by George Massee
... and Fred. V. Theobald ... Illustrated by Miss C. M.
Beard. Ed. by the Hon. secretary, under the direction of
the publications committee. ₍Croydon, Eng.₎ 1910.
  100 p. plates (VIII col.) 18½ᶜᵐ
  At head of title: The National rose society's handbook on the fungus
and insect pests of the rose.

  1, 2. Rose—Diseases and pests. ₍1. Rose—Pests₎ ₍2. Rose—Diseases₎
I. Massee, George Edward, 1850-1917. II. Theobald, Frederick Vincent,
1868-

                                          Agr 13-412 Revised

  Library, U. S. Dept. of   Agriculture 464.08N212

                WaU
NN 0064588   DNAL Or OCl NIC OrU CaBViP MBH ICJ

National rose society.
  ... The enemies of the rose. New ed. by George Massee ...
and Fred V. Theobald ... Illustrated by Miss C. M. Beard.
Ed. by the Hon. secretary, under the direction of the publications committee. ₍Croydon, Eng., Printed by J. W. Ward₎
1915.
  110 p. plates (8 col.) 19ᶜᵐ.
  At head of title: The National rose society's handbook on the fungus
and insect pests of the rose.

  ₍1. Roses—Diseases₎ ₍2. Roses—Pests₎ 1, 2. Roses—Diseases and
pests. I. Massee, George Edward, 1850-1917. II. Theobald, Frederick
Vincent, 1868-

                                          Agr 23-557

  U. S. Dept. of agr. Library   464.08N212
    for Library of Congress   ₍a41b1₎

NN 0064589   DNAL CaBVaU CaBVa CtY IaAS CU

National rose society.
  The enemies of the rose; [the National rose
society's handbook on the fungoid and insect pests
of the rose] By George Massee and F. V.
Theobald. New ed. Illustrated by Miss C. M.
Beard. [Croydon, 1919? cop. 1915]
  110 p.   13 plates (8 colored)   nar. sm. 8°.

NN 0064590   MH-A

National rose society.
  ... The enemies of the rose. New ed. by Fred. V. Theobald ... and John Ramsbottom ... With coloured plates
by Miss Frances Bunyard ... Ed. by the hon. secretary,
under the direction of the Publications committee.
₍Croydon, Eng., "Advertiser" printing works₎ 1925.
  165 p. illus., plates (XI col.) 18½ᶜᵐ.
  At head of title: The national rose society's handbook on the insect
and fungus pests of the rose.

  ₍1. Roses—Diseases₎ ₍2. Roses—Pests₎ 1, 2. Roses—Diseases and
pests. I. Theobald, Frederick Vincent, 1868- II. Ramsbottom,
John.

                                          Agr 26-644

  Library, U. S. Dept. of   Agriculture 464.08N212

NN 0064591   DNAL CaBVaU WaS OrP MBH

632.3   National Rose Society.
N21e   The enemies of the rose, by G. Fox Wilson and
1951   John Ramsbottom. Official handbook produced by
         the Publications Committee of the National Rose
         Society of Great Britain; Bertram Park, hon-
         orary editor. Westminster, London, 1951.
           153p. illus., plates(part col.) 19cm.

           1. Roses—Diseases and pests. I. Wilson,
         George Fox. II. Ramsbottom, John, 1885-

NN 0064592   IU

National rose society.
  The National rose society's handbook on pruning roses.
Comp. by a committee of the society. Illustrated by Miss
I. M. Charters. ₍Croydon, Printed by J. W. Ward, 1905₎
  83 p. illus. 19ᶜᵐ.

  1. Pruning. 2. Roses.

                                          6-2980

  Library of Congress   SB411.N27

NN 0064593   DLC

National rose society.
  The National rose society's handbook on pruning roses.
Comp. by a committee of the society. Illustrated by
Miss I. M. Charters. ₍Croydon, Printed by J. W. Ward,
1906₎
  83 p. illus. 19ᶜᵐ.

NN 0064594   ICJ

SB   National Rose Society.
411   Handbook on pruning roses. Compiled by a
N27H   committee of the society. Illustrated by I. M.
1909   Charters. New and rev. ed. Berkhamsted,
         Eng., 1909.
           91 p. illus. 19 cm.

           1. Roses. 2. Pruning. I. Title.

NN 0064595   NIC

National Rose Society

  Handbook on pruning roses. Comp. by a
committee of the society. New & ₍3d ed.₎
rev. ed. Illus. by I.M. Charters and C.M.
Beard. ₍Croyden, Printed by J.W. Ward₎
c1911.
  94 p. illus.

  1.Roses - Pruning. I.Title

NN 0064596   OrP

634.64   National Rose Society.
N21ha   Handbook on pruning roses, compiled by a com-
1912   mittee of the Society. Illustrated by I. M.
         Charters and C. M. Beard. New and rev. ed.
         Berkhamsted, Eng., 1912, c1911.
           94p. illus. 19cm.

           On cover: Third edition.

           1. Roses.

NN 0064597   IU NN MBH OCl WaS

National rose society.
  Handbook on the fungus and insect pests of the
rose
  see its   The enemies of the rose.

National rose society.
  Hints on planting roses. By a committee of the
National rose society. 12°. pp. 15. [Croydon, 1895].

NN 0064599   MBH

SB   National Rose Society.
411   Hints on planting roses. By a committee of
N27   the National Rose Society. The illus. is by
1908   C. M. Beard. 6th and rev. ed. ₍Croydon, Eng.₎
         1908.
           16 p. 18 cm.

           1. Roses. I. Title.

NN 0064600   NIC

National rose society.
  Hints on planting roses. By a committee of the National rose society. With an illustration by Miss C. M.
Beard. ₍Croydon, Eng.₎ 1912.
  20 p. 18ᶜᵐ.

  1. Rose.

                                          Agr 13-413

  Library, U. S. Dept. of   Agriculture 97N212H

NN 0064601   DNAL ICRL MBH ICJ WaS

SB   National Rose Society.
411   Hints on planting roses. By a committee
N27   of the National Rose Society. With all illus.
1914   by C. M. Beard. ₍Croydon, Eng.₎ 1914.
           23 p. 18 cm.

           "1914 edition."

           1. Roses. I. Title.

NN 0064602   NIC

National rose society.
  Hints on planting roses. [Croydon. 1919.] sm.
8°. pp. 23. Plate.

NN 0064603   MH-A

R716.2 NATIONAL Rose Society.
N213H12   Hints on planting roses. Ed. by the Hon.
         secretary. 1922 ed.
           ₍Croydon, Eng.₎ 1922. 23p. illus.

NN 0064604   WaS

VOLUME 407

National rose society.
... Hints on planting roses, ed. by the Hon. secretary. 1928
ed. ₁Croydon, Eng., J. W. Ward₁ 1923.
23 p. pl. 18½ᶜᵐ.

1. Roses.

U. S. Dept. of agr. Library　　97N212H
for Library of Congress　　₍₁41b1₁

Agr 23—1150

NN　0064605　DNAL NN

National rose society.
Official catalogue of roses. [Croydon. 1906.] nar.
sm. 8°. pp. 103.

NN　0064606　MH-A

SB　National Rose Society.
411　　Official catalogue of roses; 1910 ed.
N27 Of Compiled by a committee of the society.
1910　₁Croydon, Eng., Printed by J. W. Ward, 1910₁
c1909.
109 p.　19 cm.

1. Roses.　2. Roses - Varieties.

NN　0064607　NIC

National rose society.
The National rose society's official catalogue of roses.
1912 ed.　Comp. by a committee of the society. ₁Croydon, Eng.₁ 1911.
3 p. l., ₍9₎-119 p.　18½ᶜᵐ.

1. Rose. Varieties.

Agr 13-414

Library. U. S. Dept. of　　Agriculture 97N212N

NN　0064608　DNAL MBH CU Or OrU

National rose society.
The National rose society's official catalogue of roses.
1914 ed.　Comp. by a committee of the society. ₁Croydon,
Printed by J. W. Ward, 1914, pub. 1913₁
132 p.　18½ᶜᵐ.

1. Rose. Varieties.

Agr 13-2198

Library. U. S. Dept. of　　Agriculture 97N212N

NN　0064609　DNAL ICJ Or OCl

National Rose Society.
Report of the council
see its　Arrangements for ...

National rose society.
Report on the constitution of rose soils. By a
committee of the National rose society. 12°. pp. 22₁
[Croydon, 1899].

NN　0064611　MBH

National Rose Society.

SB411
.A1R6

The Rose annual.
₁London₁

National rose society.
Roses; hints on planting and general
cultivation ... ₍Ed. by₁ Bertram Park.
National rose society ₍1953?₁
24 p. illus.

NN　0064613　Or

National rose society.
Select list of roses and instructions for pruning. New
and revised ed. [Croydon. 1917.] sm. 8°. pp. 124.
Plates.
"This handbook is in reality a new edition of the society's Official
catalogue of roses combined with a new edition of the Handbook on
pruning roses." — Preface.

NN　0064614　MH-A NNBG CaBVaU

National rose society.
National rose society's select list of roses, and instructions for pruning.　Comp. by the Publications committee
of the society. ₁Croydon, Eng., J. W. Ward₁ 1921.
121, ₍1₁ p. illus., xiv pl. 19ᶜᵐ.

1. Pruning.　2. Roses-₍Varieties₁

Agr 21-767

Library, U. S. Dept. of　　Agriculture 97N212N

NN　0064615　DNAL WaS CaBVaU NN OCl CtY

National Rose Society.
Select list of roses and instructions for
pruning.　1925.
128 p.

NN　0064616　MBH MH-A CaBVaU

SB 125
N2　National Rose Society.
1935　Select list of roses, and instructions
for pruning.　Compiled by the Publications
Committee of the Society.　Westminster,
Page, 1935.
115 p.　illus.

1. Pruning.　2. Roses.　I. Title.

NN　0064617　CaBVaU

634.6　National rose society.
N21n　The National rose society's select list of
1940　roses, and instructions for pruning.　Compiled
by the Publications committee of the Society.
₍Westminster, 1940?₁
110p.　XXVII pl.

"New and revised edition."

1. Pruning.　2. Roses.

NN　0064618　IU MBH

SB　National Rose Society.
411　The National Rose Society's select list of
.N28 roses, and instructions for pruning.　Comp.by
1949 the Publications committee of the Society.
₁Croydon, The Croydon Advertiser, 1949?₁
96 p.　illus.　19 cm.
"New and revised edition."

1.Pruning.　2.Roses.

NN　0064619　MiU

National rose test garden, *Portland, Oregon*. [Rules and
regulations, etc.] 12°. pp. [10]. Portland, [1917].

NN　0064620　MBH

National rose test garden, *Washington, D. C.* Roses in the
garden, Arlington Farm, Va., May, 1917. N. P. N. D. l. 8°.
21 typewritten sheets.

NN　0064621　MH-A

National Rosenberg-Sobell Committee
see
National Committee to Secure Justice in the Rosenberg
Case.

National roster of realtors.
₁Clear Rapids, Iowa, Stamats Pub. Co.₁
v. illus.　30 cm.　annual.
Directory of National Association of Real Estate Boards.

1. Real estate agents—United States—Directories.　I. National
Association of Real Estate Boards.
HD253.N34　　　333.3'3　　　73-640148
ISSN 0090-1741　　　　　　　　　　MARC-S

NN　0064623　DLC IU

National Roster of Scientific and Specialized Personnel
see　U. S. *National Roster of Scientific and Specialized
Personnel.*

M1664　National Rough and ready club.
W4R6
1848　The Rough and ready minstrel.　A choice collection of songs
for the campaign.　Philadelphia, Pub. for the National
Rough and ready club by King & Baird ₍*1848₁

NATIONAL RUBBER MANUFACTURERS, LTD. Research
dept.
Rubber study series.　no.1-
Calcutta, 1948-　　　　　no.　　　　21cm.

1. Rubber—Per. and soc. publ.

NN　0064626　NN

The National rural
see　The Farmers voice, and national
rural ...

... A national rural banking system.　Outline of a plan
to establish a national rural banking system in the United
States as proposed by the bill S. 2909, a bill to provide for
the establishment, operation, management, and control
of a national rural banking system in the United States,
and for other purposes ...　Washington, Govt. print. off.,
1913.
4 p.　23ᶜᵐ.　(₍U. S.₁ 63d Cong., 1st sess.　Senate.　Doc. 158)
Presented by Mr. Fletcher.　Ordered printed August 9, 1913.
1. Agricultural credit—U. S.

13-35642

Library of Congress　　HG2051.U5N3

NN　0064628　DLC MiU OO

National Rural Electric Cooperative Association.
Bulletin
see　Rural electrification magazine.

VOLUME 407

Pam.
Coll.   **National Rural Electric Cooperative Association.**
           By-laws. Washington [195-?]
           19 p. 18 cm.

           1. National Rural Electric Cooperative
           Association.

NN   0064630   NcD

National Rural Electric Cooperative Associ-
    ation.
    Message to 1,000,000 farmers...Bulletin
    see Rural electrification magazine.

National Rural Electric Cooperative Association.
    NRECA facts. [Washington, 1954]
    28 p. illus. 21 cm.

    1. Rural electrification—U. S.
    HD9688.U52N33   54-40918 ‡

NN   0064632   DLC DNAL

National Rural Electric Cooperative Association.
    Regional meeting reports of the president, general man-
    ager and staff department directors.
    [Washington]
    v. illus. 24 cm.

    1. Rural electrification—U. S.—Societies, etc.
    HD9688.U5N34   56-19648 ‡

NN   0064633   DLC

HD9688   **National Rural Electric Cooperative Association.**
.U5N33
         Rural electrification magazine.

         Washington.

National Rural Electric Cooperative Association.
    Statement of Clyde T. Ellis

    see under

    Ellis, Clyde Taylor, 1908–

National Rural Electric Cooperative Association. *Retirement, Safety and Insurance Dept.*
    Report.
    [Washington]
    v. illus. 28 cm. annual.

    HD9688.U5N32   54-28144 ‡

NN   0064636   DLC

NATIONAL RURAL ELECTRIC PROJECT, College Park, Md.
    Electric hotbeds, cold-frames, propagating
benches and open soil heating. Section 1. Recommended construction and use. College Park, Md.
Author, 1932.
    8 p. (its Report no.5)

NN   0064637   Or

National Rural Electric Project, College Park, Md.
    Mimeo report.
    no. M

College Park, Md., 19   28cm.
    nos.
    Irregular.
    Reproduced from typewritten copy.
    No. M   called no.
    No. 1   title reads: Report.
    Ceased publication with no.E-17 (Aug.,1934).

1. Electricity in agriculture. 2. Elec-   tricity—Domestic uses.
N. Y. P. L.   January 11, 1935

NN   0064638   NN DLC

National rural electric project, *College Park, Md.*
    Report no. 1–8; Oct. 1931–June 1933. College Park, Md.,
    National rural electric project [1931–33]
    8 no. in 1 v. illus., diagrs. 28 x 21½ᶜᵐ. Irregular.
    No more published.

    1. Electricity in agriculture.
                                               41-35100
    Library of Congress   TK4018.N3

NN   0064639   DLC OrCS NN

    National rural family magazine. Detroit; Chicago,
    v.

    "1866-76 published simultaneously in Detroit
and Chicago." Cf. ULS.
    Title varies: Western rural.

NN   0064640   ICHi

    National rural family magazine. [Chicago ed.]
    v.

NN   0064641   IU

    National rural family magazine
        see also The Western rural; a weekly
    for the farm and fireside...

National rural forum, Western *Michigan University* and Kala-
    mazoo college, Kalamazoo, Mich., 1936.
    Education for democracy. [New York, 1936] folder of 6 p.
23½cm.

    Official program of that part of the conference held at Western state teachers
college, from August 11 to 13, under the auspices of the American country life association.

    1. Schools, Country—U. S.   I. American country life association.
N. Y. P. L.   September 22, 1939

NN   0064643   NN

HD6350
.P77N3   The National rural letter carrier

         Washington [C.C. McDevitt, 19
         v.   illus.(incl. ports.) 29½cm.
         weekly.
             Official organ of the National rural letter
         carriers' association.
             Absorbed R.F.D. news, Dec. 17, 1927, and
         assumed its volume numbering, Jan. 7, 1928.
             1. Postal service--U.S.--Period.   I.
         National rural letter carriers' association.

NN   0064644   DLC NN DL WHi ICRL

R331.881   National Rural Letter Carrier.
P77N21g   Golden jubilee, 1896–1946; fiftieth an-
           niversary, rural free delivery, "service
           with a smile." [Washington, D. C., 1946]
           148 p. illus., ports.

           Cover title.
           Issued as a special number of the Nation-
           al rural letter carrier, Oct. 19, 1946.
           Includes Proceedings, Golden jubilee
           convention, National Rural Letter Carriers'
           Association, Aug. 12–16, 1946, Des Moines,
           Iowa.

NN   0064645   MiD MiD-B

National rural letter carriers' association.
    Constitution and by-laws, as approved at Buffalo, New York,
August 16–19, 1955. [Washington, 1955] 46 p. 14cm.

    Cover title.

    1. Trade unions, Postal employees'   —U. S.

NN   0064646   NN

National Rural Letter Carriers' Association.
    Golden jubilee, 1896–1946 ...
        see under   National Rural Letter Carrier.

National rural letter carriers association
    **Official history of the rural free delivery
    service as revealed in the records of the
    National rural letter carriers association.**
    [The Author, n. d.)
    64 p., illus.

    Cover-title.

NN   0064648   MiD

National Rural Letter Carriers Association.

    R. F. D. news; official organ of the National rural letter
carriers' association. v. 1–   Jan. 1903–
Chicago [H. H. Windsor] 1903–

National Sabbath Convention, Saratoga Springs,
    N. Y., 1863–
        Proceedings of the National Sabbath
convention, held at Saratoga Springs, Aug. 11–13,
1863. N. Y., E. O. Jenkins, pr., 1864.
    24 p. 8°. [New York Sabbath committee.
Document 25]

NN   0064650   MB NN Nh

         National Sacramento appeal committee.
HD6515
.A52S67 **Solow, Herbert.**
             ... Union-smashing in Sacramento, the truth about the crimi-
         nal syndicalism trial, by Herbert Solow. With prefatory notes
         by Samuel S. White ... and Travers Clements ... New York
         city, The National Sacramento appeal committee, 1935.

National Saddle-Horse Breeders Association
    see American Saddle-Horse Breeders Association.

National saddlery manufacturers' association.
    Conference ... and the executive committee
of the United brotherhood of leatherworkers
on horse goods ... 1910 ... (n. p., 1910)
    20 p. 25½ cm.

NN   0064653   DL

VOLUME 407

National safe deposit company, *Washington, D. C.*
₍Circular₎ ₍Philadelphia₎ W. Mann, printer, 187–₎
₍8₎ p. 14ᶜᵐ.

ᴄᴀ 8–949 Unrev'd

Library of Congress   HG2613.W34N7

NN   0064654   DLC

National Safe Drivers Association.
Live
see under title

National safety.
₍Johannesburg₎
v. in   illus. 25 cm. monthly.
Issues for   –Aug. 1958 called also no.   –150; Nov.
1954–Apr. 1955, called v. 20, no. 104–v. 25, no. 109.
Official journal of the Safety First Association (called
Safety First Association Incorporated (Industrial)) and,
of the National Safety Council of South Africa.
Title varies: –May 1958, Industrial safety.

1. Industrial safety—Period.   ɪ. Safety First Association.
ɪɪ. National Safety Council of South Africa.

T55.A1N35   57–15273 rev ‡

NN   0064655   DLC

The national safety competitions of 1944-1947 ...
see under   Moyer, Forrest Theodore, 1906–

National Safety Congress.
Safety and its relationship to personality...
see under   National Safety Council.

National Safety Congress.
Transactions
see under   National Safety Council.

614.8   National safety council.
N213ab   The ABC's of community safety. ₍Chicago₎ National safety council, inc. ₍1937?₎
cover-title, 8p.

1. Accidents--Prevention.   I. Title.

NN   0064659   IU

HA217   National safety council.
.A4
Accident facts ...   Chicago, National safety council ₍*19

National safety council.
Accident prevention manual for industrial operations ...
Prepared by the engineering staff of the Industrial division,
National safety council, with assistance from the statistical and
traffic and transportation divisions on problems relating to their
fields ...   Chicago, Ill., Printed by Wm. H. Pool co., 1946.
x, 534 p. illus. (incl. plans) diagrs. 23ᶜᵐ.
"References" at end of each part except one.
1. Accidents—Prevention. 2. Factory management.
TS155.N27   331.823   47–40

PPT OCl OClU TU TxU ViU ICJ PPAtR
NN   0064661   DLC CLU OrCS WaS CaBVaU CaBVa PPF LN NB

National Safety Council.
Accident prevention manual for industrial operations. 2d
ed. ₍Chicago, 1951₎
1 v. illus. 23 cm.

1. Industrial accidents.   ɪ. Title.

T55.N3 1951   331.823   51–6945 ‡

   OrP
NN   0064662   DLC DI MB NN ICJ TxU NNC KU CU ViU OrPS

National Safety Council.
Accident prevention manual for industrial operations. 3d
ed. Chicago, 1955.
1 v. (various pagings) 24 cm.
Includes bibliographies.

1. Industrial safety.   ɪ. Title.

T55.N3 1955   331.823   55–4966

PPPTe DI MiD NNC IU NN MiU OCl TxU KU PPSOPR
NN   0064663   DLC KEmT FU OClU CaBVa Wa OrCS MB OU PP

National safety council.
Accident rates, 1941,
Chicago, National safety council, inc. ₍1942–
no. tables, diagrs. 28 x 21½ cm.
Planographed.
The series contains an annual pamphlet for each of 24 industries
or industry groups.

1. Industrial accidents—Yearbooks. 2. Industrial accidents—U. S.
ɪ. Title.
HD7262.N28   331.823   42—21724

NN   0064664   DLC ICJ NNC

NATIONAL SAFETY COUNCIL.
Accidental injury rates in...₍various industries₎
19

Chicago ₍19   28cm.
v. illus.

Reproduced from typewritten copy.

1. Labor—Accidents—Stat.—U.S. I. Title: Accidental injury
rates.

NN   0064665   NN DL

National Safety Council.
Aircraft sessions
see under   National Aeronautical Safety
Conference. 1st, New York, 1928.

National Safety Council
American recommended practice for compiling
industrial accident causes...
see under   American standards association.

                             331.823
                             T301
National Safety Council.
American recommended practice for window cleaning.
Approved: American Standards Association, October 3, 1933.
Sponsor: National Safety Council. ₍New York, ₎American Stan-
dards Association, 1933₎
16 p. 21ᶜᵐ.

American engineering and industrial standards.

NN   0064668   ICJ

National Safety Council.
American standard method of compiling industrial injury rates. Approved October 11, 1945
see under   American Standards Association

HD7262   National Safety Council.
.A7
1955   American Standards Association.
American standard method of recording and measuring
work injury experience. Sponsors: National Safety Council
₍and₎ Association of Casualty and Surety Companies. Approved December 16, 1954. ₍Rev. ed. New York, 1955₎

TH443   National safety council.
.A5
American standards association. *Sectional committee on
standards for safety in the construction industry, A10.*
... American standard safety code for building construction.
Approved June 7, 1944, American standards association; spon-
sors, American institute of architects ₍and₎ National safety
council. ₍New York, 1944₎

National Safety Council.
American standard safety code for floor
and wall openings, railings, and toe boards
see under   American standards association.

TS1892   National Safety Council.
.A46
American Standards Association. *Sectional Committee B28.*
American standard safety code for mills and calenders in
the rubber industry. Sponsor: National Safety Council.
Approved August 24, 1949, American Standards Associa-
tion, inc. ₍New York, 1949₎

National Safety Council.
... American standard safety code for power
presses and foot and hand presses. Approved
American standards association, October 22,
1937. Sponsor, National Safety Council. American engineering and industrial standards.
62 p.

NN   0064674   NR

National Safety Council.
American standard safety code for power presses and
foot and hand presses; sponsor, National Safety Council.
Approved January 12, 1948, American Standards Associa-
tion. ₍New York₎ American Standards Assn. ₍1948₎
43 p. illus. 28 cm. (American safety standards)
Cover title.
At head of title: ASA B11.1–1948.
Revision prepared by Sectional Committee, B11 of the American
Standards Assn.
Pub. in 1926 under title Safety code for power presses and foot
and hand presses.
1. Machinery—Safety appliances. 2. Accidents—Prevention. ɪ.
American Standards Association. ɪɪ. Title. ɪɪɪ. Series: American
Standards Association.   American safety standards.
TS253.N3 1948   331.823   48–2675*

NN   0064675   DLC MB

National Safety Council.
Analysis of national traffic safety contest
report₎ Cleveland, O., 1947 Chicago, Ill.

NN   0064676   OCl

SD
409   National Safety Council.
.N34   Anhydrous ammonia. Chicago, 1954.
₍12₎ p. illus. (Its Data sheet 251)
"Prepared for the Fertilizer Section of the
National Safety Council by Stewart A. Washburn,
senior engineer, Industrial Department ... Re-
printed from the February 1954 issue of the
National safety news."
Includes bibliography.

1. Ammonia.   I. Washburn, Stewart A.

NN   0064677   MiU

VOLUME 407

National Safety Council.
Annual green book; report on the railroad employees' national safety award class I railroads.
Chicago.
v. illus. 28 cm.

1. Railroads—U. S.—Accidents.

HE1780.A1N3   55–36684 ‡

NN   0064678   DLC MH-BA

R979.785 National safety council
N213   Annual inventory of traffic safety activities
analysis of report for 1954, Spokane, Washington.
[Chicago, Author, 1955?]. illus.

Based upon information submitted by the city
of Spokane, in cooperation with the Spokane area
safety council.

NN   0064679   WaSp

NATIONAL SAFETY COUNCIL.
Annual news letter; all industrial sections. 1936–
[Chicago]   no.   illus.   28-29cm.

Consists of material taken from news letters of the various industrial
sections of the Council.
1938 called Silver jubilee year.

Title varies slightly.
Ceased publication.

1. Accidents--Prevention--Per.   and soc. publ.

NN   0064681   NN CU DNAL

National Safety Council.
Annual report
see its   Report.

National safety council.
Nvb60   ... Annual report of the managing director...
N21b   [Chicago]
23cm.

Caption title.
Reprinted from National safety news.
Each report has an individual title.

NN   0064683   CtY

614.862 National safety council.
N21a   Auto accidents can be reduced   Chicago,
National safety council [1934?]
23, [1]p. illus., diagrs.

"A brief bibliography": p.[24]

1. Automobile drivers. 2. Automobiles--Accidents. I. Title.

NN   0064684   IU

National safety council.
Awaken your workers to the value of safety.
(Chicago, 1929)
cover-title, 8 unnumb. p. 23 cm.
The Safe worker, v. 1, no. 10, February,
1929, in pocket on front cover.

NN   0064685   DL

629.2136 National Safety Council.
N27   Be your own traffic judge. [Chicago,
°1955]
[12] p. illus. 23 cm.

Cover title.
Text on p. [2] of cover.

1. Accidents. Prevention. I. Title.

NN   0064686   N

National Safety Council.
Better street traffic, San Antonio. Consolidated report of the
San Antonio traffic survey, directed by National Safety Council,
1929. Chicago: National Safety Council, 1929.   23 p. incl.
diagrs., tables. illus. (incl. maps.) 4°.

472535A. 1. Streets--Traffic--U. S.   —Tex.--San Antonio.
N. Y. P. L.   April 28, 1930

NN   0064687   NN NNC

National safety council.
Bulletin board series.

NN   0064688   DL

National Safety Council.
Bulletin catalogue of the National Safety Council; for convenience of members in selecting bulletins for specific purposes
in promoting industrial, home, and public safety.   Chicago:
National Safety Council [1919?]. 144 p. illus. 4°.

1. Safety appliances.—Catalogues.
N. Y. P. L.   April 9, 1920.

NN   0064689   NN DL MiU MdBJ IU

National safety council.
Buyer's guide on safety equipment.   1930
edition. Chicago, National safety news (1930)
cover-title, 68 p. 23 cm.

NN   0064690   DL

NATIONAL SAFETY COUNCIL.
Catalog of occupational safety materials.
[Chicago]   v.   illus.   22 x 25cm.

Title varies slightly.

1. Accidents--Prevention--Bibl. 2. Labor--Accidents--Bibl. I. Title.

NN   0064691   NN

National safety council.
... Code for identification of gas-mask canisters. National
safety council, sponsor. American recommended practice,
approved January 7, 1930, American standards association ...
March, 1930. Washington, U. S. Govt. print. off., 1930.
v, 3 p. 23 cm. (Bulletin of the United States Bureau of labor
statistics, no. 512. Safety code series)
At head of title: United States Department of labor. James J.
Davis, secretary. Bureau of labor statistics. Ethelbert Stewart,
commissioner.
Issued also as House doc. no. 277, 71st Cong., 2d sess.
1. Gas masks. I. American standards association. II. Title.
III. Title: Gas-mask canisters.
HD8051.A62 no.   512   614.82   L 30–104
—— Copy 3.   HD7275.N3
U. S. Dept. of Labor.   Library
for Library of Congress   [a53h⅜]†

NN   0064692   DL WaWW MiU OCU OCl OU DLC

WA   NATIONAL Safety Council
250   [Collection of publications]
qN277
The library has a collection of miscellaneous publications of this organization
kept as received. These publications are
not listed nor bound separately.
1. Accidents - Prevention

NN   0064693   DNLM

HD7269 National Safety Council.
F9N3   Communications, electric utilities, gas
utilities accident rates. Chicago.
v. diagrs., tables. 22 cm.
1. Public utilities - Accidents. 2. Industrial
accidents. I. Title.

NN   0064694   DI

D614.8
N2133   [National safety council]
Community safety. [Chicago, National safety
council, inc., c1937]
cover-title, 71 p. illus. (incl. plans, tables,
diagrs., forms) 22½cm.

"This pamphlet supplants 'Safety in the small
community' issued in February, 1936."

1. Accidents - Prevention. I. Title.

NN   0064695   NNC IU IaU NN

614.8   National Safety Council.
qN275c   Community safety organization: principles,
policies, programs. Approved by Conference
of Local Safety Organizations [in October,
1955. [Chicago, 1955]
31 p. illus. 28 cm.

1. Accidents. Prevention. I. Title.

NN   0064696   N NIC

629.2136 National Safety Council.
qN27c   Complete motor transportation accident
prevention service, featuring the nation's
highest award professional safe driving
performance. [Chicago, 1955?]
16 p. illus. (part col.) 30 cm. (Its
Service guide 106.1)
"Enrollment blank including service
charge" inserted.
1. Traffic accidents. 2. Accidents.
Prevention. I. Title. (Series)   ✗

NN   0064697   N

National safety council.
... Constitution.   Pittsburgh, 1913.
12 p.   15½ cm.
——— ——   (Chicago, 1913?)
cover title, 40 p.   26cm.

NN   0064698   DL

NATIONAL SAFETY COUNCIL.
Constitution and by-laws of National Council
for Industrial Safety. Chicago, Barnard &
Miller, [191-]

Pamphlet.
Cover serves as title page.

NN   0064699   MH

National safety council.
Constitution and by-laws, National safety council, inc. [Chicago, 1944]
1 p. l., 13, [1] p. 23ᵐ.

45–1715
Library of Congress °   HV676.A1N22 1944
[2]   614.8

NN   0064700   DLC

614.8   National Safety Council.
N213co   Constitution and by-laws [adopted by the
1947   members of the National Safety Council on
October 5, 1943, with revisions made since
that date. [Chicago, 1947]
12p. 23cm.

Cover title.

NN   0064701   IU NNC

VOLUME 407

HD7260
D9N3   National Safety Council.
Construction accident rates.

Chicago.
v.   diagrs., tables.   22 cm.

1. Building - Accidents. 2. Industrial
accidents. I. Title.

NN   0064702   DI

HD7273
N7c   National Safety Council.
Construction and demolition. A reprint of
part II - Accident prevention manual for industrial operations. 1st ed.   Chicago [c1946].
p. 33-74.   illus., diagrs., tables.
23 cm.
Cover title.

1. Building. 2. Wrecking. I. Title.

NN   0064703   DI

TA192
N3   National Safety Council.
Construction job manual.   [Chicago, n.d.]
1 v. (various pagings).   illus., diagrs.
30 cm.
Cover title.
Loose-leaf.

1. Building. 2. Building - Safety measures.

NN   0064704   DI

HD7262
N26   National Safety Council.
Current safety topics in industrial safety
as presented in the subject sessions of the
1951 National Safety Congress. Sponsored by
the American Society of Safety Engineers.
Chicago, 1951.
106 p.   23 cm.
Forms vol. 15 of the Transactions, 39th
National Safety Congress.

1. Safety - Congresses. I. Nat'l. Safety Congress, 39th, 1951. II. American Society of
Safety Engineers. III. Title.

NN   0064705   DI

614.8
N21d   National Safety Council.
[Data sheets. Chicago, *1944-]
v. (loose-leaf) illus. 28 cm.

Cover title.

1. Accidents--Prevention. 2. Industrial
safety.

NN   0064706   LU

National Safety Council.
Directory [of] occupational safety posters.

[Chicago]
v. illus. (part col.) 30 cm.

1. Industrial accidents. 2. Posters--Catalogs.

HD7262.N283   331.823   49-53284 rev*‡

NN   0064707   DLC IU ICU NN CSf DI NN

National Safety Council.
Directory [of] occupational safety
posters
see also its Directory of safety
posters.

NATIONAL SAFETY COUNCIL.
Directory of safety posters. 1951-

Chicago.   v.   illus.   29cm.

Annual.
Title varies: 1951-61, Directory [of] occupational safety posters.
Cover title: 1951-61, Occupational safety poster; 1962-65, Safety posters.

United with its Catalog of occupational safety materials, to form its Catalog/Poster directory.

1. Labor--Accidents--Prevention--Posters. 2. Accidents--Prevention--Posters. I. Title. II. Title: Directory [of] occupational safety posters. III. Title: Occupational safety posters. IV. Title: Safety posters.

NN   0064710   NN

National Safety Council.
Directory of safety posters
see also its Directory [of] occupational safety posters.

National Safety Council.
District traffic court conferences and continuing
programs
see under American Bar Association.

National safety council.
Electric welding ... Chicago, National
safety council, inc., c1941.

12p. illus. 28½cm. (Its Safe practices
pamphlet. no.105)

"Prepared by J.C. Stennett, safety engineer,
Industrial division ..."--cf. p.12.

NN   0064713   MoU NcD NNC PSt MiEM

D629.2
N213   National safety council.
Enforcement for traffic safety. [Chicago]
National safety council [1938]
cover-title, 47, [1] p. illus., diagrs. 23cm.

"Sources of reference material": p. 46.

1. Traffic regulations. 2. Accidents - Prevention.

NN   0064714   NNC IU

614.862 National safety council.
N21eng   Engineering for traffic safety.   [Chicago]
National safety council, inc. [1937?]
cover-title, 32p. illus., maps, form., diagrs.

1. Traffic regulations. 2. Roads--Safety measures. I. Title.

NN   0064715   IU DNAL

National safety council.
Engineering for traffic safety. [Chicago] National safety
council inc. [1939]

cover-title, 32 p. incl. illus., diagrs., form. 23cm.

"Revised November, 1939."

1. Traffic regulations. 2. Automobiles--Accidents. 3. Accidents--Prevention. I. Title.

Library of Congress   HE369.N34 1939   41-17146

    [2]   388.2

NN   0064716   DLC

National Safety Council.
Evaluating chemical tests for intoxication.
Chicago, Ill., N.S.C., 1953?

16 p.

NN   0064717   OrU-M

614.862 National safety council.
N21e   Examining applicants for drivers' licenses; a
manual for examiners prepared under the supervision of the National safety council Committee on
the driver and approved by the Eastern conference
of motor vehicle commissioners.   Chicago, National safety council, inc. [c1934]
30p. diagrs.

NN   0064718   IU

614.862 National safety council.
N21e   Examining applicants for drivers' licenses; a
1936   manual for examiners.   Chicago, National safety
council, inc. [1936]
31p. illus., diagrs.

1. Automobile drivers. I. Title.

NN   0064719   IU

NATIONAL SAFETY COUNCIL.
Exits, fire alarms and fire drills. Chicago,
cop.1929.

pp.10. Diagrs.and other illustr.
"Safe practices pamphlet, 19."

NN   0064720   MH

National Safety Council.
Eyes saved in industry; the experience of
583 companies
see under National Society for the Prevention of Blindness.

448
N216
1949   National Safety Council.
Face the facts!   [Chicago, 1949]
[4] p.

1. Agriculture. Accidents. 2. Accidents.
Statistics.

NN   0064722   DNAL

448
N216
1951   National Safety Council.
Face the facts!   Chicago, 1951.
[4] p.

1. Agriculture. Accidents. 2. Accidents.
Statistics.

NN   0064723   DNAL

VOLUME 407

449.15
N21Fa
National Safety Council.
Falls in the farm home. Chicago
[1951]
[4] p.

1. Agriculture. Accidents. I. Heldreth,
Harold

NN 0064724 DNAL

TX150
.F2
National Safety Council.

Family safety. v. 1–   Dec. 1942–
[Chicago, National Safety Council]

296.6
N213
1952?
National Safety Council.
Farm fire prevention. Chicago [1952?]
[4] p.

1. Farm fires. Prevention.

NN 0064726 DNAL

449
N21F
National Safety Council.
Farm safety clip sheet ... for National
Farm Safety Week, 1953.   [n.p.] 1953.
sheet.

1. Accidents. Prevention.

NN 0064727 DNAL

449.15
N21F
National Safety Council.
Farm safety exhibits.   [Chicago, 1947?]
folder ([4] p.)

1. Educational exhibits. I. Title.

NN 0064728 DNAL

National Safety Council.
The fight for life
see its Report.

National safety council.
First aid reminders. [Chicago, National safety council, inc.,
©1932]
cover-title, 32 p. illus. 14½ᶜᵐ.

1. First aid in illness and injury.

Library of Congress   RC87.N3
[2]
32–31561

NN 0064730 DLC

296.6
N213F
National Safety Council.
First aids in fire fighting.   [Chicago,
194–?]
folder ([4] p.)

1. Fire extinction.

NN 0064731 DNAL

HD7273
N3
National Safety Council.
Five-minute safety talks for foremen.
Chicago, Ill. [n.d.]
[55] l. illus. 28 cm.

1. Safety appliances. 2. Accidents –
Prevention. I. Title.

NN 0064732 DI

National Safety Council.
Fleet safety manual. [Chicago, 1950–   ©1949–
pts. illus. 28 cm.
CONTENTS.—pt. 1. The fleet safety program.

pt. 4. Accident reports and records; a recommended system of accident reporting, recording, and analysis, including sample forms.

1. Automobile drivers. 2. Traffic accidents. 3. Accidents—Prevention.   I. Title.
TL152.N29   629.28   50–4401 rev

NN 0064733 DLC NNC N NN CSt

National Safety Council.
Fleet safety manual. [1953–
see under National Safety Council.
Motor Transportation Division.

National safety council, inc.
...The following lists contain the names of National safety
council trustees, directors, executive board members and officers
for the year 1944–45... [Chicago, 1944] folder of 3 p.
23cm.
Caption-title.

1. Accidents—Prevention—Assoc.   and org.—U. S.
N. Y. P. L.   April 20, 1949

NN 0064735 NN

National safety council.
... Gas welding and flame cutting. Chicago,
National safety council, inc., c1941.

15p. illus. (incl. form, diagrs.) 28½cm. (Its
Safe practices pamphlet. no. 23)

Caption title.
"This revised pamphlet was prepared by J.C.
Stennett, Industrial division ..."--cf. p.15.

NN 0064736 MoU NcD NNC MiEM PSt

q614.8
N213g
National safety council.
[General safety posters for senior high schools]
Chicago [193–?]
19 posters in envelope.

1. Accidents--Prevention. 2. Poster

NN 0064737 IU

National Safety Council.
The growing strength of the fight for life
see its
Report.

Z7164
.TS1G8
National Safety Council.
Guide to traffic safety literature.

Chicago, National Safety Council.

National Safety Council.
Handbook of accident prevention for business and industry. Chicago, ©1953.
93 p. illus. 23 cm.

1. Industrial safety.   1. Title.
HD7273.N23   331.823   53—26788 ‡

NN 0064740 DLC OrP WaS TxU OU ViU

HV675
.N34
National Safety Council.
Hazard detector; making home safety
work in the homemaking program.   [Chi-
cago, Ill., National Safety Council,
1947]
cover-title, 40p. forms. 28cm.
"Selected references" at end of each
section.

NN 0064741 NNU-W

National Safety Council.
Health practices pamphlet
see under title

449.9
N212H
National Safety Council.
Home safety guide.
Chicago [

NN 0064743 DNAL

National Safety Council.
Home Safety Inventory, 1955
see under title

National safety council, inc.
Home safety memo.
no. 1–

[Chicago] 1937–
nos.

Reproduced from typewritten copy.

1. Accidents—Prevention—Per.   and soc. publ.
N. Y. P. L.

NN 0064745 NN

National Safety Council.
Home safety news letter
see under title

National safety council.

TX150
.H6
Home safety review. v. 1–
Dec. 1942–
Chicago. Ill.. National safety council, inc. [1942–

VOLUME 407

TX321
.T6

National Safety Council.

Tolg, Myrtle Rudd, 1914–
Homemaking can be easy. Illus. by Gretchen Philips. For National Safety Council, Chicago. New York, F. Watts [1949]

RA965
.A63

National Safety Council.

American Hospital Association.
Hospital safety manual for use by hospital administrators and department heads. [Chicago, °1954]

614.862 National safety council.
H21h How long on the highway … Chicago, National safety council, inc. [c1937]
31p. illus., diagr.

"The preparation of this report was under the supervision of J. S. Baker of the staff of the National safety council." –p.31.

1. Automobiles--Accidents. 2. Automobile drivers. I. Baker, J. S. II. Title.

NN 0064750 IU NN OC1 DNAL

National safety council.

How to organize for safety. Bulletin. Chicago, (1915?).
7 p. 23cm.

NN 0064751 DL

National Safety Council
How to start a safety program. [Chicago] 1954.
48 p. illus.

1. Safety education. 2. Accidents--Prevention. I. Title.

NN 0064752 AAP

National safety council
Human engineering and safety...Chicago 1941
30 p.

NN 0064753 OU

HD7262
N23

National Safety Council.
The human side of safety in foremanship. [Chicago, c1940]
7 v. illus. 23 and 28 cm.
Contents:--1. An accident is a symptom.--2.The man who can't get it.--3.The man who can't take it.--4.The man who doesn't fit.--5.The man who day dreams.--6.The man who doesn't care.---Explanation and instructors' guide.
Booklets by J. L. Rosenstein.
1. Industrial accidents. 2. Accidents - Prevention. 3. Foremen. I. Rosenstein, J. L. II. Title.

NN 0064754 DI NNC

National safety council.

TX150
.R8

[Rupp, Francis]
Hurt at home, a survey of the causes and results of home accidents which sent 4,602 persons for treatment to Cook county hospital, Chicago. Chicago, National safety council [1936]

HV675
.N2995

National Safety Council.
Ideas in action: promoting off-the-job safety. [Chicago, n.d.]
30 p. illus. 22 cm.

Cover title.

NN 0064756 AAP

289.6
N21Im

National safety council.
Improving street traffic, Vancouver, B.C. Report of the Vancouver traffic survey directed for the city of Vancouver, B.C. by National safety council, 1936–1938. Chicago, Ill., National safety council,inc. c1938>
57 p. maps. 28cm.

NN 0064757 DNAL

National Safety Council.
Industrial accident statistics.
192

Chicago, cop. 192   4°, f°.
nos. charts.

Annual.
1929– cover the years 1928–
Title varies: 1926, Annual industrial accident experience of members; 1927, Industrial accident experience of members; 1929– Industrial accident statistics.

1. Labor—Accidents—U. S. I. Title.
N. Y. P. L. March 16, 1932

NN 0064758 NN OC1

National safety council.
Industrial data sheets... Chic. [The Author] °1939–°1942.
3 v.

v.1 is rev. ed. 1942.
Also 3 v. in 1.

NN 0064759 MiD DNAL

National safety council
Industrial housekeeping.. Chicago, Ill. National safety council, inc. c1941
8 p.

NN 0064760 OC1

National safety council.
Industrial safety and health, a bibliography. 1945 ed. Compiled by the National safety council. Chicago, Ill. [1945]
1 p. l., 54 p. 22½ᶜᵐ.
Reproduced from type-written copy.

1. Accidents—Prevention—Bibl. 2. Labor and laboring classes—Bibl. I. Title.
45–6618
Library of Congress Z7164.A17N27
[5] 016.331823

NN 0064761 DLC CtY ICU

Z7164
.A17N27
1947

National Safety Council.
Industrial safety and health, a bibliography. 1947 ed. Compiled by the National safety council. Chicago, Ill. [1947]
69 p. 23 cm. (Cover-title)

Reproduced from type-written copy.

1. Accidents--Prevention--Bibl. 2. Labor and laboring classes--Bibl. I. Title.

NN 0064762 TU DNAL PPT

614.8
N2141
Engin
Lib'y

NATIONAL SAFETY COUNCIL.
Industrial safety guide. [Chicago, c1946]
48p. illus. 23½cm.

Cover title.

1. Industrial accidents. 2. Accidents - Prevention. I. Title.

NN 0064763 TxU NNC NNU-W

[National safety council]
Industrial safety manual. [Chicago, 1944]
cover-title, 40 p. illus., diagrs. 23ᶜᵐ.

1. Labor and laboring classes—Accidents. 2. Accidents—Prevention.
3. Safety appliances. I. Title.
44–3571
Library of Congress HD7262.N285
[3] 331.823

NN 0064764 DLC

National Safety Council.
Industrial safety series pamphlet. no. F-3, 1941. Chicago, c1930, 1941.
1v. illus.

NN 0064765 ICRL

National Safety Council.
Industrial safety services. Chicago [194-]
cover-title, 24 p. illus. 24 cm.

1. Industrial accidents. I. Title.
HD7262.5.U6N3 331.823 47–41975*

NN 0064766 DLC

National safety council.
Industrial safety tomorrow; a program for industrial safety, sponsored by 38 national organizations. [Chicago, 1945] 15 p. illus. 28cm.

Cover title.

1. Labor—Accidents—Prevention t. 1945.

NN 0064767 NN

National safety council.

The Industrial supervisor; published by National safety council, inc. v. 1–
May 15, 1935–
[Chicago, 1935–

National Safety Council.
Industrial waste disposal and Bibliography on chemical wastes. Chicago, °1948.
12 p. 28 cm. (Its Industrial safety series, no. chem. 7)

1. Refuse and refuse disposal—Bibl. 2. Industrial safety—Bibl. I. Title: Industrial waste disposal. (Series: National Safety Council. Industrial safety series: Chemistry; no. 7)
TP149.N35 no. 7 016.6285 52–25266 ‡

NN 0064769 DLC

VOLUME 407

National safety council.
Industry's part in saving 38,000 lives. ₍Chicago: National safety council inc., 1935₎ 8 p. col'd illus. 23cm.
Cover-title.

1. Automobiles—Accidents— Prevention. I. Title.
N. Y. P. L. January 28, 1938

NN 0064770 NN MiU

288
N215 **National Safety Council.**
The inside story about safe farm driveways.
Chicago, 1951.
[4] p.

1. Driveways. I. Porter, Harry. II. Keldreth, Harold.

NN 0064771 DNAL

National safety council.
An introduction to safety education; a manual for the teacher, with an introductory chapter by Harold Rugg; prepared by the Education section of the National safety council. Chicago, Ill., National safety council ₍1924₎
99 p. 23ᵐ.
"Reference books": p. 99.

1. Accidents—Prevention. ɪ. Rugg, Harold Ordway, 1886–
ɪɪ Title.

Library of Congress HV676.A2N3 24—32117

NN 0064772 ₍DLC DHEW OCU OO OLak OU ICJ NN

National safety council
An introduction to safety education;
a manual for the teacher, with an introductory chapter by Harold Rugg;...3rd ed.
Chicago, 1925.

99 p.

NN 0064773 OC1 OC1h

449.15
N21K ₍National safety council₎
Keep fit for the farm front fight. ₍n.p., 194–₎
folder.

1. Agriculture. Accidents. 2. Accidents. Prevention. 3. Victory farm volunteers. I. Title.

NN 0064774 DNAL

614.862 ₍National safety council₎
N211 ₍Lest we forget … ₍Chicago, National safety council, c1936₎
cover-title, ₍26₎p. illus.

1. Automobiles--Accidents. 2. Automobile drivers. I. Title.

NN 0064775 IU

National Safety Council.
A list of employee magazines; compiled by the National Safety Council... Chicago, 1930. 15 p. 8°.
Caption-title.

1. House organs—Bibl.
N. Y. P. L. May 11, 1931

NN 0064776 NN

449.15
N21M National Safety Council.
Make your farm safe! ₍Chicago 1947?₎
folder (6 p.)

1. Agriculture. Accidents. 2. Accidents. Prevention. I. Title.

NN 0064777 DNAL

449.15
N21M National Safety Council.
1950? Make your farm safe! [Chicago, 1950?]
folder (5 p.)

1. Agriculture. Accidents. 2. Accidents. Prevention. I. Title.

NN 0064778 DNAL

HV676 National Safety Council.
.A2Y3
Yahraes, Herbert.
Make your town safe! ₍New York, Public Affairs Committee, 1947₎

National safety council.
...Manpower conservation through safety. ₍Chicago, National safety council, 1943?₎ 29 p. 23cm.
At head of title: A coordinated program for state officials.

1. Labor—Accidents—Prevention —U.S.
N. Y. P. L. November 16, 1944

NN 0064780 NN

HE National Safety Council.
5614 Manual on state traffic accident records.
.N297 ₍Chicago, 1950-
1 v.(loose-leaf) illus.,forms. 29 cm.
Caption title.

1.Traffic accidents--Forms,blanks,etc.

NN 0064781 MiU

National Safety Council.
Marine safety.
Mimeographed.

NN 0064782 DI

449
N21M National safety council.
Materials for the safety speech... Chicago, National safety council,inc.,1939.
64 p. 22½cm.

NN 0064783 DNAL DLC

National Safety Council. L331.06161 166
[Minor publications.]

NN 0064784 ICJ

HE5614.2
N27 **National Safety Council.**
Motor transportation fleets accident rates and final bulletin National fleet safety contest with award winners.
Chicago.
v. tables. 20 cm.

1. Traffic accidents – U.S. 2. Accidents. 3. Transportation, Automotive. I. Title. II. Title: National fleet safety contest.

NN 0064785 DI

National Safety Council.
A national directory of safety films.
Chicago.
v. illus. 26 cm.

1. Accidents — Prevention. 2. Industrial accidents. 3. Moving-pictures—Catalogs.

HV675.N295 371.335230838 48–35094*‡

NN 0064786 DLC NBuG WaBeW IU ICU ICJ TxU DNAL

449.15
N21Na National Safety Council.
National Farm Safety Week. ₍n.p., 1948?₎
₍2₎ p.

1. National Farm Safety Week. 2. Agriculture. Accidents. 3. Accidents. Prevention.

NN 0064787 DNAL

449.15
N21N National Safety Council.
National farm safety week, July 21-27, 1946, by proclamation of the President, Harry S. Truman Materials for United States Department of agriculture & agricultural college services. [Chicago, Ill., 1946]
14 pieces.
Consists of leaflets, posters, streamers, etc., prepared to facilitate the educational program on farm and farm home accident prevention.

NN 0064788 DNAL

449.15
N21N National safety council.
1947 National farm safety week, July 20-26, 1947, by proclamation of the President, Harry S. Truman; materials for United States Department of agriculture & agricultural college services.
Chicago ₍1947₎
11 pieces in envelope.

NN 0064789 DNAL

449.15
N21N National Safety Council.
1949 National farm safety week, July 24-30, 1949, by proclamation of the President, Harry S. Truman Chicago, 1949.
27 pieces in envelope.
1. National Farm Safety Week. 2. Agriculture. Accidents. 3. Accidents. Prevention. I. National Safety Council. The farm safety kit. II. Advertising Council.

NN 0064790 DNAL

R614.8 National Safety Council
N23n National Safety Council organization.
₍Chicago, 1955₎
79 p. illus.

Cover title

NN 0064791 MiD

National Safety Council.
National safety congress transactions
see its Transactions.

VOLUME 407

National Safety Council.
National safety news
see under title

HE
5634
C6N3
National Safety Council.
National traffic safety contest, analysis
of report, Boulder, Colorado, based on performance standards of leading cities reporting in the contest.   Chicago [1948?]
[46] p.   28cm.

1. Traffic accidents.   2. Accidents -
Prevention.   3. Traffic regulations -
Boulder, Colorado.   4. Traffic safety -
Boulder, Colorado.   I. Title.   II. Title:
Traffic safety   contest.

NN   0064794   CoU

National safety council.
The new war on accidents. [Chicago] National safety council [1936?]
cover-title, 16 p. illus. 22½ᶜᵐ.

1. Automobiles—Accidents. 2. Accidents—Prevention. ɪ. Title.

Library of Congress   HE5614.N365   38-8605

[3]   629.2136

NN   0064795   DLC Or OU IU MiU NN IaU

331.823 National Safety Council.
qN27o   Occupational safety devices. [Chicago]
1952.
N-38 p. illus. 28 cm. (Its Service
guide 2.1)

1. Accidents. Prevention. I. Title.

NN   0064796   N

M   National Safety Council.
016.6148 Occupational safety services. [Chicago]
qN277   1953.
N-51 p. illus. 28 cm. (Its Service
guide 2.1)

1. Accidents. Prevention. Bibl. I. Title.

NN   0064797   N

National safety council
The organization and operation of safety
conferences. Chicago, Ill. 194-

16, [105 p.

NN   0064798   OC1

449.15
N21   National safety council.
Organizing for farm safety; a co-operative
national program for the prevention of acci-
dents among farm people of the United
States. [Chicago, 1940]
13 p.   27 1/2cm.
Processed.
"Bibliography of farm safety": p.12-13.

1. Agriculture. Accidents. 2. Accidents.
Prevention. I. Title: Farm safety.

NN   0064799   DNAL

National safety council.
The place of the national council for
industrial safety in accident prevention work.
Chicago,   (1913?)
15 p.   18cm.

NN   0064800   DL

National Safety Council.
TP986
.5   American Society of Safety Engineers.
.E9A5   Plastic eye protectors; final report on the A. S. S. E. research
project. Chicago, American Society of Safety Engineers, Engineering Section, National Safety Council [1947]

National Safety Council.   *Cab.37.21.2
[Posters, bulletins, etc., dealing with the prevention of accidents
and the preservation of health.]
= [Chicago. 192-?]   broadsides. In portfolio.

N5770 — Safety. — Public health.

NN   0064802   MB

q614.8 National safety council.
N213po [Posters for vocational schools]   Chicago
[193-?]
15 posters in envelope.

1. Accidents--Prevention. 2. Posters.

NN   0064803   IU

National Safety Council.
Posters; 1930 safety posters.   Chicago: National Safety
Council[, 1930].   87 p.   illus.   f°.

Cover-title.

1. Accidents—Prevention—Posters.
N. Y. P. L.   April 17, 1931

NN   0064804   NN

National safety council.
...Power press safety code.   (Chicago)
1922?
18 numb. l. 28 cm.
At head of title: National safety council.
May 15, 1922.

NN   0064805   DL

National safety council.
The principles and practice of safety; a handbook for
technical schools and universities. Chicago, National safety
council, 1919.

72 p. illus. 23 cm.

Contains bibliographies.
Errata slip mounted on p. 2 of cover.
"The safety engineer, by L. A. De Blois": p. 66-70.

1. Industrial safety.   ɪ. De Blois, Lewis Amory, 1878-
ɪɪ. Title.

HD7262.N3   20—2766

NN   0064806   DLC WaS NN OC1W ICJ

National safety council.
Proceedings fall conference, community
safety councils, National safety council,
Stevens Hotel, Chicago, September 23, 24 and
25, 1927.   (Chicago? 1927)
13, (4) 2 numb. l. incl. tables. 28cm.

NN   0064807   DL

National Safety Council.
Proceedings of the annual safety congress
see its Transactions.

National Safety Council.
Proceedings of the first Co-operative
safety congress
see its Transactions.

National Safety Council.
Proceedings of the second safety congress
see its Transactions.

National Safety Council.
Product safety up to date.

[Chicago]
v. illus. 28 cm.

1. Product safety—Periodicals.   I. Title.

TS175.N37a   658.5'6   73-645874
ISSN 0091-8954   MARC-S

NN   0064811   DLC

National safety council.
Program for 18, 20th annual safety
congress....1929, 1931   Chicago, 1929-31

2 v.

NN   0064812   OCU

National safety council
Program, twenty-third annual safety
congress and exposition; hotels Cleveland
Carter, and Statler, Cleveland, Oct, 1 to
5, 1943.

NN   0064813   OC1BE

308
Z
Box 668 [National safety council]
Progress against the 5th cause of death; a
report to the nation on a movement in the national interest. [Chicago, 1944]
cover-title, [16] p. 30½ᶜᵐ.

1. Accidents - Prevention.

NN   0064814   NNC

S
629.213 National safety council.
qN277   Promoting traffic safety. [Published jointly by the National safety council ... and the
Advertising council ... in cooperation with
National committee for traffic safety. Rev.
Nov.1947] [Chic.,1947]
cover-title,51p. illus. 28cm.

1.Automobiles. Accidents. 2.Accidents.
Prevention. I.Advertising council,inc.
II.National committee for traffic safety.

NN   0064815   N

National safety council.
Proposed changes in the constitution of the National safety
council; a statement to the members of the National safety council
by the Committee on constitution and by-laws revision. [Chi-
cago, 1944] 8 p. 23cm.

Caption-title.

1. Accidents—Prevention—Assoc.   and org.—U. S.
N. Y. P. L.   March 31, 1949

NN   0064816   NN

VOLUME 407

HD7262
N25
National Safety Council.
   Psychology of safety in supervision.
[Chicago, 1950]
   7 v. illus. 23 and 28 cm.
   Contents.—1. You can't change human
nature.—2. What is your U. Q.?—3. Teaching
safety on the job.—4.People act alike.—5.
Safety takes teamwork.—6. You are human, too.
—Leader's manual.
   Booklets by J. L. Rosenstein.
   1. Industrial accidents. 2. Accidents -
Prevention. 3. Supervisors. I. Rosenstein,
J. L. II. Title.

NN   0064817   DI NNC

National Safety Council.
   Public accidents in the United States.   Chicago: National
Safety Council, 1924.   36 p. incl. tables.   8°.

1. Automobiles—Accidents.
N. Y. P. L.   March 11. 1926

NN   0064818   NN

HV675
.A1P85
National safety council.

   Public safety; published monthly by the National safety council, inc., in the interest of accident prevention on the streets
and highways and in other places and at home. v. 1–
February 1927–
Chicago, 1927–

National Safety Council.
192
   ...Public safety memo.

[New York, 192
   v.

   Irregular.
   Reproduced from typewritten copy.
   Various nos. are rev. ed.

1. Accidents—Prevention—Per. and   soc. publ. I. Title.
N. Y. P. L.   July 15, 1935

NN   0064820   NN NNC CU

National safety council.
   [Publications] Chicago [The Author]

NN   0064821   MiD

HE
372
.R3
N28
National safety council.
   Reorganizing Reading's traffic; a report to the Reading city officials based
on a traffic survey financed by the Reading automobile club and directed by the
National safety council,1928. Chicago,
National safety council [1928?]
   40 p. illus. 29½cm.
   1. Communication and traffic—Pennsylvania—Reading. 2.Traffic regulations—
Reading,Pa. I.   Reading automobile
club.

NN   0064822   MiU NNC

National Safety Council.
   Reorganizing street traffic, Richmond, Virginia.
Report of the Richmond traffic survey ...
      see under   National Safety Council.
Traffic Engineering Bureau.

National Safety Council.
   Report.
   [Chicago]

   v. illus. 28 cm.

   Issue for 1954 has also a distinctive title: The growing strength of
the fight for life; a report on the 41st year of the National Safety
Council.

HV676.A1N217   57-25370 ‡

NN   0064824   DLC DL NN CLSU

National Safety Council
   Report
      see also
   Traffic safety.

614.8
N213r
National safety council.
   A report to the members of the National safety
council, 1944-1945.   Chicago, National safety
council, inc., 1945?
   24p. illus.(ports.)

   1. National safety council.

NN   0064826   IU

National safety council.
   The Rochester public safety campaign, promoted and
managed by the National safety council, its Rochester
local council and the Rochester Chamber of commerce; a
report of organized public safety activities in the city of
Rochester, N. Y., March 1 to September 1, 1918. Julien
H. Harvey, director of the campaign. [Rochester? 1918]
   149 p. illus. 23ᶜᵐ.
   Running title: Seventh annual congress.

   1. Accidents—Prevention.   I. Harvey, Julien H. II. Rochester, N. Y.
Chamber of commerce. III. Title.

   Library of Congress   HV676.N3   19–8665

NN   0064827   DLC Or ICJ

614.8
N2133s
National safety council.
   Safe at home.   [Chicago, National safety coun-
cil incorporated, c1938]
   cover-title, 24p. illus.
      Home safety committee.

   1. Accidents—Prevention. I. Title.

NN   0064828   IU

[National safety council]
   Safe at home. [Chicago, °1943]
   23, [1] p. illus. 19ᶜᵐ.

   1. Accidents—Prevention. I. Title.

   Library of Congress °   TX150.N35   45–387
                              [3]   614.8

NN   0064829   DLC

National Safety Council.
TL152
.S27
   The safe driver.

   [Chicago, National Safety Council]

National Safety Council.
   Safe practices
      see its   Safe practices pamphlets.

National Safety Council.
   Safe practices... Metals section.
      v.

NN   0064832   DLC

National safety council.
   Safe practices... paper and pulp section. no. 1–
Chicago, [19

HD7273
.N257

NN   0064833   DLC

HD7273
N32
National Safety Council, Inc.
   Safe practices and health practices
pamphlets. Chicago, c1929–
   nos. in 2 v. illus. 29 cm.
   Safe practices pamphlets no. 1–107.–
   Health practices pamphlets no. 1–20.–
   Industrial safety series, various numberings.

   1. Accidents - Prevention. I. Title.

NN   0064834   DI

331.82
N2781
National safety council.
   Safe practices handbook for safety engineering
war training classes... Chicago, Ill.[1942]
   1 v. illus. 29ᶜᵐ.
   "Contains 15 industrial safety studies" which
are Safe practice pamphlets no.14,16,20,24,31,
41-42,65,67,70,74,75,77,93 and 103.

   1.Accidents - Prevention. 2.Safety appliances.
3.Labor and laboring classes - Accidents.

NN   0064835   CSt

National Safety Council.
   Safe practices pamphlet.
Chicago, National Safety Council.
   v.
   Began publication in 1916. Cf. ULS.
   Title varies: Safe practices.

         OrCS MH-BA OU KyU
NN   0064836   DLC MiD ICRL ICJ NcD DL NN CU Or WaS

HE1779
.S3
National Safety Council.

   Safe railroader. v. 1–
   June 1948–
   [Chicago, National Safety Council]

National Safety Council.
HD7262
.S25
   The safe worker.

   [Chicago, National Safety Council]

National Safety Council.
   Safer cities. Traffic safety activities of the
leading American communities in the National
traffic safety contest.   Chicago, National safety
council, 1932.
   39 p. illus. Q.
   1. Traffic regulations. U.S. I..Title.

NN   0064839   NcD

VOLUME 407

658.382 National Safety Council.
N277s
    Safety and its relationship to personality as presented in the early morning sessions of the 40th National Safety Congress. Chicago, National Safety Council [1952]
    23 p. 23 cm. (Its Transactions. v.24)

    Contents.—Safety and its relationship to personality.—Causes of effectiveness and ineffectiveness in speaking.—How to tell your men what you know.—Painting haystacks.

    NN 0064840   DAS

National safety council.
    The safety aspects of jig and fixture design

    see under

    Jenkins, William Loyd.

National safety council.

American drop forging institute.
    ... Safety code for forging and hot metal stamping. American drop forging institute and National safety council, sponsors. Tentative American standard approved April 8, 1927, American engineering standards committee. August, 1927. Washington, U. S. Govt. print. off., 1927.

National safety council.
    ... Safety code for paper and pulp mills, National safety council, sponsor. Tentative American standard, approved December 8, 1925, American engineering standards committee. April, 1926. Washington, Govt. print. off., 1926.

    v, 37, viii p. illus. 23ᶜᵐ. (U. S. Bureau of labor statistics. Bulletin, no. 410. Safety code series)

    At head of title: U. S. Department of labor. James J. Davis, secretary. Bureau of labor statistics. Ethelbert Stewart, commissioner.
    "The initial code was prepared by J. M. Sandel."—Introd.

    Robert M. Altman, chairman of sectional committee.
    Issued also as House doc. 132, 69th Cong., 1st sess.
    "Series of bulletins published by the Bureau of labor statistics": p. i–viii.

    1. Accidents—Prevention. 2. Paper making and trade—U. S. 3. Safety appliances.   I. Sandel, John Murdoch, 1891–   II. American standards association. III. Title.

                         L 26–153

    U. S. Dept. of labor. Library   HD8051.A5 no. 410
    for Library of Congress   HD8051.A62 no. 410

    NN 0064844   DL OrP WaWW DLC DNW

National safety council.
    ...Safety code for power presses and foot and hand presses. Approved as tentative American engineering standards committee.. Sponsor, National Safety council...(Chicago? 1922)
    cover-title, 50, (1) p. illus. 23 cm. (American engineering standards)

    NN 0064845   DL

National safety council.
    ... Safety code for power presses and foot and hand presses. National safety council, sponsor. American standard, approved November 11, 1926, American engineering standards committee ... December, 1926. Washington, Govt. print. off., 1926.

    iv, 64 p. illus. 23ᶜᵐ. (Bulletin of the United States Bureau of labor statistics, no. 430. Safety code series)
    At head of title: U. S. Department of labor. James J. Davis, secretary. Bureau of labor statistics. Ethelbert Stewart, commissioner.
    Issued also as House doc. 523, 69th Cong., 2d sess.
    1. Machinery—Safety appliances. 2. Accidents, (Industrial)—Prevention. I. American standards association. II. Title. III. Title: Power presses, Safety code for.
    U. S. Dept. of labor. Libr.   HD8051.A5 no. 430   L 27–26
    ————— Copy 2.   HD7273.U6 (no. 12)
    for Library of Congress   HD8051.A62 no. 430
    ————— Copy 2.   T5253.N3
                    (a581)   (331.06173)

    NN 0064846   DL MB DLC ICJ

National safety council.
    Safety code for the use and care of abrasive wheels... (n. p., 1915?)
    13 p. 23cm.

    NN 0064847   DL

Egleston
D614.8
N2139c   National Safety Council.
    Safety devices and ideas. Chicago (c1954-55)
    2 pts. illus.

    1. Accidents - Prevention. I. Title.

    NN 0064848   NNC DNAL OU

614.8   National Safety Council.
N21sae   Safety education data sheets. no.1–
    1945–
    (Chicago)
    v. illus. 26cm.

    "All safety education data sheets appear first in Safety education magazine."
    "Each data sheet deals with a specific subject and provides the teacher with sufficient data for the teaching of a lesson on that subject."

    NN 0064849   IU NcRS DLC

614.8   National safety council.
N2123saf   Safety education in the school shop. Chicago, National safety council, inc., c1944.
    56p. illus., form, tables. (On cover: Safety education series, School and college division, National safety council)

    1. Accidents—Prevention. I. Title.

    NN 0064850   IU IaU

614.8
N214saf
1946r   NATIONAL SAFETY COUNCIL.
Engin   Safety education in the school shop. Rev.
Lib'y   Chicago, National safety council, inc., 1946.
    64p. illus., form, tables. 24cm.

    "Revised and reprinted 1946 [c1946]

    1. Accidents - Prevention. I. Title.

    NN 0064851   TxU NNC MtU

National Safety Council.
    Safety education in the school shop, prepared by the National Safety Council in co-operation with the United States Office of Education, Vocational Division, Trade and Industrial Education Service. 2d revision. Chicago, 1948.
    68 p. illus. 23 cm.
    "References": p. 67–68.

    1. Technical education. 2. Accidents — Prevention — Study and teaching. I. U. S. Office of Education. Trade and Industrial Education Service. II. Title.
    T65.N35 1948   331.823   49–19*

    NN 0064852   DLC CaBVíP KEmT

National safety council.
    Safety exchange round table ... Chicago, National safety council, ⁗1930.
    64 p. illus. 29ᶜᵐ.

    Safety ideas selected from those published in the "Safety exchange" department of the "National safety news". cf. p. (2)

    1. Accidents—Prevention. 2. Labor and laboring classes—Accidents. I. National safety news. II. Title.
                             30–7135
    Library of Congress   HD7273.N2585

    NN 0064853   DLC

National safety council.
    Safety in foremanship; an explanation of "Safety in foremanship". (Chicago, c1931)
    (8) p. 28 cm.

    NN 0064854   DL

National Safety Council.
    Safety in foremanship. (Chicago, 1950)
    12 no. illus. 23 cm.

    1. Foremen. 2. Industrial safety. I. Title.

    TS155.N28   658.3823   51–7972 ‡

    NN 0064855   DLC IU

B614.8
N2137   National Safety Council.
    Safety in hospitals. Prepared by the National Safety Council, Chicago, in cooperation with the American Hospital Association. [Chicago] 1933.

    56 p. 24 cm.

    Cover title.

    1.Hospitals. Safety measures. 2.Accidents. Prevention.   I.American Hospital Association. II

    NN 0064856   MnU-B NcD

National safety council.
    Safety in physical education and recreation for elementary and secondary schools ... Chicago, National safety council, inc., ⁗1941.
    95 p. incl. illus., diagr., form. 23ᶜᵐ. (On cover: National safety council. Education division. Safety education series)
    Bibliography: p. 91–93.

    1. Physical education and training. 2. Accidents—Prevention. I. Title.
    Library of Congress   GV345.N35   41–16929
                        (8)   371.7822

    NN 0064857   DLC

GV
344
.N28   National safety council.
1946   Safety in physical education and recreation for elementary and secondary schools. Chicago, Ill., School and college division, National safety council, inc., 1946.
    95 p. incl. illus., diagr., form. 23 cm.
    (On cover: National safety council. School & college division. Safety education series)
    "Reprinted ... (1946)."

    NN 0064858   MiU

(National safety council)
    Safety in the small community. (Chicago, 1936?)
    cover-title, 64 p. illus., diagrs. 23ᶜᵐ.
    Prepared by the National safety council. cf. Introd.

    1. Automobiles—Accidents. 2. Traffic regulations. I. Title.
                            45–50173
    Library of Congress   HE5614. N368
                     (2)   614.862

    NN 0064859   DLC Or DNAL WaPS

National Safety Council.
    Safety manual for marine oil-fired watertube boilers. Chicago, ⁗1955.
    66 p. illus. 23 cm.

    1. Steam-boilers, Marine. I. Title.
    VM750.N3   55–30000 ‡
           *623.873 621.18422

    0064860   DLC WaS OrP MiD

VOLUME 407

National Safety Council.

Stemp, Lillian.
Safety manual for the graphic arts industry. A joint publication of the National Safety Council and the Education Council of the Graphic Arts Industry, inc. ₍Chicago!₎ ᶜ1953₎

National Safety Council.
Safety organized to reach the workmen... Chicago ₍1919?₎
4 l. illus. 8°.

1. Accidents.—Prevention.
N. Y. P. L.   December 11, 1919.

NN   0064862   NN

National safety council.
Safety poems, both serious and otherwise ... Chicago, National safety council, ᶜ1928.
40 p. 22½ᶜᵐ.

ɪ. Title.

Library of Congress   HV675.N3   28-10608

NN   0064863   DLC OC1

National safety council
Safety poems, 2d edition...Chicago National safety council, 1929
40 p. 23 cm.

NN   0064864   DL

National safety council.
Safety posters, 1929. (Chicago, 1929)
cover-title, 40 (1) p. illus. 30½ cm.

NN   0064865   DL

National safety council
Safety slogans. Chicago National safety council, 1929
31 p. 23 cm.

NN   0064866   DL

614.8   National safety council.
N213sa   Safety training for vocational schools and school shops. Chicago, National safety council, inc., c1938.
63p. illus., tables.

"Sources of material": p.61-63.

1. Accidents--Prevention. 2. Vocational education.

NN   0064867   IU IaU WaS OCU

58
N2192   National Safety Council.
Safety with the corn picker. Chicago ₍1953?₎
4 l. (RPS 9659 ag.)

1. Corn picking machinery. Accidents.
2. Radio scripts.

NN   0064868   DNAL

331.823   National Safety Council.
N27s   Safety zoo. Chicago, ᵉ 1952.
31 p. (chiefly illus.) 21 cm.

1. Safety education. Industrial.

NN   0064869   N NN

National Safety Council.
Scheme for the identification of piping systems; a systematic plan employing color and other kinds of markings based on fundamental principles
see under   American Standards Association.

614.862   National safety council.
N21sc   School buses, their safe design and operation. Chicago, The National safety council, inc. ₍c1938₎
14p.

1. motor-buses. 2. School children--Transportation. 3. Accidents--Prevention. I. Title.

NN   0064871   IU

National safety council.
Schools for foremen. Outline of lecture₍s₎.
9 pamphlets. 28 cm.

NN   0064872   DL

National safety council.
Schools for safety supervisors. Outline of lecture(s) ... (Chicago, 1920?)
12 pamphlets in binder. 28 cm.

NN   0064873   DL

National safety council.
Service guide. Chicago, National safety council, inc. ₍ᶜ1934₎
cover-title, 68 p. illus. 23ᵐ.

1. Accidents—Prevention—Societies. 2. Labor and laboring classes—Accidents.   ɪ. Title.

Library of Congress   HD7262.N33   34-2270

—— Copy 2.

Copyright AA 137009   ₍2₎   331.82306273

NN   0064874   DLC MiU NN IU

NATIONAL SAFETY COUNCIL.
Service guide. Chicago: National safety council, inc. [c1938] 71 p. illus. 23cm.

Cover—title.
"Revised edition."

1. Accidents—Prevention—U.S. I. Title.

NN   0064875   NN

National safety council.
Service guide. Rev. ed. Chicago, National safety council, incorporated ₍ᶜ1941₎
cover-title, 80 p. illus. 23ᵐ.

1. Accidents—Prevention—Societies. 2. Labor and laboring classes—Accidents.   ɪ. Title.

41-5056

Library of Congress   HD7262.N33 1941

—— Copy 2.   ₍4₎   331.82306273

NN   0064876   DLC NN

National safety council.
Shop safety. Chicago, National safety council, c1920.
40 p. illus. 17½cm.

NN   0064877   DL

National safety council.
Shop safety; illustrated. Chicago, National Safety council, Inc., c1937.

NN   0064878   InU

National safety council, inc.
Shop safety. ₍Chicago, Nat. safety council, 1945₎   32 p. illus. 21cm.

1. Safety appliances.
N. Y. P. L.   April 19, 1948

NN   0064879   NN

National Safety Council.
Showmanship in safety. Chicago, ᶜ1953.
72 p. illus. 21 cm.

1. Industrial safety.   ɪ. Title.

HD7262.N332   658.382   54-16324 ‡

NN   0064880   DLC

National safety council.

Mowery, Harold Weaver, 1883-
Slipping and tripping, the most serious public and industrial hazard, by H. Weaver Mowery ... Presented to the Philadelphia local National safety council at Franklin institute, Philadelphia, Pa. March 20, 1916. ₍New York, American abrasive metals co., 1916₎

National safety council.
Speaking for safety; a handbook for the safety speaker. Facts and figures, suggestions, and a wealth of information of practical use in preparing the address ... Chicago, National safety council, inc. ₍ᶜ1934₎
80 p. 21¼ᵐ.

1. Accidents—Prevention. 2. Oratory.   ɪ. Title.   ɪɪ. Title: Safety, Speaking for.

Library of Congress   HV675.N32   34-37671

—— Copy 2.

Copyright A 74894   ₍3₎   614.8

NN   0064882   DLC WaS OU

National safety council.
Speaking for safety; a handbook for the safety speaker. Facts and figures, suggestions, and a wealth of information of practical use in preparing the address. Chicago, National safety council, incorporated ₍ᶜ1936₎
72, ₍2₎ p. 21¼ᵐ.
Bibliography: p. ₍73₎

1. Accidents—Prevention. 2. Oratory.   ɪ. Title.   ɪɪ. Title: Safety, Speaking for.

36-20498

Library of Congress   HV675.N32 1936

—— Copy 2.

Copyright A 96904   ₍3₎   614.8

NN   0064883   DLC Or

National Safety Council.
Speed control
see under   Joint committee on post-war speed control.

VOLUME 407

HE371
.A2N34

National safety council.

National research council. *Highway research board.*
... Speed regulation and control on rural highways; report of a special investigation by Raymond G. Paustian ...
₁Washington, D. C.₁ Highway research board, 1940.

National Safety Council.
Spring clean-up and farm accident prevention. [1949]
see under National Safety Council.
Farm Division.

449.15
.N21S

National Safety Council.
Spring clean-up and farm accident prevention.
[n. p.] 1952.
sheet.

1. Accidents. Prevention. I. Cole,
Maynard H

NN 0064886   DNAL

614.862 National safety council.
N21s   Standard drivers' license and accident reporting laws. ₁Chicago, National safety council incorporated, 1938?₁
cover-title, 24p. illus., diagrs.

1. Automobile drivers. 2. Automobiles--Laws and regulations. 3. Automobiles--Accidents. I. Title.

NN 0064887   IU

614.8   National safety council.
N213st   Standard rules for operation of school safety patrols. ₁Chicago, Ill., National safety council, inc., 1937₁
₁7₁p. illus.

Caption title.

1. Accidents--Prevention. 2. Automobiles--Accidents. I. Title: School safety patrols.

NN 0064888   IU OCU

614.8   National safety council.
N213sta   State and community organization for safety. ₁Chicago, National safety council, 1936?₁
cover-title, 24p. tab.

1. Accidents--Prevention. I. Title.

NN 0064889   IU IaU

National safety council.
State and community organization for safety, National safety council. ₁Chicago, National safety council, 1945?₁   24 p. illus. 23cm.

1. Traffic accidents—Prevention   —U.S.
N. Y. P. L.   January 19, 1948

NN 0064890   NN

National Safety Council.
State traffic law enforcement
see under Committee on State Traffic
Enforcement Manual.

National safety council.

Eno, William Phelps.
Street traffic regulations (being an advance print of the more important points on traffic to appear later in book form) by William Phelps Eno ... issued under the auspices of National safety council. Chicago, 1916.

National safety council.
Student and employee safety in colleges and universities ... Chicago, National safety council, inc., *1941.
82 p. incl. illus., tables, forms. 23ᵐ.

1. Accidents—Prevention. 2. Universities and colleges.   I. Title.

Library of Congress   HV675.N33   41-11265
.3.   371.7

NN 0064893   DLC IdU CaBViP NcD OOxM O

LB1698
.N25   ₁National safety council.₁
Student safety activities; student safety organization, handbook for secondary schools. ₁Chicago, National safety council, 1945₁
cover-title, 43p. illus. 23cm.

1.Safety education. 2.Education, Secondary. I.Title.

NN 0064894   NNU-W

NATIONAL SAFETY COUNCIL.
The teaching of safety in technical schools and universities; a memorandum prepared for the aid of those desiring to undertake such work. [Chicago],1918.

pp.26.

NN 0064895   MH Or OU MiU OO DL

National safety council.

American standards association. *Textile safety code committee.*
... Textile safety code; National safety council, sponsor. American standards association. Approved September 18, 1929 ... December, 1929. Washington, U. S. Govt. print. off., 1930.

National safety council.
Too long at the wheel; a study of exhaustion and drowsiness as they affect traffic accidents. Chicago, National safety council, inc. ₁*1935₁
48 p. illus., diagrs. 23ᵐ.

1. Fatigue. 2. Automobiles—Accidents. 3. Accidents—Prevention. I. Title.

Library of Congress   HE5614.N37   35-18203
Copyright AA 164769   ₁3₁   388.3

NN 0064897   DLC OrU Or OC1

National safety council.
Toward a safer America... ₁Chicago, National safety council, 1943?₁ 31 p. 23cm.

1. Accidents—Prevention—U.S.
N. Y. P. L.   November 16, 1944

NN 0064898   NN

National safety council.
Traffic courts and violations bureaus. Chicago, National safety council ₁*1929₁
37 p. 1 l. incl. illus., tables, diagrs., forms. 23ᵐ. (Public safety series, no. 22)

"The work has been conducted by the National safety council staff under the auspices of its Public safety division Engineering committee."—p. ₁3₁

1. Traffic regulations—U. S. 2. Automobiles—Laws and regulations—U. S. I. Title. II. Title: Violations bureaus.

Library of Congress   HE371.A2N35   29-18225

NN 0064899   DLC

National Safety Council.
Traffic engineering guide, for cities under 50,000 population. Chicago ₁1955₁
28 p. illus.

NN 0064900   ICJ NcU

National Safety Council.
Traffic plan for a greater Great Falls. Consolidated report of the Great Falls traffic survey, directed by National Safety Council, 1928. Chicago: National Safety Council, 1928. 31 p. incl. diagrs., tables. illus. 4°.

472535A. 1. Streets—Traffic—U. S.   —Mont.—Great Falls.
N. Y. P. L.   April 28, 1930

NN 0064901   NN NNC

₁614.862 National safety council.
N21t   ₁Traffic safety posters for senior high schools₁ Chicago ₁193-?₁
19 posters in envelope.

1. Automobiles--Accidents. 2. Accidents--Prevention. 3. Posters.

NN 0064902   IU

614.862 National safety council.
N21t   Traffic work of police departments. Chicago [1929?]
30p. illus.incl.facsim., tables, diagrs. (Public safety series. no.18)

NN 0064903   IU OC1W

National safety council.
Transactions. 1st-   annual safety congress; 1912-
₁Chicago, 1913₁-
v. in   illus., plates (part col.) diagrs. 23 cm.

Title varies: 1912. Proceedings of the first Co-operative safety congress, held under the auspices of Ass'n of iron and steel electrical engineers. Milwaukee, Wis., Sept. 30th to Oct. 5th, 1912.
1913, Proceedings of the National council for industrial safety. Second safety congress ... New York city, September 23 to 25, 1913.
1914-25, Proceedings of the National safety council. 3d-14th annual safety congress ... 1914-

1926-   Transactions of the National safety council. 15th-annual safety congress ... 1926-
"Cumulative index to the Proceedings of the National safety council for the years 1912-1918": 7th annual congress, 1918, p. 1163-1246.

1. Industrial accidents. 2. Safety appliances.   I. Association of iron and steel engineers.

Library of Congress   HD7653.N5   15—18672

DPR CoBBS
DNLM MH TxU NcRS WaS FTaSU CLSU OrP PSt TU IU DI
NN 0064905   DLC AAP DL MB MiU OO OOxM ICJ DPU NjP

National Safety Council.
Transactions.

Film
S178   CO-OPERATIVE Safety Congress
Proceedings. 1st; 1912. ₁Princeton. Princeton Univ. Press₁
336 p. illus.
Film copy.
Continued by the Proceedings of the Safety Congress of the National Council for Industrial Safety.
Held under the auspices of the Association of Iron and Steel Electrical Engineers.

NN 0064906   DNLM

VOLUME 407

National safety council.

TX150
.N3

National home and farm safety conference.
Transactions. 1st–   1942–   Chicago, National
safety council inc. ₍1942–

HV675
.N23

National safety council.

National broadcasting company, inc.
Universal safety series. Twelve addresses by distinguished
leaders in the business, political, scientific and educational life
of the nation, as presented over the radio in the National safety
campaign conducted by the National broadcasting company,
New York city, in cooperation with the National safety council, 1929. Chicago, National safety council ₍°1929₎

National safety council.
What price 100,000 lives? By Col. John Stilwell ... The
attack on accidents, by Ned H. Dearborn ... Chicago, Ill.,
National safety council, inc. ₍1943?₎

21 p. illus. (ports.) 28 x 21½ᵐ.

"Reports by the president and the executive vice-president of the National safety council for the year ended October, 1943."—Foreword.

1. Accidents—Prevention. I. Stilwell, John, 1886–   What price
100,000 lives? II. Dearborn, Ned Harland, 1893–   The attack on accidents. III. Title. IV. Title: The attack on accidents.

44–10216

Library of Congress   HV676.A2N3
₍3₎   614.8

NN 0064909   DLC NN

National safety council.
Where shall they park? Chicago, National safety council
₍°1928₎

18, ₍2₎ p. illus. 23ᵐ.

1. Automobiles—Laws and regulations—U. S.   I. Title.

Library of Congress   HE5623.N3
                                                         28–6548

NN 0064910   DLC Or OrU

HD7268   National Safety Council.
N3   The woman in industry, her health and
              safety. Chicago ₍c1954₎

88p. 24cm.

Bibliography₍ p. 86–88.

NN 0064911   NBuG

National Safety Council.
The woman on the job, her health and safety. Chicago
₍1954₎

88 p. illus. 24 cm.

Includes bibliography.

1. Woman—Employment. 2. Industrial hygiene. 3. Industrial
safety. I. Title.

HD7268.N3   331.822   54—1875 ‡

NcC OU OCl CLU Wa PPSOPR
NN 0064912   DLC CaBViP OrU WU PP NcD NN TxU PPSKF

331.823   National Safety Council.
N27w   Working together for safety; a manual
              of safe practices. ₍Chicago, °1953₎
              32 p. col. illus. 18 cm.

Cover title.

1. Accidents. Prevention. I. Title.

NN 0064913   N

613.66   National safety council
N27y   You and your job. ₍Chicago, Na-
              tional safety council, c1933₎
              cover-title, 40p. illus.,diagrs. D.

"A trip through...an ideal plant, where
lives, limbs, pay envelopes and jobs are
preserved through common sense safety methods."

NN 0064914   IaU

National safety council
see also
Committee on state traffic enforcement manual.

TL553
.5
.A1A53

National Safety Council. Air Transport Section.

Air transport safety.
₍n. p.₎ Air Transport Section, National Safety Council.

National Safety Council. Annual Safety Congress.
Proceedings
see   National Safety Council.
Transactions.

National Safety Council. Annual Safety Congress.
Transactions
see   National Safety Council.
Transactions.

National Safety Council. Bureau of Information.
Accident prevention—health and hygine
(industrial)
see under National Safety Council.
Library.

National safety council. *Cement and quarry section.*
Safety in quarry operations, prepared by Cement and quarry
section, National safety council, inc. ₍Chicago, 1946₎

1 p. l., v–vii, 46 p. 23ᵐ.

1. Quarries and quarrying—Safety measures.   I. Title.

46–21140

Library of Congress   TN277.N32
₍2₎   331.823

NN 0064920   DLC

National Safety Council. *Cement and Quarry Section.*
Safety in quarry operations. ₍Rev.₎ Chicago ₍1954₎

30 p. illus. 23 cm.

1. Quarries and quarrying—Safety measures.   I. Title.

TN277.N32 1954   331.82°   54–20955 ‡

NN 0064921   DLC NN PSt

National Safety Council. Chemical Section.
Committee on Benzol
see National Safety Council. Committee
on Benzol.

National safety council. Chemical section.
Committee on industrial poisons.
Progress report of the sub-committee on
benzol... (Chicago, 1923–1925?)
3 pamphlets. 28–23 cm.
1st report autographed.

NN 0064923   DL

National safety council. *Chemical section. Spray coating
committee.*
Final report of the committee, Chemical section, National
safety council, on spray coating ... September, 1927. Chicago, National safety council, °1927.

53 p. illus., fold. tables. 28ᵐ.

1. Painting, Industrial. 2. ₍Painters—Diseases and hygiene₎
I. Title. II. Title: Spray coating.

Library, U. S. Dept. of   Labor   L 28–52

NN 0064924   DL OCl ICJ

National safety council. *Child education section. Elementary school committee.*
The junior safety council; a handbook for the schools, prepared by the Elementary school committee, Child education
section, National safety council ... New York, Education division, National safety council ₍1935₎

72 p. incl. illus., diagr., forms. 23ᵐ.
H. Louise Cottrell, chairman.
The edition published in 1928 was prepared by the Education division
of the National safety council.
"References": p. 69–70.

1. Accidents—Prevention.   I. National safety council. Education
division. II. Cottrell, Hélène Louise, 1893–   III. Title.

Library of Congress   HV676.A1N25 1935   35–5864
Copyright AA 171588   ₍5₎   614.8

NN 0064925   DLC ICJ

614.862   ₍National safety council. Child educa-
N27g   tion section. Secondary school
              committee₎
              Good driving; a manual outlining
              methods of organizing programs of ins-
              truction in secondary schools and pre-
              senting subject matter content on var-
              ious aspects of automobile driving...
              New York, Educational division, National
              safety council ₍c1935₎
              43p. illus.,diagrs. O.

"This pamphlet was prepared by the Secondary school committee of the Child education
section, National safety council." verso of t.-p.
"References": p.41–43.

NN 0064927   IaU

National Safety Council. Committee on Benzol.
Final report of the committee, Chemical and Rubber Sections, National Safety Council, on benzol, May, 1926. ₍New
York;₎ National Bureau of Casualty and Surety Underwriters₍,
1926₎. 128 p. incl. tables. diagrs., illus. 8°.

Bibliography, p. ₍123–₎128.

1. Benzene poisoning.
N. Y. P. L.   January 11, 1928

NN 0064928   NN OCl OClW NcRS CU DL CtY-M OU MiD

National Safety Council. Committee on Industrial
Poisons
see National Safety Council. Chemical
Section. Committee on Industrial Poisons.

National Safety Council. *Committee on Pedestrian Control
and Protection*
see
National Safety Council. *Traffic Section. Committee on
Pedestrian Control and Protection.*

VOLUME 407

National Safety Council.
Committee on post-war traffic safety planning.
Danger, traffic jam ahead; a program for post-war traffic safety sponsored by 40 national organizations. ₁Chicago, National safety council, 1944₁ 19 p. illus. 28cm.

Prepared by the Committee on post-war traffic safety planning.

1. Automobiles—Safety measures.   I. National safety council, inc.
N. Y. P. L.   January 20, 1948

NN   0064931   NN

National Safety Council. *Committee on Speed and Accidents*
     see
National Safety Council. *Traffic Section. Committee on Speed and Accidents.*

National Safety Council. *Committee on Speed Regulation*
     see
National Safety Council. *Traffic Section. Committee on Speed Regulation.*

National Safety Council. Committee on Teacher Education for Safety
    see National Safety Council. School and College Division. Committee on Teacher Education.

National Safety Council. *Committee on Tests for Intoxication*
     see
National Safety Council. *Traffic Section. Committee on Tests for Intoxication.*

614.862   ₁National safety council. Committee on
N277d   the driver₁
     ...Drivers' license eye test standards. ₁Chicago, The Council,1938₁
5p. tables. Q. (National safety council. Public safety memo, no.42)

Caption title.
Autographic reproduction of typewritten copy.

NN   0064936   IaU

National safety council. *Committee on the driver.*
Examining applicants for drivers' licenses; a manual for examiners, prepared under the supervision of the National safety council Committee on the driver, and approved by the Eastern conference of motor vehicle commissioners. Chicago, National safety council, inc. ₁c1934₁
30 p. incl. illus. diagr. form. 22½ᶜᵐ.

1. Automobile drivers. 2. Automobiles—Laws and regulations—U. S. I. Title.

Library of Congress   HE5623.N32   **34-9227**
Copyright AA 143665   ₍3₎   **388.3**

NN   0064937   DLC Or

614.862   ₁National safety council. Committee
N277r   on the driver₁
     ...Reaction time in automobile driving. ₁Chicago, The Council, 1935₁
7p. table. O. (National safety council. Public safety memo, no.95)

Caption title.
Autographic reproduction of typewritten copy.

NN   0064938   IaU

614.862   National safety council. Committee on
N277s   the driver
     ...Suggested psychological research projects for the promotion of traffic safety. ₁Chicago, The Council, 1937₁
5p. Q. (National safety council. Public safety memo, no.80)

Caption title.
Autographic reproduction of typewritten copy.

NN   0064939   IaU

National Safety Council. *Committee on Winter Driving Hazards*
     see
National Safety Council. *Traffic Section. Committee on Winter Driving Hazards.*

₁National safety council. Connecticut dimout study committee₁
^Danger in the dimout; special traffic survey. ₁Hartford?₁ Connecticut Dept. of motor vehicles ₁1943₁
cover-title, 21 l. incl. illus., map, tables. 28ᶜᵐ.

"The study was conducted by the Connecticut dimout study committee appointed by the National safety council, Chicago, Illinois."—Leaf 1.

1. Automobiles — Accidents. 2. Traffic regulations—Connecticut. 3. Blackouts in war. I. Connecticut. Commissioner of motor vehicles. II. Title.

Library of Congress   HE5614.N38   43–53146
                                      ₍3₎   **388.3**

NN   0064941   DLC NN

TL152   National Safety Council. Driver Education and
.65   Training Section.
.T43   **The Teen-age driver.** From the program of the Driver Education and Training Section, School and College Division, National Safety Council, held during the 1949 National Safety Congress and Exposition. ₁Chicago, 1950₁

National Safety Council. *Education Division*
    see National Safety Council. *School and College Division.*

National Safety Council. Education Section
    see National Safety Council. School and College Division.

449.9
N2122   National safety council. Employee publications section.
       News letter.
       Chicago,

NN   0064945   DNAL

National safety council. Employees' representation section.
Advance copy of papers to be presented before the Employees' representation section of the National safety council, eighth annual safety congress, Cleveland, October 1-4 1919. (Cleveland) 1919.
31 (1) p.   23 c..
Articles by Cyrus McCormick, jr., and E. B. Tolsted.

NN   0064946   DL

National Safety Council. Engineering Section.
American Society of Safety Engineers was founded in 1911. In 1924 the society merged with the National Safety Council, becoming its Engineering Section. In 1947 it became an independent organization again and resumed its original name American Society of Safety Engineers.

National Safety Council. Engineering Section
    see also American Society of Safety Engineers.

S565   National Safety Council. Farm Division.
.F3
    Farm safety review. v. 1–   Jan. 1943–
    ₁Chicago₁

National Safety Council. Farm Division.
National farm safety week
    see under National Safety Council.

449.15   **National Safety Council. Farm Division.**
N212P   **Planning guide: National farm safety week activities, July 19-25, 1953. [Chicago] 1953.**
      folder [5] p.

     1. **National farm safety week.**

NN   0064951   DNAL

449.15   National Safety Council. Farm Division.
N212   Spring clean-up and farm accident prevention. [Chicago? 1949]
     2 p.
     1. Accidents. Prevention. 2. Agriculture. Accidents. I. Heldreth, Harold. II. Title. III. Title: Farm accident prevention.

NN   0064952   DNAL

National Safety Council. Farm Division.
Spring clean-up and farm accident prevention. 1952
    see under National Safety Council.

614.8   National Safety Council—Farm Safety Commit-
N2126c   tee.
    Current topics in farm safety as presented in sessions of the Farm Conference at the 40th National Safety Congress. Chicago ₁c1952₁
     36p. 23cm. (National Safety Council. Transactions. 1952, v.10)

     1. Safety education—Congresses. I. Title: Farm safety. (Series)

NN   0064954   IU

National Safety Council. Higher Education Committee.
Experiencing safety in college and university living centers
    see under American Association of Colleges for Teacher Education. Personnel Section.

614.8   National Safety Council—Home Safety Commit-
N2127c   tee.
    Current topics in home safety as presented in sessions of the Home Safety Conference at the 40th National Safety Congress. Chicago ₁c1952₁
     40p. 23cm. (National Safety Council. Transactions. 1952, v.13)

     Bibliography: p.13.

     1. Safety education—Congresses. I. Title: Home safety. (Series)

NN   0064956   IU

VOLUME 407

National Safety Council. Home Safety Committee.
Safe at home
see under   National Safety Council.

National Safety Council. Industrial Division.
Accident prevention manual for industrial
operations
see under National Safety Council.

National safety council. *Industrial division.*
Hotel accident prevention. Chicago, Ill., National **safety**
council ₁1946₎
77 p. incl. illus., forms. 18ᶜᵐ.
"Prepared by the Industrial division, National safety council."

1. Hotels, taverns, etc.—Management. 2. Accidents—Prevention.
I. Title.
TX911.N34   647.94   47–20481

NN   0064959   DLC

National Safety Council. Library.
Accident prevention — health and hygiene (industrial). A
selected reading list. ₁Chicago, 1923.₎ 9 f.   f°.
Reproduced from typed copy, written on one side of leaf only.

1. Labor.—Accidents: Prevention: Bibliography.
N. Y. P. L.   December 31, 1923.

NN   0064960   NN

National Safety Council. Library.
Accident prevention — health and hygiene (industrial); a
selected reading list...compiled by Library, National Safety
Council...   Chicago, Ill., 1925.   14 f.   4°.
Caption-title.
Typewritten.

1. Labor—Accidents—Prevention—Bibl.
N. Y. P. L.   July 14, 1926

NN   0064961   NN

National safety council. *Library.*
Accident prevention — health and hygiene (industrial)
(books and pamphlets) A selected reading list ... **January,**
1932. (Rev.) Compiled by National safety council **library**
... ₁Chicago, 1932₎
28 p. 27½ᶜᵐ.
Caption title.
Mimeographed.

1. Labor and laboring classes—Accidents—Bibl. 2. Accidents—Prevention—Bibl. I. Title.
                                                 36–24040
Library of Congress   Z7164.A17N3
                                  ₍2₎   016.331823

NN   0064962   DLC

                                        L016.3318
                                        N21
National Safety Council. *Library.*
Accident prevention – health and hygiene (industrial) (Books
and pamphlets) a selected reading list ... (Revised) **Compiled**
by National Safety Council Library. Chicago, 1934.
32 p. 29ᶜᵐ.
Caption title.

NN   0064963   ICJ

National Safety Council. Library.
Accident prevention – health and hygiene
(industrial) Books and pamphlets. A selected
reading list ... April, 1938.
35 p.
Issued by the Bureau of Information.

NN   0064964   DAL

National Safety Council. Library
Classified subject list for traffic
safety. ₁Chicago, Illinois, 1939₎
19p. typed (carbon copy)

Includes subdivisions and cross references.

NN   0064965   OC1 OC1W

National Safety Council. Library.
Education in accident prevention, health and hygiene; a
bibliography for teacher and pupil; compiled by Mary Bostwick
Day...   ₁Chicago, 1923.₎   9 f.   f°.
Reproduced from typed copy, written on one side of leaf only.

1. Accidents.—Prevention: Bibliog-   raphy. 2. Day, Mary Bostwick, compiler.   piler.
N. Y. P. L.   January 2, 1924.

NN   0064966   NN

NATIONAL SAFETY COUNCIL. Library.
List of subject headings for an accident
prevention, health and hygiene information
file,/which will take care of pamphlets, clippings photographs,reports,etc., in a library
or office. Compiled by Mary B. Day. Librarian,
Chicago,1924.

4°. 11 sheets. Manifold copy.
Without title page. Carbon title.

NN   0064967   MH DL

National Safety Council. Library
Sample list of subject headings, showing
classification method. Chicago, Illinois,
₁1952₎
5p. processed.

Includes subdivisions and cross references.

NN   0064968   OC1 OC1W

Z695
.1   NATIONAL SAFETY COUNCIL. Library.
.A2N3   Subject heading list. Chicago, 1944.
              78 p.

          1. Subject headings—Accidents.

NN   0064969   ICU

National Safety Council. Library
Suggested subject file for industrial
safety publications. Chicago, Illinois,
₁1949₎
5p. processed.

Alphabetical by subject, with notation
from Cutter 2-figure table. Examples of
files with subheadings, 1p.

NN   0064970   OC1 OC1W

National safety council. Library.
Suggested subject file for industrial
safety publications. Chicago ₁1952₎
5 p. (500-9-49 Rep. 10-52-200)

"A basic list of subject headings ... selected from the files of the National safety
council library."

1. Subject headings - Accidents - Prevention.

NN   0064971   NNC

HD7269
T7N3   **National Safety Council. Motor Transportation**
Division.
Fleet safety manual. [Chicago, National
Safety Council, 1953-
1 v. (loose-leaf) illus., diagrs., tables.
30 cm.
Caption title.
Kept up to date by revisions and additions.

1. Transportation, Automotive – Safety
measures. I. Title.

NN   0064972   DI

National Safety Council. Motor Transportation Division.
Fleet safety manual
see also National Safety Council.
Fleet safety manual. [1950-

National safety council – Omaha division-
Public school committee
An outline of safety instruction and
suggestions for junior safety council
organization for Omaha elementary schools
(1925)
28 p.

NN   0064974   OC1

National Safety Council. Public Safety Division.
Making greater Flint a safer Flint; a report
to the Flint safety council and the city officials,
based on a community safety survey directed by
the public safety division, National safety council,
Chicago. 1927. Chicago, National Safety Council,
[1927]
42 p. illus. (incl. plans) 28 cm.

NN   0064975   NNC

National Safety Council. Public Safety Division.
Preventing accidents in prosperous Decatur; a
report to the Decatur safety council based on a
community safety survey directed by the Public
safety division, National Safety Council, Chicago.
September 1927. Chicago, Ill., National Safety
Council [1927]
62 numb. l. plans. 28 cm.
Reproduced from type-written copy.

NN   0064976   NNC

National safety council. Public safety
division.

₁Billings, Curtis₎
School buses; their safe design and operation. Chicago, National safety council, inc. ₁°1935₎

National Safety Council. Public Safety Division.
Street traffic regulations in South Bend, Indiana; a report to
the Citizens Traffic Committee of South Bend, based on a community safety survey directed by the Public Safety Division, National Safety Council, Chicago. Chicago: National Safety Council, 1927. 32 p. illus. (incl. diagrs., plans.)   4°.

430456A. 1. Streets—Traffic—U. S.   —Ind.—South Bend.
N. Y. P. L.   September 23, 1929

NN   0064978   NN NIC

VOLUME 407

National Safety Council. *Public Safety Section. Accident Statistics Committee.*   5579a-352
The trend of public accidents. [A report for the year 1922.]
= Chicago. 1922. 31 pp. Charts. Tables. Vignette. 23 cm.
The title is on the cover.

NN   0064979   MB

National Safety Council. *Public Safety Section.*   **614.8 S303**
Committee on Public Accident Statistics.
146922 The warning of public accident statistics. [Report of the Committee on Public Accident Statistics, Public Safety Section, National Safety Council for the year 1923.]   Chicago, National Safety Council, 1923.
36 p. incl. tables, charts. 24ᶜᵐ.
Running title: Twelfth Safety Congress. Public Safety Section.

NN   0064980   ICJ

National safety council. Rubber section.

International association of industrial accident boards and commissions.
... Safety code for rubber mills and calenders. International association of industrial accident boards and commissions and the National safety council, Rubber section, sponsors. Recommended American practice, approved March, 1927, American engineering standards committee ...   June, 1927. Washington, U. S. Govt. print. off., 1927.

National Safety Council. Rubber Section.
Committee on Benzol
see National Safety Council. Committee on Benzol.

National Safety Council. Safety Congress.
Proceedings
see National Safety Council. Transactions.

National Safety Council. Safety Congress.
Transactions
see National Safety Council. Transactions.

Z7164
.A17N28   National Safety Council. School and College Division.
Bibliography of safety materials for the use of schools, prepared by the Education division, National safety council ...   New York. [New York, 1935?]
11 p.   23cm.

Caption title.
1. Accidents.—Prevention—Bibl.   I. Title: Safety material, Bibliography of.

NN   0064985   DLC CtY

National Safety Council. *School and College Division.* **Bulletin**
see **Safety education.**

National Safety Council. School and College Division.
LB1675   A collection of safety activities and programs for
.5   senior high schools. New York, Education division, National safety council [1932]
.N27   cover-title, 11., 72 numb. 1. incl. tables, diagrs., forms, chart. 28½cm.
Mimeographed.
Contains bibliographies.

1. Safety measures.

NN   0064987   ICU

614.8   National Safety Council—School and College
N2123c   Division.
Current topics in school and college safety as presented in School and College sessions at the 40th National Safety Congress. Chicago «1952»
96p.   23cm.   (National Safety Council. Transactions.   1952, v.29)

Includes bibliographies.
1. Safety education—Congresses.   I. Title: School and college safety.

NN   0064988   IU

National Safety Council. *School and College Division.*
Foundation for safe living, a manual for elementary school teachers and principals. Chicago, National **Safety** Council, *1948.
82 p.   illus.   23 cm.
Includes bibliographies.

1. Accidents—Prevention—Study and teaching.   I. Title.
HV676.A1N27 1948   371.71   48–16778*

NN   0064989   DLC

614.8   National Safety Council—School and College Division.
N2123h   Hazard detector; making home safety work in the homemaking program. [Chicago, 1947]
40p.   illus.   28cm.

Cover title.
"Selected references" at end of each chapter.

1. Accidents—Prevention.   I. Title.

NN   0064990   IU

614.862 National Safety Council. School and College Division.
N211h   ... History and legal status of school safety patrols.   Chicago, Ill., Education division, National safety council, 1939.
7p.   (Education memo. no.6)

Caption title.
Mimeographed.

1. Traffic regulations.

NN   0064991   IU

National Safety Council. School and College Division
Led89   Home economics safety highlights.
+N31h
Chicago.
28cm.   bimonthly.

NN   0064992   CtY

National safety council. *School and college division.*
An introduction to safety education; a manual for the teacher, with an introductory chapter by Harold Rugg; prepared by the Education section of the National **safety** council. Chicago, Ill., National safety council ‹*1924›
99 p.   23 cm.
"Reference books": p. 96.

1. Accidents—Prevention—Study and teaching.   I. Rugg, Harold Ordway, 1886–   II. Title.
HV676.A1N25 1924   24–32117 rev

NN   0064993   DLC WaSp DL NN

National Safety Council. School and College Division.
The Junior Safety Council, a handbook for the schools. Prepared by the Education Division of the National Safety Council. Chicago, Ill.: National Safety Council [cop. 1926] 103 p.   23cm.

878362A. 1. Accidents—Prevention—U.S.

NN   0064994   NN ICU

National safety council. *School and college division.*
The junior safety council; a handbook for the schools, prepared by the Education division of the National safety council. New York, N. Y., Education division, National **safety** council ‹*1928›
56 p.   illus., diagr.   23 cm.
"References": p. 53–56.

1. Accidents—Prevention.   I. Title.
HV676.A1N25 1928   29–6429 rev

NN   0064995   DLC OCU OClW Or

National safety council. School and College Division.

National safety council. *Child education section.* **Elementary school committee.**
The junior safety council; a handbook for the schools, prepared by the Elementary school committee, child education section, National safety council ...   New York, Education division, National safety council ‹*1935›

614.8   [National safety council—School and college division]
N2123m   Much to do about safety.   [Chicago, Ill., The School and college division, National safety council, 1945]
cover-title, 48p.   illus.

1. Accidents—Prevention.   I. Title.

NN   0064997   IU NN NNU–W DNAL

he   National Safety Council. School and College
HV   Division.
13   Safer home living; a handbook for home
Z992   economics teachers.   Chicago, c1945.
no.1   48 p.

1. Accidents – Prevention.   2. Home – Safety measures.   I. Title.

NN   0064998   NIC

HV676   National Safety Council. School and College Division.
.A1S27
Safety education ...
[Chicago] Education division, National safety council, inc.; [etc., etc., 1924–

National safety council. *School and college division.*
Safety education in the rural school; suggested **topics for** safety lessons, prepared by the Education division of the National safety council ...   New York, Education division, National safety council ‹*1929›
38 p.   22½ cm.
Albert W. Whitney, vice-president in charge of education.
Bibliography: p. 38.

1. Accidents—Prevention—Study and teaching.   2. Rural schools—U. S.   I. Whitney, Albert Wurts, 1870–1943.   I. Title.
HV676.A1N25 1929   29–6428 rev

NN   0065000   DLC DHEW

National safety council. *School and college division.*
... Safety education in the rural school. [Chicago, Education division, National safety council, inc., *1939]
cover-title, 55 p.   illus., diagr.   23 cm.   (*Its* Safety education series)
Includes "References."

Continued in next column

VOLUME 407

Continued from preceding column

1. Accidents—Prevention—Study and teaching. 2. Rural schools—U. S.   I. Title.
HV676.A1N25   1939   372.86148   40–7478 rev

NN   0065001   DLC OU IU OOxM OrAshS

National safety council--School and college division.
Safety education in the school shop.
Published by National safety council, inc. ...
₍Chicago₎ National safety council, inc., c1944.

56p.   illus.,tables,form.   23½cm.   ₍Its Safety education series₎

NN   0065002   MoU

National Safety Council. *School and College Division.*
Safety education in the secondary school. Chicago, National Safety Council, °1949.
55 p.   illus.   23 cm.
Published in 1940 under title: Safety education methods; secondary school.
"An introductory list of safety materials for secondary teachers and students": p. ₍46₎–53.

1. Accidents—Prevention—Study and teaching.   I. Title.
HV675.N37   1949   614.8   49–49438*

NN   0065003   DLC OU AAP

National safety council. *School and college division.*
Safety education methods; elementary school. Chicago, Education division, National safety council, inc., °1940.
95 p.   illus., diagr.   23 cm.   ₍Its Safety education series₎
Bibliography: p. 85–88.

1. Safety education.
HV676.A1N25   1940   372.86148   40—7479

NN   0065004   DLC OC1W OOxM CU OU TU

National safety council. *School and college division.*
Safety education methods; secondary school. Chicago, Education division, National safety council, inc., °1940.
104 p.   illus., diagr.   23 cm.   (*Its Safety education series*)
"Materials": p. 87–94.

1. Safety education.   I. Title.
HV675.N35   1940   614.8   40–14270 rev 2

NN   0065005   DLC OC1 OOxM CU

National safety council. *School and college division.*
Safety for supervised playgrounds ... ₍New York, Education division, National safety council, °1937₎
1 p. l., 28 p.   illus., form.   23 cm.
Illustrated t.-p.
Publisher's address corrected by stamp to Chicago, Ill.
"References": p. 28.

1. Accidents—Prevention. 2. Playgrounds.   I. Title.
GV421.N45   796   39–25724 rev

NN   0065006   DLC Or IU OC1

National safety council. School and college division.
Safety materials for schools. Chicago ₍1946?₎
31 p.
1. Accidents - Prevention - Bibliography.
I. Title.

NN   0065007   NNC

National safety council. *School and college division.*
Safety teaching in the modern school; a brief outline of methods and materials. New York, N. Y., Education division, National safety council ₍1927?₎

8 p.   diagrs.   23 cm.
Bibliography: p. 7–8.

1. Accidents—Prevention.   I. Title.

E 34–336 rev

U. S. Office of Education.   Library   HV676.N23
for Library of Congress   ₍r49d₎₎

NN   0065008   DHEW

National Safety Council. School and College Division.

Safety teaching in the modern school; the problem and a brief outline of methods... New York: Education Division, National Safety Council₍, 1931?₎.   12 p.   illus. (charts.) 23cm.

739254A. 1. Accidents—Prevention—Education.

NN   0065009   NN Or

614.9   National Safety Council. School and College Division.
N2137s   Safety teaching in the modern school, the problem and a brief outline of methods.
New York, Education division, National safety council ₍1936?₎
15p.   illus.

NN   0065010   WaPS ODW OCU

National Safety Council. School and College Division
Led89   School shop safety news letter.
+N31s   Chicago.
28cm.   monthly.

NN   0065011   CtY

A614.8   National Safety Council. School and College Division.
N214s   Selected bibliography of safety materials for
1937   the use of schools ... ₍Chicago? 1937₎
12p.

Caption title.
"Revised November, 1937."

1. Accidents--Prevention--Bibl. 2. Accidents--Prevention--Study and teaching.

NN   0065012   IU

National Safety Council. School and College Division
Led89   Student safety organization news.
+N31t   Chicago.
28cm.

NN   0065013   CtY

National Safety Council. School and College Divison.
The teen-age driver
see under title

q614.8   National Safety Council. School and College Division.
N2121s   Twelve safety posters for classroom use.   New York ₍1937₎
12 posters in envelope.

1. Accidents--Prevention. 2. Posters. I. Title.

NN   0065015   IU

National Safety Council. School and College Division. Committee on Teacher Education.
... A guide for the in-service education of the school staff (Revised)   Chicago, Ill., 1942.
2 p.l., 74 p.   diagrs.   (Safety education memo, no. 21— A school safety program for the emergency)   31 cm.
At head of title: Education division National Safety Council, Chicago.
Reproduced from type-written copy.
Sources of aid on school safety problems; p. 60–61.

1. Safety education. 2. Teachers, Training of. 3. U.S. - Air defenses. I. Title. II. Title: A school safety program, for the emergency. III. Series: Safety education memo, no. 21.

NN   0065017   PSt

National Safety Council. School and College Division. Elementary School Committee.
Led89   Safety beacon.
+N32   Chicago.
28cm.   quarterly.

–Winter 1948, name of committee appears as National Elementary School Safety Committee.

NN   0065018   CtY

National Safety Council. School and College Division. Elementary School Committee.
Led89   Safety sentinel.
+N32s   Chicago.
28cm.

At head of title: Elementary school student safety organization.
–Winter 1948, name of committee appears as National Elementary School Safety Committee; Spring-Fall 1948, as Elementary School Safety   Committee.

NN   0065019   CtY

National Safety Council. School and College Division. Higher Education Committee.
Nvb60   Safety exchange.
+N21i   Chicago.
28cm.   semiannual.

–June 1948, name of committee appears as National Higher Education Safety Committee.

NN   0065020   CtY

National Safety Council. School and College Division. Secondary School Committee.
Led89   Safety scope.
+N33   Chicago.
28cm.   irregular.

name of committee appears as National Secondary School Safety Committee.

NN   0065021   CtY

VOLUME 407

National Safety Council. Spray Coating Committee.
see   National Safety Council. Chemical
Section. Spray Coating Committee.

National Safety Council. Statistics
Committee.
Accident facts...
see under title

National safety council. Statistics committee.
Public accidents statistics; their practical
application to the public safety problem. Chicago,
National safety council. 1926
22 (1) p. incl. tables diagrs. 23 cm.

NN 0065024   DL

National Safety Council. Statistics Division.
Motorcycle facts.
₍Chicago₎
v. illus. 28 cm.

1. Traffic accidents– United States—Statistics. 2. Motorcycles.
I. Title.
HE5614.2.N33a   73-644212
ISSN 0091-5798   MARC-S

NN 0065025   DLC

National Safety Council. Street and Highway
Traffic Section
see   National Safety Council. Traffic
Section.

National Safety Council. Tacoma Local, no. 23.
Safety first; references in the Tacoma Public Library on acci-
dent prevention and safety first...   Compiled for National Safety
Council, no. 23.

see under   Tacoma, Wash. Public Library.

HE
372
R5
1930
National Safety Council. Traffic Engineering Bureau.
Reorganizing street traffic, Richmond, Virginia. Report
of the Richmond traffic survey, directed for the City
of Richmond, Virginia, by National Safety Council,
1930. Chicago, National Safety Council [1930]
37 p. illus., maps. 28 cm.

Earl J. Reeder, director of the survey.

1. Traffic surveys – Richmond, Va. 2. Traffic engineering –
Richmond, Va. 3. Richmond, Va. – Streets. I. Reeder, Earl J
II. Title. III. Title: Richmond traffic survey.

NN 0065028   Vi

National Safety Council. Traffic Section.
Current topics in traffic safety, as
presented in the sessions of the Traffic
Section at the National Safety Congress.

Chicago.
v. in

Constitutes one vol. (variously numbered)

Continued in next column

Continued from preceding column

of the set of Transactions of the National
Safety Congress.
-1946 include the transactions of
various other sections of the Council.
Title varies: -1946, Transactions ...
National Safety Congress, Street and Highway Traffic ... sessions (various slightly)

NN 0065030   CU IU NNC

D629.2
N2156
1941
[National Safety Council. Traffic Section. Committee
on Bicycle Problems]

Bicycle safety. ₍Chicago, National safety
council, inc., 1941₎
31, ₍1₎ p. illus., diagrs. 23ᶜᵐ.

Final report based on the reports made in
1939 and 1940.

1. Bicycles and tricycles. 2. Accidents -
Prevention. I. Title.

NN 0065031   NNC IU IaU

614.862
N2151p
1939
National Safety Council. Traffic Section. Committee
on Bicycle Problems.
... Prevention of bicycle accidents ...   ₍Chica-
go, National safety council, inc., 1939₎
23p. illus., tables.

"1939 report ... presented at 28th National safety congress and exposition, Atlantic City, New
Jersey, October 20,1939."

1. Accidents--Prevention. I. Title. II. Title: Bicycle accidents.

NN 0065032   IU

D629.2
N2155
1938
National Safety Council. Traffic Section. Committee
on Night Accident Hazards.
Committee on night accident hazards. 1938
report to Street and highway traffic section,
National safety council, inc., Chicago, Ill.
Prevention of night accidents. Presented at
Silver jubilee safety congress and exposition,
Chicago, Illinois, October 12, 1938. ₍Chicago,
1938₎
2 p. l., 15, ₍1₎ p. illus. 23ᶜᵐ.

1.Automobiles -   Accidents. 2. Accidents -
Prevention. I.Title.   Night accident hazards.

NN 0065033   NNC

614.862
N215n
National Safety Council. Traffic Section. Committee
on Night Accident Hazards.
Night accident hazards. A progress report ...
Presented at twenty-sixth National safety congress, Kansas City, Mo., October 14,1937. ₍Chi-
cago, 1937₎
9p. diagr.

1. Automobiles--Accidents. I. Title.

NN 0065034   IU

614.862
N2774p
National Safety Council. Traffic Section. Committee on Night Traffic Hazards.
Prevention of night traffic accidents. ₍Chicago, The Council, 1940?₎
cover-title, 23p. illus., tables,
diagrs. O.

NN 0065035   IaU

614.862
N215v
1939
National Safety Council. Traffic Section. Committee
on Night Traffic Hazards.
... Visibility vs. traffic accidents... ₍Chi-
cago, National safety council, inc., 1940₎
19p. illus., tables, diagr.

"1939 report ... presented at 28th National safety congress and exposition, Atlantic City, N.J.,
October 18,1939."

1. Automobiles--Accidents. I. Title.

NN 0065036   IU

614.862
N216p
National Safety Council. Traffic Section. Committee
on Pedestrian Control and Protection.
Pedestrian control and protection. A progress
report ... Presented at the twenty-sixth National
safety congress, Kansas City, Mo., October 13,
1937. ₍Chicago, 1937₎
9p. diagrs.

1. Automobiles--Accidents. I. Title.

NN 0065037   IU

614.862
N216p
1939
National Safety Council. Traffic Section. Committee
on Pedestrian Control and Protection.
... Pedestrian control and protection ... ₍Chi-
cago, National safety council, inc., 1939₎
26p. illus., tables.

"1939 report ... presented at 28th National safety congress and exposition, Atlantic City, N.J.,
October 18,1939."

1. Automobiles--Accidents. I. Title.

NN 0065038   IU

614.862
N2773p
National Safety Council. Traffic Section Committee
on Pedestrian Control and Protection.
Pedestrian safety. ₍Chicago, The
Council₎ 1940.
cover-title, 31p. illus.,maps,
tables, diagrs. O.

NN 0065039   IaU

National Safety Council. *Traffic Section. Committee on
Pedestrian Control and Protection.*
Report.
Chicago.
v. 23 cm.

Each vol. has also a distinctive title: 1938, Safeguarding the
pedestrian.

1. Traffic safety—U. S.
HE371.A2N36   57-52458 rev ‡

NN 0065040   DLC NNC

614.862
N216s
National Safety Council. Traffic Section. Committee
on Pedestrian Control and Protection.
Safe on foot. ₍Chicago, National safety
council, inc., 1941₎
62p. illus., tables.

"Fifth annual report ... presented at the 30th
National safety congress and exposition, October 8,1941."– Foreword.

1. Automobiles--Accidents. I. Title.

NN 0065041   IU

VOLUME 407

National Safety Council. Traffic Section.
Committee on Pedestrian Control and
Protection.
Safeguarding the pedestrian
see its Report.

National Safety Council. Traffic Section.
Committee on Speed and Accidents.
Report
see under the committee's later name:
National Safety Council. Traffic Section.
Committee on Speed Regulation.

614.862
N2771r

Engin.

National Safety Council. Traffic Section.
Committee on Speed and Accidents.

...Report of a special study on speed
zoning... ₁Chicago, National safety
council, 1938₎
47p. illus., charts., tables. O.
At head of title: Committee on speed and
accidents. 1938 report to Street and highway
traffic section, National safety council,
Chicago, Ill.
D. Grant Mickle, chairman.
"Presented at Silver Jubilee safety congress
and exposition, Chicago, Ill., October 12, 1938."

NN   0065044   IaU IU NNC

National Safety Council. Traffic Section. Committee
on Speed and Accidents.
Speed and accidents, a progress report of Committee on
speed and accidents, Street and highway traffic section, National safety council, Chicago, Ill. ₁Chicago, National safety
council, 1937₎
cover-title, 33, ₁1₎ p. incl. tables, diagrs. 23ᶜᵐ.
Harry H. Harrison, chairman.
"Presented at twenty-sixth National safety congress, Kansas City, Mo.,
Oct. 11, 1937."
1. Automobile drivers.   2. Automobiles—Accidents.   3. Accidents—Prevention.   I. Harrison, Harry Howard, 1895–   II. Title.

E 38-146

U. S. Off. of educ. Library   TL152.N3
for Library of Congress   ₁3₎

NN   0065045   DHEW IU

National Safety Council. *Traffic Section. Committee on*
Speed regulation.
Report.
Chicago.
v. illus. 23 cm.
The committee's earlier name was Committee
on Speed and Accidents.

. 1. Traffic safety—Collections.

HE5614.N375   57-29170 rev ‡

NN   0065046   DLC IU IaU NNC

National Safety Council. *Traffic Section. Committee on*
Speed Regulation.
Speed regulation. ₁Chicago₎ National Safety Council
₁1941₎
63 p. illus., tables, diagrs. 23 cm.

1. Speed limits—U. S.   I. Title.

HE5620.S6N3   388.3   43–1369 rev*

NN   0065047   DLC OCl

National Safety Council. Traffic Section. Committee on
Tests for Intoxication.
Chemical texts for intoxication. [Chicago,
1938].

pp.39. Tables and charts.
"1938 Report to Street and Highway Traffic
Section, National Safety Council, Chicago, Ill."
"Presented at Silver Jubilee Safety Congress
and Exposition, Chicago, Illinois, October 12,
1938."

NN   0065048   MH-BA NNC

614.862
N217t
1939

National Safety Council. Traffic Section. Committee
on Tests for Intoxication.
... Installing tests for intoxication ...   ₁Chicago, National safety council, inc., 1939₎
23p. illus., tables.

"1939 report ... presented at 28th National safety
congress and exposition, Atlantic City, New Jersey, October 17, 1939."
"Selected references for further study": p.22-
23.

NN   0065049   IU

W 1
NA699

National Safety Council. Traffic Section. Committee on Tests for Intoxication.
Uses of chemical tests for intoxication.

Chicago, 19
v. illus.
Issued 1943, 1945 with title: Cities
using chemical tests for intoxication
(varies slightly)
1. Liquor problem - Period. 2. Liquor
problem - U. S.   Title

NN   0065050   DNLM

RC
565
.N49

National Safety Council. Traffic Section.
Committee on Tests for Intoxication.

Evaluating chemical tests for intoxication; a
report of the Michigan State College research
project on the comparability and reliability of
chemical tests for intoxication. Collaborators:
Ralph F. Turner ₁and others₎ Chicago ₁1952?₎
16 p. diagrs., tables. 23 cm.
On cover: A report of the Committee on Tests
for Intoxication, National Safety Council.
Research con-   ducted at the request of

the Committee by the Dept. of Police Administration, Michigan State College, most of the laboratory work being done by W.B. Bennett and E.S.
Cestaric.
1. Alcoholism.   I. Turner, Ralph F.   II. Bennett,
William B.   III. Michigan. State University of
Agriculture and   Applied Science, East Lansing. School of   Police Administration and
Public Safety.   IV. Title.

NN   0065052   MiU N CU CaBVaU DNLM

National Safety Council. *Traffic Section. Committee on*
Tests for Intoxication.
Progress report
see its
Report.

National Safety Council. *Traffic Section. Committee on*
Tests for Intoxication.
Report. 1937–
Chicago.
v. illus., diagrs. annual.
Title varies: 1937–   Progress report.
Issue for 1937 has also distinctive title: Tests for driver intoxi-
cation.
Issued 1937–   under the section's earlier name: Street and High-
way Traffic Section.

1. Alcoholism.

RC565.N3   42–14403 rev 2*

NN   0065054   DLC IU NN OCl CU-B CU ICJ CaBViP DPR

National Safety Council. *Traffic Section. Committee on*
Tests for Intoxication.
Tests for driver intoxication
see its
Report.

614.862
N2171h

National Safety Council. Traffic Section. Committee
on Winter Driving Hazards.
Houghton Lake skidding and traction tests.
Chicago, Committee on winter driving hazards, National safety council, inc. ₁1946₎
cover-title, 16p. incl. tables, diagrs.

1. Automobiles--Accidents.   2. Automobiles--
Safety measures.

NN   0065056   IU

National Safety Council. *Traffic Section. Committee on*
Winter Driving Hazards.
Report.
₁Chicago₎
v. illus. 23 cm. annual.
Each report has also a distinctive title: 1940, Safe winter driving.

1947, Winter accident prevention.—1948, Safety in winter driving.
Issued   under the section's earlier name: Street and
Highway Traffic Section.
1. Automobiles—Cold weather operation—Yearbooks.   2. Traffic accidents—Yearbooks.

TL152.N3   614.862   41–26904 rev*

NN   0065057   DLC OrP CU N

National Safety Council. *Traffic Section. Committee on*
Winter Driving Hazards.
Safe winter driving
see its
Report.

National Safety Council. *Traffic Section. Committee on*
Winter Driving Hazards.
Safety in winter driving
see its
Report.

National Safety Council. Traffic Section. Committee
on Winter Driving Hazards.

What about special tires for winter driving. 1951 report. Author, 1951.
19 p. diagrs. (Its Report, 1951)

NN   0065060   OrP

National Safety Council. *Traffic Section. Committee on*
Winter Driving Hazards.
Winter accident prevention
see its
Report.

D629.2
N2157
1941

₁National Safety Council. Traffic Section. Committee on Winter Driving Hazards₎
Winter traffic safety. ₁Chicago, National
safety council, inc., 1941₎
22 p., 1 l. illus.   23ᶜᵐ.

1. Accidents - Prevention.   2. Automobiles -
Accidents.   I. Title.

NN   0065062   NNC

VOLUME 407

National Safety Council. Wood Products Section.
Fire-retarding treatments for wood
see under   Miniutti, V   P

National "Safety First" Association
see
Royal Society for the Prevention of Accidents.

National safety news. Pub. by the National safety council.

₍Chicago₎ 19
v.   illus. 30½ᶜᵐ.
Weekly,   –Apr. 1921; monthly, May 1921–

1. Labor and laboring classes—Accidents—Period. 2. Accidents—Prevention—Period.   I. National saftey council.

Library of Congress   HD7260.N55   CA 22—528 Unrev'd

TxU ICJ NN DL TU OrP
CSf MsU DI OrP OrCS MB In DSI OS PPiD FM ScCleU
NN   0065065   DLC OY CSt NjR DNLM GU ICRL WvU NBuU

---

*HD7273   National Safety News.
N28   Annual safety equipment issue.

Chicago, Ill., National Safety Council.

___vols. illus. 28cm.

NN   0065066   NBuG MiD

National safety news.
...A guide to the National safety council's
services. Chicago, National safety council,
inc., 1932.
24 p. illus. 30½ cm. (National safety news.
Feb., 1932. vol. xxv, no.2)

NN   0065067   DL

National safety news.
National safety council.
Safety exchange round table ... Chicago, National safety
council, ᶜ1930.

National Safety News.
Service guide ... 1939, revised edition.

NN   0065069   DI

National Safety News.
₍Toluene and xylene₎ toluol and xylol. August, 1940.
2p. (Photostat of article in National Safety News)

NN   0065070   DAL

National Sailors' Home, Quincy, Mass.
see Quincy, Mass. National Sailors' Home.

S621.312134
qN27   National St. Lawrence Project Conference, Washington,
          Exceptions of National St. Lawrence Project Conference to decision of presiding examiner in the matter of the Power Authority
          of the State of New York, project no. 2000
          ₍St. Lawrence River International Rapids
          Project₎ before the Federal Power Commission.
          William F. Howe ₍and₎ Wiley Norton, counsel.
          Washington, D.C., 1950.
          21 ℓ. 28 cm.
            At head of title: United States of America.
          Dated January 8, 1950.
            1. St. Law-   rence. Power utiliza-
          tion. 2. Power Authority of the State .   *

NN   0065072   N

D627.1
N21   National St. Lawrence project conference,
          Washington, D. C.
          ₍Miscellaneous publications₎ 1941

          Unbound pamphlets.

          1. St. Lawrence river.

NN   0065073   NNC

National sales company, N. York.
Your war book.
The author. [1917] 96p.

NN   0065074   WaS

National sales executives, inc., New York.
Audit of responsibility and efficiency for the sales executive;
scientific appraisal of practices of sales executives.   New York
₍1954, c1952₎ 28 p. 28cm.

  Cover title; at head of title: NSE.

1. Sales management.

NN   0065075   NN

National Sales Executives, inc., New York.
Convention proceedings
see its
Proceedings of the annual international distribution congress.

National Sales Executives, inc., New York.
Current list of unpublished studies for sales executives
and specialists in marketing prepared by graduate students.
1951/52–
New York.
    v. 23 cm. annual.
  Compiled by NSE Educational Survey Committee.
  Classified list of master's and doctor's theses.

  1. Salesmen and salesmanship—Bibl. 2. Marketing—Bibl.

Z7164.C81N314   016.6588   54–17169 ‡

NN   0065077   DLC OrU

National Sales Executives, inc., New York.
A guide to films and their uses by sales executives; prepared by National Sales Executives Film Handbook Committee, Floyd A. Poetzinger, Jack J. Kielty, and Ott Coelln.
New York, 1951.
    45 p. 28 cm.

  1. Moving-pictures in industry. 2. Salesmen and salesmanship.
I. Title.
HF5438.N26   658.85   51–5680

NN   0065078   DLC FU

301.1583
N27h   National Sales Executives, inc., New York.

          How to stage a conference, convention,
          large meeting; compiled as a guide, from
          the experience of National Sales Executives
          in conducting these various functions. New
          York, Author, ᶜ1954.
          1 v.

          1. Congresses & conventions. 2. Public
          meetings.   I. Title.

NN   0065079   CaBVa FTaSU MiDW OrP

National Sales Executives, inc., New York.
          Management library. ₍New York, author,
BUS.L.   1951-55₎ v.p. illus.

Salesmanship
(sec. author) Sales Executives Club of Northern Jersey
Title

NN   0065080   NjN

658.8
N217n   National Sales Executives, Inc., New York.
          NSE planning guide for your company's,
          your industry's, your community's
          competitive markets. ₍New York, 1952₎
          63 p. illus. 28 cm.

          Cover title.

          1. Marketing. I. Title. II. Title:
          Planning guide for your company's, your
          industry's, your community's competitive
          markets.

NN   0065081   LU NBuG OCl

National Sales Executives, inc., New York.
          Proceedings of the annual international distribution congress.

          ₍New York₎
            v. illus. 28 cm.
          Title varies: Convention proceedings.
          Other slight variations in title.
          Each vol. has also a distinctive title.
          Vols. for   issued by the association under a variant name:
          National Sales Executives International.
          1. Sales management—Congresses. I. Title: International distribution congress.

          HF5438.N27   658.8106373   53–38999 rev ‡

NN   0065082   DLC NNC

National Sales Executives, inc., New York.
Retirement income plans for outside salesmen

see under

Maynard, Harold Howard, 1889-1957.

National Sales Executives, inc., New York.
          Sources of information for sales executives and specialists
          in marketing; prepared by the Committee on Bibliography
          for Sales Management: chairman, Glenn N. Merry. Rev.
          1954. New York, ᶜ1954.
          23 p. 23 cm.

          1. Marketing—Bibl. I. Title.
          Z7164.C81N316 1954   016.6588   55–19021

NN   0065084   DLC OrU NN ICU PPCuP

VOLUME 407

National sales executives, *Inc., New York*

See also

National federation of sales executives.

HF5549
.N3H6   National Sales Executives, inc., New York.
             Committee on Motivation.
           How to get others to do more and enjoy it.
           A guide to motivation and communication, for
           better understanding and development of people's
           basic desires and values: your key to success-
           ful human relations. [New York, c1955]
             20 p. charts. 30 cm.

             1. Motivation (Psychology) 2. Personnel
           management.   I. Title.

NN 0065086   NjR

R
658.72   National Sales Executives, *inc, New York.*
N2768   Distribution Congress.
           Guideposts and methods to future
           markets and sales; proceedings. 1st-
           19 -   N. Y., National Sales
           Executives, inc., 19 -

             v. illus., ports.
             Library has: v. 17-   ; 1952-
           Title varies slightly.

NN 0065087   CL

National Sales Executives International
                see
National Sales Executives, inc., *New York.*

National sales institute.
    Roofing material & construction. illus.,
    National sales institute, [c1937]

    279 p.

    Compiled for the American oil & paint company,
Cleveland, Ohio.

NN 0065089   OC1

The National salesmen's crusade
        see under [Nash-Kelvinator Corporation]

National salesmen's directory.
    Indianapolis, Ind., F. L. Schutt & Co.

NN 0065091   OC1

National salesmen's training association.
    The art and science of selling ... Chicago, New York
[etc.] National salesmens training association [*1918]-
    v. 19½ᶜᵐ.
    CONTENTS. — I. The salesman. — II. Methods of distribution. — III. The
proposition.—IV. The territory.—V. Language and persuasion.—VI. Handling the customer.—VII. Making the sale.—VIII. Personal efficiency in
selling.—IX. Selecting and securing the position.

    1. Salesmen and salesmanship.   II Title.

    Library of Congress   HF5438.N28   18-7611

NN 0065092   DLC OC1 OCU ICRL ICJ NN

NATIONAL SALESMEN'S TRAINING ASSOCIATION
    Bulletins or "Sidelights" on How to become
"A Knight of the grip". N.Y. Author c1910.
    3 v.

NN 0065093   Or MiD

NATIONAL SALESMEN'S TRAINING ASSOCIATION.
    Clever approaches and closures that made
sales... Chicago, c 1924.

    191 p.

NN 0065094   MH-BA IU

HF
5441   National salesmen's training
.A6N3   association.
1910   How to become "a knight of the grip"
           Issued by the National salesmen's
           training association. New York,
           Chicago [etc.] 1910
               v. 20 cm.

       1. Commercial travelers.   I. Title

NN 0065095   OKentU Or

National salesmen's training association.
    How to become "a knight of the grip"
Issued by the National salesmen's training association.
New York, San Francisco [etc.] *1917
    v. 19½ᶜᵐ.

    1. Commercial travelers.   I. Title.

    Library of Congress   HF5441.A6N3   17-29499

NN 0065096   DLC

NATIONAL SALESMEN'S TRAINING ASSOCIATION.
    A Knight of the grip. Chicago, etc.,
[1913].

    pp. 80.

NN 0065097   MH-BA

National salesmen's training association.
    A manual of questions and answers on Practical sales-
manship for the use of examiners and representatives.
Chicago, Ill., National salesmen's training association,
*1925.
    2 p. l., 3-59 p. 21½ᶜᵐ.

    1. Salesmen and salesmanship.   I. National salesmen's training asso-
ciation. Practical salesmanship.

    Library of Congress   HF5438.N283   CA 26-9 Unrev'd

NN 0065098   DLC

National Salesmen's Training Association.
    N. S. T. A. system of sales management...   Chicago, Ill.,
U. S. A.: National Salesmen's Training Assoc. [, cop. 1920.]
8 parts in 1 v.   20cm.

608019A. 1. Salesmanship and   salesmen.   December 6, 1933
N. Y. P. L.

NN 0065099   NN IU

National Salesmen's Training Association,   *5639.659
    N. S. T. A. Lecture series. Instruction supplementing the volumes
used as a text in teaching the art and science of selling. No. 1–
24. [1930–32.]
— Chicago. [1930–32.] 24 v. in 2. 19 cm.

D2184 — T.r. — Salesmen. Period.

NN 0065100   MB

National salesman's training association.
    Personal efficiency in selling. Chicago,
National salesmens training association
[c.1922]

    "The art and science of selling, 8."

NN 0065101   MH

National Salesmen's Training Association,   *5639.661
    Practical sales talks and demonstrations. Series no. 1–8. Sales 1–
64. [1929–32.]
— Chicago. [1929–32.] 8 v. in 2. 19½ cm.

D2100 — T.r. — Salesmen.

NN 0065102   MB NNF

National salesmen's training association.
    Practical salesmanship, demonstration method ... Chi-
cago, Ill., National salesmen's training association [*1925]
    16 v. diags. 20½ᶜᵐ.
    CONTENTS.—I. Salesmanship and your real self.—II. Salesmanship and
human needs.—III. The goods.—IV. Methods of distribution.—V. The territory.—VI. The pre-approach.—VII. The approach.—VIII. First selling talk.—
IX. Second selling talk.—X. Third selling talk.—XI. Closing the deal.—
XII. Selection and use of material.—XIII. The customer.—XIV. Safeguarding
the house.—XV. Sales management.—XVI. Selecting and securing the position.

    1. Salesmen and salesmanship.   I. Title.

    Library of Congress   HF5438.N285   25-6834

NN 0065103   DLC OC1 OrU

National Salesmen's Training Association.   *5639.660
    Practical salesmanship. Demonstration method.
— Chicago. [1931.] 16 v. 19½ cm.
    Contents. — I. Salesmanship and your real self. 2. Salesmanship and human
needs. 3. The goods. 4. Methods of distribution. 5. The territory.
6. The pre-approach. 7. The approach. 8. First selling talk. 9. Second
selling talk. 10. Third selling talk. 11. Closing the deal. 12. Selection
and use of material. 13. The customer. 14. Safe-guarding the house.
15. Sales management. 16. Selecting and securing the position.

D2225 — T.r. — Salesmen.

NN 0065104   MB

National salesmen's training association.
    Tales of unusual sales ... Chicago, Ill., National sales-
men's training association, *1923.
    210 p. 19½ᶜᵐ.

    1. Salesmen and salesmanship.   I. Title.

    Library of Congress   HF5438.N29   23-8682

NN 0065105   DLC OC1

National Sanatorium for consumption and diseases
    of the chest, Bournemouth, Eng.
        see Bournemouth, Eng. National Sanatorium
    for Consumption and Diseases of the Chest.

VOLUME 407

National Sample Survey
see
India (*Republic*) *Directorate of National Sample Survey.*

BT601   National sanctuary of Our sorrowful Mother,
.N25   Portland, Ore.
1928   The Savior's last appeal, "Behold thy
     mother." Message of National sanctuary of Our
     sorrowful Mother, her glory and her power; the
     honor and reverence we owe her. Portland, Ore.
     [1928]
         xvi, 235, [1] p.   illus. (incl. port.)
     16.5 cm.
         Illustrated t.-p.
         "Third edition, 1928."

NN   0065108   DLC

National Sand and Gravel Association,   **L691.051**
       Bulletin 1-5 ... Washington, D. C., National Sand & Gravel   **N216**
Association, Inc., 1928-1930.
     5 no. in 1 v.   tables, diagrs.   28ᶜᵐ.
     Cover-title.
     No. 1, 3d ed., 1930.
     No more published.

     DI NN WaS
NN   0065109   ICJ MtBuM DPR MnSJ ICRL DNLM NBuG

National Sand and Gravel Association,   **L691.051**
       Circular ... Washington, D. C., National Sand & Gravel   **N2161**
Association, Inc., 1929-
         illus., diagrs.   27½-31ᶜᵐ.
     Irregular.

NN   0065110   ICJ IU DNLM NN MiD WaS DPR

National sand and gravel association
Data sheets. Wash., The Author, 1929.
tables, diagr.

Loose leaf ed.

NN   0065111   MiD

National Sand and Gravel Association.
   List of laboratory investigations conducted by
National Sand and Gravel Association and Nation-
al Ready Mixed Concrete Association. no.1-
         1928-1951--   College Park, Md.

   I. National Ready Mixed Concrete Association.
016.62019051

NN   0065112   ICJ

NATIONAL SAND AND GRAVEL ASSOCIATION.
   List of laboratory investigations conducted by National sand and gravel association and National ready mixed
concrete association since 1938 at University of Maryland, College Park, Md. List compiled Jan. 1950.
[Washington, 1950]   24 p.   23cm.

1. SAND--TESTING   2. GRAVEL--TESTING
3. CEMENT AND CONCRETE--TESTING
I. National ready mixed concrete
    association   t. 1950

NN   0065113   NN

National Sand and Gravel Association.
   Manual; uniform cost accounting principles and
procedure for the industrial sand industry.
Washington, D. C., Industrial Sand Division,
National Sand and Gravel Assoc. [1936?]
   20 p.

     By Ernst & Ernst.

NN   0065114   OC1

National sand and gravel association.
   **Manual. Uniform cost accounting principles
and procedure for the sand and gravel industry.
Wash. [The Author] °1937.
   28 p.**

NN   0065115   MiD

National Sand and Gravel Association.
      The National sand and gravel bulletin
           see under title

TN939   National Sand and Gravel Association.
.N3
no.52   Operating problems of the sand and gravel
1952   industry. (A symposium of four papers, with
floor discussion, presented at the 1952
annual Operating Session of the N.S.G.A.)
Washington, 1952.
     35 p. illus.   23cm. (National Sand and Gravel
Association. Circular, no. 52)

     1. Sand. 2. Gravel. I. Title. II. Title: Sand
and gravel industry. III. Ser.

NN   0065117   ViU

National sand and gravel association.
   'Report of Washed gravel ballast committee, by Earl Zimmerman
... F. D. Coppock...[and others]   Report presented at the
tenth annual convention of the National sand & gravel association,
inc., Atlanta, January 19-20-21, 1926.   [Washington, D. C., 1928]
8 p. incl. tables.   27½cm.
     Cover-title.

     1. Railways—Track—Ballast.   2. Gravel.
N. Y. P. L.   June 12, 1940

NN   0065118   NN MiD NNC

---

q625.8   National sand and gravel association.
N213su   Summary of state highway specifications for sand for concrete pavement
construction. Comp. by Engineering
and research division.   Washington,
D. C., 1927.
     [3] p.   table, diagr

NN   0065119   IU

National sand and gravel association.
   ...Technical information letter.
no.

Washington, 19   28cm.
   v.   illus.
     Four or five times a year (irregular).
     Continuous numbering starts with no. 23 (March 24, 1941), taking into account all
letters published since the first (1936).
     Various issues include suppl. (reports, technical papers, etc.)
     Includes numerous bibliographies (no. 24 <June 16, 1941>: Selected list of
references on soundness of concrete aggregates, 1828-1940).

     1. Sand—Per. and soc. publ.   2. Gravel—Per. and soc. publ.
N. Y. P. L.   April 9, 1943

NN   0065120   NN DPR IU

National sand and gravel association.
   Year book...
19

Washington [19   23cm.
   no.   illus.

NN   0065121   NN DPR MiD

National sand and gravel association. Engineering and research
     division.
   Bibliography from current periodicals on bituminous types of
highway construction, prepared by Engineering and research division, National sand and gravel association. (Revised, September
1935.)   [Washington, D. C., 1935]   26 p.   22cm. bound
28cm.
     Caption-title.
     Photostatic reproduction of typewritten material.

—— Supplement to selected list of references to literature on
bituminous types of highway construction, prepared by Peal O.
McKim... (April, 1942.)   Washington, D. C., 1942.   12 f.
27½cm.
     Caption-title.
     Reproduced from typewritten copy.

205342B. 1. Pavements, Asphalt—   Bibl. 2. Pavements, Bitulithic—
Bibl.   November 20, 1942
N. Y. P. L.

NN   0065123   NN

National sand and gravel association. Engineering and research
     division.
   Selected list of reference [sic] to literature on miscellaneous
test methods and laboratory equipment; prepared by Pearl O.
McKim.   Washington, Engineering and research division, National sand and gravel assoc. [1942]   12 f.   28cm.
     Caption-title.

     1. Cement and concrete—Testing.   I. McKim, Pearl O., comp.
N. Y. P. L.   March 22, 1944

NN   0065124   NN

National sand and gravel association. Engineering and research
     division.
   Selected list of references on theory of design and control of
concrete mixtures; prepared by Pearl O. McKim...   [Wash-
ington, D. C., 1941]   21 f.   28cm.
     Caption-title.
     Reproduced from typewritten copy.

     1. Cement and concrete—Bibl.   I. McKim, Pearl O., comp.
N. Y. P. L.   December 21, 1942

NN   0065125   NN

National Sand and Gravel Association. Engineering and Research
     Division.
   ...Tables of quantities of materials for concrete, prepared by
the Engineering and Research Division.   Washington, D. C.:
National Sand & Gravel Assoc., Inc., 1928.   16 p. incl. tables.
4°.   (National Sand & Gravel Assoc. Bull. [no.] 4.)
     Cover-title.
     Bibliographical footnotes.

     1. Cement and concrete—Tables, calcu-   lations, etc. 2. Ser.
N. Y. P. L.   November 19, 1928

NN   0065126   NN

691.3   National Sand and Gravel Association. Engineer-
N212   ing Division.
       Report.
       [Washington?]
         v.   28cm.

       Report issued to the National Sand and Gravel
Association and the National Ready Mixed Concrete
Association.
       Issued 19   by the "Director of Engineering
of National Sand and Gravel Association and National Ready Mixed   Concrete Association."

NN   0065127   IU

VOLUME 407

The **National** sand and gravel bulletin. Vol. 1-14, no. 1; November 1919-February 1933 ... ₍Washington, etc., National Sand and Gravel Association, 1919-1933₎

14 v. in 11. illus., ports., tables, diagrs. 25-31ᶜᵐ. monthly.

Caption title; no index.
Ceased publication Feb. 1933.
Vol. 1 published in Indianapolis.

DLC: TN 789. A1 N3

NN 0065128   ICJ LU MnSJ NBuG DNLM WvU DLC NN

W 1
NA721
NATIONAL Sanitarium Association (Canada)
Annual report.
1st-   1897/98-
Toronto.
v. illus., ports.

Report year irregular.
Report for 1897/98 issued with title:
Report of the Muskoka Cottage Sanatorium
for Consumptives.
Reports for 1898/99-1899/1900 called

also Annual report of the Muskoka
Cottage Sanatorium.
Issues for 1901/02-   include
reports of the Muskoka Cottage Sanatorium
and the Muskoka Hospital for Consumptives; and 19   of the Toronto Free
Hospital for Consumptives.
I. Gravenhurst, Ont. Muskoka Cottage
Sanatorium II. Gravenhurst, Ont.

Muskoka Hospital for Consumptives
III. Toronto. Free Hospital for Consumptives

NN 0065131   DNLM CaBVaU CaBVa

National sanitarium association (Canada)
Year book and annual report
see its   Annual report.

National Sanitary Corporation. Limited [for
inspection of houses, sanitary engineering work,
etc. Prospectus]. 19 pp. 4°. London, Crown
Printing Co., [1881].

NN 0065133   DNLM

National Sanitation Clinic.
Report. 1st-
1948-
₍Ann Arbor, Mich.₎ National Sanitation Foundation.
v. 28 cm.

1. Sanitation—Congresses. 2. Health education.   ɪ. National
Sanitation Foundation, Ann Arbor, Mich.

RA422.N433   614.06373   51-33232

PPC CU DNLM
NN 0065134   DLC CaBVaU OrU Wa ICJ ICU MnU IEN NN

WA
1
qN279
NATIONAL Sanitation Foundation, Ann Arbor, Mich.
₍Collection of publications₎

The Library has a collection of
miscellaneous publications of this
organization kept as received. These
publications are not listed or bound
separately.
1. Sanitation

NN 0065135   DNLM

National Sanitation Foundation, Ann Arbor, Mich.
A bacteriological study of automatic clothes
washing
see under   Ridenour, Gerald M

National Sanitation Foundation, Ann Arbor, Mich.
Quality milk- a symbol of democracy
see under   King, James A   M.P.H.

National Sanitation Foundation, *Ann Arbor, Mich.*
Report.
Ann Arbor.
v. 28 cm. annual.

RA565.N324   55-25384 ‡

NN 0065138   DLC

RA422
.N433
National Sanitation Foundation, Ann Arbor, Mich.

National Sanitation Clinic.
Report. 1st-
1948-
₍Ann Arbor, Mich.₎ National Sanitation Foundation.

National Sanitation Foundation, Ann Arbor, Mich.
Seal of approval listing of National Sanitation
Foundation Testing Laboratory
see   National Sanitation Foundation Testing
Laboratory.
Seal of approval listing of force service equipment.

TP986
.5
.P5N3
1955
National Sanitation Foundation, Ann Arbor,
Mich.

A study of plastic pipe for potable water
supplies./ Directed by Walter D. Tiedeman
and assisted by Nicholas A. Milone. Ann
Arbor, Mich., 1955.
vi, 90 p. illus. 28cm.
Includes bibliography.

1. Water-pipes. 2. Plastics. ₍I.₎ Tiedeman,
Walter von Dohlen, 1891-   II. Title: Plastic
pipe for potable   water supplies.

NN 0065141   ViU NN MnU MiU OCl NIC

NATIONAL SANITATION FOUNDATION, Ann Arbor,
Mich.
Ten year report, 1945-1954. Headquarters: School of
public health, University of Michigan, Ann Arbor,
Mich. [Ann Arbor, Mich., 1955] 96 p. illus., group
ports. 23cm.

1. Hygiene, Public--Assoc. and org.--U. S.   ɪ. 1955.

NN 0065142   NN NIC ICJ

TX
912
N3
National Sanitation Foundation, Ann Arbor,
Mich. Joint Committee on Food Equipment
Standards.
Standard no.1-
Ann Arbor, Mich,, 1952-
v. illus. 28cm.

Some no. in rev. ed.

1. Food service-Equipment and supplies.
2. Food industry and trade-Sanitation.

NN 0065143   NBuC MiD OCl

RA
421
N335
National Sanitation Foundation Testing Laboratory.
Seal of approval listing of food service equipment.
Ann Arbor, 195 -

Title varies: 195 -62, Seal of approval listing
of National Sanitation Foundation Testing Laboratory

NN 0065144   MiU

National save-a-life league.
The 25th anniversary of the National
save-a-life league...1932. New York
1932.
19 ₍1₎ p. illus., port.

1. Suicide

NN 0065145   OO

National savings.
₍London₎
v. in   illus. 22 cm.
Title varies: v. -5. no. 2, War savings.

1. Saving and thrift — Period. 2. Saving and investment — Gt.
Brit.—Period.
HG4502.N3   58-45916 ‡

NN 0065146   DLC NN

National savings and issue bank, ltd., Amsterdam.
Ecclesiastical securities. Amsterdam, ₍1930₎.
27 p.

NN 0065147   OClFRB

The National savings and loan journal.
₍Washington, National League of Insured Savings Associations₎
v. in   illus. 29 cm. monthly.
Began publication with the Dec. 1945 issue. Cf. Union list of
serials.
Published   -Feb. 1958 by the league under its earlier name:
National Savings and Loan League.

1. Building and loan associations—Period.   ɪ. National League
of Insured Savings Associations.
HG2121.N3   64-46229

NN 0065148   DLC ICU

National Savings and Loan League
see
National League of Insured Savings Associations.

National savings and trust company, Washington, D. C.
Davis, Herbert Lewis, 1868-
Legal accounting and court auditing, with especial reference to federal and state practice in law, equity and kindred
proceedings respecting the duties and obligations of fiduciaries, court auditors, masters in chancery, referees, etc., together with analyses of cases involving the application of
principles of accounting and legal precedents, pertaining to
trust estates, partition suits, etc., by Herbert L. Davis ...
₍Washington, D. C., National savings and trust company,
ᶜ1927₎

National savings bank of the city of Albany.
Albany, birthplace of the Union; commemorating America's
oldest community, the growth of an idea, and an institution
dedicated to the advancement of each. ₍Albany₎ The National
savings bank of the city of Albany, 1940.
xi, ₍1₎, 66 p., 1 l. incl. front., illus. 27ᶜᵐ.
"First edition."
Bibliography: p. 64-65.

1. Albany—Hist. 2. Savings-banks—U. S.   ɪ. Title.
Library of Congress   F129.A3N26   40-6027
———— Copy 2.
Copyright   ₍2₎   974.743

NN 0065151   DLC NIC N-L

VOLUME 407

National savings bank of the city of Albany.
    Albany's historic street; a collection of some of the historic facts and interesting traditions relating to State street & its neighborhood; published in commemoration of its fiftieth anniversary, by the National savings bank of the city of Albany. ₍Albany₎ 1918.
    xiv, ₍4₎ 43, ₍2₎ p. incl. front., illus., ports. 23ᶜᵐ.
    "Compiled, arranged and printed by direction of Walton advertising & printing company, Boston, Mass."
    Bibliography: p. xiv–₍xv₎
    1. Albany—Streets—State street.   ɪ. Walton advertising & printing company, Boston.

    Library of Congress   F129.A3N27   18–21547

    NN   0065152   DLC ICRL NcU NN MoKU NIC OKentU MB

National Savings Bank of the City of Albany.
    Albany's historic street; a collection of some of the historic facts and interesting traditions relating to State street & its neighborhood. [2d ed.] Albany, 1928.
    xiv, 45 p. illus.
    1. Albany, N.Y. - Hist.   2. Albany, N.Y. - State Street

    NN   0065153   MH

National   savings committee, *London.*
    ... Annual report.
    London, 1917–
    v. 33½ᶜᵐ. (₍Gt. Brit. Parliament. Papers by command₎ Cd. 8516, 9112; Cmd. 194
    At head of title, 1916–   National war savings committee ...
    Chairman: R. M. Kindersley, 1916–
    1. European war, 1914–   —Finance—Gt. Brit.   2. Saving and thrift. ɪ. Kindersley, Sir Robert Molesworth, 1872–   ɪɪ. Title.

    Library of Congress   HC256.2.A6   20–4995

    NN   0065154   DLC DL FTaSU CSt ICJ MB

CBA-h   **National savings committee, London.**
1944   A map of the British army with battle honors
N3   and military achievements described: English county regiments displayed in their shires: those of Scotland, Ireland & Wales in their own countries: and regimental badges of all other units & corps circumscribed as a border. The whole forming a complete record with whose aid the reader may more easily salute the soldier in full appreciation and understanding. Issued ₍₎ by the National savings committee in London; the Scottish savings committee in Edinburgh and the

    Ulster savings committee in Belfast ₍₎ London, H. M. Stat. off., 1944.
    col.map. 97x72cm.
    No scale.
    In lower left corner: H. C. Paine. '44.
    Pictorial map.

    NN   0065156   IU

    National Savings Committee, London
National economy series. .... London, National War Savings Committee, [1919].
    no. 1–2. 22ᶜᵐ.
    Previous to June 1922: National War Savings Committee.
    Irregular.
    Reprints.

    NN   0065157   ICJ DLC

National Savings Committee, London.
    The national savings movement (founded 1916)...its origin, aims and development; a short review (with special reference to England and Wales). ₍London:₎ National Savings Committee, 1931. 46 p. illus. (facsim., ports.) 22cm.

    1. Savings and thrift—Gt. Br.
    N.Y.P.L.

    NN   0065158   NN

National savings committee, London.
    [Publications.   Westminister, 1916]–

    NN   0065159   NjP

                     SB p.v.783
    National savings committee, *London .*
    ...War savings handbook. 3. ed. reset and rev. The National war savings committee... ₍London₎ 1917. 72 p. 18cm.
    At head of title: no. 39.

    NN   0065160   NN

National Savings Committee, London.
    Why we must save and how...
    1. ed. London: Parliamentary War Savings Committee, 1915. 47(1) p. 12°.
    2. ed. ib., 1915. 31(1) p. 12°.

    1. European war, 1914–   —Economic   aspects, Gt. Br.   2. European war, 1914–   —Food supply, Gt. Br.   3. Thrift, Gt. Br.
    N.Y.P.L.   June 2, 1919.

    NN   0065161   NN

National Sawmilling Association.
    The British sawmilling classification of timbers
       see under title

National scalemen's association.

    Streeter-Amet company, *Chicago.*
    Glossary. Design, manufacture, installation, and use of weighing machines. Comprising 642 broad technical terms, colloquialisms, and local trade terms common to the art in the United States of America. Chicago, Streeter-Amet company ₍ᶜ1936₎

    National Scalemen's Association.

QC107   **Considine, Douglas Maxwell.**
.C56   Industrial weighing. New York, Reinhold Pub. Corp., 1948.

    National acalemen's association.

    ... **Specifications** for the manufacture and installation of railroad track scales. ⟨Prepared by a joint committee of the American railroad association, the American railway engineering association, the Railroad and warehouse commission of the state of Minnesota, the National scalemen's association, the Scale manufacturers association, and the Bureau of standards.⟩ Issued January 31, 1920 ... Washington, Govt. print. off., 1920.

National scalemen's association.
    Pivots and bearings; a collection of reports of experiments and studies. ₍Chicago₎ 1954. 1 v. (various pagings) illus. 28cm.
    "This work comes...in three parts. One enclosure is a reprint of Bulletin no. 242 of the Engineering experiment station, University of Illinois, entitled 'Bearing value of pivots for scales.' A second enclosure is a reprint of paper read by Mr. A. Heward before the Incorporated society of inspectors of weights and measures of England entitled 'Weighing machine pivots'. These are enclosed in the main booklet published by our committee and given the broad title 'Pivots and bearings.' This main booklet contains five articles which have been published in the Scale journal since the year 1927."

    1. Scales (Weighing instruments).   ɪ. 1954.

    NN   0065166   NN

National Scenario bureau, Washington, D. C.

    ₍May, Frederick James₎ 1871–
    How to write a scenario for a motion picture play. Washington, D. C., National scenario bureau ₍ᶜ1911₎

National Scholarship Service and Fund for Negro Students.
    Opportunities in inter-racial colleges, edited by Richard L. Plaut, executive vice-chairman. 1st ed. New York, 1951.
    vi, 240 p. 29 cm.
    1. Universities and colleges—U. S.—Direct.   2. Negroes—Education. ɪ. Plaut, Richard L., 1903–   ed. ɪɪ. Title.

    LC2801.N3   378.73   51–3585

    NN   0065168   DLC NN

National Scholarship Service and Fund for Negro Students.
    Report.
    New York.
    v. 23 cm. annual.
    Report year ends Aug. 31.

    1. Negroes—Education.

    LC2801.N35   59–52311

    NN   0065169   DLC OrPS

LC2801   **National Scholarship Service and Fund for Negro**
N32   **Students.**
    Southern project report, 1953–1955. New York [1955]
    65 p. diagrs., tables, forms.

    1. Negroes - Education.   2. Gifted children - Southern States.

    NN   0065170   CU

National scholarship service and fund for Negro students.
    10th anniversary dinner. ₍New York, Williamson Music, inc., c1949₎ 16 p. ports. 31cm.

    1. Scholarships—U. S. 2. Negro—   Education—U. S.

    NN   0065171   NN

National Scholastic Press Association.
    Helpful aids for the journalism teacher
       see under   National Association of Journalism Directors. Teaching Techniques Commission.

National Scholastic Press Association.
    A manual and scorebook for editors and staffs of scholastic newspapers
       see under   Kildow, Fred L.

J
070.48   **National scholastic press association.**
N21r   The N.S.P.A. newspaper manual. Minneapolis, National scholastic press assoc., c1944. 23p. 24cm.

    1. Journalism. 2. Newspapers. I. Title.

    NN   0065174   LU

VOLUME 407

National scholastic press association.

McMurtrie, Douglas Crawford, 1888–
Specimens showing typographic style of page headings for school and college yearbooks, prepared to illustrate an address to the yearbook group at the convention of the National scholastic press association, held at Milwaukee, December 6, 1935, by Douglas C. McMurtrie ... Chicago, Ludlow typograph company, 1935.

National Scholastic Press Association.
The yearbook manual
see under Kildow, Fred L

National School Band Association.
Standards of adjudication
see under American Bandmasters
Association. Committee on Adjudication.

National School Band Association.
State and national school music competition-festivals
see National school music competition-festivals.
Rules, music lists...

National School Band Association
see also
National Interscholastic Music Activities Commission.

National School Band, Orchestra and Vocal Association
see
National Interscholastic Music Activities Commission.

National School Boards Association.
New approaches; a report on a symposium on the problems of public education. ₍Prepared by Fred M. Hechinger₎ Chicago ₍1955₎
28 p. 16 x 23 cm.

1. Education—U. S.—1945–　ɪ. Title.

LA210.N384　1955c　　370.973　　　56–4286

NN　0065181　DLC CU

L13　NATIONAL SCHOOL BOARDS ASSOCIATION.
.N487　Proceedings of the convention. 1941?–
Evanston, Ill.

Annual.
Each vol. has also a distinctive title.
Issue for 1959, xerox copy.

1. Education--U.S.--Societies, etc.

NN　0065182　ICU IU N

National School Boards Association.

LB2831
.A4　American Association of School Administrators.
The school board member in action ₍by₎ American Association of School Administrators ₍and₎ National School Boards Association. Washington, 1949.

National School Boards Association.

LB2819
.A55　American Association of School Administrators.
What to pay your superintendent ₍by₎ American Association of School Administrators ₍and₎ National School Boards Association. Washington, 1952.

National School Boards Association.

LB2831
.A43　American Association of School Administrators.
Written policies for school boards ₍by₎ American Association of School Administrators and National School Boards Association. ₍Washington, 1955₎

National School Boards Association.
Yearbook.
Evanston, Ill.
v. illus., ports. 23 cm. annual.
Began publication with 1954 volume.

1. School boards—Congresses.

LB2804.N38　　379.153　　62–53597

NN　0065186　DLC

The National school building journal,
vol. 1, 4–5　May 1919–Nov. 1919.
Jan. 1923–Sept. 1924
Saint Paul, Minn., 1919–24
3 v. illus., plans, diagrs. 30 cm.
monthly.
Editors: 1919　Bradley, R. J.　1923–34
George L. Lockhart and others.

NN　0065187　DHEW NN

National school city league.
The school city ₍a new system of moral and civic training₎ Issued by National school city league. ₍Philadelphia? 1905?₎
cover-title, 48 p., 1 l. 23ᶜᵐ.
Ralph Albertson, secretary National school city league.
"Partial bibliography": p. 41–43.

1. School city, state, etc.　ɪ. Albertson, Ralph, 1866–

8—18770

Library of Congress　LB3093.N3

NN　0065188　DLC DHEW MB

National school city league.
The school city; a new system of moral and civic training ... Philadelphia, Boston ₍etc.₎ The National school city league ₍1906?₎
2 p. l., ₍3₎–44 p., 1 l. 23ᶜᵐ.
Ralph Albertson, secretary National school city league.
"Books on citizenship": p. 40.
"Partial bibliography": p. 41–44.

1. School city.　ɪ. Albertson, Ralph, 1866–

E 9–1449

Library, U. S. Bur. of　Education LB3094.N25

NN　0065189　DHEW ICJ

National School Digest [Lincoln, Neb.]
see American Educational Digest [Lincoln, Neb.]

National school essay contest on "What are the benefits of an enlistment in the U. S. army." Program and prizes by the War department through "The Comeback." National award day. Washington, D.C., May 5, 1920. (Washington? D. C., 1920)
11 p. ports. 23 cm.

NN　0065191　DHEW

The National school festival; an original magazine, devoted to fresh and sparkling dialogues, recitations, concert, motion and other exercises for the exhibitions, concerts, festivals, etc. of Sunday schools, day schools, and cold water temples ... no. 1–
Jan. 1870–
Chicago, A. L. Sewell; ₍etc., etc.₎ 1870–
v. 20½ᶜᵐ. quarterly.
Title varies: Jan. 1870–Jan. 1871, The Little corporal's school festival. Apr. 1871–　The National school festival. (Apr. 1871 has cover-title: The School festival; caption title, The National school festival)
Editors: Jan. 1870–Jan. 1871, A. L. Sewell.—Apr. 1871–Mar. 1873, A. L. Sewell, Mary B. C. Slade.—Apr. 1873–　T. A. Hutchins, Mary B. C. Slade.
Pub. in East Boston,　　　　　　Apr. 1873–
ɪ. Sewell, Alfred L., ed.　　　ɪɪ. Slade, Mrs. Mary B. C., ed.
ɪɪɪ. Hutchins, Thomas A.,　　　ed.
Library of Congress　　AP200.N4　　10–23468†

NN　0065192　DLC

National school for commercial and trade organization executives
see
National institute for commercial and trade organization executives.

National School for Commercial Secretaries
see
National Institute for Commercial and Trade Organization Executives.

National school for the deaf and dumb, Mexico
see Mexico (City) Escuela normal de profesores y profesoras para la ensenanza de sordo mudos.

National school furniture co.
... Illustrated catalogue of school and church furniture, and school requisites of all kinds. ₍New York and Chicago₎ 1872.
iv, 5–48 p. illus. 22½ᶜᵐ.

1. School furniture—Catalogs.

CA 10–2184 Unrev'd

Library of Congress　LB3281.N3　1872

NN　0065196　DLC

The National school law reporter. v. 1–
March. 1951–
[New London, Conn., Croft Educational Services, a division of Vision]
v. in　semimonthly.
For holdings see Shelf List.
Title varies: v. 1–4, Mar. 1951–Feb. 17, 1955, The Bi-weekly school law letter.
1. Educational law and legislation - Period.
I. Title: The Bi-weekly school law letter.

NN　0065197　HU NcD WaU-L TxLT MtU IdU MtBC OrU

[National school miscellany. 1826] v. 3.
382 p. illus. 11 cm.
t.-p. wanting.
Binder's title.

NN　0065198　RPB

VOLUME 407

ML36
.N17M2 National school music competition-festivals.
... Rules, music lists, general information ... Official manual of the National school band association, National
school orchestra association, National
school vocal association, auxiliaries of
the Music educators national conference, a
department of the National education association of the United States. Chicago,
Ill., ᶜ19
v. 22½ᶜᵐ.

At head of title: 19 State and
national school music competition-festivals.

1. Music—Competitions. 2. Musical
festivals. I. National school band association. II. National school orchestra association. III. National school vocal association.

NN 0065200 DLC OLak

National school of bridges and highways
see under Connor, William Durward, 1874-

**National school of business science for women,
Washington, D. C.**
Cummings, *Mrs.* Edith Mae (Cunliffe) 1888-
Pots, pans and millions; a study of woman's right to be in
business; her proclivities and capacity for success, by Edith
Mae Cummings. Washington, D. C., National school of busi-
ness science for women, 1929.

National school of correspondence, *Quincy, Ill.*
... A normal course in nature-science and agriculture ...
Quincy, Ill., National school of correspondence ₁1904₁
157 p. 19ᶜᵐ. (Teachers' home series)

1. Agriculture—Study and teaching. 2. Natural history—Study and
teaching.
5–5092 Additions

Library of Congress S495.N2 Copyright

NN 0065203 DLC

National school of correspondence, *Quincy, Ill.*
... Teachers' home series. L. B. McKenna ... president
and director. ₁First grade—number 1–6₁ Quincy, Ill.,
Quincy school of correspondence ₁1902₁
6 pts. in 1 v. port. 19½ᶜᵐ.
Each part has special t.-p.

I. McKenna, Llewellyn B.
4–1618 Additions

Library of Congress LC6001.N66 Copyright

NN 0065204 DLC

National school of correspondence, *Quincy, Ill.*
... Teachers' home series. A normal course in six numbers. ₁no. 1–
Quincy, Ill. ₁1905–
v. 19½ᶜᵐ.

7–31571†

Library of Congress LC6001.N7 Copyright

NN 0065205 DLC

The national school of dancing for home instruction
see under ₁Karl, Julius E ₁

National School of Dental Technics
see
American Institue of Dental Teachers.

National school of detectives, New York.
Young, George Howard, 1881–
Text book. Elementary course of the principles of detection containing methods of professional criminals,
deceptions practised by ordinary malefactors and rules
for students, by George H. Young ... for the use of students of the National school of detectives ... ₁New York,
National school of detectives, ᶜ1914₁

National School of Electricity, Chicago
see Chicago. National School of Electricity.
[supplement]

National school of elocution and oratory, Philadelphia
see Philadelphia, National school of
elocution and oratory.

National school of fine and applied, art, Washington
D.C.
see Washington, D.C. National school of
fine and applied art.

National school of keyboard fingering, Danville, Ill.
see Danville, Ill. National school of
keyboard fingering.

**National School of Library Science, Washington,
D.C.**
see Washington, D.C. National School
of Library Science.

National school of meat cutting, *Toledo*
see
Toledo. National school of meat cutting.

National school of music, Washington, D.C.
see
Washington, D.C. National school of music.

National school of podology, *Chicago.*
Podology ... based on the experience, inventions, foot comfort system and methods of Dr. William M. Scholl ... Chicago, National school of podology, ᶜ1932.
111 p. illus. (part col.) 19½ᶜᵐ.

1. Foot. 2. Chiropody. I. Scholl, William Mathias, 1882–
II. Title.

Library of Congress RD563.N3 32–5150
Copyright A 48365 ₁3₁ 617.58

NN 0065216 DLC DNLM ViU

National school of railroading, *Chicago.*
Text book for brakemen and train baggagemen. Chicago, National school of railroading ₁ᶜ1907₁
170 p. illus. fold. diagrs. 18ᶜᵐ.

1. Railroads—Trainmen's manuals.

Library of Congress TF557.N28 7–29416
Copyright A 196305

NN 0065217 DLC ICJ

National school of railroading, *Chicago.*
Text book for express company employes. Chicago, National school of railroading ₁ᶜ1907₁
76 p. 18½ᶜᵐ.

1. Express service.

Library of Congress HE5900.N3 7–36143

NN 0065218 DLC ICJ

National school of railroading, *Chicago.*
Text book for locomotive firemen. Section 1–
Chicago, National school of railroading ₁ᶜ1907–
v. illus. (partly col.) diagrs. (partly fold.) 18ᶜᵐ.

1. Locomotives—Handbooks, manuals, etc.
8–14697

Library of Congress TJ607.N64

NN 0065219 DLC ICJ

National school of railroading, *Chicago.*
Text book for station agents & telegraphers ... Chicago, National school of railroading ₁ᶜ1907₁
2 pts. in 1 v. illus. (partly col.) diagrs. 18½ᶜᵐ.
CONTENTS.—section 1. Telegraphy.—section 2. General rules, signals,
movement of trains by telegraph, station work.

1. Railroads—Station service. 2. Railroads—Telegraph.
8–14540

Library of Congress TF652.N3

NN 0065220 DLC NN

National school of salesmanship, *Minneapolis, Minn.*
The fourth profession: salesmanship. Practical, systematic one-book course. Compiled from the lessons and
lectures written by the thirty-seven authors of the complete course. Minneapolis, Minn., The National school
of salesmanship (incorporated) ₁ᶜ1912₁
4 p. l., ₁3₁–348 p. front., illus., ports. 24½ᶜᵐ.

1. Salesmen and salesmanship.

Library of Congress HF5438.N3 12–22535

NN 0065221 DLC ICJ

The National school of salesmanship, *Minneapolis, Minn.*
... Questions on the entire course of the National school
of salesmanship and answers thereto. Minneapolis,
Minn. ₁ᶜ1907₁
155 p. 17½ᶜᵐ.

1. Salesmen and salesmanship.
7–36197

Library of Congress HF5438.N27

NN 0065222 DLC DHEW

**National school of salesmanship, Minneapolis,
Minn.**
Haddock, Frank Channing.
The will in salesmanship; or, How brain-power wins
business success; a lecture written for the National school
of salesmanship, Minneapolis, Minnesota, by Frank Channing Haddock ... ₁Minneapolis, Minn., The National
school of salesmanship, ᶜ1911₁

National school of typewriting, Oklahoma City.
Karam, Ameen S.
Essentials of shorthand; a simple and practical system of
shorthand, which can be mastered and put into practical use
in 30 days. Copyright ... by A. S. Karam. Oklahoma City,
Okl., National school of typewriting, ᶜ1927.

National school of visual education, Chicago
see
Chicago. National school of visual education.

National School Orchestra Association
see also
National Interscholastic Music Activities Commission.

VOLUME 407

National school primer, or An introduction
to any spelling book, with more than one
hundred engravings. Stereotype edition.
Portland:Waterhouse & company,1845.
48p. illus. 14½cm.

Is94
t1
v.2

NN 0065227 CtY

371.206 National School Public Relations Association.
NA Annual report.

Washington.
v. 28cm.

Each issue has also a distinctive title.

NN 0065228 IU

National School Public Relations Association.
Contact plus; a handbook of ideas for improving school-
community relations. Washington ₁1954₎
64p. illus. 22 cm.

1. Community and school. I. Title.

LC215.N38 370.19 54–1358 ‡

NN 0065229 DLC OrLgE OrPS OrU Or IU TxU

LB 2846 NATIONAL SCHOOL PUBLIC RELATIONS ASSOCIATION.
.N268 Education's meeting at the summit, portfolio of reports from the White House Conference on Education designed to help you build
continuing public interest in schools.
₁Washington,D.C., 1955₎
9 v. in 1

Includes addresses by Dwight D. Eisenhower,
R.M. Nixon, M.B. Folsom, S.M. Brownell, Neil
McElroy, and J.G. Stratton.

NN 0065230 InU

LB National School Public Relations Association.
2846 It starts in the classroom; a public relations handbook for
N3 classroom teachers. Washington ₁1951₎
64p. illus. 22 cm.

1. Public relations—Schools. I. Title.

LB2846.N3 371.2 51–5548

OCU HU NIC KMK OrPS FU KEmT CaBVaU OrCS MtU
NN 0065231 DLC OrU-M CU-I Or OrU IdU CU TU TxU

LB1525 National School Public Relations Association.
.N3
National Education Association of the United States. Dept.
of Elementary School Principals.
Janie learns to read; a handbook for parents whose child
will soon learn to read. ₁Washington₎ Dept. of Elementary
School Principals ₁and₎ National School Public Relations
Association, departments of the National Education Associa-
tion ₁1954₎

National School Public Relations Association.
Let's go to press; a guide to better school news reporting.
₁Washington₎ *1954.
48 p. illus. 28 cm.

1. School publicity. I. Title.

LB2846.N313 371.2 54–14821 ‡

IU ViU TU CSt OOxM OrPS OrU PPPL
NN 0065233 DLC OrAshS IdPI Or TxU CLSU CU MiU

National School Public Relations Association.
No news is bad news where schools are concerned. Washington, National School Public Relations Association in cooperation with the Oregon Education Association, *1955.
32 p. illus. 23 cm.

1. School publicity. I. Oregon Education Association. II. Title.

LB2846.N314 371.2 55–42725 ‡

NN 0065234 DLC Or OrU CSt NbU CU PPPL

National School Public Relations Association.
₁PR tool kit; a collection of current leaflets and newsletters on various phases of
school public relations. Washington, 1954₎
1 v. (loose-leaf) illus. 28cm.

NN 0065235 OrPS

National School Public Relations Association.
Parents and teachers at work
see under National Educational Association
of the United States. Research Division.

National School Public Relations Association.
Print it right: how to plan, write, and design school public
relations materials ₁by National School Public Relations Association Handbook Committee. Washington, 1953₎
48 p. illus. 28 cm.

1. Public relations—Schools. I. Title.

LB2846.N315 371.2 53–1278 ‡

OrCS OrMonO OrP OrU MtBC Wa PPPL
NN 0065237 DLC CaBViP IdPI Or OU TxU NN AU OrAshS

LC215 National School Public Relations Associa-
qN3 tion.
Report of the executive secretary,
19

New York, 19
v. 28½cm. annual.

Report year ends May 31.
Processed.
Issued with distinctive title also.

1. Community and school. Contents for
distinctive titles. x: National
Education Association of the

NN 0065238 OrCS

National School Public Relations Association.
Teaming up for public relations; a handbook for leaders
in American education. ₁Based on recommendations of the
National Conference on Public Relations in American Education, held in Chicago, April 30–May 1, 1952₎ Washington
₁1952₎
48 p. illus. 28 cm.

1. Public relations—Schools. I. Title.

LB2846.N32 371.2 52–3227 ‡

TxU ViU DGW OrU OrPS Wa PPPL
NN 0065239 DLC OrMonO OrSaW Or RU GU PSt OU PU

National School Public Relations Association.
This business about Johnny and his reading.
[Washington, 1955]
1 v. (various pagings) illus. 28 cm.
Cover title.
A collection of reprints issued in portfolio.
1. Reading (Elementary) 2. Flesch, Rudolf
Franz, 1911– Why Johnny can't read.
I. Title.

NN 0065240 MiDW PV

National School Public Relations Association
see also
American Association for Health, Physical Education,
and Recreation and National School Public
Relations Association Joint Handbook Committee;
School Public Relations Association.

National School Public Relations Association.
Public Relations Seminar, Lake Forest, Ill., 1955.
Why do the schools teach reading as they do

see under

Smith, Nila Banton, 1896–

National school series.
New York, 1851–

NN 0065243 DLC

National school service. vol. 1. Sept. 1, 1918–May 1, 1919.
Washington, D. C. The Committee on public informa-
tion, 1918–19.
1 v. (variously paged) 30ᶜᵐ. (bimonthly)
No more published.
"With this issue (Jan. 1, 1919) National school service passes to the
Division of educational extension, Department of the interior."
Directors: Sept. 1, 1918–Dec. 15, 1918, Guy Stanton Ford; Jan. 1, 1919–
May 1, 1919, J. J. Pettijohn.
Editors: Sept. 1, 1918–May 1, 1919, W. C. Bagley and others.

1. Education—Periodicals. I. Ford, Guy Stanton, 1873– II. Pet-
tijohn, John J., 1875– III. Bagley, William Chandler, 1874– IV.
U. S. Committee on public information. v. U. S. Bureau of education.
Division of educational extension.
E 19–373
———— Copy 2.
Library, U. S. Bur. of Education. J.11.N183

NN 0065244 DHEW NN

National School of the Young Women's Christian
Associations for Professional Study, New York
see Young Women's Christian Associations.
U.S. National School for Professional Study.

371.2 National School Service Institute.
N2778p Public relations primer; a practical
presentation of public relations fundamentals, especially adapted for schools by
Lew E. Permenter ₁and₎ Otis A. Crosby.
₁Chicago₎ National School Service Institute in cooperation with National Education Association, National Association of
State Teacher Association Secretaries and
the School Public Relations Association.
₁n.d.₎
24p. 23cm.

1.Public relations - Schools. I.Per-
menter, Lew E. II.National Education
Association. III.National Association of
State Teacher Association Secretaries.
IV.The School Public Relations
Association. V.Title.

NN 0065247 CLSU TU LU

371.2 National School Service Institute.
N2778p Public relations primer; a practical pres-
1946 entation of public relations fundamentals,
especially adapted for schools by Lew E.
Parmenter, executive manager ₁and₎ Otis A.
Crosby, public relations counsel, the National School Service Institute. 2d printing.
₁Chicago?₎ National School Service Institute
in cooperation with National Education Association, National Association of State
Teacher Association Secretaries and the
School Public Relations Association.[1946?]
27p. illus. 23cm.

1.Public relations - Schools. I.Parmen-
ter, Lew E. II.National Education Association of the U.S. III.National Association
of State Teacher Association Secretaries.
IV.School Public Relations Association.
V.Title.

NN 0065249 CLSU PSt TxU

VOLUME 407

371.2　National School Service Institute.　Public
N2778b　　Relations Committee.
　　　　　Building friends for education and keep-
　　ing them; the background of good public
　　relations especially adapted for schools,
　　by Lew Parmenter, executive manager, the
　　National School Service Institute.　Work-
　　ing with the press, by Otis A. Crosby.
　　[Chicago] National School Service Institute
　　in cooperation with the National Associa-
　　tion of Secretaries of State Teachers Asso-
　　ciations [1953?]
　　　27p.　illus.　23cm.

　　"This booklet represents the joint efforts and ideas of
　the Committee on Public Relations of the National Associa-
　tion of State Teachers Associations and the Public Rela-
　tions Committee of the National School Service Institute."
　Caption title of working with the press: How to work
　with the press.
　　　1. Public relations - Schools. I. Parmenter,
　Lew E. II. National Association of State Tea-
　chers Associations　　Committee on Public
　Relations. III. National Association of Sec-
　retaries of State Teachers Associations.
　IV. Crosby, Otis A.　　　V. Title. VI. Title:
　Working with the　　　press.

　NN　0065251　　CLSU

　　　　National school singer
　　　　　　see under　Root, George Frederick, 1820-
　　　　1895, comp.

　　　　National School Supplies and Equipment Association, *Chi-
　　　　cago*
　　　　　　see
　　　　National School Service Institute, *Chicago*.

　　National school supply association, Chicago.
　　　Better country schools. Published in
　　the interest of the school children of America,
　　by the National school supply association,
　　Chicago. (Chicago, 1921?)
　　　(24)p.　illus. (1 col.) 23cm.

　NN　0065254　　DHEW

NATIONAL SCHOOL SUPPLY ASSOCIATION, *Chicago*.
　...Proceedings and addresses [at the] annual convention...
　[no.]

[Chicago, 19　　　　　　　　　　　　　　　　23cm.
　v.

　19　　　　includes its: Articles of constitution.

1. Schools—Furniture, equipment, etc.—U.S.

　NN　0065255　　NN

　　National school supply association, Chicago.
　　　A study of present practices in the selec-
　　tion, purchase, and distribution of school sup-
　　plies. Issued by the National school supply
　　association.　Chicago, Ill. [1926?]
　　　41 p.　tables, forms.　25½cm.
　　　"The first of a series of such studies." The mater-
　　ial for the investigations was collected and assembled
　　by C. J. Anderson.　cf. Introductory.

　　　1. Schools—Furniture, equipment, etc.
　　　　　　　　　　LB3261.N28

　NN　0065256　　MiU

Lfa37　　National school teaching, what it is, and
G5　　　　what it is not, by a member of the Church of
1　　　　England.　London, J. Hatchard and son, 1846.
　　　　　Pamphlet

　　　(I. A member of the Church of England.

　NN　0065257　　CtY

　　　　National School Vocal Association
　　　　　　see also
　　　　National Interscholastic Music Activities Commission.

JOURNALISM
LB 3621　National School Yearbook Association.
A1 N3　　Judging standards for scholastic & collegiate
　　　　yearbooks.

　　　Memphis, Tenn.
　　　　　v. illus. 28 cm.

　　　Official publication.

　　　1. School yearbooks.　I. Title.

　NN　0065259　　OU

　　　　National schools, *Los Angeles*
　　　　　　see
　　　　Los Angeles.　National schools.

National schools for Manitoba. Winnipeg, 1892.
44p.　　　　　YA 17505

　NN　0065261　　DLC CaBViPA CaBViP DHEW

R.B.R.　National Schuetzen Bund of the United States
　　　　of America.
　　　　　Fest-Programm Fünftes Nationales Schützen-
　　　　Bundes-Fest vom 6ten bis 14ten Mai 1907, Charles-
　　　　ton, S. C. [Charleston, S. C., 1907]
　　　　　[24] p.　17 cm.
　　　　　German and English.

　　　　　1. National Schuetzen Bund of the United
　　　States of　　　　　　America.　I. Title.

　NN　0065262　　NcD

　　National science club, *Washington, D. C.*
　　　Journal of the National science club, Washington, D. C.

　　Washington, D. C., National science club, 189
　　　illus., ports. 23ᶜᵐ.

　　1. Science—Societies.

　　　　　　　　　　　CA 6—1039 Unrev'd

　NN　0065263　　DLC DSI

National science club, *Washington, D. C.*
　Proceedings of the National science club, Washington, D. C.
Jan. 1895–Apr. 1897.　Washington, D. C., Judd & Detweiler,
printers, 1895–97.
　　3 v. in 1.　23½ᵒᵐ.
　　Vol. 1, 1895, has title: Proceedings of the National science club for
　women, Washington, D. C.
　　Continued as: Journal of the National science club.
　　List of members in each volume.

　　1. Science—Societies.

　　　　　　　　　　　　8–1236 Revised

　NN　0065264　　DLC MB

　　National Science Club, *Washington, D. C.*
　　　see also Eistophos Science Club, *Washington, D. C.*

　　　　National science club for women, Washington, D. C.
　　　　　　see
　　　　National science club, Washington, D. C.

　　National Science Council.　Medical Sciences Division
　　　see
　　National Research Council.　Division of Medical
　　Sciences.

　　National Science Council (Ireland)
　　　Progress report.
　　Dublin, Stationery Off.
　　　v.　24 cm.

　　　1. Science and state—Ireland—Collected works. 2. National Sci-
　　ence Council (Ireland)
　　Q127.I 73N37a　　　　354'.415'0085505　　　73–645585
　　　　　　　　　　　　　　　　　　　　　　　MARC-S

　NN　0065268　　DLC

　　National Science Fair.
　　　Souvenir.
　　[Karachi]
　　　v. illus., ports. 25 cm.
　　　Fairs organized by the Pakistan Association of Scientists and
　　Scientific Professions.

　　　1. Science—Exhibitions—Pakistan—Period.　I. Pakistan Asso-
　　ciation of Scientists and Scientific Professions.
　　Q105.N3　　　　　　　　　　　　　S A 67–2094

　NN　0065269　　DLC NSyU

　　National Science Foundation
　　　see U. S.　*National Science Foundation*.

　　National Science Foundation Conference on Low
　　　Temperature Physics and Chemistry
　　　　see　International Conference on Low
　　　Temperature Physics.

　　National Science Museum, *Tokyo*
　　　see
　　Kokuritsu Kagaku Hakubutsukan, *Tokyo*.

VOLUME 407

National Science Teachers Association.
A bibliography of reference books for elementary
science
see under title

National Science Teachers Association.
Combatting prejudice through science teaching

see under

Burnett, Raymond Will, 1912–

507
N213f
National Science Teachers Association.
First national convention of the National
Science Teachers Association, Pittsburgh,
Pennsylvania, March 19,20,21,1953. A summary
report of proceedings, ed. by Herbert S. Zim.
Washington ₍1953₎
33p. 30cm.

Cover title.

1. Science. Study and teaching.

NN 0065275 OrCS OrU

507
N278
National Science Teachers Association.
If you want to do a science project.
₍Washington, ₎1954₎
20 p. illus. 23 cm.

Cover title.

1. Research. 2. Science. Scholarships,
fellowships, etc. I. Title.

NN 0065276 N

507
N27721
National science teachers association
Influence of the war on science
teaching.   ₍Washington?, The Assn.₎
1944.
cover-title, 48p. O. (Its Year book,
1944)

NN 0065277 IaU

Q145
.N16
National Science Teachers Association.

NSTA membership directory and handbook. 1955–

Washington, National Science Teachers Association.

National Science Teachers Association.
NSTA news bulletin
see under title

National science teachers association.
The place of science in the education of the consumer; a
statement prepared for the Consumer education study of the
National association of secondary-school principals, by the
National science teachers association. Washington, D. C., The
Consumer education study, ₍1945.

cover-title, 32 p. 23½ᵐᵐ.

"References and sources of information": p. 31–32.

1. Consumer education. 2. Science—Study and teaching.   I. Consumer education study.   II. Title.
46–503

Library of Congress   TX335.N37
₍4₎   330.47

ICJ
NN 0065280 DLC CaBVaU OrCS OrU Or NcGU ODW ViU

National Science Teachers Association.
Proceedings of the national convention.
₍Washington₎
v. illus. 28 cm.

Began in 1953 under title: Summary report of proceedings of the
national convention. Cf. New serial titles, 1961–65.
Vols. for 1954–55 not published. Cf. New serial titles, 1961–65.
Cover title   : A report of proceedings ₍of the₎ national
convention.

1. Science—Study and teaching—Congresses.   I. National Science
Teachers Association. A report of proceedings ₍of the₎ national
convention.

Q181.A1N32   74–200688

NN 0065281 DLC OU OrP OrU

TK152
.N2
National Science Teachers Association.

National Commission on Safety Education.
Safe use of electrical equipment ₍by₎ National Commission
on Safety Education and National Science Teachers Association of the National Education Association. Washington,
1951.

HV675
.N26
National Science Teachers Association.

National Commission on Safety Education.
Safety thru elementary science ₍by₎ National Commission
on Safety Education ₍and₎ National Science Teachers Association. Washington, National Education Association, 1949.

National Science Teachers Association.
School facilities for science instruction. John S. Richardson, editor, and the following members of a committee
of the National Science Teachers Association: Philip G.
Johnson, chairman, Robert H. Carleton ₍and others₎ Washington ₍1954₎
viii, 266 p. illus. 29 cm.
Bibliography: p. 257–262.

1. Science—Study and teaching.   I. Richardson, John Sanford,
1908–   ed. II. Title.
Q181.N384   507   54–4200

NcRS MiU AAP ScU PBL PP PU PPPL KEmT
NN 0065284 DLC CU NIC IU ViU TU OU MB WaU TxU

National Science Teachers Association.
Science bibliography

see under

Mallinson, George Greisen, 1917–

330
N219
National Science Teachers Association.
Science course content and teaching apparatus
used in schools and colleges of the United States.
[Ithaca? N.Y., 1947]
186 p.
1. Science. Study and teaching. 2. Scientific
apparatus and instruments. I. American Association of the Advancement of Science. Cooperative
Committee on Science Teaching. II. Title.

NN 0065286 DNAL

Ref
LB
1585
N37
National Science Teachers Association.
Science courses of study; a compilation of those
available in elementary, junior, and senior high
schools. Compiled in 1955. Washington, D.C.,
1955.
iii, 17 numb. l. 28cm.

NN 0065287 PPT

Q181
.S38
National science teachers association.

The Science teacher. v. 1–
Feb. 1934–
₍Normal, Ill., 1934–

National Science Teachers Association.
Science teaching ideas
see under title

National Science Teachers Association.
Science teaching today...
see under   Bruce, Guy V

Q181
.S386
National Science Teachers Association.

Selected science teaching ideas. 1952–
Washington, National Science Teachers Association.

National Science Teachers Association.
Specifications for commercial supplementary teaching materials for science, pre-college level; restricted to booklets,
charts, exhibits, models, and pictures. A report prepared
for the Consumer Education Study of the National Association of Secondary-School Principals. Washington, 1946.
61 p. 28 cm.

1. Science—Study and teaching. 2. Scientific apparatus and instruments.   I. Consumer Education Study.

LB3261.N385   372.35   52–65808

NN 0065292 DLC Or

National Science Teachers Association.

Star; a selection from the winning entries in the science
teacher achievement recognition program.
Washington, National Science Teachers Association.

NATIONAL SCIENCE TEACHERS ASSOCIATION.
Teaching conditions and the work week of
high school science teachers; reported at Cleveland, Ohio, July, 1948. Author, 1948.
18 p.   (its Bulletin, 1947–48.)

NN 0065294 Or

National science teachers association.
... Year book. 1944–
₍Washington?₎ 1944–
v. 24½ᵐ.

1944–   issued as a supplement to Science teacher.
Each volume has also distinctive title: 1944. Influence of the war on
science teaching.

1. Science—Study and teaching.   I. Science teacher. Supplement.
II. Title: Influence of the war on science teaching.
45–3567

Library of Congress   Q181.N385
₍3₎   507

NN 0065295 DLC OrCS MtU OCU MsU CU ICU

National science teachers association
see also
American council of science teachers.

VOLUME 407

National Science Teachers Association. *Advisory Council on Industry-Science Teaching Relations.*
How science teachers use business-sponsored teaching aids; report of a study. Washington ₁1950₁
36 p. illus. 28 cm.

1. Science—Study and teaching. 2. Teaching—Aids and devices.

Q181.N387   507   50–2537

NN   0065297   DLC Or

National Science Teachers Association. *Committee on School Facilities for Science Instruction.*
School facilities for science instruction. John S. Richardson, editor, and the following members of a committee of the National Science Teachers Association: Philip G. Johnson, chairman, Robert H. Carleton ₁and others₁ Washington, National Science Teachers Association ₁1954₁
viii, 266 p. illus. 29 cm.
Bibliography : p. 257–262.
1. Science — Study and teaching.   I. Richardson, John Sanford, 1908–   ed. II. Title.

Q181.N3874 1954   507   54–4200 rev

TOU MeB OrMonO OrPS OrU Wa
NN   0065298   DLC MtBC MtU Or OrAshS OrCS OrLgE

National Science Teachers Association.
Committee on Special Bulletins.
Science in secondary schools today

see under

National Association of Secondary-School
Principals.

National Science Teachers Association. *Future Scientists of America Foundation*
see
Future Scientists of America Foundation.

National scientific documentation centre,
Delhi.
Report.
New Delhi, National physical laboratory of India.
v.   illus.   22cm.

Annual.
1. Science—Research—India. 2. Science—India—Bibl.

NN   0065301   NN

National scientific documentation centre, Delhi.
Union catalogue series.
Bangalore [etc.]   v.   24–27cm.

1. Bibliography--Catalogues   --Libraries--India.

NN   0065302   NN

T
1
N24   **The National scientific journal.**
v.1–
Apr.? 1881–
Chicago, The National Scientific
Association.
v. illus. 35 cm. semimonthly.

1. Technology - Period. I. National
Scientific Association.

NN   0065303   DSI ICJ ICHi

National Scientific Laboratories, *Richmond.*
Money making formulas. Richmond ₁1921₁
unpaged. 28 cm.

1. Receipts.   I. Title.

T49.N3   55–52060 ‡

NN   0065304   DLC

GC177
.B7   **National Scientific Laboratories, inc., Washington, D. C.**

Bralove, A   L
A study of the errors of the bathythermograph; final report, by A. L. Bralove ₁and₁ E. I. Williams, Jr. Navy Dept., Bureau of Ships, Electronics Division. Contract NObsr 52348, June 30, 1952. Serial no. NE 051247, task 7. Washington, National Scientific Laboratories ₁1952?₁

National Scientific Register
see U. S. *National Scientific Register.*

331.31
N21n   **National Scottish Conference on the Employment of Children and Kindred Subjects, Glasgow, 1909.**
National Scottish Conference on the Employment of Children and Kindred Subjects/ Held under the auspices of the Scottish Council for Women's Trades.   Glasgow? ₑ1909?₁
69p. 22cm.

1. Children--Employment--Scotland. 2. Children--Law--Scotland. 3. Juvenile delinquents--Scotland. I. Scottish Council for Women's Trades.

NN   0065307   IU

National scrap harvest; handbook for workers
see under   [Farm equipment institute,
Chicago]

National Screw Machine Products Association.
Basic principles of cost control for the screw machine products industry. 2d ed. Cleveland, °1951.
32 p. forms. 30 cm.

1. Screw machine products industry—Accounting.   I. Title.

HF5686.S4N3 1951   338.4721882   51–5272

NN   0065309   DLC

National Screw Machine Products Association.
Buyers' guide for design of screw machine products, prepared by Committee on Manufacturing Standards of NSMPA. 2d ed. ₁Cleveland₁ °1950.
16 p. illus. 23 cm.

1. Screws.   I. Title.

TJ1338.N3 1950   621.882   51–4891

NN   0065310   DLC

National screw machine products association.
Manual for on-the-job instruction of screw machine personnel. 1st ed. Cleveland, O., National screw machine products association, °1943.
107 p. illus. 23 x 18ᵐ.
Reproduced from type-written copy.

1. Screw-cutting machines.
                                        44–4970
Library of Congress   TJ1222.N3
                            ₁4₁   621.94

NN   0065311   DLC WaS OC1 OLak O NNC

National Screw Machine Products Association.
Manual on statistical quality control. Prepared by American Society for Quality Control and Quality Control Committee of N. S. M. P. A.   [Cleveland 1953–54]
2 v. in 1. illus.
Vol. 2 has title: Manual on quality control charts.

NN   0065312   MH–BA

National Screw Machine Products Association.
NSMPA manuals. Cleveland, National Screw Machine Products Association, 1953.
v. illus.

1. Screw-cutting machines. 2. Machine-tools.

NN   0065313   MsSM

National Screw Machine Products Association.
Relationship of thread percentage to thread strength in tapped holes; an investigation by the Manufacturing Standards Committee. Cleveland ₁°1950₁
28 p. diagrs. 28 cm.
Cover title.

1. Screw-threads, Standard.   I. Title.

TJ1340.N3   621.882   51–4889

NN   0065314   DLC

National screw machine products association.
The story of a trade association, NSMPA.   ₁Cleveland, 1945₁
10 l. illus. 28cm.

1. Trade and open prices association.   July 11, 1949
N. Y. P. L.

NN   0065315   NN MB NNC

National screw thread commission
see
U. S. *National screw thread commission.*

National script for India (A collection of the opinions of some eminent European and other scholars) [Benares, Nagari Pracharini Sabra, 1942?]

NN   0065317   MH

National sculpture review. v. 1–
Dec. 1951–
₁New York, National Sculpture Society₁
v. in   illus., ports. 28 cm. quarterly.

1. Sculpture—U. S.—Period.   I. National Sculpture Society, New York.

NB1.N29   735.73   58–31323

NN   0065318   DLC CL KU MoU OCU TxU NcGU

National sculpture society, New York.

₁Lenz, Hugh F   ₁
The Alfred David Lenz system of lost wax casting. New York, National sculpture society, 1933.

National Sculpture Society, New York.
American sculptors series
see under   American sculptors series.

VOLUME 407

National Sculpture Society, New York.   **4072.132**
Art as an educational force and a source of wealth.
= [New York. The Willett Press. 190–?] (14) pp. Plates. 8°.

F7661 — Fine arts. — Art education.

NN 0065321   MB

National sculpture society, *New York.*
... Catalogue of a collection of small bronzes, arranged
by the National sculpture society. February 8–March 2,
1913. [Buffalo? 1913]

10, [1] p. 20ᶜᵐ.

At head of title: Buffalo fine arts academy, Albright art gallery.
Caption title: Exhibition of small bronzes collected ... under the auspices
of the Art society of Pittsburgh.

1. Bronzes—Exhibitions.   I. Buffalo fine arts academy.   II. Art society
of Pittsburgh.

CA 17–2746 Unrev'd

Library of Congress   NB1230.N3 1913

NN 0065322   DLC NN

National sculpture society, *New York.*
... Catalogue of an exhibition of contemporary American
sculpture held under the auspices of the National sculpture
society; June 17–October 2 ... 1916 ... [Buffalo, Printed by
the Courier co., 1916]

118 p., 1 l. incl. front., plates, ports. 20ᶜᵐ.

At head of title: The Buffalo fine arts academy, Albright art gallery.
Last leaf blank for "Notes."
"Biographical data of sculptors represented": p. [85]–117.

1. Sculpture, American—Exhibitions.   2. Sculptors, American.   3. Artists—Portraits.   I. Buffalo fine arts academy.   II. Title: Contemporary American sculpture.

Library of Congress   NB212.N25   42–45716

NN 0065323   DLC NIC DSI IaU NBuU MiD

National sculpture society, *New York.*
... Catalogue of small bronzes collected by the National
sculpture society, December 17, 1912, to January 6, 1913.
The John Herron art institute ... [Indianapolis? 1912]

[7] p. 21ᶜᵐ.

At head of title: Art association of Indianapolis, Ind.
"Collected ... under the auspices of the Art society of Pittsburgh."

1. Bronzes—Exhibitions.   I. Art association of Indianapolis, Indiana.
John Herron art institute.   II. Art society of Pittsburgh.

CA 17–2747 Unrev'd

Library of Congress   NB1230.N3 1912

NN 0065324   DLC NN

NATIONAL sculpture society, *New York.*
Catalogue of the second annual exhibition.
[N. Y. 1895.] 52 pp. Illus. 12°.

NN 0065325   MB

National Sculpture Society, New York.
[Catalogues of exhibitions and other publications...   New
York, 1927.] 2 v.   fronts., illus., plans, plates. 12°.

Binder's title.
Some plates printed on both sides.
Pamphlets dated: 1895–1910.
Includes advertising matter.

I. Sculpture, U. S.—Exhibitions—   U. S.—N. Y.—New York.
N. Y. P. L.   March 6, 1928

NN 0065326   NN

National sculpture society, New York.
...Classified sculptural services and supplies.   [New York]
1941.   16 p.   21cm.

2. ed.

I. Sculpture—Equipment and   supplies—Direct.—U. S.—N. Y.—
New York.   New York.
N. Y. P. L.   February 28, 1944

NN 0065327   NN

National sculpture society, New York.
...A collection of small bronzes...
see under   Buffalo fine arts academy.

National Sculpture Society, New York.
Constitution.
= [New York.] 1901. 21 pp. 16°.

NN 0065329   MB NjP

National sculpture society, *New York.*
Contemporary American sculpture.   The California palace
of the Legion of honor, Lincoln park, San Francisco, April
to October, MCMXXIX.   [New York, Press of the Kalkhoff
company, ©1929]

xv p., 1 l., 352 p. incl. illus., plates. 28½ᶜᵐ.

Seal of National sculpture society on t.-p.
"Issued for the exhibition held by the National sculpture society in
co-operation with the trustees of the California palace of the Legion of
honor."
Contains biographical sketches.

1. Sculpture, American.   2. Sculptors, American.   I. California palace of the Legion of honor, San Francisco.   II. Title.
                                                    29–8040

Library of Congress   NB212.N27

OrCS NcC CoU MtBC Or
CU–I NIC PSt NcD FTaSU MeB Wa WaS WaTC IdB OrU
OO OCl OCU OO MiU OOxM OLak MH DDO TxU WaSp PLF
NN 0065330   DLC ViU WaU MdBWA MB PPPM Ok TU OFH

National Sculpture Society, *New York.*
Enduring memory, in stone, in metal, in beauty.   [New
York, 1946?]

[52] p.   illus., plates.   35 cm.

1. Sepulchral monuments.   2. Sculpture.   I. Title.

NB1800.N3   731.76   A 49—1976*
Grosvenor Library
for Library of Congress   [56f⅓]

ViU PU MB IU IaU TU NRU PV OU MiDA
DI MdBP MH AU PSt ScCleU DDO PPAmP ICRL MiD TxU
NN 0065332   NBuG MtU WaS IdU OrP OrCS Or DLC NN

National sculpture society, New York.
Exhibition catalogues.   N.Y., 1948–62
no. in   v.   21cm.

Unbound.
Contents.
1 Garden sculpture, May 19 – Sept. 15, 1948.
2 Sculpture exhibition, Mar. 23 – Apr. 13, 1962.

NN 0065333   NNMM

National sculpture society, *New York.*
Exhibition of American sculpture catalogue; 156th
street west of Broadway, New York, April fourteenth to
August first, MCMXXIII.   [New York, ©1923]

xiv p., 1 l., 372 p., 1 l. incl. illus., plates. 26ᶜᵐ.

Half-title: Exhibition of American sculpture held by the National sculpture society.

1. Sculpture, American—Exhibitions.   2. Sculptors, American.   3. Medals—Exhibitions.
                                                    23–9844

Library of Congress   NB212.N3

ViU WaSp CU MB MdBWA
MtU WaT IdU WaS TU DDO MiU OCU OClW OU OO OCl
NN 0065334   DLC NcD NcRS FMU DSI MU CoU Or OrU

National sculpture society, *New York.*
Exhibition of sculpture under the auspices of the National
sculpture society, open to the public April 3 to May 2, 1940 ...
at the Whitney museum of American art ...   New York city.
[New York, Plantin press, 1940]

[16] p. incl 144 pl. on 73 l.   25ᶜᵐ.

"Foreword" signed: Herbert Adams.

1. Sculpture, American—Exhibitions.   I. Whitney museum of American art, New York.   II. Adams, Herbert, 1858–
                                        42–2756
Library of Congress   NB212.N33
                             [2]   735.0973

NN 0065335   DLC OU DSI CU OClSA NIC NN ViU NNC

National Sculpture Society.
Guide. Exhibition of American sculpture
beginning April 27, 1929
see under   California palace of the
Legion of honor, San Francisco.

National sculpture society, New York.

Schevill, Ferdinand, 1868–
Karl Bitter; a biography, by Ferdinand Schevill; is-
sued under the auspices of the National sculpture society.
Chicago, Ill., The University of Chicago press [1917]

National Sculpture Society, New York.

NB1
N29

National sculpture review.   v. 1–
Dec. 1951–
[New York, National Sculpture Society]

National sculpture society, New York.
National sculpture society... 1948–1950.
New York, 1950.
88 p.   19 cm.

NN 0065339   PPPM

National sculpture society, New York.
National sculpture society, American fine arts building...New
York city.   [New York, 1910?]   14 p.   illus.   22½cm.

1. Sculpture—Assoc. and org.   —U. S.
N. Y. P. L.   October 17, 1938

NN 0065340   NN

National sculpture society, **New York.**
                                    FOR OTHER EDITIONS
                                    SEE MAIN ENTRY
Adams, *Mrs.* Adeline Valentine (Pond) 1859–
The spirit of American sculpture, by Adeline Adams; writ-
ten for the National sculpture society.   New York, 1929.

National sculpture society, New York.
Year book.   1948–   *New York.*
annual.

1. Sculpture — Yearbooks

NN 0065342   NNMM

National Sea Fisheries Protection Association.
International conference of representatives
of maritime powers ...
see under   International Conference of
Representatives of Maritime Powers, London,
1890.

National sea fisheries protection association.
Proposed ministry for the fisheries; mem-
orandum... for submission to the Right Hon, R. E.
Prothero, M. P., M. V. O., president of the Board
of agriculture and fisheries, by deputation on
Wednesday, November 27th, 1918 ...   London,
The association, 1918.
35 p.   F.

NN 0065344   CaBViPA

VOLUME 407

The National sea scout log. v. 1–8, no. 4; Apr. 1936–Sept. 1943. ₁New York, 1936–43₁

8 v. illus. 28ᶜᵐ. bimonthly (except July)

Caption title.
Official publication for sea scout leaders, published by Boy scouts of America.
Editor: 1936–41, T. J. Keane.—1942–43, G. E. Chronic.
Merged into Scouting.

1. Boy scouts—Period. ɪ. Keane, Thomas Joseph, 1894–   ed. ɪɪ. Chronic, George E., ed. ɪɪɪ. Boy scouts of America. ɪᵥ. Title: Sea scout log.

Library of Congress   VK544.A25   39–25109 Revised

₁r46c2₁   369.43

NN   0065345   DLC

National Seal Company.
On the science of sealing bottles and jars...
see under   Owens, R   Stuart.

National seamen's union
see
International seamen's union of America.

National Seamen's Union (*Canada*)
see
Canadian Seamen's Union.

National Secondary Education Association.
Bulletin.

L13
.N468

Secondary education. v. ₁1₁–14, no. 8; Jan. 1931–Apr./June 1950. ₁Washington, etc.₁

NATIONAL SECRET TELEPHONE COMPANY.
The telephone.

N. Y. [188–?] 14 pp. 8°.

NN   0065350   MB

National Secretaries Association
see
National Secretaries Association (International)

National Secretaries' Association (*International*)
The Secretary.

HF5547
.A2S395

₁Kansas City, Mo., National Secretaries Assn.₁

National Secretaries Association (*International*)
Some history of the organization

see under

McMahon, Blanche C

National Secretaries Association (International)
see also   Ohio Secretarial Institute, Ohio State University, Columbus.

National Secretaries Association (International)
Forest City Chapter.
Roster and officer guide.   Cleveland, O.
Cover title.

NN   0065355   OCl

National Secretaries Association (International)
St. Paul chapter.
Bulletin. 1,   1942 ?4

NN   0065356   MnHi

The National secretary

see

The Secretary.

The National secular almanack
see   National Secular Society.
Almanack.

National Secular Society.
Almanack. 1870–

K40
N22

London, Freethought Pub.Co.
22cm.   annual.

Title varies:1873–1874,The National secular almanack.
Editors: Charles Bradlaugh, and others.

NN   0065359   CtY NcU MH–AH

National secular society.
... An apology for his resignation of the office of a vice-president of the National secular society
see under   Gilmour, J   P.

National Secular Society.
Laws against religious liberty
see under title

National Secular Society.
Leaflet.
no.
London, 19
v.   8°.

NN   0065362   NN

National secular society.
National secular society ... principles, objects, and rules. ₁187–?₂
4 p.

Volume of pamphlets.

NN   0065363   NNC

National Secular Society.
The secular song and hymn book
see under   Besant, Annie (Wood),
1847–   , editor.

National Securities and Research Corporation, *New York*.
Annual report. National securities series.

₁New York₁
v. diagrs. 28 cm.
Report year ends Apr. 30.

HG4530.N3   332.63   49–21669*‡

NN   0065365   DLC OrStbM

National securities and research corporation, *New York*.
Guide book to Independence fund. New York, Independence fund of North America, inc. ₁ᶜ1932₁

1 v. tables (part fold.) diagrs. (part fold.) 19½ᶜᵐ.
Loose-leaf.

44–28261 Revised
Library of Congress   HG4497.N37

NN   0065366   DLC

National securities and research corporation, New York.

HG4501
.I 739

Investment timing; a weekly service based upon economic and technical factors; for timing major and intermediate movements of security prices and cyclical trends of business.

New York, N. Y., Economics & investment department, National securities & research corporation, 19

National securities and research corporation, New York.

HD9725
.M6

Mott, L   Scudder.
Post-war backlogs and business ₁by₁ L. Scudder Mott ... New York, National securities & research corporation, Economics and investment dept., 1943.

National securities and research corporation, New York.

HG4527
.B65

Bradshaw, Leslie Havergal.
Scientific developments from the investor's viewpoint ₁by₁ Leslie Havergal Bradshaw ... New York, N. Y., Boston ₁etc.₁ Economics and investment dept., National securities & research corporation ₁1944₁

National Securities & Research Corporation New York₁

HG
4921
N27+

What every salesman should know about mutual investment funds. ₁New York, c1951₁
1 v. (various paging) 29cm.

1. Investments, American. 2. Salesmen and salesmanship. I. Title.

NN   0065370   NIC MH–BA TxU NNU–W

NATIONAL SECURITIES and RESEARCH CORPORATION, New York.
What every salesman should know about mutual investment funds. Rev. ed. [New York, 1955, c1951] 1 v. (loose-leaf) 30cm.

"Bibliography on salesmanship, sales training, promotion and management," [2] p. at back of book.

1 Investment trusts.

NN   0065371   NN NNU–W OCl

National security act of 1947; P. L. 80–253.
₁Ithaca, N. Y., Cornell Law Library, 1947₁
1 v. (various pagings) 29cm.

Law
KF
7204
.573
A15
1947

On spine: Legislative history; unification of the armed services.

ʹ1. United States--Defenses.ʹ2. United States. Laws, statutes, etc. ₁National security act of 1947.ʹ3. Legislative histories. ʹI. Cornell University. Law School. Library. ʹII. United States. Laws, statutes, etc. ₁National secu rity act of 1947.ʹIII. Title: Unifica tion of the armed services.

NN   0065372   NIC

VOLUME 407

National Security Agency
see
U. S. *National Security Agency.*

National security and Biblical education
see under   Howard association, London.

National security association.

Twiford, William Richard.
Think or be shot! Our defense against war, Hitler, the machine and depressions, by William Richard Twiford ... **Miami,** Fla., National security association ₁*1941₎

National Security Industrial Association. Procurement Advisory Committee.
Criteria recommended to be considered by the Department of Defense in establishing policy and procedures for contractor maintenance. [Washington, 1955?]
6 p.
Letter of transmittal attached to first page.
1. U.S. - Armed Forces - Procurement.
2. Military supplies - U.S. 3. Public contracts- U.S. I. Title. II. Title: Policy and procedures for contractor maintenance.

NN 0065376   AMAU

UA23
A1N28
National Security Congress, Washington, D.C., 1916.
Proceedings of the National Security Congress, under the auspices of the National Security League, Washington, January 20-22, 1916. New York, the National Security League, ₁1916₎
407 p. 24cm.

1. U.S. - De   fenses. I. National Security League.

IaU WaU-L Or MiU MB MiD NN NBuHi
NN 0065377   CSt-H WaSp MtBC KMK ViU IU DNW NjP

National Security Congress, Washington, D. C., 1916. *4222.132
Program.
= [Washington. 1916.] (8) pp. 25 cm.
The Congress was held under the auspices of the National Security League, Inc.

K7532 — National Security League, Inc., Washington, D. C.

NN 0065378   MB

National Security Council
see U. S. *National Security Council.*

National Security Industrial Association.
Directory of officers, committees and members.

New York.
v. 28 cm.

UA18.U5N372   56-29182 ‡

NN 0065380   DLC

National Security Industrial Association.
Report.
₁New York₎
v. illus. 28 cm. annual.

Report year ends July 31.

UA18.U5N374   56-2069 ‡

NN 0065381   DLC

National security league.

Hart, Albert Bushnell, 1854–   *ed.*
America at war; a handbook of patriotic education references, ed. by Albert Bushnell Hart for the Committee on patriotism through education of the National security league, with preface by James M. Beck. New York, Pub. for the National security league by George H. Doran company, 1918.

National security league.
Americanism and the Americanization problem...
Somers, N.Y., 1918.

NN 0065383   NjP

NATIONAL SECURITY LEAGUE.
Americanization service; what you can do for America through Americanization of the foreign-born. New York city: National Security League [1918] 12 p. 22½cm.

869421A. 1. Americanization

NN 0065384   NN

National Security League.
...Americanization: what is it? What to do... What you can do for America through Americanization of the foreign-born. ₁New York, 1919.₎   11(1) p.   nar. 8°.   (National Security League. Patriotism through education; organized education series.)

1. Americanization.   2. Series.
N. Y. P. L.   January 19, 1920.

NN 0065385   NN NjP MB MH

National security league.
Annual meeting.

New York city, National security league
v. 23ᶜᵐ.

1. U. S.— Defenses. 2. European war, 1914–

                                          17–30659

Library of Congress   UA23.A1N4

NN 0065386   DLC MB

UA23
.A1N37
National security league.
...Annual report of... president.
New York.

NN 0065387   DLC

National Security League.   355.06161
                                                          1
Annual report of the National Security League, Inc. ...
New York ₁19₎
v.   23ᶜᵐ.
Title varies: 1917, Annual meeting of the National Security League.
Other variations.

NN 0065388   ICJ MB NN

National security league.
...Annual report upon the educational work of the National security league 1917/18.
New York city, National security league, 1918–
1 v. 23 cm.

NN 0065389   DHEW

National security league, inc.
... Ask me another! Questions and answers on the Constitution of the United States. 2d ed. [c1927]
(In Pamphlets, Vo. 14)

NN 0065390   NcD

National Security League,   42298.307
Before the war, during the war, after the war. [The work of the League.]
= New York. 1918. 15 pp. 23 cm.

L7438 — European War, 1914– . United States.

NN 0065391   MB

UA23
.A1N42
National security league.
...Bulletin...
v. 1, no. 1
Feb. 1918–
New York city, ₁1918–

NN 0065392   DLC NjP MB

National Security League.
By-laws of the National Security League.   New York, 1916.
4 l.   8°.
Cover-title.

1. Defence, U. S.
N. Y. P. L.   October 27, 1916.

NN 0065393   NN

National Security League.
Correspondence course in patriotism.
no. 1–
New York ₁1916?   f°.
nos.

Contents: no. 1. The importance of the war.
no. 2. The great difference.
no. 3. The meaning of America.
no. 4. True democracy.

no. 5. America — a land of opportunity.
no. 6. The road to success in America.
no. 7. Basic principles of democratic government.
no. 8. Our government protects us.
no. 9. America led the world in freedom of church, speech and press.
no. 10. The right of private property.

1. Patriotism.
N. Y. P. L.   October 1, 1923.

NN 0065395   NN

National Security League.
English-French handbook for the use of United States Soldiers
see under   Downer, Charles Alfred, 1866–1930.

National Security League.
Editorial endorsement of universal military instruction and training by leading newspapers throughout the country.   New York, National Security League, 1919.
11 p. Pamphlet. nar. 8°.
"Patriotism through education. Universal military instruction and training series."

NN 0065397   MH OO

VOLUME 407

National Security League.   4329-333
The flying squadron of speakers. A propaganda for patriotic service.
= [New York. 1919.] 19 pp. 23 cm.

L8144 — T.r. — Americanization.

NN 0065398   MB Or

NATIONAL SECURITY LEAGUE.
French-English hand book, for the use of
United States soldiers. New York, National
Security League.

pp.64.

NN 0065399   MH

NATIONAL SECURITY LEAGUE.
...Future work. New York, 1919. 8 p. 21½cm.

782402A. 1. Defense—U.S.

NN 0065400   NN

*BROAD-
SIDE   National Security League.
1917
.N27   Gen. Robt. L. Bullard becomes head of
Security League. New York [1917?]
broadside. 19 x 14cm.

      1. Bullard, Robert Lee, 1861—
I. Title.

NN 0065401   ViU

National Security League.
Germany self-convicted, by the words of her
own rulers, philosophers ...
      see under title

National security league.
                            FOR OTHER EDITIONS
                            SEE MAIN ENTRY
Hart, Albert Bushnell, 1854–
Handbook of the war for public speakers, edited by Albert
Bushnell Hart, and Arthur O. Lovejoy, for the Committee on
patriotism through education of the National security league.
New York, National security league, 1918.

National security league.
Hart, Albert Bushnell, 1854–   ed.
Handbook of the war for readers, speakers and teachers, ed.
by Albert Bushnell Hart and Arthur O. Lovejoy for the National
security league. 2d ed. New York, National security
league, 1918.

National security league.
Frothingham, Arthur Lincoln, 1859–
... Handbook of war facts and peace problems, by Arthur
L. Frothingham ... New York, Committee on organized education National security league, 1919.

National Security League.   4222.138
Home defense leagues: suggestions for their organization.
= New York. [1917.] 4 pp. 23 cm.
Deals with United States national defense.

This card was printed at the Boston   *Public Library, June 26, 1917.*

L1883 — National defense. United States.

NN 0065406   MB

BAA-fda National security league.
1917   How Germany wanted the world to look; a
N3   graphic explanation of why there is a war
New York, National security league [1917?]
col.map. 30x50cm. on sheet 47½x55cm.

No scale.
"From the World Sunday magazine, October 28,
1917."
Text in lower margin.

      1. World—1917? 2. European war, 1914-1918—
Territorial ques-   tions—Germany—1917?

NN 0065407   IU

National security league.
The Lawrence plan for education in citizenship.
No. 1-
New York, National security league, 1918-
v. 23 cm.   (Lawrence plan leaflets)

NN 0065408   DHEW

National security league.
Military training; objections and answers. New York, Nat.
security league [1926] 10 p. 18cm.

1. Military service, Compulsory.
N. Y. P. L.   June 29, 1945

NN 0065409   NN

National Security League.
[Minor publications.]
123681

NN 0065410   ICJ

National security league.
Miscellaneous pamphlets.   New York, National
security league, 1917-
Pam.   14.5-23 cm.

NN 0065411   OrPR

National Security League.
Money, munitions and ships; luncheon under auspices of
the National Security League, Hotel Astor, New York City,
April 13, 1918...   New York: National Security League [1918].
39(1) p.   8°.

Frederic R. Coudert, toastmaster; speakers, Hon. Robert L. Owen...Col.
Samuel McRoberts...Hon. Warren G. Harding.

1. European war, 1914- .—Ad-   dresses, sermons, etc. 2. Title.
N. Y. P. L.   April 29, 1919.

NN 0065412   NN OO

NATIONAL SECURITY LEAGUE.
The National Security League...before the war, during the
war, after the war... New York, 1918.   15 p.   23x10cm.

782577A. 1. Defense—U.S.

NN 0065413   NN OU

National Security League.
The National Security League, Inc. What it is and why, what
it has done and is doing; a national defense catechism for the busy
man or woman. New York: [the league.] 1917. 19(1) p.   24°.

1. Defence, U. S.
N. Y. P. L.   July 25, 1917.

NN 0065414   NN OrPR OU MB

National security league.
National security league quarterly ... v. 1–v. 6, no. 3; Mar.
1927–Sept. 1932. New York, National security league [1927–
32]
6 v. in 1. illus. 29½cm.
No more published.

                                                34-32630
Library of Congress   UA23.A1N425

NN 0065415   DLC NN MB ICJ DCaE

UA23   National security league.
.A1N43   ... Officers, committees and branches.
New York City, National Security League, Inc.,
1916.
62 p. 22.5. cm.
At head of title: The National Security League,
Inc.

NN 0065416   DLC NN

National Security League.   4229a.308
Organization of the training and instruction of men registered for
the draft.
= New York. [1918.] (8) pp. 22 cm.

L7439 — Drafts. — United States. A. .n. Army. — European War, 1914– .
United States.

NN 0065417   MB

National Security League.   *4229A.305.3
Our charter of liberty; what it means to every American. A series
of articles explaining the Constitution of the United States. Prepared for the celebration of Constitution Day, September 17,
1919.
— New York. 1919. 95 pp. [Patriotism through education. Constitution series. No. 3.] 22 cm.

N7317 — S.r.c — United States. Constitutions, etc. 1780. Works about.

NN 0065418   MB

National Security League.
... Our job
      see under Hubbard, Elijah Kent, 1869–

NATIONAL SECURITY LEAGUE.
Our peril from Germany's aggressive growth
and why she wants peace now. Designed and
compiled for the league by W.H.Gardiner,
historical text by H.E.Barnes. New York,
1917.

Maps. Broadside in folder form.

I. Gardiner, William Howard, 1875–

NN 0065420   MH

VOLUME 407

National security league.
 [Pamphlets on patriotism]   New York, The League [1917-24]
 69 pts. in 3 v.   23-31cm.

 Many items are parts of the League's "Patriotism through
education" series.
 [Vol. 3] is a portfolio.
 Imperfect: [v. 2] 10th-11th, 14th and 20th pts. wanting.

 Partial contents. - [v. 1] Libby, M. F. Suggestions for the
organization of a state for patriotic education. [1918?]- McElroy,
R. M. Annual report upon the educational work of the National
Security League, 1917-18. - Meier, A. G. How the war was made

in Germany. 1918. - Sperry, E. E. Pan-Germanism. 1918. -
Van Tyne, C. H. Democracy's educational problem. - Beck, J. M.
The six fundamental principles of the Constitution. 1919. -
Lydecker, C E. Annual report. 1919. - Lydecker, C. E.
Militia. - McElroy, R. M. The Constitution and industrial demo-
cracy. 1919. - McElroy, R. M. How the Constitution saved the
nation. 1919. - Root, E. The Constitution of the United States.
1919. - Taking his place in industry. [1919]- Willoughby, W. W.
The fundamentals of the American political system.   3d ed.
1919. - Willoughby, W. F. Some fundamental political principles.

 3d ed. 1919. - Americanization: what is it? - What to do. [1920]-
Menken, S. S Annual report. 1924. - West, H. L. A catechism
of the Constitution of the United States in twelve lessons. 21st ed.
[1924]
 Contents of [v. 2-3] listed at front of respective vols.

 1. Patriotism - U.S.

NN 0065423   CU

D570   National security league.
.A2N35   Patriotism through education.
    Congress series.   2d set.

NN 0065424   DLC

National Security League.
Congress of constructive patriotism, *Washington, D. C.*, 1917.
 Proceedings of the Congress of constructive patriotism,
held under the auspices of the National security league, Washington, D. C., January 25-27, 1917. New York, National security league, inc. [1917]

National Security League.
 Proceedings of the National Security Congress
  see under   National Security Congress,
Washington, D.C., 1916.

National security league.

Pavey, Frank Dunlap, 1860-
 ... Proposed plan for collection of the foreign debt of
the United States, settlement of German reparations and
establishment of an international gold currency, by Frank
D. Pavey ... Revised and reprinted for the National
security league. New York, N. Y. [1922]

National Security League.
 Report to members...

New York, 19   nar. f°.
 v.

 Monthly.
 Caption-title.
 Broadsides.

1. Defence—U. S.
N. Y. P. L.   January 8, 1930

NN 0065428   NN

National security league.
 Taking his place in industry. How
the disabled soldier and sailor will be
put in a good job. N.Y. , The League
[1919]

 11 p.

NN 0065429   OU 00

National security league.
 Teachers' patriotic leaflets.   New York [1918]
 v. 1-

NN 0065430   NjP

National security league.
 Universal military training; a catechism in twelve lessons,
issued by National security league...   New York, Business
men's nat. service league [1920]   18 p.   23cm.

1. Military service, Compulsory.
N.Y.P.L.   June 29, 1945

NN 0065431   NN MB

National Security League.
 Universal obligatory military training and service.   New
York [1916].   24 p.   8°.
 Cover-title.

1. Military service (Compulsory).   U.S.
N. Y. P. L.   October 27, 1916.

NN 0065432   NN

National Security League.
 The vote by states in the Senate and House of Representatives
on preparedness measures; a record of Congress prior to call for
mobilization of the National Guard, June 18, 1916.   New York:
National Security League, Inc., 1916.   20 p.   8°.

1. Defence. U. S.
N. Y. P. L.   October 27, 1916.

NN 0065433   NN OU

UA29   National security league.
.N25   We are unprepared, issued by the National security
   league.
   New York city, [1915?]

NN 0065434   DLC

National security league.
 Why we are at war; why you must help;
what you can do.   N.Y. 1917

 1 p 1, 12 [2] p.

NN 0065435   OO OU

National Security League. Bordentown Branch.
 Historic pageant of Bordentown, New Jersey
  see under title

National security league.   Bureau of pat-
 riotism through education.
  ...How to pronounce the war name.
 N.Y. National security league....B'deice.

 9.8 x 23 in. fld.

 At head of title: Courtesy of N.Y. Evening Mail

 1. Nudes, Personal, 2. Names, Geographical.

NN 0065437   OO

National Security League.   Chicago Branch.
 Purpose, organization, and a few facts as to the unprepared-
ness of our country...   [Chicago: the league, 1915]   101.   16°.

 At head of title: National Security League. Folded letter and blank form
attached to last leaf.

1. Defence. U. S., 1915.
N. Y. P. L.   December 24, 1915.

NN 0065438   NN

National security league.
 The Lawrence plan for education in citizenship.
 No. 1-
 New York National security league, 1918-
 v.   23 cm.   (Lawrence, plan leaflets)

NN 0065439   DHEW

National Security League.   Committee on
 Patriotism through education.
  Handbook of the war for readers, speakers...
  see under   Hart, Albert Bushnell, 1854-

NATIONAL SECURITY LEAGUE, Committee on Patriotism
 through Education.

 Wake up, America! A hand book of the war
for national defense, prepared for the use
of speakers and writers by the Committee on
patriotism through education. New York, The
national security league, 1917.

 nar.pf°. ff.142.
 In "June 1917, 200 copies of this pamphlet
were printed. It has not been reprinted in
any other form since

 Imperfect:- pp.117,119,136, 142 torn.
 Inserts at pp.33. and at 117.
 MS notes, corrections and additions in
the margins.
 Bibliography with each chapter.

NN 0065441   MH

National Security League.   Committee on Patriotism
 through Education.
  War points for Americans...
  see under   Libby, Melanchthon Fennessy,
  1864-

National Security League.   Committee on Physical Reserve.
 ...How to work for physical reserve <instructions to commit-
tees appointed by mayors>.   New York city: National Security
League [1918]   2 l.   23cm.

 Caption-title.
 Signed: Committee on Physical Reserve.

850731A. 1. Physical education.
N. Y. P. L.   November 10, 1936

NN 0065443   NN

National Security League,   Committee on Physical Reserve.
 A manual of physical exercise prepared for general use. 2d edition.
= New York City. [1919.] (16) pp. Illus. 23 × 11 cm.

L7869 — Gymnastics.

NN 0065444   MB CU

NATIONAL SECURITY LEAGUE.   Congressional
   Committee.
 Congressional vote on preparedness and war.
[New York, 1917?]

 Broadside 22 x 28 in.

NN 0065445   MH

VOLUME 407

National security league bulletin

    see

National security league.
   ...Bulletin.

D570 National security league. Patriotism through educa-
.A2N9   tion series.
    New York city, [1917—
        v.   23 cm

    OrCS OrPR
NN 0065447   DLC ICJ NIC ICU NN MB NjP OrU Or

D570 National security league. Patriotism through edu-
.A2N44   cation. Universal military instruction and
      training series.
    New York, [1919-
       v, 22½ cm .

NN 0065448   DLC MiD NN MB

National security league quarterly...
    see under   National security league.

National Security Resources Board
  see U. S. *National Security Resources Board.*

National security savings bank of Edinburgh.
    Report on the affairs of the National security
  savings bank of Edinburgh, by the Committee of
  accounts... for the year ending 20th November
  1854... [Edinburgh, 1855]
    8 p.   21.5 cm.
    Caption title.

NN 0065451   CtY

National security savings bank of Edinburgh.
    Report on the affairs of the National security
  savings bank of Edinburgh; presented to the annual
  general meeting of the trustees and managers, held
  on 21st February 1837; and approved of by a
  resolution of said general meeting. Prepared by a
  committee appointed by the monthly meeting held
  on 13th February 1837.   Edinburgh, 1837.
    16 p.   21.5 cm.

NN 0065452   CtY

National Security Savings Bank of Edinburgh.
  [Proposed] Rules . . . duly agreed to, and sanctioned,
in terms of the acts 9th Geo. IV. chap. 92., 3d Will. IV.
chap. 14, and 5th and 6th Will. IV. chap. 57. Established
in 1835. *Edinburgh: Neill & Co.,* 1835. 25 pp. 8°.

NN 0065453   NN

National security savings bank of Edinburgh.
    Rules of the National security savings bank of
  Edinburgh, duly agreed to ... Established in
  1836... Edinburgh, 1854.
    19 p.   21.5 cm.

NN 0065454   CtY

National Security Savings Bank of Edinburgh.
  Rules...duly agreed to, and sanctioned, in terms of the
acts 9 Geo. IV., c. 92; 3 Will. IV., c. 14; 5 & 6 Will IV.,
c. 57; and 7 & 8 Vict., c. 83. Established in 1836.
[also Report...for the year ending 20. Nov. 1844.]
  Edinburgh: Neill & Co., 1844. 19, 12 pp. 8°.

NN 0065455   NN

National Security Savings' Bank of Glasgow.
    Annual report. 9th; 1843/44
  Glasgow, 1845.
    1 v.   21 cm.   [1843/44. Pamphlets on
  banking. v. 1]
    1. Banks and banking - Scotland.

NN 0065456   CU

National Security Traders Association.
    Traders' annual.
  [New York, Investment dealers' digest]
    v. illus. 29 cm.
  Official publication of the National Security Traders Association.

    1. Investments—United States—Yearbooks. 2. Investments—
United States—Periodicals. I. Investment dealers' digest. II.
Title.

  HG4905.N37a   332.6'32'0973   73–648012
  ISSN 0092-4679   MARC-S

NN 0065457   DLC

National Security Training Commission
  see U. S. *National Security Training Commission.*

National Seeds Corporation.
    Annual report [and] statements of accounts.
  [New Delhi]
    v. illus. 27 cm.
  Report year ends Mar. 31.
    Title varies slightly.

    1. Seed industry and trade—India.
  HD9019.S432 I 45   S A 68-6818

NN 0065459   DLC NSyU

National seedsman. v. 1-8, no. 3; Sept. 1937-Mar. 1941.
  [Chicago, National seedsman publications, 1937-41]
    8 v. in 3. illus. (incl. ports.) 30cm. monthly.
  Editors: 1937–   1938, J. M. Anderson.   1938-1941, R. C.
  Helgeson.
  Merged into Seed world.
  L. C. set incomplete: v. 1, no. 2; v. 3, no. 2; v. 4, no. 5 wanting.

    1. Seed industry and trade—Period. 2. Seed industry and trade—U. S.
  I. Anderson, James M., ed. II. Helgeson, Robert C., ed.
                                     45–46078
  Library of Congress   SB117.A1N3
                    [2]   631.521105

NN 0065460   DLC

National seedsman.
  ...Yearbook, an annual ready reference for
seedsmen... Chic., National seedsman publications.

NN 0065461   MiD CSt

WA   NATIONAL Selected Morticians
840   A digest of transportation regulations;
qN277d   rules governing the transportation of
1946   dead human remains within the United
      States and Territories, and to foreign
      countries ... [4th ed.] Chicago, 1946.
      48 p.
        1. Dead - Disposal

NN 0065462   DNLM

National selected morticians.
    Proceedings of the ...   annual
  convention of the National selected morticians ...
  [Pittsburgh,
    v. 23cm.
    Editor: W. H. Putnam.

    1. Undertakers and undertaking—Societies.   I. Putnam, William H.,
ed.

  Library of Congress   RA622.A5N25   21–8297

NN 0065463   DLC

National selected morticians.
    A service book. [Chicago, Ill.] The National selected mor-
ticians [c1935]
    190 p. 16cm.
    "First printing 1925 ... revised edition, first printing 1935."
    "Prepared under the supervision of the Reverend Dr. Charles Carroll
Albertson."—Pref.

    1. Funeral service.   I. Albertson, Charles Carroll, 1865–
                                      36–16885
  Library of Congress   BV199.F8N3 1935
  ———— Copy 2.
  Copyright A 96088   [3]   265.8

NN 0065464   DLC OrStbM MSohG OU

        National selected morticians, comp.
Coll
NA872sm   Today and to-morrow. [Poems] Chicago [c1926]
Harris   [16]p.   16 cm.
Collection

NN 0065465   RPB

JS 1230 National self government committee, inc., *New York.*
1933 N35 Civics as it should be taught. New York city, National self
       government committee [1933]
      16 p. 21½cm. (On cover: Truth about politics)
      "Fourth printing."
      "Suggested reading": p. 15–16.

      1. New York (City)—Pol. & govt. 2. Citizenship—Study and teach-
ing. I. Title.
                               34–21759
    Library of Congress   JS1230.1933.N35
                   [2]   352.07471

NN 0065466   DLC DHEW CtY ViU OCU OU

National self government committee, inc., *New York.*
    Civics as it should be taught. New York city, National self
  government committee [1939]
    16 p. 20½cm. (On cover: Truth about politics for tomorrow's Ameri-
cans)
    "First printing, December 1933 ... eighth printing, November 1939."
    "Suggested reading": p. 15–16.

    1. New York (City)—Pol. & govt. 2. Citizenship—Study and teach-
ing. I. Title.
                                 40–7176
  Library of Congress   JS1228.N35 1939
                  [2]   352.07471

NN 0065467   DLC IdU

National Self Government Committee, Inc., New York.
    [Correspondence, notes, papers, questionnaires, charters, con-
stitutions, reports, clippings, pamphlets and pictures relating to
the National Self Government Committee, Inc., Richard Welling,
chairman of the Board of Directors] [New York, etc., 1909–32]
  48 letter file boxes.   38½cm.
    The boxes are numbered 1 to 45, 49 to 51.
    Gift of R. Welling.

    1. Colleges and universities—Manage-   ment and discipline. 2. School city.
  3. Schools—Management and discipline.   4. Criminals, Juvenile—Communities.
  Self governing. I. Welling, Richard,   1858–
  N. Y. P. L.   March 27, 1936

NN 0065468   NN

VOLUME 407

371.59　National self government committee,
N27s　　inc., New York
　　　　　Some facts about pupil self-
　　　government.　New York, School
　　　citizens committee ₍n.d.₎
Educ.　　cover-title, 23p. D.

　　　Richard Welling, chairman.

NN　0065469　IaU

371.59　National self government committee,
N27so　　inc., New York
　　　　　Some suggestions regarding the
　　　organization and conduct of a plan
　　　of pupil co-operation in school man-
　　　agement.　New York, Self-government
Educ.　committee ₍n.d.₎
　　　　　cover-title, 23p. O.

　　　Richard Welling, chairman.

NN　0065470　IaU

National self teacher for bugle. U. S. Army and Navy
signals and calls. Chicago, Chart Music Publishing House
₍°1945₎
　　18 p.　26 cm.
　　Cover title.
　　"Bugle calls": p. 14–18.

　　1. Bugle—Methods—Self-instruction.　2. Bugle-calls.

　　UH43.N3　　　　　　　　　　51–34246

NN　0065471　DLC

...National self teacher for German accordeon;
an easy system.... Chicago, Chart music
publishing house, c1922.

　　16 p.

NN　0065472　OC1

National selfteacher for guitar. Chords. The simplest
and most comprehensive selfinstructor for guitar
chords ever published. A new system by which anyone, with a little study, can in a short time become a
good player ... ₍n. p.₎ °1901.
　　16 p.　8°.
　　Cover-title.
　　Copyrighted by M. Atkinson.

　　　　　　　　　　　　　　　　1—389 Music div.

NN　0065473　DLC

National selfteacher for guitar. The simplest and most
comprehensive selfteacher ever published. Full and
complete instructions on position, the rudiments of
music and all necessary information . . . ₍n. p.₎
°1901.
　　16 pp. 8°.
　　Cover-title.
　　Copyrighted by M. Atkinson.　1—390—M 2 Music div.

　1. Guitar — Methods — Self-instruction.

NN　0065474　DLC

National self-teacher for harmonica, a chart system by which
after slight practice anyone can play at sight all the popular
airs and any music adapted for the instrument. ₍n. p.₎
°1901.
　　16 p. 24 cm.
　　Cover title.

　　1. Mouth-organ—Methods—Self-instruction.

　　MT682.N33　1901　　　　　　　Music—391*

NN　0065475　DLC

National self-teacher for mandolin: the simplest and most
comprehensive self-teacher ever published. Full and
complete instructions on position, the rudiments of
music and all necessary information ... ₍n. p.₎ °1901.
　　16 p. 8°.
　　Cover-title.
　　Copyrighted by M. Atkinson.

　　　　　　　　　　　　　　　1—392 Music div.

NN　0065476　DLC

786.3　National self teacher for ragtime piano play-
N277　　ing. Chicago, Chart music publishing house,
　　　　c1917.

　　　cover-title, 16 p.　26 cm.

　　1. Piano - Methods - Self instruction.
　　I. Title: Ragtime piano playing.

NN　0065477　LNHT

National self-teacher for violin: the simplest and most
comprehensive self teacher ever published. Full and
complete instructions on position, the rudiments of
music and all necessary information ... ₍n. p.₎ °1901.
　　16 p. 8°.
　　Cover-title.
　　Copyrighted by M. Atkinson.

　　　　　　　　　　　　　　　1—393 Music div.

NN　0065478　DLC

JV　　National Seminar on Citizenship,
7275　　Scarborough, Ont., 1953
A3N3　　　Report of National Seminar on Citizen-
1953　　ship, Scarborough, Ontario, May 4th–6th,
　　　　1953. Ottawa, Canadian Citizenship Branch,
　　　　Department of Citizenship and Immigration,
　　　　1953.
　　　　　167 leaves.

　　Reproduced from typewritten copy.

NN　0065479　CaOTU

National Seminar on Compulsory Primary Education.
　　Report.
　₍New Delhi₎ Government of India, Ministry of Education.
　　　v.　24 cm.　(₍India (Republic)₎ Ministry of Education₎ Publi-
cation₎

　　1. Education, Compulsory—India—Congresses.　ɪ. India (Republic)　Ministry of Education.　　(Series)

　　LC136.I 5N3　　　　　　　S A 64–8240

NN　0065480　DLC NSyU MiU NN DS

National Seminar on Elementary Education.
　　Report.
　New Delhi, Ministry of Education, Govt. of India.
　　　v. 21 cm.

　　1. Education, Elementary—India—Congresses.　ɪ. India (Republic)　Ministry of Education.

　　LB1152.N36　　　　372.9'54　　　S A 68–14685

NN　0065481　DLC NSyU

National Seminar on the Organization and Tech-
niques for the Liquidation of Illiteracy, 1st,
Jabalpur, 1950.
　　Report
　　　　see under　Indian Adult Education
Association.

National Semi-pro Baseball Congress
　　see　National Baseball Congress of America.

...National sentiment in the Poema de Fernán
　　Gonçalez and in the Poema de Alfonso Onceno
　　　see under　[Davis, Gifford]

The National series.
New York,

NN　0065485　DLC CoGrS

The national series of histories, mythology, etc.
New York, 1858.

NN　0065486　DLC

National series of juvenile speakers.
Philadelphia, 18

NN　0065487　DLC

National series of school books
　　　　see
National school series.

National, The, series of spelling blanks, in three numbers.　New
York: Potter, Ainsworth & Co. ₍cop. 1874-75₎　3 nos. in 1 v.
8°.
　　1. Words.　2. Words & definitions.　3. Words, definitions & sentences.　Title
from cover.

　1. English language.—Spelling.
N. Y. P. L.　　　　　　　　　September 28, 1911.

NN　0065489　NN

National series of standard school books
　　　　see
National school series.

National service. v. 1–10, no. 4; Feb. 1917–Nov./Dec. 1921.
₍New York, etc.₎ Military Training Pub. Corp.₎
　　10 v. in 9.　illus., ports., maps.　25–31 cm.　monthly.
　　Absorbed International military digest in Jan. 1919.
　　Vol. 1 includes a separately paged Training camps supplement,
Feb.–Apr. 1917.
　　Merged into the American Army and Navy Journal (later Army,
Navy, Air Force Journal)

　　1. U. S.—Armed Forces—Period.　2. Military education—U. S.—
Period.　3. European War, 1914–1918—Period.　ɪ. Title: Training
camps supplement.

　　UA23.A1N5　　　　　　　　　18–14113 rev*

NN　0065491　DLC OrU DNW ICJ NjP MB NN DAL TxU

National service board for religious objectors.
　　The churches look at the conscientious objector.　₍Washing-
ton₎ Nat. service board for religious objectors ₍1943?₎　8 p.
22cm.

　　1. Conscientious objectors to　　　　military service.
N. Y. P. L.　　　　　　　　　June 23, 1945

NN　0065492　NN

VOLUME 407

National service board for religious objectors.

UB342
.U5A52
1943

U.S. *Congress.*
Congress looks at the conscientious objector. Washington,
D. C., National service board for religious objectors ₁1943₁

National service board for religious objectors,
The conscientious objector under the Selective training and
service act of 1940. Washington, Nat. service board for religious objectors ₁1943₁ 15 p. 22cm.

"Revised Nov. 1, 1943."

1. Conscientious objectors to   military service—U. S.
N. Y. P. L.   May 16, 1945

NN   0065494   NN

355.22   National Service Board for Religious Objectors.
N215d   Directory of civilian public service, May,
1941 to March, 1947.   Washington ₁1947₁
xxiv, 167p. 23cm.

1. Conscientious objectors—U.S.   I. Title.

NN   0065495   IU MiD CU-B

National Service Board for Religious Objectors.
The origins of Civilian Public Service; a
review of the negotiations during the fall of
1940 between government officials and representatives of the churches most immediately
affected by the drafting of conscientious
objectors. Washington,D.C.,National Service
Board for Religious Objectors₁1941?₁
27p. 23cm.

NN   0065496   PSC-Hi CSt-H

NATIONAL SERVICE BOARD FOR RELIGIOUS OBJECTORS,

Questions and answers on the classification and
assignment of conscientious objectors. Washington,
1952. 16 p. 27cm.

1. Conscientious objectors to military service.

NN   0065497   NN

National service board for religious objectors.
Report of the executive secretary, National
service board for religious objectors; three
years of civilian public service, May 15, 1941 -
May 15, 1944. ₁Washington? 1944?₁
36 numb.l. tables,diagrs. 29cm.

Mimeographed.

NN   0065498   CU-B

National Service Board for Religious Objectors.

UB343
.R46

The Reporter. v. 1–
July 1942–
₁Washington₁

National service board for religious objectors,
Statements of religious bodies on the conscientious objector.
Rev. Washington, 1953. 59 p. 21cm.

1. Conscientious objectors to mili-   tary service—U. S.   2. Law and
religion.

NN   0065500   NN NjPT TxDaM OC1

₁National service board for religious objectors₁
They serve without weapons ... ₁Washington, 1944₁
₁8₁ p. illus. (incl. map) 23ᵐ.

1. Conscientious objectors—U. S. 2. World war, 1939-   —U. S.
I. Title.
Library of Congress   UB342.U5N3   44-39542
                    ₍2₎   355.22

NN   0065501   DLC MH-AH NN

PN2570   National Service Bureau.
A1N3   The continental theatre, a monthly bulletin.

New York.
     v.   (Its Publication)

Cover title:
Continental theatre bulletin.

NN   0065502   CU

Z5784   **National Service Bureau.**
N4   A list of Negro plays. New York, National
N37   Service Bureau, Federal Theatre Project,
Works Progress Administration, 1938.
53 p. (National Service Bureau. Publica-
tions, no.24-L)

Xerox copy of the original.

1. Negro drama - Bibliography. 2. Negroes
in art and literature. I. Title. II. Series.

NN   0065503   WaU

National service bureau.
... Old testament plays ... ₁New York₁
National service bureau, 1938.

₍ p. ₎., 50 numb. ₎. 29cm. (Publication
no. 45-L)

Mimeographed.

NN   0065504   MtU

National service bureau.
... 101 selected plays for a puppet
theatre ... ₁New York₁ National service bureau,
1938.

10 p. ₎., 101 numb. ₎. 29cm. (Publication
no. 41-L)

Mimeographed.

NN   0065505   MtU

National service bureau.

₁United New York and New Jersey Sandy Hook pilots
benevolent associations₁
Pilot lore; from sail to steam, and historical sketches
of the various interests identified with the development of
the world's greatest port. ₁New York₁ 1922.

National service bureau
...Publication...

see

Federal theatre project.
...Play bureau publication...

National service commission of the Con-
gregational churches of America
The church, the war, and the days beyond.
A patriotic service N.Y. n.d.

₍8₎, 3-11 p.

Added t. p. Supplement to a patriotic
service.

1. Patriotism. I Title.

NN   0065508   00

National service commission of the Congregational
churches of America
Report concerning the needs and problems
of negroes in war camp communities.
N.Y. n.d.

15 p. O.

NN   0065509   00

National service data
see under   National Automotive Service.

National service league, London.

₁Shee, George Richard Francis₁ 1869–
The Briton's first duty, the case for universal military
training, with an introduction by Field-Marshal Earl
Roberts ... 4th (abridged) ed. 65th thousand. ₁London₁
The National service league ₁pref. 1907₁

National service league, London.
... The causes of the great war (Revised to
September 21st 1914)... [London, Gee & co.,
ltd., 1914]
12 p. 23 cm.

NN   0065512   CSt-H

National service league, London.

Barker, J   Ellis.
... National and non-national armies. A study in mili-
tary policy. A lecture by J. Ellis Barker, delivered at the
Royal united service institution on February 27th, 1907
... Pub., with the permission of the Council of the Royal
united service institution, by the National service league
... Westminster ₁1907?₁

National service league, *London.*
The problem of invasion and how to meet it ... ₁London, Pub. by the National service league, 1909₁
1 p. l., 22, ₍4₎ p., 1 l. 21ᵐ.

1. Gt. Brit.—Defenses.
                                           9-21986
Library of Congress   UA647.N34

NN   0065514   DLC ICJ

National service league, London.

Roberts, Frederick Sleigh Roberts, *1st earl*, 1832–1914.
Speeches and letters of Field Marshal Earl Roberts, ᴋ. ɢ.
on imperial defence. ⟨Selected and arranged by Elliott E.
Mills, under the auspices of the National service league.⟩
London, Simpkin, Marshall, Hamilton, Kent & co., ltd.; ₁etc.,
etc., 1906.

VOLUME 407

National service library, Major Charles E. Kilbourne ... editor-in-chief ... ₜNew York₎ P. F. Collier & son, inc., ᵗ1917₎

5 v. col. fronts. (incl. port.) illus. 17ᶜᵐ. (The Collier classics)

Illustrated lining-papers, in colors.

Contains bibliographies.

CONTENTS.—v. 1. Universal military training, by L. Wood.—v. 2. Military strength and resources of the United States, by D. E. Aultman.—v. 3. Principles of military training, by F. R. McCoy.—v. 4. Rudiments of drill, mobile army troops, by W. T. Carpenter.—v. 5. Warfare of the future, by H. Jervey.

1. Military art and science. 2. Military education—U. S. 3. U. S.—Army.   I. Kilbourne, Charles Evans, 1872–   ed.

17—15296

Library of Congress   U15.N3

NN   0065516   DLC WaU LU ICJ NN DNW

TL152
.N26

National service manual.

National Automotive Service.

National service data. 1934—

Berkeley, Calif.

National service publications, inc., Chicago.

Seefurth, Nathaniel Henry, ed.

... Insurance estates and trusts, business and estate insurance; a loose leaf cumulative service covering the practical selling and legal phases of corporation, partnership and estate insurance and insurance trusts, including special reports, plans and data for the use of life underwriters and trust officers to promote the creation and conservation of estates and business interests. Edited by Nathaniel Henry Seefurth. Chicago, Ill., National service publications, incorporated, ᵗ1927.

National Service Publications, Inc., Chicago.

The life insurance estate and trust service. Chicago, 1928–1929.

1 v. (various pagings) illus.

Loose leaf.

NN   0065519   MH-BA

National service publishing company, Washington, D. C.

ₜThe Military engineer₎

FOR OTHER EDITIONS SEE MAIN ENTRY

The advanced engineer manual. 2nd ed. A textbook for the Reserve officers' training corps and general engineer training. Washington, D. C., The National service publishing company ₜ1933₎

National Service Publishing Company, Washington, D. C.

An index to the Gettysburg, Fort Leavenworth, and Fort Benning military and Geological Survey maps. Produced for the Infantry journal. New ed. Washington, 1931.

68 p. 25 cm.

Cover title.

Based on maps issued by the General Service Schools, Fort Leavenworth, and the Infantry School, Fort Benning.

1. Gettysburg—Environs—Maps—Indexes. 2. Leavenworth, Kan.—Environs—Maps—Indexes. 3. Fort Benning, Ga.—Maps—Indexes.   I. Infantry journal. II. U. S. General Service Schools, Fort Leavenworth. III. U. S. Infantry School, Fort Benning, Ga.

G3700 1931.U5 Index   Map 58–156

NN   0065521   DLC DNW

UF453
.A7
1933

National service publishing company, Washington, D. C.

FOR OTHER EDITIONS SEE MAIN ENTRY

ₜAntiaircraft journal₎

The R. O. T. C. manual. Coast artillery ... A textbook for the Reserve officers' training corps. Washington, D. C., National service publishing company ₜ1933₎

U133
.A6

National service publishing company, Washington, D. C.

The R. O. T. C. manual ... for all arms. Harrisburg, Pa., The Military service publishing co. ₜ1933–

National service publishing company, Washington, D. C.

see also   Military service publishing company.

National service star legion.

See

Service star legion.

National sesquicentennial exhibition commission.

see   U. S. National sesquicentennial exhibition commission.

NATIONAL sewerage and sewage utilization co.   **5763.**

The West system.   [Circular.]

N. Y. [1884?] 8 pp. 8°.

NN   0065527   MB DNLM NN

The National Sewerage and Sewage Utilization Co.

The West system of sewerage disposal and utilization.   New York [1888]

20 p. 8°.

NN   0065528   DNLM

National Sewing Machine Co., Belvidere, Ill.

Eldredge bicycles.   [Chicago, 1901]

16 p. illus. 16°.

NN   0065529   NN

National Sewing Machine Co., Belvidere, Ill.

Sewing machine service manual.   Belvidere, Ill. ₜ194?₎

59 p. illus.

Cover title.

NN   0065530   MiD

National Shade Tree Conference

see   International Shade Tree Conference.

---

*EC85
T3255
Z864n
(A)

National Shakespeare committee, London.

... Sir, We beg to inform you that a general meeting ... will be held ... January the 4th ...

[London,1863]

folder (1l.) 19cm.,in case 23cm.

At head: National Shakespeare committee. 120, Pall Mall, S.W. December 30, 1863.

Signed: W. Hepworth Dixon, J.O. Halliwell, gen. secs.

Unbound; leaf 2 (presumably blank) wanting; in half blue morocco case with The National Shakspeare committee and the late Mr. Thackeray [1864].

NN   0065532   MH

---

*EC85
T3255
Z864r
(A)

National Shakespeare committee, London.

... Sir, We beg to inform you that an adjourned general meeting ... will be held ... January the 18th instant ...

[London,1864]

broadside. 20.5x12.5cm.,in case 23cm.

At head: National Shakespeare committee, 120, Pall Mall, S.W. January 13th, 1864.

Signed: W. Hepworth Dixon, J.O. Halliwell, general secretaries.

Unbound, as issued; in half blue morocco case with The National Shakspeare committee and the late Mr. Thackeray [1864].

NN   0065533   MH

The National Shakespeare committee and the late Mr. Thackeray, ...

see under   [Clayton, Joseph] comp.

PR
2976
P21

National Shakespearian Fund.

First report of the National Shakespearian Fund, March, 1862. ₜLondon, Whittingham and Wilkins, Chiswick Press, 1862₎

8 p. illus. 21cm.

No. 6 in vol. lettered: Papers on Shakspere.

1. Shakespeare, William—Societies, periodicals, etc.

NN   0065535   NIC

NATIONAL SHARECROPPERS FUND, inc.

The condition of farm workers in 1952; report to the Board of directors of National sharecroppers fund, inc., by Fay Bennett, executive secretary. [New York, 1953] 4 l. 33cm.

Film reproduction.

Caption title.

1. Labor, Agricultural—U.S.   2. Mexicans in the U.S.   I, Bennett, Fay.

NN   0065536   NN DNAL

Nde40
U2
+N21m

National sharecroppers fund, inc.

[Minor publications]   38cm.

NN   0065537   CtY

NATIONAL SHARES CORPORATION.

Report.

[New York]   no.   23cm.

Annual.

1. Investment trusts—U. S.—N. Y.—New York.

NN   0065538   NN

National Shawmut bank, Boston.

The Anglo-French loan, conditions necessitating a foreign credit and its effect on our commerce. Boston, National Shawmut bank, 1915.

cover-title, 14 p. 23ᶜᵐ.

1. European war, 1914–1918—Finance. 2. Debts, Public—France. 3. Debts, Public—Gt. Brit. 4. Finance—U. S.   I. Title.

15—22288

Library of Congress   HJS627.N3

NN   0065539   DLC

VOLUME 407

National Shawmut bank, *Boston.*
    The bank and the individual. Boston, The National
Shawmut bank ₍1915₎
    28 p. pl. 21ᶜᵐ.

    ɪ. Title.

    Library of Congress   HG2613.B74N4   16–22970

NN 0065540   DLC ICJ

National Shawmut Bank, Boston.
    The bank and the merchant, ₍by₎ the National Shawmut Bank
of Boston. ₍Boston, cop. 1916.₎ 53 p. pl. 8°.

    67000A. 1. Banks and banking.
    N.Y.P.L.   December 30, 1922.

NN 0065541   NN NSyU

National Shawmut bank, *Boston.*
    Bank and trade acceptances. ₍Boston₎ The National
Shawmut bank of Boston ₍1919₎
    22 p. illus. (forms) 23ᶜᵐ.

    1. Acceptances. ɪ. Title.

    Library of Congress   HG1655.N35   20–4540

NN 0065542   DLC

National Shawmut Bank, Boston.
    Bank directory of New England. January, 1915.
Boston.
    nar. 24°⁄

NN 0065543   MH

National Shawmut bank, *Boston.*
    Bank directory of New England ... Maine, New Hampshire, Vermont, Massachusetts, Rhode Island, Connecticut ...
Boston, Mass., The National Shawmut bank of Boston, ₍1922–
    v. illus. (maps) 15½ᶜᵐ. (Shawmut series, no. 222)

    1. Banks and banking—New England. ɪ. Title.

    Library of Congress   HG2441.N35   22–13977

NN 0065544   DLC

National Shawmut bank, *Boston.*
    The bankers' calendar, comp. and pub. by the National
Shawmut bank. Boston, Mass., 1919.
    34 p. 17ᶜᵐ. (*On verso of t-p.:* Shawmut series, no. 112)

    1. Banks and banking—Calendars. 2. Holidays. ɪ. Title.

    Library of Congress   HG1531.N3   19–8154

NN 0065545   DLC

National Shawmut Bank, Boston.
    The bankers' calendar... compiled and published by the
National Shawmut Bank of Boston.   Boston, Mass., 1921.
34 p. 16°. (Shawmut series no. 192.)

    1. Banks and banking, U. S.   2. Holidays, U. S.
    N.Y.P.L.   February 15, 1923.

NN 0065546   NN

National Shawmut Bank, Boston.
    The bankers' calendar, 1925–1926...   Boston: National
Shawmut Bank of Boston₍, cop. 1925₎. 34 p. 16°. (Shawmut ser. no. 234.)

    1. Holidays—U. S. 2. Banks and   banking—U. S.
    N.Y.P.L.   August 10, 1925

NN 0065547   NN

National Shawmut Bank, Boston.   *9332.003A14
    The bankers' calendar 1931–1932.
    Boston. [1931.] (1), 36, (1) pp. 17 cm.
    Bank holidays in the United States and its possessions, and in Canada and Mexico.

    D1097 — Banks and banking. — Holidays.

NN 0065548   MB

National Shawmut Bank, Boston.
    Better banking under the federal reserve system...   ₍Boston, 192–?₎ 14 p. nar. 12°.
    Cover-title.

    1. Banks and banking, Federal   reserve.
    N.Y.P.L.   June 16, 1927

NN 0065549   NN

National Shawmut Bank, Boston.   9332.1744A3ᵃ
    The book of the Shawmut Bank. Illustrations by J. Albert Seaford.
=   Boston. 1923. 23 pp. Illus. Plates. [Shawmut series. No. 228.]
    26½ cm.
    Issued to commemorate the completion of the bank's building.

    D162 — S.r. — Seaford, John Albert, illus., 1858–

NN 0065550   MB

National Shawmut bank, *Boston.*
    The Boston & Maine railroad. Boston, National Shawmut bank, 1916.
    cover-title, 20 p. 23ᶜᵐ.

    1. Boston and Maine railroad.

    Library of Congress   HE2791.B85 1916   16–5075

NN 0065551   DLC 00

National Shawmut Bank, Boston, Mass.   9332.174487
    A brochure, containing a sketch of the bank, together with views
    and a brief description of the new building.
=   [Boston. Walton Advertising & Printing Co. 1907.] 32 pp.
    Plates. 8°.

NN 0065552   MB NNC

---

*9381
.A93   **National Shawmut Bank,** Boston.
         Business and Europe. [Boston, 1916]
         17 p. illus., tables. 23cm.

         1. U. S.—Comm. 2. U. S.—Econ.
         condit. I. Title.

NN 0065553   MB MH

Leavens
Collection
J   **National Shawmut Bank,** Boston.
N277c   Conserving your property at low cost.
1951   ₍Boston₎ Personal Trust Dept., The National
         Shawmut Bank ₍1951₎
             32 p. illus. 28cm.
             Cover title.

             1. Trusts and trustees - U.S. 2. Estate
         planning. I. Title.

NN 0065554   CoU

HG3765   **National Shawmut bank,** Boston, appellee.
1923
         U. S. *Court of appeals for the fifth circuit.*
             Cotton warehouse receipts, opinion by Circuit court of appeals, fifth circuit, defining rights of holders against trustee
         in bankruptcy, fully annotated by Max Isaac ... ₍Savannah, *1923₎

National Shawmut bank, *Boston.*
    ... Foreign trade report for October, 1915. ₍Boston,
G. H. Dean, printer, 1915₎
    ₍4₎ p. 28ᶜᵐ.
    Running title: Foreign trade report—port of Boston.
    "Compiled and issued by the Foreign department of the National Shawmut bank."

    1. Boston—Comm. ɪ. Title.

    Library of Congress   HF3163.B6N3   16–3642

NN 0065556   DLC

National Shawmut Bank, Boston.
    Foreign trade review.

    Boston,   4°.
    v. tables.
    Monthly.
    Title varies: April, 1920, Foreign trade report; May, 1920
                           Foreign trade review.

    1. Commerce, U. S.: Mass.: Bos-   ton. 2. Shipping, U. S.: Mass.:
    Boston.
    N.Y.P.L.   January 22, 1923.

NN 0065557   NN

National Shawmut Bank, Boston.   *9332.174A2
    Guide to transit numbers of New England and New York City
    banks, compiled for its depositors . . . from original sources
    and by kind permission of the American Bankers Association
    from its "Numerical key" to facilitate the listing of checks for
    deposit by numbers instead of the names of banks . . .
=   Boston. 1931. 70 pp. 18 cm.

    D1096 — Checks. — New York, Ci. Banks. — New England. **Banks.** —
    Transit numbers of banks.

NN 0065558   MB

NATIONAL SHAWMUT BANK, *Boston,*
    Guide to transit numbers of   New England
and New York city commercial banks, compiled
for its depositors by the National Shawmut
Bank of Boston from original sources and by
kind permission of the American bankers
association from its "Numerical key," to
facilitate the listing of checks for deposit
by numbers instead of by names of the banks.
Boston, c 1923.

    1. Banks and banking - Directories. 2.
Directories. Banks   and Banking. I.
Title.

NN 0065559   MH-BA

VOLUME 407

National Shawmut Bank, Boston.
Guide to transit numbers of New England commercial banks, compiled for its depositors by the National Shawmut Bank of Boston from original sources and by kind permission of the American Bankers Association from its "Numerical key," to facilitate the listing of checks for deposit by numbers instead of by names of the banks. ₍Boston:₎ National Shawmut Bank of Boston, cop. 1922. 36 p. nar. 12°. (Shawmut series. no. 221.)

1. Banks and banking, U. S.: New England.
N. Y. P. L. February 8, 1923.

NN 0065560 NN

₍**National Shawmut bank,** Boston₎
✕ An introduction to the Webb law; an act to promote export trade and for other purposes, approved April 10, 1918 ... ₍Boston, The National Shawmut bank of Boston, 1919₎
32 p. 23ᶜᵐ. (Shawmut series, no. 109)

1. U. S.—Comm. 2. Competition, International. I. U. S. Laws, statutes, etc. II. Title: The Webb law.
Library of Congress HF3029.N38 19–5369

NN 0065561 DLC

₍**National Shawmut bank,** Boston₎
An introduction to the Webb law; an act to promote export trade and for other purposes, approved April 10, 1918 ... Second printing. ₍Boston, The National Shawmut bank of Boston, 1919₎
32, ₍1₎ p. 23ᶜᵐ. (Shawmut series, no. 109)
Cover-title: The Webb law.

1. U. S.—Comm. 2. Competition, International. I. U. S. Laws, statutes, etc. II. Title: The Webb law.
Library of Congress HF3029.N38 1919 a 19–12650

NN 0065562 DLC NIC

HF3029 ₍National Shaumut bank, Boston₎
.N38 An introduction to the Webb law; an act to promote export trade and for other purposes, approved April 10, 1918 ... Third printing.
[Boston, 1920]

[Shawmut series, no. 109]

NN 0065563 DLC

National Shawmut bank, Boston.
Massachusetts income tax law. Boston, Trust department, National Shawmut bank, 1916.
cover-title, 39 p. 23ᶜᵐ.

1. Income tax—Massachusetts—Law. I. Massachusetts. Laws, statutes, etc. II. Title.
Library of Congress HJ4655.M38N3 16–13877

NN 0065564 DLC

NATIONAL SHAWMUT BANK, Boston.
Money rates from 1900 to 1935. [Boston: The National Shawmut Bank, 1935] 2 l. chart. 23½cm.

1. Interest, 1900–1935.

NN 0065565 NN

National Shawmut bank, Boston.
New account manual ... compiled by C. O. MacDonald. Boston, Mass., The National Shawmut bank of Boston. 1932.
1 v. 25ᶜᵐ.
Loose-leaf.

1. Banks and banking. I. MacDonald, Chester Otis, 1883– comp.
II. Title. 33–12736
Library of Congress HG1616.N35
———— Copy 2.
Copyright A 62006 ₍3₎ 332.1

NN 0065566 DLC

National Shawmut bank, Boston.
The port of Boston, a foreign market for the surplus products of New England. ₍Boston₎ National Shawmut bank ₍°1916₎
1 p. l., 57 p. diagrs. 23ᶜᵐ.
"Short list of books, pamphlets and articles on port administration and the essentials of foreign trade": p. 52–57.

1. Boston—Comm. 2. Massachusetts—Indus.
Library of Congress HF3163.B6N35 16–24951

NN 0065567 DLC OrU OU OO MB ICJ

National Shawmut Bank, Boston. 9387.9744A4
The port of Boston. [1923.]
Boston. 1923. 1 v. Illus. Plates. [National Shawmut Bank, Boston. Shawmut series, no. 227.] 23 cm.
This has no connection with the previously issued booklet bearing a similar title and published in 1916. There was no series number to that booklet, as it was published by special arrangement with some one outside of the bank.

D5538 — T.r. — S.r.c. — Boston. Harbor.

NN 0065568 MB ICJ NN MH MiD Or

National Shawmut bank, Boston.

₍**Gaston, William Alexander**₎ 1859–
The problems of peace; a study of the essential needs of Massachusetts during the reconstruction period. Boston, National Shawmut bank ₍°1918₎

National Shawmut Bank, Boston.
Scandinavia and its trade opportunities...prepared by the Publicity Department of the National Shawmut Bank of Boston. ₍Boston: National Shawmut Bank of Boston, 1919.₎ 14 p. 8°. (Shawmut series. no. 130.)

1. Economic history, Scandinavia. 2. Commerce, Scandinavia and U. S.
3. Commerce, U. S. and Scandinavia.
N. Y. P. L. July 6, 1920.

NN 0065570 NN

National Shawmut bank, Boston.
Shawmut sales manual. ₍Boston₎ The National Shawmut bank of Boston ₍°1929₎
1 v. diagrs. 28½ᶜᵐ.
Loose-leaf.
"References": verso of p. 7 of chap. XII.

1. Banks and banking—U. S. I. Title.
Library of Congress HG2613.B74N43 30–8280

NN 0065571 DLC

National Shawmut bank, Boston.
A state tax on incomes. Boston, National Shawmut bank, 1916.
cover-title, 15 p. 23ᶜᵐ.

1. Income tax. I. Title.
Library of Congress HJ4629.N3 16–13756

NN 0065572 DLC NN

₍NATIONAL SHAWMUT BANK, Boston₎
A survey of the markets of the Far East for American trade. ₍Boston, The National Shawmut Bank, cop. 1919₎

Pamphlet.
Shawmut series, no. 142.

NN 0065573 MH IU

National Shawmut bank, Boston.
Synopsis of the Massachusetts corporate excise tax law, general acts of 1919; with comparative applications of this and the older law ... ₍Boston, The National Shawmut bank, °1919₎
14 p. 23ᶜᵐ. (Shawmut series. no. 143)

1. Corporations—Taxation. 2. Taxation—Massachusetts. I. Title.
Library of Congress HD2753.U7M48 19–18664

NN 0065574 DLC

National Shawmut Bank, Boston. 9368.08
Taxation affecting life insurance, life insurance trusts and annuities. An explanation of the Federal income, gift and estate tax laws, and the State inheritance, gift and estate tax laws affecting life insurance, life insurance trusts, and annuities. 1935 edition.
[New York. Prentice-Hall, Inc.] 1935. v, 170 pp. Tables. 18.5 cm.
In the form of questions and answers.

E994 — Income tax. — Questions and answers. — Life insurance. — States of the United States. Tax. — Annuities. — United States. Tax.

NN 0065575 MB

National Shawmut Bank, Boston.
The text of the Edge law; an act to amend the act approved Dec. 23, 1913, known as the Federal reserve act, approved Dec. 24, 1919
see under U. S. Laws, statutes, etc.

D694 NATIONAL SHAWMUT BANK, Boston.
v.45 War taxes 1919 ... Philadelphia, 1919.
29 p.
₍Pamphlets on the European war, 1914–1918.
v.45, no.2₎

1. European war, 1914–1918—Finance—U. S.

NN 0065577 ICU MH

45.9 **National sheep and wool bureau of America.**
N213 Monthly bulletin v. 1, no. 1–
Apr. 1918–
[Chicago, 1919₎
illus. f°.
Ceased; cf. letter dated, July 23, 1920.

NN 0065578 DNAL

NATIONAL SHEEP AND WOOL BUREAU OF AMERICA.
Objections to truth in fabric law enumerated, analyzed and answered. Chic., Author₍n.d.₎
2 v.

NN 0065579 Or

National sheep breeders' association.
British pure-bred sheep, published by the National sheep breeders' association ... ₍Brentford, Middx., Printed by W. Pearce & co.₎ St. Georges press₎ 1946.
142 p., 1 l. illus. (incl. group port.) 21½ cm.
Map on lining-papers.
Includes advertising matter.

1. Sheep—Gt. Brit. I. Title.
SF376.N3 636.32 47–25577

NN 0065580 DLC IdU IU DNAL

VOLUME 407

45
N214
1952

National Sheep Breeders' Association

British pure-bred sheep.   Rev. ed.
London, 1952.
95 p.

1. Gt. Brit. Sheep. 2. Sheep. Breeds.
3. Sheep breeders' directories. I. Title.
II. Title: Pure-bred sheep.

NN   0065581   DNAL CaBVaU

National Sheep Breeders' Association of England
see   National Sheep Breeders' Association.

National sheep committee.
Proceedings of a joint meeting of the executive
and eastern members, Ottawa, February 8-10,
1944. n.p., The Committee, 1944.
v.p.   plates, tables.   sq. Q.

NN   0065583   CaBViP

National sheepgrowers' association.
Memorial of the National sheepgrowers'
association and others with accompanying papers
accompanying papers asking protective legislation
for sheep industry...   Washington, D.C., 1895.
254 p.   (54th Congress, 1st Sess., Document
No. 17)

NN   0065584   MtHi

National sheet metal contractor. v. 1–
Nov. 1906–
₁Pittsburgh, National association of sheet metal contractors;
etc., etc., 1906–
v.   illus.   23–29ᵐᵐ.   monthly.
Volume numbers of v. 15–16 irregular: Nov. 1920 called v. 15, no. 1;
Dec. 1920–Oct. 1921, v. 16, no. 2–12.
Official organ of the National association of sheet metal contractors
(formerly the Nationals association of master sheet metal workers)
Title varies: Nov. 1906–Oct. 1907, The Master sheet metal workers
journal.
Nov. 1907–July 1910, The Master sheet metal workers journal; de-
voted exclusively to the interests of the sheet metal trade and the
National association of master sheet metal workers of the United
States.

Aug. 1910–Oct. 1916, The Master sheet metal workers journal.
Nov. 1916–Oct. 1924 (v. 11–19), Warm air heating & sheet metal
journal.
Nov. 1924–Nov. 1926, National sheet metal contractor; published in
the interests of warm air heating, ventilating, sheet metal cornice,
skylight and general sheet metal work.
Dec. 1926–   National sheet metal contractor.
Imprint varies: Oct. 1906–Nov. 1926, Philadelphia, E. L. Seabrook
₁etc.₁–Dec. 1926–July 1927, Columbus, O., National association of
sheet metal contractors–Aug. 1927–   Pittsburgh, National
association of sheet metal contractors.
1. Sheet-metal work— Period. 2. Heating—Period.   ɪ. National
association of sheet metal contractors of the United States. ɪɪ. The
Master sheet metal workers journal. ɪɪɪ. Warm air heating & sheet
metal journal.
                                                8–13890 (rev. '30)
Library of Congress   TS200.N25

NN   0065586   DLC NN ICJ ICRL

National sheet metal roofing co., *New York.*
Practical hints to builders and those contemplating
building. 2d ed. Facts worth considering relating to
foundation, cellar, kitchen, chimney, cistern, brick-work,
mortar, heating, ventilation, the roof, and many items of
interest to builders ... The National sheet metal roofing
co., sole manufacturers of Walter's patent standard, and
Cooper's patent Queen Anne metallic shingles and siding
plates ... New York, Press of W. J. Pell, 1888.
80 p.   illus. (incl. plans)   19¼ᵐᵐ.
p. 78–80, advertising matter.
1. Roofing. 2. Building.
                                        CA 9–3640 Unrev'd
Library of Congress   TH2455.N27

NN   0065587   DLC

National Sheet Metal Roofing Co., New York.
Practical hints to builders and those contemplating building. Facts worth considering relating to
foundation, cellar, kitchen, chimney, cistern,
brick-work, mortar, heating, ventilation, the roof
... 3d ed.   New York, Press of W. J. Pell, 1889.
100 p.   illus., plans.   19 cm.
1. Building. I. Title.

NN   0065588   N

National sheet metal roofing co., *New York.*
Practical hints to builders and those contemplating
building ... Facts worth considering relating to foundation, cellar, kitchen, chimney, cistern, brick-work, mortar,
heating, ventilation, the roof, and many items of interest
to builders ... The National sheet metal roofing co., sole
manufacturers of Walter's patent standard, and Cooper's
patent Queen Anne metallic shingles and siding plates ...
₁4th ed. (145,000)₁ New York, Press of W. J. Pell, 1890.
100 p.   illus. (incl. plans)   19ᵐᵐ.
p. 95–100, advertising matter.
1. Roofing.
                                        CA 9–5124 Unrev'd
Library of Congress   TH2455.N29

NN   0065589   DLC

RA1242.T7
N21

**National shell filling factory, Chilwell, Eng-
land.**
... The occurrence and prevention of the toxic
effects on human beings brought about by the use
of T.N.T.; a report compiled by the managing
director and staff of the National shell filling
factory, Chilwell, Notts. Long Eaton, National
shell filling factory, 1917.
29 p.   fold. diagr.   33ᶜᵐ.

"For official use only, not for publication."

NN   0065590   NNC DNW DL

SH365
A2N3

National Shellfisheries Association.
Addresses delivered at the convention

[n.p.]
v.   diagrs., tables.   29 cm.

1. Shell-fish fisheries – U.S.

NN   0065591   DI NcU

National Shellfisheries Association.
Papers delivered at the convention
see its
Proceedings.

National Shellfisheries Association.
Proceedings.
Washington, Fish and Wildlife Service, U. S. Department
of the Interior.
v.   illus. 27 cm.   annual.
Title varies: Papers delivered at the convention.

1. Shell-fish fisheries—Societies, etc.   ɪ. U. S. Fish and Wildlife
Service.
SH370.A1N312   55–24650 rev

NN   0065593   DLC FTaSU LU ScU LNL AAP NcU NcD

Z5973
.S5
qN3
pam

National Shellfisheries Association.
Titles of papers presented at annual
meetings 1930–1957. ₁n.p., 1957₁
15 ɫ.   29cm.

1.Shell-fish fisheries – Bibl.   I.Title.

NN   0065594   OrCS

S352.23
qN275   The **National** sheriff.

₁Washington, National Sheriffs' Association₁
v. in   illus., ports. 29 cm.
Monthly.   –Apr. 1952; bimonthly, May/June 1952–
Began publication in 1948. Cf. N. W. Ayer & son's directory, 1958.
"Successor to the Sheriffs' news letter."

1. Sheriffs—U. S.—Period.   ɪ. National Sheriffs' Association.

HV7551.N35   352.23   59–30088

NN   0065595   DLC AAP NN FTaSU N

NATIONAL SHERIFFS' ASSOCIATION.
Directory of sheriffs of the United States.
Columbus, Ohio [etc.]   no.   28cm.

The directory for 1956 was issued as v.8, no.2, Mar./Apr. 1956, of the
National sheriff and has been bound with the periodical in M–10–48. (See
that entry.).

1. Sheriffs––U.S.   I. Title.

NN   0065596   NN

HV7551
.N35

National Sheriffs' Association.

The **National** sheriff.

₁Washington, National Sheriffs' Association₁

National Ship Buoying and Towing Company.
Prospectus...   New York, The Company, 1872.
1 p.l., p. 5–36.   2 pl.   8°.

NN   0065598   NN

---

*
TF25
.S68
1868
v.29,
no.3

National Ship–Canal Convention, Chicago, 1863.
Memorial to the President and Congress of
the United States, by the National Canal Convention, assembled at Chicago, in June, 1863.
₁Chicago, Tribune Co., 1863₁
16 p.   22cm.   (Streeter pamphlets. S.E.R.R.,
v. 29, no. 3)

1. Canals–U.S. 2. Railroads—Southeastern States.
I.U.S. President, 1861–1865 (Lincoln) II. U. S.
Congress. III. Southeastern railroads. IV. Title.

NN   0065599   ViU CtY RPB IHi

National ship-canal convention, *Chicago,* 1863.
Memorial to the president and Congress of the United
States, by the National canal convention, assembled at
Chicago, June 2, 1863. Chicago, Tribune company, print-
ers, 1863.
cover-title, 24 p.   22½ᵐᵐ.

1. Canals—U. S.
Library of Congress   TC623.3.N27   6–11636†
———— Copy 2.   ₁Miscellaneous pamphlets, v. 458, no. 13₁

NN   0065600   DLC OClWHi MnHi N IU

Microcard
TC
623.3
N27

National Ship-canal Convention, Chicago, 1863.
Memorial to the President and Congress of
the United States, by the National Ship-Canal Convention, assembled at Chicago, June 2, 1863.
Chicago, Tribune Company, printers, 1863.
24p.

Micro-opaque.
Cover-title.

1. Canals––United States.

NN   0065601   UU

VOLUME 407

National ship-canal convention, Chicago, 1863.

Chicago. *Committee on statistics.*
The necessity of a ship-canal between the East and the West. Report of the Committee on statistics, for the city of Chicago, submitted to the National convention, assembled at Chicago, June 2, 1863. Chicago, Tribune company's book and job printing office, 1863.

National ship-canal convention, *Chicago, 1863.*
Proceedings of the National ship-canal convention, held at the city of Chicago, June 2 and 3, 1863. Chicago, Tribune company's book and job printing office, 1863.

248 p. 21½ᶜᵐ.

1. Canals—U. S. 2. Inland navigation—U. S.

Library of Congress   HE395.A3N3   6—13503
———— Copy 2.   ₍Miscellaneous pamphlets, v. 458, no. 5₎
    TC623.3.N28

   ICHi ICJ MB Nh MnU NjP PSt MiU OCHP
NN   0065603   DLC CtY CU NIC ICN IEdS I NBuG MnHi

National shippers association.
New York book; express, parcel post, freight ... 1916–

Issued under the auspices of National shippers association ... N₍ew₎ Y₍ork₎, National shippers association, ₍1916–

v. 19½ᶜᵐ.
Editor: 1916–   C. J. Woodworth.

1. Parcels-post—U. S.—New York (City) 2. Express service—New York (City) ɪ. Woodworth, Clayton J., ed. ɪɪ. Title.

Library of Congress   HE6473.N7N3   16–7682

NN   0065604   DLC NN

National shippers' conference, *Chicago, 1919.*
A memorial by the National shippers' conference to the Joint conference committee of the Congress of the United States having under consideration pending railroad legislation. Chicago, Barnard & Miller print ₍1920₎

cover-title, 22 p. 23ᶜᵐ.

1. Railroads and state—U. S. ₍1. Railroad policy—U. S.—1919₎ 2. ₍Cummins bill, 1919₎ 3. ₍Esch bill, 1919₎

A 20–176

Title from Bureau of   Railway Economics. Printed by L. C.

NN   0065605   DBRE

National shippers express guide. Western ed., for the following states and territories: Alaska, Arkansas, Arizona, California, Colorado, Idaho, Iowa, Kansas, Louisiana, Minnesota, Montana, Missouri, Nebraska, Nevada, New Mexico, North Dakota, Oklahoma, Oregon, South Dakota, Texas, Utah, Washington and Wyoming ...   Des Moines, Kansas City, National shippers publishing company ₍1908–

v. 23ᶜᵐ.

Comp. by the National shippers publishing company.

1. Express service. 2. Shipping—The West—Direct. ɪ. National shippers publishing company.

8–1707

Library of Congress   11E5895.N27   Copyright

NN   0065606   DLC

National Shipping Authority
   see
  U. S. *National Shipping Authority.*

National Shoe Manufacturers' Association.
   Annual convention.
   ₍New York?₎

v. 22½ᶜᵐ.

Cover-title,   : Proceedings of the ... annual convention ...

1. Boots and shoes—Trade and manufacture—Societies. 2. Boots and shoes—Trade and manufacture—U. S.

CA 18–1451 Unrev'd

Library of Congress   HD9787.U6N25

NN   0065608   DLC OU OCl DL

National Shoe Manufacturers' Association.
   Brief in support of the retention of the present import duty on boots and shoes, filed with the Committees on ways and the means of the 62nd and 63rd congresses, by the National boot and shoe manufacturers' association, The National shoe wholesalers association, the National shoe retailers' association, The New England shoe and leather association. Rochester, N.Y.], 1913.

nar. 1.8°. pp.(3).   42. Tables.

NN   0065609   MH

L675.81
V501
National shoe manufacturers association.
Development of shoe design from one war to another, by Harold R. Quimby ... One of a series of publications devoted to shoes. New York, National shoe manufacturers association, 1945.

5, 2 p. illus. 29ᶜᵐ.

ɪ. Quimby, Harold R

NN   0065610   ICJ

National Shoe Manufacturers' Association.
Executive committee meeting of the National boot and shoe manufacturers' association, held at ... Boston, Mass., April 24, 1919. ₍Boston? 1919₎   49 p.   23ᶜᵐ.

Cover-title.

1. Boots and shoes—Manufacture   —Assoc. and org.—U. S.
N. Y. P. L.   November 27, 1941

NN   0065611   NN

National Shoe Manufacturers Association.
   Facts and figures on footwear.
   New York.

v. 29 cm. annual.

1. Boots and shoes—Trade and manufacture—U. S.

HD9787.U4N33   55–38636 ‡

NN   0065612   DLC MH-BA OrU NNC NIC OCl MiD CaBVa

National Shoe Manufacturers Association.
   Hand book of the National Boot and Shoe Manufacturers' Association. ₍New York? 1905?₎

15 p. 11 cm.

Cover-title: Constitution of the National Boot and Shoe Manufacturers Association.

Contents.—Constitution adopted at the city of New York, Feb. 22, 1905.—Order of business convention.

HD6515.B7N3   42–32004 rev*

NN   0065613   DLC

National Shoe Manufacturers' Association.
Outline for oral presentation with graphic charts before the administrator of the Wage and hour division, United States Department of labor ... By the National boot and shoe manufacturers association ... At public hearing beginning December 11, 1939. ₍New York, 1939₎   88 p.   illus. (19 col'd charts.) 21½ cm.

Cover-title.

1. Hours of labor, Shoemakers'—U. S. 3. Boots and shoes—Trade and Labor department. Wage and hour N. Y. P. L.   U. S. 2. Wages, Shoemakers'—stat.—U. S. ɪ. United States. division.   November 19, 1941

NN   0065614   NN

National Shoe Manufacturers Association.
Proceedings of the annual convention. 1st–
1905–
New York.

v. in   23 cm.

Ceased publication with no. 24 (1928) Cf. Union list of serials. Issued 1905–   by the association under its earlier name: National Boot and Shoe Manufacturers' Association of the United States.

1. Boots and shoes—Trade and manufacture—U. S.—Societies, etc.

HD9787.U6N25   55–53608

NN   0065615   DLC

National Shoe Manufacturers' Association.
   Pure shoe legislation; brief in opposition to its enactment filed by the National boot and shoe manufacturers' association, the National shoe wholesalers' association, The national shoe retailers association, the New England shoe and leather association. n.p., [1913?]

np.12.   Econ 7780.01

NN   0065616   MH

National Shoe Manufacturers Association.
Questions and answers, Fair labor standards act of 1938, particularly applying to the shoe manufacturing industry. ₍New York₎ 1939.

1 v. 30 cm.

Cover title.
Published by the association under its earlier name: National Boot and Shoe Manufacturers Association.

1. Labor laws and legislation—U. S. 2. Labor and laboring classes—U. S.—1914–   3. Wages—U. S. 4. Boots and shoes—Trade and manufacture—U. S. ɪ. Title. ɪɪ. Title: Fair labor standards act of 1938.

HD7833.N35   331.768530973   40–11502 rev*

NN   0065617   DLC

L675.81
V502
National shoe manufacturers association.
The story of footwear, by Harold R. Quimby ... One of a series of publications devoted to shoes. New York, National shoe manufacturers association, 1945.

60 p. 28ᶜᵐ.

ɪ. Quimby, Harold R

NN   0065618   ICJ TxU IEN

L675.81
V400
National shoe manufacturers association.
... The story of lasts, by Harold R. Quimby ... One of a series of publications devoted to shoes. New York, National shoe manufacturers association, 1944.

10, 2 p. 29ᵐᵐ.

ɪ. Quimby, Harold R

NN   0065619   ICJ

VOLUME 407

National shoe manufacturers association.
The story of style in shoes, by Harold·R. Quimby.
₍New York, National shoe manufacturers association, °1945₎
19 p. illus. 28ᶜᵐ.
One of a series of publications devoted to shoes.—p. 2.

ɪ. Quimby, Harold R

NN 0065620   ICJ

National shoe retailers' association.
... Fashion and footwear.
ed.
New York,
v.   illus.   35½ᶜᵐ.

Loose-leaf.
Includes sample materials.

1. Boots and shoes - Trade and manufacture.
I. title.

NN 0065621   NNC

HF
5686 National shoe retailers association.
.B4 Footwear business accounts; the N.S.R.
N28 A. system. [n.p.,192-?]
Binder's title.   forms.   29½ x 37½ᶜᵐ.
In loose-leaf binder.
"How to use National shoe retailers'
business record": 8 mimeographed leaves
laid in.

NN 0065622   MiU

National Shoe Retailers' Association.
"Go-withs" in fashion and footwear
see under title

National Shoe Retailers' Association   **4459-173**
Annual convention. 9th. Boston, 1920.
[Program.]
= Boston. [The University Press.] 1920. 29 pp. Decorated title-
page. 22½ cm.

L9811 — Boots and shoes.

NN 0065624   MB

**National shoe retailers' association. Educational
al division.**
Shoe store operations in 1931. Ohio. ₍The
Author₎ °1933.
48 p.

NN 0065625   MiD

HD9787 National shoe wholesalers' association of the U.S.
.U6N35 Constitution and by-laws. List of officers.
Constituent bodies.
[Boston, 1905]

NN 0065626   DLC

HD9787 National shoe wholesalers' association of the U.S
.U6N3 Proceedings... annual meeting...
[Boston,

NN 0065627   DLC

NATIONAL SHORT BALLOT ORGANIZATION.
Certain weaknesses in the commission plan of municipal
government. Why the commission—manager plan is better.
New York: The National short ballot organization [1916?]
15 p. 17cm.

1. Municipal government by commission—U.S.

NN 0065628   NN

JS342 National short ballot organization.
.N3 The city manager plan of municipal government.
[Reprinted from Beard's loose-leaf digest of short
ballot charters] ...
New York, 1913.
35 p.

NN 0065629   DLC NN

National Short Ballot Organization.
The city manager plan of municipal government...   New
York, 1914.   34 p. incl. table.   2. ed.   4°.

Reprinted in part from Beard's Loose-leaf digest of short ballot charters.

1. Municipal government by city   manager.
N. Y. P. L.   July 1, 1927

NN 0065630   NN MA

National Short Ballot Organization.
Commission government with a city manager.   New York
₍1915₎.   23(1) p.   12°.

1. Municipal government by city   manager.
N. Y. P. L.   June 9, 1916.

NN 0065631   NN ViU

National Short Ballot Organization.
The commission-manager plan of municipal government...
New York: The National Short Ballot Organization, 1915.   35 p.
3. ed.   4°.

Cover-title.
Repr.: Loose-leaf digest of short ballot charters.

1. Municipal government by city   manager.
N. Y. P. L.   June 26, 1916.

NN 0065632   NN

National short ballot organization.
Documents on county government (1911–1921)
see under title

National Short Ballot Organization.
The first short ballot county.   n. t.-p.   ₍New York, 1912₎
15 p.   8°.

1. Government (Local). U. S.:   Cal.: Alameda Co.
N. Y. P. L.   February 24, 1914.

NN 0065634   NN MiD

NATIONAL SHORT BALLOT ORGANIZATION.
The first short ballot county ₍Los Angeles
County, California, with copy of its charter₎
₍New York, National short ballot organization,
1913₎
15 p.

NN 0065635   Or

National short ballot organization.
Okc16 [Minor publications]
N47m   26½cm.

1. Elections - U.S.   2. Ballot.

NN 0065636   CtY

National short ballot organization.
Pamphlets on county government.   New York,
1913-1917.
v.p.

NN 0065637   WaS

NATIONAL SHORT BALLOT ORGANIZATION.
The short ballot; a movement to simplify
politics.   National short ballot organization
₍1913₎
31 p.

NN 0065638   Or

National short ballot organization
The short ballot...A movement to simplify
politics...   N.Y. 1916.

31 p. S.

NN 0065639   OO OU

JK2446 National Short Ballot Organization.
.A25
The **Short** ballot bulletin. v. 1–7 (no. 1–56); Feb. 1911–Apr.
1920. ₍New York, National Short Ballot Organization₎

National Short Ballot Organization.
Short ballot cartoons.   ₍New York, 1912.₎   61.   ob. 16°.

1. Municipal government.—Commis-   sion form, U. S. 2. Elections.—
Management, etc.—: Ballot, U. S.
N. Y. P. L.   January 16, 1914.

NN 0065641   NN

"324
N29s
National Short Ballot Organization.

₍Short ballot pamphlets₎ New York ₍1913-
1917₎

Title supplied.
Contains some issues of the Short ballot
bulletin.

1. Ballot. 2. State governments. 3. Municipal
government - U.S.   4. Municipal government
by commission.   I. Short ballot bulletin
II. Title.

NN 0065642   OrP

National short ballot organization.
The story of the short ballot cities, an
explanation of the success of the commission
form of municipal government. (Rev. ed.) N. Y.
1913.
19 p.

NN 0065643   MiD Or IU

VOLUME 407

National short ballot organization.
Suggestions for legislators of 1917. New York city, The National short ballot organization [1916]
15, [1] p. 23^{cm}.

1. Ballot. 2. State governments. 3. Municipal government—U. S. 4. Municipal government by commission. I. Title.

Library of Congress   JK2446.N3   17-233

NN   0065644   DLC NN MiU OU NIC OrU Or

National Short Ballot Organization.
Tangible results at Dayton under the commission-manager plan... A story of three years of good government on the basis of a model municipal charter. [New York, 1916.] 19(1) p. illus. (incl. port.) 12°.

1. Municipal government, U. S.:   Ohio: Dayton, 1914–16.
N. Y. P. L.   April 4, 1917.

NN   0065645   NN OU

National Short Ballot Organization.
Three years' accomplishments.   [New York, 1913.]   4 l.
16°.

1. Municipal government—Commis-   sion form, U. S.
N. Y. P. L.   February 16, 1914.

NN   0065646   NN

National short ballot organization.
Year book.
[New York,
v. 17^{cm}.

1. Ballot.

CA 15–1342 Unrev'd

Library of Congress   JF1104.N2

NN   0065647   DLC

**L653.061
P992   v.17**
The National shorthand reporter. Publisht monthly for the National Shorthand Reporters' Association as a supplement to the Phonographic magazine. Volume 1, number 1–10, January–October 1903. [Cincinnati] 1903.
75, [1] p. illus. 26^{cm}.

Caption title.
Bound with the Phonographic magazine, vol. 17.
In Nov. 1903, united with the Phonographic magazine under the title The Phonographic magazine and national shorthand reporter.

NN   0065648   ICJ NN

National shorthand reporter; official organ of the National shorthand reporters' association. v. 1–
Jan. 1913–
New York, The Association, 1913–
v. illus. 23^{cm}. monthly.

Editors: 1913, W. M. Clift.—1914–   J. N. Kimball.

1. Shorthand—Period.   I. Clift, William M., ed.   II. Kimball, James Newton, ed.   III. National shorthand reporters' association.

Library of Congress   Z54.N23   15–16982

NN   0065649   DLC MsU KMK

The **National** shorthand reporter; the journal of the National shorthand reporters association. v. 1–
Oct. 1939–
[New York, 1939–

v. illus. 26½^{cm}. monthly (except Aug. and Sept.)

Supersedes the Shorthand reporter.
Editor: Oct. 1939–   Louis Goldstein.

1. Shorthand—Period. 2. Shorthand reporting.   I. Goldstein, Louis, ed.   II. National shorthand reporters' association.

43–43832

Library of Congress   Z54.N24
[3]   653.42

NN   0065650   DLC ICJ LU NN

National Shorthand Reporters' Association.
Annual meeting at Put-in-Bay, Ohio...1900.   [Program, etc.]   [Spartanburg, S. C., 1900.]   5 l.   16°.

1. Stenographers—Associations.   BEALE SHORTHAND COLL.
N. Y. P. L.   March 7, 1913.

NN   0065651   NN

National Shorthand Reporters' Association.
Annual report.

[n. p.]
v.   23 cm.

1. Shorthand—Societies.

Z55.N26   653.06273   48–37654*‡

NN   0065652   DLC ICU

National Shorthand Reporters' Association.
Bulletin.

La Porte, Ind., 19   8°.
nos.   illus.
Irregular.

1. Shorthand—Per. and soc. publ.   HOWARD SHORTHAND COLL.
N. Y. P. L.   May 17, 1926

NN   0065653   NN

National Shorthand Reporters' Association.
Bulletin...15th annual convention.
no. [1–]4   (Aug. 19–22, 1913).

Chicago, 1913.   8°.
4 nos.

Caption-title.
No more published.

1. Shorthand—Per. and soc. publ.   HOWARD SHORTHAND COLL.
N. Y. P. L.   May 13, 1926

NN   0065654   NN

National Shorthand Reporters' Association.
...Constitution.   [New York?] 1910.   18 p.   nar. 24°.
Cover-title.

1. Stenographers—Assoc. and org.—   HOWARD SHORTHAND COLL.
N. Y. P. L.   U. S.   May 18, 1926

NN   0065655   NN

National Shorthand Reporters' Association.
Constitution and by-laws of the National Shorthand Reporters' Association; revised at Chicago convention, August 23, 1923. [Chicago? 1923.]   6 l.   12°.

NN   0065656   NN

National shorthand reporters' association.
Digest of statutes and legal decisions relating to official stenographers ... Comp. and pub. by the Committee on legislation of the National shorthand reporters association ... New Haven, Conn., The Mac printing corporation, 1906.
242 p. fold. tab. 24^{cm}.

1. Shorthand reporting.   [1. Law reporting]   2. Stenographers.

6–34055 Revised
Library of Congress

NN   0065657   DLC ICJ NN

National Shorthand Reporters' Association.
Directory of shorthand reporters and notaries.   [Louisville, Ky., 1903.]   16 p.   12°.

1. Stenographers.—Directories.   BEALE SHORTHAND COLL.
N. Y. P. L.   December 3, 1912.

NN   0065658   NN MiU MB

NATIONAL SHORTHAND REPORTERS' ASSOCIATION.
...Directory of shorthand reporters in the United States and Canada, and a two hundred year calendar. Prepared for distribution by the National Shorthand Reporters Association.   n.p.
[1932]   64 p.   22x8cm.

At head of title: 1931–1932.
Cover–title.

782400A. 1. Shorthand—Directories.

NN   0065659   NN NBuG

National Shorthand Reporters' Association.
List of officers, charter members, and constitution and by-laws.
1899
Greenvill, S. C., 1899.   16°

1. Shorthand.—Associations.   BEALE SHORTHAND COLL.
N. Y. P. L.   February 26, 1913.

NN   0065660   NN

National shorthand reporters' association.
Making the record...   Elkhart, Ind.: National shorthand reporters assoc. [1937]   24 p.   23cm.

1. Court records. 2. Shorthand—   Reporting, Court.
N. Y. P. L.   June 4, 1940

NN   0065661   NN DFT

National shorthand reporters' association.

National shorthand reporter; official organ of the National shorthand reporters' association. v. 1–
Jan. 1913–
New York, The Association, 1913–

Z54
.N24

National shorthand reporters' association.

The **National** shorthand reporter; the journal of the National shorthand reporters association. v. 1–
Oct. 1939–
[New York, 1939–

National Shorthand Reporters' Association.
Officers, charter members, and constitution and by-laws. Adopted...1899.   Greenville, S. C.: Shannon & Co., 1899.   21 p. 24°.

With manuscript notes.

1. Stenographers.—Associations.   BEALE SHORTHAND COLL.
N. Y. P. L.   March 7, 1913.

NN   0065664   NN

VOLUME 407

National Shorthand Reporters' Association.
Proceedings of the annual convention. 54th;
1955. [1955]
1 v.

NN 0065665 ICN

National shorthand reporters' association.
... Proceedings of the annual meeting ... [1st]–
1899–
Greenville, S. C. [etc.] 1899–[19
v. fronts., illus., plates, ports. 22½–25ᶜᵐ.
Title varies slightly.
Proceedings for 1902–03 were not published separately, but appeared in Phonographic magazine. cf Letter in Order div.
"Chronological list of shorthand magazines, published in Great Britain from 1842 to 1915": 1915, p. 225–245.
"Index to papers printed in the Proceedings of the N. S. R. A. from 1899 to 1917. Prepared by Forrest Clark.—List of authors": 1917, p. 242–247.
List of members in each volume.
1. Shorthand—Societies. 2. Shorthand—Bibl.

11–7057

Library of Congress Z55.N27

NN 0065666 DLC ICJ NN MB

National Shorthand Reporters' Association.
Program of annual convention.
no.
Boston[, etc.], 19 16°, 12°, 8°, 4°.
nos. illus.
Cover-title.
1922 includes Professional program.

HOWARD SHORTHAND COLL.
N. Y. P. L. May 13, 1926

NN 0065667 NN

National Shorthand Reporters' Association.
Register of attendance of members and guests at the annual convention...
Cincinnati, 8°.
no.
1903 consists of autographs of members and guests.

1. Stenographers—Assoc. and org.— U. S.
N. Y. P. L. June 28, 1926

NN 0065668 NN

National Shorthand Reporters' Association.
Report of Committee on frauds, by George Farnell...
Adopted at the seventeenth session of the National Shorthand Reporters' Association at San Francisco, California, August 17th, 1915. [La Porte, Ind.? 1915?] 2 l. 8°.

1. Shorthand. 2. Farnell, George.
N. Y. P. L. July 21, 1926

NN 0065669 NN

NATIONAL SHORTHAND REPORTERS ASSOCIATION.
Report of Committee on legislation to the Executive committee, second annual convention, Put-in-Bay, Ohio [Put-in-Bay, O., 1901?] 14 p.

Microfiche (neg.) 1 sheet. 11 x 15cm. (NYPL FSN 12, 254)
Caption title.
John Robert Gregg Shorthand Coll.
1. Shorthand--Jurisp.--U.S.

NN 0065670 NN

National shorthand reporters' association.
... Report of special committee on official organ, Philadelphia, May 1, 1939. [Philadelphia, 1939] 29 p. 23cm.

Cover-title.
Copies numbered; this copy no. 90.

1. Shorthand—Reporting.
N. Y. P. L. May 31, 1940

NN 0065671 NN

National shorthand reporters' association.
The reporters' phrasebook of standardized shorthand (Pitmanic); a complete and systematic exposition of the science and art of phrasing as developed and used by the most expert and experienced shorthand reporters of the United States and Canada, prepared by the Standardization committee of the National shorthand reporters' association, United States and Canada. [Clinton, Mass.] The Association, 1934.

239 p. incl. illus. (ports.) 22½ᵐ.

1. Shorthand—Phrase-books. I. Title.

35–23852

Library of Congress Z56.N26
[2] 653.42

NN 0065672 DLC WaE NN

National shorthand reporters' association.

New York. Public library.
The shorthand collection in the New York public library; a catalogue of books, periodicals, & manuscripts brought together by the National shorthand reporters' association and the library, compiled by Karl Brown & Daniel C. Haskell. New York, The New York public library, 1935.

Z54
.S57

National Shorthand Reporters' Association.
The Shorthand reporter. v. 2–35, no. 7; Oct. 1906–July 1939. [Chicago] A. C. Gaw [etc.]

National shorthand reporters' association.
Shorthand reporters; a digest of statutes and legal decisions relating to official stenographers and their reports ... 2d ed., 1916. Pub. by the National shorthand reporters' association. Ed. by Gordon L. Elliott ... [Des Moines, The Homestead printing co., ᶜ1916]
viii, 325 p. 24½ᵐ. $2.50
1st edition pub. in 1906 under title: Digest of statutes and legal decisions relating to official stenographers ... Comp. and pub. by the Committee on legislation of the National shorthand reporters' association.
1. Shorthand reporting. [1. Law reporting] 2. Stenographers. I. Elliott, Gordon L., ed. II. Title.

16–2141

NN 0065675 DLC NN ICJ

National Shorthand Reporters' Association. 6142.78
Souvenir program . . . Fourth annual convention, Boston, Mass., August 19–22, 1902.
= [Boston? 1902.] (12) pp. Illus. Portraits. Fac-simile. 8°.

NN 0065676 MB

National shorthand reporters' association.
Standardized reporting shorthand (Pitmanic) principles, commonest English words, word signs and contractions, prepared by the Standardization committee of the National shorthand reporters' association. [Elkhart, Ind.] The Association, 1921.
96 p. illus. 17ᵐ.

1. Shorthand. I. Title.
Library of Congress Z56.N27 22–1465
———— Copy 2.

NN 0065677 DLC

NATIONAL SHORTHAND REPORTERS ASSOCIATION.
Summary of reporting conditions in the United States and Hawaii. [Jersey City? N. J.] 1947. 51 l. 28cm.

Cover title.
Prepared by its Committee on state legislation.
John Robert Gregg Shorthand Coll.
1. Shorthand--Reporting, Court. 2. Stenographers--U.S. 3. Stenographers --Hawaii.

NN 0065678 NN

National Shorthand Reporters' Association.
Unigraphy, a complete system of shorthand
see under Baldwin, P. W.

National Shorthand Reporters' Association. Committee on Legislation.
Report [at the] annual convention.
[no.]
[Greenville, S. C.? 1 4°.
v.

NAT. SHORTHAND REP. ASSOC.
1. Shorthand.—Jurisprudence, U. S.
N. Y. P. L. December 4, 1918.

NN 0065680 NN

National Shorthand Reporters' Association. Committee on Lloyd Memorial Tablet.
[Invitation to attend dedication of tablet in memory of T. Lloyd, Philadelphia, 1903.] n. t.–p. [Boston, 1903.] 2 l. 12°.
Card of admission inserted.

BEALE SHORTHAND COLL.
1. Lloyd, Thomas.
N. Y. P. L. March 7, 1913.

NN 0065681 NN

National Shorthand Reporters' Association. Library
Z
201
.119 Catalogue of the shorthand and typewriting books, magazines, reports, etc., in the Library of the National Shorthand Reporters' Association. [n. p.]1910.
31 l. 22cm.
Cover title.
With this: 2 announcements and a card of the Chautauqua School of Shorthand and Typewriting, a folder of the Drake-Bridge Correspondence School, and 5 other pieces, by Bridge.

NN 0065682 ICN NN

National Shorthand Reporters' Association. 653.06161 S400
Silver Jubilee Committee.
187129 Our silver jubilee; record of twenty-five years of progress of the National Shorthand Reporters' Association, organized at Chicago, Ill., August 22–24, 1899; incorporated Washington, D. C., December 3, 1904. Edited, compiled and written by Herbert Dore. Chicago, Ill., Silver Jubilee Committee, [1924].
175, [1] p. illus. (incl. ports.) 23½ᶜᵐ.
"One thousand copies. No. 483."
——— In memoriam; a service dedicated to the memory of its departed members ... at its twenty-sixth annual convention held at Omaha, Nebraska, August 17, 1925.
[4] p. 21ᵐ.
Bound together.

NN 0065683 ICJ NN

National Shorthand Reporters' Association. War Record Committee.
. . .A record of the services rendered the United States government during the World War, 1917–1918... Denver, 1920.
29 l., 240 l. 28½cm.
Reproduced from typewritten copy.
Leaves printed on one side only.

NAT. SHORTHAND REP. ASSOC.
632320A. 1. Shorthand—Biog.
N. Y. P. L. 2. European war, 1914–1918—Biog.
October 20, 1933

NN 0065684 NN

VOLUME 407

National Shorthand Teachers' Association.
₍Circular.   Chicago? 1904.₎   16 p.   24°.

HOWARD SHORTHAND COLL.

1. Stenographers—Assoc. and org.
N. Y. P. L.   April 26, 1926

NN   0065685   NN

National Shorthand Teachers' Association.
₍Constitution, by-laws, history, etc.₎   n. p. ₍1902.₎   16 p.
16°.

Title from cover.

1. Stenographers.—Associations.   BEALE SHORTHAND COLL.
N. Y. P. L.   March 13, 1914.

NN   0065686   NN

National Shorthand Teachers' Association.
₍Constitution, by-laws, reports, etc.₎   n. p. ₍1900.₎   36 p.
24°.

Title from cover.

1. Stenographers.—Associations.   BEALE SHORTHAND COLL.
N. Y. P. L.   March 13, 1914.

NN   0065687   NN

National shorthand teachers' association.
Proceedings of the National shorthand teachers' association, including papers read, etc., at the
annual meeting ...
New York, E. N. Miner
v.   illus., pl.   23¼ᶜᵐ.

1. Shorthand—Societies

CA 6—1040 Unrev'd

Library of Congress   Z55.N28

NN   0065688   DLC NN

National Shorthand Teachers' Association. Summer School.
Annual announcement.
₍no.₎ 1
Ann Arbor, Mich.₍,₎ 1902   16°.
nos.

NN   0065689   NN

National Show of Bees and Honey, Sydenham, Eng.,
1926
see   Sydenham, Eng.   National Show of
Bees and Honey, 1926.

National show ... Singers, foreign, color bred
see under   American color breeders, inc.

National Shrine of Our Blessed Lady of Victory.
see   Lackawanna, N. Y.   National Shrine
of Our Blessed Lady of Victory.   [Supplement]

National shrine of St. Jude, *Chicago*
see
Chicago.   National shrine of St. Jude.

National Shrine of the Blessed Virgin Mary,
Cap de la Madeleine, Quebec
see   Cap de la Madeleine, Quebec.   National
Shrine of the Blessed Virgin Mary.   [Supplement]

National shrine of the Immaculate conception
see
Washington, D.C.   National shrine of the Immaculate
conception.

National Shropshire registry association.
The national Shropshire sheep record.   v. 1.   Published by
the National Shropshire registry association.   Edited and
compiled by S. J. Weber ...   Middleville, Mich., The Sun job
printing department, 1902.

v. front.   24ᶜᵐ.

1. Sheep—Flock-books.   i. Weber, Solomon Joseph, 1867–   ed.

Library of Congress   SF373.S56N.   3—16707

NN   0065696   DLC

The national sickness, invalidity and funeral
insurance in Denmark
see under   Denmark.   Direktoratet for
sygekassevaesenet.

The **National** sign journal ...
v.

Denver, Colo.: National sign publ. co., 19   29½ – 30½cm.
v.   illus. (incl. ports.)

Bimonthly,   – Feb., 1939 ; monthly, March, 1939 –
Organ of the National sign association.

1. Signs and signboards—Per. and   soc. publ.—U. S.   I. National sign
association.
N. Y. P. L.   March 19, 1940

NN   0065698   NN ICJ

National Silesian union
see   Národní jednota slezská.
[Supplement]

National silicosis conference.   1st, Washington, D.C., 1936.
...Proceedings at National conference on
silicosis and similar dust diseases, called
by the secretary of labor, Washington, D.C.—
April 14, 1936.   (Washington, D.C., 1936)
20 numb. l.   27 cm.
With this are filed. Silicosis and similar
dust diseases (medical aspects and control)
By R.R. Sayers and R.R.Jones, and Silicosis
as an employer problem, by A.C.Hirth, papers
presented at the conference.

--- ----Copy 2-3

NN   0065700   DL

National silicosis conference, *2d, Washington, D. C.,* **1937.**
... National silicosis conference ; summary reports submitted
to the secretary of labor by conference committees, February 3,
1937 ...   Washington, U. S. Govt. print. off., 1937.
viii, 56 p. incl. tables.   23ᶜᵐ.   (U. S. Dept. of labor.   Division of
labor standards.   Bulletin no. 13)
At head of title : United States Department of labor.   Frances Perkins,
secretary.   Division of labor standards.   Verne A. Zimmer, director.
"Committee on the prevention of silicosis through engineering control.
List of selected references" : p. 52–56.

1. Lungs—Dust diseases—Congresses.   ₍1. Silicosis—Congresses₎
2. Occupations—Diseases and hygiene.

U. S. Dept. of labor.   Libr.   HD8051.2.A2   L 37—87
———— Copy 2.   HD7264.S6N3 1937
for Library of Congress   HD7264.N3 1937 d
                                 ₍142h1₎   613.63

NN   0065701   DL WaWW WaU-L OCl OU OO OCU DLC

National silicosis conference. *2d, Washington, D. C.,* **1937.**
... National silicosis conference ...   Final report₍s₎ of the
committee₍s₎ ...   Washington, U. S. Govt. print. off., 1938.
4 v.   map, tables (part fold.) diagr.   23 cm.   (U. S. Dept. of labor.
Division of labor standards.   Bulletin no. 21)
At head of title : United States Department of labor.   Frances
Perkins, secretary.   Division of labor standards.   Verne A. Zimmer,
director.
Lists of references in parts 1 and 2.
CONTENTS.—pt. 1. Report on medical control.—pt. 2. Report on engineering control.—pt. 3. Report on economic, legal, and insurance
phases.—pt. 4. Report on regulatory and administrative phases.
1. Lungs—Dust diseases—Congresses.   2. Dust—Prevention.
3. ₍Occupations—Diseases and hygiene₎

HD7264.N3   1937c

U. S. Dept. of Labor.   Library   L 38—112 rev
for Library of Congress   ₍r55f¾₎†

NN   0065702   DL DAU WaU-L WaWW DLC

National silicosis conference. *Committee on the prevention*
of silicosis through medical control.
Etiology of silicosis.   ₍Washington? D. C., 1937₎
23, ₍3₎ p.   26¼ᶜᵐ.
Caption title.
This is the report of the sub-committee on etiology—prepared by Dr.
Sayers and Dr. Jones.
Mimeographed.

1. Lungs—Dust diseases.   i. Sayers, Royd Ray, 1882–   ii. Jones,
Roy Richard, 1890–   iii. Title.

Library of Congress   HD7264.N33   37—2ᵃ375
———— Copy 2.   ₍3₎   613.63

NN   0065703   DLC

HD9911
.N3   **National silk convention.**
Proceedings of the ... National silk conven-
tion ...
Paterson, N. J.
v.   23cm.

1. Silk manufacture and trade—Congresses.

NN   0065704   DLC DPU NN

National Silk Convention. 1st. Paterson, N. J., 1915.
First National Silk Convention ; catalogue of the historical
exhibition of textiles, by R. A. Meyer-Riefstahl ...   Paterson,
N. J., October 12th to 21st., 1915.   Paterson: Paterson Composition Co. ₍1915.₎   76 p.   8°.

1. Textile fabrics.—Exhibitions,   U. S.: N. J.: Paterson, 1915.   2.
Meyer-Riefstahl, R. A.
N. Y. P. L.   July 17, 1916.

NN   0065705   NN PPPM

National Silver Committee, 1889.   *9333.426a3
Memorial address to Congress and the people.   Issued by the Exe-
cutive Committee.
=   Washington. Gray. 1890.   17 pp. 8°.
The Committee was appointed at the First National Silver Convention,
at St. Louis, November, 1889.

E630.5 — Silver, Free coinage of.

NN   0065707   MB MH

VOLUME 407

National silver convention, *St. Louis, 1889.*
Papers and addresses before the first National silver convention, held at St. Louis, November 26, 27 and 28, 1889. ... Ed. and comp. by E. A. Elliott ... St. Louis, Buxton & Skinner stationery co., 1889.

106 p. 19ᶜᵐ.

1. Silver question.   I. Elliott, E. A., ed.

NN   0065708   MiU Nh CSmH MH

National silver convention, *St. Louis, 1889.*
Proceedings of the first National silver convention, held at St. Louis, November 26, 27 and 28, 1889 ... Ed. and comp. by E. A. Elliott ... St. Louis, Buxton & Skinner stationery co., 1889.

xii p. 1 l., xiii–xv, 283 p.   22 x 17½ᶜᵐ.

1. Silver question.   I. Elliott, E. A., ed.

6–29377

Library of Congress   HG556.N28

         Nh MH
NN   0065709   DLC MU CoU OClWHi CU OFH ViU ICJ IU

National Silver Convention. *2d, Washington, D. C., 1892.*
Proceedings, including the organization of the American Bimetallic League. Washington, G. R. Gray, printer, 1892.
284 p. 23 cm.

1. Silver question—Congresses. 2. American Bimetallic League.

HG556.N28 1892   50–49027

NN   0065710   DLC MH-BA CtY MU ICU

National silver deposit ware co. inc., *New York.*
Catalogo de artículos de cristal con adornos de plata pura de suprema calidad ... Catalog of fine crystal glass decorated and mounted with sterling silver. New York.

1 v. illus. 25½ᶜᵐ.

Only latest issue in Library is kept on shelf.

1. Glassware—Catalogs.
                                   CA 19–433 Unrev'd
Library of Congress   TP868.N4

NN   0065711   DLC

SF405 **National silver fox breeders association of America.**
.F6N3   ...Constitution, by-laws and classification of
         foxes.
         Muskegon, Mich., c1920.

NN   0065712   DLC

National Sindical Economic Council
see
Organización Sindical. *Consejo Económico Sindical Nacional.*

Mann
SF   **National Single-Comb White Leghorn Club.**
489   Catalog. 19
L5   [n. p.] 19 -
N27   v. illus. 23 cm.

1. Leghorns (Poultry) - Societies.

NN   0065714   NIC

National single tax league of the United States
The Bulletin; pub. monthly by the National single tax league. v. 1-
Jan. 1917-
Cincinnati, O. [etc., 1917-

*HD1313   **National single taxer.** v. 4–10 (no. 1); Jan.
.A38   3, 1895–Jan. 1901. New York [etc.] G. P.
           Hampton [etc., 1895–1901]
           7 v. in   illus., ports. 31–40cm.
           Vols. 7–10 incomplete.
           Weekly, Jan. 3, 1895–July 27, 1898; monthly,
           Jan. 1899–Jan. 1901.
           Official organ of Single Tax League of the
           United States and Canada, Mar. 10, 1897–July
           27, 1898.

           Title varies: Jan. 3, 1895–May 7, 1896,
           Single tax courier.
           Vol. 6, no. 46, Dec. 15, 1897, called also
           Historical series, no. 1.
           Superseded by Single tax review, later Land
           and freedom.
           1. Single tax—Period. 2. Social sciences—
           Period. 3. Periodicals, English.   I. Single
           Tax League of the United States and Canada.
           II. Title: Single tax courier.

NN   0065717   MB LNHT ICJ

National Šiptare Demokratik
see
Nacional Šiptare Demokratik.

National six-man football rules committee.

Epler, Stephen Edward, *ed.*
... Official six-man football guide and rule book, 1940, official publication of the National six-man football rules committee, consisting of Stephen Epler, chairman ... Floyd R. Eastwood ... P. F. Neverman [and others], ... Edited by Stephen Epler ... New York, American sports publishing company [*1940]

National Six-Man Football Rules Committee.
GV953
.N3
National Federation of State High School Athletic Associations.
Official six-man football rules and handbook (including touch football rules) for schools, military camps and playground groups. 1935-
[Chicago]

National Skating Association of Great Britain.
Ice dances; official steps, diagrams, and glossary of terms. [New ed.] Westminster [London, 1952?]
61 p. illus. 22 cm.

1. Skating.   I. Title.

GV849.N3   796.91   57–27812 ‡

NN   0065721   DLC NN

NATIONAL SKATING ASSOCIATION of Great Britain. *4009.246
Official handbook of the departmental committee for figure skating
1897, 98.
London. Langley. 1897, 98. v. 8°.

NN   0065722   MB

NATIONAL SKATING ASSOCIATION of Great Britain. *40
Rules and constitution.
[London, 1897.] 19 pp. 8°.

NN   0065723   MB

National skeet shooting association,
Official skeet rule and handbook.
Library has
1933.

NN   0065724   MiD

NATIONAL SKEET SHOOTING ASSOCIATION.
Skeet rules and regulations, rev. and approved January 1, 1932. [Author, 1932]
[3] p.

NN   0065725   Or

GV1181   **National Skeet Shooting Association.**
.N298
Skeet shooting review.
[Dallas]

National sketch book, Washington to Roosevelt,
containing biographical sketches of our presidents, their wives and ladies of the White house with birthdays, birthstone lore [etc.] Chicago Ill., Devereaux & Turner [c.1939]

80 p. ports. 22 cm.

NN   0065727   MH DLC

GV854   **National Ski Association of America.**
.A1A55
American ski annual and skiing journal.
[Barre, Mass.]
             v. illus., ports. 28 cm.

National Ski Association of America.
Manual of ski mountaineering
see under title

National Ski Association of America.
1950 world ski championships, U. S. A. [Denver, W. W. MacGruder] 1950.
xii, 40, xiii–xxiv p. illus. 30cm.

"Advertising matter included in paging."

NN   0065730   NcU NN OrCS WaT

National ski association of America.
Official rules for downhill and slalom racing.
[Boston, Blanchard printing co.] *19
             v. 15½ᶜᵐ.
Publication began with issue for 1939?

1. Skis and ski-running.
GV854.A1N28   796.93   47–3497

NN   0065731   DLC

National ski association of America.
The **Ski** bulletin; the national skiing weekly.
[Boston, A. B. Moorhouse, 19

GV854   **National Ski Association of America.**
.A1S58
Ski news.
Hanover, N. H.

VOLUME 407

National Ski Association of America,
. . . Year book.

Bellows Falls, Vt. ₁19
  v. illus. (incl. ports.)   25½cm.

    19   published jointly with the United States Eastern Amateur Ski
Association.

1. Ski-running—Assoc. and org.—   U.S.
N. Y. P. L.   December 13, 1935

NN 0065734   NN

National ski association of America. *National ski patrol system.*
  Annual report of the National ski patrol system, the National ski association of America ... 19
  New York, The National ski patrol system ₁*19

    v. illus., diagr., forms. 19ᵐ.

  Editor: 19   C. M. Dole.

    1. Skis and ski-running—Societies. 2. Sports—Accidents and injuries.
  I. Dole, Charles M., ed.
                                     41–9179
    Library of Congress   GV854.A1N3
                    ₁2₂   614.87

NN 0065735   DLC

National ski association of America. *National ski patrol system.*
  The National ski patrol system manual; editorial board, Charles Minot Dole, chairman, Robert Livermore, jr., Richard Rocker ₁and others₂ ... New York, The National ski patrol system ₁*1941₂

    x, 117 p. incl. illus., tables. 17ᵐ.

    1. Skis and ski-running—Societies. 2. Sports—Accidents and injuries.
  I. Dole, Charles Minot. II. Title.
                                    42–19225
    Library of Congress   GV854.N33
                    ₁4₂   614.87

NN 0065736   DLC Or CU OC1

        National Ski Association of America.   **National**
GV841   Ski Patrol System.
.W55   **Winter** sport news. v. 1–
      Jan. 2, 1947–
      New York.

National ski patrol system, National ski association of America

    see

National ski association of America. *National ski patrol system.*

NATIONAL skiing.   Denver.Col.

  2, 1949 –

NN 0065739   NhD

National skiing guide. 1947–
  New York, N. Y., A. S. Barnes & company, *1946–

    v. illus. (incl. maps) plates. 27ᵐ.

    On cover, 1947–   : The Annual almanac of skiing in the United
  States.
    Editor: 1947–   Minot Dole.

    1. Skis and ski-running—Year-books. I. Dole, Charles Minot, ed.

    GV854.A1N33   47–1588

NN 0065740   DLC OrCS WaT

National Skyway Freight Corporation
  see Flying Tiger Line, inc.

669.148 National slag association.
N21b   Blast furnace slag as concrete aggregate. Report of Committee 201, Aggregate specifications, American concrete institute. Cleveland, 1931.
    cover-title, 45p.

    "Authorized reprint from copyrighted Journal of the American concrete institute, vol.II, no.2, October, 1930 and no.6, February, 1931."
    Bibliography: p.35-37.

NN 0065742   IU

TG335 National Slag Association,
N3   Bridges and incidental structures.
    Washington, D.C., 1937.
    47 ℓ. of illus. 23cm.

    Cover title.

      1. Slag cement. 2. Bridges, Concrete. I. Title.

NN 0065743   NcRS IU DNAL WaS

National Slag Association.
  Materials required per cubic yard, of slag, stone and gravel concrete and cement mortar
    see under Hubbard, Fred.

TE   National Slag Association.
205   Methods of testing mineral aggregates and associated materials. ₁Prepared for the Committee on
.N28 Correlation of Research in Mineral Aggregates of the Highway Research Board,National Research Council. Cleveland ₁Distributed by Highway Research Board,National Research Council,Washington₂ 1931.
    1 v.(various pagings) 28 cm.
    In 7 divisions,1 and 7 originally issued July 18, 1930,and Nov.26,1929; each division with caption title: Symposium of test methods on coarse aggregates.
    1.Road materials--Testing. I.National Research Council. Highway Research Board. II.Title. III.Title: Symposium of test methods on coarse aggregates.

NN 0065745   MiU PSt

National slag association.
  ₁Miscellaneous publications₂ Cleveland, O.

NN 0065746   MiD NNC

National slag association.
  Reports ₁of committees₂ Cleveland, O.

    Library has
    Reports for Committee C-9, June 1930;
      Committee 201, Oct. '30.

NN 0065747   MiD

669.148 National slag association.
N21s   ... Symposium no.1₁-19₁ March 1928₁-October 1929₂ (1st edition) ... Cleveland, O., National slag association ₁c1928-c29₂
    19 no. tables.

    "A collection pertaining to the characteristics and uses of blast furnace slag."
    No more published.

      1. Slag.

NN 0065748   IU DPR NN MiD UU ICJ

National slate association.
  Slate roofs. ₁Philadelphia₂ The Chapman slate co., National slate assoc. ₁1926₂ 84 p. incl. diagrs., tables. illus. 28½cm.

    Prepared by the National slate association.
    "First edition, January, 1926."

    1. Roofing, Slate. I. Chapman   slate company, Bethlehem, Pa.
N. Y. P. L.   October 19, 1938

NN 0065749   NN IdU MiD OC1 MiU

                                 L695.2
National Slate Association.   S900
  Slate roofs. ₁2d ed.₂   ₁Philadelphia, Pa.₂ National Slate Association ₁1929₂

    cover-title, 84 p. incl. illus., map, tables, diagrs. 28ᵐ.

    "Second of a series ... on slate and its uses."

NN 0065750   ICJ NNC

TH2445
N3   National Slate Association.
1953   Slate roofs. [3d ed. New York, 1953]
    84 p. illus., map, diagrs., tables. 28 cm.
    Cover title.
    "Second of a series of informative literature on slate and its uses."

      1. Roofing, Slate. I. Title.

NN 0065751   DI

National Slovak Society of the United States of America.
  Almanac
  see
  Národný americko-slovenský kalendár.

4E   National Slovak Society of the United
234   States of America.
    Dejiny a pamätnica Národného slovenského spolku, 1890-1950. Sost. Juraj J. Nižnanaský, a V. S. Plátek.
    Pittsburgh [195]
    448 p.

NN 0065753   DLC-P4 NN

National Slovak Society of the United States of America.
  Kalendar
  see
  Národný americko-slovenský kalendár.

E184   National Slovak Society of the United States of
.S64N27   America.
    Národné noviny. National news.
    Pittsburgh.

AY76   National Slovak Society of the United States of
.N35   America.
    Národný americko-slovenský kalendár.
    Pittsburgh.

National Slovak Society of the United States of America.
  Oslava 35. vyrocia N. S. S. 1890-1925,v nedel'u, dňa mája 1925 v Pittsburghu. Pa.
  Pittsburgh, Pa., Narodny novin, 1925.
  14p.
  Slovak.

NN 0065757   OC1

VOLUME 407

National Slovak Society of the United States of
America.
    Regular convention.   Youngstown, Ohio.
      7 v. illus. 29 cm.

NN 0065758   OU

National Slovak Society of the United States of America.
    Souvenir book published on the occasion of the regular
convention.
    [v. p.]
      v. illus. 29 cm.
      Title varies slightly.

    1. Slovaks in the U. S.

E184.S64N3   325.24370973   56–32304 ‡

    IEN OO
NN 0065759   DLC CU WaT MiD MeB PSt CLSU IEdS MB

HS1998   National Slovak society of the United States of
N277   America.
      Stanovy Národného slovenského spolku vo
    Spojených Štátoch Amerických opravené a prijaté
    na XIII. riadnej konvencii, v McKeesport, Pa.
    Constitution and by-laws of the National Slovak
    society of United States of America, adopted at
    the XIII. regular convention, held at McKees-
    port, Pa.   [Philadelphia? 1320]
      cover-title, xxxviii [5], 6–120, 6–120, [17]
    p. incl. forms.   15ᶜᵐ.
      Slovak and English on opposite pages.
      Documents con   cerning the granting of the
    charter of the   National Slovak society:
    p.i–xxxviii.
      1. Slovaks in the U.S. I. Title.

NN 0065760   CSt-H

National Slovak society of the United States of America.
    Zápisnica...
1

Pittsburgh: P. V. Rovnianek & co. [etc.] 1   23–25cm.
    v.

    1. Slovaks—U. S.—Assoc. and   org.
N. Y. P. L.   December 31, 1937

NN 0065761   NN IEdS

625.85   National Slurry Seal Association.
N21n   NSSA specification.
    Waco, Tex.
      no. 28cm. irregular.

NN 0065762   IU

National Small Business Association.
    "Abe Lincoln's story"
      see under   Haverlin, Carl.

National small business association.
    Significant forces; the minute men arise to meet
    today's emergency in the same spirit which begat
    the new world's first true republic...
      see under   Maxwell, Perriton, 1868–1947.

Business
HD
2346
.U5   National Small Business Association.
N21   Small business bulletin and issues.

    [Washington, D. C., etc.]
      v. illus., ports. 28cm.

NN 0065765   NNC

National small business association.
    Two fronts; a brief outline of some things which need to be
done at home.   [Akron, National small business men's assoc.,
194–?] 7 p. 16cm.

    1. World war, 1939–   —Labor   —U. S.
N. Y. P. L.   January 4, 1945

NN 0065766   NN

National small business conference.
    Report of proceedings, National small business conference.
    [1st–   1942–
    [Chicago] 1942–
      v. 23ᶜᵐ.

    1. U. S.—Econ. condit.—1918–   2. U. S.—Economic policy.
    3. World war, 1939–   —Economic aspects—U. S.

    Library of Congress   HC106.4.A1N38   42–21929
                               [2]   330.6873

NN 0065767   DLC

National Small Business Men's Association
    see
National Small Business Association.

National small business research bureau,
    incorporated, Washington, D. C.
American business policy report. Document no. 1–
Washington, D. C., National small business research bureau
(incorporated) 1940–

National small business research bureau,
    incorporated, Washington, D. C.
Carruthers, John Franklin Bruce, 1889–
    ... The small business problem as I see it, by John F. B.
Carruthers. Washington, D. C., National small business re-
search bureau (incorporated) 1940.

National small homes bureau, inc.
    see
National homebuilders bureau, inc.

National small homes demonstration, inc.
    The best way to achieve low-cost housing is
to build low-cost homes. [Wash. c1939]

    32 p.

NN 0065772   OC1

NATIONAL SMALL HOMES DEMONSTRATION, INC.

    How to do more business and make more money—with
lower cost small homes this year. [Washington, D.C.:
National small homes demonstration, inc., 1940] 20 p.
incl. diagrs. illus. (incl. plans.) 28cm.

    1. Housing for the working class—U.S. I. Title.

NN 0065773   NN

[National small house competition]
    Home builder's plan book; a collection of architectural
designs for small houses submitted in competition by architects and architectural draftsmen in connection with
the 1921 Own your home expositions, New York and Chicago, 1921. [1st ed.] [New York] Building plan holding
corporation [ᶜ1921]
    84 p. illus. (incl. plans) 27¼ᶜᵐ.
    Lettered on cover : Prize and honor designs of the National small house
competition, 1921.
    Issued also, without descriptive text, under title : Prize winning small
house plans.
    1. Architecture, Domestic—Designs and plans.   ɪ. Building plan hold-
ing corporation. ɪɪ.   Title. ɪɪɪ. Title: Own your home expositions.
    Library of Congress   NA7127.N45 1921   21—6618

NN 0065774   DLC WaS OrU NcRS PP OC1 FMU IdB NN CU

[National small house competition]
    Prize winning small house plans; a collection of archi-
tectural designs for small houses submitted in competition by architects and architectural draftsmen in connection with the 1921 Own your home expositions, New York
and Chicago, 1921. [New York] Building plan holding
corporation [ᶜ1921]
    48 p. illus. (incl. plans) 27¼ᶜᵐ.
    Cover-title : Prize winning small house plans of the National architec-
tural competition, 1921.
    "Official Own your home exposition edition."
    Issued also, with descriptive text, under title : Home builder's plan book.
    1. Architecture, Domestic—Designs and plans.   ɪ. Building plan hold-
ing corporation. ɪɪ. Title. ɪɪɪ. Title: Own your home expositions.
                                        21—6619
    Library of Congress   NA7127.N45 1921 a

NN 0065775   DLC ICRL MWA

HD2346   National Small Industries Corporation Limited.
.I5N34   Administration report.
    National Small Industries Corporation Limited.
    Small industries programme; a brief report.

    [New Delhi]

HD   National Small Industries Corporation Limited.
2346   Annual report.
I5   New Delhi.
N32   v. 28 cm.
      Report year ends Mar. 31.

    1. Small business—India.
    HD2346.I5N32   S A 68–10172

NN 0065777   DLC NN NSyU

National Small Industries Corporation Limited.
    Small industries programme; a brief report.

    [New Delhi]
      v. illus. 25 cm. annual.
      Cover title.   : Administration
report.

    1. Small business—India. 2. Industry and state—India.   ɪ. Na-
tional Small Industries Corporation Limited. Administration report. ɪɪ. Title.
    HD2346.I5N34   S A 68–15652

NN 0065778   DLC

Pam.   National smelting and refining co.
Coll.
      Prospectus ... Kansas city, Mo., 1890.
14745   [4] p. 27½cm.

NN 0065779   NcD

National Smoke Abatement Society
    see
National Society for Clean Air.

VOLUME 407

96.505
N21

National Snapdragon Society.
Bulletin.

ₜColumbus, Ohioₕ

1. Antirrhinum.

NN 0065781   DNAL

National Soap Sculpture Committee, New York.
...Annual competition for prizes offered by the Procter &
Gamble Company for small sculpture, using white soap as a
medium; for professionals.
ₜno.ₕ

New York, 192   4°.
nos.

Title of committee   :192   National Small Sculpture Committee,
New York.   New York.

1. Sculpture, Soap. I. Proctor &   Gamble Company.
N. Y. P. L.   June 1, 1932

NN 0065782   NN

ₜNATIONAL SOAP SCULPTURE COMMITTEE, New Yorkₕ
Soap sculptureₜ a manual. ₜ160 Fifth Ave.,
New York 10, Authorₕ c1947.
23 p. illus.

NN 0065783   CaBViP Or PPPL

National Soap Sculpture Committee, New York.
Soap sculpture illustrated. 80 E. 11th St.,
New York, Author c1942.
23 p. illus.
Text on back cover also.
Contains announcement of 19th annual Ivory
soap sculpture competition.

NN 0065784   Or

NATIONAL SOAP SCULPTURE COMMITTEE, New York.
Soap sculpture, its place in education and
recreation. 80 E. 11th St., New York, Author
c1937.
29 p.

NN 0065785   Or

National Soaring Contest.
Official directory.
ₜn. p.ₕ Soaring Society of America.
v. illus. 31 cm. annual.
Cover title, 19   Official program.

1. Gliders (Aeronautics)   I. Soaring Society of America.

TL765.N3   55-40304 ‡

NN 0065786   DLC

HV591
.A1Z9
no. 46
... National sobriety ... London, printed by
William Clowes and sons, limited [1902]
32 p. [Pamphlets on prohibition... in
countries other than U.S. No. 16]
Reprinted from the Quarterly review,
No. 392. [Oct. 1902]

NN 0065787   DLC NN

National social directory.
New York, Society Listing.
v. 18 cm. annual.

Title varies: The List of society, national.
Issues for   Include section: Official Washington listings.

1. U. S.—Social registers.

E154.7.L47   54-26905 rev ‡

NN 0065788   DLC NcGU MsSM LU MoSW C

National social directory publishers, Chicago.
Social directory of the United States
see under title

National Social Life Conference
see
Catholic Social Life Conference.

National social purity crusade, London.
The cleansing of a city. Published ₜorₕ the National
social purity crusade ... Contributors: Rev. J. B. Paton, D. D., Dr. C. W. Saleeby ... ₜand othersₕ James Marchant (editor) London, Greening & co., ltd., 1908.
xviii, 159 p. 18¼ᶜᵐ.
"First published, December, 1908."
Contents.—I. Forewords by the Lord Bishop of Hereford, the Most
Rev. the Archbishop of Westminster, the President of the Free churches,
the chief rabbi.—II. Note by the editor.—III. The moral training of our
youth, by Rev. J. B. Paton.—IV. Parenthood and education, by C. W.

Saleeby.—V. What has been done and what might be done in the cleansing of the city, by Rev. F. B. Meyer.—VI. 1. The reading of our youth, by
Rev. J. B. Paton. 2. Unclean fiction, by Rev. William Barry. 3. Noxious
literature, by Rev. R. F. Horton. 4. The censorship of low-grade literature and illustrations, by the editor.—VII. The need of purity, by the Arch-
deacon of London.—VIII. The foreign bully, by (I) Arnold White. (II)
George R. Sims.—IX. Vice and the law, by Mrs. Bramwell Booth.—X. A
study of illegitimacy in London, by Alfred Leffingwell.—XI. Who is responsible? By the Right Rev. Bishop Welldon.

1. Social ethics. 2. London—Soc. condit. 3. London—Moral conditions.
I. Marchant, James, 1867-   ed.

                                                    9-15099

Library of Congress   HQ291.N3

NN 0065792   DLC CaBVaU ICRL ICJ

National social purity crusade, London.
Public morals conference. *London*, 1910.
The nation's morals; being the proceedings of the Pub-
lic morals conference held in London on the 14th and
15th July, 1910 ... with a preface by the Rt. Hon. Alfred
Emmott ... Pub. for the National social purity crusade.
London, New York ₜetc.ₕ Cassell and co., ltd. ₜ1910ₕ

National social purity crusade, London.
Public morals; preface by the Right Rev. the Lord Bishop of
Southwark (Edward Stuart Talbot, D.D.); edited by James Mar-
chant; published for the National social purity crusade. Lon-
don: Morgan & Scott, 1908. 254 p. 17½cm.
Various contributors.

13428B. 1. Vice—Gt. Br. 2. Great   Britain—Moral conditions. I. Marchant, Sir James, 1867-1955 ed.   II. Title.
N. Y. P. L.   March 12, 1940

NN 0065794   NN

National Social Purity Crusade, London.
Social hygienics. A new crusade by James
Marchant, ...
see under   Marchant, Sir James, 1867-1956.

⁕⁕⁕⁕ The National social science series. ... . Chicago, A. C. McClurg,
1913-.
Continued from no. 1. 18 x 10½ᶜᵐ.
Editor: Frank L. McVey.
The volumes in this series are shelved according to their subjects. Cards for the in-
dividual works follow that for the series in the author catalogue.

NN 0065796   ICJ DLC

HD
7090
N28
1953
National Social Security Conference,
Chicago, 1953.
Proceedings; National Social Security
Conference, Friday, March 27, 1953, Drake
Hotel, Chicago, Illinois. Sponsored by the
Chamber of Commerce of the United States,
its affiliated State Chambers of Commerce
and the Chicago Association of Commerce
and Industry. ₜWashington, D.C.,ₕ Chamber
of Commerce of the United States of
America, 1953ₕ

79p. 23cm. (American economic
security. v.10, no.3. Conference issue.,
1953)

1. Old age pensions - U.S.   I. American
economic security, v.10, no. 3. II.
Chamber of Commerce of the United States of
America.

NN 0065798   NRU

368.4
N2133w
National Social Security Conference, Chicago,
1953.
Weaknesses in Federal programs for the aged.
Morning session, National Social Security Con-
ference, Friday, March 27, 1953, Drake Hotel,
Chicago. Sponsored by the Chamber of Commerce
of the United States, its affiliated State
chambers of commerce and the Chicago Associa-
tion of Commerce and Industry. ₜWashington,
Chamber of Commerce of the United States of
America, 1953?ₕ
8, 9, 6p. 28cm.
Cover title.

NN 0065799   IU

National social unit organization.
Bulletin.
Cincinnati, O., National social unit organization, 1917-
v. 18¼ᶜᵐ.

1. Community centers.

Library of Congress   HN55.N4   19-14503

NN 0065800   DLC DHEW CtY ICJ MdBJ

National Social Unit Organization.   3560.123
[Papers read at the National Social Unit Conference, October 23-
25, 1919.]
— [New York City. 1920.] 8 v. in I. 30½ cm.
Contents.—I. Why community organization. By John Collier, John Love-
joy Elliott, and members of the Conference. 2. The Social Unit and
public health. By Haven Emerson and Zoe La Forge. 3. The Social
Unit. By Edward T. Devine. 4. The Social Unit and the Church. By
Charles Stelzle. 5. The Social Unit and community statistics. By Robert
E. Chaddock. 6. The Social Unit in 1920. By Wilbur C. Phillips. 7.
The Social Unit and the worker and the employer. By Mark M. Jones
and John Walker. 8. Democracy and the making of budgets. By
John Collier.
A circular is inserted.

L9558 — Community organization.

NN 0065801   MB ICJ OrU MiD DL NcU

National social unit organization.
A plan for establishing a national social
laboratory in which to develop under the
auspices of a widely representative group of
social experts a model program for community
organization, beginning with work for
children. (n. p., 1915?)
--- ---Copy 2.

NN 0065802   DL

HN55
.N3
National social unit organization.
Special report. no. [1]-
Cincinnati, 1918-
v. 28ᶜᵐ.

Mimeographed.

NN 0065803   ICU CtY

VOLUME 407

National Social Welfare Assembly.
Analysis of programs

see under

Krueger, Anna Barbara.

NATIONAL SOCIAL WELFARE ASSEMBLY.
Annual report.
New York.   v.   22-27cm.

Some reports have also distinctive titles; i.e., 1956, Serving organizations and people; 1961, New directions in social welfare; etc.

1. Charities, Private--U.S.

NN 0065805   NN

National Social Welfare Assembly.
Assembly letter. no. 1-
July 1948-

NN 0065806   AzU CU

National Social Welfare Assembly.
Employment characteristics of recent group
work graduates

see under

Kindelsperger, Walter L

NATIONAL social welfare assembly.
Field service directory.
N.Y.

NN 0065808   WaS

National social welfare assembly.
Health and welfare services in the national defense; a memorandum prepared by the National social work council, December,
1940. [New York, 1940]   11 p.   23cm.

1. Hygiene, Public--U. S., 1940.   2. Social service--U. S.
N. Y. P. L.

NN 0065809   NN IU

HV 91
N2
National Social Welfare Assembly.

The issues before social welfare today;
papers and discussion summaries from the 10th
anniversary annual meeting, December 8-9,
1955, New York City. [New York, 1955]

35 p.   31 cm.

1. Social service. I. Title.

NN 0065810   CaBVaU

NATIONAL SOCIAL WELFARE ASSEMBLY.
Juvenile delinquency and the relationship
of the police to social agencies. Author, 1953.
8 p.

NN 0065811   Or

National social welfare assembly.
Men and women discharged from the armed
forces. Addresses
see under   Martin, Helen W.

National Social Welfare Assembly.
The National Conference on Social Welfare
Needs
see under   National Conference on Social
Welfare Needs, Washington, D.C., 1948.

National Social Welfare Assembly.
A new look at governmental and...
see under   Adirondack Workshop, Silver
Bay, N.Y., 1955.

HV
41
.N29
National Social Welfare Assembly.
Personnel references in social agencies; a
guide to writing and using. Prepared by Committee on Personnel. New York, 1955.
3 p.   28 cm.

1.Recommendations for positions. 2.Social
workers.   I.Title.

NN 0065815   MiU

HV 88
N35
National Social Welfare Assembly.
Proceedings of the annual meeting.
19
[New York]
v. illus. 28 cm.

1. Social service - Societies, etc.

NN 0065816   OU CaBVaU

309.13
N21r
National Social Welfare Assembly.
The relation of national agencies to local
community study groups.   New York [1955]
11p. 22cm.

1. Social surveys. I. Title.

NN 0065817   IU DCU

National Social Welfare Assembly.
Report.
[New York]
v. 28 cm. annual.

HV88.N15   360.6273   53-20488 ‡

NN 0065818   DLC NBuU UU MiU IU

National Social Welfare Assembly.
Report of Vocational Rehabilitation Conference
see under   Vocational Rehabilitation
Conference, New York, 1955.

National social welfare assembly.
The reservation Indian comes to town.   New York [1953]
15 p.   22cm.

Cover title.
Bibliography, p. 15.

1. Indians, N. A.--Reservations.   2. Indians, N. A.--Civilization.

NN 0065820   NN MH-P PBm WaU Wa LU

National Social Welfare Assembly.
A selected bibliography

see under

National Committee on the Aging.

National Social Welfare Assembly.
Service directory of national organizations affiliated and
associated with the National Social Welfare Assembly. 1st
ed. 1951-
New York.
v. 28 cm.

1. Social service--Societies, etc.--Direct. 2. Charities--U. S.--
Direct.   I. Title.

HV89.N35   360.58   52—3715

MtU PPPHA UU CaBVaU
NN 0065822   DLC KU CU TxU MiU NN NBuU MoU CtY-M

National Social Welfare Assembly.
Service directory of national organizations
affiliated and associated with the National Social
Welfare Assembly
see also   National Assembly for Social
Policy and Development.
Service directory of national organizations,
voluntary and governmental. [Supplement]

HN
29
.N32
National Social Welfare Assembly.
Shall we make a survey? Questions to be
considered before a survey is undertaken.
New York [1949]
23 p. 21 cm.

1.Social surveys. I.Title.

NN 0065824   MiU CaBViPA

National Social Welfare Assembly.
Standards of care

see under

National Committee on the Aging.

HV88
.C6
National Social Welfare Assembly.

Committee on Income Procedures of National Membership
Organizations.
A study of the income procedures of national membership
organizations. [Report] Staff service by the National Social
Welfare Assembly. New York, 1947.

HV 91
N36
National Social Welfare Assembly.
A study of the services and support of eleven
national agencies. Prepared by Committee on Con-
tributions to National Agencies from Community
Chest Cities, National Social Work Council.
New York, 1939.
39 p. table. 23 cm.

1. Social Service - U. S. I. Title.

NN 0065827   OU NN

VOLUME 407

National Social Welfare Assembly.
Young people and citizenship

see under

Olds, Edward B

HD9000
.6
.U63

National Social Welfare Assembly.

U. S. *President's Famine Emergency Committee.*
Youth united for famine relief. Information kit from
the President's Famine Emergency Committee and the
National Social Welfare Assembly. [Washington, 1944–

National Social Welfare Assembly
see also
Committee on a Federal Department of Health,
Education, and Security.
Conference Group on Low-Income Families.
National Committee on Service to Veterans.
National Committee on the Aging.

National social welfare assembly. Aging, National
committee on the
see National committee on the aging.

National social welfare assembly. Committee on
future program.
Report ... as adopted by the National social
welfare assembly, December 4-5, 1951.
New York, National social welfare assembly, inc.
[1952?]
80 p.

NN 0065832 PU-PSW

National Social Welfare Assembly. Field Staff
Institute, Pawling, N. Y., 1948
see Field Staff Institute, National Social
Welfare Assembly, Pawling, N. Y., 1948.

361.01
N21p

National Social Welfare Assembly.
Social Casework Council.
Private lives--public funds: some
answers to current questions about al-
leged abuses in social welfare. New
York [1952]
8 p. 22 cm.

Cover-title.
1. Social case work. I. Title.

NN 0065834 LU

309.12
N214r

National Social Welfare Assembly. Social Case
Work Council.
Report of a study of volunteer services in selected case work agencies, prepared by a committee of the Social Case Work Council of the National Social Welfare Assembly. New York, 1947.
55 l. diagrs., tables. 28cm.

1. Social case work.

NN 0065835 IU MiD PBm

National social welfare assembly. Social
case work council.
Service to migrants; a statement of principles
and procedures. New York [1948] 8 p. 22cm.

1. Labor, Migratory—U.S. 2. Travelers' aid—U.S.

NN 0065836 NN MH-IR

E
169.1
.N29

National Social Welfare Assembly. Young Adult
Council.
An introduction to the United States of
America for the visitor from abroad. [1st ed.]
New York [1951]
80 p. 22 cm. (WAY Orientation pamphlet)
Bibliography: p.79-80.
Text and map on p.[2-4] of cover.

1. U.S.--Civilization.

NN 0065837 MiU InU NcD

National Social Welfare Assembly. *Young Adult Council.*
Report of the year's activities.

New York.
v. 28 cm. annual.

1. Youth—U. S.—Societies, etc.

HN55.N434 55-37088 ‡

NN 0065838 DLC

National Social Welfare Assembly. *Young Adult Council.*
Youth organizations in the United States. New York
[1952?]
68 l. 28 cm.
Cover title.

1. Youth—Societies. 2. Youth—U. S. I. Title.

HQ796.N35 *301.43 301.1584 52–29670

NN 0065839 DLC WHi OU

National Social Welfare Assembly. Youth
Division.

Presenting your opportunity in a youth
serving organization. New York, National
Social Welfare Assembly, n.d.

31 p.

NN 0065840 CaBVaU

National social welfare assembly. Youth
division.
Youth united for a better home town.
New York, n.d.
cover-title, 22 p. illus. 21 cm

NN 0065841 Mi

National Social Welfare Assembly. Youth Division.
Committee on Volunteers.

Interorganization training of volunteer
leaders in youth serving organizations.
New York, National Social Welfare Assembly
[n.d.]

9 p.

NN 0065842 CaBVaU

4HV
495

National Social Work Association.
Diagrams of social work in Japan.
[Tokyo] 1933.
48 p.

NN 0065843 DLC-P4

National social work council
see National social welfare assembly.

National socialism or the American way; which
for US?
see under [McDermott, Malcolm Mallette]
1885-

The National socialist.

The National socialist handbook, no. 1–
[Washington, D. C., *1912–

The National Socialist. [Districted]
see District citizen.

The National socialist. [National ed.] A weekly news-
paper of facts and constructive propaganda. no. 1–
Jan. 27, 1912–
Washington, D. C., 1912–
v. illus. 59cm. weekly.
Editor: 1912– Louis Kopelin.

1. Kopelin, Louis, ed.

14–2657

NN 0065848 DLC

National socialist Germany and the pursuit of
learning
see under [Rust, Bernhard] 1883-

National socialist German labor party
see Nationalsozialistische deutsche
Arbeiter-Partei.

The National socialist, devoted to the interests of the
working people. no. 1-4; Oct.–Dec. 1911. Washington, D. C., 1911.
2 v. 28cm. monthly (irregular)
Title varies: Oct.–Nov. 1911, The Washington socialist.
Dec. 1911, The National socialist.
Louis Kopelin, editor.
Superseded by the National socialist [District ed.] and the National socialist [National ed.]

1. Socialism—Period. I. Kopelin, Louis, ed.

13–24680 Revised

Library of Congress HX1.N15

NN 0065851 DLC

E 743.5
A1 N3

National socialist bulletin.
no. 1– 19 –
[Arlington, Va., American Nazi Party]
v. illus. 22 cm.

Superseded by The Stormtrooper.

I. American Nazi Party.

NN 0065852 OU

VOLUME 407

The **National** socialist handbook, no. 1–
₍Washington, D. C., ₎1912–
v. 15ᶜᵐ.
Cover-title.
"Compiled from ... the National socialist ... Washington, D. C."
Compiler: 1913– W. J. Ghent.

1. Socialism in the U. S. i. The National socialist. ii. **Ghent, William**
James, 1866– comp.

CA 25–237 Unrev'd

Library of Congress HX81.N3

NN 0065853 DLC

National society, *London*
see
**National society for promoting the education of the poor in
the principles of the Established church,** *London.*

DS651
.N3 National society--Army of the Philippines.
Year book, v. o, no. 1.
Kansas city, [c1907]
1 pam 8°

NN 0065855 DLC

National Society--Army of the Philippines
see also
Veterans of Foreign Wars of the United States.

National society Americans of royal descent.
National society. Americans of royal descent. Incorporated 2nd May, 1908. ₍Laws₎ ₍n. p.₎ 1908.
3 p. 12¼ᶜᵐ.

1. Royal descent, Families of. i. Title.
Library of Congress CS55.N3
18–15859

NN 0065857 DLC

National Society Colonial Dames XVII Century
see
Colonial Dames of the XVII Century.

National society, Daughters of colonial wars
are
Daughters of colonial wars.

National Society Daughters of the Barons of Runnemede
see **Daughters of the Barons of Runnemede.**

NATIONAL SOCIETY FOR ART EDUCATION.
Journal of the conference.
[Leicester, etc.] v. 22cm.

Annual.
Reports for 1945 and 1947 published as Conference issues of the N. S. A. E.
journal, v.15, no. 2, Oct. 1945, and v.15, no. 3, Feb. 1948.

1. Art--Education--Gt. Br. I. N. S. A. E. journal.

NN 0065861 NN

National society for art education.
N. S. A. E. membership. 1

₍Berkhamsted, Herts., Eng.₎ 1 no. 21cm.

1. Art--Assoc., clubs, etc.-- Gt. Br. 2. Art--Education--
Gt. Br.
N. Y. P. L. June 12, 1950

NN 0065862 NN

National society for broader education.
Annual report to the incorporators, associates **and fellows of**
the National society for broader education.
₍Carlisle, Pa.₎ 19
v. 26¼ᶜᵐ.

CA 33–1147 Unrev'd
Library of Congress LC5201.N3 374.06273

NN 0065863 DLC DHEW

National Society for Business Budgeting.
Business budgeting
see Budgeting.

658.154 **National Society for Business Budgeting.**
N213r **The road ahead; a review of the annual**
conference held in New York City May 15
and 16, 1952. ₍Philadelphia₎ 1952.
105 p. 28cm.

Cover title.

1. Budget in business. I.

NN 0065865 LU CoU

National Society for Business Budgeting.
Technical notes
see
Budgeting.
Managerial planning.

QZ NATIONAL Society for Cancer Relief,
200 London
N283b The book of cancer relief₎ presenting
1951 an outline of the position regarding
cancerous diseases in Britain, and of the
forces engaged in combating the scourge.
London ₍1951₎
91 p. illus., ports.
"Council and officers, 1955" tipped in.
1. Neoplasms - Gt. Brit. 2. Neoplasms - Prevention

NN 0065867 DNLM ICJ CtY-M

W 1 NATIONAL Society for Cancer Relief, London
NA735 Report.
London, 19
v. ports.

Report for 1959 called also **Ten years**
of cancer relief, 1950 to 1960.

NN 0065868 DNLM

**National Society for Central Italy and for War
Orphans.**
Holy Year; the jubilee of 1950
see under Giannini, Amedo, 1886–
ed.

**National society for checking the abuses of
public advertising**
see Scapa society, London.

TD884 **National Society for Clean Air.**
.C615
Clean air year book. 1930–
₍London, etc.₎

National Society for Clean Air.
Constitution. Westminster ₍1946?₎
8 p. 21cm.
"Adopted at a special general meeting of the society held on
19th October, 1945."

NN 0065872 ICJ

National Society for Clean Air.
Fumifugium: or, The inconvenience of the aer
and smoake of London dissipated ...
see under Evelyn, John, 1620–1706.

National Society for Clean Air.
Guilty chimneys; the evidence of authorities
against smoke. London, National smoke abatement
soc. [1948] 19 p. plates. 24cm.

Revised edition of the "Case against smoke."
"Suggestions for further reading," p. 19.

1. Smoke.

NN 0065874 NN

National Society for Clean Air.
Journal
see
Smokeless air.

National Society for Clean Air.
... Measures for smoke prevention in relation
to plans for post-war reconstruction ... [Luton,
Eng., Gibbs, Bamforth & co., 1943]
24 p. 21 cm.
Caption title.
At head of title: Proceedings of the eleventh
annual conference of the National smoke abatement
society held at the Caxton hall, London, S. W. I., on
5th November, 1943.

NN 0065876 NNC

National Society for Clean Air.
National Smoke Abatement Society. ₍Report₎
see
Clean air year book.

National Society for Clean Air.
No clean city. ₍Manchester, Eng., National smoke abate-
ment soc., 1942?₎ 14 p. illus. 21cm.
"The need for smoke prevention in post-war reconstruction."

1. Smoke--Prevention.
N. Y. P. L. November 16, 1944

NN 0065878 NN

VOLUME 407

National Society for Clean Air.
Proceedings of the annual conference.
₍London₎
v. 21 cm.
Vols. for (1943–   ) published by the society under its earlier name: National Smoke Abatement Society.

1. Smoke prevention—Congresses.

TD884.N312   628.53   49–41875 rev*‡

OU IaAS UU IU

NN   0065879   DLC MiD NN ICJ DNLM KMK CaBVaU NbU

National Society for Clean Air.
Report
see
Clean air year book.

National Society for Clean Air.
The report of the Joint conference of the Institute of fuel and the National smoke abatement society held in London on February 23, 1945 ...
see under   Joint conference of the Institute of fuel and the National smoke abatement society, London, 1945.

National society for clean air.
Smoke abatement exhibition handbook and guide. Manchester, The National smoke abatement society ₍1936₎
79, ₍1₎ p.   24½ cm.
On cover: Science museum, South Kensington (by permission of the director, Col. E. E. B. Mackintosh, b. s. o.) October 1st to October 31st, 1936.
Advertising matter: p. 65–79.

1. Smoke prevention.   ɪ. Title.

TD884.N315   628.53   37–103 rev

NN   0065882   DLC NN

National Society for Clean Air.
ɪhe smoke abatement handbook. ... Manchester ₍Eng.₎ Published for the National Smoke Abatement Society by the Service Guild ₍1931–   ₎
Library has ed. 1, 1931, *to date*. 22ᶜᵐ.

NN   0065883   ICJ OC1 NN

National society for clean air.
Smoke prevention in relation to initial post-war reconstruction, a memorandum submitted by the National smoke abatement society. ₍Manchester, Eng., Pontefract bros., printers, 1942₎
cover-title, 24 p.   21½ cm.

1. Smoke prevention. 2. Hygiene, Public—Gt. Brit.

TD884.N32   628.53   42–25223 rev

NN   0065884   DLC NN

TD884
.S855

National Society for Clean Air.
Smokeless air; the smoke abatement journal. v. 1–
(no. 1–   ) ; autumn 1929–
₍Westminster₎, National smoke abatement society; etc., etc.,
1929–

National society for clean air.
... Smokeless zones. Westminster ₍London₎ National smoke abatement society ₍1945₎
1 p. l., 12, ₍2₎ p.   illus.   21½ cm.

1. Smoke prevention—Societies, etc.   ɪ. Title.

TD884.N323   628.53   45–18557 rev

NN   0065886   DLC NN

National Society for Clean Air.
Year book
see
Clean air year book.

National Society for Clean Air
see also   Coal Smoke Abatement Society, London.

362
N21a

National Society for Crippled Children and Adults.
Achieving goals for the handicapped. Proceedings 1949 annual convention. Nov. 6–10, Hotel Commodore, New York, N.Y.   Chicago, ⁱ1950.
231p. illus. 23cm.

1. Cripples. 2. Disabled—Rehabilitation, etc. I. Title.

NN   0065889   LU

National Society for Crippled Children and Adults.
Annual report
see its   Report.

National Society for Crippled Children and Adults.
Articles on cerebral palsy in The Crippled Child, October 1930 – February 1954, a chronological listing. Rev. February 1954. Chicago, 1954.
5 p.   28 cm.

1. Paralysis – Cerebral – Bibl. I. Title. II. The Crippled Child.

NN   0065891   CaBVaU

360.6
N215
1950

National Society for Crippled Children and Adults.
Building happy, useful lives for the handicapped. A record of the 1950 convention. Oct. 26–28, 1950.   Chicago ₍1951₎
120p. illus. 23cm.

1. Cripples. 2. Disabled—Rehabilitation, etc. I. Title.

NN   0065892   LU DVA

National Society for Crippled Children and Adults.
Bulletin
see   Easter seal bulletin.

National society for crippled children and adults.
Camping for crippled children; editor, Harry H. Howett ... By Committee on camping ... Elyria, O., The National society for crippled children and adults, incorporated, 1945.
xx p., 1 l., 120 p. incl. illus., forms, diagr. 21ᶜᵐ.
Ernest B. Marx, chairman.
Plan on front lining-paper.
"Bibliography" at end of each chapter and introduction.

1. Camping. 2. Cripples. 3. Children—Care and hygiene.   ɪ. Howett, Harry H. ɪɪ. Marx, Ernest B.

		Agr 45–317
U. S. Dept. of agr. Library	280.6N215	
for Library of Congress	SK601.N47	
	₍5₎†	362.78

OC1 ODW O CU DLC TxU

NN   0065894   DNAL MtBC OrCS CaBVaU WU NcGU TU ICRL

National Society for Crippled Children and Adults.
The care, cure, and education of the crippled child
see under   Abt, Henry Edward, 1904–

National Society for Crippled Children and Adults.
Careers in service to the handicapped; information for vocational guidance specialists on the professions of physical therapy, occupational therapy, speech and hearing therapy, and special education. Published by the National Foundation for Infantile Paralysis, the National Society for Crippled Children and Adults, with the cooperation of the Federal Security Agency, Office of Vocational Rehabilitation. ₍Chicago, 1952₎
53 p. illus. 23 cm.

Prepared ₍by₎ the staff of the National Society for Crippled Children and Adults₎ in cooperation with American Occupational Therapy Association, American Physical Therapy Association, American Speech and Hearing Association ₍and₎ International Council for Exceptional Children.

1. Occupational therapy.   ɪ. Title.

RM735.N3   615.8069   53–1110 ‡

IEN PPD OC1W

NN   0065897   DLC OrPS OrU IdPI PLF DNLM WU OU IU

HD
7255
qN277

NATIONAL Society for Crippled Children and Adults
₍Collection of publications₎

The library has a collection of miscellaneous publications of this organization kept as received. These publications are not listed nor bound separately.

1. Cripples

NN   0065898   DNLM

RD701
.C6
1943

National society for crippled children and adults.
Conference on camps for crippled children, *Cleveland*, 1943.
Conference on camps for crippled children, at the Statler hotel, Cleveland, Ohio, December 11–12, 1943, arranged by the National society for crippled children, inc. Elyria, O. ₍1944₎

RA
973
N27

National Society for Crippled Children and Adults.
Convalescent care for children. Proceedings of the conference held at Hershey, Pennsylvania, April 19–20, 1945.   Chicago, 1946.
143 p. illus. 25cm.

1. Convalescence—Congresses. I. Title.

NN   0065900   NIC

RD701
.C7

National society for crippled children and adults.
The Crippled child.
₍Lorain, O.₎ National society for crippled children of the United States of America, inc.; ₍etc., etc.₎ 19

National society for crippled children and adults.
Directory.
Elyria, O. ₍19
v. 23ᶜᵐ.
Issues for 19   published under an earlier name of the society: International society for crippled children.

1. Cripples. 2. Orthopedia—Hospitals and institutions.

		40–13215 Revised 2
Library of Congress	RD726.U5N28	
	₍r45e2₎	362.7806273

NN   0065902   DLC CaBVaU NBuG

VOLUME 407

National society for crippled children and adults.
Directory, hospitals and institutions in the United States engaged in work for crippled children. 1938–   Elyria, O.
₍1938–

v. 22¼ᵐ.

1938–   published under an earlier name of the society: International society for crippled children.
Issued by the Committee on institutions.

1. Cripples. 2. Orthopedia—Hospitals and institutions.

39–11388 Revised 2

Library of Congress   RD726.U5N3

₍r4512₎   362.78058

NN   0065903   DLC NBuG MoU OU CoU DNLM

RC418
.T84
National society for crippled children and adults.

Turner, T Arthur.
The farthest corner; an outline of the cerebral palsy problem in the United States in text and pictures, prepared under the supervision of Winthrop Morgan Phelps, M. D., by T. Arthur Turner. ₍Elyria, O., National society for crippled children, 1944₎

National Society for Crippled Children and Adults.
Foundations for walking

see under

Shriner, Mildred.

RC418
N215
1951
National society for crippled children and adults.
Guide for cerebral palsy evaluation and diagnostic clinics. Chicago ₍1951?₎
24 p.

1. Cerebral palsy

NN   0065906   NNC-M NNC

796.3
N213g
National Society for Crippled Children and Adults
Guide to standards for resident camps for crippled children ₍compiled by Eveline E. Jacobs₎ Chicago ₍ᶜ1954₎
31 p. illus. (An Easter seal publication, no. E-11)

1. Camping 2. Cripples I. Jacobs, Eveline C II. Title

OU Or OrCS OrU FTaSU
NN   0065907   MiD FTaSU OrU ViU NcRS N NNC-M DNLM

National society for crippled children and adults.
International news bulletin

see its

The monthly letter.

National society for crippled children and adults.

... A list of selected references on the education and training of the cerebral palsied child ... 1940.
6 numb. l. 28ᶜᵐ.

Caption title.
At head of title: Bureau of information, National society for crippled children, Elyria, Ohio.
Reproduced from typewritten copy.

1. Paralysis, Spastic - Bibliography.

NN   0065909   NNC

National Society for Crippled Children and Adults.
A manual of cerebral palsy equipment. Chicago, 1950–

1 v. (loose-leaf) illus. 30 cm.

"Sponsored by Zeta Tau Alpha."
Includes bibliography (2 p.)

1. Paralysis, Cerebral.   ɪ. Title: Cerebral palsy equipment.

RC418.N35   616.83   50–12975

WaTC
ICRL PPC WU DNLM IEN ICU WaS OrU Or ICJ CaBVaU
NN   0065910   DLC Wa WaT OrU-M MtBC MiU KMK DPAHO

RC113
.T8
National society for crippled children and adults.

Turner, T Arthur.
Microbes that cripple. Written and illustrated under the direction of Edward L. Compere, M. D., by T. Arthur Turner. Elyria, O., The National society for crippled children, inc. ₍1944₎

National society for crippled children and adults, inc.
..."Model bill" relating to the special education of crippled and physically handicapped children. Elyria, O., 1941.   7 f. 28cm.

Caption-title.
At head of title: Special legislative bulletin.

1. Children, Crippled—Education   —U.S.
N. Y. P. L.   December 27, 1949

NN   0065912   NN

National society for crippled children and adults.
The monthly letter. v. 1–6, no. 10; July 1925–Oct. 1930. Elyria, O., 1925–30.

6 v. in 3. illus. 28ᶜᵐ.

Caption title.
Vols. 1–5, no. reproduced from type-written copy.
Issues for 1925–Oct. 1929 have title: News bulletin (International news bulletin, Apr.–June 1927)
Published under an earlier name of the society: International society for crippled children.
No more published.
L. C. set incomplete: v. 1, no. 2; v. 2, no. 3, 6; v. 3, no. 4, 12; v. 5, no. 10 wanting.

1. Cripples—Societies.

Library of Congress   RD701.N32   45–28383

NN   0065913   DLC

HD
7255
N277n
1950
NATIONAL Society for Crippled Children & Adults
A nationwide report on building happy, useful lives for the handicapped; a record of the 1950 convention, Hotel Stevens, October 26-28. Chicago, 1950.
120 p. ports.

1. Disabled - Rehabilitation

NN   0065914   DNLM

362.4
N277n
National Society for Crippled Children and Adults.
A nationwide report on building happy, useful lives for the handicapped; a record of the 1950 convention, Chicago, October 26-28, 1950. [Chicago, c1951]
120 p. illus. 23 cm.

1. Physically handicapped. Rehabilitation. U. S. I. Title: Building happy, useful lives for the handi-   capped.

NN   0065915   NcD

National society for crippled children and adults.
News bulletin

see its

The monthly letter.

National society for crippled children and adults.

League of nations. *Advisory commission for the protection and welfare of children and young people. Child welfare committee.*
... Note by the secretary. Geneva, 1933.

LC4231
.N3
National Society for Crippled Children and Adults.
Opportunities for the preparation of teachers of exceptional children; a cooperative study sponsored by National Society for Crippled Children and Adults and the United States Office of Education₍ ₎Chicago₎ 1949.
99p. 23cm.

1. Handicapped children. 2. Physically handicapped chi ldren. I. Title.

NN   0065918   NNU OrU-M DNLM

QGU
N21
Cutter
National Society for Crippled Children and Adults.
Opportunity; a short story of the development of a program for crippled children in America during the last two decades. Elyria, Ohio, National society for crippled children of the U. S. A., inc. ₍1942₎
cover-title, 20 p., 1 l. illus. 23cm.
"Designed, written, and illustrated by T. Arthur Turner."

1. Physical Handi-   capped. 2. Orthopedia
I. Title. II. Turner, T Arthur

NN   0065919   WU Or

National society for crippled children and adults.
Opportunity, a short story of the development of a program for crippled children in America during the last two decades. Elyria, O., The National society for crippled children of the U. S. A., inc. ₍1943₎

1 p. l., 20 p., 1 l. illus., diagrs. 22¼ᵐ.

"Written and illustrated by T. Arthur Turner."—Leaf at end.
"Second run, Jan. 1943."

1. Cripples.   ɪ. Turner, T. Arthur.   ɪɪ. Title.

45–15610 Revised

Library of Congress   RD701.N36

₍r46c2₎   362.7806273

NN   0065920   DLC IaU

HV3011
.T8
National society for crippled children and adults.

Turner, T Arthur.
Organizing to help the handicapped, a brief guide for voluntary associations for the crippled, by T. Arthur Turner. Elyria, O., National society for crippled children, inc. ₍1944₎

National Society for Crippled Children and Adults.
Parents' study guide; a manual for parents of cerebral palsied children. Prepared under the direction of Verna S. Carlisle. Chicago ₍1951₎
68 p. illus. 22 cm.

1. Paralysis, Spastic. 2. Cripples.   ɪ. Carlisle, Verna S.   ɪɪ. Title.

RJ496.P3N3   616.83   51–8173

NN   0065922   DLC TxU OrU Or WaS WU DNLM

W 1
NA743
NATIONAL Society for Crippled Children and Adults
₍Press release₎

Chicago, 19
v.
A file of this publication is kept as received but not bound. For numbers in library, consult assistant at Periodical Desk.

NN   0065923   DNLM

VOLUME 407

National society for crippled children and
adults.
Raney, Richard Beverly, 1906–
A primer on the prevention of deformity in childhood, by
Richard Beverly Raney ... in collaboration with Alfred Rives
Shands ... illustrated by Jack Wilson. Elyria, O., National
society for crippled children, inc., 1941.

362.78
N277pr   National society for crippled children and
adults.
The problem and the promise; a brighter
future for the crippled. A report on the
work of the Easter seal societies. Chicago
₍1953₎
₍32₎ p. illus. 28cm.
Cover title.

1. Cripples--Rehabilitation, etc. I. Easter
seal societies.   II. Title.

NN 0065925   TxDaM

National Society for Crippled Children and Adults.
Proceedings ₍of the₎ annual convention.

Chicago ₍etc.₎
v. illus. 23-29 cm.
No proceedings published for the 1st-6th conventions? Cf. Union
list of serials.
Title varies slightly.
Issues for 19   have also distinctive titles.
Proceedings for 19   issued by the society under an earlier name:
19   –38, International Society for Crippled Children.—1939– National Society for Crippled Children of the United States of America.
Proceedings for 1935–   included in the Crippled child.
1. Cripples—Societies.

RD701.N3   362.78   45-27712 rev*

NNC
NN 0065926   DLC MtU Or FTaSU CU KAS NN DNLM TU

National Society for Crippled Children and Adults.
Proceedings ₍of the Institute of Rehabilitation Centers₎
see under   Institute of Rehabilitation Centers.

RC388
.A5   National Society for Crippled Children and
Adults.

American Psychological Association. *Division of School
Psychologists.*
Psychological problems of cerebral palsy; a symposium
sponsored by Division of School Psychologists, American
Psychological Association, and the National Society for
Crippled Children and Adults, inc. ₍Chicago, 1952₎

National Society for Crippled Children and Adults.
Rehabilitation centers in the United States

see under

Redkey, Henry.

Z5704
.R4   National Society for Crippled Children and
Adults.

Rehabilitation literature.

Chicago ₍etc.₎ National Society for Crippled Children and
Adults.

National Society for Crippled Children and Adults.
Report.
₍Chicago?₎
v. illus., ports. 22 x 29 cm. annual.
Each volume has also a distinctive title: 1957, Steps to rehabilita-
tion.

I. Title: Steps to rehabilitation.

RD701.N34   58-34937

DNLM AAP
NN 0065931   DLC CaBVa ICU IU Or Wa OrU-M NNC

RA965
N21
1947   **National society for crippled children and
adults.**
Report of a study on convalescent care for
children. Chicago, 1947.
x, 144 p.

Bibliography: p. 133-134.

1. Convalescence. 2. Hospitals, Convalescent.
3. Children. I. Title: Convalescent care for
children.

NN 0065932   NNC-M OrU CU DNLM WU NNC

362.78   National society for crippled children and adults.
N21r   Report of a study on convalescent care for
children.   Chicago, The National society for
crippled children and adults, 1947.
156p. 28cm.

1. Children--Care and hygiene. I. Title.

NN 0065933   LU

W 1   NATIONAL Society for Crippled Children and
NA743   Adults
Report of the executive director to the
delegate assembly.
Chicago ₍1945?₎-
v.
Title varies slightly.

NN 0065934   DNLM

National Society for Crippled Children and Adults.
Role of the school psychologist in services to
the parents of a child with a handicap
see under   American Psychological Association. Division of School Psychologists.

HV3018
.U5   **National Society for Crippled Children and
1953   Adults.**

U. S. Federal Security Agency. *Office of Vocational Rehabilitation.*
Selected papers, National conference of rehabilitation
centers, second annual meeting, October, 1953, co-sponsors:
Office of Vocational Rehabilitation ₍and₎ National Society
for Crippled Children and Adults. ₍Washington, 1953?₎

RC423
.A48   **National Society for Crippled Children and
Adults.**

American Speech and Hearing Association.
Speech problems of children; a guide to care and correction, prepared for the National Society for Crippled Children and Adults. Wendell Johnson, editor. New York,
Grune & Stratton, 1950.

National Society for crippled children and adults.
Speech problems of school children

see under

American Psychological Association.

372.1   National Society for Crippled Children
N269   and Adults.
Understanding yourself and your child.
Chicago ₍1955?₎
20 p. 23 cm.

"An Easter Seal publication."
"Selected papers presented at the Parent
Institute and the Seminar on Developing Personality held at a National Convention of
the National Society."
1. Cripples.   2. Children. Care and
hygiene.   I. Title.

NN 0065939   N IU PU-Med-TS OrCS

360.6   National Society for Crippled Children
N215   and Adults.
1951   Voluntary effort--National strength.
Proceedings 1951 annual convention,
October 3-5, 1951, Palmer House, Chicago,
Ill.   Chicago ₍1952₎
176 p. illus. 24cm.

1. Cripples.   2. Disabled--Reha-
bilitation,   etc. I. Title.

NN 0065940   LU

National Society for Crippled Children and Adults
see also
International Society for Rehabilitation of the Disabled.

National Society for Crippled Children and Adults. *Committee on Convalescent Care*
see also **Conference on Convalescent Care for Children,**
Hershey, Pa., 1945.

National society for crippled children and adults. *Committee on legislation.*
Digest, federal and state legislation affecting crippled children and the physically handicapped. 1938. Compiled by
states, issued by the Committee on legislation. Elyria, O., The
International society for crippled children, inc. ₍1938₎
cover-title, 75 p. 22½ᵐ.

1. Children—Charities, protection, etc.—U. S. 2. Cripples. 3. Disabled—Rehabilitation, etc.—U. S. 4. Employers' liability—U. S. I.
Title.

38-39591 Revised 2

NN 0065943   DLC OrP Or MiD WU ICJ NN N

362.78   National Society for crippled children and adults.
N21re   Committee on the severely handicapped.
Rehabilitation facilities for the severely handicapped...   ₍Chicago, The National society for
crippled children and adults, inc.₎ 1947.
ix, 53p. 28cm.

Bibliographical footnotes.

1. Cripples. 2. Disabled--Rehabilitation, etc.
I. Title.

NN 0065944   LU CU MH-IR OrU CU DNLM OU NN

National Society for the Crippled Children and
Adults. Education Committee.
Progress in the education of crippled
children ...
see under   Howett, Harry H.

VNB   National Society for Crippled Children and Adults.
2N21   Library.
Cutter   A bibliography on camping with handicapped
children, an author subject index to literature
in the library of the National Society. Rev.
Sept., 1949. Chicago ₍1949₎
13 p. 29cm.

Cover title

1. Camping - Bibl. 2. Children, Abnormal & backward - Bibl.

NN 0065946   WU ICJ

ZHD
7255   **National Society for Crippled Children
N27b   and Adults. Library.**
A bibliography on employment of the
physically handicapped; an author-subject
index to literature in the Library of the
National Society, March, 1949. Chicago
₍1949₎
28p. 28cm.
Cover title.

NN 0065947   NRU ICJ MnU WU Or OrU

VOLUME 407

ZQT　　NATIONAL Society for Crippled Children
250　　　and Adults. *Library.*
qN277b　　　A bibliography on recreation for
1950　　physically handicapped children and
　　　adults. A selection of titles in the library
　　　of the National Society for Crippled
　　　Children and Adults. Rev. Dec. 1949,
　　　with suppl. Jan.-Aug. 1950. Chicago
　　　[1950]
　　　　24 p.
　　　　1. Cripples - Bibl.
　　　　2. Recreation - Bibl.

NN　0065948　　DNLM OrU CoU

National Society for Crippled Children and Adults.
Library.
　　　A bibliography on recreation for physically
handicapped children and adults; a selection
of titles in the library. Rev. February 1954.
Chicago, 1954.

　　　53 p. 28 cm.

　　　Cover title.
　　　1. Handicapped - Bibl. 2. Recreation -
Bibl.

NN　0065949　　CaBVaU

National Society for Crippled Children and
Adults. *Library.*
Bibliography on the deaf and hard of
hearing. Chicago, 1949.
17p. 28cm.

Processed.

1. Deaf. Bibliography.

NN　0065950　　Or OrU

NATIONAL SOCIETY FOR CRIPPLED CHILDREN AND
ADULTS. *Library.*
Bibliography on the deaf and hard of hearing.
[New ed.] Author, 1951.
23 p.

Mimeographed.

NN　0065951　　Or CaBVaU

ZHD　　NATIONAL Society for Crippled Children
7255　　　and Adults. *Library.*
qN277b　　　Bibliography on the psychology of the
1950　　handicapped; a selection of titles in the
　　　Library of the National Society for
　　　Crippled Children and Adults. Chicago,
　　　1950.
　　　　57 p.
　　　　1. Disabled - Rehabilitation - Bibl.

NN　0065952　　DNLM

Z5814　　National Society for Crippled Children and
P6N35　　　Adults. *Library.*
1951　　Bibliography on the psychology of the
　　　handicapped; a selection of titles in the
　　　library. Chicago, 1951.
　　　　67 p. 28cm.
　　　　1. Handicapped - Psychology - Bibl.
　　　　I. Title.

NN　0065953　　CoU NNC

Z　　　NATIONAL Society for Crippled Children
5704　　　and Adults. *Library.*
qN277b　　　Books and pamphlets on rehabilitation;
1953　　a selective checklist of publications in
　　　print, comp. by the Library. Rev.
　　　Chicago [1953]
　　　　13 p.
　　　　Caption title.

　　　　1. Disabled - Rehabilitation - Bibl.

NN　0065954　　DNLM

National Society for Crippled Children and
Adults. Library.
　　　Books and pamphlets on rehabilitation; a
selective checklist of publications in print.
Rev. [ed.] Chicago, 1954.

　　12 p. 28 cm.

　　1. Rehabilitation - Bibl. I. Title.

NN　0065955　　CaBVaU

016.37191　National Society for Crippled Children
N277b　　　and Adults. *Library.*
　　　Books in print on rehabilitation; an
　　　annotated list of selected titles from
　　　the Library of the National Society for
　　　Crippled Children and Adults. Chicago,
　　　1949.
　　　　21p. 28cm.

　　　1.Rehabilitation - Bibliography.

NN　0065956　　CLSU

HD7256.Un3
N212　　　National society for crippled children and
1952　　　adults. Library.
　　　Books in print on rehabilitation; an anno-
　　　tated list of selected titles from the library
　　　of the National society for crippled children
　　　and adults. Rev. January, 1952. Chicago
　　　[1952]
　　　　30 p.

　　　"This bibliography is supplemented by the
　　　Bulletin on current literature, a monthly
　　　bibliography for　　　workers with the
　　　handicapped."

　　　1. Disabled - Rehabilitation, etc. - Bibliog-
　　　raphy. I. Title.

NN　0065958　　NNC-M NNC CaBVaU PU PU-Med-TS

HD7256.Un3
N214　　　National society for crippled children and
1952　　　adults. Library.
　　　A checklist of books and pamphlets on
　　　exhibit, 1952 annual conference of the
　　　American physical therapy association, by
　　　the library of the Easter seal society,
　　　June 23-28, 1952. Chicago, 1952.
　　　　8 p.

　　　1. Disabled - Rehabilitation, etc. - Bibliog.
　　　II. American physical therapy association.
　　　III. Title.

NN　0065960　　NNC-M NNC

National society for crippled children and adults, inc.
Library.
　　...List of books and theses in the library of the National so-
ciety for crippled children. [Elyria, O., 1945] 10 f. 28cm.
Caption-title.

1. Children, Crippled—Bibl.
N. Y. P. L.　　　　　　　　　　　　　　March 28, 1946

NN　0065961　　NN

National Society for Crippled Children and Adults. *Library.*
Pamphlets in print on rehabilitation; a checklist of free
and inexpensive materials. Chicago, 1951.
44 p. 28 cm.
"Supplemented by the [society's] Bulletin on current literature."

1. Disabled—Rehabilitation, etc.—Bibl. 2. Children, Abnormal and
backward—Bibl.
Z5704.N33　　　　　016.3719　　　　　51-14346

NN　0065962　　DLC DNLM NNC CaBVaU

National society for crippled children and
adults. Library.
A selected list of periodicals that
publish articles concerning the handicapped.
Revised September, 1951. Chicago, 1951.
6 p.

1. Disabled - Rehabilitation, etc. -
Periodicals - Bibliography. I. Title.

NN　0065963　　NNC-M NNC

Z
695.1　　National Society for Crippled Children and
.R4　　　Adults. Library.
N28　　　A selected list of subject headings on the
　　　rehabilitation of the handicapped. 1st ed.
　　　Chicago, 1954.
　　　　51 p. 29 cm.
　　　　Caption title.

　　　1.Subject headings--Rehabilitation.

NN　0065964　　MiU OClW NNC-M NNC NcU

Z
5704　　　National Society for Crippled Children and
N38　　　Adults. *Library.*
1947　　　Selected references on the vocational counsel-
　　　ing, placement, and employment of handicapped
　　　workers. Rev. Oct.1947. Chicago [1947]
　　　　17p. 28cm.

　　　Caption title.

　　　1.Vocational rehabilitation-Bibliography. 2.
　　　Handicapped-Employment-Bibliography. I.Title.

NN　0065965　　CoFS

S
016.61683　National society for crippled children and
qN275　　　adults. *Library.*
　　　A selective bibliography on cerebral palsy;
　　　an author-subject index to literature in the
　　　library of the national society. Rev. Septem-
　　　ber, 1949. Chicago, Library, National societ;
　　　for crippled children and adults [1949]
　　　　42 p. 28 cm.

　　　1. Paralysis. Cerebral. Bibliography.

NN　0065965-1　N

ZWS　　NATIONAL Society for Crippled Children
340　　　and Adults
qN277s　　　A selective bibliography on cerebral
1951　　palsy; an author-subject index to
　　　literature in the library of the National
　　　Society. Rev., comp. and distributed
　　　by the library of the National Society for
　　　Crippled Children and Adults. Chicago,
　　　1951.
　　　　45 p.
　　　　Cover title.
　　　　1. Paralysis - Cerebral - Bibl.

NN　0065966　　DNLM

National Society for Crippled Children and
Adults. Library.
　　　A selective bibliography on cerebral palsy;
an author-subject index to literature in the
library of the National Society. Rev. Chicago, 1953.
　　57 p.

　　　1. Cerebral palsy - Bibliography.

NN　0065967　　NNC-M DNLM ICJ NNC PU WU NcU-H

VOLUME 407

National Society for Crippled Children and
Adults. Library.
Sources of information about the handicapped; a guide to nontechnical publications,
prepared by the Library, April 1953. Chicago
₁1953₎
24p. 28cm.

Caption title.

NN 0065968   PU-Med-TS

National Society for Crippled Children and
Adults. Library.
Sources of information about the handicapped;
a guide to nontechnical publications. Rev.
[ed.] Chicago, 1955.
20 p. 28 cm.

1. Rehabilitation - Bibl. 2. Handicapped -
Bibl. I. Title.

NN 0065969   CaBVaU

Z5814
C52N35   National Society for Crippled Children and
1950   Adults. *Library.*
A special education bibliography; a
selection of titles in the library. Rev.
Apr. 1950.   Chicago [1950]
42 p.   28cm.

1. Rehabilitation - Bibl.   I. Title.

NN 0065970   CoU

Z 5704
N 35   National Society for Crippled Children and
1955   Adults. Library.
A special education bibliography; a
selection of titles in the library. Rev.
[ed.] Chicago, 1955.
60 p. 28 cm.

1. Rehabilitation - Bibl. 2. Handicapped -
Bibl. I. Title.

NN 0065971   CaBVaU

616.87   National society for crippled children and
N277s   adults. Library
A speech correction bibliography; a selec-
Philos.   tion of titles in the library of the National
society for crippled children and adults.
Rev. June, 1949.   Chicago, 1949.
cover-title, 21p. Q.

1. Speech, Disorders of. Bibl. I. Title.

NN 0065972   IaU WaU WU

Z6675
S55N35   National Society for Crippled Children and
1950   Adults. *Library.*
A speech correction bibliography; a
selection of titles in the library. Rev.
Nov. 1950.   Chicago [1950]
21 p.   28cm.
1. Speech, Disorders of - Bibl.   I.
Title.

NN 0065973   CoU

ZWM   NATIONAL Society for Crippled Children
475   and Adults. *Library.*
qN512s   A speech rehabilitation bibliography:
1953   a selection of titles in the Library of the
National Society for Crippled Children
and Adults. Rev. May 1953.   Chicago,
1953.
58 p.
Cover title.
1. Disabled - Rehabilitation - Bibl.
2. Speech - Disorders - Bibl.

NN 0065974   DNLM CaBVaU

National Society for Crippled Children and Adults. *Library.*
Summary report.
Chicago.
v. 28 cm. annual.

Report year ends in Sept.

Z733.C5239   027.66   53-15678 ‡

NN 0065975   DLC DNLM

National Society for Crippled Children and
Adults. Library.
Surveying community needs in rehabilitation
services; a checklist of selected references
in the library. Chicago, 1954.
11 p.   28 cm.

1. Rehabilitation - Bibl.   I. Title.

NN 0065976   CaBVaU

National society for crippled children of the United
States of America
see
National society for crippled children and adults.

National society for curriculum study. *Committee
on courses of study.*
Samples of typical present-day courses of study
in the elementary and secondary schools...
n.p.₁c1937₎
18,₁1₎ p. 27cm.

Herbert B. Bruner, chairman of Committee on
courses of study.

NN 0065978   OrU

DB879   National Society for Foreign Travel in German
.K3A53   Bohemia.
Karlsbad, *Bohemia. Stadtrat.*
Album of the watering place of Carlsbad. ₁Issued by the
Municipal Council of Carlsbad and the National Society
for Foreign Travel in German Bohemia. Carlsbad, 19——₎

National society for historical research.

Hemstreet, Charles, 1866–
The Broadway of yesterday; a collection of 20 prints
of old Broadway, together with a full description, by
Charles Hemstreet ... With a color cover design from
painting by the artist-historian John Rae ... ₁New York,
Issued by the Cadwallader publishing co. under the direction of the National society for historical research₎ ₁1905.

W 1   NATIONAL Society for Medical Research
NA747   Annual report.

[Rochester, N. Y., etc.] 19
v. illus., ports.

1. Research - period.

NN 0065981   DNLM OrU-M

612.05   National Society for Medical Research.
NA   The bulletin for medical research.
v.1-   ; Nov./Dec. 1946-
Chicago.
v. illus. 26cm. bimonthly.

Issues for May/June-July/Aug. 1950 not pub-₁
lished.
Title varies: Nov./Dec. 1946-Nov./Dec. 1953,
Bulletin.

GEU WU-M GU NNC NIC PPULC OrCS InU-D CLWM
NN 0065982   IU ViRM MnRM CaBVaU CtY-M OU LNL DNLM

W
20.5   NATIONAL Society for Medical Research
qN277   ₁Collection of publications₎

The library has a collection of miscellaneous publications of this organization
kept as received. These publications are
not listed nor bound separately.
1. Research, Medical

NN 0065983   DNLM

National Society for Medical Research.
Events affecting research administration
see under title

448
N215T   National Society for Medical Research.
38 common questions; authoritative answers;
subject: animal experimentation.
[Chicago, 195-?]
14 p.

1. Animal experimentation.

NN 0065985   DNAL

National society for promoting religious education in
accordance with the principles of the Church of England
see
National society for promoting the education of the poor in
the principles of the Established church, *London.*

National society for promoting the education of the poor
in the principles of the Established church, *London.*
Account of the report of the National society for the
education of the poor; at a meeting held 2nd June, 1813
...
(*In* The Pamphleteer. London, 1813. 22½ᶜᵐ. v. 2, p. ₁27₎-30)

cA 5—669 Unrev'd

Library of Congress   AP4.P2 vol.2

NN 0066002   DLC ICN

National society for promoting the education of
the poor in the principles of the Established
church, London.
Annual report.

[London, 18-   ]   v.   21½cm.
[College pamphlets, v.1254]

NN 0066003   CtY DHEW RPB

National Society for Promoting the Education of the
Poor in the Principles of the Established Church,
London.
The birth of Judaism
see under   Batho, Dorothy.

National Society for Promoting the Education of the
Poor in the Principles of the Established Church,
London.
Charter of incorporation ...   London,
1817.
17 p.   21 cm.   [College pamphlets,
v. 191]

NN 0066005   CtY

VOLUME 407

National society for promoting the education of
the poor in the principles of the Established
church, London.
.rg62   Charter of incorporation ...
.21   London, 1850.   2 p.ℓ.,[3]-17pp.   21½cm.
.17no   Imprint reads:London...1817.And there re-printed
-1850.
—— London, 1817. 17pp. 21cm. [College pamphlets, v.191]

NN   0066006   CtY

YA   National society for promoting the education of
1254   the poor in the principles of the established
church , London.
Charter of incorporation... London, 1852.
12p.

NN   0066007   DLC

National society for promoting the education
of the poor in the principles of the
Established church, London.
Lfa63   Correspondence of the National society with
G5   the Lords of the Treasury and with the Com-
1   mittee of council on education. Edited by the
Rev.John Sinclair, M.A., secretary. London,
J.Murray,1839.
1v,39p. 21cm.

NN   0066008   CtY PU

646.2   National society for promoting the educa-
N27   tion of the poor in the principles of
the Established church,London.
Instructions on needle-work and knitting as derived from the practice of the
Central school... 4th ed.   Lond.,The
author, 1853.

NN   0066009   N

National Society for Promoting the Education of the
Poor in the Principles of the Established Church,
London.
Map showing the distribution of the chief
mineral productions of England and Wales, with
part of Scotland. Lond., 1848.

NN   0066010   Nh

National society for promoting the education of
the poor in the principles of the Established
church,London.
National education; or A short account of the efforts which have been made to educate the children
of the poor,according to the new system invented
by the Rev.Dr.Bell; including an account of the recent establishment of the society. To which is sub-
joined,a letter,on the subject of national education ... London, Printed and published by W.Hughes
,etc. 18--,
24 p. 18.4cm.

Bound with Gt.Brit.Parliament.1791.House of commons. The debate on a motion for the abolition of
the slave-trade ... London,1792.

1.Education of children.2.National society for
promoting the education of the poor in the principles of the Estab lished church.London.I.Ti-
tle.

NN   0066012   MiU-C

National Society for Promoting the Education of the
Poor in the Principles of the Established Church,
London.
National society's Graded hymn book with
tunes. Part I. Hymns for children under eight
years. Part II. Hymns for children between
eight and twelve years of age. [London] National
society's depository [1914]
ix, 108 p. 19 cm.
85 hymns, 3 supplemental hymns.
With music.

NN   0066013   NNUT

National society for promoting the education of
the poor in the principles of the Established
church.
The National society's monthly paper...(no.
26103) Jan. 1843-Dec. 1855.
London, The depository of the Society, 1843-55.
6 v. illus. (incl. music) 22 cm.
Lacks nos. 37-38, Jan.-Feb. 1850; no. 44. ...
1850; nos. 47-50; Jan, Feb. 1851; nos. 56-97,
Jan. Dec. 1854.

NN   0066014   DHEW CtY

321   National Society for Promoting the Education of the
N212   Poor in the Principles of the Established Church,
London,
Posture in housework; an application of the
principles of good posture to the practice of housework. London, National society's depository
[1935?]
71 p.

NN   0066015   DNAL

National society for promoting the education
of the poor in the principles of the
Established church, London.
Dean, *Rev.* James.
Religion an essential element of education. An ad-
dress to his congregation, on behalf of "The national so-
ciety for the education of the poor in the principles of
the Established church, throughout England and Wales,"
Jan. 21st, 1838. By the Rev. James Dean, A. M. ...
Derby [Eng., H. Mozley and sons, printers] 1838.

National Society for Promoting the Education of the
Poor in the Principles of the Established Church,
London.
Religious instruction in schools. London
[1872?]
23 p. 8°. [In v. 732, College Pamphlets]

NN   0066017   CtY

National Society for Promoting the Education of the
Poor in the Principles of the Established Church,
London.
Remarks on the present state of the society.
1st paper, July, 1852, [by a Committee appointed
June 10] [London, 1852]
16 p. 8°. [In v.   College Pamphlets]

NN   0066018   CtY

NATIONAL SOCIETY FOR PROMOTING THE EDUCATION OF
THE POOR IN THE PRINCIPLES OF THE ESTAB-
LISHED CHURCH,London.
Report of the proceedings at a public meeting
held in St.George's Hall,Liverpool,on April 5,
1872,in the interests of church education,in-
cluding speeches by the marquis of Salisbury,
the lord bishop of Chester,J.G.Hubbard,[and
others]. Liverpool,Lee and Nightingale,1872.

21 cm.   pp.31.

NN   0066019   MH

National Society for Promoting the Education of the
Poor in the Principles of the Established Church,
London.
The result of an inquiry concerning works of
industry connected with national schools. 1832.
Caption-title, 14 p. 22 cm.

NN   0066020   RPB

National society for promoting the education of the poor
in the principles of the Established church, *London.*
Result of the returns to the general inquiry made by
the National society, into the state and progress of
schools for the education of the poor in the principles
of the Established church, during the years 1846-7,
throughout England and Wales. London, Printed at the
School-press, for the Society, 1849.
[742] p. 34ᶜᵐ.
Various paging.

1. Education — London. 2. Poor — London. 3. Church of England —
Education.   E 11-1700

Library, U. S. Bur. of   Education   LC410.G7N23

NN   0066021   DHEW CtY

National Society for Promoting the Education of the
Poor in the Principles of the Established Church
London.
Revised code. Copy of letter from the secre-
tary of the National society to the secretary of the
Committee of council on education. [n.p., 1861]
7 p. 33 cm.
Caption title.

NN   0066022   CtY

National society for promoting the education of
the poor in the principles of the Establish-
ed church, London.
PO 1309   ...A simple exposition of the education
.R3 P2   bill, 1906, with full text of the bill. [London,
v.12   Printed by Spottiswoode and co.,ltd., 1906?]
(Binder's title:
Pamphlets, 12)

NN   0066023   MdBJ

National Society for Promoting the Education of the
Poor in the Principles of the Established Church,
London.
Statistics of Church of England schools for the
poor in England & Wales for the years 1866 & 1867.
2d ed. London,
50 p. 8°. [In v. 465, College Pamphlets]

NN   0066024   CtY

National Society for Promoting the Education of the
Poor in the Principles of the Established Church,
London.
The story of England's church
see under   Elliott-Binns, Leonard
Elliott, 1885-

National Society for the Advancement of Gastroenterology
see
National Gastroenterological Association.

National society for the blind.
Blind persons employed in war industries in the United
States as of January 1, 1943, in cooperation with Service for
the blind, U. S. Office of education. Washington, D. C., Na-
tional society for the blind, inc., 1943.
cover-title, 2, 33 numb. l. 27½ x 21½ᶜᵐ.
Reproduced from type-written copy.
Text runs parallel with back of cover.

1. Blind — Employment.   I. U. S. Office of education. Service for
the blind. II. Title.
                               44-2584
Library of Congress   HV1658.N3
                 [3]   331.59

NN   0066026   DLC TU

VOLUME 407

National society for the blind.

Lewis, Lawrence Quick, 1895– *comp.*
Blind workers in U. S. industries; photographs and letters from their employers, in cooperation with Service for the blind, U. S. Office of education, compiled by Lawrence Q. Lewis. Washington, D. C., National society for the blind, incorporated, 1943.

National society for the blind.

Lewis, Lawrence Q
Letters from sighted employers of blind employees, in co-operation with Service for the blind, U. S. Office of education, compiled by Lawrence Q. Lewis. Washington, D. C., National society for the blind, inc., 1942.

HV1596
.C56
National society for the blind.
[Clunk, Joseph F   1895–
Open letter to my newly blinded friend. [Washington] U. S. Office of education, Federal security agency [1944]

National society for the blind.

Lewis, Lawrence Quick, 1895–
Reasons for the amendment to the Randolph-Sheppard act and evidence supporting its practicability and need. Service for the blind, U. S. Office of education. Compiled by Lawrence Q. Lewis. Washington, D. C., National society for the blind, 1941.

HV1652
.N4
National society for the blind.
New York institute for the education of the blind.
Report on the vocational training and guidance program of the New York institute for the education of the blind [by] Alan R. Blackburn ... Clarence R. Athearn ... [and] Marion Shoesmith ... [New York] 1943–

HV1792
.A3W56
National Society for the Blind.
Who's who among the blind in the business and professional world. [1st–   ed.] 1950–
Washington, National Society for the Blind, inc.

National Society for the Employment of Epileptics. Report of proceedings at a meeting held at the Mansion House, January 25, 1893. With an introduction showing the objects and scheme of the society. 31 pp. 8°. *London,* 1893.

NN   0066033   DNLM

National society for the end of strife.

Batdorf, John W.
National society for the end of strife, by John W. Batdorf ... New York, Broadway publishing co. [1912]

W 1
NA748H
NATIONAL Society for the Humane Regulation of Vivisection
Proceedings of the annual meeting.

A file on this publication is kept as received but not bound. Issues in the Library may be found on the shelves under the call number.

NN   0066035   DNLM

National society for the humane regulation of vivisection.
Mercy and truth; a paper devoted to securing justice for animals. v. 1–   June 1919–
Washington, D. C., 1919–

National Society for the Prevention of Blindness.
The Americas unite to save sight [summaries of papers]
see under   Mid-Century Conference on Progress of the Pan-American Association of Ophthalmology and National Society for the Prevention of Blindness, Miami Beach, Fla., 1950.

National Society for the Prevention of Blindness.
... Annual report ...
see its   Report.

National Society for the Prevention of Blindness.

Bright eyes, how to keep them shining. New York, National Committee for the Prevention of Blindness [192–]
[8] p. illus. 23ᶜᵐ. [Its Pamphlet, no.10]

1. Eye—Care and hygiene. I. Title. II. Ser.

NN   0066039   ViU CU

National society for the prevention of blindness.
Committee of medical social eye workers, *New York.*
... Bulletin ... of the Committee of medical social eye workers ... New York, N. Y., National society for the prevention of blindness [19

National Society for the Prevention of Blindness.
Care of the eyes
see under   Metropolitan life insurance company.

National Society for the Prevention of Blindness.
... Care of your eyes- a message to you. Take care of yours eyes, your eyes are your bread-winners ... New York, National committee for the prevention of blindness [1915?]
4 p. 23 cm. (Its Publications, no. 2)

NN   0066042   CU

National   society   for the Prevention of Blindness.
[Census of causes of blindness of pupils enrolled in 31 state schools for the blind and 4 public school systems, 1915–1916.] New York, 1916. 2 l. Tables. 4°.

Typewritten.
Letter of G. L. Berry, acting secretary, included.

1. Blind.—Education, U. S.
N. Y. P. L.   October 26, 1916.

NN   0066043   NN

National Society for the Prevention of Blindness.
Classroom lighting.   N. Y., Author [1950]
15 p. illus. O. (Publication, no. 498)

NN   0066044   PPPL

HV
1573
qN277
NATIONAL Society for the Prevention of Blindness
[Collection of publications]
The Library has a collection of miscellaneous publications of this organization kept as received. These publications are not listed nor bound separately.
1. Blind

NN   0066045   DNLM

National Society for the Prevention of Blindness.
... Common causes of blindness in children. Concerning common causes of blindness in children. and the means and methods of prevention. Prepared by the Ohio commission for the blind. New York, National committee for the prevention of blindness [1915?]
cover-title, 16 p. illus. 23 cm. (Its Publications, no. 1)
1. Title. II. Ohio. Commission for the blind.

NN   0066046   CU

National Society for the Prevention of Blindness.

Common causes of blindness in children, concerning common cause of blindness in children and the means and methods of prevention. Rev. 1920. New York, National Committee for the Prevention of Blindness [1920]
cover-title, 16 p. illus. 23ᶜᵐ. ([National Society for the Prevention of Blindness] Publication, no. 1)
1. Eye—Diseases and defects. 2. Blindness. 3. Children—Diseases.   I. Title. II. Ser.

NN   0066047   ViU

WW
505
qN277c
1945
NATIONAL Society for the Prevention of Blindness
Conservation and utilization of eyesight in industry. [New York, 1945?]
1 v. (various pagings) illus.
Caption title.
"This brochure contains a selection of publications [by various organizations] on the above subject. "

1. Eye - Wounds & injuries
2. Industrial hygiene 3. Occupational diseases 4. Vision

NN   0066049   DNLM

National Society for the Prevention of Blindess.
Conserving the sight of school children; a program for public schools
see under   Joint Committee on Health Problems in Education.

National Society for the Prevention of Blindness.

Contribution of statistics to the prevention of blindness. New York [1935]
35 p. 23ᶜᵐ. (National Society for the Prevention of Blindness. Publication 164)
"Proceedings of the Statistics session, annual Conference of the National Society for the Prevention of Blindness, December, 1934."
"Reprinted from the Sight-saving review, vol. V, no. 1, March, 1935."
1. Blindness. I. Title. II. Ser.

NN   0066051   ViU

National Society for the Prevention of Blindness.
... Directions for the prevention of blindness from babies' sore eyes. Needlessly blind for life ... Prepared by the New York committee for the prevention of blindness. [New York city, National committee for the prevention of blindness 1915?]
4 p. illus. 23 cm. (Its Publications, no. 3)

NN   0066052   CU

VOLUME 407

HV1631
.H3
1947   National Society for the Prevention of Blindness.
         FOR OTHER EDITIONS
         SEE MAIN ENTRY
   Hathaway, Winifred (Phillips)
     Education and health of the partially seeing child. Rev.
ed. New York, Pub. for the National Society for the Prevention of Blindness, by Columbia Univ. Press, 1947.

National Society for the Prevention of Blindness.
   Eye hazards in industrial occupations
     see under Berry, Gordon Lockwood,
     1884-

National society for the prevention of
blindness.
Resnick, Louis, 1891–1941.
   Eye hazards in industry; extent, cause, and means of prevention, by Louis Resnick. New York, Published for the
National society for the prevention of blindness by Columbia
university press, 1941.

National Society for the Prevention of Blindness.
   Eye health, a teaching handbook for nurses. New York,
1946.
     108 p. illus. 23 cm. (*Its* Publication no. 447)
     "References": p. 101–103.

     1. Eye—Care and hygiene. 2. Eye—Diseases and defects.   I. Title.
     II. Series.

     RE1.N3 no. 447   617.7   Med 47–2282*

   NN   0066056   DLC OC1 CU MiDP WaT MtU OrU-M

National Society for the Prevention of Blindness.
   Eye health, a teaching handbook for nurses. New York,
c1947,
     108 p. illus. 23 cm. (*Its* Publication no. 447)
     "References": p. 101–103.
     "3d ed."

   NN   0066057   ICU

National society for the prevention of blindness, inc.
   Eye health & safety news ...
     see under title

National Society for the Prevention of Blindness.
   Eye health primer for nurses. New York,
n.d.
     By Francis Crocker.

   NN   0066059   OrU

National society for the prevention of blindness
   ...Eye inspection and vision testing; a
screening process. N.Y. 1942.

     7 numb. l., 6 diagrs. 28 cm.

   NN   0066060   OU

National Society for the Prevention of Blindness,
inc.
   The eye physician in industry
     see under Jones, James Guy, 1885-

National Society for the Prevention of Blindness.
   Eyes saved in industry; the experience of
583 companies. A study conducted jointly by
the National Safety Council and the National
Society for the Prevention of Blindness.
ᵣNew York, 1928ᵢ
     23 p. illus. 23ᶜᵐ. (National Society for the
Prevention of Blindness. Publication 62)
     1. Accidents—Prevention. 2. Eye—Protection.
3. Safety appliances. 4. Blindness. I. National
Safety Council. II.   Title. III. Ser.

   NN   0066062   ViU

NATIONAL SOCIETY FOR THE PREVENTION OF BLINDNESS
   An important new incentive tool for eye safe-
ty in industry; the Wise owl clubs of America.
Author c1948?ᵢ
     ᵣ11ᵢ p. illus.

   NN   0066063   Or

National Society for the Prevention of Blindness.
   Industrial aspects of ophthalmology.   New York,
1945.
     149 p.
     Proceedings of the 1944 Seminar.
     Publication No. 430.

   NN   0066064   MiDP

National society for the prevention
of blindness.
New York (State) University. Medical inspection bureau.
   ... Jamestown eye survey; a study of 8000 school children.
Report of the Medical inspection bureau in cooperation with
National committee for the prevention of blindness, New York
state commission for the blind, Jamestown board of education.
Prepared under the direction of Emily A. Pratt ... Albany,
The University of the state of New York press, 1926.

National society **for the prevention of blindness.**
   American health congress, *Atlantic City*, 1926.
   ... Joint sessions. Relation of venereal diseases to vision
impairment, American social hygiene association and National
committee for the prevention of blindness. Venereal disease
control, American social hygiene association and American
public health association ... ᵣNew York, National health council, 1926ᵢ

National society for the prevention
of blindness.
   Lighting the schoolroom. Based upon
the American standard code of lighting
school buildings... New York, The National committee for the prevention of
blindness (1924)
     (4) p.   23 cm.

   NN   0066067   DL

National society for the prevention of blindness.
   Louisa Lee Schuyler, 1837–1926. New York, N. Y., The National committee for the prevention of blindness ᵣ1926ᵢ
     24 p. front. (port.) 28ᵐᵐ.
     Short addresses by Homer Folks, secretary, State charities aid associ-
ation, New York, and others.

     1. Schuyler, Louisa Lee, 1837–1926.   I. Folks, Homer, 1867-

                                  28–5173
     Library of Congress   HV28.S3N3

   NN   0066068   DLC NIC MB NN ICJ

National society for the prevention of blindness.
   Medical social workers in eye services news
     see under title

National Society for the Prevention of Blindness.
   A mid-century conference on progress ...
     see   Mid-Century Conference on Progress
of the Pan-American Association of Ophthalmology
and National Society for the Prevention of Blindness,
Miami Beach, Fla., 1950
     The Americas unite to save sight ...

RE91
N21   National society for the prevention of blindness.
     ᵣMiscellaneous publications and reprints ...ᵢ

     In pamphlet box.

     1. Blindness - Societies.

   NN   0066071   NNC

W 1   NATIONAL Society for the Prevention of
NA748N   Blindness
no. 378   Mobilization of state forces for pre-
1942   vention of blindness; a symposium.
   New York, 1942.
     59 p. (Its Publication, no. 378)
                   W1 NA748N
     Supplement to the Sight-saving
review, v. 12, no. 1, March, 1942.
     1. Blindness 2. Vision   Title:
Sight-saving review, Supplement
Series

   NN   0066072   DNLM

National Society for the Prevention of Blindness.
   The news letter on sight conservation.

   New York.
     no. in   illus. 24 cm.
     5 no. a year, 19   ; annual, 19
     Pub. May 1915–Nov. 1942 (88 no.); superseded by Eye health &
safety news.
     Title varies: The news letter.
     No.   issued under the society's
earlier name: National Committee for the Prevention of Blindness.
     With no. 6–24 is bound Its Publication no. 4.
     1. Blindness—Societies, etc.

     RE1.N33   617.705   21–5811 rev*

     ICRL
   NN   0066073   DLC OC1W DNLM CU ICJ NBuG MiU IU DL

614.83   National society for the prevention of blindness.
N213n   1937 survey of fireworks accidents in Maryland.
   New York, N.Y., National society for the preven-
tion of blindness, inc. ᵣ1938ᵢ
     8p. tab. (Its Publication 268)

     1. Accidents--Stat. 2. Fireworks.

   NN   0066074   IU

National society for the prevention of
blindness.
   ...Organization...(New York city,
National committee for the prevention of
blindness, n.d.)
     (4) p.   23 cm.

     Caption-title

   NN   0066075   DL

National Society for the Prevention of Blindness.
   ... Photographic exhibits and slides. Loan exhibits: Babies' sore eyes (ophthalmia neonatorum)
wood alcohol, midwives, trachoma, industrial eye
accidents ... Slides ... arranged for stereopticon
lectures on the above subjects ... New York,
National committee for the prevention of blindness,
[1916?]
     [5] p. illus. 23 cm. (Its Publications,
no. 4)

   NN   0066076   CU

VOLUME 407

National society for the prevention of blindness.
(Posters 1-5)
New York city (1935?)
5 nos. 28cm.

NN   0066077   DL

RE11
.C6
1945

National Society for the Prevention of Blind-
ness.
Conference on Industrial Ophthalmology, *Columbia Univer-
sity,* 1945.
Proceedings of a Conference on Industrial Ophthalmol-
ogy, sponsored by the Columbia University College of
Physicians and Surgeons in cooperation with the National
Society for the Prevention of Blindness, May 7-11, 1945.
New York, 1947.

RE1
.N4

National society for the prevention of
blindness.
Proceedings of the ₍1st₎ ₍1915₎
annual conference...   New York, The
Society ₍1915₎
v.   23-25cm.   (Publication no.   )
Title varies: 1st-12th conference;
National committee for the prevention of
blindness.
No conferences were held 1930-1934.

1.Blindness - Societies.   2.Eye - Care
and hygiene.

NN   0066079   NNU-W MiU AzU MB MnU CU ICJ Vi NBuG

National Society for the Prevention of Blindness.
A program of eye health in a school system
(Pubn. no. 143)   New York, 1934.

NN   0066080   OrU

RE53
.P7

National society for the prevention of
blindness.
... Protecting eyes in industry; addresses presented before the
Industrial section, National society for the prevention of
blindness, at its annual conference in New York city, October
27, 1939 ...   Washington, U. S. Govt. print. off., 1940.

RE322
U5N3

National Society for the Prevention of Blindness.
The public health aspects of trachoma.   Joint
sessions of the National Committee for the Prevention of Blindness with the Eastern Association of
Indian Affairs.   [New York, 1926?]
37 p.   23 cm.
Reprinted from the Proceedings of the 12th
annual conference of the National Committee for
the Prevention of Blindness, Dec. 1-2, 1926.
1. Conjunctivitis Granular.   2. Indians of North
America - Diseases.   I. Eastern Association of
Indian Affairs.   II. Title.

NN   0066082   DI

National Society for the Prevention of Blindness.
Publication.   no. 1–
New York ₍1915–

no. in   v.   illus.   22-31 cm.

No. 1–   issued by the society under its earlier name: National
Committee for the Prevention of Blindness.
Some numbers also in rev. ed.

1. Blindness—Societies.   2. Blindness—Prevention.

RE1.N3   53-26280

DL NBuG ICJ NNU-W NN AzU MiU PBL CtNIC
NN   0066083   DLC Or NcD IU ViU Vi MB ICRL DNLM MiD

National Society for the Prevention of Blindness.
Publications on preventing blindness.   New
York ₍1938₎
23 p.   22cm.   (National Society for the Prevention
of Blindness.   Publication 32.)

1. Blindness—Bibl.   I. Ser.

NN   0066084   ViU

617.7
N213p

NATIONAL SOCIETY FOR THE PREVENTION OF BLINDNESS.
Publications relating to eye health, comfort,
and efficiency.   New York [1939-48]
27 pamphlets in 1v.   24cm.

Cover title.
Most of articles reprinted from the Sight-
Saving Review.

1. Eye - Care and hygiene.   2. Eye - Diseases
and defects.   I. Title.

NN   0066085   TxU

National Society for the Prevention of Blindness.
Report.   1st–   1915–
₍New York₎
v. in   illus.   18 x 22 x 23 cm.   annual.
1st-12th reports issued as the society's Publication no. 8, 11, 14,
15, 19, 22-25, 27, 29, 32 (RE1.N3)
Report year for 1915-16 ends Nov. 1; for 1917–   Dec. 31.
Reports for 1927–   have also distinctive titles.
Reports for 1915-26 issued by the society under its earlier name:
National Committee for the Prevention of Blindness.
1st report includes 7th Report of New York State Committee for
the Prevention of Blindness.
1. Blindness—Societies, etc.   (Series: National Society for the
Prevention of Blindness.   Publication)

RE1.N31   17-22430 rev 2*

NN   0066086   DLC DNLM CtNIC MiU DL DHEW

National Society for the Prevention of Blindness.
"Screening," eye examinations, and follow-up.
New York₍1945₎
16p.   24cm.   (Its Publication no.443)

"Reprinted from The Sight-saving review, vol.
XX, no.3."
Forms chapter 5 of Eye health - a teaching
handbook for nurses, by the National Society
for the Prevention of Blindness.

NN   0066087   PSt

**National Society for the Prevention of Blind-
ness.**
Seeing through 1931.   New York ₍1932₎
8 p.   23cm.   (National Society for the Prevention of Blindness.   Publication 90)
"Reprinted from the Sight-saving review, vol. II,
no. 1, March, 1932."

1. Eye—Care and hygiene.   2. Blindness.   I. Ser.

NN   0066088   ViU

WW
505
N277s
1953

NATIONAL Society for the Prevention of
Blindness
Sight conservation in gray iron foundries;
report of a survey made in cooperation with
the Gray Iron Founders' Society.   New
York ₍1953₎
20 p.   (Its Publication, no. #28)
Cover title.
1. Accidents - Prevention   2. Iron &
steel workers   3. Vision   I. Gray Iron
Founders' Society, Cleveland   Series

NN   0066089   DNLM

National Society for the Prevention of Blindness.
The sight saving class exchange
see under title

National Society for the Prevention of Blindness.
Sight seeing classes; their organization and
administration.   New York, n. d.

NN   0066091   OrU

National Society for the Prevention of Blindness.
Standards of school lighting.   New York.

NN   0066092   OrU

National society for the prevention of blindness.
Suggested bibliography in the fields of eye
health, treatment and related social services.
1955.

NN   0066093   PU-PSW

D621.35
N216

National society for the prevention of blindness.
Suggested regulations for lighting sight-
saving classrooms.   New York, National society
for the prevention of blindness ₍1937?₎
8 p.   23cm.   (Its Publication 249)

"Reprinted ... from the Transactions of the
Illuminating engineering society, September,
1937, and from the Sight-saving review, vol.
VII, no. 3, September, 1937."

1. Lighting.

NN   0066094   NNC

National ᴀ society for the Prevention of Blindness.
Summary of state laws and rulings relating to the prevention
of blindness from babies' sore eyes.   ₍New York? 1915?₎   2 l.
8°.
Caption-title.
At head of title: National Committee for the Prevention of Blindness...New
York City.

1. Ophthalmia neonatorum.
N. Y. P. L.   May 21, 1917.

NN   0066095   NN CU

National Society for the Prevention of Blindness.
... Summary of state laws and rulings relating
to the prevention of blindness from babies'
eyes ...   August, 1916.   [New York city, National
committee for the prevention of blindness, 1916]
[6] p.   tables.   23 cm.   (Its Publications,
no. 9)
Caption title.
1. Blind - Laws and legislation.

NN   0066096   CU

National Society for the Prevention of Blindness.
... Summary of state laws and rulings relating
to the prevention of blindness from babies' sore
eyes ...   Rev. to December, 1918 ...   [New York,
city, National committee for the prevention of
blindness, 1918]
[6] p.   tables.   23 cm.   (Its Publications,
no. 9)
Caption title.
1. Blind - Laws and legislation.

NN   0066097   CU

National society for the prevention of blindness.
Twenty-five years of saving sight ...   New York, N. Y., The
National society for the prevention of blindness, inc. ₍1933₎
14 p.   diagrs.   23cm.

1. Eye—Care and hygiene.   I. Title.

Library, U. S. Office of   Education   RE51.N2   E 34-13

NN   0066098   DHEW NIC NN NBuG NN Or

VOLUME 407

National society for the prevention of blindness.
The vision of pre-school children; an analytical study of 982 children. New York, N. Y., National society for the prevention of blindness ₁1930₎
37 p. incl. tables, diagrs. 23ᶜᵐ. (Its Publication 66)

1. Eye—Diseases and defects.   I. Title.
                                                            E 31-29
Library, U. S. Office of   Education LB3451.N2

NN   0066099   DHEW MiU CU ViU

National Society for the Prevention of Blind-ness.
What to do for cross-eyes. ₁New York, 1933₎
₁2₎ p.   23cm (National Society for the Prevention of Blindness. Publication 119.)
"Reprinted from the Sight-saving review, vol. III, no. 2, June, 1933."

1. Strabismus.   I. Title.   II. Ser.

NN   0066100   ViU

National Society for the Prevention of Blindness.
... What women's clubs and nursing organizations can do to prevent blindness ... [New York, National committee for the prevention of blindness, 1916?]
4 p.   23 cm.   (Its Publications, no. 5)
Caption title.

NN   0066101   CU

National Society for the Prevention of Blindness. Junior Committee.
Publication.
no.
₁New York, 19   8°.
no.   illus.

1. Blind—Per. and soc. publ.
N. Y. P. L.   July 31, 1928

NN   0066102   NN

National Society for the Prevention of Cruelty to Children.
Annual report
see its   Year's work.

National Society for the Prevention of Cruelty to Children.
The care and control of the feeble-minded [by] The Royal Commission and the National Society for the Prevention of Cruelty to Children
see under   Gt. Brit.   Royal Commission on Care and Control of the Feeble-Minded.

National Society for the Prevention of Cruelty to Children.
Child's guardian
see under title

NATIONAL SOCIETY FOR THE PREVENTION OF CRUELTY TO CHILDREN.
Historical tableaux. Arranged under the direction of W. Nugent Monck. The orchestral and vocal music under the direction of R.F. Ryhd, Jan.7,8,9,1909. Norwich, Jarrold & Sons Ltd., etc., etc., [1909]

4°. pp.30-. Plate and other illustr.
Words only.
Cover: Programme. Historical tableaux.

NN   0066106   MH

National Society for the Prevention of Cruelty to Children.
Pamphlets.   London, 1910-
1 v.   illus.   23.5 cm.

NN   0066107   DL

National Society for the Prevention of Cruelty to Children.
Report
see its   Year's work.

National Society for the Prevention of Cruelty to Children.
Year's work.
London.
v.   24 cm.
Title varies: Report.
Cover title,   Annual report.

HV751.A2N3   362.706242   48-44084*‡

NN   0066109   DLC DL

---

society
National ‸ for the prevention of destitution.
... The case for the national minimum, with preface by Mrs. Sidney Webb. London, Printed for the National committee for the prevention of destitution, 1913.
v, 89, ₁1₎ p. 18½ᶜᵐ.
Contains bibliographies.
CONTENTS.—I. The legal minimum wage.—II. The eight hours' problem today.—III. A minimum of child nurture.—IV. Healthy homes for all.—V. A national minimum of health.—VI. The prevention of unemployment.—VII. The abolition of the Poor law.
1. Wages—Minimum wage—Gt. Brit. 2. Eight-hour movement. 3. Unemployed—Gt. Brit. 4. Labor and laboring classes—Dwellings. ₁4. Housing—Gt. Brit.₎ 5. Poor laws—Gt. Brit.   I. Webb, Beatrice (Potter) "Mrs. Sidney Webb." II. Title.
                                                  L 13-156 Revised
Library, U. S. Bur. of   Labor Statistics HD6957.G7N3

NN   0066110   DL

HV244   National Society for the Prevention of Destitution.
.N2   [Tracts]   London, 19

NN   0066111   DLC

National Society for the promotion of industrial education
            see   National Society for Vocational Education.

National Society for the Promotion of Occupational Therapy
            see   American Occupational Therapy Association.

National Society for the Scientific Study of Education
see National Society for the Study of Education.

Per.   National Society for the Study of Communica-
P   tion.
90   Directory. 1951?-
.J6   [Chicago, etc.]
Suppl   v.   annual   (In the Journal of
         communication, issued as its supplement)

         1. Communication.   I. T.: Journal of
         communication.

NN   0066115   NBuU IU NcRS

P90   National Society for the Study of Communication.
.J6
The Journal of communication. v. 1-
    May 1951-
₁Jacksonville, Fla.₎ National Society for the Study of Communication.

National society for the study of education.
... Adapting the schools to individual differences; prepared under the direction of Carleton W. Washburne, by Franklin Bobbitt, B. R. Buckingham, Stuart A. Courtis, William S. Gray, Ernest Horn, Jessie Mackinder, Helen Parkhurst, A. H. Sutherland, Mary A. Ward, Carleton W. Washburne. Ed. by Guy Montrose Whipple ...
(*In its* 24th Yearbook. Bloomington, Ill., 1925. 23ᶜᵐ. pt. II, p. 1-363. tables, diagrs.)

CONTENTS.—Factors causing maladjustment of schools to individuals.—Typical attempts to adjust schools to individual differences.—Statistical results of experiments with individualization.—Problems involved in adapting schools to individuals.—A program of individualization.—An effort at appraisal.—An annotated bibliography on adapting schools to individual differences (p. 287-363)

1. Education—Experimental methods. 2. ₁Individual differences₎   I. Whipple, Guy Montrose, 1876-   II. Washburne, Carleton, Wolsey, 1889-
                                                            E 26-349
U. S. Off. of educ.   Library   LB5.N25
  for Library of Congress   [LB5.N25   vol. 24, pt. 2]
                                    ₁38n1₎   (370.6273)

MiU OCU OO OCl OOxM OClU
NN   0066118   DHEW MtU WaTC CaBVaU OrU IdPI PU PSt

National society for the study of education.
Addresses and discussions presenting the thirty-ninth yearbook "Intelligence: its nature and nurture" of the National society for the study of education in joint sessions with the American educational research association and the National society of college teachers of education. Edited by Guy Montrose Whipple. Salem, Mass., Printed by Newcomb and Gauss, 1940.
iii, 84 p. 23ᶜᵐ.
1. Intellect. 2. Heredity. 3. ₁Man—Influence of₎ environment. 4. National society for the study of education. Committee on intelligence: its nature and nurture. Intelligence: its nature and nurture.   I. Whipple, Guy Montrose, 1876-1941, ed.   II. American educational research association.   III. National   society of college teachers of education.
                                                            E 42-20
U. S. Off. of educ.   Library   LB5.N25   1940 a
  for Library of Congress

NN   0066119   DHEW Or OrU ICU IaU

275.1   **National Society for the Study of Education.**
N213   Agricultural education in secondary schools.
         Bloomington, Public School Publishing Co. ₁1912₎
         104 p.   (Its Yearbook, 11th, pt.2)

NN   0066120   DNAL

National society for the study of education.
... Changes and experiments in liberal-arts education, prepared by Kathryn McHale ... Edited by Guy Montrose Whipple ...
(*In its* 31st Yearbook. Bloomington, Ill., 1932. 24ᶜᵐ. pt. II, p. 1-267. fold. map)

CONTENTS.—Introduction ₁by₎ Kathryn McHale.—Current changes and experiments in liberal-arts colleges ₁by₎ C. S. Boucher.—One hundred twenty-eight outstanding changes and experiments ₁by₎ Frances V. Speek.—The major phases of experimental change with significant illustrations.—College ventures in the stimulation of the intellectual life ₁by₎

Kathryn McHale.—American and English college practices ₁by₎ Agnes L. Rogers.—Some notes on the technique of experimentation in a liberal college ₁by₎ Alexander Meiklejohn.—Liberalizing a liberal education ₁by₎ Hamilton Holt.—Future possibilities in liberal-arts education: some expert opinions.—A selected bibliography on changes and experiments in liberal-arts education ₁by₎ Frances V. Speek.

1. Education, Higher. ₁1. Higher education—U. S.₎ 2. Universities and colleges—U. S.   I. Whipple, Guy Montrose, 1876-   ed.   II. McHale, Kathryn, 1890-   III. Title.
                                                            E 33-66
Library, U. S. Office of   Education LB5.N25   1931, pt. II
Library of Congress   [LB5.N25   1931   pt. II]

NN   0066122   DHEW NcD GEU WaPS

LA   National Society for the Study of Education.
5   Commemorating a quarter of a century of
Z99   service of the National Society for the Study
no. 101 of Education. ₁Bloomington, Ill., 1926₎
         44 p.

         1. National   Society for the Study of
         Education.

NN   0066123   NIC MiU IaU OO ICU NRU NNU PSt MA

VOLUME 407

National Society for the Study of Education.
The co-ordination of the kindergarten and the elementary school
see under title

National Society for the Study of Education.
Graduate study in education, prepared by the society's board of directors: William A. Brownell ⌜and others⌝ Edited by Nelson B. Henry. Chicago, Distributed by the University of Chicago Press, 1951.

xix, 369 p. 23 cm. (Yearbook of the National Society for the Study of Education, 50th, pt. 1)

1. Education—Study and teaching. 2. Universities and colleges—Graduate work. I. Brownell, William Arthur, 1895– II. Henry, Nelson Bollinger, 1883– ed. III. Title. (Series: National Society for the Study of Education. Yearbook, 50th, pt. 1)

LB5.N25 50th, pt. 1 370.73264 51-6258

CoU NNCU-G PSt GAT NN WaPS MtBC Or OrPR WaTC WaS
NN 0066125 DLC INS OrStbM CaBVa CaBVaU NNC TxU

LB
5
.N25
1912
pt.1

National Society for the Study of Education.
Industrial education: typical experiments described and interpreted.

(In its Yearbook. Chicago, 1912, 23cm. pt. 1, p. 5-124)

1. Technical education. I. Title. II. Series.

NN 0066126 INS

National society for the study of education.
... Intelligence tests and their use. Pt. I. The nature, history, and general principles of intelligence testing. Pt. II. The administrative use of intelligence tests, prepared by the Society's committee and edited by Guy Montrose Whipple ...

(*In its* 21st Yearbook. Bloomington, Ill., 1922. 23cm. pt. I–II. ix, 207 p. tables, diagrs.)

Stephen S. Colvin, chairman.

CONTENTS.—pt. I. Measurement in education, by E. L. Thorndike. Principles underlying the construction and use of intelligence tests, by S. S. Colvin. Statistical methods applied to educational testing, by H. Rugg. An annotated list of group intelligence tests, by G. M. Whipple.—pt. II. Intelligence tests and individual progress in school work, by H. W. Holmes. The group intelligence testing program of the Detroit public schools, by W. K. Layton. The use of intelligence tests in the classification of pupils in the public schools of Jackson, Michigan, by Helen Davis. Measurement of the abilities and achievements of children in the lower primary grades, by A. J. Rogers. The significance of intelligence testing in the elementary school, by R. Pinter. The use of intelligence tests in junior high schools, by M. R. Trabue. The administrative use of intelligence tests in the high school, by W. S. Miller. Some administrative uses of intelligence tests in the normal school, by B. L. Gambrill. The use of psychological tests in the administration of colleges of liberal arts for women, by A. L. Rogers. Intelligence tests in colleges and universities, by G. M. Whipple.

1. Mental tests. I. Whipple, Guy Montrose, 1876– ed. II. Colvin, Stephen Sheldon, 1869–1923. III. Thorndike, Edward Lee, 1874– IV. Rugg, Harold Ordway, 1886– V. Holmes, Henry Wyman, 1880– VI. Layton, Warren Kenneth. VII. Davis, Helen. VIII. Rogers, Agnes Low, 1884– IX. Pintner, Rudolph, 1884– X. Trabue, Marion Rex, 1890– XI. Miller, Wilford Stanton. XII. Gambrill, Bessie Lee, 1883– XIII. Title.

E 22-508

U. S. Off. of educ. Library LB5.N25
for Library of Congress [LB5.N25 1922]

OOxM OU OO OCl OClW ICJ
NN 0066129 DHEW DLC CaBVaU WaTC Or PSt MiU OCU

National Society for the Study of Education.
The kindergarten and its relation to elementary education
see under Holmes, Manfred James, ed.

National Society for the Study of Education.
The measurement of educational products.

(In its Yearbook. Bloomington, Ill., 1918. 23cm. pt. 2, p. 9-194)

1. Educational tests and measurements. I. Title. II. Series.

NN 0066131 INS

National society for the study of education.
... Nature and nurture. Pt. I. Their influence upon intelligence. Pt. II. Their influence upon achievement. Prepared by the Society's committee ... Ed. by Guy Montrose Whipple.

(*In its* 27th Yearbook. Bloomington, Ill., 1928. 23 cm. pt. I, p. 1–460; pt. II, p. 3–353. tables, diagrs.)

L. M. Terman, chairman.

CONTENTS.—pt. 1. Introduction. By L. M. Terman. Statistical hazards in nature-nurture investigations. By Barbara S. Burks and T. L. Kelley. The resemblance of siblings in intelligence. By E. L. Thorndike ⌜and others⌝ Family similarities in mental-test abilities. By R. R. Willoughby. A first study of parent-child resemblance in intelligence. By H. E. Jones. A study of a pair of Siamese twins. By Helen L. Koch. A comparative study of identical and non-identical twins with respect to intelligence resemblances. By Gladys G. Tallman. Family resemblance in maze-learning ability in white rats, by Mildred Burlingame and C. P. Stone. The influence of environment on the intelligence, school achievement, and conduct of foster children. By F. N. Freeman, K. J. Holzinger and B. C. Mitchell. The relative influence of nature and nurture upon mental development; a comparative study of foster parent-foster child resemblance and true parent-true child resemblance. By Barbara S. Burks. Comments on the Chicago and Stanford studies of foster children. By Barbara S. Burks. The effect on the intelligence quotient of change from a poor to a good environment. By Agnes L. Rogers, Dorothy Durling and Katharine McBride. Comparison of white and negro children in the rational learning test. By J. Peterson. A study of the relation between intelligence and the acquisition of English. By Katherine Murdoch and Doris Maddow. The effect of school environment upon Stanford-Binet tests of young children. By Gertrude Hildreth. A preliminary report on the effect of nursery-school training upon the intelligence test scores of young children. By Florence L. Goodenough. The influence of improvement in physical condition on intelligence and educational achievement. By Carolyn Hoefer and Mattie C. Hardy. Notes on the mental development of children exhibiting the somatic signs of puberty praecox. By C. P. Stone and Lois Doe-Kulmann. Precocious puberty and mental maturation. By A. Gesell. Notes on factors that may alter the intelligence quotient in successive examinations. By Janet A. Matthew and Bertha M. Luckey. The influence of specialized training on tests of general intelligence. By Katharine B. Greene. Three studies on the effect of training in similar and identical material upon Stanford-Binet test scores. By Mary L. Casey, Helen P. Davidson and Doris I. Harter. The nature and limit of improvement due to training. By A. I. Gates.—pt. II. Introduction. By L. M. Terman. Children clustering at 165 I. Q. and children clustering at 146 I. Q. compared for three years in achievement. By Leta S. Hollingworth and Margaret V. Cobb. The relative influence upon educational achievement of some hereditary and environmental factors. By J. D. Heilman. The effect of length of school attendance upon mental and educational ages. By Katharine M. Denworth. The conditional value of a longer school year in one-teacher schools. By F. P. Obrien. The influence of the teacher on relative class standing in arithmetic fundamentals and reading comprehension. By H. Taylor. Grade placement versus mental age as a factor in school achievement. By M. J. Van Wagenen. Comparison of the educational progress of bright pupils in accelerated and in regular classes. By W. A. McCall. Efficiency of training as affected by the cost of instruction. By T. C. Holly and G. M. Ruch. Achievement as affected by amount of time spent in study. By L. Jones and G. M. Ruch. The relationships of certain environmental factors to measures of mechanical ability. By L. D. Anderson. Dextrality types and the preschool child. By June E. Downey. Sibling resemblance in deception. By M. A. May and H. Hartshorne. The transfer of training. By G. M. Whipple. The effects of practice on individual differences. By J. Peterson and M. C. Barlow. The effects of nature and nurture on musicality. By P. R. Farnsworth. A summary of literature on the determiners of the intelligence quotient and the educational quotient. By Barbara S. Burks.

1. Man—Influence of environment. 2. Heredity. I. Whipple, Guy Montrose, 1876– ed. II. Terman, Lewis Madison, 1877– III. Title.

[LB.N25 vol. 27, pt. 1–2] E 28—61

U. S. Office of Education. Library
for Library of Congress ⌜a66b²2⌝

MiU OOxM OO OCl OCU OU ICJ CaBVaU
NN 0066137 DHEW NcD INS OrAshS OrPR WaTC MB PSt

National Society for the Study of Education.
El nuevo programa escolar [by] W.H.Kilpatrick, Harold Rugg, Carleton Washburne [and] J.F.G.Bonser. [Traduccion del inglés por Lorenzo Luzuriago] Buenos Aires, Losada [1940]

159 p. (Publicaciones de la Revista de pedagogia: La escuela activa, 4)
Selected from the society's Yearbook no. "25", i.e. 26.

NN 0066138 MH DPU TxU

National society for the study of education.
... Preschool and parental education. Pt. I. Organization and development. Pt. II. Research and method. Prepared by the Society's committee ... Ed. by Guy Montrose Whipple ...

(*In its* 28th Yearbook. Bloomington, Ill., 1929. 23 cm. pt. I–II)
Paged continuously.
Lois H. Meek, chairman.

CONTENTS.

pt. I. Organization and development. sec. 1. General considerations: Introduction. History of the movement in preschool and parental education. General considerations underlying preschool and parental education. sec. 2. The organization of education for preschool children: The family as an educational agency. Day nurseries. Preschool and parental education promoted by maternity and infant welfare centers. The clinic as an agency for the education of parents and children. Nursery schools. The kindergarten in relation to preschool and parental education.

sec. 3. Provisions for parental and preparental education: Survey of programs in parental education. Experiments in preparental training. sec. 4. Professional training of leaders: Professional training for research and instruction in preschool education. The professional training of nursery-school teachers. Training for the field of parental education.—pt. II. Research and method. sec. 1. Research activities in the field of child development: Present status of research in child development. Studies of motor development. Studies in language development. Studies of intellectual development. Studies of emotional and social development. Studies of physical growth.

Continued in next column

Continued from preceding column

sec. 2. Methods of educating preschool children: Child activities leading to the establishment of routine habits. Child activities: play. Child activities leading to art experiences. Child activities in language and literature. Child activities leading to social development. Provision for individual differences. Records of young children: a means to education. sec. 3. Methods of educating parents: Methods and materials for the education of parents. Practical ways of educating parents and teachers to the value of mental hygiene.

1. Education of children. ⌜1. Preschool education⌝ 2. Parent and child. I. Whipple, Guy Montrose, 1876– ed. II. Meek, Lois Hayden, 1894–

E 29—88

U. S. Office of Education. Library LB5.N25
for Library of Congress ⌜LB5.N25⌝
⌜a49v1⌝ (370.6273)

OrPR WaTC MtBC CaBVaU INS MNtcA
NN 0066141 DHEW OClW OCl OO OU OCU MiU CU PSt Or

LB
5
.N25
1919
pt.1

National Society for the Study of Education.
The professional preparation of high school teachers.

(In its Yearbook. Bloomington, Ill., 1919. 23cm. pt. 1. p. 1-358. tables, diagrs.)

1. Teachers--Training--High schools. I. Title. II. Series.

NN 0066142 INS

LB
5
.N25
1914
pt.1

National Society for the Study of Education.
Some aspects of high-school instruction and administration.

(In its Yearbook. Chicago, 1914. 23cm. pt. 1, p. 5-124)

1. School management and organization. 2. Teaching. I. Title. II. Series.

NN 0066143 INS

National society for the study of education.
Yearbook. 1st–5th ⌜1895⌝–99; ⌜new ser.⌝ 1st–
1902–
Bloomington, Ill., Public school publishing company; ⌜etc., etc., 1895⌝–19

v. in illus., tables, diagrs. 22½–24 cm.

Yearbooks published under the society's earlier names as follows: 1895, Herbart society for scientific study of teaching; 1896–99 (including the two supplements for 1895) National Herbart society; 1902–09, National society for the scientific study of education.
Editors: 1895–1904, pt. 1, C. A. McMurry.—1904, pt. 2–1909, M. J. Holmes.—1910, pt. 1, J. S. Brown.—1910, pt. 2–1911, pt. 1, S. C. Parker.—1911, pt. 2, B. M. Davis.—1912, pt. 1–1915, pt. 2, S. C. Parker.—1916, pt. 1–1941, G. M. Whipple (with H. L. Miller, 1919, pt. 1; with I. L. Kandel, 1937, pt. 2).—1942– N. B. Henry.
1897–1916, pt. 2 were published in Chicago by the University of Chicago press.
1895–99 accompanied by supplements.

1. Education—Societies. 2. Education—Study and teaching. I. McMurry, Charles Alexander, 1857–1929, ed. II. Holmes, Manfred James, 1863– ed. III. Brown, James Stanley, 1863– ed. IV. Parker, Samuel Chester, 1880–1924, ed. V. Davis, Benjamin Marshall, 1867– ed. VI. Whipple, Guy Montrose, 1876–1941, ed. VII. Miller, Harry Lloyd, ed. VIII. Kandel, Isaac Leon, 1881– ed. IX. Henry, Nelson Bollinger, 1883–

LB5.N25 370.6273 6—16938

FTaSU PBa DL NcU NcC CU
MsU NN NdU PBL INS MB NBuU NcRS ScCleA KEmT
ViU OClW OCU ODW OOxM MeB KyWA IU CtNIC NcD
NjR MiU OCl OClh OU O OClCC ICJ MB OClJC MH
DNAL MiDM MBC IdPI KyMoreU PPFr GEU Or PSt
NN 0066144 DLC Wa DAU MoU ICRL KEmT IEdS

National Society for the Study of Education. *Committee on Adapting the Secondary-School Program to the Needs of Youth.*
Adapting the secondary-school program to the needs of youth. Edited by Nelson B. Henry. Chicago, Distributed by the University of Chicago Press, 1953.

xiii, 316, vi p. 23 cm. (Yearbook of the National Society for the Study of Education, 52d, pt. 1)

Includes bibliographical references.

1. Education, Secondary—Addresses, essays, lectures. I. Henry, Nelson Bollinger, 1883– ed. II. Title. (Series: National Society for the Study of Education. Yearbook, 52d, pt. 1)

LB5.N25 52d, pt. 1 373.082 53—6956

CaBVaU WaSpG CaBVa PPPL
OOxM PSt PBm PSC MiU Or WaS WaPS OrPR NNCU-G INS
NN 0066146 DLC MtBC IdPI PJB TxU OO MiD NN OU

VOLUME 407

National society for the study of education. *Committee on adolescence.*
... Adolescence. Prepared by the society's committee ... Edited by Nelson B. Henry. Chicago, Ill., The Dept. of education, The University of Chicago, 1944.
x, 358, ⌊4⌋ p. incl. tables, diagrs. 23ᶜᵐ. (National society for the study of education. 43rd Yearbook, pt. I)
"References" at end of each chapter.
1. Adolescence. I. Henry, Nelson Bollinger, jr., ed.
E 44-78
U. S. Off. of educ. Library for Library of Congress [LB5.N25 vol. 43, pt. 1]
⌊15⌋ (370.6273)

CaBVaU OrPS CU NIC PSC OCU OOxM O OO NNC Or
NN 0066147 DHEW CaBVa WaPS CoU PSt INS WaTC IdPI

National society for the study of education. *Committee on arithmetic.*
... Report of the Society's committee on arithmetic. Pt. I. Some aspects of modern thought on arithmetic. Pt. II. Research in arithmetic. Prepared by the Society's committee ... Edited by Guy Montrose Whipple.
(*In* National society for the study of education. 29th Yearbook. Bloomington, Ill., 1930. 23 cm. pt. I–II. tables, diagrs.)
F. B. Knight, chairman.
Paged continuously.
CONTENTS.—pt. I. Introduction, by F. B. Knight. The social value of arithmetic, by B. R. Buckingham. The arithmetic curriculum, by R. L. West, C. E. Greene and W. A. Brownell. Some considerations of method, by F. B. Knight.—Testing, diagnosis, and remedial work in arithmetic, by C. E. Greene and G. T. Buswell. The training of teachers of arithmetic, by B. R. Buckingham.—pt. II. The purpose and plan of part two, by G. T. Buswell. The techniques of research employed in arithmetic, by W. A. Brownell. A critical survey of previous research in arithmetic, by G. T. Buswell. The number abilities of children when they enter grade one, by B. R. Buckingham and Josephine MacLatchy. A critical evaluation of methods of analyzing practice in fractions, by L. J. Brueckner and Fred Kelly. Mixed versus isolated drill organization, by A. C. Repp. The learning of the one hundred multiplication combinations, by G. M. Norem and F. B. Knight. A measurement of transfer in the learning of number combinations, by E. A. Beito and L. J. Brueckner. An experimental study in improving ability to reason in arithmetic, by C. W. Stone. A test in arithmetic for measuring general ability of pupils in the first six grades, by Harriet S. Peet and W. F. Dearborn. The effect of awareness of success or failure, by Isidoro Panlasigui and F. B. Knight. A study of errors in percentage, by Arthur Edwards. The grade placement of arithmetic topics, by C. W. Washburne. A review of experiments on subtraction, by G. M. Ruch and C. D. Mead. Appendix: A critique of the yearbook, by L. J. Brueckner.
1. Arithmetic—1901– I. Whipple, Guy Montrose, 1876– ed. II. Knight, Frederic Butterfield, 1891–
E 30—50
U. S. Office of Education. Library LB5.N25 vol. 29, pt. 1–2 for Library of Congress [LB5.N25 vol. 29, pt. 1–2]
⌊a49j1⌋ (370.6273)

OrU CaBVaU PSt OCU OU OOxM OCl OO OClW OEac OCU DLC
NN 0066150 DHEW PSt OrPS IdPI OrP IdU-SB Or WaTC

National society for the study of education. *Committee on art in American life and education.*
... Art in American life and education. Prepared by the Society's committee ... Assisted by Milton S. Fox and William L. Longyear ... Edited by Guy Montrose Whipple ... Bloomington, Ill., Public school publishing company, 1941.
xx, 819 p. 23 cm. (National society for the study of education. 40th Yearbook)
Thomas Munro, chairman.
CONTENTS.—Introduction, by Thomas Munroe.—sec. I. Art in American life: The social background of American art, by Felix Payant. City planning, by W. C. Behrendt. Public architecture, by T. F. Hamlin. The domestic setting today, by R. J. Neutra. Landscape design, by Edwin Ziegfeld. Flower arrangements, by Margaret Fairbanks. The handicrafts, by Felix Payant. Art in industry, by Alon Bement, Sheldon Cheney and Martha Cheney. Clothing and personal adornment, by Grace W. Ripley and M. S. Fox. Art in commerce, by William Longyear. Art in printing and publishing, by William Longyear. The American theater, past and present, by B. S. Leathem. Puppets, marionettes, and shadow plays, by Louise M. Dunn. The motion picture, by Iris Barry, Edwin Ziegfeld, and M. S. Fox. Television, by A. H. Morton. Dancing, by John Martin. Photography, by R. P. Ensign and M. S. Fox. The graphic arts, by Alon Bement and H. S. Francis. Sculpture, by Felix Payant and G. J. Cox. Painting, by M. S. Fox and S. E. Lee.—sec. II. The nature of art and related types of experience: The psychological approach to art and art education, by Thomas Munro. Creative ability in art and its educational fostering, by Thomas Munro. Powers of art appreciation and evaluation, by Thomas Munro. The analysis of form in art, by Thomas Munro. A survey of recent research in art and art education, by Ray Faulkner. Recent research in the psychology of art, by N. C. Meier. Standards of value in art, by Ray Faulkner. Art and its relation to society, by Ray Faulkner.—sec. III. Art education: its aims, procedures, and agencies: Past and present trends in art education, by R. B. Farnum, R. S. Hilpert, Grace Sobotka, W. G. Whitford and Alma C. Field. Art in general education, by L. L. Winslow and others. The education of artists, by R. B. Farnum and others. Other agencies in art education, formal and informal, by R. B. Farnum and others.—sec. IV. The preparation of teachers of art: Some problems of aim and method in training art teachers, by O. F. Ege. Curricular patterns of

Continued in next column

Continued from preceding column

some institutions preparing art teachers, by G. S. Dutch. Course requirements for teachers of art in fifty institutions, by W. E. Hager and Edwin Ziegfeld. The technical preparation of the art teacher, by R. B. Farnum. The art teacher's preparation in art history and art education, by Margaret F. S. Glace. Courses other than art and education for the prospective art teacher, by Ernest Horn. The art teacher's preparation in the theory and practice of education, by Ernest Horn. Graduate work for the art teacher, by Ernest Horn. Recommended experiences in addition to school and technical training, by C. V. Kirby. The teacher of art in colleges and universities, by G. S. Dutch. The training of college teachers of art history and appreciation, by F. J. Mather, Jr. The preparation of the art supervisor, by C. V. Kirby and L. L. Winslow. Rural art supervision and teachers' extension classes, by Harold Gregg. Preparation of the general classroom teacher for teaching art, by Edwin Ziegfeld.
1. Art. 2. Art—Study and teaching. I. Whipple, Guy Montrose, 1876–1941, ed. II. Munro, Thomas, 1897– III. Title.
[LB5.N25 vol. 40] (370.6273) E 41—36
U. S. Office of Education. Library for Library of Congress ⌊a53p²5⌋

OCU OOxM OO OU OCl NcD CoU NSyU WaTC DHEW
NN 0066156 DLC INS TxU PSt CaBVa CaBVaU OrPR

National Society for the Study of Education. *Committee on Audio-Visual Materials of Instruction.*
Audio-visual materials of instruction; ed. by Nelson B. Henry. Chicago, Univ. of Chicago Press, 1949.
x, 320 p. 22 cm. (Yearbook of the National Society for the Study of Education, 48th, pt. 1)
Includes "References."
1. Visual instruction. I. Henry, Nelson Bollinger, 1883– ed. II. Title. (Series: National Society for the Study of Education. Yearbook, 48th, pt. 1)
LB5.N25 48th, pt. 1 371.333 49-8494*

TxU DCU
OrPR WaTC CaBVaU IdPI OU PPLas PBm PPEB NcD NNCU-G
NN 0066157 DLC PSt GAT WaPS CaBVa OrPS INS Or

National society for the study of education. *Committee on changing conceptions in educational administration.*
... Changing conceptions in educational administration, prepared by the society's committee ... Edited by Nelson B. Henry. Chicago, Ill., The University of Chicago press ⌊1946⌋
ix, 186, xlvii p. diagr. 22 cm. (National society for the study of education. 45th Yearbook, pt. II)
"References": p. 52.
1. School management and organization. I. Henry, Nelson Bollinger, 1883– ed. II. Title.
LB5.N25 45th, pt. 2 (370.6273) 371.2 A 46—5124
Chicago. Univ. Libr. for Library of Congress ⌊a51o²5⌋†

MiU
NN 0066158 ICU INS CoU PSt MB OCU OOxM TxU DLC

National Society for the Study of Education. *Committee on Citizen Co-operation for Better Public Schools.*
Citizen co-operation for better public schools; edited by Nelson B. Henry. Chicago, Distributed by the University of Chicago Press, 1954.
xvii, 304, vi p. 24 cm. (Yearbook of the National Society for the Study of Education, 53d, pt. 1)
Bibliographical footnotes.
1. Community and school. I. Henry, Nelson Bollinger, 1883– ed. II. Title. (Series: National Society for the Study of Education. Yearbook, 53d, pt. 1)
LB5.N25 53d, pt. 1 370.19 54—8085
Library of Congress ⌊56i²15⌋

CaBVaU CaBVa OOxM INS
N TxU PSt OO PJB PPEB MtBC Or IdPI WaS WaTC PU OU
NN 0066159 DLC PPPL WaPS OrPR ICRL PRosC PSC PBm

National society for the study of education. *Committee on curriculum making.*
... The foundations and technique of curriculum-construction, prepared by the Society's committee under the direction of Harold Rugg. Edited by Guy Montrose Whipple. Pt. I. Curriculum-making: past and present. Pt. II. The foundations of curriculum-making.
(*In* National society for the study of education. 26th Yearbook. Bloomington, Ill., 1927. 23 cm. pt. I–II, tables, diagrs.)
CONTENTS.—pt. I. A century of curriculum construction in American schools, by Harold Rugg. Current practices in curriculum-making, by S. A. Courtis, G. S. Counts, G. A. Works. Examples of progressive curriculum-construction in public school systems, by S. A. Courtis, E. M. Sipple. Carleton Washburne, J. H. Newton, A. L. Threlkeld, W. D. Cocking, Ethel I. Salisbury. Curriculum-making in private laboratory schools, by H. O. Gillet, W. C. Reavis, O. W. Caldwell, Ernest Horn, Maude McBroom Ellsworth Collings, Flora J. Cooke, R. W. Osborne, H. C. Pearson, E. R. Smith, Caroline Pratt, Margaret Naumburg, C. A. Phillips, Marietta Johnson, F. G. Bonser. Miscellaneous curriculum studies, by W. W. Charters, F. J. Kelly, J. K. Flanders, Harold Rugg, G. S. Counts, J. A. Hockett.—pt. II. The foundations of curriculum-making. Supplementary statement, by W. C. Bagley. The orientation of the curriculum-maker, by Franklin Bobbitt. The curriculum and

Continued in next column

Continued from preceding column

curriculum-making, by F. G. Bonser. Statement, by W. W. Charters. Some notes on the foundations of curriculum-making, by G. S. Counts. Reading between the lines, by S. A. Courtis. Discussion of the general statement, by Ernest Horn. Supplementary statement, by C. H. Judd. Statement of position, by W. H. Kilpatrick. Curriculum-making: points of emphasis, by Harold Rugg. Representative quotations from John Dewey's written statement on the curriculum (1900–1926) Representative quotations from the written statements on the curriculum by the Herbartians and their critics (1894–1896)
1. Education—Curricula. ⌊1. Course of study⌋ I. Whipple, Guy Montrose, 1876– ed. II. Rugg, Harold Ordway, 1886–
E 27—59
U. S. Office of Education. Library LB5.N25 for Library of Congress [LB5.N25 vol. 26, pt. 1–2]

CaBVaU OrU OrPR WaTC
NN 0066162 DHEW PSt OClW OO OCl MiU OOxM OU OrU

National society for the study of education. *Committee on curriculum reconstruction.*
... American education in the postwar period. Pt. I. Curriculum reconstruction. Prepared by the society's committee ... Edited by Nelson B. Henry. Chicago, Ill., The University of Chicago press, 1945.
x, 297 p. 23 cm. (National society for the study of education. 44th Yearbook, pt. I)
1. World war, 1939–1945—Education ⌊and the war⌋ 2. Education—U. S.⌊—Curricula⌋ 3. ⌊Course of study⌋ I. Henry, Nelson Bollinger, jr., ed. II. Title. III. Title: Curriculum reconstruction.
E 46—52
U. S. Office of Education. Library LB5 for Library of Congress ⌊a60c³5⌋

WaPS CaBVa Or OrP INS WaTC CoU
NN 0066163 DHEW OCU OU OOxM TxU PPEB NcD PSt CoU

National Society for the Study of Education. *Committee on Early Childhood Education.*
Early childhood education, ed. by Nelson B. Henry. Chicago, University of Chicago press, 1947.
xii, 390, xlix p. 23 cm. (Yearbook of the National Society for the study of Education, 46th, pt. 2)
Includes bibliographies.
1. Education of children. I. Henry, Nelson Bollinger, 1883– ed. II. Title. (Series: National Society for the Study of Education. Yearbook, 46th, pt. 2)
LB5.N25 46th, pt. 2 372.08 48—293*

CaBVaU Or OrPS IdPI WaPS CoU INS
NN 0066164 DLC MiEM OO CoU PSt NNCU-G WaTC OrPR

National Society for the Study of Education.
Committee on Economy of Education.
Fourth report of the Committee on Economy of Education.
(In its Yearbook. Bloomingtin, Ill., 1919. 23 cm. pt. 2, p. 7-123)
1. Teaching - Curricula.

NN 0066165 INS

National Society for the Study of Education.
Committee on Economy of Time in Education.
Third report of the Committee on Economy of Time in Education. Section I: Studies of minimal essentials in elementary school subjects. Section II: Symposium on the purposes of historical instruction in the seventh and eighth grades.
(In its Yearbook. Bloomington, Ill., 1918. 23 cm. pt. 1, p. 7-134)

NN 0066166 INS

National society for the study of education. *Committee on education as a science.*
... The scientific movement in education. Prepared by the Society's Committee on education as a science ... Edited by Guy Montrose Whipple ...
(*In* National society for the study of education. 37th Yearbook. Bloomington, Ill., 1938. 22½ cm. pt. II, xii, 529 p.)
Includes references.
CONTENTS.
sec. I. The contributions of research to the advancement of education: Contributions of school surveys ⌊by⌋ Charles H. Judd. Contributions of research to educational administration ⌊by⌋ William C. Reavis. Contributions of research to the education of teachers ⌊by⌋ E. S. Evenden.—Contributions of research to the curriculum: I. A generation of research on the curriculum ⌊by⌋ W. E. Peik. II. Research and public-school curriculum ⌊by⌋ C. L. Cushman and Guy Fox.—Contributions of research to general methods of instruction ⌊by⌋ Arthur I. Gates.—Contributions of research to special methods: Handwriting ⌊by⌋ Frank N. Freeman. Contributions of research to special methods: Reading ⌊by⌋ William S. Gray. Contributions of research to special methods: Spelling ⌊by⌋ Ernest Horn. Contributions of research to special methods: English usage ⌊by⌋ Harry A. Greene. Contributions of research to special methods: Mathematics. I. Contribu-

Continued in next column

VOLUME 407

Continued from preceding column

tions to elementary-school mathematics [by] G. T. Buswell. II. Contributions to secondary-school mathematics [by] E. R. Breslich. Contributions of research to special methods: Natural science [by] Samuel Ralph Powers. Contributions of research to special methods: The social studies [by] Howard E. Wilson and Wilbur F. Murra. Contributions of research to special methods: The practical arts [by] John M. Brewer. Contributions of research to special methods: Music and art [by] Willis L. Uhl. Contributions of research to special methods: Home economics [by] Clara M. Brown.—Contributions of research to the classification, promotion, marking, and certification of pupils [by] Arch O. Heck.—Contributions of research to the individualization of instruction [by] S. A. Courtis.—Contributions of research to discipline and control [by] Ruth Strang.—Contributions of research to the development of guidance in education [by] M. R. Trabue.—Contributions of research to higher education [by] Fred J. Kelly.

sec. II. The development of methods and techniques of inquiry in education: The contribution of this society to the scientific movement in education with special reference to the trends in problems and methods of inquiry [by] Guy M. Whipple.—General methods: Historical, comparative, and documentary research [by] Newton Edwards. General methods: The social survey and the study of communities [by] C. S. Marsh. General methods: Statistical analysis and comparison [by] Karl J. Holzinger. General methods: Laboratory experimentation [by] G. T. Buswell. General methods: Classroom experimentation [by] Walter S. Monroe. General methods: Case study [by] Willard C. Olson. General methods: Educational diagnosis [by] Leo J. Brueckner.—The specific techniques of investigation: Examining and testing acquired knowledge, skill, and ability [by] Ralph W. Tyler. The specific techniques of investigation: Testing intelligence, aptitudes, and personality [by] Goodwin Watson. The specific techniques of investigation: Observation, questionnaire, and rating [by] Leonard V. Koos.

sec. III. The contributions to education of scientific knowledge in particular fields: Contributions to education of scientific knowledge about the psychology of learning [by] J. F. Dashiell. Contributions to education of scientific knowledge about individual differences [by] Frank S. Freeman. Contributions to education of scientific knowledge about mental growth and development [by] George D. Stoddard. Contributions to education of scientific knowledge in mental hygiene [by] Mandel Sherman. Contributions to education of scientific knowledge about the organization of society and social pathology [by] Willard Waller. Contributions to education of scientific knowledge in economics [by] Harold F. Clark.

sec. IV. Science and philosophy: The determination of ultimate values or aims through antecedent or a priori speculation or through pragmatic or empirical inquiry [by] John Dewey.—Concluding comments and remarks on the province of scientific inquiry [by] Frank N. Freeman.

1. Educational research. [1. Research, Educational] 2. Education—U. S. 3. Education—Philosophy. I. Whipple, Guy Montrose, 1876–1941, ed. II. Title.

LB5.N25 37th pt. 2 E 38–148

U. S. Office of Education. Library
for Library of Congress [a56v2]†

OrPR Or WaTC WaS CaBVaU DLC
NN 0066173 DHEW OrPS INS OCU OOxM OU CoU PSt WaPS

National Society for the Study of Education. *Committee on Education in Rural Communities.*

Education in rural communities. Edited by Nelson B. Henry. Chicago, Distributed by the University of Chicago Press, 1952.

xiv, 259 p. 23 cm. (Yearbook of the National Society for the Study of Education, 51st, pt. 2)

Includes bibliographies.

1. Rural schools. I. Henry, Nelson Bollinger, 1883– ed. II. Title. (Series: National Society for the Study of Education. Yearbook, 51st, pt. 2)

LB5.N25 51st, pt. 2 379.173 52—7759

OrPR Or MtBC WaS CaBVaU IdPI CaBVa INS
NN 0066174 DLC PSt NNC TxU NN CoU NNC-G DNAL WaTC

National society for the study of education. *Committee on educational diagnosis.*

... Educational diagnosis, prepared by the society's Committee on educational diagnosis ... Edited by Guy Montrose Whipple ...

(*In* National society for the study of education. 34th Yearbook. Bloomington, Ill. [1935] 23 cm. x, 523 p.)

L. J. Brueckner, chairman.

CONTENTS.—sec. I. Factors associated with learning difficulty: Physical conditioning factors in learning, by J. G. Rockwell.—Intellectual factors, by L. E. Travis.—Pedagogical factors associated with learning difficulty, by L. J. Brueckner.—Emotional and social factors in learning, by W. C. Olson.—Environmental factors contributing to learning, by P. T. Rankin.—sec. II. Principles and techniques of educational diagnosis and treatment: Characteristics of a satisfactory diagnosis, by R. W. Tyler.—Elements of diagnosis, by W. R. Tyler.—Techniques of diagnosis, by L. J. Brueckner.—The place of the psychological laboratory in educational diagnosis, by G. T. Buswell.—Maturation as a factor in diagnosis, by S. A. Courtis.—The principles of developmental and remedial instruction, by L. J. Brueckner.—sec. III. Diagnosis and remedial instruction related to the unique contributions of various fields of instruction: Diagnosis and treatment of reading disabilities, by Marion Monroe.—Diagnosis of difficulties in English, by Dora V. Smith.—Diagnosis in arithmetic, by L. J. Brueckner.—Diagnosis in the social studies, by E. B. Wesley.—Diagnosis and remedial treatment in the field of science, by F. D. Curtis.—sec. IV. Diagnosis and remedial treatment related to other objectives of instruction: Diagnosis in health education, by D. W. Gudakunst.—Diagnosis and treatment of behavior disorders of children, by W. C. Olson.—Diagnosis in speech, by L. E. Travis.—Vocational interests, ability, and aptitude, by J. L. Stenquist.—The discovery and guidance of musical talent, by C. E. Seashore.—Diagnosis in art, by N. C. Meier.—Diagnosis in leisure-time activities, by Edgar

Continued in next column

Continued from preceding column

Dale.—Diagnosis and remedial instruction in creativeness, by P. T. Rankin.—sec. V. Administrative aspects of diagnosis and remedial instruction: the administration of a program of diagnosis and remedial instruction, by J. L. Stenquist.

1. Learning, Psychology of. 2. Grading and marking (Students) 3. Child study. 4. Ability—Testing. I. Whipple, Guy Montrose, 1876– ed. II. Brueckner, Leo John, 1890– III. Title.

E 35—177

U. S. Office of Education. Library
for Library of Congress [a63g^{2}¼]

WaPS OrPR WaS WaTC CaBVaU
NN 0066178 DHEW OrP OO OU OCU OClW OCl MiU PSt

National society for the study of education. *Committee on extra-curricular activities.*

... Extra-curricular activities, prepared by the Society's yearbook committee on extra-curricular activities ... Ed. by Guy Montrose Whipple ...

(*In* National society for the study of education. 25th Yearbook. Bloomington, Ill., 1926. 23 cm. pt. II, p. 1–235. tables, diagrs.)

Leonard V. Koos, chairman.

CONTENTS.—Introduction: Scope and organization of the yearbook, by L. V. Koos.—Analysis of the general literature on extra-curricular activities, by L. V. Koos.—General survey of practices: junior high schools, by P. W. Terry.—General survey of practices: four-year and senior high schools, by J. G. Masters.—General survey of practices: six-year elementary schools, by E. K. Fretwell.—Pupil participation in extra-curricular activities in the high schools of Everett and Seattle, Washington, by F. C. Ayer.—Pupil participation in the extra-curricular activities in the smaller high schools of Michigan, by Clifford Woody, and E. H. Chapelle.—Direct training in citizenship through the participation of high-school pupils in community activities, by W. C. Reavis.—Cooperation of teacher advisors, by P. W. Terry.—Financial administration of extra-curricular activities, by H. C. McKown and M. B. Horner.—Special types of activities: student participation in school government, by Earle Rugg.—Special types of activities: student publications, by W. C. Reavis.—Special types of activities; honor societies, by P. W. Terry, C. E. Hagie [and] C. J. Pieper.—Special types of activities: assemblies, athletics, music, dramatics, debating, and clubs by E. K. Fretwell [and] C. R. Foster.—Local practices: clubs in the Barbour intermediate school, Detroit, by M. P. Monroe.—Local practices: Tulsa high school, by Merle Prunty.—Local practices: Bellflower township high school, Illinois, by E. S. Simmonds.—Local practices: Langley junior-senior high school, Pittsburgh, by C. R. Foster and Frank Fickinger.—Local practices: the high-school system of Pittsburgh, by C. R. Foster.—Evaluating extra-curricular activities, by L. V. Koos.

1. Student activities. [1. Extra-curricular activities] I. Whipple, Guy Montrose, 1876– ed. II. Koos, Leonard Vincent, 1881–

[LB5.N25 vol. 25, pt. 2] E 26—228

U. S. Office of Education. Library
for Library of Congress [a59k½]

NN 0066182 DHEW PSt PU WaTC OrU CaBVaU IdPI INS

National Society for the Study of Education. *Committee on General Education.*

General education. Edited by Nelson B. Henry. Chicago, Distributed by the University of Chicago Press, 1952.

xiii, 377 p. 23 cm. (Yearbook of the National Society for the Study of Education, 51st, pt. 1)

Includes bibliographies.

1. Education—U. S.—1945– I. Henry, Nelson Bollinger, 1883– ed. II. Title. (Series: National Society for the Study of Education. Yearbook, 51st, pt. 1)

LB5.N25 51st, pt. 1 370.973 52–7760

IdPI
TxU NNC PSt PRosC NN NNCU-G CaBVa WaPS CaBVaU INS
NN 0066183 DLC WaS MtBC OrPR Or WaTC CaQML CoU

National society for the study of education. *Committee on general education in the American college.*

... General education in the American college. Prepared by the Society's committee ... Edited by Guy Montrose Whipple ...

(*In its* 38th Yearbook. Bloomington, Ill., 1939. 22½ cm. pt. II, xII, 382, xxxiv, [4] p.)

Alvin C. Eurich, chairman.

CONTENTS.—sec. I. The growing concern with general education. A renewed emphasis upon general education, by A. C. Eurich. Social factors affecting general education, by H. P. Rainey. Young as developing organisms, by D. A. Prescott. Youth and the high school, by G. N. Mackenzie. Youth in the colleges, by A. C. Eurich. Youth as a common concern of high schools and colleges, by A. J. Brumbaugh.—sec. II. College plans emphasizing the extension of general education. The junior college, by B. L. Johnson. The general colleges, by M. S. MacLean, with the assistance of W. L. Little and G. A. Works. General education in the liberal arts colleges, by J. D. Russell. General education in experimental liberal arts colleges, by D. P. Cottrell. General education in professional education, by E. J. McGrath and others. General education and teacher education, by K. W. Bigelow. Occupational motivation in general education, by Mark Ellingson, G. W. Hoke, and L. L. Jarvie. A critical appraisal of experiments in general education, by H. M. Wriston.—sec. III. Materials for general education. The choice of materials for advancing the aims and functions of general education. Samuel Ralph Powers, and others.—sec. IV. Trends. Dominant trends in general education, by K. W. Bigelow and M. S. MacLean. Selected bibliography on general education (p. 381–382)

Continued in next column

Continued from preceding column

1. Education—U. S. 2. Education, Higher. [2. Higher education—U. S.] 3. Education, Secondary. [3. Secondary education—U. S.] 4. Universities and colleges—U. S. 5. Students. I. Whipple, Guy Montrose, 1876– ed. II. Eurich, Alvin Christian, 1902–

[LB5.N25 vol. 38, pt. 2] E 39—269

U. S. Office of Education. Library LB5
for Library of Congress [a56v1]

INS MiU
NN 0066186 DHEW PSt WaPS WaTC OrPR Or WaS MtBC

National society for the study of education. *Committee on guidance.*

... Guidance in educational institutions, prepared by the Society's Committee on guidance ... Edited by Guy Montrose Whipple ...

(*In* National society for the study of education. 37th Yearbook. Bloomington, Ill., 1938. 22½ cm. pt. I, viii, 313 p.)

Grayson N. Kefauver, chairman.

Includes references.

CONTENTS.—Guidance and purposive living [by] Arthur J. Jones and Harold C. Hand.—Appraisal of student characteristics and needs [by] Alvin E. Eurich and C. Gilbert Wrenn.—Appraising certain aspects of student achievement [by] Louis Raths.—Counseling with students [by] C. Gilbert Wrenn.—Guidance through group activities [by] Richard D. Allen and Margaret E. Bennett.—The orientation of students in educational institutions [by] Margaret E. Bennett.—Guidance in personality development [by] Ruth Strang.—Guidance in transition from school to community life [by] A. H. Edgerton.—Guidance and instruction [by] Grayson N. Kefauver.—The staff needed for the development of an effective guidance service [by] Francis C. Rosecrance.—Vocational guidance in foreign countries [by] Franklin J. Keller.

1. Personnel service in education. 2. Profession, Choice of. 3. Vocational education. I. Kefauver, Grayson Neikirk, 1900– II. Whipple, Guy Montrose, 1876– ed. III. Title.

E 38—147

U. S. Office of Education. Library LB5.N25 1938 pt. 1
for Library of Congress [LB5.N25 vol. 37, pt. 1]

INS OCU OO
NN 0066188 DHEW PSt CoU OrPR Or WaS WaTC CaBVaU

National Society for the Study of Education. *Committee on Intelligence: its Nature and Nurture.*

Intelligence: its nature and nurture. Pt. 1. Comparative and critical exposition. Pt. 2. Original studies and experiments. Prepared by the Society's committee, assisted by members of the Society and others. Edited by Guy Montrose Whipple. Bloomington, Ill., Public School Pub. Co., 1940.

2 v. diagrs., tables. 22 cm. (Yearbook of the National Society for the Study of Education, 39th, pts. 1–2)

Includes bibliographies.

1. Intellect. 2. Heredity. 3. Man—Influence of environment. [3. Environment] 4. Mental tests. I. Whipple, Guy Montrose, 1876–1941, ed. (Series: National Society for the Study of Education. Yearbook, 39th, pts. 1–2)

LB5.N25 39th, pt. 1–2 E 40–580 rev*
151.082

U. S. Office of Education. Library
for Library of Congress [r58f^{2}2]†

WaTC Or WaS CaBVaU IdPI OrPS
NN 0066189 DHEW WaPS DLC INS OCU OO OU PSt CaBVa

National society for the study of education. *Committee on international understanding.*

... International understanding through the public-school curriculum, prepared by the Society's Committee on international understanding ... Edited by I. L. Kandel and Guy Montrose Whipple ...

(*In* National society for the study of education. 36th Yearbook. Bloomington, Ill., 1937. 22½ cm. pt. II, xii, 406 p.)

I. L. Kandel, chairman.

Includes references.

CONTENTS.

Sec. I. General problems: International understanding and international interdependence by J. T. Shotwell.—Nationalism, patriotism, informed citizenship, and international understanding by Paul Monroe.—The development of international attitudes by Esther Caukin Brunauer.

Sec. II. Public-school curricula and international understanding: Intelligent nationalism in the curriculum by I. L. Kandel.

Sec. III. The school curriculum. Primary grades by Evaline Dowling.—English literature in the elementary school by Henry Neumann.—English literature in the high school: a project in world literature by B. J. R. Stolper.—Mathematics: its general character by D. E. Smith.—Arithmetic in the elementary school by C. H. Judd.—Mathematics in the high school by W. Betz.—History: its general function in the school by G. S. Ford.—History in the elementary and the junior high school by K. A. Sutton.—History in the senior high school by E. M. Hunt.—Geography by D. Whittlesey.—Geography in the elementary and the junior high school by Edith P. Parker.—Geography in the senior high school by R. H. Whitbeck.—Social studies in the senior high school by W. G. Kimmel.—The natural sciences: general considerations by F. Barry.—Science in the elementary school by G. S. Craig.—Science in the high school by O. W. Caldwell.—Modern-language study by R. H. Fife.—Modern languages in the high school by Margaret B. Holtz.—The classics by W. L. Carr.—Music by P. J. Weaver.—Music in the elementary and the high school by W. Earhart.—The fine arts by F. P. Keppel.—The fine arts in the elementary and the high school by Thomas Munro.—Physical education by J. F. Williams.—Recreation in the elementary and the high school by W. W. Pangburn.

Sec. IV. Some type studies: The schools and international understanding in Canada by H. F. Munro.—Education and Canadian-United States relations by A. A. Hauck.—The Pacific area and its problems by Reginald Bell.

Continued in next column

VOLUME 407

Continued from preceding column

Sec. v. Teachers and teaching aids: The preparation of teachers by W. C. Bagley.—Leading organizations promoting the study of international relations in the United States by J. E. Harley.—Teaching aids and materials by Margaret Kiely.

1. International relations—₍Study and₎ teaching. 2. International cooperation. 3. Education—Curricula. ₍3. Course of study₎ 4. ₍International education₎ I. Kandel, Isaac Leon, 1881- ed. II. Whipple, Guy Montrose, 1876–1941, joint ed. III. Title.

[LB.N25 1937, pt. 2] E 37—172

U. S. Office of Education. Library LB5
for Library of Congress ₍a57i½₎

NN 0066194 DHEW WaPS CaBVaU MtBC INS PSt OEac OO OCU OOxM O OCl OrPR Or WaS WaTC

National Society for the Study of Education. *Committee on Juvenile Delinquency and the Schools.*
Juvenile delinquency and the schools, ed. by Nelson B. Henry. Chicago, University of Chicago Press, 1948.

x, 280 p. 23 cm. (Yearbook of the National Society for the Study of Education, 47th, pt. 1)
Includes bibliographies.

1. Juvenile delinquency. 2. Personnel service in education. I. Henry, Nelson Bollinger, 1883- ed. II. Title. (Series: National Society for the Study of Education. Yearbook, 47th, pt. 1)

LB5.N25 47th, pt. 1 371.93 48—6850*

NN 0066195 DLC MB PSt CoU NjR MoU TxU OO OU PSC WaPS WaS WaTC CaBVaU Or OrPS IdPI CaBVa CoU INS

National Society for the Study of Education. *Committee on Learning and Instruction.*
Learning and instruction. Edited by Nelson B. Henry. Chicago ₍National Society for the Study of Education₎ distributed by the University of Chicago Press, 1950.

xii, 352 p. 23 cm. (Yearbook of the National Society for the Study of Education, 49th, pt. 1)
Includes bibliographies.

1. Learning, Psychology of. I. Henry, Nelson Bollinger, 1883- ed. II. Title. (Series: National Society for the Study of Education. Yearbook, 49th, pt. 1)

LB5.N25 49th, pt. 1 370.15 50—14227

NN 0066196 DLC CoU NIC PBm TxU NNC PSt NcD MeB CoU CaBVa Or WU MiU INS MtBC NN WaPS OU OrPR WaS CaBVaU WaTC

National Society for the Study of Education. *Committee on Mass Media and Education.*
Mass media and education; edited by Nelson B. Henry. Chicago, Distributed by the University of Chicago Press, 1954.

x, 290, lxxvi p. diagrs. 24 cm. (Yearbook of the National Society for the Study of Education, 53d, pt. 2)
Includes bibliographies.

1. Communication. I. Henry, Nelson Bollinger, 1883- ed. II. Title. (Series: National Society for the Study of Education. Yearbook, 53d, pt. 2)

LB5.N25 53d, pt. 2 371.3 54—8086

NN 0066197 DLC MiU PPPL IU OU IU TxU PBm PSC PSt WaPS MtBC CaBVaU CaBVa INS OOxM PRosC PU-Penn N PIm PJB PSt OCH NNCU-G Or OrPR IdPI WaTC WaS

National society for the study of education. *Committee on maturity.*
... Child development and the curriculum ... Prepared by the Society's Committee on maturity ... Edited by Guy Montrose Whipple ...

(*In its* 38th Yearbook. Bloomington, Ill., 1939. 22½ cm. pt. I, x, 442, ₍4₎ p.)
Carleton Washburne, chairman.

CONTENTS.—Introduction, by Carleton Washburne.—sec. I. The development of the child. Child development and the growth process, by J. E. Anderson.—sec. II. Data on the relation between the curriculum and child development. Prefatory note on the use of a classification by subject matter, by Carleton Washburne. Education in motor activities, by A. T. Jersild. Health and safety education, by Ruth Strang. Early training in routine physical habits, by A. T. Jersild and Frances M. Dwyer. The practical arts, by F. D. Brooks and P. J. Fay. Music, by A. T. Jersild. Radio and motion pictures, by A. T. Jersild. The graphic and allied arts, by N. C. Meier. Reading, by W. S. Gray. The development of spoken language, by J. E. Anderson. Language: The development of ability in oral and written composition, by L. J. Brueckner. Language: The development of ability in spelling, by Ernest Horn and Paul McKee. Language: The development of ability in hand writing, by F. N. Freeman. Foreign language, by F. D. Brooks and C. O. Arndt. The development of ability in arithmetic, by L. J. Brueckner. The work of the Committee of seven on grade-placement in arithmetic, by Carleton Washburne. The social studies, by Kai Jensen. Emotional and social development in the educative process, by H. E. Jones, H. S. Conrad, and Lois B. Murphy. Some theoretical and practical implications of the data on development, by Carleton Washburne.—sec. III. Appraisal of our knowledge of the relation of the curriculum to child development and of our methods of investigating the problem. Problems of method in maturity and curricular studies, by J. E. Anderson. Needed research, by Kai Jensen. A critique, by E. O. Melby.

Continued in next column

Continued from preceding column

1. Child study. 2. Education of children. ₍2. Children—Education₎ 3. Education—Curricula. ₍3. Course of study₎ I. Whipple, Guy Montrose, 1876- ed. II. Washburne, Carleton Wolsey, 1889- III. Title.

[LB5.N25 vol. 38, pt. 1] E 39—268

U. S. Office of Education Library
for Library of Congress ₍a60u1₎

NN 0066201 DHEW CaBVaU WaTC WaS Or OrPR OO O OCU OEac CoU PSt CU-S IdPI WaPS OrPS MtBC

National Society for the Study of Education. *Committee on Mental Health in Modern Education.*
Mental health in modern education. Edited by Nelson B. Henry. Chicago, NSSE; distributed by the University of Chicago Press, 1955.

xi, 397, lxxiv p. 24 cm. (Yearbook of the National Society for the Study of Education, 54th, pt. 2)
Includes bibliographical references.

1. Mental hygiene—U. S. 2. Educational psychology. I. Henry, Nelson Bollinger, 1883- ed. II. Title. (Series: National Society for the Study of Education. Yearbook, 54th, pt. 2)

LB5.N25 54th, pt. 2 371.71 55—14176

NN 0066202 DLC INS WaTC CSt PPPL MB DI WaS IdPI OrPR MtBC PSC PSt PBm PJB PPEB PPLT MiU PPLas WaPS TxU NcD NN OO OOxM OU PU-Penn PPDrop OClJC MNtcA OrPS WaSpG CaBVaU PSt CaBVa OKU-M NNC

National society for the study of education. *Committee on minimal essentials in elementary-school subjects.*
... Report. ₍1st₎-
1915-
Chicago; ₍etc., etc.₎ 19

(*In* National society for the study of education. 14th Yearbook, Chicago ₍1915₎ 22½cm. pt. 1, p. 9-152. diagrs.; 16th Yearbook, Bloomington, Ill., 1917. 23cm. pt. 1, 204 p.)

1. Education—Curricula. ₍1. Course of study₎

E 15-406 Revised

Library, U. S. Bur. of Education LB5.N25

NN 0066203 DHEW INS PSt

National Society for the Study of Education. *Committee on Modern Philosophies and Education.*
Modern philosophies and education. Edited by Nelson B. Henry. Chicago, NSSE; distributed by the University of Chicago Press, 1955.

x, 374, vi p. 24 cm. (Yearbook of the National Society for the Study of Education, 54th, pt. 1)
Includes bibliographies.

1. Education—Philosophy. I. Henry, Nelson Bollinger, 1883- ed. II. Title. (Series: National Society for the Study of Education. Yearbook, 54th, pt. 1)

LB5.N25 54th, pt. 1 370.1 55—14177

NN 0066204 DLC NcC DNLM MiU MNtcA PSC LN WaPS INS MtBC WaS WaTC CaBVaU OrPR IdPI CaBVa OWorP WaSpG

National society for the study of education. *Committee on music education.*
... Music education, prepared by the Society's Committee on music education ... Edited by Guy Montrose Whipple ...

(*In* National society for the study of education. 35th Yearbook. Bloomington, Ill., 1936. 23cm. pt. II, xii, 260 p.)
Willis L. Uhl, chairman.

CONTENTS.—sec. I. General principles and educational relations: Principles of music education ₍by₎ James L. Mursell.—The place of music in a system of education ₍by₎ Lilla Belle Pitts.—Significant relationships of music to other subjects ₍by₎ Peter W. Dykema.—The composition of musical ability ₍by₎ Jacob Kwalwasser.—sec. II. Musical activities in the school: Typical musical activities of the school ₍by₎ Lilla Belle Pitts.—Rhythm ₍by₎ Mabelle Glenn.—Singing ₍by₎ Maybelle Glenn.—Ear-training ₍by₎ Russell V. Morgan.—Instrumental activities ₍by₎ David Mattern and Norval L. Church.—Listening ₍by₎ Lillian L. Baldwin.—Reading music ₍by₎ James L. Mursell.—Music theory ₍by₎ Louis Woodson Curtis.—Creative activities ₍by₎ Will Earhart.—sec. III. Classroom and administrative problems: The accrediting and the programming of school music ₍by₎ John W. Beattie.—The selection and organization of music materials ₍by₎ Anne E. Pierce.—Music rooms and equipment ₍by₎ Joseph E. Maddy.—A music program for rural schools ₍by₎ Marguerite V. Hood.—A program of music activities outside the school ₍by₎ Edgar B. Gordon.—Standards and the evaluation and measurement of achievement in music ₍by₎ Glenn Gildersleeve.—The selection and training of teachers ₍by₎ John W. Beattie.

1. Music—Instruction ₍and study₎—U. S. I. Uhl, Willis Lemon, 1885- II. Whipple, Guy Montrose, 1876- ed. III. Title.

E 36-112

Library, U. S. Office of Education LB5.N25 1936 pt. 2
Library of Congress [LB5.N25 vol. 35, pt. 2]

NN 0066206 DHEW OrPR WaTC Or IdPI WaS OrPS CaBVaU PSt NIC OU OO OOxM OCU OClW MiU IdU-SB WaPS

National society for the study of education. *Committee on new materials in instruction.*
Report. ₍1st₎-2d.; 1920-21.

(*In* National society for the study of education. 19th Yearbook. Bloomington, Ill., 1920. 23 cm. pt. I, p. 7-180; 20th Yearbook, Bloomington, Ill., 1921. 23 cm. pt. I, p. 1-221)
Chairman: 1920, C. H. Judd.—1921, F. J. Kelly.
Editor: 1920-21, G. W. Whipple.
First report contains references.
Bibliography: 20th Yearbook, pt. I, p. 189-221.

1. Education—Curricula. ₍1. Course of study₎ I. Judd, Charles Hubbard, 1873- II. Kelly, Frederick James, 1880- III. Whipple, Guy Montrose, 1876-

[LB5.N25 vol. 19, pt. 1; vol. 20, pt. 1] E 21—100

U. S. Office of Education. Library
for Library of Congress ₍a59t1₎

NN 0066207 DHEW PSt WaTC Or OrU CaBVaU

National society for the study of education. *Committee on philosophies of education.*
... Philosophies of education. Prepared by the Society's committee ... Edited by Nelson B. Henry ... Bloomington, Ill., Public school publishing company, 1942.

xi, 321 p. 23 cm. (National society for the study of education. 41st Yearbook, pt. I)
John S. Brubacher, chairman.

CONTENTS.—Introduction: Purpose and scope of the yearbook, by J. S. Brubacher.—Philosophy and science in the western world; a historical overview, by E. H. Reisner.—Philosophy of education from the experimentalist outlook, by W. H. Kilpatrick.—Education and the realistic outlook, by F. E. Breed.—An idealist philosophy of education, by H. H. Horne.—In defense of the philosophy of education, by M. J. Adler.—The philosophy of Catholic education, by William McGucken, S. J.—Comparative philosophy of education, by J. S. Brubacher.

1. Education—Philosophy. I. Henry, Nelson Bollinger, jr., ed. II. Title.

[LB5.N25 vol. 4] E 42—207

U. S. Office of Education. Library
for Library of Congress ₍57g²2₎

NN 0066209 DHEW OWorP INS IMunS OCU OO OU OOxM CoU NjR PSt MiU GAT Or WaTC WaPS CaBVaU OrPS IdPI

National Society for the Study of Education. *Committee on Reading.*
Reading in the elementary school, prepared by the yearbook committee under the direction of the society's Committee on Reading. Edited by Nelson B. Henry. Chicago, University of Chicago Press, 1949.

xi, 343, lvi p. 23 cm. (Yearbook of the National Society for the Study of Education, 48th, pt. 2)
Includes bibliographies.

1. Reading (Elementary) I. Henry, Nelson Bollinger, 1883- ed. (Series: National Society for the Study of Education. Yearbook, 48th, pt. 2)

LB5.N25 48th pt. 2 372.4 49—8506*

NN 0066210 DLC CaBVaU INS WaPS WaTC IdPI PU NNCU-G MtBC Or TxU NcD PSt OU PSC PBm PPLas PSt PV CU OrPS

National Society for the Study of Education. *Committee on Reading.*
Reading in the high school and college, prepared by the yearbook committee under the direction of the society's Committee on Reading; ed. by Nelson B. Henry. Chicago, University of Chicago Press, 1948.

x, 318, xlix p. 23 cm. (Yearbook of the National Society for the Study of Education, 47th, pt. 2)
Includes bibliographies.

1. Reading (Secondary education) 2. Reading (Higher education) 3. Books and reading. I. Henry, Nelson Bollinger, 1883- ed. II. Title. (Series: National Society for the Study of Education. Yearbook, 47th, pt. 2)

LB5.N25 47th, pt. 2 372.4 48—6851*

NN 0066211 DLC TxU ICU OO PV PSC PSt CaBVaU WaTC IdPI PCM MiU WaS Or OrPS WaPS INS

National society for the study of education. *Committee on reading.*
... Report of the National committee on reading. Frank W. Ballou, Rose Lees Hardy, Ernest Horn, Frances Jenkins, Sterling A. Leonard, Estaline Wilson, Laura Zirbes. William S. Gray, chairman. Ed. by Guy Montrose Whipple ...

(*In* National society for the study of education. 24th Yearbook. Bloomington, Ill., 1925. 23 cm. pt. I, p. 1-309)

1. Reading. I. Gray, William Scott, 1885- II. Whipple, Guy Montrose, 1876-

[LB5.N25 vol. 24, pt. 1] E 26—348

U. S. Office of Education. Library LB5
for Library of Congress ₍a61m½₎

NN 0066212 DHEW CU PSt OU OEac OO OClW OCl MiU OCU IdU-SB WaTC IdPI WaS Or OrCS CaBVaU INS

VOLUME 407

National society for the study of education. *Committee on reading.*
... The teaching of reading: a second report, prepared by the Society's Committee on reading ... Edited by Guy Montrose Whipple.
(*In* National society for the study of education. 36th Yearbook. Bloomington, Ill., 1937. 22½ cm. pt. I, vii, 442 p.)
William S. Gray, chairman.
Includes references.
CONTENTS.—A decade of progress by W. S. Gray.—The nature and types of reading by W. S. Gray.—The place of reading in the curriculum by Bess Goodykoontz.—The nature and organization of basic instruction in reading by W. S. Gray.—Reading in the various fields of the curriculum by Mabel Snedaker.—The development of reading interests and tastes by Jean Betzner.—The materials of reading by W. H. Uhl.—The school library by B. L. Johnson.—Vocabulary development by Paul McKee.—The improvement of oral reading by Vera Alice Paul.—Individual differences and their implications with respect to instruction in reading by D. D. Durrell.—The measurement and evaluation of achievement in reading by A. I. Gates.—Diagnosis and treatment of extreme cases of reading disability by A. I. Gates.—The reorganization and improvement of instruction in reading through adequate supervision by G. A. Yoakam.
1. Reading. I. Whipple, Guy Montrose, 1876–1941, ed. II. Gray, William Scott, 1885–
[LB5.N25 vol. 36, pt. 1] E 37—173
U. S. Office of Education. Library LB5.N25 1937, pt. 1
for Library of Congress [a54u1]

OEac OO OCU OCl OOxM OU IdPI INS OrPS WaPS MtBC
NN 0066214 DHEW PSt WaTC OrPR Or WaS CaBVaU TxU

National society for the study of education. *Committee on rural education.*
... The status of rural education; first report of the Society's Committee on rural education. Prepared by the Society's committee ... Edited by Guy Montrose Whipple ...
(*In* National society for the study of education. 30th Yearbook. Bloomington, Ill., 1931. 23 cm. pt. I, p. 1–272. tables)
Orville G. Brim, chairman.
CONTENTS.—Economic and social factors of rural life, by G. A. Works.—Pupil status in the rural elementary school, by G. C. Kyte.—Availability of schools in rural communities, by K. M. Cook and W. H. Gaumnitz.—The curriculum of the rural elementary school, by F. W. Dunn.—The curriculum of the rural secondary school, by W. H. Bristow, E. N. Ferriss, R. M. Stewart.—The preparation of teachers for rural schools, by Mabel Carney.—The supervision of rural schools, by N. Frost, M. S. Pittman, H. H. Heyl.—Problems in the organization and administration of rural schools, by T. L. Bayne, jr., J. E. Butterworth, M. G. Nelson, R. E. Jaggers.—Financing the rural school, by H. C. Morrison.—Coöperative extension work in agriculture and home economics, by T. H. Eaton.—Guiding principles in rural education, by O. G. Brim.
1. Rural schools—U. S. I. Whipple, Guy Montrose, 1876–1941, ed. II. Brim, Orville Gilbert, 1883–
[LB5.N25 vol. 30, pt. 1] E 31—415
U. S. Office of Education. Library LB5
for Library of Congress [a57o1]

PSt DHEW OCU OClW OOxM OU OCl MiU PPPL OO
NN 0066216 DHEW DNAL WaPS CaBVaU OrU WaS Or OrPR

National society for the study of education. *Committee on safety education.*
... The present status of safety education. Prepared by the Society's committee ... Ed. by Guy Montrose Whipple ...
(*In* National society for the study of education. 25th Yearbook. Bloomington, Ill., 1926. 23 cm. pt. I, p. 1–366. illus.)
G. M. Whipple, chairman.
CONTENTS.—The problem, by S. J. Williams.—Development of the safety movement, by S. J. Williams.—Realization of the educational aspect of the problem, by S. J. Williams.—The subject matter of safety education, by Mary N. Arrowsmith.—Prevalent methods of administering safety education in the schools, by Idabelle Stevenson, Harriet E. Beard, Frances H. Miner, Z. E. Scott, J. H. Harvey, Ruth C. Earle, H. S. Gruver [and] Ruth Streitz.—Courses of study and methods in safety education: elementary schools, by Evelyn T. Holston.—Courses of study and methods in safety education: junior high schools, by Idabelle Stevenson.—Courses of study and methods in safety education: senior high schools, by Idabelle Stevenson.—Courses of study and methods in safety education: rural schools, by M. S. Pittman [and] Rena Allen.—Courses of study and methods in safety education: vocational industrial schools, by M. S. Henig.—The present status of safety education in teacher training institutions, by E. G. Payne.—Training engineers in safety, by W. D. Keefer.—The fundamental significance of safety education, by A. W. Whitney [and] A. B. Meredith.—Summary and outlook: future problems, by A. B. Meredith.—An annotated bibliography on safety education, by Mary B. Day.
1. Accidents—Prevention. I. Whipple, Guy Montrose, 1876–
[LB5.N25 1926] E 26—227
U. S. Office of Education. Library
for Library of Congress [a63m¼]

OU CaBVaU WaS
NN 0066219 DHEW INS PSt PU MiU OOxM OCl OO OCU

National society for the study of education. *Committee on school buildings.*
... The planning and construction of school buildings, prepared by the Society's Committee on school buildings ... Edited by Guy Montrose Whipple ...
(*In* National society for the study of education. 33d Yearbook. Bloomington, Ill., 1934. 23 cm. pt. 1, xi, 337 p. incl. tables, forms)
N. L. Engelhardt, chairman.
CONTENTS.—sec. I. The philosophy of the school plant: Functional relationships of the school plant [by] A. B. Moehlman.—sec. II. School-plant planning policies: Thrift in capital outlay through school-building surveys [by] J. C. Miller. The influence of the city building code upon school-building construction [by] J. W. Sahlstrom. Evaluation of school-building plans appearing in the pamphlets of state educational departments [by] L. L. Chism. Relation of the public to expenditures for school-building programs [by] I. O. Friswold. The architect and school-building program-planning [by] F. Engelhardt. Economy and efficiency in the selection and purchase of school sites [by] F. W. Hart. Some underlying theories affecting plans for financing school-building programs [by] F. Engelhardt. Budget plan for checking income and costs that may be incurred in the planning of a single school building [by] S. H. Jones.—sec. III. Educational services: The work of the National advisory council on school-building problems [by] Alice Barrows. The function and program of a state bureau of buildings and grounds [by] F. H. Wood and J. H. Hixson. State control of plans and specifications for public-school buildings [by] C. E. Sohl. The rôle of the superintendent of schools in school-building planning [by] J. W. Studebaker and A. W. Merrill. Analysis of the responsibilities of the superintendent of schools [by] E. T. Peterson. The teacher as an educational planner [by] C. L. Spain.—sec. IV. Architectural services: Difficulties encountered by superintendents of schools and boards of education with respect to architectural service [by] W. W. Theisen. Selection of architectural service [by] H. W. Anderson. A proposed application form to be used by architects seeking commissions in school-building planning [by] N. L. Engelhardt. The dissemination of information concerning proposed school buildings and school-building construction [by] N. L. Engelhardt. Obstacles reported by architects in securing contracts for planning school buildings [by] N. L. Engelhardt. Obstacles reported by the school architect in rendering contractual services [by] N. L. Engelhardt. The preparation that school officials should make in order to coöperate effectively with the school architect [by] N. L. Engelhardt. The form of architect's contract advocated by the American institute of architects [by] T. C. Holy. The various forms of architects' contracts used by boards of education [by] F. W. Hosler and C. Eifler. What architects do in carrying through a school-building problem after their appointment [by] N. L. Engelhardt. Standards for architects' working drawings [by] A. M. Proctor.—sec. V. Constructional service: Legal documents [by] T. C. Holy and C. E. Sohl. The character of the contractors' bidding on school buildings [by] D. R. Pugmire. A checking list for the contract between a board of education and a building contractor [by] C. Eifler and F. W. Hosler. Precautions to be taken in preparation for school-building construction [by] E. A. Andersen. Supervision of construction [by] R. L. Hamon.—sec VI. Financial aspects of the problem: Theory of school-plant costs [by] A. B. Moehlman. Extra costs in the erection of school buildings [by] F. M. Misner. The adjustment of school-building programs to economic conditions [by] L. L. Standley.
1. School-houses—U. S. I. Whipple, Guy Montrose, 1876–1941, ed. II. Engelhardt, Nickolaus Louis, 1882– III. Title.
[LB5.N25 vol. 33, pt. 1] E 34—427
U. S. Office of Education. Library
for Library of Congress [a57o1]

OrPR CaBVaU OrPS WaPS
NN 0066225 DHEW OCl OClW OO OOxM OCU OU NNC PSt

National Society for the Study of Education. *Committee on Science Education in American Schools.*
Science education in American schools, ed. by Nelson B. Henry. Chicago, Univ. of Chicago Press, 1947.
xii, 306 p. 23 cm. (Yearbook of the National Society for the Study of Education, 46th, pt. 1)
1. Science—Study and teaching. I. Henry, Nelson Bollinger, 1883– ed. II. Title. (Series: National Society for the Study of Education. Yearbook, 46th, pt. 1)
LB5.N25 46th, pt. 1 507.12 48—294*

CaBVaU TxU OrPS CaBVa WaPS CoU INS WaTC
NN 0066226 DLC MiEM OO PSC CoU NNCU-G PSt IdPI WaS

LB5
.N25
v.46
pt.1
1955

National Society for the Study of Education. Committee on Science Education in American Schools.
Science education in American schools, ed. by Nelson B. Henry. Chicago, Distributed by University of Chicago Press, 1947 [reprinted 1955]
xii, 300, vi p. 23cm. (Yearbook of the National Society for the Study of Education, 46th, pt. 1)
Includes bibliographies.
1. Science--Study and teaching. i. Henry, Nelson Bollinger, 1883- ed. ii. t. iii. s: National Society for the Study of Education. Yearbook. v. 46, pt. 1.

NN 0066227 OrPS

National society for the study of education. *Committee on silent reading.*
... Report of the Society's committee on silent reading, prepared by the committee from material submitted by J. A. O'Brien, May Ayres Burgess, S. A. Courtis ... [and others] Ed. by Guy Montrose Whipple ...
(*In* National society for the study of education. 20th Yearbook. Bloomington, Ill., 1921. pt. II, p. 1–172. illus., tables, diagrs.)
Ernest Horn, chairman.
CONTENTS.—Introduction.—Factors affecting results in primary reading, by W. W. Theisen.—Controlling factors in the measurement of silent reading, by M. A. Burgess.—Individual difficulties in silent reading in the fourth, fifth, and sixth grades, by W. S. Gray.—The development of speed in silent reading, by J. A. O'Brien.—Motivated work in third-grade silent reading, by J. H. Hoover.—The effect of a single reading, by G. A. Yoakam.—Outlining and summarizing compared with re-reading as methods of studying, by C. E. Germane.—Measuring comprehension of content material, by H. A. Greene.—The vocabularies of ten first readers, by J. L. Packer.—The contents of readers, by D. Starch.—Exercises developed at Detroit for making reading function, by Regina R. Heller and S. A. Courtis.—Silent reading exercises developed at Denver, Cedar Rapids, Racine and Iowa City.
1. Reading (Elementary) I. Horn, Ernest, 1882– II. Whipple, Guy Montrose, 1876– III. Theisen, William Walter, 1886– IV. Burgess, May (Ayres) 1888– V. Gray, William Scott, 1885– VI. O'Brien, John Anthony, 1893– VII. Hoover, J. H. VIII. Yoakam, Gerald Alan, 187– IX. Germane, Charles E., 1885– X. Greene, Harry Andrew, 1889– XI. Packer, J. L. XII. Starch, Daniel, 1883– XIII. Heller, Regina R. XIV. Courtis Stuart Appleton, 1874–
[LB5.N25 vol. 20, pt. 2] E 21—125
U. S. Office of Education. Library
for Library of Congress [a58e²2]

MiU MB PSt WaS Or WaTC OrU
NN 0066230 DHEW CaBVaU IdPI INS OCl OCU OOxM OO

National Society of College Teachers of Education. *Committee on Social Foundations.*
The emerging task of the foundations of education; the study of man, culture and education, a statement to the profession. [Ann Arbor, Lithoprinted by Edwards Letter Shop for National Society of College Teachers of Education, 1950]
[71] p. 28 cm.
1. Teachers, Training of. 2. Education—Aims and objectives. I. Title.
A 51-4878
Wisconsin. Univ. Libr
for Library of Congress [3]

NN 0066231 WU

National society for the study of education. *Committee on structural reorganization.*
... American education in the postwar period. Pt. II. Structural reorganization ... Edited by Nelson B. Henry. Chicago, Ill., The University of Chicago press, 1945.
x, 324, xl p. 23 cm. (National society for the study of education. 44th Yearbook, pt. II)
1. Education—U. S. 2. School management and organization—U. S. 3. World war, 1939–1945—Education [and the war] I. Henry Nelson Bollinger, jr., 1883– ed. II. Title. III. Title: Structural reorganization.
E 46—51
U. S. Office of Education. Library LB5
for Library of Congress [a57v²1]

PSt CaBVaU WaPS WaTC Or OrP OrPS IdPI OrStbM
NN 0066233 DHEW INS IdPI CaBVa OCU OOxM TxU CoU

National society for the study of education. *Committee on the activity movement.*
... The activity movement, prepared by the Society's Committee on the activity movement ... Edited by Guy Montrose Whipple ...
(*In* National society for the study of education. 33d Yearbook. Bloomington, Ill., 1934. 23 cm. pt. II, xi, 320 p.)
Lois Coffey Mossman, chairman.
"A selected bibliography of the activity movement": p. 273–277.
CONTENTS.—Statement of the problem, by L. C. Mossman.—Historical sketch of activism, by T. Woody.—Definition of the activity movement to-day, by W. K. Kilpatrick.—Description of some ways of interpreting the principles of activity when applying it to school work, by Adelaide M. Ayer, Mildred English, J. F. Hosic, and L. C. Mossman.—Comments and criticisms by some educational leaders in our universities, by W. C. Bagley, B. H. Bode, J. Dewey, R. L. Finney, F. N. Freeman, M. E. Haggerty, G. Watson.—Comments and criticisms by some educational leaders in the field, by Dessalee Ryan Dudley, A. L. Hartman, Helen Hay Heyl, R. H. Lane, Maude McBroom, E. E. Oberholtzer, R. H. Palmer.—The evaluation of the learning product: The problem of evaluation: report on attempts to evaluate the work in the field, by Mildred English.—The orientation of measurement in the activity program, by Alice V. Keliher.—Comments upon relationships between the activity movement and the measurement movement, by A. I. Gates.—Controversial issues, by W. S. Gray and Adelaide M. Ayer.—Statements with which there is a measure of committee agreement.—Statements by various members of the committee, by Adelaide M. Ayer, Mildred English, A. I. Gates, W. S. Gray, Ernest Horn, J. F. Hosic, W. H. Kilpatrick, L. C. Mossman, E. E. Oberholtzer.—Appendix.
1. Project method in teaching. [1. Project work] I. Whipple, Guy Montrose, 1876– ed. II. Mossman, Lois Coffey, 1877– III. Title.
[LB5.N25 1934] E 34—428
U. S. Office of Education. Library
for Library of Congress [a58t½]

OrPR WaS WaTC CaBVaU OrPS
NN 0066236 DHEW WaPS INS OOxM OCU OClW OO OCl PSt

VOLUME 407

National Society for the Study of Education. *Committee on the Community School.*
The community school. Edited by Nelson B. Henry. Chicago, Distributed by the University of Chicago Press, 1953.
xii, 292, lxxii p. 23 cm. (Yearbook of the National Society for the Study of Education, 52d, pt. 2)
Includes bibliographical references.
1. Community and school—Addresses, essays, lectures. I. Henry, Nelson Bollinger, 1883- ed. II. Title. (Series: National Society for the Study of Education. Yearbook, 52d, pt. 2)
LB5.N25 52d, pt. 2 370.19 53-1815

NNCU-G MtBC WaTC CaBVaU PPPL WaS
MiD OO PJB NN OrPR IdPI CaBVa WaPS INS Or PSt MiU
NN 0066237 DLC TxU PU-Penn PBm PSt PSC OOxM OU

National Society for the Study of Education. *Committee on the Education of Exceptional Children.*
The education of exceptional children. Edited by Nelson B. Henry. Chicago ⌊National Society for the Study of Education⌋ distributed by the University of Chicago Press, 1950.
xiii, 350, lxii p. diagrs. 23 cm. (Yearbook of the National Society for the Study of Education, 49th, pt. 2)
Includes bibliographies.
1. Children, Abnormal and backward. I. Henry, Nelson Bollinger, 1883- ed. II. Title. (Series: National Society for the Study of Education. Yearbook, 49th, pt. 2)
LB5.N25 49th, pt. 2 371.9 50-13996

NNC DCU WaTC CaBVaU OrPR WaPS Or CaBVa INS
NN 0066238 DLC NcD PSt NN OClW IaU MtBC WaS TxU

Barnard
D371
N213
National Society for the Study of Education. Committee on the Education of Exceptional Children.
The education of exceptional children. Prepared by the Society's Committee, Harry J. Baker ⌊and others⌋ Edited by Nelson B. Henry. Chicago, University of Chicago Press, 1950 ⌊i.e. 1955⌋
xiii, 356 p. (Yearbook of the National Society for the Study of Education, 49th, pt. 2)
Includes bibliographies.

NN 0066239 NNC

National society for the study of education. *Committee on the education of gifted children.*
... Report of the Society's committee on the education of gifted children, edited by Guy M. Whipple ...
(*In* National society for the study of education. 23d Yearbook. Bloomington, Ill., 1924. 23 cm. pt. I, 443 p.)
CONTENTS.—sec. I. General reports and summaries: Historical and introductory, by G. M. Whipple. Methods of selecting superior or gifted children, by B. T. Baldwin. Problems of organization. Some administrative phases in the education of gifted children, by L. O. Smith. The curriculum for the gifted: Some principles and an illustration, by E. Horn. The curriculum for gifted children, by H. O. Rugg. Personal and social characteristics of gifted children, by Helen Davis. The democratic idea and the education of gifted children, by H. G. Townsend.—sec. II. Special studies: The physical and mental traits of gifted children, by L. M. Terman. The educational achievements of gifted children, by L. M. Terman and J. C. De Voss. Case studies of gifted children, by C. W. Waddle. Miscellaneous experimental and statistical studies of gifted children.—sec. III. Bibliography: Annotated bibliography on gifted children and their education, compiled by T. S. Henry.
1. Exceptional children—Education. 2. Ability. I. Whipple, Guy Montrose, 1876- ed.
[LB5.N25 vol. 23, pt. 1] E 24-567
U. S. Office of Education. Library
for Library of Congress ⌊65j½⌋

WaTC CaBVaU
NN 0066241 DHEW MiU OCU OOxM OU OO OClW PSt WaS

National society for the study of education. *Committee on the grouping of pupils.*
... The groupings of pupils, prepared by the society's Committee on the grouping of pupils ... Edited by Guy Montrose Whipple.
(*In* National society for the study of education. 35th Yearbook. Bloomington, Ill., 1936. 23 cm. pt. I, x, 319 p. incl. tables, diagrs., forms)
Warren W. Coxe, chairman.
1. Ability. 2. Grading and marking (Students) 3. School management and organization. 4. Mental tests. I. Whipple, Guy Montrose, 1876-1941, ed. II. Title.
LB5.N25 35th, pt. 1 E 36-111 rev
U. S. Office of Education. Library
for Library of Congress ⌊r55j2⌋†

OU MiU PSt IdPI Or WaS WaTC INS
NN 0066242 DHEW WaPS OrPS CaBVaU DLC OClW OCU OO

National society for the study of education. *Committee on the library in general education.*
... The library in general education. Prepared by the Society's committee ... Edited by Nelson B. Henry ... Chicago, Ill., The Dept. of education, The University of Chicago, 1943.
xiv, 383 p. 23 cm. (National society for the study of education. 42nd Yearbook, pt. II)
Bibliography: p. ⌊361⌋-370.
1. Libraries—U. S. I. Henry, Nelson Bollinger, jr., ed. II. Title.
[LB5.N25 vol. 42, pt. 2] E 43-38
U. S. Office of Education. Library
for Library of Congress ⌊a56p1⌋

CaBVaU IdPI WaTC CaBVa WaPS INS
NN 0066243 DHEW PSt CoU OCU OU TxU IU NNC NcRS

National society for the study of education. *Committee on the measurement of understanding.*
... The measurement of understanding, prepared by the society's committee ... Edited by Nelson B. Henry. Chicago, Ill., The University of Chicago press, 1946.
xi, 338, v p. illus. (incl. maps) diagrs. 23 cm. (National society for the study of education. 45th Yearbook, pt. I)
"References" at end of some of the chapters.
1. Learning, Psychology of. 2. Teaching. I. Henry, Nelson Bollinger, jr., ed. II. Title.
LB5.N25 45th, pt. 1 370.1544 A 46-5923
Chicago. Univ. Libr.
for Library of Congress ⌊a62k²1⌋†

WaS Or MiU NNNCU-G CaBVa WaPS INS
NN 0066244 ICU CoU OCU OOxM TxU DLC CaBVaU WaTC

National society for the study of education. *Committee on the psychology of learning.*
... The psychology of learning. Prepared by the Society's committee ... Assisted by E. R. Guthrie and Clark L. Hull ... Edited by Nelson B. Henry ... Bloomington, Ill., Public school publishing company, 1942.
xiv, 502 p. port. 23 cm. (National society for the study of education. 41st Yearbook, pt. II)
T. R. McConnell, chairman.
CONTENTS.—Introduction: Purpose and scope of the yearbook, by T. R. McConnell.—section I. Theories of learning. Conditioning: a theory of learning in terms of stimulus, response, and association, by E. R. Guthrie. Conditioning: outline of a systematic theory of learning, by C. L. Hull. Connectionism: its origin and major features, by Peter Sandiford. Connectionism: present concepts and interpretations, by A. I. Gates. The field theory of learning and its educational consequences, by G. W. Hartmann. Field theory of learning, by Kurt Lewin. Reconciliation of learning theories, by T. R. McConnell.—section II. Implications for education. Motivation in learning, by D. G. Ryans. The relation of emotional behavior to learning, by J. E. Anderson. The role of practice in learning, by J. B. Stroud. Language and meaning, by Ernest Horn. Problem solving, by W. A. Brownell. Organization and sequence of the curriculum, by G. T. Buswell.
1. Psychology. 2. Learning, Psychology of. 3. Educational psychology. I. Henry, Nelson Bollinger, jr., ed. II. Title.
[LB5.N25 vol. 41] E 42-208
U. S. Office of Education. Library
for Library of Congress ⌊a58n²1⌋

MNtcA CaBVaU WaTC OrPS IdPI WaPS
NN 0066246 DHEW INS OWorP OU OCU OO OOxM OU Or

LB
1051
.N263
National society for the study of education. Committee on the psychology of learning.
... The psychology of learning. Prepared by the Society's committee ... Assisted by E.R. Guthrie ... ⌊and others⌋ Edited by Nelson B. Henry. Chicago, Distributed by the University of Chicago press ⌊1945⌋
xiv,463 p. diagrs. 22cm. (National society for the study of education. 41st Yearbook,pt.II)
T.R.McConnell,chairman.
CONTENTS.--Introduction: Purpose and scope of the yearbook ⌊by⌋ T.R.McConnell.--section I.Theories of learning. Conditioning: a theory of learning in terms of stimulus,response,and association ⌊by⌋ E.R.Guthrie. Conditioning: outline of a systematic theory of learning ⌊by⌋ C.L.Hull. Connectionism: its origin and major features ⌊by⌋ Peter Sandiford. Connectionism: present concepts and interpretations ⌊by⌋ A.I.Gates. The field theory of learning and its educational consequences ⌊by⌋ G.W.Hartmann. Field theory of learning ⌊by⌋ Kurt Lewin. Reconciliation of learning theories ⌊by⌋ T.R. McConnell.--section II. Implications for education. Motivation in learning ⌊by⌋ D.G.Ryans. The relation of emotional behavior to learning ⌊by⌋ J.E.Anderson. The role of practice in learning ⌊by⌋ J.B.Stroud. Language and meaning ⌊by⌋ Ernest Horn. Problem solving ⌊by⌋ W.A. Brownell. Organization and sequence of the curriculum ⌊by⌋ G.T.Buswell.
1.Learning,Psychology of. 2.Educational psychology. I. Henry,Nelson Bollinger,jr., ed.

NN 0066249 MiU

LB
1051
.N27
1946
National society for the study of education. Committee on the psychology of learning.
... The psychology of learning. Prepared by the Society's committee ... Assisted by E.R. Guthrie ... ⌊and others⌋ Edited by Nelson B. Henry. Chicago, Distributed by the University of Chicago press ⌊1946⌋
xiv,463 p. diagrs. 22cm. (National society for the study of education. 41st Yearbook,pt.II)
T.R.McConnell,chairman.
"Published,February,1942 ... fourth printing,November,1946."
CONTENTS.--Introduction: Purpose and scope of the yearbook ⌊by⌋ T.R.McConnell.--section I.Theories of learning. Conditioning: a theory of learning in terms of stimulus,response,and association ⌊by⌋ E.R.Guthrie. Conditioning: outline of a systematic theory of learning ⌊by⌋ C.L.Hull. Connectionism: its origin and major features ⌊by⌋ Peter Sandiford. Connectionism: present concepts and interpretations ⌊by⌋ A.I.Gates. The field theory of learning and its educational consequences ⌊by⌋ G.W.Hartmann. Field theory of learning ⌊by⌋ Kurt Lewin. Reconciliation of learning theories ⌊by⌋ T.R. McConnell.--section II. Implications for education. Motivation in learning ⌊by⌋ D.G.Ryans. The relation of emotional behavior to learning ⌊by⌋ J.E.Anderson. The role of practice in learning ⌊by⌋ J.B.Stroud. Language and meaning ⌊by⌋ Ernest Horn. Problem solving ⌊by⌋ W.A. Brownell. Organization and sequence of the curriculum ⌊by⌋ G.T.Buswell.
1.Learning,Psychology of. 2.Educational psychology. I. Henry,Nelson Bollinger,jr., ed.

NN 0066252 MiU

National Society for the Study of Education. Committee on the Psychology of Learning.
The psychology of learning. Ed. by N.B.Henry. Chicago, Distributed by Chicago U.P. [1947]
xiv, 463 p. diagr. (National Society for the Study of Education. Yearbook, 41)

NN 0066253 MH

Agric
Library
LB
1051
N252
National Society for the Study of Education. Committee on the Psychology of Learning
The psychology of learning. Prepared by the Society's committee, assisted by E. R. Guthrie and Clark L. Hull. Edited by Nelson B. Henry. Chicago, Distributed by The University of Chicago Press ⌊1948⌋
xiv, 463p. illus. 23cm. (National Society for the Study of Education. 41st Yearbook, pt. 2)
Includes bibliography.
1. Psychology 2. Learning, Psychology of 3. Educational psychology I. Henry, Nelson Bollinger, 1883- ed.
II. Title jrr 42-208

NN 0066254 WU

Barnard
D370.1
N2121
National Society for the Study of Education. Committee on the Psychology of Learning.
The psychology of learning. Prepared by the Society's committee ... Assisted by E. R. Guthrie ⌊and others⌋ Edited by Nelson B. Henry. Chicago, Distributed by the University of Chicago Press ⌊1951⌋
xiv, 463 p. illus. (National Society for the Study of Education. 41st Yearbook, pt. II)
T. R. McConnell, chairman.

NN 0066255 NNC CaBVa

National Society for the Study of Education. *Committee on the Teaching of Arithmetic.*
The teaching of arithmetic. Edited by Nelson B. Henry. Chicago, Distributed by the University of Chicago Press, 1951.
xii, 302, lxx p. 23 cm. (Yearbook of the National Society for the Study of Education, 50th, pt. 2)
Includes bibliographies.
1. Arithmetic—Study and teaching. I. Henry, Nelson Bollinger, 1883- ed. II. Title. (Series: National Society for the Study of Education. Yearbook, 50th, pt. 2)
LB5.N25 50th, pt. 2 511.07 51-9871

MtBC NNC
WaTC CoU INS NN PSt NNCU-G IEdS OrPR WaS IdPI TxU
NN 0066256 DLC Or OrPS WaPS OrMonO CaBVaU CaBVa

VOLUME 407

National society for the study of education. *Committee on the teaching of geography.*
... The teaching of geography, prepared by the Society's Committee on the teaching of geography ... Edited by Guy Montrose Whipple ... Bloomington, Ill., Public school publishing company ₍1933₎
xviii, 615 p. facsims., tables, diagrs. 23 cm. (National society for the study of education. The 32d Yearbook)
A. E. Parkins, chairman.
CONTENTS.
sec. I. The development of geography and its general contribution to life; Nineteenth century textbooks of geography, by A. P. Brigham and R. E. Dodge. How geography contributes to general ends in education, by J. R. Smith. The place of geography in higher education, by R. H. Whitbeck.
Geographic surveys of rural and urban areas, by D. H. Davis. Uses of geography as exemplified in commerce and industry, by F. E. Williams. The place of geography in the activities of the government, by Helen M. Strong.
sec. II. Developing the science of teaching geography. Investigating the value of geographic offering, by Edith Putnam Parker. Investigating the curriculum in geography, by Edith Putnam Parker. Investigating miscellaneous aspects of the teaching of geography, by Edith Putnam Parker. Major conclusions to be drawn from the investigations, by Edith Putnam Parker.
sec. III. Geography in the curriculum. Natural environment and human activity, by D. C. Ridgley. The relation of geography to other subjects, by R. M. Brown. The study of peoples in the curriculum, by R. M. Brown.
sec. IV. The curriculum in geography. Some general curricular principles and other applications, by Zoe Thralls. Geography in the elementary school, by Zoe Thralls, Isabelle K. Hart, and Erna Grassmuck. A provisional formulation of attainments in geography for the elementary school, by Marguerite Uttley. Geography in the junior high school, by Marie Graham, H. H. Russell, and Zoe Thralls. Geography in the senior high school, by Alice Foster and Katherine L. Calloway. Geography in the junior college, by N. A. Bengston.
sec. V. The technique of teaching geography. Method in geography, by E. H. Reeder. Testing in the field of geography, by M. E. Branom, W. H. Gregory, and E. Curt Walther. The supervision of geographic education, by Erna Grassmuck, Josie M. Shea, and Francis M. Garver. The training of geography teachers, by G. J. Miller. Materials for visual instruction in geography, by W. M. Gregory, A. W. Abrams, and R. Peters. Maps and map standards, by A. G. Eldridge, A. W. Abrams, W. Jansen, and Clara M. Shryock. A bibliography of geography books for teachers and pupils, by F. K. Branom. Published materials for the teachers college library, by Elizabeth T. Platt.
sec. VI. Investigations in the teaching of geography. Eighty-two studies in the teaching of geography classified by content and technique, with selected summaries, by Norah E. Zink.—Editors prefatory note.—Minor contributions: six studies of abilities, disabilities, and difficulties in geography, by Ella Wilson, Isabelle K. Hart.—Alison Aitchison, G. F. Howe, Katheryn C. Thomas, Mary T. Thorp.—Minor contributions: five studies of instruction in geography, by Lora M. Dexheimer, Jessie M. Dillon, Laura O'Day, F. A. Carlson, W. R. McConnell.—Minor contributions: five studies of the status of geography, by H. H. Russell, Clare Symonds, F. F. Cunningham, W. B. Cochran, H. K. Hutter.—Minor contributions: two miscellaneous studies of geography, by Floy Robbins, De Forest Stull.
1. Geography—₍Study and₎ teaching. I. Whipple, Guy Montrose, 1876–1941, ed. II. Parkins, Almon Ernest, 1879– III. Title.
[LB5.N25 1933] E 33—1103
U. S. Office of Education. Library for Library of Congress ₍a58h²2₎

NcRS OrPS WaPS WaTC WaSp CaBVaU OrPR WaS IdPI
NN 0066262 DHEW PSt MiU OOxM OC1W OC1 OU OCU NcD

National society for the study of education. *Committee on the teaching of language.*
... Teaching language in the elementary school. Prepared by the society's committee ... Edited by Nelson B. Henry. Chicago, Ill., The Dept. of education, The University of Chicago, 1944.
ix, 257, xxviii p. 23 cm. (National society for the study of education. 43rd Yearbook, pt. II)
1. English language—₍Study and₎ teaching₍—Elementary schools₎ I. Henry, Nelson Bollinger, jr., ed. II. Title.
[LB5.N25 vol. 43, pt. 2] E 44—72
U. S. Office of Education. Library for Library of Congress ₍a55w½₎

CaBVaU WaTC OrPS
NN 0066263 DHEW CaBVa WaPS INS PSt CoU OO MiU Or

National society for the study of education. *Committee on the teaching of science.*
... A program for teaching science, prepared by the Society's Committee on the teaching of science ... Edited by Guy Montrose Whipple ...
(*In* National society for the study of education. 31st Yearbook. Bloomington, Ill., 1932. 23 cm. pt. I, p. 1–364, incl. tables, plans)
S. Ralph Powers, chairman.
CONTENTS.—The plan of the public schools and the program of science teaching (S. R. Powers)—Some criticisms of current practices in the teaching of science in elementary and secondary schools (S. R. Powers)—What are some of the contributions of science to liberal education? (S. R. Powers)—The objectives of science teaching in relation to the aim of education (S. R. Powers)—The psychology of science teaching (S. R. Powers)—Some contributions of educational research to the solution of teaching problems in the science classroom (F. D. Curtis)—Some contributions of educational research to the solution of teaching problems in the science laboratory (F. D. Curtis)—Investigations relating to the content of science courses (F. D. Curtis)—Curricular developments in the teaching of science (F. D. Curtis)—The program of science in the elementary school (G. S. Craig)—The technique of analysis to determine content in the elementary school (Florence G. Billig)—Suggested content for the grades of the elementary school (G. S. Craig)—Science in the seventh, eighth, and ninth grades (C. J. Pieper)—The course of study in biology (E. R.

Continued in next column

Continued from preceding column

Downing)—Instruction in physical science in the secondary schools (R. K. Watkins)—Science rooms and their equipment (Morris Meister and Lillian Hethershaw)—Science teaching on the college level (V. H. No. 1)—Programs for the education of science teachers in state teachers colleges (S. R. Powers)—Report of the reviewing committee: Comments on the Yearbook from the psychological point of view, by F. N. Freeman.—Comments on the yearbook by a school administrator, by J. C. Morrison.—General comments on the yearbook by a fellow-worker in science, by E. I. Palmer.
1. Science—₍Study and₎ teaching. I. Whipple, Guy Montrose, 1876–1941, ed. II. Powers, Samuel Ralph, 1887– III. Title.
[LB5.N25 vol. 31, pt. 1] E 33—67
U. S. Office of Education. Library for Library of Congress ₍a66w½₎

OC1 OCU OO PSt GEU OrPR WaTC WaS OrU
NN 0066266 DHEW MtBC WaPS INS CaBVaU MiU OOxM OU

LB5
.N25
v.31
pt.1
1951

National Society for the Study of Education. Committee on the Teaching of Science.
A program for teaching science, prepared by the Society's Committee on the Teaching of Science. Edited by Guy Montrose Whipple. Chicago, Distributed by University of Chicago Press c1951, °1932₎
xii, 364p. 23cm. (Yearbook of the National Society for the Study of Education, 31st, pt. 1)
S. Ralph Powers, Chairman.
Bibliographical footnotes.
1. Science--Study and teaching. I. Whipple, Guy Montrose, 1876-1941, ed. II. Powers, Samuel Ralph, 1887- III. t. iv. s: National Society for the Study of Education. ₍Yearbook, v. 31, pt. 1.

NN 0066267 OrPS

National society for the study of education. *Committee on the textbook.*
... The textbook in American education, prepared by the Society's committee on the textbook ... Edited by Guy Montrose Whipple ...
(*In* National society for the study of education. 30th Yearbook. Bloomington, Ill., 1931. 23 cm. pt. II, p. 1–323. tables)
J. B. Edmonson, chairman.
CONTENTS.—Introduction.—The textbook and methods of teaching, by W. C. Bagley.—The techniques of textbook authors, by R. Schorling and J. B. Edmonson.—The professional status of textbook authors, by H. G. Richey.—The selection of manuscripts by publishers, by F. A. Jensen.—New data on the typography of textbooks, by B. R. Buckingham.—Current practices in selecting textbooks for the elementary schools, by F. A. Jensen.—The use of score cards in evaluating textbooks, by C. R. Maxwell.—The policies of publishers in marketing textbooks, by F. A. Jensen.—The problems of publishers in making and marketing textbooks, by N. B. Henry.—The ethics of marketing and selecting textbooks, by J. B. Edmonson.—The cost of textbooks, by N. B. Henry.—The state publication of textbooks, by E. P. Cubberley.—Legislative agencies for textbook selection, by W. L. Coffey.—Judicial opinion on textbook selection, by W. L. Coffey.—Standards for evaluating proposed textbook legislation, by W. L. Coffey.—Conclusion and recommendations of the Committee.—A selected and annotated bibliography of literature relating to textbooks, by G. T. Buswell.
1. Text-books. 2. Authorship. 3. Publishers and publishing. I. Whipple, Guy Montrose, 1876–1941, ed. II. Edmonson, James Bartlett, 1882–
[LB5.N25 vol. 30, pt. 2] E 31—416
U. S. Office of Educatio: Library for Library of Congress ₍a61t1₎

OrU IdPI MtBC CaBVaU
NN 0066270 DHEW INS NcD PPPL PSt Or WaS WaTC WaPS

National society for the study of education. *Committee on vocational education.*
... Vocational education. Prepared by the Society's committee ... Edited by Nelson B. Henry ... Chicago, Ill., The Dept. of education, The University of Chicago, 1943.
xvi, 486 p. 23 cm. (National society for the study of education. 42nd Yearbook, pt. I)
1. Vocational education—U. S. I. Henry, Nelson Bollinger, jr., ed.
[LB5.N25 vol. 42, pt. 1] E 43—37
U. S. Office of Education. Library for Library of Congress ₍a55q1₎

NN 0066271 DHEW INS IU PSt CoU OrPS CaBVa

National society for the study of educational sociology.
Bibliographies on educational sociology, compiled by A. O. Bowden ... Carroll D. Champion ... F. R. Clow ... chairman ₍and others₎ ... New York city, New York university, 1928.
154 p. 24ᶜᵐ. (*Its* Yearbook, 1st, 1928)
Arranged chronologically under subjects with author index.
1. Educational sociology—Bibl. 2. Social sciences—Study and teaching—Bibl. 3. Education—Curricula. I. Clow, Frederick Redman, 1863–
Library of Congress Z5811.N27 28—8061

NN 0066272 DLC FMU OrMonO Or OrU ICJ NN WaEIN

National Society for the Study of Educational Sociology.
... Yearbook of the National Society for the Study of Educational Sociology ... New York City, 1928–1929.
Library has no. 1–2. 24ᶜᵐ.
Each volume has also individual title: no. 1. Bibliographies on educational sociology; no. 2. Objectives of education.

NN 0066273 ICJ ODW OCU OC1 MH DLC NcD PBL TxU

National Society for Vocational Education.
... Addresses delivered at the ... annual convention
see its Proceedings of ... annual meeting.

National Society for Vocational Education.
... The administration of state aid for vocational education ...
see under Bawden, William Thomas.

T61
.N28

National Society for Vocational Education.
Advance program of the ... annual convention ... Cincinnati, 1911-

NN 0066276 DLC

National society for vocational education.
Agricultural education, organization and administration, supervision, cooperation and relationships, instruction ... Addresses delivered at the fifteenth annual convention Detroit, Michigan, Nov. 29, 30, Dec. 1, 2, 1922. Issued Nov. 1, 1923, National society for vocational education ... New York city, New York. ₍Indianapolis, Ind., Printing contributed by the United typothetae of America school of printing, 1923₎
ix, 11–116 p. 23ᶜᵐ. (Bulletin no. 35)
1. Agricultural education. 2. Agriculture—₍Study and₎ teaching.
Library, U. S. Bur. of Education T61.N2 E 25–102

NN 0066277 DHEW MiU OC1 OU MB

National society for vocational education.
Agricultural education, supervision, two current problems, relations to agricultural extension ... Addresses delivered at the twelfth annual convention, St. Louis, Mo., February 20–22, 1919. Issued June, 1919, National society for vocational education ... ₍New York, Press of Clarence S. Nathan, inc.₎ 1919.
29 p. 23ᶜᵐ. (Bulletin, no. 31)
1. Agricultural education—U. S.
E 19—661
U. S. Off. of educ. Library for Library of Congress T61.N2 ₍a40f1₎

NN 0066278 DHEW MtBC OrU MiU OC1 OU MdBJ ViU

National Society for Vocational Education.
₍Amended constitution proposed for adoption at annual convention, St. Louis, Mo., February 20th, 1919. New York, 1919.₎
7(1) p. 8°.
1. Educational (Industrial and technical), U. S.
N. Y. P. L. August 27, 1920.

NN 0066279 NN

LC1045
.A25
no. 92

National society for vocational education.

U. S. *Federal board for vocational education.*
... Apprentice education in the construction industry. Discussions and papers presented at the seventeenth annual convention of the National society for vocational education, at Buffalo, N. Y., December 6, 1923. Issued by the Federal board for vocational education, Washington, D. C. Washington, Govt. print. off., 1924.

VOLUME 407

National society for vocational education.
... Apprenticeship and corporation schools. New York city, National society for the promotion of industrial education, 1911.

ix, 53–91 p. 23ᶜᵐ. (Bulletin no. 13. Proceedings, Fourth annual convention, Boston, Massachusetts, pt. II)

1. Technical education—U. S. 2. Apprentices—U. S.

E 11–378 Revised

Library, U. S. Bur. of   Education   T61.N2

NN   0066281   DHEW WaS MiU OO OU OCl ICJ

National society for vocational education.
                                    FOR OTHER EDITIONS
                                    SEE MAIN ENTRY
Richards, Charles Russell, 1865–1936.
Art in industry, by Charles R. Richards; being the report of an industrial art survey conducted under the auspices of the National society for vocational education and the Department of education of the state of New York. New York, The Macmillan company, 1922.

National society for vocational education.
... Bulletin. no. 1–
(New York, etc., 1907)–

v. 23ᶜᵐ.

At head of title: 1907–17, National society for the promotion of industrial education.—1918– National society for vocational education.

1. Technical education—Societies.

Library of Congress   T61.N27   8—11988

NN   0066283   TxLT OU OC1 OC1W OO OOxM ICJ MB MiU KEmT DHEW MB
                 DLC ScClea Vi WaSp OrPR NjP KMK MiU

National society for vocational education.
... Circular of information : constitution, state branches, officers and members. New York city, National society for the promotion of industrial education, 1908.

44 p. 23ᶜᵐ. (*Its* Bulletin no. 7)

1. National society for vocational education. 2. Technical education—U. S. 3. Manual training—U. S. (2, 3. Industrial education—U. S)

E 9–109 Revised

Library, U. S. Bur. of   Education   T61.N2

NN   0066284   DHEW OrU ICJ

National society for vocational education.
Commercial and home economics education. Part I. Commercial education. Part II. Home economics education ... Addresses delivered at the fifteenth annual convention Detroit, Michigan, Nov. 29, 30, Dec. 1, 2, 1922. Issued November 1, 1923, National society for vocational education ... New York city, New York. (Indianapolis, Ind., Printing contributed by the United typothetae of America school of printing, 1923)

viii p., 1 l., 11–103 p. 23ᶜᵐ. (Bulletin no. 36)

1. Business education. 2. Domestic economy—(Study and) teaching.

Library, U. S. Bur. of   Education   T61.N2   E 25–103

NN   0066285   DHEW MB OrU

National society for vocational education.
Commercial education, federal aid, recent developments, retail selling education ... Addresses delivered at the twelfth annual convention, St. Louis, Mo., February 20–22, 1919. Issued April, 1919, National society for vocational education ... (New York, Press of Clarence S. Nathan, inc.) 1919.

79 p. tables. 23ᶜᵐ. (Bulletin, no. 29)

1. Business education.   I. Title.

E 19—652

U. S. Off. of educ. Library   T61.N2
for Library of Congress   (a40f1)

NN   0066286   DHEW NN MB ViU

National society for vocational education.
... Evening vocational courses for girls and women. New York city, National society for the promotion of industrial education, 1917.

73 p. 23ᶜᵐ. (Bulletin no. 23)

1. Evening (and continuation) schools.   I. Title.

Library, U. S. Bur. of   Education   T61.N2   E 18–293

NN   0066287   DHEW ICJ MdBJ OrU

National Society for Vocational Education.
... The Factory school of Rochester
    see under   Forbes, George Mather, 1853–

National society for vocational education.
Federal and state-aided vocational education; the states and the vocational education act; state boards for administering the vocational education act; extent of state-aided vocational education; schools training vocational teachers; new opportunities in industrial education; new books. New York (1917)

59 p. 23ᶜᵐ.

1. Vocational education—U. S.   I. Title.

E 17–512
(33b1)
Library, U. S. Bur. of   Education   LC1045.N2

NN   0066289   DHEW MiU NN MB IU ICJ

National society for vocational education.
... Industrial education ... Communication from C. R. Richards, president of the National society for the promotion of industrial education, transmitting reports by a committee of the society on the subject, together with resolutions urging upon Congress an appropriation to enable the Department of education to develop schools for industrial training ... (Washington, Govt. print. off., 1910)

8 p. 23½ᶜᵐ. ((U. S.) 61st Cong., 2d sess. Senate. Doc. 516)

Laid before the Senate by the vice-president, referred to Committee on education and labor and ordered printed, April 30, 1910.
Includes Preliminary report of the Committee of ten, H. S. Pritchett chairman, submitted at the second annual meeting of the society, November 19–21, 1908, and Final report, submitted at third annual meeting, December 2–4, 1909.

1. Technical education—U. S.   I. Richards, Charles Russell, 1865–
II. Pritchett, Henry Smith, 1857–

10–35697 Revised

Library of Congress   T73.N4

NN   0066291   DLC OrU MiU OO DHEW

National society for vocational education.
Industrial education.   Part I. Industrial education. Part II. Training in industry ... Addresses delivered at the fifteenth annual convention Detroit, Michigan, Nov. 29, 30, Dec. 1, 2, 1922. Issued November 1, 1923, National society for vocational education ... New York city, N. Y. (Minneapolis, Minn., Printing contributed by the William Hood Dunwoody industrial institute, 1923)

vii, 123 p. incl. facsim., tables, diagr. 23ᶜᵐ. (Bulletin no. 33)

1. Industrial education.

Library, U. S. Bur. of   Education   T61.N2   E 25–104

NN   0066292   DHEW OCl OU MB

National society for vocational education.
Industrial education, trade tests, unit trade schools, general industrial schools, shopwork on productive basis, teacher training, state supervision, training and upgrading of women workers ... Addresses delivered at the twelfth annual convention, St. Louis, February 20–22, 1919. Issued June, 1919, National society for vocational education ... (New York, Press of Clarence S. Nathan, inc.) 1919.

72 p. 23ᶜᵐ. (Bulletin 30)
1. Manual training. 2. Technical education. (2. Industrial education—

E 19–662

Library, U. S. Bur. of   Education   T61.N2

NN   0066293   DHEW MiU ODW OU OCl ICJ ViU MB

National society for vocational education.
Lessons of the war, the state and the Smith-Hughes act ... Addresses delivered at the twelfth annual convention, St. Louis, February 20–22, 1919. Issued June, 1919, National society for vocational education ... (New York, Press of Clarence S. Nathan, inc.) 1919.

96 p. 23ᶜᵐ. (Bulletin, no. 28)

1. European war, 1914– ; Influence and results— U. S.

Library, U. S. Bur. of   Education   T61.N2   E 19–653

NN   0066294   DHEW OrU MiU OCl OU ViU

National Society for Vocational Education.
[Minor publications.] New York City, National Society for the Promotion of Industrial Education.
Continued.

NN   0066295   ICJ

National society for vocational education.
The National society for the promotion of industrial education. What it has done. What it is doing ... (New York? 191–?)

(8) p. 22¼ᶜᵐ.

1. National society for the promotion of industrial education.

E 16–1139 Revised

Library, U. S. Bur. of   Education   T61.N223

NN   0066296   DHEW Or

National society for vocational education.
... Newsletter, no. 1–11; Mar. 1918–June 1922. (New York, 1918–22)

11 no. in 1 v. 23ᶜᵐ.

Caption title.
At head of title: National society for vocational education.
Record has been found of an additional number (9a), Feb. 1921; this number is wanting in Library of Congress set.
Continued in Vocational education magazine.

I. Title.

Library of Congress   T61.N285   26–19501

NN   0066297   DLC Or OrU ICJ CU ICU MB DL DHEW

National Society for Vocational Education.
... Part time and evening schools. New York city, National Society for the promotion of industrial education, 1911.

ix p., p. 93–144. 23ᶜᵐ. (*Its* Bulletin no. 13, Proceedings, Fourth annual convention, Boston, Massachusetts, pt. III)

1. Cooperative system of industrial education. 2. Evening schools.

E 11–703

Library, U. S. Bur. of   Education   T61.N2

NN   0066298   DHEW ICJ

National society for vocational education.
Part-time continuation education, aim and purpose, progress, teacher training ... Addresses delivered at the fifteenth annual convention Detroit, Michigan, Nov. 29, 30, Dec. 1, 2, 1922. Issued November 1, 1923, National society for vocational education ... New York city, N. Y. (Minneapolis, Minn., Printing contributed by the William Hood Dunwoody industrial institute, 1923)

vi, 35 p. 23ᶜᵐ. (Bulletin no. 34)

1. Continuation schools.

Library, U. S. Bur. of   Education   T61.N2   E 25–105

NN   0066299   DHEW WaS OCl OU

VOLUME 407

National society for vocational education.
Principles and policies that should underlie state legislation for a state system of vocational education. A tentative statement of principles and policies formulated at a meeting of a committee of the National society for the promotion of industrial education, in annual convention, at Philadelphia, December, 1912, and approved by the Board of managers of the society, February 1913 ... ₁Philadelphia? 1913₎
6 p. 23ᶜᵐ.
Caption title.
1. Vocational training. 2. School management and organization—U. S. ₍2. School supervision—State₎

E 13-556 Revised

Library, U. S. Bur. of   Education LC1043.N22

NN 0066300   DHEW OrCS

National society for vocational education.
Problems of administering the federal act for vocational education ... Addresses delivered at the eleventh annual convention, Philadelphia, Pa., February 21–23, 1918. New York city, National society for vocational education, 1918.
83 p. 23ᶜᵐ. (Bulletin no. 26)

1. Vocational education—U. S. 2. Teachers, Training of. ₍2. Teachers—Training—Vocational education₎ I. Title: Federal act for vocational education.
E 18-985
Library, U. S. Office of   Education T61.N2 no. 26
Library of Congress   [T61.N27 no. 26]

NN 0066301   DHEW OrU MiU OU OCl ViU

National society for vocational education.
... Proceedings of ... annual meeting ... 1st–1908–
New York city, National society for the promotion of industrial education, 1908–19
v. 23ᶜᵐ. (*Its* Bulletin no. 5–6, 9–10, 13, 15–16, 18, 20, 24, 26–27.

1. Vocational education—₁U. S.₎—Societies. 2. Technical education—Societies.
——— 2d set.   E 8-610 (rev. '29)
                                     T61.N22
Library, U. S. Bur. of   Education T61.N2
Library of Congress   T61.N27

NN 0066302   DHEW ICJ TxLT OrU DLC NN N MB ICJ

National society for vocational education.
Employment managers' conference. *Minneapolis*, 1916.
... Proceedings of Employment managers' conference, held under the auspices of the National society for the promotion of industrial education and the Minneapolis civic and commerce association, January 19 and 20, 1916. May, 1916. Washington Govt. print. off., 1916.

National society for vocational education.
... Proceedings of the organization meetings. ₁New York, C. S. Nathan, 1907₎
44 p. 23ᶜᵐ. (*Its* Bulletin no. 1)
CONTENTS.—Officers.—Editorial note.—Constitution.—Minutes of organization meeting.—Address by M. P. Higgins.—Address by N. M. Butler.—Address by F. A. Vanderlip.—Address by F. P. Fish.—Address by A. Mosely.—Address by S. B. Donnelly.—Address by Jane Addams.

——— Copy 2.   E 8-466 Revised
Library, U. S. Bur. of   Education T61.N2

NN 0066304   DHEW OrU ICJ

T61   National Society for Vocational Education.
.N29   Prospectus ... [New York?] 1910.

NN 0066305   DLC

National society for vocational education.
... Report of the Committee of ten on the relation of industrial training to the general system of education in the United States. New York city, National society for the promotion of industrial education ₁1910₎
16 p. 23ᶜᵐ.
Includes Preliminary report of the committee of ten, H. S. Pritchett chairman, submitted at the second annual meeting of the society, November 19–21, 1908, and Final report, submitted at the third annual meeting, December 2–4, 1909.
1. Technical education—U. S. I. Pritchett, Henry Smith, 1857–
E 10-1387
U. S. Off. of educ. Library   T73.N3
——— Copy 2.
for Library of Congress   ₁a41d1₎

NN 0066306   DHEW MB ICJ

National Society for Vocational Education.
Report of the committee on future policy, name and organization of the National Society for the Promotion of Industrial Education. New York ₁1918₎. 15 p. 8°.
Cover-title.

1. Education (Industrial and techni-   cal).—Assoc. and organizations, U. S.
N. Y. P. L.   April 9, 1918.

NN 0066307   NN DHEW

National society for vocational education.
... Report of the committee on the selection and training of teachers for state aided industrial schools for boys and men. N₁ew₎ Y₁ork₎ city, National society for the promotion of industrial education ₁1913₎
cover-title, 86 p. 1 illus. 23ᶜᵐ.
At head of title: Tentative draft.

1. Teachers, Training of—U. S. 2. Technical education—U. S.
                                          13-23899 Revised
Library of Congress   LB1736.N3

NN 0066308   DLC Or DHEW

National society for vocational education.
... Report of the Minneapolis survey for vocational education. January 1, 1916. ₁New York? 1916₎
697 p. fold. plates. 22½ᶜᵐ. (Bulletin no. 21)

1. Education—Minneapolis. 2. Educational surveys. 3. Vocational education—Minneapolis. I. Title: Minneapolis survey for vocational education.

E 16-1096 Revised
Library, U. S. Bur. of   Education T61.N2

         DNW DL MdBJ ICJ
NN 0066309   DHEW MtU WaS KEmT MB OCl OU MiU OO

National society for vocational education.
... The selection and training of teachers for state-aided industrial schools for boys and men. (Special report) New York city, National society for the promotion of industrial education, 1914.
112 p. 23ᶜᵐ. (Bulletin no. 19)

1. Technical education—U. S. 2. Teachers, Training ₁of₎—Massachusetts. 3. ₁Teachers—Training—Industrial schools₎ I. Title: State-aided industrial schools.
                                          E 14-650
U. S. Off. of educ. Library   LB1736.N2
for Library of Congress   ₁a40d1₎

NN 0066310   DHEW OrU MiU OO OCl OU NcD ICJ

National society for vocational education.
... The selection and training of teachers for state-aided industrial schools. (Rev. ed.) Issued February, 1917. New York city, National society for the promotion of industrial education ₁1917₎
64 p. diagr. 23ᶜᵐ. (Bulletin 19. ₁Rev. ed.₎)

1. Technical education—U. S. 2. Teachers, Training ₁of₎—Massachusetts. 3. ₁Teachers—Training—Industrial schools₎ I. Title: State-aided industrial schools.
                                          E 18-622 Revised
——— Copy 2.   LB1736.N2 1917
Library, U. S. Bur. of   Education T61.N2

NN 0066311   DHEW PPT ViU

National society for vocational education.
... The social significance of industrial education. New York city, National society for the promotion of industrial education, 1911.
ix, 145–213 p. 23ᶜᵐ. (*Its* Bulletin no. 13. Proceedings, Fourth annual convention, Boston, Massachusetts, pt. IV)

1. Technical education.
                                          E 11-704 Revised
Library, U. S. Bur. of   Education T61.N2

NN 0066312   DHEW WaS MiU OCl OU ICJ

National society for vocational education.
Synopsis of recommendations for vocational education for Richmond made by the General survey committee for consideration at the eighth annual convention of the National society for the promotion of industrial education held at Richmond, Virginia, December 9–12, 1914. New York city, N. Y., National society for the promotion of industrial education ₁1914₎
29 p. 22½ᶜᵐ.
1. Professional education—₁Virginia₎—Richmond. 2. Technical education—₁Virginia₎—Richmond. 3. Vocational education—₁Virginia₎—Richmond. 4. Education—₁Virginia₎—Richmond. 5. Educational surveys—₁Richmond₎ I. Richmond. Local survey committee.
E 15-841 Revised
Library, U. S. Bur. of   Education LC1046.V8R51

NN 0066313   DHEW WaS MB NN

National society for vocational education.
... Synopsis of the findings of the vocational education survey of the city of Richmond by the General survey committee. New York city, National society for the promotion of industrial education ₁1914₎
62 p. 23ᶜᵐ.
At head of title: National society for the promotion of industrial education.
1. Professional education—₁Virginia₎—Richmond. 2. Technical education—₁Virginia₎—Richmond. 3. Vocational education—₁Virginia₎—Richmond. 4. Education—₁Virginia₎—Richmond. 5. Educational surveys—₁Richmond₎ I. Richmond. Local survey committee.
E 14-2226 Revised
Library, U. S. Bur. of   Education LC1046.V8R5

NN 0066314   DHEW Or MiU MB IU NN

National Society for Vocational Education.
Three lectures on vocational training
    see under Kerschensteiner, Georg
Michael Anton, 1854–

National society for vocational education.
... Trade education for girls. New York city, National society for the promotion of industrial education, 1911.
ix, 51 p. 23ᶜᵐ. (Bulletin no. 13)
Proceedings, Fourth annual convention, Boston, Massachusetts, pt. I.

1. Vocational education. 2. Woman—Employment. ₁1, 2, Girls—Industrial education₎
                                          E 11-879
U. S. Off. of educ. Library   T61.N2
for Library of Congress   ₁a40f1₎

NN 0066316   DHEW WaS MiU OCl OO OU ICJ

National society for vocational education.
Vocational education magazine. v. 1–2, v. 3, no. 1; Sept. 1922–Jan. 1925. Philadelphia, Pub. by J. B. Lippincott company for the National society for vocational education, 1922–25.

National society for vocational education.
Vocational education, one of the significant problems of the day. Pub. for thirteenth biennial convention, General federation of women's clubs, New York city, May, 1916, by the National society for the promotion of industrial education ... New York city. ₁New York, Press of C. S. Nathan, inc., 1916₎
11, ₁1₎ p. illus. 23ᶜᵐ.
Illustrated t.-p.
1. Manual training—U. S. 2. Technical education—U. S. ₁1, 2. Industrial education₎ I. Title.

E 16-920 Revised
Library, U. S. Bur. of   Education LC1081.N2

NN 0066318   DHEW OrU MiU

VOLUME 407

National society for vocational education.

HD8051
.A62
no. 199

U. S. *Bureau of labor statistics.*

... Vocational education series, no. 1. Vocational education survey of Minneapolis, Minn., made by the National society for the promotion of industrial education. **December, 1916.** Washington, Govt. print. off., 1917.

National society for vocational education.

... Vocational education survey of Minneapolis, Minn., made by the National society for the promotion of industrial education. December, 1916. Washington, Govt. print. off., 1917.

502 p. fold. tab. 23½ᵐ. (Bulletin of the United States Bureau of labor statistics, whole no. 199. Vocational education series, no. 1)

At head of title: U. S. Department of labor. Bureau of labor statistics. Royal Meeker, commissioner ...

Issued also as House doc. 1158, U. S. 64th Cong., 1st sess.

Revised edition of Bulletin no. 21 of the National society for the promotion of industrial education. Issued January 1, 1916.

1. Vocational education—Minnesota—Minneapolis. ₍1. Industrial education—Minneapolis₎ 2. Education—Minnesota—Minneapolis. 3. Educational surveys. 4. Profession, Choice of. ₍4. Vocational guidance₎ I. ₍U. S.₎ Bureau of labor statistics. II. Title.

L 17–12

U. S. Dept. of labor. Library   H9051.A5 no. 199
  for Library of Congress   H9051.A62 no. 199
  —— Copy 2.   T73.M6N3
                ₍a57m1₎   (331.06173)

NN 0066320   DL NIC OU OCU MB NN DHEW ICJ

National society for vocational education.

... Vocational education survey of Richmond, Va. **August,** 1915. Washington, Govt. print. off., 1916.

333 p. fold. tables. 23ᵐ. (Bulletin of the United States Bureau of labor statistics, whole no. 162. Miscellaneous series, no. 7)

At head of title: U. S. Department of labor. Bureau of labor statistics. Royal Meeker, commissioner ...

"The Executive committee of the National society for the promotion of industrial education arranged with the Richmond Board of education to make ₍this survey₎"

Issued also as House doc. 1445, U. S. 63d Cong., 3d sess.

1. Technical education—Virginia—Richmond. ₍1. Industrial education—Richmond, Va.₎ 2. Educational surveys. 3. ₍Industrial surveys—Richmond, Va.₎ 4. Profession, Choice of. ₍4. Vocation, Choice of₎ 5. Richmond—Industries. 6. Occupations—Description₎ I. Richmond. School board. II. Title.

L 16–8

U. S. Dept. of labor. Libr.   HD9051.A5 no. 162
  for Library of Congress   H9051.A62 no. 162
                ₍a39q2₎   (331.06173)

NN 0066321   DL MiU OCU NN DHEW ICJ DLC

National society for vocational education.
... Vocational training for women in industry
see under   Murtland, Cleo.

National society for vocational education.

Vocational training in war time ... Addresses delivered at the eleventh annual convention, Philadelphia, Pa., **February** 21–23, 1918. New York city, National society for vocational education, 1918.

93 p. 23ᵐ. (Bulletin no. 27)

1. Vocational education—U. S. 2. European war, 1914–1918—U. S.—Influence and results. I. Title.

E 18–986

Library, U. S. Office of   Education T61.N2 no. 27
  Library of Congress   [T61.N27 no. 27]

NN 0066323   DHEW IdU OrU MiU OC1 OU ViU ICJ MB

National society for vocational education.

... War demands for industrial training; the situation, responsibility of the industries for training needed workers, what some industrial plants are doing in emergency training, the contribution industrial schools can make for emergency training, industrial schools and the branches of military service, what some industrial and technical schools are doing for emergency training, items of interest. New York city, 1917.

40 p. 23ᵐ. Prepared by E. E. MacNary

1. Technical education—U. S. I. Title.

17–29560 Revised

Library of Congress   T73.N45

NN 0066324   DLC DHEW MiU IaU NN MB

T73 National society for vocational education.
.N34 ...War news.
  [New York,

NN 0066325   DLC

National society for vocational education.

... What is the Smith-Hughes bill, providing federal grants to vocational education? and What must a state do to take advantage of the federal vocational education law? New York city, National society for the promotion of industrial education, 1917.

48 p. tables. 23ᵐ. (Bulletin no. 25)

1. Vocational education—U. S.   I. Title: Smith-Hughes bill.

E 18–294

U. S. Off. of educ. Library   T61.N2
  for Library of Congress   [T61.N27 no. 25]

OO OU ViU ICJ

NN 0066326   DHEW OrU WaU-L ICJ MdBJ KEmT MiU OC1

National Society for Vocational Education
see also American Vocational Association.

National society for vocational education. *Executive committee.*

Report presented to the Executive committee of the National society for the promotion of industrial education by the special committee appointed to consider Senate bill number three. ₍n. p., 1912₎

11 p. 23ᵐ.

Caption title.

David Snedden, chairman.

1. Agriculture—₍Study and₎ teaching—U. S. 2. Technical education—U. S. 3. Domestic economy—₍Study and₎ teaching—U. S. 4. ₍Page vocational bill₎   I. Snedden, David Samuel, 1868–

E 13—199

U. S. Off. of educ. Library   T73.N37
  for Library of Congress   ₍a41d1₎

NN 0066328   DHEW

National society for vocational education. *New York state branch.*

... Constitution and list of officers and members of advisory board and address by Dr. William H. Maxwell, at the organization meeting, New York city, November 13, 1908. ₍New York, 1909?₎

16 p. 22½ᵐ.

1. Technical education—U. S.   I. Maxwell, William Henry, 1852–

E 11–380 Revised

Library, U. S. Bur. of   Education T61.N3

NN 0066329   DHEW NN

NATIONAL SOCIETY FOR WOMEN'S SUFFRAGE
  Declaration in favour of women's suffrage, being the signatures received at the office of the central committee.
=   [Westminster, 1889.] 20, (2) pp. 8°.

NN 0066330   MB

NATIONAL SOCIETY for women's suffrage.
  Memorial to the Hon. the Marquis of Salisbury, K.G., and the Hon. W H. Smith, M.P., First lord of the Treasury.
=   Westminster, 1891. 12 pp. 8°.
  Issued by the society's Central Committee.

NN 0066331   MB

National Society for Women's Suffrage.
  Occasional paper . . . March 17, 1896.
=   London. [1896.] 7, (1) pp. 8°.
  Contents. — Women's franchise bill. — Parliamentary notes. — Committee notes.
  The title is on the cover.

F9518 — Woman suffrage.

NN 0066332   MB

JN
981
.N28

National society for women's suffrage.
  Opinions of women on women's suffrage.
London, 1879.
61 p. 21½cm.

1.Woman—Suffrage. I.Title.

NN 0066333   MiU

HOOSE
192
M64
Xbr

National Society for Women's Suffrage.
  Report of a meeting held at the gallery of the Architectural Society in Conduit Street, Saturday, July 17th, 1869. ₍London, 1869₎
34p. 22cm.

Includes speech by John Stuart Mill.
Bound with British Quarterly Review.
John Stuart Mill.

✓1.Woman –   Suffrage - Gt.Brit. I.Mill,
John Stuart,   1806–1873.

NN 0066334   CLSU MB

HOOSE
192
M64
Xbr

National Society for Women's Suffrage.
  Report of a meeting held at the Hanover Square Rooms, on Saturday, March 26th, 1870. ₍London, 1870₎
34p. 22cm.

Includes speech by John Stuart Mill.
Bound with British Quarterly Review.
John Stuart Mill.

✓1.Woman – Suffrage - Gt.Brit. I.Mill, John Stuart,   1806–1873.

NN 0066335   CLSU

NATIONAL SOCIETY for women's suffrage.
  Speeches made at the general annual meeting, Westminster, July 2 1895.
=   [Westminster.] 1896. 15 pp. 8°.
  Issued by the society's Central Committee.

NN 0066336   MB

National Society for Women's Suffrage. Bristol and Clifton Branch.
  Report of the committee to the council, Nov. 14, 1868. [Bristol, Arrowsmith, 1868]
7 p. 8°.

NN 0066337   MB CtY CSmH

National Society for Women's Suffrage. Edinburgh.Branch.
  ... Annual meeting of the Edinburgh National Society for Women's Suffrage. .... Edinburgh, 1875–1901.
No. 7, 10, 13, 15, 17, 19–26, 28–30, 1875, 1878, 1881–1882, 1884, 1886–1894, 1898–1901. 22½ᵐ.
At head of title: Women's suffrage.

NN 0066338   ICJ CtY

National Society for Women's Suffrage, Edinburgh branch.
  Speech of the late John Stuart Mill at the great meeting in favour of women's suffrage ...
  see under   Mill, John Stuart, 1806–1873.

National Society for Women's Suffrage, Edinburgh branch.
  Women's Suffrage. Public meeting in Edinburgh in Queen St. Hall ... Edinb., 1870.
31 p. 8°. [In v. 463, College Pamphlets]

NN 0066340   CtY

VOLUME 407

National Society Magna Charta Dames.
₍Addresses delivered at meetings of the society₎

₍Philadelphia?₎

v. illus., ports. 24–27 cm.

1. Magna Carta. 2. U. S.—Pol. & govt.—Addresses, essays, lectures.

CS42.N47   369.11   36–1634 rev

NN   0066341   DLC Wa MB MiD-B PHi OrP Or NN MtHi

F   NATIONAL SOCIETY MAGNA CHARTA DAMES.
83193   ₍Annual celebration, June 15, 1943₎ **Magna**
.61   charta – at home and abroad, by Capt. H.Cotton
      Minchin.   ₍Philadelphia,1943₎
1943   cover-title,24p. 24½cm.

NN   0066342   ICN

CS55   National Society Magna Charta Dames.
.N35   The barons for the Magna Charta and lines of
      descent from some of their descendants,
      members of the National Society Magna Charta
      Dames ... [Phila., 1927]

NN   0066343   DLC CU NcU

National Society Magna Charta Dames.
      The barons for the Magna Charta and lines of descent from
them of some of their descendants, members of the National Society
Magna Charta Dames; edited for the society by John S. Wurts...
Germantown, Pa.₍, 1929?₎ 20–31 p. 4°.

"Preliminary pages, issued by the society, suggesting arrangement of the
pedigrees."

445974A. 1. United States—Geneal.   2. Wurts, John Sparhawk,
1876–   , editor.
N. Y. P. L.   February 13, 1930

NN   0066344   NN PHi

National Society Magna Charta Dames.
      A message to its members of all Fellow
Descendants of Magna Charta ... n.p., 1932.
      32 p.

NN   0066345   PHi

National society Magna charta dames.
      The National society Magna charta dames ... October, 1935.
₍Philadelphia?₎ 1935₎

30, ₍2₎ p. incl. front., illus. (ports.) geneal. tab. 26½ᶜᵐ.

List of officers, and proceedings of the society at the Huntingdon
valley country club meeting, June 18, 1935, in celebration of the 720th
anniversary of the granting of Magna charta, including "The Constitution and Magna charta, an address by Gilbert H. Montague" (p. 13–29)

1. Magna charta. 2. U. S.—Constitutional history. I. Montague,
Gilbert Holland, 1880–

                                    36–1634
Library of Congress   CS42.N473A5 1935 a
                         ₍3₎   369.1

NN   0066346   DLC NN Or

National society Magna charta dames.
      The National society Magna charta dames, instituted **March**
1, 1909. June 1, 1935. ₍Philadelphia? 1935₎

78, ₍2₎ p. incl. front., plates, ports. 24½ᶜᵐ.

                              CA 36–324 Unrev'd
Library of Congress   CS42.N473A5 1935
                         ₍2₎   369.11

NN   0066347   DLC WaS ViU NN

National society Magna charta dames.
      The National society Magna charta dames. Addresses **by**
Daniel R. Randall. Daniel O. Hastings ₍and₎ George H. Houston ... ₍Philadelphia? 1936₎

cover-title, 69, ₍1₎ p. incl. illus., ports. 23ᶜᵐ.

List of officers and proceedings of the society at the meetings at
Baltimore, November 11–12, 1935; Washington, March 3, 1936; and the
Huntingdon valley country club, June 16, 1936; with the respective
addresses: Lest we forget ... by Hon. Daniel R. Randall; Our democratic
form of government shall endure ... by Hon. Daniel O. Hastings; The
American system ... by Mr. George Harrison Houston.

1. U. S.—Pol. & govt.   I. Randall, Daniel Richard, 1864–1936. II.
Hastings, Daniel Oren, 1874–   III. Houston, George Harrison, 1883–
                                    37–20764
Library of Congress   CS42.N473A5 1935 b
                         ₍3₎   369.1

NN   0066348   DLC Or NN

National society Magna charta dames.
      The National society Magna charta dames, instituted March
1, 1909 ... ₍Philadelphia₎ 1939.

cover-title, 79 p. illus. (incl. ports.) 25ᶜᵐ.

List of officers and proceedings of the society at the meetings at New
York, November 10, 1936; Philadelphia, June 15, 1937; Louisville, Kentucky, November 9, 1937; Philadelphia, June 20–21, 1938; Hartford, Connecticut, November 1, 1938; with the respective addresses: The influence
of Magna charta in our times ... by Clarence Blair Mitchell; Magna
charta in the home ... by Frances Lester Warner; The cornerstone of the
Constitution ... by James A. Emery; The tripod of freedom ... by Henning Webb Prentis; The Magna charta and liberty ... by Walter Phelps
Hall.

1. U. S.—Pol. & govt.   I. Mitchell, Clarence Blair, 1865–   II. War-
ner, Mrs. Frances Lester, 1888–   III. Emery, James Augustin, 1876–
IV. Prentis, Henning Webb,   1884–   v. Hall, Walter Phelps,
1884–
                                    39–14750
Library of Congress   CS42.N473A5 1936–38
———— Copy 2.   ₍2₎   369.11

NN   0066349   DLC

National society Magna charta dames.
      The National society Magna charta dames.   ₍Philadelphia₎
1943.   24 p. illus. 24cm.

"Magna charta at home and abroad...by Captain Humphrey Cotton Minchin,"
p. 13–18.

1. Societies, National and patriotic   —U. S. I. Minchin, Humphrey
Cotton.
N. Y. P. L.   August 12, 1947

NN   0066350   NN

National society Magna charta dames.
      The National society Magna charta dames, 1948...   ₍Phila-
delphia?₎ 1948₎   48 p. illus. 27cm.

1. Societies, National and patriotic   —U. S.
N. Y. P. L.   December 12, 1949

NN   0066351   NN

CS
42   National Society Magna Charta Dames.
N473   The National Society Magna Charta Dames,
A5   1952 and 1953. ₍Philadelphia, 1954₎
1952   29, ₍8₎ p. illus., ports., geneal. table. 26 cm.

List of officers, and proceedings at meetings held
in Washington, D. C., April 17, 1952, and April 23,
1953, with addresses: World government in the light
of Magna Charta, by G. L. H. Brosseau; Constitutional
government and treaty-making powers, by J. M. Butler.
Queen Elizabeth's American cousins, by J. S. Wurts:
p. 27–₍81₎

1. Magna Carta. 2. U. S. – Pol & govt. 3. Elis-
abeth II, Queen of Great Britain, 1926–   4. Royal
descent, Families of ? Brosseau, Grace Lincoln (Hall)
1872–   II. Butler,   John Marshall, 1897–
III. Wurts, John   3   1876–

NN   0066352   Vi

National Society Magna Charta Dames.
      The National Society Magna Charta Dames to its members
and all fellow descendants of the barons for the Magna Charta...
₍Philadelphia? 1930.₎   16 p. illus. (incl. facsim.) nar. 16°.

1. Societies, National and patriotic—   U. S.
N. Y. P. L.   June 17, 1931

NN   0066353   NN

929.1
N2₍p   National Society Magna Charta Dames.
Gene-   A priceless heritage, a sacred trust, a mes-
alogy   sage to its members and all fellow descendants
      of the barons for the Magna Charta. [Philadel-
      phia, 1932?]
      31p. illus. 16cm.

1.National Society Magna Charta Dames. I.Title

NN   0066354   Mi OC1 OC1WHi

National Society of Accountants for Cooperatives.
      The Cooperative accountant
      see under title

657.4   National Society of Accountants for Coopera-
N217a   tives—Committee on Auditing Standards and
      Terminology.
      Accounting practices, auditing standards,
      and terminology for agricultural cooperatives
      Columbus, Ohio ₍1953?₎
      30p. 23cm. (National Society of Account-
      ants for Cooperatives. Pamphlet no. 1)

      Cover title.

      1. Agriculture, Cooperative—Accounting.
      I. Title.

NN   0066356   IU

National society of Americans of royal descent.
      ...The constitution of the National society Americans of royal
descent, incorporated May 2, 1908 — Washington, D. C. Registered College of arms, January 1, 1936 — London, England.
₍Washington? 1936?₎   11 p.   22cm.

1. Royal descent, Families of.
N. Y. P. L.   October 15, 1937

NN   0066357   NN PHi

National society of art masters, *ed.*
      Some aspects of art education, pub. under the auspices
of the National society of art masters, with a foreword
by Sir James Yoxall. London, G. Allen & Unwin ltd
₍1921₎

143, ₍1₎ p. 18½ᶜᵐ.

CONTENTS.—Foreword, by Sir J. Yoxall.—Creative instinct in education,
by W. G. Raffé.—The co-ordination of drawing and art in elementary and
other schools, by J. W. T. Vinall.—Art instruction in secondary schools, by
R. Hall.—Drawing and art as a means of expression: their place in education,

by C. W. Hobbis.—Civic art, by G. C. Duxbury.—Art education for industry,
by W. H. Helm.—Colour, by H. B. Carpenter.—Possible careers in art, by
A. F. R. Fowkes.—Art school libraries and collections, by C. A. Eva.—The
training of public taste, by F. P. Brown.—The museum as a factor in education, by Ethel M. Spiller.—A minister of arts, by P. J. Keelan.—The National society of art masters.—N. S. A. M. panel of lectures.

1. Art—Study and teaching. I. Title.
                                    22–3200
Library of Congress   N85.N3

NN   0066359   DLC WaS MiU OC1 OC1MA NN

National Society of Autograph Collectors
      see **Manuscript Society.**

National society of brass and metal mechanics.
      ... **Annual report and financial statement...**
      32d –   ; 1903/04
      Birmingham ₍1904–
      1 v. 21½cm

NN   0066361   DL

VOLUME 407

National society of brass and metal mechanics
  General rules...1904.
  Birmingham, 1904-
    1 v. 16½cm.

NN 0066362   DL

National society of children's nurseries (Gt. Brit.)
  Babies...Report of the International
  conference of the National society of day
  nurseries held in London...May 29, 30, & 31,
  1923.   Lond. 1923,

    56 p.

NN 0066363   OC1

National Society of Childrens Nurseries (Gt. Brit.)
  Everyday psychology in the nursery. A selection from courses of lectures delivered under the
  auspices of the National society of day nurseries.
  London, The National league for health maternity
  and child welfare, 1925.
    viii, 44 p.   18.5 cm.
    Bibliography at end of each lecture.

NN 0066364   DL

National society of children's nurseries (*Gt. Brit.*)
  A four years plan for children's nurseries, by the chairman,
  National society of children's nurseries. (London, The Na-
  tional society of children's nurseries (1943)
    1 p. l., 18, (2) p. 21½cm.
    Foreword signed : Cyril H. Nathan, chairman.

    1. Day nurseries.   I. Nathan, Cyril H. II. Title.
                                                    43–17732
    Library of Congress   HV861.G6N3
                                (3)   362.71

NN 0066365   DLC

National Society of Children's Nurseries (Gt. Brit.)
  Report
  London, 1914-34.
    16 v.   17-18 cm.
    1912 - Annual report in the Year book of the
  National Society of Children Nurseries for 1913.
    1915/16 Annual report in The Creche news,
  v. 1. no. 11. May 1916.

NN 0066366   DL

National society of children's nurseries (*Gt. Brit.*)
  Group committee on the training of the nursery nurse
      see
  Group committee on the training of the nursery nurse.

National society of college teachers of education.
  ... College courses in education, committee reports presented as a basis for discussion, presented at the meeting
  of the Society of college teachers of education, Chicago,
  February 24–25 ... Marshalltown, Ia., Marshall printing
  company, 1919.
    86, (1) p. 23cm. (Educational monographs, no. VIII, 1919)
    Publications of the society, no. 13.

    1. Universities and colleges—Curricula.   I. Title.
                                                 E 20–518 Revised
    Library, U. S. Bur. of   Education LB2361.S2

NN 0066368   DHEW ViU WaU

L13
.N5
(Ed)
National society of college teachers of educa-
  tion.
  [Constitution and by-laws and membership
  list 1910-11] [n.p.,1911?]
    [11]p. 25ᶜᵐ.

NN 0066369   ICU

National Society of College Teachers of Education.
  Current educational readjustments in higher
  institutions
      see under   Courtis, Stuart Appleton,
  1874-   ed.

Labor and
Management
Center
L101
U6
N3
28
National Society of College Teachers of Education
  The discipline of practical judgment in a dem-
  ocratic society. General editor: Clifford Woody,
  secretary-treasurer. Chicago, University of
  Chicago Press [pref. 1943]
    vii, 268 p. 24 cm. (*Its* Yearbook, no. 28)

    1. Democracy. 2. Judgment. 3. Politics
  and education. I. Woody, Clifford, 1884-
  II. Title.

NN 0066371   CtY

National Society of College Teachers of Education.
  Educational monographs
      see its   Yearbook.

National society of college teachers of education.
  Burnham, William Henry, 1855–
    ... The history of education as a professional subject, by
  Professor William H. Burnham ... and Professor Henry Suz-
  zallo ... New York, Teachers college. Columbia university,
  1908.

National Society of College Teachers of Education.
  History of education journal
      see under title

National Society of College Teachers of Education.
  Monograph.
  (Austin, University of Texas, Print. Division (*19
    no. 25 cm. (Studies in education)
  Running title, : Educational monographs.

    1. Education—Collections.

    LB5.N28   53–1930 †

        LU MiD TxLT
NN 0066375   DLC OC1 NIC CtY ICU OCU TxU NBC CoU

National society of college teachers of education,
  The National society of college teachers of
  education; organized 1902, in connection with the
  Department of superintendence of the National education association... [n.p., 1909?]
    [11] p. 28cm.

    Includes Constitution and Membership list.

    1. Education - Societies. 2. Education -
  U. S.

NN 0066376   MdBJ

National society of college teachers of education.
  Observation and practice teaching in college and university
  departments of education, by Frederic Ernest Farrington ...
  George Drayton Strayer ... (and) Walter Ballou Jacobs ...
  Papers prepared for discussion at the meetings of the National
  society of college teachers of education, Auditorium hotel,
  Chicago, Tuesday, February twenty-third, at one-thirty p. m.,
  and Wednesday, February twenty-fourth, at one-thirty p. m.,
  nineteen hundred nine. Pub. by the National society of college teachers of education. (Iowa City, Ia., Printed by the
  C. A. Webber printing company, 1908)
    80 p. fold. tab. 23ᶜᵐ.

    CONTENTS.—Practice work in university departments of education, by
  F. E. Farrington.—Observation in connection with college and university
  schools or departments of education, by G. D. Strayer.—Practice teaching
  at Brown university, by W. B. Jacobs.

    1. Universities (and colleges,—(Pedagogical departments) 2. Teachers,
  Training of. (2. Teachers—Training—Universities)   I. Farrington,
  Frederic Ernest, 1872-1930. II. Strayer, George Drayton, 1876–   III.
  Jacobs, Walter Ballou, 1861-1932.
                                                            E 9–956
    U. S. Off. of educ. Library   LB2165.N2
      for Library of Congress   (a37b1)

NN 0066378   DHEW OU MiU ICJ WaU MH

National Society of College Teachers of Education.   L370.6161 30
  73338 [Papers prepared for discussion.] Syracuse, New York, Journal
  of Pedagogy, [etc., etc.], 1907–.
    Continued from 1907. 24½–26½ᶜᵐ.
    The papers for the different years are published with individual titles only and not as
  a set.

NN 0066379   ICJ

370.6
N214pa
National Society of College Teachers of Education.
  Papers presented at the Educational Psychology
  Section, the ... (annual) meeting.
    [v.p.]
      v. 23cm.
    Cover title.
    Reprints from the Journal of educational psy-
  chology.
    At head of title, 1948-   : Studies in education.

    Title varies: 1948-49, Reprints, papers in Sec-
  tion 2 at the ... (annual) meeting.
    Each vol. has also a distinctive title.

    1. Education –   Societies.

NN 0066381   TxU

National society of college teachers of education.
  ... Practice teaching for prospective secondary teachers. Committee reports and papers by A. R. Mead,
  Romiett Stevens, H. G. Childs, W. G. Chambers, and
  co-operating members, presented at the meeting of the
  Society of college teachers of education, Detroit, February 21–22, 1916 ... Cedar Rapids, Ia., The Torch press
  (1916)
    74 p. 24ᶜᵐ. (Educational monograph, no. VII)
    Publications of the society, no. 12.
    1. Teachers, Training (of)—(Secondary schools)   I. Title.
                                                 E 18–348 Revised
    Library, U. S. Bur. of   Education LB1737.U6S6

NN 0066382   DHEW OCU OU ViU

National society of college teachers of education,
  ... Practices of American universities in granting higher degrees in education; a series of official
  statements...
      see under   Freeman, Frank Nugent, 1880–

National)
(Society of College Teachers of Education.
  (Program and membership list Feb. 1917) (New York?
  1917) 8 l. 22cm.

    796625A. 1. Education—Assoc. and   org.—U. S. 2. Schools, Normal—
  Assoc. and org.—U. S.
    N. Y. P. L.   February 17, 1936

NN 0066384   NN

VOLUME 407

National society of college teachers of education.
Publications.

[Analyzed]

NN 0066385   DLC NN

National Society of College Teachers of Education.
Quantitative measurement in institutions of
higher learning
see under   Courtis, Stuart Appleton,
1874-   ed.

National society for vocational education.
...Special bulletin prepared by David Snedden...for use at
the annual convention, St. Louis, February 20–22, 1919...   New
York: National headquarters, 1919.   24 p.   8°.

Contents: Section 1. "High spots" in vocational education as reported from
the several states. Section 2. Future policies of the national society as suggested by
members.

1. Education (Industrial and techni-   cal), U. S. 2. Snedden, David
Samuel, 1868-   October 30, 1919.
N. Y. P. L.

NN 0066387   NN OU ICU NBuG

National Society of College Treachers of Education.
Studies in education ...
see its   Yearbook.

National Society of College Teachers of Education.
... The use of background in the interpretation
of educational issues
see under   Brooks, Fowler Dell, 1885-

National society of college teachers of education.
Yearbook... no. 1–
Chicago, Ill., The University of Chicago press ₁1911–
v. in   diagrs. 24ᶜᵐ.
₁No. 13₁ published in the Oct. 1924 issue of the Journal of educational
research.
Nos. 1–12, 14 issued as its Publications, no. 6–18.
Nos. 1–14 issued under the society's earlier name: The Society of
college teachers of education.
Title varies: no. 1–   The School review monographs.
no.   –14, Educational monographs.
no. 15–16, Studies in education. Yearbook.
no. 17–   Yearbook.
Nos. 1–12, 14 issued as its Publications, no. 6–18.
1. Education—Societies.   2. Education—U. S.
                                              27–22784 Revised
Library of Congress   L101.U6N3
                                                   370.6278

ICJ NcD CoU KMK IU IdPI MtBC CaBVaU ViU
OrPR WaWW WaS OrLgE OrMon0 OrCS OrAshS Or
OCU OC1CC DHEW CU KEmT NN WaTC OrU MtU IdU
NN 0066390   DLC PSt OU ODW MiU OC1 OC1W OO

LB2157   National Society of College Teachers of
.A3N3   Education.

Association for Student Teaching.
Yearbook.

₁Dubuque, Iowa, etc.₎

National Society of College Teachers of **Education.** *Committee on Curriculum and Instruction.*
Preparation of teachers in the area of curriculum and
instruction. Henry Harap. editor. ₁Austin₎ **University of**
Texas, Print. Division ₁1951₎
xi, 89 p. 25 cm. (National Society of College Teachers of **Educa-**
tion. Monograph no. 2)

Studies in education.
Includes bibliographies.

1. Teachers, Training of.   (Series)

LB5.N28 no. 2   370.7322   53–1929

IdU
NN 0066392   DLC MiD CU NIC KEmT CU CoU TxU OrPS

National Society of College Teachers of Education. **Com**
mittee on *Educational Psychology.*
Educational psychology in teacher education, a guide **for**
instructors, by the Committee on Educational Psychology:
Walter W. Cook and Wm. Clark Trow, co-chairmen. **With**
chapters contributed by Warren R. Baller ₁and others₎ Ann
Arbor, National Society of College Teachers of Education
₁ᶜ1953₎
90 p. 23 cm. (National Society of College Teachers of Education.
Monograph no. 3)

1. Educational psychology—Outlines, syllabi, etc.

LB5.N28 no. 3   370.15   54–4083 ‡

PU–Penn PSC OCU
NN 0066393   DLC CaBVaU CoU PPPL CU NIC ViU TxU OU

LB   National Society of College Teachers of
1055   Education. Committee on Educational
.N38   Psychology.
Educational psychology in the education
of teachers; papers in section 2 at the
St. Louis meeting. Reprints. Baltimore,
Warwick and York, 1949.
257–294 p. (Studies in education)

Reprinted from Journal of Educational

Psychology.
Cover title.

#Educational psychology--Addresses, essays,
lectures.

NN 0066395   MoU

National Society of College Teachers of Education. *Committee on Social Foundations.*
The emerging task of the foundations of education; **the**
study of man, culture and education, a statement to the profession. ₁Ann Arbor, Lithoprinted by Edwards Letter **Shop**
for National Society of College Teachers of Education, 1950₎
₁71₎ p. 28 cm.

1. Teachers, Training of. 2. Education—Aims and objectives.
ɪ. Title.
                                                    A 51–4878
Wisconsin. Univ. Libr
for Library of Congress   ₁3₎

NN 0066396   WU OrU CaBVaU TxU CU ICU ViU OrCS

National Society of Colonial Dames of America
see
National Society of the Colonial Dames of
America.

National society of craftsmen, *New York.*
A national directory of workers in the artistic **crafts**
₁v. 1₎– 1906–1907–   Prepared and issued by **the**
National society of craftsmen ... New York ₁The **Trow**
press, ᶜ1906–
v. 20½ᶜᵐ.

1. Art industries and trade—Direct.   7–2757

Library of Congress   TT12.N2 (Copyright A 162479)

NN 0066398   DLC ICRL MB

National Society of Daughters of Founders and
Patriots of America
see   Daughters of Founders and Patriots
of America.

National society of day nurseries (*Gt. Brit.*)
see
National society of children's nurseries (*Gt. Brit.*)

National Society of Denture Prosthetists
see Academy of Denture Prosthetics.

W 1   NATIONAL Society of Electro-Therapeutists
NA75   Transactions of the annual meeting.
1st-13th; 1893-1901. New York
13 v.   W1 NA75
Title: Transactions of the annual
meeting of the National Society of
Electro-Therapeutists

NN 0066402   DNLM MiDW MiU

National Society of India for Malaria & Other Mosquito-
borne Diseases.
Bulletin.
Delhi.
v. 24 cm. bimonthly.
Superseded by Indian Society for Malaria and Other Communicable Diseases. Bulletin.

1. Malarial fever — India — Prevention — Period. 2. Anopheles —
Period. 3. Mosquitoes—India—Period.
[RC164]   S A 68–4329
Printed for PL 480   PL 480: I–D–E–331
by Library of Congress

NN 0066403   ICU MiU NNC–M

National Society of Industrial Realtors
see
Society of Industrial Realtors.

National Society of Literature and Science.   5590.12
A general statement of the plan of the National Society of Litera-
ture & Science.
New York. [Oliver.] 1841. 4 pp. F°.
Cut from Literary Advertiser, vol. 2, no. 2.

NN 0066405   MB

National Society of Literature and Science.
The monthly lecturer
see under title

National society of mural painters, *New York.*
... Catalogue of the ... exhibition of the National society **of**
mural painters ... 1st–   1925–
₁Brooklyn, Brooklyn museum press, 1925–
v. front., plates. 21½ᶜᵐ.

1. Paintings, American—Exhibitions. 2. Mural painting and decoration.
Library of Congress   ND2608.N3   42–49854
                                   ₂₎   751.73

NN 0066407   DLC ViU MiU

National society of mural painters, **New York.**

Smithsonian institution. *National collection of fine arts.*
The George Washington bicentennial frieze, painted **by a**
group of members of the National society of mural painters to
commemorate the two hundredth anniversary of the birth of
George Washington. Washington, D. C., National gallery of
art, 1932.

National society of mural painters, New York.
News bulletin.
v.

New York, 1940   24½ – 28cm.
v.
Irregular.
Title varies: v.   · News letter; v.   News
bulletin.

1. Painting, Mural—Per. and soc.   publ.
N. Y. P. L.   January 18, 1943

NN 0066409   NN

VOLUME 407

759.1 National Society of Mural Painters.
N21p   A portfolio of the work of members of the
       National Society of Mural Painters, designed
       and produced by William Hill Field.   New
       York ₍194-?₎
           ₍45₎ℓ. illus. 29cm.

       Issued in portfolio.

           1. Mural painting and decoration. I. Field,
       William Hill.

NN 0066410   IU MiD

N   National Society of Mural Painters, New York.
751.73   A portfolio of the work of members of the
qN276   National Society of Mural Painters, designed
       and produced by William Hill Field.   New
       York ₍1950?₎
           ₍3₎ ℓ., 36 plates (in portfolio) 29 cm.

           1. Mural painting and decoration. I.
       Field, William Hill. II. Title.

NN 0066411   N WaS

National society of mural painters, New York.
    A portfolio of the work of members of the National society of
mural painters... Designed and produced by William Hill Field.
₍New York, 1950?₎   2 p.l., 42 pl., 1 l.   28cm.

    With biographical sketches.

595567B. 1. Paintings, Mural—U. S.   I. Field, William Hill, ed.
N.Y.P.L.   October 10, 1951

NN 0066412   NN CU MB

National Society of New England Women.
    Constitution and by-laws. ₍New-York, 1895.₎   29 p.   24°.

    Three appendices inserted giving lists of officers and committees through the year
1899.

1. Societies (National and historic),   U. S. 2. Woman.—Assoc. and organizations, U. S.   ganizations, U. S.
N. Y. P. L.   September 29, ₍924

NN 0066413   NN

National society of New England women.
    Constitution and by-laws of the National society of New
England women. ₍New York, 191–?₎
    29 p. illus. 12½ x 10ᵐᵐ.

                                                        22–742
    Library of Congress   F1.N27

NN 0066414   DLC NBhi NN

National society of New England women.
    Dramatic and scenic reproduction of American history,
1620–1865 ... under the auspices of the National society
of New England women, assisted by genealogical and
patriotic societies, at the Metropolitan opera house, November 30th and December 1st, 1897. Mrs. Charles Elliot Fitch, historical director. ₍New York? 1898?₎
    ₍22₎ p. 9 pl. 30ᵐᵐ.
    Title vignette.

    1. U. S.—Hist.—Drama.   I. Title.

                                                        2–6103
    Library of Congress   E179.N27

NN 0066415   DLC WHi

National Society of New England Women.
    Tidings from far and near
₍no.₎
₍New York?₎ 19   8°.
    v.   ports.

1. Societies (National and patriotic),   U. S. 2. Woman.—Assoc. and
organizations, U. S.   organizations, U. S.
N. Y. P. L.   July 16, 1924

NN 0066416   NN

National Society of New England Women. Brooklyn.
    Colony.
        Address book.   [Brooklyn]
        v.

NN 0066417   NBLiHi

        National society of New England women.   Buffalo
Buffalo colony.
E186.99
N4A5   ₍Year book₎

       ₍Buffalo?₎, National society of New England women₎
       Buffalo colony, 19__

           __ vols.   front.,col.illus.   15½cm.

           1. Woman.—Societies and clubs.   2. United
       States.—History.—Colonial period.—Societies.

NN 0066418   NBuG

F   National society of New England women—
84   Chicago colony.
.605   ...Year book,
       ₍Chicago
       v.

       "Organized April 11th, 1907."
       "Colony number twelve.

NN 0066419   ICN

       National society of New England Women – Cleveland
       colony

           ₍Year book₎   ₍Cleveland₎

NN 0066420   OCl

       **National society of New England women. Davenport
       colony.**
           ₍Year book₎ n. imp.
           v.

NN 0066421   MiD-B

       **National society of New England women. Detroit
       colony.**
           ₍Year book₎

NN 0066422   MiD-B

       **National society of New England women. Hartford
       colony.**
           ₍Year book₎ n. imp.
           v.

NN 0066423   MiD-B

---

                                                  *4459A-330
National Society of New England Women. Los Angeles Colony.
    Year book. 1932/33.
= [Los Angeles. 1932.]   v. Portrait. 18½ cm.

D1910 — Annuals and year-books. — Women's clubs. Period.

NN 0066424   MB

**National society of New England women. Miami
colony.**
    Year book. n. imp.
    v.

NN 0066425   MiD-B

**National society of New England women.
Minneapolis colony.**
    ₍Year book₎ n. imp.

NN 0066426   MiD-B

**National society of New England women. New
Haven colony.**
    Year book. n. imp.

NN 0066427   MiD-B

**National society of New England women. *New York city
colony.***
    Year book.
    ₍New York₎
    v. 16¼ x 13ᵐᵐ.
                pub. by the National society of New England women.
Upon the reorganization of that society in 1913, the publication was continued by the National society of New England women, New York city
colony.

                                                        16-3019
    Library of Congress   F1.N34

NN 0066428   DLC MiD MB NN

**National society of New England women. Rochester
colony.**
    ₍Year book₎ n. imp.

NN 0066429   MiD-B

**National society of New England women. Syracuse
colony.**
    ...Year book. n. imp.

NN 0066430   MiD-B

       National Society of New England Women.
           Toledo colony.
           ...Year book.   Fourth year, 1909–1910..
       n.p.   n.d.

           Also: 1928–29
                           1929–30

NN 0066431   OClWHi

       National society of non-smokers.
HV5733
.T3   Taylor, T   F   *of Clovelly, Eng.*
           Don't smoke! An address by T. F. Taylor ... ₍London,
       National society of non-smokers₎ 1944.

       National society of operative printers and assistants.
           Journal.
       London.

NN 0066433   NN

VOLUME 407

Law
National society of operative printers and assistants, defendant.

Ward, Lock and company, ltd., *publishers, plaintiff.*

Litigation! Ward and Lock *v.* N. S. O. P. A. and E. Smith. Full report of the above-named action, before Mr. Justice Darling and special jury, in the High court of justice, King's bench division, and also the unabridged report of the successful appeal of the National society of operative printers' assistants and E. Smith, against the decision of Mr. Justice Darling, heard in the Supreme court of judicature (Court of appeal) before the appeal judges: Lord Justice Vaughan Williams, Lord Justice Stirling, and Lord Justice Fletcher Moulton ... ₁London, Cooperative printing society limited, 1906₁

Z120
.I 632
I 78
National society of operative printers and assistants.

₁Isaacs, George Alfred₁ 1883–
The Pressmen's home, Tennessee. The report of the general secretary's second visit as a fraternal delegate from the National society of operative printers and assistants, to the 1916 convention of the International printing pressmen and assistants' union of North America. ₁London₁ Executive council of the National society of operative printers and assistants ₁1916₁

Law
National Society of Operative Printers and Assistants.

Gt. Brit. *Court of Inquiry into a Dispute Between D. C. Thomson and Company Limited and Certain Workpeople, Members of the National Society of Operative Printers and Assistants.*

Report. London, H. M. Stationery Off., 1952.

National society of operative printers and assistants.

Isaacs, George Alfred, 1883–
With the pressmen and assistants of North America. The report of George A. Isaacs upon his visit as a fraternal delegate from the National society of operative printers and assistants, to the 26th annual convention of the International printing pressmen and assistants' union of North America, held in June at Rogersville, Tennessee ... London, The National society of operative printers and assistants ₁1914₁

National Society of Penal Information.
Bulletin.
no. ₁1–₁

₁New York,₁ 1922–
nos.

Irregular.
Cover-title.
At head of title: no. 5, The Death penalty; no. 6, Probation; no. 8, The Colorado report.

1. Prisons—Per. and soc. publ.
N. Y. P. L.

March 15, 1928

NN 0066438   NN MH–L MiD MB ICJ DL

National society of penal information.

MacCormick, Austin Harbutt, 1893–
The education of adult prisoners, a survey and a program, by Austin H. MacCormick ... New York, The National society of penal information, 1931.

HV9471
.H3
National Society of Penal Information.

Handbook of American prisons and reformatories. ₁1st₁ ed.; 1925–
New York.

National society of penal information.

Rector, Frank Leslie, 1879–
Health and medical service in American prisons and reformatories, prepared by Frank L. Rector, M. D. New York, N. Y., The National society of penal information, inc., 1929.

National society of penal information.

Osborne association.
News bulletin. v. 1–
New York ₁1930–

Apr. 1930–

National Society of Penal Information.
On the first anniversary of the death of Thomas Mott Osborne, the addresses given at the memorial meeting on February twenty-seventh, nineteen hundred and twenty-seven, are printed by the National Society of Penal Information and the Welfare League Association, which he organized, as a testimonial to his inspiring and continuing leadership. ₁New York, 1927.₁ 26 p. (incl. port.) 12°.

395967A. 1. Osborne, Thomas Mott, 1859–1926. 2. Welfare League Association, New York.
N. Y. P. L.
January 28, 1929

NN 0066443   NN MH

NATIONAL SOCIETY OF PENAL INFORMATION, INC.
Report...presented at the annual meeting.
192

New York₁, 192
nos.
22–28cm.
Title varies: 192 , Report of the secretary...; 19 , Report...presented at the annual meeting.

1. Prisons—Assoc. and org.—U.S.

NN 0066444   NN

National society of penal information
see also Osborne association.

National society of physical therapeutics.
Papers treating on physical therapeutics read by Dr. G. H. Patchen ... Dr. Oscar Jones ... Dr. J. F. Roemer ... at the National society of physical therapeutics, Detroit, Michigan, Wednesday, June 19, 1918 ... ₁Waukegan, Ill., Printed by Gazette pub. co.,₁ ⁽1918₁
cover-title, 30 p. 22ᶜᵐ.
One illus. and text on p. ₁3₁ and ₁4₁ of cover.
CONTENTS.—Skeletal misalignment the primary and perpetuating physical cause of disease, by G. H. Patchen.—Spinal therapy—a neglected field, by Oscar Jones.—Chronic troubles treated with the leucodescent lamp and the tension table, by J. F. Roemer.
1. Physical therapy. I. Patchen, George Henry, 1845– II. Jones, Oscar, 1877– III. Roemer, Jacob F., 1861–
18–22903

Library of Congress   RM702.N2

₁a44b1₁

NN 0066446   DLC

National society of pottery workers.
...Reconstruction in the pottery industry. Manchester, Cooperative prtg. soc., 1945. 40 p. 25cm.

1. Pottery—Trade and stat.— Gt. Br. 2. World war, 1939–1945—
Post-war problems, Economic— Gt. Br.
N. Y. P. L.
February 10, 1948

NN 0066447   NN CU

TA157
qN25
National Society of Professional Engineers.
Conference proceedings.
19

₁Washington, D.C., 19
nos. in v. ports. 24–28cm.

Conferences sponsored in conjunction with the society's annual meeting.
Each issued with distinctive title or theme.

1. Engineers - Societies. 2. Engineering - Cong. Contents for distinctive title.

NN 0066448   OrCS

National Society of Professional Engineers.
Digest of professional engineers' income and salary survey. Washington ₁1955?₁
₁8₁ p. Illus. 23 cm.

1. Engineers—U. S.—Salaries, pensions, etc. I. Title.

TA157.N32   56–16662 ‡

NN 0066449   DLC

TA157
.N35
1953
National Society of Professional Engineers.
Executive research survey no. 1₁–4₁
Washington, D. C. ₁1953–55₁
4 pts. illus. 23cm.
In case.
Numbers 3–4: Prepared by Professional Engineers Conference Board for Industry in cooperation with the National Society of Professional Engineers.
Each number includes bibliography.
CONTENTS.—no.1.How to improve engineering-management communications. 1953.—no.2. How to improve the utilization of engineering manpower. 1953.—no.3.How to attract and hold engineering talent. 1954.—no.4. How to train engineers in industry. 1955.
1. Engineering. 2.Engineering as a profession. I. Professional Engineers Conference Board for Industry.

NN 0066450   ViU NN TxHU NIC MH–BA OrCS MtBC

HD69
R4N36
National Society of Professional Engineers.
How to improve engineering-management communications, prepared by the National Society of Professional Engineers under the direction of the Professional Engineers Conference Board for Industry. Washington, D.C., ₁1952₁
46 p. illus. (Its Executive research survey, no.1)

Bibliography: p.46.

OrP OrU NcD
NN 0066451   CU NjR IaU MiD ICJ OCU PSt OU DI IdU

TA157
N3
National Society of Professional Engineers.
How to improve the utilization of engineering manpower. Washington, D.C. [c1952]
55 p. illus. 23 cm. (Its Executive research survey, no. 2)

1. Engineers. 2. Engineering as a profession. I. Title. (Series)

NN 0066452   DI NcD PU–E1 NBuG MH–BA MiD

National Society of Professional Engineers.
How to train engineers in industry

see under

Professional Engineers Conference Board for Industry, Washington, D. C.

620.07
N21ℓ
National Society of Professional Engineers.
Legislative bulletin.
v. 1–
₁1946₁–
Washington.
v.

NN 0066454   IU NcRS

National Society of Professional Engineers.
₁Minor publications₁
Washington.

NN 0066455   ICJ Wa

VOLUME 407

National Society of Professional Engineers.
Panel discussion on "The St. Lawrence
waterway, pro and con. Remarks made at
Seventeenth annual convention ...
    see under   Kelly, Walter J., 1877–

National Society of Professional Engineers.
Professional development, the responsibility of industry
and the engineer; conference proceedings, June 2, 1955,
Philadelphia, Pennsylvania, sponsored by the National Society of Professional Engineers in conjunction with its 21st
annual meeting. ₍Washington, 1955₎
    56 p. ports. 24 cm.

    1. Engineering—Congresses.   I. Title.

    TA5.N3 1955   620.6273   56–1024

        ScC1eA LU   AAP
NN 0066457   DLC PPD MtBuM CU PBL NIC IU TxU OrP

National Society of Professional Engineers.
Professional engineers; autobiography of National Society of
Professional Engineers. Washington ₍1946?₎
    12 p. 22cm.

NN 0066458   ICJ

National Society of Professional Engineers.
Professional engineers' income and salary survey. 1st–
1952–
Washington.
    v. illus. 23 cm. biennial.

    1. Engineers—U. S.—Salaries, pensions, etc.   I. Title.

    TA157.N33   A 55–10041
    Georgia. Inst. of Tech   Library
    for Library of Congress   ₍r60(2),† rev 2

        PBL ICJ MiD MiU OrP CL N PWpM PPPL
NN 0066459   GAT PU-W PSt NNC MH-BA PPD NIC DLC CU

NATIONAL SOCIETY OF PROFESSIONAL ENGINEERS.
Report.
Washington.   no.   illus.   28cm.

    Annual.

NN 0066460   NN InLP

National society of professional engineers.
Committee on the economic status of the
531.116 engineer.
C734M   Manual on collective bargaining for professional employees ... Washington, National
society of professional engineers, 1947–
    3 v. 28cm.

    Contents.–1. The national labor relations
act and professional employees.–2. Collective
bargaining, mediation and arbitration.–3. The
objectives, structure and tactics of labor
organizations.

NN 0066461   NcD

National Society of Professional Engineers. *Employment
Practices Committee. Engineer-in-Industry Subcommittee
see
National Society of Professional Engineers. Engineer-in-
Industry Committee.*

National Society of Professional Engineers. *Engineer-in-
Industry Committee.*
A professional look at the engineer in industry. Wash-
ington, National Society of Professional Engineers, ʰ1955.
    124 p. illus. 23 cm.

    1. Engineering as a profession.   I. Title.

    TA157.N34   620.69   55–1505 rev 2 ‡

        AU TU
        PPD AAP ScC1eA NcRS ICJ MtBC OrCS PMarshSO PU-EI
NN 0066463   DLC IEN TxU PBL PWpM PSt NcD NN DI OC1W

National Society of Professional Musicians
    see   Incorporated Society of Musicians.

National Society of Public Accountants.
Membership directory.
₍n. p.₎
    v. 23 cm.

    1. Accountants—U. S.—Direct.

    HF5601.N34   58–31623

NN 0066465   DLC TxU WaS FU CSf P OrP

National Society of Public Accountants.
HF5601   The National public accountant. v. 1–6, no. 8; Oct. 1949–
.N334   Aug. 1956. Washington ₍etc.₎ National Society of Public
Accountants.

National Society of Public Accountants.
Yearbook.
Washington.
    v. illus., ports. 23 cm.

    1. Accountants—U. S.—Societies, etc.

    HF5601.N342   657.6′062′73   78–485

NN 0066467   DLC IU TxU

National society of real Americans, New York.
Democracy; a magazine of opinion. v. 1–
Feb. 1918–
Philadelphia, 1918; New York, 1918–

National Society of Sales Training Executives.
Attitude and preparation. Reported for the
Committee for Economic Development. ₍Chicago₎
c1943₎
    28p. (Selecting and training post-war sales
personnel. 1)

    Cover-title.

NN 0066469   ICRL

National Society of Sales Training Executives.
Checking results and following through.
Reported for the Committee for Economic Development. ₍Chicago, c1943₎
    16p. (Selecting and training post-war sales
personnel. 4)

    Cover-title.

NN 0066470   ICRL

National Society of Sales Training Executives.
Getting action. Reported for the Committee
for Economic Development. ₍Chicago,
c1943₎
    28p. (Selecting and training post-war sales
personnel. 3)

    Cover-title.

NN 0066471   ICRL MH-BA OC1

National Society of Sales Training Executives.
Handbook of sales training. New York, Prentice-Hall,
1949.
    viii, 415 p. 22 cm.
    Bibliography : p. 396–399.

    1. Salesmen and salesmanship—Study and teaching.

    HF5438.N352   658.85   49–3974*

NN 0066472   DLC OrCS WaT OrU CaBVaU CU PP OEac WaS

National Society of Sales Training Executives.
Handbook of sales training. New York, Prentice-Hall,
c1950, c1949₎
    viii, 415 p. 22 cm.
    Bibliography : p. 396–399.
    "Second printing, April, 1950."

NN 0066473   PPT

658.85   National Society of Sales Training Execu-
N2133h   tives.
1949r   Handbook of sales training. New York,
Prentice-Hall [1951, c1949]
    viii, 415p. 22cm.

    "First printing May, 1949 ... Third print-
ing October, 1951."
    Bibliography: p.396–399.

    1. Salesmen and salesmanship - Study and
teaching.

NN 0066474   TxU

National Society of Sales Training Executives.
Handbook of sales training. 2d ed., rev. by James H.
Davis. New York, Prentice-Hall, 1954.
    402 p. 22 cm.

    1. Salesmen and salesmanship—Study and teaching.

    HF5438.N352 1954   658.85   54–10568 ‡

        CaBVa
        KMK CoU TU OU NcG PU-W PPT PCM OC1 TxU NN MB WaS
NN 0066475   DLC IdU Or KEmT LU OC1W PP MiU ScU

NATIONAL society of sales training executives.
    [Pamphlets on selection & training of
salesmen] Reported for the Committee for
economic development.
    N.Y. 5 nos. in 1v. [c1943–44]

    With this are bound its: Meeting guides
and suggested introductory remarks. [1]–4.

NN 0066476   WaS

National Society of Sales Training Executives.
Planning the program. Reported for the
Committee for Economic Development. ₍Chicago,
c1943₎
    28p. (Selecting and training post-war sales
personnel. 2)

    Cover title.

NN 0066477   ICRL

VOLUME 407

National Society of Sales Training Executives.
 Post-war outlook for sales training. Reported
for the Committee for Economic Development.
₍Chicago, ₎c1943₎
 12p. (Selecting and training post-war sales
personnel. 5)

NN 0066478   ICRL

National society of sales training executives.
 Selecting and training post-war sales per~
sonnel; report for the Committee for economic
development. ₍c1943₎
 5 pts. in 1 v.

 1. Salesmen and salesmanship.

NN 0066479   NNC KMK MiEM

National Society of Sales Training Executives.
 Selecting and training post-war sales personnel.
 3. Getting action
  see its Getting action.

National Society of Scabbard and Blade
 see Scabbard and Blade.

National society of scientific research, *Washington, D. C.*
 ... Official bulletin ... Paper no. 1. Discussion of the
atomic theory. Aug. 18, 1909. Washington, D. C., 1909.
 8 p. 20ᶜᵐ.
 Caption title.
 No more published.

 1. Science—Societies.
 Library of Congress   Q11.N295
                                    10-3895 Revised

NN 0066482   DLC

National society of the Children
 of the American revolution

   see

Children of the American revolution.

National Society of the Colonial Dames of America.
 Acts in council
18
Manchester, N. H. ₍etc., 1898–1910.₎   8°.

 Biennial.
 Title varies: 1910– Constitution, acts in council, constitutional amendments, committees.

 1. Societies (National and patriotic),   U. S.
 N. Y. P. L.   January 26, 1916.

NN 0066484   NN Nh NbHi NcD ViU CSmH

National society of the colonial dames of America.

 American war songs; published under supervision of National
committee for the preservation of existing records of the National society of the colonial dames of America. Philadelphia,
Pa., Priv. print., 1925.
 xxvii p., 2 l., ₍3₎–202 p. front. (port.) facsims. 24½ᶜᵐ.
 Without music.

 1. War-songs, American.   I. Title.
                                        44-31505
 Library of Congress   M1628.N2₍5₎A5

   NBuG
   NIC GU MH ICN NN ViU MiU DSI LU OU NBuC RPJCB IEN
NN 0066485   DLC P NcD NcU DN MB IdU WaTC OrU WaS

Film
E
69
.611 NATIONAL SOCIETY OF THE COLONIAL DAMES OF AMERICA
 Applications for membership. ₍Washington,
 D.C.,n.d.
 5 reels.

 Microfilm from manuscript and typescript
copies.

NN 0066486   ICN OC1

National society of the colonial dames of America.
 Book guide to the separate states of these United States of
America, May, 1933, suggested by the Patriotic service com-
mittee of the National society of colonial dames of America.
₍Providence, R. I., E. A. Johnson co., 1933₎
 ₍51₎ p. 18 x 13½ᶜᵐ.
 Foreword signed : Mrs. Arthur T. Holbrook, chairman.

 1. U. S.—History, Local—Bibl.   I. Holbrook, Mrs. Bertha Matson
(Andrews)   II. Title.
                                                33-21029
 Library of Congress   Z1250.N27
                        ₍2₎   016.973

NN 0066487   DLC MiD

National society of the colonial dames of
 America.
 Calder, Isabel MacBeath, ed.
 Colonial captivities, marches and journeys, edited, under the
auspices of the National society of the colonial dames of America, by Isabel M. Calder ... New York, The Macmillan company, 1935.

National society of the colonial dames of America.
 ... Constitution and eligibility lists of the National
society of the colonial dames of America. Baltimore,
Printed by Guggenheimer, Weil & co. ₍1896₎
 3 p. l., ₍5₎–46 p. 18 x 14½ᶜᵐ.

                                    2-11922 Additions
 Library of Congress   E186.4.A¹

NN 0066489   DLC

National society of the colonial dames of America.
 The constitution and officers of the Society of
the colonial dames of America. Richmond, Va.,
West, Johnston & co., 1893.
 30 p. form. 17 cm.

 "The constitution and by-laws of the Society of
the colonial dames of America in the state of Virginia ...": p. ₍13₎–30.
 "Officers of the Society in the state of Virginia": p. ₍15₎–₍16₎
 1. Virginia – Hist. – Colonial period – Societies.
 I. National society   of the colonial dames of
America. Virginia.

NN 0066490   Vi

National society of the colonial dames of
 America.
 Pitt, William, *1st earl of Chatham, 1708–1778.*
 Correspondence of William Pitt, when secretary of state,
with colonial governors and military and naval commissioners in America; ed. under the auspices of the National society
of the colonial dames of America, by Gertrude Selwyn Kimball ... New York, The Macmillan company; London, Macmillan & co., ltd., 1906.

National society of the colonial dames of
 America.
 Shirley, William, 1694–1771.
 Correspondence of William Shirley, governor of Massachu-
setts and military commander in America, 1731–1760, ed. under
the auspices of the National society of the colonial dames of
America, by Charles Henry Lincoln ... New York, The Mac-
millan company, 1912.

National society of the colonial dames of
America.
 Bradstreet, Howard.
 Dark days of the Republic. Farmer Washington's
vision. The catching of Moses Dunbar. By Howard
Bradstreet. Hartford, Conn., Printed by the Americani-
zation committee of the National society of the colonial
dames of America, 1925.

National society of the colonial dames of America.
 ... Directory, 1898. Manchester, N. H., Printed by the
John B. Clarke company, 1898.
 68 p. 18½ x 15ᶜᵐ.

 Library of Congress   E186.4.A12   98-1868 Revised

NN 0066494   DLC ICJ NbHi CU-B NcD NN

National society of the colonial dames of
America.
 Eligibility lists. Charleston, S. C., Walker,
Evans & Cogswell co., ptrs., n. d.
 78 ₍1₎ p.

NN 0066495   MiD

National Society of the Colonial Dames of America.
 Eligibility lists of the colonial state societies. ₍New York,₎
the society. 1900.   12°.

 1. Societies (Patriotic), U. S.
 N. Y. P. L.   January 15, 1914.

NN 0066496   NN

E186.4
.A112 National Society of the Colonial Dames of
       America.
 The National Society of the Colonial Dames
of America; eligibility lists of the Colonial
state societies. ₍n.p.₎ Printed for the
Society, 1914.
 61 p., 1 l. 24 cm.

 1. U.S.—Hist.—Colonial period—Societies.

NN 0066497   T

National Society of the Colonial Dames of
 America.
 First address of Miss Anne Hollingsworth
Wharton
  see under Wharton, Anne Hollingsworth,
1845–1928.

National Society of the Colonial Dames of America.
 Historian's report.
 Washington.
 v. 23 cm.

 E186.4.A114   369.123   57-32284

NN 0066499   DLC OC1WHi MB OO NbHi MiD NcD NN

National society of the colonial dames of
 America.
 Lee, Richard Henry, 1732–1794.
 The letters of Richard Henry Lee, collected and ed. by
James Curtis Ballagh ... New York, The Macmillan com-
pany, 1911–14.

VOLUME 407

National society of the colonial dames
of America.
Hamilton, Stanislaus Murray, 1855–1909, ed.
Letters to Washington, and accompanying papers;
published by the Society of the colonial dames of America, ed. by Stanislaus Murray Hamilton ... Boston and
New York, Houghton, Mifflin and company, 1898–1902.

National society of the colonial dames of
America.
Dunbar, William, 1749–1810.
Life, letters and papers of William Dunbar of Elgin, Morayshire, Scotland, and Natchez, Mississippi, pioneer scientist of
the southern United States; compiled and prepared from the
original documents for the National society of colonial dames
in America, by Mrs. Dunbar Rowland (Eron Rowland) ...
Jackson, Miss., Press of the Mississippi historical society, 1930.

718   National society of the Colonial dames of America.
N277   A memorial to the soldiers and sailors of the
United States who gave up their lives for their
country in the war of 1898–1899 with Spain.
₍Springfield, Mass.₎ Pr. under the supervision
of Clifton Johnson, 1902₎
    ₍22₎ p. front. illus., ports. 22cm.

       1. Monuments. 2. U.S. – Hist. – War of 1898.
    I. Title.

NN   0066503   LNHT CtY NN MiD-B MH

E186   National Society of the Colonial Dames of
.4   America.
.A06   **The Messenger.**
       ₍Richmond?₎ National Society of the Colonial Dames of
America.

National Society of the Colonial Dames of America.
    Minutes of the council...
₍no.
Baltimore, Md. ₍etc.₎, 18   8°.
    v.
Biennial.

1. Societies (National and patri-   otic), U. S.
N. Y. P. L.   January 21, 1916.

NN   0066505   NN MB MiD-B ViU CSmH

*
E186
.4   National Society of the Colonial Dames of
.A1   America.
1893
       The National Society of the Colonial Dames
of America. Organized May 23d, 1890.
Incorporated April 13th, 1891. "Colere
Coloniarum Gloriam." New York: H. H. B.
Angell, 1893.
       105 p. 21cm.
       This edition is limited and this copy is no. 95,
issued to Miss Elise Willing Balch (Ms. note on
front lining paper)
       1. U. S.—Hist.   —Colonial period—
Societies.

NN   0066506   ViU

National society of the colonial dames of America.
    The National society of the colonial dames of America,
its beginnings, its purpose and a record of its work, 1891–
₍1913. ₍n. p.₎ Printed for the Society, 1913.
    vi, 7–141, ₍1₎ p. 24½ᵐ.

    1. U. S.—Hist—Colonial period—Societies.

Library of Congress   E186.4.A11
                                                   14–3724

NN   0066507   DLC OClWHi InU NN ViU

National society of the colonial dames of America.
Officers and members. n.p., n.d.

NN   0066508   Nh

National society of the colonial dames
of America.
    Officers of the National society of
the colonial dames of America and of the
state societies. 1903. ₍Manchester, N.H.
Printed by the J.B. Clarke co.₎ 1904

    39 p.

NN   0066509   OClWHi

National society of the colonial dames of America.

    Rines, Edward Francis, 1905–
       Old historic churches of America; their romantic history
and their traditions, by Edward F. Rines. Published under
the auspices of the National society of colonial dames of
America. New York, The Macmillan company, 1936.

National society of the colonial dames of
America.
Jones, Edward Alfred, 1872–
    The old silver of American churches, by E. Alfred Jones ...
Letchworth, England. Priv. print. for the National society
of colonial dames of America, at the Arden press, 1913.

National Society of the Colonial Dames of America.
    Order of exercises for the dedication service held by the
National Society of the Colonial Dames of America at the presentation of the memorial commemorating the three hundredth
anniversary of the landing of the pilgrims. Plymouth, Mass.,
1921. 24 p. front. 8°.

1. Pilgrim Fathers.
N. Y. P. L.   September 27, 1922.

NN   0066512   NN

**National society of the colonial dames of
America.**
    Jameson, John Franklin, 1859–   ed.
    Privateering and piracy in the colonial period: illustrative
documents, edited under the auspices of the National society of
the colonial dames of America, by John Franklin Jameson ...
New York, The Macmillan company, 1923.

National Society of the Colonial Dames of America.
    The record of those who gave to a fund collected by the
National Society of the Colonial Dames of America for the
reconstruction of Gunston Hall, Fairfax County, Virginia,
the home of George Mason, author of the Virginia Declaration of rights. ₍Morristown? N. J.₎ 1954.
    117 p. 39 cm.

    1. Gunston Hall, Fairfax Co., Va.

F234.G86N3   975.529   55–19266 ‡

NN   0066514   DLC Vi

National society of the colonial dames of America.
    The record of those who gave to an endowment fund
collected by the National society of the colonial dames of
America for the maintenance of Sulgrave manor, the
home of the ancestors of George Washington in Sulgrave,
Northamptonshire, England. ₍Boston₎ Printed for the
National society, 1925.
    x, 108 p., 3 l. 49ᵐ.
    Half-title: Sulgrave endowment record.
    Lettered on cover: Sulgrave manor endowment record.
    "Forty-eight copies of this book were printed ... by D. B. Updike, the
Merrymount press, Boston ... This is number 4."
    1. Sulgrave manor house.   I. Title: Sulgrave endowment record.

Library of Congress   E312.195.N2?₎
                                                   26–4802

NN   0066515   DLC ViU CSmH MWA NSyU

National society of the colonial dames of
America.
Prince Frederick parish, S. C.
    The register book for the parish, Prince Frederick, Winyaw
Ann: Dom. 1713. Pub. by the National society of the colonial
dames of America. Baltimore, Williams & Wilkins company,
1916.

National society of the colonial dames of America.
    ... Report of the Committee on relics; uniforms of
women worn during the war. Washington, 1922.
    cover-title, 28 p. 23ᶜᵐ.
    Signed: Carolyn Gilbert Benjamin, chairman.

    1. European war, 1914–1918—Women's work.   I. Benjamin, Mrs. Carolyn (Gilbert)   II. Title: Uniforms of women worn during the war.

Library of Congress   D639.W7N5
                                                   22–16086

NN   0066517   DLC

National society of the colonial dames of America
    ... A report on the status of the societies
composing the National society of the colonial
dames of America. Adopted by the Executive
committee of the National society on November 5,
1908. ₍Washington, D.C.₎ 1908?₎
       cover-title, 33 p.   23ᶜᵐ.

    1. U.S.—Hist.—Colonial period—Societies.

NN   0066518   ViU NN

National society of the Colonial Dames of
America.
Reports, rules, registers, etc.
    open. binder

NN   0066519   DNW

National Society of the Colonial Dames of America.
    ₍Roster₎

    ₍New York, 19   no.   15cm.

    1. Societies, National and   patriotic—U. S.
N. Y. P. L.   October 3, 1944.

NN   0066520   NN

National society of the colonial dames
of America.
₍Hancock, Eliza Penn-Gaskell₎
    A short account of Penn of Pennsylvania and his family. Philadelphia, The Historical register publishing co.,
1895.

National Society of the Colonial Dames of America.
    Some historic houses
    see under Fitzpatrick, John Clement,
    1876–

National society of the colonial dames of America.
Hopewell, N. J.
    The town records of Hopewell, New Jersey, compiled by
Lida Cokefair Gedney, registrar. Published by authority of
the Board of managers of the New Jersey society of the
Colonial dames of America. ₍New York, Printed by Little
& Ives company₎ 1931.

VOLUME 407

National society of the colonial dames of
America.

Mereness, Newton Dennison, *ed.*
Travels in the American colonies, ed. under the auspices of
the National society of the colonial dames of America, by
Newton D. Mereness. New York, The Macmillan company,
1916.

**National society of the colonial dames of
America.**
Torrence, Clayton, *comp.*
Virginia wills and administrations, 1632–1800, an index of
wills recorded in local courts of Virginia, 1632–1800, and of
administrations on estates shown by inventories of the estates
of intestates recorded in will (and other) books of local courts,
1632–1800. Compiled by Clayton Torrence ... Richmond,
Va., The William Byrd press, inc. ₁1931₎

National society of the colonial dames of America.
see also
Colonial dames of America.

National society of the colonial dames of
America. De Soto committee
Report of the De Soto committee on the
celebration of the four hundredth anniversary
of the discovery of the Mississippi River, May
6, 1937. Washington, D. C. ₁1937?₎
1p.*l.* ₁5₎ p. 24cm.

1. Mississippi River.

NN 0066527 LNHT

National Society of the Colonial Dames of America. Publication Committee.
Year book...
₁no. 1
Boston: The Barta Press ₁1914   8°.

1. Societies (National and patri-   otic), U. S.
N. Y. P. L.   August 7, 1916.

NN 0066528 NN

National Society of the Colonial Dames of America. Alabama.
Directory and by-laws.
1
₁Mobile, Ala.?,₎ 1   8°.
no.

1. Societies, National and patriotic—   U. S.
N. Y. P. L.   August 27, 1929

NN 0066529 NN

Z731
.B87   National society of the colonial dames of
America. California.
Bruner, Helen Marcia, 1890–
Books and libraries in colonial America, by Helen Marcia
Bruner. Prepared for the National society of colonial dames
of America resident in the state of California. San Francisco,
Calif., 1947.

National society of the colonial dames of
America. California.
Watkins, *Mrs.* **Eleanor Preston.**
The builders of San Francisco, and some of their early
homes; prepared for the National society of colonial dames of
America in the state of California, by Eleanor Preston Wat-
kins. San Francisco, Calif., 1935.

F864
.B78   National society of the colonial dames of
America. California.
Bruner, Helen Marcia, 1890–
California's old burying grounds, by Helen Marcia Bruner.
Prepared for the National society of colonial dames of Amer-
ica resident in the state of California. San Francisco, Calif.
₁Portal press₎ 1945.

National Society of the Colonial Dames of America. California.
...The Colonial Dames of America in the state of California
... Organized October 8, 1895. ₁San Francisco, Cal.: Cubery
& Co. 1897?₎ 31 p. 12°.

Includes: Constitution, list of members, etc.

1. Societies (National and patri-   otic), U. S.
N. Y. P. L.   August 15, 1923.

NN 0066533 NN

National society of the colonial dames of
America. California.
Gardner, Frances Tomlinson.
Early California navigators and their maps, by Frances
Tomlinson Gardner. Prepared for the National society of
colonial dames of America resident in the state of California.
San Francisco, Calif., 1941.

F868
.S156P6   National Society of the Colonial Dames of
America. California.
Potter, Elizabeth Gray.
Early Mexican ranchos in the San Francisco Bay region.
Prepared for the National Society of Colonial Dames of
America resident in the State of California. San Francisco,
1951.

National society of the colonial dames of
America. California.
Livermore, Helen Ells.
Early Mexicans, prepared for the National society of colo-
nial dames of America in the state of California, by Helen
Ells Livermore. San Francisco, Calif., 1932.

National society of the colonial dames of
America. California.
Allen, Alice Mayhew.
Early roads and trails in California, by Alice Mayhew Allen,
prepared for the National society of colonial dames of America
resident in the state of California. San Francisco, Calif., 1942.

National society of the colonial dames of
America. California.
Nickelsburg, Stephen.
... Hernado ₁!₎ de Soto, agent of Spanish imperialism, by
Stephen Nickelsburg. ₁Stanford University? Calif., 1940₎

National society of the colonial dames of
America. California.
Deering, Margaret (Perkins) *"Mrs.* James Henry Deering,*"*
1865–
The hills of San Francisco, prepared for the National society of colonial dames of America in the state of California,
by Margaret Perkins Deering. San Francisco, Calif., 1936.

National society of the colonial dames of
America. California.
Killinger, Emily Tibbey.
The islands of San Francisco bay, prepared for the National
society of colonial dames of America in the state of California,
by Emily Tibbey Killinger. San Francisco, Calif., 1934.

**National society of the colonial dames
of America. California.**
Davidson, Ellinor Campbell, 1877–
Notes on California Indian shellmounds, prepared for the
National society of colonial dames of America in the state of
California. by Ellinor C. Davidson. San Francisco, Calif.,
1930.

National Society of the Colonial Dames of America.
California.
[Publications] S. F., 1929–38.
9 v. in 1. illus. pl. maps.

NN 0066542 WaS

National Society of the Colonial Dames of America.
California.
₁Register₎
₁1
₁San Francisco, 1   12°.
v.

1. Societies (National and patriotic),   U. S.
N. Y. P. L.   August 22, 1923.

NN 0066543 NN

National society of the colonial dames of
America. California.
Tibbitts, Grace Cilley.
Rivers of California, by Grace Cilley Tibbitts. Prepared
for the National society of colonial dames of America in the
state of California. San Francisco, Calif., 1938.

National Society of the Colonial Dames of
America. California.
"The Russians in California" ...
see under Stow, Nellie.

National Society of the Colonial Dames of America. Colorado.
₁Officers and members.₎
₁18
₁Denver, 18   12°.
no.

1. Societies (National and patriotic),   U. S.
N. Y. P. L.   September 22, 1923.

NN 0066546 NN

National society of the colonial dames of America. *Connecticut.*
Connecticut circa 1625, its Indian trails, villages and sach-
emdoms ... published by the Connecticut society of the colonial
dames of America, inc., from data collected by Mathias Spiess;
edited by Elinor H. Bulkeley Ingersoll ... ₁Wethersfield,
Conn., *1934₎

26, ₁3₎ p. 23ᵐᵐ.

This information is published to accompany a map of Connecticut
before its occupation by the white man. The original map, drawn by
Mr. Hayden Griswold from data furnished by Mr. Mathias Spiess, was
presented to the Connecticut society of the colonial dames by Mr. and
Mrs. Horace Bushnell Cheney. *cf.* Foreword.
Bibliography: p. ₁27–28₎

1. Indians of North America—Connecticut. 2. Indian trails. I. Ingersoll, Mrs. Elinor Houghton (Bulkeley) 1893– ed. II. Spiess, Mathias. III. Title.

Library of Congress   E78.C7N26
————— Copy 2.   34–16116
Copyright A 71712   ₁3₎   970.4

NN 0066548 DLC DSI

VOLUME 407

National society of the colonial dames of America. *Connecticut.*

Connecticut houses; a list of manuscript histories of early Connecticut homes, presented to the Connecticut state library by the Connecticut society Colonial dames of America. Comp. by Mrs. Elford Parry Trowbridge, chairman, Committee on old houses. Hartford, Connecticut state library, 1916.

33 p. 23ᶜᵐ. (*On verso of t.-p.:* Bulletins of the Connecticut state library, Hartford.

1. Connecticut—Historic houses, etc. 2. Manuscripts. U. S.—Catalogs. 3. Connecticut—Hist.—Bibl. ɪ. Trowbridge, Anna Bertha (Chadwick) "Mrs. Elford Parry Trowbridge," 1866– ɪɪ. Title.

16–14829

Library of Congress   F95.N27

NN   0066549   DLC OC1WHi NN NNC MiU OC1 OU CtY WaU

National society of the colonial dames of America. *Connecticut.*

... Connecticut houses; a list of manuscript histories of early Connecticut homes, compiled by and presented to the Connecticut state library by the Connecticut society, Colonial dames of America ... Hartford, Conn., The State, 1924.

27 p. 23ᶜᵐ. (Bulletin of the Connecticut state library, Hartford. no. 10)
"Compiled in co-operation with Mrs. Elford Parry Trowbridge, chairman, Committee on old homes."
"A list of ... four hundred manuscript histories of 'Early Connecticut houses' ... arranged alphabetically by towns in which the houses are located."
1. Connecticut—Historic houses, etc. 2. Manuscripts. U. S.— Catalogs. 3. Connecticut—Hist.—   Bibl.   ɪ. Trowbridge, Anna Bertha (Chadwick) "Mrs. Elford   Parry Trowbridge," 1866– ɪɪ. Title.
25–27094

Library of Congress   F95.N272

NN   0066550   DLC MH NN OC1 OC1WHi

National society of the colonial dames of America. *Connecticut.*

... Connecticut houses, a list of manuscript histories of early Connecticut homes, compiled by and presented to the Connecticut state library by the Connecticut society, Colonial dames of America; compiled in co-operation with Mrs. Alfred H. Terry, chairman, Committee on old homes. Hartford, Conn., The State, 1931.

39 p. 23ᶜᵐ. (Bulletin of the Connecticut state library, Hartford. no. 16)
"A list of ... six hundred and fifty-five manuscript histories ... arranged alphabetically by towns in which the houses are located."
1. Connecticut—Historic houses, etc. 2. Manuscripts. U. S.—Catalogs. 3. Connecticut—   Hist.—Bibl.   ɪ. Terry, Marian Dickinson (Campbell)   Mrs. Alfred H. Terry", comp. ɪɪ. Title.
32–27310

Library of Congress   F95.N2722
ᵢ₃ᵢ   016.91746

NN   0066551   DLC NN PPB CtY OC1

National society of the colonial dames of America. *Connecticut.*

... Connecticut houses, a list of manuscript histories of Connecticut houses, compiled by and presented to the Connecticut state library by the Connecticut society, Colonial dames of America. Compiled by Historic buildings committee: Mrs. Alfred Howe Terry, chairman. Hartford, Conn., Connecticut state library, 1942.

cover-title, 1 p. l., 47 numb. l. 21½ x 36ᶜᵐ. (Bulletin of the Connecticut state library, Hartford. No. 17)

Reproduced from type-written copy.

"This bulletin comprises a complete list of the nine hundred four manuscript histories of early Connecticut houses which have thus far been compiled and permanently deposited in the Connecticut state library through the Historic buildings committee (formerly Committee on old houses) of the Connecticut society of colonial dames of America."— Prelim. leaf.

1. Architecture, Domestic—Bibl.—Catalogs. 2. Manuscripts. U. S.— Catalogs. ɪ. Terry, Marian Dickinson (Campbell) ɪɪ. Title.
43–53110

Library of Congress   Z5943.D7N3
ᵢ₃ᵢ   016.9746

NN   0066553   DLC OU

National Society of the Colonial Dames of America. Connecticut.
Constitution and by-laws. [Tuttle, Morehouse & Taylor press, 1904]
28 p.

NN   0066554   MiD–B

National society of the Colonial Dames of America. Connecticut.
The constitution of the National society of the Colonial Dames of America and by-laws of the Connecticut society of the Colonial Dames of America. n. p. 1906.
18 p.

NN   0066555   OC1WHi

National society of the colonial dames of America. Connecticut.
Wadsworth atheneum and Morgan memorial, *Hartford.*
... The early plate in Connecticut churches prior to 1850, collected by the Connecticut society of the colonial dames of America, catalogued by Florence Paull Berger ... exhibited in the Morgan memorial, Hartford, Connecticut, May 1919. ᵢHartford? 1919ᵢ

NN   0066555   OC1WHi

National society of the colonial dames of America. Connecticut.
C143   ... Form of record for —————— house in the
015   town of —————— ... [n.p.,191–?]

NN   0066557   CtY

National society of the colonial dames of America. Connecticut.
A history of the National society of the colonial dames of America in the state of Connecticut, November, 1893. December, 1937
see under   Daggett, Eleanor E (Cutler) "Mrs. Leonard M. Daggett, " ed.

974.6   National society of the colonial dames of
N27h   America. Connecticut.
The house of hope of the first Connecticut settlers. A paper read before the Connecticut society of the colonial dames of America, in Hartford,November 19,1895, by Mrs.Charles Frederick Johnson,historian of the society. ᵢHartford?,n.d.ᵢ
46p. 23cm.
1.Connecticut. History. Colonial period. 2.Connecticut. I.Title. II.Series:National society of the   Colonial dames of America. Connecti-   cut. ᵢAddresses,

NN   0066559   N

National Society of the Colonial Dames of America. Connecticut.
[List of early settlers, 1639–1675; Historical events, 1639–1790; and Ancient sites and historical houses of Fairfield, Conn.] Fairfield, Conn., 1905.
1 p.l., 9 p. 15.5 x 12.5 cm.

NN   0066560   CtY

WF846   National Society of the Colonial Dames of
.NA   America. Connecticut.
List of old colonial houses still standing in the state of Connecticut. [n.p.] 1903.
22 p. 15 cm.

1. Connecticut – Historic houses, etc.

NN   0066561   WHi NN

National Society of the Colonial Dames of America. Connecticut.
... Memorial in celebration of the tenth anniversary of the founding of the Connecticut Society of the Colonial Dames of America. [New Haven, 1903]
2 p.l., [3]–65 p. 21 cm.
At head of title: 1893–1903.

NN   0066562   CtY MiD–B

National Society of the Colonial Dames of America. Connecticut.
Officers and members. [The society]

NN   0066563   MiD–B NN

National society of the colonial dames of America. *Connecticut.*

Old houses of Connecticut, from material collected by the Committee on old houses of the Connecticut society of the Colonial dames of America, edited by Bertha Chadwick Trowbridge, chairman, with the assistance of Charles McLean Andrews ... New Haven, Yale university press; ᵢetc., etc.ᵢ 1923.

xxvii, 519 p. col. front., illus. (incl. plans) 29½ cm.

"Of this Limited edition ... there have been printed from type one thousand copies of which this is number 490."
"Published on the foundation established in memory of Calvin Chapin of the class of 1788, Yale college."

1. Connecticut—Historic houses, etc. 2. Architecture, Domestic—Connecticut. 3. Architecture, Colonial. ɪ. Trowbridge, Anna Bertha (Chadwick) "Mrs. Elford Parry Trowbridge," 1866– ed. ɪɪ. Andrews, Charles McLean, 1863–1943, joint ed. ɪɪɪ. Yale university. Calvin Chapin memorial publication fund. ɪᴠ. Title.

F95.N273   23–17387
———— Copy 2.   NA7235.C8N3

NcD MeB CaBVaU KyU MoU GU FTaSU OrPS
NN   0066565   DLC OC1 OU OC1W OO MB OC1WHi NBuU DEU

---

                                    the
National Society of ᵢ Colonial Dames of America. — Connecticut.
Old houses of Connecticut; historical and technical information in regard to... Collected and compiled by the Connecticut Society of Colonial Dames of America. ᵢHartford, Conn., 1916?ᵢ
15 l. (incl. forms, plans.) f°.

Lettered on cover: Form of record...
Printed on one side of leaf only.
Blank leaves at end for "Early traditions and history."

1. Historic houses, U. S.: Conn. 2.   Title.
N. Y. P. L.   May 25, 1917.

NN   0066566   NN

---

                                    the
National Society of ᵢ Colonial Dames of America. Connecticut.
Old houses of Connecticut; historical and technical information in regard to the Doctor Henry Skilton house, Southington, Hartford county, Connecticut...collected and compiled by the Connecticut Society of Colonial Dames of America. ᵢCheshire? 1929.ᵢ   10 l., 17 l. facsims., illus., plans, plates. 4°.

Typewritten, main text lettered a–p.

466893A. 1. Historic houses—U. S.   —Conn.—Southington. 2. Skilton, Henry, 1718–1802.   April 29, 1930
N. Y. P. L.

NN   0066567   NN

National society of the colonial dames of America. *Connecticut.*

Old inns of Connecticut; edited by Marian Dickinson Terry from material collected by the Committee on historic buildings of the National society of the colonial dames of America in the state of Connecticut. Hartford, Conn., The Prospect press, 1937.

253, ᵢ1ᵢ p. incl. illus., plates, facsims. front. 29½ cm.
Maps on lining-papers.
"One thousand copies printed."
Bibliographical note: p. 253.
1. Hotels, taverns, etc.—Connecticut. 2. Connecticut—Historic houses, etc. ɪ. Terry, Marian Dickinson (Campbell) "Mrs. Alfred H. Terry," ed. ɪɪ. Title.

F95.N28   917.46   38–17265

NN   0066568   DLC CU GU OO OU OC1MA PSC NIC

National society of the colonial dames of America. Connecticut.
Newton, Caroline Clifford.
Once upon a time in Connecticut, by Caroline Clifford Newton. Boston, New York ᵢetc.ᵢ Houghton Mifflin company ᵢ1916.

National Society of the Colonial Dames of America. Connecticut.
Pictures loaned to libraries by Connecticut Society of Colonial Dames of America
see under   Connecticut. Public Library Committee.

VOLUME 407

National Society of the Colonial Dames of
America. Connecticut.
Pictures loaned to schools by
Connecticut Society of Colonial Dames of
America
see under Connecticut. Public
Library Committee.

National Society of the Colonial Dames of America.
Connecticut.
Proceedings of the dedication of the memorial
gateway to Jonathan Edwards at the Old Burying
Ground, South Windsor, 25 June, 1929, by the
Connecticut Society of the Colonial Dames of
America. New Haven, Priv. print. [Printing-
Office of the Yale University Press] 1929.
61 p. 24 cm.
Title vignette.

NN 0066572 NIC MH-AH CtY

the
National Society of Colonial Dames of America. Connecticut.
Progress of work upon the public records and archives and
early Connecticut houses. Hartford, 1914. 16 p. 8°.
(Connecticut. State Library. Bull. no. 6.)
Repr.: Librarian's report, 1913-14.

1. Historic houses, U. S.: Connecti-   cut. 2. Archives, U. S.: Connecticut.
3. Series.
N. Y. P. L.   February 28, 1919.

NN 0066573 NN

National society of the colonial dames of America. Connecticut.
Register of the Connecticut society of the Colonial
dames of America. 1893-1907. [Hartford] The Connecticut society [1907]
334 p. front., plates, ports., facsims. 24½ᶜᵐ.
Five hundred copies printed. no. 448.

1. U. S.—Hist.—Colonial period—Societies. 2. Connecticut—Geneal.
16-2780
Library of Congress   E186.4.C75

NN 0066574 DLC OFH OClWHi

E186.4
.C75
1922
National Society of the Colonial Dames of
America. Connecticut.
Register of the Connecticut Society of the
Colonial Dames of America 1893-1922. [Hart-
ford, 1922]
416 p. front. 24 cm.

1. U.S.--Hist.--Colonial period--Societies.
2. Connecticut--Geneal.

NN 0066575 T MiD ICN NN

National society of the colonial dames of America. Connecticut.
Register of the Connecticut society of the colonial dames of
America. 1893-1939. [Hartford?] Published by the Connecticut society [1940]
464 p. front., ports. 23½ᶜᵐ.

1. U. S.—Hist.—Colonial period—Societies. 2. Connecticut—Geneal.
A 41-2357
Yale univ. Library
for Library of Congress   [E186.4.C   ]

NN 0066576 CtY OFH

National Society of the Colonial Dames of America.
Connecticut.
... Special votes and usages governing the
action of officers and committees ... supplementary
to the Constitution and by-laws of the society.
[n.p.] 1906.
20 p. 18.5 cm.

NN 0066577 CtY

National Society of the Colonial Dames of
America. Connecticut.
Traveling schools libraries loaned
by Connecticut society of Colonial dames'
of America
see under Connecticut. Public
library committee.

National Society of the Colonial Dames of America.—Connecticut.
Committee on Old Houses.
List of slides. [Hartford, 1913.] 11 p. 8°.
Caption-title.
List of lantern slides available for use in connection with lectures on Connecti-
cut history.

1. Historic houses, U. S.: Conn.   2. Stereoscopic views.
N. Y. P. L.   January 25, 1916.

NN 0066579 NN

National society of the colonial dames of America. Delaware.
A calendar of Delaware wills, New Castle County,
1682-1800, abstracted and compiled by the Historical research committee of the Colonial dames of Delaware.
New York, F. H. Hitchcock [ᶜ1911]
218 p. 24½ᶜᵐ. $3.50

1. Wills—New Castle Co., Del. 2. New Castle Co., Del.—Geneal.
11-14184
Library of Congress   F172.N5N2

NN 0066580 DLC C NN OClWHi ICU

National Society of the Colonial Dames of America.
Delaware.
Constitution and by-laws ... [Wilmington,
Del., C.L. Story co., print.] 1924.
26, [1] p.

NN 0066581 MiD-B

D 975.1
N 277g
National Society of Colonial Dames of America.
Delaware.
A guide to some historic points in Delaware,
1916. [Wilmington,Del.,1916]
26p.

1. Delaware - Historic houses, etc. 2.
Delaware - Hist. - Colonial Period. I.
Title.

NN 0066582 DeU

National Society of the Colonial Dames of
America. Delaware.
... The Nanticoke and Conoy Indians with
a review of linguistic material from manuscript
and living sources ...
see under Speck, Frank Gouldsmith,
1881-

National society of the Colonial dames of
America. Delaware.
Pyle, Katharine.
Once upon a time in Delaware, by Katharine Pyle, ed. by
Emily P. Bissell, drawings by Ethel Pennewill Brown.
[Wilmington, Del., Mercantile printing company, 1911]

National Society of the Colonial Dames of America. Delaware.
Portraits in Delaware, 1700-1850; a check list. Wilmington, 1951.
176 p. illus. 25 cm.
Bibliography: p. [169]

1. Portraits, American. 2. U. S.—Biog.—Portraits.   I. Title.
N7593.N25   704.942   51—7662

NN 0066585 DLC MH NN ViU DSI

National Society of the Colonial Dames of America. Delaware.
Register.
Wilmington.
v. 23 cm.

1. Delaware—Geneal. 2. U. S.—Geneal.
E186.4.D4   56—33360 ‡

NN 0066586 DLC WaS

National society of the colonial dames of
America. Delaware.
Harrington, Jessie.
Silversmiths of Delaware, 1700-1850, by Miss Jessie Har-
rington, & Old church silver in Delaware. [Wilmington?]
National society of colonial dames of America in the state of
Delaware, 1939.

Pam.
Coll.
39410
National Society of the Colonial Dames of
America. District of Columbia.
National constitution of the Society of the
Colonial Dames of America and by-laws of the
National Society of the Colonial Dames of Amer-
ica in the District of Columbia, [Washington?]
189-]
35 p. 14 cm.

NN 0066588 NcD

National society of the colonial dames of America. District of Columbia.
... Preservation of Niagara Falls ... Petition from the
National society of colonial dames of America in the
District of Columbia, praying for the preservation of
Niagara Falls, with indorsements from several states.
[Washington, Gov't print. off., 1906]
8 p. 23ᶜᵐ. (U. S. 59th Cong., 1st sess. Senate. Doc. 217)
Presented by Mr. Gallinger.

1. Niagara Falls.
6-16721 Additions
Library of Congress   F127.N8N27

NN 0066589 DLC MiU OO DNW

the
National society of colonial dames of America,
Florida
[Directory] [Jacksonville] 19-
v.
Library has
1927, 1928.

NN 0066590 MiD-B

National Society of the Colonial Dames of America.
Florida.
Register and historian's report.
v.

NN 0066591 NbHi

VOLUME 407

Ga
E186.4
G44   National Society of the Colonial Dames of America.
1927   Georgia.
      By-laws of the Georgia Society of the Colonial
    Dames of America, incorporated January 24, 1894,
    as amended through April, 1927. ₍n.p.₎ Pomar's
    Print Shop ₍1927₎
    15 p. 15cm.

    Cover title.
    Title varies slightly from earlier editions.

    1. National Society of the Colonial Dames of
America. Georgia.   I. Title.

NN   0066592   GU

Ga
E186.4
G42   National Society of the Colonial Dames of
1931   America. Georgia.
      By-laws of the Georgia Society, Colonial
    Dames of America, incorporated January 24,
    1894, amended April, 1927, amended April,
    1931. ₍Savannah? 1931?₎

    1. National Society of the Colonial Dames
of America. Georgia.   I. Title.

NN   0066593   GU

Ga
E186.4
G42   National Society of the Colonial Dames of
1940   America. Georgia.
      By-laws of the Georgia Society of the
    Colonial Dames of America, incorporated Janu-
    ary 24, 1894, as amended to 1940. ₍Savannah?
    1940?₎
    15 p. 21cm.

    Cover title.

    1. National Society of the Colonial Dames of
America. Georgia.   I. Title.

NN   0066594   GU

Ga
E186.4
G4A4   **National Society of the Colonial Dames of**
1932   **America. Georgia.**
      Constitution and by-laws: Georgia Society
    Colonial Dames, XVII century. Atlanta, 1932.
    24 p. 23cm.

    Cover title.
    Charter members: p. 17-24.

NN   0066595   GU

Ga
F292
F7N3   National Society of the Colonial Dames of
    America. Georgia.
      Frederica; unveiling of the tablet placed
    in the old fort of Oglethorpe by the Georgia
    Society of The Colonial Dames of America
    on St. Simon's Island, Georgia, April 22,
    1904. ₍n.p., 1904₎
    1 v. (unpaged) illus. 22cm.

    Cover title.

    1. Fort Frede-   rica National
Monument.

NN   0066596   GU NN GU-De

NN   0066597   DLC TxU OC1 OU ViU NcD KEmT OkU

Ga
E186.4
G4A43   National Society of the Colonial Dames of
1950   America. Georgia.
      A history of the Georgia Society of the
    Colonial Dames of America from April 1893 to
    January 1950. Comp. by Mary Savage Anderson.
    Rev. ₍n.p., 1950?₎
    76 p. 23cm.

    1. National Society of the Colonial Dames
of America. Georgia.   I. Anderson, Mary
Savage (Jones) 1873–   comp. II. Title.

NN   0066598   GU

F314
.M24   **National society of the colonial dames of**
      America. Georgia.
    McQueen, John, 1751–1807.
      The letters of Don Juan McQueen to his family, written **from**
Spanish East Florida, 1791–1807; with a biographical **sketch**
and notes by Walter Charlton Hartridge. Columbia, S. C.,
Pub. for the Georgia society of the Colonial dames of America
by Bostick & Thornley, 1943.

CT275
.M4347   **National Society of the Colonial Dames of**
A4   **America. Georgia.**
    Mackay, Robert, 1772–1816.
      The letters of Robert Mackay to his wife, written from
ports in America and England, 1795–1816. With an introd.
and notes by Walter Charlton Hartridge. Athens, Pub-
lished under the auspices of the Georgia Society of the
Colonial Dames of America by the University of Georgia
Press ₍1949₎

      National society of the Colonial dames of
      America. Georgia society.

    Charlton, Walter Glasco, 1851–1917.
      The making of Georgia ; Oglethorpe; two addresses by Hon.
Walter Glasco Charlton ... ₍Savannah? 190–?₎

Ga
E186.4
G44   National Society of the Colonial Dames of
1913   America. Georgia.
      National constitution and by-laws.
    ₍Savannah, Braid & Hutton, Printers, 1913₎
    26 p. 18cm.

    Cover title.

NN   0066602   GU

      National Society of the Colonial Dames of America.
      Georgia.
        Order of service for laying the cornerstone
    of the George Whitefield Memorial Chapel at
    Bethesda, Chatham County, Ga. The Georgia
    Society of Colonial Dames of America, April 28th,
    1916, 4 P.M.   [Savannah, 1916]
        [4] p.   8vo.

NN   0066603   GU-De

      National Society of the Colonial Dames of America.   Georgia.
189   ₍Register of members.₎

Augusta, Ga., 189   **12°.**
v.

NN   0066604   NN GU

      National society of the colonial dames of America
      Georgia.
      Register of the Georgia society colonial dames
    of America ... Savannah [Register committee?]
    1914.
      [3]–125, viii p.   23 cm.

NN   0066605   ViLxW NN

      National society of the colonial dames of
    America. Georgia.
      Register of the Georgia society colonial dames
    of America... Savannah, Ga., ₍Braid & Hutton,
    inc.,₎ 1926.
    190 p.

    Bound with this is: Supplement to Register...
Savannah, 1928.
    56 p.

NN   0066606   MiD-B

NN   0066607   DLC GU

NN   0066608   DLC AU GASC NjP NcD GMW

F
83195
.26   National society of the colonial dames
      of America—Illinois.
        Constitution, by-laws and annual
    reports...

    [Chicago]

NN   0066609   ICN

      National Society of the Colonial Dames of America.
    Indiana.
      Rules for admission of members.
    = N. p. 3 pp. 16°.

NN   0066610   MB

      National Society of the Colonial Dames of
      America. Iowa.
        Early social and religious experiments
    in Iowa ...
            see under   McCarty, Dwight Gaylord.

      National Society of the Colonial Dames of
      America. Kansas.
        Constitution, by-laws and membership ...
    [Lawrence, Kansas]
        Library has
    1907.

NN   0066612   MiD-B

NN   0066613   NN

VOLUME 407

E
186.4
.K4
National Society of the Colonial Dames of
America. Kentucky.
History of the Colonial Dames in the Commonwealth of Kentucky, 1897-1947. [n.p.]
1946.
56 p. illus. 22cm.

1. U.S.—History—Colonial period—Societies.
I. Title.

NN 0066614 KyLoU

E186.4 National society of the colonial dames
.K25   of America. Kentucky.
1930   The National society of the colonial
dames of America in the commonwealth of
Kentucky. [Louisville, Ky., Press of
G.G. Fetter company, inc.] 1930.
5 p. l.,9-139 p. 23cm.

Pages [93]-[98] left blank.

NN 0066615 MnHi

National society of the colonial dames of America.
Kentucky.
Register of the National society of the colonial dames of America in the commonwealth of
Kentucky, 1947. [Louisville, Ky., From the
press of the Franklin printing co., inc., 1947]
3 p. l., 179 p. 23.5 cm.

Half-title: Kentucky register.
On cover: 1897-1947.

1. Kentucky – Geneal. 2. U. S. – Geneal. 3.
U. S. – Hist. – Colonial period – Biog. 4.
U. S. – Hist. – Colonial period – Societies. I.
Title: Kentucky register.

NN 0066617 Vi MiD

Microcard
929
National Society of the Colonial Dames of
America. • Kentucky.
Register of the National Society of the
Colonial Dames of America in the Commonwealth of Kentucky. [Louisville, Ky.,
1947?]
179p. 23cm.

Micro-opaque. Louisville, Lost Cause
Press, 1969. 5 cards. 7.5 x 12.5cm.
(Kentucky culture series)

√1.Kentucky –   Biog. √2.Kentucky –
Geneal. √I.   Title. √(Series)

NN 0066618 CLSU

L976.3 National society of the Colonial dames of
(920)   America. Louisiana.
N277e   Early settlers of Rapides parish, portraits
and land grant [Alexandria, La., 1952]
116, [3] p. ports., facsims. 30 cm.
Compiled by the Historical activities
committee of the Alexandria committee.

Loose-leaf.

1. Rapides parish, La. – Hist. 2. Rapides
parish, La. – Geneal. 3. Louisiana – Geneal.
4.Louisiana –   Biog. I. Title.

NN 0066619 LNHT

National Society of the Colonial Dames of
America. Louisiana.
Marriage records, Parish of Ouachita,
Louisiana. Ouachita Parish Court House,
Monroe, La.
see under title

National Society of the Colonial Dames of America.
Louisiana.
The National Society of the Colonial Dames of
America resident in the state of Louisiana.
[n.p.] 1917.
28 p. plates. 22.5 cm.

NN 0066621 CtY

E186.4 National society of the colonial dames
.L85   of America. Louisiana.
1931   The National society of the colonial
dames of America in the state of Louisiana, organized by Mrs. Francis Daniel
Blake, 1895. Register, 1931. [New
Orleans, Press of Dameron-Pierson co.,
ltd.] 1931.
55,[1] p. 23cm.

Pages [47]-[52] left blank.

NN 0066622 MnHi

369.123
L93n
National Society of the Colonial Dames of
America. Louisiana.
The National Society of the Colonial Dames
of America in the State of Louisiana, 1895-
1948. [n.p., 1948?]
67p. 23cm.

1. U.S. – Hist. – Colonial period – Societies, etc. 2. Louisiana – Hist. – Colonial
period – Societies, etc. 3. Louisiana –
Geneal. Sp.: Littlefiend Fund.

NN 0066623 TxU

La
641.5
N21t
1952
National Society of the Colonial Dames of
America. Louisiana.
To a king's taste. [New Orleans?]
1952.
183 p. illus. 23 cm.

1. Cookery, American—Louisiana.
2. Cookery, Creole. I. Title.

NN 0066624 LU

F379
.N5N53
National Society of the Colonial Dames of
America. Louisiana.
New Orleans. Christ Church Episcopal Cathedral.
Transcription [of] baptismal, marriage and death records,
1849-1900, comp. by the National Society of the Colonial
Dames of America resident in Louisiana. [New Orleans,
1948?]

National Society of the Colonial Dames of
America. Maine.
Constitution, by-laws and members.
n. imp.
Library has
1907.

NN 0066626 MiD-B

National Society of the Colonial Dames of America.
Maine.
Officers and constitution. n.p., n.d.

NN 0066627 Nh

National Society of the Colonial Dames of
America. Maine.
Register of the National Society of
Colonial Dames of America in the state of
Maine. [Boston, 1928]
100 p.

NN 0066628 OClWHi

National society of [the] colonial dames of America.
Maryland.
Ridgely, Helen West, ed.
A calendar of memorial inscriptions collected in the state of
Maryland by the Maryland society of the Colonial dames of
America. Ed. by Helen West Ridgely ... [New York? 1906]

National Society of the Colonial Dames of America
Maryland.
Historic graves of Maryland and the District
of Columbia....
see under Ridgely, Helen West, ed.

National society of the colonial dames of America. Maryland.
The Maryland society of the Colonial dames of America. 1899. Baltimore, Guggenheimer, Weil & co., 1899.
163 p. 23ᵐ.
Errata slip inserted between p. 162 and 163.

1. U. S.—Hist.—Colonial period—Societies.

12-15157

Library of Congress   E186.4.M24

NN 0066631 DLC NcD

National society of the colonial dames of America. Maryland.
"Mount Clare", Carroll Park, Baltimore; an historical
sketch issued under the auspices of the Maryland society of the colonial dames of America. [Baltimore]
°1926.
[18] p. front., illus. 24ᵐ.
"The material for this brochure is taken from the notes of Mrs. Albert
Sioussat, on 'Old Baltimore'."

1. Mount Clare, Baltimore. 2. Carroll family. I. Sioussat, Mrs.
Annie Middleton (Leakin)

Library of Congress   F189.B1N2   26-12324

NN 0066632 DLC NcD

National society of the colonial dames of
America. Maryland.
Sioussat, *Mrs*. Annie Middleton (Leakin)
Old Baltimore, by Annie Leakin Sioussat. Published under
the auspices of the Maryland society of the colonial dames of
America, in honor of the author. New York, **The Macmillan**
company, 1931.

National society of the colonial dames of America. Maryland.
Register of the Maryland society of the colonial dames
of America, 1891-1915. Baltimore, The Society, 1915.
viii, 254 p. 24ᵐ.
Second lineage book; first lineage book pub. under title: **The Maryland**
society of the colonial dames of America. 1899. Baltimore, 1899.

1. U. S.—Hist.—Colonial period—Societies. 2. Maryland—Hist.—
Colonial period—Societies.

16-11144

Library of Congress   E186.4.M245

NN 0066634 DLC WaS ViU OClWHi NN

National society of the colonial dames of
America. Massachusetts.
Bolton, *Mrs*. Ethel (Stanwood) 1873–
American samplers, by Ethel Stanwood Bolton and Eva
Johnston Coe. [Boston] The Massachusetts society of the
colonial dames of America, 1921.

National Society of the Colonial Dames of
America. Massachusetts.
Annual report. Boston.

NN 0066636 MiD-B NbHi NN

VOLUME 407

Typ
870
98.5980

National society of the colonial dames of
America. Massachusetts.
An exhibition & competition of colonial
pictures under the auspices of the Colonial
dames of Massachusetts, held at the Boston art
club from Tuesday, December sixth, to Saturday,
December seventeenth, and open daily from nine
in the morning to six o'clock at night.
Printed for the Colonial dames at Boston,
Massachusetts, MDCCCXCVIII.

7,[1]p. 16cm., in folder 17cm.

Title vignette.
"Printed at The Merrymount press, Boston."
Original marble wrappers, label on front
cover; in cloth folder.
Inserted at end is a blank printed admittance
ticket to the exhibition.

NN   0066638   MH NN

National Society of the Colonial Dames of
America. Massachusetts.
History of the Quincy homestead.
[Boston, Mass.] Massachusetts society
of Colonial Dames, 1920.
14 p.   illus.

NN   0066639   MiD-B

F
83195
.42

National society of the colonial dames
of America—Massachusetts.
Members and ascendants of the Massachusetts society of colonial dames of
America.   Boston, 1898.

--   ----- Supplement... Members admitted November to May, 1898-99.   Boston, 1899.

--   ----- Supplement no.2... Members admitted
November, 1899, to May, 1901.   Boston,
1902.

NN   0066641   ICN MB OClWHi MH

National society of the colonial dames of America. *Massachusetts.*
Register of the Massachusetts society of colonial dames
of America ... 1893–1905. Boston, Printed for the Society, 1905.
31, [1], 32–428 p. front., port., facsims. 24½cm.
E186.4.M28
—— Supplement ... 1905–1909. Boston, Printed for the
Society, 1909.
2 p. l., 429–548 p. 24½cm.
1. Massachusetts—Geneal. 2. U. S.—Geneal.
5–35978
Library of Congress   E186.4.M281

NN   0066642   DLC WaS MB NBuU OClWHi

National society of the colonial dames of America. *Massachusetts.*
Register of the Massachusetts society of the colonial
dames of America, 1893–1917. Boston, Printed for the
society, 1917.
599 p. 25cm.

1. U. S.—Hist.—Colonial period—Societies. 2. Massachusetts—Geneal.
17–19082
Library of Congress   E186.4.M282

NN   0066643   DLC WaSp

National society of the colonial dames of America. *Massachusetts.*
Register of the Massachusetts society of the colonial dames
of America, 1893–1927. Boston, Printed for the Society, 1927.
iv, 496 p., 1 l. front., ports. 23½cm.

1. Massachusetts—Geneal. 2. U. S.—Geneal. 3. U. S.—Hist.—Colonial period—Biog.
27–27477
Library of Congress   E186.4.M35

NN   0066644   DLC WaS Or

National society of the colonial dames of America. *Massa-
chusetts.*
Register of the Massachusetts Society of the colonial dames of
America, 1893–1944. Boston, The Society, 1944.
659 p. 23½cm.
"Entirely the work of ... Mrs. Elizabeth French Bartlett."—Introd.

1. Massachusetts—Geneal. 2. U. S.—Geneal. 3. U. S.—Hist.—Colonial
period—Biog. I. Bartlett, Elizabeth French.
44–51981
Library of Congress   E186.4.M35 1944
[3]   369.123

NN   0066645   DLC WaS

National Society of the Colonial Dames of
America. Massachusetts.
[Report of historian] n.p., n.d.
Library has
v. 1- 1904/04, v. 2 1905/06.

NN   0066646   MiD-B

National Society of the Colonial Dames of America.
Massachusetts.
Reports of officers and standing committees 1907–1908.
= [Boston. 1908.] 29 pp. 8°.

NN   0066647   MB

National Society of the Colonial Dames of
America. Massachusetts.
The story of America
see under   Pecorini, Alberto.

National Society of the Colonial Dames of
America. Massachusetts.
Summary of reports of officers and standing
committees 1910–1911.   [Boston? 1911]
16 p.

NN   0066649   MH MiD

National Society of the Colonial Dames of America.
Massachusetts.
Supplement to members and ascendants of the...Society.
1898–1899.   Boston: the society, 1899. 53 p.   8°.

1. Societies (Patriotic), U. S.
N. Y. P. L.

NN   0066650   NN

national society of the colonial dames of America.
Massachusetts.
Bolton, *Mrs.* Ethel (Stanwood) 1873–
Wax portraits and silhouettes, by Ethel Stanwood Bolton;
with an introduction by Charles Henry Hart, esq. Boston,
The Massachusetts society of the colonial dames of America,
1914.

National Society of the Colonial Dames of America. Michigan.
Constitution and by-laws...officers and members.
19
Detroit[, 19   8°.
no.

1. Societies, National and patriotic   —U. S.
N. Y. P. L.
February 11, 1930
NN   0066652   NN MiD

National society of the colonial dames of
America. Michigan.
History and register, 1897–1937. n. imp.
153 p.

First lineage book published under title:
List of members...1898.

NN   0066653   MiD-B

National Society of the Colonial Dames of America. Michigan.
List of members.
18
[Detroit, 18   8°.
no.

1. Societies, National and patriotic   —U. S.
N. Y. P. L.
February 11, 1930
NN   0066654   NN MiD

National Society of the Colonial Dames of
America. Michigan.
[Report of historian] n.p., n.d.

NN   0066655   MiD

National Society of the Colonial Dames of America.
Minnesota.
A brief history of the National society of the
colonial dames of America in the state of Minnesota,
1896–1935 ...
see under   Janney, Frances Wheaton,
comp.

*E186.4
.M6
1901

National Society of the Colonial
Dames of America. Minnesota.
The constitution and by-laws;
officers and members, 1901.
[St. Paul? 1901].
32 p. 19cm.

NN   0066657   MnHi

National society of the colonial dames of
America. Minnesota.
Hennepin, Louis, *17th cent.*
Father Louis Hennepin's Description of Louisiana, newly
discovered to the southwest of New France by order of the
king; translated from the original edition by Marion E. Cross,
with an introduction by Grace Lee Nute. [Minneapolis, Pub.
for the Minnesota society of the Colonial dames of America,
The University of Minnesota press, 1938.

National society of the colonial dames
of America. Minnesota.
Gates, Charles M   *ed.*
Five fur traders of the Northwest; being the narrative of
Peter Pond and the diaries of John Macdonell, Archibald N.
McLeod, Hugh Faries, and Thomas Connor; edited by
Charles M. Gates, with an introduction by Grace Lee Nute.
[Minneapolis] Pub. for the Minnesota society of the colonial
dames of America, The University of Minnesota press, 1933.

National society of the Colonial dames of America. *Mis-
souri.*
Register of the National society of the Colonial dames of
America in the state of Missouri ... Saint Louis, 1932.
240 p. plates. 23½cm.
" Edited by Katharine Twining Moody, historian."
E186.4.M65
—— Supplement, 1940. [St. Louis? 1940]
1 p. l., 23 p. 21½cm.
I. Moody, Katharine Twining, ed.
42–10023
Library of Congress   E186.4.M65 Suppl.
[2]   369.123

NN   0066660   DLC ICN MoSU NN

VOLUME 407

National Society of the Colonial Dames of America.
Nebraska.
Fontenelle. ₍Omaha, 1916₎
29 p. illus. 19 cm.

Cover title.
In slip case.
"Logan Fontenelle, last ruling chief of
the Omahas", by H.F.Childs: p.13-19.

NN 0066661   NjP

National Society of the Colonial Dames of
America. Nebraska.
A history of the National Society of the
Colonial Dames of America in the state of
Nebraska
see under   Learned, Mary Poppleton.

National Society of the Colonial Dames of
America. Nebraska.
Officers and Board of Managers of the
Nebraska Society of the Colonial Dames of
America ...
v.
Title varies slightly.

NN 0066663   NbHi

National society of the colonial dames of
America. Nebraska.
Troup, Elsie De Cou, *"Mrs. Alexander C. Troup."*
Once upon a time in Nebraska, comp. for the Colonial
dames by Mrs. Alexander C. Troup ... illustrations con-
tributed by Thomas R. Kimball ... 2d ed. Omaha, 1916.

National society of the colonial dames of
America. Nebraska.
...Sketch of Logan Fontenelle, the last
ruling chief of the Omahas... n. imp.
29 p. port.

NN 0066665   MiD-B

National society of the colonial dames of
America. Nebraska.
The story of the Missouri river
see under   Learned, Mary Poppleton.

National Society of the Colonial Dames of
America. New Hampshire.
Addresses. Manch., n.d.

NN 0066667   Nh

National society of the colonial dames of
America. New Hampshire.
Colonial garrisons of New Hampshire. Pub. by
the New Hampshire society of the colonial dames
of America. Comp. for the Historic activities
committee by Mrs. Wendell Burt Folsom. Exeter,
N. H., News-letter press, 1937.
62 ₍4₎ p. front., illus.

NN 0066668   MiD-B Nh MH

National society of the colonial dames of
America. New Hampshire.

Goss, Winifred (Lane)
Colonial gravestone inscriptions in the state of New Hampshire, published by the Historic activities committee of the National society of the colonial dames of America in the state of
New Hampshire, from collections made by committees from
1913 to 1942. Compiled by Mrs. Charles Carpenter Goss ...
Dover, N. H., 1942.

National society of the colonial dames of America. *New
Hampshire.*
Gravestone inscriptions gathered by the Old burial
grounds committee of the National society of the colonial
dames of America in the state of New Hampshire; comp.
by Mrs. Josiah Carpenter, chairman. Cambridge, Printed at the Riverside press, 1913.
2 p. l., 63 p. 20ᵐᵐ.

1. Epitaphs—New Hampshire.   ɪ. Carpenter, Georgia Butters (Drake)
"Mrs. Josiah Carpenter," comp.

14-11195

Library of Congress   F33.N27

NN 0066670   DLC NBuG WHi NhD ICN MnHi CtY

National Society of the Colonial Dames of
America. New Hampshire.
House of the first minister of Concord,
New Hampshire. 1733-4. Meeting of Colonial
Dames. Concord, N.H., June 17, 1899.

NN 0066671   NhDo

National society of the colonial dames of
America. New Hampshire.
Orcutt, Philip Dana.
The Moffatt-Ladd house, its garden and its period, 1763,
Portsmouth, New Hampshire, by Philip Dana Orcutt, A. ɪ. A.
₍Portsmouth₎ The New Hampshire society of colonial dames
of America, 1935.

E186.4   National society of the colonial dames
.N45   of America. New Hampshire.
1930   The New Hampshire society of the
         colonial dames of America. Directory,
         1930. Dover, N.H., C.F. Whitehouse,
         printer, 1930.
         51 p. 24cm.

NN 0066673   MnHi

National Society of the Colonial Dames of
America. New Hampshire.
Register. Manch., 1898.

NN 0066674   Nh NN

National society of the colonial dames of America. *New
Hampshire.*
The register of the New Hampshire society of the
colonial dames of America ... Manchester, The Society,
1910.
147 p. 23½ᵐᵐ.

1. U. S.—Hist.—Colonial period—Societies.

16-9477

Library of Congress   E186.4.N3

NN 0066675   DLC

National society of the colonial dames of America. *New
Hampshire.*
The register of the New Hampshire society of the
Colonial dames of America ... ₍Dover, N. H.₎ The So-
ciety, 1926.
202 p. 23½ᵐᵐ.

1. U. S.—Hist.—Colonial period—Societies. 2. U. S.—Hist.—Revolution—Registers, lists, etc.

26-13613

Library of Congress   E186.4.N3 1926

NN 0066676   DLC MB

National society of the colonial dames of
America. New Jersey.

Lawrenceville, N. J. Presbyterian church.
The church records of the Presbyterian church of Lawrenceville, New Jersey, and the Bible records from the Bibles in
the library of the church, edited and compiled by Lida Cokefair
Gedney ... Published by authority of the Board of managers
of the New Jersey society of the colonial dames of America.
₍Somerville, N. J.₎ Somerset press, inc.₎ 1941.

National Society of the Colonial Dames of America. New Jersey.
Constitution, charter and by-laws of the New Jersey society of
the Colonial Dames of America... Trenton, N. J.: MacCrellish
& Quigley Co., 1916. 40 p. 16°.

1. Societies (National and patriotic),   U. S.
N. Y. P. L.   January 11, 1918.

NN 0066678   NN

National Society of the Colonial Dames of America. New Jersey.
Directory and proceedings of the annual meeting.
1
Trenton,   sq. 16°.
v.

1. Societies (National and patriotic).   U. S.
N. Y. P. L.   June 24, 1918.

NN 0066679   NN MiD

National society of the colonial dames of
America. New Jersey society.
Furman, Moore, 1728-1808.
The letters of Moore Furman, deputy quarter-master general
of New Jersey in the revolution, comp. and ed. with genealog-
ical notes by the Historical research committee of the New
Jersey society of the Colonial dames of America. New York,
Pub. for the Society by F. H. Hitchcock, 1912.

National Society of the Colonial Dames of America. New Jersey.
The register of the New Jersey Society of the Colonial Dames
of America... Trenton: The society, 1914. xxvi, 415 p.
front., plates. 8°.

50452A. 1. Societies (National   and patriotic), U. S.
N. Y. P. L.   August 22, 1922.

NN 0066681   NN OC1WHi CtY

E186.4   National Society of the Colonial Dames of
.N4   America. New Jersey.
         Register of the New Jersey Society of the
         Colonial Dames of America, 1892-1928. ₍New
         Haven, Quinnipiack Press₎ 1928.
         viii, 707 p. front.,plates. 24 cm.

Each plate preceded by descriptive letter
press.

1. U.S.—Hist.—Colonial period—Biog.
2. New Jersey—Geneal. 3. U.S.—Geneal.

NN 0066682   T MiD-B NcD ICN NN ICU NjP

National society of the colonial dames of America.
New Jersey.

Hopewell, N. J.
The town records of Hopewell, New Jersey, compiled by
Lida Cokefair Gedney, registrar. Published by authority of
the Board of managers of the New Jersey society of the
Colonial dames of America. ₍New York, Printed by Little
& Ives company₎ 1931. *

National society of the colonial dames of America. *New
York.*
Annual register of the Colonial dames of the state of New
York, 1893-1898 ... Published by authority of the Board of
managers. New York ₍H. K. Brewer & co., printers₎ 1898.
231, ₍1₎ p. front., col. pl. 26ᵐᵐ.

1. New York (State)—Geneal.

96-62 Revised

Library of Congress   E186.4.N63

NN 0066684   DLC OrU IU OC1WHi

National society of the colonial dames of
America. New York.
Fernow, Berthold, 1837-1908, comp.
Calendar of wills on file and recorded in the offices of the
clerk of the Court of appeals, of the county clerk at Albany,
and of the secretary of state, 1626-1836, comp. and ed. by
Berthold Fernow ... under the auspices of the Colonial dames
of the state of New York, and published by the Society. New
York ₍The Knickerbocker press₎ 1896.

VOLUME 407

NATIONAL SOCIETY OF THE COLONIAL DAMES OF
AMERICA - New York.
Catalogue, colonial education, Van Cortlandt
House Museum. [New York], 1924.

Plates and facsim. plates.
Cover serves as title page.

NN 0066686   MH NN

National Society of the Colonial Dames of America.
New York.
Catalogue, Van Cortlandt House Museum, for
the Hudson-Fulton Celebration, September, 1909
    see under   Van Cortlandt Mansion, New
York.

National Society of the Colonial Dames of
America. New York.
Catalogue, Van Cortlandt House Museum.
Huguenot memorials of the refugees who came to
America ...
    see under   Van Cortlandt Manson,
New York.

National Society of the Colonial Dames of America. New
York.
A collection of tea sets; comprising specimens from the colonial period, with a few of later date, 1910. [New York, 1910?]
8 p.   8°.

1. Pottery.—Exhibitions, U. S.:   N. Y.
N. Y. P. L.

NN 0066689   NN

National Society of the Colonial Dames of
America. New York.
Eighteen colonial recipes
    see under title

National society of the colonial dames of
America. New York.
Robison, *Mrs.* Jeannie Floyd (Jones) 1853-   *ed.*
... Genealogical records; manuscript entries of births,
deaths and marriages, taken from family Bibles, 1581–
1917, ed. by Jeannie F-J. Robison and Henrietta C. Bartlett ... New York, 1917.

National Society of the Colonial Drames of America. New
York.
List of members.
Fishkill, N. Y.,   16°.

1. Societies (Patriotic), U. S.
N. Y. P. L.

NN 0066692   NN

National society of the colonial dames of America. *New
York.*
Loan exhibition of colonial book-plates, Society of colonial dames, state of New York. April first to June first,
1908. [New York, The De Vinne press, 1908]
iv, 39, [1] p. front., plates. 18°.

1. Book-plates, American.   I. Title: Colonial book-plates.

                            18–1705

Library of Congress   Z994.A5N2

NN 0066693   DLC

National society of the colonial dames of America,
New York.
Publications of the committee on history and tra-
dition of the Colonial dames of the state of New York
New York, 1902-

[Analyzed]

NN 0066694   DLC

National society of the colonial dames of America. *New
York.*
Register of the Colonial dames of the state of New
York, 1893–1901 ... New York, Pub. by the authority of
the Board of managers, 1901.
373 p. front., plates. 24°.

1. New York (State)—Geneal.

Library of Congress   E186.4.N64   6—22

NN 0066695   DLC WaS MB OClWHi

National society of the colonial dames of America. *New
York.*
Register of the Colonial dames of the state of New
York, 1893–1913 ... New York, Pub. by the authority of
the Board of managers, 1913.
432 p. 24°.

1. New York (State)—Hist.—Colonial period—Societies.

                     13–25651

Library of Congress   E186.4.N65

NN 0066696   DLC WaS NIC IU OClWHi

National society of the colonial dames of America. *New
York.*
Register of the National society of colonial dames in
the state of New York, 1893–1926 ... New York, Pub. by
authority of the Board of managers, 1926.
534 p. 24°.

                     26–20949

Library of Congress   E186.4.N66

NN 0066697   DLC NN ViU WaS NIC OClWHi

F
83195
.13
1941
NATIONAL SOCIETY OF THE COLONIAL DAMES OF AMERICA.
New York.
Register of the National society of colonial
dames in the state of New York. Containing the
new members and the supplemental papers accumulat-
ed between the 1926 register and February 1941.
New York, Published by authority of the Board of
managers, 1941.
204p. 24p.

NN 0066698   ICN

National society of the colonial dames of America.
New York.
... Report of officers and standing committees
New York, 180-
-vols. 22½cm.

At head of title: The colonial dames of the
state of New York.

NN 0066699   NBuG NN CtY

National Society of the Colonial Dames of America. New York.
Six colonial recipes, a Dutch sausage and a
colonial punch. Printed by the City History
Club Committee of the Colonial Dames of the
State of New York... New York:[Irving Press],
1908. 9 l. 8°.

1.Cookery (American) 2. Title.

NN 0066700   NN

National Society of the Colonial Dames of America. New York.
Some Colonial and Revolutionary landmarks, Manhattan, 1609–
1800; illustrated by Elizabeth Shippen Green Elliott... [New
York] 1932. 24 p. illus. (incl. plans.) 26 x 13½cm.

"New revised edition."
"Printed under the auspices of the Historical Activities Committee of the National
Society of the Colonial Dames in the State of New York."
"Bibliography," p. 24.

869647A. 1. New York (City)—   Hist.—Landmarks, historic buildings,
etc.
N. Y. P. L.   March 2, 1937

NN 0066701   NN NBhi

National Society of the Colonial Dames of America. New York.
The story of Van Cortlandt Park. New York: Irving Press,
1911. 24 p., 1 l., 4 pl. 4°.

1. New York city.—Parks: Van   Cortlandt.
N. Y. P. L.

NN 0066702   NN OClWHi

National Society of the Colonial Dames of America. New
York.
Van Cortlandt House Museum. A special exhibition
in connection with the Mayor's Catskill aqueduct
celebration. N.Y., 1917.
15 p. (In N.Y. City The Mayor's Catskill Aqueduct
Celebration Committee.)

NN 0066703   OO

[National Society of the Colonial Dames of America. New York.]
Van Cortlandt House Museum, Van Cortlandt Park, New
York. Special exhibition Wedgwood cameo portrait medallions,
china, portraits and other eighteenth century articles... [New
York,] 1922. 42 p. 12°.

1. Pottery (British) : Wedgwood.   2. Pottery.—Exhibitions, U. S.:
N. Y. : New York City. 3. Title.
N. Y. P. L.   May 2, 1924.

NN 0066704   NN

National society of the colonial dames of
America. New York.
[Ferris, Mary Lanman (Douw) "*Mrs. Morris P. Ferris*"] 1855–
1932.
Van Cortlandt mansion, erected 1748, now in the custody of
the Colonial dames of the state of New York. [New York,
The De Vinne press, 1897]

NN 0066705

National society of the colonial dames of America. *New
York. Library.*
Catalogue of the genealogical and historical library of
the Colonial dames of the state of New York. New York,
The Society, 1911.
518 p. 25°.

"Limited edition. Only two hundred and fifty copies have been printed
from type. This is number 41."

1. U. S.—Geneal.—Bibl.

                     12–11415

Library of Congress   Z5313.U5N2

NN 0066706   DLC MiU

NATIONAL SOCIETY OF THE COLONIAL DAMES OF AMERICA. New York. Library.
Catalogue of the genealogical and historical library of the Colonial
dames of the state of New York. New York, The Society, 1912.
518 p. 25cm.

574018B. 1. United States—Geneal.—Bibl. 2. New York (State)—Hist.—
Bibl.

NN 0066707   NN

VOLUME 407

National Society of the Colonial Dames of
369.123   America. North Carolina.
N873A
    Addresses delivered under the auspices of
the North Carolina Society of the Colonial Dames
of America, 1900–1926. ₍Wilmington, N. C.,
Press of Jackson & Bell Company, 1926?₎
    192 p.   22½cm.

    1. North Carolina. History. Colonial
period. Addresses, essays, lectures

NN   0066708   NcD ViU

National Society of the Colonial Dames of
America. North Carolina.
    ... Annual report of the National Society
of the Colonial Dames of America in the state of
North Carolina.

NN   0066709   NbHi

National society of the colonial dames of America.
North Carolina.
    ₍Wilmington, 1905?₎
By-laws and directory, 1904–5.

NN   0066710   NcU

National society of the colonial dames of
America. North Carolina.
Sprunt, James.
    A colonial apparition, a story of the Cape Fear. By
James Sprunt. Wilmington, N. C., Le Gwin bros., 1898.

F   National society of the colonial dames
83195   of America—North Carolina.
.648   The constitution and by-laws of the
North Carolina society of the colonial
dames of America. Officers and members.
Wilmington, N. C., 1903.

NN   0066712   ICN NcU

National Society of the Colonial Dames of
America. North Carolina.
    Constitution and by-laws.   Wilmington, N. C.,
1921.
    32p. 22cm.

    Cover title.
    Includes the national constitution and the
constitution of the North Carolina society .

    1. U. S. - History - Colonial period - Societies.
I. Title.

NN   0066713   NcRS

National society of the colonial dames of America. *North Carolina.*
    ... Historical addresses delivered at the ruins of Saint
Philip's church under the auspices of the North Carolina
society of colonial dames. ₍Wilmington, N. C., The De Rosset
press₎ 1901.
    ₍53₎ p. illus., pl. 23¾ᶜᵐ.
    Cover-title: Old Brunswick pilgrimages.
    Contents.—Waddell, A. M. Early explorers of the Cape Fear.—
Sprunt, J. Old Brunswick.—Martin, E. S. Defense of Fort Anderson,
1865.—Sprunt, J. Spencer Compton, earl of Wilmington.
    1. Brunswick, N. C. (Brunswick Co.) 2. North Carolina—Hist.—
Colonial period. 3. Anderson, Fort, Capture of, 1865. 4. Wilmington,
Spencer Compton, earl of, 1673?–1743.   I. Waddell Alfred Moore,
1834–1912. II. Sprunt,   James, 1846–1924. III. Martin, Eugene S.
                                 4—31165
    Library of Congress   E186.4.N86

NN   0066714   DLC NcD ViU ICN NcU NN

Pam.   National Society of the Colonial Dames of
Coll.   America. North Carolina.
    A history of the North Carolina Society
41948   of the Colonial Dames of America, from March
1894 to March 1935, by Jean Dalziel Wood ₍his-
torian. n. p., 1935?₎
    52 p. 23 cm.

    1. National Society of the Colonial
Dames of America. North Carolina. I. Wood,
Jean Dalziel.

NN   0066715   NcD

National Society of the Colonial Dames of America.
North Carolina.
    Jamestown day for the public schools of
North Carolina ...   [Wilmington, 1907]

NN   0066716   NcU

National society of the colonial dames of
America. North Carolina.
₍Schaw, Janet₎
    Journal of a lady of quality; being the narrative of a jour-
ney from Scotland to the West Indies, North Carolina, and
Portugal, in the years 1774 to 1776. Edited by Evangeline
Walker Andrews, in collaboration with Charles McLean An-
drews ... New Haven, Yale university press; ₍etc., etc.₎ 1921.

National society of the colonial dames of
America. North Carolina.
Lawson, John, *d.* 1712.
    Lawson's History of North Carolina, containing the exact
description and natural history of that country, together with
the present state thereof and a journal of a thousand miles
traveled through several nations of Indians, giving a particular
account of their customs, manners, etc., etc., by John Lawson
... London, Printed for W. Taylor and F. Baker, 1714. Richmond, Va., Garrett and Massie, 1937.

National   society of the colonial dames
of America, North Carolina.   N.p., 1894–
Minutes of the annual meeting.

NN   0066719   NcU MiD

National Society of the Colonial Dames of
369.123   America. North Carolina.
N873N
    The North Carolina Society of the Colo-
nial Dames of America ... Wilmington,
N. C., Jackson & Bell Co., 1900.
    58 p. 24 cm.

    On spine: Register of the North Carolina
Society of Colonial Dames.
    1. North Carolina. History. Colonial
period. Societies

NN   0066720   NcD MiD-B NN NcU ICN NcRS MnHi

National Society of the Colonial Dames of America.
North Carolina.
    Register...   Raleigh, 1912.
    233p 24cm

    Half-title: Society of Colonial Dames.

NN   0066721   MnCS NcD NcU

E186.4   National Society of the Colonial Dames of
.N87   America. North Carolina.
    Register of the North Carolina Society of
the Colonial Dames of America.   Wilmington,
N.C., National Press, 1924.
    289 p. 24 cm.

    1. U.S.--Hist.--Colonial period--Biog.
2. North Carolina--Geneal. 3. U.S.--Geneal.

NN   0066722   T Vi NcC

NATIONAL society of the Colonial dames of America,
North Carolina.
    Register of the North Carolina society of the
Colonial dames of America.
    Wilmington. 1939. 378p.

    Compiled by Anne Thornton Spence Bellamy.

NN   0066723   WaS

National society of the colonial dames of
America. North Carolina. Craven County
Waters, Mary Louise.   Committee.
    A short historical sketch ₍of₎ New Bern, N. C., by Mary
Louise Waters ... New Bern, N. C., O. G. Dunn, printer
₍1924₎

National Society of the Colonial Dames of America.
Ohio.
    Constitution of the National Society of
Colonial Dames of America and by-laws of
Colonial Dames of America in the state of Ohio.
n.p., 1903.
    27 p.

NN   0066725   OClWHi

National Society of the Colonial Dames of
America. Ohio.
    Directory of the National Society of
the Colonial Dames of America in the state
of Ohio ... June 1938. n.p., 1938.
    30 p.

NN   0066726   OClWHi

F   NATIONAL SOCIETY OF THE COLONIAL DAMES OF
83195   AMERICA. Ohio.
.7   Directory.   ₍n.p.₎1950.
    31p. 23cm.

NN   0066727   ICN

National society of the colonial dames of
America, Ohio.
Putnam, Rufus, 1738–1824.
    The memoirs of Rufus Putnam and certain official papers
and correspondence, published by the National society of the
Colonial dames of America in the state of Ohio; comp. and
annotated by Miss Rowena Buell ... Boston and New York,
Houghton, Mifflin and company, 1903.

National Society of the Colonial Dames of America. Ohio.
    Studies in the colonial period for use in the public schools.
₍no.₎
    Cincinnati: The Ebbert & Richardson Co., 19   8°
    v.
    no.   cover-title.
    Contents:

    no. 3. Phillips, M. S. Colonial Massachusetts. 1916.

    1. U. S.—History: Colonial: Per. and   soc. publ.
N. Y. P. L.   April 25, 1918.

NN   0066729   NN DLC OCU MiD

National Society of the Colonial Dames of
America. Oregon.
    Circular letter by the Recording Secre-
tary, 19
    v.

NN   0066730   NbHi

VOLUME 407

979.5
N2125
National Society of the Colonial Dames of America. Oregon.
The Oregon country ₍by Eliza Parker
Anderson, historian.. Portland?₎ 1943.
₍9₎p. 23cm.

Cover title.

1. Oregon. Hist. To 1859. I. Anderson, Eliza (Parker)

NN   0066731   OrU

National society of the colonial dames of America. *Pennsylvania.*
... Annual report of the Pennsylvania society of the Colonial
dames of America ...

₍Philadelphia₎
v. 23½ᶜᵐ.

CA 35–612 Unrev'd
Library of Congress   E186.4.P32   369.123

NN   0066732   DLC MiD P NbHi

National Society of the colonial dames of America.
Pennsylvania.
Catalogue of the exhibition of the John Hays
Hammond, Jr. collection of early American glass..
    see under   Hammond, John Hays, 1888–
1965.

National society of the colonial dames of America. *Pennsylvania.*
... Church music and musical life in Pennsylvania in the
eighteenth century ... prepared by the Committee on historical research ... Philadelphia, Printed for the Society, 1926–
47.

3 v. in 4. front. (v. 3, pt. 2) illus. (incl. ports.) facsims. (1 fold.)
25 cm. (Publications of the Pennsylvania society of the colonial
dames of America. IV)

Includes facsimiles of "The hymn book of Magister Johannes Kelpius, translated by Dr. Christopher Witt" (v. 1, p. ₍19₎–165) and of
the 1731 edition of the libretto of "The fool's opera" by Anthony
Aston, with "A sketch of the author's life written by himself" (v. 3,
pt. 1, p. ₍103₎–137)
Bibliography: v. 1, p. ₍251₎–255; v. 2, p. ₍273₎–278; v. 3, pt. 2,
p. ₍541₎–550.

1. Church music — Pennsylvania. 2. Music — Pennsylvania.
I. Kelpius, John, 1673–1708. II. Aston, Anthony, fl. 1682–1747.

E186.4.P33   no. 4   783   27—16256
——— Copy 2.   ML3111.P3N18

FTaSU NcD DSI WaU InU WaU
NN   0066735   DLC PU–FA NNUT MH MB NN PU MWA KU CoU

ML200
.7
.P3V3
**National Society of the Colonial Dames of
America. Pennsylvania. Church music and
musical life in the eighteenth century.**
Vail, George.
Backgrounds of Welsh music in Pennsylvania. ₍n. p.,
1947?₎

National society of the colonial dames of America. *Pennsylvania.*
... Forges and furnaces in the province of Pennsylvania,
prepared by the Committee on historical research. Philadelphia, Printed for the Society, 1914.

vii, 204 p. front., plates. 25 cm. (Publications of the Pennsylvania society of the colonial dames of America. III)

1. Iron industry and trade—Pennsylvania. 2. Pennsylvania—
Hist.—Colonial period.
                          14—18402
Library of Congress   E186.4.P33   vol. 3
——— Copy 2.   F152.N27

NNC MiU OC1WHi TxU ICJ CSmH NjP GU
NN   0066737   DLC TU OKentU CU NBuU ScC1eA CU MnHi

National Society of the Colonial Dames of America. — Pennsylvania.
In memoriam, Elizabeth Duane Gillespie, 1821–1901. ₍Philadelphia? 1901.₎   4 l.   12°.

1. Gillespie, Elizabeth Duane, 1821–   1901.
N.Y.P.L.   September 13, 1915.

NN   0066738   NN

National Society of the Colonial Dames of America. Pennsylvania.
Publications.
₍no.₎
Philadelphia, 19   8°.
v. illus., plates.

1. Pennsylvania.—History: Per.   and soc. publ.
N.Y.P.L.   April 2, 1919.

NN   0066739   NN CtNIC DLC MB PHi NNUT OO

369.123
P415R
National Society of the Colonial Dames of America.
Pennsylvania.
    Register of Pennsylvania Society of the
Colonial Dames of America.
₍Philadelphia, etc.₎
v. 24 cm.

NN   0066740   NcD ICN WaS

National society of the colonial dames of America. *Pennsylvania.*
Register of Pennsylvania society of the colonial dames
of America ... Philadelphia ₍Printed for the Society by
J. B. Lippincott company₎ 1895.
129 p. col. front. 25½ᶜᵐ.

1. Pennsylvania—Geneal.   6–1860 Additions

Library of Congress   E186.4.P32

NN   0066741   DLC

National society of the colonial dames of America. *Pennsylvania.*
Register of Pennsylvania society of the colonial dames
of America ... Philadelphia ₍Printed for the Society by
J. B. Lippincott company₎ 1898.
193 p. col. front. 23½ᶜᵐ.

1. Pennsylvania—Geneal.

                     2–10954   Additions
Library of Congress   E186.4.P33

NN   0066742   DLC NcD ViU MiD–B

National society of the colonial dames of America. *Pennsylvania.*
Register of Pennsylvania society of the colonial dames of
America ... Philadelphia ₍Printed for the Society by J. B.
Lippincott company₎ 1902.
238 p. col. front. 23½ᶜᵐ.
                    E186.4.P34 1902
——— Supplemental register ... 1902. Philadelphia ₍Press of
Ferris & Leach, 1902₎
18 p., 1 l. 23ᶜᵐ.
                    E186.4.P34 1902 a
——— Supplemental register ... 1903. Philadelphia ₍Press of
the New era printing company, Lancaster, Pa., 1903₎
18 p., 1 l. 23ᶜᵐ.

——— Supplemental register ... 1904. Philadelphia ₍Press of
the New era printing company, Lancaster, Pa., 1904₎
14 p. 23ᶜᵐ.
                    E186.4.P34 1904
——— Supplemental register ... 1905. Philadelphia ₍Press of
the New era printing company, Lancaster, Pa., 1905₎
12 p. 23ᶜᵐ.

1. Pennsylvania—Geneal.   6–1960–34

Library of Congress   E186.4.P34 1905

NN   0066744   DLC WHi ViU

National society of the colonial dames of America. *Pennsylvania.*
Register of Pennsylvania society of Colonial dames of
America ... Philadelphia ₍Printed for the Society by Wickersham company, Lancaster, Pa.₎ 1907.
304 p. col. front. 23½ᶜᵐ.

1. Pennsylvania—Geneal.

Library of Congress   E186.4.P35   7–22169 Revised

NN   0066745   DLC ViU

National society of the colonial dames of America. *Pennsylvania.*
Register of Pennsylvania society of Colonial dames of
America ... Philadelphia ₍Printed for the Society by Wickersham company, Lancaster, Pa.₎ 1911.
358 p. col. front. 23½ᶜᵐ.

NN   0066746   ViU IHi MnHi PSt MiD–B

National society of the colonial dames of America. *Pennsylvania.*
Register of the Pennsylvania society of the colonial dames
of America ... Philadelphia ₍Printed for the Society by W. J.
Dornan₎ 1928.
499 p. front., plates. 24ᶜᵐ.

"The National society of the colonial dames of America. The national officers, 1928": p. 5.

1. Pennsylvania—Geneal.
                           30–12821
Library of Congress   E186.4.P34 1928
                     ₍2₎   369.123

NN   0066747   DLC NjP

National Society of the Colonial Dames of America.
Pennsylvania.
Susanna Wright, 1697–1784. ₍Philadelphia, 1906₎
48 p. illus. 20 cm. (Publications of the Pennsylvania Society
of the Colonial Dames of America, no. 2)
Caption title.

1. Wright, Susanna, 1697–1784. I. Series: National Society of
the Colonial Dames of America. Pennsylvania. Publications, no. 2.

E186.4.P33   no. 2   920.7   48–31846*
——— Copy 2.   CT275.W75N3

NN   0066748   DLC MiD–B

National society of the colonial dames of America. *Pennsylvania.*
... Three centuries of historic silver; loan exhibitions under
the auspices of the Pennsylvania society of the colonial dames
of America, compiled and edited by Mrs. Alfred Coxe Prime,
chairman. Philadelphia, The Society, 1938.
191, ₍1₎ p. incl. plates, ports., facsims. 24ᶜᵐ. (Fifth publication of
the Pennsylvania society of the Colonial dames of America)

"One thousand copies ... have been printed."

1. Silversmithing—U. S. 2. Silversmithing—Exhibitions. I. Prime,
Phoebe P., "Mrs. Alfred Coxe Prime," ed. II. Title.
                           39–5235
Library of Congress   E186.4.P33   no. 5
——— Copy 2.   NK7112.N3
Copyright A 125673   (369.123)   739

NN   0066749   DLC OC1 OC1MA FTaSU CU Wa MiU DSI

HJ9307
.P685A45
National Society of the Colonial Dames of America.
Pennsylvania. Allegheny County Committee.
Pine Township, Pa. *(Allegheny Co.)*
Copy of duplicate-tax-books of Pine Township, Allegheny
County, Pennsylvania, 1801, 1804–1809 ... Transcribed
from original assessments and tax lists for Pine Township
by the Committee on Preservation of Records and Historical Research, 1941–1942 ... ₍n. p., 1942₎

**National society of the colonial dames
of America. Pennsylvania. Allegheny
county committee.**
Forbes, John, 1710–1759.
Letters of General John Forbes relating to the expedition
against Fort Duquesne in 1758; compiled from books in the
Carnegie library of Pittsburgh for the Allegheny County committee, Pennsylvania society of the Colonial dames of America,
by Irene Stewart ... to which is added a list of references on
the expedition. Pittsburgh, Allegheny County committee,
1927.

VOLUME 407

National society of the colonial dames of
America. Pennsylvania. Allegheny county
committee.
Forbes, John, 1707-1759.
   Writings of General John Forbes relating to his service in
North America, compiled and edited by Alfred Procter James
... for the Allegheny county committee of the Pennsylvania
society of the colonial dames of America. Menasha, Wis., The
Collegiate press, 1938.

National society of the colonial dames of America. *Pennsylvania. Committee on historical research.*
   An evening of music of the colonial period, including
songs by Francis Hopkinson, the first American poet-com-
poser. The Historical society of Pennsylvania ... Pennsylvania society of the colonial dames of America, Committee on historical research. Wednesday evening, November 12th, 1919 ... ₍Philadelphia, The Society, 1919₎
   cover-title, ₍10₎ p. incl. facsims. port. 24½ᶜᵐ.
   Includes facsimile of autograph letter of Washington to Hopkinson ; also
words and music of "the first American song, 'My days have been so won-
drous free.'"
   I. Hopkinson, Francis, 1737-1791. II. Washington, George, 1732-1799.
                                                        20-8703
   Library of Congress   ML410.H81N2

NN   0066753   DLC PHC MWA MB MiU OO NN

National society of the colonial dames of America. *Pennsylvania. Junior committee.*
   The A B C book of colonial Pennsylvania, by the Junior
committee of the Pennsylvania society of the National colonial
dames of America ; verse by Mrs. Moreau Delano Brown, Miss
Harriet H. Bland; and Mrs. Louis H. Twyeffort; drawings by
Miss Margaret Aumont Moore. ₍Philadelphia, The Pennsylvania society of the National colonial dames of America, 1942₎
   ₍30₎ p. illus. (incl. map)   13½ x 20½ᶜᵐ.

   1. Pennsylvania—Hist.—Colonial period.   I. Title.
                                                        43-3258
   Library of Congress   F152.N28
                                  ₍3₎   974.8

NN   0066754   DLC

National Society of the Colonial Dames of
   America. Rhode Island.
      Addresses delivered before the Society of the
Colonial Dames in Rhode Island at their third
annual celebration held in the rooms of the Newport
Historical society, Aug. 31, 1894.   Newport, R.I.
1894.
      40 p.   27 cm.

NN   0066755   RPB

National society of the Colonial Dames of
   America-Rhode Island
   ...Annual meeting... Newport, Daily news
job print,
   v.   25 cm.

NN   0066756   DNW

National society of the colonial dames
   of America. Rhode Island.
      The constitution and by-laws of the Societ₍
of colonial dames in the state of Rhode
Island and Providence plantations. Institute
anno domini, 1892. (₍.p., n.p.,n.d)
      30 p. 1 p₁. (insignia) 18 cm.

NN   0066757   DNW RPB

National Society of the Colonial Dames of
   America. Rhode Island.
      The correspondence of the colonial
governors of Rhode Island, 1723-1775
            see under   Rhode Island (Colony) Gover-
nors.

National Society of the Colonial Dames of
   America. Rhode Island.
      Dedication of the R.I. bay in the cloister
of the colonies. Washington Memorial Chapel,
Valley Forge, Pa., May 29, 1921.   Providence,
1921?
      10 p.   23 cm.

NN   0066759   RPB

National society of the colonial dames of America. *Rhode
Island.*
   First record book of the Society of colonial dames in
the state of Rhode Island and Providence plantations.
Ending August 31, 1896 ... Providence, Snow & Farn-
ham, printers, 1897.
   xvi, 196 p. 24½ᶜᵐ.

   1. Rhode Island—Hist.—Colonial period—Societies.
                                                        17-21054
   Library of Congress   E186.4.R43

NN   0066760   DLC CtY ICN

National Society of ₜₕₑ Colonial Dames of
   America. Rhode Island.
   The Mercury and Gazette
      see under title

National society of the Colonial Dames of
   American-Rhode Island .
   (Miscellaneous publications)
   Open binder containing reports, rules,
etc.

NN   0066762   DNW

National Society of the Colonial Dames of
   America. Rhode Island.
      The National Society of Colonial Dames in
the state of Rhode Island and Providence plantations. [Charter, constitution and bylaws]   [Pro-
vidence, 1905?]
      55 p.   illus.   15 cm.

NN   0066763   RPB

National society of ₜₕₑ **colonial dames of America.**   Rhode Island.
   News letter ₍of₎ the Rhode Island society of the National
society of colonial dames of America.
   v. 1

   ₍Providence, R. I.? 1936   23½cm.
   no.   illus.

   Annual.

NN   0066764   NN

National society of the colonial dames of America. *Rhode
Island.*
   Old houses in the south county of Rhode Island, compiled
by the National society of the colonial dames in the state of
Rhode Island and Providence plantations ... Providence,
Printed for the Society ₍Boston, D. B. Updike₎ 1932.
   v. illus. (incl. plan) map. 27½ᶜᵐ.

   Maps on lining-papers.

   1. Rhode Island—Historic houses, etc. 2. Architecture, Domestic—
Rhode Island.   I. Title.
                                                        33-5291
   Library of Congress   F80.N26
   ——— Copy 2.
   Copyright A 59542   ₍3₎   917.459

             OrU CU MB
NN   0066765   DLC MH NcD OrU MiU FU MsU MB OCl Or

National society of the colonial dames of
   America. Rhode Island.
Pyle, Katherine.
   Once upon a time in Rhode Island, by Katherine Pyle,
illustrated by Helen B. Mason. ₍Garden City, N. Y.,
Doubleday, Page & company, ₍1914₎

National society of ₜₕₑ colonial dames of Ameri-
   ca- Rhode Island.
   ...Record book... Providence, Snow &
Faraham
   v. 25 cm.

NN   0066767   DNW Nh OClWHi

National Society of the Colonial Dames of
   America. Rhode Island.
      Requirements for admission.   ₍Provi-
dence? 1894-95₎
      16-17 cm.
      Cover title.
      1895 printed at Newport.

NN   0066768   RPB

National society of the colonial dames of America. *Rhode
Island.*
   Year book and register of members of the National
society of colonial dames in the state of Rhode Island and
Providence plantations ... 1910/12–
Providence, 1912–
   v. 23ᶜᵐ.

   1. Rhode Island—Hist.—Colonial period—Societies.
                                                        15-28181
   Library of Congress   E186.4.R47

NN   0066769   DLC MB OClWHi ICN

National society of the colonial dames of
   America. South Carolina.

Charleston, S. C. St. Philip's parish.
   Register of St. Philip's parish, Charles Town, or Charleston,
S. C., 1754-1810. Edited by D. E. Huger Smith and A. S.
Salley, jr. Charleston, S. C., The South Carolina society,
Colonial dames of America, 1927.

E186.4   National society of the colonial dames of
S62   America. South Carolina.
1945   Register of the National society of the co-
          lonial dames of America in the state of South
          Carolina, incorporated 1893; eligibility list
          by Alexander S. Salley, genealogist. Regis-
          ter of members, by 1945 register committee ...
          Charleston, 1945. Charleston ₍Baltimore,
          Waverly press₎ 1945.

          176p. 23cm.

NN   0066771   NBuG Vi MiD-B NNC OClWHi NjP

National society of the colonial dames of America. *South
Carolina.*
   Register of the South Carolina society of colonial dames of
America ... Compiled by Mrs. Joseph Ioor Waring, Mrs.
George F. Vonkolnitz, Mrs. Ernest W. King ₍and₎ Mrs. Edmund Felder, chairman. Revised by Miss Mabel L. Webber,
₍genealogist. Charleston ₍Baltimore, Printed at the Waverly
press₎ 1935.
   119 p. 23ᶜᵐ.

   1. U. S.— Hist.— Colonial period — Societies. 2. South Carolina—
Hist.—Colonial period—Societies₎
                                                        A 41-2417
   Enoch Pratt free library
      for Library of Congress   ₍2₎

NN   0066772   MdBE IHi

National society of the colonial dames of
   America. South Carolina. Columbia committee.
St. Matthew's parish, *Orangeburg district, Calhoun co., S. C.*
   Minutes of the vestry of St. Matthew's parish, South Caro-
lina, 1767-1838, edited by A. S. Salley. Columbia, S. C.,
Printed for the Columbia committee, South Carolina society,
Colonial dames of America, by the State company, 1939.

VOLUME 407

BX5980
.C3S3
National Society of the Colonial Dames of
America. South Carolina. Historical
Activities Committee.
Charleston, S. C. St. Michael's Church.
The minutes of St. Michael's Church of Charleston, S. C.,
from 1758-1797. Prepared for publication by Mrs. C. G.
Howe, chairman, and Mrs. Chas. F. Middleton, member of
committee. ₍Charleston?₎ Historical Activities Committee
of the South Carolina Society of Colonial Dames of Amer-
ica ₍1950?₎

National Society of the Colonial Dames of
America. Tennessee.
Historian's report.
v.

NN   0066775   NbHi

E77
.A22
National Society of the Colonial Dames of
America. Tennessee.
Adair, James, ca. 1709-ca. 1783.
History of the American Indians, edited under the aus-
pices of the National Society of the Colonial Dames of
America, in Tennessee, by Samuel Cole Williams, LL. D.
Johnson City, Tenn.. The Watauga Press, 1930.

F
83195
.415
National society of the colonial dames
of America—Texas.
Directory...
1909.
[Austin,Tex.]1909.   (with its
[Report of the annual meeting] 1909)

NN   0066777   ICN

E186.4
.T45
1930
National society of the colonial dames
of America. Texas.
National society of colonial dames of
America resident in the state of Texas.
Directory, 1930.   ₍n.p.₎ 1930.
58 p.   23cm.

NN   0066778   MnHi

F
83195
.415
National society of the colonial dames
of America—Texas.
[Report of the annual meeting]
1908/09.
[Austin,Tex.]1909.

Report year ends in May.

NN   0066779   ICN

National Society of the Colonial Dames of
America. Vermont.
Constitution, by-laws and members.
n.p., n.d.
Library has
1908.

NN   0066780   MiD-B

National society of the colonial dames of America. *Vermont.*
... Dedication of the monument to Ann Story ... Salisbury, Vermont, July twenty-seventh, nineteen hundred
and five ... ₍Salisbury, Vt., The Vermont society of colonial dames, 1905₎
47 p. 2 pl., 2 port. 23½ᵐ.
On cover: 1774, Ann Story; dedication of monument to her memory ...
At head of title: Erected by the Vermont society of colonial dames.
1774-1905.
1. Story, Mrs. Ann, 1742-1817. 2. Salisbury, Vt. Ann Story monument. I. Title.
                                13-23468

Library of Congress   F59.S16N2

NN   0066781   DLC RPB MiU MiU-C ViU

National Society of the Colonial Dames of
America. Vermont.
Directory. n.p., 19-
v.
Library has
1935.

NN   0066782   MiD-B

E186.4
V3
National Society of the Colonial Dames of
America. Vermont.
... Preamble, constitution and by-laws, with
a brief sketch of the history and purpose of
the society. ₍No imprint, 1903?₎

45p.   20cm.

1. Vermont.-Hist.-Colonial period.-
Societies.
2. National Society of the Colonial Dames
of America. Vermont.

NN   0066783   NBuG

NATIONAL SOCIETY OF THE COLONIAL DAMES OF AMERICA. Virginia. By-laws of the Society of colonial dames of America in the state of Virginia and the constitution of the National
society of the colonial dames of America. *Richmond,Rich-
mond press,n.d.*   27 p.

NN   0066784   TKL

Pam
F
226.5
.N3
₍National Society of the Colonial Dames of
America. Virginia.₎
Celebration of the three hundredth anniversary
of the first legislative assembly in America.
₍n.p., 1919?₎
19 p. 23cm.

1. Virginia - History - Addresses, essays,
lectures. 2. Virginia. General Assembly -
History - Address-   es, essays, lectures. I.
Title.

NN   0066785   GU ViN NcWsW MiU

National Society of the Colonial Dames of
America. Virginia.
The constitution and officers of the Society of
the Colonial Dames of America. Richmond, Va.,
West, Johnston & Co., 1893.

NN   0066786   CSmH

V
25
W67
Ee
v
National Society of the Colonial Dames of
America. Virginia.
Exercises accompanying the unveiling of a
tablet to the memory of the founders of
William and Mary college, on Tuesday, October
twenty-second, nineteen hundred and one,
under the auspices of the Colonial Dames of
America in the state of Virginia.
₍Williamsburg, 1901₎
cover-title, ₍1₎ p. 23cm. ₍With this
are bound: Edmonds,   R. H. Training
Southern boys for   their mighty task.
₍n.p., n.d.₎ -   Armstrong, Mrs. F.M.₎

The Symes-Eaton free school. ₍Hampton, Va.,
n.d.₎ - Virginia. Eastern State Hospital,
Williamsburg, Va. By-laws and regulations.
Williamsburg, 1901. - The Ku Klux Klan, or
Carpet-bagger in   New Orleans.
Memphis, 1877. -   Tucker, J. R. The

public services of St. George Tucker. ₍n.p.,
1896₎ - Richmond and Newport News Railway.
Second report of A. C. Dunn, Chief engineer. -
A directory and handbook of the City of
Williamsburg and   the county of James
City, Virginia.   Williamsburg, ₍1898?₎

- Thomas, A. F. The Virginia constitutional
convention and its possibilities. Lynchburg,
Va., 1901. - National Society of the Colonial
Dames of America. Virginia. The unveiling
of a tablet ... to the founders of the College
of William and   Mary ₍Richmond,
1901?₎ - Sherwood,   G. F. T.
Sherwood mss.   London, 1900. -

Continued in next column

Continued from preceding column

Thruston, G. P. George Rogers Clark and the
pioneers of Kentucky. ₍Nashville, 1900?₎ -
Westminster abbey and Stratford-on-Avon.
Chicago, 1901. - Business Men's Association of
the City of Williamsburg, Va. Facts about
Williamsburg and   vicinity. - Tyler,
John. The address   delivered by His

Exc'y John Tyler, and the poem recited by St.
George Tucker, esq., on the 166th anniversary
of the College of William and Mary. ₍Williams-
burg₎ 1859. - Virginia Navigation Co.
Afloat on the James. New York ₍n.d.₎

   I. William and   Mary College,
Williamsburg, Va.   Anals.

NN   0066792   ViW

---

*
E186
.4
.V83
1903
National Society of the Colonial Dames of
America. Virginia.
The first field day of the Colonial Dames
of America in the state of Virginia, Yorktown,
May 27, 1903. Richmond, Wm. Ellis Jones,
Book and Job Printer, 1903.
19 p.   24 cm.

Original blue paper wrappers.
Stamp of the Virginia Historical Society on
title page.
I. Title.

NN   0066793   ViU CSmH

F229
.M13
National society of the colonial dames of
America. Virginia.
McCabe, William Gordon, 1841-1920.
The first university in America, 1619-1622; an address de-
livered by W. Gordon McCabe ... before "the Colonial dames
of America in the state of Virginia," May 31, 1911, at Dutch
gap on James river. ₍n .p.₎ The Virginia society of "colonial
dames," 1914.

National society of the colonial dames of America. *Virginia.*
History and register of ancestors and members of the
Society of the colonial dames of America in the state of
Virginia, 1892-1930. Richmond ₍Printed for the Society by
the William Byrd press, inc.₎ 1930.
c, 544 p. front., plates, ports. 24 cm.

1. Virginia—Hist.—Colonial period—Societies, etc. 2. Virginia—
Geneal.—Sources.

E186.4.V84   369.123   31—14199

NN   0066795   DLC OClWHi ViU WaS

**National society of the colonial dames of
America. Virginia.**
Robins, *Mrs.* Sally (Nelson)
Love stories of famous Virginians, by Sally Nelson Robins
... published under the auspices of the National society
colonial dames of America in the state of Virginia. Richmond, Va., The Dietz printing co., 1923.

929.3
qN277P
National Society of the Colonial Dames of America. Virginia.
Parish record series. no. 1-3.
Richmond, 1897-1905.
3 v. 24- 29 cm.

No more published?-cf. Union list of serials.

NN   0066797   NcD NbHi

National society of the colonial dames of
America. Virginia.

Christchurch, Va. Christ church.
The parish register of Christ church, Middlesex county, Va.,
from 1653 to 1812, published by the National society of the
colonial dames of America in the state of Virginia. Richmond,
W. E. Jones, printer, 1897.

VOLUME 407

National society of the colonial dames of
America. Virginia.
St. Peter's parish, *New Kent co., Va.*
The parish register of Saint Peter's, New Kent county, Va.
from 1680 to 1787, pub. by the National society of the colonial
dames of America in the state of Virginia ... Richmond, W.
E. Jones, printer, 1904.

NN 0066800 ViU NcWsW

---

*
F234
.J3C65 National Society of the Colonial Dames of
1922 America. Virginia.

Presentation of the Robert Hunt Memorial
Shrine to the Association for the Preservation
of Virginia Antiquities, and programme of its
dedication at Jamestown Island, Va., June 15,
1922 (Magna Charta Day) ₁Richmond, Va.,
Whittet & Shepperson, Printers, 1922₂
unpaged. 24cm.
Cover title.
1. Hunt, Robert, 1586 (ca)-1608. 2. Jamestown,
Va.—Hist. I. Assoc iation for the Preservation of Virginia Antiquities.

NN 0066800 ViU NcWsW

National society of the colonial dames of America.
Virginia.
... ₁Report₂
₁Richmond, Va.₂
v. 26.5 cm.

1. U. S. – Hist. – Colonial period – Societies.
2. Virginia – Hist. – Colonial period – Societies.

NN 0066801 Vi

National society of the colonial dames of
America. Virginia.
Roster of the colonial dames of America in the
state of Virginia, May first 1932. Compiled by
Katherine D. W. Ferrell, registrar ... ₁New
York? 1932₂
32 p. 19 cm.

"Published through the co-operation of the
National Americana society, New York."
Bookplate: From the library of Gen. John E.
Roller ... by his daughter.

1. Virginia – Hist. – Colonial period – Societies. 2. Virginia – Geneal. – Sources. I. Han-
cher, Katherine Douglas (White) Ferrell, comp.
II. National Americana society, New York. III.
Title.

NN 0066803 Vi

National Society of the Colonial Dames of
America. Virginia.
The Society of the Colonial Dames of
America in the state of Virginia, 1894. Richmond
Press of William Ellis Jones, 1894.
Sm. 8 vo. White paper covers.

NN 0066804 CSmH

National Society of the Colonial Dames of
America. Virginia.
The Society of the Colonial Dames of
America in the state of Virginia, 1896. Richmond,
West, Johnston & Co., publishers [1896]
8vo. Unbound and uncut.

NN 0066805 CSmH

National Society of the Colonial Dames of
America. Virginia.
The Society of the Colonial Dames of
America in the state of Virginia. 1899. Rich-
mond, Va., J.L. Hill Printing Company, 1899.
8vo. White paper covers.

NN 0066806 CSmH

National society of the colonial dames of America. *Virginia.*
The Society of the colonial dames of America in the
state of Virginia. 1908 Richmond, Va., Mitchell &
Hotchkiss, 1907.
127b. 24cm.
CONTENTS.—List of members.— List of ancestors.

NN 0066807 ViU

National society of the colonial dames of America. *Virginia.*
The Society of the colonial dames of America in the
state of Virginia. 1913. Richmond, Va., Mitchell &
Hotchkiss, 1913.
208 p. 24cm.
CONTENTS.—List of members.—Register of ancestors.

1. Virginia — Hist. — Colonial period—Societies. 2. Virginia—Geneal.—
Sources.
14-4050
Library of Congress E186.4.V8

NN 0066808 DLC Vi ViU

V
30
N21s National society of the colonial dames of
1922 America. Virginia.
v The Society of the colonial dames of America
in the state of Virginia ... Richmond, Va.,
Whittet & Shepperson, printers, 1922.
30 p. 23½cm.

1. Va. - Hist. - Colonial period - Soc.
2. Va. - Geneal. - Sources.

NN 0066809 ViW

National society of the colonial dames of America. *Virginia.*
The unveiling of a tablet, erected by the Colonial
dames of America in the state of Virginia, to the founders of the college of William and Mary. October 22, 1901.
₁Richmond, I. N. Jones & son print, 1901?₁
47 p. 23¼cm.
Address of Col. William Lamb: p. 11-45.

1. William and Mary college, Williamsburg, Va. I. Lamb, William,
1835-1909. II. Title.

Library of Congress LD6051.W513A3
14-14109

NN 0066810 DLC ViW ViU

National society of the colonial dames of
America. Virginia.
St. Peter's parish, *New Kent co., Va.*
The vestry book of Saint Peter's, New Kent county, Va.
from 1682-1758. Pub. by the National society of the colonial
dames of America in the state of Virginia ... Richmond,
W. E. Jones, book and job printer, 1905.

National society of the colonial dames of
America. Virginia.
Tyler, Lyon Gardiner, 1853-
Virginia first ₁by₂ Dr. Lyon G. Tyler ... ₁Richmond₂
Colonial dames of America in the state of Virginia ₁1921₂

National society of the colonial dames of America. *Virginia.*
Albemarle club.
Historical guide to Albemarle county, including Monticello,
the University of Virginia and Charlottesville ... Published
under the auspices of the Albemarle club of Colonial dames
and the Albemarle chapter, Daughters of the American revolution. Charlottesville, Va. ₁The Michie company, printers₂
1924.
64 p., 1 l. front. (fold. map) plates. 16½cm.
Advertising matter: p. 51-64.

1. Albemarle co., Va. I. Daughters of the American revolution.
Virginia. Albemarle chapter
37-9459
Library of Congress F232.A3N3
₁8₂

NN 0066813 DLC ICN ViU OClWHi IEN ViN TxU OKentU

ND1301
.N3 National Society of the Colonial Dames of
1951 America. Virginia. Blue Ridge Committee.

An exhibition of portraits owned in Albemarle County, Virginia, painted before the
year 1830. Presented ... April 8-30, 1951,
Museum of Fine Arts, Bayley Memorial Building, University of Virginia. ₁Charlottes-
ville? Va., 1951₂
10 p. 23cm.
"Addendum" (typed leaf) tipped in at end.
1. Portraits—Ex hibitions. 2. Paintings—
Albemarle Co., Va. —Exhibitions.

NN 0066814 ViU

---

*
F229
.M27 National Society of the Colonial Dames of
1940 America. Virginia. Blue Ridge Committee.

Our county origins, ₁comp. by₂ Sally M.
Hamilton, historian and chairman. ₁Rich-
mond, 1940?₂
69 p. 22cm.
"References": p. 41.
CONTENTS.—Albemarle County, by Mrs. Carter Har-
rison.—Orange County, by D.M. Davidson.—Augusta
County, by A.M. Pritchard.—Rockbridge County, by
Ellen Graham Anderson.—Louisa County, by Jane
Lewis Hart.—Bath and Alleghany Counties,
by Rives Cosby Ford —Waynesboro and

CONTENTS—Continued.
vicinity, by Juliet Hite Gallaher.

1. Va.—Hist.—Colonial period. 2. Albemarle
Co., Va.—Hist. 3. Orange Co., Va.—Hist. 4.
Augusta Co., Va.—Hist. 5. Rockbridge Co., Va.—
Hist. 6. Louisa Co., Va.—Hist. 7 Bath Co., Va.—
Hist. 8 Alleghany Co., Va.—Hist. 9. Waynesboro,
Va.—Hist. I. Hamil ton, Sally Parke
(Wellford) comp. II. Title.

NN 0066816 ViU ViLxW

E186.4 National society of the colonial dames
.W25 of America. Washington.
1931 The National society of the colonial
dames of America in the state of Washington, organized March 31st, 1910, in-
coporated April 7th, 1910. ₁Seattle?
1931?₂
59 p. incl.front. 24cm.

NN 0066817 MnHi

National Society of Colonial Dames of America. — West Virginia.
The National Society of Colonial Dames of America in the
State of West Virginia in reply to the circular letter of the
National Honorary President Mrs. Justine V. R. Townsend.
₁Washington, D. C.: W. F. Roberts, 1903.₂ 8 p. 8°.

I. Societies (Patriotic). U. S.
N. Y. P. L. December 30, 1913.

NN 0066818 NN

E186.4 National society of the colonial dames
.W45 of America. West Virginia.
1930 The National society of the colonial
dames of America in the state of West
Virginia, directory, 1930. ₁Charleston,
W.Va.?₂ 1930.
30 p. 24cm.

Pages ₁23₂-₁28₂ left blank.

NN 0066819 MnHi

National society of the Colonial dames of
America. Wisconsin.
The A B C of Wisconsin
see under Holbrook, Bertha Matson
(Andrews)

National Society of the Colonial Dames of America.
Wisconsin.
Wisconsin historic calendar, 1935. ₁Milwaukee,
E. F. Schmidt co., 1935₂
Cover-title: 12 plates.

Sponsored by the Colonial dames of Wisconsin;
pub. for the benefit of their restoration of the
old Indian agency house at Portage, Wisconsin.

NN 0066821 MiD-B

VOLUME 407

F
83195
.978   NATIONAL SOCIETY OF THE COLONIAL DAMES OF AMERICA.
     Wisconsin.
     ...Year book. 1941.
     ₍Washington,D.C.,₎1941.
       1v. 23cm.

     NN   0066822   ICN

National society of the colonial daughters of America.
     Certificate of incorporation ... ₍n. p., ᶜ1920₎
     ₍8₎ p. 15½ᶜᵐ.

                                       26–23758
     Library of Congress   E186.99.N33

     NN   0066823   DLC

National society of the colonial daughters of America.
     ... ₍Constitution and by-laws. n. p., 191–?₎
     8, ₍2₎ p. 1 l. 19½ᶜᵐ.

                                         26–23756
     Library of Congress   E186.99.N372

     NN   0066824   DLC

National society of the colonial daughters of America.
     ... Constitution and by-laws. ₍n. p., ᶜ1920₎
     1 p. l. 15 p. 13½ᶜᵐ.

                                         26–23757
     Library of Congress   E186.99.N374

     NN   0066825   DLC

National society of the colonial daughters of America.
     National charter of the National society of the colonial daughters of America. ₍n. p., ᶜ1920₎
     ₍7₎ p. 15ᶜᵐ.

                                         26–23752
     Library of Congress   E186.99.N35

     NN   0066826   DLC

National society of the Daughters of the American colonists
          see
Daughters of the American colonists.

National Society of the Daughters of the American Revolution
          see
Daughters of the American Revolution.

The National society of the deaf and the
     hard of hearing.
     Annual report, 19 –19 . [Tor.The
     Soc.19 –19].
       v.0.

     NN   0066829   CaBViP

National society of the fine arts, *Washington, D. C.*
     see
Washington society of the fine arts, *Washington, D. C.*

National Society of the Sons and Daughters
     of the Pilgrims.
          see   Sons and Daughters of the Pilgrims.

National Society of the Sons of the American Revolution
     see
Sons of the American Revolution.

F
821
N3   **National Society of the Sons of Utah Pioneers**
     By-laws.
     Salt Lake City.
       v. 16cm.

       1. Utah--History--Societies, etc.

     NN   0066833   UU

National society of United States daughters of 1812.
     ₍Bulletin₎ vol. ɪ–
     Dec. 1906–
     New York, 1906–
       v. 26ᶜᵐ.

                                       15–25683
     Library of Congress   E351.6.A13

     NN   0066834   DLC

E
351
6
A17
1923   **National Society of United States Daughters of 1812.**
     Charter and constitution ... Little Rock, Ark., 1923.
     20 p. 15 cm.

     Errata slip tipped to t. p.

       1. U. S. – Hist. – War of 1812 – Societies, etc.

     NN   0066835   Vi MiD

E
351
6
A17
1924   **National Society of United States Daughters**
     of 1812.
     Charter and constitution. ₍Little Rock?
     Ark.₎ 1924.
     20 p. 15 cm.

       1. U. S. – Hist. – War of 1812 – Societies.

     NN   0066836   Vi ViU

E
351
6
A17
1936   **National Society of United States Daughters**
     of 1812.
     Charter, constitution, and by-laws.
     ₍Washington? D. C.₎ 1936.
     23 p. 15 cm.

       1. U. S. – Hist. – War of 1812 – Societies.

     NN   0066837   Vi

E351
.6
.A15   **National Society of United States Daughters of**
     1812.
     [Circulars] [Washington, 1907]

     NN   0066838   DLC

National Society of United States Daughters of
     1812.
     The Club woman
         see under   Club woman. Boston.

E351.6
A13   **National society of United States daughters of**
     1812.
     Constitution and by-laws ... 1926. [Narberth, Pa.?] National society, 1926.
     23p. 15½cm.
     Laid in "As amended April, 1930."

     1. United States.-History.-War of 1812.-Societies.

     NN   0066840   NBuG

F
833601
.91   **National society of United States**
     daughters of 1812.
     Constitution of the National Society of United States Daughters of 1812. Adopted January 8th, 1909.
     n.p.n.d.

—   —— ——— Amended to April, 1913.
     n.p.[1913]

—   —— ——— Amended to April, 1915.
     n.p.[1915]

     NN   0066841   ICN OClWHi

National society of United States daughters of 1812.
     Constitution of the National society of United States daughters of 1812. Amended to April, nineteen hundred and fifteen. ₍New York, 1915₎
     27 p. 15ᶜᵐ.

                                     15–25680
     Library of Congress   E351.6.A17

     NN   0066842   DLC MB OClWHi

National society of United States daughters of
     1812.
     Dedication of the memorial vases given by the National society United States daughters of 1812 in honor of George Washington, first president of the United States of America, Washington memorial chapel, Valley Forge, October 3, 1918.
     ₍n. imp.₎
     ₍10₎ p. illus.

     NN   0066843   MiD

E362
.C21
Rare Bk.
Coll.   **National society of United States daughters of**
     1812.
     Canada. *Public archives.*
     General entry book of American prisoners of war at Quebec. ₍Hartford, Conn., pref. 1923₎

National society of United States daughters
     of 1812.
     Carr, Deborah Edith (Wallbridge) *"Mrs. Henry James Carr,"* 1854– *comp.*
     Index to certified copy of list of American prisoners of war, 1812–1815, as recorded in General entry book, Ottawa, Canada. List of American prisoners of war, who died at Princetown, Dartmoor, England, 1812–1815, compiled by Mrs. Henry James Carr. ₍n. p.₎ Association of state presidents, past and present, and charter members, of the National society, United States daughters of 1812 ₍1924₎

VOLUME 407

National Society of United States Daughters of
1812.
Inspection returns of the 5th company,
6th regiment of Connecticut militia ...
see under   Welles, Edwin Stanley, ed.

National society of United States daughters of 1812.
Log book of the "Old Ironsides" fair
see under title

E.F
+8N27
N
National Society of United States Daughters
of 1812.
News-letter.

Washington.
v. in   illus.   21-28 cm.   quarterly.

Frequency varies, 1907-June 1927.

ViU ICN NIC NBuG
NN   0066848   WHi FM T MiD NN OrP MB Or MtHi NbHi

Geneal.
Case
E   NATIONAL SOCIETY OF UNITED STATES DAUGHTERS OF
69   1812.
.613   A partial roster of the soldiers of 1812,
as represented by members of the various state
societies…   ₍n.p.,n.d.₎
v.   27½cm.

Loose leaf.
Deposited by the National society, United
States daughters of 1812, Illinois society.

NN   0066849   ICN

National society of United States
daughters of 1812.
...Report of board of directors meeting
of April 9 and 10, Chicago, Illinois.
₍Washington,D.C.,1946₎
118p.   23cm.

NN   0066850   Mi

National society of United States daughters of
1812.
Report of the president national...
Washington.

NN   0066851   MiD-B DLC

National society of United States daughters of 1812.
... Report of the work of the National society of United
States daughters of eighteen hundred and twelve, from
1897 to 1915, during the presidency of Mrs. William Gerry
Slade. ₍New York, 1915₎
54 p. front. (port.) 21ᶜᵐ.

Library of Congress   E351.6.A4
15-25681

NN   0066852   DLC NN OO ICN

National society of United States daughters of
1812.
₍Shotwell, *Mrs*. Margaret Badollet Caldwell₎ *comp*.
Stories of 1812, prize winning reminscences ₍₎ submitted
by U. S. D. 1812, 1926-1927. ₍Omaha? °1927₎

E351
.6
.A45
National society of United States daughters of
1812. Associate council.
Proceedings ...
Washington, D. C.
v.   illus.   23cm.

NN   0066854   DLC Mi MiD FM MdBJ C NdHi

E351
.6
.A56
National Society of United States Daughters of
1812. Association of State Preisents and
Charter Members.
[List of members,   Narberth?
Pa.₎
v.   23 cm.

NN   0066855   DLC MB

National society of the United States daughters of 1812.
Association of state presidents and charter members.
... ₍Yearbook₎ 192
₍Washington? D. C.₎ 192
v. ports. 23ᶜᵐ.
Compiler: 192   Mrs. Henry James Carr.

1. Carr, Deborah Edith (Wallbridge) "Mrs. Henry James Carr,"
1854-   comp.
37-15399
Library of Congress   369.142

NN   0066856   DLC ICN OC1 NN

National society of the United States daughters of 1812.
Arkansas.
Annual council,
₍n. p., 19
v. front. (port.) 23ᶜᵐ.

18-16078
Library of Congress   E351.6.A72

NN   0066857   DLC

National society of United States daughters of 1812.
Georgia.
History of the National society United States daughters of
1812, state of Georgia, 1901-1942. Fiftieth anniversary of the
National society, United States daughters of 1812. 1942. ₍At-
lanta, J. T. Hancock, 1943₎
104 p. incl. front., ports. 23½ᶜᵐ.

43-6214
Library of Congress   E351.6.G4
₍2₎   369.142

NN   0066858   DLC AAP NN OC1

[NATIONAL SOCIETY OF UNITED STATES DAUGHTERS
OF 1812. Illinois]
Alphabetical list of ancestors and their descendants
and The alphabetical list of members [1903-1955] and
their ancestors, compiled by Mrs. E. Julius Albrecht,
honorary state president and Mrs. Wendell W. Hall,
Illinois state registrar. [Lockridge, Iowa, Print. by
Times, 1955]   [61]   79 l.   29cm.

1. Societies, National and patriotic—U. S. 2. United States— Hist. --
War of 1812—Registers, lists, etc. I. Albrecht, Lucie Cable Weston .

NN   0066860   NN N PHi IHi   ICN OC1WHi WaS C

F
333601
.916
National society of United States
daughters of 1812-Illinois.
[Officers, members, constitution
and by-laws]
1904,1906,1908,1909,1915/16.
[Chicago?,1904-16]   5v.

NN   0066861   ICN

F
833601
.62
National society of United States daughters of 1812-Illinois.
State society year book...annual announcement
[1st] (1904)
[3d] (1906)
[5th-6th] (1908-09)
[12th] (1915-16)
26th (1929-30)

[Chicago?1904-

NN   0066862   ICN MiD-B

National society of United States daughters of
1812. Illinois. Kaskaskia chapter, Greenville.
₍Year book₎
Library has
1931/32, 1937/38, 1938/39.

NN   0066863   MiD-B

National society of United States daughters of 1812. Kansas.
History of the Kansas state society, 1912-1946, compiled by
Mrs. Wayne F. Shaw, State president ₍and₎ Lena M. Scurlock,
State vice president. ₍Kansas City, Kan., 1946₎ 45 p. illus.,
ports. 23cm.

1. Societies, National and patriotic   —U. S.₋—Kansas.

NN   0066864   NN

National society of United States daughters of
1812. Michigan.
...Constitution, by-laws and roster. n. p.,
19 -
v.
Library has
1923, 1937, 1941

NN   0066865   MiD-B

National society of United States daughters of
1812. Michigan.
...History of the Michigan state society,
1896-1942. Compiled by Mrs. Lloyd DeWitt
Smith... ₍Detroit, 1942₎
103 p.

I. ₍Smith, Mrs. Mabel (Gale), comp.

NN   0066866   MiD-B

National society of United States daughters of
1812. Michigan.
...Lineage book... Detroit, Mich., 1904.
₍33₎ p. front. (port.)

NN   0066867   MiD-B

National Society of United States Daughters
of 1812. Michigan
Membership roll and lineage, 1896-1940.
Compiled by Mrs. Lynn T. Miller. Ithaca,
Mich. ₍1940?₎
38 p.

₍Supplement (in pocket)₎ Michigan "1812"
roll of honor continued from 1940 state
lineage book, covering state numbers 314
through 407, and supplementals. ₍Listed by
Ruth S. Peter-   son. n.p., 1947₎ (8 ₍.
typescript)

NN   0066868   MiD

VOLUME 407

National society of United States daughters of 1812. Michigan.
Programme for bronze statue of Major General Alexander Macomb. n. imp.
₍8₎ p. illus.

NN   0066869   MiD-B

National society of United States daughters of 1812. Michigan. General Alexander Macomb chapter, Detroit.
Year book and by-laws.

Library has
1933/34–1939/40, 1942/43, 1947/48₎   Open entr₎

NN   0066870   MiD-B

M369.142
N27s
Vault   **National Society of United States Daughters of 1812. Michigan. General Isaac Shelby Chapter, Grand Rapids.**
Minutes. October 1943-Dec.1955.
112p.   27cm.

Manuscript, from Muriel Link Collection, Michigan State Library.
Inserted: Program of 52d state council meeting, National Society, United States Daughters of 1812, State of Michigan, 1951.
    I.Muriel Link   Collection, Michigan State Library.

NN   0066871   Mi

National Society of United States Daughters of 1812. Michigan. Lansing Chapter.
Cemetery tombstone inscriptions. Copied and compiled by Lansing chapter, U.S. Daughters 1812. Index arranged by Mrs. Otto Hartig and Mrs. L.T. Miller.   n.p., 1938-39.
631 l.

NN   0066872   Mi

---

*E351.6   **National society of United States**
.M65   **daughters of 1812. Minnesota.**
1942   Minnesota state society United States daughters of 1812 ... Anniversary report, ₍compiled by Mrs. Clara G. Smith. Minneapolis, Minn., 1942₎
141 l.   mounted front.   28cm.

One of three typewritten copies.
Leaves ₍64–66₎ printed.
Seal of National society mounted on title page.

"Tributes to the American flag and the Minnesota state flag, by Mrs. O.D. Wisner": folder (3.p.) mounted on p.1.
"Association of state presidents... and charter members": printed leaf mounted on l.₍139₎

NN   0066874   MnHi

National society of United States daughters of 1812. Missouri.
... Proceedings of the ... annual council ...

₍St. Louis, Mo., 19
    v. ports. 21ᶜᵐ.

At head of title, : National society United States daughters of 1812, state of Missouri.
19   includes: Roster–soldiers of war of 1812 buried in Missouri.
    1. U. S.—Hist.—War of 1812—Societies. 2. U. S.—Hist.—War of 1812—Registers, lists, etc. 3. Missouri—Biog.

                 CA 35–611 Unrev'd
Library of Congress   E351.6.M5   369.142

NN   0066875   DLC

National society of United States daughters of 1812. Nebraska.
Heroes of 1812, written by the members of the Nebraska society of United States daughters of 1812, 1930. Compiled by the publishing committee of the Nebraska society of United States daughters of 1812 ... ₍Omaha, Citizen printing company, ᶜ1930₎
2 p. l., ₍7₎-228 p. 22½ᶜᵐ.

"Ancestry and service of their forfathers ₍!₎ who fought in that war."—p. ₍7₎
    1. Nebraska—Hist.—War of 1812—Societies. 2. U. S.—Hist.—War of 1812—Biog. 3. Nebraska—Geneal.   I. Title.

Library of Congress   E351.6.N34   30–18181
——— Copy 2.
Copyright A 24960   ₍3₎   369.142

NN   0066876   DLC WaS KyHi OClWHi CLU

National society of United States daughters of 1812. Nebraska.
₍Year book₎

Library has
1937/38.

NN   0066877   MiD

National society of United States daughters of 1812. New Jersey.
...Year book.
19

₍Trenton, N. J., 19   19cm.
   no.

NN   0066878   NN

National Society of United States Daughters of 1812. New Jersey. Captain James Lawrence Chapter, Haddonfield
Ancestor list of the Captain James Lawrence Chapter, U.S.D., 1812 ₍Haddonfield, New Jersey₎. Prepared from the registrar's book. Hurffville, N. J., 1950.
1 v. (loose-leaf) typescript (carbon)

   Registrar: Hazel B. Simpson (Mrs. Walter A.)

   1. New Jersey   Genealogy

NN   0066879   MiD

National society of United States daughters of 1812. New Jersey. Commodore Stephen Decatur chapter of Essex county.
Year book.
1928/29

₍Newark, N. J., 1928–   19cm.
   nos.   mounted photos (1928/29).

NN   0066880   NN

National society of United States daughters of 1812. New York.
Constitution and by-laws, National society of United States daughters of 1812, state of New York; adopted and put in effect May second, nineteen hundred fifteen, rev. January second, nineteen hundred twenty-three. ₍New York, 1923₎
21 p. 15 x 8½ᶜᵐ.

                24–8631
Library of Congress   E351.6.N52 1923

NN   0066881   DLC

E351.6   **National society of United States daughters**
NG   **of 1812. New York**
    ... Newsletter.   no.

New York City, National society of United States daughters of 1812, state of New York, 19

    vols.   25½cm.

    Caption-title.

NN   0066882   NBuG

E351.6   **National society of United States daughters of**
N65   **1812. New York.**
    Ritual used in placing grave markers ... N. p., National society United States daughters of 1812, State of New York, 1927.

    cover-title₍4₎p.   23cm.

    1. Cemeteries.   I. Title.   II. Title: Grave markers.

NN   0066883   NBuG

National Society of United States Daughters of 1812. New York. Mohawk Valley Chapter, Amsterdam.
Records of 703 men

see under

Becker, Edith (Van Heusen) comp.

National society of United States daughters of 1812. Ohio.
... Ancestor roster ... ₍Columbus? O.₎ 1943.
29 numb. l.   28 x 21½ᵐ.

Caption title.
"Compiled by Mrs. Lowell K. Weaver, state pres., Mrs. Charles A. Dillon, state treas., Mrs. Loren E. Souers, state registrar ₍and₎ Mrs. Roy B. Fink, state secretary."—Leaf 29.
"Published ... in memory of Mrs. Albert M. Reiser, state historian from April 2, 1941 to October 26, 1942, by the Ohio state society."

    1. U. S.—Hist.—War of 1812—Biog.   I. Weaver, Mrs. Lowell K. II. Title.

Library of Congress   E351.O64   45–12733
    ₍2₎   369.142

NN   0066885   DLC OCl OClWHi

National Society of U.S. Daughters of 1812. Ohio.
By-laws of National Society of U.S. Daughters of 1812, State of Ohio. As adopted at meeting held in Cleveland, June 17, 1911.

    7 p. 16cm.

NN   0066886   OClWHi

National society of United States daughters of 1812. Ohio.
Lineage book, National society, United States daughters of 1812, state of Ohio ... ₍Cleveland, Printed by A. J. Watt₎ 1915–
    v. ports, facsim. 23ᵐ.

"Compiled by Mrs. Perry Lynes Hobbs, Miss Effie Serena Wagar."

    1. U. S.—Hist.—War of 1812—Societies.   I. Hobbs, Mrs. Mary Everett (Marshall) 1863–   comp. II. Wagar, Effie Serena, joint comp.

Library of Congress   E351.6.O37   16–23518

NN   0066887   DLC OClWHi

National society of United States daughters of 1812. Ohio.
National society United States daughters of 1812, state of Ohio. ₍Columbus? O.₎ 1932.
    cover-title, 35 p. 23ᵐ.

"Record of its membership and recent work."—p. ₍1₎

Library of Congress   E351.6.O67   CA 33–279 Unrev'd

NN   0066888   DLC

National Society of United States Daughters of 1812. Ohio.
Year book.
₍n. p.₎
    v. 21 cm.

    E351.6.A3   369.142   48–34891*↑

NN   0066889   DLC MiD OCl

VOLUME 407

F 833601 .92 National society of United States daughters of 1812-Ohio-Commodore Perry chapter, Cleveland.
[Program]

[Cleveland,1912-

NN 0066890   ICN OC1 OC1WHi

National society of U.S. daughters of 1812 - Ohio - General Duncan McArthur chapter
₍Year book₎ 1934.35-1935.36.

₍Grenfeidld, O.₎

NN 0066891   OC1

National society of United States daughters of 1812. Pennsylvania.
... Lineage book 1895-1929, compiled by Mrs. Henry James Carr ... Scranton, Pa., Westmoreland chapter U. S. D. 1812 ₍1929₎
cover-title, 175 p. 1 illus., ports. 23ᵐ.

I. Carr, Deborah Edith (Wallbridge) "Mrs. Henry James Carr." 1854- comp. II. National society of United States daughters of 1812. Pennsylvania. Westmoreland chapter, Scranton. III. Title.

Library of Congress   E351.6.P39   32-11071
—————— Copy 2.   ₍2₎   369.141

NN 0066892   DLC WaS MiD-B PHi MB ICN NN OC1

National society ₒf United States daughters of 1812. Pennsylvania.
[List of members
Scranton, Pa.,

E351 .6 .P41

NN 0066893   DLC

F 833601 .925 National society of United States daughters of 1812-Pennsylvania-Dolly Madison chapter, Pittsburgh.
By-laws and history of Dolly Madison chapter, National society, U.S.D. of 1812 of Pennsylvania, 1897-1915.
[Pittsburgh,1915]

NN 0066894   ICN

National society of United States daughters of 1812. Pennsylvania. Stephen Decatur chapter, Philadelphia.
...Year book and register. n. imp.

Library has:
1935/36, 1939/40.

NN 0066895   MiD-B PHi

National society of United States daughters of 1812. Pennsylvania. Westmoreland chapter, Scranton.
National society of United States daughters of 1812. Pennsylvania.
... Lineage book 1895-1929, compiled by Mrs. Henry James Carr ... Scranton, Pa., Westmoreland chapter U. S. D. 1812 ₍1929₎

National Society of United States Daughters of 1812. Tennessee.
Tennessee soilders in the war of 1812 ... see under Allen, Penelope Johnson.

National society of United States daughters of 1812. Tennessee. Volunteer chapter, Chattanooga.
Allen, Penelope Johnson, comp.
Guide book of Chattanooga and vicinity, compiled by Penelope Johnson Allen. Chattanooga, Tenn., 1935.

F 831998 .613 NATIONAL SOCIETY, WOMEN DESCENDANTS OF THE ANCIENT & HONORABLE ARTILLERY COMPANY.
Brief histories of the London company. The artillery company of Massachusetts. National society of women descendants. Membership roll. Ancestor sketches. ₍n.p.₎1940.
195p. 23cm.

On cover: History and lineage book.
"Compiled by Mrs. Edward Perry Walsh."

NN 0066899   ICN

National Society of Women Descendants of the Ancient and Honorable Artillery Company.
Directory of officers and committe₍e₎s; year book.
₍n. p.₎
v. 21 cm.

E186.99.N42   59-A547.

NN 0066900   TxU

National society ₒf women descendants of the ancient and honorable artillery company.
The Herald. no.

₍St. Louis₎ 19   nos.   18cm.
Irregular.
Includes supplementary material.

NN 1. Societies, National and patriotic—   U. S. I. Title.

NN 0066901   NN

National Society of Women Descendants of the Ancient and Honorable Artillery Company.
History and lineage book. ₍Washington, 1940₎-
v. illus., ports. 23 cm.

1. Massachusetts. Ancient and Honorable Artillery Company. 2. Massachusetts — Hist. — Colonial period — Societies, etc. 3. U. S. — Geneal.

E186.99.N423   369.12   45-30968 rev*

MiD
NN 0066902   DLC NbHi NN WaS CSf MnHi OC1 TxU WHi

National Society of Women Descendants of the Ancient and Honorable Artillery Company.
Membership of the Ancient and honorable artillery company, from organization in 1637 to 1775
see under Massachusetts. Ancient and Honorable Artillery Company.

National Society, Women Descendants of the Ancient and Honorable Artillery Company.
Report of the annual rendezvous...
₍no.₎

Washington, D. C.₍, 19   20½cm.
no.
19   includes the Annual report of the president-general.

1. Societies, National and patriotic   —U. S.
N. Y. P. L.   July 17, 1934

NN 0066904   NN

National society, painters, sculptors, engravers, potters.
Catalogue of the exhibition. 1st-   ; 1930-
[London]   no.   19cm.

Annual.
No exhibitions held 1941-43, 1945.
1930-46, name of society as: National society, painters, sculptors, engravers, potters.
Title varies.
1. Art, British--Exhibi-   tions--Gt.Br.--Eng.-- London.

NN 0066905   NN

National society, women descendants of the Ancient and honorable artillery company
see
National society of women descendants of the Ancient and honorable artillery company.

National Society's Training College of Domestric Subjects
see   National Society for Promoting the Education of the Poor in the Principles of the Established Church, London.

HM13 .N27 1898 National Sociological Convocation, Lake Bluff, Ill. July 1-17, 1898.

₍Program₎ n.p., 1898.

1. Sociology--Congresses.

NN 0066908   IEG

National sociological society.
How to solve the race problem
see under Washington conference on the race problem in the United States, Washington, D.C., 1903.

National Soil and Fertilizer Research Committee.
Fertilizer use and crop yields...
₍Washington, D.C.₎ 1951.
5 nos. 26 cm. (Its Report. no.1-5)

"Preliminary draft."
Contents.--no.1. In the Southern Region.-- no.2. In the North Central Region.--no.3. In the Northeastern Region.--no.4. In the Western Region.--no.5. In the United States.

NN 0066910   TU

National Soil and Fertilizer Research Committee.
Fertilizer use and crop yields in the United States ₍by₎ the Fertilizer Work Group, National Soil and Fertilizer Research Committee, in cooperation with the Soil and Water Conservation Research Branch and the Production Economics Research Branch, Agricultural Research Service, U. S. Dept. of Agriculture. Washington ₍U. S. Govt. Print. Off.₎ 1954.
iv, 75 p. illus., tables. 26 cm. (U. S. Dept. of Agriculture. Agriculture handbook no. 68)

1. Fertilizers ₍and manures₎—Stat. 2. Crop yields. 3. Field crops— U. S.—Stat.   (Series)

SB187.U6N3   Agr 54-358
U. S. Dept. of Agr. Libr.   1Ag84Ah no. 68
for Library of Congress   ₍5*₎†

NN 0066911   DNAL NNBG DLC

S631 N33 National Soil and Fertilizer Research Committee.
Report no.

₍Washington, D.C.₎ 19
nos. 26cm.

Preliminary draft, no.
Processed.

1. Fertilizers and manures.
Contents.

NN 0066912   OrCS

VOLUME 407

National Soil and Fertilizer Research Committee. *Fertilizer Work Group*
see
National Soil and Fertilizer Research Committee.

National Soil and Fertilizer Research Committee. *Soil Test Work Group.*
Soil testing in the United States. ₍Washington, U. S. Govt. Print. Off.₎ 1951.
117 p. 27 cm.

1. Soil mechanics.   I. Title.

TA710.N33   631.42   52–60320 ‡

WaTC MB
NN 0066914   DLC NIC OrP OrCS CaBVaU ICJ OU MtBC

The National stamp exhibition of 1934, sponsored by the New York American ...
see under   New York American.

National soil fertility league.
The National soil fertility league ... Chicago, 1911.
cover-title, 32 p. 17ᶜᵐ.

1. Soils.

Library of Congress   S591.N3   12–31428

NN 0066916   DLC DNAL TU NN

National soil fertility league.
Post-prandial proceedings...   1913.
48 p.

NN 0066917   DNAL

National sojourners, inc.
The sojourner
see under title

The National Soldier.   Kearney, Nebr., 1882–
v.

Semi-monthly.
"Devoted exclusively to the interests of the soldiers and sailors who served in the Union army in the late war of the rebellion."

NN 0066919   NbHi

National soldiers' and sailors' orphan home, Washington, D.C.
see
Washington, D.C. National soldiers' and sailors' orphan home

National soldiers historical association.
Plan of organization of National soldiers historical association. T. Buchanan Read, president. John D. Caldwell, secretary. Cincinnati, C. Clark, printer, 1865.
Cover-title, 14 p. 15½ᶜᵐ.
"Organized for the purpose of publishing in a substantial form a minute and reliable history of the country during the great rebellion, as far as practicable, from official and reliable sources."

Continued in next column

Continued from preceding column

Subject entries: U. S.—Hist.—Civil war—Societies.   3–957

Library of Congress, no.   F462.98.A11.

NN 0066921   DLC OClWHi

National Soldiers' Home near Dayton, Ohio
see under   National Home for Disabled Volunteer Soldiers. Central Branch, Dayton, O.

National soldiers' home, near Milwaukee
see under   National Home for Disabled Volunteer Soldiers. Northwestern Branch, Milwaukee.

National soldiers home, Tennessee
see
National home for disabled volunteer soldiers. Mountain branch, Johnson City, Tenn.

National soldiers home, Va. U.S. Army. General hospital no. 43
see
U.S. Army. General hospital no. 43, Hampton, Va.

25.3   The national soliciting company of New York and
2355a   New Jersey.
Cash draft book. ₍New York, 1894₎
288 p. 18°.

NN 0066926   DLC

National solidarity
see
Min tsu t'uan chieh.

The National song book. A collection of original and selected songs ... Toledo, O., 1878.
32 p. 16 cm.
Published by the National executive committee.

NN 0066928   RPB

The **National** song book; a complete collection of the folk-songs, carols, and rounds, suggested by The Board of Education, 1905. Edited and arr. for the use of schools by Charles Villiers Stanford. London, New York, Boosey, ᶜ1906.
240 p. 28 cm.
With piano acc.

1. School song-books. 2. Folk-songs, British. I. Stanford, Sir Charles Villiers, 1852–1924, ed.

M1994.N273 1906a   M 58–376

NN 0066929   DLC NN MH OCl

The **National** song book; a complete collection of the folk-songs, carols, and rounds, suggested by The Board of Education, 1905. Edited and arr. for the use of schools by Charles Villiers Stanford. Ed. with words and voice parts only. London, New York, Boosey, ᶜ1906.
280 p. 18 cm.

1. School song-books. 2. Folk-songs, British. I. Stanford, Sir Charles Villiers, 1852–1924, ed.

M1994.N273 1906   M 58–377

NN 0066930   DLC MH

A **National** song-book, being a collection of patriotic, martial, and naval songs and odes, principally of American composition. Trenton, Comp. and pub. by James J. Wilson, 1813.
xii, ₍13₎–204 p. 13½ᶜᵐ.
Without music; tunes to many of the songs indicated by title.

1. National songs, American. 2. U. S.—Hist.—Revolution—Poetry. 3. U. S.—Hist.—War of 1812—Poetry. I. Wilson, James Jefferson, 1775–1824, comp.

17–7243

Library of Congress   PS593.L8N3

NN 0066931   DLC MiU-C InU RPB

32   The national song folio. no. 3–4. Chicago,
national music co. [1889]
2 v. 4°.

NN 0066932   DLC

32   National songs for male voices. Columbia, the
10062   gem of the ocean; or, the red, white and blue.
My country, 'tis of thee. Star Spangled banner.
Hail Columbia, Yankee Doodle. [anon]
Boston, O. Ditson & co. [1876]
1 p.l., 67–75 p. obl. 8°.

NN 0066933   DLC

M1628   National songs of America. "America, My
.N38   country 'tis of thee," "The star-spangled
1889   banner," "Columbia, the gem of the ocean."
Profusely illus. in colors and in monotints.
With the music. New York, F.A. Stokes, 1889.
19 l. illus., 18 col. plates. 24cm.
1. National songs, American. 2. Patriotic music, American. I. Key, Francis Scott, 1779–1843. The Star-spangled banner. II. Shaw, David T. Columbia, the gem of the ocean. III. Smith, Samuel Francis, 1808–1895. America, My country 'tis of thee.

NN 0066934   ViU OrU

784.4   National songs of America ... Profusely illustrated
N2132   in colors and in monotints. With the music.
New York, F. A. Stokes & brother, 1889.
37 l. incl.front., illus., plates(part col.)

Each part has separate t.-p.
Contents.– America, my country 'tis of thee.– The star-spangled banner.– Columbia, the gem of the ocean.

1. National songs, American. 2. U.S.—Descr. & trav.—Views.

NN 0066935   IU DLC

National songs of the Allies and others
see under   ₍Grenville, Arthur₎ ed.

M   The national songs of the allies, harmonized
1646   for mixed voices. Boston, O. Ditson; New
N3   York, C. H. Ditson, 1918.
1918
19p. music. 28cm.

1. European War, 1914–18 – Songs and music.

NN 0066937   WU

National songs of the Allies ₍United States, Great Britain, France, Italy₎ Boston ₍c1918₎
12 p. 27 cm. (The Beacon series)
Cover title.

NN 0066938   RPB

MISSISSIPPI

MsG	William Alexander Percy Memorial Library, Greenville.
MsSC*	Mississippi State University, State College.
MsSM	Mississippi State University, State College.
MsU	University of Mississippi, University.

MONTANA

MtBC	Montana State University, Bozeman.
MtBozC*	Montana State University at Bozeman.
MtU	University of Montana, Missoula.

NEW YORK

N	New York State Library, Albany.
NAlU	State University of New York at Albany.
NAurW	Wells College, Aurora.
NB	Brooklyn Public Library, Brooklyn.
NBB	Brooklyn Museum Libraries, Brooklyn.
NBC	Brooklyn College, Brooklyn.
NBM	Medical Research Library of Brooklyn.
NBPol	Polytechnic Institute of Brooklyn, Brooklyn.
NBSU-M	State University of New York, Downstate Medical Center Library, Brooklyn.
NBiSU-H	State University of New York, Harpur College, Binghamton.
NBronSL	Sarah Lawrence College, Bronxville.
NBu	Buffalo and Erie County Public Library, Buffalo.
NBuC	State University of New York, College at Buffalo.
NBuG	Grosvenor Reference Division, Buffalo and Erie County Public Library, Buffalo.
NBuU	State University of New York at Buffalo.
NCH	Hamilton College, Clinton.
NCaS	St. Lawrence University, Canton.
NCorniC	Corning Glass Works Library, Corning. (Includes Corning Museum of Glass Library)
NCoxHi	Greene County Historical Society, Inc., Coxsackie.
NFQC	Queens College Library, Flushing.
NGrnUN*	United Nations Library.
NHC	Colgate University, Hamilton.
NHi	New York Historical Society, New York.
NIC	Cornell University, Ithaca.
NJQ	Queens Borough Public Library, Jamaica.
NL*	Newberry Library, Chicago.
NLC	Not a library symbol.
NN	New York Public Library.
NNAB	American Bible Society, New York.
NNAHI	Augustinian Historical Institute, New York.
NNAJHi	American Jewish Historical Society, New York.
NNB	Association of the Bar of the City of New York, New York.
NNBG	New York Botanical Garden, Bronx Park, New York.
NNC	Columbia University, New York.
NNC-T	— Teachers College Library.
NNCFR	Council on Foreign Relations, New York.
NNCoCi	City College of New York, New York.
NNE	Engineering Societies Library, New York.
NNF	Fordham University, New York.
NNFI	French Institute in the United States, New York.
NNG	General Theological Seminary of the Protestant Episcopal Church. New York.
NNGr	Grolier Club Library, New York.
NNH	Hispanic Society of America, New York.
NNHeb	Hebrew Union College, Jewish Institute of Religion Library, New York.
NNHi	New York Historical Society.
NNJ	Jewish Theological Seminary of America, New York.
NNJIR*	Jewish Institute of Religion, New York.
NNJef	Jefferson School of Social Science, New York. (Library no longer in existence)
NNM	American Museum of Natural History, New York.
NNMM	Metropolitan Museum of Art Library, New York.
NNMor*	Pierpont Morgan Library.
NNNAM	New York Academy of Medicine, New York.
NNNM	New York Medical College, Flower & Fifth Avenue Hospitals, New York.
NNNPsan	New York Psychoanalytic Institute, New York.
NNPM	Pierpont Morgan Library, New York.
NNQ*	Queens Borough Public Library, New York.
NNQC*	Queens College Library, Flushing.
NNRI	Rockefeller Institute for Medical Research, New York.
NNSU-M*	State University of New York College of Medicine at New York City.

NEW YORK continued

NNU	New York University Libraries, New York.
NNU-W	— Washington Square Library.
NNUN	United Nations Library, New York.
NNUN-W	— Woodrow Wilson Memorial Library.
NNUT	Union Theological Seminary, New York.
NNUT-Mc	— McAlpin Collection.
NNWML	Wagner College Library, Staten Island.
NNYI	Yivo Institute for Jewish Research, New York.
NNZI	Zionist Archives and Library of Palestine Foundation, New York.
NNerC	College of New Rochelle, New Rochelle.
NNiaU	Niagara University, Niagara University.
NPV	Vassar College, Poughkeepsie,
NRAB	Samuel Colgate Baptist Historical Library of the American Baptist Historical Society, Rochester.
NRU	University of Rochester, Rochester.
NSchU	Union College, Schenectady.
NSyU	Syracuse University, Syracuse.
NUt	Utica Public Library.
NWM	U.S. Military Academy, West Point.
NYPL*	New York Public Library.
NYhI	International Business Machines Corporation, Thomas J. Watson Research Center, Yorktown Heights.

NEBRASKA

NbOC	Creighton University, Omaha.
NbU	University of Nebraska, Lincoln.

NORTH CAROLINA

Nc	North Carolina State Library, Raleigh.
Nc-Ar	North Carolina State Department of Archives and History, Raleigh.
NcA	Pack Memorial Public Library, Asheville.
NcA-S	— Sondley Reference Library.
NcAS*	Sondley Reference Library, Asheville.
NcC	Public Library of Charlotte & Mecklenburg County, Charlotte.
NcCC	Charlotte College Library, Charlotte.
NcCJ	Johnson C. Smith University, Charlotte.
NcCU	University of North Carolina at Charlotte.
NcD	Duke University, Durham.
NcDurC	North Carolina College at Durham, Durham.
NcGU*	University of North Carolina at Greensboro.
NcGW	University of North Carolina at Greensboro.
NcGuG	Guilford College, Guilford.
NcR	Olivia Raney Public Library, Raleigh.
NcRR	Richard B. Harrison Public Library, Raleigh.
NcRS	North Carolina State University at Raleigh.
NcU	University of North Carolina, Chapel Hill.
NcWfC*	Wake Forest College, Winston-Salem.
NcWfSB	Southeastern Baptist Theological Seminary Library, Wake Forest.
NcWilA	Atlantic Christian College, Wilson.
NcWilC	Carolina Discipliniana Library, Wilson.
NcWsW	Wake Forest College, Winston-Salem.

NORTH DAKOTA

NdFA	North Dakota State University, Fargo. (Formerly North Dakota Agricultural College)
NdHi	State Historical Society of North Dakota, Bismarck.
NdU	University of North Dakota Library, Grand Forks.

NEW HAMPSHIRE

Nh	New Hampshire State Library, Concord.
NhD	Dartmouth College, Hanover.
NhU	University of New Hampshire, Durham.

NEW JERSEY

NjGbS	Glassboro State College, Glassboro.
NjHi	New Jersey Historical Society, Newark.
NjMD	Drew University, Madison.
NjN	Newark Public Library.
NjNBR*	Rutgers–The State University, New Brunswick.
NjNbS	New Brunswick Theological Seminary, New Brunswick.
NjNbT*	New Brunswick Theological Seminary.
NjP	Princeton University, Princeton.
NjPT	Princeton Theological Seminary, Princeton.
NjR	Rutgers–The State University, New Brunswick.
NjT	Trenton Free Library, Trenton.

NEW MEXICO

NmA	Albuquerque Public Library, New Mexico.
NmU	University of New Mexico, Albuquerque.
NmUpU	New Mexico State University, University Park.

NEVADA

NvU	University of Nevada, Reno.

OHIO

O	Ohio State Library, Columbus.
OAU	Ohio University, Athens.
OAkU	University of Akron, Akron.
OBerB	Baldwin-Wallace College, Berea.
OBlC	Bluffton College, Bluffton.
OC	Public Library of Cincinnati and Hamilton County, Cincinnati.
OCH	Hebrew Union College, Cincinnati.
OCHP	Historical and Philosophical Society of Ohio, Cincinnati.
OCLloyd	Lloyd Library and Museum, Cincinnati.
OCU	University of Cincinnati, Cincinnati.
OCX	Xavier University, Cincinnati.
OCl	Cleveland Public Library.
OClCS	Case Institute of Technology, Cleveland.
OClFC	Cleveland State University, Cleveland. (Formerly Fenn College)
OClJC	John Carroll University, Cleveland.
OClMA	Cleveland Museum of Art, Cleveland.
OClSA	Cleveland Institute of Art, Cleveland.
OClW	Case Western Reserve University, Cleveland.
OClWHi	Western Reserve Historical Society, Cleveland.
ODW	Ohio Wesleyan University, Delaware.
ODa	Dayton and Montgomery County Library, Dayton.
ODaStL	St. Leonard College Library, Dayton.
ODaU	University of Dayton, Dayton.
OEac	East Cleveland Public Library.
OFH	Rutherford B. Hayes Library, Fremont.
OGK	Kenyon College, Gambier.
OHi	Ohio State Historical Society, Columbus.
OKentC	Kent State University, Kent.
OO	Oberlin College, Oberlin.
OOxM	Miami University, Oxford.
OSW	Wittenberg University, Springfield.
OTU	University of Toledo, Toledo.
OU	Ohio State University, Columbus.
OWibfU	Wilberforce University, Carnegie Library, Wilberforce.
OWicB	Borromeo Seminary, Wickliffe.
OWoC	College of Wooster, Wooster.
OWorP	Pontifical College Josephinum, Worthington.
OYesA	Antioch College, Yellow Springs.

OKLAHOMA

Ok	Oklahoma State Library, Oklahoma City.
OkEG	Graduate Seminary Library, Enid.
OkS	Oklahoma State University, Stillwater.
OkT	Tulsa Public Library.
OkU	University of Oklahoma, Norman.

OREGON

Or	Oregon State Library, Salem.
OrCS	Oregon State University Library, Corvallis.
OrHi	Oregon Historical Society, Portland.
OrP	Library Association of Portland, Portland.
OrPR	Reed College, Portland.
OrPS	Portland State College, Portland.
OrSaW	Willamette University, Salem.
OrStbM	Mount Angel College, Mount Angel Abbey, Saint Benedict.
OrU	University of Oregon, Eugene.

PENNSYLVANIA

PBL	Lehigh University, Bethlehem.
PBa	Academy of the New Church, Bryn Athyn.
PBm	Bryn Mawr College, Bryn Mawr.
PCA*	Samuel Colgate Baptist Historical Library of the American Baptist Historical Society, Rochester, N. Y.
PCC	Crozer Theological Seminary, Chester.
PCamA	Alliance College, Cambridge Springs.
PCarlD	Dickinson College, Carlisle.
PHC	Haverford College, Haverford.
PHi	Historical Society of Pennsylvania, Philadelphia.
PJA	Abington Library Society, Jenkintown.
PJAlG	Alverthorpe Gallery, Rosenwald Collection, Jenkintown.
PJB	Beaver College, Jenkintown.